Letter to Readers

Our goal in writing *Fundamentals of HVAC/R* is to encourage a high level of professionalism for future and current technicians in the HVAC/R industry by producing a text that is both accessible and thorough. To accomplish this, we followed a few guiding principles:

- Explain why things work.
- Organize material so that it progresses from fundamental concepts to specific applications of those concepts.
- Organize the material so that it progresses in difficulty from easily understood ideas to more challenging concepts and applications.
- Write a text that is accessible to readers while still providing the detailed information necessary to be successful.
- Write a book that HVAC/R students will want to keep for reference when they become professionals.

The "HVAC/R Science" section lays the foundation for understanding virtually all the concepts and applications introduced later in the book. Taking the time to understand the science behind HVAC/R systems is an investment in the reader's future. The specific details of individual units change over time, but the science that governs how they operate stays the same.

The most difficult part of writing a comprehensive text is deciding what material to include. Everything there is to know simply won't fit into a single book. When deciding what material to include, we fell back on one simple question: Does the material help the reader understand how to install, maintain, and service HVAC/R systems?

The presentation of the material is equally important. There is always more than one way to describe or explain something. We tried to choose the most transparent and easily understood explanations possible without leaving out crucial detail. Concepts and applications are reinforced with specific, real-world examples. We aimed to make the writing style engaging to draw the students in. There is really no reason a textbook can't be written in a style that encourages the reader to read out of interest rather than obligation.

HVAC/R students and technicians are our target audience. Most technicians are visually oriented learners. A good picture or illustration can often explain more than several pages of text. We have included many pictures, illustrations, graphs, and diagrams to show everything from basic concepts to operational sequences.

One of the great things about teaching is sharing in other people's success. There is nothing more gratifying than seeing your students succeed. We hope that this book launches you on a successful HVAC/R career and finds a permanent place in your library or service truck.

Fundamentals of
HVAC/R

CARTER STANFIELD
Athens Technical College

DAVID SKAVES
Maine Maritime Academy

 Air-Conditioning, Heating, and Refrigeration Institute

Prentice Hall
Upper Saddle River, New Jersey
Columbus, Ohio

Library of Congress Cataloging-in-Publication Data

Stanfield, Carter.
    Fundamentals of HVAC/R / Carter Stanfield, David Skaves.
        p. cm.
    Includes index.
    ISBN-13: 978-0-13-222367-6
    ISBN-10: 0-13-222367-8
    1. Heating. 2. Ventilation.   3. Air conditioning. 4. Refrigeration and refrigerating machinery.
        I. Skaves, David.   II. Title.
    TH7012.S695 2010
    697--dc22

                                                                    2008043251

Editor in Chief: Vernon Anthony
Acquisitions Editor: Eric Krassow
Editorial Assistant: Sonya Kottcamp
Production Coordination: Aptara, Inc.
Project Manager: Louise Sette
AV Project Manager: Janet Portisch
Operations Supervisor: Laura Weaver
Art Director: Diane Ernsberger
Cover Designer: Bryan Huber
Cover Image: Getty One
Director of Marketing: David Gesell
Marketing Manager: Derril Trakalo
Senior Marketing Coordinator: Alicia Wozniak
Copyeditor: Carol Mohr

This book was set in Minion by Aptara, Inc. and was printed and bound by Courier Kendallville, Inc. The cover was printed by Phoenix Color Corp.

Copyright © 2010 by Pearson Education, Inc., Upper Saddle River, New Jersey 07458.
Pearson Prentice Hall. All rights reserved. Printed in the United States of America. This publication is protected by Copyright and permission should be obtained from the publisher prior to any prohibited reproduction, storage in a retrieval system, or transmission in any form or by any means, electronic, mechanical, photocopying, recording, or likewise. For information regarding permission(s), write to: Rights and Permissions Department.

Pearson Prentice Hall™ is a trademark of Pearson Education, Inc.
Pearson® is a registered trademark of Pearson plc
Prentice Hall® is a registered trademark of Pearson Education, Inc.

Pearson Education Ltd., London
Pearson Education Singapore Pte. Ltd.
Pearson Education Canada, Inc.
Pearson Education—Japan

Pearson Education Australia Pty. Limited
Pearson Education North Asia Ltd., Hong Kong
Pearson Educación de Mexico, S.A. de C.V.
Pearson Education Malaysia Pte. Ltd.

Prentice Hall
is an imprint of

www.pearsonhighered.com

10 9 8 7 6 5 4 3 2 1
ISBN-13: 978-0-13-222367-6
ISBN-10:   0-13-222367-8

Fundamentals of
HVAC/R

CARTER STANFIELD
Athens Technical College

DAVID SKAVES
Maine Maritime Academy

Air-Conditioning, Heating,
and Refrigeration Institute

Prentice Hall
Upper Saddle River, New Jersey
Columbus, Ohio

Library of Congress Cataloging-in-Publication Data

Stanfield, Carter.
    Fundamentals of HVAC/R / Carter Stanfield, David Skaves.
        p. cm.
    Includes index.
    ISBN-13: 978-0-13-222367-6
    ISBN-10: 0-13-222367-8
    1. Heating. 2. Ventilation.   3. Air conditioning. 4. Refrigeration and refrigerating machinery.
        I. Skaves, David.   II. Title.
    TH7012.S695 2010
    697--dc22

                                            2008043251

Editor in Chief: Vernon Anthony
Acquisitions Editor: Eric Krassow
Editorial Assistant: Sonya Kottcamp
Production Coordination: Aptara, Inc.
Project Manager: Louise Sette
AV Project Manager: Janet Portisch
Operations Supervisor: Laura Weaver
Art Director: Diane Ernsberger
Cover Designer: Bryan Huber
Cover Image: Getty One
Director of Marketing: David Gesell
Marketing Manager: Derril Trakalo
Senior Marketing Coordinator: Alicia Wozniak
Copyeditor: Carol Mohr

This book was set in Minion by Aptara, Inc. and was printed and bound by Courier Kendallville, Inc. The cover was printed by Phoenix Color Corp.

Copyright © 2010 by Pearson Education, Inc., Upper Saddle River, New Jersey 07458.
Pearson Prentice Hall. All rights reserved. Printed in the United States of America. This publication is protected by Copyright and permission should be obtained from the publisher prior to any prohibited reproduction, storage in a retrieval system, or transmission in any form or by any means, electronic, mechanical, photocopying, recording, or likewise. For information regarding permission(s), write to: Rights and Permissions Department.

Pearson Prentice Hall™ is a trademark of Pearson Education, Inc.
Pearson® is a registered trademark of Pearson plc
Prentice Hall® is a registered trademark of Pearson Education, Inc.

Pearson Education Ltd., London
Pearson Education Singapore Pte. Ltd.
Pearson Education Canada, Inc.
Pearson Education—Japan

Pearson Education Australia Pty. Limited
Pearson Education North Asia Ltd., Hong Kong
Pearson Educación de Mexico, S.A. de C.V.
Pearson Education Malaysia Pte. Ltd.

Prentice Hall
is an imprint of

www.pearsonhighered.com

10 9 8 7 6 5 4 3 2 1
ISBN-13: 978-0-13-222367-6
ISBN-10:   0-13-222367-8

Preface

Fundamentals of HVAC/R provides comprehensive coverage of heating, ventilation, air conditioning, and refrigeration (HVAC/R) topics for students in vocational schools and technical colleges as well as field technicians. Based on input from industry experts and many academics, this comprehensive, reader-friendly text offers fundamental concepts, current trends, and practical applications in the field.

THE STORY BEHIND THE BOOK

Having always supplemented the texts we use with articles, we realized that this "supplementary" information often exceeded the information in the text. Available air conditioning texts seem either to be too technical—aimed at engineers, or too low level—simply glossing over detailed subject matter. And so, this text was born—an accessible book that provides a good depth of subject matter aimed squarely at installing, servicing, and maintaining HVAC/R systems. Unlike other texts that continue to add content edition after edition, this book was crafted from scratch, starting with the table of contents. After extensive reviews, we found out what you, the readers, require. Thus we have produced a superb, heavily illustrated text with logical organization that flows extremely well and suits today's visual learner.

ORGANIZATION OF THE BOOK

Structured to prepare students to enter the industry, the book is divided into 10 sections with each section covering a general subject area. Each section is composed of units, with each unit targeting a specific topic beginning with the simplest and progressing to the most complex. The final section pulls all the information together to present detailed coverage of installation, maintenance, and troubleshooting of all system types. The 86 units are shorter than chapters found in more traditional texts so that instructors can cover an entire unit in a reasonable amount of time.

PREPARE FOR A CAREER IN HVAC/R WITH CONFIDENCE!

Unlike other texts in the marketplace, *Fundamentals of HVAC/R* offers:

- Detailed examples and applications of R-410A throughout the text

- A unique section on HVAC/R Science (Units 4–8) that clearly explains the application of fundamental scientific concepts essential to understand air conditioning system operation

- Superb coverage of the basic refrigeration cycle and refrigeration components (Section 4: Refrigerants and the Refrigeration System, Units 17–27)

- Extensive coverage of new refrigerants, including R-410A (Unit 23: Refrigerants and their Properties)

- Detailed explanations for using service valves to access all types of refrigeration systems (Unit 25). This is the only text that offers in-depth coverage on how to use the most common types of refrigeration system access valves in one concise unit.

- Referenced EPA Certification Outline showing a cross-reference listing of each specific EPA competency document (Unit 26: Refrigerant Management and the EPA)

- Construction section (Unit 54: Basic Building Construction)

- Blueprint reading (Unit 55: Drawing and Blueprint Reading)

- Consolidation of all types of systems covering installation, maintenance, and troubleshooting in one place, and offering a logical culmination in Section 10: Units 84–86 (Unit 84: Installation Techniques, Unit 85: Planned Maintenance, and Unit 86: Troubleshooting)

Take the Guided Tour

We now invite you to take the Guided Tour, which will familiarize you with *Fundamentals of HVAC/R*. Easy to navigate, the text is broken down into bite-sized subsections as reflected in the Contents to help optimize your learning.

FEATURES OF THE TEXT

Learning Objectives

Each unit begins with clearly stated objectives that enable you to focus on what you should achieve by the end of the unit.

> **OBJECTIVES**
>
> After completing this unit you will be able to:
>
> - describe the different types of refrigeration service valves.
> - explain the operation of gauge manifold valves.
> - explain how to properly install and remove a gauge manifold set on manual service valves.
> - explain the operation of split system installation valves.
> - explain how to properly install and remove a gauge manifold set on Schrader valves.
> - describe how to gain access to systems without

Unit Summary

These summaries pull together the main points of the unit and help reinforce learning.

> **UNIT 25—SUMMARY**
>
> Service valves are used to gain access to the refrigeration system. Type II and Type III systems all have service valves installed at the factory, Type I systems have process tubes. Commercial refrigeration systems typically use manual stem service valves on the suction and discharge sides of the compressor and on the liquid receiver. The normal operating position of a manual stem service valve is back seated. In the

Unit Introduction

These introductions are organized topically and progress from basic fundamentals to practical application with each topic supporting the next topic.

> **25.1 INTRODUCTION**
>
> One of the last things a service technician should do when troubleshooting a system is attach a set of gauges to the system. Each time a sealed system is accessed there is a chance that some contaminants can be introduced to the system, or refrigerant can be lost. However, there are times when a refrigeration system's operating conditions cannot be accurately assessed without accessing the system's refrigerant piping to

Service Tickets

Appearing at the end of most units, this feature provides examples of the types of problems service technicians encounter and how the information in the unit helps solve them.

> **Service Ticket 2501**
>
> **Customer Complaint: Air Conditioner Freezes Up**
>
> **Equipment: Packaged Terminal Air Conditioner (PTAC) Using R-22 Refrigerant**
>
> A service technician for the Rest Easy Motel chain is asked to look at a PTAC in one of the rooms because it cools poorly and freezes over. Like most PTACs, this one has no service valves of any kind. The technician knows that the two most common causes of air conditioning evapora-

Review Questions

Each unit has a set of review questions to help the reader assess his or her understanding of the material. The questions range from simple identification to more complex questions that require application and analysis of the material in the unit.

UNIT 25—REVIEW QUESTIONS

1. What do technicians use the gauge manifold for?
2. What are the colors used on a gauge manifold set and what do they indicate?
3. What is the term for slightly opening a valve?
4. List three cautions when handling a gauge manifold set.
5. Why is the low side gauge called a compound gauge?

Safety Tips

Safety tips highlight safety issues relevant to the immediate material.

SAFETY TIP

The proper personal protective equipment, PPE, for installing refrigeration gauges and manipulating valves includes safety glasses and gloves. When liquid refrigerant escapes into the atmosphere it boils at extremely cold temperatures. Liquid refrigerant sprayed in the eyes can cause blindness, sprayed on the skin can cause frostbite.

Service Tips

Service Tips are practical applications of the information in the unit that help technicians perform their jobs more efficiently.

SERVICE TIP

Refrigeration gauges have a small adjustment screw that allows the gauge to be zeroed. The gauge is adjusted to zero with the hoses open to atmospheric pressure. However, it is possible for a gauge to zero out but not read other pressures accurately. From time to time the technician should attach the gauges to a new cylinder of refrigerant at a known temperature and compare the pressure reading to the temperature-pressure chart so that the gauge can be checked for accuracy. Gauges that are zeroed and are still inaccurate should be replaced.

Caution

Caution boxes contain information the student should know to properly operate and protect equipment.

CAUTION

Having the proper fire extinguisher is not enough if it is not large enough to do the job. Make sure that your fire extinguisher is large enough to handle the size of fire that might occur in your work area. If there are a lot of combustible materials, you need a bigger fire extinguisher. In some cases you may want to have more than one fire extinguisher available.

Tech Tips

Tech Tips provide extra detail and information for students who want to go beyond the minimum daily requirement of knowledge.

TECH TIP

An operating room is cooled to aid with the surgery as well as for the comfort of the patient or surgeon. Therefore, an operating room is an example of process cooling even though it may be within the normal air conditioning temperature range.

English- and Spanish-Language Glossaries

The glossaries help students with both English and Spanish language skills understand the terms used in the HVAC/R field.

COMPREHENSIVE TEACHING AND LEARNING PACKAGE
FOR THE INSTRUCTOR

To access supplementary materials online, instructors need to request an instructor access code. Go to **www.pearsonhighered.com/irc,** where you can register for an instructor access code. Within 48 hours after registering, you will receive a confirming e-mail, including an instructor access code. Once you have received your code, go to the site and log on for full instructions on downloading the materials you wish to use.

Visit **www.pearsonhighered.com/educator** to access the following:

Instructor's Manual with Lesson Plans and Correlation Guide (ISBN: 0-13-505720-5)

Adopters can access a complete supplements integration guide, including media topics, to assist in selecting appropriate assessment materials for each lesson. Unlike most instructor manuals, this supplement provides detailed lesson plans to walk new and experienced instructors through every unit of the text, integrating each teaching supplement with the text.

We've also included a correlation guide to show you where content in our text addresses the standards and competencies of the ICE and NATE Certification exams.

PowerPoint Slides (ISBN: 0-13-222406-2)

This comprehensive and colorful PowerPoint presentation includes photos from the book as well as dozens of animations that illustrate HVAC/R equipment and concepts.

Lab Manual (ISBN: 0-13-222410-0)

This rich resource provides instructors with 80 different labs that drive home the main theory/principle for each unit.

TestGen (Computerized Test Bank) (ISBN: 0-13-222409-7)

TestGen contains pre-test and post-test questions pertaining to online content, plus over 1,000 questions independent of the text, with varying levels of difficulty.

FOR THE STUDENT AND INSTRUCTOR

My HVAC Lab   myhvaclab

(Stand-Alone Student Access Code Card: 0-13-505406-0)
(Packaged with textbook: 0-13-222367-8)
The ultimate in technology, My HVAC Lab provides an experience unrivalled in the industry. It features robust testing, multimedia, and diagnostic materials to reinforce the classroom and hands-on experience.

- Each unit will have
  Objectives and outlines
  eBook version of the printed textbook
  Homework questions
  PowerPoint slides
  Electronic flashcards of glossary terms
  Animations of key concepts
  Interactive matching and terminology exercises
  Short video clips to accompany text and lab manual

- Pre-test/Post-test/Study Plan
  This supercharged study guide allows students to take a test and receive a customized study plan based on their results and where they scored poorly. The customized study plan links students directly to all relevant content and media for specific objectives. When they're ready, students can then take the post-test and gauge their improvement!

- AHRI Correlation Guide
  Content for NATE and ICE exams are correlated to content within the text.

- Instructor Resources
  Instructors will have access to all of the appropriate resources online, including the Instructor's Manual, PowerPoint slides, TestGen (Computerized Test Bank), homework questions from the text, and the Appendix.

- HVAC Interactive!
  Ten gaming simulations will provide students with the experience they need in a safe learning environment! From dispatch through completion, users will navigate their way through an entire service call. During the course of each simulation, students will be asked what tests and tasks to perform while images from the text appear throughout to help them visualize and identify problems. Scoring is based on time taken and executing the correct steps, with a homework sheet provided at the end of the simulation.

Supplemental Text

Guide to the NATE/ICE Certification Exams, Featherstone and Riojas (ISBN: 0-13-231970-5)

Letter to Readers

Our goal in writing *Fundamentals of HVAC/R* is to encourage a high level of professionalism for future and current technicians in the HVAC/R industry by producing a text that is both accessible and thorough. To accomplish this, we followed a few guiding principles:

- Explain why things work.
- Organize material so that it progresses from fundamental concepts to specific applications of those concepts.
- Organize the material so that it progresses in difficulty from easily understood ideas to more challenging concepts and applications.
- Write a text that is accessible to readers while still providing the detailed information necessary to be successful.
- Write a book that HVAC/R students will want to keep for reference when they become professionals.

The "HVAC/R Science" section lays the foundation for understanding virtually all the concepts and applications introduced later in the book. Taking the time to understand the science behind HVAC/R systems is an investment in the reader's future. The specific details of individual units change over time, but the science that governs how they operate stays the same.

The most difficult part of writing a comprehensive text is deciding what material to include. Everything there is to know simply won't fit into a single book. When deciding what material to include, we fell back on one simple question: Does the material help the reader understand how to install, maintain, and service HVAC/R systems?

The presentation of the material is equally important. There is always more than one way to describe or explain something. We tried to choose the most transparent and easily understood explanations possible without leaving out crucial detail. Concepts and applications are reinforced with specific, real-world examples. We aimed to make the writing style engaging to draw the students in. There is really no reason a textbook can't be written in a style that encourages the reader to read out of interest rather than obligation.

HVAC/R students and technicians are our target audience. Most technicians are visually oriented learners. A good picture or illustration can often explain more than several pages of text. We have included many pictures, illustrations, graphs, and diagrams to show everything from basic concepts to operational sequences.

One of the great things about teaching is sharing in other people's success. There is nothing more gratifying than seeing your students succeed. We hope that this book launches you on a successful HVAC/R career and finds a permanent place in your library or service truck.

Preface

Fundamentals of HVAC/R provides comprehensive coverage of heating, ventilation, air conditioning, and refrigeration (HVAC/R) topics for students in vocational schools and technical colleges as well as field technicians. Based on input from industry experts and many academics, this comprehensive, reader-friendly text offers fundamental concepts, current trends, and practical applications in the field.

THE STORY BEHIND THE BOOK

Having always supplemented the texts we use with articles, we realized that this "supplementary" information often exceeded the information in the text. Available air conditioning texts seem either to be too technical—aimed at engineers, or too low level—simply glossing over detailed subject matter. And so, this text was born—an accessible book that provides a good depth of subject matter aimed squarely at installing, servicing, and maintaining HVAC/R systems. Unlike other texts that continue to add content edition after edition, this book was crafted from scratch, starting with the table of contents. After extensive reviews, we found out what you, the readers, require. Thus we have produced a superb, heavily illustrated text with logical organization that flows extremely well and suits today's visual learner.

ORGANIZATION OF THE BOOK

Structured to prepare students to enter the industry, the book is divided into 10 sections with each section covering a general subject area. Each section is composed of units, with each unit targeting a specific topic beginning with the simplest and progressing to the most complex. The final section pulls all the information together to present detailed coverage of installation, maintenance, and troubleshooting of all system types. The 86 units are shorter than chapters found in more traditional texts so that instructors can cover an entire unit in a reasonable amount of time.

PREPARE FOR A CAREER IN HVAC/R WITH CONFIDENCE!

Unlike other texts in the marketplace, *Fundamentals of HVAC/R* offers:

- Detailed examples and applications of R-410A throughout the text

- A unique section on HVAC/R Science (Units 4–8) that clearly explains the application of fundamental scientific concepts essential to understand air conditioning system operation

- Superb coverage of the basic refrigeration cycle and refrigeration components (Section 4: Refrigerants and the Refrigeration System, Units 17–27)

- Extensive coverage of new refrigerants, including R-410A (Unit 23: Refrigerants and their Properties)

- Detailed explanations for using service valves to access all types of refrigeration systems (Unit 25). This is the only text that offers in-depth coverage on how to use the most common types of refrigeration system access valves in one concise unit.

- Referenced EPA Certification Outline showing a cross-reference listing of each specific EPA competency document (Unit 26: Refrigerant Management and the EPA)

- Construction section (Unit 54: Basic Building Construction)

- Blueprint reading (Unit 55: Drawing and Blueprint Reading)

- Consolidation of all types of systems covering installation, maintenance, and troubleshooting in one place, and offering a logical culmination in Section 10: Units 84–86 (Unit 84: Installation Techniques, Unit 85: Planned Maintenance, and Unit 86: Troubleshooting)

Take the Guided Tour

We now invite you to take the Guided Tour, which will familiarize you with *Fundamentals of HVAC/R*. Easy to navigate, the text is broken down into bite-sized subsections as reflected in the Contents to help optimize your learning.

FEATURES OF THE TEXT

Learning Objectives

Each unit begins with clearly stated objectives that enable you to focus on what you should achieve by the end of the unit.

> **OBJECTIVES**
>
> After completing this unit you will be able to:
>
> - describe the different types of refrigeration service valves.
> - explain the operation of gauge manifold valves.
> - explain how to properly install and remove a gauge manifold set on manual service valves.
> - explain the operation of split system installation valves.
> - explain how to properly install and remove a gauge manifold set on Schrader valves.
> - describe how to gain access to systems without

Unit Summary

These summaries pull together the main points of the unit and help reinforce learning.

> **UNIT 25—SUMMARY**
>
> Service valves are used to gain access to the refrigeration system. Type II and Type III systems all have service valves installed at the factory, Type I systems have process tubes. Commercial refrigeration systems typically use manual stem service valves on the suction and discharge sides of the compressor and on the liquid receiver. The normal operating position of a manual stem service valve is back seated. In the

Unit Introduction

These introductions are organized topically and progress from basic fundamentals to practical application with each topic supporting the next topic.

> **25.1 INTRODUCTION**
>
> One of the last things a service technician should do when troubleshooting a system is attach a set of gauges to the system. Each time a sealed system is accessed there is a chance that some contaminants can be introduced to the system, or refrigerant can be lost. However, there are times when a refrigeration system's operating conditions cannot be accurately assessed without accessing the system's refrigerant piping to

Service Tickets

Appearing at the end of most units, this feature provides examples of the types of problems service technicians encounter and how the information in the unit helps solve them.

> **Service Ticket 2501**
>
> **Customer Complaint: Air Conditioner Freezes Up**
>
> **Equipment: Packaged Terminal Air Conditioner (PTAC) Using R-22 Refrigerant**
>
> A service technician for the Rest Easy Motel chain is asked to look at a PTAC in one of the rooms because it cools poorly and freezes over. Like most PTACs, this one has no service valves of any kind. The technician knows that the two most common causes of air conditioning evapora-

Review Questions

Each unit has a set of review questions to help the reader assess his or her understanding of the material. The questions range from simple identification to more complex questions that require application and analysis of the material in the unit.

UNIT 25—REVIEW QUESTIONS

1. What do technicians use the gauge manifold for?
2. What are the colors used on a gauge manifold set and what do they indicate?
3. What is the term for slightly opening a valve?
4. List three cautions when handling a gauge manifold set.
5. Why is the low side gauge called a compound gauge?

Safety Tips

Safety tips highlight safety issues relevant to the immediate material.

SAFETY TIP

The proper personal protective equipment, PPE, for installing refrigeration gauges and manipulating valves includes safety glasses and gloves. When liquid refrigerant escapes into the atmosphere it boils at extremely cold temperatures. Liquid refrigerant sprayed in the eyes can cause blindness, sprayed on the skin can cause frostbite.

Service Tips

Service Tips are practical applications of the information in the unit that help technicians perform their jobs more efficiently.

SERVICE TIP

Refrigeration gauges have a small adjustment screw that allows the gauge to be zeroed. The gauge is adjusted to zero with the hoses open to atmospheric pressure. However, it is possible for a gauge to zero out but not read other pressures accurately. From time to time the technician should attach the gauges to a new cylinder of refrigerant at a known temperature and compare the pressure reading to the temperature-pressure chart so that the gauge can be checked for accuracy. Gauges that are zeroed and are still inaccurate should be replaced.

Caution

Caution boxes contain information the student should know to properly operate and protect equipment.

CAUTION

Having the proper fire extinguisher is not enough if it is not large enough to do the job. Make sure that your fire extinguisher is large enough to handle the size of fire that might occur in your work area. If there are a lot of combustible materials, you need a bigger fire extinguisher. In some cases you may want to have more than one fire extinguisher available.

Tech Tips

Tech Tips provide extra detail and information for students who want to go beyond the minimum daily requirement of knowledge.

TECH TIP

An operating room is cooled to aid with the surgery as well as for the comfort of the patient or surgeon. Therefore, an operating room is an example of process cooling even though it may be within the normal air conditioning temperature range.

English- and Spanish-Language Glossaries

The glossaries help students with both English and Spanish language skills understand the terms used in the HVAC/R field.

COMPREHENSIVE TEACHING AND LEARNING PACKAGE

FOR THE INSTRUCTOR

To access supplementary materials online, instructors need to request an instructor access code. Go to **www.pearsonhigh-ered.com/irc,** where you can register for an instructor access code. Within 48 hours after registering, you will receive a confirming e-mail, including an instructor access code. Once you have received your code, go to the site and log on for full instructions on downloading the materials you wish to use.

Visit **www.pearsonhighered.com/educator** to access the following:

Instructor's Manual with Lesson Plans and Correlation Guide (ISBN: 0-13-505720-5)

Adopters can access a complete supplements integration guide, including media topics, to assist in selecting appropriate assessment materials for each lesson. Unlike most instructor manuals, this supplement provides detailed lesson plans to walk new and experienced instructors through every unit of the text, integrating each teaching supplement with the text.

We've also included a correlation guide to show you where content in our text addresses the standards and competencies of the ICE and NATE Certification exams.

PowerPoint Slides (ISBN: 0-13-222406-2)

This comprehensive and colorful PowerPoint presentation includes photos from the book as well as dozens of animations that illustrate HVAC/R equipment and concepts.

Lab Manual (ISBN: 0-13-222410-0)

This rich resource provides instructors with 80 different labs that drive home the main theory/principle for each unit.

TestGen (Computerized Test Bank) (ISBN: 0-13-222409-7)

TestGen contains pre-test and post-test questions pertaining to online content, plus over 1,000 questions independent of the text, with varying levels of difficulty.

FOR THE STUDENT AND INSTRUCTOR

My HVAC Lab   myhvaclab

(Stand-Alone Student Access Code Card: 0-13-505406-0)
(Packaged with textbook: 0-13-222367-8)
The ultimate in technology, My HVAC Lab provides an experience unrivalled in the industry. It features robust testing, multimedia, and diagnostic materials to reinforce the classroom and hands-on experience.

- Each unit will have
  Objectives and outlines
  eBook version of the printed textbook
  Homework questions
  PowerPoint slides
  Electronic flashcards of glossary terms
  Animations of key concepts
  Interactive matching and terminology exercises
  Short video clips to accompany text and lab manual

- Pre-test/Post-test/Study Plan
  This supercharged study guide allows students to take a test and receive a customized study plan based on their results and where they scored poorly. The customized study plan links students directly to all relevant content and media for specific objectives. When they're ready, students can then take the post-test and gauge their improvement!

- AHRI Correlation Guide
  Content for NATE and ICE exams are correlated to content within the text.

- Instructor Resources
  Instructors will have access to all of the appropriate resources online, including the Instructor's Manual, PowerPoint slides, TestGen (Computerized Test Bank), homework questions from the text, and the Appendix.

- HVAC Interactive!
  Ten gaming simulations will provide students with the experience they need in a safe learning environment! From dispatch through completion, users will navigate their way through an entire service call. During the course of each simulation, students will be asked what tests and tasks to perform while images from the text appear throughout to help them visualize and identify problems. Scoring is based on time taken and executing the correct steps, with a homework sheet provided at the end of the simulation.

Supplemental Text

Guide to the NATE/ICE Certification Exams, Featherstone and Riojas (ISBN: 0-13-231970-5)

ACKNOWLEDGMENTS

Contributors

Special thanks to our contributing authors:

Freddie Williams (MyHVAC Lab Author)
HVAC/R Instructor at Lanier Technical College, Oakwood, GA; N.A.T.E. Certified Service Technician

Dan Leathers
Instructor teaching Controls, Hydronics, and Home Inspection at College of DuPage, Glen Ellyn, IL; HVAC contractor

Joe Marchese
HVAC Instructor at Community College of Allegheny County, Pittsburgh, PA; HVAC contractor; monthly columnist for THE NEWS; webmaster for www.rvactools.com

Scott McClure
HVAC Instructor at Vernon College, Vernon, TX

Patrick Heeb
Refrigeration and Air Conditioning Department Head, Long Beach City College, Long Beach, CA

William J. Parlapiano III
President of BP Consulting, serves on the NATE, ARI-ICE and BPI Technical Committees.

Tom Kissell
Terra Community College, Fremont, Ohio

Reviewers

We would like to acknowledge the reviewers of this text:

Michael Brock, Florida Community College at Jacksonville
Terry M. Rogers, Midlands Technical College
Freddie Williams, Lanier Technical College
Patrick Heeb, Long Beach City College
Daniel Foust, Austin Community College
Richard McDonald, Santa Fe Community College
Whit Perry, Northwest Mississippi Community College
Rick Marks, Cisco Junior College
David Shehadeh, UALR, Morrilton College
Peter J. Correa, TCI College of Technology
Dalton W. Thacker, Augusta Technical College
Alan R. Mercurio, Oil Tech Talk
Danny Burris, Eastfield College of Dallas County
    Community College District

Hugh Cole, Certification & Training Services
Scott McClure, Vernon College
Joel Owen, Alabama Power/HVAC Training Center

We would also like to acknowledge both Maine Maritime Academy, Castine, ME, and Eastern Maine Community College, Bangor, ME, for allowing photographs to be taken of their equipment for use in this text. Our thanks also to Charlie Veilleux for his help with the photos taken at Eastern Maine Community College. Finally, we thank Tom Kissell, who took many of his photos at Terra Community College, Fremont, OH.

About the Authors

Carter Stanfield is Program Director of the Air Conditioning Technology Department at Athens Technical College, where he has taught since 1976. His industry credentials include both an RSES CM and NATE Certification and a State of Georgia Unrestricted Conditioned Air Contracting License. He graduated from the University of Georgia in 1995 with a Bachelor of Science Degree, Magna Cum Laude, in Education. Mr. Stanfield believes that successful educational programs are focused on what the students do. Students start with a strong background in fundamental concepts and theory and then actively apply them to solve real problems. Practice and active application are the keys to students building both confidence and competence.

The Air-Conditioning, Heating, and Refrigeration Institute (AHRI) is the trade association representing manufacturers of air conditioning, heating, and commercial refrigeration equipment. AHRI's 350+ member companies account for more than 90 percent of the residential and commercial air conditioning, space heating, water heating, and commercial refrigeration equipment manufactured and sold in North America. AHRI participates as a contributing author to this text.

David Skaves, P.E. has been a faculty member at the Maine Maritime Academy since 1986, primarily teaching marine refrigeration and air conditioning. He was the first faculty member to receive the teaching excellence award at the college in 2006. Prior to his appointment at the college, Professor Skaves was employed as a Production Planner at Bath Iron Works Shipyard and as a Marine Engineer sailing on deep-sea tankers. From 2001 through 2003 he was employed during the summers as an engineering consultant for the power plant performance group McHale & Associates, based out of Sammamish, Washington, conducting performance tests at many newly built natural gas combined cycle power plants throughout the U.S. and Mexico. In addition to his MBA from the University of Maine at Orono, Professor Skaves is a registered Professional Engineer, First Class Stationary Engineer, and Chief Engineer for marine vessels of unlimited horsepower. Also a former Chairman for the Maine State Board of Boiler and Pressure Vessels, Professor Skaves currently continues to serve the Board as a public member.

Contents

*Units covering energy efficiency, environmental impact, and green construction.

Fundamentals

Introduction to Heating, Ventilation, Air Conditioning, and Refrigeration

OBJECTIVES

After completing this unit you will be able to:

- give a brief history of HVAC/R.
- define environmental heating and air conditioning.
- give the advantages of freezing foods quickly.
- explain the importance of having a clean background.
- list the various types of HVAC/R jobs and explain what they might do.
- list the HVAC/R professional organizations.

1.1 INTRODUCTION

Mankind has long known that controlling our environment can make us more productive and improve our quality of life. Having our environmental conditions, including air temperature, air motion, moisture level, dust, and other air pollutants, controlled can even help our health. Some of us could sleep in an unheated or uncooled room even if it was stuffy, damp, and dirty—but not very well. And if we did, how effective would we be at work the next day? Over time these conditions could ultimately cause lower productivity and long-term health problems.

Throughout history, famines have caused misery and death. Most have been caused by drought and crop failure, which decimated the annual food supply. Had there been a method for long-term preservation of food gathered from times of plenty, many of these famines could have been prevented. In ancient times before refrigeration, people only had a short time to eat a slaughtered animal before the meat began to turn rancid. The use of ice and, later, mechanical refrigeration improved our world's food supply and eliminated most widespread famines.

The fundamentals of air conditioning and heating are that heat is removed (cooling) by rapidly expanding a liquid into a vapor, and heat is generated by burning a fuel. The fuel burned for heat can be gas, oil, or coal. Technology has significantly increased the efficiencies and improved the comfort and quality of life we have today. As energy consumption becomes a greater concern, higher and higher efficiency levels will become standard.

1.2 HISTORY OF HEATING AND REFRIGERATION

A brief history of heating and cooling gives you an appreciation of the depth and importance this industry has played in the evolution of society. It will also dispel the popular myth that central heating, central air conditioning, and refrigeration are recent developments.

Figure 1-1 Before gaining the ability to use fire, early humans were confined to the warmer climates around the equator

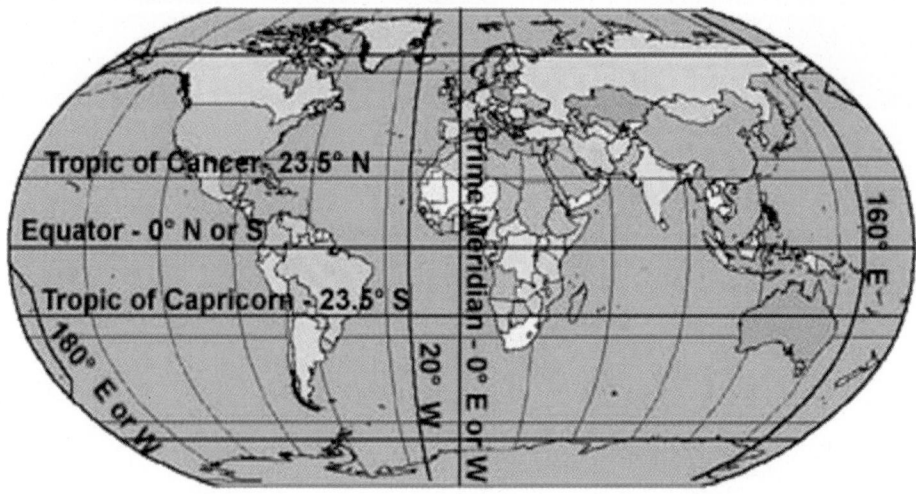

Heating for Warmth

The history of heating a space by burning wood starts in our earliest times and continues to the present. In the temperate regions around the equator early humans were able to live out of doors or with limited shelter without the possibility of freezing to death, Figure 1-1. The discovery of fire allowed early mankind to venture beyond this temperate region. We think of early humans using fire as a way of preparing food, but more importantly it was a source of heat. Campfires allowed these early settlers to move into the colder climates and still survive. Fire burning in an open fireplace remained the primary source of heat for centuries. Elaborate systems using firewood heated Roman buildings. The early Romans built channels underneath the floors to draw heat from a fire, thus warming the building and creating the first central heating systems, Figure 1-2.

Wood, peat, and coal remained the primary heating fuels for centuries. Many early buildings had open fireplaces. But fireplaces are an inefficient way of heating because too much of the heat produced is drawn up the chimney. Although early seventeenth century European masonry type stoves burned wood safely at high efficiency, the next major step in heating technology in America was the metal stove. Benjamin Franklin is credited with inventing a cast-iron stove that was several times more efficient than any other stove at that time. Today many people use decorative efficient stoves to provide much, if not all, of their heating needs, Figure 1-3.

Cooling for Food Preservation

The first use of refrigeration was for the preservation of food. Ice was harvested from frozen lakes and stored for later use. Sometimes it could be kept all summer long in ice houses. Ice harvesting remained a flourishing industry well into the twentieth century.

Archeologists have discovered that the first evidence of man making ice appeared more than 3,000 years ago, about 1,000 B.C. Peoples living in northern Egypt, the Middle East, Pakistan, and India made ice using evaporation. Archeological excavations in these regions have discovered ice-producing fields that covered several acres. The ice was produced in shallow clay plates, about the size of a saucer. The water in these clay plates wept through the clay. This water dampened the small straw mats holding the clay plates in racks a few feet above the ground, Figure 1-4. The straw aided evaporative cooling of the water. Under the right conditions a thin film of ice would form overnight on each clay plate.

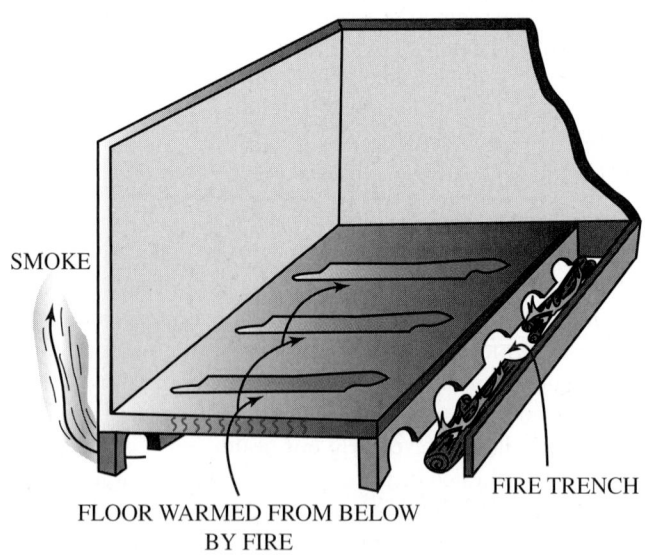

SMOKE

FLOOR WARMED FROM BELOW BY FIRE

FIRE TRENCH

Figure 1-2 Romans used fires channeled below floors as early heating systems

Figure 1-3 Woodstove

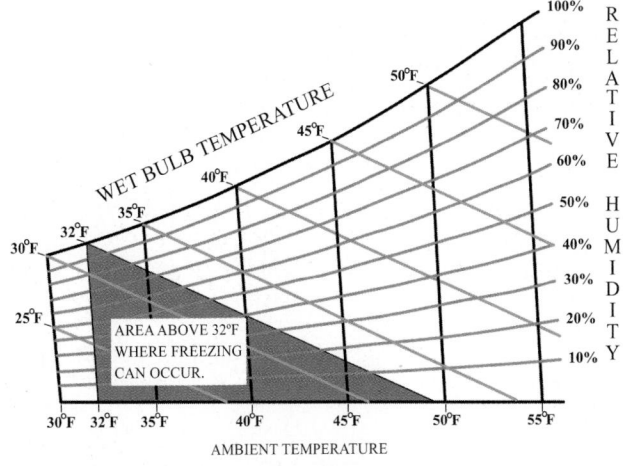

Figure 1-5 Psychrometric chart shows that water can be cooled below freezing if the relative humidity is low enough

The key to ice forming at night in these arid regions is their relative humidity being low enough, around 5%. With very low relative humidity, evaporation can cool water to its freezing point even though the evening air temperature is well above freezing. Figure 1-5 shows a chart of relative humidity at various temperatures to demonstrate this cooling effect. Although these shallow dishes would produce only thin skins of ice, it was sufficient to be harvested early in the morning and placed in straw insulated caves where food was then stored.

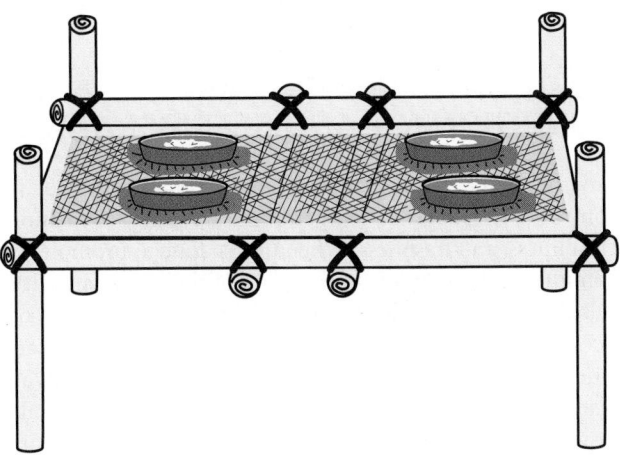

Figure 1-4 Ice was first artificially produced to be used for food preservation more than 3,000 years ago

Evaporative Cooling to Make Ice Still Used Today

Evaporative cooling is also the principle behind modern snow-making equipment. A snow producing machine like the one in Figure 1-6 can make snow by evaporative cooling even when the temperatures on the ski slopes are above freezing.

Cooling for Comfort

Artificially cooling the air in a living space also dates back to the earliest centuries. In ancient Greece, large wet woven tapestries were hung in natural drafts so that the air flowing through and around the tapestries was cooled by the evaporating water. Some manufacturers sprayed water in factories for cooling as early as the 1720s. Evaporative cooling is still used extensively in residences and businesses throughout the Southwest United States where typical summer conditions are very hot and dry, Figure 1-7.

Mechanical Refrigeration

The mechanical process of compressing a gas to produce cooling can be traced back to the coal mines in England. Large steam-driven or water-powered compressors were used to force air into the deepest mines so miners could work in a safe atmosphere. Over long hours of operation, miners observed the formation of ice around the air nozzles, Figure 1-8. This ice was collected and used for food preservation. The construction of steam-powered compressed-air ice-producing plants soon followed. The first maritime refrigeration units were made by putting steam powered compressors on sailing ships to make it possible for beef to be shipped from Australia to England starting in 1876.

Figure 1-6 Snow blowers can produce artificial snow by evaporative cooling
(Courtesy of Red River Ski Area)

Figure 1-7 Evaporative cooler used to cool a store in New Mexico

Air Conditioning Begins

Ice was the primary means of cooling air for many years. The Romans packed ice and snow between double walls in the

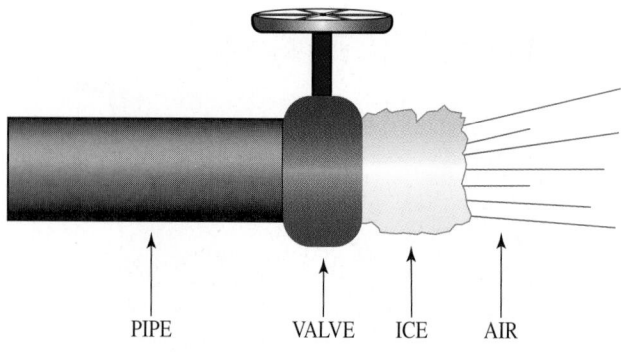

Figure 1-8 Ice forming around an air nozzle

emperor's palaces. John Gorrie patented the first mechanical air conditioned system in 1844. His system was used to cool sick rooms in hospitals in Florida. The United States capitol building in Washington, DC, was first air conditioned using ice in 1909. Rumor has it that when the legislators got really involved in controversial debates, more ice was required to keep the building cool. The phrase "ton(s) of air conditioning" we use today came from this era in history when tons of ice were used for cooling.

TECH TIP

Refrigerant capacity is measured in tons. One ton of capacity is equivalent to the amount of heat that 2,000 lb of ice could absorb in one day. The amount of latent heat required to change 1 ton of ice into 1 ton of water is 288,000 Btu. If this amount is divided by 24 hr per day, the equivalent is 12,000 Btu/hr.

1.3 TODAY'S HEATING, AIR CONDITIONING, AND REFRIGERATION

Environmental heating and air conditioning refers to the control of a space's air temperature, humidity, circulation, cleanliness, and freshness. When this is done to promote the comfort, health, and/or productivity of the inhabitants, it is called environmental heating or air conditioning. Homes, offices, schools, colleges, factories, sporting arenas, hotels, cars, trucks, and other vehicles such as aircraft and spacecraft are heated and cooled. The main purpose of environmental heating or cooling is to help maintain the body temperature within its normal range. Generally, the term air conditioning is used when the space temperature is above 60°F (15°C), and refrigeration is the term that is used when the space temperature is below 60°F (15°C).

TECH TIP

Without our ability to control the environment, it would be impossible for us to be exploring space, the bottom of the ocean, or even enjoying the comfort of a transcontinental jet ride at 35,000 ft. So our ability to control our environment has served both to improve the quality of life and to enhance our scientific endeavors.

Process heating and cooling are used to aid in manufacturing or to keep equipment at the desired temperature. An area used to process meat or vegetables may be cooled to help preserve the product. Computer rooms are cooled so the equipment lasts longer and is able to stay online due to the heat being removed from the space. Computers would not operate properly if heat were not absorbed from the space. Remote pumping stations may be heated to prevent pipes from freezing. The main purpose of process heating or cooling is to maintain the temperature of things or processes within their required range.

TECH TIP

An operating room is cooled to aid with the surgery as well as for the comfort of the patient or surgeon. Therefore, an operating room is an example of process cooling even though it may be within the normal air conditioning temperature range.

Modern Heating

Central heating of homes and businesses dates back to ancient times; however, the first commercial warm-air fan-driven system was marketed in the 1860s. By the 1900s a number of different central warm air systems were available for residential and commercial applications. In 1908, the essential elements for heating, cooling, humidifying, dehumidifying, and filtering air were defined.

Today central heating systems can use warm air, hot water, steam, electric resistance, or a reverse refrigeration cycle (heat pump). The basic theory for the heat pump dates back to 1852.

Modern Air Conditioning

The development of modern air conditioning is often credited to Dr. Willis Carrier. Dr. Carrier, an engineer, was confronted with a problem facing printers. As paper was printed with one color, the dampness in the ink caused the paper to stretch slightly, and it was nearly impossible for the second color to be printed without being misaligned. Dr. Carrier determined that a means for controlling the humidity was necessary and developed the first air conditioning system for the printing industry. His invention, called an "Apparatus for Treating Air," was patented in 1906, Figure 1-9. His invention quickly found favor not only for dehumidifying, but also for cooling. Through the 1940s and 1950s, businesses would

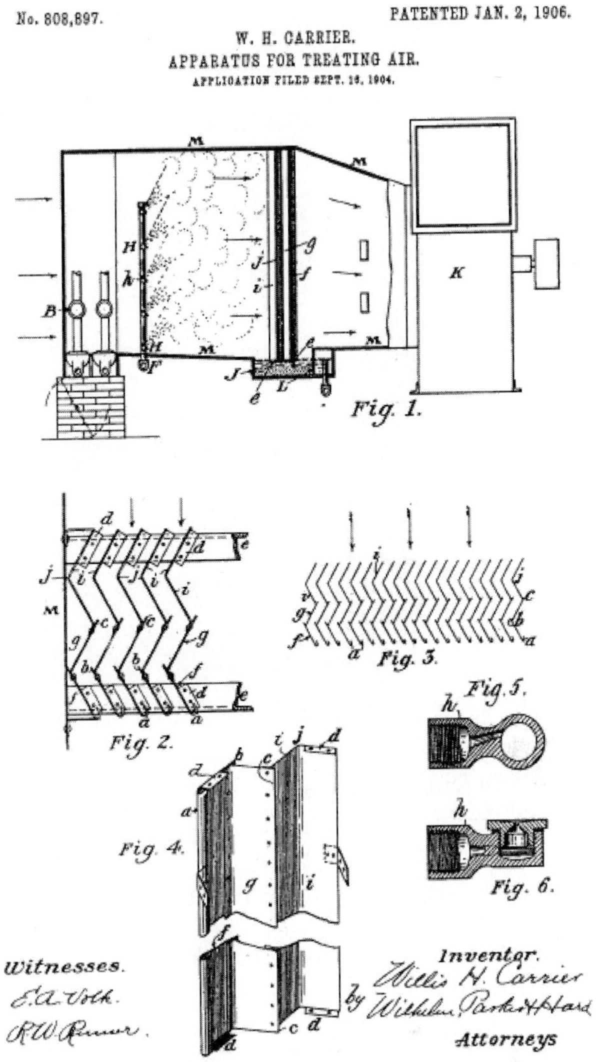

Figure 1-9 Patent for the first apparatus for cooling air, invented by Willis Carrier

proudly display signs reading "Air Conditioned." Dr. Carrier designed the psychrometric chart as we know it today.

Mass air conditioning of homes began in the late 1950s with window air conditioners. Central residential air conditioning started to become popular in the mid-1960s. Today most of us cannot imagine living in a home anywhere in the country that does not have air conditioning.

Modern Refrigeration

Clarence Birdseye made another major contribution to the industry. He developed the process of freezing foods in 1922. Today, supermarket freezer displays provide us with a variety of food products that would not be possible to preserve any other way, Figure 1-10. In 2006, a new era in eating occurred when the American public purchased more heat-to-eat and thaw-to-eat foods than any other type of food.

- **Frozen Foods** Before Clarence Birdseye began commercially freezing food, people had allowed food to

Figure 1-10 Modern refrigeration display cases provide us with a variety of food products that would not be available without refrigeration *(Courtesy of Hussmann Corporation, an Ingersoll-Rand Business)*

freeze naturally during the winter months as a way of preserving it to be eaten later. Food frozen this way did not always taste that good. The trick was to come up with a way of freezing food and having it still taste good when it was thawed.

■ **Quick Freezing** The process of rapidly freezing food using air blast, contact, and/or immersion freezing, was the key ingredient in improving the quality and taste of thawed frozen foods. The problem with freezing food slowly is that when ice crystals form over time, they become much larger. These large sharp ice crystals grow through the cell walls of the food; and when the food thaws, all of the nutrients in the food are allowed to drain away. Quick freezing causes the ice crystals to be very small and they are less likely to penetrate cell walls. So the food retains nutrients and flavor when it is thawed.

1.4 EMPLOYMENT OPPORTUNITIES

The HVAC/R industry represents one of the largest employment occupations in the country. Our industry, for example, is one of the largest consumers of electric and gas utilities in the nation. More electricity and natural gas is consumed producing heating and cooling as compared to most any other single use. The size of the industry has been growing steadily since the late 1960s when residential central systems became popular. The installation and servicing of HVAC/R systems will always be an expanding occupation. No one builds a home or business without some type of heating and/or

cooling system, which requires designing, installing, and servicing by skilled and trained technicians.

Residential Air Conditioning and Heating

Most residential heating systems have a heating capacity of 50,000 to 150,000 Btu/hr. The majority of residential air conditioning systems are 5 tons or less. Both of these sizes will obviously vary greatly depending on the region of the country you are working in. In addition, there are many new very large homes being built requiring systems that could easily be classified as light commercial because of their size and/or complexity.

TECH TIP

To protect the public from potentially dangerous individuals, some businesses and/or local and state governments require criminal background checks on anyone involved with in-home service work. These checks may go back 25 years or more into an individual's past. Check with your local or state governmental department that regulates in-home service work if you feel there is something in your past that might affect your ability to work in residential service. In most states these checks are only required for in-home service work, so you may still be able to work in new construction or in the commercial or industrial areas.

Commercial Air Conditioning and Heating

The term commercial is used to refer to any system that is used in commercial buildings that provides cooling or heating. These systems may be as small as a fraction of a ton in size to several thousand tons in cooling capacity and/or from a thousand Btu/hr to hundreds of thousands of Btu/hr.

Commercial systems may be operated independently of any other system or be integrated with a building automation system. Because of the vast differences in the types of equipment and system complexity, commercial technicians often specialize in a single type of system or group of systems.

Commercial and Industrial Refrigeration

The terms commercial and industrial refrigeration are applied to retail food and cold storage equipment and facilities. Examples of commercial equipment and systems include refrigeration equipment found in supermarkets, convenience stores, restaurants, and other food service establishments. Industrial refrigeration can include long-term storage either as cold storage, medium, or low temperature refrigeration systems that are generally larger-scale operations.

Types of Jobs

There are a variety of occupational specialties offered within the HVAC/R industry. These occupations range from the basic entry-level helper to the systems designer. Although the work of heating, air conditioning, or refrigeration equipment and systems are similar in theory, there is a significant difference between the work done in the areas of residential, light commercial, commercial, and industrial. These areas of heating, air conditioning, and refrigeration generally relate to the size (capacity) and complexity of the system. However, technicians may find the exact same equipment used in one home being used in a commercial shop or factory. In these cases the distinguishing factor is whether you are working in someone's home or in a business.

- **Entry-Level Helper**   The entry-level helper (first year apprentice) provides the senior technician with assistance installing and servicing equipment. Most medium and large mechanical contracting companies use a number of helpers to assist with the installation and service of residential and commercial systems. A helper may be expected to assist in lifting, carrying, or placing equipment or components. They may also run errands to pick up parts and clean up the area following installation or service. Helpers receive basic safety training and if they will be driving, they must have good driving records.
- **Rough-in Installer**   The initial installation process is referred to as rough-in. In this process the technician (first through third year apprentice) will install the refrigerant lines, electrical lines, thermostat and control lines, duct boots and duct run, as well as setting the indoor and outdoor units. The rough-in technician must have an understanding of duct layout, blueprint reading, basic hand tools, and good brazing skills.
- **Start-up Technician**   Once the system has been installed and all of the components are ready for operation, a start-up technician (fourth and fifth year apprentice) will go through the manufacturer's recommended procedures to initially start a system. Because much of the HVAC system has been field installed, this checkout procedure is essential to ensure safe and efficient operation. The start-up technician records all of the information requested by the manufacturer's warranty. Start-up technicians must be skilled with electrical troubleshooting, refrigerant charging, and have good reading comprehension skills and writing skills.
- **Service Technician**   The service technician (fourth year apprentice to journeyman) is the individual who provides the system owner with repair and maintenance. Service technicians are the people who must be able to diagnose system problems and make the necessary repairs. Service technicians must be skilled in diagnosing electrical problems, refrigerant problems, and air distribution problems.

TECH TIP

Technology has enabled the field tech to stay in close contact with his service manager. This allows the highly experienced service managers to provide assistance to technicians as they come upon new problems. The technician can also call upon the office to research unique problems to determine the best, most efficient way of making the repair.

- **Sales**   HVAC/R sales are divided into two major categories, inside sales and outside sales. Inside sales deal primarily with system sales to other air conditioning contractors. Outside sales may be to both contractors and end users. Working in outside sales or consumer sales requires the technician to have a good understanding of cost and value of equipment so that the owner can make an informed choice.
- **Equipment Operators**   Equipment operators are required by local ordinance and state law to be present any time large central heating and air conditioning plants are in operation. Their primary responsibility is to ensure the safe and efficient operation of these large systems. They must have a good working knowledge of the system's mechanical, electrical, and computer control systems in order to carry out their job. They sometimes need to hold a city or state license to become an operator. Equipment operators generally work by themselves or as part of a small crew. They often are required to have good computer skills when buildings have computerized building management systems.

- **Facilities Maintenance Personnel** Facilities maintenance personnel are responsible for planned maintenance and routine service on systems. They may work at a single location or have responsibilities for multiple locations, such as school systems. Facilities maintenance personnel typically maintain systems and provide planned maintenance. They may work alone or as part of a crew, depending on the size of the facility. Maintenance personnel may from time to time have duties and responsibilities outside of the HVAC/R trades, such as doing minor electrical plumbing and carpentry projects for the upkeep of the building.
- **Service Manager** A service manager is typically a skilled HVAC/R technician with several years of experience. This individual oversees the operation of a company or maintenance department. They must have good management skills, communication skills, and technical expertise. Service managers typically assign jobs to other technicians and employees. They must then oversee these individuals' jobs.
- **Systems Designer** For small buildings, contractors normally size and select HVAC systems and equipment. There are many industry standard sizing and design guides available from trade associations such as the ACCA (Air Conditioning Contractors of America). For larger buildings, mechanical, architectural, or building services engineers may be required by law to design and specify the HVAC systems. Specialty mechanical contractors will work with the design plans to build and commission these systems.

1.5 TRADE ASSOCIATIONS

With the rapid growth and variety of interests, trade associations naturally evolved to represent specific groups. The list includes manufacturers, wholesalers, contractors, sheet metal workers, and service organizations. Each is important and makes a valuable contribution to the field. Space does not permit a detailed examination of all of these organizations, or all of their activities, but throughout the book many of these associations will be acknowledged as specific subjects are covered.

Air Conditioning, Heating, and Refrigeration Institute (AHRI)

The Air Conditioning, Heating, and Refrigeration Institute (AHRI) is a national trade association representing manufacturers of over 90% of United States-produced central air conditioning, gas appliances, and commercial refrigeration equipment. AHRI was formed in 2007/2008 when ARI (Air Conditioning and Refrigeration Institute) merged with GAMA (Gas Appliance Manufacturer's Association). ARI, now AHRI, was originally formed in 1954 through a merger of two related trade associations and traces its history back to 1903 when it started as the Ice Machine Builders Association

of the United States. Today AHRI has over 180 companies as members.

Many services are provided by AHRI to assist HVAC/R technicians. Some of these services, which would supplement this text, are listed below:

- ICE is an industry competency exam. This test is made available to students of educational institutions to test their knowledge of fundamental and basic skills necessary for entry level HVAC/R technician positions. The information in this text covers the topics in the AHRI curriculum guide and would assist the student in taking this examination. A directory of those who pass the examination is published nationally to assist prospective employers in identifying job candidates.
- Equipment donations to schools participating in the ICE competency exam. AHRI contacts industry sources having no-cost or low-cost equipment available to supply a school's laboratory needs.
- Technician certification program. In accordance with EPA's (the Environmental Protection Agency) enforcement of the Clean Air Act, the sale of refrigerants is made only to those technicians who have been certified. AHRI is among the many approved by EPA to administer the test for certification. In addition, AHRI provides study material to prepare for the test.
- Reclaimer certification program. EPA also requires certification of any processor of recovered refrigerant for resale. AHRI is among those assigned by EPA to carry out a certification program for companies that seek to reclaim refrigerants. Technicians handling reclaimed refrigerant should become familiar with the *Directory of Certified Reclaimed Refrigerants,* published every March and September by AHRI.
- Certification program for equipment used to recover and recycle refrigerant. AHRI is one of the companies approved by EPA to certify equipment used to recover and recycle refrigerants. Technicians should become familiar with the *Directory of Certified Refrigerant Recovery/Recycling Equipment,* published every March and September by AHRI.
- HVAC/R equipment certification program. AHRI maintains a certification service, which tests a wide variety of equipment and products to verify the performance described by the manufacturer. Certified directories for various products are published semiannually and annually.

AHRI has a full program of educational activities geared toward helping the nation's vocational and technical schools improve and expand their education and training programs. Under the direction of AHRI's education director and its Education and Training Committee, AHRI serves as a resource from the manufacturers to school instructors, department heads, and guidance counselors. In addition to this textbook and its companion materials, AHRI produces the *Bibliography of Training Aids,* a career brochure, and a promotional video for schools to use to recruit students into HVAC/R programs. Many schools around the country have adopted the ICE competency exams as final exams for their programs. AHRI's most recent efforts involve participation in efforts to develop national HVAC/R competency standards.

Having students pass the ICE competency exams and training toward national competency standards will improve the quality of installation and service. New HVAC/R technicians will be better prepared, resulting in three basic advantages:

- Limited training required for contractors.
- Limited rework or repeat calls due to error.
- Limited warranty/replacement for manufacturers.

The cost of repeat service calls, which is born by contractors, may be reduced substantially by employing properly trained technicians. Every new technician receives training and serves as an apprentice for a period of time. That is essentially a period where contractors pay two people to do one job. A properly trained technician will generally require less training time and function sooner than a poorly trained technician.

In co-sponsorship with AHRI, ASHRAE holds an annual international Air Conditioning Heating Refrigeration Exposition, which may draw 30,000 to 50,000 people in the field. Product exhibits, technical displays, and business seminars highlight the event.

American Society of Heating, Refrigeration, and Air Conditioning Engineers (ASHRAE)

The American Society of Heating, Refrigeration, and Air Conditioning Engineers is an organization started in 1904 as the American Society of Refrigeration Engineers (ASRE) with 70 members. Today its membership is composed of thousands of professional engineers and technicians from all phases of the HVAC/R industry. ASHRAE also creates equipment standards for the industry. Its most important contribution probably has been a series of books that have become the reference books of the industry. These include the *Guide and Data Books for Equipment, Fundamentals, Applications, and Systems*.

TECH TIP

Becoming an active participating member in a professional trade association will provide you with an opportunity to continue your HVAC/R education. The HVAC/R field is such a dynamic and evolving industry that in order to stay competitive you must continually attend seminars and take classes. This is a field where your success will depend on your continued education.

American Society of Mechanical Engineers (ASME)

The American Society of Mechanical Engineers is an organization composed of engineers in a wide variety of industries. Among other functions, ASME writes standards related to safety aspects of pressure vessels.

Air Conditioning Contractors of America (ACCA)

The Air Conditioning Contractors of America is a service contractor's association concerned with the education of technicians and service managers with business improvement techniques. ACCA provides technician EPA certification.

Refrigeration Service Engineers Society (RSES)

The Refrigeration Service Engineers Society is the international professional association for all HVAC/R workers and is dedicated to education and certification of technicians in the HVAC/R industry. RSES offers Specialist Certification for senior technicians in eight HVAC/R areas and has a technician EPA certification program. RSES chapters conduct classroom training in technical areas and are a source for educational printed material and books.

SERVICE TIP

The AHRI list of certified equipment is available to anyone through the internet. This material is very helpful when trying to make a determination of the best equipment to recommend for a customer and their specific application needs. On the web, very often all of the various pieces of equipment are available.

UNIT 1—SUMMARY

Since the beginning of time, people have had a desire to control their environment to live and work more comfortably. That trend will not stop, and that is the good news for anyone entering this ever-growing, financially rewarding, and personally satisfying field. HVAC/R technicians are required to understand the theory to design, install, and service a wide range of systems. This diversity ensures that each day on the job will be new and unique; ever changing and challenging.

UNIT 1—REVIEW QUESTIONS

1. How has refrigeration helped to reduce famines?
2. What were some of the primary heating fuels that early civilizations used?

3. When is it believed that ice was first artificially made for food storage?

4. How did early man make ice?

5. Why did some manufacturers spray water in factories in the early 1700s?

6. How did early Romans cool palaces?

7. What do the terms "environmental heating" and "air conditioning" refer to?

8. What does the term "process heated and cooled" refer to?

9. When did central warm air systems for residential and commercial applications become well defined?

10. Who developed what is referred to as modern air conditioning?

11. When did mass air conditioning of homes with window units begin?

12. Why is it important to freeze foods quickly?

13. Why do some businesses and/or local and state governments require criminal background checks?

14. What size range might a commercial air conditioner fit into?

15. Give an example of some of the types of equipment that a commercial refrigeration technician might work on.

16. What type of things might an entry-level helper do?

17. Whose job is it to do the initial installation process such as install the refrigerant lines, electrical lines, thermostat and control lines, duct boots and duct run, as well as setting the indoor and outdoor units?

18. What skills must a service technician have?

19. What are some of the things that a service manager must be able to do?

20. What is the ICE exam and who might take it?

21. What are some of the RSES organization's activities?

UNIT 2

Being a Professional
HVAC/R Technician

OBJECTIVES

After completing this unit you will be able to:

- list some of the most popular HVAC/R publications.
- explain the importance of professional certifications.
- list the seven specialty areas of NATE specialty certification.
- explain the value of taking the Industry Competency Exam (ICE).
- list the items that help make for a professional appearance while on the job.
- describe how to develop good communication with the customer.

2.1 INTRODUCTION

The air conditioning and refrigeration industry has more professional organizations, trade associations, publications, and other related organizations than most any other technical field. These groups provide the HVAC/R industry with the most up to date and current information. As a student, you should consider becoming involved with a student organization such as ACCA's student club, RSES student club, or ASHRAE's student club. These will give you an opportunity to begin developing extremely important business and technical contacts in the local HVAC/R industry. These contacts will serve you very well as you enter the profession.

As a professional in the trade, it is to your advantage to maintain a close relationship with one or more of these professional organizations. Each group provides its members with the latest trends and most current technical information. This gives members a significant edge. Most of the organizations provide ongoing technical and business training classes. Many of the classes cover the latest trends in equipment, regulations, codes and standards, local building regulations, and business practices. Being able as a member to participate in these ongoing educational opportunities will keep you at the leading edge of your new profession.

Each of these professional organizations has publications and many provide the industry with codes and standards. These publications would be an excellent addition to your technical library. Having a current and up-to-date library will help you provide your employer and customers with the best possible service while making you significantly

more valuable to your employer. HVAC/R is an ongoing learning process for even the most skilled technician.

Figure 2-1 lists a number of these professional associations. Most have websites that are accessible through the internet and many have local, regional, and state chapters that you can become affiliated with.

Many of the HVAC/R professional organizations have industrial trade shows. These shows are an excellent opportunity for you to see the various manufacturer's latest equipment, tools, supplies, and services. Some of the trade shows are local, others may be regional, some are national, and a few are international, Figure 2-2.

TECH TIP

Once you enter the profession as an HVAC/R technician, all costs associated with taking additional classes, purchasing books, and membership dues may be tax deductible.

2.2 PUBLICATIONS

Another excellent way of keeping up with the latest information in the HVAC/R field is by subscribing to one or more of the HVAC/R publications, Figure 2-3. Some of these publications are weekly, while others are monthly. They all contain well written articles specifically addressing HVAC/R industry concerns. Many of them are written to teach their readers troubleshooting skills. Their articles are very valuable even to the skilled technician.

Some of the professional organizations have their own newsletters that are published and provided to their members. Some local and state chapters of these organizations have additional newsletters that are provided to their members.

2.3 PROFESSIONAL CERTIFICATION

Every HVAC/R technician must become certified under the EPA Section 608 regulations. Compliance with these regulations regarding the management of refrigerants is mandatory for everyone in the trade. Following your successful

Figure 2-1 United States organizations.

ACCA—Air Conditioning Contractors of America
AFEAS—Alternative Fluorocarbons Environmental Acceptability Study
AGA—American Gas Association
AHAM—Association of Home Appliance Manufacturers
AMCA—Air Movement & Control Association
ANSI—American National Standards Institute
AHRI—Air-Conditioning, Heating, & Refrigeration Institute
ARWI—Air-Conditioning & Refrigeration Wholesalers International
ASAE—American Society of Association Executives
ASHRAE—American Society of Heating, Refrigerating and Air-Conditioning Engineers
ABC—Associated Builders & Contractors
Boiler and Refrigeration Engineers
BOMA International—Building Owners and Managers Association
COBRA—The Association of Cogeneration
CDA—Copper Development Association
EEI—Edison Electric Institute
EPRI—Electrical Power Research Institute
EHCC—Eastern Heating & Cooling Council
Envirosense Consortium Inc.
EPEE—European Partnership for Energy and the Environment
FMI—The Food Marketing Institute
Geothermal Heat Pump Consortium
GMA—Grocery Manufacturers of America
HARDI—Heating, Airconditioning and Refrigeration Distributors International
HPBA—Hearth, Patio and Barbeque Association
HI—Hydraulic Institute
HRAI—Heating, Refrigerating, & Air-Conditioning Institute of Canada
IDDBA—International Dairy, Deli, Bakery Association
IFPA—International Fresh-Cut Produce Association
IIAR—International Institute of Ammonia Refrigeration
IHACI—Institute of Heating and Air Conditioning Industries
ISA—The Instrumentation, Systems, and Automation Society
MCAA—Mechanical Contractors Association of America
MSCA—Mechanical Service Contractors of America
NACS—National Association of Convenience Stores
NADCA—National Air Duct Cleaners Association
NAHB—National Association of Home Builders
NAFEM—National Association of Food Equipment Manufacturers
NAM—National Association of Manufacturers
NATE—North American Technician Excellence Program
National Restaurant Association
NEMA—National Electrical Manufacturers Association
NFFS—Non-Ferrous Founders' Society
NIPC—National Inhalant Prevention Coalition
PHCC—Plumbing Heating Cooling Contractors Association
PIMA—Polyisocyanurate Insulation Manufacturers Association
PMA—Produce Marketing Association
RACCA—Refrigeration & Air Conditioning Contractors Association
RSES—Refrigeration Service Engineers Society
SMACNA—Sheet Metal and Air Conditioning Contractors' National Association
UL—Underwriters Laboratories Inc.

completion of any and all of the appropriate levels, it remains your responsibility to stay current with any changes in these regulations. As unfair as it may seem, you can be fined significantly for violating an EPA regulation pertaining to refrigerants even if that regulation took effect after your successful completion of the certification. In addition, it is your sole responsibility to remember and follow all of the EPA regulations pertaining to refrigerant management. For that reason, it would be a good business practice to occasionally take a refresher course in EPA rules and regulations.

CANMET Energy Technology Centre
EPEE—European Partnership for Energy and the Environment
EUROVENT-CECOMAF—European Committee of Air Handling & Refrigerating Equipment
EUROVENT Certification
ICARMA—International Council of Air-Conditioning and Refrigeration Manufacturers' Association
globalEDGE International Business Resources Desk
International Energy Agency (IEA) Heat Pump Centre
IIAR—International Institute of Ammonia Refrigeration
IIR—International Institute of Refrigeration
JRAIA—Japan Refrigeration and Air-Conditioning Industry Association
LATCO's Tools of the Trade—(Latin American International Trade Sites)
Strategic Information for Trade Efficiency (UN-ETO)
Trade Compass
United Nations Environment Programme (UNEP)
USA*Engage
The World Bank
World Trade Point Federation
Worldclass

Figure 2-2 International Organizations

The Air-Conditioning, Heating & Refrigeration (ACHR) News
American School & University (AS&U)
APPLIANCE Magazine
Appliance Manufacturer
ASHRAE Journal
Buildings
Building Design and Construction
Consulting-Specifying Engineer
Contracting Business
Contractor Magazine
Energy User News
Engineered Systems
Facilities Net
Heating/Piping/AirConditioning (HPAC)
Japan Air Conditioning, Heating & Refrigeration News (JARN)
Japan Refrigeration & Air Conditioning News
Plant Engineering
RSES Journal
SchoolDesigns.com
Skylines
Supply House Times
Western HVAC/R News

Figure 2-3 Publications

2.4 INDUSTRY COMPETENCY EXAM (ICE)

The Air-Conditioning, Heating, and Refrigeration Institute (AHRI); the Air Conditioning Contractor's of America (ACCA), the Heating, Air Conditioning, and Refrigeration Distributors International (HARDI); the Plumbing, Heating, Cooling Contractors Association (PHCC); the North American Technician Excellence (NATE); the Partnership for Air-Conditioning, Heating, Refrigeration Accreditation (PAHRA); and the Refrigeration Service Engineers Society (RSES) have established a competency examination that is designed for students who have completed or nearly completed a technical training program. This examination is voluntary; but it does provide students leaving a training program, whether from high school, trade school, or community college, with an opportunity to evaluate their knowledge with an industry standardized test.

The ICE exam has been developed over the years with input from manufacturers, trade associations, instructors, and other industry experts. This exam can also provide your institution with an overall evaluation of its training program. Upon your successful completion of the ICE exam, your name, along with your school's name, is published and made available to area contractors who might be looking for new skilled employees. In short, the successful completion of the ICE exam can put you well ahead of other graduates from programs not participating in the ICE examination. The ICE examination is in three parts—Residential Heating and Air Conditioning, Light Commercial Heating and Air Conditioning, and Commercial Refrigeration. A good student will make testing and certification achievement a challenge for him or herself, always setting goals high.

AHRI and its affiliates provide training institutions with incentives as encouragement to participate in the ICE examination by directing many of its manufacturing members' equipment donation programs toward the schools, institutes, and colleges that participate in the ICE program. These equipment donations can become an excellent source of the latest equipment you will be seeing in the field.

2.5 SKILLS USA

Skills USA is a vocational industrial club for students in high schools, trade schools, and community colleges. Skills USA clubs are open to students in all areas of specialties including HVAC/R. The national organization provides local chapters and students with many opportunities to develop leadership, citizenship, and interpersonal skills that are invaluable to the success of individuals in any profession. The Skills logo is shown in Figure 2-4a.

In addition to the opportunities of individual professional growth, Skills USA sponsors regional, state, national, and international skills competitions. These skills competitions are available on the secondary and post-secondary levels. By participating in the competition students are given the opportunity to demonstrate their troubleshooting skills in diagnosing real world problems under the supervision of highly skilled individuals serving as judges.

The winners of local, state, and national competitions move on to the international skills competition held in a different country each year. At the international competition the best and brightest students from around the world compete to see who has the greatest knowledge and expertise in each of the technical areas including HVAC/R. Every student who participates in these skills Olympics at any level receives recognition. Students involved in this program are shown in Figure 2-4b,c. This recognition is invaluable to the students because prospective employers value such recognition.

2.6 COUNCIL OF AIR CONDITIONING AND REFRIGERATION EDUCATORS (CARE)

The Council of Air Conditioning and Refrigeration Educators (CARE) is an organization that was founded in the late 1990s by a group of air conditioning educators, counselors, and administrators responsible for the various aspects of HVAC/R training. This group is made up of individuals from secondary schools, post-secondary schools, and colleges representing institutions from various regions of the country.

The purpose of CARE is to educate in order to meet or exceed the needs of the industry.

CARE membership is open to instructors, counselors, and administrators who are involved in some aspect of HVAC/R training. Through this organization, individuals can come together to learn and share experiences for the betterment of the HVAC/R students and program.

2.7 NORTH AMERICAN TECHNICAL EXCELLENCE (NATE)

NATE is an independent, third party certification body formed in the 1997 as a result of a concern expressed by many in the industry that there was not a way of distinguishing quality, highly skilled HVAC/R technicians from every other

(a)

(b)

(c)

Figure 2-4 (a) Skills USA logo; (b,c) Students competing in the National Skills Olympics

person working in the field. NATE is supported by all of the major equipment manufacturers, major component manufacturers, professional and trade associations, and the National Skills Standard Board. Figure 2-5 shows a technician with a patch showing NATE certification working on a system.

The NATE certification program has either a service or installation path for each specialty area. Installation certification

Figure 2-5 NATE certified air conditioning technician checking the refrigerant charge in a residential system

is primarily designed for the technician who is involved with the installation or removal of HVAC equipment. Installers assemble the system and fabricate the necessary connections to complete an efficient system. They also set up the operational controls under the supervision of a service technician. After the system is started, the installation technician records the readings for temperature, pressure, voltage, current, and any other measurements required by the manufacturer or service company for the completion of the warranty paperwork.

The service technician must have all of the skills of the installation technician plus be able to work independently. Service technicians must be able to perform field diagnostics to determine the cause of system failures and to make the needed repairs. There are currently seven specialty areas for service technicians. They are:

1. Air conditioning
2. Air distribution
3. Gas heating
4. Heat pumps
5. Oil heating
6. Hydronics gas service
7. Hydronics oil service

In addition to the technical skills required to pass the various areas of specialization, each technician must take as part of the exam process a core exam. The core test covers basic math, customer relations, comfort, heat transfer, and the fundamentals of electricity. A well trained, experienced technician should be able to take and pass both the core and area specialty exams. A number of organizations provide NATE pretest tutorial classes to bring technicians' skill levels up to pass the exam. The exam passing score is 70% or better. Certification lasts for five years, after which a technician must

recertify. There are many classes which qualify for credits that can be used toward recertification. If a technician receives 60 hours of credit, the technician does not have to take a test at five years. If the technician obtains 30 credit hours, he or she will only be required to take a 50 question specialty test instead of 100 questions.

NATE recommends that you have at least one year of field experience before taking an installation series test, and at least two years of experience before taking a service series test. It is further recommended that you have some instruction from an educational institution or trade association.

NATE has provided technicians with Knowledge Areas of Technician Expertise (KATEs) which give detailed outlines of all of the material that a technician can expect to be questioned about on an exam. These KATEs represent all of the knowledge and skills that a quality HVAC/R technician should have. The KATEs also help the prospective test candidate to focus on those areas that the industry feels are most important.

2.8 CODES AND STANDARDS

There are many organizations and agencies that provide codes that are used throughout the HVAC/R industry. Figure 2-6 lists many of these organizations. In addition to codes there are standards that are provided. The difference between a code and a standard is that codes often carry with them the force of law and standards do not. Organizations providing standards to the HVAC/R industry are listed in Figure 2-7.

The HVAC/R industry has many consumer groups that over the years have worked with the industry and industry

International Association of Plumbing and Mechanical Officials (IAMPO)
Building Officials and Code Administrators International, Inc. (BOCA)
International Code Council (ICC)
International Conference of Building Officials (ICBO)
International Fire Code Institute (IFCI)
National Conference of States on Building Codes and Standards (NCS/BCS)
National Fire Protection Association (NFPA)
Southern Building Code Congress International Inc. (SBCCI)

Figure 2-6 Code groups

Figure 2-7 Standards

AFNOR—Association Francaise de Normalisation
ANSI—American National Standards Institute
BSI—British Standards Institution
CSA International—Canadian Standards Association
DIN—Deutches Institut für Normunge. V.
CEN—The European Committee for Standardization
CENELEC—The European Committee for Electrotechnical Standardization
EU—European Union
IEC—International Electrotechnical Commission
ISO—International Organization for Standardization
JIS—Japanese Industrial Standards
NSSN—National Standards Systems Network
SASO—Saudi Arabian Standards Organization
SES—Standards Engineering Society

Figure 2-8 Consumer information

Buying Energy Efficient Products (DOE Federal Energy Management Program)
Consumer Information Center (GSA)
North American Technician Excellence Program (NATE)
Consortium for Energy Efficiency (CEE)

leaders to help us provide consumers with the most efficient and effective service. Some of these consumer information groups are listed in Figure 2-8.

2.9 THE PROFESSIONAL TECHNICIAN'S APPEARANCE

As a service technician you are seen by the customer as a representative of your company. Customers often assume the appearance and professionalism of the technician is a reflection on the technician and company's technical skills. It is, therefore, important that you present yourself in a very clean and neat professional manner to the customer. In some cases you might find during the course of the day that your uniform becomes soiled. It is, therefore, a good idea to carry at least an extra clean shirt in the service van so that you can change if necessary.

If your company does not provide uniforms, you should dress appropriately. In some cases, blue jeans and a jersey or denim shirt are acceptable. However, in other cases where you might be working in an office building, slacks and a shirt

would be appropriate. Check with your employer to see what the company dress code is. In addition to your clothing, you must have a clean and neat professional appearance. That means clean well kept hair, for men, either clean shaven or well kept beard, and for everyone, clean hands.

You must keep your service vehicle clean and neat. It is a rolling billboard for your company and it is important that it look sharp. A clean service van provides a better, more efficient work area, making it easier to find tools and supplies. A clean and neat service vehicle also makes a better impression on the customer. Unless you have permission from residential customers, you should not park your service vehicle in their driveway. Always make it a habit to park your vehicle on the street. You do not want to be responsible for cleaning up an oil spill; and your vehicle can obstruct their access, which to some customers is very aggravating.

When you present yourself to a customer's door, you should have your hands in plain sight either at your side or holding your tools and clipboard. When the customer opens the door, if you take one step back, it will give the customer a greater sense of comfort. Many companies provide photo ID badges, and you must have yours clearly displayed. If it is necessary for you to enter a dwelling for service, ask permission from the homeowner before entering.

2.10 WORKING NEAT

Some companies provide technicians with paper shoe covers to prevent tracking dirt into residences. If you suspect your shoes are dirty, either remove them or use the covers. You and your company can be responsible for cleaning the carpet if it becomes soiled. When working on an indoor furnace, place a drop cloth on the floor in front of the furnace so that any debris will be contained. When you are finished working in the furnace area, a small battery powered vacuum cleaner can be used to pick up loose dirt and debris in the area. Use a damp rag to wipe down any fingerprints that are on the equipment or that may be on the door or woodwork.

TECH TIP

Cleaning up the equipment area in a residence is an excellent PR move. You should vacuum up all of the debris in the area including all the burnt matches that have been left there by the customer over the years as they may have lit the pilot. Many customers judge your work by appearance. All they may understand is neat and clean. When changing out a unit, electricians or plumbers may also be involved. You should clean up any mess even if you did not make it. Leaving behind a mess will reflect on you, since the final repair is still your responsibility.

In many residences, the air handler is located in an attic. If access to the unit is through a pulldown staircase, make certain that any dirt on debris that falls from the stairs when it is pulled down is cleaned up. If you are going to be going in and out of the attic a number of times during the service, place a drop cloth on the floor below the stairs to catch any insulation or other debris that might fall on the floor. Do not attempt to carry a large number of tools up and down the stairs. This can cause you to be caught off balance and possibly drop your toolbox. In addition, most attic stairs have a weight limit that could be exceeded by you and a large toolbox. Attic stair treads, like any ladder, are strongest next to the side rail. For that reason, when you ascend and descend the stairs, place your foot as close as possible to the side next to the side rail to reduce the possibility of breaking the stairs. Always be careful in an attic so that you do not step through the homeowner's ceiling.

Many customers have extensively landscaped their homes including the area around an outdoor condensing unit. Even though their landscaping may encroach within the manufacturer's recommended free air space around the unit, do not remove this landscaping; but notify the homeowner as to how it should be trimmed so that they or their landscaper can remove the vegetation. When working around vegetation, it is important

that you be as careful as possible so as not to damage any plants. On very soft, wet ground your repeated trips to the service van can wear a path. To avoid this, each time you have to cross soft, wet ground, take a slightly different route when possible.

It is considered a bad practice to leave packaging and boxes left over from the installation of new equipment in the customer's trash receptacles. This material should be taken with you so as not to overload their receptacle.

TECH TIP

Working in air conditioning and refrigeration is often a very hot job. From time to time customers may offer you a glass of water, tea, or cold drink. Use your discretion on accepting these offers. However, it is never appropriate for you to accept a beer or other alcoholic beverage from a customer. Even if you do not open the drink but take it with you, you have significantly damaged your credibility with the customer and your boss. If you take a beer, even though you do not drink it, and there is a problem with the service you provided the customer, the first thing the customer is going to tell your boss and everyone else is that you were drinking on the job, in spite of the fact they gave you the beer. Do not take any alcoholic beverages that are offered by customers.

2.11 TECHNICIAN AND CUSTOMER COMMUNICATION

A large part of the technician's job is to educate the customer as to the problem that was found and the available options for its repair. Tell the customer what failed, why it failed, and the options to fix the problem. Do not simply tell the customer that they need a part, and you are going to replace it.

Many customers would like an estimate of the job's cost. In some municipalities you are obligated under consumer protection laws to provide customers with such a quote. In some cases the quote must be in writing. If, however, as part of your service you uncover a situation that could not have been foreseen or was not visible in your initial evaluation that will require additional work, immediately stop and inform the customer of the new problem. Do not simply make the repairs and expect the customer to accept the higher charge at the conclusion of the job.

TECH TIP

If you locate an additional problem or pending problem with a customer's system and after notifying the customer of your concerns they choose not to have you provide that repair, you should note that on the customer's invoice as part of your service call record keeping and get them to sign the acknowledgment.

Under no circumstance should you tell a customer that the previous technician messed up their system when they did the last service. All that will result from such statements is the loss of faith the customer may have in you and your professionalism; but more importantly, you might find out that it was one of your colleagues who works for your company that did the last service job.

TECH TIP

Good professional technicians never knock the competition. Their skill and knowledge will set them apart from everyone else without the need to brag.

One of the primary complaints customers have on any service call is punctuality. It is not always possible to be at a job exactly when you anticipated being there. Earlier service calls may take more time than you initially estimated. However, as soon as you realize you are not going to make the schedule and as early as possible, let the customer know and give them an opportunity, if they so choose, to reschedule. If you do reschedule, you must be at the next scheduled appointment on time. It is extremely important that you provide a very clear, clean, and legible invoice or bill to the customer. If it is necessary for you to get prices, look up information, or check your spelling, you should do all of that in your service vehicle and not in front of the customer. Even though you may not be a literary expert, customers do expect you to provide them with clear, concise, well written statements. If you have a problem writing clear and concise statements, you may want to invest in a PDA (Personal Data Assistant) device. There are many of these devices on the market and many can have spell check and writing programs installed.

TECH TIP

Some air conditioning and refrigeration work in the summer requires that the technician work in relatively hot environments such as attics or buildings without working air conditioning systems. To prevent heat stress injury, it is important that you guard against dehydration by drinking large quantities of water or sports drinks. You must drink enough so that you have to use the restroom at least once every couple of hours throughout the day. In addition to dehydration, you may also develop kidney and bladder problems if you do not drink enough fluids while working in hot environments.

Carbonated beverages, milk, fruit juice, beer, and other beverages do not replace the body's electrolytes. Without replacing the electrolytes, you can feel fatigue, and may experience cramps. For that reason, only sports drinks with the essential electrolytes and water are recommended as your primary drinks when working in the heat.

UNIT 2—SUMMARY

You should become familiar with the various professional organizations and trade associations that support the air conditioning and refrigeration industry and consider joining those that are suitable to your career goals. Read the many available publications so that you may keep up to date with the latest changes in industry practices and standards.

As a refrigerant technician, you must become certified under the Environmental Protection Agency (EPA) Section 608 regulations. To further demonstrate your ability as a service technician, you may also consider taking an industry standardized test such as the Industry Competency Exam (ICE). There are also certification programs such as North American Technical Excellence (NATE) that allow you to focus on specialty areas.

Always remember to present yourself to the customer as a neat and clean professional. Carry an extra set of clothes in the event you need to change because your uniform becomes soiled. Think of using paper shoe covers rather than tracking dirt across the customer's carpet. Finally, always be polite to the customer and make sure that you communicate clearly. A large part of your job is to provide guidance for the customer by explaining the nature of the equipment-related problem. Be prepared to tell the customer what failed, why it failed, and the options to fix the problem.

UNIT 2—REVIEW QUESTIONS

1. List three student organization clubs.
2. What does RSES stand for?
3. What does ACCA stand for?
4. What does AHRI stand for?
5. What does ASHRAE stand for?
6. What does NATE stand for?
7. What section of the EPA regulations requires technician certification?
8. The _____ exam has been developed over the years with input from manufacturers, trade associations, instructors, and other industry experts.
9. What is the name of the vocational industrial club for students in high schools, trade schools, and community colleges?
10. What organization was founded in the late 1990s by a group of air conditioning educators, counselors, and administrators responsible for the various aspects of HVAC/R training?
11. List the seven specialty areas for the NATE service technician certification program.
12. The core exam for the NATE certification program covers what topics?
13. What is the difference between a code and a standard?

14. What precaution should be taken if you find that during the course of the day your uniform becomes soiled?

15. When might it be necessary for you to use a drop cloth?

16. When making a repair, what information should you relay to the customer?

17. If you locate an additional problem or pending problem with a customer's system and they choose not to have you provide that repair, what should you do?

18. What is one of the primary complaints that customers have regarding service calls?

19. Why are many common drinks, such as sodas, not adequate for your protection against heat stress injury?

20. When would it be appropriate to tell the customer that the previous technician messed up their system when performing the last service call?

UNIT 3

Safety

OBJECTIVES

After completing this unit you will be able to:

- explain how to work safely to avoid accidents.
- discuss the material that appears on all Material Safety Data Sheets (MSDS).
- discuss how to safely use hand and power tools.
- discuss how to practice safety in the shop.
- describe four types of fire extinguishers.
- demonstrate a safe method of lifting heavy objects.
- discuss safe welding and cutting practices.
- discuss electrical safety rules.
- discuss the safe use of refrigerants, their storage, and proper disposal.
- tell how to safely handle refrigerant cylinders.
- discuss refrigerant system safety.
- name three major hazards of pressure vessels.
- discuss how a technician's driving record can affect employability.
- tell what steps should be followed in case of an accident.

3.1 INTRODUCTION

In every trade, safety is a major concern, and safety is everyone's first job responsibility. Accidents, no matter how minor, can cost the technician, the company, and the customer unnecessary losses of time and money. There is no reason to feel that accidents are inevitable and something you must just accept. Good working habits, good tools, and being vigilant to potential hazards can virtually eliminate accidents. Never do anything you feel is unsafe. When working with new equipment or tools, read all the safety instructions and follow them.

Most companies require some type of safety training for all their employees. In addition some of the businesses where you may be asked to do HVAC/R work at may have their own safety program that you must pass before beginning work at their site.

Most accidents are caused by carelessness, as well as lack of awareness of proper safety procedures. This unit deals with some of the safety tips and procedures the installer and service technician should follow—whether on the job site or at related locations where hazards could exist.

This unit will cover many of the basic safety facts; additional specific safety facts will be covered in each unit. Read and follow all safety rules.

3.2 PERSONAL PROTECTIVE EQUIPMENT

Personal Protection Equipment (PPE) is designed to reduce your exposure to hazards that cannot be eliminated or controlled. PPE may include equipment or devices to protect your head, face, eyes, ears, respiratory system, hands, and feet. Some devices, such as safety glasses, are commonly used while others, such as respiratory protection, may be less frequently used.

If PPE is required for any job, OSHA (Occupational Safety and Health Administration) recommends that all employees be trained. This training may be as short as a few minutes to several hours or more. The length of the training time depends on the level of hazard and the complexity of the PPE to be used.

Keeping all PPE clean and in good working condition is essential to ensure that, when needed, they will work properly.

Head Protection

An approved hard hat, Figure 3-1, should be worn whenever there is a danger of things dropping on the head or where the head may be bumped. On a construction site proper safety head gear is a must.

Eye and Face Protection

The majority of eye injuries are the result of flying or falling objects. Most of these objects are smaller than the head of a pin but can cause serious injury. Approved eye or face protectors, Figure 3-2, must be worn whenever there is a

Figure 3-1 Hard hats are required to be worn on many job sites

Figure 3-2 Eye protection equipment: (a) these safety goggles can be worn over glasses; (b) safety glasses with side protection

danger of objects striking the eyes or face. Side shields must be part of any safety glasses worn even if they are prescription eyeglasses. Safety glasses or goggles must be worn over pre-scription eyeglasses if they do not have side shields. Eye and face protectors have various shapes and sizes and some of them are very specialized.

Special eye protectors must be worn when arc welding, spot welding, and burning in order to cut out harmful light radiation. These special face visors come with various shades of viewing eyepieces that filter out the harmful emissions. Take time to identify the right one for the job. For example, never wear oxyacetylene welding goggles when an arc weld-ing face shield is needed.

Confine long hair and loose clothing before operating rotating equipment.

TECH TIP

In order to control insurance costs, many air conditioning companies have adopted very stringent policies on per-sonal protection equipment. Unlike your shop teacher who may have reminded you each day about safety glasses, ear protection, and so on, many employers may terminate you with a single safety infraction. Others may warn you once or twice about wearing proper safety equipment while working. But no HVAC/R companies are going to give you unlimited warnings before your em-ployment with them is terminated. These policies are good for you and the company, because they reduce the likelihood of your being injured on the job.

Ear Protection

Hearing protection devices, Figure 3-3, must be worn when-ever there is exposure to high noise levels of any duration. These devices are of two types: (1) ear plugs, which are in-serted in the ear, and (2) headphones, which cover the ear. Either one must be properly selected on the basis of how much protection is required.

Respiratory Protection

There are two main types of respirators as shown in Figure 3-4: (1) *air-purifying respirators* are ones that purify the air by

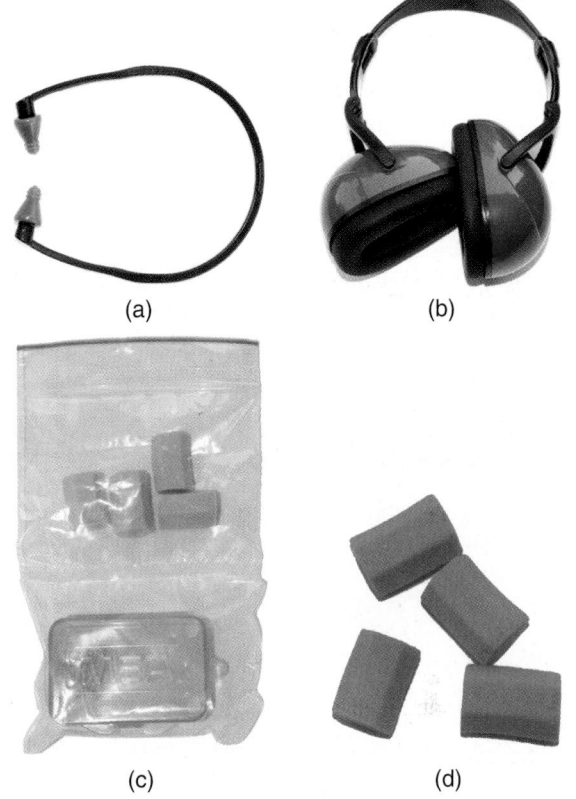

Figure 3-3 Ear protection equipment: (a) disposable earplugs on a lanyard (that fits around the neck) allow for easy removal and reuse; (b) headphones protect both ears and hearing; (c, d) disposable, one time use ear plugs

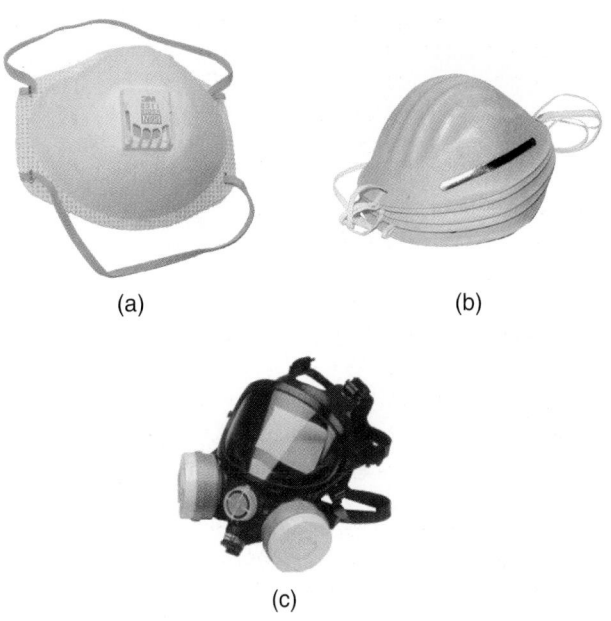

Figure 3-4 Filtration masks: (a, b) light duty filter; (c) respirator with replaceable filters

filtering out harmful dust, mist, metal, fumes, gas, and vapor; and (2) *atmosphere-supplying respirators* are ones that supply clean breathing air from a compressed air source. The second type should always be worn when working in a confined space where concentrations of harmful substances are very high or where the concentration is unknown. Remember that most refrigerants are odorless, tasteless, and invisible, and can cause asphyxiation in a very short time.

Respirators must fit tightly against the skin so that there is no leakage from the outside into the face. Workers who are required to use respirators at any time must be instructed in their use, care, maintenance, and limitations.

TECH TIP

Respirators are required to be located in all equipment rooms where that equipment contains large quantities of refrigerant. These respirators are provided in case there is a massive refrigerant leak. If you work in one of these areas, you must familiarize yourself with where the respirators are located and how to quickly put them on. You may have only a matter of seconds once a refrigerant leak alarm is sounded to safely put on this equipment.

Hand, Foot, and Back Protection

There are many different kinds of gloves used for hand protection, as shown in Figure 3-5. Some are made for special usages, such as gloves of steel mesh or Kevlar to protect against

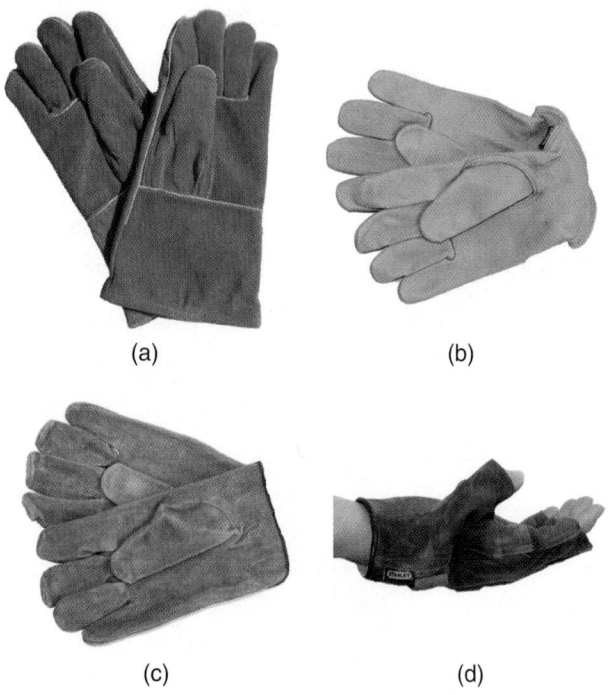

(a)   (b)

(c)   (d)

Figure 3-5 (a) Gauntlet-type work gloves; (b) work gloves, (c) welding gloves; (d) open-tipped gloves

Figure 3-6 High-top work boots

cuts and puncture wounds. Different glove materials are needed to protect against a variety of different chemicals. Choose the right kind from a dependable supplier who can supply this information. Discard the damaged ones.

Lifting heavy objects improperly can lead to back injury. Always bend at the knees and lift straight upward rather than bending over, which will place undue stress on the spine. There are a number of different types of back support belts available. These should be used if heavy lifting is expected to be performed on a regular basis.

When choosing foot protection, as shown in Figure 3-6, use the following guidelines:

1. All footwear must be well constructed to support the foot and to provide secure footing.
2. Where there is danger of injury to the toes, top of the foot, or from electrical shock, the proper shoe or boot, such as steel toe, must have Construction Safety Approval (CSA) indicated.
3. Where there is danger of injury to the ankle, footwear must cover the ankle and have a built-in protective element/support.
4. If there is danger of harmful liquids dropping on the foot, the top of the shoe must be completely covered with an impervious material or treated to keep the dripped substance from contacting the skin.

3.3 LADDERS AND SCAFFOLDS

Access equipment refers to ladders and scaffolds that are used to reach locations not accessible by other means. The following precautions should be practiced in the use of ladders.

1. Only use CSA- or ANSI-approved ladders. Maintain ladders in good condition. Inspect ladders before each use. Discard ladders needing frequent repairs or showing signs of deterioration.
2. All portable ladders must have no-slip feet.

3. Place ladders on a firm footing, no farther out from the wall than one quarter of the height required, as shown in Figure 3-7.
4. Ladders must be tied, blocked, or otherwise secured at the top where the ladder meets the building to prevent them from slipping sideways.
5. Never overload a ladder. Follow the maximum carrying capacity of the ladder, including the person and equipment. The American National Standards Institute (ANSI) sets the standard for ladders.
6. Only one person should be on a ladder, unless the ladder is designed to carry more people. Follow maximum load rating.
7. Never use a broken ladder. Never place a ladder for use on top of scaffolding. And never use a borrowed ladder on someone's property. Always use your own ladder even if you need to leave the job site to go get it.
8. Always face the ladder and use both hands when climbing or descending a ladder.
9. Use fiberglass or wood ladders when doing any work around electrical lines, Figure 3-8.

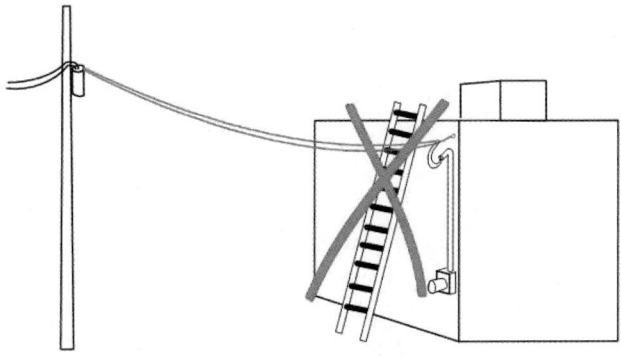

Figure 3-8 Never use a metal ladder near electrical wires!

10. Ladders should be long enough so you can perform the work comfortably, without leaning or having to go beyond the two rungs below the top rung safety barrier.
11. Stepladders should only be used in the fully open position.

CAUTION

Ladders must be inspected from time to time to ensure their safety. Some companies will require that a company safety official inspect the ladders you carry on your service van. Damaged or worn ladders must be repaired or removed from service.

The following recommendations apply to scaffolds.

1. Scaffolds must be supported by solid footings.
2. A scaffold having a height exceeding three times its base dimension must be secured to the structure.
3. When rolling scaffolds are used, the wheels must be locked when there are workers on the scaffold.
4. No worker is to remain on the scaffold while it is being moved. All equipment should also be removed before moving a scaffold.
5. Access to the work platform must be a fixed vertical ladder or other approved means.

3.4 FALL PROTECTION

Two methods of preventing injury from falling are: (1) fall prevention equipment, and (2) fall arresting equipment. Either of these methods is required when working at heights over 10 ft above grade when no other means has been provided for preventing falls. Figure 3-9 illustrates a safety belt.

In fall prevention, a worker is prevented from getting into a situation where a fall can occur. For example, a safety belt attached to a securely anchored lanyard will limit the distance a worker can move.

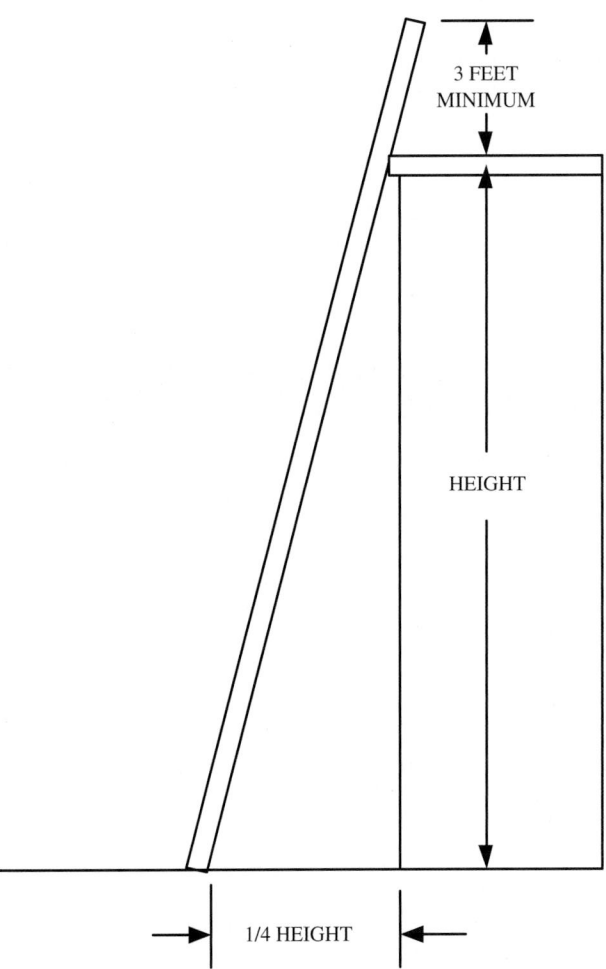

3 FEET
MINIMUM

HEIGHT

1/4 HEIGHT

Figure 3-7 A ladder must be placed so the top is at least 3 ft above the roof and at an angle in which the distance from the building is one-fourth the height of the building

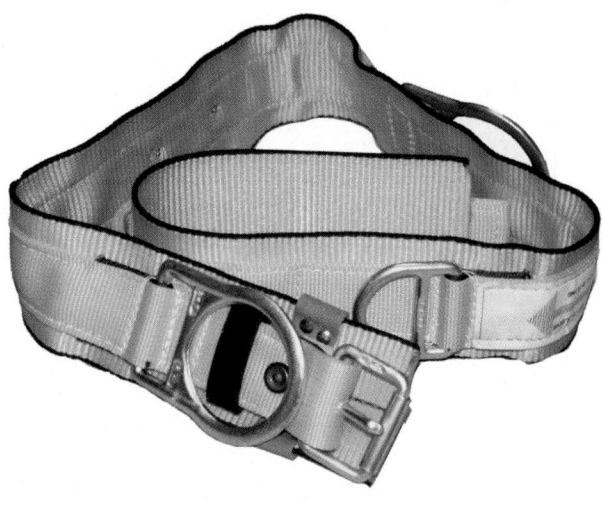

Figure 3-9 Safety equipment for heights over 10 ft above grade—a safety lanyard would be attached to this safety belt

In fall arresting, the worker must wear a safety harness attached to a securely anchored lanyard, which will limit the fall to a safe distance above impact. The harness helps prevent the worker from suffering internal damage. Belts should not be used to arrest a fall because they do not provide the measure of safety that harnesses do. Where a fall arresting system is not practicable, a safety net should be suspended below the work activity. The worker should be secured separately from the tools and equipment.

CAUTION

Fall protective harnesses are designed to suspend you in a vertical position if you accidentally slip and fall from a height. These harnesses, however, are not designed to suspend you for long periods of time. In recent years, workers have survived a fall, only to die in the safety harness. The safety harness can constrict blood flow to your legs as you dangle at the end of the safety line. The restriction of blood flow to your legs can cause enough blood to pool in your legs so that you might pass out or even die if allowed to dangle motionless for a long period of time. If you are the victim of a fall and are suspended on your safety line, you should remember to move your legs to help keep the blood flowing until you are rescued.

3.5 HOT AND COLD

HVAC/R technicians often work with extremely hot or extremely cold vapors, liquids, and solid objects. Similar personal protection equipment is required for both extremely hot and extremely cold work because of the potential for burns. Burns can occur on your skin from accidentally contacting either extremely hot or extremely cold material. It is easy to see how a hot material can cause a burn but more difficult to see how something that is cold can burn your skin.

When you touch something that is extremely cold, your body heat is drawn out so quickly that your own body's heat causes the surface of your skin to burn and blister. Remember that refrigerant will cause frostbite, so be careful.

3.6 HARMFUL SUBSTANCES

Workers in the mechanical trades can be exposed to a variety of harmful substances, such as dust, asbestos, carbon monoxide, refrigerants, resins, adhesives, and solvents.

All dust can be harmful. Where dust cannot be controlled by engineering methods, an approved respirator designed to filter out specific dust must be worn.

When asbestos containing material (insulation) is being cut or shaped, the particles must be removed by a ventilation system that discharges the particulate matter through a High Efficiency Particulate Air (HEPA) filter. All waste materials that contain asbestos must be placed in impervious bags for transfer to an approved disposal site. These fibers, when inhaled, are considered carcinogenic. Even if you are asked to remove asbestos from a piece of equipment such as an old boiler, do not attempt this. You do not want to put anyone's life at risk, so do not be forced into improperly removing asbestos. Improper removal of asbestos can lead to serious fines.

Engine-driven mobile equipment operating in an enclosed area can produce dangerous levels of carbon monoxide (CO). Oil-fired or gas-fired space heaters without suitable vents can also produce carbon monoxide. Areas must be well ventilated while being heated with these devices.

TECH TIP

Read and follow all label safety and user instructions on any materials you use in the HVAC/R field. Some of these materials can be hazardous to your health if you do not follow the label's directions.

Some refrigerants are more dangerous than others. All refrigerants are dangerous if they are allowed to replace the oxygen in the air. Even the so-called safe refrigerants can produce a poisonous phosgene gas when heated to high temperatures. Refrigerants sprayed on any part of the body can quickly freeze tissue.

Resins, adhesives, and solvents can be dangerous if not properly handled. Ensure that the workspace is continuously ventilated with large amounts of fresh air.

Never use carbon tetrachloride for any purpose because it is extremely toxic, either inhaled or on the skin. Even slight encounters with it can cause chronic problems.

To provide workers and health care professionals with specific reactions and treatments for exposure to materials on the job, all manufacturers must provide, on request, Material Safety Data Sheets (MSDSs) on all of their products. It is your responsibility to request MSDSs for all of the products you work with or carry on your service vehicle. Some site safety officers, building inspectors, or job managers may even ask to see your MSDSs before you are allowed to start or continue work.

3.7 MATERIAL SAFETY DATA SHEETS (MSDSs)

Material safety data sheets are required by law and have specific important information listed in specific areas so that emergency personnel can easily read them. If an area does not apply to the product, the manufacturer must mark the space as being nonapplicable. No blank spaces are allowed on MSDSs. This is done so that there will not be any confusion regarding the safety or reactions to any products. You should read MSDSs on any material before you use it so you know how to use it properly and safely as well as knowing what to do if there is an accident involving the material.

Figure 3-10 is an example of an MSDS for a coil cleaner. The following material appears on all MSDSs:

1. **Identity.** This section gives the name of the product.
2. **Section I.** This section gives the manufacturer's name and address. This section contains the emergency contact phone number and company phone number.
3. **Section II: Hazardous Ingredients/Identity Information.** A list of the hazardous ingredients by chemical name is given here. If a material has a secret ingredient,

Material Safety Data Sheet
May be used to comply with
OSHA's Hazard Communication Standard,
29 CFR 1910.1200. Standard must be
consulted for specific requirements.

U.S. Department of Labor
Occupational Safety and Health Administration
(Non-Mandatory Form)
Form Approved
OMB No. 1218-0072

(1) IDENTITY *(As Used on Label and List)* Coil Master Non Acid Coil Cleaner CMD-2A

Note: Blank spaces are not permitted. If any item is not applicable, or no information is available, the space must be marked to indicate that.

(2) Section I

Manufacturer's Name Crow Marketing & Distribution, Inc.	Emergency Telephone Number 800-255-3924
Address *(Number, Street, City, State, and ZIP Code)* P. O. Box 29171, Dallas, TX 75229	Telephone Number for Information 214-241-3049
	Date Prepared 08-23-95 reviewed 12/01/99
	Signature of Preparer *(Optional)*

(3) Section II -- Hazardous Ingredients/Identity Information

Hazardous Components (Specific Chemical Identity; Common Name(s)	OSHA PEL	ACGIH TLV	Other Limits Recomended	% (optional)
NaOH Sodium Hydroxide 50%	2mg/m^3	2mg/m^3		
CAS#1310-73-2 NA1824 Corrosive				

(4) HMIS INFORMATION

Health	2
Reactivity	1
Flammability	0

(5) Section III -- Physical/Chemical Characteristics

Boiling Point	180°F	Specific Gravity (H_2O = 1)	1.01
Vapor Pressure (mm Hg.)	760	Melting Point	N/A
Vapor Density (AIR = 1)	1	Evaporation Rate (Butyl Acetate = 1)	N/A

Solubility in Water
Complete - 100%

Appearance and Odor
Yellow to gold liquid, characteristic odor

(6) Section IV -- Fire and Explosion Hazard Data

Flash Point (Method Used) None	Flammable Limits None	LEL	UEL

Extinguishing Media
N/A

Special Fire Fighting Procedures
Will react with metals to produce flammable hydrogen gas

Unusual Fire and Explosion Hazards
None known. Contents under pressure. Exposure to temperatures above 120°F may cause bursting.

Figure 3-10 Sample of a completed Material Safety Data Sheet (MSDS)

the company must either list it or provide it to a health worker on request. The item listed as OSHA PEL stands for the *personal exposure limit*. This is the maximum safe amount of contact or exposure time that is allowed. The ACGIH TLV is the time weighted average exposure over an 8 hr period of time. It is the maximum amount of contact or exposure allowed during an 8 hr working day. Any other specific limitations are given in this section.

4. **HMIS Information.** The information in this section refers to the hazardous material identification system (HMIS). This information tells health care workers a relative number according to how significantly the material will affect health, how reactive it is, and its flammability.

5. **Section III: Physical/Chemical Characteristics.** This section gives the properties of the material, such as its boiling point, vapor pressure, solubility in water, specific gravity, melting point, evaporation rate, and its appearance or odor.

6. **Section IV: Fire and Explosion Hazard Data.** Gives the flammability of the material and lists its flash point, flammability limits, extinguishing media, any special firefighting procedures, and any unusual fire or explosion hazards.

In addition to the information on the MSDS you must read and follow all manufacturers' listed instructions for proper use and handling of every material you use on the job. Many companies have policies that require that you be fired if you do not follow these instructions. These policies are both for your protection and the protection of the company and to customers. Handle all material properly according to the manufacturer's instructions.

SERVICE TIP

It is a good work practice to request MSDSs on all products that you get from the supply house. Some job site safety officials require that you have MSDSs on all of the products you will be using at their job site. An easy way of maintaining these documents is to put them all in a large manila envelope that is labeled MSDS and keep this envelope in your service vehicle.

3.8 SAFE WORK PRACTICES

The installer and service technician works in many areas: in the shop, in various types of buildings, in equipment rooms, on rooftops, under houses, and on the ground outside buildings. Each location requires different activities where safe performance is essential.

In addition, the worker deals with many potentially dangerous conditions, such as handling pressurized liquids and gases, moving equipment and machines, working with electricity and chemicals, and exposure to heat and cold. It is important, therefore, that the technician practice good safety procedures wherever or whatever the work is.

Confined Space Entry

A confined space is an area that has been closed off from any outside source of ventilation and is a space large enough for a person to enter and perform work. Entering a storage tank through a manhole opening would be an example of this. Never enter such a space unless the atmosphere has been checked to ensure that no hazardous vapors exist. Even without the presence of hazardous vapors, the space could be potentially deadly due to a lack of oxygen. A person entering an oxygen deficient space may not realize it until too late and suddenly pass out unconscious. Never enter a confined space until the air quality in the space has been verified as acceptable. Even then, always leave someone standing outside the space with emergency breathing apparatus available and ready.

3.9 TOOLS

All tools come with safety instructions. Do not assume you know how to use a tool; read and follow the manufacturer's safety instructions. These instructions have been developed and tested to ensure that, when followed, you are not likely to be injured.

Part of the manufacturer's literature may include instructions on how to service or repair the tool. Make sure to follow these instructions so that the tool will last longer and you can use it safely.

Hand Tools

1. Keep all hand tools sharp, clean, and in safe working order.
2. Defective tools should be repaired or replaced.
3. Use correct, proper fitting wrenches for nuts, bolts, and objects to be turned or held.
4. Do not work in the dark; use plenty of light.
5. Do not leave tools on the floor. Keep them properly put away neatly in your vehicle.

Power Tools

1. Only use power tools that are properly grounded.
2. Stand on dry nonconductive surfaces when using electrical tools.
3. Use only properly sized electrical cords in good condition with a GFI or GFCI.
4. Turn on the power only after checking to see that there is no obstruction to proper operation.
5. Disconnect the power from an electrical tool (or motor) before performing any maintenance.
6. Disconnect the power supply when equipment is not in use.

CAUTION

Never use portable electrical equipment unless it is connected to a Ground Fault Circuit Interrupter (GFCI) or Ground Fault Interrupter (GFI). GFI is the term that is sometimes used when referring to a GFCI. A GFCI is a safety device that cuts off electric current to a circuit when a short or ground is detected. These devices are designed to prevent burns and electrocution if a portable electric tool is being used. OSHA requires that all extension cords used for outside service work be equipped with GFCIs. Some extension cords now come with these devices built into the plug. If your extension cords do not have GFCIs built in, one can be purchased and added to the end.

3.10 SHOP SAFETY

1. Keep the shop or laboratory floor clear of scraps, litter, and spilled liquid.
2. Store oily shop towels or oily waste in metal containers in an open, airy place.
3. Clean the chips from a machine with a brush; do not use a towel, bare hands, or compressed air.
4. Keep safety glasses and gloves in a prominent location adjacent to machinery used for grinding, buffing, or hammering and where material with sharp edges is handled.
5. Establish cleaning periods regularly, at least on a daily basis. Make sure everyone is clear when using compressed air to clean.

Maintaining an Orderly Shop

1. Arrange machinery and equipment to permit safe, efficient work practices and ease in cleaning.
2. Materials, supplies, tools, and accessories should be safely stored in cabinets, on racks, or in other readily available locations.
3. Working areas and workbenches should be clear. Floors should be cleaned on a daily or more frequent basis. Keep aisles, traffic areas, and exits free of materials and obstructions.
4. Combustible materials should be properly disposed of or stored in approved containers.
5. Drinking fountains and wash facilities should be clean and in good working order at all times.
6. Eyewash stations should be periodically tested to make sure that they work properly and they should not be blocked and should always be readily accessible.

Fire Extinguishers

The danger of fire is always present. Rags soaked in oil, grease, or paint can ignite spontaneously. Keep used rags in tightly closed approved metal containers.

Sparks, open flames, and hot metal can ignite many materials. Always have a fire extinguisher close at hand when welding or burning.

CLASS A EXTINGUISHERS

CLASS B EXTINGUISHERS

CLASS C EXTINGUISHERS

CLASS D EXTINGUISHERS

Figure 3-11 Fire extinguisher classification symbols

Extreme caution should be taken with highly flammable and volatile solvents. Due to its low flash point (the temperature at which vapors will ignite), gasoline should never be used as a cleaning solvent.

Fire extinguishers should be readily accessible, properly maintained, regularly inspected, and promptly refilled after use. Fire extinguishers are classified according to their capacity for handling specific types of fires, Figure 3-11.

1. **Class A Extinguishers.** These are used for fires involving ordinary combustible materials such as wood, paper, and textiles, where a quenching, cooling action is required.
2. **Class B Extinguishers.** These are for flammable liquid and gas fires involving oil, gas, paint, and grease, where oxygen exclusion or flame interruption is essential.
3. **Class C Extinguishers.** These are for fires involving electrical wiring and equipment where nonconductivity of the extinguishing agent is critical. This type of extinguisher should be present whenever functional testing and system energizing take place.
4. **Class D Extinguishers.** Some metals, such as magnesium, can actually catch fire. Class D extinguishers are used to put out combustible metal fires.

CAUTION

Having the proper fire extinguisher is not enough if it is not large enough to do the job. Make sure that your fire extinguisher is large enough to handle the size of fire that might occur in your work area. If there are a lot of combustible materials, you need a bigger fire extinguisher. In some cases you may want to have more than one fire extinguisher available.

Material Handling

Use mechanical lifting devices whenever possible. Use a hoist when lifting tools or equipment to a roof. If you are required to lift a heavy object, get help. In order not to strain your back, the following procedures should be observed when lifting heavy objects.

1. Bend your knees and pick up the object, keeping your back straight up.
2. Gradually lift the weight using your leg muscles, continuing to keep your back vertical.

3.11 WELDING AND CUTTING

Welding and cutting is a specialized skill and requires special training. Many refrigeration and air conditioning technicians require this training due to the need to perform some of these operations as part of their work. It must be recognized, strictly from a safety standpoint, that this work should not be attempted without adequate knowledge and instruction.

Acetylene

Acetylene gas under high pressure is unstable, so to make it safe to use it is absorbed in acetone inside the acetylene cylinder. However, an acetylene cylinder can explode if it is struck or jarred severely, so keep the cylinders secured so they cannot be accidentally knocked over or fall. Because acetylene can explode at high pressures, it is illegal to operate a torch with an acetylene pressure greater than 15 psi. For HVAC/R work, we generally use pressure less than 5 psi. Most acetylene gauges have a red mark indicating 15 psi, Figure 3-12.

CAUTION

The acetone which is used to stabilize the acetylene is absent in the neck of the tank. For this reason, never store or transport an acetylene cylinder in the horizontal position. Storage in this manner even for short periods is *very* dangerous.

Oxygen

Oxygen is provided in highly pressurized cylinders. A full oxygen cylinder contains approximately 2000 pounds per square inch (psi) of oxygen. Because the oxygen is under such great pressure, care must be taken to ensure that the oxygen cylinder valve is not damaged or knocked off. If the oxygen cylinder valve were to be broken off of a full oxygen cylinder, the cylinder could fly around the room much like a child's balloon. To prevent possible damage to the valves and regulators on oxygen and acetylene cylinders they should be securely attached to a frame or cart when they are in use, Figure 3-13.

Figure 3-12 Acetylene regulator with gauges

Figure 3-13 Portable oxyacetylene welding and cutting rig
(Courtesy Victor Equipment Company)

CAUTION

Certain materials react explosively if exposed to high pressure pure oxygen. Never use oil or grease on any part of the oxygen or acetylene regulator, hoses, or torch and tips. Ensure that all fittings are clean and dry when assembling. Repair using only manufacturer approved replacement parts.

Air acetylene torches are used by HVAC/R technicians to produce sufficient heat for silver (hard) soldering brazing. These torches use a mixture of air and acetylene as a fuel.

Oxyacetylene torches are used for brazing, welding, and cutting. These torches mix oxygen and acetylene gases to produce a very intense hot flame.

The following safety rules should be practiced when using this equipment.

1. Always use a welding regulator on acetylene and oxygen cylinders.
2. Never use oil or grease on a regulator. This could cause a violent explosion with compressed oxygen.
3. Always secure the cylinder to something solid to prevent it from being accidentally knocked over.
4. Wear the proper colored safety glasses.
5. Open the valve on the acetylene cylinder only one and one-quarter turns.
6. Light the torch with a striker.

SAFETY TIP

Always remove regulators from oxygen and acetylene cylinders before you put them back in your service vehicle. In many states and cities it is against the law to transport oxygen and acetylene cylinders in a motor vehicle with the regulators attached. The danger is that in an accident the regulators could be broken off, causing a fire or explosion.

CAUTION

All oxygen and acetylene cylinders should be stored and used in secure racks or carts. Federal safety regulations (OSHA) require 55 ft³ cylinders and larger to be safety chained to carts or structures any time the cylinder is being used with its safety cap removed. There are no exceptions to these OSHA regulations regarding cylinders.

3.12 FIRST AID

Refrigeration and air conditioning workers are advised to enroll in an approved first aid course. Some vocational programs and technical colleges offer first aid as an elective course. Be sure to talk to your advisor about taking a first aid course. Prompt and correct treatment of injuries not only reduces pain but could also save lives. A classification of accidents that occur to HVAC/R personnel, related to the hazards described, include the following:

1. Injuries due to mechanical causes.
2. Injuries due to electrical shocks.
3. Injuries due to high pressure.
4. Injuries due to burns and scalds.
5. Injuries due to explosions.

6. Injuries due to breathing toxic gases.
7. Never play with electricity. Joking around could cause you or someone you are with to receive serious injury or death.
8. Heat exhaustion or heat stress.

3.13 ELECTRICITY SAFETY

All possible precautions must be practiced to prevent electrical shock, that is, current passing through the body. Very few realize the damage that can be done by even a small amount of current.

The following information applies to low voltage circuits where current is measured in milliamps (mA). One amp (A) is equal to 1,000 mA.

The illustration in Figure 3-14 indicates the effect on the body when various amounts of current pass through the body at 100 mA or less.

Noncontact voltage (NCV) testers should be a standard tool for all HVA/CR service technicians. Some digital multimeters incorporate an NCV feature.

Electrical Safety Rules

1. Check all circuits for voltage before doing any service work. Tag and lock out all electrical disconnects when working on live circuits.
2. Stand on dry nonconductive surfaces when working on live circuits.
3. Work on live circuits only when absolutely necessary.
4. Use only properly insulated tools to work on electrical circuits.

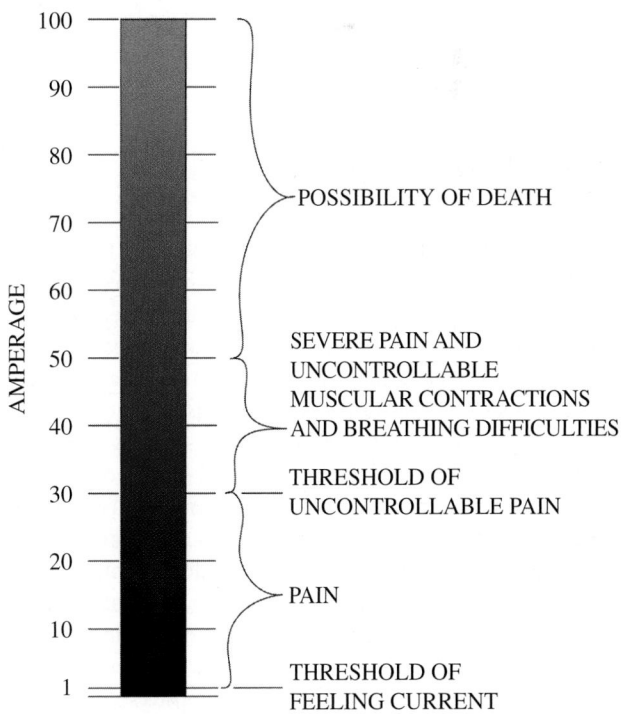

Figure 3-14 Amperage rating of electric current creating various shock effects from 1 mA up to 100 mA
(Courtesy of Workers Compensation Board of British Columbia)

5. Never bypass an electrical protective device.
6. Properly fuse all electrical lines.
7. Properly insulate all electrical wiring.
8. Use ground fault circuit interrupters whenever using power tools.

3.14 REFRIGERATION SAFETY

The hazards associated with refrigeration service are principally associated with the proper use of refrigerants and their storage in closed containers and systems. A large improvement was made when the HVAC industry started using the so-called safe refrigerants (Class I or fluorocarbons), which were nontoxic and nonflammable. Dangers now relate to the use of pressurized gas or liquid and the fact that these chemicals, when released accidentally, can replace oxygen in a confined space without sensory detection.

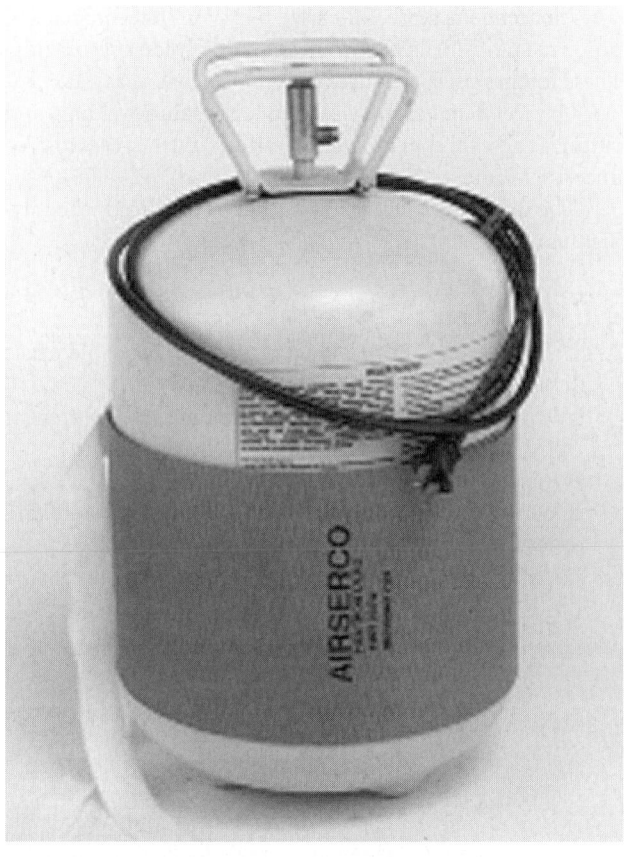

Figure 3-15 An electrical cylinder heater can be used to safely raise cylinder temperature
(Courtesy of Airserco Manufacturing Company)

CAUTION

From time to time it may be necessary to warm a refrigerant cylinder so that system charging can proceed. Never heat a refrigerant cylinder with an open flame. This could cause two problems. The open flame could cause a rapid rise in cylinder pressure above the rupture point of the cylinder, and the high heat can cause the refrigerant to decompose. Three safe ways of warming cylinders are to place the cylinder in a warm bath of water; or to place the cylinder in the warm discharge air from the condenser fan; or to wrap an electrical cylinder heater around the cylinder, Figure 3-15.

CAUTION

It is illegal to sell any used CFC or HCFC refrigerants that have not been reclaimed by an EPA-certified reclaimer.

Used Refrigerants and Refrigerant Oils

The EPA classifies all used refrigerants and used refrigerant oils as hazardous waste that must be disposed of properly. They must be taken to a state or locally approved recycler that specializes in used refrigerants and used refrigerant oils. Often these recyclers have local or state certifications that you can obtain copies of for your records. It is a good idea to keep accurate and complete records showing how and where all of the used refrigerant and used oil you collect was disposed. Although these records are not required by the EPA, you may be asked to prove that you are complying with all disposal requirements. Having good documentation can help show the EPA if your records are audited that you are complying with all the laws and regulations regarding disposal of hazardous waste.

Used refrigerant oil and used automotive oils are not compatible and cannot be mixed for disposal. That is why used refrigerant oil cannot be disposed of at an automotive oil recycler unless they have special containers just for used refrigerant oil.

Handling Refrigerant Cylinders

1. Do not fill a cylinder with liquid refrigerant to more than 80% of its volume. Heat can expand the liquid enough so that it fills the cylinder. Once that occurs, the cylinder will rupture. Space must be available inside the cylinder for proper expansion of the liquid to take place. In recovering refrigerants, this is particularly important. Special cylinders have been designed for recovery that have an automatic volume limiting device.
2. In using a cylinder or transporting it, the cylinder must be secured with a chain or a rope in an upright position. Do not drop a cylinder.
3. Mixing refrigerants is dangerous. Cylinders are color coded to help identify each refrigerant. Each system has an identifying label. Do not mix refrigerants. Maintain the identification system.

4. Never apply a torch to a system containing refrigerant. If heat is needed to vaporize refrigerant, use hot water at a temperature not to exceed 125°F (52°C).
5. Do not refill disposable refrigerant cylinders.
6. Replace the cylinder cap when not using a cylinder. The cap protects the valve. Do not lift or carry a cylinder by the valve.

SERVICE TIP

Most refrigerant cylinders come in cardboard boxes. These boxes contain important safety information. Some industrial plant safety officers will require that you maintain these cardboard containers with the safety material listed whenever you are working on their job site.

Refrigerant System Safety

1. Never use oxygen or acetylene to pressurize a system because an explosion can occur. Use dry nitrogen or carbon dioxide from a tank properly fitted with a pressure regulator.
2. When isolating a section of piping or component of a system, exercise caution to prevent damage and potential hazard from liquid expansion.
3. Always charge refrigerant vapor into the low side of the system. Liquid refrigerant entering the compressor could damage the compressor or cause it to burst.
4. Never service a refrigeration system where an open flame is present. The flame must be enclosed and vented outdoors. If a fluorocarbon refrigerant comes in contact with intense heat, it can produce poisonous phosgene gas.

3.15 PRESSURE VESSEL SAFETY

Pressure vessels pose three major hazards if they rupture. The blast from the sudden explosion can cause serious internal injury. The pressurized liquid can cause severe burns. In addition, fragments of metal thrown from the exploding vessel can cause lacerations and punctures. All pressure vessels pose some degree of hazard to individuals working in the area; that is why they must be inspected for flaws that might weaken their integrity.

There are a number of pressure vessels used in the HVAC/R field. These include accumulators, receivers, refrigerant cylinders, low-pressure boilers, high-pressure boilers, and hot water tanks. Both low and high pressure boilers and many commercial hot water tanks are required to be inspected periodically. The type and frequency of inspection varies depending on the type of pressure vessel. There must be a placard displayed on or near the pressure vessel showing when it was inspected and giving the date when it needs to be reinspected.

Some pressure vessels such as accumulators and receivers may not have to be inspected. It is, however, a good idea to inspect them for rust, corrosion, cracks, or other signs of physical damage that may render them unfit for service.

Refillable refrigerant cylinders, such as those that are used for refrigerant recovery, must be inspected every five years. The inspection date must be stamped on the top of the cylinder. Cylinders that have not been inspected within five years cannot be used.

3.16 DRIVING SAFETY

A good driving record is essential for any job that requires that you drive. Almost all HVAC/R work requires that you do some driving as part of your job. Outside service technicians may spend much of their day driving from one job to another.

Your driving record will affect the insurance rate the company must pay. In some cases a very bad driving record could make you unemployable due to the high insurance rates your employer would have to pay so you could drive their service vans.

You cannot speed or drive recklessly or aggressively in a service vehicle. To do so could result in bad public relations for your company. In addition, with almost everyone having a cell phone, the chance that someone would call your boss and report your actions is very high. Even worse would be if they use their cell phone to take a picture or video of your driving and send that to your boss. You might be the best technician the company has, but you can still lose your job because of your actions behind the service vehicle's wheel.

If you are involved in an accident, make sure to get all of the other driver's information. You should also get any contact information from anyone who may have witnessed the accident.

TECH TIP

Carrying a disposable camera in the vehicle glove box will let you take photos of the accident and of any cars in the area. Make sure to get photos of the license plates of potential witnesses to the accident. A few photos taken shortly after the accident can help you prove your side of the story, if necessary.

3.17 STEPS TO BE FOLLOWED IN CASE OF AN ACCIDENT

1. If the injuries appear to be serious, call 911 or your local emergency number.
2. First aid should be administered, if needed, only by those qualified to do so.
3. All accidents, injuries, and illnesses should be reported to your boss or supervisor no matter how minor the injuries may seem.

4. An accident report form should be filled out and turned in to your company office.
5. An investigation of the accident may be done to determine the cause of the accident.
6. Clean up the area before resuming work.

UNIT 3—SUMMARY

Schools provide a safe environment to learn. However, it is your responsibility to always work safely. You must follow all of the rules because electricity, compressed gases, and other potential hazards do not know you are a student; you may not get to make a safety mistake more than once.

If you have not been trained on the safe operation of any tool, equipment, or device, do not attempt to use it.

Safe working habits can last a lifetime. Start now and learn everything you can to make your HVAC/R career a long and safe one.

UNIT 3—REVIEW QUESTIONS

1. Tell what causes accidents and how they can be eliminated on the job site.
2. What are PPE's?
3. Discuss ladder safety.
4. Discuss scaffold safety.
5. What is the difference between fall prevention equipment and fall arresting equipment?
6. Describe how cold can cause a burn on skin.
7. List harmful respiratory substances.
8. Explain some of the dangers of refrigerants.
9. Explain what material appears on all Material Safety Data Sheets (MSDSs).
10. Discuss how to safely use hand tools.
11. Discuss how to safely use power tools.
12. Discuss how to practice safety in the shop.
13. List four types of fire extinguishers.
14. Tell how to safely lift heavy objects.
15. Discuss safe welding cylinder practices.
16. Discuss electrical safety rules.
17. When a refrigerant cylinder needs to be warmed, how should it be done?
18. How should used refrigerants and refrigerant oils be disposed of?
19. Discuss refrigerant system safety.
20. List three major hazards of pressure vessels.
21. Discuss how a technician's driving record can affect employability.
22. Tell what steps should be followed in case of an accident.

HVAC/R Science

UNIT 4
Properties of Matter

OBJECTIVES

After completing this unit you will be able to:

- explain why the properties of matter are important to the HVAC/R field.
- explain the law of conservation of matter and give an example.
- discuss the unique characteristics of the three states of matter.
- name the physical and thermal properties of matter and tell why it is important for the HVAC/R worker to understand them.
- explain the difference between weight and mass.
- explain the importance of testing standards.
- demonstrate how to calculate the density, specific volume, and specific gravity of a material and discuss how this information is used.
- identify the common temperature reference points.

4.1 INTRODUCTION

Matter is all around us; matter is what makes up the earth and everything in and on the earth. Understanding the states and properties of matter is important to the HVAC/R technician because all heating and cooling requires some change to matter. During both the heating and cooling process, matter may expand or contract, melt or freeze, or even appear to vanish through evaporation or combustion.

Some types of matter are easily heated or cooled while other types of matter take more heat to get a temperature change. Different forms of matter respond differently when heated or cooled. To better understand what happens when things are heated and cooled and why it happens, you must understand matter and its properties.

Matter can be identified by its properties because each type keeps its own unique set of properties regardless of the sample size. A single drop of water reacts and responds to pressure and temperature just like an ocean of pure water would.

4.2 MATTER

Matter is anything that has mass and occupies space. Here on earth, matter may be thought of as anything that has weight and occupies space. Water and air are example of matter; light and sound are not matter. Only a limited amount of water or air can be put in a container until it is full and there is no more space inside. However, a container will not "fill up" with light or sound because they do not occupy space.

The law of conservation of matter states that we cannot create or destroy matter. Matter can change its form, but it cannot disappear. We can grind, crush, or burn matter, but it still exists in the same quantity, just in a different form. When a log burns in a fire, its matter is not destroyed; it simply changes from one form to another form. The log is mainly made up of carbon and hydrogen atoms. When it burns up in a fire, much of it is changed from a solid to a gas. The carbon and hydrogen combine with oxygen to form carbon dioxide, carbon monoxide, and water. Some unburned carbon leaves as smoke and some minerals and carbon are left as ash. If you could capture all of the products of combustion and weigh them, they would weigh the same as the wood and oxygen you started with.

4.3 THE STRUCTURE OF MATTER

Everything on earth consists of different combinations of 94 naturally occuring chemicals called elements. We are familiar with some elements because they are used in their pure form. For example, metals like gold, platinum, lead, mercury, iron, copper, and aluminium can be used in their pure element form. Some gases like argon and nitrogen are used as pure elements.

Atoms

The smallest piece of an element that can exist and still retain the same chemical properties is the atom. Atoms are made of small particles called protons, neutrons, and electrons. Protons are positively charged, electrons are negatively charged, and neutrons have no charge. Atoms have a nucleus composed of protons and neutrons. Clouds of negatively charged electrons orbit around this nucleus, Figure 4-1. However, most matter does not exist as an element, but a compound made up of more than one atom.

Molecules

The smallest part of anything that is not an element is a molecule. When the atoms of an element join together with themselves or with other types of atoms, they form molecules. Energy binds atoms to each other to form molecules, Figure 4-2. Because of their atomic structure, some materials have a predisposition to combine with other material. Oxygen is an example of an element that is normally only found in molecules made up of the same type of atoms. Two oxygen atoms join to form one molecule of O_2 (pronounced O-two), the air we breathe.

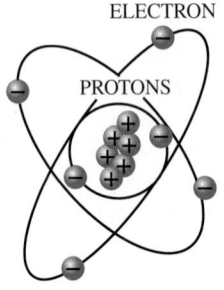

Figure 4-1 The carbon atom has six protons and six electrons

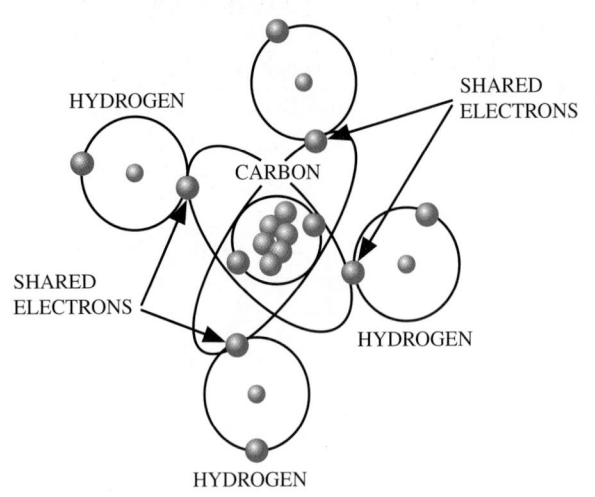

Figure 4-2 The methane molecule is composed of one atom of carbon and four atoms of hydrogen

Different types of atoms can also join to form different types of matter. Water (H_2O), for example, is formed when two hydrogen (H + H) atoms and one oxygen (O) atom unite. The amount of energy holding the atoms together changes when they combine to form molecules. This change absorbs or releases energy. When hydrogen combines with oxygen, large amount of heat is released. Chemical energy is the energy change that takes place when the atoms of materials rearrange themselves to form entirely new materials from the same atoms. It is important to remember that no matter or energy is "lost," just changed.

4.4 STATES OF MATTER

In air conditioning and refrigeration work, you will encounter matter in three states: solid, liquid, and gas, as shown in Figure 4-3. The state that a substance is in depends upon its physical properties, the pressure applied to it, and its temperature. Water is an example of matter that is commonly found at standard atmospheric pressure in three states. It is a solid (ice) at 32°F (0°C), a liquid between the temperature of 32°F (0°C) and 212°F (100°C), and a vapor or gas at 212°F (100°C) and above. These three different states of matter each represent a different level of molecular energy. The energy levels from lowest to highest are solid, liquid, and gas.

4.5 SOLID

Solids are the lowest energy level of these three physical states. The molecules of a solid remain basically fixed in place. They do vibrate, but they do not move about. Solids have a definite shape and they will hold their shape under some stress. Gravitational force on solids creates downward pressure on the surface that the solids rests on. Small changes in the volume of a solid occur from temperature change.

SERVICE TIP

The specific gravity of a fuel gas is important when using pipe sizing charts. A pipe's resistance to flow changes with the specific gravity of the gas traveling through it. Gas piping offers more resistance to gases with higher specific gravities than to gases with lower specific gravities. For this reason, gas piping charts specify the specific gravity of the gas they are designed for.

4.17 EXAMPLE CALCULATIONS

The AHRI definition of standard air will be used as the reference temperature and pressure for all our examples. Take the example of a gas with a weight of 4 lb and a volume of 64 ft³. To calculate density, divide 4 lb by 64 ft³ to arrive at a density of 0.0625 lb/ft³. To calculate specific volume: divide 64 ft³ by 4 lb to get a specific volume of 16 ft³/lb. You can easily convert between density and specific volume by dividing them into 1. In our above example, dividing 16 into 1 yields 0.0625; and dividing 0.0625 into 1 yields 16.

For another example, examine a solid that weighs 300 lb and takes up 3 ft³. To calculate density, divide 300 lb by 3 ft³ arrive at a density of 100 lb/ft³. To calculate specific volume, divide 3 ft³ by 300 lb to get a specific volume of 0.01 ft³/lb. You can easily convert between density and specific volume by dividing them into 1. In our above example, dividing 0.01 into 1 yields 100; dividing 100 into 1 yields 0.01.

Notice that in each case density and specific volume are "opposites." If something has a high density, it will have a low specific volume. Likewise, if it has a low density, it will have a high specific volume. In general, solids and liquids have high densities and low specific volumes. Gases are just the opposite; they tend to have high specific volumes and low densities.

To calculate specific gravity of a solid or liquid, divide its density by the density of water. You only need to remember to compare apples to apples. If you state water's density in pounds per cubic foot, you also must state whatever you are measuring in pounds per cubic foot.

The density of water in traditional units is usually stated as 62.4 lb/ft³ at standard conditions. Applying this to the solid in the second example above, the specific gravity of the solid would be 100 divided by 62.4, or 1.6 (rounded). This substance would be much heavier than water and would sink.

For gases, the density of the gas is compared to the density of air. The density of air at standard conditions is usually stated as 0.075 lb/ft³. The specific gravity of the gas used in the first example would be 0.0625 lb/ft³ divided by 0.075 lb/ft³ or 0.83 (rounded). This substance is lighter than air and would rise.

SI Calculations

SI calculations for density and specific volume are performed in the same way as for traditional units, just using SI units. For example, density can be calculated in kilograms per liter while specific volume would be liters per kilogram. Take the example of a liquid with a weight of 3 kg and a volume of 4 L. To calculate density, divide 3 kg by 4 L to arrive at a density of 0.75 kg/L. To calculate specific volume: divide 4 L by 3 kg to get a specific volume of 1.3 (rounded) L/kg.

Metric units provide a shortcut when determining specific gravity. Since 1 L of water weighs 1 kg, the density of water is 1 kg/L. This means that densities calculated in kilograms per liter also represent the specific gravity. In the example above, the specific gravity of the liquid is 0.75 because it is equal to the density. This also works for the smaller units of grams and milliliters. A substance's density in grams per milliliter is also its specific gravity.

4.18 MELTING AND FREEZING POINTS

The melting point of a material is the temperature where the material begins to change from a solid state to a liquid state when heat is added. When a substance changes from a solid to a liquid, the potential energy of the molecules increases, but the temperature stays the same. This means that when a solid melts, the liquid being formed is the same temperature as the solid it came from.

The freezing point of a material is the temperature where the material begins to change from a liquid state to a solid state when heat is removed. The melting point and freezing point are the same except for the direction of heat flow. If heat is flowing into the material, it is melting; and if it is flowing away from the material, it is freezing. Figure 4-9 lists a single temperature for both the melting and freezing temperature for the materials shown.

Mixtures of two or more substances can create a solution with a substantially lower freezing point than either substance alone. Ethylene glycol and water is a good example. Pure ethylene glycol, the primary component in antifreeze,

Material	F°	C°
Ethanol	−173°F	−114°C
Mercury	−38°F	−39°C
Beeswax	145°F	65°C
Copper	1,984°F	1,085°C
Aluminum	1,220°F	660°C
Ethylene glycol	8.6°F	−13°C

Figure 4-9 Melting points for several materials

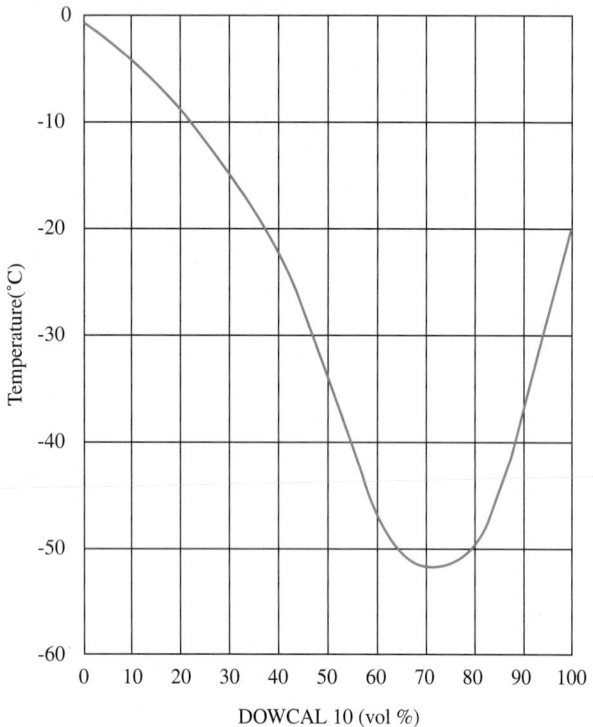

**Freezing point of aqueous solution of
Dowcal 10 (Ethylene Glycol 94%)**

Figure 4-10 The freeting point of water/glycol solutions changes depending on the percentage of glycol

freezes at around 8°F and water freezes at 32°F. Systems exposed to cold winter temperatures easily freeze at these temperatures. But a solution of 60% ethylene glycol and 40% water freezes at a much lower –48°C, Figure 4-10.

4.19 EVAPORATION

Evaporation is gradual change of state from liquid to gas that occurs when the liquid is below the boiling point. Only the molecules at the surface of the liquid can evaporate. The molecules in the liquid are in constant motion, but traveling at different speeds. Liquid molecules are frequently colliding with each other. If a molecule at the surface is struck hard enough by another molecule, it may gain enough kinetic energy for it to leave the liquid and become a gas molecule even though the temperature of the liquid is below the boiling point.

Since higher temperatures mean higher average molecular speed, evaporation increases as the temperature of the liquid increases. Increased surface area also increases evaporation because evaporation only occurs at the surface. A third factor is the concentration of the gas molecules around the liquid. Water evaporates more slowly when the air around it is at a high relative humidity.

TECH TIP

Evaporation is very important to everyday life. If water did not evaporate at temperatures below the boiling point, after mopping a floor the water would remain on the floor indefinitely.

Some liquids, like oils, do not appear to evaporate. If you spill some on the counter today it will still be there tomorrow. This is because their molecules do not strike each other hard enough or at the correct angle to eject the surface molecules from the liquid.

4.20 BOILING AND CONDENSING POINTS

Boiling describes a rapid change from a liquid state to a gaseous state. The boiling point of a liquid is the temperature where the saturated vapor pressure of the liquid equals the surrounding atmospheric pressure. The difference between evaporation and boiling is that when a liquid is boiling, molecules are changing throughout the liquid and forming gaseous bubbles, while evaporation takes place only on the surface. Heat is required to make a substance boil. When a liquid boils, the potential energy of the molecules increases, but the temperature stays the same. This means that when water boils, the water and the steam coming off the water are both 212°F, Figure 4-11.

The condensing point is the temperature where gaseous molecules are releasing heat and joining together forming a liquid. Condensation of a vapor occurs when the molecules of gas slow down as heat is removed. The molecules begin to clump together and form a liquid. Condensing releases

Figure 4-11 Both the water and the steam are 212°F

the potential energy that was absorbed when the molecules changed from a liquid to a gas. The difference between the boiling point and the condensing point is which direction heat is flowing.

4.21 EFFECT OF PRESSURE ON BOILING POINT AND CONDENSING POINT

The boiling and condensing point of any liquid is controlled by the pressure. Remember that the boiling point occurs when the vapor pressure of the gas bubbles in the liquid equal the pressure surrounding the liquid. When that pressure is increased, the liquid molecules have to gain more kinetic energy in order to reach escape velocity to become a gas. Thus, increasing the pressure on a liquid increases the boiling point.

For example, the boiling point of water at atmospheric pressure is 212°F. When the pressure on the water is increased to 15 psig, the boiling point is increased to 257°F. This is the secret of pressure cookers. By increasing the pressure, the water in the pressure cooker heats to a temperature higher than 212°F, Figure 4-12.

This same principle is used in car radiators. The radiator cap maintains a pressure above atmospheric pressure in the engine's cooling system, effectively raising the boiling point of the engine coolant to prevent it from boiling, Figure 4-13.

A lower pressure will result in a lower boiling point. Reducing the pressure below atmospheric with a vacuum pump will lower the boiling temperature of water. Figure 4-14 shows the boiling point of water at different pressures.

The refrigerant cycle is based on changing the pressure of a liquid to change its boiling and condensing temperatures. By lowering the pressure, the boiling point of the refrigerant

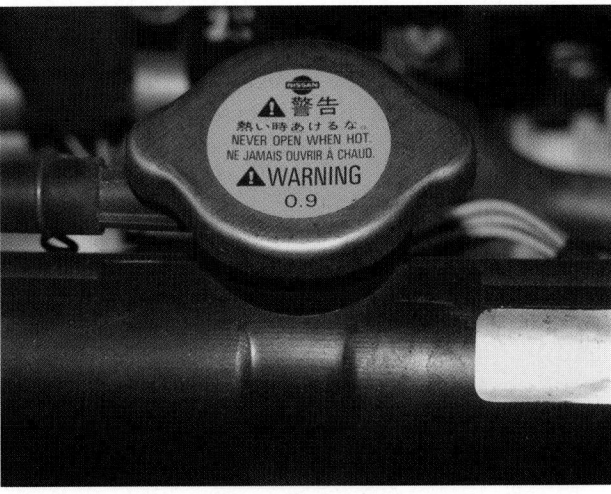

Figure 4-13 The cap on a car radiator increases the boiling point of the engine coolant by increasing the pressure in the radiator.

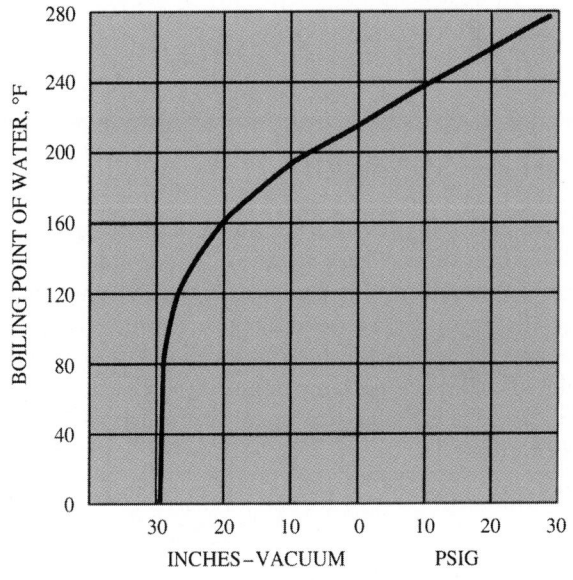

Figure 4-14 Pressure-temperature curve for water

is lowered enough so it can boil and pick up heat at a lower temperature. Raising the pressure on the refrigerant vapor makes it possible to condense the vapor back into a liquid at a higher temperature by removing heat.

Figure 4-12 The water in a pressure cooker boils at 257°F under a pressure of 15 psig

SERVICE TIP

The purpose of a vacuum pump is to ensure that the refrigeration system has no air or moisture in it before charging it with refrigerant. The low pressure created by the vacuum pump causes any water droplets in the system to boil to a gas so the water can be removed by the vacuum pump.

Library, Nova Scotia Community College

4.22 SUBLIMATION AND DEPOSITION

When a solid changes to the gaseous state without forming a liquid, it is called sublimation. Under some condition, molecules at the surface of the solid can change from a solid to a gas. An example of sublimation is ice that disappears in a frost-free refrigerator. The ice has not truly disappeared, it has sublimated to a gas. The water vapor is then deposited on the evaporator as frost, changing from a gas back to a solid. When a gas changes to a solid without going through the liquid phase, that process is called deposition.

SERVICE TIP

"Freezer burn" is caused by sublimation. The water in frozen food slowly sublimes out, leaving the food dry and tough. Freezer burn can be reduced by using heavy duty plastic wrap and containers designed to reduce the amount of water that can pass through the container.

UNIT 4—SUMMARY

Matter exists in three forms, solids, liquids, and gases Adding heat can change a solid to a liquid, and a liquid to a gas. Solids and liquids do not change size by adding increased pressure. Gases do change size with changes in pressure. An increase in pressure can increase the boiling point of a liquid, or the temperature at which a liquid turns to a gas. This is the basic principle on which all HVAC/R systems work.

UNIT 4—REVIEW QUESTIONS

1. What is matter?
2. What is the difference between an atom and a molecule?
3. List the three states of matter in order of their energy level from lowest to highest.
4. Explain the difference between the weight of an object and the mass of an object.
5. Calculate the density, specific volume, and specific gravity of a gas that occupies 20 ft^3 and weighs 2 lb.
6. If the gas in question 5 was released in a room, would it be more likely to be found near the ceiling or near the floor?
7. Calculate the density, specific volume, and specific gravity of a solid that occupies 3 ft^3 and weighs 9 lb.
8. If the solid in question 7 was placed in water, would it sink or float?
9. Explain the relationship between specific volume and density.
10. What is the AHRI definition of standard air?
11. Why are testing standards important when specifying density and specific volume?
12. What is the difference between the melting and freezing points?
13. What effect does pressure have on the boiling temperature of a liquid?
14. What is the temperature of the water formed when ice melts?
15. Give a practical application in the HVACR industry for specific gravity.
16. State the law of conservation of matter.
17. What is a substance's critical point?
18. What are the two general categories for properties of matter?
19. What physical change of state is the opposite of boiling?
20. What physical change of state is the opposite of sublimation?

Library, Nova Scotia Community College

UNIT 5

Types of Energy and Their Properties

OBJECTIVES

After completing this unit you will be able to:

- explain the difference between potential and kinetic energy.
- list common forms of energy and the units used to measure them.
- explain how the structure of molecules and atoms affects chemical and electrical energy.
- explain the relationship between energy, work, and power.
- calculate energy conversions using Watts, BTU, foot-pounds, and joules.
- diagram the electrical distribution system.

5.1 INTRODUCTION

At its most fundamental level, heating and air conditioning is about controlling energy. Many tasks performed by air conditioning technicians involve controlling and measuring energy. Heating is the process of adding thermal energy; air conditioning and refrigeration are processes that remove thermal energy. Other types of energy are often used when transferring thermal energy. Understanding energy and how it affects our world is crucial to understanding heating, air conditioning, and refrigeration.

5.2 ENERGY, WORK, AND POWER

The world and everything in it can be divided into two large categories: matter and energy. On earth, matter has weight and takes up space; everything around us is made of matter. Energy affects matter, but energy has no weight and does not take up any space.

Energy acts on matter to perform work. Work is done when energy is transferred to an object. For example, the mechanical energy used to compress a spring is transferred to the spring. The spring contains more energy than it did before it was compressed. When energy is transferred into an object, the object is changed in some way. Energy makes matter move, changes its temperature, or even changes its physical state.

The relationship between energy, work, and power is typically explained using the example of a moving object. Mechanical work is defined as force multiplied times distance. A footpound of mechanical work is performed when 1 lb is moved a distance of 1 ft, Figure 5-1. Moving

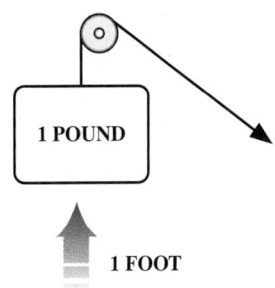

Figure 5-1 A footpound of work is moving 1 lb 1 ft

5 lb a distance of 2 ft would represent 10 ft lb of work. This describes the amount of work done, but it does not describe how long it took. Horsepower measures the rate of mechanical work. One horsepower (hp) is a rate of work equal to 33,000 ft lb/min. Moving 33,000 lb a distance of 1 ft in 1 min would require 1 hp, Figure 5-2. The relationship between energy, work, and power can be stated as follows: energy is the ability to do work, work is the result of transferring energy, and power is the rate at which the work is accomplished.

5.3 POTENTIAL AND KINETIC ENERGY

Something that has potential has ability. Potential energy is energy that is stored, waiting to perform work. Something that is kinetic is in motion. Kinetic energy is energy in motion performing work. A battery is a good example of potential energy. The battery has the potential to create a flow of electrical current, but current does not flow until a circuit is created. When a path is formed, electrons flow from one pole to the other, creating a flow of electrical current. This

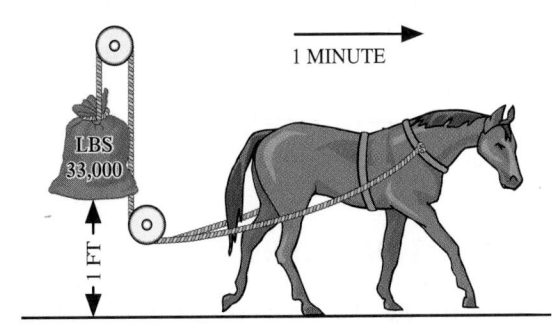

Figure 5-2 One horsepower is moving 33,000 lb 1 ft in 1 min

Figure 5-3 Flowing water is an example of kinetic energy
(Courtesy of Tennessee Valley Authority)

converts some of the potential energy in the battery to kinetic energy because the electrons in the circuit are in motion. Other examples of potential energy include a compressed spring or water held in a reservoir behind a dam. Releasing the spring releases the mechanical energy by putting the spring in motion, converting potential energy to kinetic energy. Releasing water through the spillway of the dam converts the water's potential energy into kinetic energy because the water is in motion, Figure 5-3.

Potential and kinetic energy are also present at the molecular level. At temperatures above absolute zero, all molecules move or vibrate. The vibrations and movements are examples of kinetic energy because they are associated with motion. As the temperature of the molecules increases, the motion and kinetic energy also increases.

The physical state of the matter determines the molecule's potential energy. It takes energy to change the state of matter. The molecules of a liquid have less attraction for each other than the molecules of a solid. They move about freely because they have a higher level of potential energy than the molecules of a solid. Similarly, the molecules of a gas have an even higher amount of potential energy than a liquid. The energy that goes into changing the state of a substance is potential energy because it does not affect the motion of the molecules, only their positioning relative to each other. Large amounts of energy are required to change the state of a substance, but its temperature remains the same during this change of state. At the molecular level, energy that is associated with molecular motion and temperature is kinetic energy while energy that is associated with a physical change of state is potential energy.

5.4 FORMS OF ENERGY

We all use energy hundreds of times a day while going about our daily routine. Driving a car, heating a home, operating a computer, and even playing music all use energy. Energy exists in many forms. Some common forms of energy used in heating and air conditioning are

- Chemical
- Thermal (heat)
- Radiant (light)
- Electrical
- Magnetic
- Mechanical

This is by no means a complete list of energy forms, just the forms of energy most often involved in the air conditioning trade.

5.5 CHEMICAL ENERGY

The smallest part of anything that is not an element is a molecule. Energy binds atoms to each other to form molecules, Figure 5-4. Because of their atomic structure, some materials have a predisposition to combine with other materials. The amount of energy holding atoms and molecules together changes when atoms combine with each other to form new molecules. This change absorbs or releases energy. Chemical energy is the energy change that takes place when the atoms of materials rearrange themselves to form entirely new materials from the same atoms. It is important to remember that no matter or energy is "lost," just changed.

One common use of chemical energy is for the generation of electricity. Batteries are an example of chemical energy. A chemical change in the materials of the battery creates electrical potential, Figure 5-5. Many tools use batteries, and some thermostats are operated by batteries instead of power from the system.

Burning hydrocarbons, like natural gas, is also another form of chemical energy. Large amounts of chemical energy are used to produce heat in gas burning appliances. The carbon combines with oxygen to form carbon dioxide and the

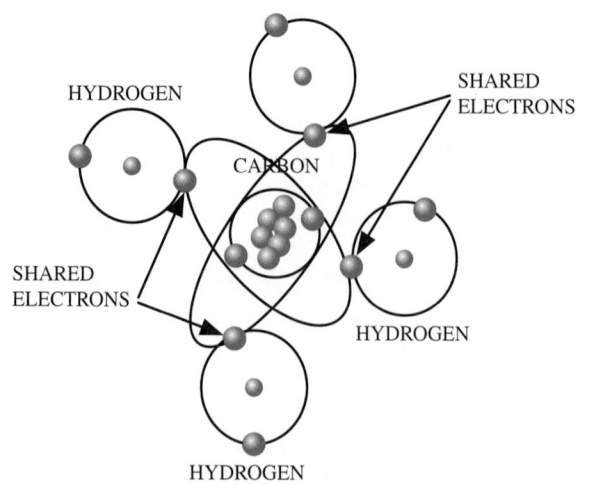

Figure 5-4 Methane molecule

Figure 5-5 Batteries convert chemical energy into electrical energy

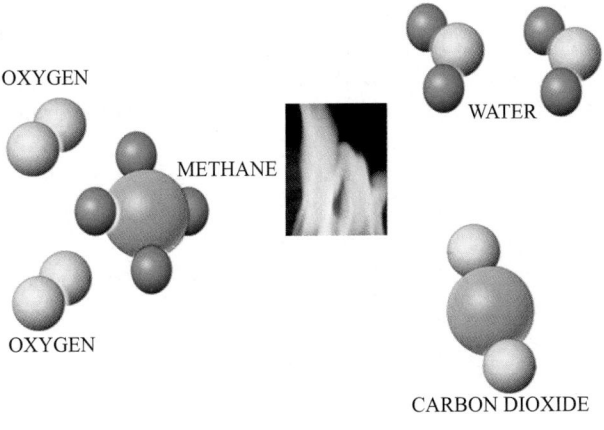

Figure 5-6 Combustion turns chemical energy into heat energy

hydrogen combines with oxygen to form water, Figure 5-6. The combustion of hydrocarbons is still the primary source of energy in the world.

5.6 THERMAL ENERGY—HEAT

All molecules are in motion. Not only are the electrons in motion as they orbit the nucleus, the entire molecule vibrates with a random motion. Heat is the form of energy that gives molecules their motion. For the same state, more heat equals

faster molecular motion, while less heat equals slower molecular motion. Temperature increases or decreases as molecular motion increases or decreases. A change in thermal energy that results in a change in temperature is called a sensible heat change because the temperature change can be sensed. But not all changes in thermal energy result in a temperature change. Some changes result in a physical state change.

The arrangement and energy level of the molecules in a substance determine its physical state: solid, liquid, or gas. Solids are at the lower end of the energy spectrum. The molecules of a solid vibrate, but remain more or less in the same spot. As their energy level increases, the temperature of the substance increases. When they reach the melting point, the molecules cannot stand still any longer and they begin to freely move about. Now they are forming a liquid. As a liquid, all the molecules can move about; but they still maintain close contact with each other. As more energy is added, they move about faster and faster and their temperature increases. At the boiling point their energy level is too high to tolerate each other, and they separate from each other as much as possible. Now they are forming a gas, Figure 5-7.

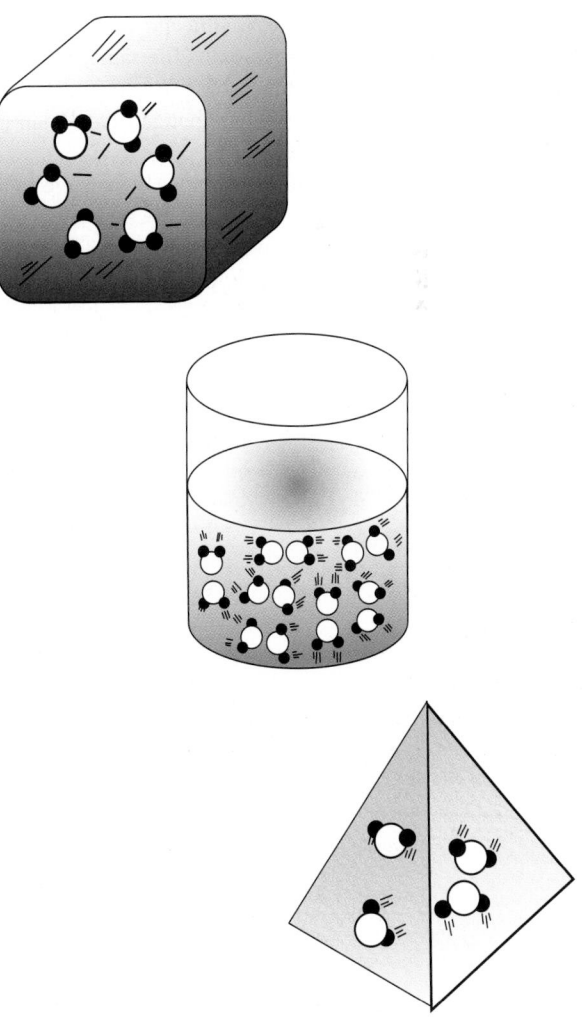

Figure 5-7 Matter can exist as a solid, liquid, or gas

Figure 5-8 The water and ice are both 32°F

Each of these state changes requires an enormous amount of energy. The energy added to a material at the melting point or boiling point does not result in a temperature change because all the energy is used to change the state of the substance. This is a crucial concept: when matter is changing state its temperature remains the same. When ice melts, both the ice and the water melting from the ice are 32°, Figure 5-8. Once all the material has changed state, then the temperature can start to change.

Changes in heat that result in a change in state are called latent heat, meaning hidden heat. This is because there is no temperature change accompanying the heat change. Of course, it is possible to see the steam coming off of boiling water, but it is not possible to measure a temperature difference between the water and the steam, because the boiling water and the steam are the same temperature.

Controlling thermal energy is usually the desired end result in heating and air conditioning. The end product of operating a furnace is supplying heat to the house. The end product of operating an air conditioner is removing heat from the house. Heat is also involved in the generation of most of the world's electrical power. Chemical energy is used to make heat, the heat is used to make motion, and motion and magnetic energy are used to make electrical energy.

5.7 RADIANT ENERGY

Radiant energy is electromagnetic energy that travels in waves. Heat, light, radio waves, and x-rays are examples of radiant energy. Radiant energy is measured by its wavelength and frequency. Wavelength refers to the distance between the peaks of the waves; frequency refers to the number of complete waveforms per second. Lower frequencies have longer wavelengths; higher frequencies have shorter wavelengths. Figure 5-9 illustrates the relationship between frequency and wavelength. The electromagnetic energy spectrum extends from radio waves at the lowest energy level, to gamma rays at the highest energy level.

5.8 ELECTRICAL ENERGY

Electrons are the subatomic particles whizzing around the outside of an atom. Electricity is basically the flow of electrons. It is not like pouring electrons in one end of a wire and

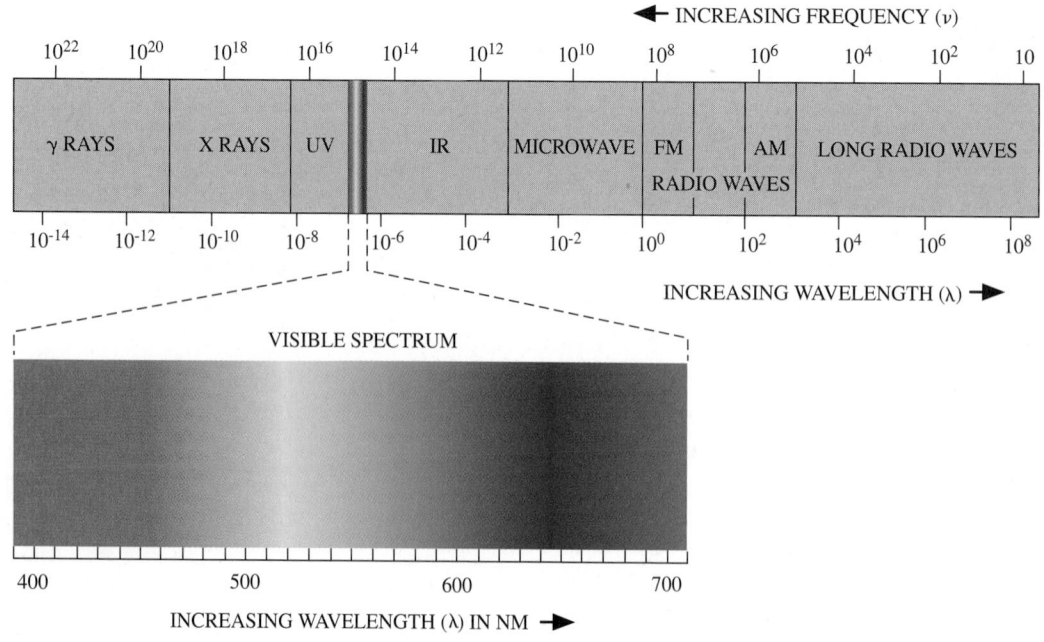

Figure 5-9 As the frequency increases, the wavelength gets shorter
(NASA)

dumping them out the other end. Rather, electricity is more like a string of dominoes. One bumps the next and the energy flows from one end to the other, but no individual domino moves very far. With electricity, an electron moving from one atom to another creates an imbalance in that atom which causes it to reject an electron. This electron then has a similar effect on a neighboring atom. This chain reaction carries through the wire to provide an electrical current.

Electricity is the mainstay of all heating and air conditioning systems. The controls are all electrical and many of the systems use electricity exclusively for their power source. While it is true that hydrocarbon combustion powers the world, a large percentage of that heat energy is used to generate electricity.

5.9 MAGNETIC ENERGY

Magnetic energy is created by the alignment of electric charges. This occurs when all the molecules of a polar material are aligned so that the positive ends of all the molecules face the same direction in the material. This alignment gives the entire object a polarity and sets up an invisible magnetic field. Some materials, like iron, are attracted to this field. A magnetic field is also created around a wire that has an electrical current flowing through it, Figure 5-10. Conversely, moving a magnetic field past a wire will "pull" electrons in the wire in the direction of the magnetic field. This creates an electric current in the wire. This relationship between magnetic fields and electrical flow is the foundation of electrical generators and motors.

It might appear that making electricity by moving a magnet past a wire is "free" energy because it is difficult to see anything happening. Turning a generator by hand will dispel this misconception. When the generator is not connected to an operating circuit, it is relatively easy to turn. When an electric circuit with a small light is connected, the generator gets considerably harder to turn. If the light is replaced with a larger one, the difficulty increases. With a large enough electrical load, the generator becomes nearly impossible to turn. However, if the load is turned off, the generator turns easily again. This is just another illustration of the law of conservation: you cannot get energy for free!

Magnetic energy is usually not an end result but a way of transferring mechanical energy into electrical energy or electrical energy into mechanical energy. All electric motors used in air conditioning use a magnetic field to turn an electric current into mechanical energy. Many controls that operate motors also rely on magnetism to turn electrical energy into mechanical energy. Although magnetic energy is seldom the end result, it has a part in nearly all electrical generation.

5.10 SOURCES OF ENERGY

We depend on a variety of energy sources to maintain the lifestyle enjoyed by people in the United States. Many of the energy sources we currently use cannot be replenished; after we use them up, they are gone. These are called nonrenewable energy sources. Other energy sources can be replenished, and so they are called renewable energy sources.

TECH TIP

Conservation of the limited supply of nonrenewable natural resources is important. There is a great deal of interest by citizens' groups and the government behind the HVAC/R industry's push for higher efficiency equipment. Heating and air conditioning accounts for approximately 50% of the energy used in most homes. Selling, properly installing, and properly servicing high efficiency equipment is good for the environment. Properly working high efficiency equipment will result in our using less of these valuable nonrenewable sources of energy. Properly working high efficiency equipment is also good for the customer because their utility bills will be lower as a result of consuming less energy.

Nonrenewable Energy Sources

Nonrenewable energy sources have a limited supply. Currently, most of the world's energy is supplied by nonrenewable energy sources. Oil, natural gas, coal, and uranium are examples of nonrenewable energy sources, Figure 5-11.

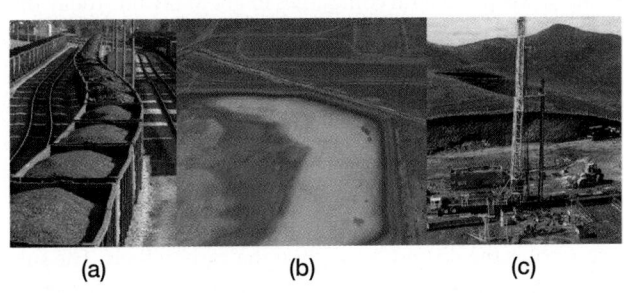

(a)   (b)   (c)

Figure 5-11 (a) Coal cars—non-renewable energy sources *(Courtesy of Indiana Office of Energy)*; (b) Uranium mining in the Navajo Nation *(Courtesy of Sprol.com)*; (c) Drilling for petroleum-based energy *(OSHA)*

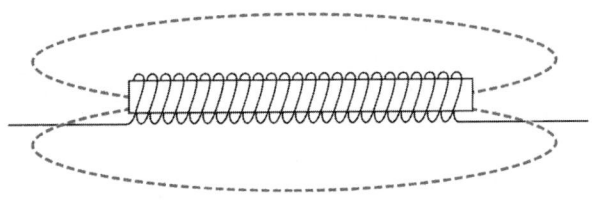

Figure 5-10 Electromagnetism produced by current flowing through a conductor

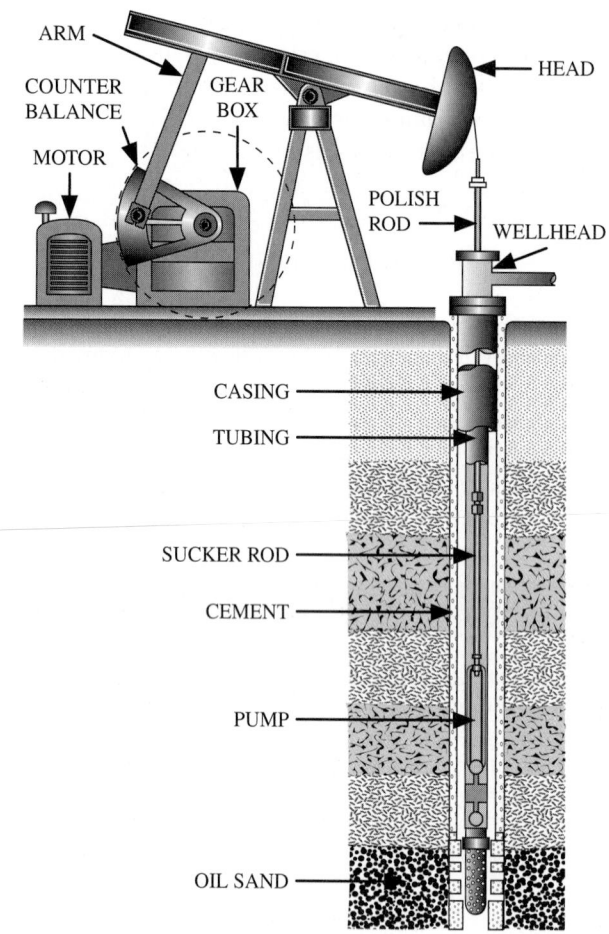

Figure 5-12 Oil well cross section
(Source: California Department of Conservation.)

Figure 5-13 Surface coal mine
(Courtesy of Peter Gunn)

Crude oil is recovered from wells, Figure 5-12, and distilled into a large number of hydrocarbon fuels including fuel oil and gasoline. These refined products are used for heating, electricity generation, and transportation.

Natural gas also comes from wells in the ground. Gas is frequently found on top of oil reserves. Like oil, natural gas is a hydrocarbon. In years past, when natural gas was encountered during petroleum exploration, the gas was burned off to allow the petroleum companies to get to the oil. Today the gas is considered as valuable as the oil. It is collected, refined, and distributed nationally through pipelines for heating and electrical generation. Gas is the cleanest burning of all the carbon based fuels.

Coal is essentially carbon. It must be mined by digging it out of the ground, Figure 5-13. Coal is still plentiful in the United States, but many problems come with increased coal use. Coal is the dirtiest burning of the carbon fuels. The sulfur content in coal contributes to acid rain. Like all carbon based fuels, coal produces carbon dioxide when burned. However, since coal is nearly all carbon, it produces more carbon dioxide than either gas or oil. Because the United States has such large coal reserves, many studies are underway to

find cleaner uses of coal. The primary use for coal today is generating electricity.

Uranium is a radioactive element used today in nuclear power plants. It is possible to split uranium atoms to form two smaller atoms and release vast amounts of energy. The energy released from the fission, or splitting, of the uranium atom is used to heat water to steam to generate electricity. Nuclear power holds great promise, but also a great potential for catastrophe, as was demonstrated at Chernobyl. Public opinion has turned against nuclear power because of concern for the safety of nuclear power plants. Another concern with nuclear power is managing the radioactive material left over from operating the plant.

The world's growing energy demands have strained the current methods of retrieving and distributing these nonrenewable resources. The increasing energy demands of the world cannot be supported indefinitely. We are using up finite sources of energy at an ever increasing rate.

Renewable Energy Sources

Renewable energy sources can be replenished. Interest in renewable energy sources is increasing as researchers look for long-term solutions to the world's energy appetite. Some of the renewable energy sources that have been explored include solar, wind, hydro, ocean, geothermal, and biomass.

Solar energy can be used to generate electricity using photovoltaic cells, or it can be converted into thermal energy for heating water and buildings. A few large-scale solar generating stations have been constructed in the southwestern United States that generate electrical power and distribute it over the existing electrical grid, Figure 5-14.

Wind energy is primarily used to generate electricity. Wind generators are in use from small windmills to generate electricity in homes to large scale projects that harvest wind power with hundreds of large strategically placed windmills, Figure 5-15. One concern with windmill farms has been the large number of birds killed by the windmills.

Figure 5-14 Large-scale solar power generating plant
(Office of Energy Efficiency and Renewable Energy, U.S. Department of Energy)

Hydroelectric power has been used for years. Projects like the Tennessee Valley Authority, TVA, have sought to turn the raw power of large rivers into electricity. However, the potential is somewhat limited and environmental concerns have been raised regarding the drastic changes in the ecosystem that a large scale hydroelectric plant brings. Even in the TVA, one of the world's most ambitious uses of hydroelectric power, only 10% of the electricity is generated by hydroelectric power.

Figure 5-15 Wind farms use multiple large wind turbines to generate electrical power
(By the permission of Endless Energy Corporation.)

Figure 5-16 This plant produces biodiesel fuel from soybeans
(Courtesy Minnesota Soybean Processing Plant)

Ocean energy can be harnessed from the waves or from the rising and falling tide. The wave motion has been used to turn generators. The tidal change can be used in coastal areas that have a high degree of tidal change between high and low tide. Gates are constructed that control the flow of sea water into and out of large areas, trapping water at high tide. The water is then released through a turbine to generate electricity.

Geothermal energy is heat from inside the earth. Hot water and steam flowing out of the ground can provide heat in areas with active thermal springs or geysers. Geothermal heat pumps can extract heat from the ground, even at relatively low temperatures. A geothermal heat pump can move three times as much heat as it consumes.

Biomass energy refers to energy derived from plants and animals. This can be as simple as burning plants for heat, or as complex as converting garbage into gas and oil. Decaying trash, plants, animals, and animal wastes can be used to produce methane, the main component of natural gas. Plant and animal materials can also be used to produce fuels like bio-diesel or ethanol. Figure 5-16 shows a plant that produces biodiesel fuel from soybeans.

5.11 ENERGY CONVERSION

Energy can be converted from one form to another. The energy conversions required to operate an air conditioner are listed below.

1. Coal or natural gas is burned at the generating plant to produce steam; converting chemical energy into thermal energy.
2. The steam is used to turn a turbine; converting thermal energy into mechanical energy.
3. The turbine turns a generator; converting mechanical and magnetic energy into electrical energy.

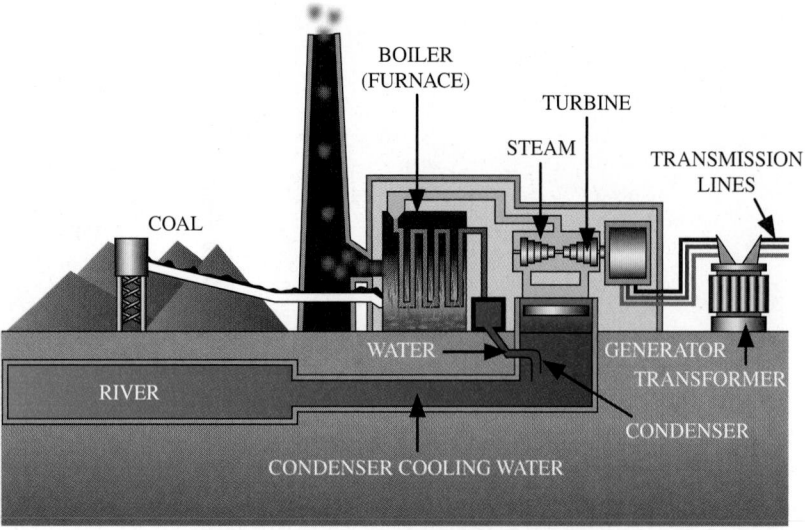

Figure 5-17 Diagram of a coal fired electric generating plant
(Courtesy of Tennessee Valley Authority)

4. The electricity is used to operate electric motors; turning electric energy into magnetic energy.
5. The electric motors use the spinning magnetic field to turn the compressor and fans; converting magnetic energy into mechanical energy.
6. The mechanical energy is used to transfer thermal energy, heat, from where it is not wanted to where it is unobjectionable, Figure 5-17.

Note that the whole process began by turning some matter, coal and oxygen, into other forms of matter, water and carbon dioxide. When hydrocarbons are burned, the carbon is combined with oxygen to form carbon dioxide while the hydrogen is combined with oxygen to form water. The coal does not disappear; it is changed into carbon dioxide gas and water vapor. When the entire process is through, there is just as much matter as before. Also, there is just as much energy as before, just converted into heat.

These conversions are not perfect. Some energy is "lost" with each conversion. But energy is not really "lost." Some of it is not directed toward the desired outcome. When the coal is burned, some of the heat leaves with the hot combustion gases. This energy is not lost in the sense that it no longer exists. It still exists; some of the heat energy was not captured when it was converted. Likewise, all the heat energy that is captured is not used to turn the turbine; there is still a considerable amount of energy in the steam after it has passed through the turbine. Once again, all the energy was not completely captured, but the "missed" energy still exists. In virtually any energy conversion there is "lost" energy. However, it is important to understand that when energy is "lost" it does not disappear, it just does not go where it is supposed to go.

Common Energy Conversions

It would be accurate to say that the modern lifestyle we enjoy depends upon energy conversions taking place all around us that we take for granted. Operating any appliance, heating and cooling our homes, and transporting people and goods all depend upon energy conversion. Even enjoying your favorite music on your MP3 player requires converting chemical energy into electrical energy to operate, converting that electrical energy into magnetic energy to drive a speaker or headset, converting that magnetic energy into mechanical energy to make the speaker cone move, and finally converting the mechanical movement of the speaker into sound energy so that it can be heard. Some common energy conversions are shown in Figure 5-18.

Energy Conversion Is Reversible

Not only can energy be converted from one form to another, the conversion can be reversed. A car battery is a good example of a practical use for reversible energy conversion.

Type of product/action	Energy conversion	
	From	To
Gasoline in a car	Chemical	Mechanical
Electricity going through a light bulb	Electrical	Radiant
Water turning a turbine	Mechanical	Electrical
Heat energy producing steam to turn a turbine	Thermal	Mechanical
Chemical in a battery	Chemical	Electrical
Burning coal moving the wheels on a steam engine	Chemical	Mechanical
Windmill	Mechanical	Electrical
Electricity in a heater	Electrical	Thermal
Natural gas burning	Chemical	Thermal
Light on a photocell	Radiant	Electrical

Figure 5-18 Examples of energy conversion

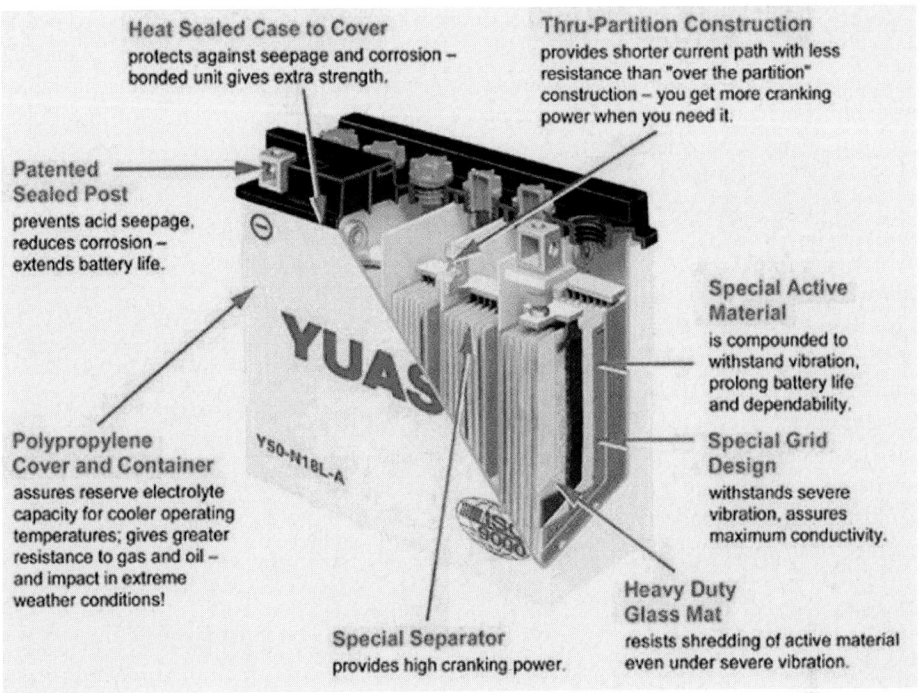

Figure 5-19 Typical wet cell battery
(Courtesy of Yuasa Battery, Inc.)

A car battery is basically a tank full of acid with two different types of metal plates dipped in the acid, Figure 5-19. The chemical reaction between the acid and one set of metal plates produces an excess of electrons on the metal plate. The reaction between the acid and the other set of metal plates produces a lack of electrons. When an electrical circuit is connected between the two plates, electrons run from the plate with an electron surplus to the plate with an electron deficit; providing electricity. This is a chemical to electrical conversion. As electricity is used, the chemicals that supply this reaction are changed. This is how a battery is "used up." The chemicals which react to provide the electron difference are changed to chemicals that do not support this chemical reaction. If an electrical current is applied across the set of metal plates, the chemical reaction is reversed and the chemicals are restored to their original state. This is how a battery is recharged. Most energy conversions are reversible.

Conversion Formulas

The most common energy conversion calculations are electricity to heat and electricity to mechanical energy. Table 5-1 lists the formulas for some of the most common energy and power conversions.

For example, a 5 kW electric heater can produce 17,050 Btu of heat if operated for an hour: 5,000 W × 3.41 Btu/W = 17,050 Btu. A 3 hp electric motor will produce the equivalent of 2,238 W of work: 3 hp × 746 W/hp = 2,238 W. If the motor is 75% efficient, it will consume 2,984 W to produce 3 hp of work: 2,238 W/0.75 = 2,984 W.

Table 5-1 Power and Energy Conversions

Conversion	Formula
Electricity to heat	Watt-hours × 3.41 = Btu
Electric power to mechanical power	Watts/746 = horsepower
Electricity consumed by electric motor	(horsepower × 746)/motor efficiency*

*Efficiency should be expressed as a decimal.

5.12 ENERGY CONSERVATION

The subject of energy conversion brings up an important concept in dealing with matter and energy: matter and energy cannot be created or destroyed. This is the first law of thermodynamics, often referred to as the law of conservation. It is not possible to increase the amount of heat somewhere by "making heat." It is necessary to convert another form of energy into heat or move heat from somewhere else to where it is needed. Likewise, it is not possible to simply "destroy" the heat to reduce the amount of heat somewhere. It is necessary to convert the heat to another form of energy or move it somewhere else.

The operation of an electric heater is an example of how the law of conservation works. The heat produced by the heater represents the same amount of energy as the electricity used to produce the heat.

5.13 ENERGY DISTRIBUTION

Most of the energy we use is produced in a central location and distributed throughout the country. The two forms of energy used most in heating and cooling are electricity and natural gas.

Electrical Distribution

The laws of physics work against distributing large amounts of electrical power over long distances. According to Ohm's law, the voltage lost through a conductor will equal the resistance of that conductor multiplied by the current traveling through the wire. Power lines have resistance. The longer the wire is, the higher its electrical resistance. To reduce the loss through the line it is necessary to reduce the current traveling through it. Power distribution systems accomplish this by using high voltages. Electrical work, Watts, is a product of volts times amps. A comparison of two 1-kW electrical systems can illustrate the point. See Table 5-2.

Note that the higher voltage in Table 5-2 delivers 99.5% of the original power while the lower voltage loses half of its power through the wire.

Table 5-2 Comparison of Two 1-kW Electrical Systems on a 5-Ω Conductor

	1 A at 1,000 V	**10 A at 100 V**
Voltage loss	5 V (1 A $\times$ 5 Ω)	50 V (10 A $\times$ 5 Ω)
Lost power	5 W (5 V $\times$ 1 A)	500 W (50 V $\times$ 10 A)
Delivered power	995 W	500 W
Percent of power delivered	99.5%	50%

Figure 5-20 Electrical power distribution system *(OSHA)*

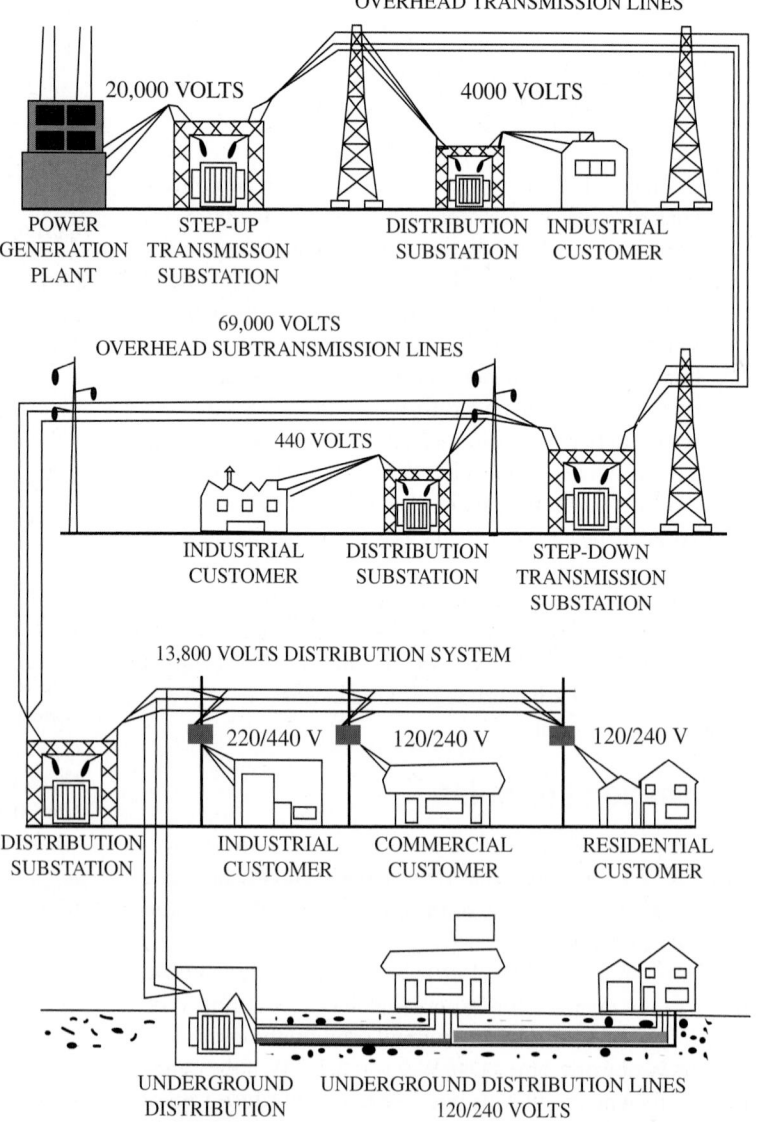

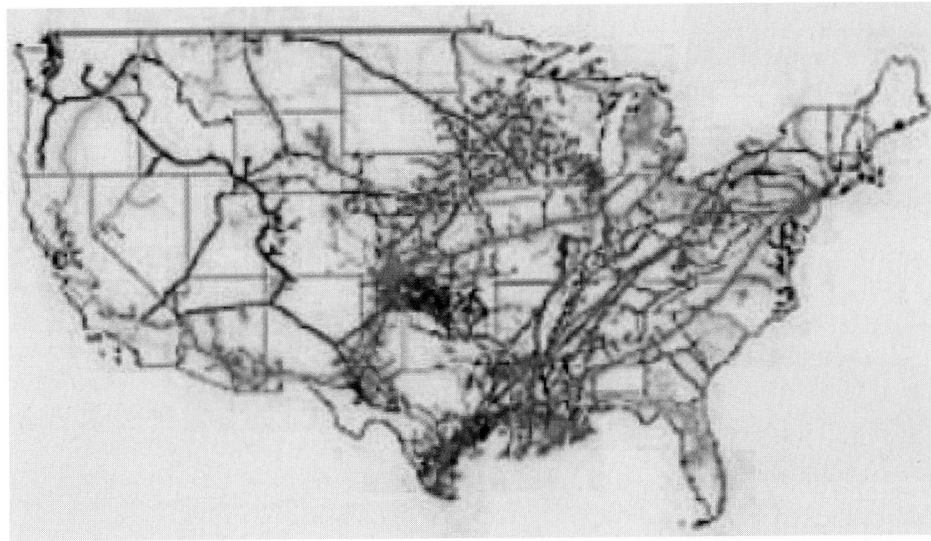

Figure 5-21 Interstate natural gas pipelines
(Courtesy of Energy Information Administration)

In practice, the voltage is changed to a very high voltage for transmission over long distances and then lowered to a safer level for use. Alternating current is used for our power distribution because it is much easier and cheaper to accomplish the required voltage changes. The voltage is changed, or transformed, through a device called a transformer. Transformers can either increase or decrease voltage. The steps taken from the plant to your house are shown in Figure 5-20.

1. Electricity is generated at a high voltage: 20,000–33,000 V.
2. It is transformed to a higher voltage: 69,000–500,000 V.
3. It is transmitted long distances at this voltage.
4. It is transformed to subtransmission voltages at a sub station: 34,500–69,000 V.
5. It is transmitted to regional substations at this voltage.
6. The voltage is transformed to a distribution voltage: 4,800–13,800 V.
7. It is distributed to pole transformers.
8. The pole transformer drops the voltage to the end user: 120–240 V.

Natural Gas

Natural gas is collected, refined, and distributed through a nationwide network of pipelines. Figure 5-21 shows a map of the major gas pipelines in the United States. Compressors are used to reduce the volume and raise the pressure of the gas in the large interstate pipelines. These large interstate pipelines typically have a 16–48 in diameter and operate at pressures ranging 200–1,500 psig. Compressor stations, Figure 5-22, are located at 40–100 mi intervals along the pipeline to maintain the pipeline pressure. Lateral pipelines deliver the gas from the main pipelines to local distribution networks.

While large gas consumers like electric utilities and industrial plants may get their gas directly from the main pipeline, most users rely on local distribution networks. The gas pressure is reduced before entering the local distribution system. Line pressure may be as low as 3 psig because of the reduced volume of gas. Compressor stations may still be

Figure 5-22 Typical natural gas compressor system
(Photo courtesy of El Paso Corporation)

required for large local distribution systems, but they are much smaller than the stations used in the interstate pipelines. Finally, the gas passes through a regulator at each customer's location and its pressure is reduced to very low pressures. Delivery pressure for residential natural gas is typically 6 in water column. The cost of building and maintaining these local distribution networks represents almost half of the price of natural gas to residential consumers.

5.14 STANDARD AND SI UNITS OF WORK

Mechanical Work–Traditional Units

Mechanical work is measured by the weight of an object and how far the object is moved. In traditional English units this is foot-pounds. A foot-pound is the product of multiplying the weight in pounds times the distance in feet. Moving a 50 lb weight a distance of 2 ft requires 2 ft $\times$ 50 lb = 100 ft lb of mechanical work. The torque wrench is commonly used in many mechanical fields to measure the mechanical force

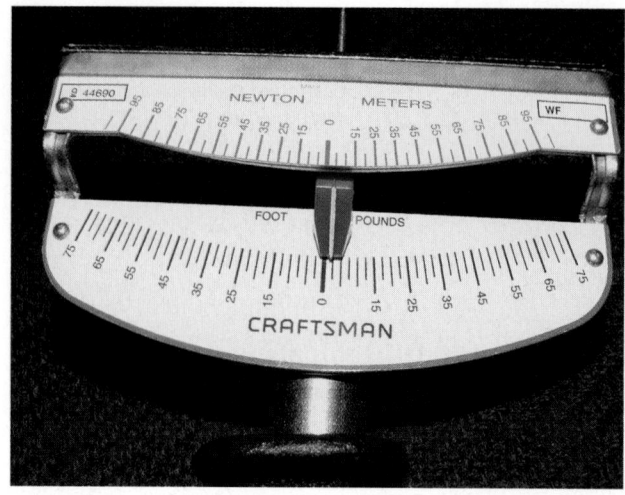

Figure 5-23 Torque wrench calibrated in footpounds in black, and Newton meters in red

used when tightening bolts. Standard torque wrenches are calibrated in footpounds, Figure 5-23. The United States is one of the few countries still using traditional (standard) units of weight and measure.

Mechanical Work—SI Units

Mechanical force in the SI system is measured in Newton meters. This is the force of 1 N times the distance of 1 m. Metric torque wrenches are calibrated in Newton meters, Figure 5-23.

Thermal Work

When asked for a measurement of heat, most people respond with a temperature. In fact, they are partly correct. Temperature is a measure of the concentration of heat. But if a quantity is needed, then temperature will not work. Temperature is a comparative measurement; it compares the concentration, or level, of heat against known standards. It does not measure the amount of heat energy in a substance. There is a difference between heat intensity and heat quantity and how each is measured. Heat intensity describes how concentrated heat is. Heat quantity describes the amount of heat in something.

Thermal work is measured in British thermal units (Btu), calories, or joules, Figure 5-24. The definitions for both Btu and calories are similar. A Btu is the amount of heat required to raise 1 lb of water 1°F. A calorie is the amount of heat required to raise 1 g of water 1°C.

None of these units of heat can be directly measured, they all require calculation. Calculating the amount of heat transferred in water is easy because both Btu and calories are defined by a temperature change in water. The formulas below show how to calculate heat quantity based on the temperature change of water.

$$Btu = \text{(water temp difference in °F)}$$
$$\times \text{(water weight in pounds)}$$
$$calories = \text{water temperature difference in °C}$$
$$\times \text{(water weight in grams)}$$

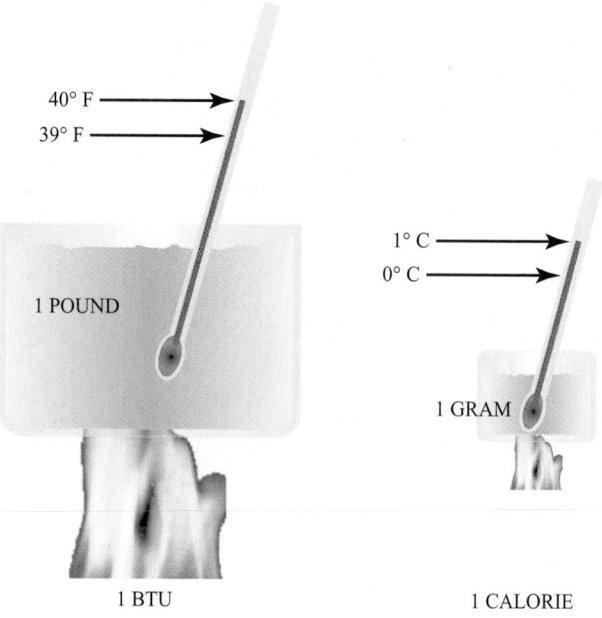

Figure 5-24 (a) 1 Btu raises the temperature of 1 pound of water 1°F; (b) 1 calorie of heat raises 1 gram of water 1°C.

Both Btu and calories represent relatively small amounts of heat. One Btu is roughly equivalent to the heat given off by a single wooden kitchen match. A calorie is even smaller, it takes approximately 250 cal to equal 1 Btu! Larger units of heat quantity have been derived for many real world applications.

In the United States we use the therm to count very large quantities of heat. A therm is equal to 100,000 Btu. Natural gas is sold by the therm. For metric heat measurement, the kilocalorie (k cal) is used. The kilocalorie is equivalent to 1,000 cal. Frequently kilocalories are referred to as Calories. The capital C differentiates the large Calorie from the small calorie. So 1,000 calories equals 1 Calorie.

TECH TIP

Kilocalories, Calories with a capital C, are the same Calories people watch when they are dieting! The phrase "burning Calories" is actually quite accurate. Your body is oxidizing the energy stores and converting chemical energy into heat energy.

Electrical Work

Since electricity is the flow of electrons, a logical unit of electricity would measure the flow of electrons. This unit is the ampere, abbreviated amp or A as a unit. One amp is a flow of one coulomb in 1 second. But electron flow is only part of the picture. There must be a difference in electrical charge from one side of the circuit to the other before current will flow. This difference is called potential difference and is measured in volts. A volt is defined as the potential difference across a conductor when a flow of 1 A dissipates 1 W of electrical power. The Watt is the unit used to measure the rate of electrical work.

TECH TIP

A coulomb is the SI unit of electric charge. This amounts to a quantity of 6.241506×10^{18} electrons. The ampere was originally a derived unit, based on the coulomb with the coulomb being the original SI base electrical unit. The ampere was named the SI base electrical unit in 1960. The ampere is a commonly used unit in air conditioning work.

Figure 5-25 Typical kiloWatt hour meter

Since the ampere is a rate and not a quantity, the Watt is also a rate. To measure the quantity of electrical work, it is necessary to state how long work is being done at the rate of 1 W. The watt hour is the amount of electrical work done at the rate of 1 W for 1 hr. Watt hours is the product of watts and hours. Operating a 100 W light for a period of 2 h requires 100 W × 2 h = 200 W hr.

In practical terms, the Watt-hour is a relatively small unit. Power companies use kiloWatt-hours to measure the amount of electrical work used during the month. Figure 5-25 shows a typical kiloWatt hour meter. This is calculated by measuring the kiloWatt use over time. It can be expressed using the formula V × A × 0.001 × hr = kW hr. Operating 10 100 = W lightbulbs for 1 hr would require 10 × 100 W × 1 hr × 0.001 = 1 kW hr.

Why is something with "hour" in its name a quantity and not a rate? Remember that amperes is a rate of electron flow. The hour in kiloWatt-hour makes the kWhr a quantity by giving a specific amount of time to work at that rate. A comparison with water would be to specify the amount of water pumped at a rate of 5 gal/min (GPM) for the period of 1 hr. The 5 GPM measure just tells the rate of water flow, but does not tell how much water is pumped altogether. By specifying a time the total quantity of water pumped can be determined to be 300 gal: 5 GPM × 60 min.

Joules—SI Unit of Energy

One problem with units of measurement based on the temperature change of water is that the specific heat of water changes slightly as its temperature changes. So the amount of heat represented by a temperature change in water depends upon the starting temperature. This has led to the development of many different definitions of both calories and Btus, each based on a different starting temperature and representing a slightly different heat value. For this reason, joules have replaced calories in SI measurements of thermal energy.

Joules are a heat equivalent for mechanical energy but are used today in the SI system for all forms of energy. One joule is the work done by a force of 1 N moving an object 1 m. Consuming electrical power at the rate of 1 W for 1s is the electrical equivalent of 1 j. Today, the joule represents the standard SI measurement of energy for all types of energy.

5.15 STANDARD AND SI UNITS OF POWER

Most of the terms used to describe the capacity of air conditioning systems and components are rate measurements. Rate measurements always measure a quantity over and time. Power is a measure of the rate of work; it measures a quantity of work over time. Although any form of energy can produce power, in air conditioning the three primary types of power measured are mechanical power, thermal power, and electrical power.

Figure 5-26 Btu/hr input and output rating of gas fired heating equipment

AIR TEMP RISE	MAX EXTERNAL STATIC PRESSURE		
20-50F	0.5WC/0.12KPA		
11.1-27.8C			

ALTITUDE IN FEET	GAS ORIFICE		INPUT MAX	OUTPUT CAP	THERMAL EFFICIENCY	EQUIPED FOR USE WITH
0 - 2000	NO. 44	BTU/HR	40000	32800	81.9 %	NATURAL GAS
■	SIZE 0.086	KW	11.71	9.59		
2000 - 4500	NO. 49	BTU/HR	33300	27300	81.9 %	
	SIZE 0.073	KW	9.75	7.98		
GAS SUPPLY PRESSURE		13.0WC/3.2KPA MAX		4WC/0.99KPA MIN		
MANIFOLD PRESSURE		3.5INWC/0.87KPA				

Mechanical Power

Horsepower is a rate of doing mechanical work. Like foot-pounds, horsepower involves distance and weight. Unlike foot pounds, horsepower also uses a time component because it is a rate, not a quantity. One horsepower is defined as producing 33,000 ftlb of mechanical work in 1 min. Horsepower is literally supposed to be the amount of work a horse can do, as shown earlier in the unit in Figure 5-2. Motors are still rated by this somewhat archaic term. For electric motors 1 hp is defined as 746 W. This does not mean that a 1 hp motor consumes 746 W; it means that the mechanical work performed by the motor is equivalent to the electrical work rate of 746 watts. An electric motor consumes more than 746 W per hp because electric motors are not 100% efficient.

Thermal Power

A very common rate used to specify the capacity of heating and cooling systems is Btu per hour. A heating system with a rating of 40,000 Btu/hr would provide 40,000 Btu of heat energy for every hour of operation, Figure 5-26. A common rating for refrigeration equipment is the ton. A ton of cooling is defined as the amount of cooling accomplished by melting a ton of ice over a 24-hour period. Notice this specifies both a quantity, the cooling done by 1 ton of ice; and a time, 24 hr. This quantity of cooling is 288,000 Btu because it takes 144 Btu to melt 1 lb of ice: 144 Btu × 2,000 lb = 288,000 Btu. This time period is not usually the most convenient. Dividing both the quantity and time by 24 gives an hourly rate of 12,000 Btu/hr. This is what is more commonly thought of as a ton. Do not forget the per hour part. A ton is not 12,000 Btu, but 12,000 Btu/hr. A ton can also be stated as 200 Btu/min: 12,000 divided by 60. All three of these rates are identical; the only difference is whether you prefer to measure by the minute, the hour, or the day.

Electrical Power

The ability of electricity to do work depends on two factors: voltage and current. Voltage is a measure of the potential difference. Potential difference provides the electrical pressure, which makes current flow possible. Without a difference in voltage from one end of the wire to the other, there will be no current flow. Watts is a measure of the rate at which electrical work is done. Wattage depends upon both voltage and current. A watt is defined as 1 A of current flowing at a potential difference of 1 V. Wattage can be calculated using the formula V × A = W. Wattage measures the rate at which work is accomplished. Wattage is a rate because it is calculated using amps, a measure of electrical current flow. Flows are always measured as a rate.

Wattage is a reasonable measure for small appliances and lightbulbs, but for jobs like heating a house, something is needed that works better for large measurement. KiloWatts, abbreviated kW, are used to specify the energy use of heating and air conditioning equipment. A kiloWatt is equal to 1000 W. The formula is simply W/1,000 = kW.

Watts—SI Unit of Power

Although the Watt was originally conceived as a unit of electrical power, it is used today as the standard SI unit of power for all types of power. The Watt is a rate of power equal to one joule of energy per second. In SI measurement systems Watts are used to measure the output of engines, electric motors, or furnaces.

UNIT 5—SUMMARY

Heating, air conditioning, and refrigeration are about controlling energy. Energy that is stored is called potential energy, while energy that is in use is called kinetic energy. There are many forms of energy including chemical, thermal, radiant, electrical, magnetic, and mechanical. Energy can be converted from one form to another, but it cannot be created or destroyed. There is a definite relationship between energy, work, and power. Energy is the ability to do work, work is the amount of energy transferred, and power is the rate of energy transfer. The difference between work and power is that work is a quantity while power is a rate.

UNIT 5—REVIEW QUESTIONS

1. List the forms of energy used in the heating, air conditioning, and refrigeration industry.

2. What units are used to measure heat quantity?

3. What units are used to measure heat intensity?

4. Explain the relationship between energy, work, and power.

5. How many Btu will a 5-kW heater produce if operated for 1 hr?

6. How many Btu are required to raise the temperature of 15 lb of water from 100°F to 120°F?

7. A heat transfer process results in 20 kcal of heat being absorbed by 1 L (1 kg) of water. What temperature will the water be if it started at a temperature of 25°C?

8. Describe chemical energy and give an example.

9. How much mechanical force is required to lift a 250 lb compressor 2 ft?

10. What energy unit is used today in the SI system for all forms of energy?

11. How many joules of heat does a 100 Watt heater produce if it is operated for 5 min?

12. Use a block diagram to outline a common electrical distribution system from the power plant to your house.

13. What units of measurement are used in the United States to rate the cooling capacity of conditioning equipment?

14. Arrange the following heat quantities from smallest to largest.
    a. The Btu
    b. The Joule
    c. The calorie
    d. The kilocalorie
    e. The therm

15. Explain the difference between a renewable energy resource and a nonrenewable energy resource.

16. Explain the difference between potential and kinetic energy.

17. Describe the natural gas distribution system.

18. Explain the relationship between Watts and joules in the SI system.

19. What is the required input in Watts to operate an 80% efficient 5 hp electric motor?

20. Explain the units used to measure torque.

UNIT 6

Temperature Measurement and Conversion

OBJECTIVES

After completing this unit you will be able to:

- define temperature and explain the effect it has on a substance.
- discuss the concept of absolute zero.
- compare various temperature measuring devices.
- explain the concept of absolute temperature scales.
- explain the four types of temperature scales: Fahrenheit, Celsius, Rankine, and Kelvin.
- demonstrate how to convert temperature from one scale to another.

6.1 INTRODUCTION

Temperature control is the primary function of most air conditioning and refrigeration systems. Temperature measurements are among the most important measurements an air conditioning technician will make. Taking accurate temperature readings is crucial in analyzing system performance; incorrect readings can lead to incorrect system diagnosis. This unit will discuss what temperature is, the different methods of measuring temperature, and how to take accurate temperature readings.

6.2 WHAT IS TEMPERATURE?

Temperature is the measure of the average kinetic energy in a substance. Kinetic energy makes molecules move: the molecules of solids vibrate in place; the molecules of liquids and gases move about. All the molecules are not moving at exactly the same speed, this is why temperature is defined as a measure of the average kinetic energy of a substance. The higher the temperature, the faster the molecules move. The lower the temperature, the slower the molecules move, Figure 6-1.

Temperature does not measure the amount of heat in a substance because molecules have both potential and kinetic energy. Temperature can only measure kinetic energy; it cannot measure potential energy. A 40°F gas will have more heat in it than a 100°F liquid because the gas has a much higher potential energy than the liquid.

6.3 TEMPERATURE AND RADIANT ENERGY

Solids both absorb and emit radiant energy. They emit radiant energy at any temperature above absolute zero. The frequency of the radiant energy wave increases as the temperature increases. At around 1,000°F, the radiant energy is in the red spectrum of visible light and the object glows a dull red. As the temperature increases, the frequency of the light increases, producing shifts in the color of the visible light emitted by the solid. Figure 6-2 shows the visible light spectrum associated with different temperatures.

Below 1,000°F, materials are not hot enough to produce visible light. They still produce radiant energy, but at a lower frequency. This unseen light is called infrared light because it has a wavelength that is longer than red light. This is the light that an infrared thermometer sees when reading the temperature of a material's surface from several feet away. As the temperature increases, the color of the object changes because the wavelength of the radiation it is emitting gets shorter and shorter.

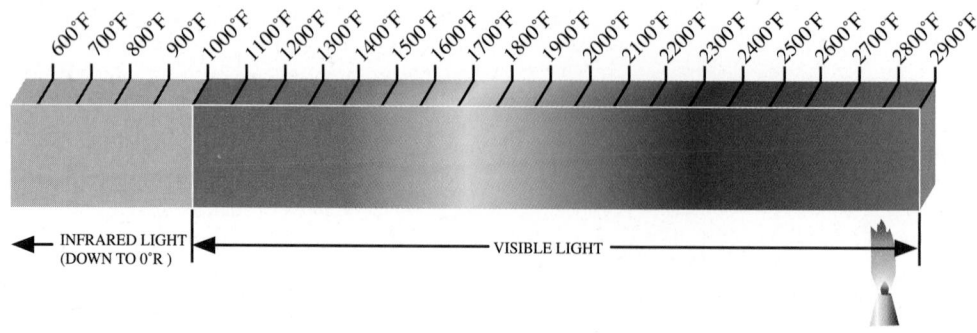

Figure 6-1 Above 1,000°F, the vibrations are fast enough to begin emitting a dull red visible light. As the temperature continues to rise, the color of the light changes. When it is very hot, it glows white

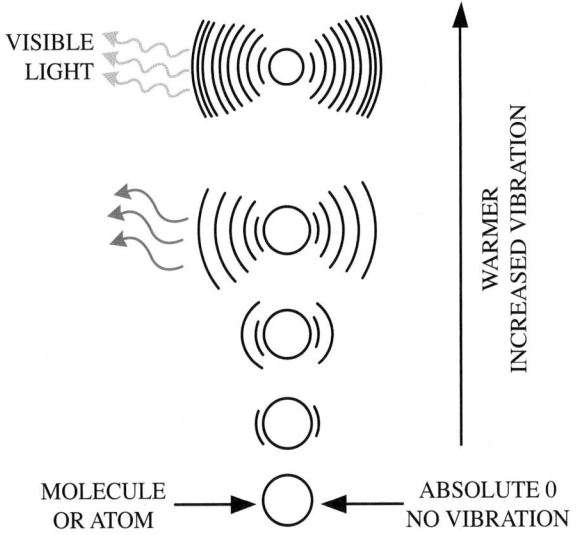

Figure 6-2 As the temperature rises above absolute zero, the molecules begin to vibrate. The hotter the material, the faster the vibrations

6.4 EARLY THERMOMETERS

Scientists have been devising methods of measuring temperature for nearly 2,000 years. In the first century, Hero of Alexandria published his studies on pneumatics in which he described a tube with the top closed and the bottom open. The bottom is submerged in a container of water and the tube is filled with air at the top and water at the bottom. When the air that is trapped in the top of the tube was heated, the expanded air would push the water down the tube. When the air cooled, the air would contract and water would rise in the tube. This made a sort of backwards thermometer, Figure 6-3. Later, in the eleventh century, Abu Ali ibn Sina developed air thermometers based on this same principle. In the early seventeenth century Galileo experimented with a device called a thermoscope, Figure 6-4. It consisted of a column of liquid with several glass balls partially filled with water to give them different densities. The density of the fluid they were immersed in changed with temperature, causing them to rise or fall. The position of the glass balls indicated the relative temperature.

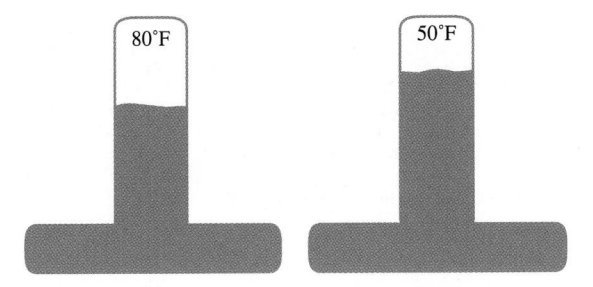

Figure 6-3 The volume of the trapped air changes with temperature, changing the level of the water

Figure 6-4 In a thermoscope the position of the balls in the fluid changes with temperature
(Courtesy of GalileoShop.com)

All of these early instruments were affected by atmospheric pressure changes as well as temperature changes. In 1654 Ferdinando II de Medici made the first modern-style thermometer that was not affected by changes in atmospheric pressure. His thermometer used sealed tubes that were partially filled with alcohol. Many scientists experimented with different styles of thermometers using different liquids. Unfortunately, each thermometer and scale was unique and no accepted standard existed. In 1724, Daniel Fahrenheit began producing thermometers that used mercury. Mercury's large coefficient of expansion allowed a scale with a wider range and greater precision than previous thermometers. The superiority of Fahrenheit's thermometer led to its wide adoption resulting in the Fahrenheit temperature scale becoming the first widely used temperature scale.

6.5 GLASS STEM THERMOMETERS

Glass stem thermometers are still used today. An advantage of glass stem thermometers is that they are highly reliable because they rely on properties of physics, not on a mechanical

Figure 6-5 Glass stem thermometer

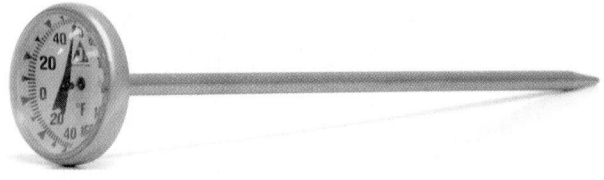

Figure 6-7 Analog pocket thermometer

or electronic device. The temperature is measured on a scale as compared to the tip of the expanding or contracting liquid inside the thin tube. When the liquid is heated, it expands and pushes further up the glass tube. When it is cooled, it contracts, and the liquid level falls. Any liquid can be used, but mercury or alcohol are the most commonly used liquids. Mercury looks metallic in color, and alcohol is usually dyed red, Figure 6-5. The thinner the size of the hollow glass tube, the greater the movement per degree of temperature change. Longer, more accurate models for laboratory work are available as well as pocket sizes. Breakage is a problem since glass thermometers are fragile.

6.6 DIAL THERMOMETERS

Dial thermometers indicate temperature by a pointer moving over a circular scale, Figure 6-6. The pointer moves because it is attached to a bimetal spring. The spring may be wound into a spiral or twisted. A bimetal is made by joining together two metals with different rates of expansion. When the bimetal is heated, one metal expands more than the other and the bimetal spring opens; when it is cooled, the spring tightens. This creates a turning motion that is used to move the pointer on the thermometer.

An advantage of dial thermometers is that they are more rugged than glass stem thermometers and can be used for a wide variety of applications. They are also relatively inexpensive. Service technicians have used dial type pocket thermometers for years. Figure 6-7 shows a typical dial type pocket thermometer. The disadvantage of dial thermometers is that they are not very accurate compared to other types of thermometers.

6.7 INFRARED THERMOMETERS

Infrared thermometers can "see" the temperature of a surface from a distance, Figure 6-8. What they are seeing is the color of the invisible infrared (IR) light given off by the object. A detector is located inside the instrument that senses the infrared light waves. A change in the IR light's color occurs as a result of temperature changes, which results in a change in the electrical output of the detector. A small integrated circuit converts that electrical output into a displayed temperature.

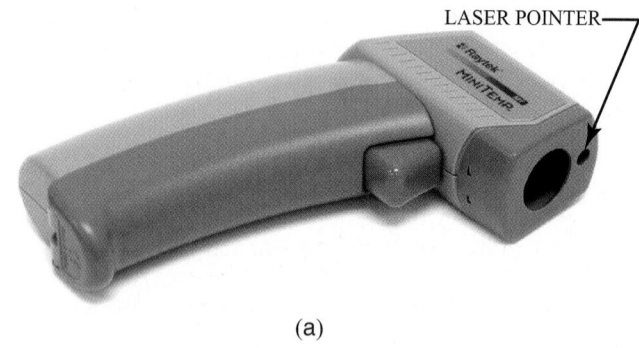

LASER POINTER

(a)

Figure 6-6 Each increment on this dial thermometer represents 2°F—this thermometer is reading 84°F

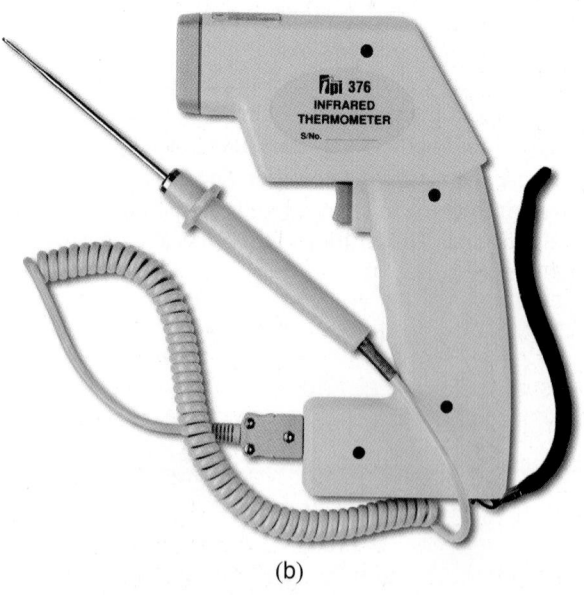

(b)

Figure 6-8 (a) Infrared thermometer; (b) infrared thermometer with a temperature contact probe
(Courtesy Test Products International, Inc.)

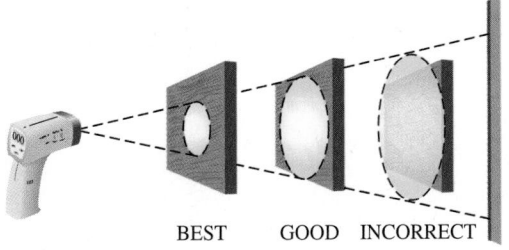

BEST   GOOD   INCORRECT

Figure 6-9 Distance to spot ratio
(Photograph copyright © by Cole-Parmer Instrument Company. Used with permission)

The distance the detector is from the object, the surface color, and its reflectivity all affect the accuracy of the temperature reading. The most accurate reading is obtained when the object whose temperature is being read is a black dull surface. IR thermometers are generally not useful for measuring air, liquids, shiny metal objects, or small objects.

One difference between different IR thermometers is their distance to spot ratio. This ratio tells how large the target area is compared to the distance, Figure 6-9. An instrument with a 10 to 1 ratio will measure an area of 1 in diameter when the target is 10 in away. Inexpensive tools have ratios of 4:1, while more expensive models have ratios of 12:1. More expensive models also have adjustable emissivity, so that they can be used on different surfaces.

Not all HVAC/R field work requires extreme accuracy. Technicians are often looking for trends in temperature change. For example, during an air balancing job in a residence the technician may need to know if the air coming out of the duct is colder or warmer than it was before the dampers were adjusted.

SERVICE TIP

A disadvantage of IR thermometers is that they cannot detect air temperatures; however, they can detect the temperature of the grill or register that the air is passing through. To obtain the most accurate estimate of the actual duct air temperature, point the detector into the louvers so it is pointed at the inside of the duct boot. Some IR thermometers have a laser pointer to make this easier. Move the instrument around and watch the temperature display. Watch for the highest or lowest temperature (highest for heating and lowest for AC) indicated on the display. That temperature is going to be the closest to the actual air temperature. Practice will help develop your skill in obtaining accurate temperature readings with an IR thermometer.

There are many advantages of infrared thermometers. The fact that a temperature reading can be made from a distance may mean that you do not need to climb a ladder to get air duct readings. It may also mean that you can get a reading from the back of a hard-to-reach space. The temperature is displayed instantaneously, which speeds up your work.

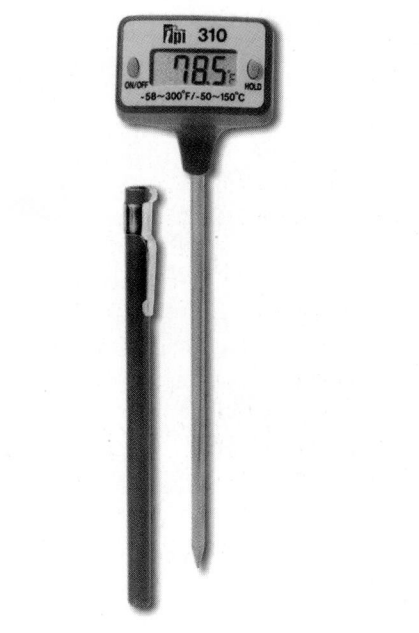

Figure 6-10 Digital pocket thermometer

6.8 DIGITAL THERMOMETERS

Digital thermometers with compact sensing elements are popular due to their speed in sensing a change in temperature and the ease in reading the alphanumeric display instead of a dial or a scale. Figure 6-10 shows a digital pocket thermometer. Most digital thermometers require batteries or a source of electrical power to produce the digital display.

Digital thermometers can perform many functions that analog instruments cannot. These include recording temperature differences between two or more sensing elements, remembering the highest and lowest temperatures from several readings, and averaging the temperature of several readings. The display on most digital thermometers can easily be changed to show the temperature reading as Fahrenheit or Celsius.

6.9 ELECTRONIC TEMPERATURE SENSORS

Digital thermometers use three different types of temperature sensors: wire wound elements, thermistors, or thermocouples.

Wire Wound Sensors

A wire wound temperature sensor changes resistance with temperature change. The resistance of most conductors increases with an increase in temperature. Normally this change is very small. This resistance change can be magnified by winding many turns of small diameter wire into a coil that is used as a sensor. Wire wound sensors are very accurate, but they are also the most expensive of the three types of electronic sensors.

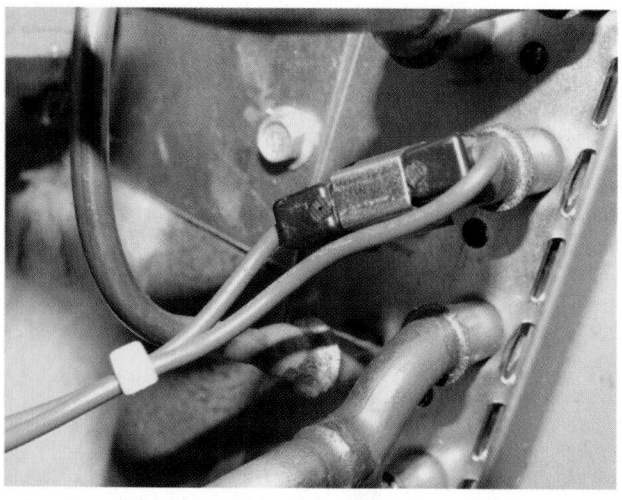

Figure 6-11 Outdoor air thermistor

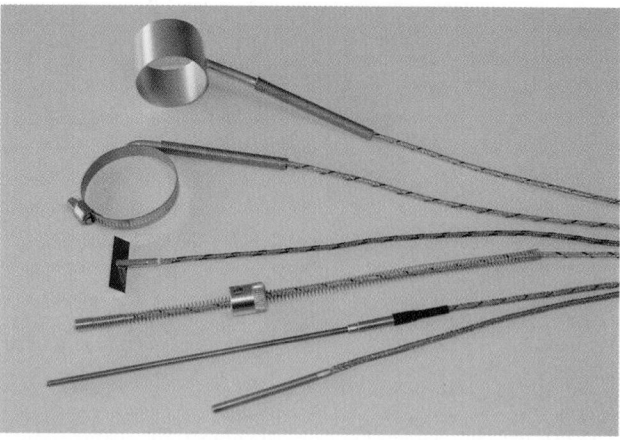

Figure 6-12 Variety of type J thermocouple probes
(Courtesy of Ivaldi, www.ivaldi.Fr)

Thermistors

A thermistor is a semiconductor that changes resistance with temperature. Thermistors are inexpensive and fairly rugged, but they are the least accurate of the three types of digital temperature measurement because their resistance change is not linear. Themistors are frequently used as temperature sensing devices on air conditioning equipment. Figure 6-11 shows a thermistor used to measure the outdoor coil temperature on a heat pump.

Thermocouples

Thermocouple temperature sensors can be used to detect temperatures that are displayed on analog or digital instruments. The thermocouple produces a small voltage when two dissimilar metal wires are joined forming a tip or junction that can be heated or cooled. The two most common thermocouple types are chromel and alumel, type K, and iron and constantan, type J. Type J (iron and constantan) sensors have been used for years and are still very popular. Type K (chromel and alumel) is gaining in popularity because of its lower cost. Any manufacturer's thermocouple will work with any manufacturer's digital thermometer as long as they are both the same type. This standardization has led to the development of a wide array of different probes for many specialized applications, Figure 6-12.

Thermocouples are less accurate than wire wound sensors but more accurate than thermistors. They may provide a temperature that is 2°F higher or lower than the actual temperature. You can test the accuracy of a thermocouple by checking the temperature of ice, which should read 32°F. Once you know the temperature error factor, you can mark it on the thermocouple. That way you can add or subtract a degree or two as needed to keep the error factor within an acceptable range for most HVAC/R work.

Thermocouples are relatively inexpensive and flexible. They can be attached to several locations inside of the equipment, and the equipment cover panels can then be replaced

Figure 6-13 Thermocouple soldered to line in unit

so the equipment can operate normally, Figure 6-13. With the thermocouple leads run so that they are outside the cabinet, the equipment can be operated normally. This allows technicians to diagnose what is happening to temperatures inside operating equipment.

TECH TIP

Sometimes people confuse thermometers and thermostats. The difference between a thermometer and a thermostat is that a thermometer simply indicates the temperature. A thermostat controls equipment based on the temperature it reads.

6.10 COMMON TEMPERATURE SCALES

Every day temperatures are indicated using either the Fahrenheit or Celsius temperature scales. The Fahrenheit scale is still predominant in the United States, but is seldom used anywhere

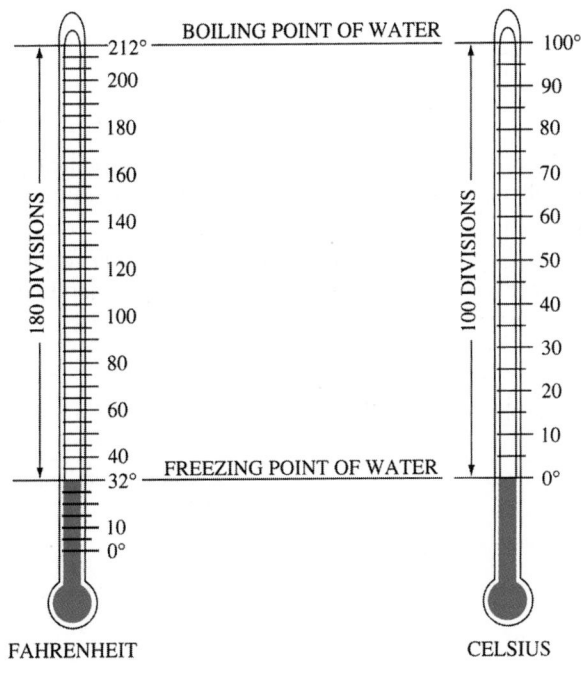

Figure 6-14 Comparison of the Fahrenheit and Celsius temperature scales

else. The Celsius scale is part of the SI system of measurement and is used throughout the world. Figure 6-14 shows a comparison of the two scales.

Fahrenheit

By the early eighteenth century, many different temperature scales were proposed and used, but no clear standard had emerged. Daniel Fahrenheit produced the Fahrenheit scale in 1724. The Fahrenheit scale was based on three temperatures. The temperature of 0° was set at the lowest temperature he could produce in his lab using ice and salt; the freezing point of water was set at 32°; and the human body temperature was set at 96°. The boiling point of water on the Fahrenheit scale is 212° at sea level.

Celsius

In 1742 Anders Celsius proposed a temperature scale with 100° as the freezing point of water and 0° as the boiling point of water. Linnaeus reversed this, placing 0° at freezing and 100° at boiling. This scale was widely adopted by scientists and was known as the Centigrade scale because of its division into 100° from freezing to boiling. The name was changed to Celsius in 1948 to honor the scientist who first conceived the scale.

6.11 ABSOLUTE TEMPERATURE

Once scientists had a way to measure temperature, they began to speculate what the coldest temperature possible would be. Most agreed that there must be a bottom, or starting point.

Charles' Law was used to determine the temperature of absolute zero. In theory, if the volume of a gas keeps contracting with temperature, at some point the volume and temperature will be nothing. Scientists plotted the decrease in volume of different gases and extended the line representing the change in volume with each gas. Regardless of the gas or the starting quantity of gas, the lines all intersect at the same point, absolute zero. The coldest temperature possible where all molecular motion stops is absolute 0. This is −460°F or −273°C.

Both the Fahrenheit and Celsius scales depend on reference points. What 5°C really means is that the temperature is 5°C warmer than the freezing point of water. A more exacting place to start measuring temperature would be at absolute zero (0°). There are two scales that do start measuring temperature from absolute zero; they are the Rankine and Kelvin scales, Figure 6-15. There are no negative temperatures in either Rankine or Kelvin because they start at absolute zero.

Both Rankine and Kelvin scales are primarily used for scientific measurements. All gas law problems require absolute temperatures. The lack of negative temperatures makes absolute temperature scales work correctly with the ratios set up in the ideal gas law. If measurements are taken in Fahrenheit or Celsius they must be converted to Rankine or Kelvin before being used in a gas law problem.

Rankine

The Rankine temperature scale is named after William Rankine who proposed it in 1859. Rankine is the absolute temperature scale for Fahrenheit and has the same spacing

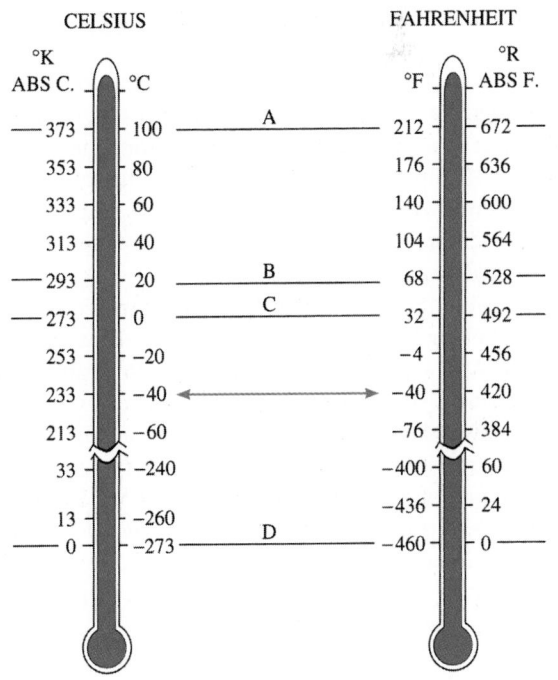

Figure 6-15 Fahrenheit, Celsius, Rankine, and Kelvin temperature scales: (A) boiling temperature of water; (B) standard temperature; (C) freezing temperature of water; (D) absolute zero; note that −40°C (red arrow) equals 40°F

between degrees as does the Fahrenheit scale. The numbers are just shifted so that 0° starts at absolute zero. Just as there are 180°F between freezing and boiling on the Fahrenheit scale, there are 180°R difference between freezing and boiling on the Rankine scale as well.

Because their degree spacing is the same, conversion between Fahrenheit and Rankine is simple. Adding 460° to Fahrenheit yields Rankine; subtracting 460° from Rankine yields Fahrenheit.

Kelvin

The Kelvin temperature scale is named in honor of William Thomson, the first Baron Kelvin. Kelvin is the absolute temperature scale for Celsius and is the official temperature scale for the SI system. It has the same spacing between degrees as does the Celsius scale, just shifted so that 0° starts at absolute zero.

Because their degree spacing is the same, conversion between Celsius and Kelvin is simple. Adding 273° to Celsius yields Kelvin; subtracting 273° from Kelvin yields Celsius.

TECH TIP

Temperature scales can go higher or lower depending on the use of the instrument. Outdoor thermometers usually have scales from –60°F to 120°F and indoor thermometers usually range from 50°F to 90°F.

6.12 TEMPERATURE CONVERSION

So long as the United States continues to measure temperature in degrees Fahrenheit while the rest of the world uses Celsius, we will need to make conversions from one system to the other. Two primary differences in how the scales are established must be addressed. The reference point for each system is different, and the amount of temperature change represented by a degree is different.

There are 180° on the Fahrenheit scale between the freezing and boiling points of water, while the Celsius scale only has 100°C between freezing and boiling. This can be converted using a ratio. 180 divided by 100 gives us a ratio of 1.8°F for every 1°C. For people who prefer fractions, 9/5 does the trick. This would be all we needed if 0 represented the same temperature on both scales, but it does not. Since water freezes at 32°F and 0°C, we can adjust for this by adding 32. The traditional formula for converting from Celsius to Fahrenheit is

$$(Celsius \times 1.8) + 32 = Fahrenheit$$

or if you prefer fractions

$$(Celsius \times 9/5) + 32 = Fahrenheit$$

This can be rearranged algebraically to get the formula for converting from Fahrenheit to Celsius.

$$(Fahrenheit - 32)/1.8 = Celsius$$

or if you prefer fractions

$$(Fahrenheit - 32) \times 5/9 = Celsius$$

Notice that when converting Celsius to Fahrenheit, you multiply first and then add; but when converting Fahrenheit to Celsius, you subtract first and then divide. This standard conversion process is based on comparing the freezing points of the two scales. Unfortunately, the subtle variation in execution has vexed many an aspiring technician.

6.13 CONVERSION EXAMPLES

To illustrate how this formula works we will convert 212°F to Celsius; a temperature for which we know the answer.
    The basic formula is

$$(F - 32)/1.8 = C$$

Substituting the temperature we want to convert

$$(212°F - 32)/1.8 = C$$

That works out to

$$180°F/1.8 = 100°C$$

Next we will convert 100°C to Fahrenheit.
    The basic formula is

$$(C \times 1.8) + 32 = F$$

Substituting the temperature we want to convert

$$(100°C \times 1.8) + 32 = F$$

That works out to

$$180 + 32 = 212°F$$

Now we will do a couple of examples where the answer is not as obvious. It would be useful to know what temperature Celsius is equivalent to a normal Fahrenheit temperature, so we will convert 75°F to Celsius.
    The basic formula is

$$(F - 32)/1.8 = C$$

Substituting the temperature we want to convert

$$(75°F - 32)/1.8 = C$$

That works out to

$$43°F/1.8 = 26.9°C$$

Next we will convert 40°C to Fahrenheit.
    The basic formula is

$$(C \times 1.8) + 32 = F$$

Substituting the temperature we want to convert

$$(40°C \times 1.8) + 32 = F$$

That works out to

$$72 + 32 = 104°F$$

SERVICE TIP

While the two scales do not correspond at freezing, there is a temperature where the two scales align: –40°. Forty degrees below zero Fahrenheit is exactly the same temperature as 40° below zero Celsius. We can use this coincidence to build an easier system. The system has three short steps. The first and last steps are always the same regardless of which direction you are going. Only the middle step changes; and it is relatively easy to remember.

1. Add 40.

2. Multiply or divide by 1.8.
   Multiply by 1.8 when converting from Celsius to Fahrenheit.
   Divide by 1.8 when converting from Fahrenheit to Celsius.

3. Subtract 40.

6.14 TEMPERATURE CONVERSION TABLES

The easiest way of making the conversion is to use a conversion table, like the one on the back cover. Regardless of whether the starting temperature is Fahrenheit or Celsius, you start by finding the temperature you are converting in the center column. Look across to the number in the right column if you are converting from Fahrenheit to Celsius. If you are converting from Celsius to Fahrenheit, look at the number in the left column. To convert 75°F to Celsius, find 75 in the middle column. Looking at the right-hand column you can see that 77°F is equal to 25°C. To convert 25°C to Fahrenheit, find 25 in the center column. Looking at the left-hand column you can see that 25°C is equal to 77°F. Referring to the back cover, it is interesting to note that –40°F is equivalent to –40°C. This is the only place where the two scales coincide.

6.15 ABSOLUTE TEMPERATURE CONVERSION

The most useful conversions to absolute temperatures will be between each regular scale and its corresponding absolute scale: Fahrenheit to Rankine or Celsius to Kelvin. Fortunately these are very easy conversions to make. Fahrenheit can be converted to Rankine by adding 460; Rankine can be converted to Fahrenheit by subtracting 460. Celsius and Kelvin work in a similar manner. Adding 273 to Celsius produces Kelvin; subtracting 273 from Kelvin produces Celsius.

Since Rankine and Kelvin both start at absolute zero, they can be converted from one to the other by either multiplying or dividing by 1.8. There is no need to adjust the scales as is done with Fahrenheit and Celsius. This method produces results that are off by a little less than a degree because the temperatures for absolute zero are approximated at –460°F or –273°C.

6.16 TAKING ACCURATE TEMPERATURE READINGS

Getting accurate temperature readings requires the right equipment and the right techniques. Common temperatures read while working on HVAC/R equipment include air, water, and refrigerant line temperatures.

Air temperature can be read with dial type pocket thermometers, digital pocket thermometers, or electronic temperature testers. Infrared thermometers are less desirable for air temperature readings, because they must read the temperature of objects. However, an infrared thermometer can be used to measure air by targeting the grill.

Water temperature readings can also be read with dial type pocket thermometers, digital pocket thermometers, or electronic temperature testers. If possible, the thermometer should be inserted directly into the water stream. When using electronic thermometers, be sure that the sensor is rated for liquid immersion. Infrared thermometers do not work well for measuring liquid. An infrared thermometer can be used if the water is contacting an object that the infrared can target.

Pipe temperatures are best taken with a thermocouple type temperature tester. Probes are available with clamps that hold the thermocouple against the pipe, Figure 6-16. Bead type thermocouples can be held against the pipe with a Velcro strap for an accurate reading, Figure 6-17. Pocket type thermometers can be used only if the tip can be held securely against the pipe and insulated from the surrounding air. A Velcro strap or perma-gum can be used to hold the tip of the thermometer against the pipe and insulate it from the surrounding air. Most infrared thermometers are not suited for measuring pipe temperature because of their distance to spot ratio. The emissivity of the pipe can also be a problem for shiny materials like copper. Infrared thermometers with a spot ratio of 10:1 or greater will work fine with dull pipes larger than $1/2$ in.

Some systems are equipped with thermometer wells. These are designed for use with thermometers that have metal stems, like pocket thermometers, Figure 6-18. The well

Figure 6-16 Thermocouple clamp on pipe

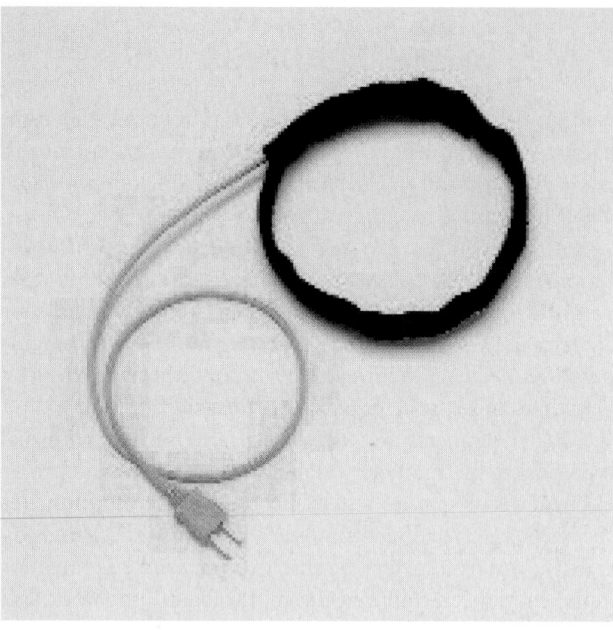

Figure 6-17 Thermocouple bead with Velcro
(Reproduced with Permission of Fluke Companies)

Figure 6-18 Thermometer well with stem thermometer in it

should be filled with mineral oil to ensure good thermal contact between the well and the thermometer.

6.17 AIR TEMPERATURES

Three air temperatures are commonly read when working on air conditioning equipment: the outdoor ambient temperature, the return air temperature, and the supply air temperature. Ambient temperature is the temperature around the unit, typically outside. Return air is the air returning to the system from the conditioned space. Supply air is the conditioned air being supplied to the conditioned space.

Outdoor Ambient Temperature Readings

Outdoor ambient temperature readings should be taken in areas that are free from discharge air from condensing units or dryer vents and out of direct sunlight. Holding the thermometer in front of the air intake grill of the outdoor unit normally works well.

Return Air Temperature

Accurate return air temperatures can be obtained by holding a pocket or digital thermometer in front of the return air grill. Infrared thermometers can be used with return air grills by targeting the grill.

Supply Air Temperature

Supply air temperatures can be more difficult. The unit should operate long enough for supply air temperatures to stabilize. If possible, the thermometer should be inserted inside the supply air register, Figure 6-19. When the supply air leaves the register, it mixes with room air, affecting the temperature of the supply air. Infrared thermometers can be used with supply air registers by targeting the supply air register. When measuring supply air temperature with an infrared thermometer, the unit must run long enough for the register to be the same temperature as the supply air.

Duct Temperatures

The temperatures read at the registers will be different than the temperature at the unit because of duct loss and gain. When checking a system performance specification, such as furnace temperature rise, it is best to check temperatures at the unit. Drilling a small hole in the ductwork allows temperature readings of the air just as it enters and leaves the unit. Holes should generally not be drilled in the actual unit or in flex duct. A hole in the wrong place in the unit can damage

Figure 6-19 Thermometer

Figure 6-20 Thermometer placed in hole in supply duct

the unit. Flex ducts should not be pierced; poking holes in a flex duct allows air to pass between the inner and outer jacket. This increases duct loss and can lead to condensation on and inside the duct.

The return air plenum is the best location for checking return air temperatures, especially if there are several return ducts. The thermometer will read the mixed air temperature, which may be different from the temperature in individual returns.

The supply air plenum can be used on systems with a radial duct design using flex duct. The hole in the plenum should not be too close to where the plenum connects to the unit. If there are any components installed in or on the plenum be careful to avoid them. Airflow from the return air through a bypass humidifier or bypass damper will be a very different temperature than the supply air in the plenum.

When possible, take supply air temperatures in a trunk duct leaving the plenum, Figure 6-20. This avoids the problems of radiant heat from furnace heat exchangers or return air being bypassed through a humidifier or bypass damper.

SAFETY TIP

When drilling holes in ductwork to measure temperature, make certain you know what is on the other side of the duct; hopefully just air. Contacting a set of electric heat strips with a metal thermometer that is sticking through a metal duct can cause a direct short on a high current device and give you a serious shock!

UNIT 6—SUMMARY

Understanding temperature measurements and conversions is essential to every aspect of HVAC/R work. Most HVAC/R jobs require temperature measurement. Temperature is the measure of the average molecular kinetic energy of a substance. The faster the molecules move, the higher the temperature. A solid emits radiant energy that is proportional to its temperature. Different types of thermometers include glass stem, dial, digital, and infrared. Thermocouples are the most common type of electronic temperature sensors. They produce a small DC voltage in response to temperature. There are four widely used temperature scales: Fahrenheit, Celsius, Rankine, and Kelvin. Fahrenheit is primarily used in the United States while Celsius is used throughout the world. Rankine and Kelvin are absolute temperature scales whose zero point is absolute zero. Getting accurate temperature readings depends upon using the correct equipment and technique.

UNIT 6—REVIEW QUESTIONS

1. What is temperature?
2. What is the first color of light that can be seen when a piece of metal is being heated?
3. How does a glass stem thermometer measure temperature?
4. What is an advantage of a glass stem thermometer?
5. What causes the pointer to move on a dial type thermometer?
6. What is an advantage of digital thermometers?
7. Which type of thermometer can see the temperature of a surface from a distance?
8. What is a disadvantage of an IR thermometer?
9. What two metals are joined to create a Type K thermocouple?
10. What are the two points used to create the Celsius temperature scale?
11. The Rankine temperature scale uses the same spacing between degrees as which other system?
12. What would an indoor thermometer range usually be?
13. Convert the following Celsius temperatures to Fahrenheit.
    a. 50°C
    b. 25°C
    c. 150°C
    d. 350°C
14. Convert the following Fahrenheit temperatures to Celsius.
    a. 50°F
    b. 104°F
    c. 158°F
    d. 356°F
15. Convert the following temperatures.
    a. −60°F to Rankine
    b. 30°C to Kelvin
    c. 630°R to Fahrenheit
    d. 200°K to Celsius
16. Convert the following temperatures.
    a. 125°K to Rankine
    b. 300°K to Rankine
    c. 540°R to Kelvin
    d. 378°R to Kelvin

UNIT 7

Thermodynamics—The Study of Heat

OBJECTIVES

After completing this unit you will be able to:

- state the first and second laws of thermodynamics.
- compare and contrast the three basic methods of heat transfer.
- explain the factors that affect the rate heat transfers through various materials.
- explain the difference between heat energy and temperature.
- compare sensible heat to latent heat.
- calculate heat change.
- differentiate between saturated, superheated, and subcooled refrigerant.

7.1 INTRODUCTION

Almost everything we do in HVAC/R involves adding or moving thermal (heat) energy. For example, in heating we may be converting chemical energy, such as a natural gas flame, to thermal energy and distributing it through the building. In refrigeration and air conditioning we are removing heat from inside the refrigerator or house and sending it outside.

It is important to understand thermal transfer. The reason we have to heat or cool areas is because heat transfers through the walls. In the heating season it transfers out, and in the cooling season it transfers in. Put simply HVAC/R technicians work with thermal energy. In this unit, we cover thermodynamics and then look at heat transfer more deeply.

7.2 FIRST LAW OF THERMODYNAMICS

Thermodynamics is the branch of science dealing with heat and the movement of energy. There are four laws of thermodynamics that describe how heat and energy behave. Two of these are of particular interest in HVAC/R applications. The first law of thermodynamics states that "energy can neither be created nor destroyed." Heat cannot be "made," but other forms of energy can be converted to heat because different forms of energy can be converted from one form to another. Energy itself is defined as the ability to

do work, and heat is the transfer of energy due to temperature difference. Other common forms of energy are: mechanical, electrical, and chemical, which may be converted easily from one form to another. The steam-driven turbine generator of a power plant is a device that converts heat energy into electrical energy. Chemical energy may be converted into electrical energy by the use of a battery. Electrical energy is converted into mechanical energy through the use of an electromagnetic coil to produce a push-pull motion or the use of an electric motor to create rotary motion. Electrical energy may be changed directly to heat energy by means of heating resistance wires such as in an electric toaster, grill, or furnace. In all of these transformations energy is neither created or destroyed, just changed from one form to another.

7.3 SECOND LAW OF THERMODYNAMICS

The second law of thermodynamics states that "to cause heat energy to travel, a temperature difference must be established and maintained." Heat energy travels downward on the intensity scale. Heat from a higher temperature (intensity) material will travel to a lower temperature (intensity) material, and this process will continue as long as the temperature difference exists. The rate of travel varies directly with the temperature difference. The higher the temperature difference, commonly called the delta temperature or ΔT, the greater the rate of heat travel. The lower the ΔT, the lower the rate of heat travel.

7.4 METHODS OF HEAT TRANSFER

There are three principal ways that heat is transferred:

1. Conduction.
2. Convection.
3. Radiation.

Most refrigeration systems utilize all three methods. These three methods of heat transfer are shown in Figure 7-1.

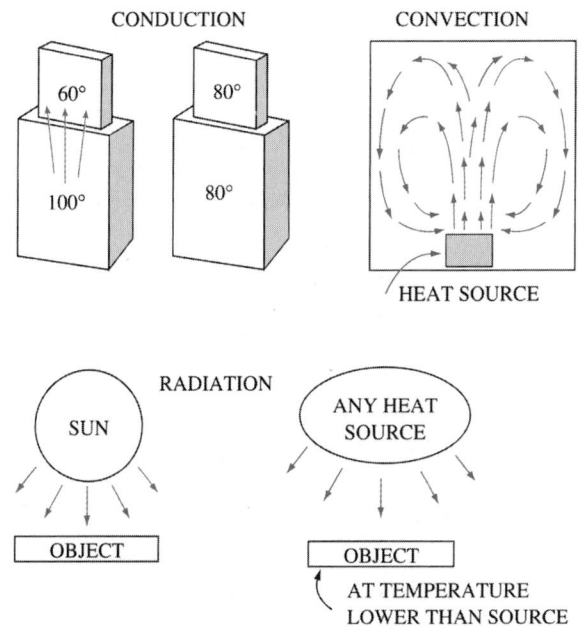

CONDUCTION · CONVECTION

60° · 80°

100° · 80°

HEAT SOURCE

RADIATION

SUN

ANY HEAT SOURCE

OBJECT

OBJECT
AT TEMPERATURE
LOWER THAN SOURCE

Figure 7-1 Three methods for transferring heat

The rate of heat transfer will vary according to the ability of the material to conduct heat. Solids, on the whole, are much better conductors than liquids; in turn, liquids conduct heat better than gases or vapors.

Most metals, such as silver, copper, steel, and iron, conduct heat fairly rapidly. Many other solids such as glass, wood, or other building materials, transfer heat at a much slower rate and therefore are used as insulators.

TECH TIP

Materials that are excellent electrical conductors also tend to be excellent thermal conductors. Similarly, materials that are good electrical insulators also tend to be good thermal insulators. Of course there are exceptions. Materials such as ceramics can be designed to be either an insulator or a conductor of electricity or heat. One particular type of ceramic is actually considered to be a superconductor, meaning it has extremely low electrical and heat resistance.

Copper is an excellent conductor of heat, as is aluminum. These substances are ordinarily used in the construction of heat transfer coils like evaporators and condensers. Steel and iron are also used for some types of heat transfer devices.

The rate at which heat may be conducted through any material is dependent on factors like the thickness of the material, its cross-sectional area, the temperature difference between the two sides of the material, the heat conductivity (k factor) of the material, and the time duration of the heat flow. The table in Figure 7-2 gives the heat conductivities (k factors) of some common materials.c

Note that the k factors are given in Btu/hr/ft^2/°F/in of thickness of the material. The formula for heat transfer using these factors is shown below.

$$\text{Btu} = \frac{A \times k \times \Delta t}{X} \qquad (7\text{-}1)$$

Material	Conductivity k
Plywood	0.80
Glass fiber—organic bonded	0.25
Expanded polystyrene insulation	0.25
Expanded polyurethane insulation	0.16
Cement mortar	5.0
Stucco	5.0
Brick (common)	5.0
Hardwood (maple, oak)	1.10
Softwood (fir, pine)	0.80
Gypsum plaster (sand aggregate)	5.6

Figure 7-2 Conductivities for common building and insulating materials; k values expressed in Btu/hr/ft^2/°F/in thickness of material

TECH TIP

Heat is always on the move. It is moving constantly from a warmer body to a cooler body. This movement can be slowed with insulation, but no matter how thick the insulation is, heat will continue to move through it until both bodies have reached equilibrium and are at the same temperature. For this reason it is very difficult to store heat for long periods of time without significant loss in the quantity of heat being stored.

7.5 CONDUCTION

Conduction is described as the transfer of heat between the closely packed molecules of a substance, or between substances that are in good contact with one another. When heat transfers by conduction in a single substance, such as a metal rod, movement of heat continues until there is a temperature balance throughout the length of the rod. With one end of the rod in a flame and the other end in the air, heat will travel from the end in the flame to the end in the air. Heat will continue to travel through the rod as long as one end is hotter than the other. Even after the rod is removed from the flame, heat will continue to travel from the hotter end to the cooler end until both ends are the same temperature.

If the rod is immersed in water, the rapidly moving molecules on the surface of the rod will transmit some heat to the molecules of water, and still another transfer of heat by conduction takes place. As the outer surface of the rod cools off, there is still some heat within the rod, and this will continue to transfer to the outer surfaces of the rod and then to the water, until a temperature balance is reached.

where

A = cross-sectional area, ft^2
k = heat conductivity, Btu/hr/ft^2/°F/in
Δt = temperature difference between the two sides, °F
X = thickness of material, in

Metals with a high conductivity are used within the refrigeration system itself because it is desirable that rapid heat transfer occur in both evaporator and condenser. The evaporator is where heat is removed from whatever is being cooled; the condenser dissipates this heat to another medium or space.

In the case of the evaporator, the product or air is at a higher temperature than the refrigerant within the tubing and there is a transfer of heat from the warm air into the cool refrigerant in the evaporator. In the condenser, however, the refrigerant vapor is at a higher temperature than the cooling medium traveling through the condenser and heat transfers out of the warm refrigerant in the condenser into the cooler surrounding air.

Plain tubing, whether copper, aluminum, or another metal, will transfer heat according to its conductivity or k factor, but this heat transfer can be increased through the addition of fins on the tubing. They will increase the area of heat transfer surface, thereby increasing the overall efficiency of the system. If the addition of fins doubles the surface area, it can be shown by the use of Equation 7-1 that the overall heat transfer will be doubled compared to that of plain tubing.

7.6 CONVECTION

Another means of heat transfer is by motion of the heated material itself. Convection is limited to heat transfer within a liquid or a gas. When a material is heated, convection currents are set up within it, and the warmer portions of it rise, since heat brings about the decrease of a fluid's density and an increase in its specific volume.

SERVICE TIP

Homeowners and building operators sometimes like to put up their own thermometers in a room. That thermometer reading sometimes is the one you will hear them talking about when they complain about room temperature. There are several factors that will affect the thermometer reading that may result in it being different from the room thermostat. First, the room thermostat is usually close to a height of five feet and should be located on an inside wall. If their thermometer is higher or lower than that, it will read a different temperature. Second, if their thermometer is near an outside wall, it will read higher or lower depending on the season of the year. Certainly a thermometer that is in a window can have wide swings in temperature. One common thermometer people use gives indoor and outdoor temperature readings. By its design, it must be located on an outside wall so that its probe can go to the outside of the building. Those temperature readings will be significantly different most of the time from the room thermostat.

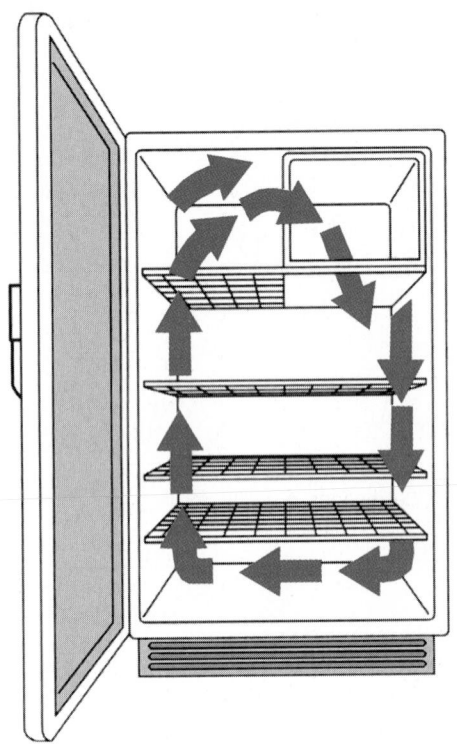

Figure 7-3 Convection currents caused by temperature differential

Natural Convection

Natural convection occurs when fluid circulates because of the density changes that are the result of the fluid heating up and cooling down. Systems that rely entirely on natural convection are called passive systems. Air within a refrigerator is a prime example of the results of convection currents, Figure 7-3. The air in contact with the cooling coil of a refrigerator becomes cool and, therefore, denser and begins to fall to the bottom of the refrigerator. In doing so, it absorbs heat from the food and the walls of the refrigerator, which, through conduction, has picked up heat from the room. After heat has been absorbed by the air it expands, becoming lighter, and rises until it again reaches the cooling coil where heat is removed from it. The convection cycle repeats as long as there is a temperature difference between the air and the coil. In commercial units, baffles may be constructed within the box to direct the air in the desired airflow patterns.

Water heated in a pan will be affected by the convection currents set up within it through the application of heat. The water nearest the heat source absorbs heat, becomes warmer, and expands. As it becomes less dense, it rises and is replaced by the other water, which is cooler and denser.

Forced Convection

Forced convection is the process of moving a fluid using mechanical means to increase heat transfer. Fans are used to move gases; pumps are used to move liquids. Systems that use fans or pumps to increase convection are called active systems.

Figure 7-4 Ceiling fans in vaulted ceilings can help redistribute warm air that has collected at the top of the ceiling

Natural convection currents in air or water distribute the temperature only to a certain extent. Natural convection currents will not keep a room's temperature consistent from floor to ceiling. A temperature difference of 10°F from floor to ceiling in a room with a wood stove is common. When there is a large temperature difference from the floor to the ceiling, additional air circulation is needed to break up the stratified air temperature. Ceiling fans like the one shown in Figure 7-4 can help distribute the heated air more evenly.

7.7 RADIATION

A third means of heat transfer is through radiation. Radiant heat energy travels by waves similar to light or sound waves. These waves travel in a straight path and require no medium between the heat source and the heated object. The sun's rays heat the earth by means of radiant heat waves, which travel through space to heat the earth. Four factors control the amount of energy transmitted between a radiation source and an object: the frequency of the radiation, the absolute temperature of the source, the surface area of the source, and the distance between the source and the object.

Radiant energy waves exist at many different frequencies. The frequency is related to the distance between the peaks of the waves. The shorter the distance, the higher the frequency, Figure 7-5. Higher frequency radiation is more powerful than lower frequency radiation.

The total amount of radiant energy emitted by an object increases dramatically as its absolute temperature increases. Doubling the absolute temperature increases the emitted energy by a factor of 16. The amount of radiant energy emitted by a radiation source is also directly related to its surface area. Twice as much surface area produces twice as much radiant energy.

Heat transfer through radiation does not result in an even distribution of heat. The amount of radiant energy transferred decreases with the square of the distance. This

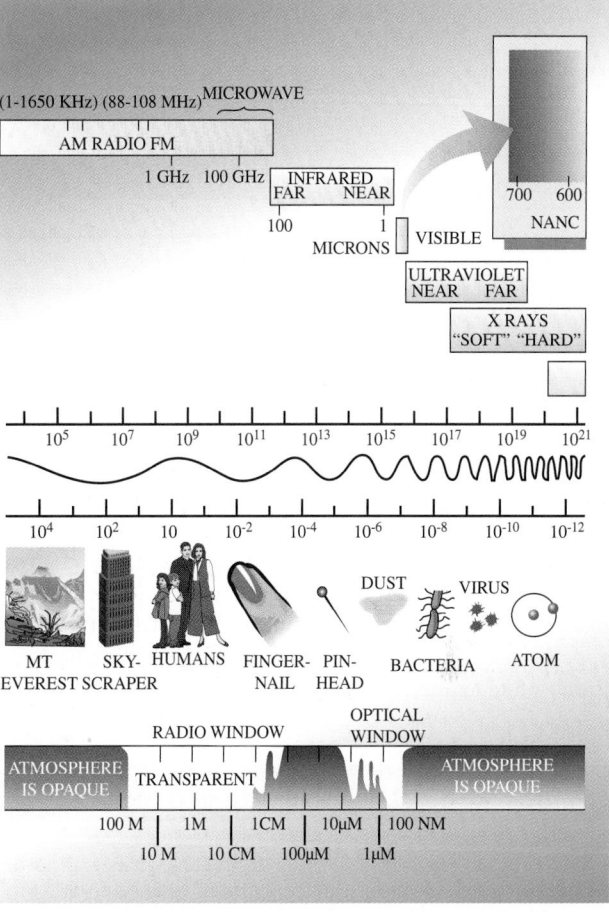

Figure 7-5 Illustration of the correlation between wavelength and frequency
(Fig. 3.9, p. 70 from Astronomy Today *by Eric Chaisson and Steve McMillan. Copyright © 2005 Pearson Education, Inc. Reprinted by permission.)*

means that doubling the distance decreases the amount of energy transmitted to a fourth of the original amount. A fireplace heats through radiation. The further you get away from the fireplace, the colder it is. Next to the fireplace is very warm, but a few feet away can feel much cooler.

Radiant energy travels in straight lines and heats objects, not air. While facing the fireplace in a cold room, your front is warm but your back is cold because it is turned away from the fire. If someone steps between you and the fireplace, your source of heat is cut off and you feel instantly cold.

All objects absorb radiant energy to some extent. When radiant energy strikes matter it can be absorbed, reflected, or transmitted. The amount of energy absorbed versus the amount of energy reflected and transmitted depends on the characteristics of the material. Solids absorb more radiant energy than liquids; liquids absorb more than gases. Dark colored solids absorb more energy than they reflect, while light colored solids reflect more than they absorb. The name for an object that is a perfect absorber of radiation is a black body.

All objects whose temperature is above absolute zero also emit radiation. The amount of radiant energy emitted equals

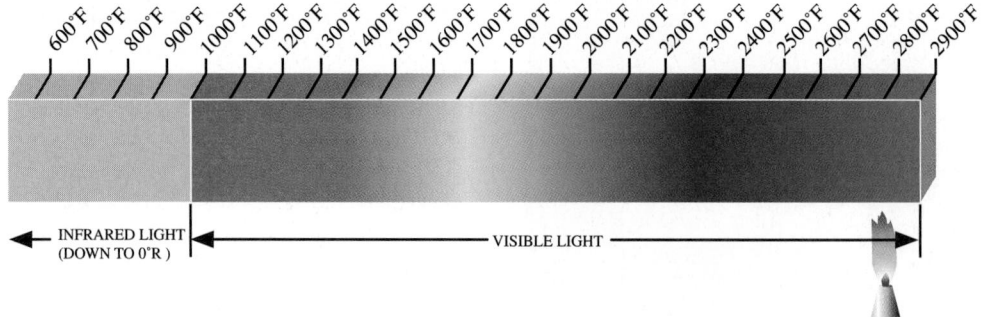

Figure 7-6 Correlation between the absolute temperature of an object and its color

the amount of energy absorbed by the object. Black bodies are also perfect radiation emitters. Radiant objects emit many frequencies of radiation, but they tend to emit more radiation of one particular frequency. This primary frequency changes with the absolute temperature of the object. When the primary frequency is within the visible light spectrum, the object appears that color. Figure 7-6 shows the correlation between the absolute temperature of an object and its color.

TECH TIP

Since radiant energy has little effect on gases, radiant heaters tend to heat the objects in a room without heating the air in the room. This has the advantage of heating people quickly. It also can mean that people can be comfortable at lower room temperatures. The air temperature does rise because the air is heated by the objects in the room, but the primary purpose of radiant heat is not to heat the air, but the objects.

7.8 HEAT TRANSFER PROCESSES

Heat is the transfer of energy because of a difference in temperature. The reaction of matter to the addition or deletion of heat is described as either a sensible, or a latent process. A sensible process results in a temperature change while a latent process results in a physical state change. Notice that these terms describe how heat affects substances, they are not names for different types of heat.

7.9 SENSIBLE HEAT

Heat that can be felt or measured is called sensible heat because it can be sensed. A sensible heat process causes a change in the temperature of a substance but not a change in state. For example, hot air travels across a cold evaporator coil and is reduced in temperature. This is called a sensible heat process because the air temperature was changed when heat was removed from it. Any time a heat transfer results in a temperature change, that process can be called a sensible heat process.

7.10 SPECIFIC HEAT CAPACITY

Specific heat capacity is a factor that allows technicians to calculate the exact amount of heat required to produce a specific temperature rise in a substance. Calculating how much heat it takes to change the temperature of water is relatively easy. In either the traditional or SI measurement systems, the weight of the water is multiplied by the difference in temperature. This is because the units of heat are defined by a temperature change in water.

However, everything does not take the same amount of heat to change temperature. For example, it takes far less heat to change the temperature of metal than glass. Each substance has its own specific heat. The specific heat is also different for different states of the same substance. For example, the specific heat of water is 1.0 Btu/lb, while the specific heats of both ice and steam are approximately 0.5 Btu/lb. Figure 7-7 shows the specific heat capacity of several common substances. It is important to use the correct specific heat value when calculating heat change in a substance.

In traditional units, the specific heat capacity is the number of Btu required to change temperature of 1 lb of a substance 1°F. Water has a specific heat capacity of 1 since the definition of the Btu is based on a 1°F temperature change in water. A substance that requires only half as much heat as water would have a specific heat capacity of 0.5 Btu/lb, while something that takes twice as much heat would have a specific heat capacity of 2 Btu/lb. Things that are easily heated have low specific heat capacities, while things that are slow to heat have high specific heat capacities.

The formula for changing the temperature of anything is:

$$\text{heat quantity} = \text{weight} \times \text{temperature difference} \times \text{specific heat}$$

In traditional units the weight is measured in pounds and the temperature in degrees Fahrenheit. The formula becomes

$$\text{Btu} = \text{lb} \times °F\,\Delta T \times \text{specific heat capacity in Btu lb}$$

In the SI system, specific heat capacity is commonly given as the number of kilojoules required to change 1 kg of a substance 1°K. The formula becomes

$$\text{kJ} = \text{kg} \times °K\Delta T \times \text{specific heat capacity in kJ/kg}$$

Water	1.00
Ice	0.50
Air (dry)	0.24
Steam	0.48
Aluminum	0.22
Brass	0.09
Lead	0.03
Iron	0.10
Mercury	0.03
Copper	0.09
Alcohol	0.60
Kerosene	0.50
Olive oil	0.47
Glass	0.20
Pine	0.67
Marble	0.21

Figure 7-7 Specific heats of common substances (Btu/lb/°F)

7.11 LATENT HEAT

The word latent means hidden. Latent heat is hidden heat because there is no accompanying temperature change to sense. Of course the heat exists, it goes into the molecules to change their state. Latent heat refers to a heat transfer that causes a change in state but not a change in temperature. For example, the refrigerant in the evaporator coil of an air conditioner boils from a liquid to a gas while it is absorbing heat from the warm air passing over the coil. Since the refrigerant is changing state and not temperature, this heat transfer process is called a latent heat process because the result of the heat transfer is a change in state, not a change in temperature. Latent heat is always involved in a change of state. There are several possible state changes, each with its own latent heat value. Each of these changes has a name which identifies the state change. Figure 7-8 lists the different types of state changes.

It takes a lot more energy to change the state of a substance than is does to change its temperature. It takes 144 Btu to change 1 lb of ice to water, but it only takes 0.5 Btu to change the temperature 1°F. The state changes involving gas require even more heat. It takes 970 Btu to boil a pound of water, but it only takes 180 Btu to raise the temperature of 1 lb of water from 32°F to 212°F. The formula for calculating a state change is

$$Btu = weight \times latent\ heat\ factor$$

The latent heat factor is different for different substances. It is also different for different state changes of the same substance. Figure 7-9 lists the latent heat factors for a few common substances.

Process	Common name	Description	Result	Example
Fusion	Freezing	Liquid to solid	Releases heat	Water freezing
Liquification	Melting	Solid to liquid	Absorbs heat	Ice melting
Vaporization	Boiling	Liquid to gas	Absorbs heat	Water boiling
Condensation	Condensing	Gas to liquid	Releases heat	Dew
Sublimation		Solid to gas	Absorbs heat	Dry ice sublimating
Deposition		Gas to solid	Releases heat	Frost forminc

Figure 7-8 Physical changes of state

Substance	Melting point Fahrenheit°	Heat of fusion Btu/lb	Boiling point Fahrenheit	Heat of vaporization Btu/lb
Water	32	144	212	970
Copper	1,981	91	5,301	2,176
Mercury	−38	5	674	226
Paraffin	133			
Ethyl alcohol	−179	45	172	369
Oxygen	−362	6	−298	92
Carnauba wax	120	54	320	
Beeswax	144	75	650	

Figure 7-9 Table of latent heat values

7.12 APPLICATION OF HEAT TRANSFER PROCESSES

Simply stated, a sensible heat process causes a change in temperature; a latent heat process cause a change in state. A substance can either change temperature or change state, but cannot change both at the same time. Water will not boil until it reaches 212°F, but once it does, its temperature will not change. A heat transfer process requires a heat source to supply the heat, and a heat sink, to absorb the heat. One can undergo a sensible change while the other undergoes a latent change. In the evaporator coil shown in Figure 7-10, the refrigerant is boiling from a liquid to a gas and absorbing heat. This is a latent change. The fact that the refrigerant is changing state keeps it cold even as it is absorbing heat. The air blowing over the evaporator is changing temperature from warm to cool. This is a sensible change. The sensible change in air temperature is the goal.

7.13 CALCULATING HEAT CHANGE

The specific heat formula is used to calculate the amount of heat required to change the temperature of a substance; the latent heat formula is used to calculate the amount of heat required to change the state of a substance. Both formulas must be used if the change will involve both a temperature change and a state change. Something cannot change state and temperature at the same time, but it can change temperature and

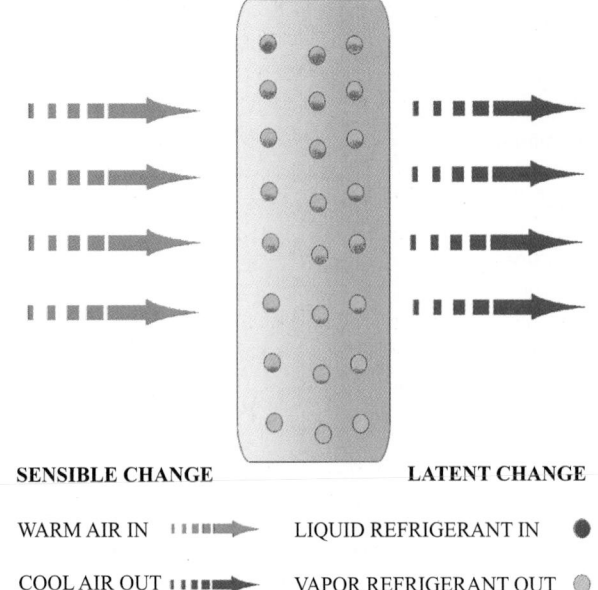

SENSIBLE CHANGE   LATENT CHANGE

WARM AIR IN ▐▐▐▬▬▶   LIQUID REFRIGERANT IN ●

COOL AIR OUT ▐▐▐▬▬▶   VAPOR REFRIGERANT OUT ○

Figure 7-10 The refrigerant in this coil is undergoing a latent change from liquid to vapor while the air is undergoing a sensible change from warm to cool

then change state. The process of changing water from below freezing ice to superheated steam is illustrated in Figure 7-11.

The line from A to B in Figure 7-11 shows the temperature change in the ice from 10°F to 32°F. The line from B

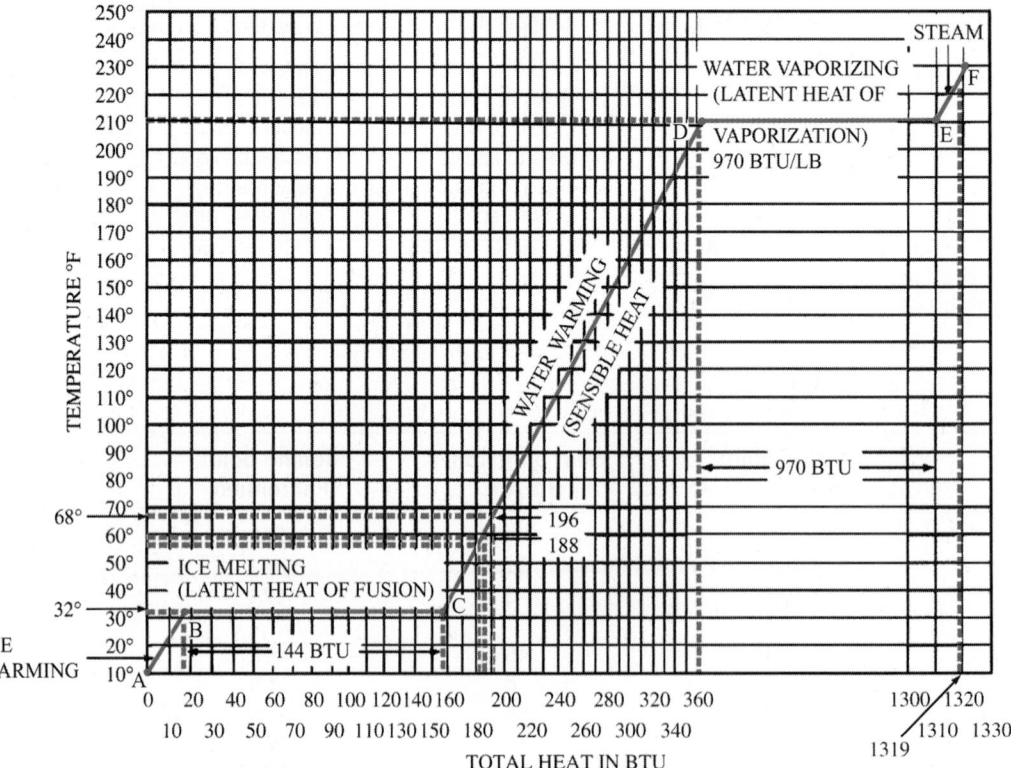

Figure 7-11 Chart demonstrating sensible and latent heat relationships in melting ice, changing ice to water and water to steam

to C shows the 32°F ice melting to 32°F water. Notice that the temperature of the water is the same as the ice. The line from C to D shows the water temperature rising from 32°F to 212°F. The line from D to E shows the 212°F water boiling to 212°F steam. Notice that the steam temperature is the same as the water temperature. Finally, the line from E to F represents raising the steam temperature from 212°F to 230°F. Each of these steps is solved independently and the results are summed to solve for the overall amount of heat required.

- The heat required to increase the temperature of 1 lb of ice from 10°F to 32°F is calculated using the specific heat formula:

  Btu = lb × °F ΔT × specific heat capacity in Btu/lb.
  Btu = 1 lb × 22 × 0.5 = 11 Btu

- The heat required to melt 1 lb of ice is calculated using the latent heat formula:

  Btu = weight × latent heat factor
  Btu = 1 × 144 = 144 Btu

- The heat required to increase the temperature of 1 lb of water from 32°F to 212°F is calculated using the specific heat formula:

  Btu = lb × °F ΔT × specific heat capacity in Btu/lb.
  Btu = 1 lb × 180 × 1 = 180 Btu

- The heat required to boil 1 lb of water is calculated using the latent heat formula:

  Btu = weight × latent heat factor
  Btu = 1 × 970 = 970 Btu

- The heat required to increase the temperature of a pound of steam from 212°F to 230°F is calculated using the specific heat formula:

  Btu = lb × °F ΔT × specific heat capacity in Btu/lb
  Btu = 1 lb × 18 × 0.5 = 19 Btu

It is evident that changes of state require much more heat than changes in temperature. The total amount of heat required for the temperature change from 10°F to 230°F is 210 Btu while the total amount of heat required to change state from ice to water and from water to steam is 1,114 Btu. The latent heat is the turbocharger of the refrigeration cycle. Much greater amounts of heat can be moved by changing the refrigerant's state than by changing its temperature.

7.14 EXAMPLE HEAT CALCULATION

Calculate the amount of heat needed to change 10 lb of ice at −20°F to steam at 250°F.

- The heat required to increase the temperature of 10 lb of ice from −20°F to 32°F is calculated using the specific heat formula:

  Btu = lb × °F ΔT × specific heat capacity in Btu/lb
  Btu = 10 lb × 52 × 0.5 = 260 Btu

- The heat required to melt 10 lb of ice is calculated using the latent heat formula:

  Btu = weight × latent heat factor
  Btu = 10 × 144 = 1,440 Btu

- The heat required to increase the temperature of 10 lb of water from 32°F to 212°F is calculated using the specific heat formula:

  Btu = lb × °F ΔT × specific heat capacity in Btu/lb
  Btu = 10 lb × 180 × 1 = 1,800 Btu

- The heat required to boil 10 lb of water is calculated using the latent heat formula:

  Btu = weight × latent heat factor
  Btu = 10 × 970 = 9,700 Btu

- The heat required to increase the temperature of a pound of steam from 212°F to 250°F is calculated using the specific heat formula:

  Btu = lb × °F ΔT × specific heat capacity in Btu/lb
  Btu = 10 lb × 38 × 0.5 = 190 Btu

- Finally, sum the results
  260 Btu + 1,440 Btu + 1,800 Btu + 9,700 Btu + 190 Btu = 13,390 Btu

7.15 SATURATED LIQUID-GAS MIXTURES

The word saturated means completely full. When a sponge is saturated with water, it is holding all the water it can possibly hold. If you try to add more water, some water will spill out because there is nowhere for it to go. When a liquid is saturated with heat, it has all the heat is can hold and still remain a liquid. When you add additional heat to a saturated liquid, some of the liquid changes to a gas. The gas that boils off of a saturated liquid is called a saturated gas. If heat is removed from a saturated gas, some of the gas will condense to a liquid. The saturation point is the boiling point. As long as the liquid-gas mix remains at a constant pressure and some liquid remains, the temperature will remain the same. Additional heat does not change the temperature; it simply makes more saturated gas. This concept of saturation helps explain why a liquid's temperature remains stable when it boils. After you reach the boiling point, any extra heat goes into turning some of the liquid to gas rather than raising the temperature of the liquid.

While it is technically possible to have a saturated gas and not have any saturated liquid along with it; in practice, where there is saturated gas there is also saturated liquid. For this reason many texts refer to saturated mixtures when discussing either saturated gases or saturated liquids.

Saturated gases do not follow the ideal gas laws. The liquid in a saturated mixture will continue to vaporize until the gas pressure reaches the saturation point for the temperature of the mixture. The pressure of a cylinder of saturated refrigerant with 5 lb of refrigerant will have the same pressure

100 °F 124 PSIG   100 °F 124 PSIG

Figure 7-12 Even though these cylinders have different amounts of liquid refrigerant in them, they are the same pressure because they are the same temperature

as a cylinder with 20 lb of refrigerant if they are both at the same temperature. For saturated mixtures, the pressure is determined entirely by the temperature and not by the quantity of refrigerant, Figure 7-12.

SERVICE TIP

A drop in cylinder pressure is a common problem encountered when charging refrigerant vapor from a cylinder into a system. This does not happen because there is less refrigerant in the cylinder, but because the remaining liquid in the cylinder cools off as the vapor leaves. When vapor boils off of the liquid, it removes heat from the liquid, dropping its temperature. When the temperature of a saturated mixture drops, so does the pressure. Heating the cylinder with warm water can offset this. When the liquid temperature is raised, the pressure comes up as well.

7.16 USING PRESSURE-TEMPERATURE CHARTS

Remember that the boiling point, or saturation temperature, is controlled by pressure. The higher the pressure is, the higher the saturation temperature will be. The pressure and temperature of any saturated mixture go up and down together. If you know one, you can find the other. Charts called pressure-temperature charts, or PT charts for short, are commonly used in refrigeration, Figure 7-13. These charts correlate the saturation temperature and pressure for commonly used refrigerants. Most of these charts list temperature in a column on the left-hand side of the chart and corresponding pressures

in columns on the right-hand side of the chart. To use the chart, find the saturation temperature in the left column and follow across that same row to the column under the refrigerant being used. That lists the pressure of that refrigerant which corresponds to that particular saturation temperature. In Figure 7-13 for example, 40°F in the left-hand column corresponds to 69 psig in the column under R-22.

Of course the chart can be used the other way also. Find the pressure in the column under the refrigerant and then follow across that same row to the temperature column on the outside. This lists the saturation temperature for the refrigerant at that particular pressure. In Figure 7-13 for example, 124 psig under the R-134a column corresponds to 100°F in the temperature column on the left-hand side.

7.17 SUPERHEATED GAS

Remember that when heat is added to a saturated mix, the temperature does not change. More liquid turns to gas, but the temperature remains the same. However, what happens if enough heat is added to a saturated mixture until all the liquid has turned to gas? Now, if more heat is added, the gas temperature will rise because there is no more liquid to boil. When a gas is heated above its boiling point, it is called a superheated gas. In theory it is possible to have a gas that has no liquid in it and is still at the saturation point. However, in practice, if there is only gas present, it is usually superheated. What happens when heat is removed from a superheated gas? The temperature of a superheated gas drops as it is cooled until it reaches the saturation point. If heat continues to be removed after the gas reaches the saturation point, some of the gas will turn back to liquid. When the saturated gas begins to change to liquid, the temperature remains the same.

Temp (°F)	11	12	22	113	114	500	502	134a	123
	VAPOR PRESSURE, PSIG								
5	*23.9*	11.8	28.2	*27.9*	*16.2*	16.4	35.9	9.1	*25.3*
10	*23.1*	14.6	32.8	*27.6*	*14.4*	19.7	41.0	11.9	*24.6*
15	*22.1*	17.7	37.7	*27.2*	*12.4*	23.3	46.5	15.0	*23.7*
20	*21.1*	21.0	43.0	*26.8*	*10.2*	27.2	52.5	18.4	*22.8*
25	*19.9*	24.6	48.7	*26.3*	*7.8*	31.5	58.8	22.1	*21.8*
30	*18.6*	28.4	54.9	*25.8*	*5.2*	36.0	65.6	26.0	*20.7*
35	*17.2*	32.5	61.5	*25.2*	*2.3*	40.8	72.8	30.3	*19.5*
40	*15.6*	36.9	68.5	*24.5*	*0.4*	46.0	80.5	35.0	*18.1*
45	*13.9*	41.6	76.0	*23.8*	2.0	51.6	88.7	40.0	*16.6*
50	*12.0*	46.7	84.0	*22.9*	3.8	57.5	97.4	45.4	*15.0*
55	*10.0*	52.0	92.5	*22.2*	5.8	63.9	106.6	51.1	*13.1*
60	*7.8*	57.7	101.6	*21.0*	7.9	70.6	116.4	57.3	*11.2*
65	*5.4*	63.7	111.2	*19.9*	10.1	77.8	126.7	63.9	*9.0*
70	*2.7*	70.2	121.4	*18.7*	12.6	85.4	137.6	71.0	*6.6*
75	0.0	76.9	132.2	*17.3*	15.2	93.4	149.1	78.6	*4.0*
80	1.5	84.1	143.6	*15.8*	18.0	101.9	161.2	86.6	*1.2*
85	3.2	91.7	155.7	*14.3*	20.9	111.0	174.0	95.1	0.9
90	4.9	99.7	168.4	*12.5*	24.1	120.5	187.4	104.2	2.5
95	6.8	108.2	181.8	*10.6*	27.5	130.5	201.4	113.8	4.2
100	8.8	117.1	195.9	*8.6*	31.1	141.1	216.2	124.1	6.1
105	10.9	126.5	210.7	*6.4*	35.0	152.2	231.7	134.9	8.1
110	13.2	136.4	226.3	*4.0*	39.1	164.0	247.9	146.3	10.3
115	15.6	146.7	242.7	*1.4*	43.4	176.3	264.9	158.4	12.6
120	18.3	157.6	259.9	0.7	48.0	189.2	282.7	171.1	15.1

Temp. Deg. F	R-408A (FX-10) Liquid Pressure	R-404A (FX-70) Liquid Pressure	R-409A (FX-56) Liquid Pressure	R-409A (FX-56) Vapor Pressure	R-407C Liquid Pressure	R-407C Vapor Pressure	R-410A Liquid Pressure
	PRESSURE/TEMPERATURE CHART						
5	34.2	38.6	18.1	9.7	33.0	22.9	55.2
10	39.3	44.0	21.7	12.5	38.0	27.3	62.3
15	44.8	49.9	25.5	15.4	43.5	32.0	70.0
20	50.7	56.2	29.6	18.7	49.3	37.2	78.3
25	57.0	63.0	34.0	22.2	55.7	42.7	87.3
30	63.7	70.3	38.7	26.0	62.5	48.7	96.8
35	71.0	78.1	43.8	30.1	69.8	55.2	107.0
40	78.7	86.4	49.2	34.5	77.6	62.1	118.0
45	87.0	95.2	54.9	39.2	86.0	69.5	129.7
50	95.8	104.7	61.0	44.3	94.9	77.5	142.2
55	105.1	114.7	67.6	49.8	104.5	86.0	155.2
60	115.1	125.3	74.5	55.6	114.6	95.1	169.6
65	125.6	136.6	81.8	61.9	125.4	104.8	184.6
70	136.8	148.6	89.5	68.6	136.9	115.2	200.6
75	148.7	161.2	97.7	75.8	149.1	126.2	217.4
80	161.2	174.6	106.4	83.4	162.1	137.8	235.3
85	174.4	188.8	115.5	91.5	175.8	150.2	254.1
90	188.4	203.7	125.2	100.2	190.2	163.4	274.1
95	203.1	219.4	135.3	109.4	205.5	177.4	295.1
100	218.7	235.9	146.0	119.2	221.6	192.1	317.2
105	235.0	253.4	157.2	129.6	238.5	207.8	340.5
110	252.1	271.7	169.0	140.6	256.4	224.4	365.0
115	270.2	290.9	181.4	152.3	275.1	241.9	390.7
120	289.1	311.1	194.4	164.7	294.7	260.5	417.7

Figure 7-13 The pressure of common refrigerants at 40°F saturation is shown in the highlighted band
(Courtesy of Arkema Inc.)

7.18 SUBCOOLED LIQUID

As long as there is some gas in a saturated mix, the removal of heat will result in some of the gas changing to liquid at the same temperature. After all the gas has turned to liquid, if more heat is removed the liquid temperature will drop because there is no more gas to turn into liquid. When a liquid is cooled below its boiling point it is called a subcooled liquid.

7.19 DISTINGUISHING BETWEEN SATURATED, SUPERHEATED, AND SUBCOOLED

Refrigerant can be found in a refrigeration system as a superheated gas, a saturated mixture, or a subcooled liquid. Determining the condition of the refrigerant is an important step in working on refrigeration systems. It is not really difficult to determine if the refrigerant in a part of a refrigeration system is saturated, superheated, or subcooled. All that is needed is

- An accurate temperature reading.
- An accurate pressure reading.
- A pressure-temperature chart for the type of refrigerant involved.

Take accurate pressure and temperature readings where the state of the refrigerant is to be identified. Use a saturated pressure-temperature chart to look up the saturation temperature that corresponds to the pressure reading.

Saturated Mix

If the actual temperature reading is within 3° of the temperature on the chart, the refrigerant is most likely saturated. Ideally it should be dead on, but a slight measurement error on either the pressure or temperature reading can make it difficult to get a perfect reading.

Superheated Vapor

If the actual temperature reading is more than 3° above the temperature on the chart, the gas is superheated.

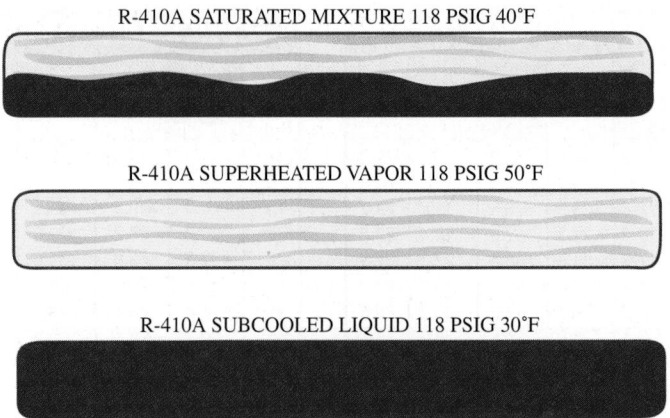

Figure 7-14 Comparison of a saturated mixture of liquid and vapor, a superheated vapor, and a subcooled liquid

Subcooled Liquid

If the actual temperature reading is more than 3° degrees below the saturated temperature on the chart, the liquid is subcooled.

This procedure is summarized below.

1. Measure the refrigerant pressure and temperature.
2. Look up the saturation temperature for the refrigerant pressure on a PT chart.
3. Compare the chart temperature to the actual temperature.

Figure 7-14 illustrates the difference between a saturated mix, a superheated vapor, and a subcooled liquid.

UNIT 7—SUMMARY

Thermodynamics is the study of heat. The first law of thermodynamics states that energy cannot be created or destroyed; the second law of thermodynamics states that heat travels from hot to cold. Heat can travel through conduction, convection, or radiation. Conduction is the transfer of heat through a material by physical contact, convection is heat transfer by fluid circulation, and radiation is heat transfer by waves of radiant energy.

A sensible heat transfer process results in a temperature change; a latent process results in a change of state. It takes more heat to change the state of matter than to change its temperature. Heat changes that involve both temperature changes and state changes must be broken down into steps before solving.

A saturated mixture is a mixture of liquid and vapor at the boiling point. The pressure or temperature of a saturated mixture can be predicted using a pressure-temperature chart. A gas whose temperature is above the saturation temperature contains no liquid and is called a superheated gas. A liquid whose temperature is below the saturation temperature contains no gas and is called a subcooled liquid.

UNIT 7—REVIEW QUESTIONS

1. Summarize the first and second laws of thermodynamics.
2. How does temperature difference affect the rate that heat travels?
3. List the three methods of heat transfer and give an example of each.
4. What is the relationship between electrical conductivity and thermal conductivity?
5. List two materials that are considered to be good thermal conductors.
6. According to their *k* values, which material is a better insulator: expanded polystyrene or expanded polyurethane?
7. Explain why the addition of fins on the tubing will increase the rate of heat transfer.
8. Describe the process of natural convection.
9. What factors determine the amount of radiant energy that is transferred between two objects?
10. Explain the relationship between radiant energy and color.
11. Can a substance change temperature and state at the same time? Explain.
12. Describe the following terms: fusion, liquefaction, vaporization, condensation, deposition, and sublimation.
13. Define sensible heat.
14. Define latent heat of fusion.
15. What is a saturation pressure-temperature chart?
16. The refrigerant R-22 in a system component has a pressure of 70 psig and a temperature of 50°F. Is it saturated, superheated, or subcooled?
17. The refrigerant R-134a in a system component has a pressure of 35 psig and a temperature of 40°F. Is it saturated, superheated, or subcooled?
18. The refrigerant R-410a in a system component has a pressure of 340 psig and a temperature of 95°F. Is it saturated, superheated, or subcooled?
19. Calculate the amount of heat in Btu required to change the temperature of 6 lb of copper from 75°F to 100°F.
20. Calculate the amount of heat in Btu required to turn 5 lb of 10°F ice to 242°F steam.

UNIT 8

Pressure and Vacuum

OBJECTIVES

After completing this unit you will be able to:

- explain the relationships between atmospheric pressure, gauge pressure, and absolute pressure.
- convert atmospheric, absolute, gauge, and vacuum pressures to different scales.
- define head pressure and tell how it is used.
- explain how a manometer measures pressure.
- explain how a refrigeration gauge measures pressure.
- describe how gas responds to changes in temperature, volume, and pressure.
- solve for new pressure, temperature, or volume using the ideal gas law.

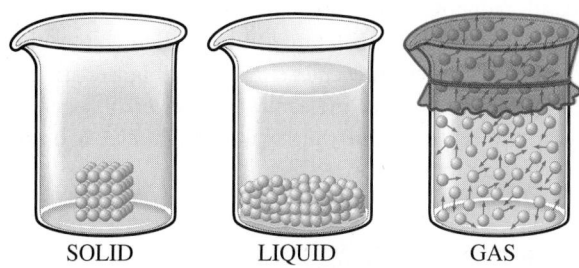

Figure 8-1 A solid exerts pressure down, a liquid exerts pressure down and to the sides, and a gas exerts pressure in all directions

8.1 INTRODUCTION

Pressure is a fundamental physical property that is measured when servicing HVAC/R equipment. Hydronic, pneumatic, refrigeration, and air systems all depend upon pressure differences to create flow. That is why HVAC/R technicians must be familiar with pressure and vacuum readings so they can properly install, service, and repair these systems. The operation of HVAC/R equipment depends on controlling system pressures. This unit will cover the different types of pressure readings and how to convert one type of reading into another.

8.2 PRESSURE

Pressure is a comparative measurement. It compares force pushing on a surface to the area supporting the force. Pressure is uniformly distributed over the surface it is pushing on. The pressure on any surface can be determined by dividing the force applied by the area it is pushing against.

Different states of matter exert pressure in different ways. A solid exerts pressure downward because of gravity. Liquids exert pressure downward and outward because of gravity. Gases exert pressure in all directions against the walls of their container, Figure 8-1.

The force is normally expressed as weight. The pressure created by an object that weighs 100 lb and has a base of 100 in^2 is 100 lb/100 in^2 = 1 pound per square inch. We abbreviate this as 100 psi. If the object weighed 100 lb, but had a base area of only 50 in^2, the pressure would be 100 lb/50 in^2 = 2 psi, because the same weight is supported by a smaller area.

If the same 100 lb was supported by a larger base of 200 in^2, the pressure would be 100 lb/200 in^2 = 0.5 psi. All that is necessary to calculate pressure is to divide the force by the area. In standard units, pressure is measured in pounds per square inch (psi).

8.3 LIQUID COLUMN PRESSURE

Another common way to measure pressure is to measure how high a column of liquid the pressure will support. In the case of atmospheric pressure, the atmosphere will support a column of mercury about 30 in high. What this means is that a column of mercury 30 in high weighs the same as the column of air pushing on it.

Higher pressures are measured in inches of mercury because mercury is heavy. Lower pressures are measured in inches of water column, because water is much lighter. While atmospheric pressure will support a column of mercury 30 in high, it will support a column of water 34 ft high! In air conditioning, we use mercury columns to measure vacuum. Water columns are used to measure the air pressure in ductwork and the gas pressure in gas furnaces.

8.4 ATMOSPHERIC PRESSURE

The air around us exerts a pressure because it has weight. The weight of all the air sitting on top of each square inch of surface area is about 15 lb at sea level. This varies depending upon the elevation of your location. The higher the elevation is, the lower the atmospheric pressure is. Since higher elevations have less air above them, the column of air weighs less, making the air pressure lower. Standard atmospheric pressure at sea level with a temperature of 59°F is 14.7 psi or

101.325 kilopascals (kPa) for SI. In mercury column measurement, that is 29.92 in of mercury (in Hg) or 760 mm of mercury (mm Hg).

The atmospheric pressure at any location on earth will also change with the weather. Both temperature and humidity changes affect the atmospheric pressure. Higher temperature and higher relative humidity both produce lower atmospheric pressure. Higher temperature causes the air to expand, reducing its density and weight, which reduces the atmospheric pressure. Water molecules are lighter than either nitrogen or oxygen molecules. Air with a high relative humidity has more water molecules and fewer nitrogen and oxygen molecules than dry air, making high relative humidity air lighter than dry air.

8.5 BAROMETRIC PRESSURE

Barometric pressure is a term that is used for the current atmospheric pressure. Meteorologists study barometric pressure to predict weather patterns. A barometer is a device designed to measure the atmospheric pressure. Atmospheric pressure was first demonstrated by the type of simple barometer shown in Figure 8-2.

Early experimenters used a glass tube about 36 in long and closed at one end, an open bowl, and a supply of mercury. They filled the tube with mercury and inverted it in the bowl of mercury, holding a finger at the open end to keep the mercury from spilling out while the tube was inverted. Upon removal of the finger, the level of the mercury in the tube dropped somewhat, leaving a vacuum at the closed top of the tube. The atmospheric pressure bearing down on the open

bowl of mercury forced the mercury in the tube to stand up to a height determined by the air pressure. Standard air pressure at sea level and 59°F is 29.92 in Hg. That is 760 mm in SI. That is how barometric pressure came to be measured in inches of mercury (in Hg).

SAFETY TIP

Mercury is considered to be a hazardous chemical and it must be disposed of properly when an instrument containing mercury is to be disposed of. Mercury can contaminate an area resulting in an expensive cleanup operation if it is carelessly discarded on the floor of an office, school, hospital, or any other public area. Mercury vapors have been associated with a number of health issues. Therefore, any time mercury is spilled you must notify the proper authorities so that its potential threat can be determined and an appropriate method of removing the contamination can be done. Be very careful when instruments are used that contain mercury to avoid any accidental spillage.

Although early scientists did touch mercury with their hands, this is not safe, because mercury is toxic. Handling of mercury should be avoided.

One problem with this type of instrument is that it is not very portable. The aneroid barometer was developed as a more portable instrument. Its operating mechanism is an evacuated bellows called an aneroid cell, Figure 8-3. All the air is removed from the bellows but it has a spring

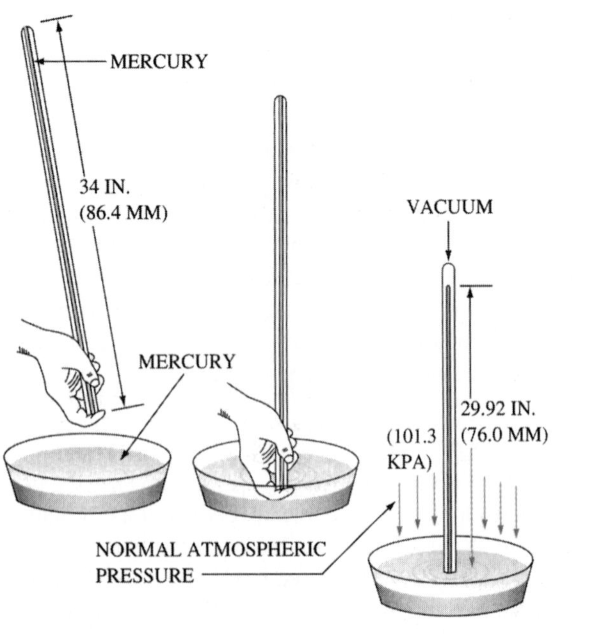

Figure 8-2 Column of mercury supported by normal atmospheric pressure

Figure 8-3 Aneroid cell barometer

inside that balances standard atmospheric pressure and prevents the bellows from collapsing. An increase in the atmospheric pressure causes the bellows to contract; a decrease in pressure causes it to expand. The movement of the bellows moves a needle that indicates the atmospheric pressure.

8.6 LIQUID COLUMN PRESSURE MEASUREMENT

A manometer is one type of device used in the refrigeration and air conditioning field for the measurement of pressure. This type of pressure gauge uses a liquid, usually mercury, water, or gauge oil, as an indicator of the amount of pressure involved. The water column manometer is customarily used when measuring pressures like gas pressures or pressures in air ducts because the low density of water makes it suitable for measuring small amounts of pressure.

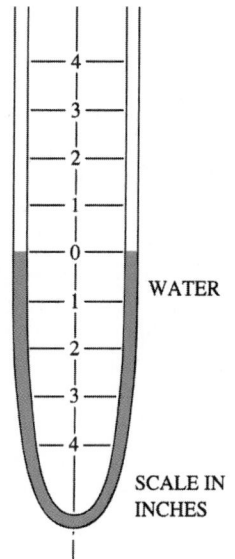

Figure 8-4 U-tube manometer

SERVICE TIP

There are electronic devices that can measure air pressure so accurately that they can tell the difference in altitude of a distance as little as 5 ft. These devices use small electronic sensors to determine the difference in pressure. Most of these instruments use a piezo crystal as their sensor. A piezo crystal is a crystal that changes its electrical resistivity as a result of external force. As the cost of piezo crystal sensors decreases, their use in air conditioning will increase.

A simple open arm manometer is shown in Figure 8-4. The U shaped glass tube is partially filled with water and is open at both ends. The water is at the same level in both arms of the manometer, because both arms are open to the atmosphere, and no external pressure is being exerted on them.

Figure 8-5 shows the manometer in use with one arm connected to a source of positive pressure that is being measured. The amount of pressure being applied is shown by the difference in fluid level from one side to the other. In this case the pressure is 2 in water column.

A space that is void, or lacking any pressure, is described as having a perfect vacuum. If the space has pressure less than atmospheric pressure, it is defined as being a partial vacuum. It is customary to express this partial vacuum in inches of mercury vacuum, abbreviated as in Hg vacuum.

If a vacuum pump pulls a partial vacuum on the left arm of the manometer, as shown in Figure 8-6, atmospheric pressure will push the mercury in the right arm lower and the mercury on the left higher. The measured vacuum is the

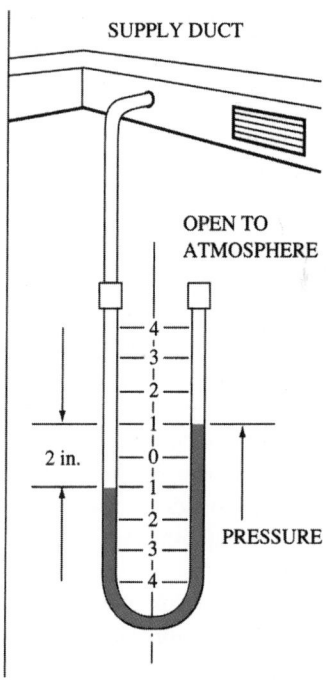

Figure 8-5 When pressure is applied to one side of the manometer, the liquid in that side is forced down and the other side is forced up

difference between the two sides of the manometer, in this case 2 in Hg vacuum.

Liquid column measurement in SI uses millimeters of mercury. Atmospheric pressure is equal to 760 mm of mercury.

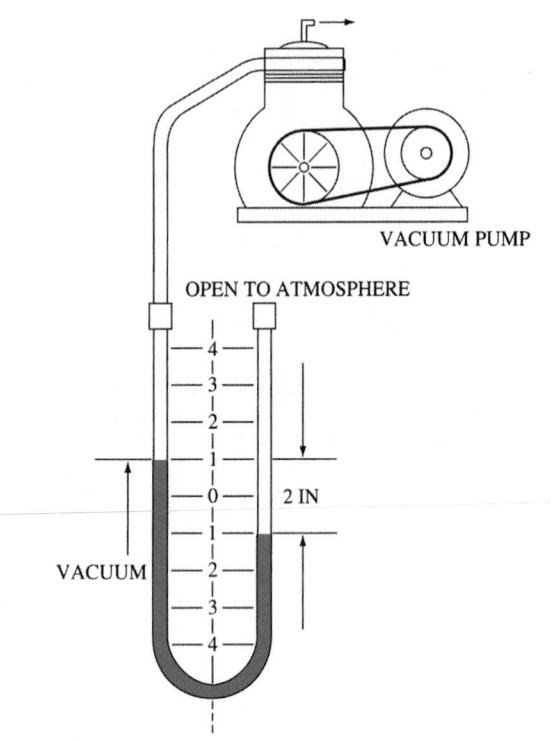

Figure 8-6 When a vacuum is applied to one side of the manometer, the liquid in that side is forced up and the other side is forced down

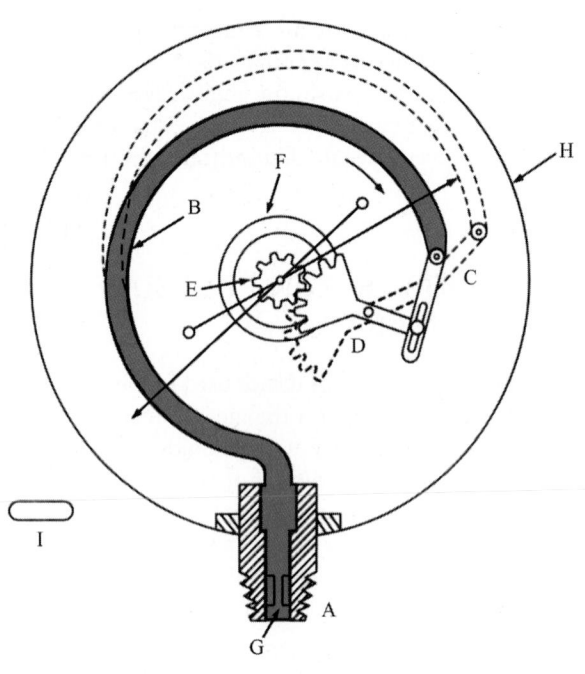

Figure 8-7 Internal construction of a pressure gauge: (A) adapter fitting, usually a $\frac{1}{8}$ in pipe thread; (B) Bourdon tube; (C) link; (D) gear sector; (E) pinter shaft gear; (F) calibrating spring; (G) restricter; (H) case; (I) cross section of the Bourdon tube; the dashed lines indicate how the pressure in the Bourdon tube causes it to straighten and operate the gauge

8.7 GAUGE PRESSURE

The gauges used in the HVAC/R field typically measure pressure compared to atmospheric pressure. Atmospheric pressure is used as the starting point, so the gauges are calibrated to read 0 at atmospheric pressure. Pressures above atmospheric pressure register as a positive pressure while pressures below atmospheric pressure register as a vacuum. A "g" is added to the end of psi to indicate gauge pressure. A pressure of 20 psig would mean 20 psi gauge, or 20 psi above atmospheric pressure.

Pressure gauges most commonly used in the field by service technicians, to determine pressure within the refrigeration system, are of the Bourdon tube type. As is shown in Figure 8-7, an internal view, the essential element of this type of gauge is the Bourdon tube. This oval metal tube is curved along its length and forms an almost complete circle. One end of the tube is closed, and the other end is connected to the equipment or component being tested.

High pressure gauges, as shown in Figure 8-8, are preset at 0 lb, which represents atmospheric pressure of 14.7 psi. Any additional pressure applied when the gauge is connected to a piece of equipment will tend to straighten out the Bourdon tube, thereby moving the needle or pointer and its mechanical linkage, thus indicating the amount of pressure being applied. High pressure gauges can only indicate pressures above atmospheric pressure.

Figure 8-8 A refrigeration pressure gauge measures pressure above atmosphere pressure

Compound gauges are used to measure pressures above and below atmospheric pressure, Figure 8-9. Pressures below atmospheric are customarily expressed in units of in Hg. There is an indication of the range between 0 gauge and 30 in Hg on the compound gauge.

Figure 8-9 A refrigeration compound gauge measures pressure above and below atmospheric pressure
(Courtesy of Ritchie Engineering Company, Inc.–YELLOW JACKET Products.)

8.8 ABSOLUTE PRESSURE

Of course atmospheric pressure is not 0, it is approximately 15 psi. Some applications require true, or absolute pressure. Absolute pressure is simply the real pressure. In absolute pressure, 0 means 0. There is no pressure lower than 0 absolute pressure. Absolute pressure is normally stated in pounds per square inch absolute. The abbreviation psia indicates pounds per square inch absolute pressure.

Absolute pressure is the pressure without regard to the current atmospheric pressure. Where atmospheric and gauge pressures may vary from time to time based on when and where they are taken, absolute pressure never changes. The same absolute pressure can give different gauge pressure readings if the gauges used to measure the pressure are calibrated to different atmospheric pressures. For example, a cylinder containing a quantity of refrigerant at a set temperature might have a gauge pressure of 85 psig down at the coast. That same cylinder at the same temperature might only have a gauge pressure of 87 psig in the mountains. However, the cylinder's absolute pressure at both locations would be 100 psia.

8.9 VACUUM

A vacuum is any pressure less than atmospheric pressure. Mercury columns can be used to measure vacuum by measuring how much pressure has been removed. A pressure of

20 in Hg vacuum means that the pressure is 20 in of mercury less than atmospheric pressure. Since atmospheric pressure is 29.92 in of mercury, a perfect vacuum would be 29.92 in Hg vacuum. This would indicate that all the pressure had been removed. There is no vacuum using absolute pressure because absolute pressure starts with 0 equal to a perfect vacuum. It is impossible to have less pressure than no pressure at all.

Absolute pressure can be used to measure vacuums by measuring how much pressure is left. In the case of a pressure of 20 in Hg vacuum, the absolute pressure would be 9.92 in Hg absolute because 9.92 in of the original 29.92 in of pressure is left. A perfect vacuum using absolute measurement would be 0 in of mercury absolute. This indicates that no pressure remains.

8.10 SI PRESSURE MEASUREMENT

The SI system has a unit made specifically to measure pressure: the Pascal. A Pascal is equal to a Newton per square meter. This is too small a pressure for air conditioning purposes, so many gauges that read pressure using SI units use kilopascals (kPa). A kilopascal is still a much smaller unit of pressure than psi. A pressure of 100 kilopascals is roughly equivalent to 15 psi. That means that 1 kPa is about one-seventh of 1 psi.

Some metric gauges use bars. A bar is equivalent to 100 kPa and is roughly equal to atmospheric pressure. The bar and barometric pressure both get their names from the same Greek root "baros" meaning weighty.

8.11 CONVERTING GAUGE AND ABSOLUTE PRESSURES

There are times when it will be necessary to convert between gauge pressure and absolute pressure. Calculating compression ratio is an instance when a service technician will need to convert gauge pressure to absolute pressure. A set of refrigerant gauges shows the system pressure in gauge pressure, but absolute pressures are needed to calculate compression ratio.

Absolute pressure equals gauge pressure plus atmospheric pressure. Use 14.7 if the actual local atmospheric pressure is not known. For most air conditioning work, the atmospheric pressure can be approximated at 15 psi.

$$\text{psia} = \text{psig} + 14.7 \quad \text{or} \quad \text{psia} = \text{psig} + 15$$
$$\text{psig} = \text{psia} - 14.7 \quad \text{or} \quad \text{psig} = \text{psia} - 15$$

For example, to convert the low side pressure gauge reading of 65 psig to absolute pressure:

$$\text{psia} = \text{psig} + 14.7$$
$$\text{psia} = 65 + 14.7$$
$$\text{psia} = 79.7$$

or rounded to

$$\text{psia} = 80$$

To convert a chart reading of 105 psia to the gauge reading you would see in gauge pressure:

$$psig = psia - 14.7$$
$$psig = 105 - 14.7$$
$$psig = 90.3$$

or rounded to

$$psig = 90$$

SERVICE TIP

Many refrigerant pressure charts and psychrometric charts are based on sea level readings. You must use the correct chart when working at altitudes that are significantly above sea level. The pressure-temperature chart used by a technician in Denver, Colorado is going to be different from one used by a technician in Dallas, Texas. If you look at the bottom of the chart, there is often a small note stating the barometric pressure, altitude, or other indications as to the chart's intended use.

8.12 CONVERTING MERCURY COLUMN PRESSURE TO PSI

Standard atmospheric pressure is stated as 14.7 psia or 29.92 in Hg. This means there are approximately 2 in Hg for every psi; 2.04 to be more precise. To convert from inches of mercury to psi, divide inches of mercury by 2.04, or simply use 2 for an easy estimate.

$$psi = in\ Hg/2.04 \quad or \quad psi = Hg/2\ for\ an\ easy\ estimate$$

For example, to estimate the psi equivalence for 18 in of mercury, divide 18 by 2 to get 9 psi (psi = 18 in Hg/2 = 9 psi). For a more precise conversion, divide 18 by 2.04 (18/2.04 = 8.8 psi).

To convert from psi to inches of mercury, simply multiply by 2.04 for precision, or by 2 for a quick estimate. For example, 8 psi would be 16.32 in of mercury (8 × 2.04 = 16.32).

Most positive mercury column measurement is absolute. One end of the tube that the mercury is in is sealed and the space between the mercury and the sealed end of the tube is in a vacuum, Figure 8-10. When converting gauge pressure, psig, to mercury column pressure absolute, the gauge pressure should first be converted to absolute pressure, psia.

8.13 VACUUM CONVERSIONS

Sometimes vacuums are measure by how much pressure has been removed, as in inches of mercury vacuum, and sometimes the vacuum is measured by how much pressure is left, as in inches of mercury absolute. To convert between the two, subtract the value you want to convert from 29.92. You can use

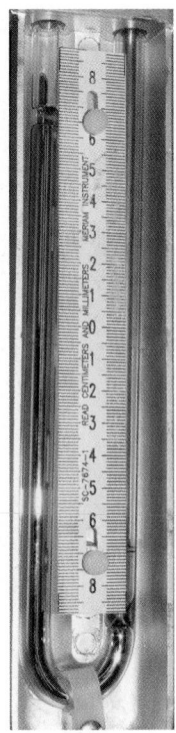

Figure 8-10 Mercury manometer

30 for a very close estimate. For example, an 18 in Hg vacuum is approximately 12 in Hg absolute. Subtracting either one from 30 will produce the other. 30 − 18 in Hg vacuum = 12 in Hg absolute; 30 − 12 in Hg absolute = 18 in Hg vacuum.

SERVICE TIP

Parts of low pressure refrigeration systems operate in a vacuum. Some manufacturers specify their pressures in psia while others specify their pressures in inches Hg vacuum. For a close estimate of psia from inches Hg vacuum, first subtract the inches of Hg vacuum from 30, and then divide the answer by 2. In the case of 16 in Hg vacuum:

$$30 - 16 = 14$$
$$14/2 = 7\ psia$$

For more precision, use 29.92 and 2.04:

$$29.92 - 16 = 13.92$$
$$13.92/2.04 = 6.8\ psia$$

8.14 FLUID PRESSURE

A fluid is a substance that deforms and flows under pressure. Fluids change shape and move from one point to another because of pressure difference. Both liquids and gases are considered fluids because both can take the shape of their container and can flow from one place to another because of pressure difference. Like all matter, fluids have weight, even gases.

The weight of any solid material acts as a downward force on whatever is supporting it. The force of a solid object is the overall weight if the object, which is distributed over the area on which it lies. The weight of a given volume of water, however, acts not only as a force downward on the bottom of the container holding it, but also as a force laterally on the sides of the container. If a hole is made in the side of the container below the water level, as in Figure 8-11, the water above the hole will be forced out because of its force acting downward and sideways.

TECH TIP

The most commonly overlooked fluid that affects air conditioning performance is air. Many people do not realize that air is a fluid. However, either a liquid or a gas can be a fluid because a fluid is anything that can flow. That makes air a fluid with all of the associated characteristics of weight, density, inertia, and pressure.

Fluid pressure is the force per unit area that is exerted by a gas or a liquid. Fluid pressure varies directly with the density and the depth of the fluid. At the same depth below the surface, the pressure is equal in all directions. Notice the difference between the terms used: force and pressure. Force means the total weight of the substance; pressure means the unit force or pressure per square inch.

The tank in Figure 8-11 measures 1 ft in all dimensions holds exactly 1 ft^3 of water. The weight of 1 ft^3 of water is approximately 62.4 lb; therefore, the total force being exerted on the bottom of the tank is 62.4 lb. The force is spread

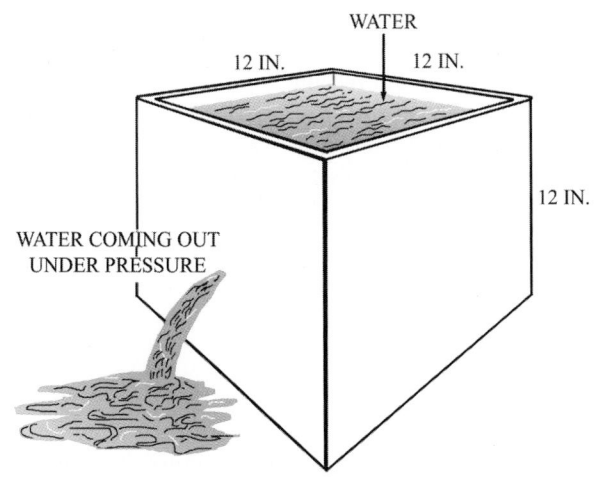

Figure 8-11 Water pressure in a container exerts pressure in all directions

over an area of 144 in^2 (12 in × 12 in = 144 in^2). Using the equation

$$\text{Pressure} = \frac{\text{Force}}{\text{Area}}$$

a pressure of 0.433 psi is exerted on the bottom of the tank (62.4/144 = 0.433).

8.15 HEAD PRESSURE

Pressure and depth have a close relationship when a fluid is involved. The head is the height of water expressed in feet and is used to express water pressure in a system. Water pressure varies directly with its depth. As an example, if the tank in Figure 8-11 was 2 ft high and filled with water, it would contain a volume of 2 ft^3 of water and would weigh 2 × 62.4 lb, or 124.8 lb. Now the force of the water on the bottom of the tank would still be distributed over 144 in^2 and the unit pressure would be 0.866 psi (124.8 lb ÷ 144 in^2). This is twice the amount of pressure that was exerted when the head of water was only 1 ft. Therefore, in an open top container, the pressure of the water will equal 0.433 psi for each foot of head.

SERVICE TIP

A pump only moves fluid—it does not create pressure. The resistance to the flow of a fluid is what results in pressure. A pump that has a fully unrestricted outlet will have zero or nearly zero pressure reading. It is only when a pipe is attached to the outlet and the water directed through the pipe or up some distance that the pressure in the system is created.

The same relationship follows when pumping water in a system. The head is the height difference from the lowest point to the highest point. An increase in the height that a pump must move the water increases the pressure. The head pressure can be determined by multiplying 0.433 times the height. If the height is 10 ft, the pressure will be 0.433 × 10 or 4.33 psi.

The tank in Figure 8-11 has an area of 1 ft^2 with 1 ft of head; therefore, the pressure on the bottom of the tank is 0.433 psi. If there is a fish pond covering an area of 50 ft^2, and the depth of water in it is 1 ft, the pressure on the bottom of the pond will still be just 0.433 psi, even though there is a larger total volume of water. The pressure is determined by the depth of the water, not the volume.

8.16 GAS PRESSURE

An ideal gas is one in which the molecules of the gas have no attraction for each other. An important characteristic of an ideal gas is that it will expand to take up the entire volume

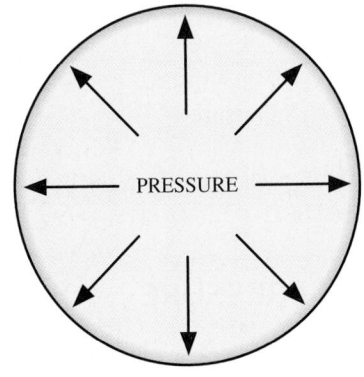

Figure 8-12 Gas exerts force evenly against all sides of its container

that it is contained in. When gas is confined, it pushes against the sides of its container, creating pressure, Figure 8-12. This pressure is created by the kinetic energy of the gas molecules as they strike the surface of the container. If more molecules are put into the same container, the pressure goes up because now there are more molecules to strike the surface, Figure 8-13.

TECH TIP

Nitrogen is stored as a compressed gas in cylinders at very high pressures. The pressures are high because so much nitrogen gas is stuffed into the cylinder. Immediately after the cylinders are filled, the pressure is as high as 2,400 psig. As nitrogen is used out of the cylinder, the cylinder pressure decreases because there is less nitrogen in the cylinder.

If the temperature of the gas is increased, the increased speed and kinetic energy of the molecules increases the number of times molecules strike the surface and increases

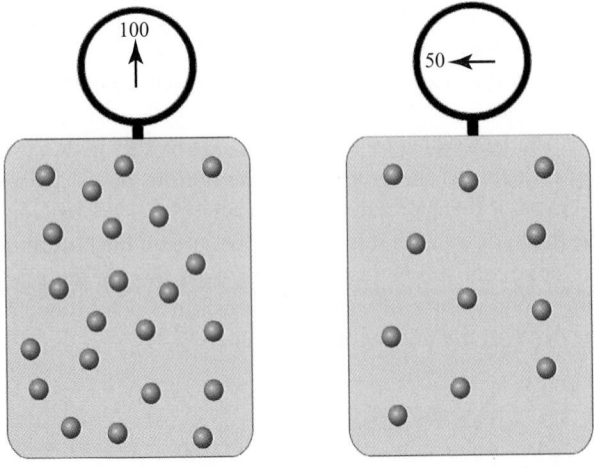

Figure 8-13 Increasing the number of gas molecules in the container increases the pressure on the sides of the container

the pressure. If the volume of the container is reduced, the pressure increases because the molecules are packed in more closely and strike the surface more often. Therefore, the three ways that gas pressure can be increased are by increasing the quantity of gas in the container, increasing the temperature of the gas, or decreasing the size of the container. Naturally these all work in reverse as well. Gas pressure can be reduced by removing some of the gas from the container, decreasing the gas temperature, or increasing the size of the container.

8.17 GAS LAWS

Many scientists have studied the behavior of gases and contributed to our knowledge of gas laws. Several scientists published their findings demonstrating a particular aspect of gas behavior. The math formulas describing the particular gas behavior they studied have become known as the gas laws. Each law is named after the scientist credited with creating it. The laws governing gas behavior are summarized in the list below.

- **Pascal's Law** Pascal's law states that gas pressure is exerted uniformly everywhere on its container.
- **Boyle's Law** Boyle's law states that pressure increases as volume decreases.
- **Charles's Law** Charles's law states that volume increases as temperature increases.
- **Gay-Lussac's Law** Gay-Lussac's law states that the pressure increases as the temperature increases.
- **Ideal Gas Law** The ideal gas law is a combination of all of these laws that describes the behavior of gases.
- **Dalton's Law** Dalton's law states that the total pressure of a mixture of gases is equal to the sum of their individual pressures.

Absolute Pressure and Temperature

All pressures and temperatures must be converted to absolute temperatures and pressures before attempting to solve any of the equations because the gas law formulas only work for absolute temperature and absolute pressure. This is because ratio and proportion will not give correct results for any system that uses both positive and negative values. Absolute temperature and absolute pressure have no negative numbers. The coldest temperature on an absolute scale is 0°; there are no negative temperatures. The lowest pressure on an absolute pressure scale is 0; there is no vacuum.

8.18 PASCAL'S LAW

Pascal's law describes how a gas reacts in a confined space. Pascal's Law states that when a gas is confined, it exerts equal pressure in all directions. This means that if the pressure were measured from the outside or inside or from the top or bottom, the pressure readings would all be the same, Figure 8-14.

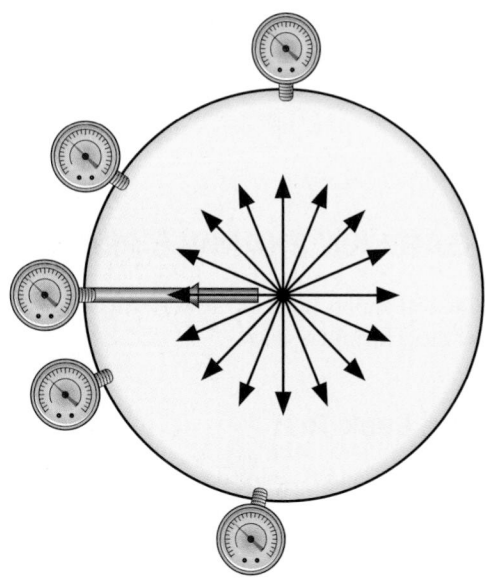

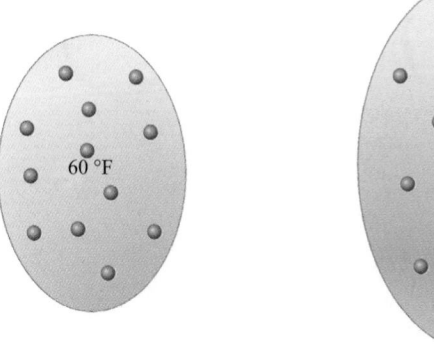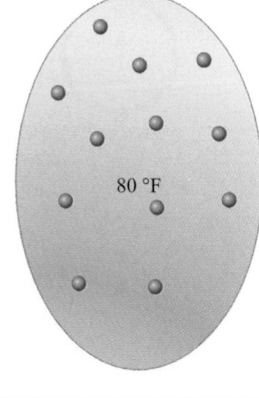

Figure 8-16 The same number of gas molecules take up more space at a higher temperature

Figure 8-14 Pascal's law states that gas pressure is applied evenly on all surfaces of its container

shows a fixed quantity of gas before and after being compressed.

8.19 BOYLE'S LAW

Boyle's law describes the relationship between the volume and pressure of a gas. Boyle's law states that the volume of a gas varies inversely with its pressure if the temperature of the gas remains constant. This means that if the volume increases, the pressure will decrease. For example, if the volume of a gas is doubled, the pressure will be halved. This also works the other way. When the volume decreases, the pressure increases. If the volume is halved, the pressure is doubled. This is the operating principle of compressors. Figure 8-15

8.20 CHARLES'S LAW

Charles's law describes how a gas volume reacts to changes in temperature. Charles's law states that the volume of a gas is in direct proportion to its absolute temperature, provided that the pressure is kept constant. This means that a gas will expand in volume with an increase in temperature, and contract in volume with a decrease in temperature. Figure 8-16 shows a balloon at two different temperatures. When the gas in the balloon is at a higher temperature, the gas volume expands, making the balloon larger.

> ### TECH TIP
>
> The increase in gas volume that accompanies an increase in gas temperature is the operating principle of hot air balloons. The heated air inside the balloon expands, making it less dense than the surrounding air.

8.21 GAY-LUSSAC'S LAW

Gay-Lussac's law describes the relationship between gas pressure and gas temperature. Gay-Lussac's law states that the pressure of a gas is directly proportional to its temperature with the volume remaining constant. This means that increasing the temperature increases the pressure, or decreasing the temperature will decrease the pressure. Figure 8-17 shows two identical volumes of gas at different temperatures. The volume at a higher temperature is also at a higher pressure.

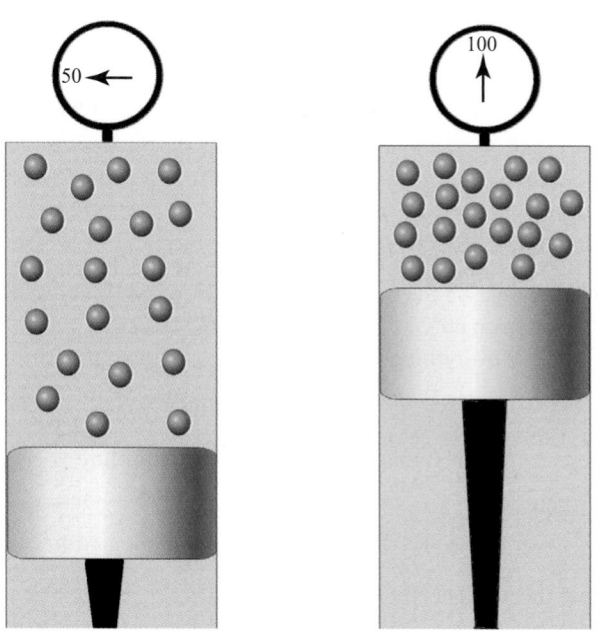

Figure 8-15 Confining the same number of gas molecules in a smaller space increases the gas pressure

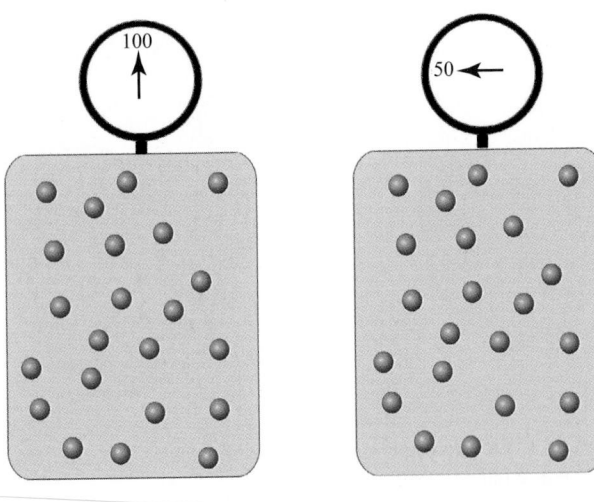

800° RANKINE   400° RANKINE

Figure 8-17 With the same number of molecules and the same amount of space the container with the higher temperature will have a higher pressure

8.22 IDEAL GAS LAW

A combination of all of the above laws is called the ideal gas law. All of the previous relationships assumed that one of the variables remained constant. In reality, this is seldom the case. The ideal gas law makes predictions of gas behavior possible even when all of the variables are changing. Mathematically, the ideal gas law may be written as

$$P_1V_1/T_1 = P_2V_2/T_2$$

where
V_1 = the starting volume
V_2 = the ending volume
P_1 = the starting pressure
P_2 = the ending pressure
T_1 = the starting temperature
T_2 = the ending temperature

The basic formula can be rearranged to show the solution for new volume, new pressure, or new temperature

New volume

$$V_2 = (T_2 \times V_1 \times P_1) \div (T_1 \times P_2)$$

New pressure

$$P_2 = (T_2 \times V_1 \times P_1) \div (T_1 \times V_2)$$

New temperature

$$T_2 = (T_1 \times V_2 \times P_2) \div (V_1 \times P_1)$$

Just plug in the relevant numbers to solve for new volume, new pressure, or new temperature. When working a problem that does not use all three variables, just leave off the variable you are not using. For example, to solve for new pressure when the volume remains constant, the formula becomes

$$P_2 = (T_2 \times P_1) \div T_1$$

8.23 GAS LAW EXAMPLE PROBLEMS

A few practical applications of the perfect gas law will illustrate how these formulas work.

Standing Leak Test

A refrigeration system is charged with nitrogen to check for leaks. The temperature of the system and surroundings is 100°F when the system is charged to 100 psig. The pressure is checked the following morning after the temperature has dropped to 50°F. The pressure will have dropped slightly even if no nitrogen has escaped. What should the pressure be if no nitrogen has escaped?

The formula to use is

$$P_2 = (T_2 \times V_1 \times P_1) \div (T_1 \times V_2)$$

Since the space in the system, the volume, is staying the same this can be shortened to

$$P_2 = (T_2 \times P_1) \div T_1$$

Convert the pressures and temperatures to absolute.

100 psig + 15 = 115 psia
100°F + 460 = 560°R
50°F + 460 = 510°R

Plug the numbers into the formula.

$$(510°R \times 115 \text{ psia}) \div 560°R = 105 \text{ psia}$$

convert 105 psia to psig

$$105 \text{ psia} - 15 = 90 \text{ psig}$$

Compressed Gas

What would be the final volume of 4 ft³ of gas that is compressed from 60°F at 70 psig to 150°F at 210 psig?

Since everything is changing, the formula to use is

$$V_2 = (T_2 \times V_1 \times P_1) \div (T_1 \times P_2)$$

Convert the pressures and temperatures to absolute.

70 psig + 15 = 85 psia   210 psig + 15 = 225 psia
60°F + 460 = 520°R   150°F + 460 = 610°R

Plug the numbers into the formula.

$$V_2 = (610°R \times 4 \text{ ft}^3 \times 85 \text{ psia}) \div (520°R \times 225 \text{ psia})$$
$$V_2 = 1.8 \text{ ft}^3$$

Compressed Air Cooling

One of the more interesting air conditioning systems that have been developed works by compressing and expanding air. Air is compressed, raising its pressure and temperature. It is then cooled to outdoor ambient temperature by passing it through a cooling coil. Finally, the compressed air is passed through an orifice where its pressure is dropped and it is expanded back to its original volume, but with less heat. Calculate the leaving air temperature of a system which is expanding air from 5 ft^3/lb at 30 psig and 100°F to a new volume of 14 ft^3 at 0 psig.

Since everything is changing, the formula to use is

$$T_2 = (T_1 \times V_2 \times P_2) \div (V_1 \times P_1)$$

Convert the pressures and temperatures to absolute.

30 psig + 15 = 45 psia   0 psig + 15 = 15 psia

100°F + 460 = 560°R

Plug the numbers into the formula.

T$_2$ = (560° R $\times$ 14 ft^3 $\times$ 15 psia) $\div$ (5 ft^3 $\times$ 45 psia) = 523°R

Convert 523°R to °F

$$523°R - 460 = 63°F$$

8.24 DALTON'S LAW

Dalton's law states that the total pressure of a gas mixture is equal to the sum of all the gas partial pressures in the mixture. This means the total pressure of a mixture of gases can be determined by adding each of the individual gas pressures, Figure 8-18. Dalton's law is a logical extension of Avogadro's law which states that equal volumes of gases, at the same temperature and pressure, contain the same number of atoms or molecules. The type of the gas has no effect on the gas pressure, only the number of molecules in the container.

TECH TIP

In the field, you can easily check to see whether a cylinder of refrigerant is contaminated with air. If a cylinder of refrigerant is contaminated with air, the pressure gauge reading will be equal to the reading for the refrigerant and the air added together. Take the cylinder's pressure and temperature, and compare it to a refrigerant chart. If the pressure you obtained is higher, the cylinder contains something other than pure refrigerant, and that is usually air.

8.25 SATURATED GAS

So far, all the discussion has related to the behavior of an ideal gas in which the molecules have no attraction for one another. However, when a gas is at the saturation point, the molecules have enough attraction for each other that removing heat from them will cause them to condense to a liquid. A saturated gas behaves very differently from an ideal gas because the gas can change state at the saturation point. For this reason, saturated gases do not follow the ideal gas laws.

The temperature and pressure changes of a saturated mixture are far greater than those of an ideal gas. Adding heat to a saturated mixture in a container creates more gas molecules while leaving the volume the same. More gas molecules create more gas pressure. This increase in pressure is much more dramatic than the increase in pressure due to simply increasing the temperature of the molecules that are already there, as in an ideal gas.

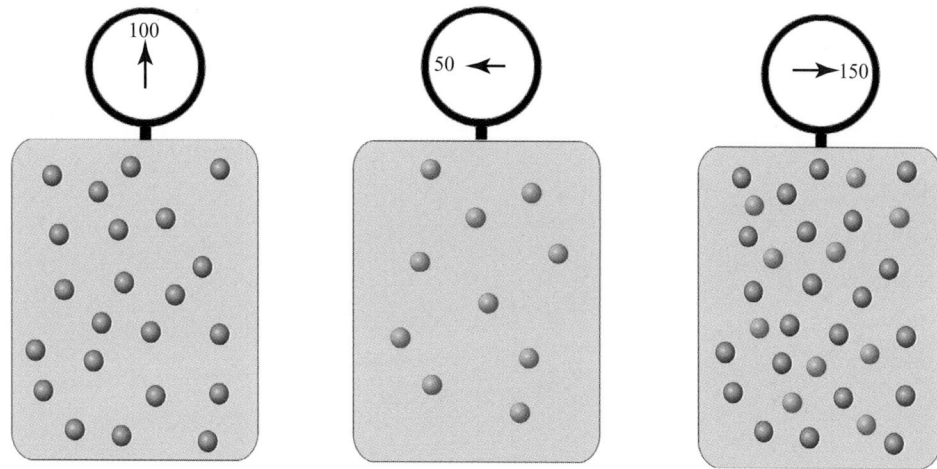

Figure 8-18 When two separate gases are put in the same container the total pressure in the container is the sum of the individual pressures

UNIT 8—SUMMARY

Hydronic, pneumatic, refrigeration, and air systems all depend upon pressure differences to create flow. That is why HVAC/R technicians must be familiar with pressure and vacuum readings so they can properly install, service, and repair these systems.

Absolute pressure is the only pressure reading that is not dependant on the surrounding atmospheric pressure. Absolute pressure is not often used by the HVAC/R field technician; however, it is important to know about and may be a factor in some refrigeration applications. For example, low temperature refrigeration often operates in a vacuum. As you now know, the total pressure difference between an absolute vacuum and atmospheric pressure is 14.7 psi. That is not very much pressure to work with as compared to air conditioning that might have 300–400 psi. Therefore, in some low temperature refrigeration service, technicians may have to convert gauge reading to absolute to know exactly how the system is working and at what temperature.

UNIT 8—REVIEW QUESTIONS

1. How does atmospheric pressure affect a gauge pressure reading?
2. What is a fluid?
3. Define pressure.
4. What creates atmospheric pressure?
5. What is the difference between absolute pressure and gauge pressure?
6. What causes atmospheric pressure to change?
7. What is the relationship between atmospheric pressure and barometric pressure?
8. The reading on a low side pressure gauge is 65 psig. What is the absolute pressure?
9. Convert a chart reading of 100 psia to the reading you would see in gauge pressure.
10. Convert a barometric pressure reading of 26 in Hg to psia.
11. Convert a reading of 20 in Hg vacuum to psia.
12. Define a vacuum and tell how it is measured.
13. Why are some vacuum pressures expressed in inches of water and others in inches of mercury?
14. What causes fluid pressure?
15. What is the pressure at the bottom of a square tank that has a cross section of 5 ft^2 and is filled with water to a depth of 4 ft?
16. What is the pressure in psi required to lift water 15 ft?
17. Explain how a simple open arm manometer measures pressure.
18. Explain how a Bourdon tube gauge works.
19. Briefly summarize Dalton's Law.
20. What temperature in degrees Fahrenheit would a fixed volume of gas need to be heated to in order to double its pressure if it starts out at 25°F?
21. A volume of 4 ft^3 of gas is compressed from 50°F at 70 psig to 2 ft^3 with the resulting temperature of 100°F. What is the new pressure?
22. Explain the bar pressure measurement system.
23. Which is a larger unit of pressure: 1 kPa or 1 psi?
24. Why do saturated gases not follow the ideal gas law?
25. Explain Pascal's law.

Tools and Equipment

UNIT 9

Hand and Power Tools

OBJECTIVES

After completing this unit you will be able to:

- identify the major tools used in HVAC/R work.
- describe how the major HVAC/R tools are used.
- explain the process for flaring tubing.
- demonstrate how to care for tools.

TECH TIP

Air conditioning and refrigeration hand tools do not get as dirty as most mechanics' tools will. However, it is a good idea to wipe them down with a clean, dry rag after each use. In addition, from time to time they should be rubbed with a lightly oiled cloth to protect them from rusting.

9.1 INTRODUCTION

The care and use of tools are important considerations for the technician. The customer often judges a technician on the appearance of their tools. They often assume that a technician that has a dirty, poorly maintained, and disorderly tool bag will provide the same type of service. To a large extent this is true, because it is harder to work with poorly maintained tools, and a tool bag that is not well organized makes it take longer to locate the tools for the job. The way you maintain your tools reflects on your quality of workmanship. In addition, injury can frequently be traced to a lack of, or improper use of, hand tools. Clean, sharp tools are better to work with and safer to use.

The common hand tools needed by an HVAC/R technician are described in this chapter.

9.2 WRENCHES

The term wrench is used to describe tools that grip and turn threaded parts such as nuts, bolts, valves, and pipes. Some wrenches are adjustable, so they will fit a range of sizes of nuts, bolts, or pipes, as shown in Figure 9-1. Other wrenches have fixed sizes and come as sets to fit common sizes, as shown in Figure 9-2. Some wrenches are specifically designed for HVAC/R jobs such as the service valve wrench, as shown in Figure 9-3.

9.3 SERVICE VALVE WRENCHES

Service valves on some compressors and condensers are $1/4$ in (6 mm) square stems and require a special service valve wrench as shown in Figure 9-3. Service valve wrenches

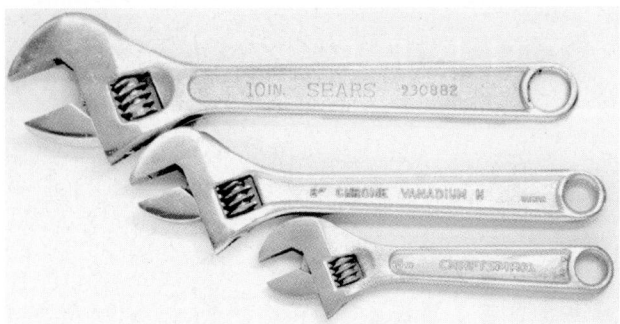

Figure 9-1 Adjustable wrenches come in a variety of sizes

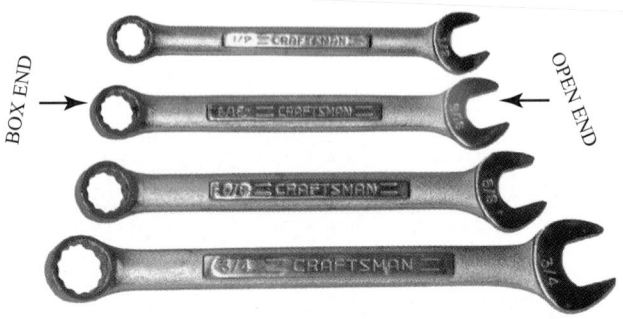

Figure 9-2 Combination wrenches—one end is open and the other end is boxed

Figure 9-3 Refrigerant service valve wrenches have square openings

come in several styles and shapes. Some service valve wrenches use a ratchet mechanism. The ratchet may be fixed in one direction so the wrench has to be removed and turned over to change directions. Other service valve wrenches may have a lever for reversing the rotation of the wrench as required for either opening or closing the valve, Figure 9-4. Reversible ratchet service valve wrenches can have up to four fixed sizes of square openings ranging from $^3/_{16}$ in, $^1/_4$ in, $^5/_{16}$ in, and $^3/_8$ in (4 mm, 6 mm, 8 mm, and

Figure 9-4 Ratchet service valve wrench

(a)

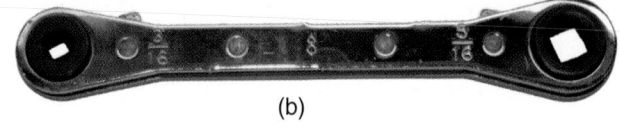

(b)

Figure 9-5 Some ratcheting refrigerant service valve wrenches provide four different size openings by having two different sizes on each end: (a) front, $^1/_4$ and $^3/_8$ in sizes; (b) back, $^3/_{16}$ and $^5/_{16}$ in sizes

9 mm), Figure 9-5. These service wrenches look similar to the ratchet wrenches used by auto mechanics, but those wrenches have hex openings to fit the heads of standard nuts and bolts.

The handles on service valve wrenches can be flat or offset. The offset gives your hand a little more clearance in tight places, Figure 9-6. Most HVAC/R technicians carry more than one type of service valve wrench to meet the varying job needs.

SERVICE TIP

From time to time it is necessary to use an extension on a socket to reach way down inside a piece of equipment to remove or install a bolt or a nut. For example, the mounting bolts on a compressor inside of a residential condensing unit may require a foot long extension or more. A problem can exist when you try to reach back in this tight space to reinstall the bolts. There may not be room for your hand and wrench. However, if you use a small piece of paper, possibly folded one or two times, and place it over the head of the bolt before pushing the head into the socket, this can be used to hold the bolt or nut in the socket as it is lowered down into the confined space. This trick can save a lot of aggravation. Some manufacturers do provide small magnets that can be placed in the sockets which can serve the same purpose. However the paper trick works when you do not have the magnets.

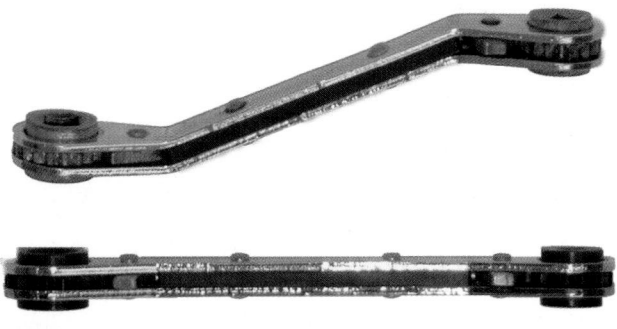

Figure 9-6 Refrigerant service valve wrenches are available with offsets to provide some hand clearance when using the wrench

9.4 SOCKET WRENCHES

Socket wrenches are made to slip over the heads of bolts and nuts, Figure 9-7. They are made of tool steel. Sockets usually come as sets in either standard or metric sizes.

Although standard sockets are available in sizes ranging from $\frac{1}{16}$ in up to several inches in size, the most common set would have sockets sizes starting with $\frac{1}{4}$ in up to 1 in by $\frac{1}{8}$ in or $\frac{1}{16}$ in increments, Figure 9-8. Common metric socket sets range from 6 mm up to 25 mm.

Both standard and metric socket sets for standard hexagonal nuts or bolts can be either 6 point or 12 point, Figure 9-9. The 6 point sockets are stronger; but the 12 point sockets allow easier alignment and shorter swing for tight locations. Swivel sockets and universal joints are also useful for reaching bolts that are hard to get at.

Socket Handles

A number of designs of socket wrench handles, referred to as socket handles, are available. Socket handles range from

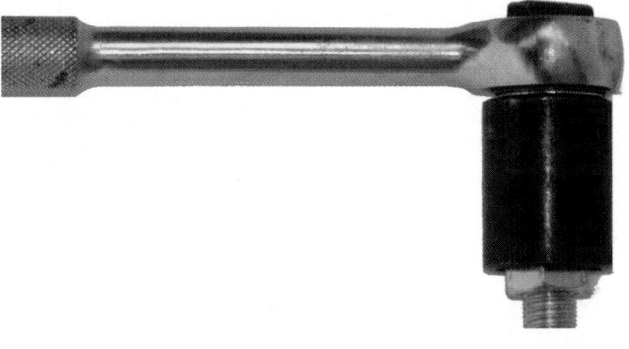

Figure 9-7 The socket slides over the heads of nuts and bolts

Figure 9-8 Socket set

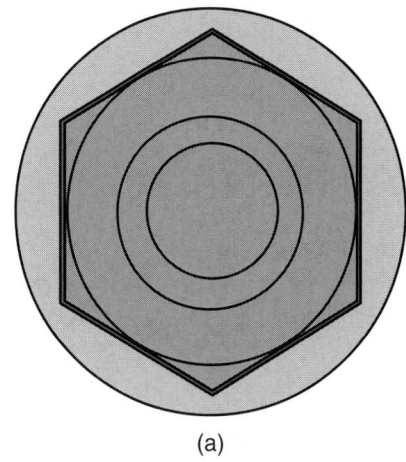

(a)

(b)

   AREA OF CONTACT BETWEEN SOCKET AND BOLT

Figure 9-9 (a) Six point sockets provide greater contact with the head of the nut or bolt than (b) twelve point sockets

the most common ratchet type to the breaker bar to specialty designs such as tee driver and torque wrench handle, Figure 9-10. There are two dimensions used to refer to socket handles: length and size. The length refers to the distance from the tip of the handle to the head. The size refers to the dimension of the square shank that fits into the socket. The three common sizes for this shank are $\frac{1}{8}$ in, $\frac{1}{4}$ in, and $\frac{3}{8}$ in. Adapters are available to allow larger or smaller shank sizes to be used with different sized socket sets, Figure 9-11.

Ratchet Socket Wrench Handles

Ratchet socket wrench handles are the most common type of handles because they can be used to quickly loosen and remove or install and tighten nuts and bolts. Some ratchets have swivel heads that are helpful for working in tight places, Figure 9-12.

Figure 9-10 Torque wrench

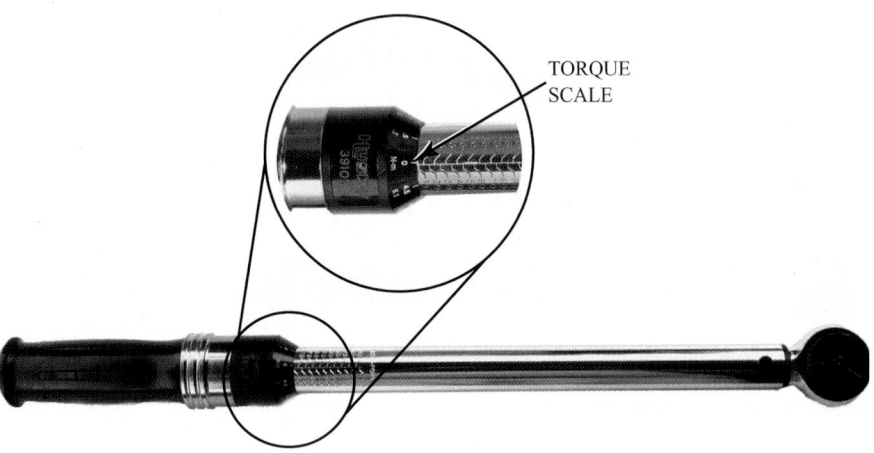

TORQUE SCALE

than ratchets. However, never use a cheater bar or pipe to extend the handle for more leverage because this could damage the wrench.

9.5 TORQUE WRENCHES

Torque wrenches have a gauge to measure the force being applied. Making sure the same force is used on nuts and bolts is important especially when tightening the heads on compressors. Uneven tightening can result in the head being warped or bolts being stripped or broken. Either case can render the compressor unusable or more expensive to repair. Equipment manufacturers have recommended torque specifications that must be followed to ensure a quality assembly, Figure 9-13. Typical specifications will give both the torque and the tightening sequence. A good torque practice is to first apply only a light torque to each bolt in the recommended sequence. Then repeat the tightening sequence and each time increase the torque slightly until the required torque is reached.

The dial on the wrench indicates the amount of pressure being applied to turn the bolt. Torque is a twisting action. Torque is measured in inch pounds (in lb), foot pounds (ft lb), or Newton meters (Nm) as applied to the wrench handle.

1/4"

3/8"

1/4"

1/8"

Figure 9-11 Socket wrench adaptors are available that permit more than one size socket to be used with different sized wrenches

9.6 BOX END AND OPEN END WRENCHES

Box end wrenches, Figure 9-14, are strong and are resistant to slipping. They are ideal for working on long shaft bolts where a socket would not fit. The open end wrench is excellent for work on bolts or nuts where access is limited or the end of the bolt cannot be reached, Figure 9-15a. Some wrench sets, called combination box open end wrenches, have one end open and one box end, Figure 9-15b. All of these types of wrenches may have straight or offset handles.

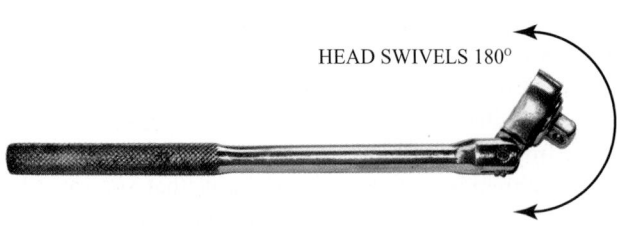

HEAD SWIVELS 180°

Figure 9-12 Swivel head ratchet handle

Breaker Bar

Breaker bar socket wrench handles are used when a great deal of force is required to remove a stuck or stubborn bolt or nut. They are designed to take significantly more force

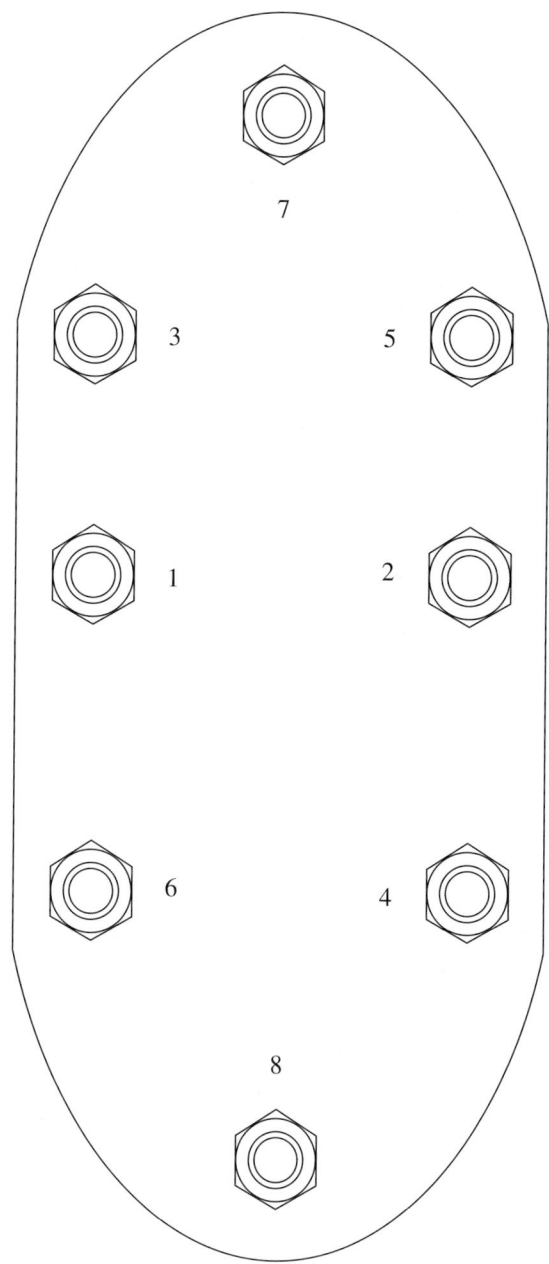

Figure 9-13 Typical head torquing sequence—check with the manufacturer for specific torquing sequences and torque specifications

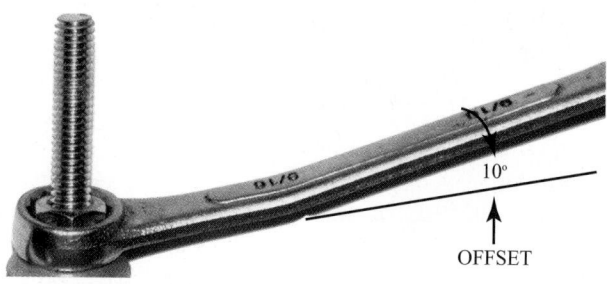

Figure 9-14 Offset box end wrench

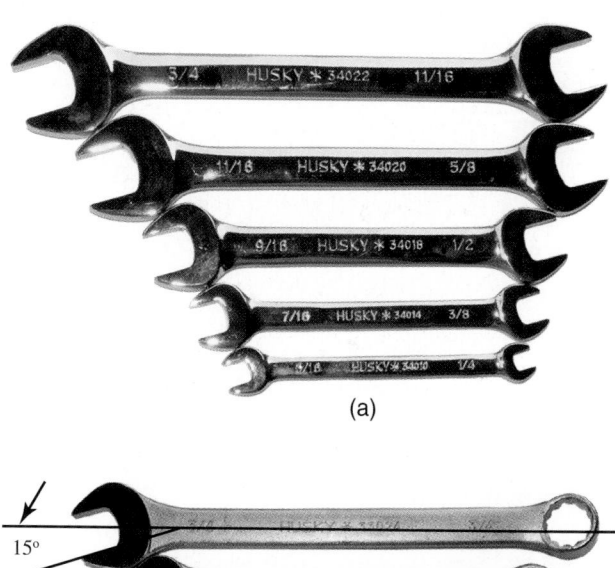

Figure 9-15 (a) Open end wrench with 15° offset openings, both ends; (b) open end wrench with 15° and 75° openings

9.7 FLARE NUT WRENCHES

The flare nut wrench is a special variation of the box wrench in that the heads are slotted to allow the wrench to slip over the tubing and then onto a flare nut, Figure 9-16.

Figure 9-16 Tubing wrenches

Figure 9-17 Adjustable wrench

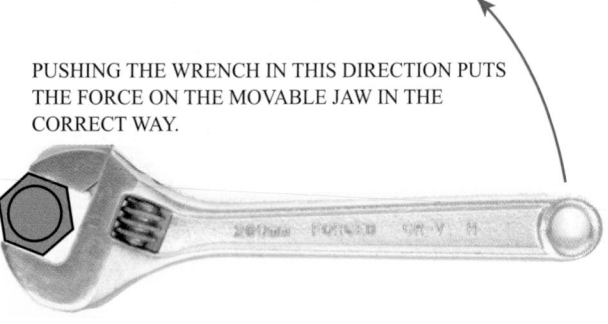

PUSHING THE WRENCH IN THIS DIRECTION PUTS THE FORCE ON THE MOVABLE JAW IN THE CORRECT WAY.

Figure 9-18 Always push an adjustable wrench so that the force is correctly applied to the movable jaw and the wrench is less likely to slip

9.8 ADJUSTABLE WRENCHES

The Crescent Tool Company was the first to introduce the adjustable wrench, Figure 9-17. The adjusting wheel permits fitting the flat to any size object within the maximum and minimum opening. Always use this type of wrench in a manner such that the force is in a down or clockwise direction with the movable jaw on the bottom when tightening a bolt. This keeps the force against the fixed head so the wrench is less likely to suddenly slip and injure you, Figure 9-18. Adjustable wrenches are available in sizes from 4 in to 12 in (102 mm to 305 mm).

9.9 TUBING AND PIPE CUTTERS

Tubing and pipe cutters both use a hardened steel rolling cutter. The cutter parts the tube or pipe as it is repeatedly rolled around the pipe with an ever-increasing pressure being applied. The pressure is applied as the cutter's handle is turned slightly inward after each revolution around the pipe. The pressure is applied by rollers.

As the cutter is rotated around the pipe, the cutting tool does not remove metal but simply forces an ever deepening groove into the pipe or tube surface until it has been cut through. If excessive pressure is put on the cutting tool as it is used, the pipe can be bent or deformed. Ideally, only enough pressure should be applied with the handle to cut the pipe as smooth and clean as possible. The inside lip of the cut end of the pipe will have a burr. The burr is a result of the pipe being cut. The burr needs to be removed following the cut.

Figure 9-19 Compact tubing cutter
(Courtesy of Terra Community College HVAC Program, Fremont, Ohio)

Most tubing cutters have a ream that can be used to remove this burr. Special deburring tools are available.

There are a number of different types and sizes of tube and pipe cutters. Standard tubing cutters will cut tubes or pipe ranging in size from a $\frac{1}{8}$ in to a 1 in diameter. Larger tube and pipe cutting tools are available to cut pipe up to a 4 in diameter. Larger diameter tubing and pipe are usually cut with a portable band saw or other such power tool.

There are small diameter and compact cutters that can be used in tight or limited spaces, Figure 9-19. These cutters are a little more difficult to use, but work very well when cutting tubing that is close to other tubes or otherwise has restricted access. There are other specialty pipe cutting tools for limited access, one of which is shown in Figure 9-20. This tubing cutter sits around the pipe, and a ratcheting mechanism turns the cutter around as the handle is moved back and forth.

When a tubing cutter is used, the blade should track in the groove. However, occasionally, the tubing cutter will cut a spiral through the groove along the pipe. The groove may resemble the threads on a pipe. This occurs as a result of a slight misalignment of the cutting tool or the cutting tool

Figure 9-20 Ratcheting tubing cutter
(Courtesy of Stride Tool Inc.)

rollers. If this happens, the pipe can be cut satisfactorily by rotating the tool once completely around the pipe in one direction, stopping, increasing the pressure on the cutting tool handle slightly, and rotating it back in the opposite direction once. Repeat this process until the pipe is completely cut. Tubing cutter wheels are replaceable because they may be chipped or become dull. It is important when buying a replacement wheel to only purchase one for the specific make and model tubing cutter, to ensure that it fits properly.

9.10 DEBURRING TOOLS

There are deburring tools other than those often found on tubing cutters. Pipe cutters leave a small burr inside the cut end of pipe and tubes. This burr must be removed. There are deburring tools made for this purpose. One deburring tool has a swivel cutting edge that rotates around inside the pipe as the tool is drawn around, Figure 9-21. This type of deburring tool can be used on any size pipe. The cone shaped barrel reamer is held firmly in the end of the pipe with one hand, and the ratchet handle is operated with the other hand. This turns the reamer inside the end of the pipe, removing the burr. Do not remove an excessive amount of metal from the inside of the pipe by overusing this tool.

CAUTION

Small metal chips removed during the deburring process must not be allowed to drop inside of the pipe being deburred. When possible, hold the pipe being deburred vertically, open end pointed down, so that the deburred chips fall away from the pipe. These small metal chips can cause serious mechanical and electrical problems inside the refrigeration system. If the metal chips get lodged in the compressor motor winding, they can cause spot burns or short out the winding. If they get lodged in the small orifice of a metering device or in a compressor valve, the chips can prevent them from working properly.

9.11 FLARING TOOL

The end of a tube may be flared outward so that it can be secured using a flare nut and fitting. The two most popular flare fittings used in HVAC/R work are the National Pipe and the Society of Automotive Engineers standard thread fittings. In order for these fittings to be used a flare must be formed at the end of the tubing.

To form the flare end of the tubing, a flaring block, shown in Figure 9-22, is placed around the end of the tube to be flared. The flaring block has various sized openings for each tubing size to be flared. Clamp the tubing in the flaring block so that the end of the tubing extends approximately $\frac{1}{8}$ in above the surface of the flare block, Figure 9-23. If the tubing extends too high up, the flare may be too large

Figure 9-22 Tubing flaring block
(Courtesy of Terra Community College HVAC Program, Fremont, Ohio)

Figure 9-23 Tube extends slightly above the surface of the flaring block
(Courtesy of Terra Community College HVAC Program, Fremont, Ohio)

Figure 9-21 Pipe deburring tool
(Courtesy of Terra Community College HVAC Program, Fremont, Ohio)

to fit inside of the flare nut. If the tubing does not extend up high enough, the flare formed will be too small to properly seal.

With the tubing securely clamped, a pointed mandrel is used to form the flare against the tubing block. The mandrel is centered in the tubing end and tightened using the handle. For best results, do not overtighten the mandrel. Once the flare has been formed, loosen and remove the mandrel and tubing block. Not overtightening allows the flare nut and fitting to finish the flaring of the pipe as they are tightened for use. This helps ensure a tight leak-free joint.

Note that any burr in the end of the tubing must be removed before making a flared fitting. A pipe burr inside the pipe or tube may split, causing a crack, or may fold inward, restricting the flare's formation. Either way, a proper seal may not be produced when the joint is assembled.

Double Flaring Tool

A double flare may be required on some hardened tubing, for example mild steel and stainless steel tubing and for some high pressure applications. A double flare is used on harder piping materials because they tend to crack easily during the flaring process. The double flare thicker rim acts like a washer forming a tighter leak-free seal on high pressure tubing fittings.

A double flaring tool must be used to form double flares, Figure 9-24. A double flare is formed in two steps. Begin by clamping the tube in the flaring block following the manufacturer's recommendation for tubing extension. Insert the first mandrel in the end of the tubing and tighten it. This forms a slight inward bend at the tubing end, Figure 9-25. Remove this mandrel and finish the process using the pointed mandrel.

TECH TIP

The flared end on tubing can be cut just after the flare if a tubing cutter with a grooved roller is used. The flared end of the tubing fits into the tubing cutter roller groove, Figure 9-26, so that the cutter wheel can part the tubing very close to the flare. This minimizes the length of tubing that must be cut off when removing a flared end.

Swaging Tool

Swaging is sometimes used to join copper tubing, however it is not as popular as flaring. It is the process of joining two pieces of copper tubing together by brazing or soldering without the use of fittings. The end of one piece of copper tubing is expanded so that the other piece will fit into it. Hand punch swaging tools of different sizes are shown in Figure 9-27.

Figure 9-24 Double flaring tool
(Courtesy of Terra Community College HVAC Program, Fremont, Ohio)

Figure 9-25 First step in making a double flare
(Courtesy of Terra Community College HVAC Program, Fremont, Ohio)

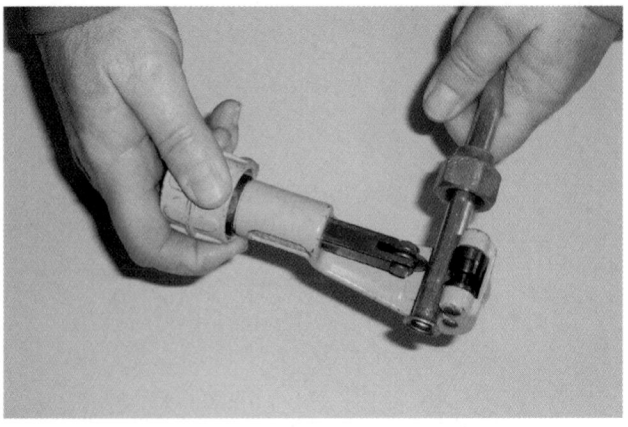

Figure 9-26 Tubing cutter grooved roller cutting off the flare end
(Courtesy of Terra Community College HVAC Program, Fremont, Ohio)

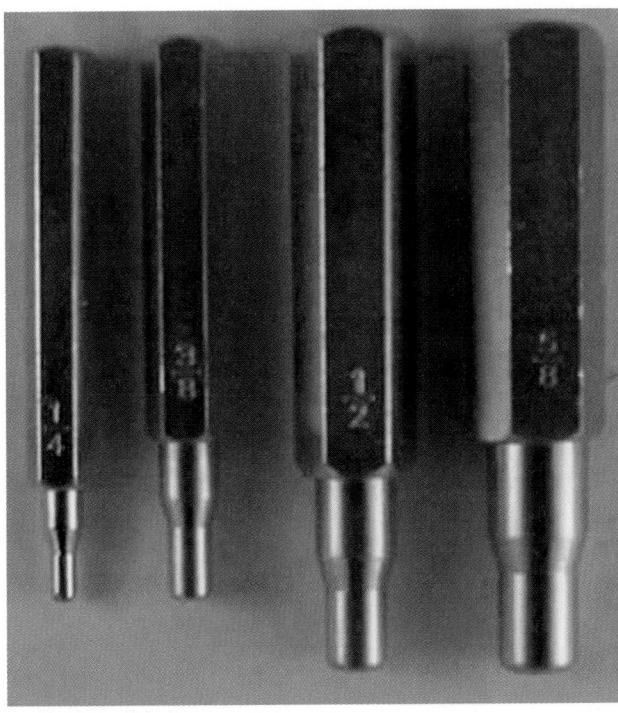

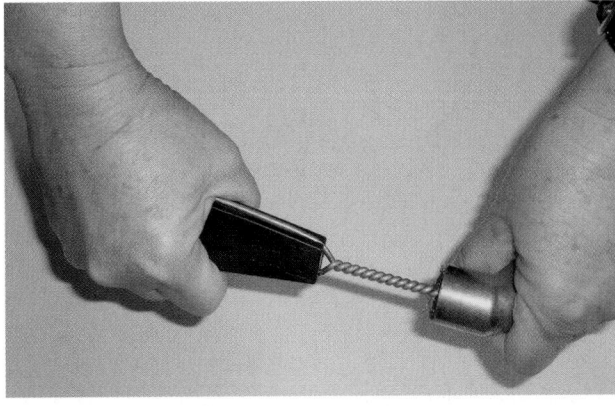

(a)

Figure 9-27 Swaging tool set
(Courtesy of Northway's Machinery, Inc.)

9.12 TUBING BRUSHES

It is often necessary to clean oxides, oil, or dirt off of copper tubing so it can be soldered or brazed. Tubing brushes, Figure 9-28a, come in a variety of sizes for cleaning out the inside of fittings. Figure 9-28b shows three sizes of tubing brushes. One end is designed to clean the outside of the pipe, and the other end is designed to clean the inside of the fitting. These are available in sizes to fit most standard air conditioning and refrigeration tubing.

A solder flux brush is also recommended in applying paste. A paintbrush is useful to brush dirt or dust out of a control box, for example, or it may be used to apply cleaning solvent to an object.

9.13 TUBE BENDING TOOLS

Often it is necessary for HVAC/R technicians to bend copper tubing during installation and service work. Being able to form smooth radius bends in copper tubing is important for a number of reasons.

- Bending tubing reduces the need for additional fittings and brazed joints, thus reducing costs and the possibility of leaking joints
- Bending tubing speeds installation. Bending tubing is much faster than cutting and installing 90° or 45° fittings.
- Bending tubing does not create oxide formation inside the pipe such as that formed during brazing and soldering.
- Long smooth radius bends are less restrictive to refrigerant flow than fittings.

Always use the largest radius bend as possible to minimize the possibility of kinking, crimping, or flattening the

(b)

Figure 9-28 (a) Tubing brush (b) three different sized tubing brushes
(Courtesy of Terra Community College HVAC Program, Fremont, Ohio)

tubing. Kinking occurs when the copper tubing collapses at a bend, severely restricting refrigerant flow. The radius of a tubing bend is somewhat dependant on the diameter of the tubing. Smaller diameter tubing may be bent with a radius as small as five times the tube diameter; however, larger diameter tubing may only be bent with a radius equal to 10 times the tubing diameter, Figure 9-29.

Large radius copper tubing bends can often be made by hand; however, this can result in the crimping of the copper tubing.

SERVICE TIP

If copper tubing is crimped accidentally, the crimped portion must be cut out and replaced with a copper fitting.

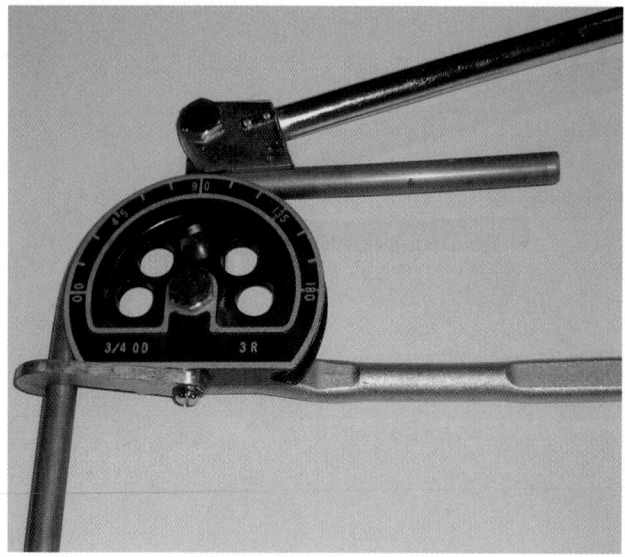

Figure 9-29 Large diameter tubing bent to a radius equal to 10 times its diameter
(Courtesy of Terra Community College HVAC Program, Fremont, Ohio)

There are a number of specialized bending tools that allow technicians to safely form bends without crimping the copper tube.

Spring Benders

A spring bender is made up of a coil steel spring. It slips over the tube being bent and provides lateral support to the side of the copper tube as it is bent. This lateral support prevents the tubing from crimping by keeping the tube relatively round, Figure 9-30. Different sized spring bending tools are available to fit various sized refrigeration tubing. Spring bending tools are limited to smaller tubing sizes.

Hand Benders

Hand benders are tools that can be used to make accurate short radius bends in copper tubing, Figure 9-31. These tools are available for various diameters of copper tubing

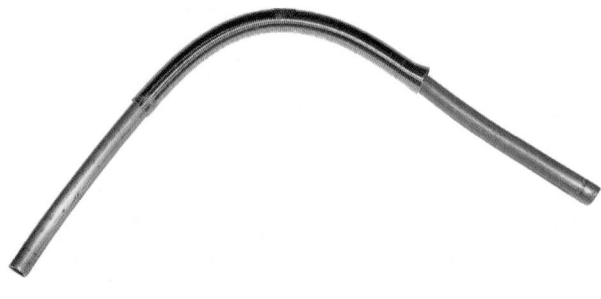

Figure 9-30 Spring type tubing bender
(Courtesy of Terra Community College HVAC Program, Fremont, Ohio)

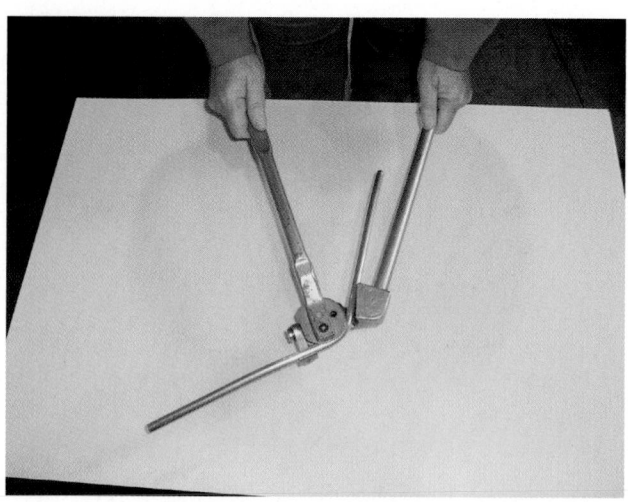

Figure 9-31 Copper tubing hand bender
(Courtesy of Terra Community College HVAC Program, Fremont, Ohio)

and are available in several different radiuses. The copper tubing is slid into the groove on the tool and held in place by a swivel clamp. The bending arm may or may not have a roller. The bending arm is rotated around to the desired bend angle. The tool is marked for bending radiuses from 0° to 180°.

The groove the tube fits into supports the side of the tube during the bending, so that little or no side deforming occurs.

9.14 PIPE WRENCHES

The pipe wrench is used in refrigeration installation and service work to assemble or disassemble threaded pipe, Figure 9-32.

At least two sizes are recommended. An 8 in (203 mm) wrench can handle up to 1 in (25 mm) diameter pipe and a 14 in (356 mm) size can handle up to 2 in (50 mm) diameter pipe. Some have replaceable jaw inserts to extend the life of the tool.

The chain wrench is another form of adjustable pipe wrench. This wrench can make work easier in a confined area or on round, square, or irregular shapes.

Figure 9-32 Pipe wrench

Self-Drilling

Self-drilling sheet metal screws have a tip built like a small drill bit as can be seen in the inset in Figure 10-4e. Self-drilling sheet metal screws predrill the hole as the screw goes in. Self-drilling sheet metal screws can be used in metal thicknesses from 30 gauge to 16 gauge.

TECH TIP

The purpose of using round tipped sheet metal screws is to eliminate the possibility of a sharp point damaging electrical wire insulation.

An electric drill with a magnetic nut driver can be used to spin in self-starting and self-tapping sheet metal screws. Self-starting sheet metal screws are commonly used for on-site sheet metal duct fabrication and installation. When using an electric drill with self-starting or self-tapping sheet metal screws, the technician must be careful not to strip out the screw by overtightening it. Practice is required to develop the skill required to stop the drill the moment the screw is tight without overtightening. Some electric drills have torque adjustments, such as the dial on the drill in Figure 10-5, that allow the operator to set the drill so that it will apply enough force to sink the screw into the sheet metal but not strip it out.

SERVICE TIP

When using a magnetic nut driver and a drill, be certain that the head of the screw is completely in the end of the nut driver. If the nut is not completely in or is in at a slight angle, the screw head can slip inside the nut driver. This will quickly hollow out the end of the nut driver, rendering it useless.

Flat blade screwdrivers and Phillips head screwdriver tips may be used on some sheet metal screws. The flat blade screwdriver tip works well when manually removing or inserting screws, but it is very difficult to keep the bit aligned in the slot if a drill on power screwdriver is being used. Phillips head screws can be used with a Phillips bit chucked in a drill or power driver more successfully than the flat head type bit. Unfortunately, when the screwdriver bit begins to wear, it is more difficult to tighten and loosen screws.

Figure 10-5 Cordless electric drill with adjustable torque chuck

Screw Head Design

Screws can have several different head designs, shown in Figure 10-6, including hex (a), round (b), pan (c), and flat (d). Hex head screws are the most common type used in HVAC/R work. They are used for almost everything inside and outside of the units. The round head screw and the pan head screw may be found inside electrical boxes and on electrical terminals. Round and pan head screws can have flat or Phillips slots and some even have combination flat/Phillips slots, shown in Figure 10-7. Phillips and slot

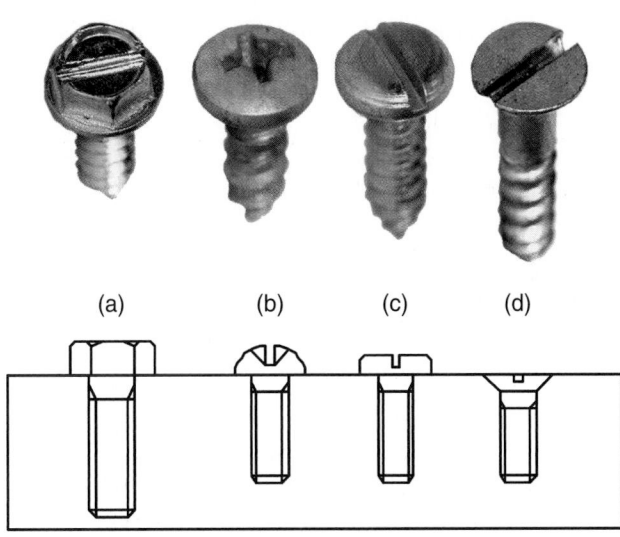

(a)　　　(b)　　　(c)　　　(d)

Figure 10-6 Common types of screw heads: (a) hex; (b) round; (c) pan; (d) flat; the bottom half of the figure shows how each screw will be represented in a drawing

Figure 10-7 Combination Phillips and slot-headed screw

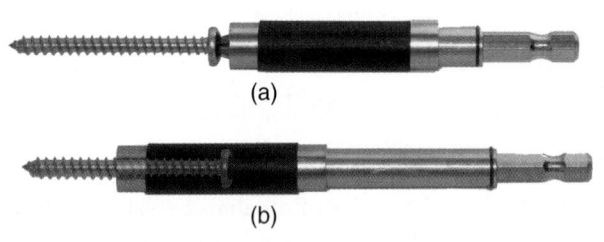

(a)

(b)

Figure 10-8 Screwdriving adapter: (a) with collar retracted to put Phillips bit into screw head; (b) with collar extended to keep contact between Phillips bit and screw head

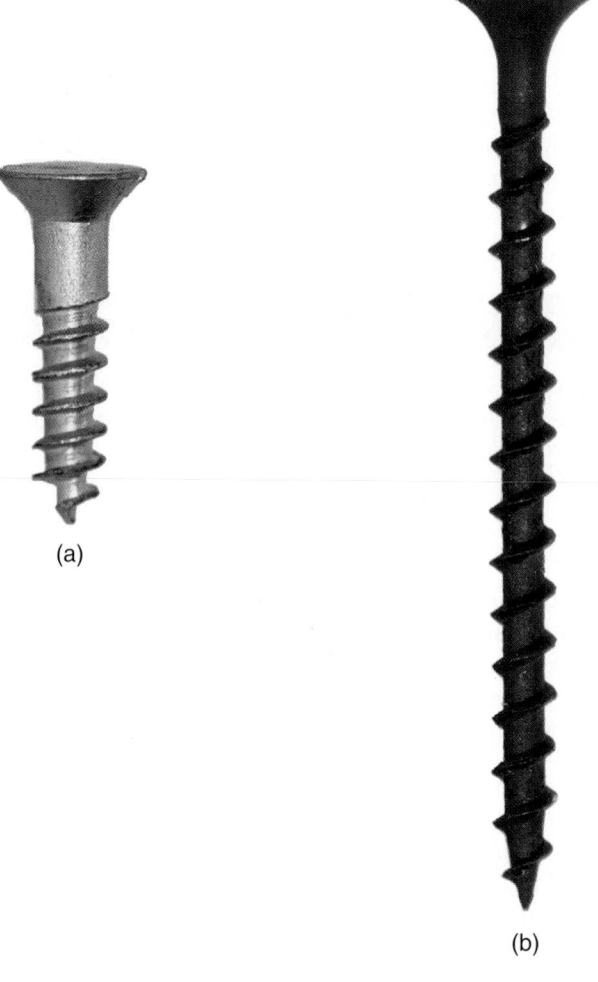

(a)

(b)

Figure 10-9 (a) Wood screw; (b) sheetrock screw

head screws can be used in drills or power screwdrivers with an adaptor, Figure 10-8. The adaptor has a magnetic screwdriver bit inside a collar. The collar slides down over the screw so it can be held straight as it is driven in with a power screwdriver or drill. Wood screws are the most common type of flat head screws. They are used to attach strapping to beams and joists.

Wood and Sheetrock Screws

Wood screws and sheetrock screws, Figure 10-9a,b, are often used in the HVAC/R industry to attach hanging straps to wooden structures. Wood screws for attaching hanging straps (a) are most often flat head screws. Sheetrock screws are almost exclusively Phillips heads. The major difference in appearance between wood screws and sheetrock screws is that the wood screw is shiny and has a portion of the shank that does not have any thread. Sheetrock screws are almost always black and their thread extends the full length of the screw.

10.4 BOLTS AND NUTS

Bolts and nuts have machined threads. These threads will only work when matched parts are used. A typical specification for a bolt would be $3'' \times \frac{1}{2}''$ NC-13 hex head, which is shown in Figure 10-10. The first dimension given, $3''$, is the length of the bolt. The second dimension, $\frac{1}{2}''$, is the outside or major diameter of the bolt. The letters NC refer to the fact that this a national coarse threaded bolt. It has 13 threads per inch, and the bolt has a hex head. The length of the bolt is measured from the base of the head to the tip. The diameter

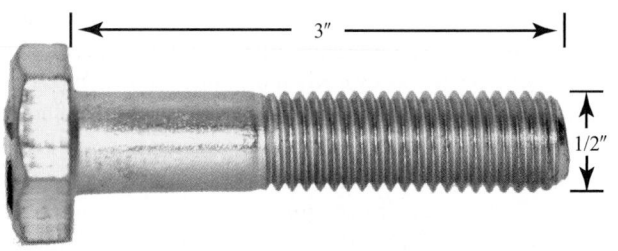

$3''$

$1/2''$

Figure 10-10 Bolt, $3'' \times \frac{1}{2}''$ NC-13 hex head

of a bolt is measured across the threads. The type of thread is listed as either NC for national coarse or NF for national fine. Each standard diameter bolt has a uniform number of threads per inch depending on whether it is coarse or fine. Although most of the bolts used are hex head bolts, other head designs may include carriage bolt, square, and Allen wrench. Square head and Allen wrench bolts are typically used on fans to hold the blades to the rotating motor shaft.

10.5 NAILS

Nails come in a variety of sizes, lengths, materials, and with different types of heads. The most commonly used nail material for HVAC/R work is steel, and they may be zinc coated to resist rusting.

Nail Types

Figure 10-11a,b illustrate some of the common nail types and sizes used in HVAC/R work.

- **Common Nails**   Large diameter, flat-headed nails used for general wood frame construction.
- **Box Nails**   Similar to common nails in shape and use but they are thinner in diameter.
- **Finishing Nails**   Small diameter, small-headed nails used to attach trim boards to door casings and floor molding. These nails are generally designed to be countersunk or recessed for a finished appearance.

Nail Sizes

Penny is the term commonly used for nail sizes. It is abbreviated as "d" and is used with the wire gauge number. (Note: This notation is actually a carryover from English unit weight measurement. Even the penny coin was abbreviated "d.") The wire gauge number refers to the size wire used to make the nail. The larger the number, the smaller the nail size. Some

nails are sold with both their penny size and length, which can make choosing the correct size nail easier.

10.6 CONCRETE FASTENERS AND ANCHORS

The terms concrete fastener and concrete anchor are often used interchangeably; however, fasteners are nonstructural while anchors can be used for both nonstructural and structural attachments. Concrete fasteners can be grouped into two general categories: driven-in and predrilled. Anchors are almost always predrilled; however, some can be preplaced before the concrete is poured.

Driven-in concrete nails can be installed using a hammer or with a gun and ballistic charge. The hammered-in concrete nails are usually short and work best when driven in with the fewest hammer blows. Repeatedly hammering the nail can loosen it in the concrete.

Ballistic concrete nail guns may be trigger activated or hammer strike activated. In both cases they use a small charge that resembles a .22 caliber blank cartridge to drive the nail in quickly. The nail lengths and cartridge power must be matched to the job so that the nail is driven into its desired depth.

> ### CAUTION
> Always wear proper eye and face protection when nailing, and read and follow all manufacturer's safety instructions. Special safety protection should always be used when driving ballistic concrete nails in anticipation of chips of cracking or exploding concrete.

Early concrete anchors used lead sleeves placed in a drilled hole. These type of anchors are still used today. One drawback, however, is that the hole drilled into the concrete had to be a lot larger in diameter than the anchor. This meant that the holes had to be accurately predrilled so they aligned with the part being attached. Newer type anchors can fit into the same diameter hole as the anchor itself. This allows the preplacement of the part being attached, so hole alignment is not as much a problem. Figure 10-12a–c shows concrete anchors, drill bits, and the drilling through concrete for an anchor hole.

> ### TECH TIP
> Concrete is the most widely used material on earth. It is used for all types of construction. Masonry is a type of construction using bricks, stones, blocks, and so on. Masonry construction is held together with mortar or similar type materials. Concrete fasteners can be used on most masonry construction.

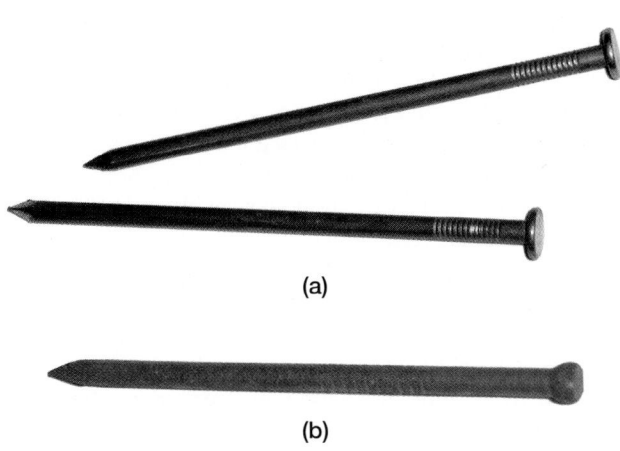

(a)

(b)

Figure 10-11 (a) Common nails; (b) finishing nail
(Courtesy of HVAC Department, Terra Community College, Fremont, Ohio)

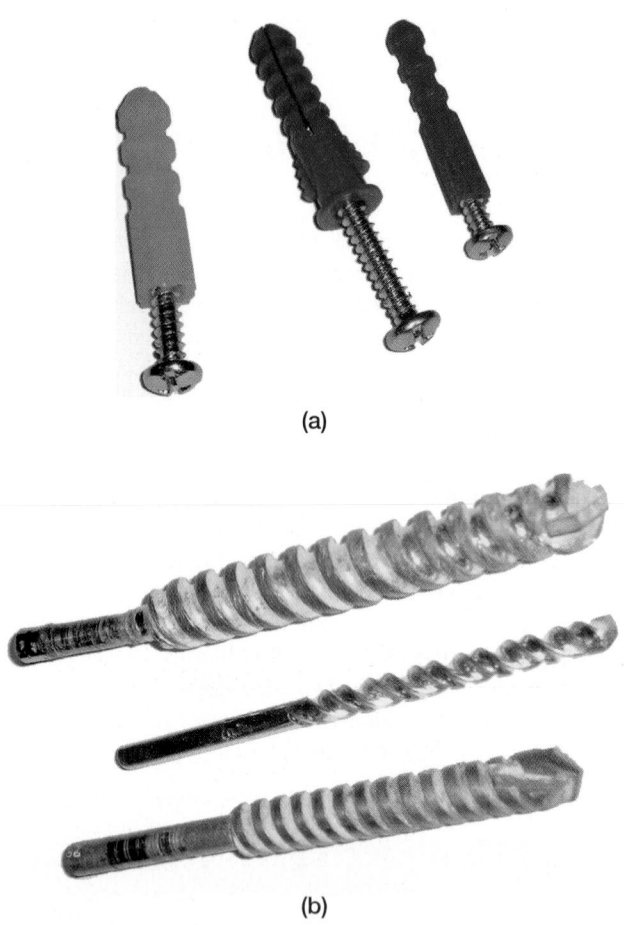

(a)

(b)

Figure 10-13 Pop rivets come in a variety of types and sizes

(c)

Figure 10-12 (a) Concrete anchors; (b) concrete drill bits; (c) drilling concrete anchor holes
(Courtesy of HVAC Department, Terra Community College, Fremont, Ohio)

10.7 RIVETS

A rivet is a small unthreaded piece of metal that is installed through a predrilled hole. Once it is through the hole, the end of the rivet is enlarged so it will not fit back through the hole.

The process of enlarging the end is called "upsetting the rivet." Over the centuries, rivets that had to be upset by hammers were in common use, but today this type is seldom used. Pop rivets have replaced the older style rivets.

Pop rivets are usually made out of aluminum but other metals including copper and stainless are available. A variety of pop rivets is shown in Figure 10-13. A pop rivet has a central shaft that is placed in a pop rivet gun, shown in Figure 10-14. The sequence showing the installation of a rivet is represented in Figure 10-15. The central shaft is withdrawn back through the center of the hollow rivet shaft. As the bead on the end of the center shaft is pulled through the rivet sleeve, the sleeve deforms outward. When the bead at the end of the central shaft is pulled snugly against the back side of the drilled metal it pops off so that the nail-like shaft can be removed and discarded.

Pop rivets come in a variety of sizes ranging from the most popular $\frac{1}{8}$ in diameter up to $\frac{1}{4}$ in diameter. The length of a pop rivet is determined by the distance from the tip to the head of the pop rivet. You should select a pop rivet that

Figure 10-14 Pop rivet gun

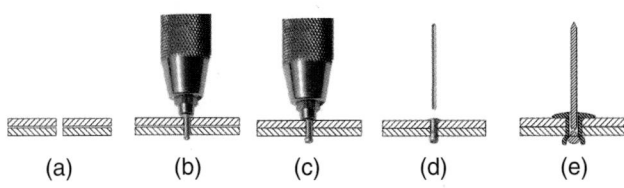

(a)   (b)   (c)   (d)   (e)

Figure 10-15 Steps in pop riveting: (a) drill a hole; (b) insert a pop rivet into the hole; (c) depress the pop rivet gun handle to upset the rivet; (d) rivet stem pops off when blades are pulled tight and rivet is seated; (e) cross section of pop rivet

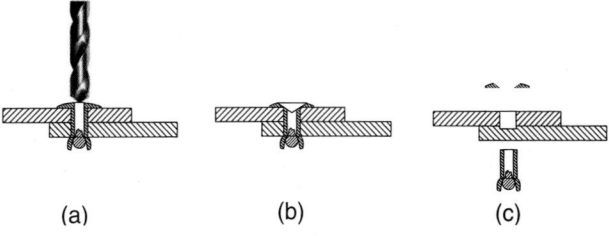

(a)   (b)   (c)

Figure 10-16 Steps in removing a pop rivet using a drill: (a) the drill bit should be slightly larger than the original pilot hole; (b) the drill only cuts out the rivet head; (c) the head and the shaft fall away

drilling out just the rivet head (b), and the pop rivet, with its head drilled out, falling away (c). Take care not to drill through and increase the size of the rivet hole.

SERVICE TIP

Sometimes the drill will grab the rivet and the rivet will spin. If this is happening, you cannot drill out the rivet head. But by angling the drill bit slightly to one side, the bit will begin cutting again. Only angle the bit enough for it to start cutting. Too much angle may cause the bit to slip off of the head, damaging the finish of the part.

10.8 STAPLES

Staples hold by either driving their points into a soft material such as wood, or having the legs folded as with a paper stapler. Staples come in one standard width, Figure 10-17. Staples can be purchased with a variety of lengths of leg, from $\frac{1}{4}$ in to $\frac{15}{16}$ in.

Specially designed staples are used to attach fabric or vinyl backed duct insulation, Figure 10-18a. Duct staplers are designed so that the tips of the staple are bent outward as

will extend through the joint materials by at least $1\frac{1}{2}$ times the diameter of the pop rivet. For example, a $\frac{1}{8}$ in diameter pop rivet should extend through the material being joined by at least $\frac{3}{16}$ in and a $\frac{1}{4}$ in diameter pop rivet should extend $\frac{3}{8}$ in through the material.

SERVICE TIP

Usually rivets have limited field applications in the HVAC industry because of the time required to predrill the holes. However, a $\frac{1}{8}$ in pop rivet will fit into a #8 sheet metal screw hole. Placing one pop rivet in the corner of a panel will reduce the possibility of unauthorized people tampering with the system.

The best way to remove rivets without damaging the base metal is to drill them out. Pop rivets can be easily drilled using a bit slightly larger than the original shaft of the hole. As the drill cuts through the rivet head, the shaft of the rivet will be removed once the head has been cut free. Figure 10-16 shows the sequence of the drill bit next to the rivet (a),

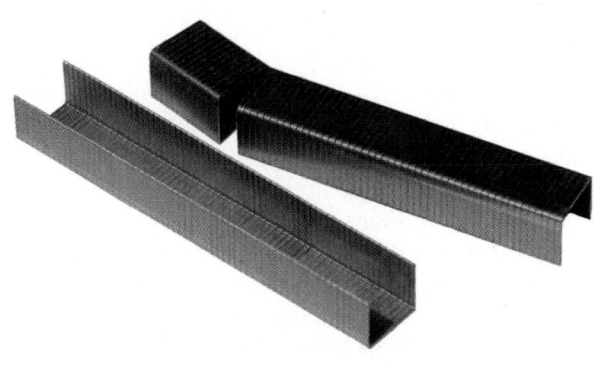

Figure 10-17 Staples come as preassembled strips

(a)

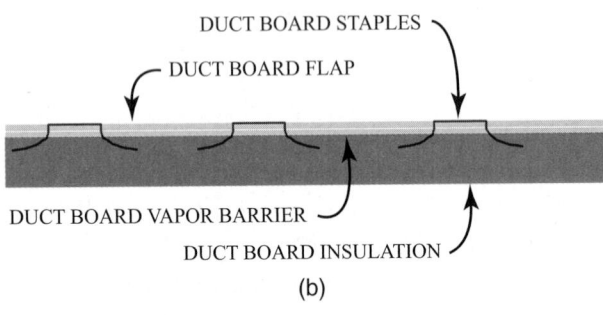

DUCT BOARD STAPLES

DUCT BOARD FLAP

DUCT BOARD VAPOR BARRIER

DUCT BOARD INSULATION

(b)

Figure 10-18 Staple gun used to (a) attach duct insulation or (b) seal duct board flaps

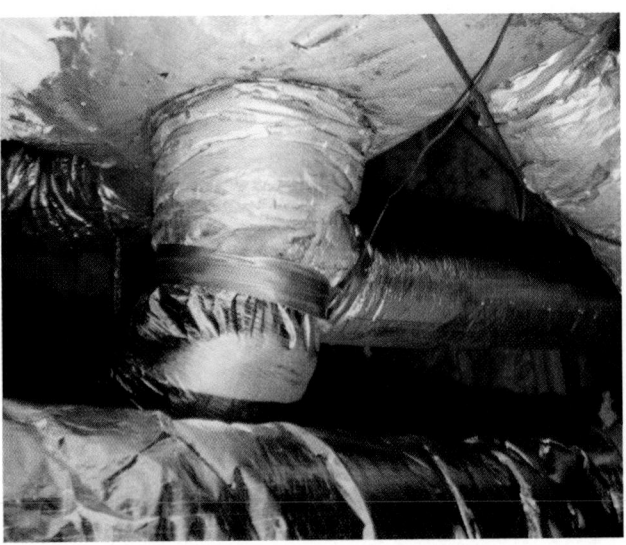

Figure 10-19 A number of products have been used in the past to seal duct and duct insulation such as this system that used cloth duct tape

Table 10-2 UL Listings for Duct Tape

Flex duct
UL-181B-FX Pressure sensitive tape, for flexible ducts

Duct board
UL 181A-P Pressure sensitive tape, for duct board
UL 181A-H Heat activated tape, for duct board

Metal duct connectors to flex or duct board
UL 181 A-P or UL181 B-FX

the staple is driven through the fabric, Figure 10-18b. Duct staples are the most commonly used method of attaching external insulation to sheet metal ducts.

10.9 TAPE

Two of the most commonly used types of tape in the HVAC/R industry are duct tape and electrical tape. Tape is manufactured to a variety of specifications but new codes require that all duct tape meet UL 181 standards. The quality of tape used will directly affect the length of time it stays in place to seal the duct. For example, some vinyl gray duct tape is sold at deep discounts because it does not contain fabric reinforcement. There may even be a pattern embossed in the plastic giving it the illusion of having cloth reinforcement, however, no reinforcement exists.

Because of the heat in the attic, vinyl or cloth duct tape mastic will dry out over time and become hard and brittle. When this happens, no tackiness is left in the tape and it simply turns loose, Figure 10-19. It is not a matter of whether the tape will dry out and fail, but when the tape will dry out and fail. For this reason most codes require UL 181 for duct closing systems. There are several different types of tape under the UL 181 listing. Each of these tapes has a different purpose, Table 10-2.

Aluminum pressure sensitive tapes are easily formed to the surface, creating a tight fit. They have a rubber or acrylic adhesive that is protected on the roll with a paper backing. The paper backing is removed when the tape is being used, Figure 10-20. Cloth tapes have a mylar coating. They are designed for application on flex ducts, Figure 10-21. All approved UL 181 tapes must be identified with lettering on the face of the tape.

The adhesive on foil tapes is very tacky. If it is accidentally touched to any surface before it is in place it is difficult if not impossible to remove it. Foil tape comes with a paper backing to keep it from being stuck permanently to itself in the roll. This paper must be peeled back as the tape is applied to the surface. Once the tape is in place it should be smoothed down securely to ensure a proper seal. Failure to wipe the tape down can result in air gaps beneath the tape, which will allow its mastic to dry out. Keeping duct tape securely in place over time is the only way to ensure that conditioned air does not leak out of the duct system.

Vinyl electrical tape is often referred to as electrical tape or simply black tape. As with duct tape there is a range of

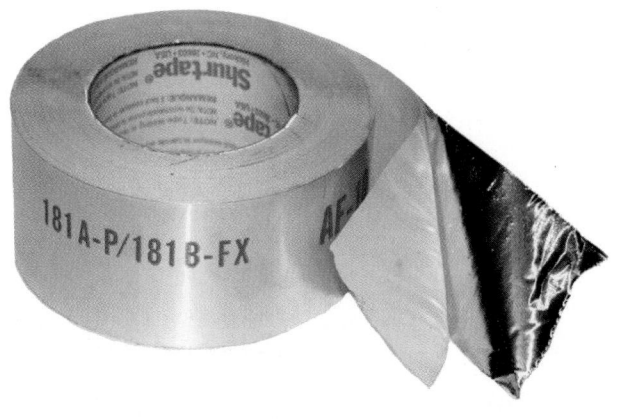

Figure 10-20 Aluminum foil pressure sensitive duct tape

Figure 10-21 Mylar coated pressure sensitive duct tape

quality in the tape available. A good vinyl electrical tape should have some stretch so it can form itself around the wires or connection. Too much stretch and the tape cannot be pulled tightly around the parts. The tape must resist heat without loosening or softening.

10.10 ADHESIVES

There are a number of adhesives used in HVAC/R work. The three general groupings of adhesives are mastics, glues, and caulk. Generally in HVAC/R work mastics are used to seal large areas such as duct joints, glues are used to hold items together, and caulks are used to seal cracks. All three types of material are classified as adhesives. *Adhesion* is their ability to stick to a surface and *cohesion* is their ability to stick to themselves.

When using any adhesive, it is important that the surface is clean, dry, and free of loose material. Any of these surface conditions can prevent adhesion. Some adhesives have reinforcing fibers to add to their cohesive strength, while others do not have reinforcing fibers.

Adhesives may be water based or use another type of volatile organic compound (VOC) as their solvent. Some VOCs are flammable and others can produce hazardous fumes. Adequate ventilation must be provided to prevent the buildup of hazardous or explosive fumes in the work area.

Some adhesives are paintable and some are not. Check to see whether the product you plan to use on any interior or exterior surfaces can be painted before you use it. Not being able to paint the caulk can be a problem, especially when it is used around public areas such as the trim around a supply grill, and so on.

CAUTION

Always follow all manufacturer's instructions when using adhesives. Wear all personal protection equipment suggested by the manufacturer.

TECH TIP

If you pull a glued component apart and the glue comes off of the surface, that is an adhesion failure. If the glue separates itself, it is a cohesive failure.

10.11 TIE STRAPS (DRAW BANDS)

Tie straps or draw bands are usually made out of nylon and are widely used in the HVAC/R industry. Large sizes are used to secure flexible duct to start collars or boots, shown in the installation sequence in Figure 10-22a–d. These tie straps must be resistant to ultraviolet light (UV), have a tensile strength of 150 lb and a service temperature of 165°F. When nylon straps are used on duct installations, a special tool called a strap tensioner must be used. The strap-tensioning tool pulls the strap tight, reducing the likelihood of air leaks, and securely mechanically connecting the duct to the sheet metal boot or collar. Once the proper tension has been applied, a lever on the strap-tensioning tool extends a razor knife to cut off the unused nylon strap end.

Smaller ties are used to secure wires into bundles inside of units. When the nylon straps are used around electrical wires, they are simply pulled tight by hand or with a pair of pliers, and the unused portion is cut off, as shown in the installation sequence in Figure 10-23a–d.

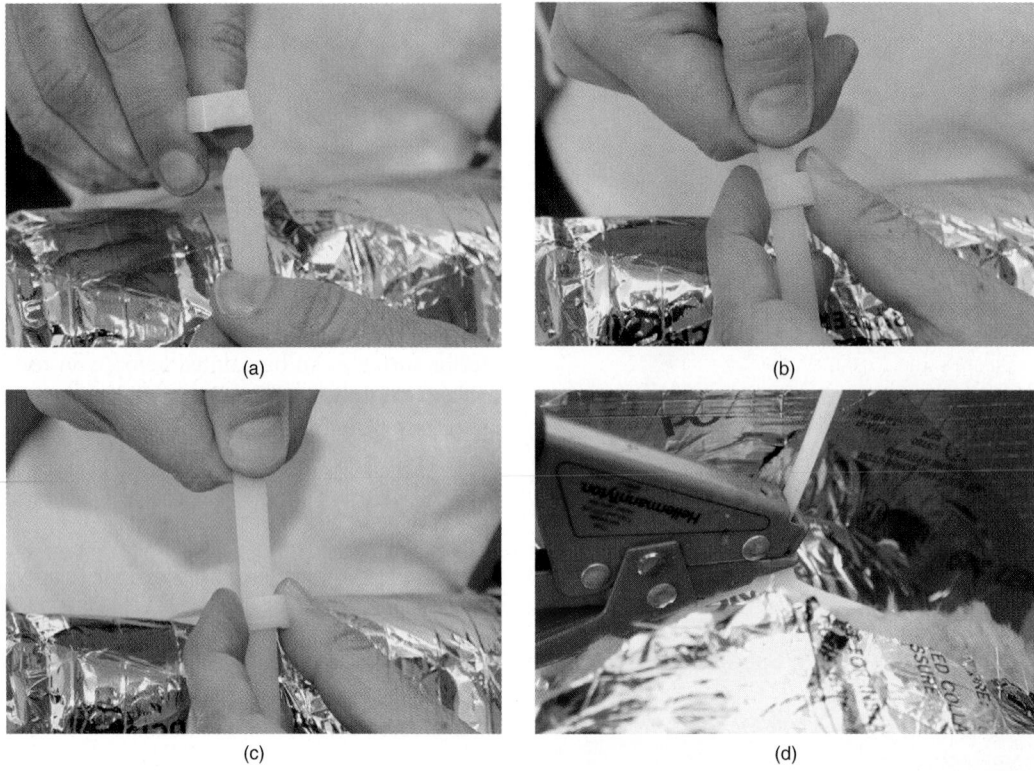

Figure 10-22 (a) Insert the end of the tie strap through the ratchet mechanism; (b) use your hand to pull the strap through; (c) pull the strap with your hand as tight as possible; (d) use a duct strap tightening tool to finish tightening and cut the end of the strap

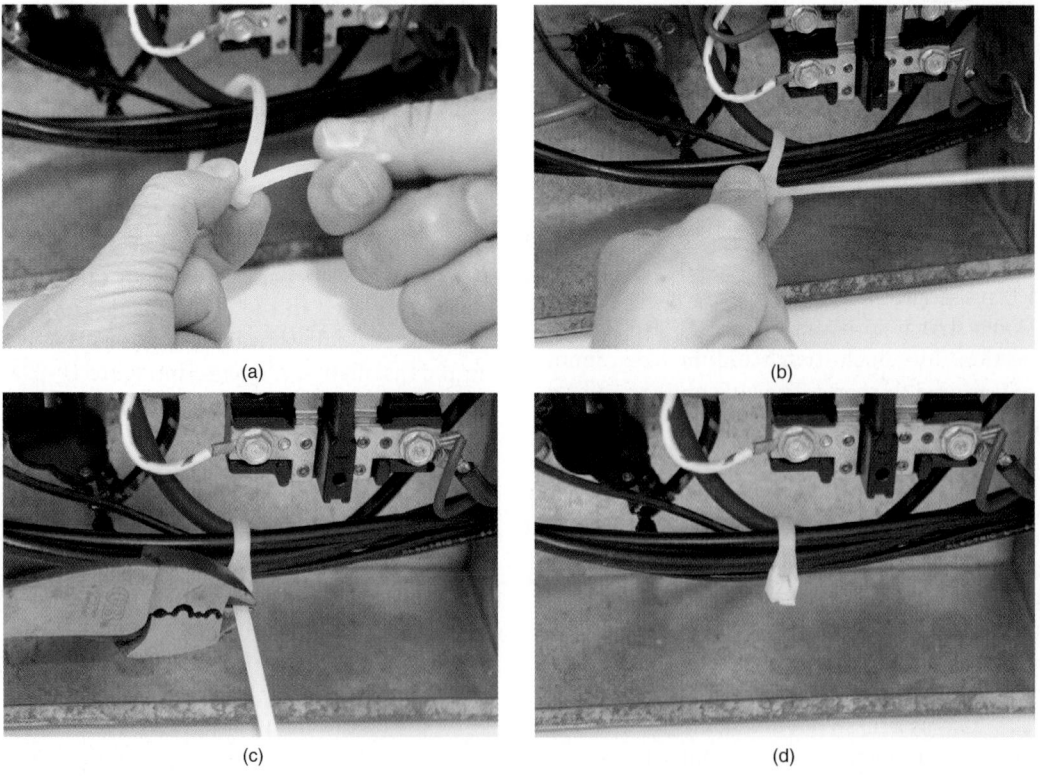

Figure 10-23 (a) Small wire tie size straps; (b) pull tight by hand; (c) clip the strap; (d) finally, with the end cut off, the job looks neater

SERVICE TIP

From time to time a tie strap may be put in place and only later is it found that it has to be removed. Ties may need to be removed when a wire must be added or removed from the bundle, or when a duct needs to be cut shorter or straightened. Tie straps are expensive and must not be wasted. They can be removed easily, if the end has not been cut off, by placing the tip of a small screwdriver under the ratchet mechanism, Figure 10-24a,b. By putting just a little force on the corner of the screwdriver blade, the tie will be able to slip through the mechanism. Do not force the screwdriver tip under the mechanism. You can damage the ratchet, or the screwdriver could slip and stick your finger. As a precaution you might want to use pliers to hold the strip the first few times you try this. Once the ratchet is released, use your thumb to slide the end up and off to remove the tie strap.

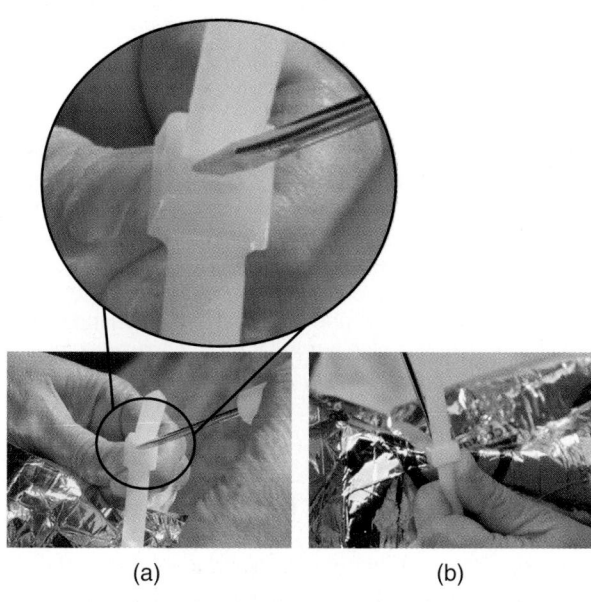

(a)   (b)

Figure 10-24 Use a screwdriver to release the ratchet mechanism so that a duct strap can be removed and reused

UNIT 10—SUMMARY

Thread gauges and screw and bolt size gauges are available to help you find the correct sized threaded fastener for the job. Never force a nut, bolt, or screw if it does not fit correctly. You can cross thread the part and strip the threads, which can result in a significantly longer time to repair. You may also break the bolt or screw off in the part, which will require a lot of work to remove.

Although there are many different types and sizes of fasteners that can be used in HVAC/R work, you will find that the number and type you use on a regular basis is relatively small. The commonly used ones are the ones you will have in your tool bag and stock in your service vehicle.

Most HVAC/R parts houses carry the commonly used fasteners. You may need to go to a nut and bolt supply store to locate the specialty fasteners you need for some jobs.

UNIT 10—REVIEW QUESTIONS

1. What are the typical types of screws used on HVAC/R jobs?
2. How are the length and diameters of screws given?
3. List the common shaped tips found on sheet metal screws.
4. What is the difference between the way a self-threading and a self-drilling sheet metal screw is used?
5. Why are rounded tipped sheet metal screws used?
6. What is a common use for self-starting sheet metal screws?
7. Why are flat blade screwdrivers usually used manually to remove or install slotted head screws?
8. List the common screw head designs.
9. What is a common use for wood screws and sheetrock screws in HVAC/R work?
10. Explain the significance to each part of this bolt specification: $2'' \times \frac{1}{4}''$ NC-20 hex head.
11. List three comon types of nails.
12. What is the difference between a concrete fastener and concrete anchor?
13. What drives a ballistic concrete nail in?
14. What is the term used to describe the enlarging of the end of a rivet?
15. What metals are commonly used to make pop rivets?
16. What is the best way of removing a pop rivet?
17. How does the tip of an installed duct staple differ from other types of staples?
18. Duct tape must meet what standard?
19. What is the problem with using vinyl or cloth duct tape in an attic?
20. What are two qualities that a good vinyl electrical tape must have?
21. List the three common types of adhesives used in HVAC/R work and tell how they are used.
22. Why is it better to use water based adhesives as apposed to VOC based solvent adhesives?
23. Why must a tensioner tool be used on duct tie straps?

UNIT 11

Electrical Measuring and Test Instruments

OBJECTIVES

After completing this unit you will be able to:

- list the major types of electrical test instruments and explain how they are used.
- explain what factors should be considered when purchasing a meter.
- explain the difference between weighted average meters, true RMS meters, and RMS meters.
- identify the CAT rating on meters and explain its importance.
- describe the difference between analog and digital meters.
- demonstrate how voltmeters, ohmmeters, and ammeters are used.
- discuss the importance of data loggers.

11.1 INTRODUCTION

The terms *test instrument* and *test meter* are used interchangeably in the HVAC/R field to describe devices that are used to detect some aspect of an electrical system's operation. Usually they are used to determine how a system is operating or why it is not operating. The information they supply can then be used for servicing and troubleshooting.

The information in this unit is not intended to replace any operating instructions provided by the meter's manufacturer. Read and follow all manufacturers' operating and safety instructions; failing to do so can damage the equipment and may result in your being injured.

11.2 ELECTRICAL AND ELECTRONIC INSTRUMENTS

Testing electrical circuits is an important skill that each technician needs to develop. Although practice and experience are significant, a high degree of success is obtainable by following a proven procedure, such as the following:

1. Know the unit electrically. This means understanding the proper function of each control and the sequence of the control operation. It is as important to know what a meter does not measure as well as what it does.
2. Be able to read schematic wiring diagrams and have them available.
3. Be able to use the proper electrical test instruments. Know the instrument. Read instructions carefully before using.

In the following section, various electrical and electronic instruments will be described along with information on how they are best used. For electrical troubleshooting, the instruments most commonly used are:

- A voltmeter to measure electrical potential,
- An ammeter to measure electrical current,
- An ohmmeter to measure electrical resistance,
- A megohm meter to measure very high electrical resistance(a megohm is the same as a mega ohm),
- A capacitor checker to measure capacitor microfarad capacitance, and
- A wattmeter to measure electrical power.

TECH TIP

Electronic meters are expensive and relatively easily damaged if they receive rough treatment. To ensure that your instruments last as long as possible they should be cleaned after each use and stored in their own individual case or pouch. It is also a good idea to carry your instruments in a separate bag away from your hand tools.

11.3 SELECTING A TEST INSTRUMENT

There are a large number of test instruments and meters that are available for HVAC/R technicians to select from. There are traditional volt ohm meters (VOMs) and newer multifunction meters, Figure 11-1. You can select digital, analog, or digital with an analog display. If you are like most HVAC/R technicians, your first meter will not be the only meter you purchase during your career. Your first choice of a meter may be affected by price, while your later purchases may be based more on features, reliability, accuracy, durability, and safety.

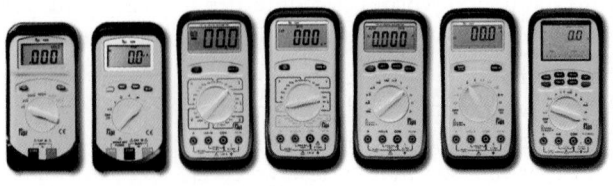

Figure 11-1 Multimeters come in a variety of sizes with a variety of functions
(Courtesy Test Products International, Inc.)

Consider keeping a less expensive or older meter as a backup in case your primary meter fails.

Rugged and Durable Meters

Some meters are more rugged and durable than others. A rugged meter is one that is capable of being dropped. Much of HVAC/R service work is done outside of a shop. It is not unusual for service technicians to work on ladders or on top of buildings. Some meters are padded and others may have padded cases that can be purchased separately.

HVAC/R meters must be durable because they will be subjected to oils, dirt, water, and other contaminants. Better meters are oil and water resistant, and the best are oilproof and waterproof. No one ever intends to drop a meter in a condensate pan full of water or have vacuum pump oil spill over the tools and meters inside the service vehicle. Accidents happen at the least opportune time, but a good meter will survive.

VOMs vs. Multi Function Meters

Most test instruments HVAC/R technicians use are called VOMs. *VOM* actually stands for *volt ohm meter*, although the term is often misused to include meters that may test additional items, such as amperage and temperature. These volt ohm meters have been around for many years and have provided great service. Technicians add to their ability by purchasing additional meters to test for amperage, capacitance, temperature, and mega ohms. Having dedicated meters for each test has its advantages. You can get readings from each of the meters simultaneously, and they can easily be used in different locations.

Having separate meters was the only choice for years, until the introduction of the multi function meter. Many of these meters have been specifically designed for the HVAC/R technician.

Multi Function Meters

One major consideration in selecting a multi function meter is to choose one that is specifically for the HVAC/R trade. These meters have the most features that you will use all in one instrument. Some of the functions should include the testing of AC and DC voltage, AC and DC amperage, capacitance, temperature, ohms, and possibly megohms.

Range, Resolution, and Accuracy

Range, resolution, and accuracy are three terms used to differentiate all meters. Understanding test instrument terminology will help you make the best selection of the instrument for your specific job requirements.

Range The range tells you how low and how high a reading the meter will provide for each function the meter can perform.

- Voltmeters should be able to read voltages from a fraction of a volt up to 600 V AC and DC.
- Ohmmeters should be able to read ohms from a fraction of an ohm to 20,000 (20K) ohms.
- Mega ohm (megohm) meters should be able to read up to 40,000,000 (40M) ohms.
- Amp meters (ammeters) should be able to read AC amperage from 1 A up to 200 A and DC amps from 200 mA to 4,000 mA and from 0 to 20 μA (microamps).
- Capacitance meters should be able to check from 1 μF (microfarad) up to 200 μF.
- Thermocouples should be able to read temperatures from 1°F to 1,000°F.

Resolution The resolution tells you what units of measure are used for each function. On a digital meter specification it may be expressed as the number of digits or decimal points. This can range from three to four digits and one to three decimal places.

Accuracy The accuracy is how close to the actual value the meter is going to read. These values are usually given as a percentage ± (plus or minus) of the reading. Meters may vary from ±0.5% up to ±3% depending on the function and scale. All meters become less accurate at their higher and lower scale settings. The more expensive meters have higher accuracies over their complete range. This accuracy is usually stated as a percentage of a full scale reading.

Instrument Overvoltage Safety Protection

Any time you are working with electricity, there is a possibility of an overvoltage situation occurring. We use surge protectors on our computers to protect them from overvoltages. A momentary surge or spike of voltage can be several times the normal circuit voltage. These surges, called transient voltages, can be caused by electrical storms, even miles away, or they can be caused when a major load is added or dropped from the system. Some of the things causing shifts in the load could be an auto accident where a utility pole was damaged, or a large piece of equipment starting or stopping.

The closer you are working to the power pole or main power box, the more dangerous transient spikes can be. A category, or CAT rating system, has been established by IEC (International Electrotechnical Commission) which provides the technician with information about the level of safety provided by their meter. Not all meters are rated. The lowest rating is a CAT I and the highest is a CAT IV. A CAT I meter is designed to be used on protected equipment like a gas furnace in a hallway, equipment room, or attic. CAT II meters can be used on backup heat strips found in the indoor part of a heat pump. CAT III meters can be used on condensers. CAT IV meters can be used on any branch circuit inside or outside of the building. The CAT rating on a meter will list the maximum circuit voltage that the meter can be used on, Figure 11-2.

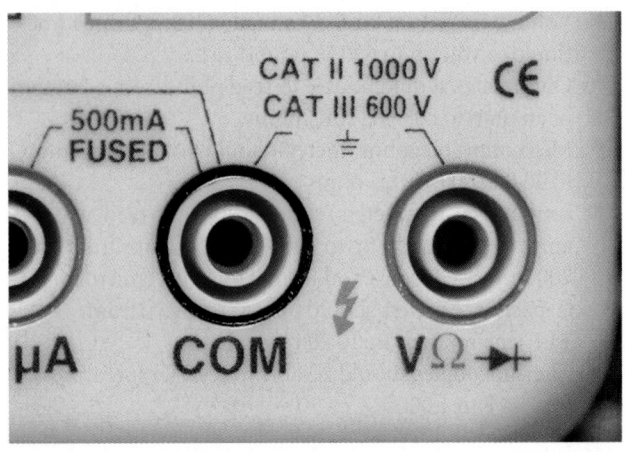

Figure 11-2 Category ratings of two voltage levels, CAT II 1000 V, and CAT III 600 V

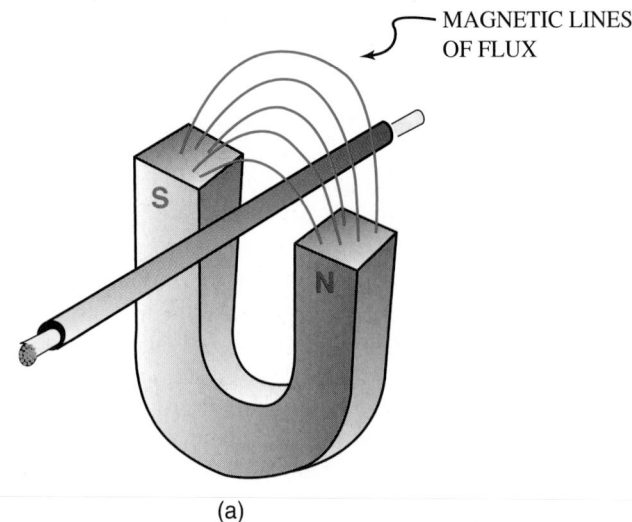

(a)

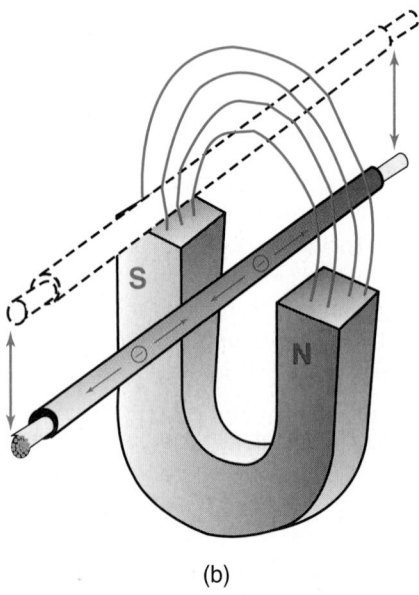

(b)

Figure 11-3 (a) If a wire is stationary in a magnetic field, no current is induced in the wire; (b) If the wire is moved up and down in the magnetic field, electrons in the wire flow forming an electric current

11.4 ANALOG METERS

All analog meters operate on the same principle. When the current flows through a conductor, it produces a magnetic field around the conductor. If a magnetic needle is placed close to the current, the needle will attempt to line up with the field, Figure 11-3.

Analog meters use a mechanical needle that swings across the dial to a point over a scale, Figure 11-4. The meter reading is taken by looking directly at the face of the meter dial and comparing the needle location to the appropriate scale. Analog meters are almost never autoranging. If too high a voltage is being tested for the scale setting, then the meter can be damaged.

TECH TIP

Many people feel that digital meters are superior to analog meters in that they show you discrete values for voltage, amperage, and ohm readings. However, the analog meter will give you more of a relative reading that can be often understood more easily. For example, during the late 1980s and early 1990s, many car manufacturers provided digital speedometers for cars. These turned out not to be very popular because with digital displays it was no longer possible to simply glance at the speedometer needle to see your relative speed. In the same way analog meters allow the technician to glance at the meter and make a determination. Some digital meters have incorporated an analog sliding scale that appears across the digital meter face so that it is possible for the technician to have both the digital number and an analog reference.

Three important characteristics of analog meters need to be considered by those who use them:

- The most accurate reading is at the midpoint of the scale. This is because the spring that opposes the deflection of the meter does not exert constant pressure across the scale. The meter may be inaccurate near either end of the scale. So whenever the operator has a choice of scales, the one selected should place the pointer in the most favorable (central) position.

- Analog meters periodically need to recalibrated. Most ohmmeters include some type of adjustment and instructions for calibration.

- The small coil of wire that forms part of the meter movement is sensitive to excessive current. The meter may be made completely inoperable if subjected to excessive current. In using a meter with multiple scales to choose from, always use the higher scale first and move down to the scale required.

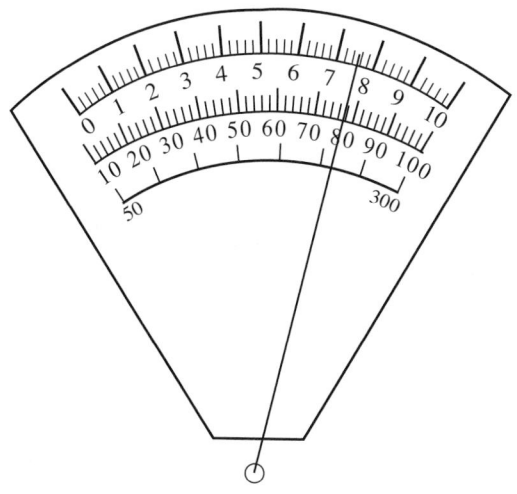

Figure 11-4 An analog multimeter has several scales, so you must know which range you are measuring and read the appropriate scale

Analog meter accuracy is normally specified as a percent of full scale reading, so readings should be taken in the upper two-thirds of the scale for testing accuracy.

More expensive (and more accurate) analog meters are often furnished with a mirror scale to enable more accurate readings. The mirror aids in minimizing parallax, an apparent difference in readings taken from different sight perspectives. When reading the meter correctly, the pointer and scale are aligned so the mirror image of the pointer disappears behind the pointer. This gives the most accurate reading.

TECH TIP

Because of the mechanical movements in an analog meter they tend to be more easily damaged as a result of rough treatment. Some analog meters have a cage for the meter movement which locks it down so that it does not bounce around and become damaged during transport.

SERVICE TIP

Many service technicians will want to have both analog and digital meters. Just like analog watches, analog meters have advantages such as the ease in reading changes and variations in the measurements.

11.5 DIGITAL METERS

Digital meters offer a number of advantages. Rugged versions are available and recommended. It is important that the technician be thoroughly familiar with the use of both types. Some of the advantages of digital meters are:

- They are direct reading. There is no need to interpret the scale.
- Digital meters can be obtained that will give accurate readings to three decimal places.
- They have no moving parts and are less likely to fail or get out of calibration than analog meters.
- They often have automatic scaling features.

SERVICE TIP

Some digital meter displays are susceptible to water or humidity damage. It is important that these meters be kept as dry as possible so that they do not become damaged. In some cases a digital display can be reconditioned by placing the meter in a warm location such as the cab of your service van to allow it to dry out and possibly begin working.

11.6 VOLTMETERS

Two leads from the voltmeter are connected to the circuit being tested, Figure 11-5. Voltmeters are connected in parallel with the load to read the voltage drop or potential difference.

Figure 11-6 shows an analog voltmeter that has multiple scales. Each scale has a different resistance in the meter placed in series with the circuit being tested. A knob in the center face of the meter adjusts the meter to the scale being used. When using a multirange meter, always start to measure voltage using the highest range on the meter. When the approximate voltage is read, the meter range can then be reduced to the proper range for greater reading accuracy. Also, using the meter with a higher voltage than the range of the meter could cause burnout or otherwise damage the meter. Some digital voltmeters provide an auto-scaling function.

Figure 11-5 Using a volt ohmmeter to check the voltage at a compressor disconnect box

Figure 11-6 Analog meters sometimes must have their needles zeroed by turning a small screw on the meter face

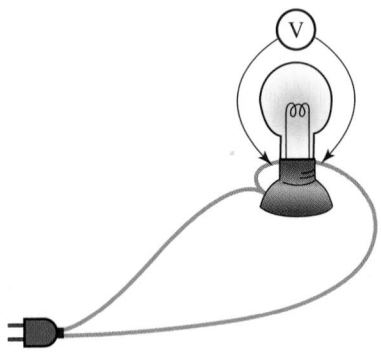

Figure 11-7 A voltmeter is connected parallel to the load

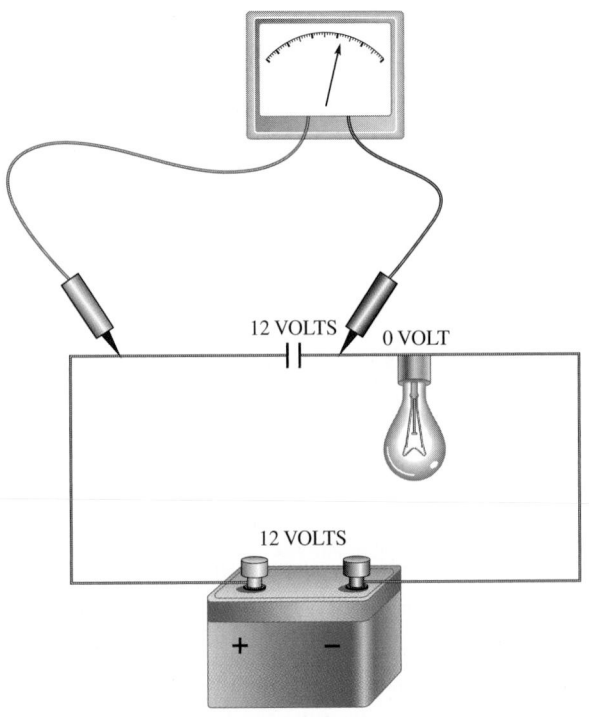

Figure 11-8 Open switch and a positive measured voltage

In DC circuits, verify the correct polarity of the probes that are used before connecting the meter to the circuit. This can be accomplished by observing negative signs on a digital meter and pegging of the needle on an analog meter.

In testing a motor to see that it has proper voltage, one lead goes on each side of the load, as shown in Figure 11-7. On a DC circuit the polarity of the leads must be observed.

The voltmeter can also be used to determine if a hidden switch is open or closed. This is very helpful in troubleshooting. If there is power in the circuit, and the leads of the voltmeter are placed on each side of the switch, a voltage reading indicates the switch is open, Figure 11-8, and a zero reading indicates the switch is closed, Figure 11-9 (if no other open switches are in the circuit).

11.7 AMMETERS

Amp meters (ammeters) are used to measure current flow through a circuit. There are two types of ammeters, clamp-on and inline. An advantage of the clamp-on meter is that it is not necessary to disconnect or make contact with any wires to obtain a reading; this is very convenient. Inline meters can provide very accurate current reading because all of the system current flows through the meter.

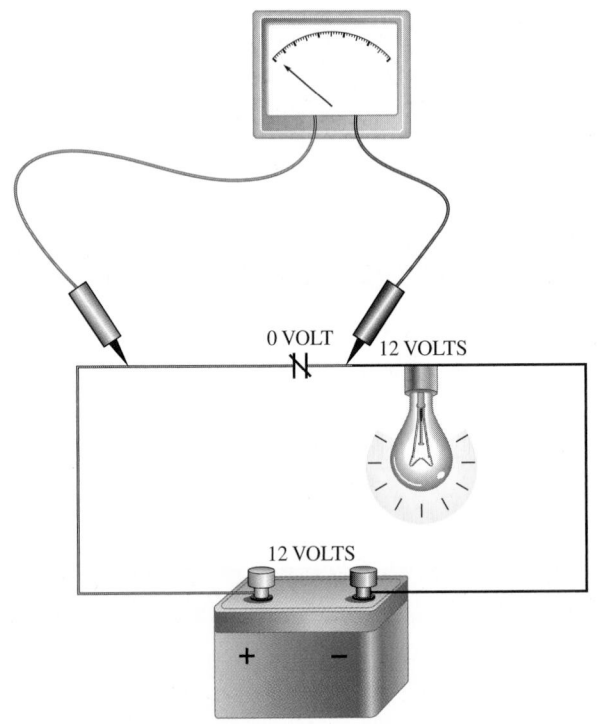

Figure 11-9 Closed switch and no measured voltage

Clamp-on Ammeters

The clamp-on ammeter is one of the most useful of the electric meters for HVAC/R technicians. It is used to measure current flow through a single wire by enclosing the wire within the jaws of the instrument as shown in Figure 11-10.

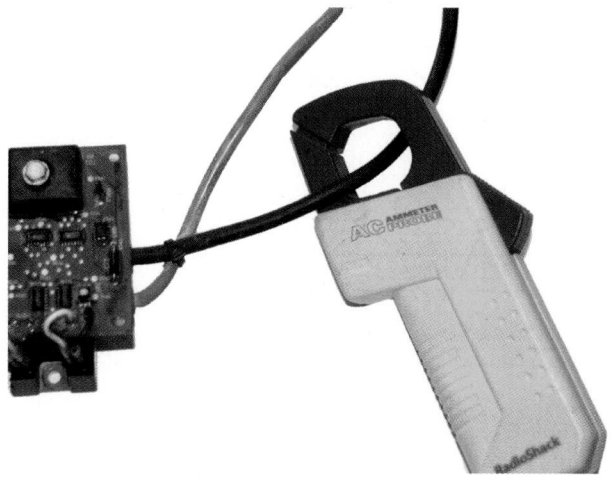

Figure 11-10 The most accurate amp measurement is when the wire passes through the center of the meter jaws

This instrument functions like a transformer. The primary coil is the test wire encircled by the jaws of the instrument. The secondary is a coil of wire within the instrument that is connected to the current-indicating mechanism. The current in the primary wire induces a flow of current in the secondary winding, measuring the current flow. The greater the current flow through the test wire, the greater the induced current and the greater the deflection of the needle reading on the scale.

Inline Ammeter

Occasionally it is desirable to use an inline ammeter. The proper location for its connections in a circuit is shown in Figure 11-11. Note that it is connected in series with the circuit being tested. In DC circuits, verify the correct polarity of the ammeter used before energizing the circuit. Never connect an ammeter across a load. It will be destroyed by line current as there is no load to limit it!

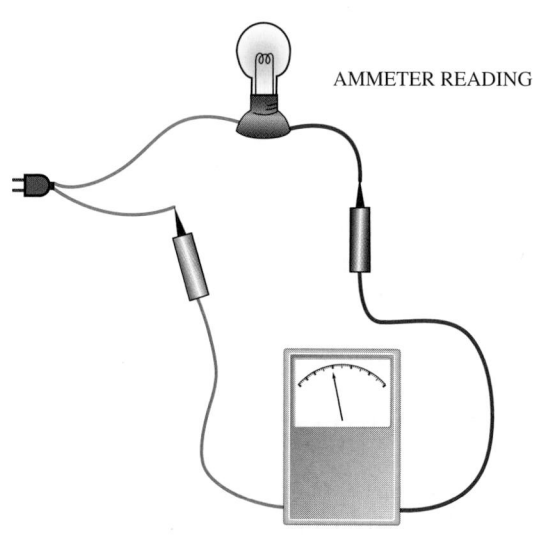

AMMETER READING

Figure 11-11 An ammeter is connected in series with the load

11.8 TRUE RMS METERS

The term *RMS* is an abbreviation for *root-mean square*, a mathematical formula for calculating the electrical power passing through an alternating current circuit. *True RMS* meters have sensitive electronic circuits that can accurately measure voltage and amperage. Most meters called *weighted average meters* display the sensed voltage and amperage by averaging the readings over a short time period. However, some weighted average meters provide RMS readings by applying a correction factor to the sensed voltage or amperage. These RMS meters may be more accurate than standard meters, but they are only averaging the true voltages and amperages.

Why Is True RMS Needed?

In the past, almost all of the equipment an HVAC/R technician serviced had linear loads. Linear loads, like transformers, resistant heat strips, and so on, do not affect the power line sine wave, Figure 11-12a. Standard meters work well on linear load circuits. However, more and more HVAC/R systems and other building loads are using semiconductors in their power and control circuits, Figure 11-12b.

The new semiconductor circuits are faster switchers and more reliable than the ones they are replacing. Their ability to energize and deenergize equipment so quickly causes changes in the power line's smooth waveform. They disrupt the electric power line's smooth waveform much like a speedboat's wake disrupts the uniform smoothness on a lake. At times the speedboat's wake can make the waves coming ashore larger, and other times they can be smaller. If you took the wave heights over time, you would not perceive any difference in wave power. But the occasional large boat wave comes crashing ashore with higher energy, which could cause damage.

True RMS meters can measure that momentary change in incoming line voltage. If there were only an occasional power peak, no long term problem would occur. Unfortunately, this is not the case, because equipment like variable speed motors so common in HVAC/R equipment

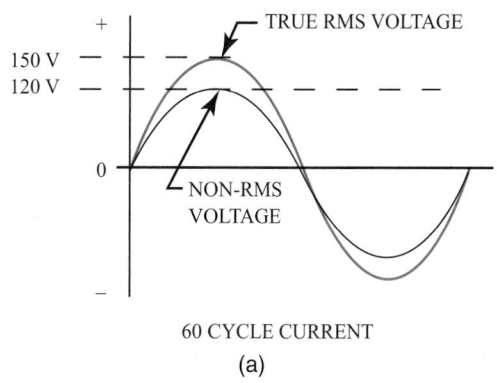

Figure 11-12a True RMS voltage plotted against non-RMS voltage

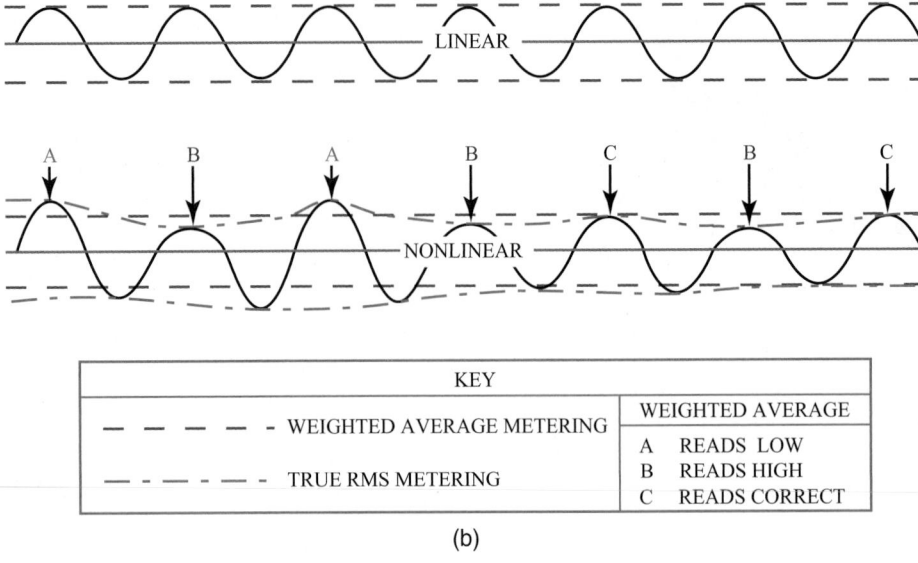

(b)

Figure 11-12b Weighted average metering plotted against true RMS metering

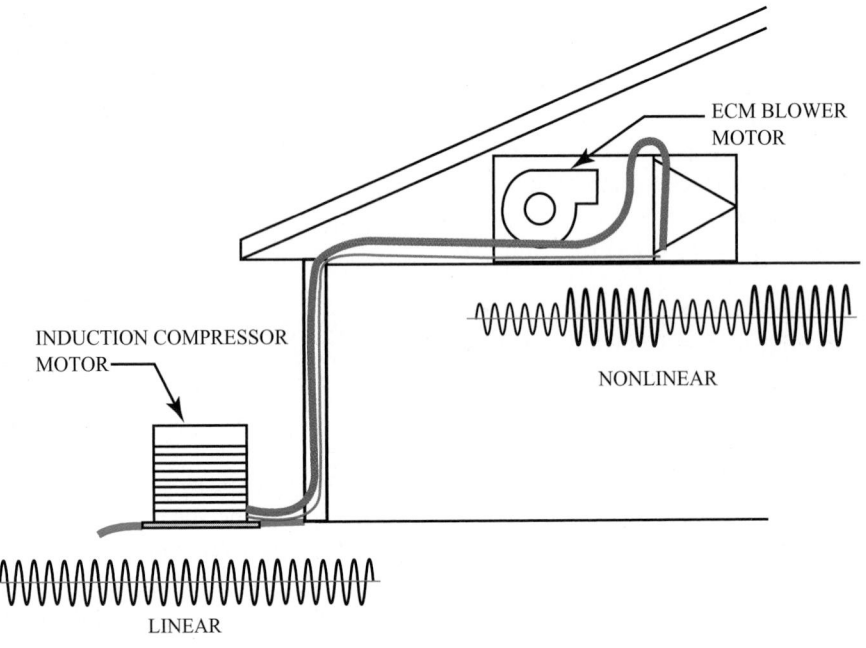

Figure 11-13 Linear vs. nonlinear power supply

today constantly disrupts the wave power. They use power in very short pulses which disrupts the normally smooth linear line current making it rough and choppy. The rough choppy power other equipment in the area has to use is nonlinear, Figure 11-13.

The weighted averaging that most meters do with voltage and amperage can result in readings that are 5% to 40% lower than the values that are actually being seen by the equipment. Small changes in operating voltages on induction motors can significantly affect current draw. Lower voltages cause higher amperage draws through the motor, which increases motor heat. A 20°F rise in motor temperature can

cut the motor's life in half. Higher voltages can cause excessively high inrush currents at startup which can also damage motors.

Using a true RMS meter is the only way to accurately measure voltage and amperage in nonlinear power.

11.9 OHMMETERS

Ohmmeters measure the electrical resistance and can be used to check a circuit for continuity. *Continuity* means there is a complete electrical path. Not every circuit that tests OK for continuity is actually good. For example, a circuit that is

Figure 11-14 The current through the very fine meter needle coil wire causes a magnetic field to form, which causes the meter needle to move

grounded (shorted) to the unit case would show continuiety to the case. All ohmmeters can check for continuity but some have a special position that sounds a beep when there is continuity. The ohmmeter is different from an ammeter or a voltmeter in that it uses a battery as a power supply. The battery furnishes the current needed for resistance measurements.

The function of an ohmmeter is a direct application of Ohm's law. The higher the resistance, the lower the current flow. For analog meters, this produces reduced meter deflection, as shown in Figure 11-14. The resting place for the needle is on the left of the scale. For a high resistance the deflection is small or not at all. For a small resistance, the deflection is large.

One thing that is extremely important is that the power to the circuit being tested must be turned off. Further, if there are any capacitors in the circuit, they must be discharged before the meter is used. There can be only one source of power to the meter and that must be from the battery within the meter itself.

TECH TIP

An ohmmeter can be used as a quick check to test for a shorted or open capacitor. Analog meters are better for this because you can more easily see the meter movement. The test is performed by placing the two leads of the ohmmeter on each of the capacitor terminals for a few seconds and then swapping the leads. What this will do is charge the capacitor with the very low voltage used for ohm checking. In a functioning capacitor, when the leads are reversed, at first there will be a bump in the reading. Then, as the voltage bleeds off the capacitor, the needle will slowly swing back to the infinity (∞) position. If the capacitor is shorted out, there will be no bump and the reading will stay at zero. If there is no needle movement at all, then the capacitor is open.

Using the ohmmeter to check for open circuits is called continuity testing. Figure 11-15 shows three diagrams representing the three possible responses that the meter can give.

- In Figure 11-15a, the meter is measuring the resistance through wire in a circuit and it registers zero. This indicates maximum current flow or 0 Ω resistance. This is the measurement of a short circuit or a good set of closed contacts.
- In Figure 11-15b, the meter is measuring the resistance of a coil, which has a measurable resistance that is read on the meter.
- In Figure 11-15c, the meter is measuring the resistance of an open circuit, which is read on the meter as infinity. Infinity means that the resistance is so large that it cannot be measured. It means that at this point there is a lack of continuity or no current could flow.

Some ohmmeters must be able to read resistances of tens of millions of ohms (megohms), Figure 11-16. The higher amount of power is required for higher resistances.

One very handy feature on an analog ohmmeter is the zero ohm adjustment, shown in Figure 11-17. This knob makes possible a quick and easy method of calibrating the instrument each time it is used. To test the adjustment, the two leads are touched together and if the reading is not zero, the zero ohm adjustment knob is turned until the needle on the analog meter reads exactly zero.

Unlike the voltmeter, one scale of an analog meter is used to read all resistance ranges. To determine the resistance value, multiply the meter reading by the number shown next to the selector switch setting. For example, in Figure 11-18, a meter reading of 5 Ω would be multiplied by the selector setting (R × 1), giving a resistance of 5 Ω.

Some ohmmeters have a selector position of R × 100,000, which is used in measuring very high resistances such as motor windings to ground.

Care must be taken to prevent errors in reading resistance when two or more circuits are connected in parallel, as shown in Figure 11-19. The meter in the illustration is actually reading the combined resistance of two parallel resistances, HTR1 and blower.

In order to read only one resistance, one side of the component being tested is disconnected, as shown in Figure 11-20.

One caution needs to be followed: do not use an ohmmeter to test a solid state circuit unless the manufacturer specifically allows it. The internal battery voltage of the ohmmeter can damage an integrated circuit chip, as shown in Figure 11-21.

11.10 WATTMETER

This instrument reads true power, including an allowance for the power factor (the ratio of real power to apparent power expressed as a percentage). The meter makes the necessary

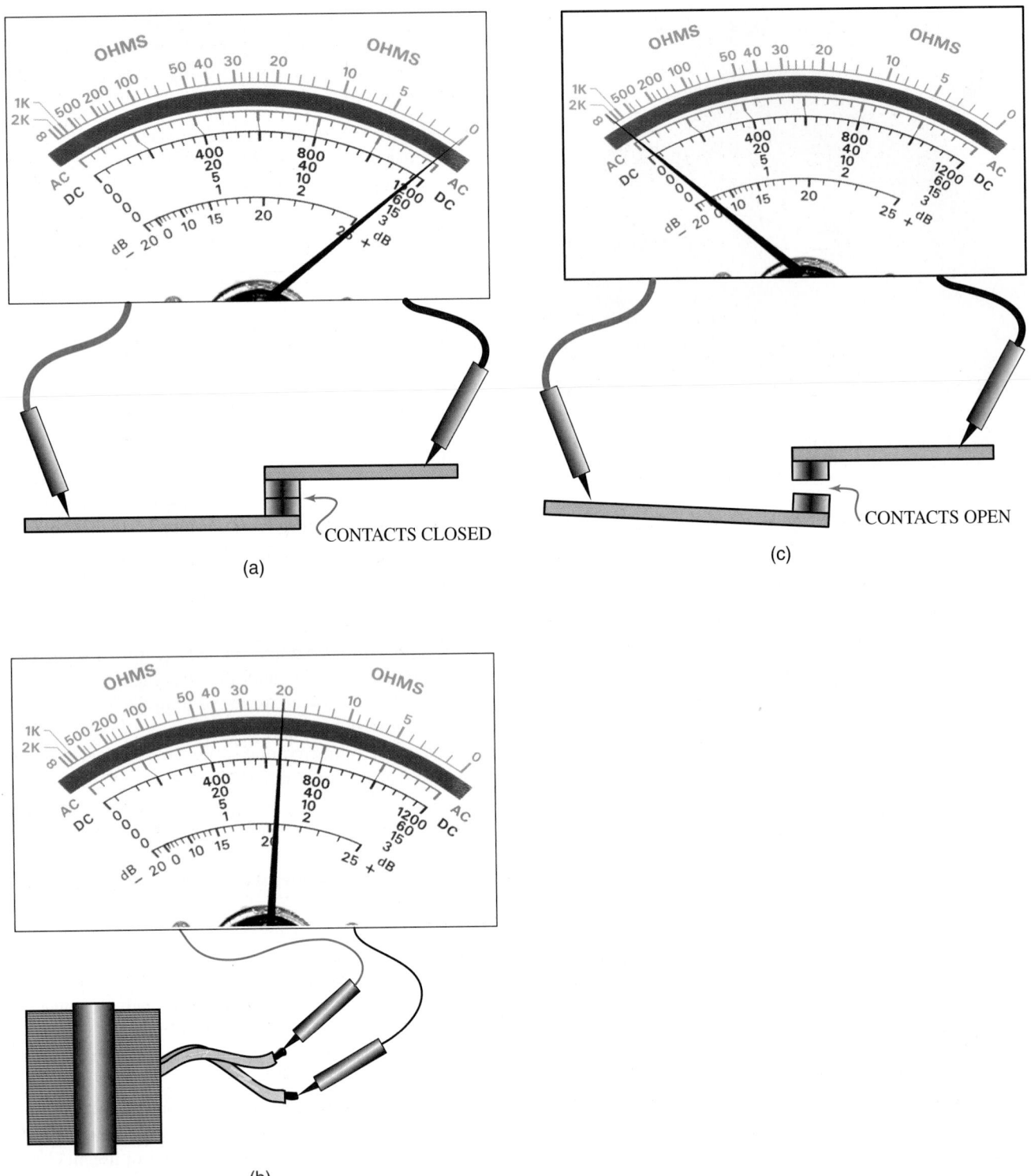

Figure 11-15 (a) Closed contacts or a short will read as 0 Ω; (b) A coil resistor will have a resistance reading between 0 and infinity; (c) An open contact or broken circuit will have an infinite (∞) resistance

calculations for power, in accordance with the power formula:

watts = volts × amps × power factor

The wattmeter zeros itself when not in use and automatically selects the proper range when used. It can be used to measure watts on single, split-phase, and three-phase power sources.

To mathematically calculate watts using the measured volts and amps, it is necessary to know the power factor.

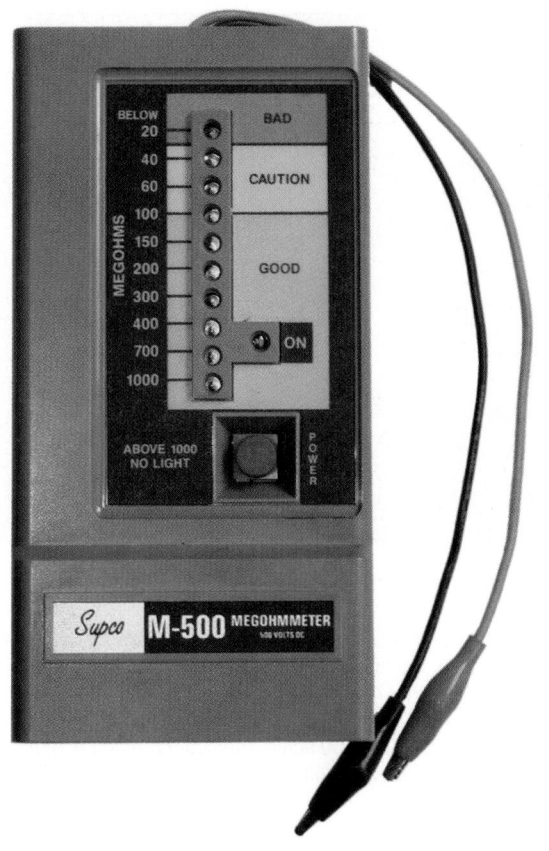

Figure 11-16 Megohmmeter

Figure 11-17 With the meter leads touching each other, zero the ohm needle

11.11 DATA LOGGING INSTRUMENTS

Data logging instruments can be set up to record any number of data points from a few seconds to a month or more. These instruments are extremely valuable when dealing with customers' complaints like, "My unit runs all the time," or "It's always hot in here," and so on. A data logger can prove or disprove these too common and often frustrating complaints. They can also help to solve troublesome intermittent problems that never seem to happen while you are working on the system.

Some data loggers display the logged data directly on the equipment display panel, while others can download the data to a computer for a comprehensive graphic analysis, Figure 11-22.

The newest line of data logging instruments prompts the technician for information. They can connect the proper test device to the data logger where it can collect the information directly from the device. With all of the data collected and the system equipment model number entered, the data logger will provide a comprehensive evaluation of the system's operation and its current level of efficiency. This data is automatically compared to the manufacturer's data, so the report can include specific recommendations if the system is not within the manufacturer's operating specifications.

11.12 INSTRUMENT CALIBRATION

All test instruments need periodic calibration. Unit 14 has specific information on calibrating meters.

11.13 GENERAL METER PRINCIPLES

Before specific types of meters and their applications are described, a number of general principles should be observed in the use of meters, as follows:

- Always use the highest scale on the meter first, then work down to the appropriate scale. This prevents damaging a meter by applying excessive power. An autoranging voltmeter will do this automatically.
- Always check the function of a meter before using it. Do not just assume a meter is working. If it is a battery operated meter, the batteries may be run down. The meter could be damaged during transportation. Other things could happen to affect the readings.
- In using a clamp-on ammeter, be sure the jaws are around only one wire. If it is around two wires of the same circuit, there will be no reading at all as they will cancel each other out. Start at the high range and work down as described above.

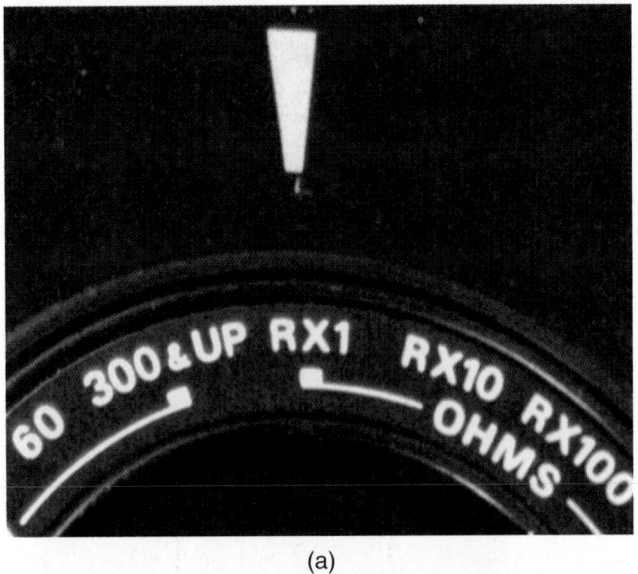

(a)

(d)

(b)

(c)

Figure 11-18 The range must be set to the proper scale. (a) On the R × 1 scale, the number on the scale is the same as the ohms being read; (b) On the R × 10 scale, the number shown on the scale is multiplied by 10, so a reading of 5 Ω would actually be 50 Ω; (c) On the R × 100 scale, the scale reading is multiplied by 100; (d) On the R × 1K scale, the number is multiplied by 1000

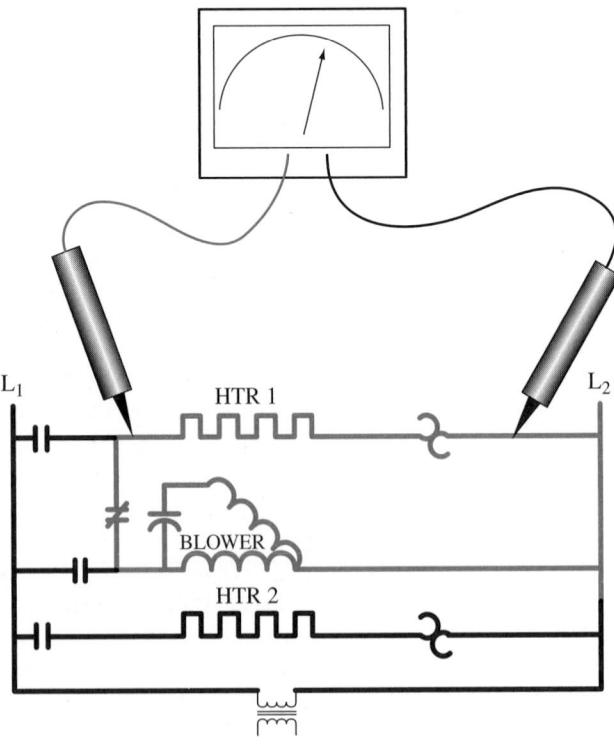

Figure 11-19 The ohm reading for Heater 1 would not be accurate because there are two paths, as shown in red

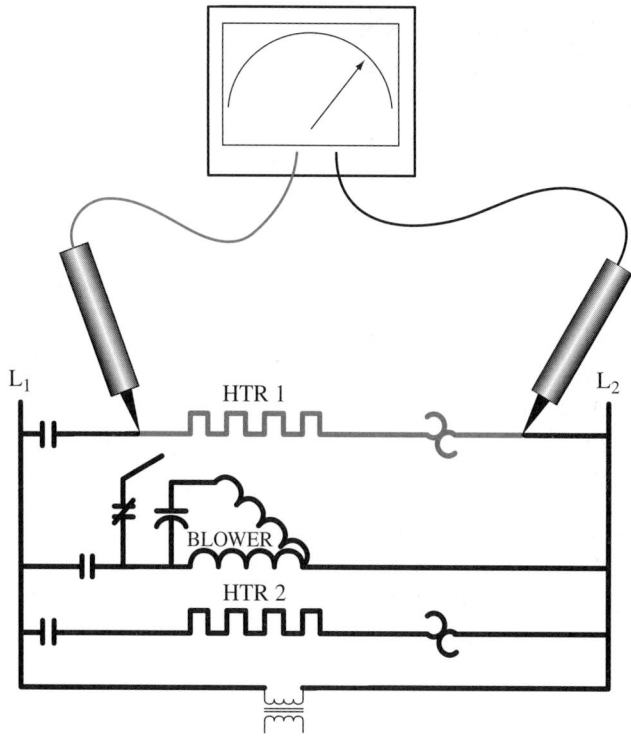

Figure 11-21 NEVER use a multimeter to check an integrated circuit board chip

Figure 11-20 The ohm reading would be accurate because the second path is now broken at the normally closed contacts

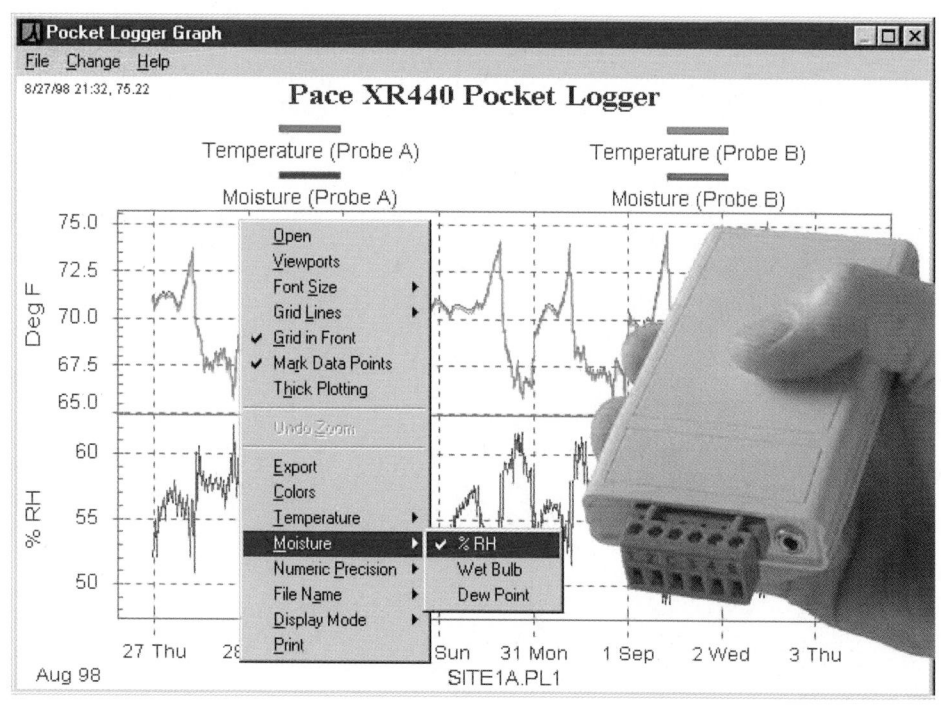

Figure 11-22 Data logger
(Courtesy of Pace Scientific Inc.)

- Always have an extra set of meter fuses on hand for replacement. Sometimes the proper fuses are difficult to obtain when you need them.
- Never use an ohmmeter in a circuit that is powered. An ohmmeter has its own power supply and can be destroyed by connecting to a live power source.
- If the meter uses batteries, have replacement batteries available. Older batteries can affect the readings the instrument provides. Colder batteries provide less voltage and current than warmer batteries. The condition of the batteries is not as important on digital meters, because they can compensate for low battery voltages automatically. Usually, digital meters will continue to operate until a LOW BATT icon is displayed.

UNIT 11—SUMMARY

Good quality meters can provide years of safe reliable service for an HVAC/R technician. They are an essential part of the tools that, when used properly, can provide you with all of the information to assess a system and keep it running properly. It is usually a good idea to start with the highest quality meter you can afford now while you are in school and add to your collection of meters later as you begin working in the field.

It is important for both functionality and appearance to keep your meters clean and in good working order. Although a dirty meter may work well, it does not instill a strong sense of confidence in your customer that you know what you are doing when they see you working with rag-tag meters.

UNIT 11—REVIEW QUESTIONS

1. List five meters commonly used for troubleshooting.
2. What does the term VOM stand for?
3. Why should you purchase a rugged meter?
4. Explain the terms range, resolution, and accuracy as they relate to meters.
5. What is a transient voltage?
6. Where are transient voltages most dangerous?
7. What are the lowest CAT and highest CAT ratings for meters?
8. What could happen to an analog meter if too high a voltage is tested?
9. Why have some digital meters added an analog sliding scale?
10. What part of an analog scale gives the most accurate reading?
11. List three advantages of digital meters.
12. What do voltmeters test?
13. What can a voltmeter show about a hidden switch?
14. What do ammeters test?
15. How are clamp-on ammeters used?
16. What do the letters RMS stand for?
17. How does the voltage reading made with a True RMS meter differ from a voltage reading taken with an RMS meter?
18. What can cause a nonlinear power?
19. What does the beep indicate on some ohmmeters?
20. What does a wattmeter read?
21. What instrument can be used to solve troublesome intermittent problems?

UNIT 12

Refrigerant System Servicing and Testing Equipment

OBJECTIVES

After completing this unit you will be able to:

- list the different types of meters that can be used to measure temperature.
- identify temperature measuring meters.
- demonstrate how to use temperature measuring instruments.
- list the different types of gauges that can be used to measure pressure.
- identify pressure measuring gauges.
- demonstrate how to use pressure measuring gauges.

12.1 INTRODUCTION

Knowing the temperatures and pressures within a refrigeration system is the primary information that all HVAC/R service technicians need to diagnose refrigerant problems. In most cases if you know the temperature and type of refrigerant, you can find the system pressure. Likewise, if you know the system pressure and type of refrigerant, you can find the system temperature. There are times when you need to know both the temperature and pressure to solve a refrigerant problem.

Most of the instruments used are digital, although many analog instruments are still in use. The introduction of digital electronics to temperature and pressure sensing has greatly increased both accuracy and speed. Today's test instruments can provide readings to one or more decimal points. That level of accuracy is often important to ensure that the system is not only running but also operating at the highest efficiency.

12.2 TEMPERATURE

Temperature is the measurement of the speed of molecular movement or vibration in a substance. Temperature can be defined in relative terms as a sensation of hot or cold. This definition in terms of human sensation may be acceptable for heating and cooling. But it is not accurate enough to provide the service technician with what is needed to diagnose refrigerant or heating systems. In HVAC/R installation and service work, temperature is defined as a thermal state of two adjacent substances that determines their ability to exchange heat.

The whole field of HVAC/R is involved in moving heat from places where it is not wanted to places where it can be tolerated, or creating heat to satisfy the occupant's needs for comfort.

There are a variety of instruments that technicians can use to obtain that degree of accuracy in temperature measurement.

Glass Stem Thermometers

Glass stem thermometers once were commonly used by refrigeration service people. The temperature is measured on a scale as compared to the tip of the expanding or contracting liquid inside the thin tube. Any liquid can be used, but mercury and alcohol are the most commonly used. Mercury looks metallic in color, and alcohol is usually dyed red, Figure 12-1. The thinner the size of the hollow glass tube, the greater the movement per degree of temperature change. Longer, more accurate models for laboratory work are available as well as pocket sizes. Breakage is a problem since glass thermometers are fragile. Many technicians would consider the slow response time of this type of thermometer to be a disadvantage.

An advantage of the glass stem thermometer is that they are highly reliable. They do not rely on any mechanical or electronic device that might stick or quit working, Figure 12-2. Their reliability and relative low price is one reason they are extensively used on large central heating and cooling plants used in large buildings or factories.

Figure 12-1 Glass stem thermometer

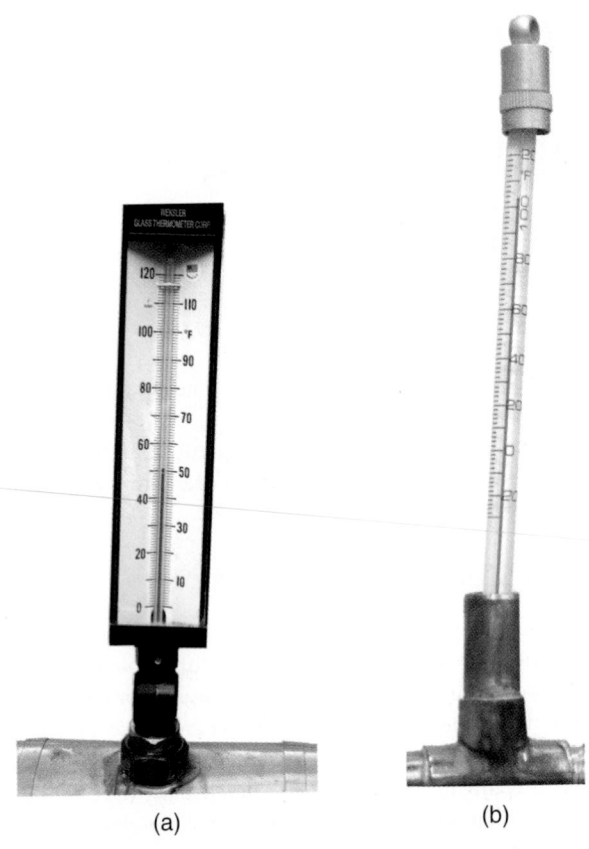

(a)   (b)

Figure 12-2 Glass tube thermometers: (a) In protective case; (b) With glass tube exposed

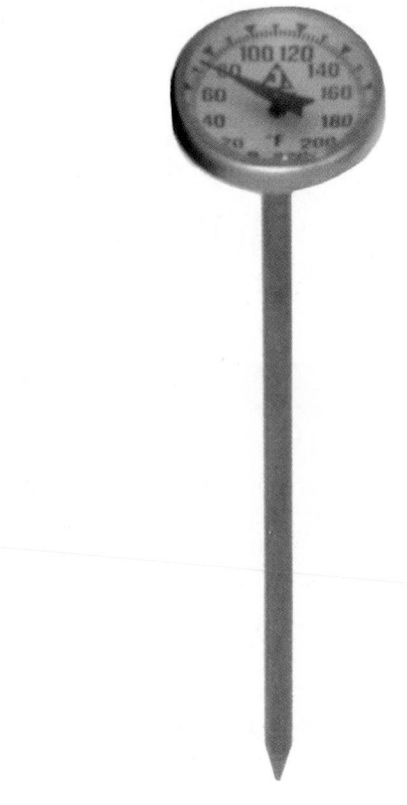

Figure 12-3 Dial-type pocket thermometer

Dial Thermometers

Dial thermometers indicate temperature by a pointer moving over a circular scale, Figure 12-3. The pointer moves because it is attached to a piece of metal inside the thermometer that has a high rate of thermal expansion and contraction with temperature changes. The metal inside the thermometer can be straight or it may be wound into a spiral or spring. If it is straight, it would expand linearly; if it is in a spiral or spring, it rotates, Figure 12-4. Spiral- or spring-wound metal strips are constructed from two different types of metal attached together. Because each strip of metal has a different rate of thermal expansion, the twisting or bending motion is greater than it would be if a single type of metal were used.

An advantage of dial thermometers is that they are more rugged than glass stem thermometers and can be used for a wide variety of applications.

Digital Thermometers

Digital thermometers with compact sensing elements are popular due to their speed in sensing a change in temperature and the ease in reading the alphanumeric display instead of a dial or a scale, Figure 12-5. Most digital thermometers require batteries or a source of electrical power to produce the digital display. The display can be easily changed to display the temperature reading in the Fahrenheit or Celsius scales.

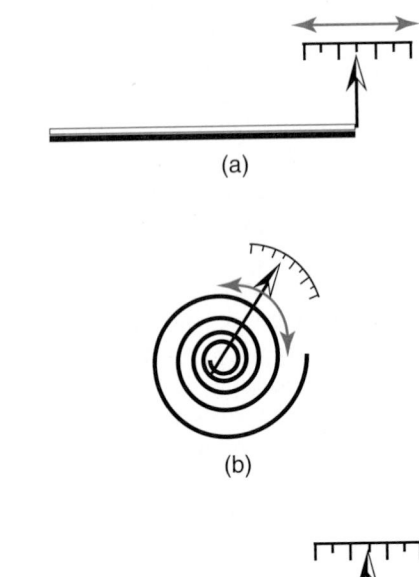

(a)

(b)

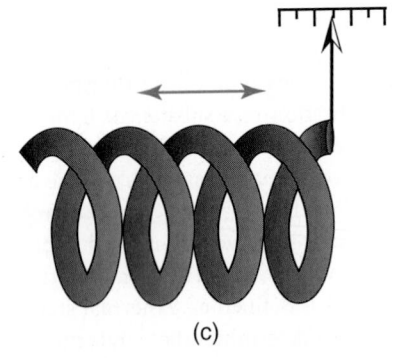

(c)

Figure 12-4 Spiral or spring wound dial thermometer operation

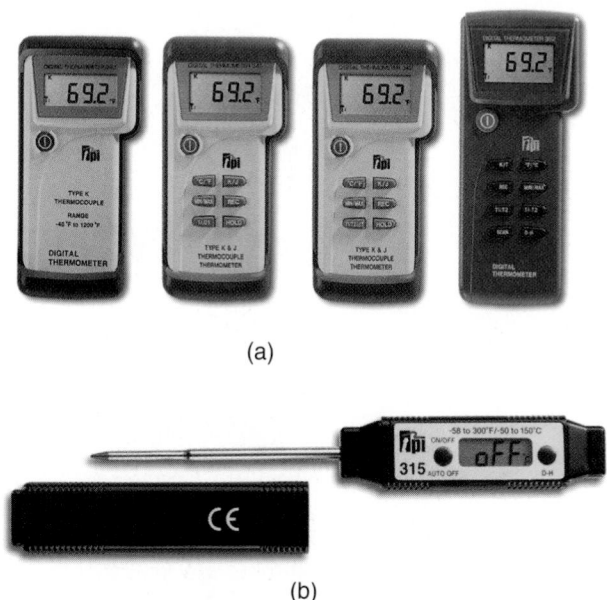

(a)

(b)

Figure 12-5 Digital thermometers
(Courtesy Test Products International, Inc.)

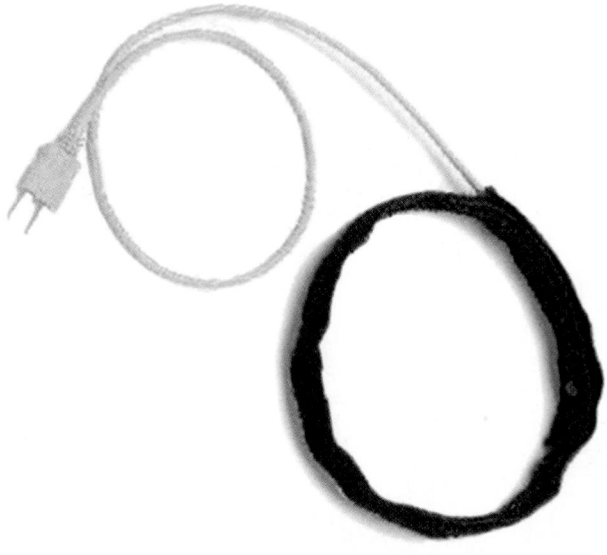

Figure 12-6 Thermocouple bead with Velcro from http://us.fluke.com/usen/products/AccessoryDetail. htm?cs_id=35952(FlukeProducts)&catalog_name= FlukeUnitedStates&Category=PRTP(FlukeProducts)
(Reproduced with permission of Fluke Companies)

Advantages of digital thermometers are the many features available on some models including temperature differences between two or more sensing elements, highest and lowest temperatures, average temperature, lighted displays, and others. They are useful in measuring surface temperatures, such as suction superheat temperatures when adjusting an expansion valve.

Thermocouple Temperature

Thermocouple temperature sensors can be used to detect temperatures that are displayed on analog or digital instruments. The thermocouple produces a small voltage when two dissimilar metal wires are joined forming a tip or junction that can be heated or cooled. A number of dissimilar metals such as chromel and alumel or iron and constantan are used in commercially available thermocouple wires. Type J (iron and constantan) sensors have been used for years but are being replaced with the more popular type K (chromel and alumel) because of its lower cost. One problem with thermocouple sensors is their accuracy. They may provide a temperature that is 2°F higher or lower than the actual temperature. You can test the accuracy of a thermocouple by comparing its temperature reading with another type of thermometer. Once you know the temperature error factor, you can mark it on the thermocouple. That way, you can add or subtract a degree or two as needed to keep the error factor within an acceptable range for most HVAC/R work.

Some of the advantages of thermocouples are their relative low cost, which makes them readily available, and their flexibility. They can be attached to several locations inside of the equipment, and the equipment cover panels can then be reinstalled. With the thermocouple leads run so they are outside the cabinet, the equipment can be operated normally.

Now the technician can better diagnose what is happening to temperatures inside the operating equipment.

When taking the temperature of a refrigerant line, make sure the tip of the thermocouple is tightly pressed against the line. You should also insulate the tip because thermocouples are very sensitive to their surrounding temperature. Some meter manufacturers supply a short strip of Velcro to wrap around the thermocouple tip to hold the tip securely against the refrigerant line and insulate it, Figure 12-6.

To make it easier to get accurate refrigerant line temperatures, some manufacturers produce line clamping thermocouple heads, Figure 12-7. These clamping thermocouples provide both a tight connection and insulation from ambient air.

TECH TIP

Sometimes the thermocouple leads used with digital temperature gauges may have a slight error in the temperature reading. For this reason it is a good idea to test a new set of temperature probes against each other or against another temperature measuring instrument. This comparison will allow you to determine the accuracy and any variance in readings that you may receive from these leads. If you find a variance greater that 1° consistently between any lead and other test instruments, then you should mark that lead with a small piece of tape with the number of degrees plus or minus that it is off. This will allow you to make corrections in temperature readings when using this probe.

A digital thermometer can be used with a wide variety of probes, three of which are shown in Figure 12-8. The different probes allow the single thermometer to be used for more different types of jobs.

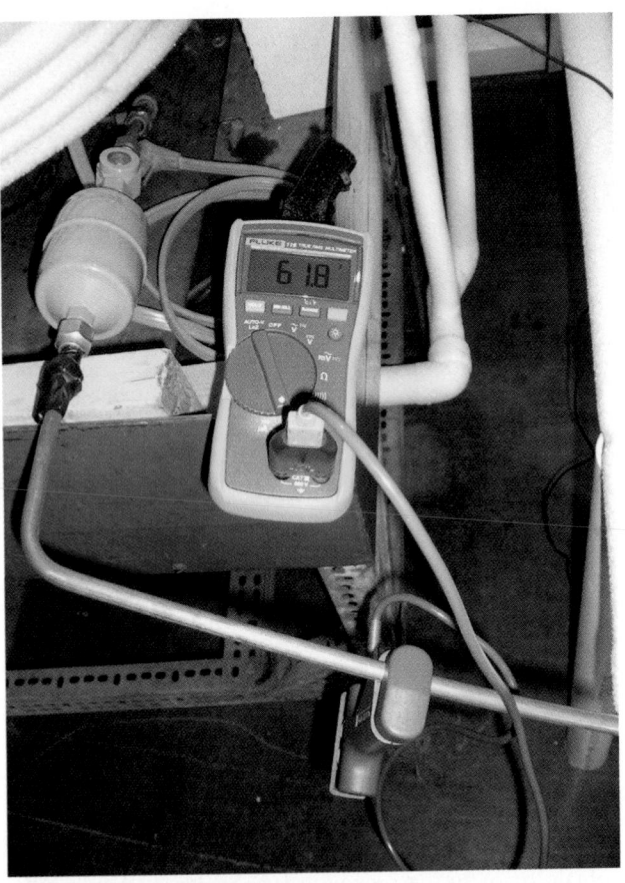

Figure 12-7 Line clamping thermocouple head
(Courtesy of HVAC Department Terra Community College, Freemont, Ohio)

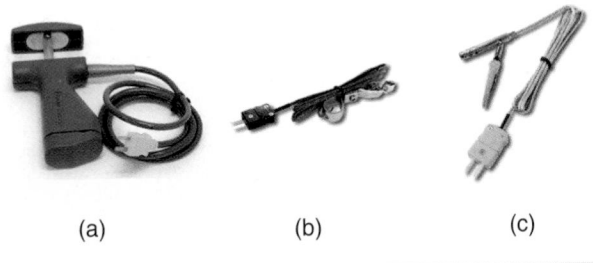

(a)   (b)   (c)

Figure 12-8 Temperature sensor probes: (a) Temperature sensor for refrigerant piping; (b) Ambient temperature sensor with clamp; (c) Flame sensing temperature probe

12.3 INFRARED THERMOMETERS

Infrared thermometers can "see" the temperature of a surface from a distance. What it is seeing is the color of the invisible infrared (IR) light given off by the object. A detector is located inside the instrument that senses the infrared light waves. A change in the IR light's color occurs as a result of temperature changes, which results in a change in the electrical output of the

Figure 12-9 Using an infrared thermometer for measuring air damper temperature

detector. A small integrated circuit converts that electrical output into a displayed temperature. The distance the detector is from the object, the surface color, and its reflectance or reflectivity all affect the accuracy of the temperature read. The most accurate reading obtained is when the detector is closest to a black dull surface. However, not all HVAC/R field work requires extreme accuracy. Technicians are often looking for trends in temperature change. For example, during an air balancing job in a residence, is the air coming from the duct colder or warmer than it was before the dampers were adjusted, Figure 12-9?

TECH TIP

A disadvantage of IR thermometers is that they cannot detect air temperatures; however, they can detect the temperature of the grill or register that the air is passing through. To obtain the most accurate estimate of the actual duct air temperature, point the detector into the louvers so it is pointed at the inside of the duct boot. Some IR thermometers have a laser pointer to make this easier. Move the instrument around and watch the temperature display. Watch for the highest or lowest temperature (highest for heating and lowest for AC) indicated on the display. That temperature is going to be the closest to the actual air temperature. Practice will help develop your skill in obtaining accurate temperature readings with an IR thermometer.

There are many advantages to infrared thermometers. The fact that a temperature reading can be made from a distance may mean that you do not need to climb a ladder to get air duct readings. It may also mean that you can get a reading from a hard-to-reach space. The temperature is displayed instantaneously, which speeds up your work. This instrument may, in some circumstances, also allow the technician to identify or "spot" air leaks.

12.4 PRESSURE

Pressure in a refrigeration system is a force that is uniformly distributed. When the system is operating, there will be one pressure on the high side and another pressure on the low side. Knowing the system's pressures will allow you to find the temperatures.

In standard units, pressure is measured in pounds per square inch (psi). The SI base unit of pressure is given in kilopascals (kPa). In HVAC/R work pressure measurements are referred to in one of three ways: atmospheric, gauge, or absolute. HVAC/R system pressures are measured in gauge pressure. Since air distribution is a function of pressure, the technician will be concerned with the various types of pressure in ductwork and the flow/pressure relationships.

12.5 GAUGE MANIFOLD SETS

Gauge manifold sets are often referred to as AC gauges or just gauges. They are available in a variety of styles as shown in Figure 12-10a–c. The combination (compound) low side gauge in Figure 12-10a reads from 30 in Hg (vacuum) to 350 psi (gauge pressure). The high side gauge reads from 0 to 500 psi. The R410A refrigerant manifold gauge low side reads from 30 in Hg to 500 psi and the high side reads from 0 to 800 psi. Manifold gauge sets are available in both standard and metric scales.

CAUTION

Do not use any refrigerant gauge sets on R410A that are not rated for its higher pressures. It is dangerous to use older gauge sets designed for R22 because they can be damaged by the higher R410A system pressures.

These liquid filled analog gauges contain glycerin to dampen pulsations, lengthen service life, and improve accuracy. The low side gauge in Figure 12-10b reads pressures from 30 in Hg to 120 psi. The four-way block in Figure 12-10c is equipped with three refrigerant hoses and one evacuation hose.

The gauge manifold is used for checking operating pressures, adding or removing refrigerant, adding oil, and performing other necessary operations.

The bottom of the manifold has three connections. High vacuum hoses, usually capable of being leak-tight down to 50 microns or less, are attached to these openings. The left hose is connected to the low side of the refrigeration system being serviced. The right hose is connected to the high side of the system. The center hose has a number of uses, all associated with servicing the system.

TECH TIP

Manifold gauge sets have screw fittings for the system end of the hoses to be attached when the gauges are not in use. It is important that you attach the hose end to these fittings every time you finish a job. These fittings are there to keep dirt out of the hose end because any dirt that gets into the hose end will be pushed into the next system you access. When purchasing a manifold set, the technician should consider the purchase of "low-loss" fittings.

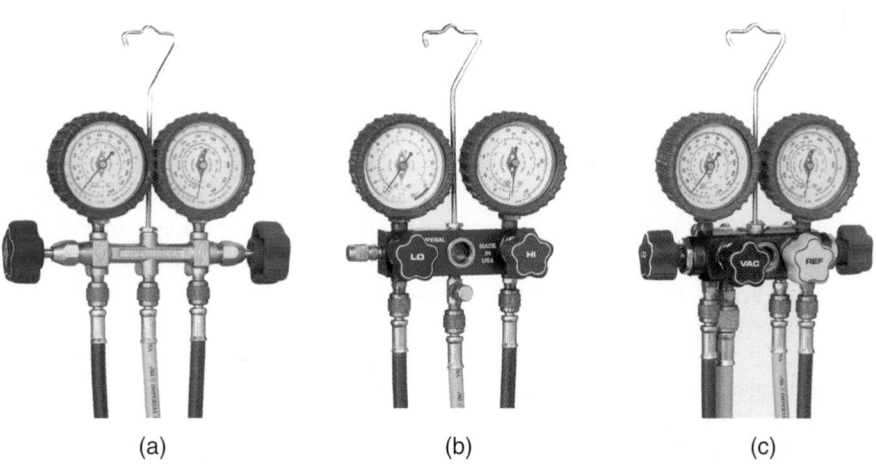

(a)　　　　　(b)　　　　　(c)

Figure 12-10 Gauge manifold sets: (a) Standard gauge manifold set; (b) Six quart manifold set; (c) Six quart four valve manifold set
(Courtesy Imperial)

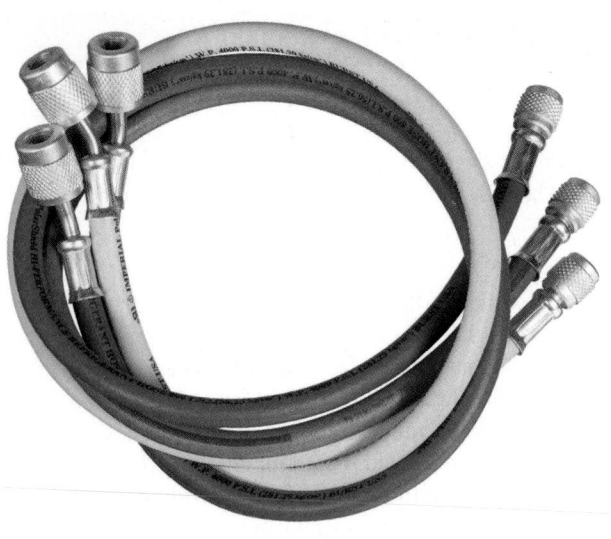

Figure 12-11 Refrigerant hoses
(Courtesy Imperial)

The hand wheels that control the valves on the end of the manifold can be set in one of three positions; fully closed, fully open, or partially opened. When both hand wheels are closed and the hoses are connected to the system, the low side gauge will indicate the system low side pressure and the high side will indicate the system high side pressure, Figure 12-13b.

When the low side hand wheel is turned open slightly, a partially open path around the valve and valve seat is opened from the low side to the center hose, Figure 12-13c. This is the way a system can be charged with refrigerant. The slight opening allows the technician to control the flow of refrigerant into the system.

As the valve is fully opened, free flow between the low side and the center hose can occur, Figure 12-13d. This is the position that would be used to recover only vapor refrigerant from the low side of the system.

When the high side hand wheel is turned open slightly, a partially open path around the valve and valve seat is opened from the high side to the center hose, Figure 12-13e. This is how the valve is operated when a little liquid refrigerant is being removed from the system. The slight opening allows the technician to control the flow of refrigerant out of the system.

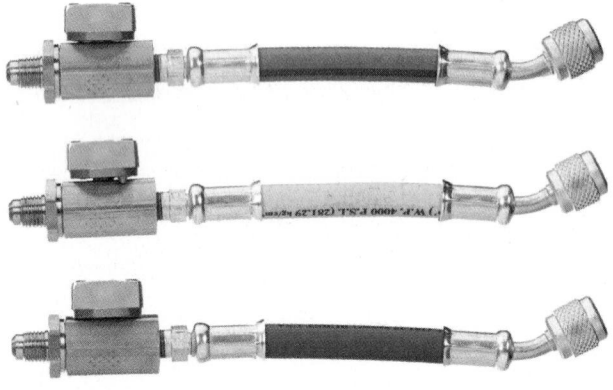

Figure 12-12 Refrigerant hose extensions with mechanical shutoff valve
(Courtesy Imperial)

TECH TIP

The small O-ring in the end of the service valve hose is a replaceable part. These O-rings will become damaged over time and will need to be replaced to prevent refrigerant and vacuum leaks from occurring at the service valve connections. It is a good idea to carry a small package of these replacement seals with your tools because from time to time the O-rings will need to be replaced and occasionally one may fall out. When the O-ring falls out of the hose end, the hose cannot be used until a new O-ring has been installed.

Refrigerant hoses are available in different lengths and colors, as shown in Figure 12-11. The longer hoses give you more working room but are more expensive and can get in the way in small work areas. Hoses are available with check valves to prevent venting of refrigerant, as shown in Figure 12-12.

The exteriors of gauge manifolds are often color-coded. The compound gauge and low side hose are blue. The high side gauge and high side hose are red. The center utility hose is usually white or yellow. The center hose, Figure 12-13a, is useful for connecting to the charging refrigerant cylinder, vacuum pump, or recovery machine.

As the valve is fully opened, free flow between the low side and the center hose can occur, Figure 12-13f. This is the position that would be used to recover liquid refrigerant from the high side of the system.

When both hand wheels are fully opened, a free flowing path between the low side, high side, and center port is provided, Figure 12-13g. This is the position for the valves when a vacuum is being pulled on the system or when the entire refrigerant charge is being recovered.

Gauge manifolds designed especially for evacuating and dehydrating a system have larger hose connections and use larger diameter hoses, Figure 12-14. The larger, usually $3/8$ in, inside diameter of the hoses and valves reduces the pressure drop that occurs when pulling a vacuum.

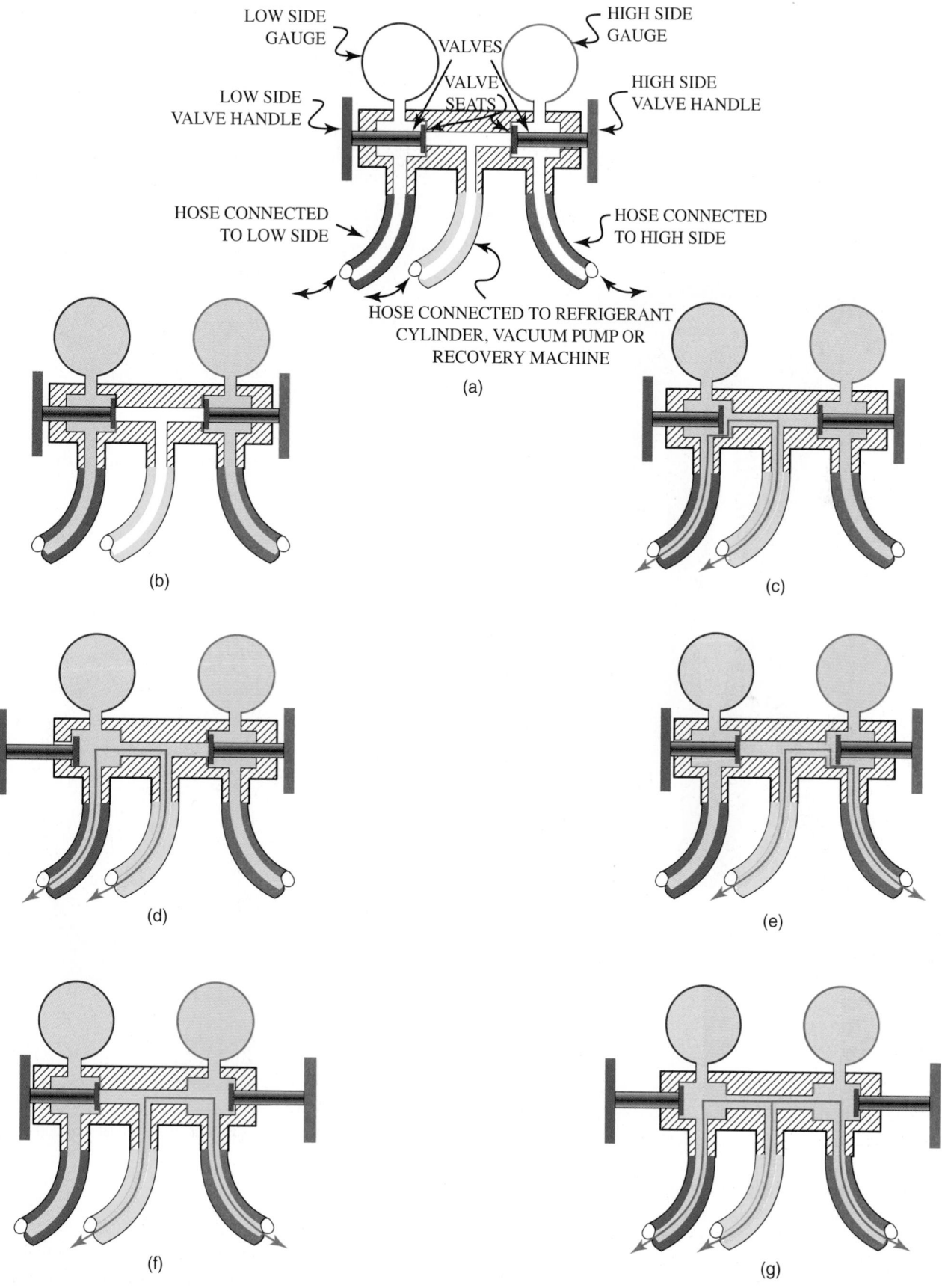

Figure 12-13 Function of the gauge manifold set: (a) Parts of the gauge; (b) Area pressurized with both valves closed; (c) Area pressurized with low side valve slightly open; (d) Area having full flow with low side valve open; (e) Area pressurized with high side valve slightly open; (f) Area pressurized with high side valve completely open; (g) Area pressurized with both low and high side valves open

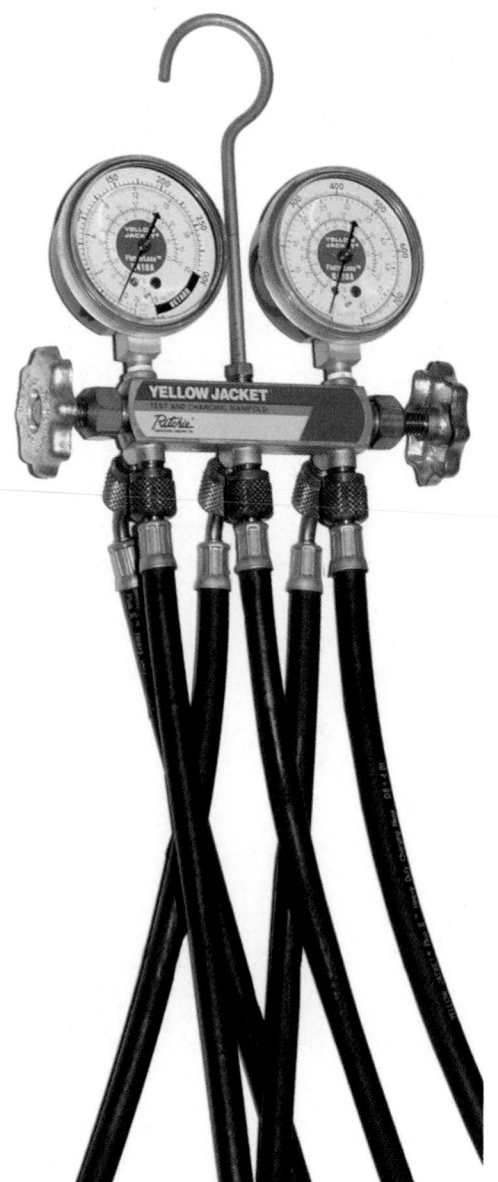

Figure 12-14 Gauge manifold set specifically designed for vacuum
(Courtesy yellow Jacket Division, Ritchie Engineering Company)

Figure 12-15 High pressure needle vibrating due to compressor pulsing

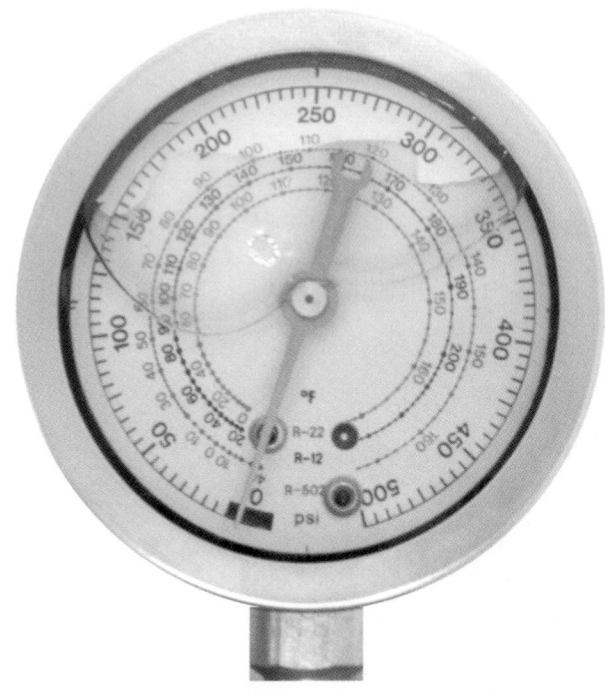

Figure 12-16 Liquid filled gauges dampen needle vibration

Reducing even the very small pressure drop that occurs in normal gauge manifolds can cut the evacuation time by up to 90%.

Some gauge manifolds have multiple openings on the utility connection to accommodate various devices being used simultaneously. The additional connections allow you to change from evacuation to charging without losing any of the system vacuum or refrigerant.

During operation of an AC or refrigeration system, the high side pressure may rapidly pulsate as the compressor valves open and close. This pulsation can cause the high side gauge needle to flutter or vibrate, Figure 12-15. Oil filled gauges are available, and they stop this fluttering from happening, Figure 12-16.

SERVICE TIP

The needle does not flutter when the gauges are first attached. That is because the needle flutters when the high side hose and valve get full of liquid refrigerant. Liquid refrigerant is drawn to the cooler hose as vapor condenses in the manifold and hose. Liquids are noncompressible, so the pulsing pressure in the high side line is transmitted directly to the gauge when the hose fills with liquid, Figure 12-17a. First close the cylinder valve so none of the system refrigerant charge will be lost. Now slightly open the high side valve to let the liquid flow into the center hose, Figure 12-17b. This will dampen the needle fluttering for a moment, allowing you to get a pressure reading. After you have the pressure reading, close the high side valve. Next slightly open the low side valve to let the liquid refrigerant that collected in the hose be drawn back into the system through the low side service valve, Figure 12-17c. By putting the refrigerant back into the system the refrigerant charge is not changed.

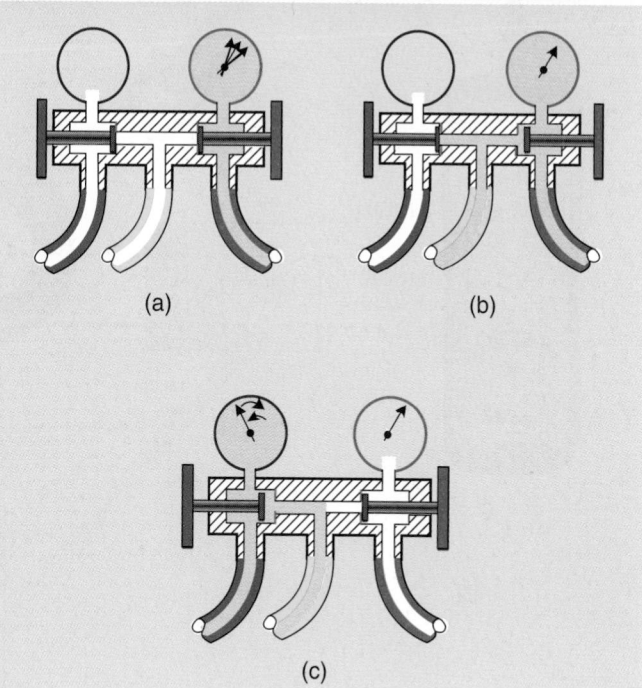

Figure 12-17 Illustration of Service Tip: (a) High side gauge needle vibrating due to liquid flooding; (b) Gauge needle dampened as liquid is slowly bled into center hose; (c) Liquid from center hose has bled back into system

12.6 SUPERHEAT AND SUBCOOLING INSTRUMENTS

There are a number of combination temperature and pressure test instruments available for HVAC/R service work. These combination instruments are most often used to compare the system's high or low side pressure to the actual refrigerant line temperature. This is done to determine the system's subcooling (high side) or superheat (low side). Subcooling and/or superheat measurements are used to determine how a system is operating. Subcooling and superheat measurements are also used to determine if the system's refrigerant charge is correct or needs to be adjusted.

Subcooling and superheat meters have a pressure port that is attached to the refrigerant's access valve and a thermocouple that is attached to the refrigerant line, Figure 12-18. For checking the subcooling, both the pressure port and thermocouple are attached to the high side. To check the superheat, both the pressure port and thermocouple are attached to the low side. The meter calculates and displays the subcooling or superheat reading.

Some of these meters are classified as data loggers because they record the pressures and temperatures over a period of time. A graph or report can be displayed on the meter or downloaded to a computer. This feature is very important when there is an intermittent problem.

12.7 LEAK DETECTORS

Ideally no refrigeration system should leak; however, leaks are a major problem with HVAC/R systems. Electronic leak detection instruments have made this process much faster, more accurate, and easier. It is important that all leaks be located and repaired. Some leak detectors work better in some locations than others. You should have more than one leak detection method available.

Some methods are better for locating the area of a leak and others are better for pinpointing the exact spot of the leak. Soap bubbles are an example of a leak detection procedure that can pinpoint a leak.

TECH TIP

Never use homemade soapy solutions for leak checking. They may be corrosive to the coil or refrigerant piping.

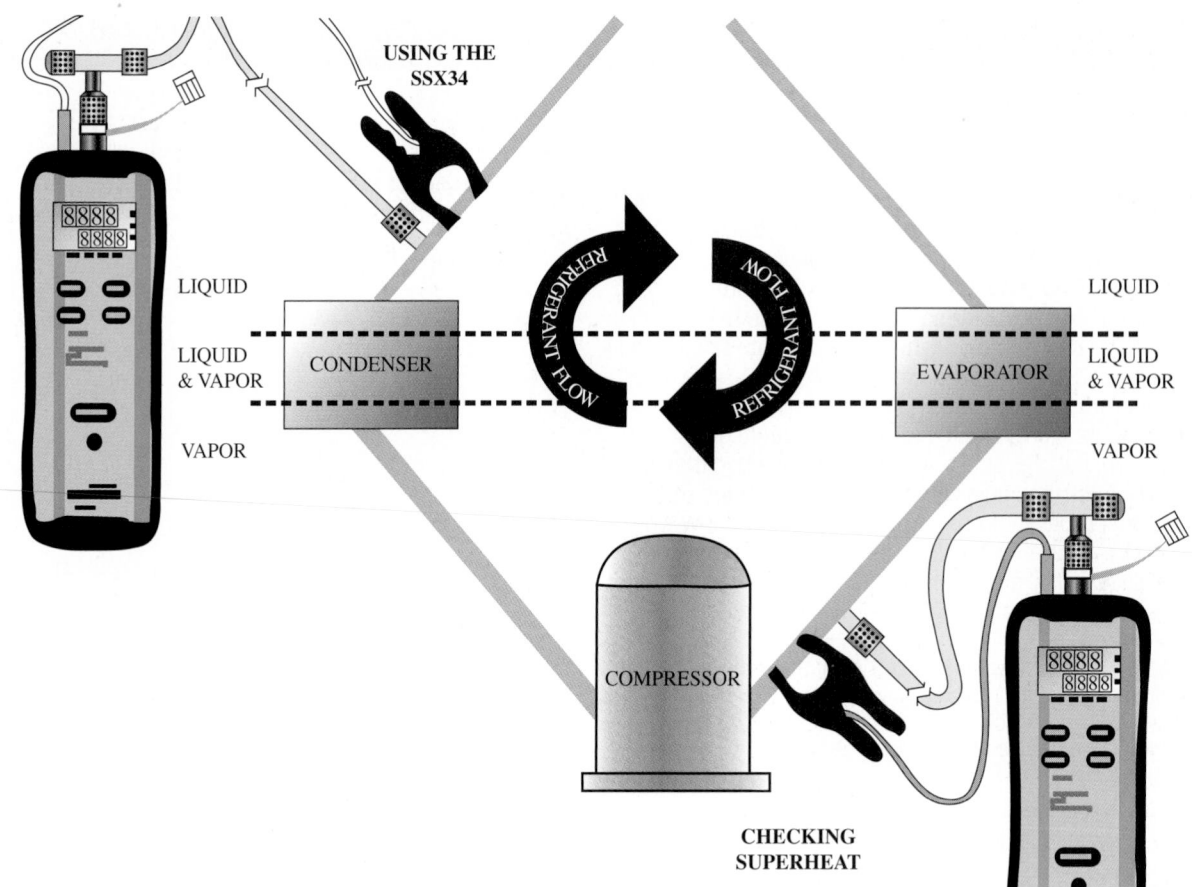

Figure 12-18 Subcooling and superheat meter with pressure port and thermocouple
[Courtesy of Fieldpiece Instruments (J. Gilley)].

CAUTION

Large leaks of refrigerant in confined spaces are danger-ous because they can replace all of the oxygen leading to asphyxiation. If you suspect there is a significant leak, ventilate the area before entering. Equipment rooms with systems that have large refrigerant charges must have self-contained breathing apparatuses available in case of a major refrigerant leak.

12.8 ELECTRONIC LEAK DETECTOR

An electronic leak detector is shown in Figure 12-19. A small pump draws air over a platinum diode located at the end of the test wand.

Electronic leak detectors are capable of detecting leaks as low as 0.4 ounce per year. They can be used for HCFC, CFC, and HFC gases. A pump located in the device draws air directly to the sensing tip. No calibration is required. It is battery operated and has both a visual and an audible signal,

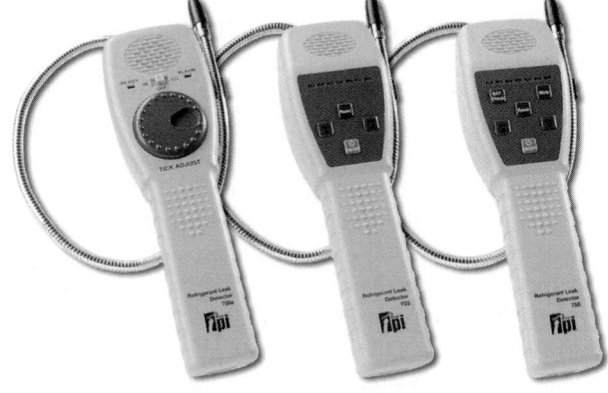

Figure 12-19 Electronic leak detectors
(Courtesy Test Products International, Inc.)

which increase in frequency as the leak source is approached. Detectors identified as halide leak detectors will only respond to refrigerants containing halogens such as chlorine and fluorine.

If you are looking for a leak in an enclosed space, the leak detector may sense the refrigerant in the air. Calibrate the meter, or adjust its sensitivity to background refrigerant levels, by manually turning the adjustment knob. Some meters calibrate automatically by turning the instrument off and back on.

12.9 ULTRASONIC-TYPE LEAK DETECTOR

An ultrasonic type leak detector instrument, shown in Figure 12-20, will detect any gas leaking through an orifice. As refrigerant is escaping from a system, it will generate a sound at a higher than normal frequency. An ultrasonic leak detector can be used to pick up these sound waves. This method works well as long as there are no other sources within the system area that produce sound waves at the same frequency. The ultrasonic leak detector is typically somewhat more expensive as compared to the other leak detection devices.

The features and specifications for this meter are as follows:

- Detects pressure or vacuum leaks.
- Unaffected by windy, rooftop conditions.
- Unaffected by background noise.
- Detects ultrasonic noise from arcing electrical switchgear.
- Can be used for finding leaks in ductwork.

Figure 12-20 Ultrasonic leak detector
(Courtesy Robinair SPXIOTC)

12.10 FLUORESCENT DYE LEAK CHECKING

A small quantity of fluorescing oil is put into the system. Use only oil dyes that have been approved by the equipment manufacturer as safe to use in their system. The system is operated for a period of time. As refrigerant leaks, it takes with it a small quantity of oil. Once a UV lamp shines on the system, even the smallest of leaks is easily found.

The advantages of this leak detection method are that it can pinpoint leaks; and once the dye is in the oil, rechecking for leaks is easy and fast.

12.11 MICRON VACUUM GAUGE

Micron gauges are used to measure deep vacuums below the level that a compound gauge on a manifold gauge set can display. The compound gauge can only show that a vacuum had been pulled down to 29 in Hg. The micron gauge can display vacuums down to around 50 microns, Figure 12-21. Microns are very small measurements. There are 25,000 microns in 1 in, which means there are about 400 microns in $\frac{1}{64}$ in.

The display on micron gauges can show the reading as a number on a numeric display, as in Figure 12-22a, or by lighting an LED next to the micron scale, as in Figure 12-22b.

A micron gauge can be a very effective leak check for HVAC/R systems. When a system has been evacuated down to 50 microns, isolate the system from the vacuum pump by shutting off the service valve to the vacuum pump. By watching the micron gauge for any release in pressure, leaking systems can be identified. One note, however, is to be certain that all of your connections are tight and leak free. The micron leak check will be adversely affected by any leak, whether it is in the refrigerant system or in your gauges or hoses.

Several concerns associated with a vacuum leak check include:

1. It does not pinpoint the leak
2. It has the potential of pulling moisture and corrosion into the system.
3. Even at maximum potential vacuum it effectively leak checks for atmospheric pressure only. Low side pressures are normally higher than that.

12.12 ELECTRONIC SIGHT GLASS

An electronic sight glass is shown in Figure 12-23. This ultrasonic instrument has both visual and audible bubble detection. The display indicates when there are actual bubbles passing between the sensor clamps. Transducer clamps fit tubing from $\frac{1}{8}$ in to $1\frac{1}{8}$ in (3 mm to 32 mm) in diameter.

Figure 12-21 Micron vacuum gauge

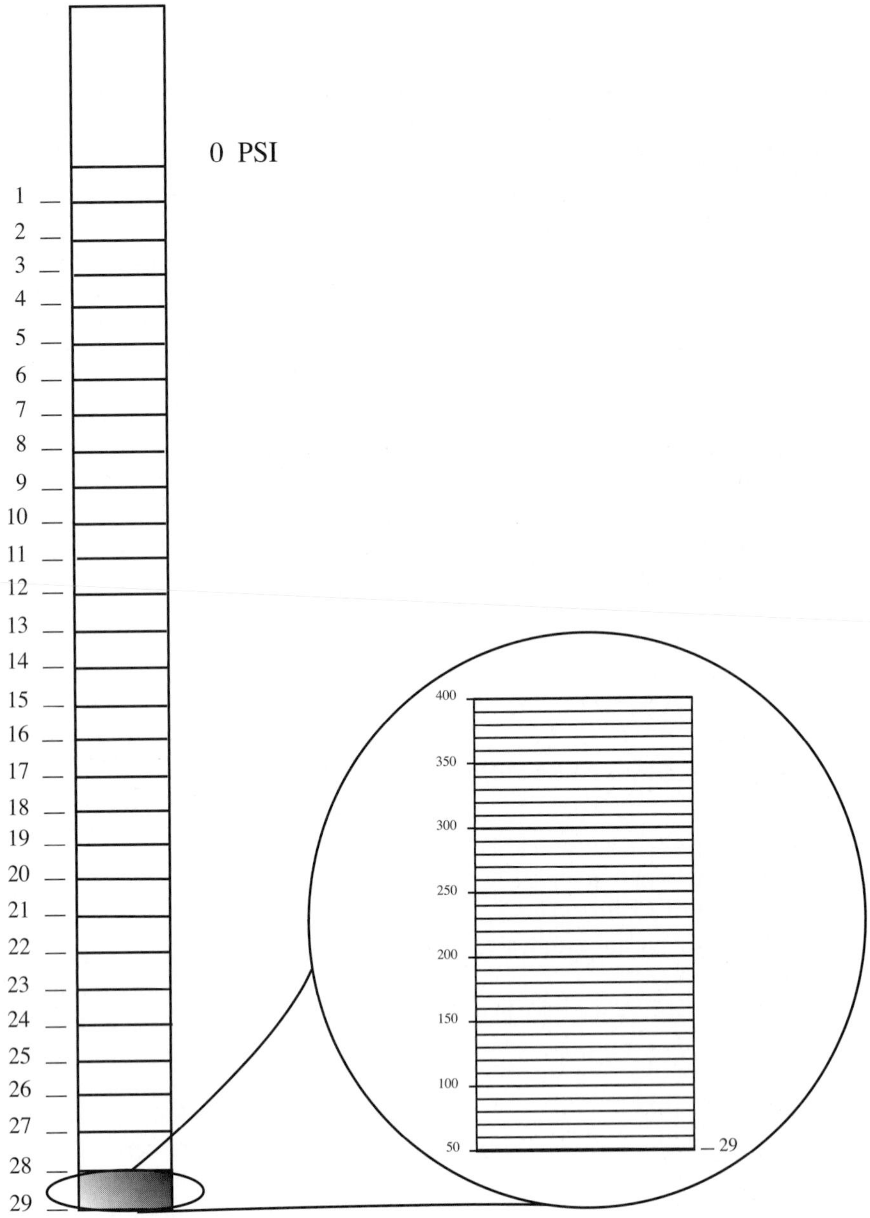

0 PSI

1
2
3
4
5
6
7
8
9
10
11
12
13
14
15
16
17
18
19
20
21
22
23
24
25
26
27
28
29

400
350
300
250
200
150
100
50
— 29

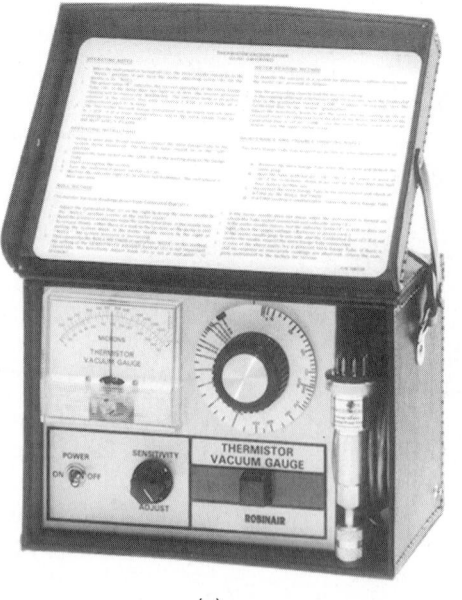
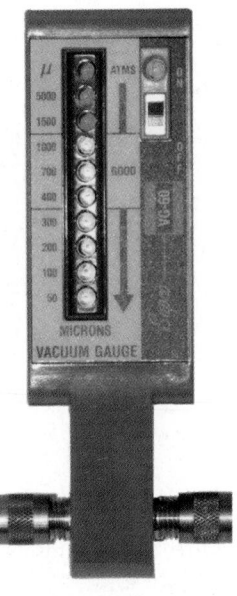

Figure 12-22 (a) Numeric display micron gauge; (b) LED display micron gauge
(Courtesy Robinair SPXIOTC)

(a)

(b)

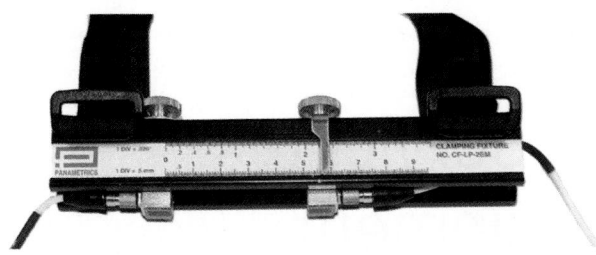

Figure 12-23 Electronic sight glass

UNIT 12—SUMMARY

Making accurate temperature and pressure measurements is essential to all refrigerant system service. For example, electric utilities are one of the major expenses for both home and business owners. Keeping the air conditioning and refrigeration systems operating at peak performance and efficiency will help to reduce electric bills.

Inaccurate readings can result in unnecessary work or system failure. If the readings are wrong and indicate the system is undercharged, overcharging may occur. If the readings are wrong and indicate the system is operating properly, the compressor may die from a low refrigerant charge.

To ensure that your test instruments are working properly, you should calibrate them according to their manufacturer's recommendation. Unit 14 covers the basic information regarding instrument calibration.

UNIT 12—REVIEW QUESTIONS

1. Why would a service technician need a system's temperature and pressure?
2. What does a temperature meter measure?
3. What liquids may be used in a glass stem thermometer?
4. What is an advantage of the glass stem thermometer?
5. What is the pointer of a dial thermometer attached to that causes it to move?
6. Why are digital thermometers popular?
7. What temperature scales can a digital meter display?
8. What are the two thermocouple temperature sensor types commonly used in HVAC/R work?
9. What are some advantages of thermocouples?
10. Why must the thermocouple tip be tightly pressed against the line?
11. How does an infrared thermometer measure temperature?
12. What color surface temperature can be read most accurately with infrared thermometers?
13. What units are used to measure pressure in HVAC/R systems?
14. What is the approximate maximum high side pressure on an R22 gauge?
15. What is the approximate maximum high side pressure on an R410A gauge?
16. Why is it dangerous to not to use R410A gauges on a R410A system?
17. What is a refrigerant gauge manifold is used for?
18. What are the three positions that the hand wheels that control the valves on the end of the manifold can be set in?
19. What happens when the low side hand wheel is turned open slightly?
20. Why would some test instruments sense both the low side pressure and the low side line temperature?
21. Why would a large refrigerant leak be dangerous?
22. How does an electronic leak detector work?
23. How does an ultrasonic type leak detector work?
24. What type of dye can be used for a fluorescent dye leak checker?
25. How many microns are in 1 in of mercury?

UNIT 13

Heating System Servicing and Testing Equipment

OBJECTIVES

After completing this unit you will be able to:

- explain the purpose for heating system servicing and testing equipment.
- describe acceptable and unacceptable ranges of furnace CO_2 output.
- demonstrate the proper way of using heating system servicing and testing equipment.
- list the warning and alarm levels for an oxygen depletion monitor.

CAUTION

Many CO_2 (carbon dioxide) detectors used in the HVAC/R industry must be calibrated to ensure their accuracy. Calibration of CO_2 detectors and other similar instruments must be done by a certified calibration company. Check with the instrument's manufacturer, if necessary, to locate an appropriate company to provide this service.

13.1 INTRODUCTION

Heating systems are tested for both safety and efficiency. In many cases, both safety and efficiency are interconnected. Safety is the primary reason most heating systems are tested. If a system is not properly working, it can be deadly to the occupants. Carbon monoxide is a colorless, odorless, deadly gas that is produced by most fuel furnaces when complete or stoichiometric combustion is not achieved. When the furnace is working properly, this gas poses no danger to the occupants.

The high cost of fuel has brought about an increase in the demand for efficiency testing of heating systems. When fuel costs were low, it was not cost effective to spend a lot of time to fine tune a system to get the last bit of heat from the fuel. Today testing for efficiency has become a standard part of all system service. In addition, a system that is working efficiently is less likely to pose safety problems.

13.2 MEASUREMENT OF CO_2

In the operation of heating systems, it is essential that the CO_2 (carbon dioxide) content of flue gases be maintained as high as practical to improve the efficiency of the heating unit while keeping a low smoke level. In practice, as far as oil furnaces are concerned, 10–12% CO_2 is desirable. For natural gas furnaces, the CO_2 range should be 8.25–9.50%. The CO_2 measurement, plus the stack temperature measurement, can be used with a special slide rule to indicate the efficiency of the furnace.

13.3 DRAFT GAUGE

The draft gauge is supplied with a draft tube to be inserted in the flue pipe with a rubber tubing extension, Figure 13-1.

There are two places where the draft is usually taken. One is in the flue pipe at the furnace exit and the other is in the inspection port of the furnace (over the fire). By taking

Figure 13-1 Draft gauge
(Courtesy of Bacharach, Inc.)

these two measurements, draft problems can be analyzed. The draft tube is inserted in the flue pipe opening and the meter registers the amount of draft, in inches of water column. The probe is then inserted through the inspection port of the furnace to read the draft at this location. If there is less draft at the inspection port, it is an indication that there is a leak in the heat exchanger that needs to be corrected.

13.4 SMOKE TESTER

The tube from the smoke tester is inserted in one of the test holes during operation of the furnace and a sample of the flue gas is passed through a filter, Figure 13-2. Ten pump strokes of the tester are required to get a proper sample. The pump stroke must be pulled in a smooth steady motion.

The shade (color) of the smoke spot on the filter is compared to the standard smoke scale. Compare the shade of the smoke spot to the numbered scale by holding the scale and sample filter at arm's length and in a well lit area. The normal smoke spot reading for oil burners is usually scale number 0 or 1 on a scale of 0–9. Any reading above 1 would require adjusting the burner.

TECH TIP

Keep the smoke spot scale clean and free of dirt that could make comparing the test spot to the scale unreliable.

To ensure that the tests are accurate, the sampling tube must be periodically cleaned of loose soot, dirt, rust, or other debris. The sampling tube should also be cleaned any time it appears to be dirty. Some manufacturers recommend cleaning the tube once every 10 times the smoke tester is used.

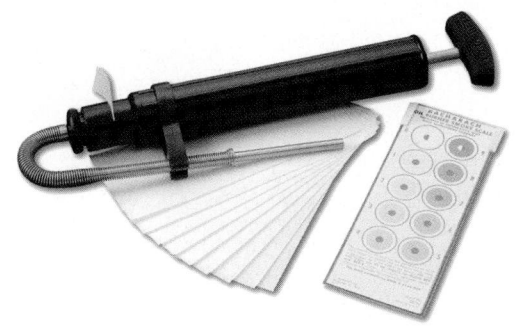

Figure 13-2 Smoke tester
(Courtesy of Bacharach, Inc.)

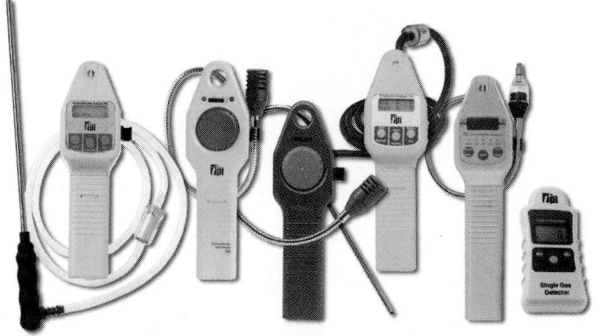

Figure 13-3 CO_2 testers
(Courtesy Test Products)

13.5 FLUE GAS ANALYZER

Some flue gas analyzers can measure carbon monoxide (CO), carbon dioxide (CO_2), oxygen (O_2), nitrous oxide (NO), pressure, and efficiency, Figure 13-3. The probe is inserted in the flue pipe during the operation of the furnace. You may also use a CO_2 probe that plugs into a multimeter, Figure 13-4.

SERVICE TIP

Flue gas analyzers can be used to help the technician set up a furnace so that it is operating at peak energy efficiency. In the past, many technicians simply looked through the inspection port into the fire box and made a visual determination that the flame looked OK. With today's rising energy costs and concerns over the environment, it is important that a complete and accurate analysis of the flue gas products be taken so that the furnace can be set at its peak performance.

13.6 GAS IDENTIFIERS AND MONITORS

Gas identifiers and monitors are available as portable or fixed detectors. The introduction of new sensor technology has expanded the types and levels of gases that can be detected. Some of the gases that can be detected include:

- bromine
- carbon monoxide
- chlorine
- chlorine dioxide
- ethylene
- ethylene oxide
- formaldehyde
- hydrazine(s)
- hydrogen bromide
- hydrogen

Figure 13-4 CO₂ tester adapter for multimeters
(Courtesy Test Products International, Inc.)

- hydrogen chloride
- hydrogen cyanide
- hydrogen sulfide
- nitric oxide
- nitrogen dioxide
- ozone
- propylene oxide
- sulfur dioxide

The presence of any of these gases may or may not be an equipment problem. A comparative check of the environmental air outside the structure is a prudent component of any serious analysis.

There are a number of uses for gas identifiers and monitors:

- To notify the owner of a refrigerant leak.
- To protect anyone entering a room where refrigerants are stored or used. Refrigerants can displace oxygen, and therefore become dangerous. Most refrigerants do not have an odor and are not normally detected.
- To identify the CO content in the air, and in some cases, to automatically control the addition of outside air. There is an increasing amount of concern about indoor air quality and particularly the need for ventilation to prevent the buildup of CO in enclosed spaces.

The refrigerant identifier is a microprocessor-based instrument that extracts a sample of the refrigerant and analyzes it to determine the type of refrigerant, Figure 13-5. A refrigerant identification tag should always appear on a system. However, it is possible for the tag to be faded and difficult to read or even missing altogether. The service technician MUST be certain of the refrigerant that has been installed in order to perform any service necessary.

Figure 13-5 Electronic analyzer to determine refrigerant types

13.7 OXYGEN-DEPLETION MONITOR

The oxygen depletion monitor has a remote oxygen sensor and a controller, which are normally mounted outside the mechanical equipment room door, Figure 13-6. It is designed to continuously monitor the oxygen level in mechanical equipment rooms where class A, group I refrigerants are

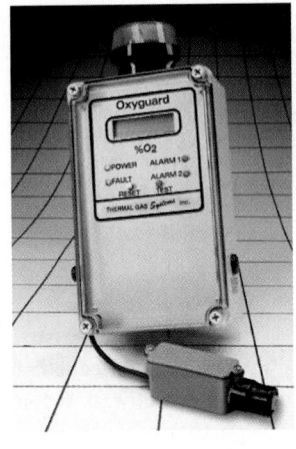

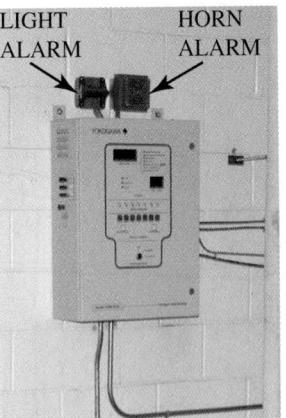

Figure 13-6 Oxygen deprivation monitors for equipment rooms
(Courtesy OI Analytical)

used. These refrigerants are odorless. A large refrigerant leak in a confined equipment room could displace the oxygen. A person could enter the space unaware of the danger and quickly fall unconscious. Oxygen is normally about 20% of the atmosphere, and when levels drop to 19.5% an amber warning light goes on, starting a mechanical exhaust. If the oxygen level continues downward to 18.5%, a red warning light goes on and an alarm will sound. Relays provide an option for sending the warning to remote locations. A "purge" switch permits the fan to run continuously or only when signaled by the monitor. The alarm turns off automatically when normal levels of oxygen return, or may be turned off manually—at which time there is automatic reset.

CAUTION

Oxygen deprivation monitors are mandated by OSHA regulations for most commercial and light commercial mechanical equipment rooms. These monitors are also a good investment for use in those few situations not mandated under the OSHA regulations. Oxygen deprivation can quickly render a technician unconscious and could result in death.

UNIT 13—SUMMARY

The use of heating system servicing and testing equipment is essential for safe and efficient operation. The presence of combustible gases, heat, flames, and products of combustion all must be properly controlled to ensure a safe environment.

Read and follow all test equipment instructions provided by the equipment manufacturer and all of the heating system equipment manufacturer's instruction. They are the experts on the test equipment and the heating system equipment. Sometimes the instructions for a specific piece of equipment may have been lost or damaged. Replacement documentation can often be downloaded and printed from the Internet.

UNIT 13—REVIEW QUESTIONS

1. Why is it important to use heating system testing equipment?
2. What is the range for CO_2 for oil and natural gas furnaces?
3. Who should calibrate HVAC/R CO_2 detectors?
4. What two places might a draft gauge be placed to analyze a furnace?
5. How should the smoke tester pump be pulled?
6. How often must the sampling tube be cleaned to ensure that the tests are accurate?
7. What are some of the gases that can be measured by a flue gas analyzer?
8. List five gases that a gas identifier may detect.
9. At what level of oxygen should the first warning be given by an oxygen-depletion monitor?
10. At what level of oxygen should the main alarm be sounded by an oxygen-depletion monitor?

UNIT 14
Calibrations of Meters and Instruments

OBJECTIVES

After completing this unit, you will be able to:

- use the correct terminology when talking about instrument calibration.
- perform simple procedures to verify the calibration of temperature measuring instruments.
- demonstrate that pressure readings are within tolerance.
- verify the proper operation and accuracy of leak detection instruments.
- perform calibration verification checks of flue-gas analysis instruments.

14.1 INTRODUCTION

Instruments are calibrated for several reasons, including improved troubleshooting accuracy and to ensure that a system is working according to design specifications. If the instruments the technicians use are not calibrated and are not providing accurate information, it will be difficult to make a determination of actual equipment performance. Many commercial buildings and some residential homes are now being commissioned. *Commissioning* is the process of testing all the building's systems and certifying to the owner that they are all operating according the manufacturer's specifications. To commission a system or building, technicians must be using instruments that are calibrated.

14.2 CALIBRATION

Calibration is a baseline testing and adjustment procedure performed on instruments to ensure that the measured indication or output is an accurate representation of the process. The technician may calibrate some instruments, and others may need to be sent to a meter shop to be calibrated.

The instrument manufacturer may specify how often an instrument must be calibrated. In some cases, local codes may require some critical instruments to be calibrated and recertified on a regular time schedule. The instrument used to certify the calibration of your instrument will have its calibration traced back to the National Institute of Standards and Technology. Certified calibrated equipment will have a sticker on the instrument listing who performed the calibration, the date of the calibration, the date the calibration expires, and any error factor that must be used to correct the instrument's reading, Figure 14-1.

Not all instruments can be calibrated. Some electronic instruments cannot be calibrated but must be tested periodically to ensure that they are working accurately. If they are found to be out of calibration beyond the acceptable limits, they must be replaced.

SERVICE TIP

The meter movement on many analog meters is very sensitive. In some cases the weight of the instrument needle can affect the reading. The needle's weight is less when the meter is laying flat as compared to when it is set upright.

The faceplate is typically made of plastic (not glass) to provide a more robust instrument capable of handling the rough environment and conditions to which it may be exposed. Static electricity on the plastic faceplate can affect the reading. To test for static buildup on the plastic face, slowly wave your hand over the top of the faceplate without actually touching it. If the indicator needle moves, static is present. The static electricity can be removed using an anti-static spray available from either the manufacturer or a supply house.

Calibration Terminology

Accuracy Accuracy is how exact a device is when making a measurement. An example is a meter measuring a conductor carrying 100 V. If the meter is 100% accurate, it indicates exactly 100 V with no tolerance. Highly accurate instruments are those used in a laboratory environment.

Range The range is the difference between the smallest indication on the scale and the largest indication on the scale. When talking about an instrument with a 0% reading of 4 mA and a 100% reading of 20 mA, the range is 16 mA.

Span The span is the value that represents 100% of the scale of an instrument. When talking about an instrument with a range of 4 mA to 20 mA, the span is 20 mA.

Tolerance The tolerance is the amount of variation allowed from a standard. Typically tolerance is expressed in percent (%). Your digital volt-ohmmeter may have a

instrument. Adjust this knob until the needle indicates the value stamped into the transducer, in this case 30.25. Place the switch into the READ position. The instrument is now ready for use.

There is one consideration with this type of instrument. Be careful not to expose the transducer itself to oil or liquid refrigerant. This contamination will render the transducer useless and another one will have to be obtained.

Digital Electronic Vacuum Instruments

There is no user calibration required on digital electronic vacuum instruments. Calibration has been performed by the manufacturer and will last the life of the instrument.

14.6 ELECTRICITY MEASURING INSTRUMENTS

Electronic instruments such as volt meters, ohm meters, and ammeters, along with wattmeters, power meters, and phase angle meters, may be out of calibration. If the readings provided are not within tolerance, these instruments must be returned to the manufacturer for calibration. There are no user level adjustments that can be made and, typically, even removing the cover to gain access to the circuit board will void the warranty.

14.7 REFRIGERANT LEAK DETECTION INSTRUMENTS

Analog Leak Detectors

Analog detectors have a small sensing wand connected to the main body of the instrument. This sensing wand is used to "sniff" along the system tubing/piping in its entirety. There is a small pump in the body of the instrument. There is usually a small filter at the end of the sensing tube that should be changed before calibration begins.

It is important to note that the sensing tips of these wands should never come in contact with refrigerant. If they are exposed to refrigerant they must be replaced. There is little that can be adjusted other than using a small screwdriver to adjust the meter movement for a zero reading. Calibration of the most complex leak detection instruments is beyond the scope of the technician. These instruments must be returned to the manufacturer where the calibration can be performed in an instrument calibration laboratory.

To perform a calibration verification procedure, test gases of 0% and 100% concentration must be purchased. These are available from the manufacturer and some supply houses. First the sensor is exposed to a gas with no refrigerant or zero concentration. At this point the minimum or zero indication is adjusted mechanically by slightly rotating a limit screw on the face of the meter or electronically by carefully adjusting a potentiometer on the circuit board to a value speci-

fied in the manufacturer's calibration procedures. Next the sensor is exposed to a gas of 100% concentration. At this point there are no mechanical adjustments, electronic only. Access to the circuitry inside is required and a potentiometer must be adjusted to provide the voltage recommended by the manufacturer or until a 100% maximum (span) reading is indicated on the meter. With all mechanical 0% (zero) and electronic 100% (span) adjustments, one adjustment affects the other. This requires you to go back and check 0% again because it will be off just a bit. Then recheck the 100% adjustment. Continue checking both the minimum and maximum indications until both are accurate. Electronic adjustments are not so inter-related; however, it is good practice to check 0% and 100% several times to ensure both are correct.

Digital Leak Detectors

These detectors have some of the same limitations as the analog models. Exposing the wand sensing tips to refrigerant renders them useless. These types of instruments have removable/replaceable tips that can be installed if needed. They operate on a slightly different principle from the analog units. Digital instruments do not draw in an air sample. They measure the conductivity between two sensor plates. Clean air provides less conductivity as compared to air with refrigerant in it. The amount of difference in conductivity is the input, which is then converted into audible signals via microprocessors or integrated circuits.

Given this principle of operation, it should be understandable that these instruments are more effective in enclosed spaces as compared to operating on a roof at a building with the wind blowing. There is no calibration on these instruments that the technician can perform. You can verify operation by first purposely exposing the wand tip to a refrigerant source and listen for the audible indication. Next, proceed to a location where there is no refrigerant and here no audible detection signal should be heard.

14.8 FLUE GAS ANALYSIS INSTRUMENTS

The newer types of instruments have a small pump built into them. Like its predecessor, it must be inserted into the flue pipe but its location is not as critical. When the sensing tip is inserted, the technician initiates the test. The small internal pump takes an air sample for X amount of seconds, and electronically performs an analysis of the gases it has drawn in. A digital display is provided although attachments can be purchased that provide a printout of the results. The newer types of instruments perform many tests on the exact same sample of flue gas. This helps eliminate an inaccurate reading caused by the improper placement of the sensing tip. The calibration of this type of instrumentation varies according to functionality.

Analog Flue Gas Instruments

For analog flue gas instruments compensation must be made for the condition of the batteries in the unit. When batteries are new, they provide more voltage and current than older batteries. This can affect instrument readings. You must also compensate for the temperature of the batteries. Even with new batteries, the amount of voltage and current provided varies with the temperature. Colder batteries provide less voltage and current than warmer batteries. Placing a selector switch to the BATT, or CAL, position and adjusting a knob for the desired indication on the faceplate will compensate for both of these battery conditions.

Digital Flue Gas Instruments

Unlike their analog counterparts, digital displays are not affected by static electricity. The condition of the batteries is not as important either. Usually, digital display models will continue to operate with the advertised accuracy until a LOW BATT icon is displayed. There is also no zeroing of the display required.

Calibration Verification of Flue Gas Instruments

The calibration verification of both types of these instruments is accomplished in the same way. Sample gases must be purchased from the manufacturer of the instrument. The sensing tip is then exposed to these gases and an indication provided.

If the indication is within tolerance, calibration verification is complete and no further action is required. If the indication provided is not within tolerance, the instrument must be returned to the manufacturer for calibration. There are no user level adjustments that can be made, and typically, even removing the cover to gain access to the circuit board will void the warranty.

UNIT 14—SUMMARY

Technicians use a variety of electronic instruments to provide an accurate picture of exactly how a specific HVAC/R system is performing. Most of these parameters cannot be visually observed, therefore the use of instrumentation is required.

It is the responsibility of the technician to determine whether or not the electronic instruments are operating correctly. If the instruments are not operating correctly, the faulty measurement could waste the technician's valuable time when troubleshooting a condition that does not exist, or even worse, to miss a condition that needs to be rectified.

Manufacturer level calibration is available for a fee and expedited work for an increased fee is available from some manufacturers. This service is one that should be considered when initially purchasing your particular instrument.

UNIT 14—REVIEW QUESTIONS

1. What is "calibration"?

2. Why is it important for your instrumentation to give you accurate readings?

3. If your voltmeter was 100% accurate and you applied 68.7 V DC to it, what would you expect your voltmeter reading to be?

4. If your voltmeter had a tolerance of $+/- 2\%$ and you applied 68.7 V AC to it, any reading between _____ and _____ would be considered within tolerance.

5. What is the range of an instrument whose 0% output is 3 psig and whose 100% output is 15 psig?

6. Resistance thermal devices come in two basic types. Name them.

7. If the RTD you are using is a negative temperature coefficient type and the temperature is increasing, the resistance output would be _____.

8. What is an easy way for you to generate 212°F

9. What type of instrument would you use to generate temperatures in excess of 212°F

10. The output signal a thermocouple generates is in units called _____.

11. In a thermocouple, the point at which the two dissimilar wires are connected to each other is called the _____.

12. Briefly describe the construction of a bi-metallic device.

13. The two types of bi-metallic devices are _____.

14. A sand bath is used to calibrate conical bi-metallic devices. TRUE or FALSE?

15. Units of vacuum are expressed in what?

16. Why is it important to use only the special dyes made to color the water in your physical vacuum indicator?

17. Mercury spillage/contamination is reportable to _____.

18. What information is located on the transducer of the micron gauge?

19. To perform a calibration of a leak detector, _____ of _____ must be purchased.

20. How do digital refrigerant leak detectors differ from analog refrigerant leak detectors?

UNIT 15
Piping and Tubing

OBJECTIVES

After completing this unit you will be able to:

- list the pipe and tubing materials used for air conditioning and refrigeration.
- discuss the characteristics of copper tubing.
- describe the characteristics of ACR copper tubing.
- discuss the methods of joining copper tubing.
- discuss the characteristics of iron and steel pipe.
- describe how to thread iron pipe.
- describe how to cut and join PVC and CPVC pipe.

15.1 INTRODUCTION

Heating and air conditioning equipment needs refrigerants, fuels, and fluids to operate. All of these travel through piping or tubing, both inside and outside the equipment. Working with the different piping materials is a key component of installing and servicing air conditioning and refrigeration equipment. Understanding the material properties and connection techniques is essential knowledge for air conditioning and refrigeration technicians.

15.2 TYPES OF TUBING AND PIPING MATERIALS

In the air conditioning and refrigeration industry, the most commonly used materials for piping and tubing are copper, iron, steel, aluminum, PVC, and CPVC. The preferred choice of material depends upon the pressure the tubing must contain, compatibility with the chemical it will be used with, ease of working the material, and the cost of the material.

Pipe Versus Tubing

Pipe is always named by its approximate inside diameter and schedule, or wall thickness. This can be confusing because the actual inside diameter is usually slightly larger than the nominal size. In other words, neither the inside nor the outside diameter of $\frac{1}{2}''$ iron pipe is $\frac{1}{2}$ in. Tubing is usually measured by its outside diameter. Unlike pipe, the outside diameter of tubing is accurate. This means that $\frac{1}{2}$ in OD tubing actually measures $\frac{1}{2}$ in. However, tubing sold in hardware stores for water piping is commonly sold by its nominal size, which is its approximate inside diameter. Figure 15-1 shows the difference between $\frac{1}{2}$ in steel pipe and $\frac{1}{2}$ in OD copper tubing. This nominal size is arrived at

1/2 INCH COPPER TUBING   1/2 INCH IRON PIPE

Figure 15-1 Comparison $\frac{1}{2}$ in OD copper tubing and $\frac{1}{2}$ in nominal iron pipe

by subtracting $\frac{1}{8}$ in from the tubing outside diameter. Air conditioning and refrigeration tubing is always specified by outside diameter. Copper tubing suitable for air conditioning and refrigeration use, whether rigid or coiled annealed, is dehydrated and marked "ACR."

Refrigeration Lines

Most refrigeration lines are made of copper. However, lines for ammonia systems are made of steel because ammonia chemically reacts with copper. Aluminum is used for internal piping of some air conditioners and appliances, but it is not used for field piping because of the difficulty in joining aluminum tubing.

Fuel Gas Lines

Black iron is used for piping natural gas. Galvanized iron pipe should not be used for natural gas because of the reaction between the odorant in the gas and the zinc in the galvanized coating. The residue generated by this reaction can migrate into the gas valve. Gas piping is being run in new flexible plastic covered corrugated steel piping, Figure 15-2. This material costs more than black iron, but is quicker and easier to run. There are limitations on where it can be used, so even systems run with the new material generally have some black iron pipe. Copper is commonly used for LP gas lines, but it should not be used with natural gas because the odorant added to natural gas reacts with copper. The flexibility of the aluminum tubing has made it the primary material used for piping the pilot gas for standing pilot systems on both natural and LP gas systems.

Figure 15-2 Flexible corrugated steel tubing used for gas lines (*Courtesy of OmegaFlex, Inc.*)

Type	Diameter OD (in)	Diameter ID (In)	Wall thickness (in)	Weight per foot (lb)
K	$\frac{1}{2}$	0.402	0.049	0.2691
	$\frac{5}{8}$	0.527	0.049	0.3437
	$\frac{3}{4}$	0.652	0.049	0.4183
	$\frac{7}{8}$	0.745	0.065	0.6411
	$1\frac{1}{8}$	0.995	0.065	0.8390
	$1\frac{3}{8}$	1.245	0.065	1.037
	$1\frac{5}{8}$	1.481	0.072	1.362
	$2\frac{1}{8}$	1.959	0.083	2.064
	$2\frac{5}{8}$	2.435	0.095	2.927
	$3\frac{1}{8}$	2.907	0.109	4.003
	$3\frac{5}{8}$	3.385	0.120	5.122
L	$\frac{1}{2}$	0.430	0.035	0.1982
	$\frac{5}{8}$	0.545	0.040	0.2849
	$\frac{3}{4}$	0.666	0.042	0.3621
	$\frac{7}{8}$	0.785	0.045	0.4518
	$1\frac{1}{8}$	1.025	0.050	0.6545
	$1\frac{3}{8}$	1.265	0.055	0.8840
	$1\frac{5}{8}$	1.505	0.060	1.143
	$2\frac{2}{8}$	1.985	0.070	1.752
	$2\frac{5}{8}$	2.465	0.080	2.479
	$3\frac{1}{8}$	2.945	0.090	3.326
	$3\frac{5}{8}$	3.425	0.100	4.292

Figure 15-3 Specification of common copper tubing sizes

Water Piping

Galvanized iron, copper, PVC, and CPVC have all been used for water piping. Black iron should not be used with water because it rusts. Copper was the material of choice for water systems before the advent of PVC and CPVC plastic pipe. PVC and CPVC plastic piping have replaced copper for water lines in most new construction because the material is very inexpensive and is easy to join. Drain lines are usually run in PVC, but can be run in CPVC or copper if the drain water is high temperature.

15.3 COPPER TUBING

Types of Copper Tubing

Copper is available in three wall thicknesses: K (heavy), L (medium), and M (light). Type K heavy wall tubing is meant for special use where abnormal conditions of corrosion might be expected. Type M thin wall tubing is not used on pressurized refrigerant lines because it does not have the wall thickness to meet the safety codes. It can be used for water lines and condensate drains. Type L is most

frequently used for normal refrigeration applications. Figure 15-3 provides specifications for both type K and type L tubing.

ACR Copper Tubing

Copper tubing intended for refrigeration and air conditioning work is designated as ACR tubing, Figure 15-4. ACR tubing must be either type L or type K. ACR tubing is cleaned, degreased, dehydrated, and sealed to keep its inside clean. It is purged by the manufacturer with nitrogen gas to seal against air, moisture, and dirt, and also to minimize the harmful oxides that are normally formed during brazing. The ends are plugged to keep out air and moisture. These plugs should be replaced after cutting a length of tubing.

Figure 15-4 ACR tubing is suitable for air conditioning and refrigeration use

Copper Tubing Sizes

ACR tubing is measured by outside diameter. The outside diameter of all three wall thicknesses stays the same; $^5/_8$ in outside diameter copper tubing will be $^5/_8$ in outside diameter regardless of the wall thickness. The inside dimension does change as the wall thickness changes. The approximate inside dimension is given as the nominal size. Since the wall thickness is approximately $^1/_{16}$ in, the nominal size is $^1/_8$ in smaller than the outside diameter. Figure 15-5 compares the dimensions of the three types of copper pipe.

ACR tubing is available in $^1/_8$ in increments from $^1/_4$ in to $^7/_8$ in and in $^1/_4$ in increments from $1^1/_8$ in up. There is an exception: $^5/_{16}$ in copper is often used for the refrigerant lines on household refrigerators and occasionally is used as a liquid line on residential air conditioners. To determine the size of ACR tubing, simply measure the outside diameter of the tubing. To find the nominal size, you measure the outside diameter and subtract $^1/_8$ in.

Soft Copper Tubing

ACR copper tubing is available in two tempers: 50 ft rolls of annealed soft copper tubing, or 20 ft straight sections of hard drawn copper tubing. Soft copper tubing is tubing that has been softened by annealing. Annealing is the process of heating the tubing up to a temperature of 1,300°F and letting it cool. This permanently softens the copper and makes it malleable enough to mechanically form bends and flares in the tubing. Soft copper tubing is used extensively for

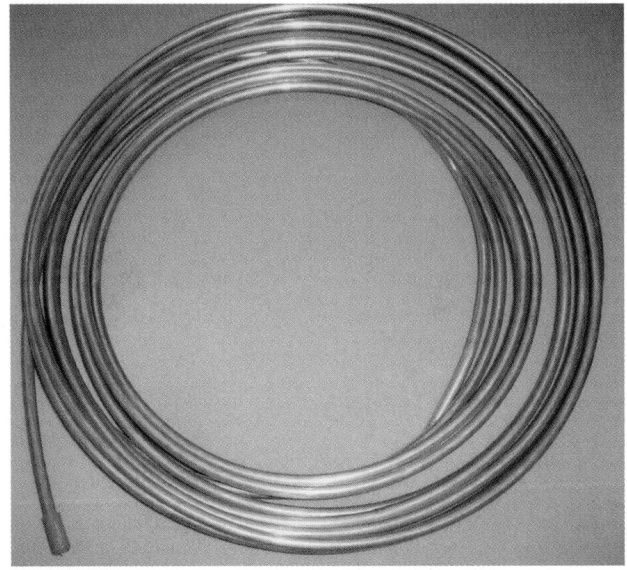

Figure 15-6 Annealed soft copper ACR tubing

refrigeration lines in residential air conditioning systems, Figure 15-6.

Soft copper must be unrolled before it can be used. It is much easier to straighten the tubing while it is still on the roll. The end on the outside of the roll should be held firmly against a flat surface and the coil slowly rolled out, Figure 15-7.

As copper is bent, it will become work hardened. The more it is bent, the harder it becomes. If excessive work hardening has occurred, it may crack or buckle when formed. Work hardened copper can be reannealed by heating the

1" NOMINAL, 1.125" OD

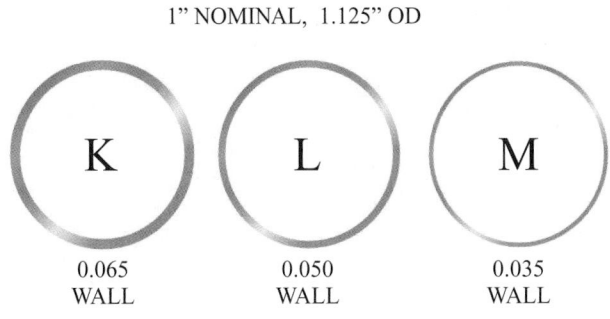

K	L	M
0.065 WALL	0.050 WALL	0.035 WALL

Figure 15-5 The tubing outside diameter is the same for types M, L, and K

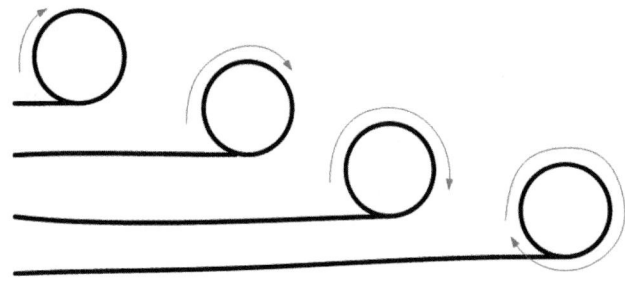

Figure 15-7 To use copper tubing, take the whole roll and unroll what you need from the outside edge across a clean, flat surface

Figure 15-8 Lengths of hard copper tubing

copper to a dull red and allowing it to cool. If this is done quickly with a large hot flame, a minimum of oxides will form on the copper tubing. Slow heating can cause excessive oxides which can cause problems with system operation once installation is complete.

Hard Copper Tubing

Hard copper is used extensively in commercial refrigeration and air conditioning systems. Unlike soft tubing, it is hard and rigid and comes in straight lengths, Figure 15-8. Hard copper cannot be mechanically formed; it will crush or buckle rather than bend. It is intended for use with formed fittings to make the necessary bends or changes in direction. Because of its rigid construction, it is more self-supporting and needs fewer supports than soft copper. Sizes range from $\frac{1}{4}$ in OD to over 6 in OD. Hard-drawn tubing comes in standard lengths of 10 ft and 20 ft. It is dehydrated, charged with nitrogen, and plugged at each end to maintain a clean, moisture-free internal condition. The use of hard-drawn tubing is most frequently associated with large line sizes or where neat appearance is desired.

Joining Copper Tubing

Soft copper tubing can be connected in many ways including compression, flaring, soldering, and brazing. Compression fittings are typically used to connect water lines to icemakers in household refrigerators. They are also used on split system air conditioners to connect the refrigerant lines to the evaporator and condenser. Soft copper is also connected by flare connections. Flaring is used commonly on refrigeration lines and water lines. Both hard and soft copper may be soldered or brazed together. Soldering and brazing are the only two methods used to connect hard copper tubing.

15.4 CUTTING COPPER TUBING

Copper tubing should be cut using a tubing cutter. Tubing cutters are preferable for refrigeration work because they do not generate chips that can get in the system. Tubing cutters

also have the advantage of producing a cut that is perpendicular to the length of the tubing, called a square cut. Tubing cutters are available in different sizes to accommodate different sizes of tubing. A standard tubing cutter typically can cut tubing from $\frac{1}{8}$ in OD up to $1\frac{1}{8}$ in OD, Figure 15-9. Larger cutters handle from $\frac{3}{8}$ in up to $2\frac{5}{8}$ in, Figure 15-10. Traditional tubing cutters will not fit everywhere. Smaller cutters are made that make it possible to cut tubing in confined spaces, Figure 15-11.

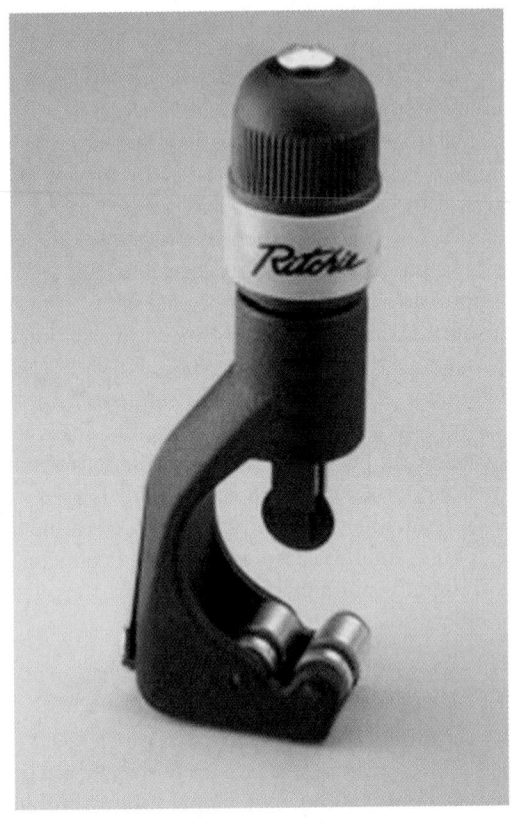

Figure 15-9 Standard tubing cutter used for $\frac{1}{8}$ in to $1\frac{1}{8}$ in copper tubing
(*Courtesy of Ritchie Engineering Company, Inc. – YELLOW JACKET Products*)

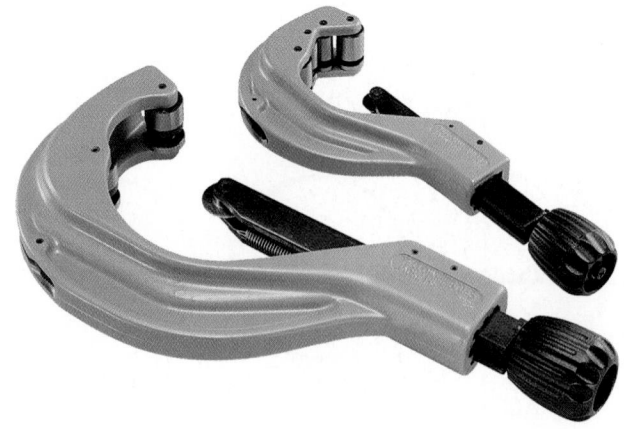

Figure 15-10 Large tubing cutters are used for $\frac{3}{8}$ in to $2\frac{5}{8}$ in copper tubing
(*Courtesy of Ritchie Engineering Company, Inc. – YELLOW JACKET Products*)

Figure 15-11 Small tubing cutters are useful for cutting $\frac{1}{8}$ in to $\frac{7}{8}$ in tubing in tight spaces
(Courtesy of Ritchie Engineering Company, Inc. – YELLOW JACKET Products)

All these tubing cutters work by rolling a sharp wheel around the outside of the tubing. The wheel scores the tubing as it rolls around it. The cutter must roll around the tubing several times to properly cut; it does not cut through in one pass. The wheel should be adjusted until it contacts the tubing with a slight pressure. Roll the cutter around the tubing, pulling the cutter so that the cutting wheel leads the cut,

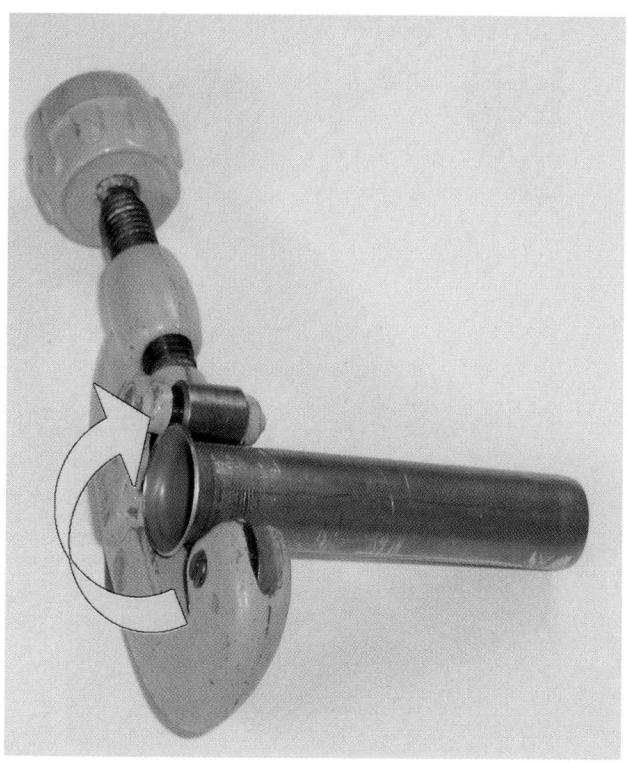

Figure 15-12 Arrow shows direction to pull tubing cutter
(Courtesy of HVAC Department, Terra Community College, Fremont, Ohio)

Figure 15-13 Tubing that is cut too quickly will have a much larger burr than tubing that is cut slowly
(Courtesy of HVAC Department, Terra Community College, Fremont, Ohio)

Figure 15-12. Increase the tension slightly with each rotation by turning the adjusting knob in a clockwise direction. Continue rolling and tightening until the tubing is cut through. Attempting to cut the tubing too quickly will pinch the tubing in and cause constriction. Figure 15-13 compares an improper cut to a correct cut. Even when done correctly, tubing cutters leave a small burr on the inside of the tube. This burr should be removed using the reamer built into the tubing cutter, Figure 15-14.

Most tubing cutters have a groove that can be used for cutting off the flare on a flared piece of tubing, Figure 15-15. This lets the technician cut off a flare with a minimal loss of pipe.

15.5 BENDING COPPER TUBING

Tubing can be bent with accuracy if the right tools are used and care is taken. It is very important not to crimp the tubing because this can restrict the flow of refrigerant through the tubing. Never get in a hurry when bending tubing.

When using lever or wheel type benders, be sure that the groove in the bender is for the size of tubing you are working with. A tool designed for tubing larger than the tubing you

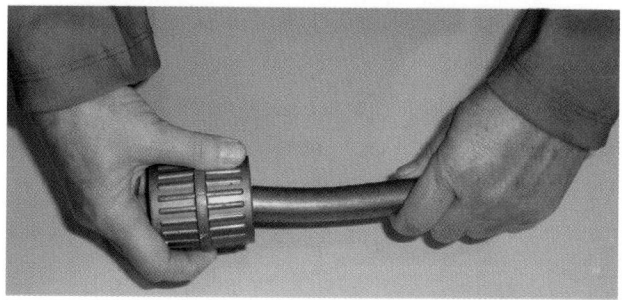

Figure 15-14 The burr should be removed after cutting
(Courtesy of HVAC Department, Terra Community College, Fremont, Ohio)

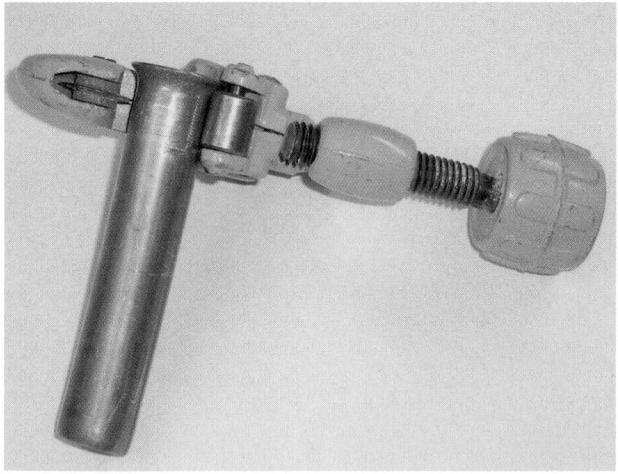

Figure 15-15 The groove in the tubing cutter rollers allows the flare to be cut off
(Courtesy of HVAC Department, Terra Community College, Fremont, Ohio)

are working with will flatten the tubing, Figure 15-16. The work should be done slowly and steadily to avoid buckling or crimping the tubing.

Most lever type benders have an "R" mark, which will help you determine the distance from the end of the completed bend to center of the pipe. To use the mark, first measure the distance you want from the end of the pipe to the center of the bend after the bend is completed. This mark lines up on the R mark on the bender. On most benders the distance

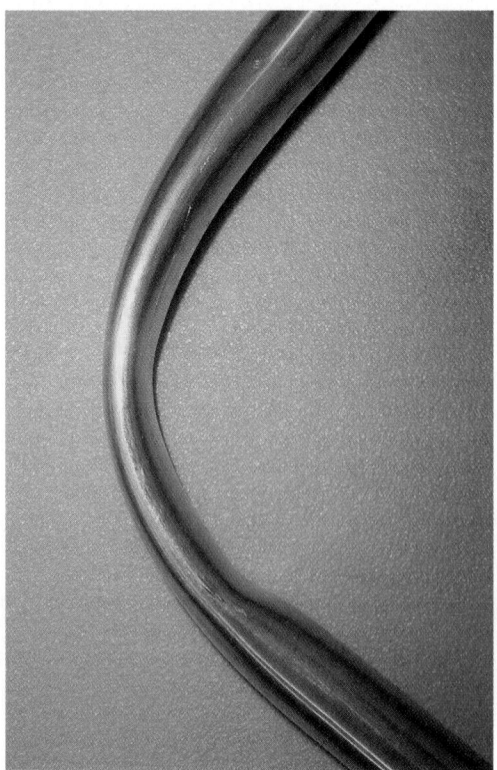

Figure 15-16 Using the wrong sized bender can flatten the tubing

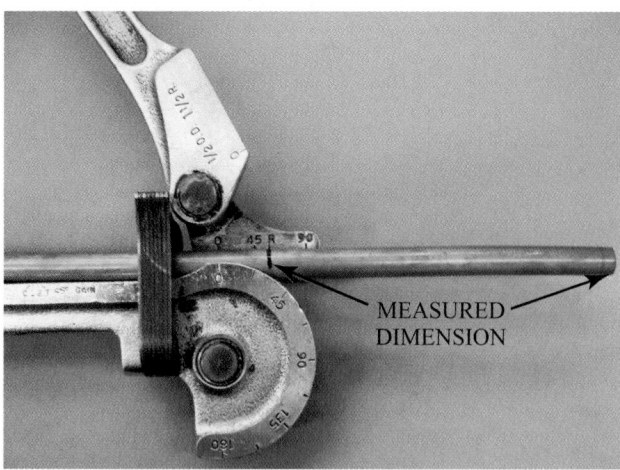

Figure 15-17 The desired dimension is measured from the right to the R mark

is measured from the right to the R mark, Figure 15-17. Bend the tubing with a slow, steady pull until the degree mark lines up to the desired angle. The dimension of the completed bend should now be correct.

When making several successive bends on one piece of pipe, it is necessary to calculate the total pipe length needed. To do this, you will need to know the radius of the tubing bender you will be using. The radius is the distance from the center of the bending wheel to the outside of the bending wheel and should be marked on the bender. Because of the many sizes and designs of tubing benders, there is no standard set of radii to remember. The technician must look on the actual tool that will be used, Figure 15-18.

Figure 15-18 The tubing bender radius

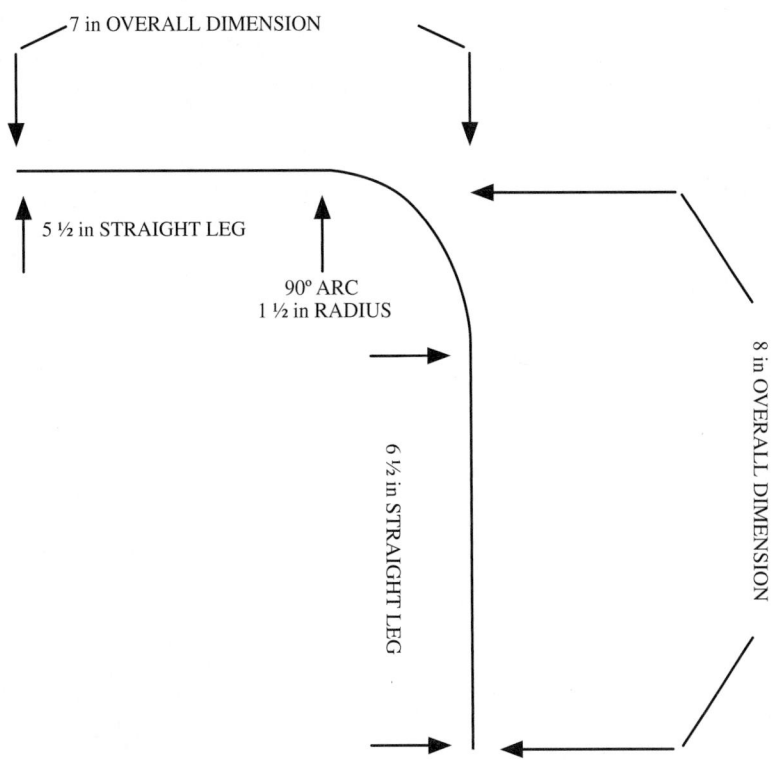

Figure 15-19 Diagram of example bend dimensions

Example Bend Calculation

Tubing $\frac{1}{2}$ in OD ACR annealed tubing
Bend 90°
Legs 7 in on one side and 8 in on the other
Bender Radius $1\frac{1}{2}$

The total length of pipe should be the sum of the two straight lengths plus the length of the 90° arc that connects them. First, calculate the actual straight length of each leg. The actual straight length will be the desired leg length minus the radius of the bender. In this example, the actual straight lengths will be 7 in $-$ $1\frac{1}{2}$ in $=$ $5\frac{1}{2}$ in, and 8 in $-$ $1\frac{1}{2}$ in $=$ $6\frac{1}{2}$ in, Figure 15-19.

To calculate the arc length, first calculate the circumference of a full circle with a radius equal to the radius of the tubing bender. In the example the circumference would be $1\frac{1}{2}$ in $\times$ 2 $\times$ (3.14). This equals 3 in $\times$ 3.14 $=$ 9.42″. Since a 90° bend is one-quarter of a circle, the arc length is $\frac{1}{4}$ of the entire 9.42 in circumference. This is $\frac{1}{4}$ $\times$ 9.42 in $=$ 2.355 in.

The entire length of tubing needed is $5\frac{1}{2}$ in $+$ $6\frac{1}{2}$ in $+$ 2.355 in $=$ 14.355 in. The 0.355 portion must be estimated to the nearest $\frac{1}{8}$ in or nearest $\frac{1}{16}$ in. To estimate to the nearest $\frac{1}{8}$ in, divide the decimal remainder by 0.125. Therefore, 0.355 would round off to $\frac{3}{8}$ in. To estimate to the nearest $\frac{1}{16}$ in, divide by 0.0625. Therefore, 0.355 would round to $\frac{6}{16}$ $=$ $\frac{3}{8}$. In this case, there is no difference.

The total length needed is then $5\frac{1}{2}$ in $+$ $6\frac{1}{2}$ in $+$ $2\frac{3}{8}$ in $=$ $14\frac{3}{8}$ in. A piece of tubing cut to this length, marked correctly and bent with the R mark, will produce a 90° bend with a 7 in leg and an 8 in leg.

Notice that the total required length is actually slightly less than the simple sum of the two center distances, 8 in $+$ 7 in $=$ 15 in. This is because it requires less tubing to make a rounded turn than a square turn. Simply adding the center distance dimensions will yield an approximate length needed to make the bend. If some waste is allowed, the length can be figured in this manner and the excess cut off at the completion of the bend. The estimation method works for bends of 90° or less, but does not work for bends over 90° because of the extra length of the arc.

15.6 JOINING COPPER TUBING USING COMPRESSION FITTINGS

The compression joint is composed of a compression sleeve, a ferrule, and a compression nut. The copper tubing fits through the nut and the ferrule into the sleeve, Figure 15-20. The nut threads over the sleeve. As the nut is tightened, it squeezes the ferrule around the tubing. The compression of the ferrule around the tubing seals the joint. The sleeve and nut can be reused but the ferrule cannot since it is irrevocably squeezed around the tube, Figure 15-21. To redo the joint, the old ferrule must be cut off and a new ferrule used. It is extremely important that the tubing is clean and straight where the joint is to be made and that the nut is not overtightened. It is very easy to assemble a leaky compression joint and very difficult to correct a leaking compression joint.

Figure 15-20 Compression fittings, ferrule, and compression nut
(Courtesy of HVAC Department, Terra Community College, Fremont, Ohio)

Figure 15-22 Flared end on copper tubing

Figure 15-21 Once ferrule is compressed it cannot be removed from the tubing
(Courtesy of HVAC Department, Terra Community College, Fremont, Ohio)

Figure 15-23 The flared end of the copper tube is squeezed between the male and female flare fittings

15.7 MAKING FLARE JOINTS

A flared piece of copper tubing has a conical appearance, something like the end of a trumpet, Figure 15-22. The flared end of the tubing is squeezed between two brass fittings, which have complementary 45° angles, Figure 15-23. A flaring tool is used to make the flare on the end of the tubing, Figure 15-24.

A good flare starts with properly cutting and preparing the tubing. The tubing should be cut slowly to minimize the burr left by the tubing cutter. There will still be a small burr which should be removed with a reamer. The tubing is clamped in the flaring block with approximately $\frac{1}{8}$ in above the block, Figure 15-25. The spinner is locked in place over the tubing, Figure 15-26. Put a few drops of refrigerant oil on the spinner before making the flare. The spinner is turned until the flare is formed by pressing the tubing between the spinner and the block. Slide a flare nut to the flared end of the tubing to check the completed flare. The flare should clear the threads of the flare nut but still fill the chamfer on the inside of the nut. The flare is too large if it catches on the

Figure 15-24 Typical flaring tool

Figure 15-25 Copper tubing loaded in flaring block ready for flaring

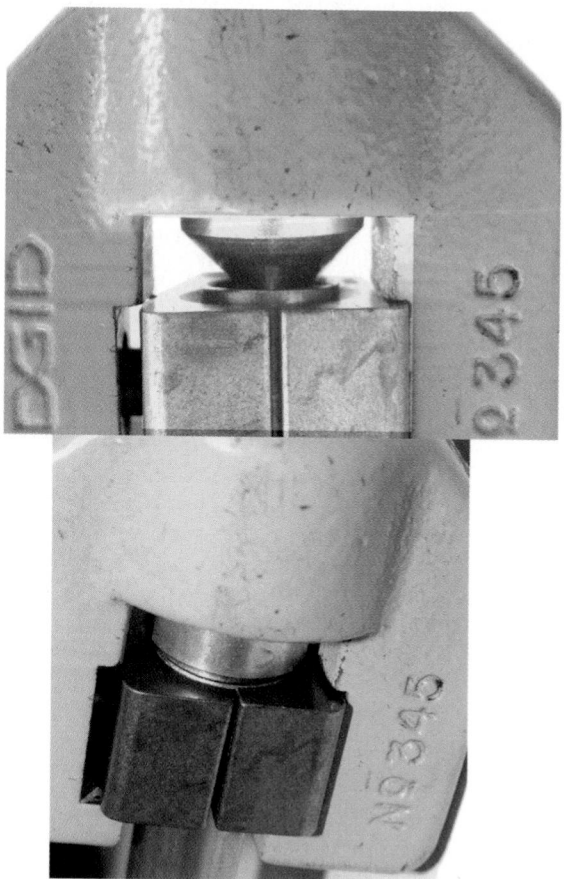

Figure 15-26 The spinner is positioned over the tubing in the flaring block

Figure 15-27 The flare on the left is too large, the flare on the right is too small, and the flare in the center is the correct size *(Courtesy of HVAC Department, Terra Community College, Fremont, Ohio)*

ROLLED BEAD

Figure 15-28 When the tubing is not correctly cut and deburred, the burr forms a "rolled bead" which holds the flare off of the flare face, creating a leak

not properly deburred, the flaring tool will generate a "rolled bead" around the flare and this will be the only point of flare surface contact, Figure 15-28.

SERVICE TIP

It may be necessary to put the flare nut on the pipe before making the flare. If the pipe has bends, or flares on both ends, it will be impossible to slide the flare nut on after the flare is made. If you forget and flare the tubing before putting the nut on, the only fix is to cut off the flare, put the nut on, and reflare the tubing.

threads of the nut. The flare is too small if it does not fill the inside chamfer on the nut, Figure 15-27. If the flare is not the right size, it should be cut off and redone. A good flare does not require thread sealant because the threads are not what is sealing the joint, the flare face is. If the end of the tubing is

15.8 MAKING FLARE JOINTS FOR R-410A REFRIGERANT

Operating pressures for systems using R-410A refrigerant are 40-60% higher than systems using R-22 refrigerant. Flares for systems using R-410A refrigerant are the same 45° angle as regular flares, but the cone shape on the end is larger. Figure 15-29 shows a comparison between a normal flare and a flare that is R-410A compliant. R-410A compliant flaring tools have a larger chamfer and use an offset roller to make more uniform flares, Figure 15-30.

R-410A compliant flare fittings are not interchangeable with traditional flare fittings. Flare fittings designed for R-410A are heavier wall and have a larger chamfer area to accommodate the increased flare cones.

15.9 MAKING A DOUBLE-THICKNESS FLARE

A double flare has two thicknesses of metal at the flare face instead of one. This gives the flare more strength. Double flares are more suited for applications where the flared connection

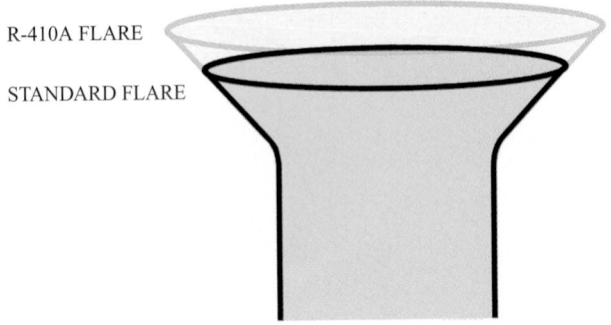

R-410A FLARE

STANDARD FLARE

Figure 15-29 The larger pink cone represents the area of an R-410A compliant flare

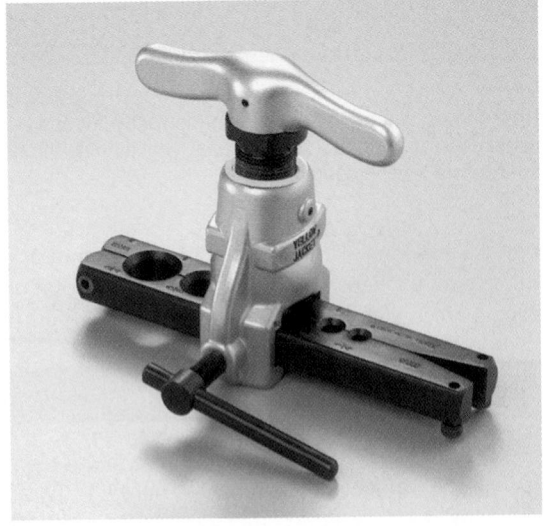

Figure 15-30 R-410A compliant flaring tool
(Courtesy of Ritchie Engineering Company, Inc. – YELLOW JACKET Products)

Figure 15-31 The tubing is formed into a "mushroom top" by the double flare adapter
(Courtesy of HVAC Department, Terra Community College, Fremont, Ohio)

Figure 15-32 Completed double flare
(Courtesy of HVAC Department, Terra Community College, Fremont, Ohio)

will be repeatedly loosened and retightened. The most common application of double flares is on brake lines for cars.

Double flares are made using a double flare adapter. The adapter folds over the end of the tubing so that there are two layers of copper at the flare face after the flare is formed, Figure 15-31. After the double flare adapter has been used, it is removed and the flare is finished with the spinner, Figure 15-32. Figure 15-33 shows the steps in making a double thickness flare.

15.10 SWAGING TECHNIQUES

A swage joint is used to allow two pieces of copper tubing to be joined by soldering or brazing. A swaging tool expands the end of a piece of copper tubing so that it will fit over the end of another tube the same size, Figure 15-34. The depth of the cup on the swage should be equal to the diameter of the pipe

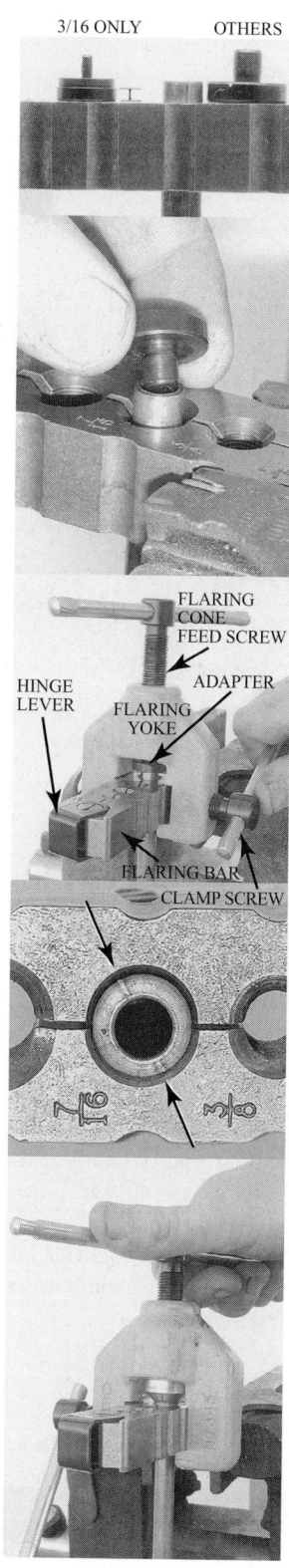

3/16 ONLY   OTHERS

FLARING
CONE
FEED SCREW

HINGE   ADAPTER
LEVER
FLARING
YOKE

FLARING BAR
CLAMP SCREW

Figure 15-33 The tubing is first folded inward by the double flare adapter and the flare is finished with the spinner
[Images courtesy Ridge Tool Co. (RIDGID)]

Figure 15-34 Swaged copper tubing
(Courtesy of HVAC Department, Terra Community College, Fremont, Ohio)

The hammer style is the least expensive and most common. Hammer swages can be sized for each pipe size, or they can be a multitaper tool that fits many sizes, Figure 15-35. The tubing is held in a flaring block. It should be high enough in the block that the swage shoulder does not compress against the block. The swage tool is inserted into the tubing and struck lightly with several small taps, Figure 15-36. Large blows will deform and buckle the copper.

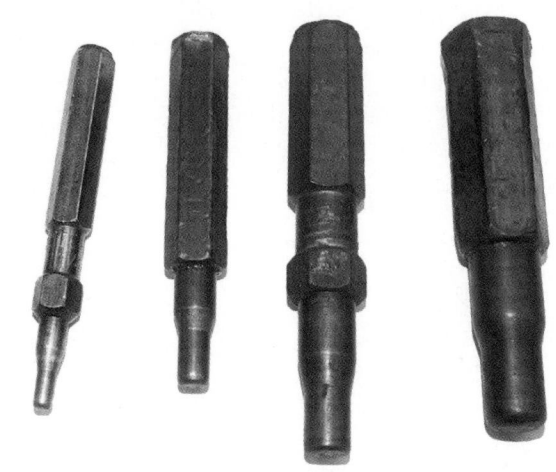

being joined. Three types of swaging tools are commonly used: tools that hammer in like a punch, tools that work like a flaring tool, and lever type tube expanders.

Figure 15-35 Hammer style swage tools

Figure 15-36 The copper is held in a flaring block when using a hammer type swage tool

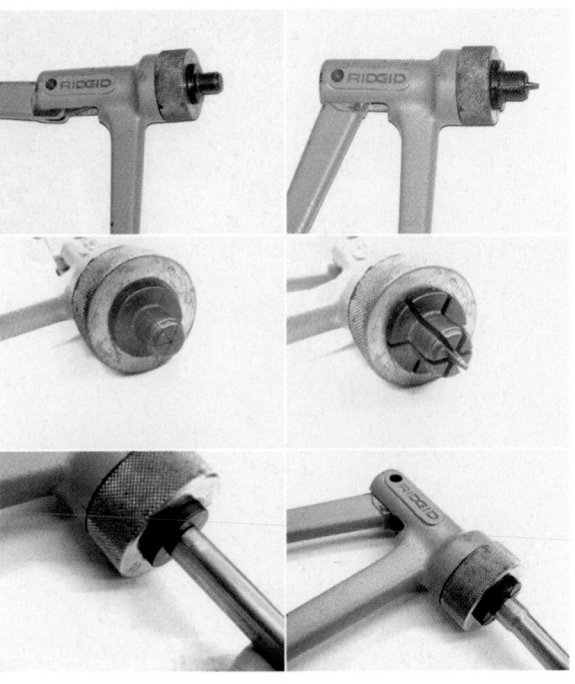

Figure 15-38 Lever type tubing expander

The flaring style swage tool works similarly to flaring, but uses a tip that expands the tubing rather than flaring it, Figure 15-37.

The lever type expander uses cylinders with segments that look like pie slices. When the lever is pulled, the cone slides into the center of the cylinder and the wedges expand outward, Figure 15-38. The lever should be pulled slowly to avoid splitting the copper. Lever tools make consistent swage joints and are easier to use than hammer types, but they are considerably more expensive.

15.11 IRON AND STEEL PIPE

Iron and steel pipe are available in different strengths, called schedules. The higher the schedule number, the stronger the pipe. Available strengths range from schedule 5 to schedule 160. Figure 15-39 summarizes the characteristics of standard iron and steel pipe. The most common schedules used for air conditioning and refrigeration work are schedules 40 and 80. Another system of strength designation simply refers to the pipe as standard, extra strong, or double extra strong. Standard generally equates to schedule 40, and extra strong equates to schedule 80. Double extra strong is somewhat heavier than the highest schedule pipe, schedule 160. Figure 15-40 shows a cross section comparison of standard, extra strong, and double extra strong pipe.

Figure 15-37 This tool swages copper tubing using a spinner with a swage tip
(Courtesy of HVAC Department, Terra Community College, Fremont, Ohio)

TECH TIP

The original idea behind pipe schedules was for the schedule number to have a uniform relationship of 1,000 times the pressure to tensile strength ratio in the modified Barlow equation that is commonly used to determine how much pressure a pipe can hold. This proved to be impractical, but the schedule numbers remained as a common designation for different strengths of pipe.

Figure 15-39 Pipe specifications

IRON PIPE SPECIFICATIONS (all dimensions in inches)				
Normal Size	Outside Diameter	Inside Diameter	Wall Thickness	Weight Pounds per foot
Schedule 40, Standard Strength Pipe				
$\frac{1}{8}$ Std	0.405	0.269	0.068	0.24
$\frac{1}{4}$ Std	0.540	0.364	0.088	0.43
$\frac{3}{8}$ Std	0.675	0.493	0.091	0.57
$\frac{1}{2}$ Std	0.840	0.622	0.109	0.85
$\frac{3}{4}$ Std	1.050	0.824	0.113	1.13
1 Std	1.315	1.049	0.133	1.68
1 $\frac{1}{4}$ Std	1.66	1.38	0.140	2.27
1 $\frac{1}{2}$ Std	1.9	1.61	0.145	2.72
Schedule 80, Extra Strong Strength Pipe				
$\frac{1}{8}$ XS	0.405	0.215	0.095	0.31
$\frac{1}{4}$ XS	0.540	0.302	0.119	0.54
$\frac{3}{8}$ XS	0.675	0.423	0.126	0.74
$\frac{1}{2}$ XS	0.840	0.546	0.147	1.09
$\frac{3}{4}$ XS	1.050	0.742	0.154	1.48
1 XS	1.315	0.957	0.179	2.17
1 $\frac{1}{4}$ XS	1.660	1.278	0.191	3.00
1 $\frac{1}{2}$ XS	1.900	1.500	0.200	3.63
Schedule 160 Pipe				
$\frac{1}{2}$	0.840	0.464	0.188	1.31
$\frac{3}{4}$	1.050	0.612	0.219	1.95
1	1.315	0.815	0.250	2.85
1 $\frac{1}{4}$	1.660	1.16	0.250	3.77
1 $\frac{1}{2}$	1.900	1.338	0.281	4.86
Double Extra Strong Strength Pipe				
$\frac{1}{2}$ XXS	0.840	0.252	0.294	1.72
$\frac{3}{4}$ XXS	1.050	0.434	0.308	2.44
1 XXS	1.315	0.599	0.358	3.66
1 $\frac{1}{4}$ XXS	1.660	0.896	0.382	5.22
1 $\frac{1}{2}$ XXS	1.900	1.100	0.400	6.41

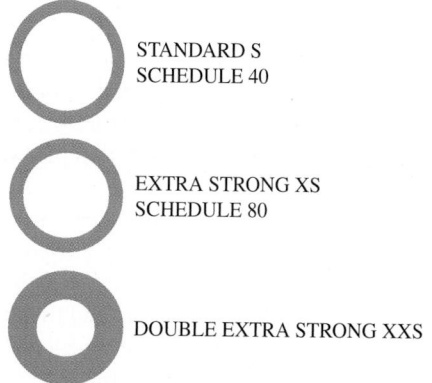

STANDARD S
SCHEDULE 40

EXTRA STRONG XS
SCHEDULE 80

DOUBLE EXTRA STRONG XXS

Figure 15-40 Standard, extra strong, and double extra strong pipe are differentiated by their wall thickness

Iron pipe is available in two finishes: black iron and galvanized, Figure 15-41. Black pipe is iron pipe that has its natural finish while galvanized is iron pipe that has been dipped in molten zinc to make it corrosion resistant. Galvanized has a silver appearance similar to steel. Steel pipe is made from steel, which is made by alloying iron with carbon for added strength. Iron and steel pipe come in 21-ft lengths, threaded on each end. Typically pipe is supplied with a coupling on one end.

Iron pipe is measured by its approximate inside diameter and comes in $\frac{1}{8}$ in increments from $\frac{1}{8}$ in to $\frac{1}{2}$ in, $\frac{1}{4}$ in increments from $\frac{1}{2}$ in to $1\frac{1}{2}$ in, and in $\frac{1}{2}$ in increments from $1\frac{1}{2}$ in and up. The nominal size is the approximate inside diameter; however, the actual inside diameter is slightly larger than the nominal size. The most consistent measurement is the outside diameter. The outside diameter is

Figure 15-41 Iron pipe in black and galvanized

approximately $1/4$ in larger than the nominal size. To determine the size of iron pipe measure the outside diameter and subtract $1/4$ in. To measure a pipe fitting: measure the threads and subtract $1/4$ in. This applies to both internal and external threads. For $1/8$ in and $3/8$ in pipe, the measurement needs to be to the nearest $1/8$ in.

15.12 JOINING IRON AND STEEL PIPING

Iron and steel pipe may be joined by welding, flanges, or threaded connections, Figure 15-42. Flanged and welded connections are only used in large industrial and commercial applications. Most iron and steel piping used in air conditioning is joined by cutting threads on the end of the pipe and

Figure 15-42 Examples of welded, flanged, and threaded pipe joints

Figure 15-43 Pipe threads are tapered; the starting threads are smaller in diameter than the last threads

Nominal size	Threads per inch
$1/8$	27
$1/4$, $3/8$	18
$1/2$, $3/4$	14
1, 1 $1/4$, 1 $1/2$, 2	11 $1/2$
2 $1/2$ up	8

Figure 15-44 National pipe thread specifications

joining the pipe with threaded fittings. Pipe threads are tapered $1/32$ of an inch per inch of threads; they have a slightly larger outside diameter at the end of the threads than at the beginning, Figure 15-43. The first seven threads are fully formed, but the threads at the back are not. The taper allows pipe threads to tighten and seal. The number of threads per inch decreases as the pipe size increases. Figure 15-44 lists the threads per inch for different size pipe.

Pipe sealant is used when assembling the threads to lubricate the threads and help seal the joint. Check the sealant to make sure it is compatible with the gas or liquid that the pipe will carry. Not all sealants are compatible with all gases and liquids. Some pipe sealants specifically warn against using them with LP gas. Pipe sealant should not be allowed to get inside the pipe when assembling it. Insert the male threads into the female threads for a full turn before applying the pipe sealant, Figure 15-45. This will keep pipe sealant out of the inside of the pipe.

Teflon tape can be used as a pipe sealant, however some mechanical and gas codes prohibit its use. Make sure that Teflon tape is acceptable for your application before using it. Teflon tape is applied by wrapping it around the threads in a direction opposite to the direction the pipe will be turned, Figure 15-46. If it is applied in the same direction, it will bunch up when the joint is tightened. Take care not to have tape all the way to the end of the pipe; the first couple of threads should not have tape on them.

Figure 15-45 The pipe should be started before thread sealer is applied

Figure 15-46 Teflon tape should be wrapped opposite to the direction the pipe will be turned, leaving the first threads exposed

Figure 15-47 Portable tripod pipe vise

Figure 15-48 Pipe vise jaws are designed to hold pipe

15.13 CUTTING AND THREADING IRON AND STEEL PIPE

When installing a piping system with iron pipe, the pipe must be cut and fitted. The cut ends have to be threaded before they can be joined. The pipe is held in a pipe vise while it is being cut and threaded. The most common vises used in the field are tripod vises which can be transported to the job, Figure 15-47. Vises with regular flat jaws cannot hold pipe properly. The jaws of a pipe vise are semicircular with ridges designed to hold the pipe, Figure 15-48. Manual pipe threading tools typically include a pipe cutter, a pipe reamer, a ratchet handle, and several die heads that fit in the ratchet handle. The pipe cutter works just like the tubing cutters used on copper; it is just larger. The reamer is used to cut out the burr left from the pipe cutter. The ratchet handle holds the die heads. A typical ratchet handle can accommodate heads for pipe sizes from $\frac{1}{2}$ in up to $1\frac{1}{4}$ in. The steps to cut pipe to length and thread it are listed below and shown in Figure 15-49. ·

1. Mount the pipe in a pipe vise.
2. Cut the pipe to the desired length using the pipe cutter.
3. Use the pipe reamer to remove the burr left by the pipe cutter.
4. Insert the correct die in the ratchet handle.
5. Apply thread cutting oil to the pipe.
6. Slide the die over the pipe. Make sure that the end without teeth showing is the end that goes over the pipe first. Also, check the direction of the arrow on the ratchet handle. It should be pointing to the right. If it is not, pull it out and flip it around so that it points to the right.
7. Apply pressure to the die with the heel of your hand while turning the ratchet handle. After one or two full turns it should not be necessary to keep applying pressure.
8. Continue to turn the ratchet handle, stopping every couple of turns to lubricate the threads and die with cutting oil.

Figure 15-49 (1) Mounted pipe in vise; (2) Ream pipe to remove burr; (3) Deburred pipe; (4) Lubricate with cuting oil; (5) Load die on pipe; (6) Place ratchet in clockwise direction; (7) Turn die clockwise to cut threads; (8) Place ratchet in counter clockwise position to remove die; (9) Finished threads

9. Continue until the end of the pipe is flush with the teeth on the back side of the die.
10. Flip the arrow on the ratchet handle and turn the ratchet handle in the opposite direction to remove the die head.

SAFETY TIP

Always wear gloves and safety glasses when handling, cutting, and threading pipe. The chips created by the threading process are quite sharp and can easily cut you.

15.14 PLASTIC PIPE

Plastic pipe is becoming more popular due to its inexpensive price, ease of use, and relative strength. The most common forms of plastic pipe used in air conditioning and refrigeration are PVC, CPVC, and HDPE, Figure 15-50. Polyvinylchloride, PVC, is normally used for cold water lines and drainage lines. It can withstand high pressures at low temperatures. It should not be used for hot water lines. In the air conditioning industry it is primarily used on condensate drain lines.

PVC pipe comes in 10-ft lengths and ranges in size from $3/8$ in to 6 in. PVC and CPVC sizes are nominal sizes, like iron pipe. The nominal size is the approximate inside diameter of the pipe. The size and schedule of PVC and CPVC pipe are stamped all along the pipe length, Figure 15-51. The size of PVC and CPVC fittings is molded into the fitting, Figure 15-52.

Chlorinated polyvinylchloride, CPVC, is more rigid than PVC and can be used for hot water lines. It can withstand pressures up to 100 psig at 180°F. It is seldom used for drain lines simply because it is more expensive than PVC.

High density polyethylene, HDPE, is used for water distribution systems, underground gas distribution systems, and large scale drainage systems. HDPE tubing is

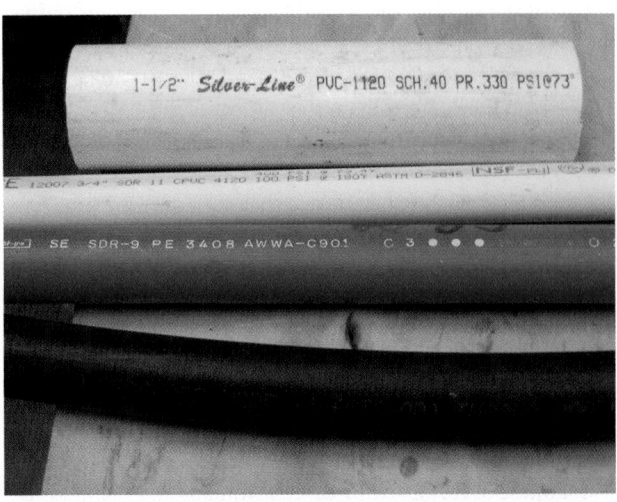

Figure 15-50 Plastic tube comes in many varieties

Figure 15-51 PVC pipe specifications
(Courtesy of HVAC Department, Terra Community College, Fremont, Ohio)

Figure 15-52 PVC fitting size is molded into fitting
(Courtesy of HVAC Department, Terra Community College, Fremont, Ohio)

Figure 15-54 Plastic tube being cut by a shear

not used much in air conditioning and refrigeration, but it is used for the water loops in ground source heat pump systems.

15.15 CUTTING AND JOINING PLASTIC PIPE

Plastic pipe can be cut with a fine tooth saw or a plastic tubing shear. The shear is preferable because it produces a clean, square cut with no chips, shavings, or burrs. Figure 15-53 compares the end of a pipe cut with a hacksaw to one cut with a shear. The shear uses two large, sharp blades to slice through the tubing, Figure 15-54. The shear uses a ratcheting action to producer enough leverage to easily cut through the plastic pipe.

PVC and CPVC are "glued" together. The "cement" used is not a glue in the traditional sense. Instead, it is a solvent that literally dissolves the pipe, allowing it to fuse together.

PVC and CPVC are both very easy to join. Joining requires only four simple steps:

1. Clean the pipe to be joined.
2. Prime the pipe.
3. Apply solvent evenly to the primed pipe.
4. Insert the pipe in the fitting and turn it slightly to help spread the cement.

If primer is used first to clean the joint and solvent is applied evenly to the joint, PVC and CPVC joints will seldom leak. PVC and CPVC joints cannot be undone. Mistakes must be cut out.

SERVICE TIP

CPVC pipe requires CPVC solvent; PVC solvent will not work with CPVC. Some solvents will work with either, but not all PVC solvents will work with CPVC pipe. Check to make sure the solvent will work with the type of pipe being assembled to avoid embarrassing joint "blowouts" when pressure is applied.

HDPE pipe is most commonly joined by heat fusion. First, a tool is used that squares the ends of the two pieces of tubing to be joined. Next, the ends of the tubing to be joined are heated until the plastic begins to melt. Last, the two pieces are forced together until the melted plastic cools. When done properly, heat fusion makes a very strong joint.

UNIT 15—SUMMARY

The materials most commonly used for piping and tubing in the air conditioning and refrigeration industry are copper, iron, steel, aluminum, PVC, and CPVC. Copper tubing is available in three wall thicknesses: M, light; L, medium; and K, heavy. Only types L or K may be used for refrigeration lines. ACR tubing is cleaned, dehydrated, and purged with

Figure 15-53 PVC shear produces a clean, square cut; the hacksaw cut produces chips which must be cleaned off before assembly

nitrogen. ACR tubing is measured by its outside diameter. Copper tubing is available in two tempers: hard drawn sticks or annealed rolls. Annealed tubing can be formed; hard drawn tubing cannot be formed. Soft copper tubing can be joined by compression fittings, flare fittings, soldering, or brazing. Hard drawn must be soldered or brazed. Iron pipe is available in several strengths, called schedules. The most common strength used is schedule 40. It is available in two finishes: natural black iron and galvanized. Gas lines are run in black iron. The nominal size of black iron pipe is the approximate inside diameter of the pipe. Iron pipe is threaded and assembled with fittings. PVC is used for drain lines on air conditioning systems. It is joined using a primer and solvent.

WORK ORDERS

Service Ticket 1501

Customer Complaint: Hot Water Pouring Out of Broken Joint

Equipment: Combination Furnace and Hot Water Heater

A heating and air conditioning contractor has just installed a new gas fired combination furnace and hot water heater. The installers had worked with PVC for drain lines, but had never performed any hot water work. They knew to use CPVC instead of PVC, but they did not know that PVC solvent will not work with CPVC pipe. After the system had operated for a short time, one of the joints gave way and water started gushing out. The service technician recognized the problem and repaired the system with the correct solvent.

Service Ticket 1502

Customer Complaint: Poor Cooling

Equipment: Split System Air Conditioner

The split system air conditioner in a new home is performing poorly. The service technician notices that the lines are bent at a sharp angle where they come out of the wall. Both are kinked. The liquid line is cool just past the kink. The technician realizes that the kinked lines are restricting refrigerant flow, causing the liquid to flash at the kink in the liquid line. The technician recovers the system refrigerant, cuts out the kinked sections, and brazes in elbows to make the sharp turn. After the system is evacuated and charged, it operates correctly with the line kinks removed.

Service Ticket 1503

Customer Complaint: LP Gas Leak

Equipment: 80% LP Gas Furnace

A customer calls and says that she smells gas near the furnace which was installed last year. The technician arrives and checks for leaks around the furnace. The threaded joint where the gas line enters the gas valve is leaking. The technician recognizes the color of the pipe sealant and remembers that that product is not listed for use with LP gas. The joint is redone with thread sealant that is listed for LP gas.

Service Ticket 1504

Customer Complaint: Deer Cooler Not Cooling

Equipment: Field Assembled Walk-in Cooler

A hunting club calls a refrigeration mechanic to look at their deer cooler. They built the deer cooler themselves and hired someone to install it on the weekend in exchange for hunting privileges. The initial installer has not been able to make the cooler work correctly and has said the equipment is faulty. Everything is running, but the compressor is hot and the suction pressure is very low. There is frost on the expansion valve, but the evaporator is not even cool. The technician recognizes that there is a restriction at the metering device. Looking at the copper tubing used for the refrigeration lines, the technician notices that it is hard copper, type L, $3/4$" nominal size. It does not say that it is ACR tubing. The hunting club members confirm that the copper came from a hardware store that one of them manages. The technician explained that ACR tubing is cleaned and dehydrated, which plumbing tubing is not. There was probably moisture in the tubing that is causing the system to freeze up at the expansion valve. The technician recovers the refrigerant, installs a large filter drier and a moisture indicator in the liquid line, evacuates the system down to 500 microns, and recharges the system with clean refrigerant. The system works for now, but the technician explains that the drier may need to be changed a few more times before all the water is removed.

UNIT 15—REVIEW QUESTIONS

1. What is the difference between pipe and tubing?
2. What materials are used for piping and tubing in heating, air conditioning, and refrigeration systems?
3. What materials are used for refrigerant piping?
4. What materials are used for fuel gas piping?
5. What materials are used for water piping?
6. What materials are used for drain lines?
7. What is the difference between hard and soft copper?
8. Why should copper tubing be cut with a tubing cutter instead of a hacksaw?
9. How is copper annealed?
10. What methods can be used to join soft copper?
11. What methods can be used to join hard copper?
12. What is the difference between schedule 40 and schedule 80 iron pipe?

13. What is the difference between black iron and galvanized iron pipe?

14. List the steps for threading iron pipe.

15. What is the difference between PVC and CPVC pipe?

16. Why should PVC pipe be cut with a plastic tubing shear instead of a hacksaw?

17. What is the difference between type M, L, and K copper tubing?

18. What is the difference between ACR copper tubing and tubing for water lines?

19. Why are pipe threads tapered?

20. What is the difference between nominal size and outside diameter?

21. What is the inside diameter of schedule 40, $\frac{3}{4}''$ black iron pipe?

22. How many threads per inch are there on the threaded portion of $1''$ iron pipe?

23. Explain how a compression fitting works.

24. List the steps for flaring the end of copper tubing.

25. What is the difference between a flare for an R-410A system and an R-22 system?

UNIT 16

Brazing, Soldering, and Welding

OBJECTIVES

After completing this unit you will be able to:

- describe the proper clothing that must be worn during welding.
- identify the equipment used for brazing, soldering, welding, and cutting.
- demonstrate safe practices for brazing, soldering, welding, and cutting.
- explain the advantages and disadvantages of brazing, soldering, welding, and cutting.

16.1 INTRODUCTION

The processes of brazing, soldering, and welding are often misidentified as all being welding. In the process of welding the base metal itself is melted as additional metal from the electrode is added to the joint. However, during brazing and soldering, only the metal being added to join the base parts is melted. The difference between brazing and soldering is temperature. Soldering takes place at a lower temperature than brazing, but other than that both processes are similar.

16.2 SAFETY

Because of the large quantity of hot sparks produced by most welding processes, proper protective clothing must be worn during welding. In addition, arc welding produces a great deal of ultraviolet (UV) light. That is why a welder's safety shield must be worn over the face at all times when arc welding. UV light can cause skin burns similar to sunburn. However, because of the intensity of the arc light, these burns can occur very quickly to any unprotected skin surface. Properly worn protective clothing will prevent both burns from hot sparks and burns from the welding light.

16.3 CLOTHING

One hundred percent cotton or leather clothing is the best material to wear while brazing, soldering, or welding. Because synthetic materials, such as nylon, are so easily burned by welding sparks, they should never be worn while welding, cutting, soldering, or brazing. Shirts worn during welding should have long sleeves and either have no shirt pocket or have flaps that cover the pocket to prevent sparks from collecting. They should have a collar and be able to be buttoned securely around the neck. One hundred percent cotton blue jeans are ideal pants for welding.

A welder's cap should be worn to protect your head from flying sparks. Earplugs can be used to protect your ears by keeping hot sparks from flying into your ear. Ear protection can be provided by earplugs that fit into the ear or by special headphones that cover the entire ear.

Often HVAC/R technicians wear work gloves, Figure 16-1a. However, for welding, leather gauntlet type welding gloves are preferred, Figure 16-1b. The gauntlet keeps both sparks and welding light from burning your exposed wrists. Leather shoes with high tops are required, Figure 16-2. Tennis shoes should never be worn when welding. Safety glasses must be worn at all times.

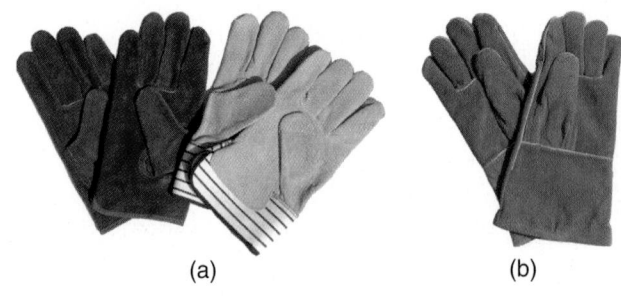

(a)   (b)

Figure 16-1 (a) Work gloves may be cloth, leather palm, or all leather; (b) Welding gloves are gauntlet-type gloves with high cuffs

Figure 16-2 Welding boots should have smooth toes to prevent sparks from being trapped.

16.4 OXYGEN AND ACETYLENE EQUIPMENT

HVAC/R technicians often use oxygen and acetylene cylinders, torches, and regulators to solder, braze, weld, and cut. When properly used, this equipment can be safe and provide years of service. If improperly handled, oxygen and acetylene cylinders, regulators, and torches can be extremely dangerous. The material in this unit is designed to provide the safest way of handling and using this equipment.

Acetylene Cylinders

Acetylene gas is provided in two common cylinder sizes for HVAC work. The MC acetylene cylinder contains approximately 10 ft^3 (cubic feet) of acetylene, Figure 16-3a, and the B acetylene cylinder contains approximately 40 ft^3 of acetylene, Figure 16-3b. Acetylene gas under high pressure is unstable. It can explode as the result of being struck or jarred severely. For this reason, acetylene gas must be stabilized in the cylinder with acetone. The acetone is capable of absorbing 28 times its own weight in acetylene gas. Acetone reacts with acetylene similarly to carbon dioxide and water. Carbon dioxide can be dissolved in water forming a carbonated beverage. As the pressure on a carbonated drink bottle is slowly released, you can observe bubbles being formed within the liquid. These bubbles are CO_2 gas being released. The acetone in an acetylene bottle works the same way. To prevent the acetone from simply being poured out accidentally, the acetylene cylinder is filled with an absorbent coarse material during manufacturing, Figure 16-4.

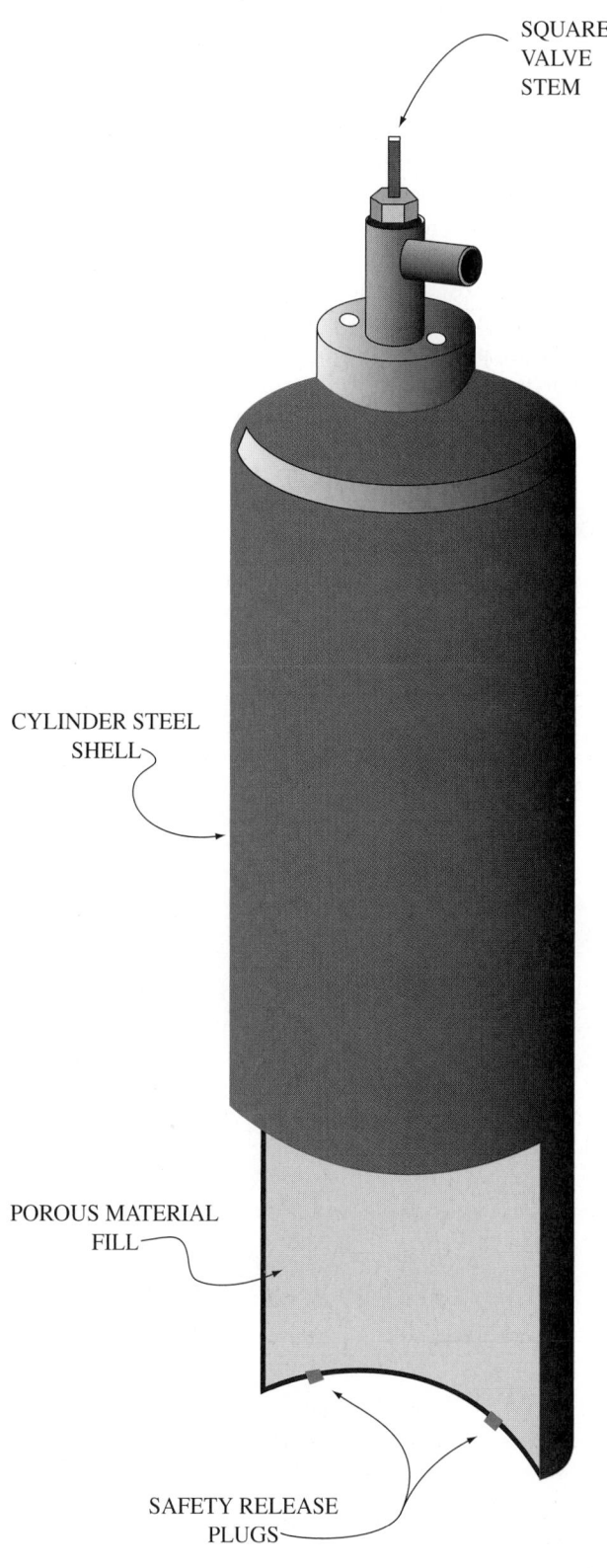

Figure 16-3 (a) The MC acetylene tank holds 10 ft^3; (b) The B acetylene tank holds 40 ft^3

Figure 16-4 Diagram of a cutaway section of a B acetylene tank showing the porous absorbent section

SQUARE VALVE STEM

CYLINDER STEEL SHELL

POROUS MATERIAL FILL

SAFETY RELEASE PLUGS

(a)   (b)

CAUTION

Acetylene cylinders must be used only in the upright position to prevent the acetone from being pulled out of the cylinder with the acetylene.

Because of acetylene's instability, it is illegal to operate a torch with an acetylene pressure greater than 15 psi. Most acetylene gauges have a red mark indicating 15 psi, Figure 16-5. Torch manufacturers have designed their equipment so that a torch will operate properly with acetylene pressures from 1–5 psi for most air conditioning and refrigeration applications. Turning the acetylene pressure up beyond the recommended pressure value for a specific torch will not make the torch operate better. It does, however, present a greater safety issue. Do not exceed the recommended pressure for any given torch and application.

Oxygen Cylinders

Oxygen is provided in highly pressurized cylinders. A full oxygen cylinder contains approximately 2,000 pounds per square inch (psi) of oxygen. The two most common sized cylinders used for the air conditioning and refrigeration trades are the 22 ft³ (cubic feet) and the 55 ft³ cylinders, Figure 16-6a–b.

Figure 16-6 (a) 22 ft³ oxygen cylinder; (b) 55 ft³ oxygen cylinder

CAUTION

Federal safety regulations (OSHA) require 55 ft³ cylinders and larger to be safety chained to a cart or structure any time the cylinder valve cap is removed. If one of these high-pressure cylinders falls over and the valve breaks off, the entire tank will fly around the room like a released balloon.

CAUTION

Always remove regulators from oxygen and acetylene cylinders before you put them back in your service vehicle. In many states and cities it is against the law to transport oxygen and acetylene cylinders in a motor vehicle with the regulators attached. The danger is that in an accident the regulators could be broken off, causing a fire or explosion.

Oxygen is not flammable; however, because of its high pressure and level of purity, even small quantities of oil that may get on the oxygen gauge, valve, or hoses can cause an explosion when subjected to high-pressure oxygen. It is very important that you never allow oil to come in contact with oxygen and acetylene equipment.

Figure 16-5 Acetylene regulator with gauges

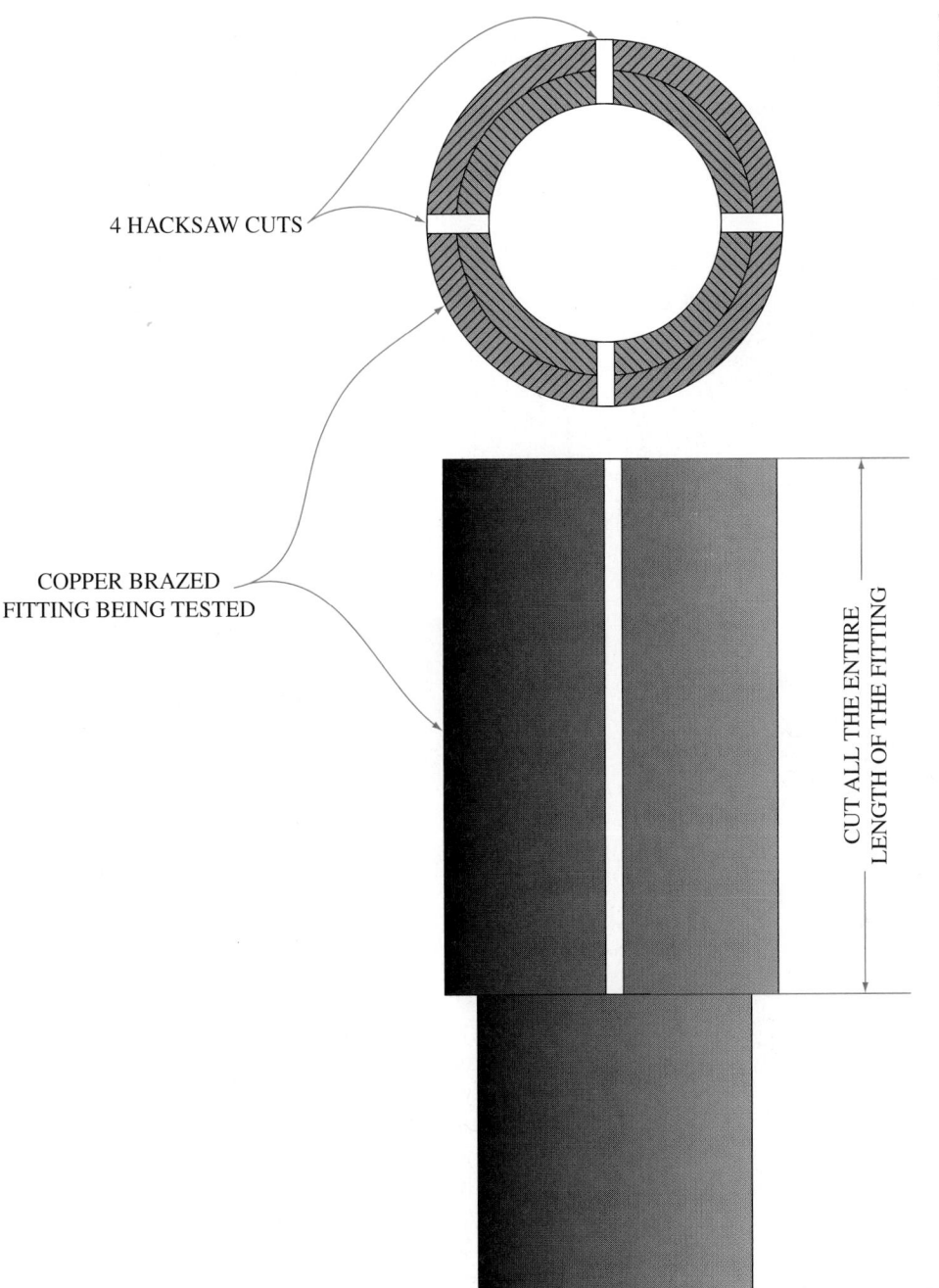

4 HACKSAW CUTS

COPPER BRAZED
FITTING BEING TESTED

CUT ALL THE ENTIRE
LENGTH OF THE FITTING

Figure 16-32 Use a hacksaw to make two cuts through the entire length of the fitting

SERVICE TIP

If the soldering gun is placed against the component being soldered before the gun has heated up, the copper wire will pull heat away from the joint rapidly. This will significantly slow the soldering process and can overheat the part or wire insulation. To prevent this from occurring, turn on the soldering gun and allow the tip solder to melt before it is brought into contact with the part being joined.

Most electrical soldering uses a flux-cored wire. The flux for electrical applications is rosin. Rosin is inactive at low temperatures and will not corrode the electrical parts even if the rosin is left on following soldering. Acid and acid core solders are reactive and will damage electrical components. Even after a thorough cleaning of an electrical component joined with acid core solder, the joint will often still corrode at some later time. It is difficult if not impossible to remove all the acid from within the fine wires of an electrical connection.

Torch Soldering

Air acetylene or air propane/air Mapp torches are all ideal for soldering copper piping. The flame produces a uniform heating of the joint, Figure 16-42. Uniform heating of the joint is important to provide a complete joint fill with the solder alloy.

(a)

(b)

Figure 16-33 (a) Use a pair of pliers to bend each quarter section out; (b) Flatten each section using a ball peen hammer and anvil

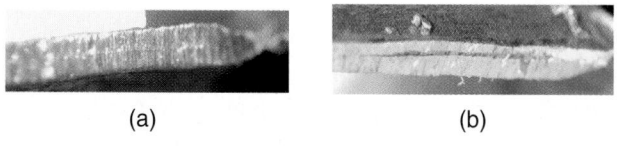

(a)   (b)

Figure 16-34 (a) A thin layer of brazed metal can be seen between the pipe and fitting; (b) Area not filled with brazed metal will allow the pipe and fitting to slip, slightly revealing a very small shelf between the pipe and fitting; this area was not properly filled with brazing metal

Begin by cleaning the copper pipe and fitting using abrasive cloths like those shown in Figure 16-43. A wire brush or sand cloth may be used for this purpose. When the part is cleaned of all contamination, such as oil, paint, or dirt, it must not be touched with your hand. Just as before, with

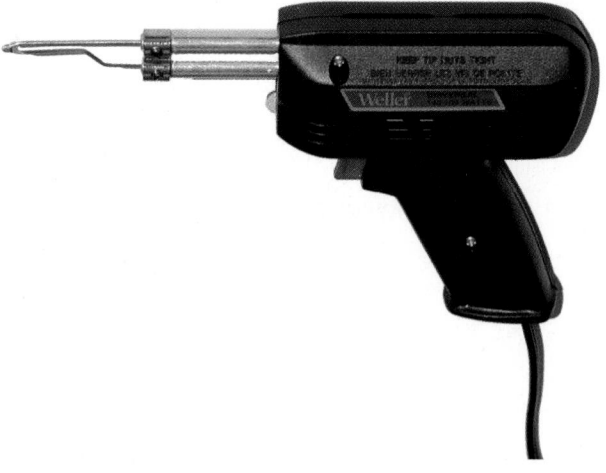

Figure 16-35 Electric resistance soldering gun

Figure 16-36 Cleaning soldering gun tip

brazing, oil from your fingers can prevent solder from flowing completely into a joint. The cleaned end should look like the one in Figure 16-21.

With the joint clean, use a brush to apply the flux. Do not apply flux to the very end of the pipe. Apply the flux up to approximately $^1/_{16}$ in to $^1/_8$ in from the end of the pipe as shown in Figure 16-44. This will help prevent flux contamination into the system. Insert the flux-covered pipe into the copper fitting. Twist the copper pipe inside the copper fitting. This will spread the flux around inside the joint.

Use an air fuel torch. Begin by heating the pipe. As the pipe expands, it will make firm mechanical contact with the inside of the copper fitting, Figure 16-45. This mechanical contact will aid in capillary attraction, which pulls the solder into the joint. The mechanical contact also aids in thermal conductivity so that the entire pipe and joint become uniformly heated. As the pipe begins to be heated, move the torch onto the fitting and pipe. Periodically test the backside of the joint with the tip of the solder. Once the solder begins to melt, remove the torch. Continue adding the solder until the joint is filled. Ideally a small fillet of solder should be left at the joint surface, Figure 16-46. Three quarters of an inch of solder is adequate to make soldered joints in $^1/_2$ in through 1 in diameter copper pipe. To prevent overfilling of the

Figure 16-37 Fluxing soldering gun tip in preparation for tinning

joint, before you start, bend the solder approximately three quarters of an inch from the end. Pushing more solder into the joint simply results in solder BB's being formed inside the piping system. In the field these BB's of solder can circulate back to water pumps where they can cause damage to the pump's impellers.

Testing Soldered Joints

Once the solder joint has been completed, allow it to cool before cutting a slice into the pipe fitting at approximately a 45° angle using a hacksaw, Figure 16-47. Use a slight rocking motion as the cut progresses, so that you are only cutting through the fitting, and not the pipe, Figure 16-48a–b. The cut is done when the appearance resembles that in Figure 16-49. Using a flat blade screwdriver placed into the slot cut in the fitting, apply pressure and twist, Figure 16-50. This will cause the pipe fitting to release from the copper pipe. Using a pair of pliers, peel back the copper fitting, exposing the soldered surface. If the surface is smooth and has no large voids, the

Figure 16-38 Tinning soldering gun tip

soldering job was successful, Figure 16-51. Some small flux-filled pockets may remain. These voids are acceptable as long as they do not run from near the inside of the joint to near the outside. Obviously, this test will render the joint unusable. The technician may use this test for the practice and development of brazing skills.

Some of the common problems with soldering include overheating and underheating. Overheating is indicated by tiny bubbles in the solder, Figure 16-52. The bubbles are formed as the solder boils. Underheating is indicated if the solder does not flow into the joint. If the joint were heated first instead of the pipe first, then during soldering the pipe would separate so that heat would not transfer to the pipe from the joint. The solder on the outside of the joint may look great as in Figure 16-53. The solder even flowed down

Figure 16-39 Loop wire through terminal lug to make a mechanical connection

Figure 16-40 Hold the soldering gun against one side of the wire and lug as the solder is introduced to the opposite side

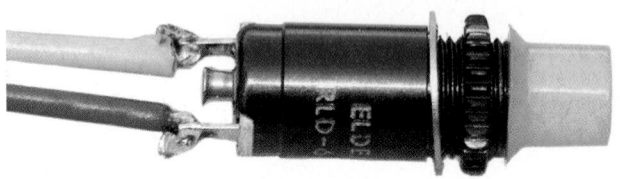

Figure 16-41 Clip the ends of the wire as necessary to complete the job; when connecting multiple wires, have the insulation always on the inside so there is less chance of an electrical short

Figure 16-43 A variety of sanding cloths are available

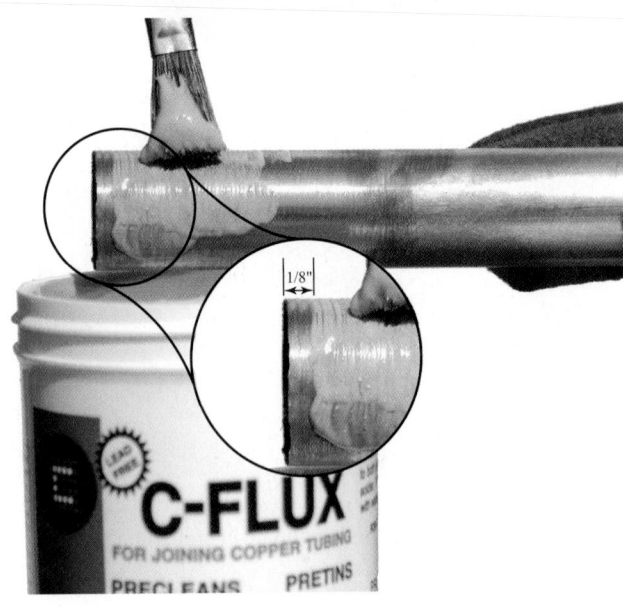

Figure 16-44 Apply the flux up to approximately $1/8$ in from the end of the copper pipe

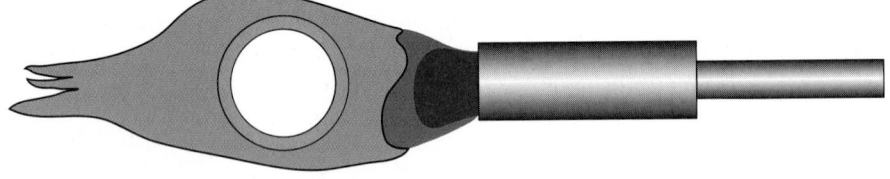

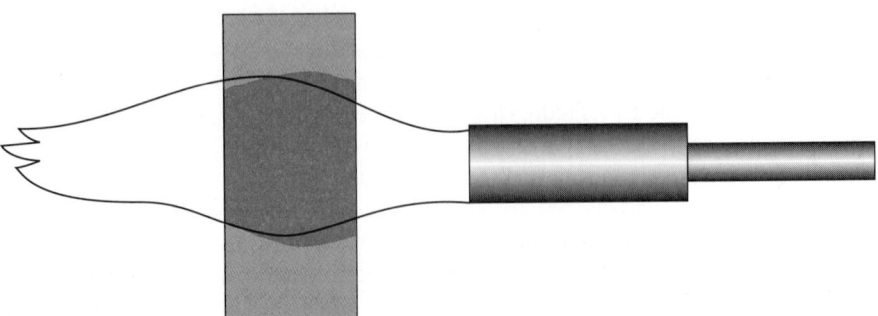

Figure 16-42 Air Mapp and air propane flames wrap around the pipe for more uniform heating than oxyacetylene

drops as it goes through the small opening of the metering device, eventually reaching a saturation point at a low pressure and temperature. In passing through the metering device to the low pressure evaporator, some refrigerant is evaporated, cooling the remaining liquid. The refrigerant is typically a mixture of 75% liquid and 25% vapor at this point.

H. Evaporator in 118 psig 40°F 75% Liquid-25% Gas Saturated Mix   As the refrigerant enters the evaporator, the air (or liquid, or whatever is being cooled) gives off heat to the refrigerant. The refrigerant takes in this heat as latent heat of vaporization. The refrigerant is about 25% vapor and 75% liquid at this point.

I. Evaporator Center 118 psig 40°F 50% Liquid-50% Gas Saturated Mix   Heat from the air or the product being cooled in the evaporator is absorbed by the liquid refrigerant and causes the refrigerant to boil or vaporize. As the compressor draws the vaporized gas from the evaporator, the metering device admits more refrigerant, continuing the process. The refrigerant is about 50% vapor and 50% liquid at this point.

J. Nearing the End of Evaporator 118 psig 40°F 25% Liquid-75% Gas Saturated Mix   As the refrigerant continues through the evaporator, the mixture becomes more saturated gas than saturated liquid. However, while there is still liquid in the tube, the temperature remains at the saturation temperature of the refrigerant. The refrigerant is a saturated mixture of liquid and gas.

K. Leaving the Evaporator 118 psig 50°F 100% Superheated Gas   After all the saturated liquid has boiled to a vapor, the refrigerant vapor starts to increase in temperature in the final evaporator circuit. Superheating is the process of continuing to heat the refrigerant after sufficient latent heat has been added to vaporize all the liquid. Superheating ensures no liquid slugs will reach the compressor and cause damage to the valves and pistons. The state of the refrigerant is 100% gas.

17.5 HEAT FLOW IN THE REFRIGERATION CYCLE

Heat is added to the refrigerant in the evaporator. Heat from the product load is transferred to the refrigerant as it boils in the evaporator. This is the majority of heat absorbed by the refrigerant. A small heat gain occurs in the piping from the evaporator up to where the refrigerant enters the compressor. Heat gain in the suction line is not desirable and can be reduced by insulating the suction line. The compressor adds a sizable quantity of heat to the refrigerant. This heat is equivalent to the work done in compressing the refrigerant. In a suction gas cooled semi-hermetic or hermetic motor compressor unit, the motor heat is also transferred to the refrigerant.

The heat added in the evaporator and by the compressor is removed in the condenser. The heat is transferred from the refrigerant in the condenser to the air or water flowing over the condenser. Some relatively small additional losses occur in the receiver and the liquid line piping up to the metering device. The heat balance of the overall system is shown in the following formula: Heat added in the evaporator + heat of compression = heat rejected in the condenser.

17.6 THE COMPRESSOR

The compressor is a mechanical device for pumping refrigerant vapor from the low pressure evaporator to the high pressure condenser. The compressor increases the refrigerant pressure and temperature by decreasing the gas volume. The main types of compressors are: reciprocating (piston), rotary, centrifugal, screw, and scroll, shown in Figures 17-6 to 17-10.

The compressor type describes the mechanical operation of the compressor. In the reciprocating compressor, a piston travels back and forth (reciprocates) in a cylinder. Gas is compressed in a reciprocating compressor by squeezing it between the piston and a valve plate at the top of the cylinder. The rotary compressor has a roller that rotates in an orbital motion within a cylinder. Gas is compressed by squeezing it between the roller and a spring-loaded vane. The centrifugal compressor has a very high speed centrifugal impeller that spins within a housing. The gas enters the impeller in the center and

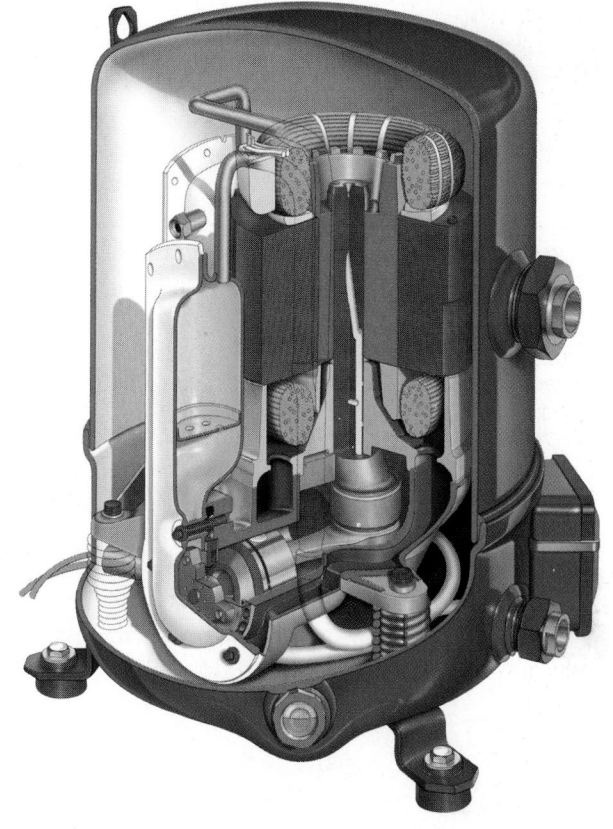

Figure 17-6 Cutaway of a piston (reciprocating) compressor (*Courtesy Danfoss Inc.*)

Figure 17-7 Cutaway of a rotary compressor

Figure 17-8 Cutaway of a centrifugal compressor
(Photo courtesy of McQuay International)

Figure 17-9 Cutaway of a screw compressor
(Courtesy of Carrier © 2008 Carrier Corporation)

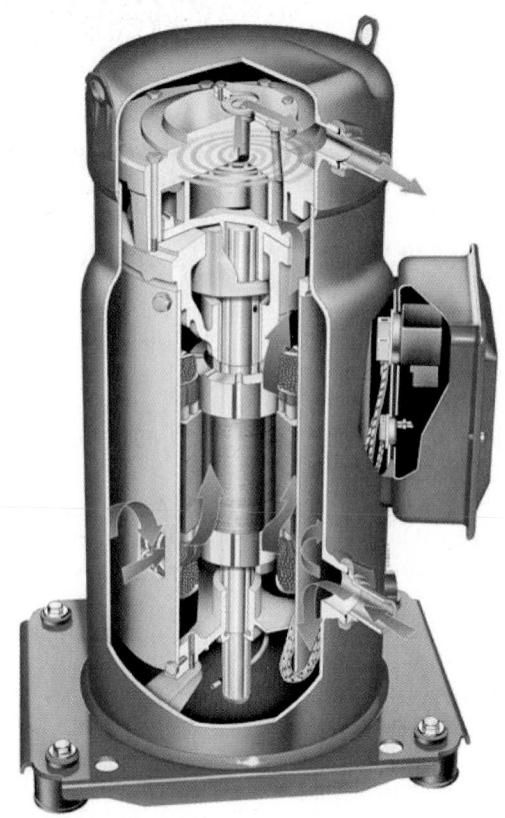

Figure 17-10 Cutaway of a scroll compressor
(Courtesy Danfoss Inc.)

is thrown outward by centrifugal force, compressing the gas. The screw compressor uses two rotating screws shaped like augers. Gas is compressed by squeezing it between the two screws. The scroll compressor has a stationary scroll and an orbiting scroll that moves within the stationary scroll. Gas is compressed by squeezing it between the two scrolls.

TRI-ROTOR SHORTENS
ROTOR LENGTH, INCREASES
COMPRESSION EFFICIENCY

TECH TIP

Air conditioning and refrigeration compressors have very large motors. Most of these motors are located inside of the refrigerant system so that the refrigerant can keep the motor cooler. Some large compressors actually have the cold suction vapor come into the compressor at the motor end to provide even greater motor cooling.

17.7 HEAT TRANSFER AND COIL DESIGN

Heat is always trying to reach a state of balance by flowing from a warmer object to a cooler object. Heat only flows in one direction, from warmer to cooler. Temperature difference (TD) is what allows heat to flow from one object to another. The greater the temperature difference, the more rapid the heat flow. For the high side of a refrigeration unit to reject heat, its temperature must be above the ambient or surrounding temperature. Also, for the evaporator to absorb heat, its temperature must be below the surrounding ambient temperature, Figure 17-4.

The two factors that affect the quantity of heat transferred between two objects are the temperature difference and the mass of the two objects. The greater the temperature difference between the refrigerant coil and the surrounding air, the more rapid the heat transfer. Increasing the coil size and the amount of refrigerant in the coil also increases the rate of heat transfer. Engineers can either design coils to have high temperature differences or larger areas to increase the heat transfer rate.

New high SEER systems are designed with larger coils to increase energy efficiency. Larger coils can operate with a lower temperature difference between the coil and the surrounding air. Less energy is required to produce the lower condensing temperature, improving system efficiency. Manufacturers of new high efficiency air conditioning systems use this principle. That is why the newer high SEER outdoor condensing units are significantly larger than older models having the same capacity, Figure 17-11.

The same principle has been applied to the evaporator coils of new high SEER systems. The temperature difference between the evaporator coil and the entering air is less than on older systems. Higher temperature evaporator coils can pick up the same amount of heat as lower temperature coils if the coil has greater surface area. The expanded area allows more refrigerant exposure to the air stream for absorbing heat, Figure 17-12.

SERVICE TIP

The larger size of the new high efficiency equipment may make replacing older equipment more difficult. The increased size of newer equipment may make it impossible to fit it in the same location as an older, smaller, low efficiency system. Check with the manufacturer for the size of new equipment before starting to change out older equipment.

Air conditioning and refrigeration design engineers must take into consideration a variety of factors when designing systems for higher efficiency. For example, the higher evaporative coil temperature may produce less dehumidification.

Figure 17-11 These two condensing units have the same cooling capacity; the larger unit is a higher efficiency unit

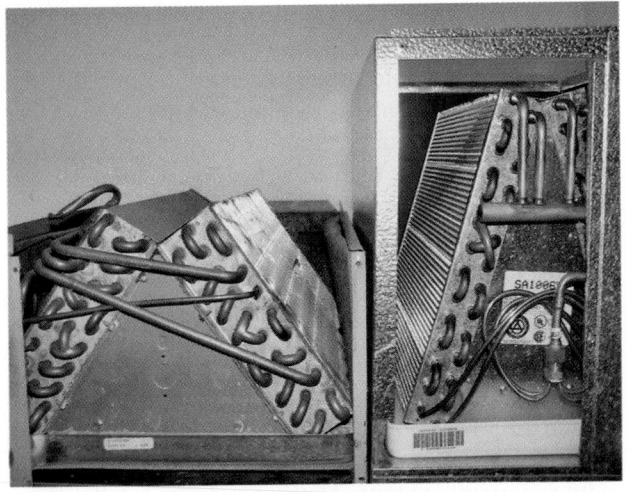

Figure 17-12 These two evaporators have the same cooling capacity; the larger coil is a new higher efficiency evaporator coil

In humid climates, dehumidification can be an important part of the total air conditioning. Manufacturers spend thousands of hours and tens of thousands of dollars researching the effective energy efficiency of systems. These tests are carried out in large calibration rooms where the condenser operates at specific temperature and humidity conditions in one area and the evaporator operates under separate conditions in another area.

The results of manufacturing research are incorporated within the manufacturer's technical data sheets provided to the technician during installation. This material may also be found in AHRI's certified equipment guides.

17.8 THE CONDENSER

The condenser is a device for removing heat from the refrigeration system. In the condenser, the vapor at high temperature and high pressure transfers heat through the condenser tubes to the surrounding medium, usually air or water. The first portion of the condenser cools off the superheated gas and lowers its temperature to the saturation point. This part of the condenser is called the desuperheating section. When the temperature of the vapor reaches the saturation temperature, the additional latent heat removed causes condensation of the refrigerant, producing liquid refrigerant. The refrigerant temperature remains the same while it is changing state. The end of the condenser subcools the refrigerant, lowering the refrigerant temperature below the saturation point. This is called the subcooling section of the condenser. There are three types of condensers: air cooled, water cooled, and evaporative, Figure 17-13. The air cooled condenser uses air as the condensing medium, the water cooled condenser uses water as the condensing medium, and the evaporative condenser uses both air and water.

AIR-COOLED CONDENSER

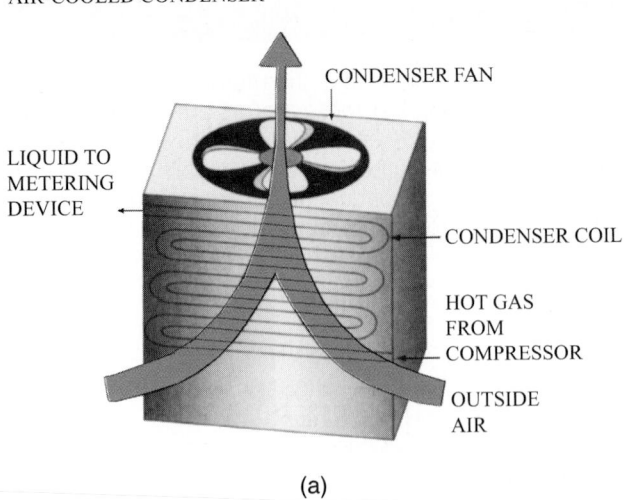

(a)

WATER-COOLED CONDENSER

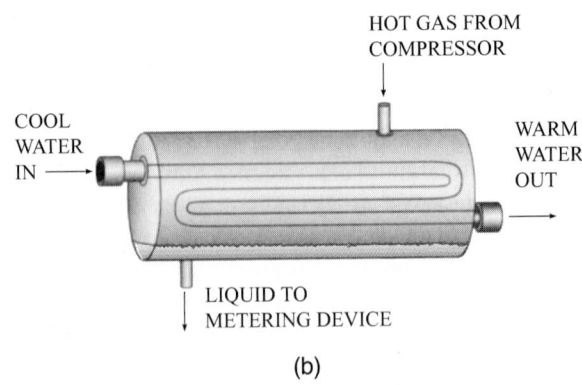

(b)

EVAPORATIVE CONDENSER

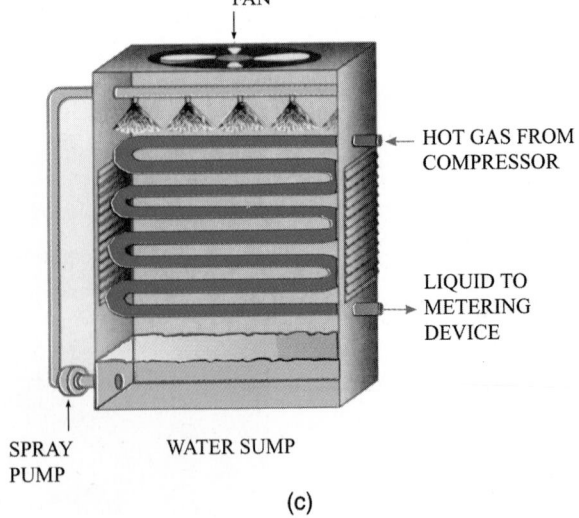

(c)

Figure 17-13 Condensers: (a) Air cooled; (b) Water cooled; (c) Evaporative condenser, also called a sump

Figure 17-14 Natural draft condenser

Air Cooled Condensers

Air cooled condensers consist of three types: natural draft, forced draft, and induced draft. Natural draft condensers do not have fans; they rely on natural air currents for air movement across the condenser, Figure 17-14. Forced draft condensers use a fan to force air across the condenser. In a forced draft condenser, the cups of the fan blade will be facing toward the coil, Figure 17-15. Induced draft condensers use a fan to suck air across the condenser. In an induced draft

Figure 17-16 The cups of the fan blades face away from the coil on an induced draft condenser

condenser the cups of the fan blade will be facing away from the coil, Figure 17-16.

SERVICE TIP

Many units with induced draft condensers require the cabinet panels to be in place for proper airflow. Without the panels in place air can enter without going across the condenser, reducing the airflow across the condenser.

Water Cooled Condensers

Water cooled condensers typically operate at a lower condensing temperature than air cooled condensers. This produces a lower high side pressure on water cooled systems. There are four types of water cooled condensers: (1) double pipe, (2) open vertical shell and tube, (3) horizontal shell and tube, and (4) shell and coil.

Double pipe condensers can be a single continuous loop, as shown in Figure 17-17, or several parallel pipes, as shown in Figure 17-18. In either case, the water and refrigerant should flow through the condenser in opposite directions. This is called counterflow, Figure 17-19. This is more efficient because the coldest water contacts the coldest refrigerant and the hottest water contacts the hottest refrigerant. Single circuit double pipe condensers can be constructed using a tube in tube, as shown in Figure 17-20, or two tubes soldered together and wrapped in a protective outer tube, Figure 17-21.

Figure 17-15 The cups of the fan blades face the coil on a forced draft condenser

Figure 17-17 The tube-in-tube single circuit condenser

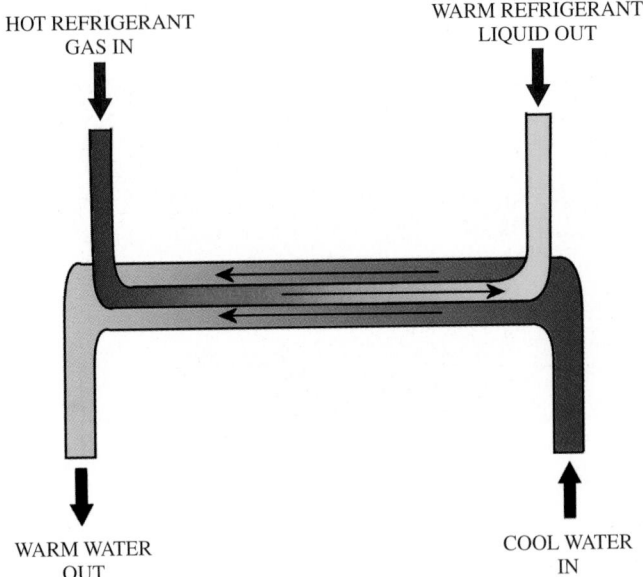

HOT REFRIGERANT
GAS IN

WARM REFRIGERANT
LIQUID OUT

WARM WATER
OUT

COOL WATER
IN

Figure 17-19 The water and refrigerant travel in opposite direction in a counterflow heat exchange

Figure 17-20 Cross section of tube-in-tube coil

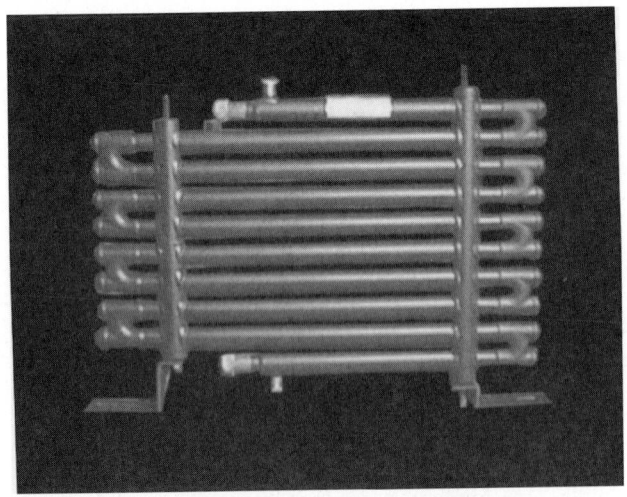

Figure 17-18 Tube-in-tube multiple circuit condenser
(Courtesy of Doucette Industries, Inc.)

REFRIGERANT   WATER

Figure 17-21 Schematic cross section of tube-by-tube coil

Figure 17-22 Operating evaporative condenser
(Courtesy of Evapco, Inc.)

Evaporative Condensers

Evaporative condensers use water evaporation to help cool the refrigerant. Evaporation of the water running over the condenser surface cools the condenser faster than air alone can. Evaporative coolers require makeup water to replace the water that evaporates. Evaporative condensers also require more maintenance than air cooled systems because the warm open water sump is a perfect place to grow bacteria, mold, and fungus. Also, evaporation causes mineral scale to build up. If the scale is not removed, the condenser's efficiency will drop off. Figure 17-22 shows a typical evaporative condenser.

17.9 THE METERING DEVICE

A metering device controls the flow of refrigerant to the evaporator. It separates the high and low pressure sides of the system. High pressure, high temperature subcooled liquid enters the metering device and exits as low pressure, low temperature saturated mixture. The pressure is low because the compressor is continuously pumping vapor from the evaporator. Two actions occur in the metering device: (1) the pressure of the refrigerant is reduced to a pressure corresponding to the evaporator temperature at the saturated condition, and (2) the refrigerant liquid is cooled to the evaporator temperature by

Figure 17-23 Capillary tube metering device

actual evaporation of some of the liquid refrigerant. The saturated mix leaving the metering device is typically 25% vapor and 75% liquid. There are two general types of metering devices commonly used in modern refrigeration systems: fixed bore expansion devices and thermostatic expansion valves.

Fixed Bore Expansion Devices

Fixed bore expansion devices work by limiting the amount of refrigerant that can pass through the restriction. Fixed bore expansion devices are best suited for constant heat loads because they cannot adjust to changing load conditions. The pressure difference across a fixed bore expansion device affects the refrigerant flow through it. A higher pressure difference produces more refrigerant flow; lower pressure differences produce less refrigerant flow. Two types of fixed bore expansion devices are used: capillary tubes and orifices, Figure 17-23 and Figure 17-24. The capillary tube's length and inside diameter determine the correct amount of liquid flow into the evaporator and the correct pressure drop.

Thermostatic Expansion Valves

Thermostatic expansion valves can adjust to varying load conditions. Thermostatic expansion valves are designed to maintain a constant superheat. The valve measures the suction line temperature with a refrigerant-filled sensing bulb that

Figure 17-24 Orifice type metering device

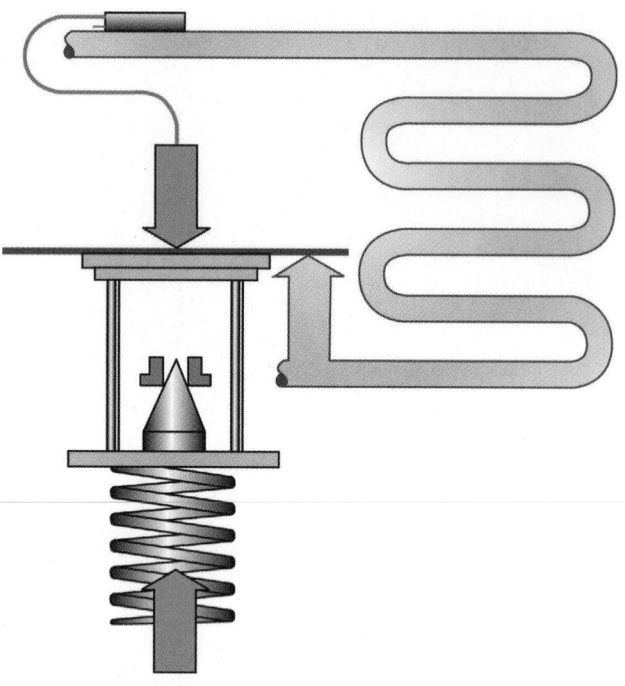

Figure 17-25 The TEV bulb pressure is balanced by the evaporator pressure and spring pressure
(Courtesy of Sporlan Division-Parker Hannifin Corporation)

Figure 17-26 Thermostatic expansion valve on high efficiency coil

installs on the suction line leaving the evaporator. The pressure from the sensing bulb is balanced by the evaporator pressure and the adjustment spring pressure. The sensing bulb pressure tends to open the valve as the suction line temperature increases; the evaporator pressure tends to close the valve as the evaporator pressure increases, Figure 17-25.

Thermostatic expansion valves are used on systems with varying loads because of their ability to adjust to varying load conditions. They are also used frequently on high SEER systems because of their ability to allow a fully active evaporator under all load conditions, Figure 17-26.

17.10 THE EVAPORATOR

The evaporator is a device for absorbing heat into the refrigeration system. In the evaporator, the saturated refrigerant absorbs heat from its surroundings and boils into a low pressure vapor. Refrigerant enters the evaporator from the metering device as a saturated mixture. The saturated liquid turns to saturated vapor as the refrigerant travels through the evaporator. The refrigerant is superheated in the end of the evaporator after all the liquid has boiled off. Some superheat is desirable to ensure that no liquid enters the compressor because liquid refrigerant could damage the compressor.

TECH TIP

Because it takes heat to vaporize water, removing humidity from air also removes heat from the air. The more humidity there is in air, the more heat the air contains. Condensing water on an evaporator coil uses system cooling capacity and reduces the amount of cooling capacity available for changing the air temperature. As the relative humidity of the return air increases, the temperature drop across the evaporator coil decreases.

The evaporator or cooling coil is fabricated from metals such as copper or aluminum or both. These metals are selected because of their good thermal conductivity. Although there are many variations and modifications of evaporators, there are three basic types of construction: bare pipe, finned tube, and plate, Figure 17-27. On finned tube evaporators the tubing is interconnected by aluminum fins that serve to both direct the airflow through the coil and increase heat transfer by increasing the surface area of the evaporator, Figure 17-28. Like condensers, evaporators can be forced air or natural draft.

Most evaporators operate below the dew point of the air being cooled. This causes water to condense on them. The condensed water vapor drains into a collection pan and is routed to a drain by tubing, Figure 17-29.

The fin spacing on an evaporator is partly determined by its intended operating temperature. Evaporators that constantly

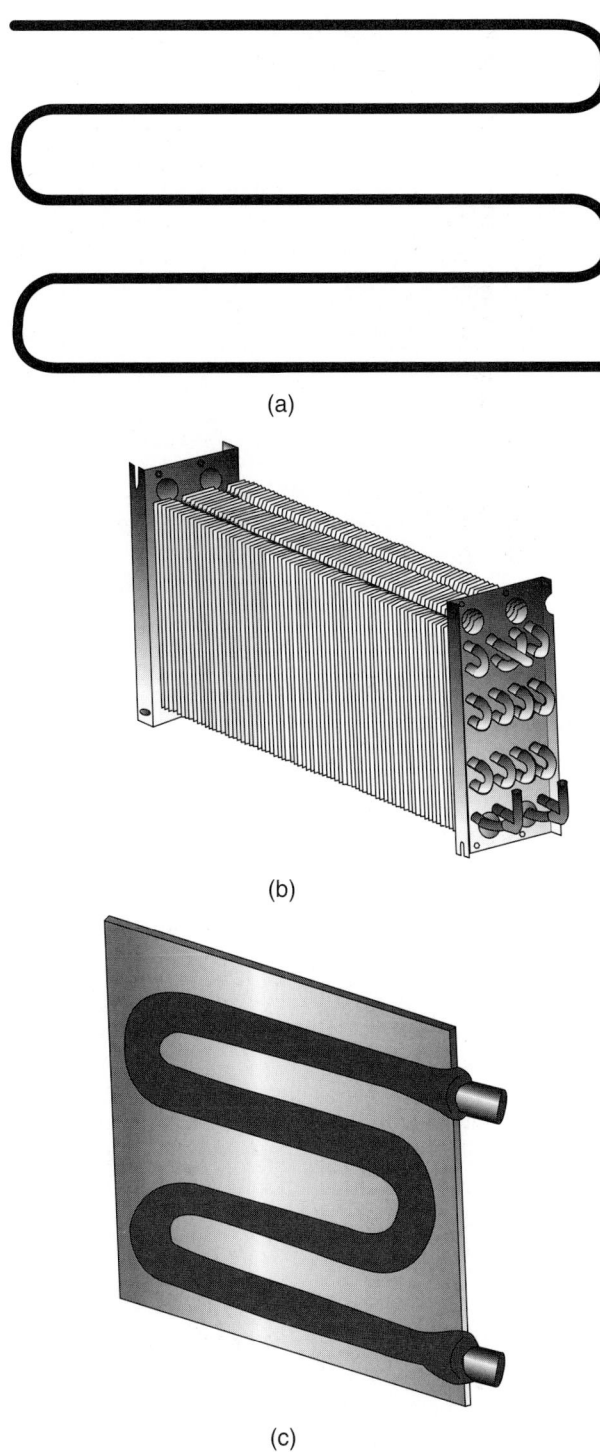

Figure 17-27 Different types of evaporators; (a) Bare pipe; (b) Finned tube; (c) Plate

Figure 17-28 Cross section of typical finned tube coil construction

Figure 17-29 Evaporator coil drain pan

operate below freezing have a wider fin spacing, so frost accumulation does not interfere as much with airflow. Evaporators that typically operate above freezing can use a closer fin spacing because frost does not accumulate. Figure 17-30 shows the difference in fin spacing between a frosting and nonfrosting evaporator coil.

17.11 REFRIGERANT LINES

The components of the refrigeration system are connected by three refrigerant lines: the discharge line, the liquid line, and the suction line. The discharge line is the smaller of the

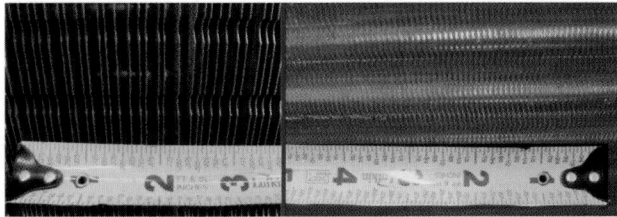

Figure 17-30 The fins are spaced wider apart on coils that operate below freezing

two lines connected to the compressor, Figure 17-31. The discharge line carries the high pressure, hot superheated gas from the compressor to the condenser. It is called the discharge line because refrigerant is discharged from the compressor into it. The liquid line carries the high pressure, warm subcooled liquid from the condenser to the metering device. The suction line is the larger of the two lines connected to the compressor, Figure 17-31. The suction line carries the low pressure, cool superheated vapor from the evaporator coil to the compressor inlet.

Units with all the refrigeration components in one piece of equipment are called packaged units. The discharge, liquid, and suction lines of a packaged unit are contained within the unit. A split system is a unit with parts of the refrigeration system located in different pieces of equipment. Most split system refrigeration units have the evaporator and metering device located inside and the condenser and compressor located outside. The piece of equipment located outside is called a condensing unit. The two lines connecting these systems are the large suction line and the small liquid line, Figure 17-32. The discharge line is not actually an external line in these systems,

Figure 17-32 Suction and liquid lines on a residential split system air conditioner

but part of the outdoor condensing unit. A few split systems locate all the components except the condenser in one piece of equipment, and locate the condenser in a separate piece of equipment. These systems also have two lines connecting them together, but they are the lines that go to and from the condenser: the discharge line and the liquid line. On these systems the suction line is an internal line.

Split system heat pumps have two lines. The large line's function changes depending upon the operating cycle of the unit. During cooling, the large line is the suction line and the small line is the liquid line. During heating, the large line is the discharge line and the small line is still the liquid line. To avoid confusion, the large line on split system heat pumps is often called the gas line because that is what travels through it in either cycle.

17.12 REFRIGERANT STORAGE

The capacity of many refrigeration systems varies depending upon their operating conditions. Capacity changes also produce different refrigerant flows. An increase in refrigeration capacity circulates more refrigerant, a decrease in capacity circulates less refrigerant. This can make it difficult for systems operating under a broad range of temperature conditions to maintain the desired level of subcooling and superheat. The extra refrigerant needs a place to sit when it is not circulating. Liquid receivers and suction accumulators provide a place for the surplus refrigerant to sit until it is needed. Systems do not usually have both receivers and accumulators. Typically, systems using thermostatic expansion valves use liquid receivers and systems using fixed bore expansion devices use accumulators.

Figure 17-31 The suction line entering the compressor is the large line, the discharge line leaving the compressor is the small line

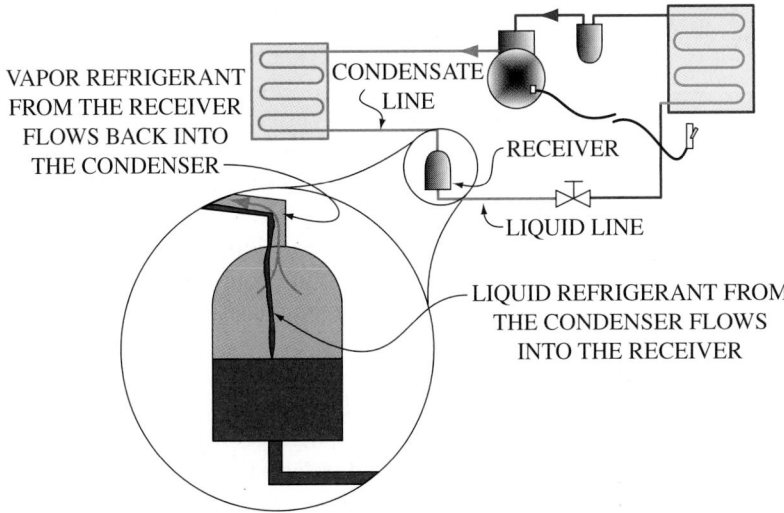

VAPOR REFRIGERANT
FROM THE RECEIVER
FLOWS BACK INTO
THE CONDENSER

CONDENSATE
LINE

RECEIVER

LIQUID LINE

LIQUID REFRIGERANT FROM
THE CONDENSER FLOWS
INTO THE RECEIVER

Figure 17-33 Liquid refrigerant drains into the receiver, and vapor flows back to the condenser through the condensate line

Liquid Receivers

Liquid receivers are located at the end of the condenser outlet to collect liquid refrigerant, Figure 17-33. The liquid receiver allows the liquid to flow into the receiver and any vapor collected in the receiver to flow back into the condenser to be converted back into a liquid. The line connecting the receiver to the condenser is called the condensate line and must be large enough in diameter to allow liquid to flow into the receiver and vapor to flow back into the condenser. The condensate line must also have a slope toward the receiver to allow liquid refrigerant to freely flow from the condenser into the receiver. The outlet side of the receiver is located at the bottom where 100% liquid can flow out of the receiver into the liquid line.

Receivers should be sized so that 100% of the refrigerant charge can be stored in the receiver. When the receiver is properly sized, it can be used to store the refrigerant during a pump down cycle or for some types of approved system service.

Some refrigeration condensing units come with receivers built into the base of the condensing unit, Figure 17-34.

Accumulators

An accumulator is a device located at the end of the evaporator that allows liquid refrigerant to be collected in the bottom of the accumulator and remain there as the vapor refrigerant is returned to the compressor. The inlet side of the accumulator is connected to the evaporator where any liquid refrigerant and vapor flow in. The outlet of the accumulator draws vapor through a U shaped tube or chamber, Figure 17-35. There is a small port at the bottom of the U shaped tube or chamber that allows liquid refrigerant and oil to be drawn into the suction line. Without this small port, refrigerant oil would collect in the accumulator and not return to the compressor. The small port does allow some liquid refrigerant to enter the suction line. However, it is such a small amount of liquid refrigerant that it boils off rapidly, so there is no danger of liquid refrigerant flowing into the compressor.

Accumulators are often found on heat pumps. During the changeover cycle, liquid refrigerant can flow back out of the outdoor coil. This liquid refrigerant could cause compressor damage if it were not for the accumulator, which blocks its return.

RECEIVER TANK

Figure 17-34 Receiver tank as part of a refrigeration condensing unit
(Courtesy Danfoss, Inc.)

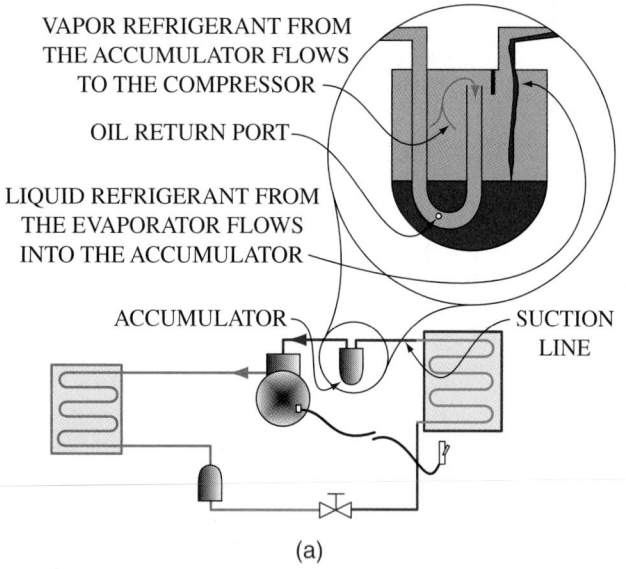

VAPOR REFRIGERANT FROM THE ACCUMULATOR FLOWS TO THE COMPRESSOR

OIL RETURN PORT

LIQUID REFRIGERANT FROM THE EVAPORATOR FLOWS INTO THE ACCUMULATOR

ACCUMULATOR

SUCTION LINE

(a)

OUTLET   INLET

VAPOR RETURN TO COMPRESSOR

SCREEN COVERED OIL RETURN PORT

(b)

Figure 17-35 Unevaporated liquid refrigerant flows into the accumulator; vapor refrigerant is drawn off the top of the accumulator. A screen covers the oil return port to prevent debris in the system from plugging the port; (a) Diagram; (b) Accumulator

17.13 OTHER REFRIGERATION SYSTEM COMPONENTS

All mechanical refrigeration systems have a compressor, a condenser, a metering device, and an evaporator, but many systems have additional components that help the system perform its job. Other refrigeration system components that may be found on some refrigeration systems include discharge line muffler, oil separator, liquid receiver, liquid line filter-drier, sight glass, liquid line solenoid, suction to liquid heat exchanger, evaporator pressure regulator, suction line filter, suction accumulator, crankcase pressure regulator, and oil level control. Some of these components improve the efficiency or reliability of the refrigeration system, while others are essential for specialized systems to operate correctly.

Optional High Side Components

The discharge line muffler dampens pulsations and noise created by the compressor. The oil separator removes the oil entrained in the discharge gas and returns it to the compressor crankcase. The liquid line filter-drier removes moisture and impurities from the liquid refrigerant. The liquid line filter-drier helps protect the system, especially the metering device. A sight glass allows the technician to visually see the condition of the refrigerant in the line. Many sight glasses also have a moisture indicator which changes color when exposed to moisture. A liquid line solenoid is an electrically operated valve used to control the flow of liquid refrigerant. With a normally closed solenoid valve, refrigerant will only flow through when the solenoid is energized. When the solenoid is deenergized, refrigerant does not flow through the solenoid valve. The suction to liquid heat exchanger exchanges heat between the warm liquid line and the cool suction line. This increases both the suction gas superheat and the liquid line subcooling.

Optional Low Side Components

The evaporator pressure regulator controls the pressure in the evaporator. It will not allow the evaporator pressure to drop below the EPR setpoint. EPR valves are used on systems with multiple evaporators operating at different pressures and temperatures. The evaporators share a common suction line but are able to maintain separate evaporator pressures because of the evaporator pressure regulators. Suction line filters are used to protect the compressor from contaminants. Typically suction line filters are used when replacement compressors are installed. The filter is removed after the system has operated long enough for the filter to do its job. Suction line accumulators are used to ensure that no liquid enters the compressor. They are commonly used on heat pumps. Crankcase pressure regulators are used to keep the suction pressure to the compressor from rising above the setpoint of the CPR valve. CPR valves are commonly used on commercial freezers. They keep the compressor from being overloaded when the evaporator temperature is above its normal operating temperature. Oil level controls are used on systems with multiple compressors which are piped into common discharge and suction headers.

17.14 ABSORPTION REFRIGERATION SYSTEMS

Absorption refrigeration systems use heat and the process of absorption to move the refrigerant instead of a compressor. The absorption process takes advantage of the fact that some chemicals have an affinity for other chemicals. One of the most common combinations is to use ammonia as the refrigerant and water as the absorbent. This combination is used in most smaller absorption systems. Large absorption chillers use water as the refrigerant and lithium bromide as the absorbent. Absorption systems really have two cycles: a refrigerant cycle and an absorbent cycle. Some systems use a third gas, typically hydrogen, to help the refrigerant move from the low side of the system back to the high side without using any mechanical devices. Other systems use a solution pump to move solution from the low side to the high side. This discussion will focus on ammonia-water absorption systems used for residential chillers. Figure 17-36 shows a simplified drawing of an ammonia-water absorption cycle.

SAFETY TIP

Ammonia is a poisonous and somewhat flammable gas! Do not attempt to service an ammonia system unless you have received specific training in the safe handling of ammonia refrigerant.

The transfer of heat is essentially the same in the absorption system as in the traditional mechanical compression cycle. Heat is absorbed in the evaporator and rejected in the condenser. Under a high pressure, the ammonia refrigerant condenses from a gas to a liquid in the condenser, yielding its latent heat in the process. The high pressure liquid now passes through a refrigerant restrictor where its pressure and temperature are reduced. This low-pressure liquid boils inside the evaporator to a gas, absorbing latent heat in the process and cooling off the water passing over the evaporator coil. So far, the compression and absorption systems are identical. The difference is in how the low and high pressures are created.

In a compression system, the compressor provides the force to create both the high and low side pressures. In an absorption system, the compressor is replaced by three components: the generator, the absorber, and the solution pump.

One component that absorption systems have that is not found on compression systems is the absorber. In the absorber, a second fluid that has an affinity for the refrigerant absorbs the refrigerant. This has the effect of "sucking" the refrigerant out of the evaporator and creating a low refrigerant pressure in the evaporator. This replaces the suction stroke of the compressor. When the vapor refrigerant is absorbed into the solution, it condenses back into a liquid. This gives off a great deal of heat, normally called the heat of absorption. If the heat of absorption is not removed from the solution, the absorption process will stop. Some units actually have two absorbers: a solution-cooled absorber and an air-cooled absorber.

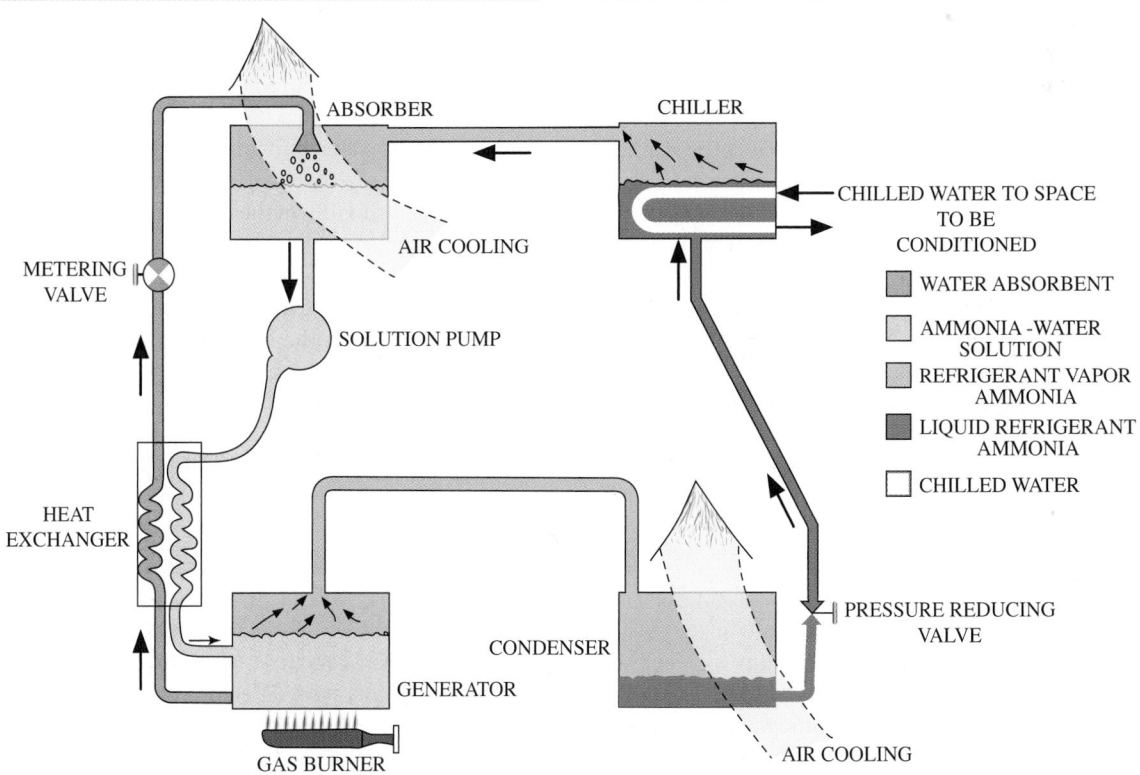

Figure 17-36 Simplified ammonia-water absorbtion cycle. The solution cycle is on the left; the refrigeration cycle is on the right
(From Advanced Course in Gas Air Conditioning, 1965, courtesy of the Southern Gas Association in cooperation with the Texas College of Arts and Industries, Kingsville, Texas)

The solution-cooled absorber is where the refrigerant and weak solution are first mixed. The solution-cooled absorber cannot cool the solution adequately enough to remove all the heat of absorption; therefore, much of the refrigerant remains in a vapor state inside the solution. To remove the heat of absorption, the solution passes through the air-cooled absorber where the heat of absorption is removed and the refrigerant vapor is condensed. A solution pump is used to pump the solution from the low-pressure absorber to the high-pressure generator.

The solution pump is the closest thing to a compressor in concept. The solution pump used in many units is a diaphragm pump and pumps somewhat like a heart, in pulses of pressure that are directed by check valves. On the suction stroke: the valve to the absorber opens, the valve to the generator closes, and solution is drawn into the pump from the air-cooled absorber. On the pressure stroke, the valve to the generator opens, the valve to the absorber closes, and the solution is forced into the generator. The pulsing action of the solution pump causes the solution level in the solution-cooled absorber to rise and fall. This helps entrain refrigerant vapor in the weak solution before it is circulated through the air-cooled absorber. The solution pump and the restrictors are the dividing points between high and low pressures on the system. Of course, the absorbing solution can only absorb a limited amount of refrigerant. In the case of water and ammonia, water will absorb about half its weight in ammonia. At this point the water-ammonia solution needs to be regenerated for the system to keep operating. The generator does this.

The generator separates the refrigerant and the absorbent by boiling the refrigerant out of the absorbent. This also creates a high pressure on the high side of the system. The refrigerant vapor is sent on its way toward the condenser and the weak solution is sent through a restrictor, back to the solution cooled absorber. The solution cycle is now complete. In addition to the components mentioned, there are a number of other components added to the system for increased efficiency.

SERVICE TIP

Never use standard brass gauges to service an ammonia system! Ammonia attacks the brass. Ammonia systems require gauges made specifically for ammonia.

17.15 EVAPORATIVE COOLING SYSTEMS

Evaporative cooling reduces the air temperature by evaporating water. The heat to evaporate the water comes from the air, reducing its temperature. After going through an evaporative cooler, the air still has the same amount of heat, but its temperature is lower and its humidity is higher. This method works well in dry climates, such as the southwestern United States. It does not work as well in humid climates, such as coastal areas or the southeastern United States. The installation

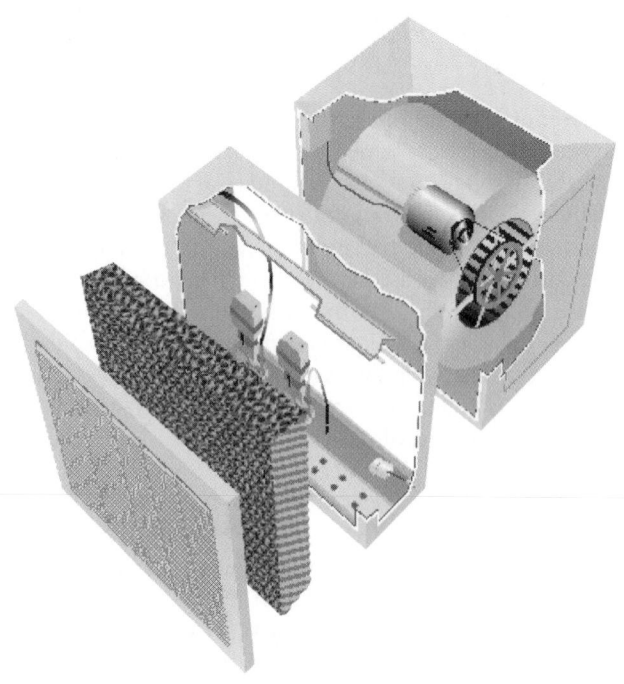

Figure 17-37 Evaporative cooler
(Image property and courtesy of AdobeAir, Inc.)

and operation costs for an evaporative cooler are much lower than conventional air conditioning using a refrigeration cycle. This makes evaporative cooling popular in large factories and plants where traditional refrigerated air conditioning would be prohibitively expensive.

A typical evaporative cooler, also called a "swamp cooler," is shown in Figure 17-37. The unit consists of a water sump, a pump, wetted media to increase the surface area for evaporating water, and a blower to move air. The pump pumps the water in the sump at the bottom to the top of the media where it runs down the media. A float controls the water level in the sump by allowing makeup water to fill the sump when the water level drops. The blower moves outside air across the media and into the house. For this system to operate correctly, air in the house must be allowed to escape. This is normally done by opening the windows.

17.16 THERMOELECTRIC REFRIGERATION

A thermocouple is a device composed of two dissimilar metal wires joined on both ends, but separated or insulated from each other in between. Thomas Seebeck discovered that small amounts of electrical current flow through the wires if the two junction points are at different temperatures, Figure 17-38. This effect has been used for years as a flame safety device in gas burning appliances. While studying the Seebeck effect in 1834, Jean Pelletier discovered that if a current is imposed on the thermocouple, one end will heat up and the other will cool off. Reversing the direction of the current will swap the hot and cold junctions. This is called the Pelletier effect,

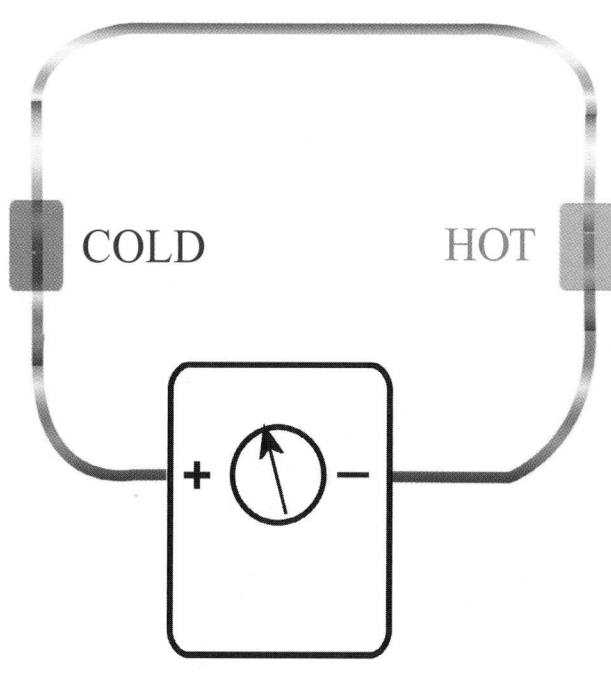

Figure 17-38 Temperature difference between the two junctions creates a DC current flow

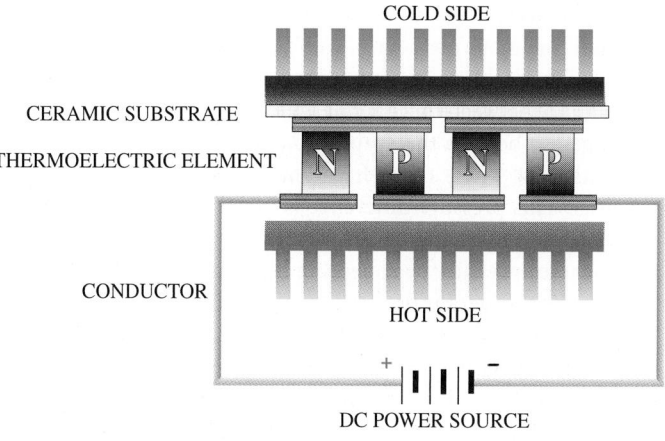

Figure 17-40 Modern thermoelectric modules use semiconductors to create the Peletier effect

Figure 17-39. This characteristic is exploited in thermoelectric refrigeration.

Today's thermoelectric modules typically use semiconductors rather than metal. Figure 17-40 shows the construction of a typical thermoelectric module. These modules can be sandwiched between two heat sinks to produce a unit capable of moving heat. Figure 17-41 shows a complete thermoelectric cooling module including the heat sinks.

Thermoelectric refrigeration is not very energy efficient, and is best suited for small loads. Thermoelectric cooling does provide a small, lightweight cooling system for areas that would be difficult to cool with a traditional refrigeration

Figure 17-41 Complete thermoelectric cooling module including heat sinks

(Courtesy of ThermoElectric Cooling America (TECA) Corp.)

system. Thermoelectric cooling has been applied to electronic systems, space ships, and picnic coolers.

UNIT 17—SUMMARY

The purpose of a refrigeration system is to move heat from where it is not wanted to where it is unobjectionable. There are several kinds of cooling systems including absorption, evaporative, thermoelectric, and mechanical compression. The mechanical compression refrigeration cycle is the most common. The four main components of the mechanical

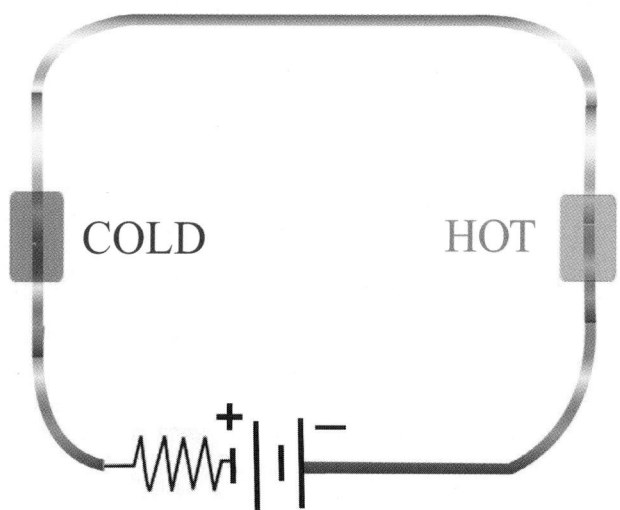

Figure 17-39 A DC current imposed a cross the two junctions creates a temperature difference

compression refrigeration cycle are the compressor, the condenser, the metering device, and the evaporator. The refrigeration cycle is made possible by maintaining a pressure difference between the low side which absorbs heat when the refrigerant boils in the evaporator, and the high side which rejects heat when the refrigerant condenses in the condenser. This pressure difference is maintained by the compressor and metering device. The compressor increases the refrigerant pressure by squeezing it; the metering device reduces the refrigerant pressure by restricting its flow into the evaporator.

Other cooling mechanisms include evaporative coolers which cool the air by evaporating water, the absorption cycle which uses heat and an absorbent fluid to create the needed system pressure difference, and thermoelectric cooling which transfers heat using electric current and the Pelletier effect.

UNIT 17—REVIEW QUESTIONS

1. List the different types of cooling mechanisms.
2. Briefly explain the fundamental principles which make the compression refrigeration cycle work.
3. Explain why boiling is considered a cooling process.
4. List the four major components of the compression refrigeration cycle in order.
5. Why do both the compression cycle and absorption cycle have a high pressure side and a low pressure side?
6. What components are responsible for maintaining the high and low pressures in a compression refrigeration system?
7. What components are responsible for maintaining the high and low pressures in an absorption refrigeration system?
8. Explain how an evaporative cooling system works.
9. Where is evaporative cooling the most effective?
10. Explain how a thermoelectric refrigeration system works.
11. Where in the compression refrigeration cycle is the refrigerant superheated?

12. Why is superheating desirable?
13. Where in the compression refrigeration cycle is the refrigerant subcooled?
14. Why is subcooling desirable?
15. Where in the compression refrigeration cycle is the refrigerant saturated?
16. Explain the heat balance in a compression cycle refrigeration system.
17. What is the difference between a liquid receiver and a suction accumulator?
18. List some of the optional components that can be found on the high side of a refrigeration system.
19. List some of the optional components that can be found on the low side of a refrigeration system.
20. List the types of compressors and briefly explain how they operate.
21. List the three types of air cooled condensers and briefly explain the difference between them.
22. List the different type of water cooled condensers and give a description of each type.
23. What are the two large classes of metering devices?
24. Which type of metering device provides the most efficient operation?
25. Compare coil design between older, less efficient air conditioning systems and newer high SEER air conditioning systems.
26. Name the three common refrigerant lines found on compression systems.
27. Which line is the larger of the two lines going to the compressor?
28. Which two lines connect the inside and outside units of a split system?
29. Why is the refrigeration cycle called a cycle?
30. Draw the basic refrigeration cycle. Label the four main components and the refrigerant lines. List the pressure, temperature, and state going in and out of each major component. Be sure to indicate where the refrigerant is superheated, saturated, or subcooled. Note: the pressure and temperature can simply be "high" or "low." Specific numbers are not required.

Plotting the Refrigeration Cycle

After completing this unit you will be able to:

- explain how refrigerant heat, pressure, and temperature change as it flows through a refrigeration system.
- identify the lines and scales on a PH (pressure-enthalpy) diagram.
- draw a PH diagram of a basic refrigeration cycle.
- calculate the pounds of refrigerant flowing through a system for a given set of operating conditions and capacity.
- explain the difference in PH diagrams for compounds and zeotropes.

18.1 INTRODUCTION

PH diagrams are primarily used for designing refrigeration systems. All aspects of system performance can be predicted using a PH diagram. A system's refrigeration capacity, the amount of refrigerant that must be circulated, the amount of heat absorbed by the evaporator, the amount of heat rejected by the condenser, and the required compressor capacity can all be determined using a PH diagram. Technicians can use PH diagrams to troubleshoot systems by comparing a plot of what a system is doing to what it should be doing.

18.2 PRESSURE-ENTHALPY DIAGRAMS

Pressure-enthalpy diagrams are referred to as PH diagrams. Enthalpy is the amount of heat in a substance, represented by the uppercase letter H. Specific enthalpy is the amount of heat per pound, represented by the lowercase h. PH diagrams show the relationship of a refrigerant's pressure, heat, temperature, volume, and state. The lines and scales used on PH diagrams represent the same thing on every PH diagram, each refrigerant just has different values. So once you understand the R–410A PH diagram shown in Figure 18-1, you can work with any other refrigerant's PH diagram.

18.3 PH DIAGRAM LINES AND SCALES

Saturation Curve

The large hump in the middle of the PH chart is the saturation curve, Figure 18-2. Every point on or inside the satura-tion curve is saturated. The critical point is at the very top of the hump. The critical point is the pressure and temperature at which liquid and vapor are indistinguishable; refrigerant cannot be saturated above the critical point. The left side of the curve is the saturated liquid line and everything to the left of the saturation curve is subcooled. The right side of the curve is the saturated vapor line and everything to the right of the curve is superheated. Everything inside the curve is saturated.

Constant Quality

The constant quality area is the area inside the dome shape outlined by the saturated liquid and saturated vapor lines. The constant quality lines start at the bottom and extend upward toward the critical point located in top center of the dome, Figure 18-3. These lines represent the percentage of vapor in the saturated refrigerant. Any point along the line marked 20% would have 20% vapor and 80% liquid. The lines run from 0% vapor at the saturated liquid line on the left, to 100% vapor at the saturated vapor line on the right. As you move from left to right across these lines, there is more vapor and less liquid refrigerant. Moving from the right to the left increases the percent of liquid as compared to percent of vapor.

During the evaporation process in the evaporator, the percentage of vapor will increase and the percentage of liquid will decrease. This is shown as a left to right movement across the area. During the condensation process in the condenser, the percentage of vapor will decrease and the percentage of liquid will increase. This is shown as a right to left movement across the area, Figure 18-4.

Pressure

The pressure lines run horizontally from the right side to the left side of the diagram, Figure 18-5. The line spacing becomes closer together as they go up from the bottom. Each line is one-half the space of the previous line. If all the lines were drawn with the same scale units, by the time they got to the top of the diagram, they would be so close that it would appear as a single line. To make the pressure scale readable, the unit spacing changes from the bottom to the top.

The pressure scales shown on the right and left sides of PH diagrams are given in pounds per square inch absolute, psia. Notice that the scale changes three times from the bottom to the top. The bottom lines are drawn to represent incre-ments of one psia with every other line identified as: 1, 2, 4,

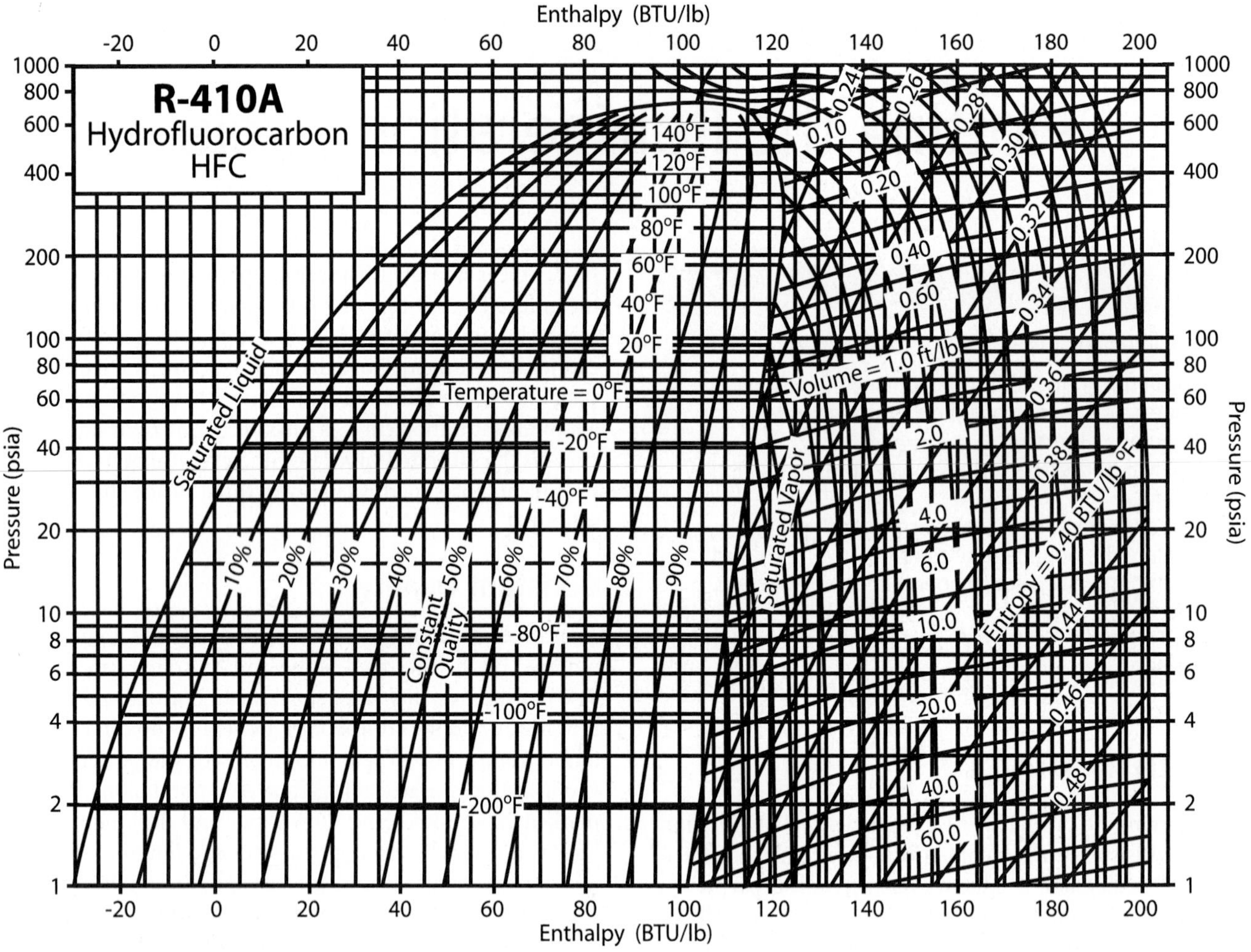

Figure 18-1 Pressure-enthalpy diagram for refrigerant R–410A

Figure 18-2 The saturation curve

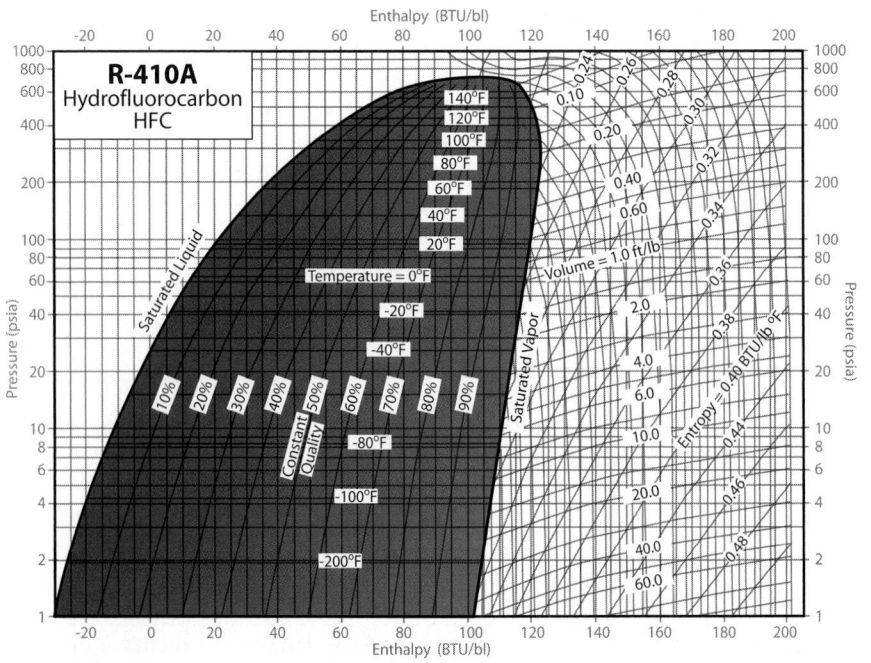

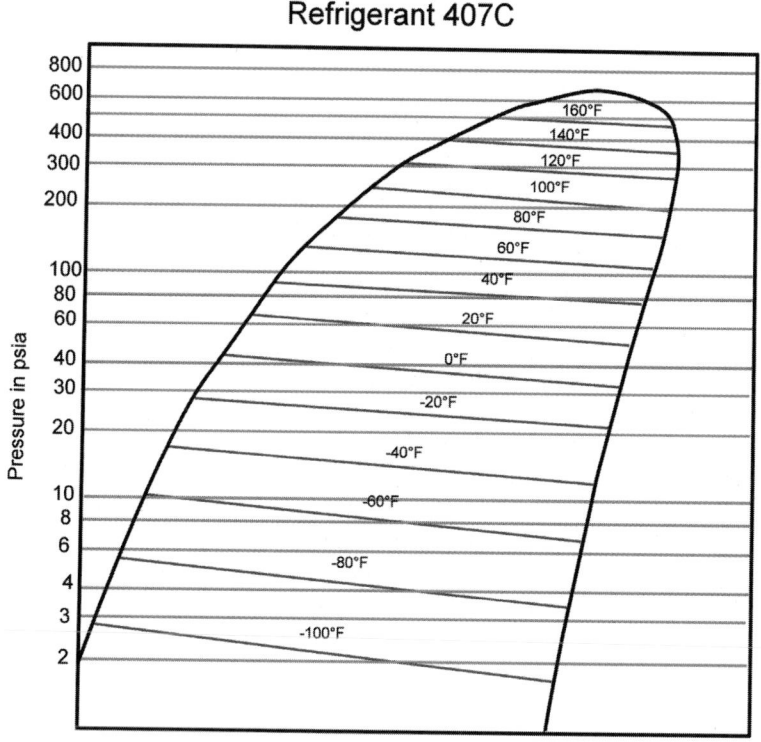

Refrigerant 407C

of 119.8 Btu/lb while saturated liquid has an enthalpy of 16.2 Btu/lb.

18.6 REFRIGERATION CYCLE PH DIAGRAM

PH diagrams can be used to show what happens in a refrigeration cycle. A basic refrigeration cycle is plotted on the PH diagram in Figure 18-12. A refrigeration cycle PH diagram contains four lines, each representing one of the four major components. Each line shows how the refrigerant changes in temperature, pressure, heat content, and state as it travels through the cycle.

Compressor

The line between points A and B in Figure 18-12 represents the compression process. The compressor line follows the entropy lines up. This line travels up because the refrigerant pressure is increased in the compressor, and to the right because of the heat added by the compressor. Heat of compression is the amount of heat energy added by the compressor due to mechanical work. The discharge temperature predicted by the enthalpy diagram is the theoretical discharge temperature based solely on heat added by mechanical work. In actual operation, the discharge temperature may be 20–35°F higher because of the heat added by the compressor motor in systems with hermetic or semi-hermetic compressors.

Condenser

The line between points B and E in Figure 18-12 represents the condenser. The line is horizontal because the pressure

remains the same through all the condenser processes. The portion of the line from point B to the saturation curve represents the desuperheating portion of the condenser. Here, the refrigerant temperature drops until it reaches the saturation point. The refrigerant temperature remains the same from the intersection with the saturated vapor line until the intersection of the saturated liquid line. This portion of the process is called isothermal because the temperature remains the same while the refrigerant changes state from a gas to a liquid. At the saturated liquid line the refrigerant is all liquid. The portion of the line between the intersection of the saturated liquid line and point E is the subcooling portion of the condenser. The liquid temperature drops in the subcooling section.

Metering Device

The line between point E and point G in Figure 18-12 represents the metering device. This line drops straight down because no heat is gained or lost in the metering device, but the pressure drops dramatically. The refrigerant increases in volume through the metering device. This is why one of the most common metering devices is called an expansion valve. This type of expansion without adding heat is called adiabatic expansion. Adiabatic means without heat. The metering device line starts in the subcooled region and ends up in the saturated region of the PH diagram.

Evaporator

The line between point G and point A in Figure 18-12 represents the evaporator. It travels horizontally because the

Thermodynamic Properties of Forane® 410A - Saturation

Saturation Temperature (°F)	Liquid Pressure (psia)	Vapor Pressure (psia)	Liquid Density (lb/ft³)	Vapor Density (lb/ft³)	Liquid Enthalpy (BTU/lb)	Vapor Enthalpy (BTU/lb)	Liquid Entropy (BTU/lb °R)	Vapor Entropy (BTU/lb °R)
-50	20.04	20.01	82.82	0.342	-3.1	111.8	-0.007	0.273
-45	22.72	22.68	82.30	0.385	-1.5	112.5	-0.004	0.272
-40	25.68	25.63	81.78	0.431	0.0	113.2	0.000	0.270
-35	28.94	28.88	81.24	0.482	1.5	113.9	0.004	0.269
-30	32.53	32.46	80.70	0.538	3.1	114.6	0.007	0.267
-25	36.46	36.38	80.15	0.599	4.7	115.3	0.011	0.266
-20	40.77	40.67	79.59	0.666	6.3	116.0	0.015	0.264
-15	45.48	45.36	79.02	0.738	7.9	116.6	0.018	0.263
-10	50.61	50.47	78.45	0.817	9.5	117.3	0.022	0.262
-5	56.18	56.03	77.86	0.902	11.2	117.9	0.025	0.261
0	62.24	62.06	77.26	0.995	12.8	118.6	0.029	0.259
5	68.80	68.60	76.66	1.095	14.5	119.2	0.033	0.258
10	75.89	75.67	76.04	1.204	16.2	119.8	0.036	0.257
15	83.54	83.29	75.41	1.322	18.0	120.3	0.040	0.256
20	91.79	91.51	74.76	1.449	19.7	120.9	0.043	0.255
25	100.65	100.35	74.11	1.586	21.5	121.4	0.047	0.254
30	110.18	109.85	73.44	1.735	23.3	121.9	0.051	0.253
35	120.39	120.03	72.75	1.895	25.1	122.4	0.054	0.251
40	131.32	130.93	72.05	2.067	27.0	122.9	0.058	0.250
45	143.00	142.58	71.33	2.254	28.8	123.3	0.062	0.249
50	155.46	155.01	70.60	2.455	30.8	123.8	0.065	0.248
55	168.75	168.27	69.85	2.671	32.7	124.1	0.069	0.247
60	182.89	182.38	69.07	2.905	34.7	124.5	0.073	0.246
65	197.92	197.38	68.28	3.157	36.7	124.8	0.077	0.245
70	213.88	213.31	67.46	3.429	38.8	125.1	0.080	0.244
75	230.80	230.21	66.61	3.724	40.9	125.3	0.084	0.242
80	248.72	248.10	65.74	4.042	43.1	125.5	0.088	0.241
85	267.67	267.03	64.84	4.387	45.3	125.6	0.092	0.240
90	287.69	287.04	63.90	4.762	47.5	125.7	0.096	0.238
95	308.82	308.16	62.92	5.169	49.9	125.7	0.100	0.237
100	331.10	330.43	61.91	5.613	52.3	125.7	0.104	0.236
105	354.56	353.89	60.84	6.098	54.8	125.5	0.109	0.234
110	379.25	378.58	59.72	6.630	57.3	125.3	0.113	0.232
115	405.19	404.53	58.54	7.216	60.0	125.0	0.117	0.231
120	432.44	431.79	57.29	7.867	62.8	124.6	0.122	0.229
125	461.02	460.40	55.94	8.593	65.7	124.0	0.127	0.227
130	490.97	490.40	54.49	9.412	68.7	123.2	0.132	0.224
135	522.34	521.81	52.91	10.348	72.0	122.3	0.137	0.222
140	555.16	554.70	51.15	11.439	75.4	121.0	0.143	0.219
145	589.47	589.08	49.14	12.747	79.2	119.4	0.149	0.215
150	625.31	625.01	46.75	14.403	83.5	117.2	0.155	0.211

Figure 18-11 Thermodynamic properties of Forane® R–410A saturation table from http://www.arkema-inc.com/index.cfm?pag=37
(Copyright© Arkema Inc. Used by permission)

pressure remains the same in the evaporator. The line between point G and the intersection with the saturated vapor line represents the portion of the evaporator where refrigerant is changing state from a liquid to a gas. The temperature remains the same from point G to the intersection of the saturated vapor line because evaporation is an isothermal process. This is where the vast majority of the heat is gained in the evaporator. All the liquid refrigerant has changed to vapor by the end of the evaporator. The portion between the

intersection of the saturated vapor line and point A represents the superheat added to the refrigerant in the end of the evaporator.

18.7 SEVEN STAGES OF REFRIGERANT TRANSFORMATION

Now that the four lines representing the four major system components are in place, let's examine the entire process in more detail using a specific example. There are seven stages of refrigerant transformation within a refrigeration system. These are: compressing, desuperheating, condensing, subcooling, expanding, evaporating, and superheating. Figure 18-13 shows a PH diagram of an air cooled air conditioning system using refrigerant R–410A operating with an outdoor ambient of 95°F and an indoor return air temperature of 80°F. The condenser temperature is 120°F, 25°F warmer than ambient. The evaporator temperature is 40°F, 40°F cooler than the return air temperature. The following explanation of each stage will refer to Figure 18-13.

Stage 1—Compression

At point A the cool refrigerant vapor enters the compressor suction valve at 133 psia and 60°F. The compressor raises its temperature and pressure to approximately 175°F and 433 psia at point B. The temperature and pressure are raised by reducing the gas volume from 0.5 ft³/lb to 0.17 ft³/lb. The compressor line follows the constant entropy lines. Vertical lines drawn from points A and B to the constant enthalpy line show the heat added to the refrigerant by the compressor, Figure 18-14. The difference between the enthalpy at point A and the enthalpy at point B is the heat of compression. In this case the heat of compression is 145 Btu/lb − 127 Btu/lb = 18 Btu/lb.

Stage 2—Desuperheating

Desuperheating, cooling off of the hot vapor refrigerant, occurs along the line between points B and C. Desuperheating decreases the sensible temperature and heat, but the pressure remains the same. Vertical lines drawn from points B and C to the constant enthalpy line show the heat removed from the refrigerant during desuperheating, Figure 18-15. The amount of desuperheating accomplished is the difference between the enthalpy of the vapor refrigerant at point B and point C. In this case 145 Btu/lb − 122 Btu/lb = 23 Btu/lb of heat removed by desuperheating the vapor refrigerant.

Stage 3—Condensing

Condensation begins after all the refrigerant superheat has been removed. Condensation of the refrigerant vapor into a liquid begins at point C where the condenser line crosses the saturated vapor line. The temperature stops dropping; it is

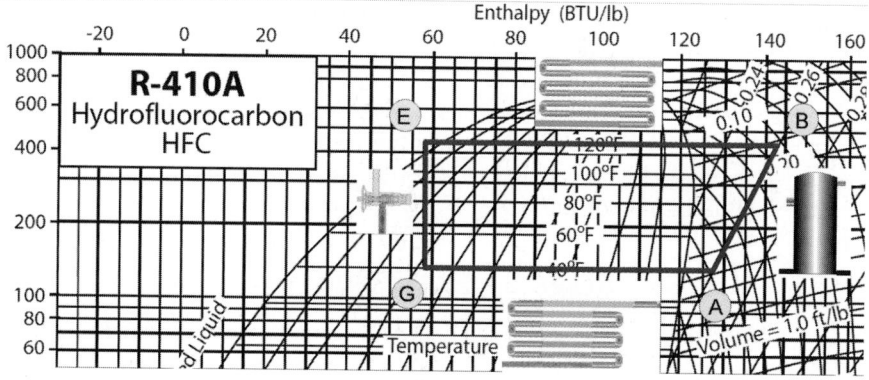

Figure 18-12 Pressure-enthalpy (PH) diagram of the operation of the basic refrigeration cycle

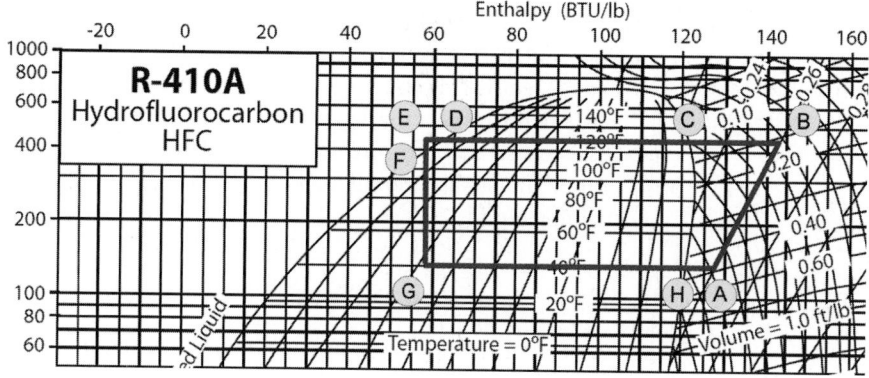

Figure 18-13 Pressure-enthalpy (PH) diagram of the operation of the basic refrigeration cycle showing stages of refrigerant transformation

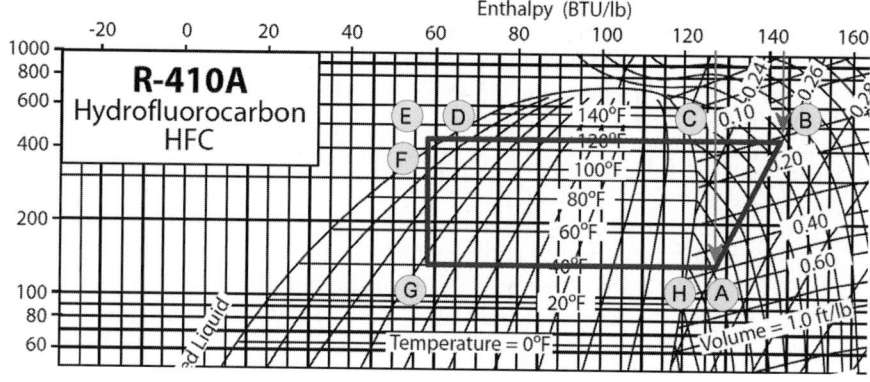

Figure 18-14 The heat of compression is the difference in the enthalpy at points A and B

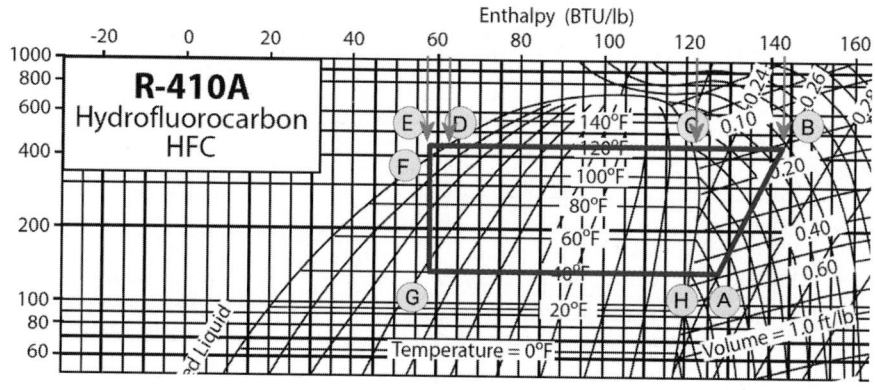

Figure 18-15 The condenser desuperheats the refrigerant between point B and point C, condenses the refrigerant between points C and D, and subcools the refrigerant between points D and E

now 120°F. That is the saturated vapor-liquid temperature for 433 psia R–410A. Condensing continues to take place with no change in pressure or temperature until the refrigerant reaches point D on the condenser line. Vertical lines drawn from points C and D to the constant enthalpy line would show the heat removed from the refrigerant during condensation, Figure 18-15. In this case 122 Btu/lb − 62 Btu/lb = 60 Btu/lb of heat removed by condensing the refrigerant.

Stage 4—Subcooling

Subcooling is the lowering of a liquid's temperature below its saturated liquid pressure. Subcooling begins as the condenser line crosses the saturated liquid line between points D and E. If 10°F of subcooling occurs, the refrigerant temperature lowers to 110°F; but the pressure remains at 433 psia. Vertical lines drawn from points D and E to the constant enthalpy line show the heat removed from the refrigerant during subcooling, Figure 18-15. In this case 62 Btu/lb − 57 Btu/lb = 5 Btu/lb.

Total Condenser Heat Rejection

Notice that the condenser must dissipate more heat than the evaporator absorbs. The condenser must dispose of the heat of compression as well as the heat picked up in the evapora-

TECH TIP

Although subcooling accounts for a very small amount of heat compared to the rest of the process, it is still very important. Subcooling ensures that the refrigerant entering the metering device is 100% liquid. Any pressure drop in the liquid line between the condenser and the metering device will cause a saturated liquid to flash, creating gas bubbles. Bubbles of refrigerant vapor decrease the amount of refrigerant the metering device feeds, reducing the system's operating efficiency.

tor. The total amount of heat rejected by the condenser is the total of desuperheating, condensing, and subcooling. That would be 23 Btu/lb desuperheating + 60 Btu/lb condensing + 5 Btu/lb subcooling = 88 Btu/lb total heat rejection. This can be found directly by subtracting the enthalpy at point E from the enthalpy of point B. In this case 145 Btu/lb − 57 Btu/lb = 88 Btu/lb.

Stage 5—Expansion

The subcooled liquid refrigerant enters the metering device at point E with a pressure of 433 psia and a temperature of 110°F. It exits the metering device at point G as a saturated mixture of 30% vapor and 70% liquid with a pressure of 133 psia and a temperature of 40°F. No heat is added or removed from the refrigerant, so the enthalpy remains 57 Btu/lb, Figure 18-16. Expanding without adding heat is called adiabatic expansion. Point F is inside the metering device. This is where the refrigerant first starts to flash from a liquid to a gas because the pressure has dropped to the saturation point. The small amount of liquid flashing cools the remaining liquid.

Stage 6—Evaporating

Refrigerant enters the evaporator at point G. As this point approximately 30% of the liquid refrigerant has flashed to vapor to cool the remaining liquid to 40°F. The 133 psia 40°F refrigerant flows into the evaporator where it can begin to pick up heat. Along the line from point G to point H, heat is added to the refrigerant, causing it to evaporate, increasing the percentage of vapor to 100%. The 100% vapor point occurs at the saturated vapor line, point H. Note that the pressure of 133 psia and temperature of 40°F did not change because this is an isothermal process. Point H is inside the evaporator.

Vertical lines drawn down from points G and H to the constant enthalpy line can be used to find the amount of heat that was added to the refrigerant as it changed from approximately 30% vapor to 100% vapor. In this case,

Figure 18-16 The pressure and temperature drops in the metering device are shown between points E and G

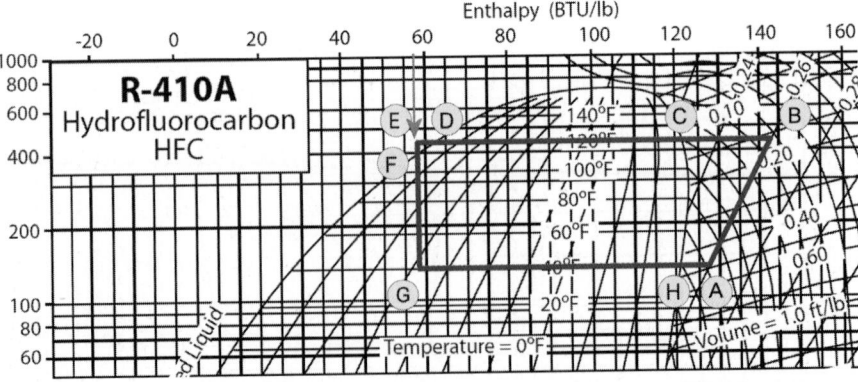

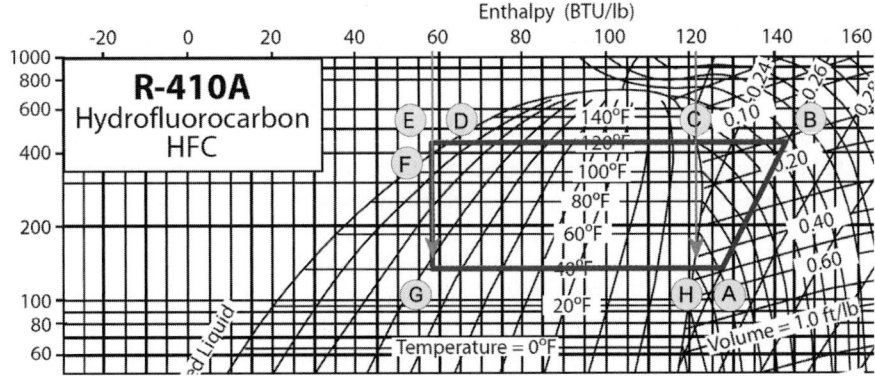

Figure 18-17 The refrigerant change of state in the evaporator from 30% vapor to 100% vapor takes place between points G and H

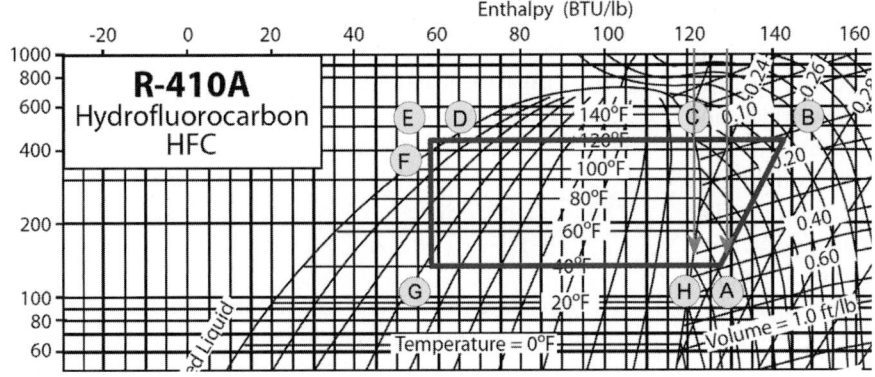

Figure 18-18 The evaporator superheat is shown between points H and A

122 Btu/lb − 57 Btu/lb = 65 Btu/lb heat gain through evaporation, Figure 18-17.

Stage 7—Superheating

From point H to point A the pressure remains at 133 psia, but without any liquid refrigerant, the vapor refrigerant is superheated approximately 20°F. Point A is located at the point where the 133 psia line crosses the 60°F temperature line in the superheat section. The portion of the line from point H to point A shows the evaporator superheat. Vertical lines drawn from points H and A to the constant enthalpy line

show the heat added to the refrigerant due to superheating, Figure 18-18. In this case 127 Btu/lb − 122 Btu/lb = 5 Btu/lb heat added due to evaporator superheat.

18.8 CALCULATING REFRIGERATION EFFECT

The refrigeration effect is the difference in the enthalpy of the refrigerant entering the evaporator and the enthalpy of the refrigerant leaving the evaporator. The refrigeration effect is rated in Btu per pound of refrigerant (Btu/lb). Referring to Figure 18-19, the enthalpy of the refrigerant at point G where

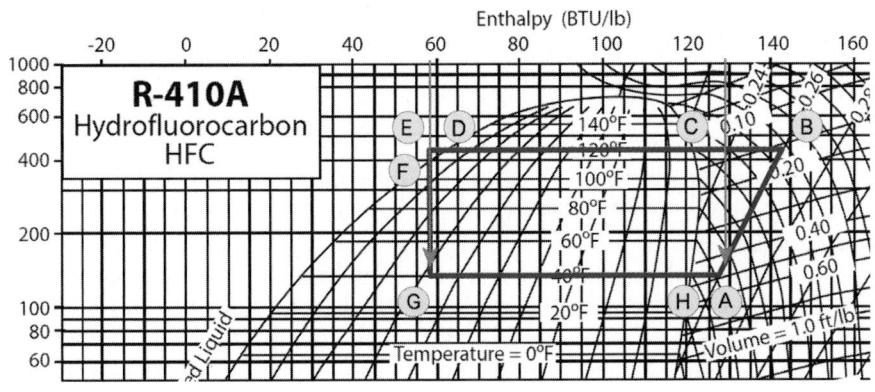

Figure 18-19 The refrigeration effect is the difference in enthalpy between points G and A

the refrigerant enters the evaporator is 57 Btu/lb and the enthalpy of the refrigerant leaving the evaporator at point A is 127 Btu/lb. The refrigeration effect is then 127 Btu/lb − 57 Btu/lb = 70 Btu/lb.

The refrigeration effect can be used to determine the amount of refrigerant that needs to be circulated to meet any particular load. This can then be used to determine the required compressor capacity.

18.9 REFRIGERATION SYSTEM CAPACITY

Once we know how many Btus a pound of refrigerant can pick up each time it passes through the evaporator, we can determine the pounds of refrigerant that must flow through the system to meet the system's load requirements. The amount of refrigerant that must be circulated can be calculated by dividing the system load in Btu per minute by the refrigeration effect. One ton of refrigeration is a rate of 200 Btu per minute. For a refrigeration capacity of 1 ton, this system would need to circulate (200 Btu/min)/(70 Btu/lb) = 2.9 lb/min. The required capacity per ton can be determined by dividing 200 Btu/min by the system's refrigeration effect as determined by the PH diagram.

18.10 NET REFRIGERATION EFFECT

AHRI defines net refrigeration effect as "the rate of total heat absorption by the refrigerant, at stated evaporator conditions, of the complete refrigeration system. This effect is equal to the product of the refrigerant mass flow rate through the system and the enthalpy difference between the refrigerant vapor leaving the evaporator and the refrigerant liquid entering the liquid control device of the evaporator, Btu/h." The refrigeration effect in the example was determined to be 70 Btu/lb and the mass flow required 2.9 lb/min. Therefore the net refrigeration effect is 70 Btu/lb × 2.9 lbs/minute = 200 Btu/min. The system's net refrigeration effect should match the heat load. (Note: the result of multiplying 2.9 × 70 is actually 203. The result should be 200, but compound error from rounding both the mass flow and enthalpy numbers yields the slight discrepancy.)

18.11 COMPRESSOR CAPACITY

In order for design conditions to be maintained within a refrigeration circuit, there must be a balance between the requirements of the evaporator coil and the capacity of the compressor. The compressor must have enough capacity to remove all the refrigerant that has vaporized in the evaporator and send the same weight of refrigerant vapor on to the condenser. If the compressor is too small, it will be unable to move all the vaporized refrigerant, some of the vapor

will remain in the evaporator. This will cause an increase in evaporator pressure and temperature and a decrease in system capacity.

Compressors are rated by the volume of gas they can move at particular low and high side pressures. The pressures the compressor must operate at are determined by the evaporating and condensing temperatures. The volume of gas to be moved is determined by the system capacity calculation. In this example, the amount of refrigerant to be circulated is 2.9 lb/min. The units of pounds per minute (lb/min) need to be turned into a volume: cubic feet per minute (ft³/min). The enthalpy diagram shows that the volume of the refrigerant where it enters the compressor at point A is 0.5 ft³/lb. Multiplying 0.5 ft³/lb × 2.9 lb/min gives the required total gas volume of approximately 1.5 ft³/min. The compressor in this example must be able to move 1.5 ft³/min at a suction pressure of 133 psia and a head pressure of 433 psia to produce a capacity of 200 Btu/min. This is equivalent to one ton of refrigeration.

18.12 REFRIGERANT COEFFICIENT OF PERFORMANCE

The refrigerant coefficient of performance (RCOP) is a ratio of the efficiency of a specific refrigerant in the refrigeration cycle comparing the utilization of expended energy during the compression process in a ratio to the energy that is absorbed in the evaporation process. RCOP is expressed as a ratio of the refrigeration effect to the energy used. RCOP may be calculated by dividing the refrigeration effect by the heat of compression: RCOP = refrigeration effect/heat of compression.

In Figure 18-19, the refrigeration effect would be the enthalpy of point A minus the enthalpy of point G: 127 Btu/lb − 57 Btu/lb = 70 Btu/lb refrigeration effect. The heat of compression would be the enthalpy of point B minus the enthalpy of point A: 145 Btu/lb − 127 Btu/lb = 18 Btu/lb. The RCOP would then be (70 Btu/lb)/(18 Btu/lb) = 3.9.

The RCOP for this refrigeration cycle is 3.9:1 (pronounced 3.9 to 1). That means 3.9 Btu of heat are removed for every Btu of heat added by the compressor. The less energy expended in the compression process, the larger the RCOP ratio of the system would be. When comparing refrigerants and operating conditions, the refrigerant and condition having the highest RCOP would be the best choice for energy efficiency.

18.13 PLOTTING AN OPERATING SYSTEM

Four measurements are all that are required to plot an operating system on a PH diagram: low side pressure, high side pressure, suction line temperature, and liquid line temperature. The system should be operating long enough

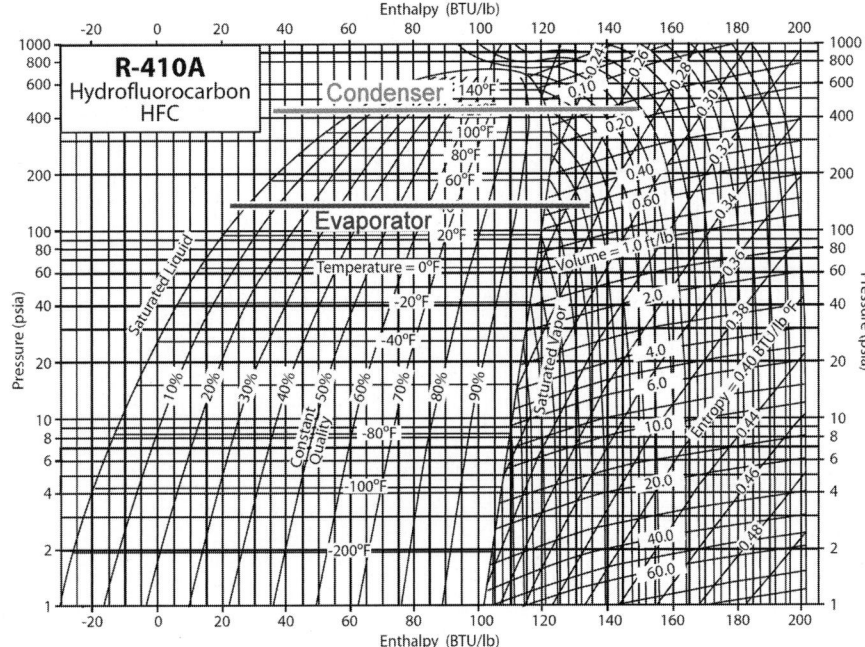

Figure 18-20 The evaporator line is drawn in blue at 40 psia; the condenser line is drawn in red at 200 psia

for these reading to be stable before taking them. This example will use a system with R–410A, operating with a suction pressure of 116 psig, a head pressure of 417 psig, a suction line temperature of 40°F, and a liquid line temperature of 110°F.

Evaporator and Condenser Lines

The first step in plotting a refrigeration cycle on a PH diagram is to establish the condensing and evaporating lines. Take the system operating pressures and convert them to absolute pressure by adding 15. These pressures will be used to establish the evaporator and condenser lines. For example, with an R–410 system operating with pressures of 116 psig on the low side and 417 psig on the high side, the absolute pressures would be 131 psia and 432 psia. Draw a horizontal line across the saturation curve at 131 psia for the evaporator line and at 432 psia for the condenser line. Do not worry about exactly where the lines should start and stop, just make sure they go all the way across the saturation curve on both sides. Figure 18-20 shows the evaporator line in blue and the condenser line in red.

Compressor Line

Measure the suction line temperature entering the compressor. Find where the evaporator line crosses this suction line temperature in the superheated area. In our example this is 40°F. This is where the compressor line starts. Follow the entropy lines up until they cross the condenser line. This is where the compressor line ends. Figure 18-21 shows the compressor line in green.

Metering Device Line

Measure the temperature of the liquid line entering the metering device. Follow the condenser line until it crosses this liquid line temperature in the subcooled area. In our example this is 110°F. This is where the metering device lines starts. Draw a line straight down until it crosses the evaporator line. This is where the metering device line ends. Figure 18-22 shows the metering device line in purple. Figure 18-23 shows the completed plot of the cycle with the evaporator and condenser lines cleaned up.

UNIT 18—SUMMARY

A refrigerant pressure-enthalpy diagram, called a PH diagram, shows the relationship of all the physical characteristics of a refrigerant including pressure, temperature, heat, volume, and state. PH diagrams can be used to determine a system's refrigeration capacity, the amount of refrigerant that must be circulated, the amount of heat absorbed by the evaporator, the amount of heat rejected by the condenser, or the required compressor capacity. PH diagrams have a large hump in the middle called the saturation curve. Everything inside the curve is a saturated mixture of liquid and gas. Everything to the right of the curve is superheated gas, and everything to the left of the curve is subcooled liquid. Enthalpy is the amount of heat in something; specific enthalpy is the amount of heat per pound. The specific enthalpy lines are vertical and marked in Btu/lb. The pressure lines are horizontal lines that are

Figure 18-21 The compressor line, drawn in green, starts where the evaporator line intersects the 40°F temperature line and follows the entropy lines up to the condenser line

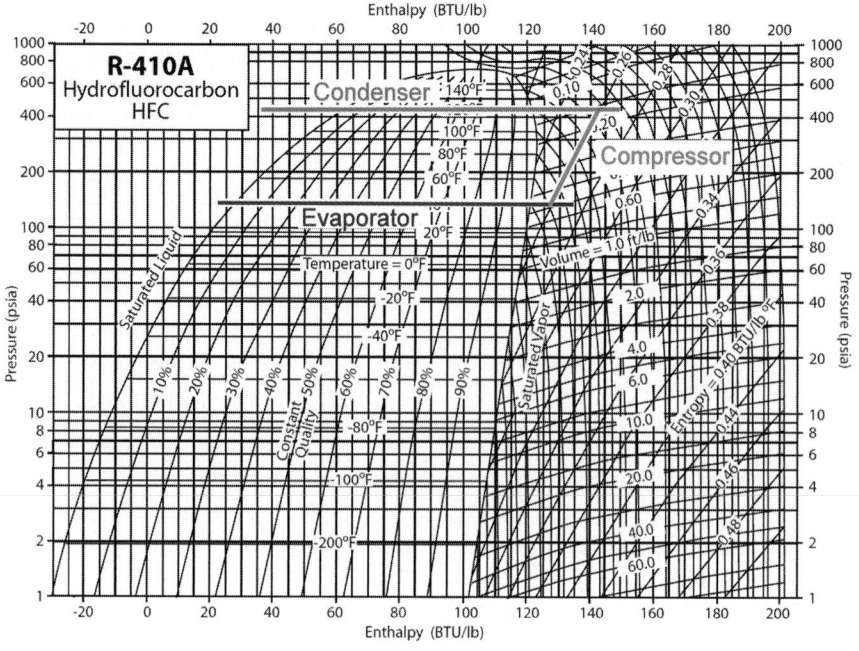

Figure 18-22 The metering device line, shown in purple, starts where the condenser line intersects the 110°F temperature line and drops straight down to the evaporator line

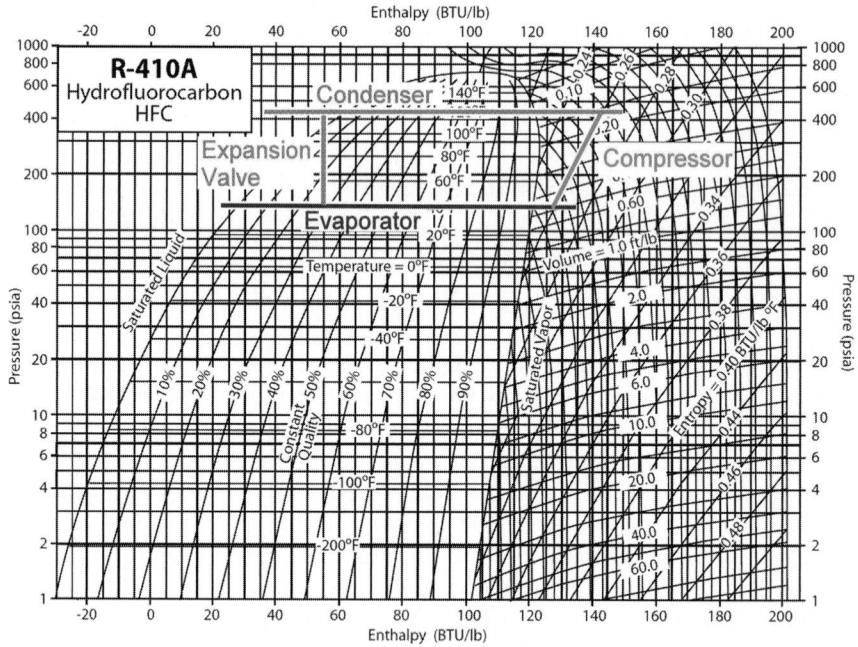

marked in absolute pressure, psia. The temperature lines are nearly vertical in the vapor and liquid areas, but horizontal in the saturated area, giving them a zigzag appearance. The temperature remains constant when heat is added inside the saturation curve. This is called an isothermal process. The refrigeration cycle is shown with four lines. A horizontal line at the bottom shows the evaporator, and a horizontal line at the top shows the condenser. They are connected by the compressor line which follows the entropy lines up. Entropy is the amount of heat per pound per degree in the refrigerant and is measured in Btu/lb/°F. No heat is added or lost when the refrigerant passes

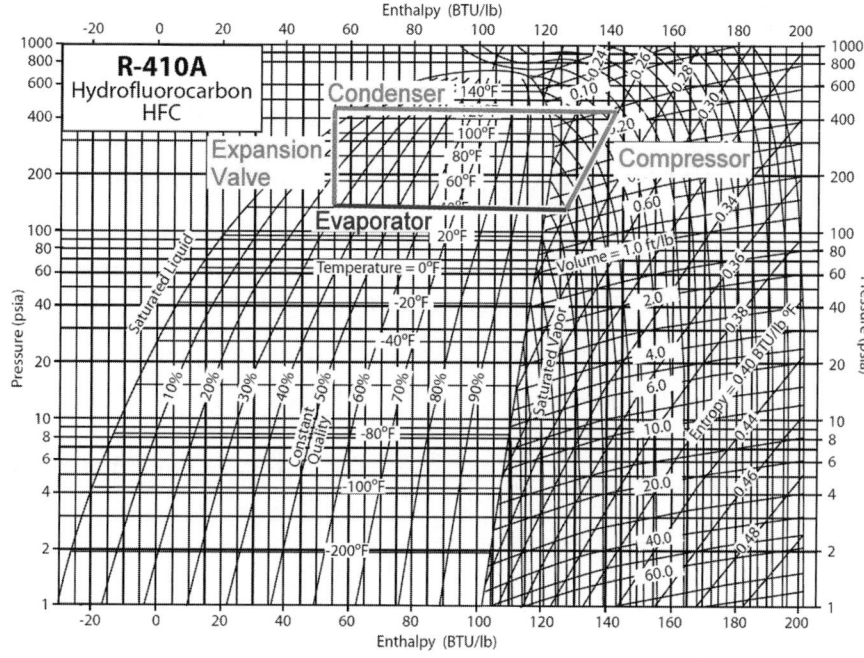

Figure 18-23 Completed plot of refrigeration cycle

through the metering device. This is why the metering device is shown as a vertical line dropping straight down form the condenser line to the evaporator line.

UNIT 18—REVIEW QUESTIONS

1. List the refrigerant characteristics that are shown on a pressure-enthalpy diagram (PH)

2. What is the saturation curve?

3. Where are the pressure lines and how are they marked?

4. Define enthalpy.

5. Explain the difference between enthalpy and specific entyhalpy.

6. Where are the specific enthalpy lines and how are they marked?

7. Why are the temperature lines horizontal inside the saturated curve?

8. What are the constant quality lines?

9. As you move to the right or left along a constant pressure line in the saturated liquid area, what happens to the temperature?

10. As you move to the right or left along a constant pressure line what happens to the specific enthalpy?

11. As you move up or down along a constant enthalpy line, what happens to the pressure?

12. As you move up along a constant enthalpy line in the constant quality area, what happens to the temperature?

13. In refrigeration, how do we define entropy?

14. Why does some of the refrigerant liquid flash vaporize in the metering device?

15. At what point in the refrigeration cycle does the last of the liquid vaporize?

16. What happens to the refrigerant pressure during desuperheating?

17. When does liquid refrigerant first begin forming in the condenser?

18. What is subcooling?

19. How much heat enters the refrigerant in the metering device when some of it flashes to a vapor, cooling the remaining liquid to the evaporator temperature?

20. What can bubbles of refrigerant vapor do to the metering device's operating efficiency?

21. When does a refrigerant pick up most of the heat as it circulates through a system?

22. Define adiabatic.

23. Define isothermal.

24. Explain how a system's refrigeration effect can be determined.

25. Determine the refrigeration effect of the following system. The liquid entering the evaporator has an enthalpy of 64 Btu/lb and the vapor leaving the evaporator has an enthalpy of 121 Btu/lb.

26. What is the net refrigeration effect for the system in question 25 if the system is circulating 4 lb of refrigerant each minute?

27. When drawing a PH diagram of an operating system, how is placement of the condenser and evaporator lines determined?

28. When drawing a PH diagram of an operating system, how is placement of the compressor line determined?

29. When drawing a PH diagram of an operating system, how is placement of the metering device line determined?

30. Why is the condenser line wider than the evaporator line in a PH diagram of a refrigeration cycle?

31. How can a PH diagram be used to determine the compression ratio?

32. How can a PH diagram be used to determine the heat of compression?

33. How can a PH diagram be used to determine the RCOP for a particular system?

34. How many pounds of refrigerant must flow through a 4 ton evaporator each minute if each pound has an enthalpy of 50.0 Btu/lb?

35. What will happen in the evaporator if the compressor capacity is not large enough to remove all of the vapor?

36. On a blank sheet of paper, sketch a typical PH diagram for a refrigeration system. You do not need to duplicate all the scales on the PH diagram. Just show the saturation curve and the four cycle lines.

Compressors

After completing this unit you will be able to:

- identify the major types of compressors.
- explain how each type of compressor works.
- give examples of applications for each type of compressor.
- explain horsepower and compressor capacity.
- explain common compressor problems.

19.1 INTRODUCTION

The compressor is a mechanical device for pumping refrigerant vapor from the low pressure side in the evaporator to the high pressure side in the condenser. The word compress means to squeeze. The compressor reduces the volume of the refrigerant gas by squeezing it. Since gas volume, pressure, and temperature are related, reducing the volume causes an increase in both pressure and temperature.

Compressors are identified by the mechanical parts that perform the actual pumping of the refrigerant vapor. In the reciprocating compressor a piston travels back and forth in a cylinder, Figure 19-1. The scroll compressor has a stationary scroll and an orbiting scroll that moves within the stationary scroll, Figure 19-2. The centrifugal compressor uses an impeller rotating within a housing at very high speed, as shown in Figure 19-3. The screw compressor uses a rotating screw within a tapered housing, Figure 19-4. The rotary compres-

sor uses an offset rolling piston that orbits within a cylinder, Figure 19-5.

The type of compressor used depends on the application. Application factors include the type of refrigerant, the size (tonnage), the pressure difference, the evaporator and condenser saturation temperatures, and the type of cooling available for the compressor. Figure 19-6 indicates the various applications for the different types of compressors.

19.2 COMPRESSOR TYPES

Compressors can be classified by their physical and operational characteristics. They are classified by general operating principle, physical enclosure, mechanical design, cooling mechanism, and evaporator temperature. The different classifications are listed below.

General Operating Principle

- Positive displacement
- Nonpositive displacement

Physical Enclosure

- Open
- Hermetic
- Semi-hermetic

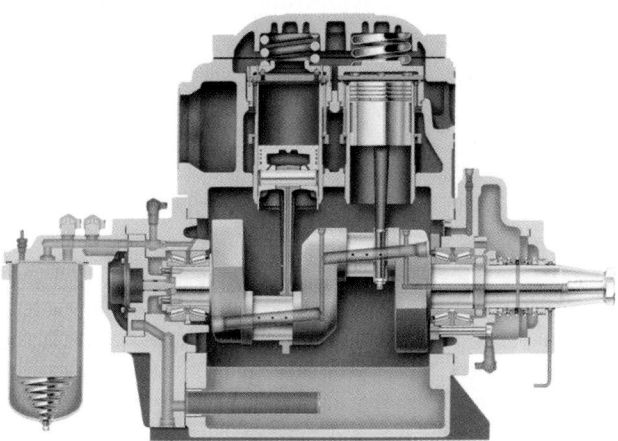

Figure 19-1 Open drive reciprocating compressor
(Courtesy Vilter Manufacturing)

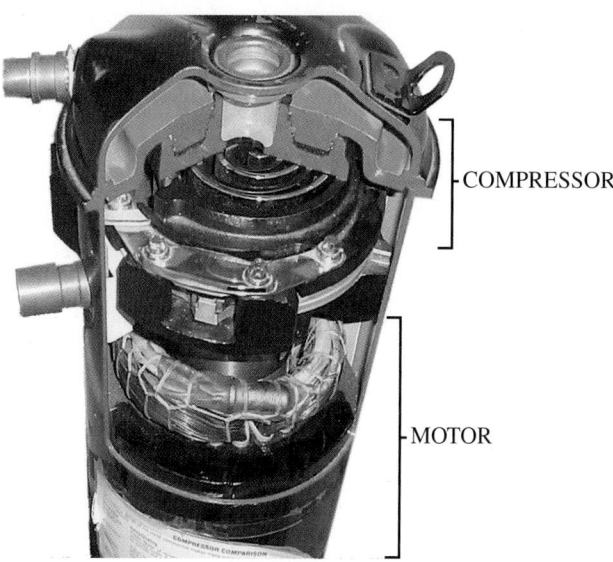

COMPRESSOR

MOTOR

Figure 19-2 Scroll compressor

Figure 19-3 Centrifugal compressor

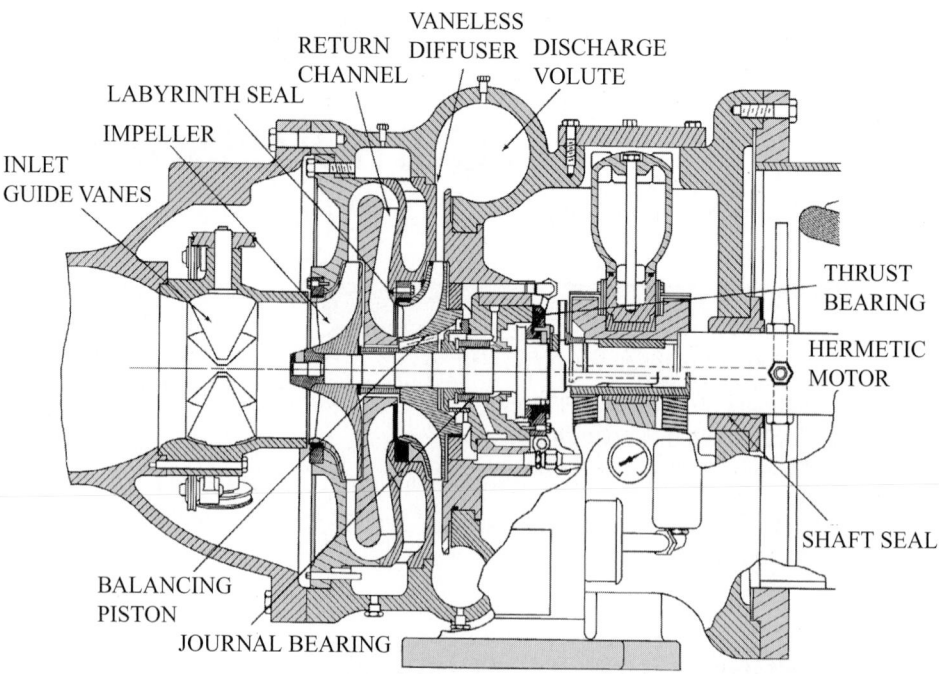

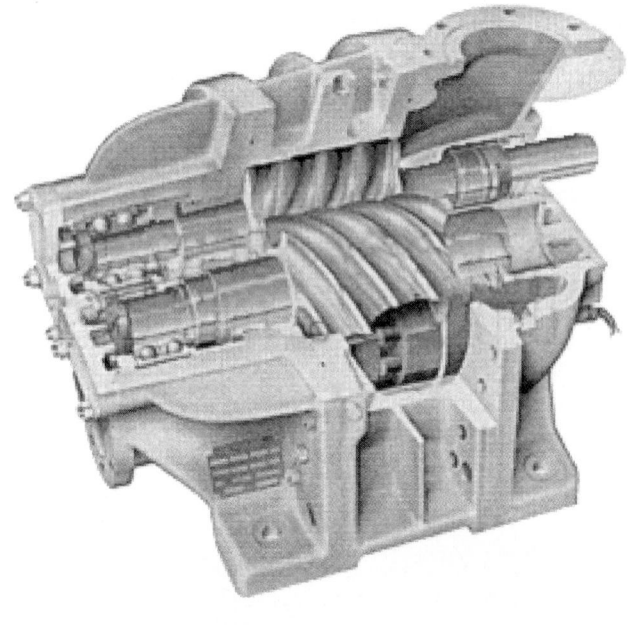

Figure 19-4 Screw compressor

Figure 19-5 Rotary compressor

Evaporator Saturation Temperature

- High
- Medium
- Low
- Ultra low

19.3 POSITIVE DISPLACEMENT COMPRESSORS

Compressors are commonly divided into two large groups by their operating principle: positive displacement and nonpositive displacement. Positive displacement compressors move the gas by taking gas into a space and then replacing that space with something physical, like a piston. Basically, whatever is in the space is positively shoved out by the mechanism. Blocking the discharge port of a positive displacement compressor can cause compressor damage because the gas must go somewhere.

Mechanical Design

- Reciprocating
- Rotary
- Scroll
- Screw
- Centrifugal

Cooling Mechanism

- Air
- Water
- Refrigerant

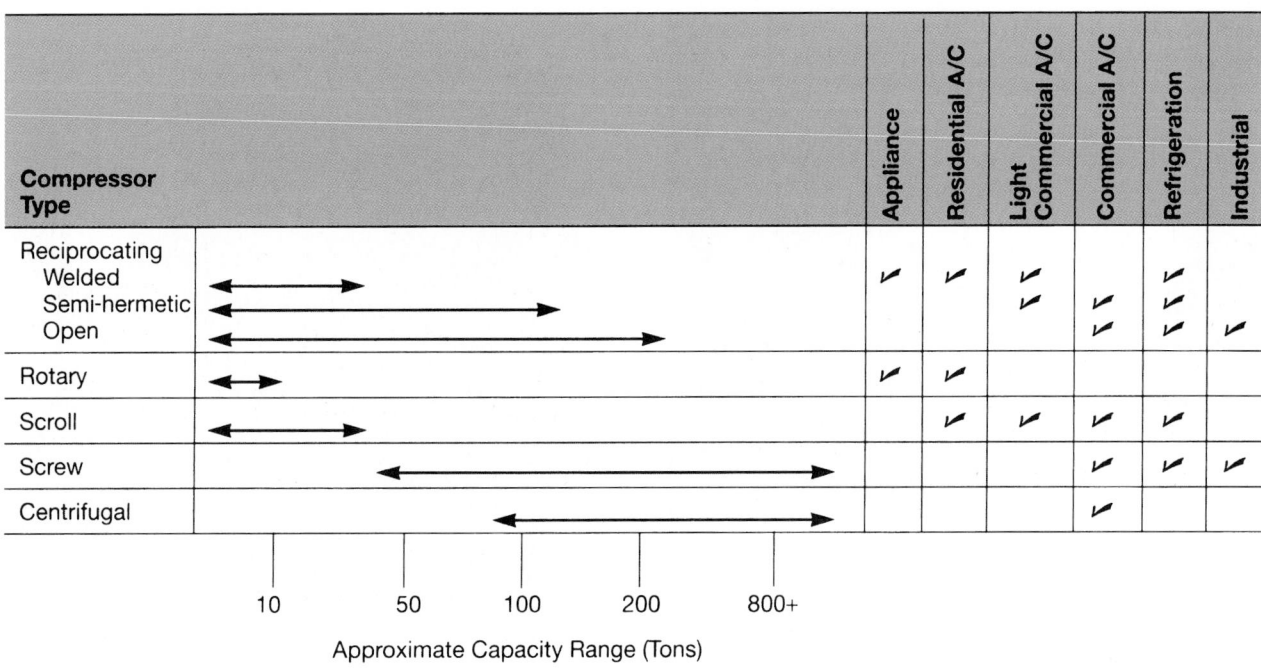

Compressor Type		Appliance	Residential A/C	Light Commercial A/C	Commercial A/C	Refrigeration	Industrial
Reciprocating Welded Semi-hermetic Open		✔	✔	✔ ✔	✔ ✔	✔ ✔ ✔	✔
Rotary		✔	✔				
Scroll			✔	✔	✔	✔	
Screw						✔	✔	✔
Centrifugal					✔		

10   50   100   200   800+

Approximate Capacity Range (Tons)

Figure 19-6 Compressor application by types

SAFETY TIP

Closing off or blocking the discharge valve on a positive displacement compressor while it is operating can be dangerous. With no place to go, the discharge pressure increases rapidly, creating extremely high pressures.

19.4 NONPOSITIVE DISPLACEMENT COMPRESSORS

Nonpositive displacement compressors do not fill the gas space with something else. These machines operate like giant fans or turbines turning at very high speeds. They basically throw the refrigerant outward, creating an increase in pressure and temperature. This outward force is like the centrifugal force you feel on those spinning pieces of playground equipment, merry-go-rounds. These compressors are called centrifugal compressors after the physical force that makes them work. The discharge of a centrifugal compressor should not be blocked because it can set up a condition known as surging, which can damage the compressor.

19.5 OPEN DRIVE COMPRESSORS

The oldest compressor design is the open type compressor shown in Figure 19-7. Open compressors may be driven by means of a pulley on a shaft that extends through a seal. The pulley is driven by a separate motor or engine. Open compressors have performed reliably over the decades, but have

Figure 19-7 Open compressor

been largely superseded by newer designs. Open machines (unlike hermetic) can be used with ammonia (NH_3) refrigerant as long as all components and accessories are made of iron or steel (or other suitable materials). Open compressors

Figure 19-8 Industrial duty open type compressor

range in size from less than a ton capacity to several hundred tons in capacity. They are often used for refrigeration and industrial applications where rugged, serviceable machinery is required. Figure 19-8 shows an industrial duty open compressor.

All open compressors use a shaft seal to prevent refrigerant from leaking around the crankshaft. These seals are subject to forming leaks and need to be checked during planned maintenance or service.

In direct drive compressors, Figure 19-9, the motor shaft is coupled to the compressor shaft and driven at motor speed.

Belt driven machines offer the flexibility of selecting a compressor speed to match the load. The belts require additional space and a protective guard. They require increased maintenance and increased power due to operational losses. An example of a belt driven compressor is shown in Figure 19-10.

One advantage of an open drive compressor is that the motor and compressor are separate units so that the motor or

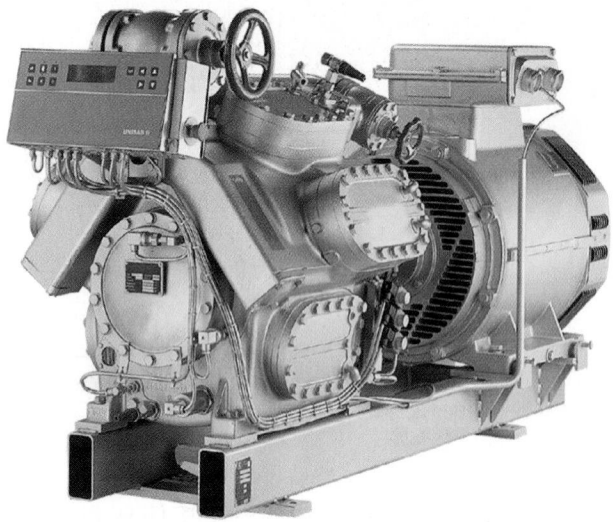

Figure 19-9 Direct drive compressor
(Courtesy Frick, York Refrigeration Systems)

Figure 19-10 Open type direct drive compressor
(Courtesy Hampden Engineering Corporation)

compressor can be repaired or replaced without having to buy a complete system. Another advantage is that the motor's heat is not absorbed in the refrigerant, so it does not have to be rejected in the condenser like most other compressor types.

The most common use of open compressors is for automobile air conditioning. In automobiles, the air conditioning compressor is driven by a pulley and belt off of the main vehicle engine. Open compressors are also used for transport refrigeration on trucks, tractor trailers, and shipping containers. These applications generally use a separate engine to drive the compressor.

19.6 HERMETIC COMPRESSORS

Hermetic compressors have their mechanical components and electric motor enclosed in a single welded shell, Figure 19-11. The compressor crankshaft extends into the rotor of the electric motor, eliminating the need for drive components. The benefits of hermetic compressors include:

- Reliable operation due to the direct connection between the motor and compressor with no belts or couplings to wear or break.
- No shaft seal to leak because the motor and compressor are sealed in welded steel shell.
- Very compact in size, permitting increased refrigerated storage space.
- Lower sound level, ideal for domestic appliances.

One challenge with hermetic compressor design is to pass electrical connections through the welded steel shell

Figure 19-11 Hermetic compressor

Figure 19-13 Hermetically sealed electric motor compressor units
(Courtesy Danfoss Inc.)

without grounding out to the shell. This is accomplished by passing the electrical connections through glass or ceramic insulators. High strength glass insulates the terminals from the metal that the terminals pass through, Figure 19-12.

SAFETY TIP

The terminal cover should always be in place when operating a hermetic compressor. Abnormally high current can create enough heat to crack the glass holding the terminals in and the electrical terminals can shoot out under high pressure. This is usually followed by ignition of the refrigerant oil. This acts like a bullet followed by a flame thrower. This is known as terminal venting. It is rare, but potentially deadly.

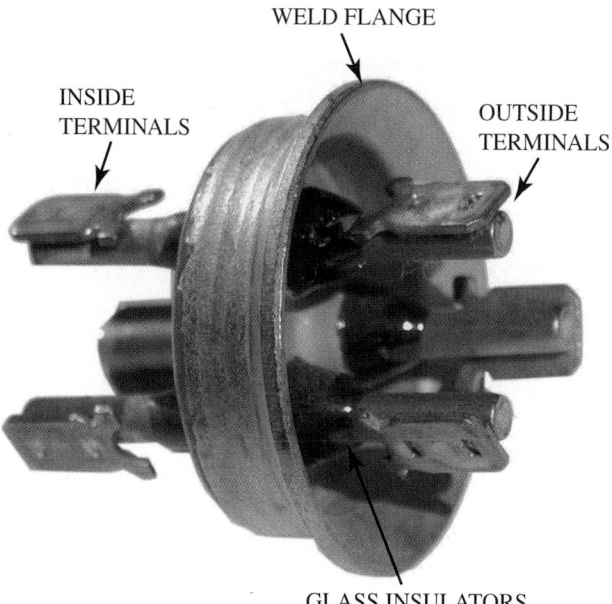

Figure 19-12 A glass to metal connection is used to isolate the electrical terminals from the metal compressor shell

The shells on reciprocating hermetic compressors are called low-side shells because the suction gas enters the shell. The motors in hermetic compressors are cooled by the refrigerant vapor traveling over them. Operating a hermetic compressor on a low charge can cause the motor to overheat because of poor motor cooling. Many hermetic compressor manufacturers do not like their compressors operating in a vacuum. The motor varnishes used in the motor winding lose some of their insulating ability under deep vacuums and motors can arc out very quickly, even before they have time to overheat. Keeping the refrigerant clean is especially important in a system with a hermetic compressor because the refrigerant and oil flow directly over the motor and all internal electrical connections.

Hermetic compressor units, Figure 19-13, are made in a variety of sizes, from tiny fractional horsepower units meant for small appliances, to larger units up to about 20 tons for air conditioning use. They are sometimes called welded hermetics, full hermetics, or sealed hermetic compressors.

The welded steel shell prevents any field service access, so there are no service procedures to replace damaged internal components such as motors, bearings, valves, and so on. If damaged or defective, the entire hermetic compressor is replaced. Reciprocating hermetic compressors are usually internally spring isolated to reduce the inherent vibration caused by the reciprocating action of the pistons, Figure 19-14.

19.7 SEMI-HERMETIC COMPRESSORS

Semi-hermetic compressors also have the motor and mechanics in one enclosure, but the enclosure has some form of access, like bolted plates and gaskets. The semi-hermetic motor compressor unit, which is field serviceable by virtue of its bolted construction, has evolved over the past 50 to 60 years. It may have a bolted cast iron construction or bolted, flanged, drawn steel shell. An advantage of semi-hermetic compressors is that they provide the advantages of hermetic

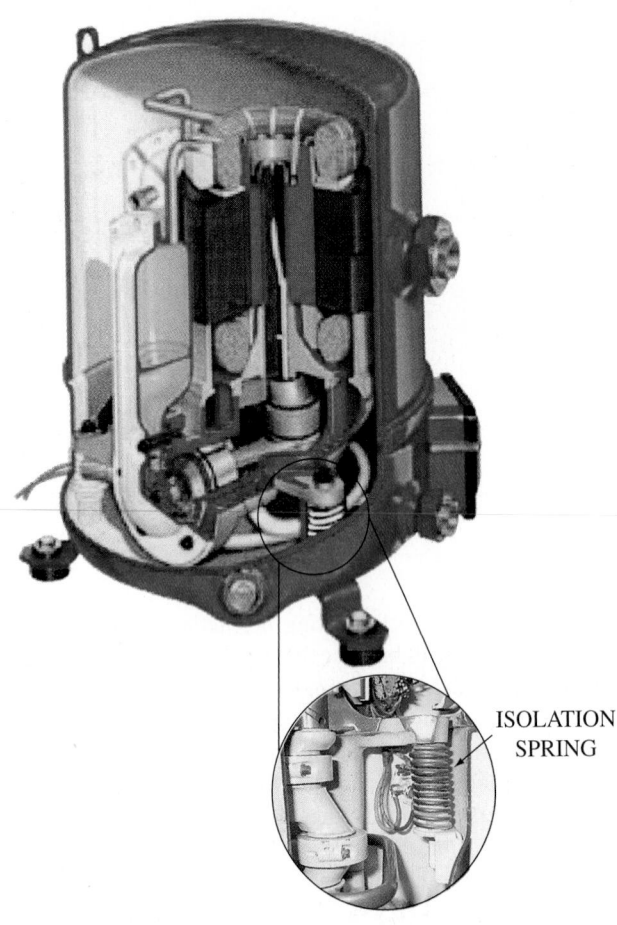

Figure 19-15 Semi-hermetic compressor used for medium and low temperature refrigeration

ISOLATION
SPRING

Figure 19-14 Cutaway view of hermetic compressor showing internal isolation spring inset
(Courtesy Danfoss Inc.)

compressors but are still field or factory repairable. Parts such as valve reeds, gaskets, bearing inserts, or motor stators may be replaced on various units. These machines are known by a variety of names: semi-hermetic. serviceable hermetic, accessible hermetic, and bolted hermetic. The units are available in sizes that range from approximately 0.25 to 125 tons cooling capacity. Figure 19-15 shows a semi-hermetic compressor used for medium and low temperature refrigeration.

Cooling

Semi-hermetic compressors can be classified by their means of motor cooling: air cooled or refrigerant cooled. Air cooled semi-hermetic compressors use airflow over the motor portion of the compressor to cool the compressor motor. The refrigerant goes straight into the cylinders on these compressors. Maintaining a minimum superheat of 20°F at the compressor is critical for air-cooled semi-hermetic compressors. Refrigerant cooled compressors use the refrigerant gas for cooling, much like hermetic compressors. They can operate safely at a much lower superheat because the refrigerant goes over the motor first before entering the cylinders.

Duty

The size and type of motor a compressor needs depends upon the job it is required to do. Hermetic and semi-hermetic compressors come with a motor already matched to the compressor. For this reason, hermetic and semi-hermetic compressors are classified by the saturation temperature of the returning suction gas they are designed to handle. Two semi-hermetic compressors can be identical mechanically, but have different motors because they are intended for different applications. In general, semi-hermetic compressor applications are classified as high temperature, medium temperature, low temperature, and ultra-low temperature.

SERVICE TIP

Although semi-hermetic compressors are field serviceable, for cost reasons many are removed and sent to companies that specialize in remanufacturing compressors. These facilities are set up to thoroughly clean and inspect the entire compressor and replace those parts that have worn beyond tolerance. Field service work is commonly done for large compressors that would be extremely difficult or expensive to remove.

19.8 RECIPROCATING COMPRESSORS

Reciprocating compressors have been used in refrigeration service for a long time. The reciprocating compressor is used in the majority of domestic, small commercial, and industrial condensing unit applications. Reciprocating compressors are available in open, hermetic, and semi-hermetic designs.

In a reciprocating compressor the piston is driven up and down in the cylinder by the connecting rod and crankshaft, Figure 19-16. Besides the compressor body, the basic mechanical components of a reciprocating compressor are the crankshaft, connecting rods, piston, wrist pin, valves, and valve plate, Figure 19-17.

The crankshaft operates like a rotating lever. Two types of crankshafts are the crankthrow and the eccentric. Crankthrow crankshafts look like the crankshaft on an engine; they have

Figure 19-18 Crankthrow crankshaft

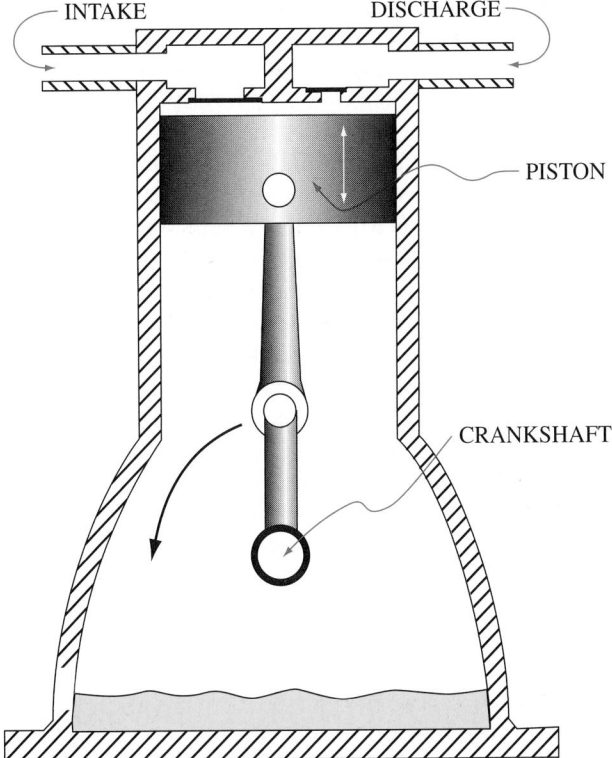

Figure 19-16 The crankshaft rotates while the piston moves up and down

Figure 19-19 Eccentric crankshaft

Figure 19-17 Reciprocating compressor parts

offset sections where the rods attach, Figure 19-18. The ends of the rods bolt around the crankshaft on a crankthrow crankshaft. Eccentric crankshafts look like the cam on an engine. An eccentric crankshaft is a straight shaft with offset lobes, Figure 19-19. The connecting rods slide over these lobes. The connecting rods used with eccentric crankshafts are one piece; they slide over the crankshaft when the compressor is assembled. An eccentric crankshaft provides smoother operation than a crankthrow crankshaft.

The connecting rods are either two piece for crankthrow crankshafts, or one piece for eccentric crankshafts, Figure 19-20. The shaft on some connecting rods has a hole which carries oil up the piston wrist pin. Other systems use oil in the refrigerant vapor inside the compressor to lubricate the piston wrist pin.

The pistons are usually manufactured slightly smaller in diameter than the cylinder they will operate in. Piston rings are used on large compressors to fill this gap, Figure 19-21.

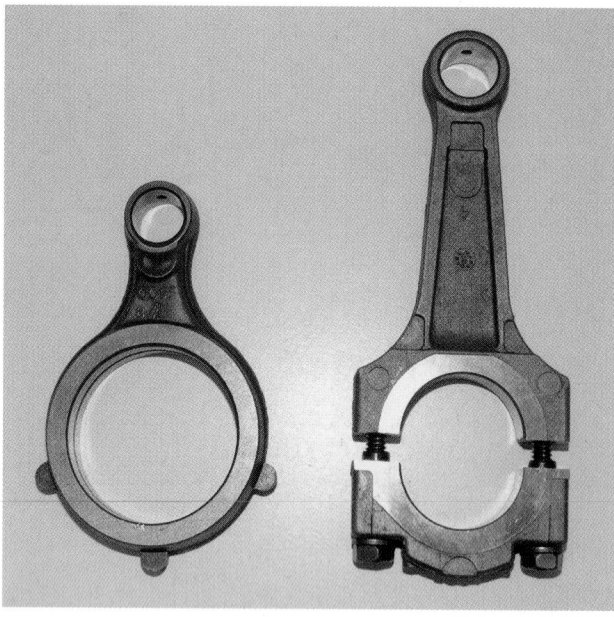

Figure 19-20 One piece and two piece connecting rods

Figure 19-21 Compressor piston with rings

Small compressors do not have rings, but "oil grooves" where oil collects to help block gases from "blowing by" the pistons during the compression stroke.

The valve plate serves as the top of the cylinder and holds the valves. Typically, the discharge valves are located on top of the valve plate and the suction valves are located on the underside of the valve plate. The valves are self-operating: they open and close due to pressure difference. They are sometimes spring loaded, but the principle is the same. Note that

this is quite different from an automobile engine, where the valves are mechanically opened and closed by a camshaft synchronized to the crankshaft.

Figure 19-22 shows the different types of reciprocating cylinder valves: (a) the flexing reed valve; (b) the floating reed valve; (c) the ring valve; and (d) the reduced clearance poppet valve used for the discus compressor.

Pistons within the compressors may have the suction valve located in the top of the piston; this is classified as a valve-in-head type, or the piston may have a solid head, with the suction and discharge valves located in a valve plate or cylinder head.

Figure 19-23a–f shows the complete compression cycle of a reciprocating piston compressor. Position (a) shows the beginning of the intake cycle; the suction valve has not opened because the pressure in the cylinder is still above the system suction pressure. As the piston strokes down in the cylinder, the pressure will drop to a point where it is below the pressure in the suction manifold. At (b), the higher pressure in the suction line forces the suction valve open and low pressure, cold (but superheated) suction gas from the evaporator will flow into the cylinder. At (c), the piston continues downward, drawing in refrigerant vapor. At (d), the refrigerant pressure above the rising piston forces the suction valve closed and the discharge valve open. At (e), the rising piston pushes the high pressure and temperature refrigerant out the discharge valve. At position (f), the suction valve remains closed and the discharge valve also closes because the system discharge pressure is greater than the pressure left in the cylinder.

19.9 CYLINDER GAS REEXPANSION

The clearance volume is the space between the top of the piston and the cylinder head. During the compression stroke, gas leaves the cylinder and passes into the discharge manifold until the pressure in the cylinder is the same as the discharge manifold pressure. At the completion of the compression stroke, this space is filled with compressed gas that is not going anywhere. This gas will have to expand on the downstroke before the pressure can drop to a point to admit fresh suction gas. This reexpansion represents wasted work and lost capacity. The compressor designer strives to minimize the clearance volume while at the same time leaving adequate room for thermal expansion and for unwanted incompressible slugs of oil and liquid refrigerant. These slugs can enter the cylinder, and possess the ability to do great damage to the valves, piston, and cylinder head. Theoretically, 0% clearance volume would be good; practically, it would be disastrous.

Figure 19-24 shows a pressure-volume plot that is used to study reciprocating compressor performance. The horizontal axis represents the cylinder volume and the vertical axis represents the cylinder pressure. A piston, cylinder, and valves have been added to graphically illustrate the stroke.

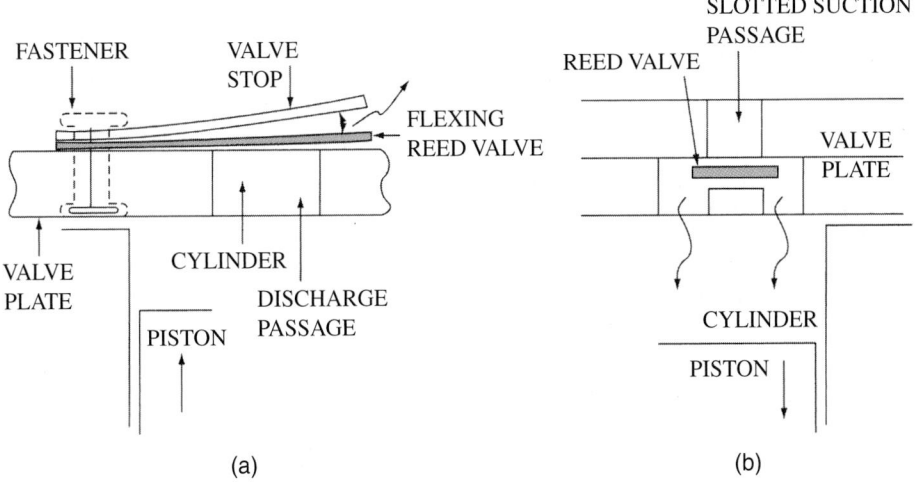

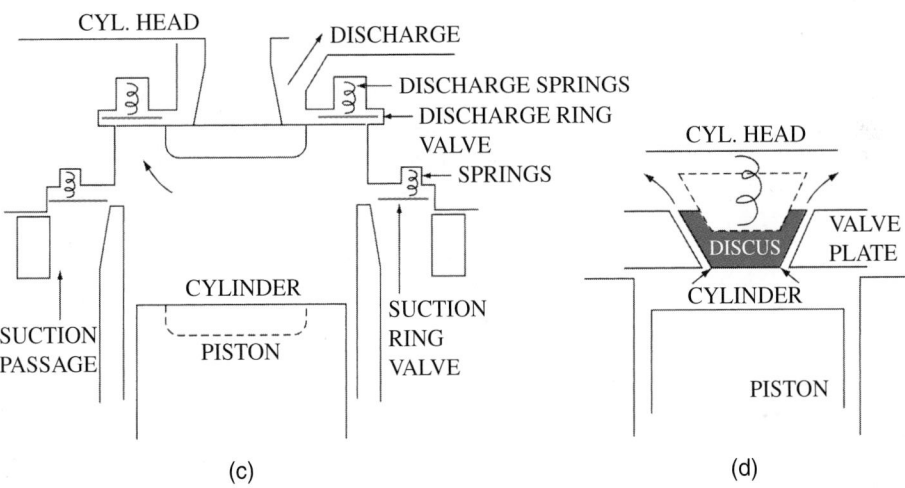

Figure 19-22 Typical reciprocating compressor cylinder valves: (a) Flexing reed valve; (b) Floating reed valve; (c) Ring valves; (d) Reduced clearance poppet valve, discus compressor

Figure 19-25 uses this type of graph to show the reexpansion volume at the beginning of the downstroke. Point A represents top dead center of the piston stroke and shows the clearance volume and discharge pressure. As the piston travels down, the trapped compressed clearance volume gas has to reexpand until it reaches suction pressure at point B. Figure 19-26 illustrates the useful portion of the intake stroke. As the downstroke continues from point B to point C, the cylinder pressure is below the suction manifold pressure and the pressure difference opens the suction valve and fills the cylinder with new refrigerant vapor. The suction valve closes at the bottom of the stroke.

Figure 19-27 shows the compression stroke from bottom dead center (C) to point D. This compresses the gas to a point about equal to discharge manifold pressure. During the compression stroke, both suction and discharge valves are closed. The piston has traveled from 100% of cylinder volume to a point about 20% of cylinder volume. On air conditioning R-410A applications, the suction pressure would be about 118 psig (40°F saturation) and the discharge pressure about 417 psig (120°F saturation).

Figure 19-28 shows the completion of the compression stroke from point D to A (top dead center). The cylinder pressure exceeds the discharge manifold pressure and forces the gas out. The gas occupying the clearance volume space (approximately 4% volume) remains. This trapped gas will remain and must reexpand with the next intake stroke.

The previous illustrations assume an ideal world with no pressure losses across the valves and minimum turbulence. A more realistic view is found in Figure 19-29, which shows pressure losses. The area enclosed by points A, B, C, and D on the pressure-volume plot represents the work done by the compressor on the gas passing through the cylinder.

Cylinder gas reexpansion causes inefficiency because part of the intake stroke is not used to bring in new gas. Some other types of positive displacement compressors (scroll, rotary, and screw) do not have trapped reexpansion gas to deal with and, thus, have inherently higher efficiencies.

Increasing the discharge pressure and/or reducing the suction pressure reduces the output of the compressor. Increased pressure difference increases the amount of cylinder gas reexpansion because the distance the piston must

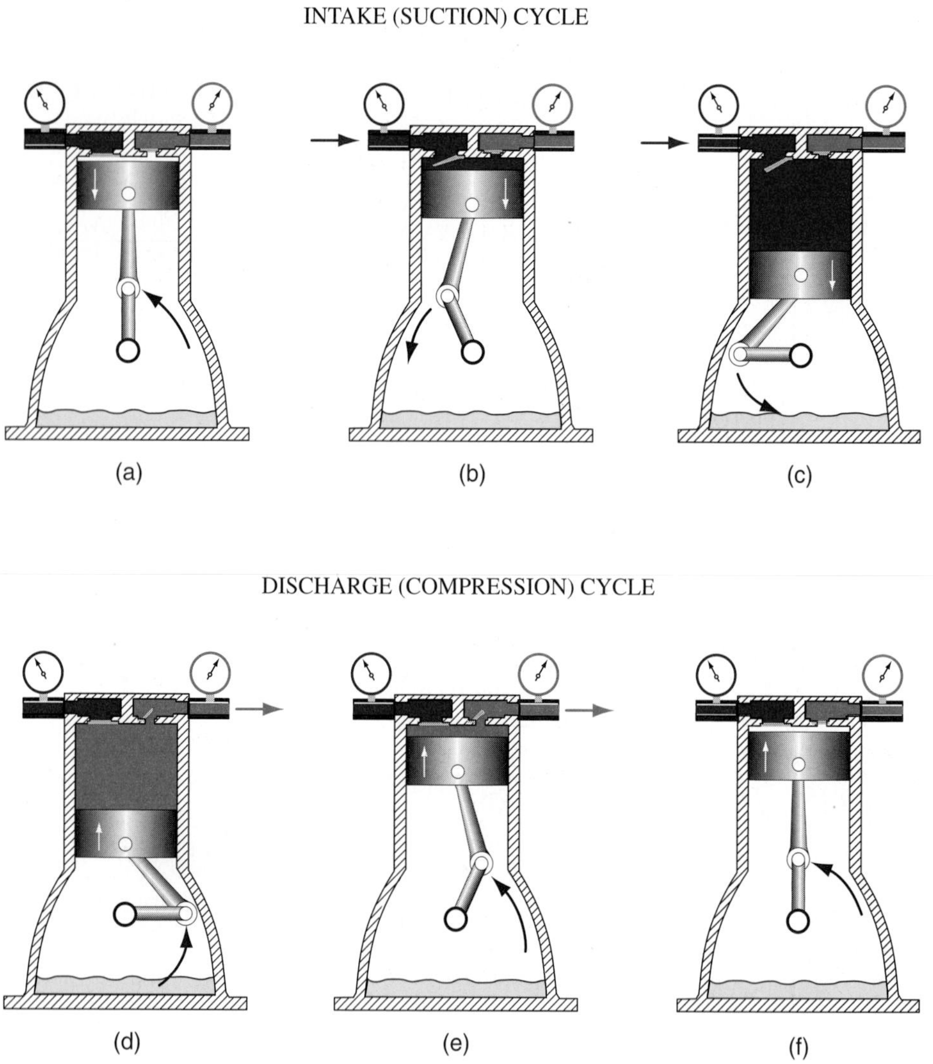

Figure 19-23 Complete compression cycle of a reciprocating piston compressor

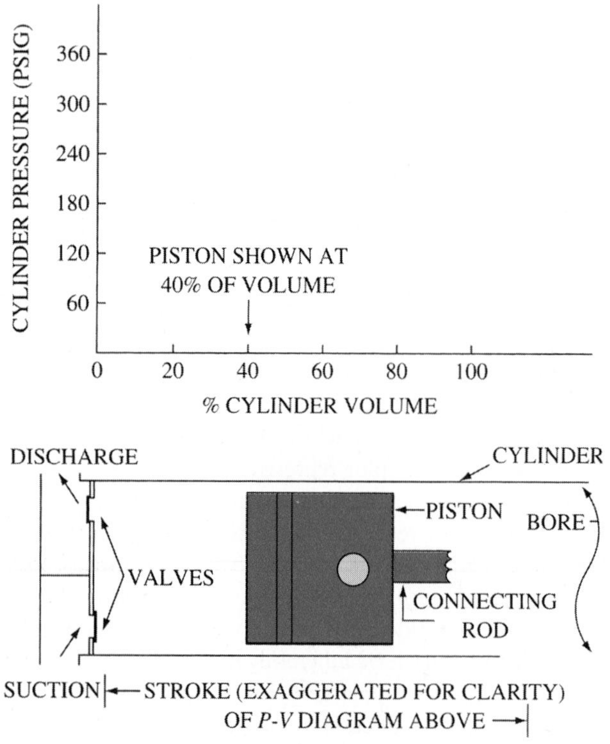

INTAKE (SUCTION) CYCLE

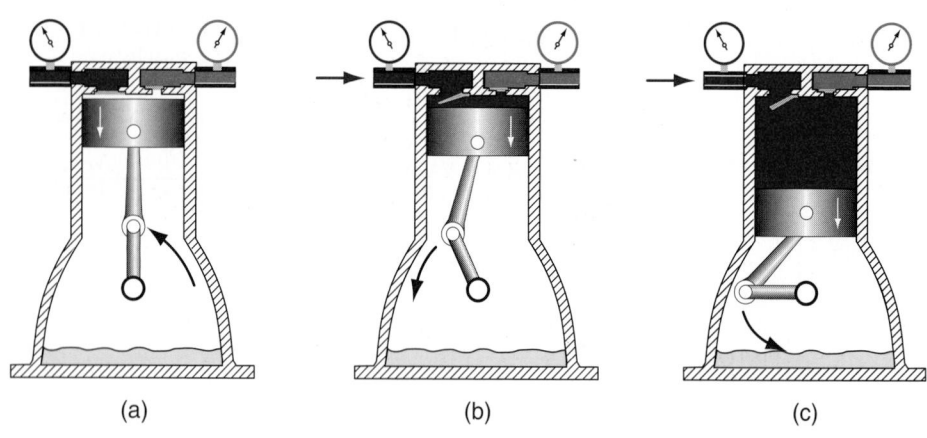

(a)　　　　　　(b)　　　　　　(c)

DISCHARGE (COMPRESSION) CYCLE

(d)　　　　　　(e)　　　　　　(f)

PISTON SHOWN AT
40% OF VOLUME
↓

CYLINDER PRESSURE (PSIG)

360 / 300 / 240 / 180 / 120 / 60

0　20　40　60　80　100

% CYLINDER VOLUME

DISCHARGE — CYLINDER

VALVES — PISTON — BORE

CONNECTING ROD

SUCTION |— STROKE (EXAGGERATED FOR CLARITY) OF *P-V* DIAGRAM ABOVE —|

Figure 19-24 The two elements of a pressure-volume plot, used in the study of reciprocating compressor performance

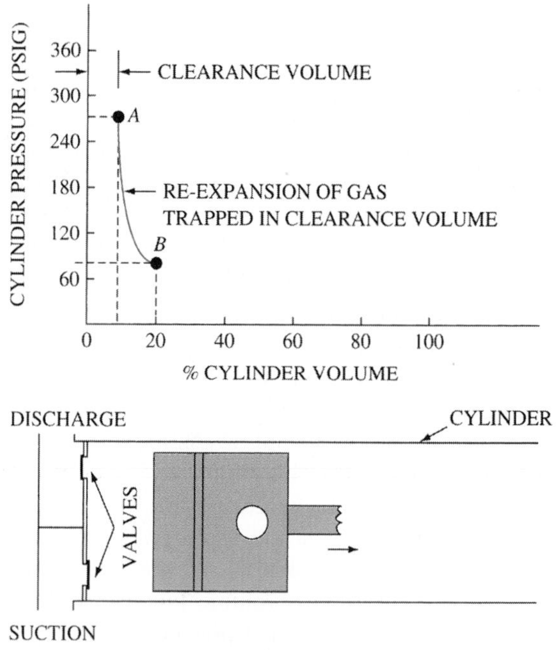

CYLINDER PRESSURE (PSIG)

CLEARANCE VOLUME

360 / 300 / 240 / 180 / 120 / 60

● *A*

RE-EXPANSION OF GAS
TRAPPED IN CLEARANCE VOLUME

B

0　20　40　60　80　100

% CYLINDER VOLUME

DISCHARGE — CYLINDER

VALVES

SUCTION

Figure 19-25 Beginning of the intake stroke; *A*: Top dead center; *B*: Suction valve ready to open

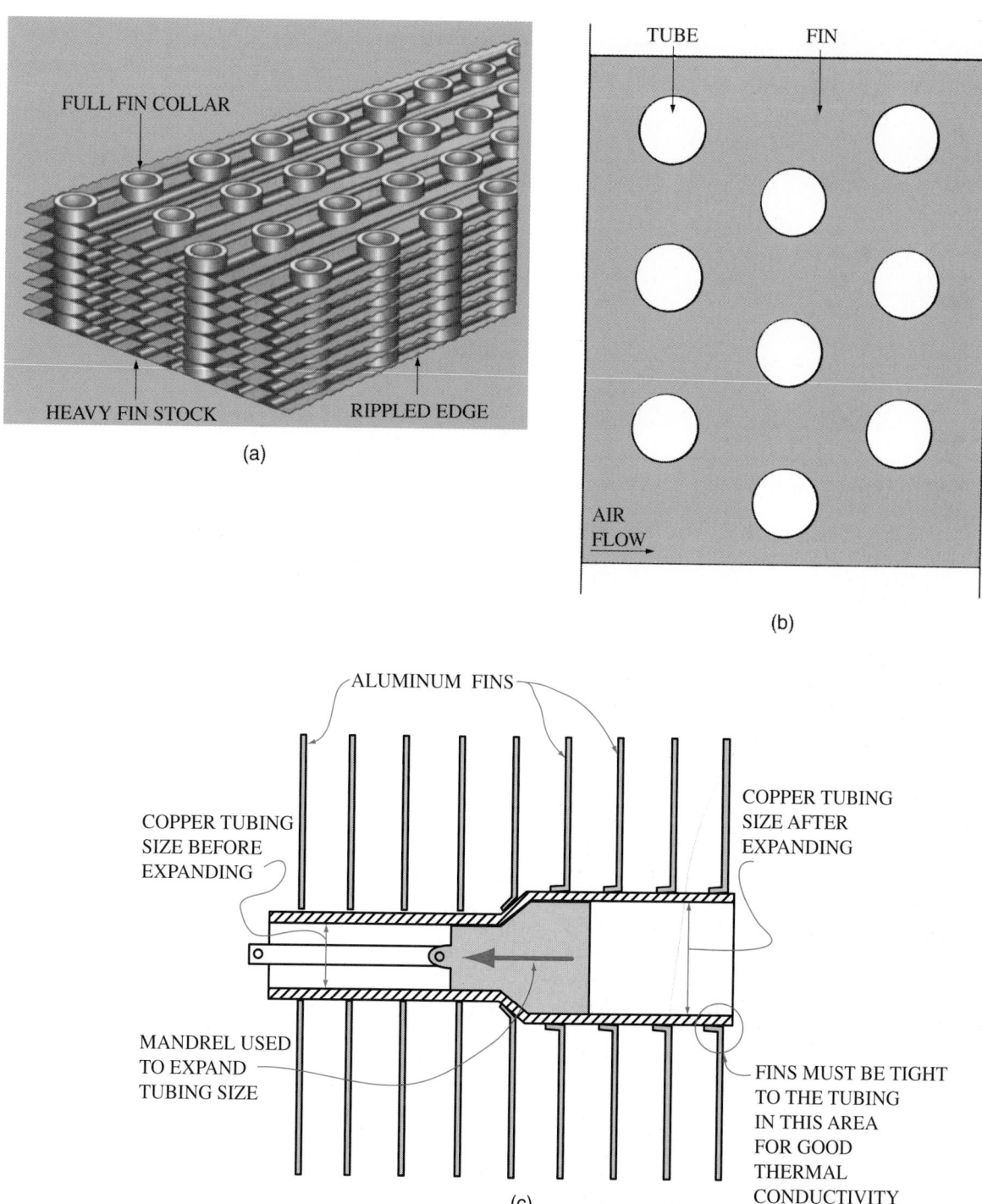

Figure 20-13 Plate fin coil details: (a) four row coil construction; (b) staggered tubes; (c) cross section of finned tube assembly

temperature can cause thermal expansion valves to under-feed as well.

The solution to the problem of low ambient operation is to maintain a minimum head pressure in order to ensure proper feeding of refrigerant to the evaporator. There are several different ways of doing this. The most common are fan cycling, fan speed control, damper control, and condenser flooding.

The use of improved expansion devices is reducing the need for head pressure control in some systems. Head pressure controls force the system to work as if it is 95°F outside all the time. Improved metering devices that can regulate with very low pressure drop reduce the need for head pressure control and save energy by allowing the system to operate against lower head pressures.

Figure 20-14 Aluminum strips are wrapped around tubing to create spine-fin coils

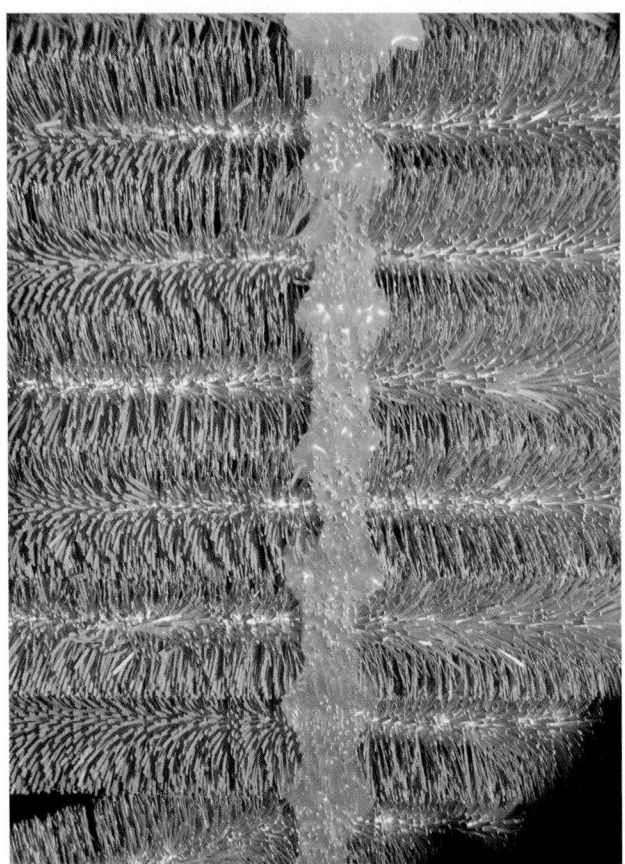

Figure 20-15 Spine-fin coils are glued together at the corners

20.11 FAN CYCLING LOW AMBIENT CONTROL

Where multiple condenser fans are employed on a single coil, the control system of the condensing unit can be equipped with devices to switch or cycle off the fans in stages. These

Figure 20-16 The 13 SEER condenser on the right is considerably larger than the 10 SEER condenser on the left, even though they are the same capacity
(Courtesy of NACHI)

controls are usually sensors that measure outdoor ambient temperature, or pressure controls that sense actual head pressure, Figure 20-17. The airflow across the coil is reduced as fans are turned off. Condensing temperatures rise with the reduced airflow. Under very low ambient conditions all of the fans can be turned off.

One disadvantage of fan cycling is that the condenser pressure can swing rapidly between the low and high set points of the fan control. Although the system works with these swings in pressure, they can result in a loss of efficiency. Another disadvantage is that on windy days even with the fans off there may be too much cooling of the condenser to maintain minimum high side pressure for the system to work properly.

Systems with a single condenser fan are generally not good candidates for fan cycling because of undesirable pressure swings. Fan cycling should never be used with air cooled compressors if there is only one fan. Air cooled compressors depend on the airflow across them to stay cool. Shutting off the fan, even at low ambient temperatures, can overheat an air cooled compressor.

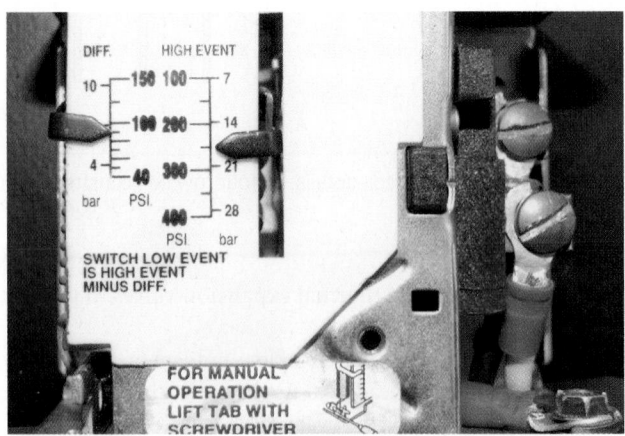

Figure 20-17 A close on rise high pressure switch with an adjustable differential can be used to cycle condenser fans

Figure 20-18 This control will vary the speed of a single phase fan motor to keep the head pressure from dropping below its set point

20.12 FAN SPEED CONTROL

Where only one condenser fan is used, air capacity can be reduced by employing a two speed motor or an electronic speed control. The electronic speed controls designed for head pressure control work by chopping part of the sine wave out, reducing the amount of current delivered to the motor, Figure 20-18. This is the same type of control often used for ceiling fans. These controls can maintain a very steady head pressure. Speed controls should not be used with condenser fan motors that have sleeve bearings. Sleeve bearings depend on a minimum speed to maintain lubrication. Turning too slowly will grind up their bearings.

20.13 DAMPER LOW AMBIENT CONTROL

Another technique of restricting airflow across the condenser coil is the use of dampers on the fan discharge. These are used on nonoverloading centrifugal type fans, not propeller fans. Blocking the discharge of a centrifugal fan will cause a reduction in amp draw, but blocking the discharge of a propeller fan will increase the amp draw. Dampers modulate from a head pressure controller to some minimum position, at which time the fan motor is shut off. This type of head pressure control is generally only used on larger systems.

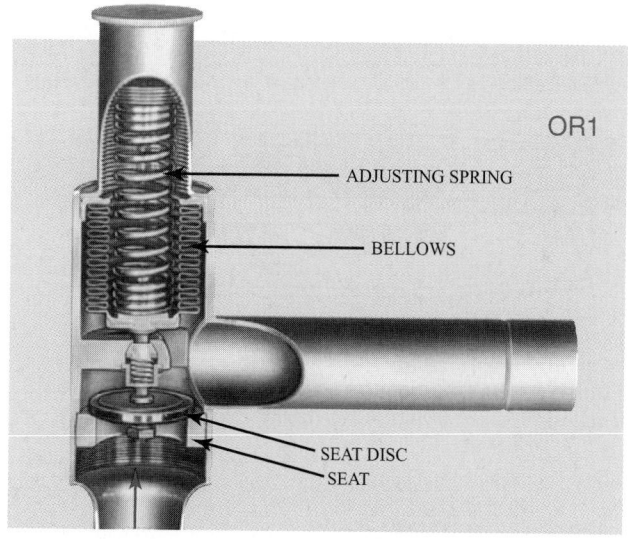

Figure 20-19 ORI, open on rise of inlet pressure valve
(Courtesy of Sporian Division-Parker Hannifin Corporation)

One common and important characteristic of the airflow restriction methods is that the full charge of refrigerant and entrained oil is in motion at all times, ensuring positive motor cooling and oil lubrication to the compressor.

20.14 FLOODED CONDENSER LOW AMBIENT CONTROL

Condenser flooding pressure control systems are common on commercial refrigeration systems and rare on air conditioning systems. This is because condenser flooding controls normally require a liquid receiver. Receivers are common in commercial refrigeration, but unusual in air conditioning.

Flooding controls artificially raise the head pressure by backing the liquid refrigerant up into the condenser tubes. An open on rise of inlet pressure control valve, ORI, is used to accomplish this, Figure 20-19. The ORI control is placed in the outlet of the condenser, which closes when the condenser pressure starts to drop. This restricts drainage of the liquid refrigerant out of the condenser, flooding it. The pressure in the flooded condenser increases because less condenser area is available for condensing refrigerant. When the condenser pressure is at or above the valve's setpoint, the ORI control opens and allows liquid refrigerant to leave the condenser. Used by itself, this valve would keep the condenser pressure at the required level, but the liquid pressure after the condenser would actually drop even further when the valve is closed.

An open on rise of differential pressure control, ORD, keeps the receiver pressure at the required setting, Figure 20-20. The ORD valve bypasses hot gas from the beginning of the condenser to the top of the liquid receiver. The

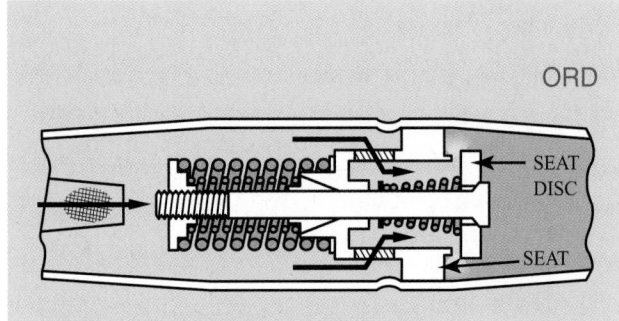

Figure 20-20 ORD, open on rise of differential pressure valve
(Courtesy of Sporlan Division-Parker Hannifin Corporation)

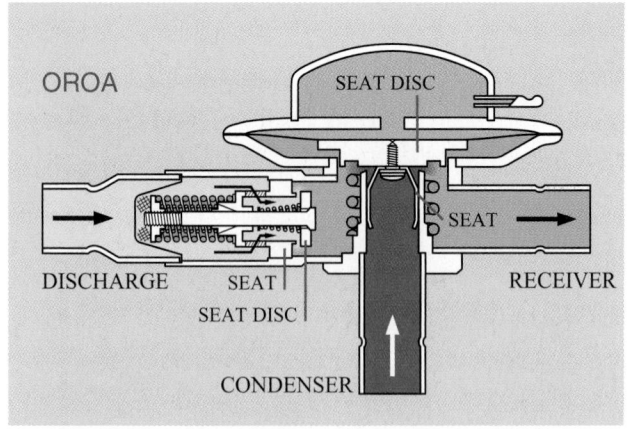

Figure 20-22 An OROA, open on rise of outdoor ambient valve, can be used by itself to control head pressure
(Courtesy of Sporlan Division-Parker Hannifin Corporation)

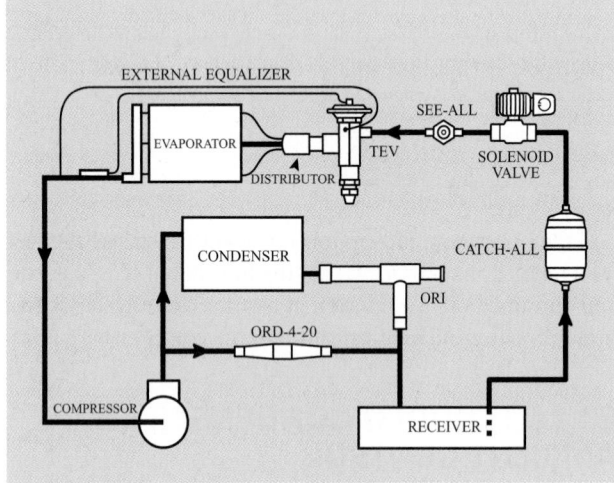

Figure 20-21 Piping diagram for application of ORI and ORD valves to control head pressure
(Courtesy of Sporlan Division-Parker Hannifin Corporation)

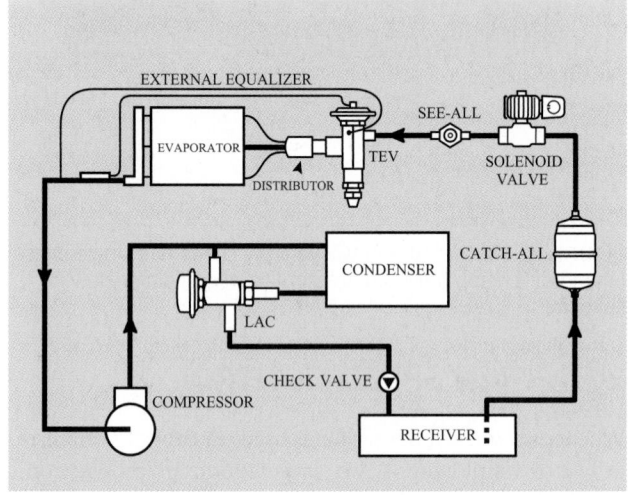

Figure 20-23 Piping diagram for application of an OROA valve to control head pressure
(Courtesy of Sporlan Division-Parker Hannifin Corporation)

purpose of this valve is to ensure enough pressure on the liquid receiver to keep the liquid in the liquid line at the minimum required pressure. The receiver is necessary because there must be a supply of liquid to the system while the condenser is being flooded. These two valves combined, the ORI and ORD, provide effective head pressure control under a wide range of operating conditions, Figure 20-21.

The functions of these two valves have now been incorporated into a single control, called an open on rise of outdoor ambient, OROA, Figure 20-22. This single, non-adjustable control simplifies selection and application of condenser flooding head pressure controls, Figure 20-23. However, it is available only for certain refrigerants. It floods the condenser and bypasses gas to the receiver based on the ambient temperature to maintain a minimum pressure.

Condenser flooding head pressure controls do not suffer from pressure swings the way fan cycling controls do, but they are more difficult to install in the field since they are piped into the refrigeration system.

TECH TIP

It is an unacceptable practice to overcharge a condenser during winter months to artificially increase the head pressure by flooding the condenser. This practice is not recommended by any manufacturer because the first warm summer day can result in compressor failure.

20.15 SERVICING AIR-COOLED CONDENSERS

Most condenser problems are related to some type of restriction of the air. When a new condenser is installed, the operating pressures and temperature need to be recorded. These values can be referred to each time the system is serviced. A change in the observed operating conditions is a good indication that additional service work is needed.

CAUTION

If the condenser becomes dirty, its condensing pressure increases. This can be a serious problem when high-pressure refrigerants like R-410A are used. R-410A operates at normal head pressure of around 400 psig, but a dirty condenser can cause these pressures to greatly increase. Condensers are designed to withstand some amount of pressure beyond normal operating pressures. However, over time, the condenser can get progressively more dirty, resulting in elevated pressures. Catastrophic failure of the refrigerant circuit can result from excessively high pressures. It is very important that condensers containing high-pressure refrigerant, such as R-410A, be thoroughly cleaned on a regular basis.

Accumulation of dirt on the condenser will reduce the heat transfer rate, and the compressor head pressure can rise to damaging levels, Figure 20-24. High head pressures will result in decreased system capacity, increased operating cost, and possible compressor damage. Air-cooled condenser coils will naturally collect dirt over a period of time. Annual cleaning is sufficient under normal operating conditions. More frequent cleaning may be necessary in particularly dirty environments. Light surface accumulation can be cleaned with a stiff bristle brush and vacuum cleaner. Grease or heavy accumulations will require coil cleaning chemicals. The equipment manufacturer should be consulted regarding acceptable cleaning products. Not all condenser coils can be chemically cleaned. Read and follow both the coil manufacturer's literature and the coil cleaning chemical manufacturer's instructions before starting. The wrong chemical cleaner can attack the condenser and do more harm than good.

SAFETY TIP

Proper personal protection equipment should always be used when applying chemical cleaners. Typically this includes safety goggles for eye protection, gloves to protect your hands, and a long sleeve shirt to protect your arms.

Coils may need repairing because they have been damaged mechanically or as a result of corrosion. Mechanical damage can be weather related, such as from ice and sleet, or from vandalism. Corrosion can result from environmental pollution, sprinklers, or pets.

Mechanical damage of the fins can be straightened with a fin comb, Figure 20-25. If more than 20% of the fins have been damaged, the condenser's efficiency will be so low that under heavy summer loads, the compressor is likely to fail. Light corrosion of the condenser fins can be removed with an approved coil cleaner. Severe corrosive damage to condenser fins may not be reparable, so the condenser coil must be replaced.

Figure 20-24 Accumulated dirt can restrict airflow and raise the head pressure

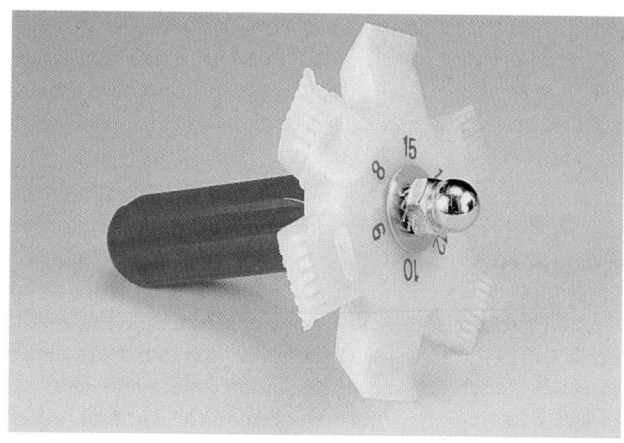

Figure 20-25 Damaged fins can be straightened using a fin comb
(Courtesy of Ritchie Engineering Company, Inc.—YELLOW JACKET Products)

20.16 WATER-COOLED CONDENSERS

Water is a more efficient heat transfer medium than air. The temperature difference between the refrigerant and the cooling medium is lower with a water-cooled condenser than with an air cooled condenser. The temperature differential between the refrigerant and the leaving water is typically 10°F. Water-cooled condensers normally operate with a 15°F lower compressor discharge temperature than air-cooled units. This allows the compressor to operate at a lower discharge pressure, increasing its capacity and lowering the power requirements. This makes water-cooled units potentially more energy efficient than air-cooled units. Water-cooled condensers are also smaller and more compact than comparable air-cooled condensers.

Water-cooled systems are more expensive to install and require more maintenance than air-cooled condensers. The water must be tested and treated regularly to prevent corrosion, fouling, and scaling. While most air-cooled condensers only need an annual inspection and cleaning, the water in a water-cooled condenser may need to be checked as often as once a week and chemical treatment is an ongoing process.

Water cooled systems require a good source of cooling water. Typical water sources include

- Waste water systems.
- Open loop cooling towers.
- Closed loop cooling towers.
- Ground loops.

The water can be used once and sent down the drain, or it can be recirculated. Systems that use the water only once and then put it down a drain are appropriately called wastewater systems. Water-cooled systems typically use 1.5 to 3 gallons of water per minute per ton. This makes waste water systems prohibitively expensive to operate on city water for all but small systems. With water resources becoming a precious commodity in many parts of the country, wastewater systems appear to be an extravagant use of a precious resource. Recirculating systems must find a way to cool the water before returning it to the condenser. The most common method is to use a water tower that cools the majority of the water by evaporating a small portion of the water. Cooling towers can be either open loop or closed loop. Open loop cooling towers are called open loop because the water in the cooling tower is open to the air and the cooling tower water is the same water that circulates through the condenser. Closed loop cooling towers use built-in heat exchangers to separate the cooling tower water from the recirculating condenser water. Another method is to use a loop of pipe buried in the ground. The water is cooled by the ground and returned to the system. These systems are called closed loops because they are not open to the atmosphere.

20.17 TYPES OF WATER-COOLED CONDENSERS

There are three basic types of water-cooled condenser construction:

- Tube in tube (coaxial).
- Shell and coil.
- Shell and tube.

20.18 TUBE IN TUBE CONDENSERS

Double pipe condensers can be a single continuous loop, as shown in Figure 20-26, or several parallel pipes as shown in Figure 20-27. In either case, the water and refrigerant should flow through the condenser in opposite directions. This is

Figure 20-26 Continuous loop coaxial water cooled condenser

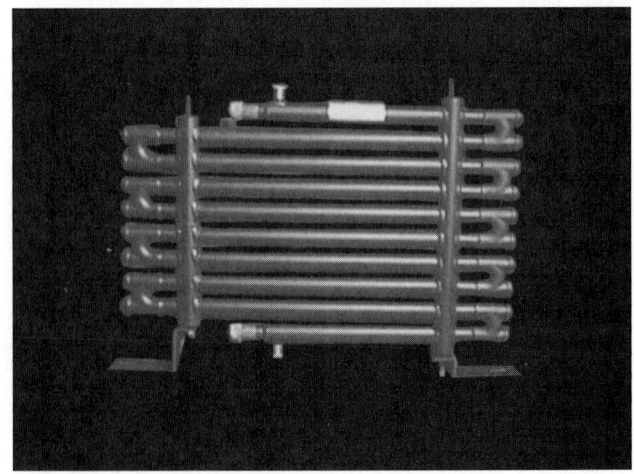

Figure 20-27 Parallel flow double tube water-cooled condenser
(Courtesy of Doucette Industries, Inc.)

HOT REFRIGERANT VAPOR IN

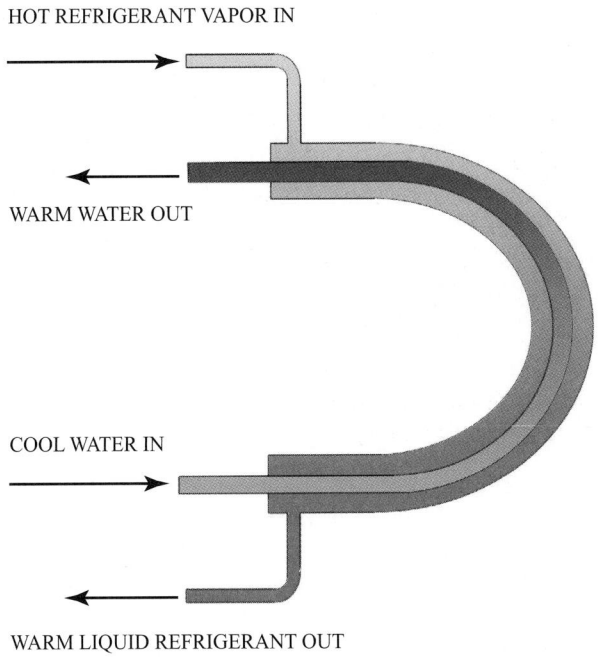

WARM WATER OUT

COOL WATER IN

WARM LIQUID REFRIGERANT OUT

Figure 20-28 The water and refrigerant flow in opposite directions to improve efficiency

called counterflow. Counterflow is more efficient because the coldest water contacts the coldest refrigerant and the hottest water contacts the hottest refrigerant, Figure 20-28. Single circuit double pipe condensers can be constructed using a tube in tube, as shown in Figure 20-29, or two tubes soldered together and wrapped in a protective outer tube, Figure 20-30. The tube in tube construction is more efficient, but cross contamination between refrigerant and water is possible if the inside tube leaks. The tube beside a tube arrangement makes cross contamination less likely because the refrigerant and water are separated by two tube walls.

The usual arrangement for tube in tube coils is for a smaller tube to be placed inside a larger tube, which is sealed at the end. Water travels through the smaller tube and refrigerant travels through the larger tube.

Figure 20-29 Cross section of a tube in tube coaxial water-cooled condenser

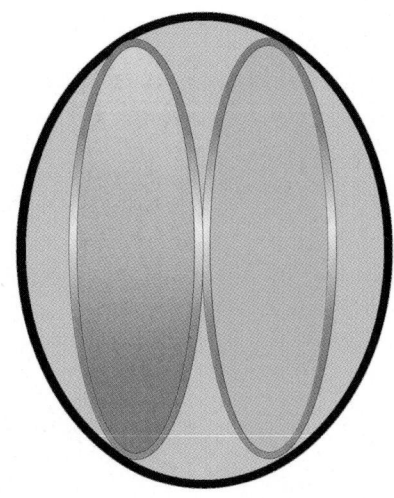

Figure 20-30 Cross section of a double-walled water-cooled heat exchanger

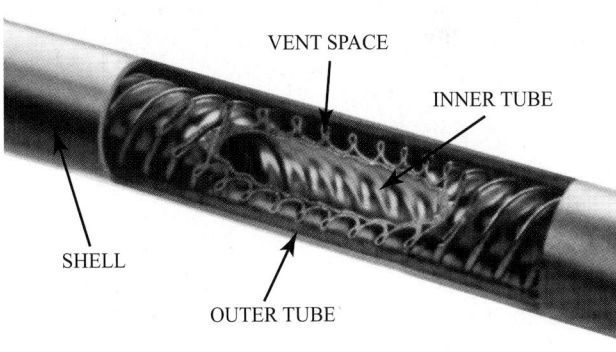

Figure 20-31 The twisted tubing shape improves heat transfer by creating turbulence in the water
(Courtesy Turbotec Products, Inc.)

When multiple tubes are used, they connect to the headers. The water flows through the inner tube and the refrigerant flows through the angular space between the tubes. The inner tube may have a spiral surface, Figure 20-31. This agitates the water as it flows through the tube so that it does not stratify with the cooler water flowing in the center of the tube. An advantage of this design is that it can be wrapped into a shape to fit the space available. For example, the packaged condensing unit shown in Figure 20-32 uses the tube-in-tube condenser.

Single circuit tube in tube condensers are used on most water source heat pumps. They are generally not accessible and can only be cleaned and descaled chemically. Parallel circuit condensers with headers can usually be mechanically cleaned by removing the header access plates on each end.

The water tubes of a double pipe condenser are typically made of copper, while the refrigerant pipe is made of copper or steel. The pipes can be constructed of stainless steel or cupro-nickel if more resistance to corrosion is required. Cupro-nickel coils are made of an alloy of 90% copper and 10% nickel that is more resistant to corrosion than copper.

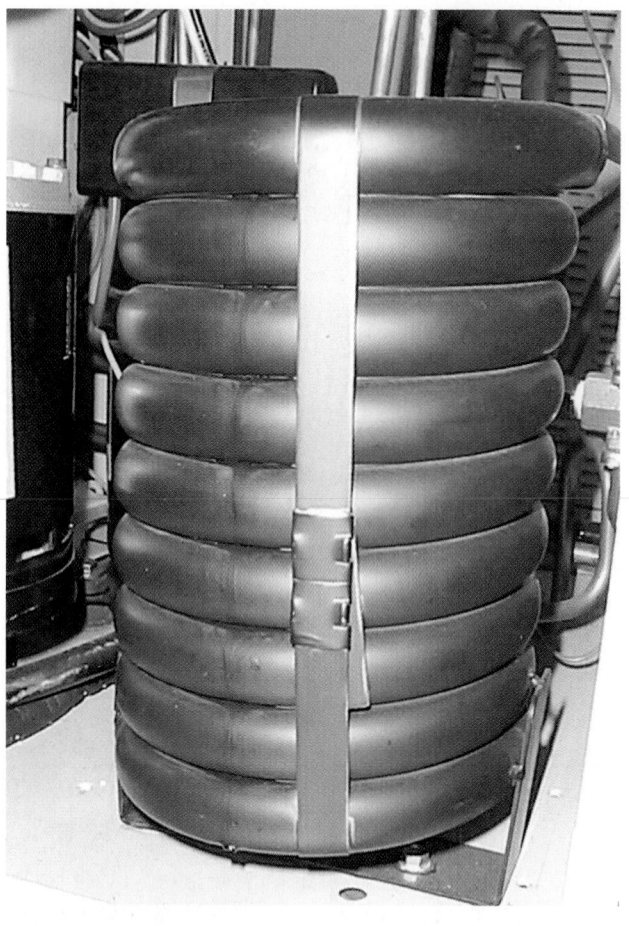

Figure 20-32 Typical use of a tube in tube condenser designed for in-the-room installation

CAUTION

Care is required when recovering refrigerant from a water-cooled condenser. During the recovery process, liquid refrigerant in the water-cooled condenser can vaporize and draw the temperature down to below the freezing temperature of water. Ice formed inside any sealed container such as a water cooled condenser can rupture the vessel or damage the internal piping. To avoid this, liquid refrigerant should be recovered first to avoid boiling the refrigerant at a low pressure and temperature. The water must either be continuously circulated or else completely drained before recovering the refrigerant.

20.19 SHELL AND COIL CONDENSERS

Shell and coil condensers are typically used in larger systems than double pipe condensers, but smaller systems than shell and tube condensers. Shell and coil condensers are constructed with a welded steel shell and an internal finned copper tubing coil, Figure 20-33. Water flows through the finned coil and the refrigerant in the shell condenses on the coil. The shell can run vertically for better heat transfer through convection, or horizontally to meet possible space requirements. Shell and coil condensers also act like liquid receivers.

Figure 20-33 Cutaway view of shell and coil condenser
(Courtesy of Refrigeration Research, Inc.)

In a vertical shell and coil condenser, the water enters at the bottom of the coil and travels up. The refrigerant enters at the top of the shell, condenses, and leaves at the bottom of the shell, Figure 20-34.

Shell and coil condensers are sometimes used with water source heat pumps and can be combined with the compressor to form a condensing unit package. These units are usually limited to 20 tons or less. Vertical packaged air conditioning units from 20 to 60 tons use shell and coil condensers due to their compact dimensions.

Shell and coil condensers are difficult to service in the field because of their construction. Shell and coil condensers

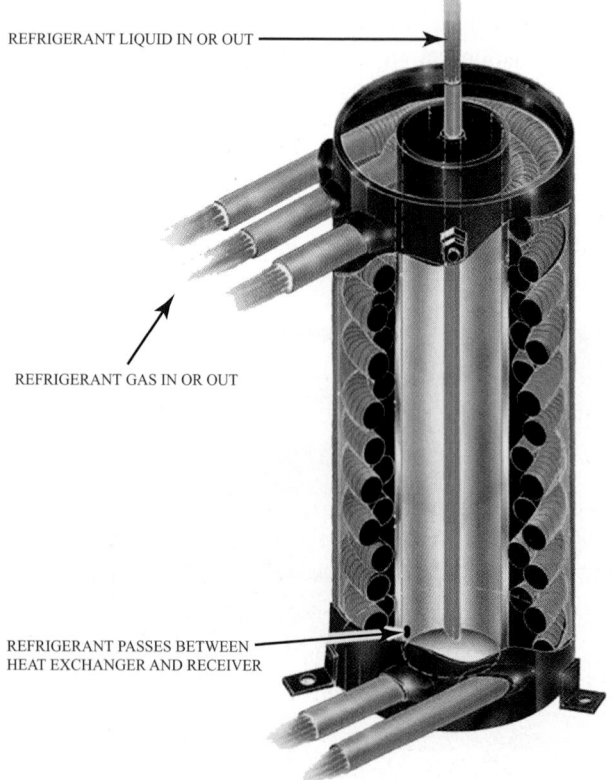

HEAT EXCHANGER/BI-DIRECTIONAL RECEIVER
REDUCED PIPING AND INSULATION
INCREASED HEAT EXCHANGE IN CONDENSER MODE
HELPS TO BALANCE REFRIGERANT CHARGE

REFRIGERANT LIQUID IN OR OUT

REFRIGERANT GAS IN OR OUT

REFRIGERANT PASSES BETWEEN
HEAT EXCHANGER AND RECEIVER

Figure 20-34 Cutaway view of shell and coil condenser
(Courtesy of Aqua Systems Inc., USA)

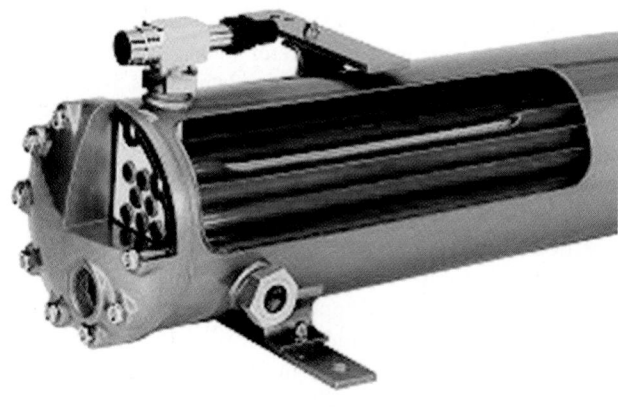

Figure 20-35 The water travels through the tubes and the refrigerant in the shell and tube condenser from page 1 of the Alfa-Laval brochure shell&tube.pdf
(© Alfa Laval. Used with permission.)

Figure 20-36 Shell and tube condenser header configuration from lower right corner page 5 of shell&tube.pdf
(© Alfa Laval. Used with permission.)

cannot be cleaned mechanically, and can only be cleaned and descaled chemically.

20.20 SHELL AND TUBE CONDENSER

The shell in tube type condenser, Figure 20-35, is used in the largest condensers. Capacities extend to 1,000 tons. Water flows through the tubes (the tube side of the condenser) and refrigerant flows on the outside of the tubes (the shell side of the condenser). These condensers have long, straight finned tubes, connected to a steel plate (tube sheet) at each end. At each end, water manifolds, called heads, are bolted to the shell, Figure 20-36. These heads direct the water to make from one to eight passes, depending on the size and design of the condenser. The heads can be removed to permit cleaning the individual tubes. Rubber gaskets provide a watertight seal.

The entering water in recirculated systems is typically warmer than with wastewater systems. Single and double pass designs are used for water tower systems to keep the difference between the condenser saturation and incoming water temperatures as low as possible, improving the efficiency of the refrigeration system. A higher water flow rate is required with fewer water passes because the condenser is operating at a lower water temperature rise. Multiple pass designs are used to minimize water use by increasing the amount of heat picked up by each pound of water. Multiple pass configurations operate with a higher temperature difference between the condenser saturation and incoming water temperatures. Multiple pass systems are used when water is scarce or expensive, such as for city wastewater systems, Figure 20-37.

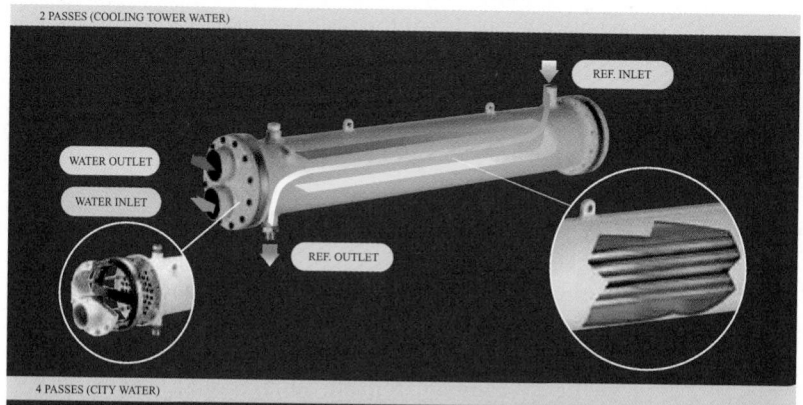
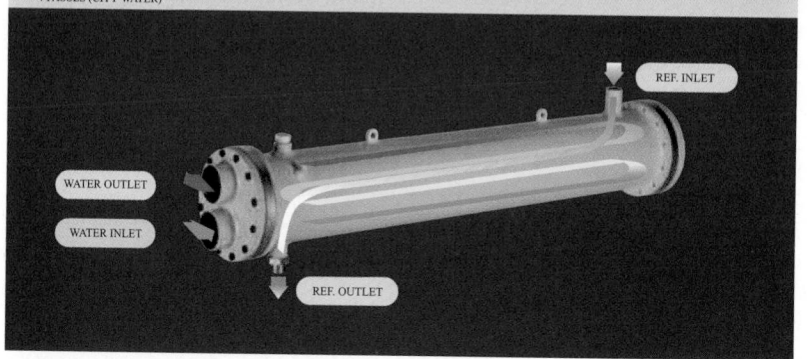

Figure 20-37 Water flow through a shell and tube condenser from 2 pictures at top of page 8 of shell&tube.pdf
(© Alpha Laval. Used with permission.)

Figure 20-38 Typical packaged liquid chiller unit with a shell-in-tube condenser

In a typical water condenser, the hot gas inlet and purge valve are on the top, the liquid outlet valve is on the bottom, and the pressure relief valve is on the side. Many of these shell and tube condensers are used in large water-cooled condensing units ranging in size from 5 to 150 tons. A common use of the shell and tube condenser is as a component of a water chiller, as shown in Figure 20-38.

20.21 WASTEWATER SYSTEMS

In earlier applications of water-cooled condensers to refrigeration and air conditioning, it was common practice to tap the water supply and then waste the discharge water to a drain connection as shown in Figure 20-39. An adjustable automatic water regulating valve was placed in the line of the flow of incoming water to control the condenser operating head pressure and temperature. It gets the system pressure through a pressure tap.

The temperature of the incoming water would naturally affect the condenser performance and flow rate of any heat load. Depending on the geographic location, water temperatures in city water mains rarely rise above 60°F in summer and frequently drop to much lower temperatures in winter.

RATE 1 TO 2 GAL/MIN/TON OF REFRIGERATION

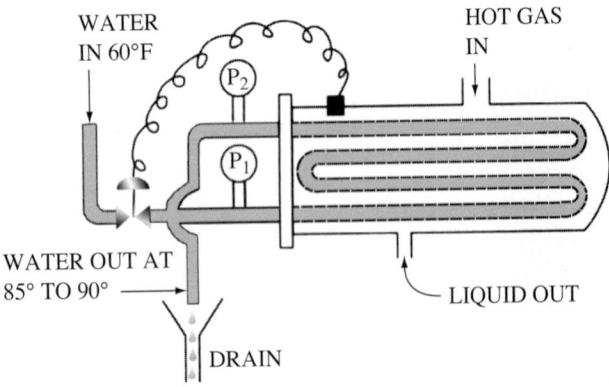

Figure 20-39 Wastewater system using water regulating valve

Condensers piped for tap water flow were always arranged for series flow, circuited for several water passes to achieve maximum heat rejection to the water, which was then wasted, Figure 20-37. Condensers drawing on city water used only 1 to $1\frac{1}{2}$ gpm (gallons per minute) per ton of refrigeration. The multipass circuit created high water pressure drops ($P_1 - P_2$) of 20 psi or more; however, most city pressures were able to supply the minimum pressure requirement (usually 25 psig).

Because of water shortages experienced in many areas of the country, water cooled condensers that waste water are not recommended. The cost and scarcity of water (unless drawn from a lake or wells and returned) has become prohibitive and is even outlawed for refrigeration and air conditioning use by many local city codes. Ordinances restricted the use of water to the point where such installations were forced to use all air cooled equipment. Some water regulations are so restrictive that they may even require existing waste water cooled systems to be replaced. Most system operators have switched to water saving devices such as the evaporative condenser, or a water tower.

Residential Well Systems

Many residential water cooled systems have been installed as wastewater systems on private wells. Even well water is not free, because energy is required to pump the water. Operating a $\frac{1}{2}$ hp water pump to move the water from the well to the unit can be a significant additional operating expense. Wastewater systems are more prone to mineral scaling than other types of water cooled systems because the continual supply of fresh water also provides a continual supply of fresh minerals. The condenser efficiency drops off as scale builds inside it, insulating the tube walls from the water.

The head pressure of a water cooled system is affected by the inlet water temperature. Wastewater systems use a water regulating valve to control head pressure by adjusting the water flow through the condenser. The water regulating valve measures the head pressure, increases the water flow when the head pressure increases, and decreases the water flow when the head pressure decreases.

20.22 COOLING TOWER SYSTEMS

In most installations using water cooled condensers, water is supplied to the condenser from a cooling tower. The heated water from the condenser is returned to the tower to dissipate the heat picked up from the refrigerant, as shown in Figure 20-40. There are four steps in the process

- Heat is transferred from the refrigerant to the water in the condenser.
- The water is pumped from the indoor condenser to the cooling tower outdoors.
- At the tower, the heat is rejected to the outdoor air, cooling the water.
- The cooled water is returned to the condenser to pick up more heat, making a continuous process.

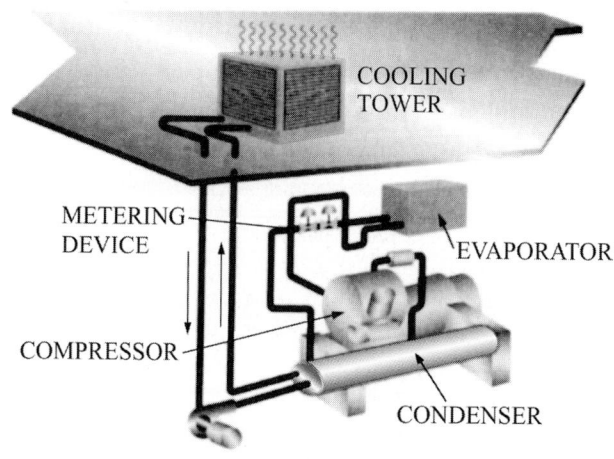

Figure 20-40 The cooling tower cools off the water from the water-cooled condenser and returnsit to the condenser

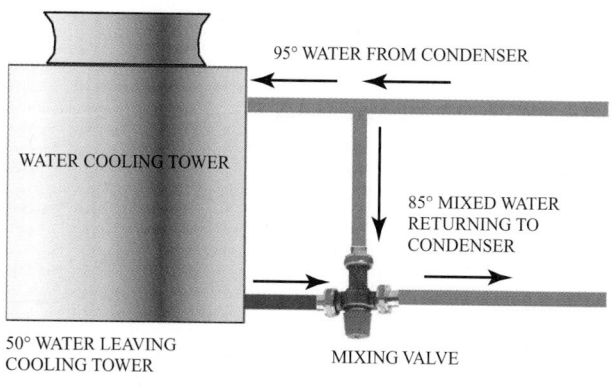

Figure 20-41 A mixing valve mixes hot water form the condenser with cold water from the cooling tower to keep the returning water from being too cold

Typical operating conditions for a water tower system are:

- The refrigerant condensing temperature is about 105°F.
- The water entering the condenser is approximately 85°, 20°F lower than the condensing temperature.
- The water temperature rises about 10°F in passing through the condenser, leaving the condenser at about 95°F
- The leaving water is only 10°F below the saturated refrigerant temperature.

When the water gets to the cooling tower, it is at 95°F. The warm water drops over the cooling tower's wetted decking, while outside air moves past it in the opposite direction, causing evaporation. Each pound of water that is evaporated removes 970 Btu from the remaining water, cooling it. A 10°F drop in temperature occurs by the time the water reaches the bottom of the tower. This 85°F water is returned to the condenser to absorb more heat. Water is lost by evaporation, drift, and blowdown. Drift is atomized water that has not vaporized, but is caught by airstreams and carried away. Blowdown is the periodic intentional release of water to reduce the mineral concentration in the water. This water is replaced by make up water, which is regulated by a float valve in the sump of the tower.

20.23 CONTROLLING WATER-COOLED CONDENSER CAPACITY

The capacity of water-cooled systems using water towers can be affected by the outdoor temperature and humidity. It is possible for the cooling tower to cool so well that a minimum desired head pressure is not maintained. On water-cooled condenser systems, a temperature-controlled water valve that bypasses the tower and mixes cooling tower water with condenser water can be used. With this arrangement the desired condenser water temperature can be maintained, Figure 20-41. The temperature-sensing element

for the bypass valve is placed at the water entrance to the condenser.

20.24 COOLING TOWERS

A cooling tower is a large evaporative cooler that is used to reject heat from water. They are used with water-cooled condensers to cool the warm water leaving the condenser and return it to the condenser ready to absorb more heat. Cooling towers can be either open loop, or closed loop. The water circulating in an open loop system is also the water circulating through the condenser. Closed loop systems use a heat exchanger to separate the water in the condenser loop from the water in the tower. That way only the tower water is exposed to the air. Closed loop systems reduce the amount of water maintenance required for the water in the condenser loop. Closing the loop reduces the opportunity for contaminants to be introduced into the condensing loop.

The primary cooling of the circulating water is provided by latent heat of evaporation. Each pound of water evaporated by the cooling tower removes 970 Btu of latent heat. At that rate it takes about 12 lb of water being evaporated to remove each ton of heat from the circulating water: 12,000 Btu/ton ÷ 970 Btu/lb = 12.3 lb of water. This amounts to approximately 1.5 gallons per hour. Compared to 1.5 gallons per minute for wastewater systems, it is easy to see that cooling towers save water.

TECH TIP

Water-cooled condensers are far more efficient than air-cooled condensers. This does not mean that a homeowner should put a sprinkler on an air-cooled condenser to increase its efficiency. Continuous watering of an air-cooled condenser coil will result in mineral buildup on the coil, which will ultimately reduce the coil's efficiency. In addition many minerals are corrosive to the fin material, so that over time the aluminum fins will be corroded away.

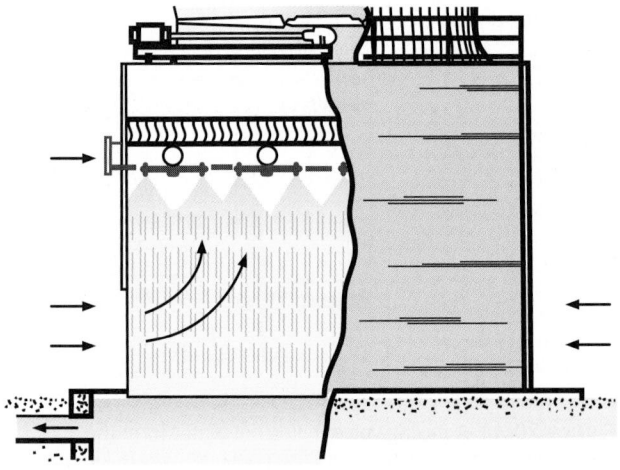

Figure 20-42 Air flows through the "raining" water to evaporate some of the water; the evaporation cools the remaining water
(Image courtesy of SPX Cooling Technologies)

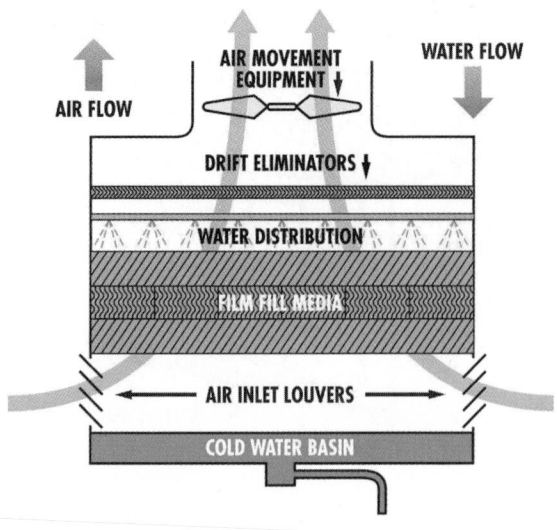

Figure 20-43 The air and water travel in opposite directions in counterflow cooling towers
(Courtesy of Brentwood Industries)

Cooling towers cool the circulated water through evaporation by spraying water through a moving air stream. In a typical tower, water "rains" down while air is pulled through the water spray using a fan, Figure 20-42. The middle of the tower is filled with wetted media to increase the surface area of the water exposed to the air. The fill increases the exposure of the water to the air and increases evaporation.

Cooling tower performance is governed by the entering air wet bulb temperature. Dry air has a lower wet bulb temperature than wet air because the rapid evaporation of water cools the sock on the wet bulb thermometer. Dry air can more easily evaporate water, so cooling tower capacity is highest with dry air. Nominal tower capacities are sized to cool the incoming water 10°F, from 95°F to 85°F with an outdoor wet bulb temperature of 78°F.

20.25 TYPES OF COOLING TOWERS

Cooling tower designs fall into one of three categories:

- Natural draft.
- Mechanical draft counterflow.
- Mechanical draft crossflow.

Natural Draft Cooling Towers

Natural draft cooling towers rely on prevailing winds and convection currents to move air across the wetted media in the tower. Natural draft towers are normally larger than mechanical draft towers for the same capacity. A properly sized natural draft tower normally has a low operating cost since

no power is used to move air. Natural draft cooling towers are frequently used in power generating plants.

Mechanical Draft—Counterflow Cooling Towers

Counterflow construction is a very common design for mechanical draft cooling towers. Figure 20-43 shows the basic construction of a counterflow mechanical draft cooling tower. The air and water flow in opposite directions in a counterflow design. Air enters at the bottom of the tower and is pulled up through the fill by a large fan. Warm water from the condenser enters at the top, is spread out across the top of the tower by a distribution deck, flows down through the fill, and collects in the sump. A pump takes the cool water from the sump and pumps it to the water cooled condenser. Some of the water evaporates during this process. The fill valve in the sump replaces the evaporated water with new water to maintain the sump level. This valve uses a ball float. When the water level drops, the float drops, opening the valve and allowing more water to enter. When the water level rises, the float rises to shut the valve. The water used to replace the water used by the tower is called makeup water.

Mechanical Draft—Crossflow Cooling Towers

Another common design is for the air to flow horizontally through the tower while the water flows from top to bottom, Figure 20-44. The operation is similar to a counterflow tower, except for the direction of airflow.

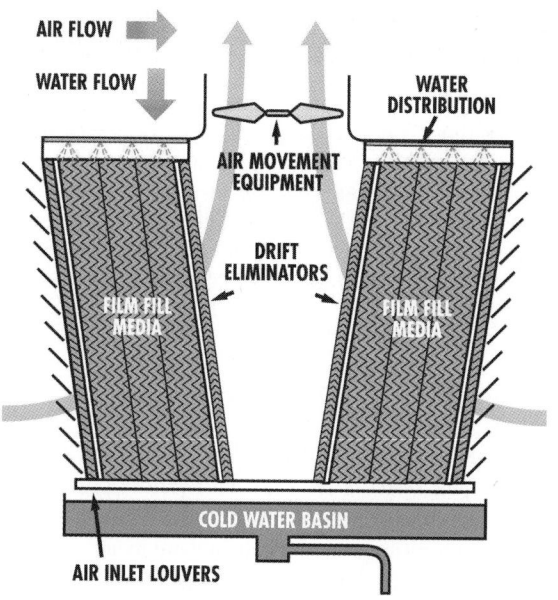

Figure 20-44 The air and water travel perpendicular to each other in crossflow cooling towers
(Courtesy of Brentwood Industries)

20.26 FREEZE PROTECTION

Cooling towers can freeze during very cold weather. With enough heat load, the water in the tower will not freeze. Freezing is more likely to occur when operating at reduced load in cold weather. Ice accumulation on towers can add considerable weight to the tower, resulting in collapse of overloaded components, Figure 20-45. The first line of defense is to drain the tower if it will not be used during the winter. The use of sump heaters and fan cycling may be necessary if the tower must be operated during freezing weather. Turning off the fan in cold weather can reduce the possibility of freezing. Sump heaters can be thermostatically controlled to keep the sump above 40°F. Finally, automatic thermostatically controlled draindown solenoids can drain all the water out of the sump if the water temperature approaches freezing.

Figure 20-45 Ice accumulation can overload cooling towers operating at reduced load in cold weather
(Courtesy of Cooling Technology Institute www.cti.org)

Antifreeze chemicals can be added to protect the condenser water loop in closed loop towers during the winter, but it is not normally used in the tower water. The addition of antifreeze to the condenser water loop changes the specific heat value of the circulating water. The specific heat drops, requiring more water to be circulated to accomplish the same amount of heat removal.

20.27 CONDENSER WATER TREATMENT

When a water-cooled condenser is used, a constant supply of water is needed. If the water is being recirculated through a cooling tower, it must be treated to prevent corrosion and scaling, as well as the formation of algae. If the water treatment is not maintained, the tower will become fouled and stop working. Regular testing of the condenser water is the key to maintaining a healthy water-cooled system. Three different aspects of water conditioning must be monitored:

- Water pH.
- Mineral content.
- Biological growth.

Water pH Control

The pH scale is a measure of the concentration of hydrogen ions in solution. It runs from 0 to 14. Lower numbers represent acidic conditions and higher numbers represent alkaline conditions. A neutral solution is 7 on the pH scale. Typically, cooling tower water is maintained at a pH between 6.5 and 9. The circulating water can become corrosive if it is too acidic. A pH lower than 6 will aggressively attack metal surfaces. High pH will encourage mineral deposits. Biological growth tends to raise the water pH level, leading to scaling. Most tower water will be alkaline, high pH, if left alone. Small amounts of acid are added to keep the pH down.

Scaling

Scaling occurs when minerals dissolved in the water precipitate out on the condenser and cooling tower surfaces, Figure 20-46. The hard scale deposits act like an insulator. Heat exchange surfaces that have $\frac{1}{16}$ in of scale have a 50% reduction in capacity. Scaling can be controlled by pH control, the addition of inhibitors that discourage mineral precipitation, and with water bleed off.

The concentration of minerals in the cooling tower increases as the tower is operated. When water evaporates it leaves its mineral behind, effectively increasing the mineral concentration of the remaining water. A small amount of water is intentionally drained off of the bottom of the cooling tower sump to keep mineral concentration under control. The high mineral concentration water is replaced with relatively low mineral concentration water, reducing the overall mineral concentration in the sump.

Figure 20-46 Scale deposits on cooling tower components reduce the tower's cooling capacity
(Courtesy of www.chemfresh.com)

Biological Fouling

Biocides are added to the water to prevent growth of organisms in the cooling tower water. Water is a fundamental requirement for life. Leave some water sitting around in the open, and soon it will be teeming with life. The warm, untreated cooling tower water becomes a Petri dish and an impressive array of bioorganisms springs forth, including bacteria, fungi, algae, and even protozoa organisms. As the organisms flourish, they attach themselves to all the tower surfaces, creating a coating called a biofilm. A well-established biofilm can be difficult to remove. Biological fouling is considered by many to be the root of most cooling-loop water treatment problems. Problems created by biological fouling include reduction in heat transfer efficiency, clogged cooling tower fill, water-flow blockages, corrosion, and hazards to human health, like *Legionella*. Figure 20-47 shows tower fill that is clogged with algae.

Figure 20-47 Biological fouling in cooling tower
(Image courtesy of SPX Cooling Technologies)

SAFETY TIP

Legionella was discovered because of an outbreak in 1976 at the American Legion Convention, where 221 people became ill and 34 people died. Investigation revealed *Legionella* was growing in cooling tower water and was spread through the mist created by the cooling tower. Failure to control its growth can lead to illness and death of people who come in contact with the spray from the tower.

Water Control in Open Systems

Water treatment is very different in open systems and closed systems. Open systems are exposed to more potential contaminants. Typically chemicals are added to maintain the proper pH, to inhibit scale formation, and to act as a biocide. Chemical treatment is usually done continuously using automatic chemical feed devices. Figure 20-48 shows an automated water treatment system. Even with an automated system, the water should be tested and monitored on a weekly basis. The types and amount of chemicals used may need to be adjusted as conditions change.

Water Control in Closed Systems

Water control is easier in closed systems because the water is not exposed to the atmosphere and makeup water is not continuously bringing in new minerals. A single chemical charge is usually sufficient when the loop is filled. The water should be tested quarterly because the water conditions will change over time, even in a closed system.

20.28 EVAPORATIVE CONDENSERS

Evaporative condensers are similar to closed loop cooling towers, except the coil is a refrigeration coil instead of a water coil. They work by evaporating water to cool the refrigeration coil. Hot refrigerant vapor travels through the inside of the copper coil as cold water is sprayed over the exterior of the coil. Fresh air is pulled up over the exterior of the coil while cold water is sprayed down over the coil. Heat from the refrigerant is transferred to the spray water, causing the refrigerant to condense from a gas to a liquid. Heat from the spray water is discharged to the atmosphere through evaporation of the spray water. Evaporative condensers provide lower condensing temperatures and can offer significant horsepower savings over conventional air-cooled and water-cooled condensing systems. Figure 20-49 shows an evaporative condenser.

The condensing coil rejects heat through both evaporative cooling using the fresh air stream and through sensible cooling using the precooled recirculating spray water. The recirculating spray water falls from the coil to a fill surface section where it is cooled by a second fresh air stream using both evaporative and sensible heat transfer processes. The cooled water increases the temperature differential between the water and the refrigerant. This cool water is then pumped back up to the spray heads to absorb more heat from the condenser.

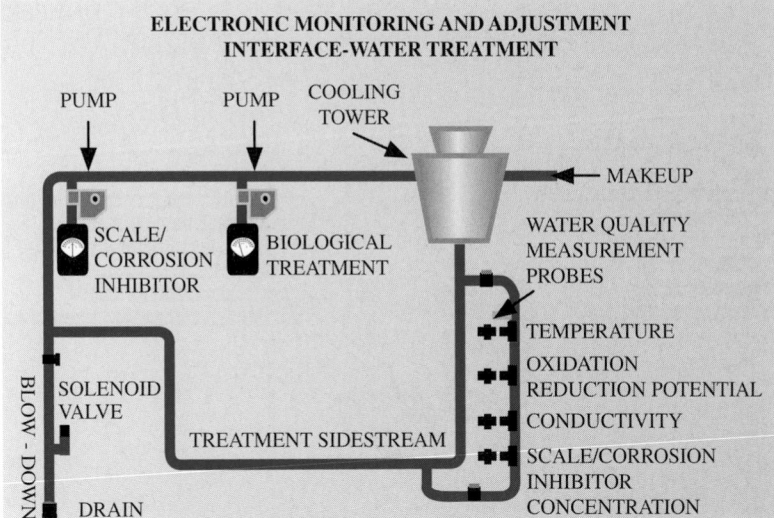

Figure 20-48 Automated water treatment system
(Image courtesy of SPX Cooling Technologies)

Figure 20-49 Evaporative condensers use water evaporation to cool the condenser coil
(Courtesy of SPX Cooling Technologies, Inc.)

20.29 CONTROLLING EVAPORATIVE CONDENSER CAPACITY

There are a number of arrangements for controlling the capacity of evaporative condensers:

- Shut off the water sprays. This reduces the evaporative condenser to an air cooled condenser. The air cooled capacity is about 50–60% of the wetted capacity. This,

however, is a huge step in capacity reduction. Shutting off the water may increase scaling.

- The fan can be cycled. This can shorten the belt life.
- Modulate the fan speed. This method gives better control with less likelihood of increased scaling.
- The airflow through the condenser can be controlled using dampers.

Airflow can be controlled using dampers in the outlet of the blower, in the outlet of the tower, or in a bypass duct. Warm humid air from the condenser discharge can be mixed with outdoor air by the use of bypass dampers and ductwork. This increases the relative humidity of the air entering the unit, reducing evaporation and, therefore, reducing the condenser capacity. Figure 20-50 shows three ways to control the capacity of an evaporative condenser by controlling the airflow.

20.30 SERVICING WATER-COOLED CONDENSERS

The first step in servicing water-cooled equipment is to check the water flow. All other checks on a water-cooled system are useless if the water flow and temperature are not right! The water flow rate can be checked by checking the pressure drop through the unit and comparing it to the manufacturer's specifications. Some systems have water flow indicators that make checking the water flow as easy as looking at a gauge. Check the water flow against the manufacturer's specifications. If the system has a log book, check the data in the log book and compare the current water flow against the baseline. Once the water flow is correct you can proceed to check the other system operating characteristics.

Fouled Condenser

Fouled condensers are the most common problem with water-cooled equipment, Figure 20-51. A fouled condenser is indicated by a higher than normal discharge pressure and a

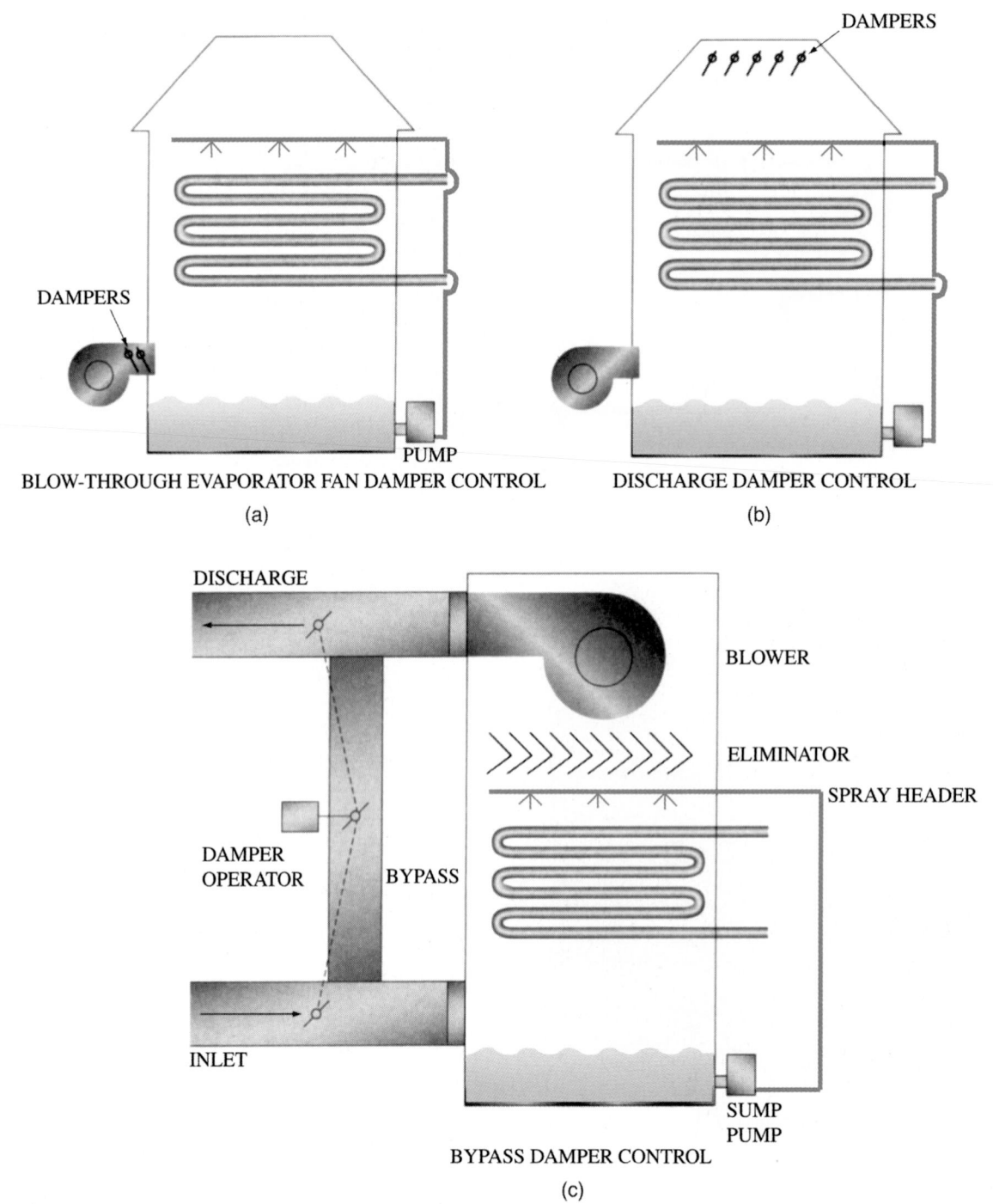

Figure 20-50 Three ways to control the airflow on the evaporative condenser

higher than normal temperature difference between the condenser saturation temperature and the leaving water temperature. In cooling tower systems, the normal temperature difference between the condenser saturation temperature and the leaving water temperature is 10°F. Wastewater systems commonly operate at a slightly higher temperature difference of 15°F. Fouled condensers do not dissipate heat as well, so the condenser temperature rises. The water pressure drop across the condenser will also increase because the condenser tubing will be effectively smaller. On wastewater systems with water pressure regulating valves, more water will be flowing than normal as the valve attempts to compensate for the high head pressure. The combination of increased water flow and poor heat exchange will cause the temperature difference across the condenser to decrease. The normal temperature difference across the condenser on cooling tower systems is 10°F. Wastewater systems using city water can vary widely because of large temperature differences in the incoming water.

	Inlet	Outlet
Volume	28 in³/lb	268 in³/lb
Pressure	418 psig	118 psig
Saturation temperature	120°F	40°F
Actual temperature	105°F	40°F
State	Subcooled liquid 100% liquid	Saturated mixture 30% vapor/70% liquid
Specific enthalpy	55 Btu/lb	55 Btu/lb

Figure 21-2 Typical values for 410a air conditioning system at ARI rating condition

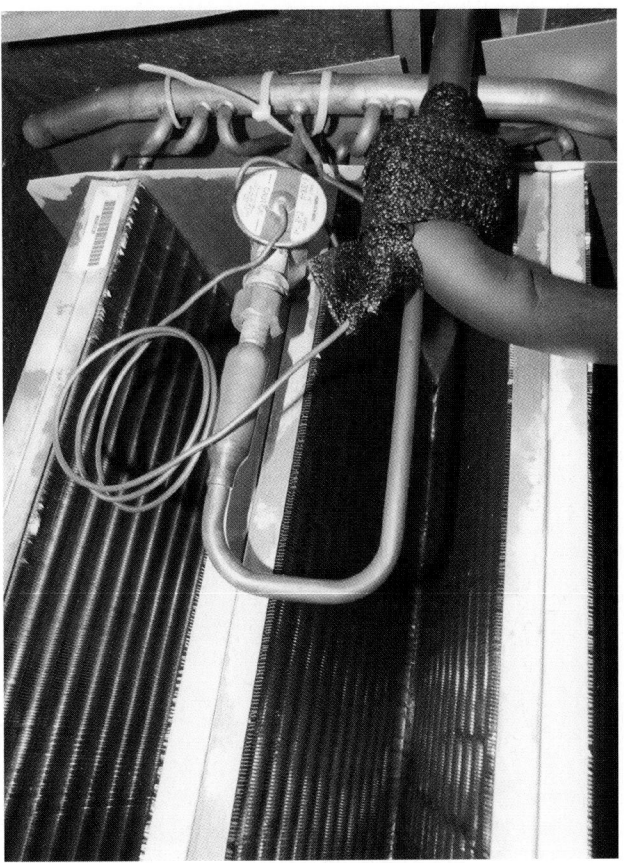

Figure 21-3 The metering device comes installed as part of a conditioning evaporator

liquid refrigerant boil. Since no heat is being added, the heat must come from the remaining liquid refrigerant. The flashing refrigerant absorbs heat from the remaining liquid refrigerant, reducing the temperature of the remaining liquid. Between 25% and 30% of the liquid typically flashes to vapor as the refrigerant flows through the metering device. Expansion that occurs without adding any heat from outside the process is called adiabatic expansion.

Referring to Figure 21-2; the volume of the refrigerant increases from around 28 in³/lb entering, to approximately 268 in³/lb leaving. This expansion creates a large pressure drop from 418 psig to 118 psig. The pressure drop causes a corresponding temperature drop from 105°F to 40°F. The specific enthalpy is unchanged because of the heat required to vaporize the flash gas came from the remaining liquid.

21.4 METERING DEVICE LOCATION

The metering device is located between the condenser and the evaporator. Typically the metering device is actually connected to the evaporator. The metering device is supplied with most air conditioning evaporator coils. Air conditioning evaporators are typically manufactured with the metering device as an integral component, Figure 21-3. Ductless mini-split systems are a notable exception. Many of these systems have the metering device located in the outdoor condensing unit, Figure 21-4. The liquid line on these systems must be insulated because they carry cold saturated liquid rather than a warm subcooled liquid. The metering device is more commonly field installed in commercial refrigeration. It is still attached to the evaporator, but the installation technician must install it in the field, Figure 21-5.

21.5 FIXED METERING DEVICES

There are two types of fixed metering devices: the capillary tube and the fixed orifice, Figure 21-6. Fixed restriction metering devices operate best where the load is nearly constant. Their operating principle is simple: when a pressurized fluid passes through a small hole, the resistance to flow through the hole causes a drop in pressure. While the operating concept is simple, the design and application of fixed restriction metering devices is anything but simple. Since a fixed hole cannot adjust itself to pressure changes, improper sizing can easily lead to flooding or starving the evaporator; both of which may be harmful to the compressor. The size of that opening and the amount of charge are critical to correct operation.

Many technicians expect a fixed amount of refrigerant to pass through a fixed metering device since the device cannot adjust. However, changes in pressure difference across a fixed metering device will cause changes in flow precisely because the device cannot adjust. The reason refrigerant goes through a restriction at all is because of a difference in pressure across it. Both the low and high side pressures tend to

Figure 21-4 The metering device on this mini-split system is located ouside where the liquid line connects

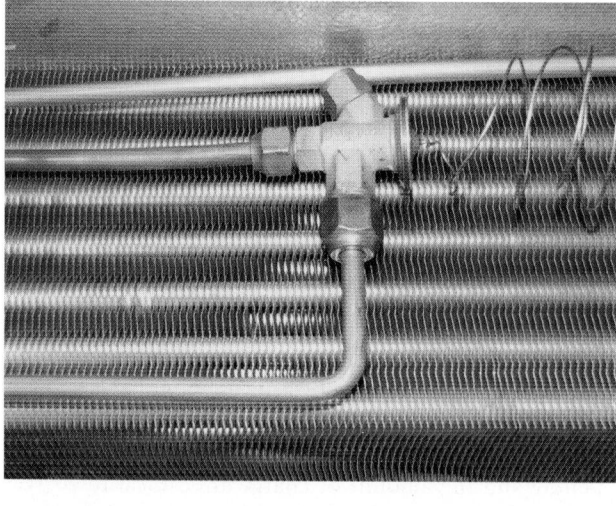

Figure 21-5 Commercial refrigeration evaporators typically do not come with a metering device already installed, this expansion valve was installed in the field

be influenced by factors such as the outdoor temperature which are beyond the control of the machine. In an air conditioning system, the head pressure increases as the outdoor temperature rises. This increase in head pressure causes an

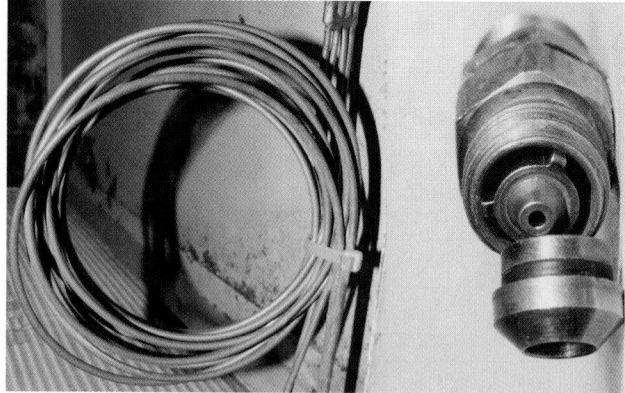

Figure 21-6 The capillary tube on the left and the orifice on the right are the primary types of fixed restriction metering devices

increase in pressure difference across the orifice. As the pressure difference across the restriction increases, more refrigerant will go through it. This increased flow will cause a rise in suction pressure, but the suction pressure will not increase quite as much as the head pressure increase that caused the increased flow. The increased flow will also have the effect of reducing superheat since more refrigerant is now being delivered to the evaporator. A check of the compressor motor amperage will reveal a relatively higher current draw from an increased system load.

Lower outdoor ambient temperatures will produce lower head pressures, reducing the pressure drop across the fixed restriction. This reduced pressure difference will result in reduced refrigerant flow to the evaporator. Decreased flow will cause a drop in suction pressure and an increase in superheat, since less refrigerant is now being delivered to the evaporator. A check of the compressor motor amperage will reveal a decrease in the system load. Figure 21-7 shows the operating characteristics of an air conditioner with a fixed restriction at different outdoor ambient temperatures.

Changes in temperature at the evaporator have an opposite effect from changes in condenser temperature. An increase in temperature at the evaporator causes an increase in evaporator pressure. This has the effect of reducing the pressure difference across the metering device, which reduces the refrigerant flow to the evaporator and raises the superheat. Decreased temperature at the evaporator decreases the evaporator pressure, increasing the refrigerant flow through the metering device, and decreasing the superheat. Figure 21-7 shows the effect of indoor wet bulb temperature on system operation.

Because the flow through a fixed restriction changes depending upon the operating conditions, the only time a system with a fixed metering device produces its full capacity is at design conditions. The AHRI standard design conditions for air conditioning are 95°F outdoor ambient temperature, 80°F indoor dry bulb temperature, and 67°F indoor wet bulb

Outdoor temperature	Indoor wet bulb temperature	Temperature drop across evaporator	Suction pressure	Discharge pressure	Superheat	Amp draw
100	77	10	145	530	24	15.3
	72	14	142	523	20	14.9
	67	17	135	417	15	14.5
	62	21	130	410	4	14.1
95	77	10	144	402	23	15.6
	72	14	135	396	20	14.5
	67	17	132	390	17	14.1
	62	21	128	382	6	13.7
90	77	11	140	378	25	14.2
	72	14	134	372	24	13.8
	67	18	130	365	19	13.5
	62	20	120	355	8	13.1
85	77	11	139	346	27	13.3
	72	15	132	340	24	13
	67	18	128	334	21	12.6
	62	21	119	328	10	12.2
80	77	11	135	335	26	12.4
	72	15	131	329	24	12.0
	67	18	126	323	23	11.6
	62	22	119	317	14	11.2
75	77	12	134	320	25	11.7
	72	15	130	314	25	11.2
	67	18	120	308	25	10.8
	62	22	118	300	17	10.5

Figure 21-7 Operational characteristics of R-410a Air Conditioner with fixed restriction

temperature. A 24,000 Btu, AHRI rated air conditioner with a fixed expansion device will not produce 24,000 Btu worth of cooling at an outdoor ambient of 75°F.

This change in capacity shows up in the system superheat. Most manufacturers using orifices or cap tubes publish superheat charts that specify what the system superheat should be at any operating condition that falls within the operating range of the unit. A look at one of these charts will show that as the outdoor ambient goes up, the system superheat goes down; and conversely, as outdoor ambient goes down, the system superheat goes up. In fact, most air conditioners with fixed restriction metering devices are operating under starving conditions at ambient temperatures less than 95°F. An orifice-equipped unit can have a superheat as high as 45°F at its lowest operating limit. This superheat is what determines the system's lowest operating temperature limit. The compressor on a system using a fixed restriction can overheat due to lack of cooling for the compressor motor when operating at low ambient conditions. That's correct, low ambient operation can cause overheated compressors! Adding charge at the low ambient condition will produce a more fully active evaporator and reduce the superheat, but then the system will flood back at higher ambient temperatures when the superheat naturally drops.

A characteristic of systems using fixed restriction metering devices is that the system high side and the low side pressures equalize when the compressor shuts off. Since the metering device is simply a hole, refrigerant will to continue to flow through it until the pressures on both sides of it are the same. This can be an advantage in system design because the compressor does not have to start against a pressure differential. This permits the use of a low starting torque compressor motor. This can also be a disadvantage since the evaporator can be filled with liquid on shutdown. On the next startup, the liquid can flood back to the compressor and cause damage. System equalization also encourages refrigerant migration to the compressor crankcase. When the system starts, the oil and refrigerant mixture foams violently, reducing lubrication. Neither of these problems is pronounced on small systems with limited charge. But they can become serious on larger systems. Crankcase heaters and suction line accumulators can be employed to mitigate these problems on larger systems.

Systems using fixed restriction metering devices do not use liquid receivers. Without a receiver, if refrigerant is condensing faster than it is flowing through the metering device, liquid starts to pile up in the bottom of the condenser. This raises the head pressure, and helps force more refrigerant through the metering device. Any refrigerant storage must be accomplished on the low side of the system with a suction accumulator.

Systems can counteract the problem of refrigerant floodback by using a suction line accumulator at the entrance to the compressor, as shown in Figure 21-8. This captures

OUTLET INLET

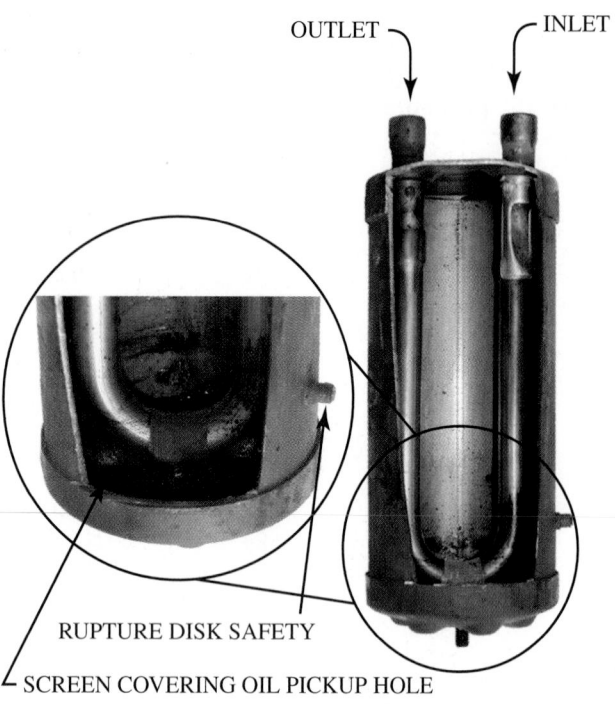

RUPTURE DISK SAFETY

SCREEN COVERING OIL PICKUP HOLE

Figure 21-8 A suction line accumulator can trap liquid refrigerant before it reaches the compressor
(Courtesy Marilyn Burris)

Figure 21-9 Rust formed on the accumulator due to condensation

the liquid refrigerant and returns it to the system as vapor. Because liquid refrigerant is evaporated from an accumulator, these devices get very cold and often sweat. This condensation can cause accumulators to rust over time as in Figure 21-9. On older units the rust can weaken the accumulator to the point where it can fail.

SERVICE TIP

It is easy to overcharge an air conditioning system with a fixed restriction in mild weather. For example, suppose a technician is checking an air conditioner on a 75°F day. The unit operates with a moderately high superheat of 30°F. The suction line feels cool, but not really cold. Since the evaporator is obviously starved, the technician adds refrigerant until the suction line is cold and the superheat is 10°F. The unit begins cooling a little better. The customer is happy until the temperature climbs to 95°F outside. As the outdoor temperature rises, the superheat drops. Since the unit has been charged to operate at a low superheat under a 75°F ambient, the evaporator will flood at a 95° ambient. The flooded evaporator does not cool as well as it should, so the capacity of the unit is reduced just when it is needed the most. Since the unit is operating at reduced capacity and increased pressure, it uses more electricity, costing the customer more money. Because the evaporator is flooded, liquid will be returned to the compressor and damage it, further reducing its capacity of the system. The moral: air conditioning systems with fixed restriction metering devices should operate at relatively high superheats in moderate weather. Do not overcharge them.

21.6 CAPILARY TUBES

The capillary tube is probably the simplest of all metering devices. It is constructed of a seamless copper tube with an inside diameter ranging in size from 0.026 in to 0.090 in, Figure 21-10. Capillary tubes may be found on older models of central air conditioners, but are seldom used today in residential air conditioning systems. Capillary tubes are still commonly used as a metering device on domestic refrigerators, window units, and other small appliances. In these appliances the capillary tube doubles as a metering device and the liquid line; the refrigerant travels from the condenser to the evaporator through the capillary tube, Figure 21-11. Capillary tubes are frequently longer than the distance they must travel, and are sometimes coiled to conserve space, as in Figure 21-12.

Small systems like refrigerators typically use a single capillary tube for their metering device. The evaporator coil on these systems is a single circuit coil: refrigerant enters at the start of the coil and exits at the end of the coil. Larger units using capillary tubes may use multiple capillary tubes feeding multi-circuit coils. A multi-circuit coil has several entry points and exits. Essentially, a multi-circuit coil is like several small coils manufactured together. Each circuit has its own capillary tube, Figure 21-13. Systems with multiple capillary tubes use a small distributor tube to feed all the capillary tubes, Figure 21-14.

The size and the length of the tube are carefully selected to match the pumping capacity of the compressor at full load. Capillary tubes depend on their length as well as their diameter to determine their total restriction. Increasing the

Figure 21-10 Typical capillary tube metering device

Figure 21-11 The capillary tube in a window unit runs from the outlet of the condenser to the inlet of the evaporator

Figure 21-12 The capillary tube is coiled when it is longer than the distance it must travel

Figure 21-13 The coil has four circuits, each fed by its own capillary tube

Figure 21-14 The four capillary tubes for this multi-circuit coil are fed by a capillary tube disributor

Figure 21-15 A small triangular file like this one can be used to cut capillary tubing
(Courtesy of Snap-On Tools)

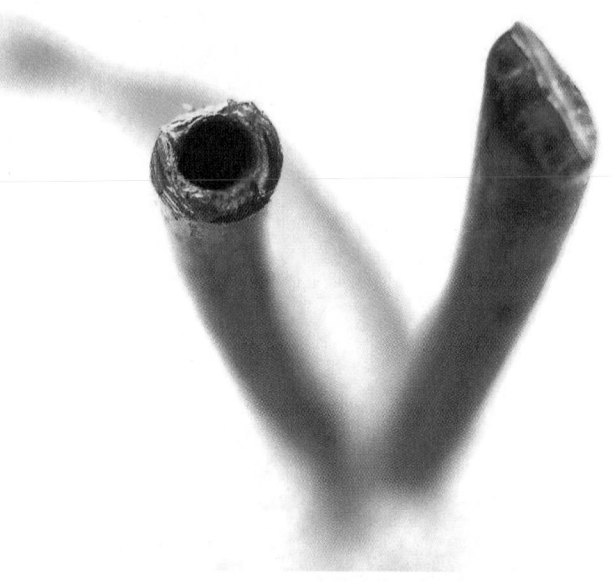

Figure 21-16 The capillary tube on the left was cut with a file; the capillary tube on the right was cut with wire pliers

diameter or decreasing the length of the capillary tube decreases the pressure drop through it, increaseing its capacity. Decreasing the diameter or increasing the length of the capillary tube increases the pressure drop through it and decreases its capacity. The pressure of the liquid refrigerant passing through the capillary tube drops slowly in the first 25% of the capillary tube length. When the pressure has dropped to the saturation pressure for the refrigerant temperature, the liquid starts to flash. The flash gas causes a rapid drop in pressure starting at that point. This point on the capillary tube can be felt. The first part is still warm to the touch; the part containing flash gas is cool to the touch.

Systems using capillary tube metering devices have no provision for refrigerant storage. The charge in these systems is critical because the capillary tube cannot adjust, the systems have no provision for refrigerant storage, and a small change in charge can have a large impact on system pressures. Most systems that use a capillary tube as their metering device are packaged units such as domestic refrigerators, freezers, and window air conditioners. These systems are evacuated and charged at the factory.

21.7 INSTALLING CAPILLARY TUBES

Capillary tubes are not generally field selected components. However, capillary tubes may occasionally need replacing. The best sizing procedure is to replace the capillary tube with exactly the same size and length. Even the coiling makes a difference. Many manufacturers sell replacement capillary tubes that are the exact replacement, including the shaping of the capillary tube. If a capillary tube must be cut during installation, it should be cut with a small triangle file, Figure 21-15. File a groove all the way around the tube and then bend the tube back and forth until it breaks at that point without creating a burr. Capillary tubes are too small for most tubing cutters. Even if a tubing cutter manages to cut a capillary

tube, it leaves a large burr which adds additional restriction. This additional restriction will create an excessive pressure drop. Wire cutting pliers will actually pinch the tubing shut. Figure 21-16 compares a capillary tube that has been cut using wire pliers with a capillary tube that has been cut with a small file. When installing a capillary tube, the capillary tube should be inserted at least an inch past the point it enters to prevent brazing material from plugging the end of the capillary tube, Figure 21-17.

Due to the small size of the tube, it can be easily plugged. Metal shavings, dirt, moisture, filings, flux, or oxides from brazing can all enter the system during manufacture and installation. Every precaution should be taken to keep these contaminants from entering the system during the installation

Figure 21-17 The capillary tube should be inserted for enough into the coil that the end will not get plugged with brazing alloy

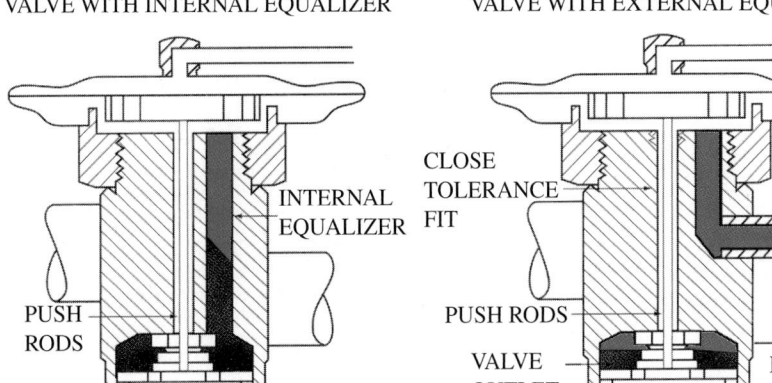

VALVE WITH INTERNAL EQUALIZER

VALVE WITH EXTERNAL EQUALIZER

INTERNAL EQUALIZER

PUSH RODS

CLOSE TOLERANCE FIT

EXTERNAL EQUALIZER FITTING

PUSH RODS

VALVE OUTLET PRESSURE

EVAPORATOR OUTLET PRESSURE

Figure 21-32 Evaporator pressure must reach the underside of the diaphragm for the thermostatic expansion valve to operate

the valve. A decrease in evaporator pressure decreases the pressure on the underside of the diaphragm, decreasing the closing force on the valve. The addition of a spring on the underside of the diaphragm adds additional closing pressure, producing superheat.

Figure 21-33 shows an R-410a system in equilibrium. The pressure on the bottom of the diaphragm exactly balances the bulb pressure on the top of the diaphragm when the system operating superheat is at the valve setpoint and the flow of refrigerant through the valve matches the load. If the suction pressure is 118 psig and the temperature of the bulb is 50°F, the superheat is 10°F. To calculate this, look up the saturation temperature for 118 psig R-410a: it should be 40°F. Subtract the 40°F saturation temperature from the 50°F actual suction line temperature for the superheat: 50°F − 40°F = 10°F.

21.18 INTERNALLY EQUALIZED VALVES

Thermostatic expansion valves must be able to sense the evaporator pressure in order to operate correctly. The port or line that transmits the evaporator pressure to the underside of the diaphragm is called an equalizer line. On internally equalized valves this is done with a passageway through the valve from the valve outlet to the underside of the diaphragm. Often the passageway is nothing more than a clearance around the push rods, Figure 21-34. This type of valve is called an internally equalized valve because the equalizer port is inside the valve. Internally equalized valves are easier to install than externally equalized valves because they do not require any connection to the suction line. However, since internally equalized valves measure the evaporator pressure at the beginning of the evaporator, they will not work well with evaporators that have a large pressure drop. The pressure drop causes the saturation temperature to drop also. The actual saturation temperature at the end of the evaporator will be considerably lower than the saturation temperature the valve sees at the beginning of the coil. This is why

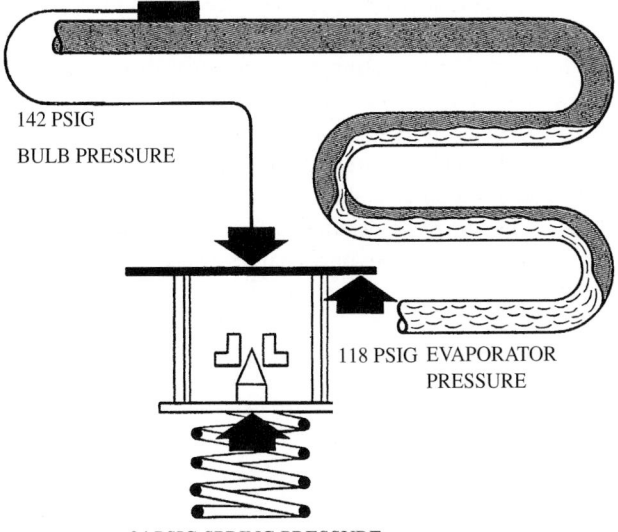

142 PSIG

BULB PRESSURE

118 PSIG EVAPORATOR PRESSURE

24 PSIG SPRING PRESSURE

Figure 21-33 The valve is in equilibrium when the system is operating at the valve set point
(Courtesy of Sporlan Division-Parker Hannifin Corporation)

Figure 21-34 Evaporator pressure passes through the holes around the triangular push rods on this internally equalized thermostatic expansion valve

Refrigerant	Evaporating temperature F°				
	40°F	20°F	0°F	−20°F	−40°F
	Pressure drop in psi				
R-134a	2	1.5	1	0.75	NR
R-22	3	2	1.5	1.0	0.75
R-404a, R-507	3	2.5	1.75	1.25	1.0

Figure 21-35 Maximum recommended pressure drop for R-134a, R-22, R-404a, and R-507

internally equalized valves are normally limited to single circuit evaporators with a maximum pressure drop that is equivalent to a 2°F saturated temperature drop. Figure 21-35 lists the maximum recommended pressure drop for several refrigerants and evaporator temperatures. Notice that less pressure drop can be tolerated at lower evaporator temperatures than at higher evaporator temperatures.

21.19 EXTERNALLY EQUALIZED VALVES

It is necessary to use an externally equalized thermal expansion valve to obtain an accurate superheat setting when the pressure drop in the evaporator (including the distributor) is sizable, Figure 21-36. Externally equalized valves measure the evaporator pressure through a separate line connected to the suction line. The underside of the diaphragm is isolated from the outlet of the valve so that the only pressure influencing the operation of the valve is the suction pressure coming in at the external equalizer line. To ensure that the valve outlet is isolated from the evaporator side of the diaphragm, the push rods are tightly fitted, Figure 21-37. Externally equalized valves are named for the line external to the valve that provides the evaporator pressure that balances the bulb pressure. Thus, the difference between an internally equalized valve and an externally equalized valve is where the evaporator pressure is sensed. If the evaporator pressure reaches the

Figure 21-37 The push rods on this externally equalized expansion valve fit tightly in the guide holes, evaporator pressure is provided by a separate, external tube and passes through the hole shown in the picture

underside of the diaphragm via a passageway inside the valve, it is an internally equalized valve. If the evaporator pressure reaches the underside of the diaphragm through a separate line external to the valve, it is externally equalized, Figure 21-32.

External equalizers must also be used when a distributor is used. Distributors are devices that divide the refrigerant evenly between several different refrigerant circuits in a multiple circuit evaporator. A pressure drop is created across the distributor. This prevents the use of an internally equalized valve because the pressure at the valve outlet will not be the same as the pressure at the evaporator inlet.

21.20 BULB CHARGES

The conventional thermostatic expansion valve uses a remote sensing bulb with a mixture of liquid and vapor refrigerant in it. They typically use the same refrigerant that the system uses. However, bulb charges are frequently designed to produce specific operating characteristics that cannot be obtained with a traditional charge. The bulb charge is what primarily determines how a TEV will respond to system changes. The perfect charge for one type of system might be a disaster in another system. TEVs are not plug and play devices; they must be carefully selected for their particular application. The types of bulb charges available include:

- Liquid charge.
- Liquid cross charge.
- Gas charge.
- Gas cross charge.
- Adsorption charge.

Liquid Charge Bulb

Liquid charged bulbs are the standard charge. They are charged with the same type of refrigerant as is in the system. Enough charge is put in the bulb so that there is always liquid

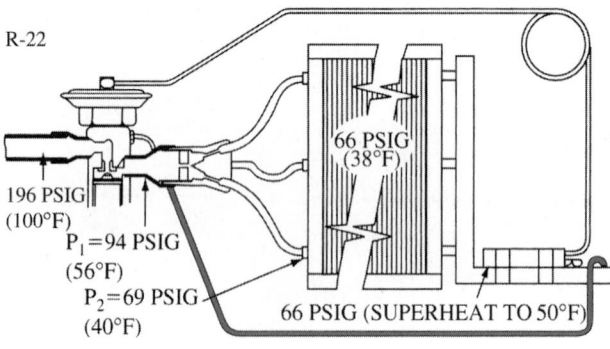

R-22

196 PSIG
(100°F)

P_1 = 94 PSIG
(56°F)

P_2 = 69 PSIG
(40°F)

66 PSIG
(38°F)

66 PSIG (SUPERHEAT TO 50°F)

Figure 21-36 Effect of an external equalized thermostatic expansion valve on the operation of the system
(Courtesy Sporlan Valve Company)

in the bulb. A liquid charged bulb will exert an opening force equal to the saturation pressure for bulb temperature. An advantage to this type of charge is that the sensing bulb will never lose control over the valve as can happen with some other types of charge. A disadvantage of this type of charge is that it will cause high suction pressures on system startup and will also cause slow pulldown times.

Liquid Cross Charge

A cross charge contains a liquid that is different from the system refrigerant, usually a mixture of refrigerants. The components in the bulb charge are selected to produce a pressure response that is different from the saturation curve of the refrigerant in the system. If the bulb response and the refrigerant saturation pressure were graphed, they would cross each other at some point; thus the name cross charge.

A valve with a traditional liquid charge requires more superheat to open at low pressures than at higher pressures. Liquid cross charges help address this by flattening out the valve response. Valves with liquid cross charges require about the same amount of superheat to open at low temperatures as at higher temperatures. Liquid cross charges are often used on commercial refrigeration systems.

Gas Charge

A standard gas charge uses the same refrigerant as is in the system, but does not have enough liquid refrigerant in the bulb to ensure liquid at all temperatures. At normal operating temperatures the gas charged bulb will respond more quickly than a liquid charged bulb because of the limited charge in the bulb. The liquid will all be vaporized at or above the maximum operating pressure of the valve. Additional temperature rise will produce very little pressure rise because these is no more liquid in the bulb to vaporize. This is used to produce a valve with a maximum operating pressure.

A potential problem with this charge is that the liquid refrigerant can migrate from the bulb to the diaphragm if the valve body becomes colder than the sensing bulb. Once the liquid has migrated to the diaphragm, the sensing bulb no longer controls the valve operation.

Gas Cross Charge

A gas cross charge uses a refrigerant or mixture of refrigerants that are different from the system refrigerant. There is limited charge in the bulb, giving this type of charge a maximum operating pressure feature. The pressure response of a gas cross charge is different from a traditional gas charge because the fluid in the bulb is different. One application of a gas cross charge is to produce a flat response at normal operating pressures and temperatures, and still have a maximum operating pressure.

Gas cross charges are subject to charge migration just like traditional gas charges. It is important that the bulb remain cooler than the valve body.

Adsorption Charge

The adsorption charge uses an adsorbent material in the bulb and a noncondensable gas charge. The amount of gas the adsorbent material will adsorb depends upon its temperature. It tends to adsorb more gas at lower temperatures and release gas at higher temperatures. The variation in the amount of gas absorbed changes the gas pressure in the power element. One advantage of this type of charge is that it will not lose control due to charge migration because there is no adsorbent in the diaphragm. However, the adsorption charge will not provide a maximum operating pressure.

21.21 MAXIMUM OPERATING PRESSURE (MOP) VALVES

The conventional sensing bulb can cause operating problems during the off cycle as well as on startup. This type of charge can cause excess pressure buildup in the evaporator during the off cycle. This type of valve can cause compressor overloading on startup. When the system starts, the valve opens wide open because the suction line is warm, creating high suction pressures that can overload the compressor. This can be prevented by using a maximum operating pressure (MOP) valve. As the name implies, the valve has a maximum pressure that it will let through, regardless of the superheat. Maximum operating pressure valves have a gas charged sensing bulb. The charge in the bulb is a mixture of liquid and gas at normal operating conditions, but turns to all gas at the maximum operating pressure point, Figure 21-38. An increase in

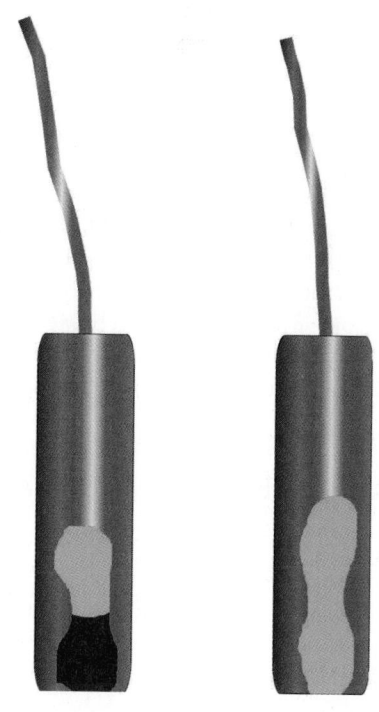

Figure 21-38 There is a small amount of liquid at normal operating temperatures in a gas-charged valve with MOP. When the temperature reaches the maximum operating pressure point, all the liquid has vaporized, so the pressure levels off.

temperature of a vapor past the normal operating temperature range produces only a slight increase in pressure. Nearly all air conditioning systems using thermostatic expansion valves limit the amount of pressure that can develop in the evaporator.

21.22 VALVE SUPERHEAT SETTING

All systems do not operate at the same superheat setting. The "correct" superheat for any system can only be determined by consulting the equipment manufacturer. However, there are standards that are widely used throughout the industry. First, a lower superheat setting delivers a higher capacity by using more of the evaporator coil to boil refrigerant. All systems should operate at the lowest possible superheat that will ensure dry vapor returning to the compressor. Next, the desired operating superheat decreases as the temperature difference between the evaporator and the load decreases. The evaporators in low temperature refrigeration systems operate as little as 5°F lower than the freezer they are cooling, while the evaporators in air conditioning systems can be 40°F cooler than the air they are cooling. Low temperature freezers often operate with superheat as low as 4°F, while air conditioning systems typically have superheat settings as high as 15°F. In general, the lower the operating temperature, the lower the normal operating superheat. As always, the manufacturer's recommendations should be the deciding factor in what a superheat setting should be. One manufacturer recommends 3–5°F superheat for low temperature systems, 5–9°F superheat for medium temperature systems, and 10—15°F superheat for high temperature systems. An all purpose superheat for generic refrigeration systems would be somewhere around 10°F.

Many manufacturers put nonadjustable TEVs on their systems, Figure 21-39. These valves have no provision for adjusting the superheat because the manufacturer has them made for one particular application. Most over the counter valves are adjustable. They typically have an adjustment stem, as in Figure 21-40, or an adjustment screw, as in Figure 21-41. They usually come from the factory set between 8°F and 12°F. These valves may need setting when they are installed because they are not manufactured for any particular system.

21.23 MEASURING SUPERHEAT

Operate the system long enough for the system pressures to stabilize before trying to read the superheat. This can take 15–30 min. To adjust a thermostatic expansion valve accurately, it is first necessary to measure its operating superheat. The basic formula for determining superheat is

superheat = (suction line temperature)
　　　　　　 − (evaporator saturation temperature).

This is illustrated in Figure 21-42.

Figure 21-39 some thermostatic expansion valves are not field adjustable
(Courtesy of Sporlan Divison-Parker Hannifin Corporation.)

Figure 21-40 Most adjustable thermostatic expansion valves have square adjustment stems that must be turned with a refrigeration wrench

　　　Suction line temperature can usually be obtained quite easily by measuring the temperature of the suction line at or near the expansion valve bulb. The temperature should be measured at the bulb since that is the point at which the valve

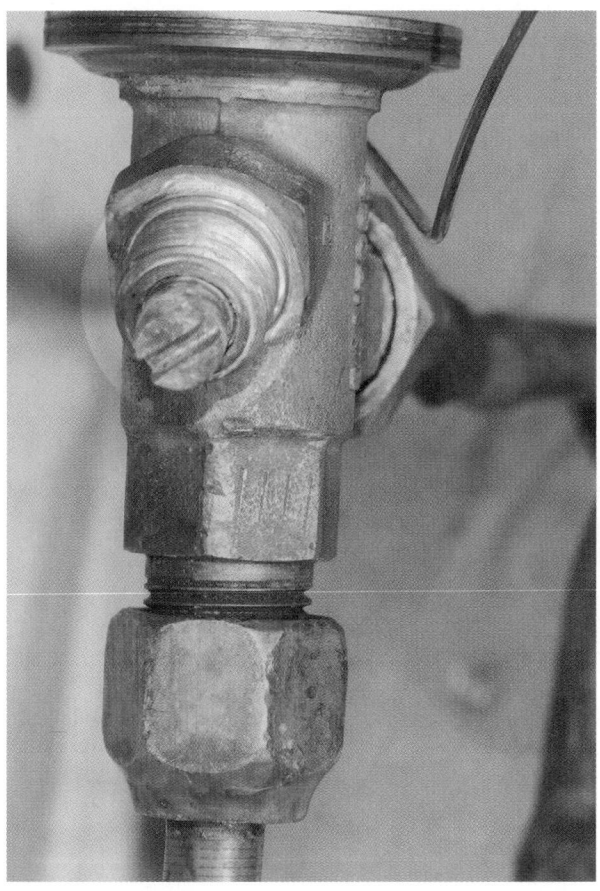

Figure 21-41 Some adjustable thermostatic expansion valves have adjustments that are turned with a screwdriver

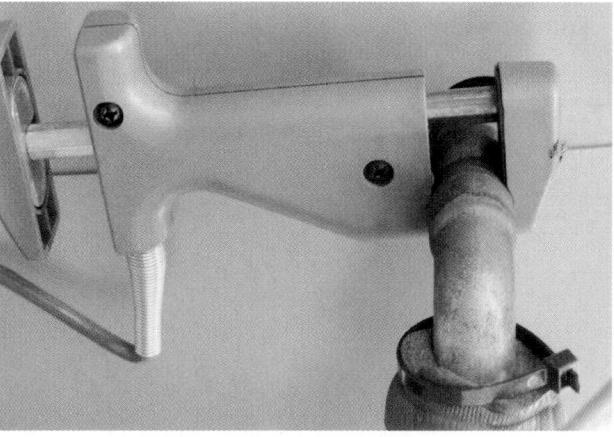

Figure 21-43 Clamp on thermocouple temperature probes can be used to get an accurate suction line temperature measurement

is measuring the suction line temperature. An accurate electronic thermometer is recommended, Figure 21-43. Infrared thermometers are usually not accurate for suction line temperature measurements. The line is usually smaller than the smallest point they can focus on, and the surface emissivity of the copper tubing is not close to the 0.95 that most infrared thermometers expect.

Evaporator saturation temperature is not as easily measured. To begin with, just getting to a spot where the evaporator saturation temperature can be measured is usually not practical. Therefore, the saturation temperature must be approximated since it cannot be directly measured. Secondly, the saturation temperature does not remain constant throughout the evaporator because the pressure does not remain the same. The most accurate way to determine the saturation temperature of the evaporator is to measure the suction pressure as close to the outlet of the evaporator as possible. If appreciable pressure drop exists between the evaporator outlet and where you actually measure the suction line pressure, this pressure drop must be added to the actual pressure reading in order to obtain an accurate evaporator saturation pressure reading.

Next, refer to a pressure/temperature chart to determine the evaporator saturation temperature, Figure 21-44. Finally, subtract the evaporator saturation temperature from the suction line temperature: the difference in the two is the operating superheat of the valve.

The obvious limitation is knowing the pressure drop between the outlet of the evaporator and the nearest suction line port. On split systems, this is usually outside at the condensing unit. Standard line sizing practice is to design for a 2°F saturated temperature drop in the suction line. The amount of pressure would vary depending upon the evaporator temperature and type of refrigerant. The pressures in Figure 21-35 will apply here as well. Some manufacturers do provide a pressure tap at the indoor coil, making the process much easier, Figure 21-45.

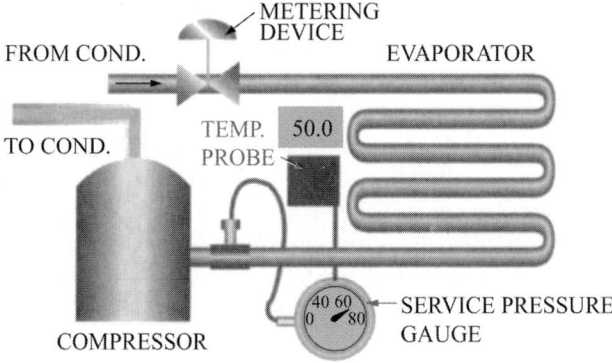

TO MEASURE SUPERHEAT:
1. FIND SUCTION PRESSURE
2. FIND MATCHING SATURATION TEMPERATURE
3. READ TEMPERATURE LEAVING EVAPORATOR
4. SUPERHEAT = TEMP. LEAVING — SATURATION TEMP.

Figure 21-42 Superheat is measured by subtracting the evaporator saturation temperature from suction line temperature

Temperature	R-134a	R-22	R-410a
-25	7" Hg	7	23
-20	4" Hg	10	27
-15	0	13	32
-10	2	17	37
-5	4	20	43
0	7	24	49
5	9	28	55
10	12	33	62
15	15	38	70
20	18	43	78
25	22	49	87
30	26	55	97
35	30	62	107
40	35	69	118
45	40	76	130
50	45	84	142
55	51	93	155
60	57	102	170
65	64	111	185
70	71	121	201
75	79	132	217
80	87	144	235
85	95	156	254
90	104	168	274
95	114	182	295
100	124	196	317
105	135	211	340
110	146	226	365
115	158	243	391
120	171	260	418
125	185	278	446
130	199	297	476
135	214	317	507
140	229	337	539
145	246	359	573
150	263	382	608

Figure 21-44 Saturated refrigerant pressure-temperature chart

Figure 21-45 The coil has a schrader valve connection that can be used to take an accurate evaporator saturation pressure reading

you have solved the original problem. For example, a high superheat can be caused by a system undercharge or a liquid line restriction. The valve cannot feed more refrigerant if it is not available. On the other hand, a system with a very low load may have a low superheat.

The superheat is adjusted by turning the valve stem in small increments to change spring tension. Increasing the spring tension increases the superheat setting; decreasing the spring tension decreases the superheat setting. The adjustment on most valves is clockwise (cw) to increase superheat and counterclockwise (ccw) to decrease superheat, Figure 21-46. Small adjustments can make big changes, especially if the operating superheat is within a few degrees of the desired superheat. Usually a $\frac{1}{4}$ turn at a time is sufficient. A $\frac{1}{2}$ turn might be warranted if the setting is off by 10°F or more. Time is required after each adjustment for the system pressures and temperatures to stabilize. This is an operation where being patient and taking your time will save time in the long run.

21.24 ADJUSTING VALVE SUPERHEAT

Before attempting to adjust the superheat on an expansion valve, make sure that some other system problem is not causing the incorrect superheat. Adjusting a valve that does not need adjusting will just create another problem to solve once

21.25 LIQUID DISTRIBUTORS

The refrigerant leaving the expansion valve must be distributed evenly to each circuit of multiple circuit coils. This cannot be done using a common header because the refrigerant leaving the metering device is a mixture of liquid and gas. Since the liquid and gas are different densities, they will

Figure 21-46 Turning the adjustment clockwise increases the superheat, turning the adjustment counterclockwise decreases the superheat

not flow through the header the same way, Figure 21-47. The result will be that some circuits are flooded while others are starved. Distributors are used to equally distribute the refrigerant to each circuit on a multiple circuit coil. They are placed between the expansion valve and the evaporator, as shown in Figure 21-48. Distributors are usually supplied by the coil manufacturer and are used where one metering device serves from 2 to 40 evaporator circuits, using connecting tubes ranging from $\frac{5}{32}$ in OD to $\frac{3}{8}$ in OD. The distributor consists of a nozzle, a conical divider, and multiple holes evenly spaced around the divider cone, Figure 21-49. The liquid and gas are evenly mixed when they pass through the nozzle. This homogenous mixture is then split evenly by the divider cone which sends equal amounts to each of the holes around it.

There is a pressure drop across the distributor. The effect of the distributor pressure drop is to reduce the amount of pressure drop across the expansion valve. Expansion valves with external equalizers must be used when a distributor is used because the pressure leaving the valve is higher than the pressure entering the evaporator coil.

MANIFOLD FEED

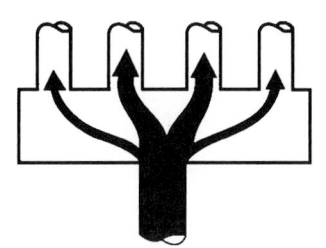

UP FEED

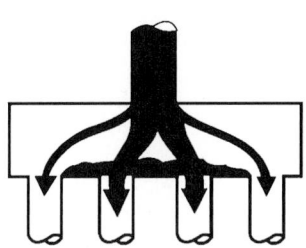

DOWN FEED

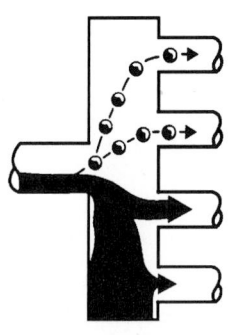

SIDE FEED

Figure 21-47 TA typical header will not evenly distribute the liquid gas mixture leaving on expansion valve
(Courtesy of Sporlan Divison-Parker Hannifin Corporation.)

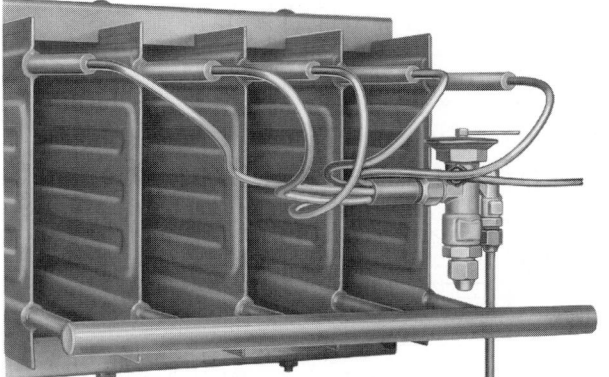

Figure 21-48 The distributor allows the thermostatic expansion valve to feed five circuits evenly
(Courtesy Sporlan Valve Company)

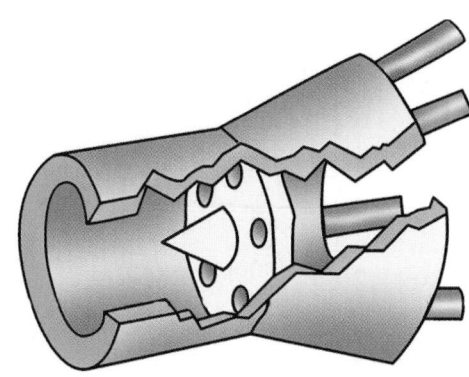

Figure 21-49 The distributor has a conical point that spreads the refrigerant evenly to all its circuits
(Courtesy Sporlan Valve Company)

21.26 LOW LOAD LIMITS

Both distributor nozzles and thermostatic expansion valves have low load limitations. A distributor will usually operate properly between 50% and 200% of its design capacity. When the flow through the nozzle drops below 50%, the gas and liquid refrigerant are not equally mixed. The superheat in the top circuits of the evaporator can be excessive due to liquid starving. The liquid floods back to the compressor from the lower circuits. This can easily be checked by measuring the temperature difference between the top and the bottom circuits of the coil. This problem can sometimes be solved by replacing the nozzle with the next smaller size.

The minimum load for most traditional thermostatic expansion valves is 35% to 50% of their capacity. When the flow through a thermostatic expansion valve drops below 30%, the valve will not hold constant settings. The valve will alternately overfeed the coil, and then underfeed the coil. This condition is called hunting. Under these conditions superheat values fluctuate. Using a smaller expansion valve can sometimes correct this condition.

Systems that must operate over a wide capacity range can solve the problem of underloading the expansion valve and distributor by using two expansion valves and distributors. Each valve would be sized for approximately 50% of the coil capacity. The control system can operate a solenoid to cut off one section of the evaporator when the load drops below 50% capacity, Figure 21-50.

21-27 BALANCED PORT EXPANSION VALVES

The primary reason for the operating limits of traditional thermostatic expansion valves is the design of the port and pin in the valve. Typically, the valve pin seats in a hole to oppose flow through the seat. The pressure on one side of the seat is much higher than on the other. This pressure difference acts as another opening force, lifting the pin off the seat, Figure 21-51. The problem is that this extra opening force changes as the system pressure drop changes. When the head pressure decreases, the pressure drop across the port decreases, and this lifting force decreases. The result is less refrigerant flow, and a starved evaporator. When the evaporator pressure decreases, the pressure drop increases, increasing this lifting force. The result is a flooded evaporator.

A solution to these problems is to design the port in the expansion valve to minimize the effect of pressure drop across the valve. These valves are called "balanced port" or "double ported" valves. Although there are several designs of balanced port valves from different manufacturers, the operating concept remains the same: refrigerant inlet pressure is applied at more than one point on the modulating assembly so that it counterbalances itself. One design is shown in Figure 21-52. Balanced port valves can operate within a much wider range of operating conditions including both low ambient and low load operation. Balanced port valves can typically operate properly on air cooled

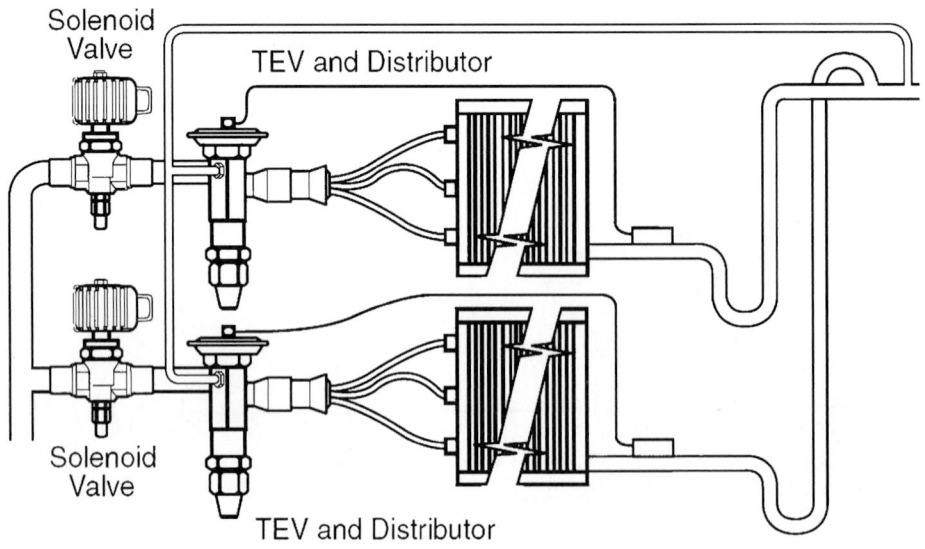

Figure 21-50 System capacity can be more easily controlled with two valves feeding a dual circuited coil
(Courtesy of Sporlan Divison-Parker Hannifin Corporation.)

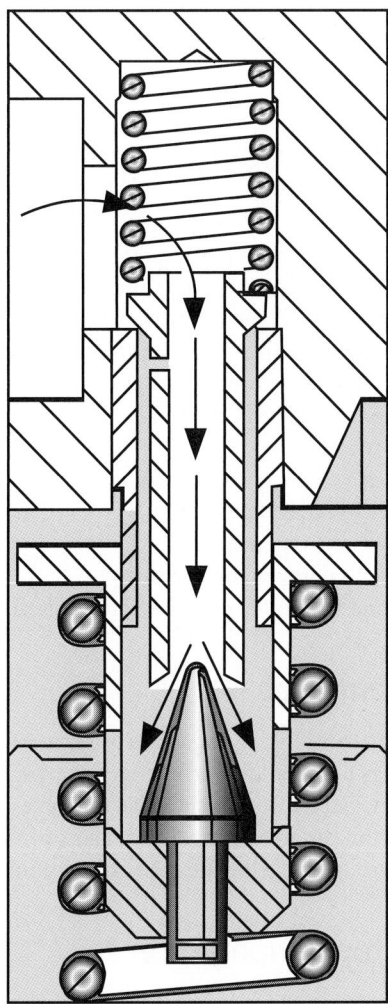

Figure 21-51 The pressure difference across the pin on a traditional valve tends to lift the pin off its seat
(Courtesy of Sporlan Divison-Parker Hannifin Corporation.)

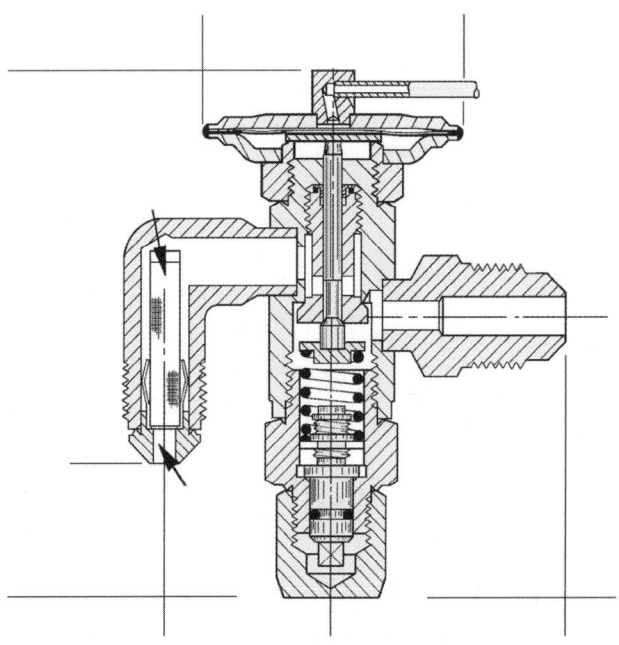

Figure 21-52 The balanced port expansion valve is not affected by pressure drop across the port
(Courtesy of Sporlan Divison-Parker Hannifin Corporation.)

Figure 21-53 Bi-flow expansion valves are used in water source heat pumps because they meter refrigerant in both directions

condensers down to 35°F without the need for condenser head pressure control. They can modulate correctly down to 15% of full evaporator load.

21.28 BI-FLOW EXPANSION VALVES

For years, expansion valves have been one way devices; they were made to only operate in one direction. Most still are designed this way. However, thermostatic expansion valves are now available that are specifically designed to allow refrigerant flow in both directions. Some of these valves meter the refrigerant in both directions, while others have built in check valves that allow unrestricted flow in the "reverse" direction.

The valves that meter in both directions are used on close coupled systems like water source heat pumps, Figure 21-53. This way the system can be manufactured with a single metering device. Since these valves meter in both directions,

they are not directional. These valves must be externally equalized and the equalizer line must run to a common suction that is suction in both heating and cooling. Likewise, the sensing bulb must be attached to a suction location that is always on the low side, regardless of the operating cycle.

The valves with built in check valves are typically used with split system heat pumps, Figure 21-54. This eliminates an external check valve that would normally be used to bypass flow around the expansion valve in the reverse direction. Even though these are also called bi-flow valves, they are

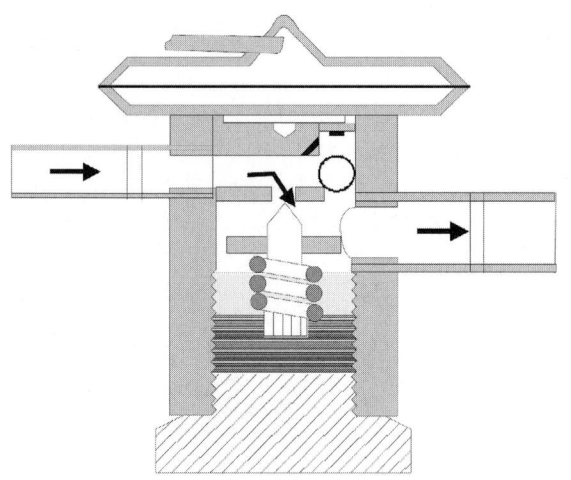

METERED FLOW

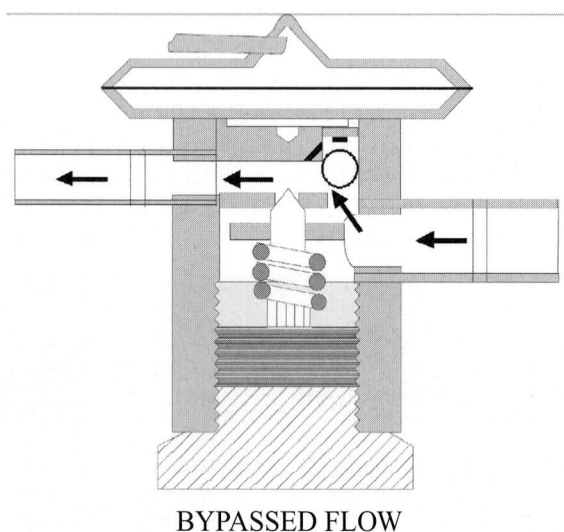

BYPASSED FLOW

Figure 21-54 Expansion valves with built in check relief valves are used on air source heat pumps at both the indoor coil and outdoor unit

directional because they meter refrigerant in one direction and let it flow unrestricted in the other direction.

21.29 THERMOSTATIC EXPANSION VALVE SIZING

Although most TEVs are labeled with a nominal capacity, the operating conditions used to produce this rating may not match the actual operating conditions for the system the valve will be installed in. Extended capacity charts give the valve ratings after considering all the factors that affect the valve capacity, Figure 21-55. The factors that affect the valve capacity are

- The type of refrigerant.
- The evaporator temperature.
- The pressure drop across the valve.
- The actual temperature of the liquid entering the valve.

Refrigerant Type

Selection charts are typically organized by refrigerant type, with a different selection chart for each refrigerant type. The heading of the table in Figure 21-55 specifies that this table is for R-410A valves. Sometimes refrigerants with similar operating characteristics are grouped together on the same selection chart.

Evaporator Temperature

A range of possible operating evaporator saturation temperatures is listed under each type of refrigerant. A typical selection chart has columns for temperatures from 50°F to −40°F. Select the column that is closest to the evaporator saturation temperature for the system. In general, the valve capacity will decrease as the evaporator saturation temperature decreases.

R 410A Thermostatic Expansion Valve Extended Capacity Table												
Valve Capacity in Tons of Refrigeration												
	40°F Evaporator						20°F Evaporator					
Nominal	Pressure Drop in psi						Pressure Drop in psi					
Capacity	120	160	200	240	280	320	120	160	200	240	280	320
1.5	1.3	1.5	1.7	1.8	2.0	2.1	1.3	1.5	1.6	1.8	1.9	2.1
3	2.6	3	3.4	3.4	4.0	4.2	2.6	2.9	3.3	3.6	3.9	4.2
5	4.3	5	5.6	6.1	6.6	7.0	4.2	4.9	5.5	6.0	6.5	6.9
7	6.0	7	7.8	8.6	9.3	9.9	5.9	6.9	7.7	8.4	9.1	9.7
9	7.8	9	10.0	11.0	11.9	12.7	7.6	8.8	9.9	10.8	12.5	12.5

Figure 21-55 Thermostatic expansion valve extended capacity selection chart

Pressure Drop Across the Valve

A range of possible operating pressure drops across the valve is listed under the evaporator temperature column. In Figure 21-55 there are six pressure drops to choose from under each temperature column. The highlighted 160 psi column under the 40°F temperature column is the nominal rating condition for these valves. To determine what the pressure drop at the valve will be, start by determining the condenser and evaporator saturation temperatures for the system. Convert these saturation temperatures to pressures using a saturation pressure-temperature chart. Subtract the evaporator pressure from the condenser pressure. Next, subtract any additional pressure drops that do no occur at the expansion valve, including:

- Pressure drop through the refrigerant lines.
- Pressure drop across any accessories in the liquid line, such as filter driers.
- Pressure drop due to vertical lift in the liquid line.
- Pressure drop through the distributor if a distributor is used.

Looking Up the Correct Nominal Size

Look under the pressure drop column which most closely matches the actual pressure drop across the valve. Go down the column until you find an actual capacity that is close to the capacity needed. Frequently the desired capacity falls between two valve ratings. In general, a slightly smaller valve will control better than a slightly larger valve. Look to the left to find the nominal size of the valve that delivers the correct capacity at the system's specific operating conditions. The extended sizing tables can also be used to determine what the actual capacity of any particular valve is at any given condition.

Actual Liquid Temperature

Most valve extended capacity charts assume a liquid temperature of 100°F. Correction factors are applied to the capacities listed in the extended capacity chart for liquid temperatures other than 100°F, Figure 21-56. Take the case of a 3 ton nominal capacity R-410A valve with an evaporator saturation temperature of 20°, a pressure drop across the valve of 200 psi, and an entering liquid temperature of 80°F. In Figure 21-55, the 3 ton nominal capacity valve has an actual capacity of 3.3 tons at 20°F with a pressure drop across the valve of 200 psig. The liquid correction factor shown in Figure 21-56 for 80°F R-410A liquid is 1.06. The capacity of the valve would be $3.3 \times 1.06 = 3.5$ tons. On the other hand, if the liquid were 120°F, the correction factor from Figure 21-56 would be 0.93. Then the valve capacity would be $3.3 \times 0.93 = 3$ tons.

21.30 INSTALLING THERMOSTATIC EXPANSION VALVES

Thermostatic expansion valves should be mounted as close to the evaporator as is practical. When using a distributor, it should be mounted directly to the expansion valve outlet. The valve body itself can be in any position, but it should be in a position that allows access to the adjusting stem in case the valve needs setting. Be careful when soldering or brazing in an expansion valve. The valve body can be wrapped with wet rags or heat absorbing paste to keep it cool. In particular, the power head and bulb should not be overheated.

> ### SERVICE TIP
>
> Many air conditioning manufacturers are now supplying evaporator coils for high efficiency units with thermostatic expansion valves installed inside the case of the coil. The thermal bulb is already attached to the suction line inside the coil. It is easy to destroy the expansion valve when brazing in the suction line on these coils. The heat conducts through the suction piping to the bulb which is fastened to the suction line on the other side of the coil casing. The pressure created from the extreme heat destroys the valve. When possible, remove the bulb from the suction line before brazing the suction line, and then reattach it when the line cools.

Liquid Refrigerant Temperature Correction Factors								
Liquid Line	70°F	80°F	90°F	100°F	110°F	120°F	130°F	140°F
R-134a	1.21	1.11	1.07	1.00	0.93	0.87	0.81	0.71
R-22	1.18	1.12	1.06	1.00	0.94	0.88	0.82	0.77
R-410A	1.09	1.06	1.03	1.00	0.97	0.93	0.89	0.84

Figure 21-56 Valve capacity correction factors for entering liquid temperature

Bulb Location

The thermal sensing bulb should ideally be located on a clean horizontal section of suction line as close to the evaporator as possible. The sensing bulb should never be located on the bottom of the suction line. Liquid and oil can puddle at the bottom of the line and affect the temperature on the bottom of the line. The bulb is normally mounted at the 4 or 8 o'clock positions on suction lines that are $^7/_8$ in OD or larger, Figure 21-57. The bulb may be mounted anywhere except on the bottom on lines that are smaller than $^7/_8$ in OD.

If a vertical bulb installation cannot be avoided, the bulb may be installed on a descending vertical line with the capillary tube end at the top, Figure 21-58. The bulb should never be located in a trap or downstream from a trap. Liquid collecting in the trap can throw off the temperature reading at that point.

Good thermal contact is essential for the valve to operate correctly. The bulb should be fastened to the line with copper straps that will not only hold the bulb securely, but also help improve the thermal contact between the line and the bulb. Finally, the bulb should be insulated from the surrounding air so that the temperature the bulb is sensing is the suction line temperature, not the air temperature.

External Equalizer Connection

If a valve has an external equalizer it must be connected; an externally equalized valve cannot operate without its equalizer line being connected. The equalizer connection normally penetrates the suction line 6 or 8 in downstream from the sensing bulb, unless the manufacturer's instructions advise differently. The equalizer line should come off the top of the

Figure 21-58 The capillary tube should come off the top if the bulb must be mounted on a vertical line

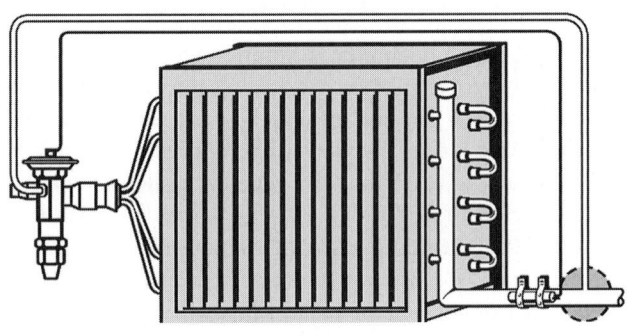

Figure 21-59 The external equalizer connection should come off the top of the suction line, downstream from the bulb
(Courtesy of Sporlan Divison-Parker Hannifin Corporation.)

suction line, never off the bottom, Figure 21-59. Piping the equalizer off the bottom creates a potential trap that can interfere with the proper operation of the valve.

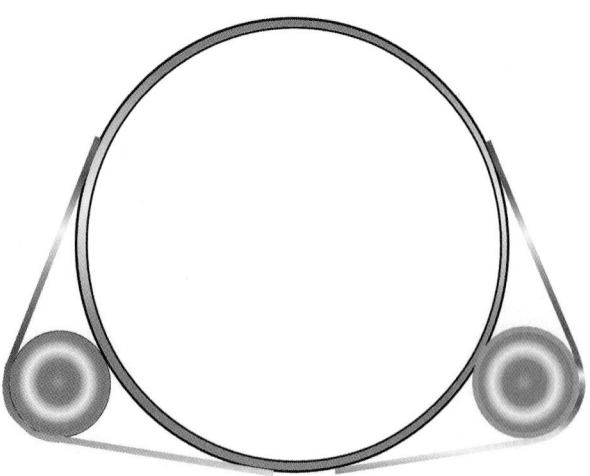

Figure 21-57 The sensing bulb should be mounted at the 4:00 or 8:00 position on lines that are $^7/_8$ in outside diameter or larger

SERVICE TIP

The external equalizer line should never be upstream of the bulb. Although refigerant is not supposed to flow through the eqalizer line from the expansion valve, small internal leaks in the valve can allow a small flow of liquid through the equalizer line. If the equalizer line enters upstream of the bulb, this small flow of liquid can fool the bulb into thinking there is liquid leaving the evaporator. This will cause the valve to underfeed and starve the evaporator.

21.31 TROUBLESHOOTING THERMOSTATIC EXPANSION VALVES

Thermostatic expansion valve problems fall into three general categories:

- The valve overfeeds—flooding the evaporator.
- The valve underfeeds—starving the evaporator.
- The valve hunts—alternately overfeeding and underfeeding.

Valve Overfeeding

Valve overfeeding is most often caused by incorrect thermal bulb installation. The valve overfeeds because it cannot accurately sense the suction line temperature. The thermal bulb should be securely fastened to a straight, clean, horizontal section of suction line. The bulb should also be insulated from the surrounding air. The bulb should sense the suction line temperature, not the air temperature. If a bulb is loose or poorly insulated it will be reading a temperature that is higher than the suction line temperature, and the valve will overfeed. Overfeeding can also be caused by improper valve sizing, incorrect application, or improper adjustment. In the case of valves that are assembled in the field from a kit of components, improper component selection can easily result in overfeeding. However, before investigating any of these possibilities, make sure the sensing bulb is correctly installed and insulated.

Valve Underfeeding

Check the system charge before assuming that the expansion valve is underfeeding. A valve cannot supply refrigerant that is not there. Also check for restrictions in the liquid line like a plugged filter drier. Typically, a restriction in the liquid line will cause a temperature drop across the restriction. This can be checked by checking the temperature difference across the suspected restriction.

A common cause of underfeeding on valves in systems with HFC refrigerant and POE lubricant, like R-410a systems, is clogged screens and valves. Many valves have screens at their inlet to prevent foreign debris from entering the valve. A system with scale inside the lines caused by brazing can become clogged with this scale when the refrigerant and oil scrub it off the inside of the refrigerant lines and deposit it at the expansion valve. If the valve does not have a screen, the debris may become lodged in the valve itself. This usually requires changing the valve. One equipment manufacturer has had so many problems with debris clogged valves that they now require the liquid line filter to be installed as close to the indoor unit as possible.

A TEV that has lost the charge in its bulb will underfeed severely. Often, systems that have valves with dead power elements will pull a vacuum on the low side. One way to diagnose a dead power element is to remove it from the suction line and hold it in your hand during system operation.

The suction pressure should rise. If there is no change, the power element is probably dead. Some valves have replaceable power elements. The parts on the valve shown in Figure 21-60 can be replaced. The entire valve must be replaced on one piece valves, Figure 21-61.

Valve Hunting

A valve that is too large for the load it is trying to control will alternately overfeed and underfeed the evaporator. This happens when the smallest amount that the valve can open lets too much refrigerant through. When the valve opens to minimum position, it floods the evaporator. It will sense this and then shut. This causes the evaporator to starve. It will

Figure 21-60 The powerhead on some expansion valves can be replaced
(Courtesy of Sporlan Divison-Parker Hannifin Corporation.)

Figure 21-61 Some thermostatic expansion valves are constructed with a one-piece body; if the power head dies, the entire valve must be replaced
(Courtesy Emerson Climate Technologies)

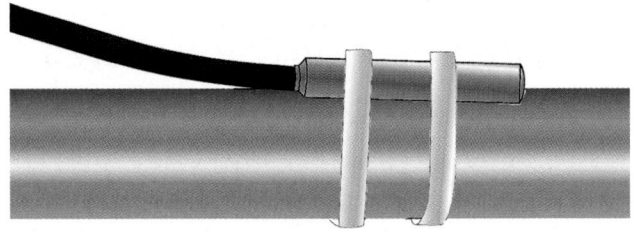

Figure 21-62 Thermistors are used to sense the line temperature for electronically controlled valves

sense this, and open again. The low side pressure will actually rise and fall on systems with severe hunting problems. Hunting is usually the result of an oversized valve or a lower than normal evaporator load.

SERVICE TIP

Manufacturers that sell systems with orifice metering devices often offer high efficiency upgrade kits that can be field applied to their units. These kits are essentially a thermostatic expansion valve with all the necessary fittings to connect it to the system. Replacing the orifice with a thermostatic expansion valve increases the efficiency of most units by about 1 point on the SEER rating: a 12 SEER unit with a fixed restriction becomes a 13 SEER unit with an expansion valve. Remember that the charging chart on the units are for the orifice, not the TEV that was just installed. The charging charts on an orifice unit will not work with a TEV. Typically orifice charging charts specify the operating superheat at different conditions. Since TEVs try to maintain a stable superheat, these charts will not work with a TEV. Normally there is a statement to this effect in small print somewhere beside the charging chart. A few manufacturers provide a new chart to paste on the panel, but most do not.

21.32 ELECTRONICALLY CONTROLLED EXPANSION VALVES

A number of mechanisms have been developed to control refrigerant flow with electric valves. Electronically controlled valves sense the evaporator saturation temperature and the suction line temperature using thermistors, Figure 21-62. A thermistor is a device that changes resistance when its temperature changes. The thermistors are wired to electronic controls which control the operation of the valves. One advantage of using electronic temperature sensing is being able to have the valve and the temperature sensing device in different locations. These valves are all controlled by electronic signals, but the mechanisms used are quite different from one another. Types of electronically controlled valves that have been successfully applied include:

- Pulse width modulated solenoid valves.
- Magnetically controlled analog valves.
- Heat motor valves.
- Stepper motor valves.

Pulse Width Modulated Solenoid

A pulse width modulated solenoid valve is shown in Figure 21-63. Unlike the TEV, which can modulate to positions between fully open and fully closed, solenoid valves are either open or closed. Pulse modulated valves control flow by increasing or decreasing open time during each cycle. When coupled with the proper electronic control system, a solenoid valve can pulse rapidly, opening and closing quickly in response to the cooling load. The illustration on the left in Figure 21-64 shows the valve closed, and the solenoid valve is deenergized; the view on the right shows the energized condition. This valve also serves the function of a liquid line solenoid valve, blocking flow to the evaporator during the OFF-cycle and at other times when refrigerant flow is not required.

Magnetic Analog Valves

The magnetic analog valve is really a specially designed solenoid valve that can modulate. It is controlled by a variable magnetic field. These valves have been used successfully in transport refrigeration, but are not common. They are difficult to control and their repeatability is poor.

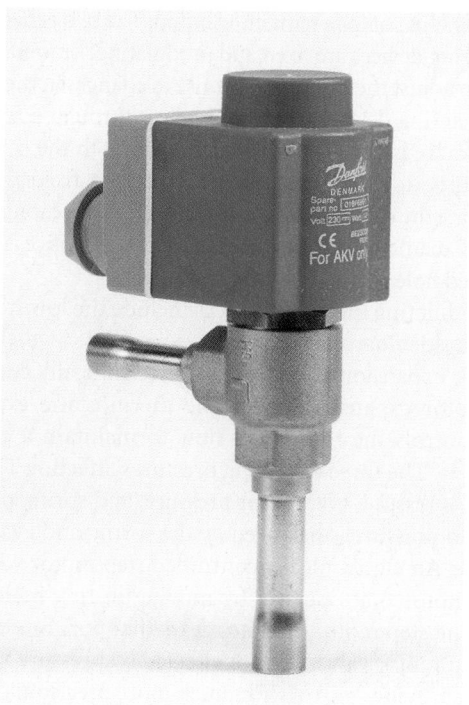

Figure 21-63 Pulse width modulated solenoid valve
(Courtesy of Donfoss, Inc.)

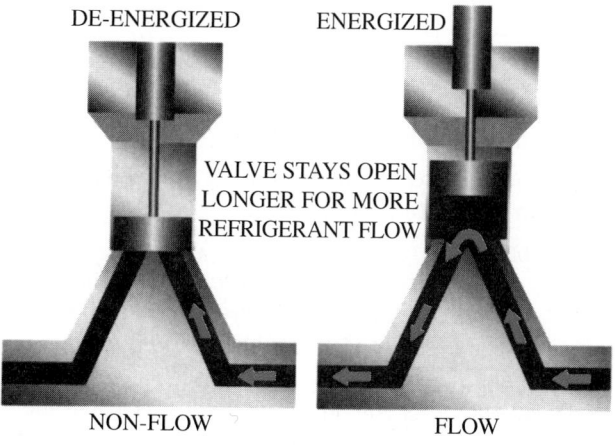

DE-ENERGIZED   ENERGIZED

VALVE STAYS OPEN
LONGER FOR MORE
REFRIGERANT FLOW

NON-FLOW   FLOW

Figure 21-64 Pulsating solenoid valve, both energized and deenergized

Heat Motor Valves

Heat motor valves operate somewhat like traditional thermostatic expansion valves. They are filled with a fluid that expands when it is heated, and contracts when it cools. A small heater that is controlled by an electronic circuit is immersed in the fluid. When the heater heats the fluid, it expands and increases the valve's opening force. When less heat is produced and the fluid cools, it contracts and the opening force is reduced.

Step Motor Valves

The pulse modulated solenoid valve, the magnetic analog valve, and the heat motor valve all have been successfully applied, but they all share some limitations. Getting consistent control from these is generally difficult. Their repeatability is poor. That is, they do not always behave the same way under the same conditions. All three are essentially fairly old electromechanical technology being controlled by sophisticated controls.

Step motor valves are truly a more advanced technology. They can deliver more precise control and their repeatability is excellent. A step motor does not spin like a regular motor, but moves in fractions of a revolution, or steps. The motor winding is actually a group of electromagnet pairs. Typically there are anywhere from 24 to 100 pairs of electromagnet pairs arranged in a circle around the step motor. The motor moves in steps from one pair of magnets to the next. In the case of a motor with 100 pairs of magnets, the motor would take 100 small steps to make one revolution.

An electronically controlled step motor valve is shown in Figure 21-65. The motor shaft rotates in tiny steps to control a set of gears that position a pin in a seat. The operation of step motor valves is governed by the software and electronics used to drive the valve, Figure 21-66. The step motor gets its signal from an electronic control panel that is attached to an electronic sensor that measures refrigerant superheat. Since the step motor valve is controlled independently of pressure, this valve is able to provide safe startup, shutdown, and operation, and high energy efficiency through its full range of operating conditions. One particular step motor valve has 1,596 steps in a 0.125 in stroke and can operate at a rate of 200 steps per second. Not only can this provide very precise control,

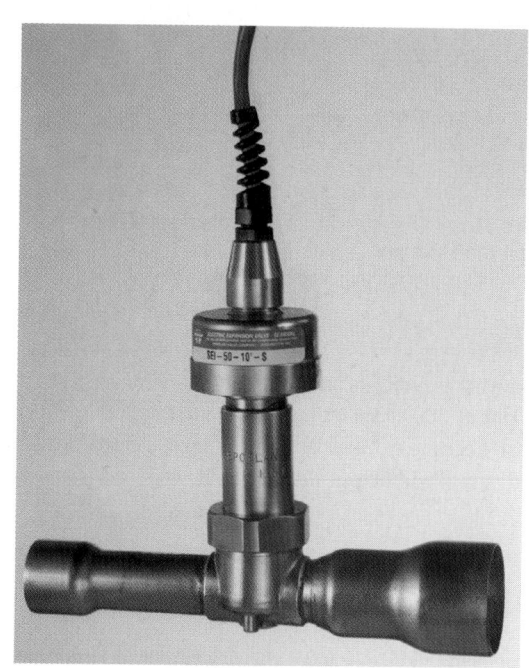

Figure 21-65 Step motor expansion valve
(Courtesy of Sporlan Divison-Parker Hannifin Corporation.)

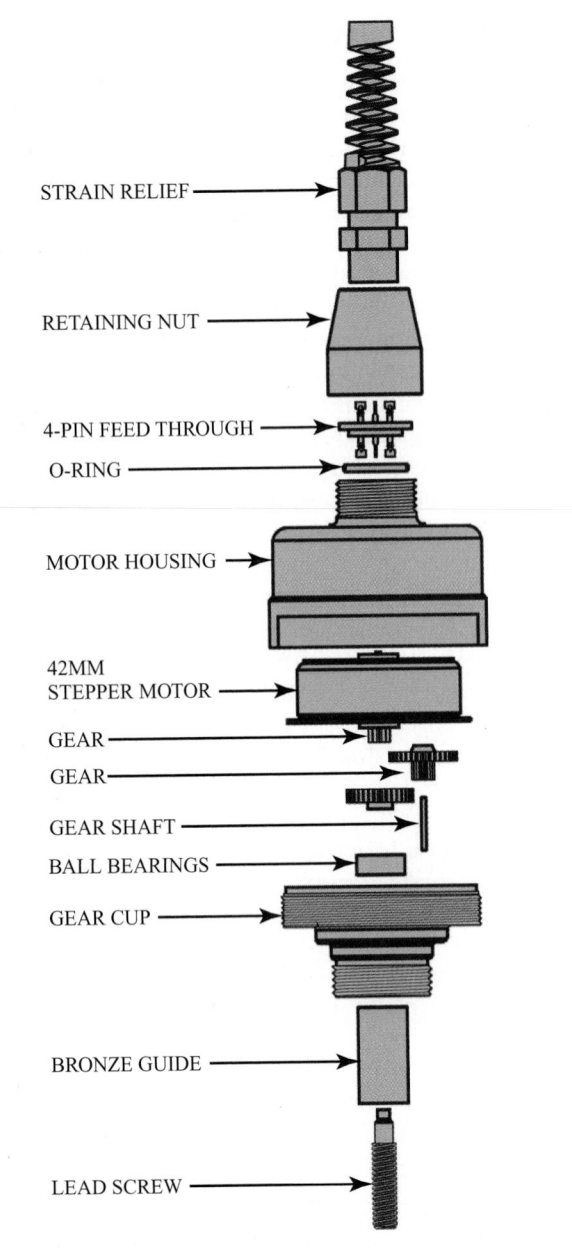

STRAIN RELIEF

RETAINING NUT

4-PIN FEED THROUGH

O-RING

MOTOR HOUSING

42MM
STEPPER MOTOR

GEAR

GEAR

GEAR SHAFT

BALL BEARINGS

GEAR CUP

BRONZE GUIDE

LEAD SCREW

Figure 21-66 The step motor controls a set of gears that position the valve pin
(Courtesy of Sporlan Divison-Parker Hannifin Corporation.)

the control points are very repeatable. The position of the valve pin at 500 steps will always be the same. As electronic control becomes more popular, more electronically controlled valves will be put into use.

UNIT—21 SUMMARY

The metering device reduces the pressure and temperature of the refrigerant entering the evaporator by restricting how much refrigerant can pass through the metering device. All metering devices have some amount of flash gas. The evaporation of the

flash gas helps cool the remaining liquid. The two general types of metering devices are fixed and modulating. Modulating devices can adjust their flow in response to changes in the system; fixed metering devices cannot. The flow through a fixed metering device is not fixed, but varies with both the condenser and evaporator temperature. Two types of fixed metering devices are the capillary tube and the orifice. The capillary tube is a small diameter, seamless copper tube. The orifice is a small, calibrated hole.

Modulating metering devices include the low side float, the high side float, the automatic expansion valve, the thermostatic expansion valve, and the electronically controlled step motor expansion valve. The thermostatic expansion valve controls the refrigerant flow to maintain a constant superheat. The three operating pressures affecting TEV flow are bulb pressure, evaporator pressure, and spring pressure. The bulb pressure is balanced by the spring and evaporator pressure. An electronically controlled step motor valve uses a step motor that operates by moving in tiny incremental steps. The step motor operates gears that position the valve pin. Step motor valves are not affected by pressure variables and can provide control with much more precision than traditional thermostatic expansion valves. The electronic controls that operate step motors use thermistors to sense system temperatures.

WORK ORDERS

Service Ticket 2101

Customer Complaint: Poor Cooling

Equipment: Recently Installed R-22 Split System with an Orifice Metering Device

A customer has recently installed a new split system. The system does not seem to be cooling well. The technician notices that the high side pressure is a little low, the low side pressure is a little high, and both the subcooling and superheat are low. The service technician calls in and asks the installation mechanics if they remember what orifice they used. The installation mechanics reply that they do not know what number the orifice is, they simply left in the orifice that came with the coil. The service mechanic looks up the match between the coil and the condensing unit because the nominal coil rating is 12,000 Btu/hr larger than the nominal rating of the condensing unit. The coil is an AHRI match for the condenser, but the manufacturer specifies a smaller orifice for the match than is normally shipped with the coil. The technician closes the liquid line valve, pumps the system refrigerant into the condenser, and then closes the suction line valve. The orifice is replaced with the correct size, the coil and line set are evacuated, and the system valves are opened. The unit now operates within manufacturer's specifications.

Service Ticket 2102

Customer Complaint: Refrigerator Stops Cooling

Equipment: Household Refrigerator with a Recently Replaced Compressor

A customer has just had the compressor replaced in their refrigerator. The refrigerator starts and begins to cool, but stops cooling a little while after starting. The technician starts the refrigerator and monitors its pressure. The pressures appear normal and the temperature begins to drop. However, after a few minutes the suction pressure pulls into a vacuum and the refrigerator begins to warm up again. The technician notices that although the compressor has been changed, the filter drier appears to be the original. The technician explains that the cause of the problem is most likely moisture freezing at the capillary tube as a result of not getting all the moisture out of the system when the compressor was changed. The refrigerant is recovered, the filter drier replaced, and the system is evacuated and charged with new, clean refrigerant. The refrigerator now stays cold after pulling down.

Service Ticket 2103

Customer Complaint: Air Conditioner Not Cooling

Equipment: Newly Installed Split System with a Factory Installed Thermostatic Expansion Valve in the Evaporator Coil

A customer has just had a new high efficiency air conditioning system installed. The system uses a thermostatic expansion valve that is factory installed inside the evaporator coil. The technician notices that the suction pressure is very low, and both the superheat and subcooling are very high. The system is doing very little cooling. The technician takes the front cover off of the evaporator and removes the TEV bulb from the suction line. The evaporator pressure does not change, even while holding the bulb. The technician notices that the paint on the coil casing is burned around the suction line and that the TEV bulb is installed just on the other side of the coil casing. The technician determines that the TEV power element was destroyed during installation from overheating when the suction line was brazed in. The technician recovers the system refrigerant, replaces the TEV, evacuates and recharges the system. The suction pressure rises to the factory specified level and the system begins cooling.

Service Ticket 2104

Customer Complaint: Poor Cooling and Noisy Compressor

Equipment: Walk In Cooler with a Thermostatic Expansion Valve

A new technician changed the thermostatic expansion valve on a walk in cooler last week. The system owner

noticed that the compressor seemed noisier than usual and also noticed that the system was not cooling well. The company's senior technician is sent to see what is going on. There is no superheat and the evaporator is flooding back to the compressor, causing the noise and poor cooling. The technician decides to check the bulb installation and finds that insulating gum is between the bulb and the suction line, keeping the bulb from sensing the suction line temperature. The senior technician asks the new technician about the gum and he replies that he was instructed to insulate the bulb well, so he wrapped insulating gum all the way around the bulb. The senior technician explains that the purpose of the insulation is to ensure the bulb senses the suction line temperature, so insulation between the bulb and suction line is not a good idea. The senior technician corrects the bulb installation and the system operates with an 8°F superheat and a much quieter compressor.

UNIT 21—REVIEW QUESTIONS

1. What happens to the refrigerant as it passes through the metering device?
2. Explain the difference between a fixed metering device and a modulating metering device.
3. What are the two types of fixed metering devices?
4. Explain how an air conditioner with a fixed metering device reacts to changes in outdoor temperature.
5. Explain how an air conditioner with a fixed metering device reacts to changes in indoor temperature.
6. List the advantages of the capillary tube.
7. What advantages are there to orifice type metering devices?
8. List types of modulating metering devices.
9. What is the most common application of the high side float?
10. What is the difference between the low side float and the high side float?
11. Explain the basic operation of the automatic expansion valve.
12. Why is the automatic expansion valve not suited for systems with varying loads?
13. Which way would the adjustment on top of an automatic expansion valve be turned to increase the evaporator pressure?
14. What does a thermostatic expansion valve try to regulate and keep stable?
15. What is the difference between internally and externally equalized thermostatic expansion valves?
16. How does a TEV with MOP work?
17. What is the difference between a traditional TEV and a balanced port TEV?
18. What is the difference between a traditional liquid charged TEV bulb and a liquid cross charged TEV bulb?
19. What is the purpose of a liquid distributor?

20. The electronic expansion valve is activated by a(n) _____ .

21. How do pulse modulated valves control flow?

22. How do electronically controlled step motor valves work?

23. An R-22 TEV is set for a 12°F superheat. The system is operating with a suction pressure of 76 psig and a suction line temperature at the bulb of 50°F. What is the actual operating superheat?

24. Which way would the adjusting stem on an expansion valve be turned to increase the superheat?

25. Which way would the adjusting stem on an expansion valve be turned to decrease superheat?

26. What types of problems could cause a TEV system to operate at too high a superheat?

27. Why must technicians be careful when brazing lines to evaporator coils that have thermostatic expansion valves?

28. How can a capillary tube that is restricted with debris be differentiated from a capillary tube that is restricted with ice?

29. What is a bi-flow expansion valve?

30. An R-134a TEV is set for an 8°F superheat. The system is operating with a suction pressure of 22 psig and a suction line temperature at the bulb of 50°F. What is the actual operating superheat?

31. What system operating characteristics would you expect from a system that has a TEV with a dead power element?

32. What system operating characteristics would you expect from a system that has a TEV with a loose sensing bulb?

33. What system operating characteristics would you expect from a system that has a restricted orifice type metering device?

34. What system operating characteristics would you expect from a system that has an oversized orifice type metering device?

35. Why is nitrogen brazing so important with systems using R-410a refrigerant?

UNIT 22

Evaporators

OBJECTIVES

After completing this unit you will be able to:

- identify the four broad categories of evaporator application.
- discuss the concepts of sensible and latent cooling as they relate to evaporators.
- explain how bypass air and dehumidification work.
- list the types of water cooling evaporators.
- explain the difference between flooded and direct expansion evaporators.
- explain the purpose of the condensate drain trap in air conditioning evaporators.
- list the three most common types of defrost in commercial refrigeration systems.
- discuss the importance of using an evaporator coil that is an ARI match to the condensing unit it will be paired with.

22.1 INTRODUCTION

The evaporator is a device for absorbing heat into the refrigeration system. The evaporator is named for the refrigerant evaporation taking place inside it. In the evaporator, the refrigerant absorbs heat from its surrounding load as it evaporates from a low pressure saturated liquid to a low pressure vapor. The evaporator is a heat exchanger with the refrigerant contained within tubes, passages, or a vessel. The load or product is separated from the refrigerant by the heat exchanger walls or shell. The heat flows into an evaporator because the temperature of the refrigerant is lower than the temperature of the product being cooled. The refrigerant temperature is set by its pressure. The evaporator pressure is maintained by the metering device.

22.2 EVAPORATOR LOADS

In refrigeration, the term product refers to anything that is being cooled or frozen. The term product is often used in reference to food, but it can be used to describe things being manufactured such as plastics and electronics; health products such as medicines and medical labs; and products that help in manufacturing like solvent baths, machining coolants, hydraulic fluids, and soon. It is not normally used to describe air, water, or brine, although they can also be considered products.

The evaporator heat load is the quantity of heat the refrigeration system must remove from the product. The product can be anything that contains a quantity of heat. An evaporator can be used to cool gases, liquids, or solids. Air is the most common gas cooled, water and brine are the most common liquids, and ice or other frozen products are the most common solids.

When evaporator coils are used to cool air, the heat load can be both sensible and latent. The sensible load is the amount of temperature change in the air as it passes through the coil. Sensible heat change results in a temperature change that can be measured by a thermometer.

Most air contains some water vapor. That water vapor will condense to a liquid as it passes over the evaporator if the evaporator temperature is below the dew point. As the water vapor changes from a vapor state to a liquid state, it releases its latent heat to the refrigerant. Latent heat reduces the amount of water vapor in the air. This requires refrigeration capacity, but it does not result in a temperature change in the air. A cooling process that is entirely latent will result in no temperature change in the air. In air conditioning, the load is typically both sensible and latent. Figure 22-1 shows how an increase in latent capacity corresponds to a decrease in sensible capacity.

Indoor wet bulb temperature	Total capacity	Latent capacity	Sensible capacity	Temperature drop
62°F WB	31,000 Btu/hr	0 Btu/hr	31,000 Btu/hr	21°F
67°F WB	34,000 Btu/hr	6,000 Btu/hr	28,000 Btu/hr	19°F
72°F WB	37,000 Btu/hr	16,000 Btu/hr	21,000 Btu/hr	14°F

Figure 22-1 Evaporator sensible and latent capacity vs. entering air wet bulb

Dehumidifying the air is the process of removing water vapor from the air. In mechanical, refrigeration, water vapor is condensed to form liquid water. Dehumidifying takes a lot of energy and can be a major load on a cooling coil. It takes approximately 970 Btu of heat to vaporize 1 lb of water. A pint weighs about 1 lb, so it takes 970 Btu to change it all to vapor. This has the effect of adding 970 Btu of heat to the air. The same quantity of heat, 970 Btu, has to be removed when that water vapor condenses on the evaporator. The cooling capacity that is used to condense water vapor out of the air does not change the air temperature. In humid climates like the southeastern United States, dehumidification is just as important as temperature reduction.

22.3 PRESSURE-ENTHALPY DIAGRAM AND THE EVAPORATOR

A plot of a refrigeration cycle using R410A is shown in Figure 22-2. The line representing the evaporator is shown in green; the lines representing the other three components are shown in gray. Refrigerant enters the evaporator as a saturated mixture at the point indicated by the blue arrow. At this point the refrigerant is a 30% vapor saturated mix with a pressure of 133 psia, a temperature of 40°F, with a heat content of approximately 58 Btu/lb. As the mixture travels through the evaporator, the vapor percentage increases as the liquid percentage decreases. This causes an increase in enthalpy, but the temperature remains 40°F and the pressure remains 133 psia. Eventually, the refrigerant is 100% vapor near the end of the evaporator at the point indicated by the purple arrow. At this point the refrigerant is still 133 psia, and 40°F, but its enthalpy has risen to approximately 120 Btu/lb. The last part of the evaporator is used to superheat the refrigerant. By the time the refrigerant leaves the evaporator at the point indicated by the red arrow, the refrigerant has changed to a superheated gas with a pressure of 133 psia, a temperature of 60°F, and a heat content of 135 Btu/lb.

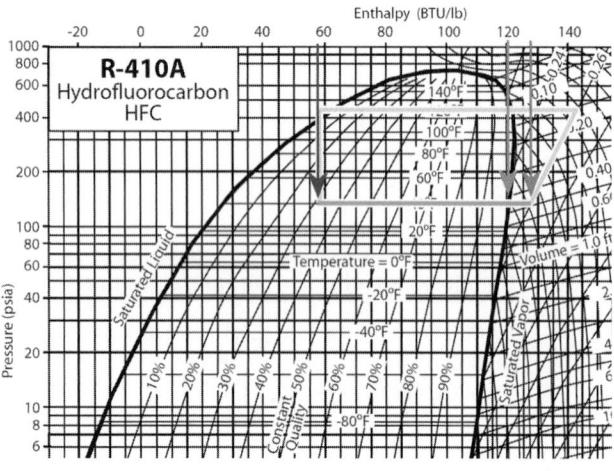

Figure 22-2 Enthalpy change through the evaporator

22.4 TYPES OF EVAPORATORS

Evaporators are made for many diverse applications. They can be classified by their application, general operating principle, physical construction, and normal operating temperature range. Evaporators can be grouped by application into four broad categories:

- Domestic refrigeration.
- Commercial refrigeration.
- Air conditioning.
- Chillers.

Domestic refrigeration includes household appliances such as refrigerators, freezers, and dehumidifiers. Figure 22-3 shows evaporators for two domestic refrigeration appliances. The top picture is the evaporator for a dehumidifier; the bottom picture is the evaporator for a frost free refrigerator. Notice that they are both constructed of aluminum.

Commercial refrigeration would be the large refrigerated cases and freezers in grocery stores and restaurants, Figure 22-4. Air conditioning coils would include residential and light commercial air conditioners and heat pumps.

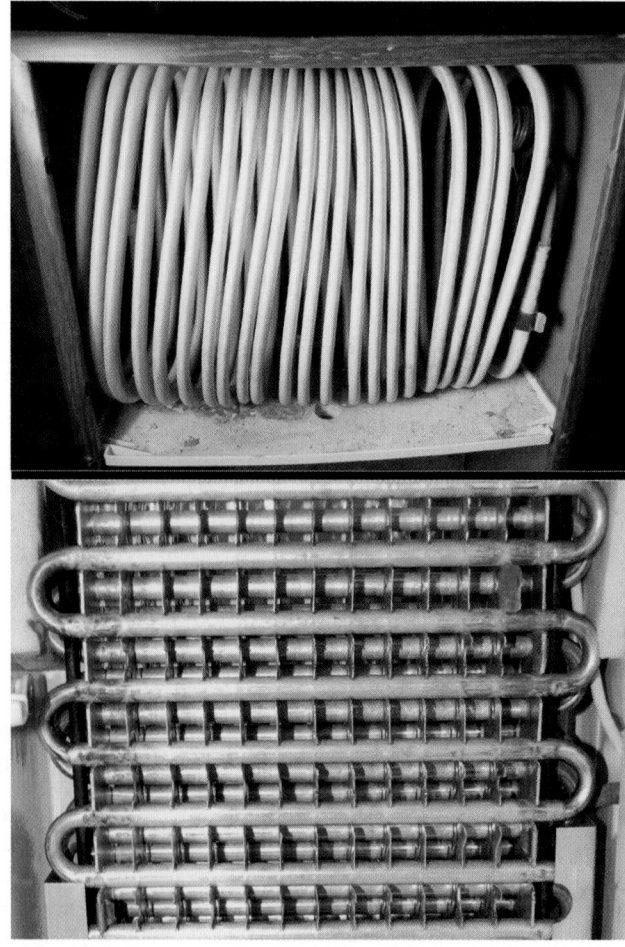

Figure 22-3 Two aluminum domestic refrigeration evaporators

Figure 22-4 Commercial refrigeration evaporator for walk in cooler
(© 2008 Heatcraft Refrigeration Products LLC.)

Chillers are systems that cool water or water and antifreeze solutions, Figure 22-5. Each of these groups can be broken down further by such characteristics as physical construction, operating principle, or normal temperature range.

Domestic and commercial refrigeration evaporators can be listed both by their construction and operating temperature range. By construction, the types of domestic refrigeration evaporators are:

- Bare pipe, Figure 22-6.
- Plate, Figure 22-7.
- Tube and fin, Figure 22-8.

Figure 22-5 Large tonage chiller

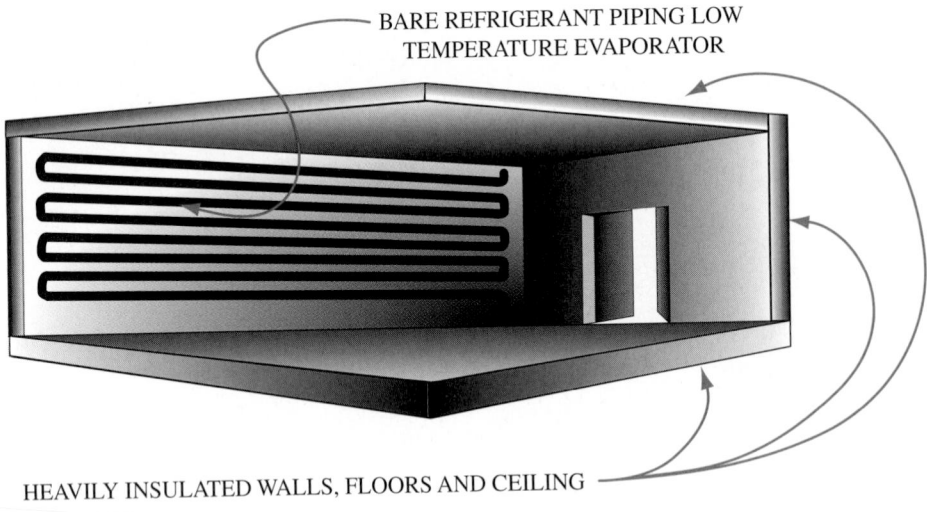

BARE REFRIGERANT PIPING LOW
TEMPERATURE EVAPORATOR

HEAVILY INSULATED WALLS, FLOORS AND CEILING

Figure 22-6 Bare pipe evaporator coil with gravity air circulation

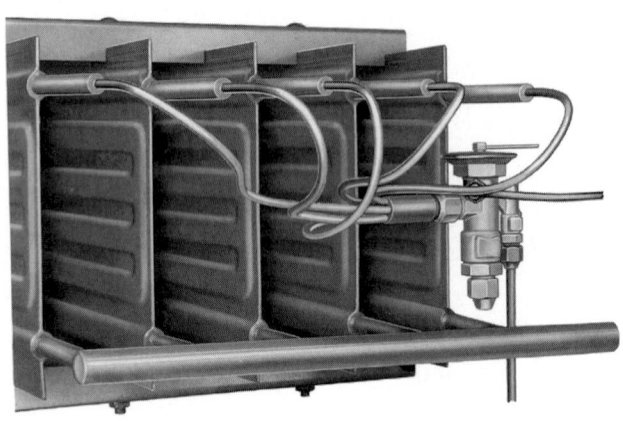

Figure 22-7 Plate-type evaporator
(Courtesy Sporlan Valve Company)

Listed by their temperature range, they can be

- High temperature, 47°F to 60°F.
- Medium temperature, 28°F to 40°F.
- Low temperature, −20°F to 32°F.

High temperature applications are generally for storage of such items as flowers, candy, and dry goods. Medium temperature applications are typically used for perishable fresh foods that must stay above freezing, such as eggs, produce, and fresh meat. Meat cases actually operate below 32°F, but the meat does not begin to freeze until around 28°F. Low temperature applications are for ice and frozen food. Everything does not freeze at the same temperature. Ice cream needs to be −20°F to be frozen hard, but ice only has to be 32°F.

Air conditioning evaporator coils are all tube and fin coils operating at about the same temperature range.

However, there are many variations of shape and thickness in tube and fin air conditioning coils. Figure 22-9 shows the four most common types of air conditioning coil shapes. They are:

- Slab coils, Figure 22-9 top left.
- Slant coils, Figure 22-9 top right.
- "A" coils, Figure 22-9 bottom right.
- "N" or "M" coils, Figure 22-9 bottom left.

Air conditioning coils can also be listed by the direction that air flows through them. Listed by airflow, they can be:

- Upflow, the air blows up through the coil.
- Downflow, the air blows down through the coil.
- Horizontal, the air blows horizontally through the coil.
- Multi-position, combines one or more of the other positions.

Figure 22-10 shows the airflow direction for each of these types of coils.

Chiller evaporators can be listed both by their general operation and by their construction. By construction they can be:

- Tube in tube, Figure 22-11.
- Shell and coil, Figure 22-12.
- Shell and tube, Figure 22-13.

By operating principle, chillers can be either direct expansion or flooded.

Evaporator design is specific to the intended application. An evaporator that performs perfectly in one application might not work at all in a different application.

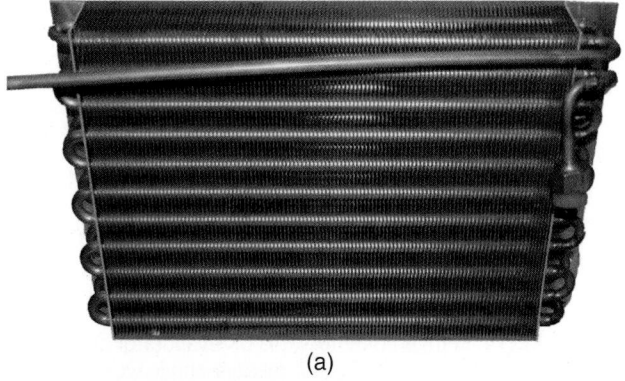

(a)

(b)

Figure 22-8 Tube and fin evaporator
(Courtesy Hampler Engineering Corporation)

22.5 FLOODED AND DIRECT EXPANSION EVAPORATORS

Two general operating principles are used in evaporator design: direct expansion evaporators and flooded evaporators.

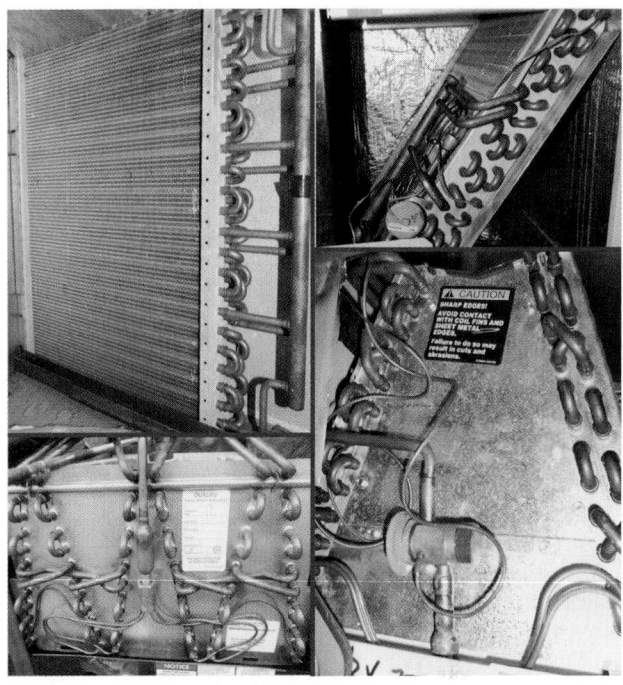

Figure 22-9 Four styles of air conditioning coils, from top left clockwise, slab, slant, "A," and "M"

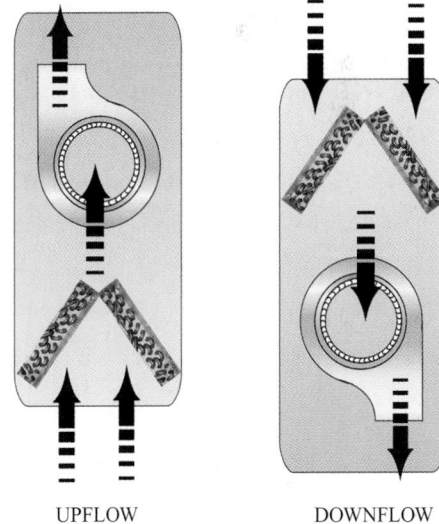

UPFLOW   DOWNFLOW

HORIZONTAL

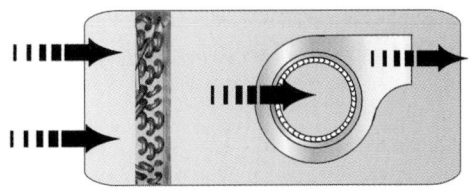

Figure 22-10 Three directions of airflow through an evaporator coil

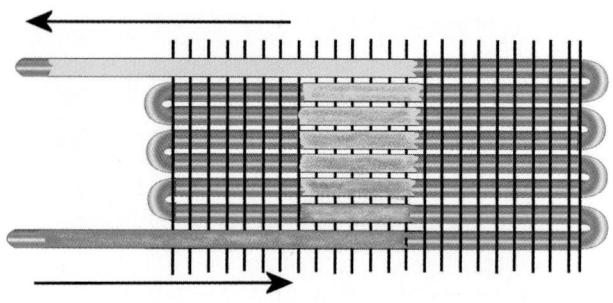

Figure 22-14 Refrigerant enters this DX evaporator at the bottom as a saturated liquid/vapor mixture and leaves at the top as a superheated vapor

Figure 22-11 Cross section of a tube in tube evaporator, the water travels through the inside copper tube and the refrigerant travels through the steel tube in the opposite direction

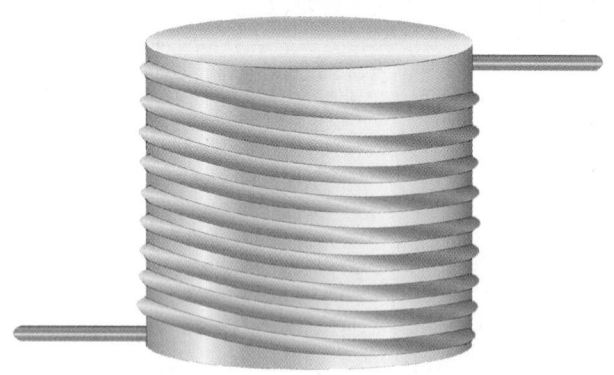

Figure 22-12 The water in the tank is cooled by the refrigerant in the tubing which is wrapped around the tank

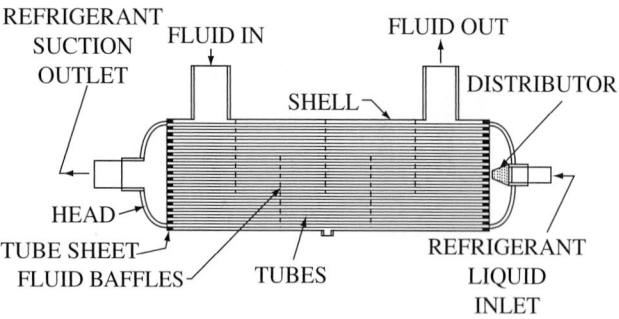

Figure 22-13 Direct expansion chiller; refrigerant tubes, water in the shell

Direct Expansion Evaporators

Most air conditioning and refrigeration systems use direct expansion evaporators. The refrigerant travels through tub-

ing in a direct expansion evaporator. It enters as a saturated mixture and leaves as a superheated vapor. The refrigerant entering a direct expansion evaporator is a saturated mixture of liquid and vapor. Generally 25% to 30% of the refrigerant entering a direct expansion evaporator is vapor. This refrigerant flashed to vapor as it was expanding in the metering device. All the refrigerant is a vapor by the time it reaches the end of a direct expansion evaporator. The very last portion of a direct expansion evaporator is used for superheating the refrigerant, Figure 22-14.

Flooded Evaporators

The refrigerant enters a flooded evaporator as all saturated liquid and there is saturated liquid throughout the evaporator. If an evaporator does not have to superheat refrigerant vapor, it can produce more cooling capacity. Flooded evaporators can circulate more pounds of refrigerant (more cooling capacity) per square foot of heat transfer surface than direct expansion evaporators because no evaporator surface needs to be used to superheat the suction vapor. On small systems the difference is negligible, but on very large systems, the increase in evaporator performance can be significant.

Large water chillers use flooded evaporators. A flooded evaporator is shown in the example in Figure 22-49. The evaporator in a flooded chiller is basically a large tank full of low pressure, low temperature liquid refrigerant with water lines submerged underneath the liquid.

Flooded evaporators typically use a float mechanism as their metering device. One of the advantages of a flooded evaporator is its ability to maintain a very accurate temperature across the entire evaporator surface. Some large ice rinks use flooded evaporators so that the rink temperature can be maintained very closely. This is particularly important for Olympic skating competitions. Skaters can tell the difference in ice temperature of a few tenths of a degree. Very cold ice sticks to the skate and is more difficult to glide across than slightly warmer ice.

It is very important to ensure that the saturated refrigerant flowing to the compressor does not contain quantities of liquid that could cause mechanical damage. Flooded chiller

Figure 22-15 The evaporator tubing in this freezer also servers as the shelves
(Courtesy of General Electric.)

evaporators have eliminators whose function is to catch droplets of liquid in the returning suction vapor and prevent them from entering the compressor.

22.6 EVAPORATOR CONSTRUCTION

The three most common types of evaporator construction are:

- Bare pipe evaporators.
- Plate evaporators.
- Tube and fin coil evaporators.

Bare Pipe Evaporators

Bare pipe evaporators are used in domestic upright freezers. The evaporator tubing also serves as the freezer shelves, Figure 22-15. In commercial refrigeration, bare pipe evaporators may be used for low temperature refrigeration, liquid cooling, ice skating rinks, and thermal storage applications. Because air is not blown across low temperature bare pipe evaporators, ice buildup on them will not significantly reduce the evaporator's efficiency, unless the ice becomes very thick.

Plate Evaporators

Plates such as those shown in Figure 22-16 are a special form of extended heat transfer surface used in refrigeration and freezer applications. The plate surfaces may be fabricated in a variety of shapes. The refrigerant passages are formed into the evaporator plates. The most common process for manufacturing plate evaporators is called roll-bond. This type of panel starts as two aluminum sheets. The two sheets are bonded into a single piece by rolling them together. The refrigerant circuit is printed onto the sheets with graphite before the sheets are bonded. After rolling, the channels are created by pressurizing the panel at between 1,500–2,250 psig.

Plate evaporators can also be made by brazing tubing to the plate, Figure 22-17. Either way works well as long as the mechanical contact between the plate and the refrigerant passages is tight. A tight connection is needed for good thermal conductivity of heat from the plate to the refrigerant.

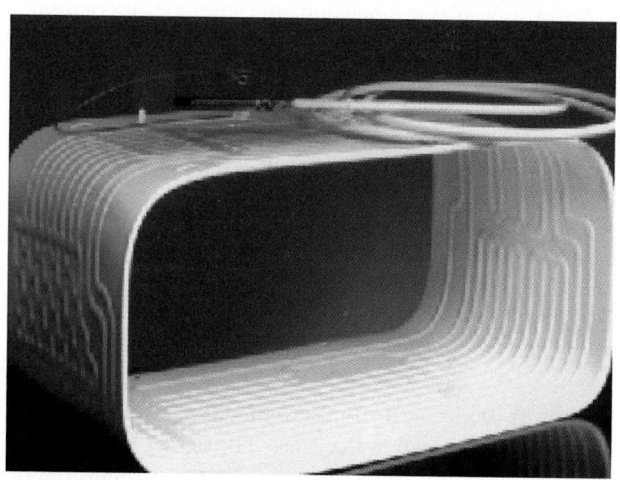

Figure 22-16 Roll-bond refrigerator evaporator
(Courtesy of Bundy Refrigeration, www.bundyrefrigeration.com.)

Figure 22-17 Plate evaporator with tubes brazed to a galvanized plate

SERVICE TIP

Many plate evaporators are used in small residential refrigerators. Under the counter refrigerators do not defrost automatically. When manually defrosting these units, individuals often puncture the evaporator refrigerant passages with a sharp metal object. These punctures can be repaired using a two-part epoxy specifically designed for repairing holes in plate evaporators. Follow the manufacturer's instructions on using the epoxy and only use those epoxies specifically designed and approved for this application. Some epoxies may have toxic substances that would not be appropriate to have in a domestic refrigerator freezer where food is stored.

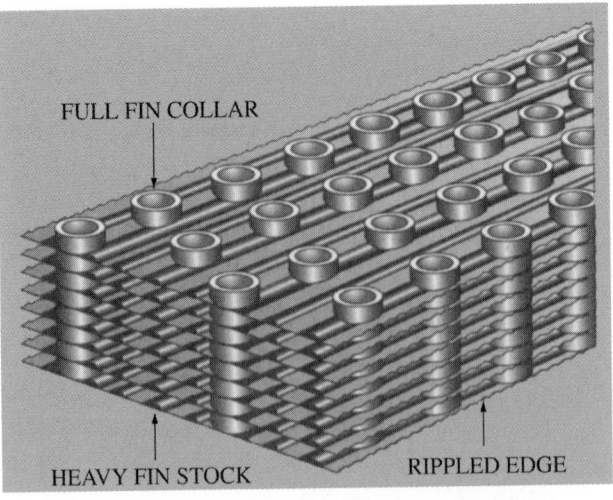

Figure 22-18 Tube and fin coil construction

Tube and Fin Coils

The most common evaporator for cooling air is the tube and fin coil. This applies to small refrigerated reach-in and walk-in boxes, as well as to small and large comfort air conditioning units. The most common tube material is copper.

Fins are added to the copper tubing to increase the surface area. This is done to help accelerate the heat transfer rate into refrigerant evaporator tubes when cooling air. Air is not good as a conductor of heat. By adding tight fitting aluminum fins to the refrigerant circuit's copper tubes, the air side surface and corresponding heat transfer can be greatly increased.

22.7 TUBE AND FIN COIL CONSTRUCTION

To ensure good heat transfer, the fins must be tightly mechanically bonded to the tubes. The tighter the bond, the better the heat can be conducted from the fins into the refrigerant tubing and refrigerant. The fins are prestamped from thin sheets of metal, usually aluminum, Figure 22-18. They may be left flat or embossed forming curves or waves in their surfaces. The fin sheets are stacked with even spacing on the copper tubing. The tubes are then mechanically or hydraulically expanded into the tube collar. Figure 22-19 shows the manufacturing process of expanding the tubes within the fin sheets.

The fins are most often formed out of aluminum; however, other materials can be used to increase the fins' corrosion resistance. Light protection can be provided with a baked on powdered coating that is applied to the fin sheets before assembly. The baking process melts the powder, and it flows evenly over the fin surface and bonds much like paint.

Figure 22-19 Tubes are expanded into the fins to form a tight mechanical bond

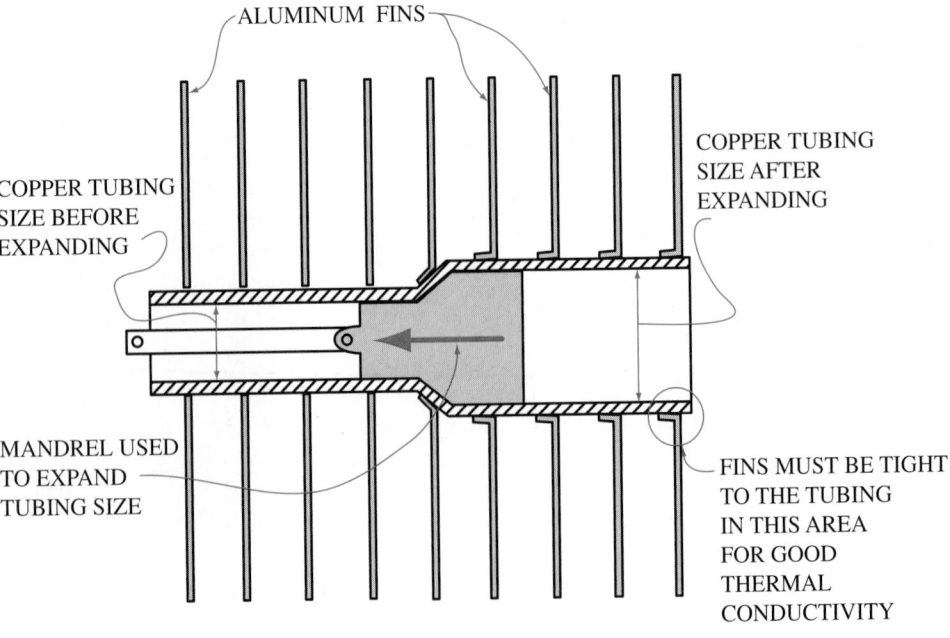

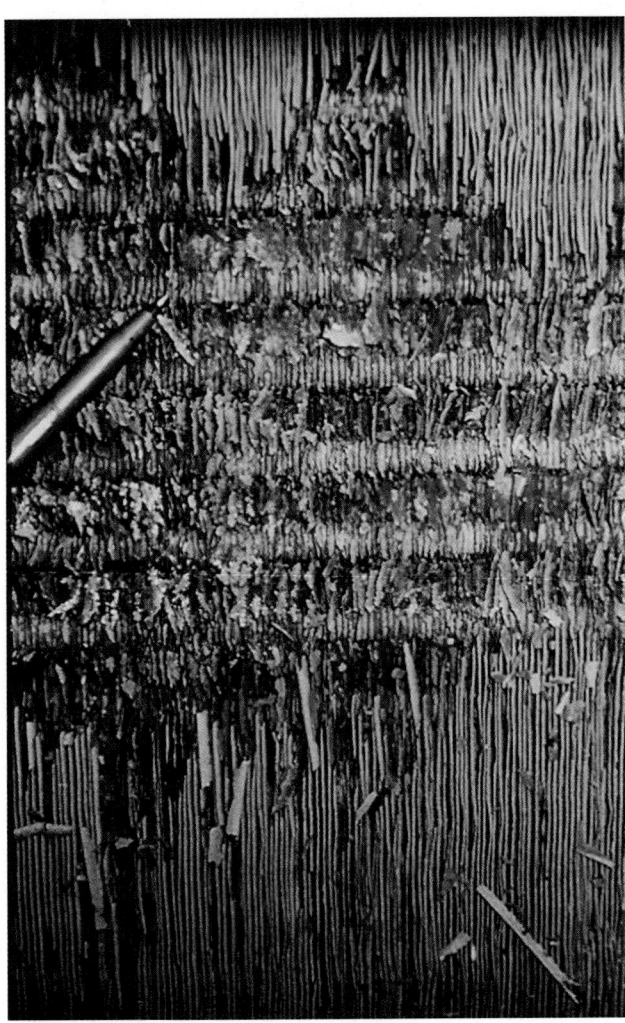

Figure 22-20 Effect of a corrosive environment on a copper tube, aluminum finned coil
(Courtesy of Broz-Dlow Technologies)

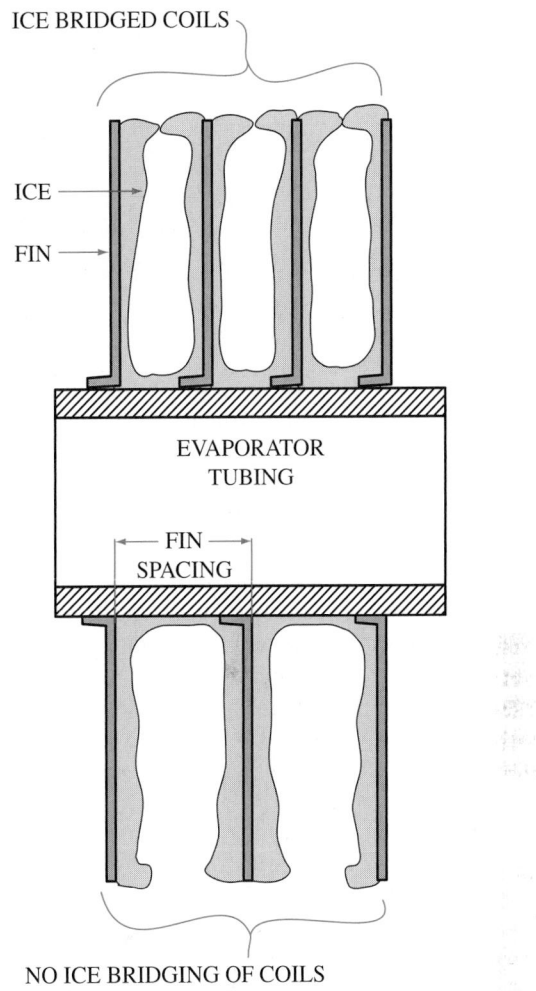

Figure 22-21 Ice bridging between fins on a tube and fin coil

It is possible to order coils with special protective coatings for industrial use where ordinary fins may be attacked by corrosion. The heaviest protection is provided when the finished coil is dipped in a thin epoxy. The epoxy cures and covers all of the fins, tubing, and coil headers. These coils provide the longest service in industrial applications where corrosive fumes are present, but they may reduce capacity.

For sprayed-coil dehumidifiers, where water sprays on the coil fins to maintain close temperature and humidity conditions, copper fins would be recommended. Because both the fins and tubing are made from copper, galvanic corrosion is eliminated. This is also important for marine or coastal applications. Figure 22-20 shows the effects of a corrosive environment on a copper tube, aluminum finned coil.

Fin Spacing

The distance between fins is called "fin spacing" or "fin pitch" and is expressed as the number of fins per inch. The fin spacing on low temperature coils can be 1–4 fins per inch to reduce ice bridging. Ice bridging is the term for what happens when the ice on one fin joins up with the ice formed on the adjoining fin. As shown in Figure 22-21, it restricts all airflow through the coil.

For air conditioning applications, fin spacing ranges from 8 to 14 fins per inch. Figure 22-22 compares the fin spacing on a low temperature refrigeration coil, a medium temperature refrigeration coil, and an air conditioning coil. The closer fin spacing produces increased heat transfer per square foot of coil, but the additional fins require more fan energy to move the air through them. This type of tradeoff in design is not unusual.

Tube and Fin Coil Tubing

The number of refrigerant tube rows in each refrigerant circuit and their spacing has a great influence on heat transfer in fin coils. The number of refrigerant tubing rows can range from 1 to 10. Two to four rows are most common for residential and light commercial air conditioning, while commercial air conditioning coils may have 10 or more rows.

Figure 22-22 Comparison of fin spacing on coils for three different applications; the low temperature is on the left, medium temperature is in the middle, and air conditioning on the right

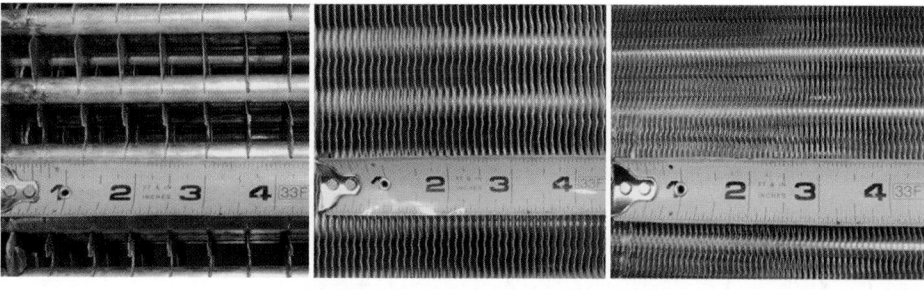

Liquid refrigerant absorbs more heat than does refrigerant vapor. There are improvements in the tubing designs to increase the area wetted by liquid, including creating internal tubing grooves. These grooves churn the liquid up onto the tubing sides as it flows through the evaporator, Figure 22-23. This increases the wetting of the internal tubing walls for better heat transfer. Another improvement has been to make the tubing oval shaped. This, too, increases the area inside the tubing that is exposed to liquid refrigerant.

Tube and Fin Coil Thickness

The more rows a coil has, the thicker it is. The thickness of fin coils greatly affects the coil's heat transfer and air resistance. Fin coils range in thickness from 1 in to about 1 ft. Residential and light commercial air conditioning coils range from 1 in to 4 in thick. Commercial refrigeration coils may be up to 12 in thick.

Thin coils offer less air resistance and provide mostly sensible cooling. Many high efficiency air conditioning coils are built today that have only one row of tubing. This provides the maximum possible heat transfer between each tube row and the air. Single row coils operate at a slightly higher saturation temperature than multi-row coils, so they fre-

quently operate above the dew point. Thin coils offer great economy of operation in dry arid areas where little or no dehumidification is required.

Thicker multi-row coils are advantageous for nearly all other areas where some degree of dehumidification is required. Multi-row coils use multiple rows of copper tubing held together by aluminum fins, Figure 22-24. The tubing in multi-row coils is staggered so that the front row does not block the airflow to the succeeding rows. Multi-row coils

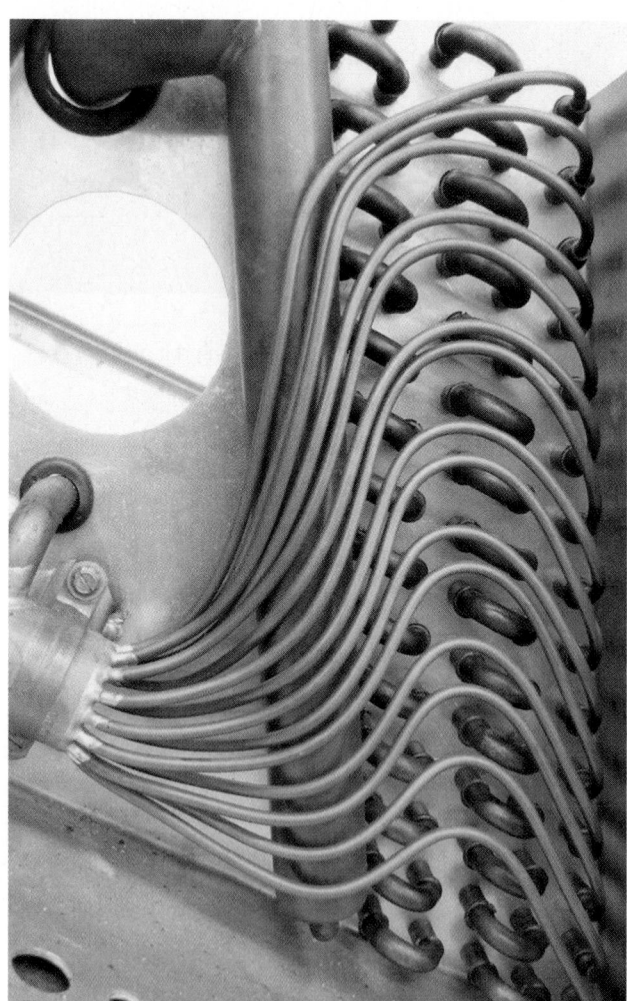

Figure 22-24 Multi-row coil used in commercial refrigeration application

Figure 22-23 The grooves, or rifling, on the inside of this tubing increase heat transfer by creating turbulent flow from http://www.processcooling.com/CDA/Archives/ e973 bde5c95b7010VgnVCM100000F932a8c0___, by Michael Scholnick, Garratt-Callahan Co.
(Courtesy of Garratt-Callahan Company)

typically operate below the dew point. The air temperature is decreased further because the air that has already been cooled by one tube row is cooled even further by the following tube rows. Multi-row coils offer greater resistance to airflow and require more material to manufacture because their heat transfer efficiency is less than single row coils.

22.8 AIR CONDITIONING COIL DESIGN

Air conditioning evaporators use tube and fin coils. Air conditioning coils are manufactured in many shapes including slab coils, slant coils, "A" coils, and "N" or "M" coils. Slab coils are rectangular in shape and are usually installed vertically or at a slight angle. The airflow through them is horizontal. Slab coils are usually multi-row coils to keep their size down. Slab coils are common in air conditioning packaged units.

Slant coils are a variation of a slab coil. They are essentially a slab coil installed diagonally, Figure 22-25. Slant coils are usually provided with drain pans that allow both vertical and horizontal installation of the equipment. Slant coils are common in heat pump blower coils.

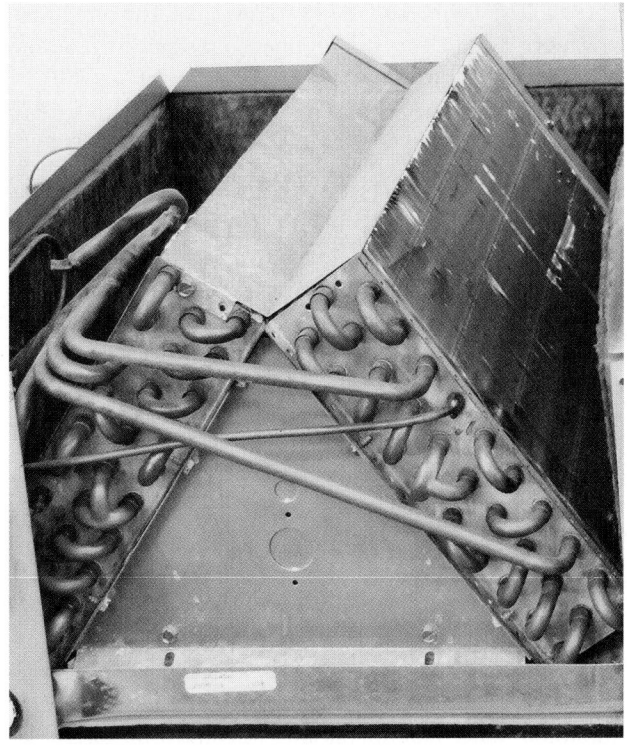

Figure 22-26 Air conditioning "A" coil

"A" coils are shaped like the letter A. They look like two slab coils joined at the top, Figure 22-26. "A" coils are popular with split system air conditioners and heat pumps. Most "A" coils are designed to be installed in the upflow position, with air coming up through the wide opening. Some have been designed for use in counterflow or horizontal positions as well. Most "A" coils are multiple row coils, but there are many being manufactured today that are single row coils. These are typically taller because each side must be larger.

Coils shaped like the letter "N" or "M" use many smaller slabs to get more coil surface into a smaller space, Figure 22-27.

Figure 22-25 Slant evaporator used in a heat pump blower coil

Figure 22-27 Air conditioning "M" coil

These coils are typically one or two row coils. They are trying to achieve the efficiency improvement of a single row coil and keep the physical size down.

22.9 TYPICAL AIR CONDITIONING EVAPORATOR OPERATION

The saturation temperature in an air conditioning coil is typically 30–40°F below the return air temperature entering the coil. The air temperature drop across the coil is usually between 10°F and 20°F.

For years the standard design evaporator saturation temperature was 40°F at ARI rating conditions. The standard ARI rating condition includes 80°F dry bulb and 67°F wet bulb return air. Thus, the evaporators were designed to operate 40°F below the return air temperature at the rating condition. Now many manufacturers are designing the evaporator to operate at 45°F under the same conditions.

The evaporator saturation temperature and the temperature drop across the coil are largely affected by the entering air wet bulb temperature. A high wet bulb indicates a large amount of water vapor in the air. The condensing of the water vapor on the coil reduces the system's sensible capacity, so the temperature difference across the coil is decreased. The evaporator temperature is increased because the air and coil do not get as cold since more of the cooling capacity is going toward condensing water on the coil. Lower entering air wet bulb temperatures produce the opposite effect. With less latent cooling to do, more of the cooling capacity goes into reducing the air's temperature. This decreases the coil saturation temperature and increases the temperature differential across the coil.

Standard airflow across an air conditioning evaporator is 400 CFM (cubic feet per minute) per ton. However, the airflow can be adjusted to get the correct amount of sensible and latent cooling from the evaporator. Decreasing the airflow increases the latent cooling and decreases the sensible cooling. Increasing the airflow does just the opposite; it increases the sensible cooling and decreases the latent cooling. Equipment manufacturers provide system performance data that shows the system's latent and sensible capacities at different airflow rates, Figure 22-28.

22.10 AIR CONDITIONING COIL FACE AREA AND FACE VELOCITY

The face area of a coil limits the face velocity of air that can pass through the coil without causing the water that is condensed on the coil to blow off. Condensate blowoff and moisture carryover are terms that refer to the small droplets of water that are blown free from the coil and travel a short distance down the duct. Coil manufacturers list the maximum volume in CFM and/or the maximum face velocity in feet per minute (fpm) for each coil they produce. Typically, the air face velocity for coils ranges form 300 fpm to 500 fpm. The face velocity should not exceed 550 fpm. If the condensate blowoff carries past the drain pan, it can leak from the air handler cabinet and may cause expensive water damage to the building or its contents. It is important to stay within the manufacturer's published airflow limits to avoid condensate blowoff.

22.11 BYPASS FACTOR

Not all of the air that passes through a coil comes in contact with the coil, even though the fins are very closely spaced. The bypass factor is a term used to quantify the air that gets through the coil without touching anything. The bypass factor for a coil is listed as a percentage of the total air volume. Manufacturers often list an evaporator's bypass factor in the performance data, Figure 22-28.

PERFORMANCE DATA
COOLING CAPACITIES (MBH) – PURON® REFRIGERANT

CNPV UNIT SIZE	INDOOR COIL AIR		SATURATED TEMPERATURE LEAVING EVAPORATOR (°F)															
			30			35			40			45			50			
	CFM	EWB	TC	SHC	BF	TC	SHC	BF	TC	SHC	BF	TC	SHC	BF	TC	SHC	BF
	450	72	31.00	15.20	0.00	28.60	13.90	0.00	25.80	12.50	0.00	22.80	11.10	0.00	19.30	9.60	0.00
		67	26.00	15.70	0.00	23.50	14.30	0.01	20.70	12.80	0.01	17.60	11.30	0.01	14.10	9.80	0.01
		62	21.50	16.00	0.01	18.90	14.50	0.01	16.10	13.00	0.01	13.00	11.50	0.01	10.10	10.10	0.03
1814	600	72	38.30	18.70	0.00	35.30	17.10	0.00	32.00	15.50	0.00	28.20	13.80	0.00	23.90	12.00	0.01
		67	32.30	19.50	0.01	29.20	17.80	0.02	25.70	16.10	0.02	21.80	14.30	0.02	17.50	12.40	0.02
		62	26.70	20.10	0.02	23.50	18.40	0.02	20.00	16.60	0.02	16.20	14.80	0.02	12.90	12.90	0.06
	750	72	44.30	21.50	0.00	40.90	19.90	0.00	37.00	18.10	0.00	32.70	16.10	0.02	27.70	14.00	0.02
		67	37.40	22.80	0.03	33.90	20.90	0.03	29.90	19.00	0.03	25.40	16.90	0.03	20.40	14.70	0.04
		62	31.10	23.80	0.04	27.40	21.80	0.04	23.40	19.80	0.04	19.10	17.70	0.04	15.60	15.60	0.10

Figure 22-28 R-410a cooling capacities
(Courtesy of Carrier © 2008 Carrier Corporation.)

(a)

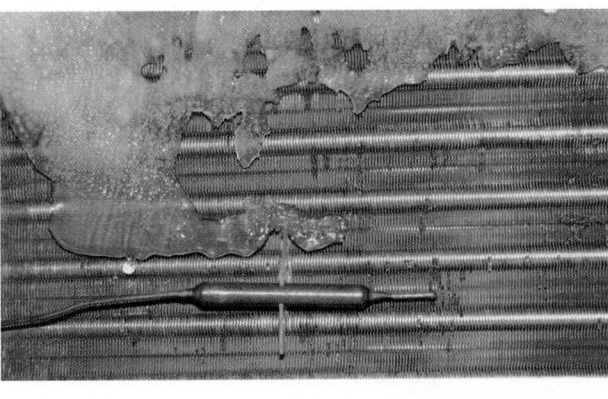

(b)

Figure 22-40 (a) Air defrost evaporator unit (*Courtesy Toco Bueno*); (b) The air moved over the coil during the off cycle melts the ice

22.20 ELECTRIC DEFROST

The electric defrost cycle is simple and widely used because of its simplicity and effectiveness. Electric defrost uses electric resistance heaters to melt ice off the coil, the drain pan, and the drain line, as shown in Figure 22-41.

Defrost is usually initiated by a time switch, Figure 22-42, although pressure or temperature sensors have also been used. When defrost is initiated, both the liquid refrigeration solenoid valve and evaporator fan motor are deenergized. The solenoid stops flow through the liquid line and the compressor pumps the system down. The low pressure switch opens, deenergizing the compressor. At the same time this is happening, the coil heater and drain pan defrost heaters activate. The cycle is usually temperature terminated with a backup time termination provision to prevent the box from overheating should the temperature control fail for any reason. When the coil reaches the termination temperature, the defrost termination thermostat energizes the termination solenoid in the defrost timer. The evaporator fan is wired through the defrost termination thermostat which is a single pole, double throw switch. The termination thermostat opens the circuit to the evaporator fan when it terminates the defrost cycle. This allows the coil to cool down before the fan comes on. The liquid line solenoid is energized, allowing flow into the evaporator. The pressure increases, closing the low pressure switch and starting the compressor. Once the coil is cold again, the termination thermostat will close the circuit to the evaporator fan.

22.21 HOT GAS DEFROST

Using hot gas available from the refrigeration cycle can be an attractive means of defrost. Hot gas is common in large systems with multiple evaporators. A correctly designed hot gas defrost system is faster than most electric defrost systems. The basic concept of a hot gas defrost system is that the condenser is bypassed, sending hot gas directly to the evaporator. Returning liquid slugs to the compressor is a potential pitfall with hot gas defrost because the hot gas can easily condense in the frozen evaporator. This problem is usually addressed in one of two ways:

- The pressure in the evaporator is limited, preventing the gas from condensing.
- The refrigerant is allowed to condense and is then returned to a liquid receiver.

Limited Evaporator Pressure

On single evaporator systems, hot gas defrost sets up a short cycle between the compressor and the evaporator. To prevent liquid refrigerant from returning to the compressor, it is necessary to keep the refrigerant from condensing in the evaporator. If the pressure is maintained below the saturation point, the refrigerant will not condense. This type of system feeds hot gas through a side port in the refrigerant distributor; so there is an appreciable pressure drop through the distributor nozzle. This system uses only the sensible heat from the compressor.

Liquid Receiver Return

In a multiple evaporator system, the evaporator that is defrosting temporarily becomes a condenser. The liquid that condenses in the evaporator is returned to the receiver via the liquid line. Figure 22-43 shows how this system is piped. This type of system uses an electrically controlled evaporator pressure regulator and a defrost solenoid valve for each coil. When an evaporator coil is being defrosted, the solenoid on the electrically controlled pressure regulator is deenergized, closing the connection to the suction line. The defrost solenoid is energized at the same time, sending hot gas into the evaporator through the suction line. Liquid is condensed in the evaporator and returned through a solenoid to the

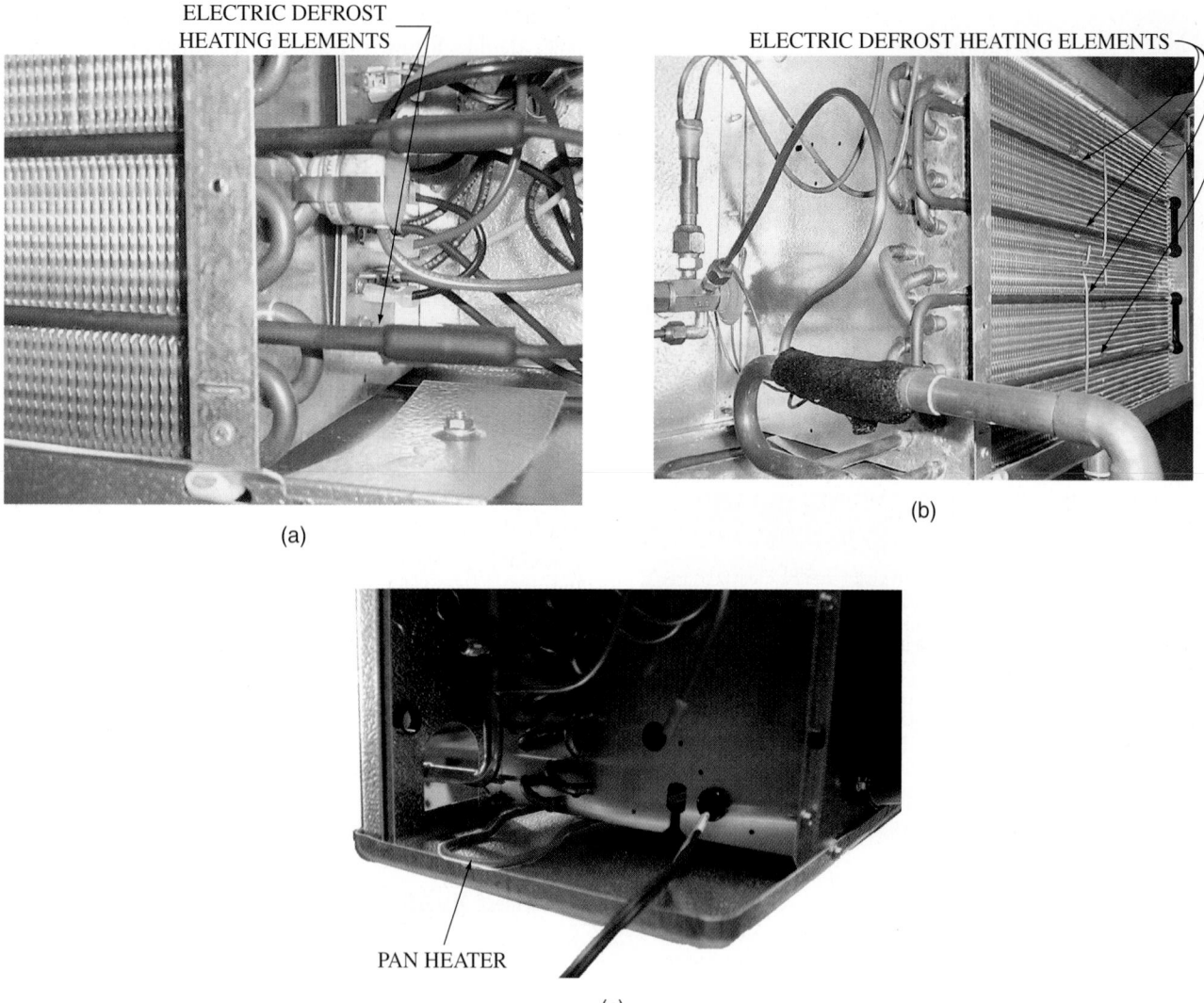

Figure 22-41 Electric defrost evaporator unit: (a) End cover removed; (b) Bottom cover removed; (c) Electric resistance pan heater to prevent ice from forming during the defrost cycle
(Courtesy Hampden Engineering Corporation)

liquid receiver. A check valve must be used to allow the liquid to bypass the TEV. Alternately, a TEV with a built in check valve can be used.

22.22 CONDENSATE DRAINAGE IN COMMERCIAL REFRIGERATION

All defrost systems must have provisions to allow the melted condensate to drain clear of the coil before the system restarts. Otherwise, the condensate can freeze. This can block drain lines and create slabs of ice in the bottom of the evaporator. A time delay between the end of the defrost cycle and

the restarting of the compressor and refrigerant cycle helps ensure all condensate is drained and not refrozen.

Drain lines from condensate drain pans in freezers must be free and clear to handle the drainage during the defrost cycle. The entire drain should be continuously heated by an electric heater cable, as shown in Figure 22-44. They should have a steep pitch (4 in drop per 12 in run) for good drainage and be insulated. Line sizes are typically a minimum of $^7/_8$ in OD tubing, with cleanout tees provided for maintenance.

Heater cable capacity should be sized in accordance with supplier recommendations. A typical capacity is about 6 W per lineal foot. It is also possible to run a hot gas line strapped to the drain line as a heat source.

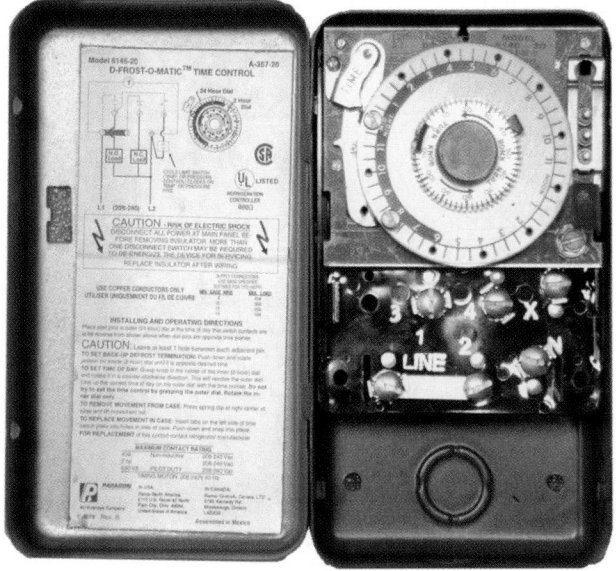

Figure 22-42 Typical commercial refrigeration defrost timer

S E R V I C E   T I P

Some coils that are used in medium temperature applications where the space temperature is above 32°F may still form ice because the evaporator temperature is below 32°F. These coils may require some form of defrost either using air or other artificial heating systems, such as electric or hot gas. Coils that ice over without defrost systems may result in a compressor tripping on low pressure. The problem for the technician is when they arrive on the job, the ice has melted and there is no evidence of a problem. For that reason, it may be necessary to temporarily install a temperature recorder on the system to ascertain if the system at times is dropping down below freezing and forming ice. Temperature plotters are available as electronic recorders or paper tape.

22.23 EVAPORATOR EFFICIENCY

The physical construction of the coil affects its efficiency. Decreasing the coil's bypass factor improves the efficiency because more of the air comes into contact with the coil. Decreasing the number of tube rows increases the heat transfer efficiency of each row because all of the rows are exposed to the warm air.

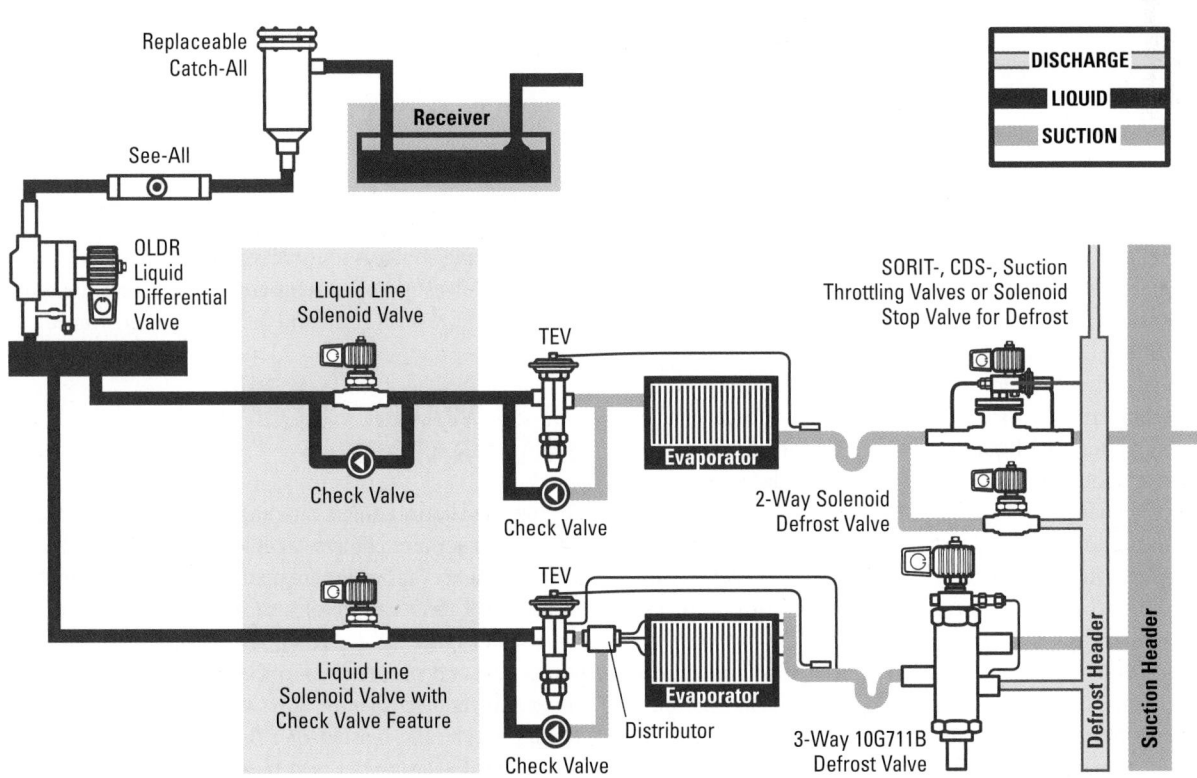

Figure 22-43 Typical piping of hot gas defrost system using solenoid operated evaporator pressure regulating valves
(Courtesy of Sporlan Division-Parker Hannifin Corporation.)

Figure 22-44 Drain line heaters; (a) Wrong application; (b) Correct application
(Courtesy of Kramer Refrigeration)

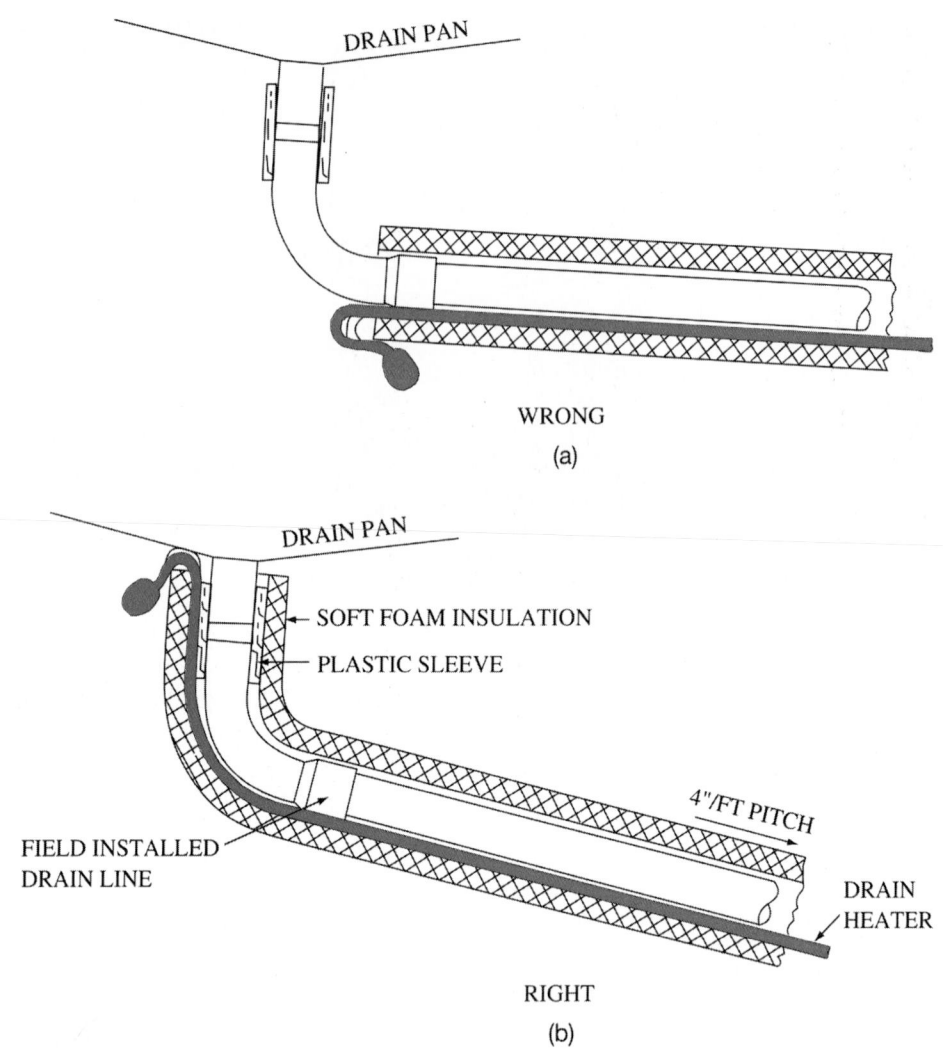

The closer to the end of the evaporator that the last bit of refrigerant evaporates, the more of the coil is being used to absorb heat. That makes the evaporator perform the most cooling for the highest level of efficiency. However, if there is too little superheat added to the refrigerant, some liquid refrigerant may return to the compressor. Floodback is the term used to describe liquid refrigerant flowing back to the compressor. Floodback can cause compressor damage.

Direct expansion evaporators are commonly fed refrigerant into the lower tubing circuits, and the vapor is drawn out of the top tubing circuits. This reduces the possibility of liquid leaving the evaporator; helping to prevent floodback while still operating at a high level of efficiency.

The overall system efficiency is improved by maintaining as high an evaporator saturation temperature as possible. Higher evaporator temperatures mean higher suction pressures and a lower system pressure differential. The compressor can more easily move the refrigerant in a system with a lower pressure differential. This is especially crucial in low temperature applications. A freezer operating at −20°F can consume 50% more energy than a similar freezer operating at 0°F. Setting controls to force refrigeration systems to operate at the lowest possible temperature increases the required system compression ratio and consumes energy needlessly.

22.24 WATER COOLING EVAPORATORS

Refrigerated liquid coolers can range from small drinking fountains to huge water chillers capable of cooling large buildings. Water cooling evaporators are made in a variety of sizes and designs. Small units can be of a tube-in-tube coaxial design, as shown in Figure 22-45. A common construction is copper water tube and steel refrigerant tube. Water flows through the inner tube and refrigerant flows through the outer tube. The tubing is typically twisted or rifled to create turbulent flow. Turbulent flow improves heat transfer by ensuring that all the water passing through touches the surface of the tubing. The water and refrigerant flow in opposite directions. This counterflow design improves efficiency. Coaxial tube in tube evaporators are normally not used for systems above 5 tons in capacity.

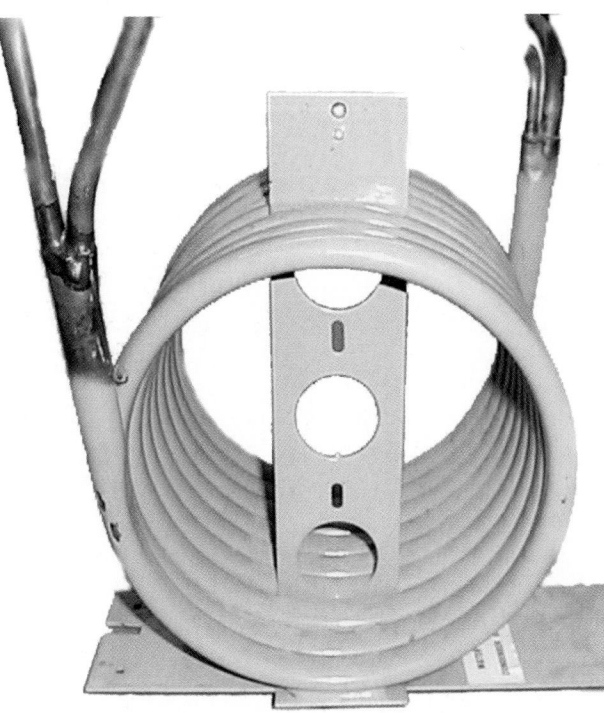

Figure 22-45 Coaxial tube heat exchanger

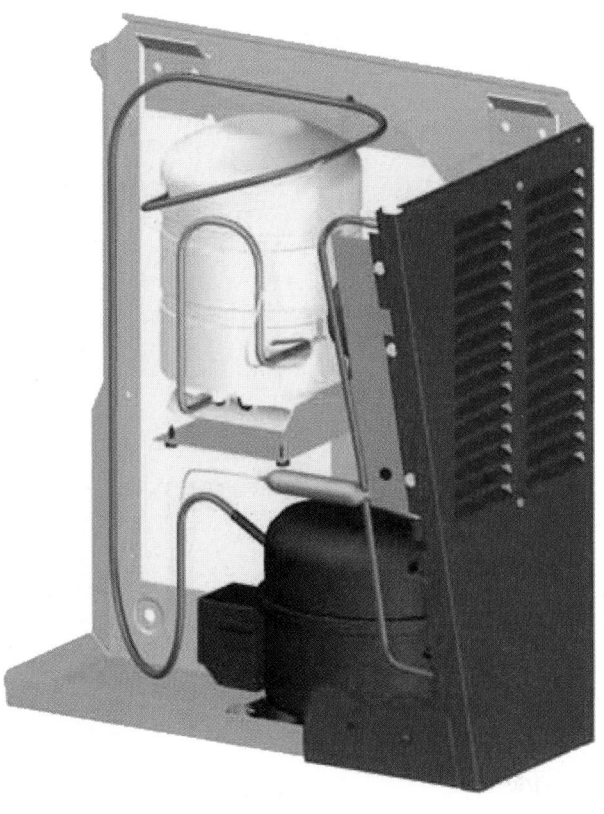

Figure 22-46 The highlighted area shows the evaporator in this water cooler
(Courtesy of Elkay Manufacturing Company.)

Larger chillers use shell and tube designs. Both direct expansion and flooded shell and tube chillers are available. The shell in a direct expansion chiller is filled with water, while the shell in a flooded chiller is filled with liquid refrigerant. The largest chillers usually use flooded evaporators.

SERVICE TIP

It is important that chiller evaporator temperatures stay above freezing to avoid damaging the chiller. It is possible to let the refrigerant pressure and temperature drop below freezing when adding or removing refrigerant from the chiller. Evacuated chillers should be charged with vapor until the vapor pressure in the chiller corresponds to a 36°F saturation temperature. Liquid refrigerant can then be added without freezing the water in the chiller. Liquid refrigerant should be recovered first when a chiller is being evacuated. After all the liquid has been removed, vapor recovery may proceed.

22.25 DRINKING WATER FOUNTAINS

Water fountain evaporators are shell and coil evaporators. The evaporator consists of a small storage tank cooled by an external coil of tubing wrapped around the tank and insulated with a styrofoam cover. This is called double wall construction. Double wall construction is required for potable water for safety. Refrigerant and/or oil would have to pass through both the wall of the refrigerant coil and the water tank in order to get into the water. Incoming water can be precooled by the cold water draining from the fountain to enhance capacity. Figure 22-46 shows the evaporator on a typical water cooler.

SERVICE TIP

Any time you are working around systems that have potable water (drinking water) you must keep the system clean. It is a violation of many local and state health codes to return a system to service that has not been thoroughly sanitized. Refer to the manufacturer's guidelines on proper system cleanup before putting the system back in service.

22.26 WATER CHILLERS

The most common application for shell and tube water chillers is to provide a secondary coolant, namely chilled water. Chilled water is used in air conditioning for cooling

Figure 22-47 Roof mounted, air cooled packaged water chiller

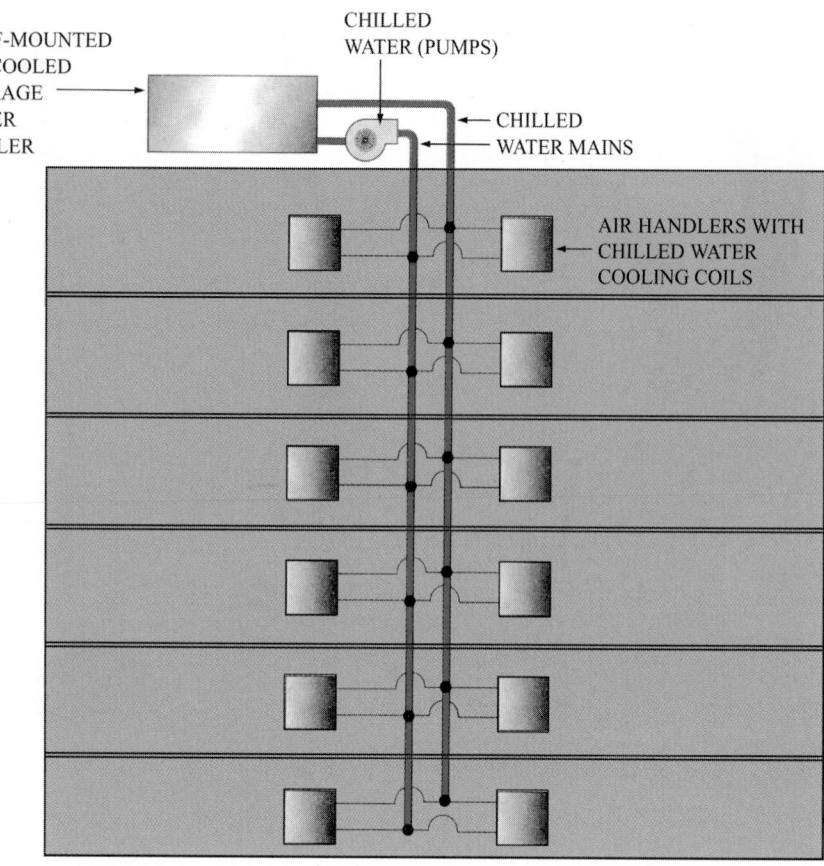

SIX-STORY BUILDING

multiple remote air handling units where it would be impractical to run long multiple refrigerant lines. The chilled water can be pumped wherever required through insulated piping, as shown in the roof mounted unit in Figure 22-47. The air handlers have water coils instead of direct expansion refrigerant coils. Water coils are usually several rows deeper than an equivalent DX coil to get an equivalent cooling performance. They are normally the same size in face area.

Chilled water is also used in process cooling. Many industries have machines that are cooled by water jackets. Chillers are used to remove the heat from the water that is circulated through the machines.

22.27 DIRECT EXPANSION CHILLERS

In direct expansion water chillers, the shell is filled with water and refrigerant flows through the tubes. A direct expansion shell and tube design is shown in Figure 22-48. The shell is usually steel, although brass pipe has been used in some smaller diameters. The refrigerant tubes are copper. Some have an integral rolled fin to increase the heat transfer surface. Some designs utilize metal inserts or turbulators in the tubes to enhance heat transfer on the refrigerant side.

The shell holds the water and baffles provide for even water flow and loading of all circuits. Like all direct expansion evaporators, the refrigerant is superheated before leaving the chiller.

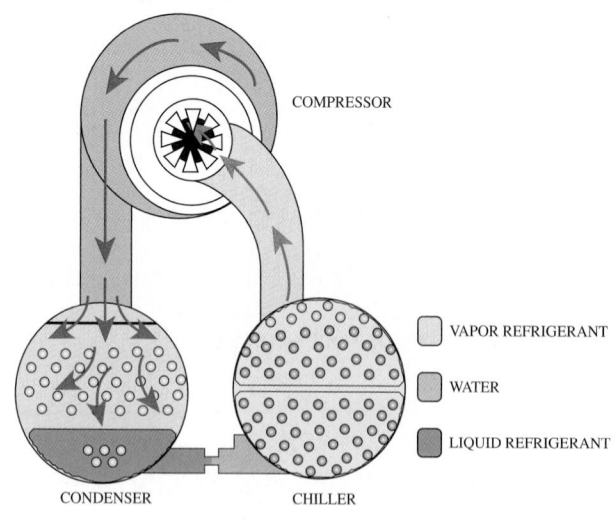

Figure 22-48 Water is in the shell of this DX chiller; liquid refrigerant flows through the tubes, which are submerged in the water; the refrigerant is superheated before leaving the chiller to prevent any liquid from returning to the compressor

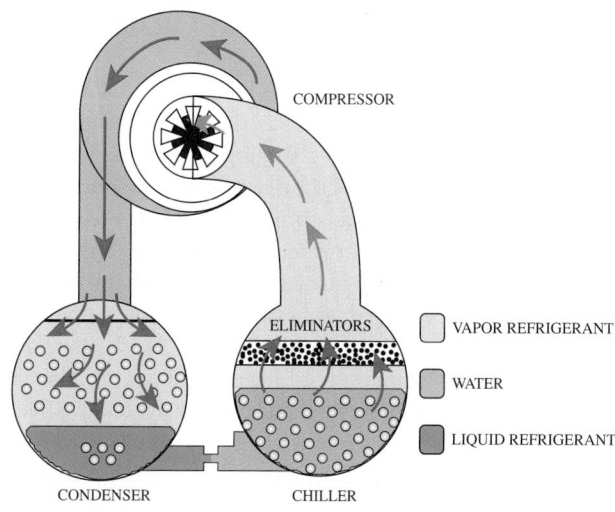

Figure 22-49 Liquid refrigerant is in the shell of this flooded chiller; the water flows through the tubes that are submerged in the liquid refrigerant; the eliminators prevent any liquid from returning to the compressor

Figure 22-50 Packaged brine cooler

22.28 CHILLERS—FLOODED

For larger capacity systems, several hundred tons and up, it is common to use flooded chillers, Figure 22-49, instead of direct expansion chillers. Flooded chillers also use a shell and tube construction. However, the fluids are reversed from the DX chiller construction. The refrigerant fills the shell and water (or brine) passes through the tubes. They use enhanced surface tubing for improved refrigerant heat transfer. The tubes are submerged in liquid refrigerant and fill the lower portion of the shell. Refrigerant is controlled by a float valve or orifice, and the shell can act as a surge chamber, permitting separation of refrigerant vapor from liquid. Closely spaced chevron-type eliminator baffles or mesh screens are normally provided to ensure satisfactory separation of dry vapor from liquid. Flooded chillers do not superheat suction vapor, and provide very efficient heat transfer.

22.29 CHILLER CAPACITY CONTROL

Controlling the chiller cooling capacity is important. Excess capacity can freeze the water circulating through the chiller. The capacity of the system load is controlled by controlling the water flow. Water flow to small and large cooling coils is controlled by modulating valves controlled by room thermostats or other system controls. The chiller capacity can exceed the load when the valves on the water coils start throttling. It is better to avoid starting and stopping the chiller compressor. Instead, the chiller capacity can be reduced by unloading the compressor. Chillers can usually be unloaded down to 25% capacity. Beyond that, the water circulating in the system provides a reserve load to be cooled and provides enough

cool water permitting satisfactory operation during light load conditions without excessive on/off cycling.

22.30 BRINE COOLERS

Chillers are also used to cool brine. Brine is a solution of salt and water. The saltwater solution can be cooled below 32°F without freezing. Other secondary coolants such as ethylene glycol or propylene glycol and water (antifreeze) are used to make water solutions that can be cooled below 32°F. A brine cooler is shown in Figure 22-50. These are found in skating rink applications and can also be used to produce ice for thermal storage.

Brine often also contains corrosion inhibitors. The same chemical companies that manufacture antifreeze for automobiles manufacture antifreeze for chillers. However, the two are not the same. The corrosion inhibitors added to automobile anti freeze are not the same as the inhibitors needed for chiller systems. These chemicals can actually create problems in the water circulation system.

SERVICE TIP

Check to make sure the antifreeze you intend to use with a chiller is approved for that use. Normally the equipment manufacturer can provide a list of recommended products. Antifreeze solutions will normally identify their intended use on the contaner.

22.31 SERVICING CHILLERS

When servicing chillers, care should be taken to avoid possible damaging freeze ups. Water expands when it freezes, destroying the chiller tubes. Chillers normally have flow interlocks that will not let the chiller operate if the water is not flowing. Make sure the flow interlocks are working, so the chiller cannot operate until water flow is established. Check to see that the chilled water thermostat is correctly set. The usual minimum exiting water temperature is about 36°F. Glycol is normally used when chiller temperatures will approach freezing.

Chillers have many safeties including freezestats, low suction pressure cutouts, and low refrigerant temperature cutouts. Make certain they are set to the manufacturer's specifications, wired correctly, and operating. Safeties should never be jumped or bypassed.

22.32 OVERSIZED EVAPORATOR AND HIGH LOAD

The effect of an oversized evaporator and a system operating with a high load are similar. In both cases there will be more heat entering the refrigerant, and the evaporator temperature will be high. Compressors rely on the returning cool vapor to keep the motor from overheating. A high heat load will cause the compressor to work harder and may cause it to overheat. The temperature of the vapor returning to the compressor will be increased, so it will be less effective in cooling the compressor.

The space temperature will rise; and if the system is on a medium or low temperature walk-in, the food product may spoil.

22.33 UNDERSIZED EVAPORATOR AND LOW LOAD

The effect of an undersized evaporator and a system operating with a low load are similar. In both cases there is less heat being transferred to the refrigerant, and the evaporator pressure and temperature will be low. The evaporator pressure and temperature will become lower and lower until a new balance point is reached. There will be little or no superheat, and liquid refrigerant may flood back to the compressor.

If the system is designed for air conditioning, the evaporator temperature can drop below freezing, and the coil will begin to ice up. The formation of ice on the coil can further reduce the temperature, causing more ice to form. If the evaporator temperature drops too low, the compressor can experience an excessively high compression ratio. Excessively high compression ratios are associated with compressor damage and failure.

Some of the reasons that an evaporator temperature and pressure will drop are listed below. Restricted air flow can be caused by:

- A dirty evaporator coil.
- A dirty air filter.
- A bad blower motor.
- Ice on the coil.

22.34 MISMATCHED EVAPORATOR PERFORMANCE

In the past, many contractors have routinely changed out a condensing unit without changing the existing coil. Typically, the SEER rating of the new condensing unit would be mentioned when the new unit was quoted. Frequently, the customer was not informed that the SEER that was quoted only applied to a matched system; and that there was no practical way of determining the result from matching a new condenser to an older, unmatched coil which may have been designed for a different SEER condensing unit. The actual performance of these mismatched systems seldom lived up to the rating.

It is important to understand that a system's SEER rating only applies to matched systems. Coils do not have to be manufactured by the same company that manufactured the condensing unit, but they should be tested and listed with that unit as an AHRI match. Just matching components by their nominal rating does not ensure correct operation. AHRI maintains an online directory that allows anyone to check a system match at http://www.ahridirectory.org/. Certificates verifying the system rating and performance can be printed from this site as well, Figure 22-51.

In January 2006, 13 SEER became the minimum efficiency for new equipment. There is a significant difference in system design between 13 SEER and the previous 10 SEER minimum. If a high efficiency (SEER) air conditioning condensing unit has been installed and the old evaporator coil is left in service, the coil may be inadequate. The newer units are designed to run at higher evaporating temperatures and need more evaporator coil surface to achieve a satisfactory balance. Also, the older fixed orifice metering devices are designed to operate with a higher pressure difference. These metering devices will not operate properly when left installed with newer higher efficiency condensing units as the liquid pressure in these units is lower. Manufacturers recommend changing the evaporator coil when a new high-efficiency unit is installed, to ensure a proper equipment match.

TECH TIP

One major equipment manufacturer installed a new 13 SEER condenser with a new 10 SEER coil and took accurate measurements of the system performance. Using the factory system charge, the system capacity went down and the overall SEER dropped from 10 to 8. Installing a new higher efficiency condenser on an old lower efficiency coil actually dropped the system efficiency.

Certificate of ARI-Certified Performance

The following

RCU-A-C

Outdoor Unit Model Number: AY018MA322

Manufactured by: YORK, UNITARY PRODUCTS GROUP

combined with

Indoor Unit Model Number: HD47436+TD

Manufactured by: ADVANCED DISTRIBUTOR PRODUCTS

under the Trade/Brand name: ADP

has been rated in accordance with

ARI Standard 210/240-2005 for UNITARY AIR-CONDITIONING AND AIR-SOURCE HEAT PUMP EQUIPMENT

and is certified by the Air-Conditioning and Refrigeration Institute to meet

the following product performance ratings:

Cooling Capacity (Btuh):	18000
EER Rating (Cooling):	12.00
SEER Rating (Cooling):	14.00

* Voluntarily revised, unless accompanied with a WAS in which case the change is involuntary.

We Encourage
Professionalism

NATE

Through Technician
Certification by NATE

PERFORMANCE
CERTIFIED ™
www.aridirectory.org

ARI Reference #:	1402949
Today's Date:	2/5/2008
Status:	**Active**

CERTIFIED RATINGS ARE VALID ONLY FOR THE PARTICULAR COMBINATION OF INDOOR AND OUTDOOR UNITS LISTED IN THE AIR-CONDITIONING AND REFRIGERATION INSTITUTE'S DIRECTORY OF CERTIFIED EQUIPMENT. VISIT WWW.AHRIDIRECTORY.ORG TO VERIFY THAT THIS COMBINATION IS AN ACTIVE LISTING AND THE DATA LISTED ON THIS CERTIFICATE IS ACCURATE. SEARCH ON THE ARI REFERENCE # TO QUICKLY LOCATE THIS COMBINATION IN THE DIRECTORY

TERMS AND CONDITIONS

This Certificate shall be used for individual, personal, and confidential reference purposes only, and may be used only pursuant to the terms and conditions listed. This Certificate and the contents hereof are proprietary products of ARI. The contents of this Certificate may not, in whole or in part, be reproduced;copied; disseminated; entered into a computer database; or otherwise utilized, in any form or manner or by any means, except for the user's individual, personal and confidential reference. Contained herein are product information and certified ratings. ARI does not endorse the product(s) listed in this Certificate and makes no representations, warranties or guarantees as to, and assumes no responsibility for, the product(s) listed in this Certificate ARI expressly disclaims all liability for damages of any kind arising out of the use or performance of the product(s), or the unauthorized alteration of data, listed in this Certificate.

Figure 22-51 This certificate shows that these two pieces of equipment will work properly together to give the results listed

UNIT 22—SUMMARY

Evaporators are manufactured for four broad types of application: domestic refrigeration, commercial refrigeration, air conditioning, and chillers. Air cooling evaporators can be listed by their construction as bare pipe, plate, and tube and fin coil. Evaporators may be divided by general operating principle as either direct expansion or flooded. A small percentage of the refrigerant entering a direct expansion chiller is already gas. The refrigerant leaving a direct expansion chiller is superheated. The refrigerant entering a flooded chiller is all liquid and the refrigerant leaving is a saturated gas.

Domestic and commercial refrigeration evaporators may be further listed by their operating temperature: high, medium, and low. The fin spacing on medium temperature coils is closer together than on low temperature coils. Most refrigeration evaporators typically operate below freezing and require defrosting. The most common forms of defrost in commercial refrigeration systems are air, electric, and hot gas defrost. When they are coming out of defrost the high evaporator temperature can create high pressures, temperatures, and superheat. This is known as hot pulldown.

Air conditioning evaporators are tube and fin type. They may be single row coils or multi-row coils. Single row coils produce more sensible cooling and less latent cooling than multi-row coils do. Air conditioning coils may be listed by their shape as slab, slant, "A," "N," or "M." By airflow, air conditioning coils can be upflow, downflow, horizontal, or multi-position. The evaporator pressure and temperature are affected by the return air wet bulb temperature. High wet bulb temperatures produce high evaporator saturation temperatures. The drain on air conditioning evaporators should include a trap that is at least 3 in deep to keep negative air pressure from preventing the condensate from draining.

Chillers can be constructed as tube in tube, shell and coil, or shell and tube. Tube in tube evaporators are used for small applications up to 5 tons. The water flows in the inner copper tube while the refrigerant flows in the opposite direction through the outer steel tube. Shell and coil chillers are used for domestic water coolers. The evaporator is coiled around the outside of the water tank, providing double wall protection for the potable water in the cooler. Large chillers up to several hundred tons are typically shell and tube construction. They may be either direct expansion, or flooded. Direct expansion chillers have the refrigerant in the tubes and the water in the shell, while flooded chillers have the refrigerant in the shell and the water in the tubes.

WORK ORDERS

Service Ticket 2201

Customer Complaint: Poor Cooling and Iced Suction Line

Equipment Type: R-22 Split AC System

A customer has called because their system is not cooling well.

They mention that there is ice visible on the unit outside. The service technician arrives and sees ice on the suction line and all over the compressor. The customer is surprised that the system can make ice, but not cool the house.

The technician explains that ice on an air conditioner does not mean it is working well. In fact, ice is a bad sign in an air conditioning system. When the technician opens the blower door the air filter is completely plugged up with dust and the coil is completely iced over. The technician explains that the dirty filter restricted the airflow over the evaporator, causing its temperature to drop below freezing. Once the ice started forming, it also caused airflow restriction. Liquid refrigerant then slowly worked its way down the suction line to the compressor.

The technician turns system off and turns the fan to "on" in order to melt the ice. This way, the ice melts slowly enough for the drain pan to handle the water. When the ice is clear, the technician restarts the system with a clean air filter and measures the airflow. After determining that the airflow is correct, the system pressure, superheat, and subcooling are all checked. The system is operating within the manufacturer's specifications with the correct airflow.

Service Ticket 2202

Customer Complaint: Chiller Not Working

Equipment Type: R-134a Flooded Chiller Used for Process Cooling

A customer calls to say that their process chiller is not working. Occasionally the plant maintenance crew had found the chiller off on the freeze-stat. When they pushed it, the chiller would work for a while until it went off again on the freeze-stat. Eventually, they jumped out the freeze-stat to keep the chiller operating. This worked for about a day, but now it does not work at all. The technician checks system refrigerant pressure and notices that the pressure is very low. Suspecting ruptured chiller tubes, the technician drains some water from the chiller loop and notices that it is murky and oily. The chiller is drained, the tubes are pressure tested, and the rupture is confirmed.

The technician explains that the freeze-stat was probably tripping because the exiting water temperature was getting too close to freezing. The freeze-stat tripping was not the problem, but a symptom. Jumping the safety only forced the chiller to operate at a dangerous condition, freezing the water in the chiller and rupturing the tubes. The chiller has been ruined. The technician warns that the original problem may still exist if something in the water loop outside the chiller was causing low water flow.

Service Ticket 2203

Customer Complaint: Poor Cooling and High Electric Bills

Equipment Type: R-22 Split System with New Condenser and Old Evaporator

A customer calls a company to look at a new air conditioning unit that is not cooling properly. The unit was installed by the customer's brother-in-law while he was visiting from out of state. The compressor in the old system died and the brother-in-law changed out the entire condensing unit with a new 13 SEER model. The new condensing unit was connected to the 20-year-old capillary tube evaporator coil. The technician checks the system airflow and refrigerant pressures. The airflow is normal, but both pressures are low and the superheat is high. The technician suspects that the condenser and coil are not an ARI match. A quick check of the ARI online directory confirms that the system is not an approved match. The technician explains to the customer that the problem is that condenser and evaporator are not matched and suggests that the customer have a matched coil installed.

23.3 TEMPERATURE-PRESSURE RELATIONSHIPS

The pressure inside a refrigerant cylinder, or inside a system is created by vapor. If all the vapor inside a closed cylinder condenses, there is no pressure. The boiling temperature of any liquid is controlled by the vapor pressure exerted on the liquid. The pressure and temperature of any saturated liquid tend to go up and down together. If you know one, you can find the other.

Charts called pressure-temperature charts, or PT charts for short, are commonly used in refrigeration. These charts correlate the saturation temperature and pressure of commonly used refrigerants, Figure 23-2. The vapor pressure of most common refrigerants can be found by consulting a pressure-temperature chart. If the temperature of a saturated refrigerant can be determined, its pressure can be determined. Most of these charts list temperature in a column on the left-hand side of the chart. To use the chart, find the saturation temperature in the left hand column and follow

across that same row until, reaching the column of the refrigerant being used. That gives the pressure of that refrigerant corresponding to that particular saturation temperature. In Figure 23-3, at a temperature of 40°F, saturated R-134a will have a pressure of 35 psig. Of course the chart can also be used the other way. Find the pressure in the column under the refrigerant being used and then follow accoss that same row to the temperature column on the outside. This gives the saturation temperature of the refrierant at that particular pressure. In Figure 23-4, saturated R-22 with a pressure of 43 psig will have a temperature of 20°F.

There is an important point that must remembered: these charts are specifically for saturated refrigerant only. They do not work with superheated gas or subcooled liquid. To be saturated, the refrigerant must be ready to evaporate or condense. In practical terms, saturated refrigerant is usually a mixture of liquid and vapor, not all vapor or all liquid. It is true that PT charts are used to calculate superheat and subcooling, but PT charts cannot be used to predict the pressure or temperature of a superheated gas or a subcooled liquid.

Figure 23-2 Saturated refrigerant pressure-temperature chart
(Courtesy of Arkema Inc.)

VAPOR PRESSURE, PSIG

Temp (°F)	11	12	22	113	114	500	502	134a	123
-50	28.9	15.4	6.2	–	27.1	12.8	0.2	18.7	29.2
-45	28.7	13.3	2.7	–	26.6	10.3	1.9	16.9	29.0
-40	28.4	11.0	0.5	–	26.0	7.6	4.1	14.8	28.9
-35	28.1	8.4	2.6	–	25.4	4.6	6.5	12.5	28.7
-30	27.8	5.5	4.9	29.3	24.6	1.2	9.2	9.8	28.4
-25	27.4	2.3	7.4	29.2	23.8	1.2	12.1	6.9	28.1
-20	27.0	0.6	10.1	29.1	22.9	3.2	15.3	3.7	27.8
-15	26.5	2.4	13.2	28.9	21.8	5.4	18.8	0.1	27.4
-10	26.0	4.5	16.5	28.7	20.6	7.8	22.6	1.9	27.0
-5	25.4	6.7	20.0	28.5	19.3	10.4	26.7	4.1	26.5
0	24.7	9.1	23.9	28.2	17.8	13.3	31.1	6.5	25.9
5	23.9	11.8	28.2	27.9	16.2	16.4	35.9	9.1	25.3
10	23.1	14.6	32.8	27.6	14.4	19.7	41.0	11.9	24.6
15	22.1	17.7	37.7	27.2	12.4	23.3	46.5	15.0	23.7
20	21.1	21.0	43.0	26.8	10.2	27.2	52.5	18.4	22.8
25	19.9	24.6	48.7	26.3	7.8	31.5	58.8	22.1	21.8
30	18.6	28.4	54.9	25.8	5.2	36.0	65.6	26.0	20.7
35	17.2	32.5	61.5	25.2	2.3	40.8	72.8	30.3	19.5
40	15.6	36.9	68.5	24.5	0.4	46.0	80.5	35.0	18.1
45	13.9	41.6	76.0	23.8	2.0	51.6	88.7	40.0	16.6
50	12.0	46.7	84.0	22.9	3.8	57.5	97.4	45.4	15.0
55	10.0	52.0	92.5	22.2	5.8	63.9	106.6	51.1	13.1
60	7.8	57.7	101.6	21.0	7.9	70.6	116.4	57.3	11.2
65	5.4	63.7	111.2	19.9	10.1	77.8	126.7	63.9	9.0
70	2.7	70.2	121.4	18.7	12.6	85.4	137.6	71.0	6.6
75	0.0	76.9	132.2	17.3	15.2	93.4	149.1	78.6	4.0
80	1.5	84.1	143.6	15.8	18.0	101.9	161.2	86.6	1.2
85	3.2	91.7	155.7	14.3	20.9	111.0	174.0	95.1	0.9
90	4.9	99.7	168.4	12.5	24.1	120.5	187.4	104.2	2.5
95	6.8	108.2	181.8	10.6	27.5	130.5	201.4	113.8	4.2
100	8.8	117.1	195.9	8.6	31.1	141.1	216.2	124.1	6.1
105	10.9	126.5	210.7	6.4	35.0	152.2	231.7	134.9	8.1
110	13.2	136.4	226.3	4.0	39.1	164.0	247.9	146.3	10.3
115	15.6	146.7	242.7	1.4	43.4	176.3	264.9	158.4	12.6
120	18.3	157.6	259.9	0.7	48.0	189.2	282.7	171.1	15.1
125	21.0	169.0	277.9	2.2	52.8	202.8	301.4	184.5	17.7
130	24.0	180.9	296.8	3.7	58.0	217.0	320.8	198.7	20.6
135	27.1	193.5	316.5	5.4	63.4	231.9	341.2	213.6	23.6
140	30.4	206.5	337.2	7.2	69.0	247.4	362.6	229.3	26.8
145	34.0	220.2	358.8	9.2	75.0	263.7	385.0	245.7	30.2
150	37.7	234.5	381.5	11.2	81.3	280.7	408.4	263.0	33.8

Bold Numbers - Inches Hg. Below 1 ATM

PRESSURE/TEMPERATURE CHART

Temp. Deg. F	R-408A (FX-10) Liquid Pressure	R-404A (FX-70) Liquid Pressure	R-409A (FX-56) Liquid Pressure	R-409A (FX-56) Vapor Pressure	R-407C Liquid Pressure	R-407C Vapor Pressure	R-410A Liquid Pressure
-50	1.6	0.6	12.4	17.2	2.9	11.4	3.5
-45	1.1	2.7	9.7	15.2	0.4	8.5	8.5
-40	3.3	5.0	6.8	13.1	2.5	5.2	11.6
-35	5.6	7.0	3.5	10.7	4.8	1.5	14.9
-30	8.2	10.4	0.0	8.1	7.3	1.3	18.5
-25	11.0	13.4	2.0	5.1	10.1	3.6	22.5
-20	14.1	16.8	4.1	1.9	13.1	6.1	26.9
-15	17.5	20.5	6.5	0.8	16.5	8.8	31.7
-10	21.2	24.5	9.0	2.8	20.1	11.9	36.8
-5	25.2	28.8	11.8	4.9	24.0	15.2	42.5
0	29.5	33.5	14.8	7.2	28.3	18.9	48.6
5	34.2	38.6	18.1	9.7	33.0	22.9	55.2
10	39.3	44.0	21.7	12.5	38.0	27.3	62.3
15	44.8	49.9	25.5	15.4	43.5	32.0	70.0
20	50.7	56.2	29.6	18.7	49.3	37.2	78.3
25	57.0	63.0	34.0	22.2	55.7	42.7	87.3
30	63.7	70.3	38.7	26.0	62.5	48.7	96.8
35	71.0	78.1	43.8	30.1	69.8	55.2	107.0
40	78.7	86.4	49.2	34.5	77.6	62.1	118.0
45	87.0	95.2	54.9	39.2	86.0	69.5	129.7
50	95.8	104.7	61.0	44.3	94.9	77.5	142.2
55	105.1	114.7	67.6	49.8	104.5	86.0	155.2
60	115.1	125.3	74.5	55.6	114.6	95.1	169.6
65	125.6	136.6	81.8	61.9	125.4	104.8	184.6
70	136.8	148.6	89.5	68.6	136.9	115.2	200.6
75	148.7	161.2	97.7	75.8	149.1	126.2	217.4
80	161.2	174.6	106.4	83.4	162.1	137.8	235.3
85	174.4	188.8	115.5	91.5	175.8	150.2	254.1
90	188.4	203.7	125.2	100.2	190.2	163.4	274.1
95	203.1	219.4	135.3	109.4	205.5	177.4	295.1
100	218.7	235.9	146.0	119.2	221.6	192.1	317.2
105	235.0	253.4	157.2	129.6	238.5	207.8	340.5
110	252.1	271.7	169.0	140.6	256.4	224.4	365.0
115	270.2	290.9	181.4	152.3	275.1	241.9	390.7
120	289.1	311.1	194.4	164.7	294.7	260.5	417.7
125	308.9	332.3	208.0	177.8	315.2	280.1	445.9
130	329.7	354.5	222.3	191.6	336.7	300.9	475.6
135	351.5	377.8	237.2	206.3	359.2	322.9	506.5
140	374.3	402.2	252.9	221.8	382.6	346.2	539.0
145	398.1	427.7	269.3	238.2	407.0	370.8	572.8
150	423.0	454.4	286.4	255.5	432.4	396.9	608.1

Bold Numbers - Inches Hg. Below 1 ATM

FOLD

VAPOR PRESSURE, PSIG

Temp (°F)	11	12	22	113	114	500	502	134a	12:
	23.9	11.8	28.2	27.9	16.2	16.4	35.9	9.1	25.
10	23.1	14.6	32.8	27.6	14.4	19.7	41.0	11.9	24.
15	22.1	17.7	37.7	27.2	12.4	23.3	46.5	15.0	23.
20	21.1	21.0	43.0	26.8	10.2	27.2	52.5	18.4	22.
25	19.9	24.6	48.7	26.3	7.8	31.5	58.8	22.1	21.
30	18.6	28.4	54.9	25.8	5.2	36.0	65.6	26.0	20.
35	17.2	32.5	61.5	25.2	2.3	40.8	72.8	30.3	19.
40	15.6	36.9	68.5	24.5	0.4	46.0	80.5	35.0	18.
45	13.9	41.6	76.0	23.8	2.0	51.6	88.7	40.0	16.

Figure 23-3 Saturated R-134a at 40°F has a pressure of 35 psig
(Courtesy of Arkema Inc.)

VAPOR PRESSURE, PSIG

Temp (°F)	11	12	22	113	114	500	502	134a	12:
	23.9	11.8	28.2	27.9	16.2	16.4	35.9	9.1	25.
10	23.1	14.6	32.8	27.6	14.4	19.7	41.0	11.9	24.
15	22.1	17.7	37.7	27.2	12.4	23.3	46.5	15.0	23.
20	21.1	21.0	43.0	26.8	10.2	27.2	52.5	18.4	22.
25	19.9	24.6	48.7	26.3	7.8	31.5	58.8	22.1	21.
30	18.6	28.4	54.9	25.8	5.2	36.0	65.6	26.0	20.
35	17.2	32.5	61.5	25.2	2.3	40.8	72.8	30.3	19.
40	15.6	36.9	68.5	24.5	0.4	46.0	80.5	35.0	18.
45	13.9	41.6	76.0	23.8	2.0	51.6	88.7	40.0	16.

Figure 23-4 Saturated R-22 with a pressure of 43 psig has a temperature of 20°F
(Courtesy of Arkema Inc.)

PRES

Temp. Deg. F	R-410A Liquid Pressure
40	118.0
45	129.7
50	142.2
55	155.2
60	169.6
65	184.6
100	317.2
105	340.5
110	365.0
115	390.7
120	417.7
125	445.9

Figure 23-5 The saturation temperature of the evaporator and condenser can be determined using the pressure-temperature chart
(Courtesy of Arkema Inc.)

Rather, superheat and subcooling are calculated by comparing the saturation temperature on the PT chart to the actual refrigerant temperature.

Saturated pressure temperature charts are very useful for determining the actual evaporating and condensing temperatures of the refrigerant in the system. Generally, the pressure-temperature charts will yield a much more accurate evaporating or condensing temperature than attempts to measure them directly with a thermometer. For example, an R-410a system operating at pressures of 118 psig on the low side and 365 psig on the high side would have an evaporator saturation temperature of 40°F and a condenser saturation temperature of 110°F, Figure 23-5.

23.4 REFRIGERANT CLASSIFICATION

Refrigerants have many physical and chemical characteristics that determine their suitability for any particular system. There are many groupings of refrigerants based on these characteristics. The most common characteristics used for grouping refrigerants are:

- Operating pressure.
- Chemical composition.
- Formulation.
- Toxicity.
- Flammability.
- Ozone depletion potential.
- Global warming potential.

23.5 OPERATING PRESSURE

The EPA regulations for preventing the release of ozone depleting substances divide refrigerants into three categories of operating pressures: low pressure, high pressure, and very high pressure. The recovery methods and levels specified for each refrigerant depend upon the refrigerant's operating pressure range. The operating pressure range is determined by the boiling point of the refrigerant at atmospheric pressure. Low pressure refrigerants have a boiling point at atmospheric pressure above 10°C (50°F). High pressure refrigerants have a

Operating Pressure	Refrigerants
Low pressure	R-11, R-123
High pressure	R-12, R-22, R-134, R-502, R-507
Very high pressure	R-503, R-410A

Figure 23-6 Refrigerants listed by operating pressure

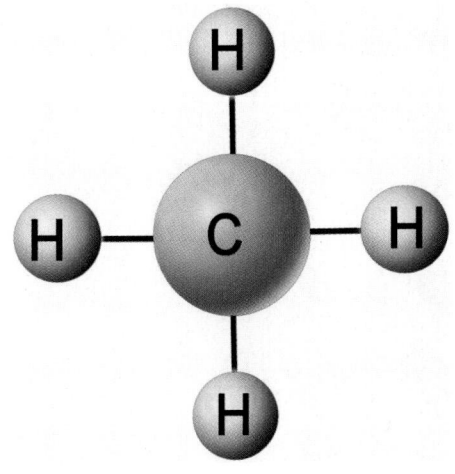

Figure 23-8 Methane molecule

boiling point at atmospheric pressure between −50°C (−58°F) and 10°C (50°F). Very high pressure refrigerants have a boiling point at atmospheric pressure below −50°C (−58°F). Generally speaking, the lower the refrigerant's operating pressure, the higher the evaporator saturation temperature. Systems using low pressure refrigerant typically have an evaporator saturation temperature of 40°F or higher. Systems using very high pressure refrigerant typically have evaporator saturation temperatures −40°F and lower. High pressure refrigerants are used in the widest variety of applications. Systems using high pressure refrigerant may have an evaporator saturation temperature between −20°F and 50°F. Figure 23-6 shows examples of refrigerants according to their operating pressure range.

23.6 REFRIGERANT CHEMISTRY

Refrigerants can be divided into five major chemical categories based on their chemical composition:

- Hydrocarbons.
- Chlorofluorocarbons.
- Hydrofluorocarbons.
- Hydrochlorofluorocarbons.
- Natural refrigerants.

Refrigerants are now frequently referred to by their chemical family using the first letters of each chemical component in the refrigerant to produce an acronym. Common refrigerant chemical families are shown in Figure 23-7.

Compounds

Until recently, most refrigerants were compounds. Water is a good example of a compound. Take a highly flammable gas,

hydrogen, combine it chemically with oxygen, a gas that is necessary for combustion, and the result is water, a chemical that does not burn and is widely used to extinguish flames. Two chemicals have been combined to make a new chemical with distinct chemical properties that are completely separate from the properties of the original chemicals. Further, these chemicals cannot be separated by physical means. The hydrogen cannot be distilled from the oxygen by boiling the water. Any pure chemical or compound has a specific saturation temperature for any given pressure. The boiling temperature can be precisely determined if the pressure on the liquid is known. Examples of refrigerants that are compounds include some of the old standards: R-11, R-12, and R-22. These are all based on the same molecule, methane, Figure 23-8.

23.7 HC REFRIGERANTS

Hydrocarbons are compounds consisting of carbon atoms tied to each other in chains surrounded by hydrogen atoms. Figure 23-9 shows the arrangement of hydrogen and carbon atoms in several common hydrocarbons. Normally, hydrocarbons are thought of as fuels; they are burned for energy. Hydrocarbons make excellent refrigerants. In addition to being excellent refrigerants, they are environmentally friendly. Hydrocarbons have zero ozone depletion because they contain

Symbol	Refrigerant family	Chemical components
HCs	Hydrocarbons	Hydrogen and carbon
CFCs	Chlorofluorocarbons	Chlorine, fluorine, carbon
HFCs	Hydrofluorocarbons	Hydrogen, fluorine, carbon
HCFCs	Hydrochlorofluorocarbons	Hydrogen, chlorine, fluorine, carbon
CO_2, NH_3	Natural refrigerants	Carbon, oxygen, nitrogen, hydrogen

Figure 23-7 Refrigerant chemical families

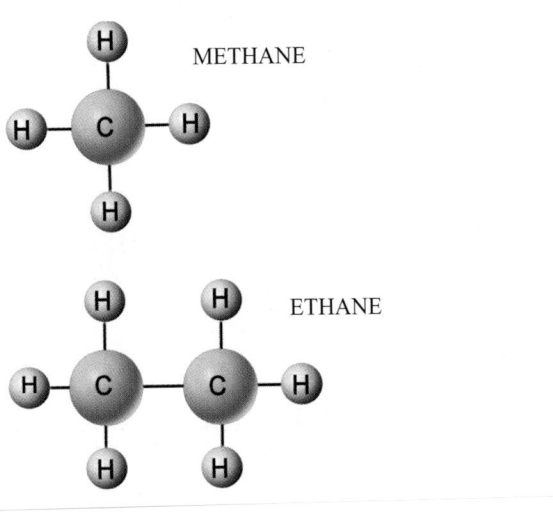

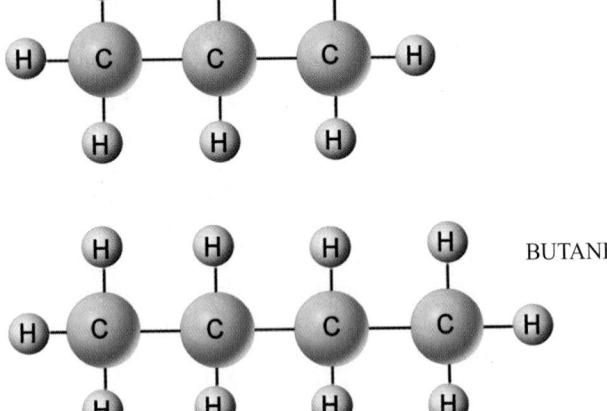

Figure 23-9 Hydrocarbon refrigerants

23.8 HALOGENATED REFRIGERANTS

All halogenated refrigerants are based on hydrocarbons, like methane. Halogenated refrigerants are formed by combining a hydrocarbon with halogens. Halogens are a group of five highly reactive chemicals:

- Chlorine.
- Fluorine.
- Bromine.
- Iodine.
- Astatine.

Chlorine and fluorine are the primary halogens used to make halogenated refrigerants. The halogens replace hydrogen atoms in the hydrocarbon molecules. If only some of the hydrogen atoms are replaced, the refrigerant is partially halogenated. If all of the hydrogen atoms are replaced, the refrigerant is fully halogenated. Fully halogenated CFC refrigerants are more chemically stable than partially halogenated HCFC and HFC refrigerants. Partially halogenated HCFC and HFC refrigerants can be more easily broken down because of the presence of hydrogen. One advantage of halogenated refrigerants is that they are generally nonflammable, low in toxicity, and do not chemically react with many materials. This is primarily because they are very chemically stable molecules. The chlorine in halogenated refrigerants and the bromine in halon fire suppressant are the halogens responsible for ozone depletion. Chemicals that contain either chlorine or bromine contribute to ozone depletion.

23.9 CFC REFRIGERANTS

CFC is short for chlorofluorocarbon. CFC refrigerants contain chlorine, fluorine, and carbon. They are fully halogenated refrigerants with chlorine and fluorine replacing all the hydrogen atoms of a hydrocarbon compound. Most CFC rerigerants are built around the methane or ethane molecules. Figure 23-11 shows the chemical structure of R-12, which is built on a methane molecule.

CFC refrigerants were once the most common type of refrigerants in use. However, CFC refrigerants are the worst offenders in terms of ozone depletion; they have the highest ozone depletion potentials of any group of refrigerants. CFCs also have a relatively high global warming index and a long atmospheric lifetime. CFCs make good refrigerants because they are very chemically stable. This stability is also what makes

no chlorine or bromine and their global warming potential is very low compared to halogenated refrigerants. Unfortunately hydrocarbons are not just flammable, but explosive. Hydrocarbons are only approved for limited applications in the United States. They are more widely used in Canada and Europe. Hydrocarbons are sometimes used in small quantities in zeotropic blends to help with oil return. The amount of hydrocarbons used in these blends is so low that the mixture retains a nonflammable safety rating. Figure 23-10 shows a list of common hydrocarbon compounds and their refrigerant number.

Figure 23-10 Hydrocarbon refrigerants

Methane	R-50	4 hydrogen atoms	1 carbon atom
Ethane	R-170	6 hydrogen atoms	2 carbon atoms
Propane	R-290	8 hydrogen atoms	3 carbon atoms
Butane	R-600	10 hydrogen atoms	4 carbon atoms

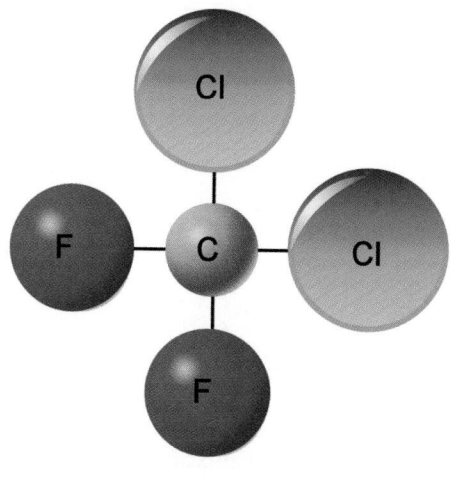

Figure 23-11 CFC-12 is based on the methane molecule

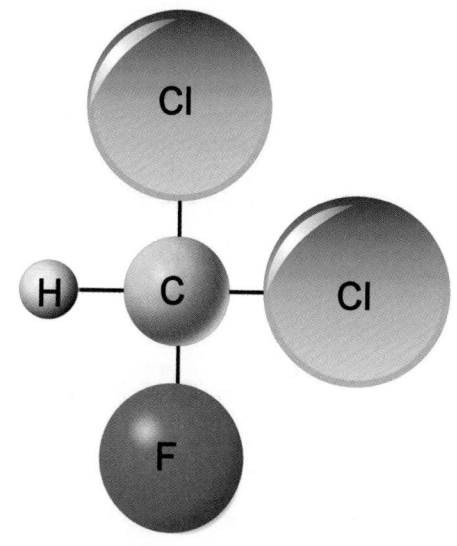

Figure 23-13 HCFC-22 is based on the methane molecule

them an environmental liability. CFCs do not break down in lower earth atmosphere. They find their way up to the stratosphere where the high intensity ultraviolet light breaks the CFCs apart, releasing the chlorine in the stratosphere.

It has been illegal to intentionally vent CFC refrigerants into the atmosphere sine July, 1, 1992, and 1995 was the last year that CFCs were allowed to be manufactured or imported into the United States, so the supply of CFCs is very low. Some CFC refrigerant is still available at very high prices; however, there is now very little demand for CFC refrigerant. Figure 23-12 lists some of the most common CFC refrigerants.

23.10 HCFC REFRIGERANTS

HCFC is short for hydrochlorfluorocarbon. HCFCs contain hydrogen, chlorine, fluorine, and carbon. Most HCFC rerigerants are built around the methane or ethane molecules. Figure 23-13 shows the chemical structure of R-22, which is built on a methane molecule.

HCFCs are only partially halogenated because they still have some hydrogen atoms. This makes them less stable than CFC refrigerants and more environmentally friendly. HCFCs still have an ozone depletion potential because they still have chlorine. Their ozone depletion potential is far less than the ozone depletion potential of CFC refrigerants because HCFCs are more likely to break down in the lower atmosphere. Once the chlorine is released in the lower atmosphere it finds plenty of chemicals to attack, so it will not reach the stratosphere.

The most common HCFC refrigerant is R-22. New equipment using R-22 cannot be manufactured or imported beginning January 1, 2010. R-22 is scheduled for a total phaseout on January 1, 2020. All HCFC refrigerants are scheduled to be phased out on January 1, 2030. R-22 has been the least expensive halogenated refrigerant available, but the price of R-22 is rising quickly because its production has been cut back. Figure 23-14 lists some of the most common HCFC refrigerants.

23.11 HFC REFRIGERANTS

HFC is short for hydrofluorocarbon. HFCs contain hydrogen, fluorine, and carbon. Most HFC refrigerants are built around the ethane molecule. Figure 23-15 shows the chemical structure of R-134a, which is built on an ethane molecule.

HFC refrigerants are only partially halogenated because they still have some hydrogen atoms. This makes them less stable than CFC refrigerants. They are more environmentally friendly than either CFC or HCFC refrigerants because they contain no chlorine; and therfore, have no ozone depletin potential. However, HFC refrigerants do still have a global warming potential. It has been illegal to intentionally vent HFC refrigerants into the atmosphere since November 15, 1995. Figure 23-16 lists some of the most common HFC refrigerants.

Refrigerant number	Refrigerant name	No. carbon atoms	No. chlorine atoms	No. fluorine atoms
R-11	Trichlorofluoromethane	1	3	1
R-12	Dichlorodifluoromethane	1	2	2
R-13	Chlorotrifluoromethane	1	1	3

Figure 23-12 CFC refrigerants

Refrigerant number	Refrigerant name	No. carbon atoms	No. hydrogen atoms	No. chlorine atoms	No. fluorine atoms
R-22	Monochlorodifluoromethane	1	1	1	2
R-123	Dichlorotrifluoroethane	1	1	2	3
R-124	Chlorotetrafluoroethane	2	1	1	4
R-142b	Chlorodifluoroethane	2	3	1	2

Figure 23-14 HCFC refrigerants

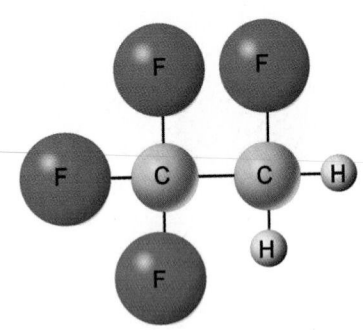

Figure 23-15 HFC 134a is based on the ethane molecule

23.12 FORMULATION

All refrigerants are combinations of two or more chemicals, but there are differences in how these chemicals are combined. The chemicals used to form a refrigerant can be combined in one of three ways. They may be

- Compounds.
- Zeotropes.
- Azeotropes.

TECH TIP

The terms zeotropic and azeotropic derive from Greek. "Zeo" means to boil and "trope" means to turn. Thus, zeotropic refrigerants turn, or change as they boil. The mixture changes (trope) as it boils (zeo). The prefix "A" means not. Placing the prefix "A" in front of a word effectively turns the word upside down. For example an amoral person is one who does not have morals. An azeotropic refrigerant does not change as it boils.

23.13 ZEOTROPES

One result of the demise of CFC refrigerants has been the proliferation of refrigerant mixtures. Unlike compounds, these are combinations of chemicals that do not form a new chemical and whose physical properties are a sort of blending of the physical properties of the individual components. Zeotropic refrigerants change in percentage mixture as they change state. A more common term that is widely used for zeotropic refrigerants is blends. Sometimes the number of components in the blend is mentioned. Ternary blends are mixtures of three refrigerants, while binary blends are made up of two refrigerants. All refrigerants whose number is in the 400 series are zeotropes, Figure 23-17.

The behavior of a zeotropic refrigerant can be compared to a mixture of alcohol and water. The alcohol can be separated from the water through distillation. The alcohol tends to boil before the water, leaving more water and less alcohol in the remaining liquid. The boiling point of the mixture changes as the percentage of the two components in the mixture changes. The mixture changes as it boils.

From the standpoint of refrigeration, this change in composition is significant because the boiling temperature of the remaining liquid also changes as the mixture percentage changes. This is not like a normal refrigerant that maintains a fixed boiling temperature for any particular pressure. Zeotropic refrigerants will boil within a range of temperatures for any given pressure.

Bubble Point and Dew Point

When heating a saturated liquid mixture, the temperature at which small vapor bubbles first begin to form is known as the bubble point. Coming the other way, the temperature at

Figure 23-16 HFC Refrigerants

Refrigerant number	Refrigerant name	No. carbon atoms	No. hydrogen atoms	No. fluorine atoms
R-125	Pentafluoroethane	2	1	5
R-134a	Tetrafluoroethane	2	2	4
R-23	Trifluoromethane	1	1	3
R-32	Difluoromethane	1	1	2
R-143a	Trifluoroethane	2	3	3
R-152a	Difluoroethane	2	4	2

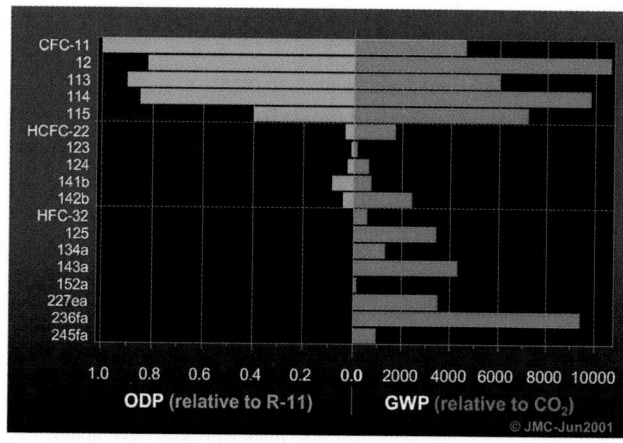

Figure 23-27 Comparison of both ozone depletion potential and global warming potential for several halogenated refrigerants *(From "Refrigerant Data Summary," by J. M. Calm and G. C. Hourahan, as appeared in* Engineered Systems, *18(11):74–88, November 2001. Copyright © 2007 Games M. Calm. Reproduced with permission of J. M. Calm)*

GWP of HFCs is generally worse than for HCFCs. Figure 23-27 shows the relative ozone depletion and global warming potential for several common refrigerants.

23.18 NAMING REFRIGERANTS

All modern refrigerants are named using a system of chemical nomenclature. The name describes a compound's chemicals and their arrangement. For example, monochlorodifluoromethane is the chemical name for R-22. This tells the reader that the chemical is composed of one chlorine (mono chloro) and two fluorines (di fluoro) attached to a methane molecule. However, these names are more useful to chemists than to air conditioning technicians. Some simpler refrigerant naming conventions exist that help identify the makeup of some types of refrigerants in a more user-friendly manner.

Refrigerant Pseudonyms

Halogenated refrigerants are identified by a series of letters indentifying the chemical element in the compound. The letters C, F, and H are used to represent chlorine, fluorine, and hydrogen. A final C is used to represent carbon.

These letters combine to identify the chemical components of the refrigerant.

- **CFC** Contains chlorine, fluorine, and carbon.
- **HFC** Contains hydrogen, fluorine, and carbon.
- **HCFC** Contains hydrogen, chlorine, fluorine, and carbon.

Trade Names

Some manufacturers have created trade names to help promote their products. One of the most successful is "Freon." Freon is DuPont's trade name for their line of CFC and HCFC refrigerants. Freon does not refer to a single refrigerant, but a family of refrigerants. Another popular trade name is "Puron." Puron is the Carrier corporation's trade name for R-410a. Puron does refer to a single refrigerant.

23.19 NUMBER DESIGNATION

Refrigerants are identified by number, preceded by the letter "R" for refrigerant. Some refrigerant numbering conventions exist that help identify the makeup of some types of refrigerants. These numbering designations were originally developed by DuPont, have been established by the American Society of Heating, Refrigeration and Air Conditioning Engineers, ASHRAE, and are used throughout the industry.

Decoding Halogenated Refrigerant Numbering

The refrigerant number assigned to single component, halogenated refrigerants describes the number of each type of atom in the refrigerant molecule. Adding 90 to the refrigerant number yields a three digit number with each digit representing the number of a particular type of atom. The first digit on the left represents the number of carbon atoms, the second digit represents the number of hydrogen atoms, and the last digit on the right represents the number of fluorine atoms. Look at HCFC-22 for example: 22 + 90 = 112.

The number shows that HCFC-22 contains one carbon, one hydrogen, and two fluorine atoms.

The number of chlorine atoms can be calculated using the information about the other components. The number of bonds available on a carbon-based molecule is twice the number of carbon atoms plus two. For HCFC-22, which has one carbon atom, there are four bonds. Chlorine atoms occupy any remaining bonds after the fluorine and hydrogen atoms. Since HCFC-22 has four bonds and three of them are occupied, HCFC-22 contains one chlorine atom.

Let's look at another example: HFC-134a.

$$134 + 90 = 224$$

This indicates that R-134 contains two carbon atoms, two hydrogen atoms, and four fluorine atoms.

There are six bonds: $2 \times 2 + 2$. There are no bonds left over, so there are no chlorine atoms.

Isomers

Some halogenated refrigerants have a lower case letter after their number, such as HFC-134a. The "a" at the end describes how these atoms are arranged. Isomers of a given compound contain the same atoms but are arranged differently. The atoms in compounds containing more than one carbon atom can usually be arranged in more than one way. Isomers usually have different properties from each other. Simply moving the components around changes the properties of the chemical. The letter following the number helps identify which isomer of the compound is being used.

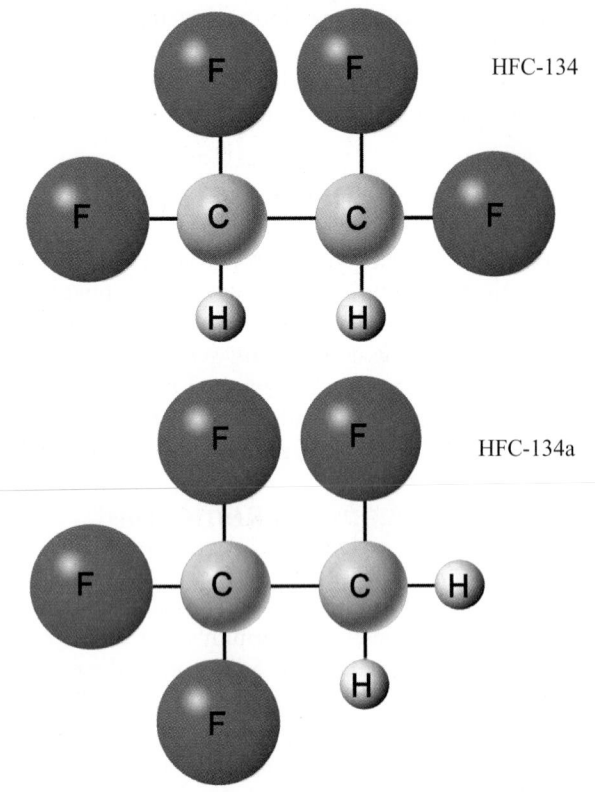

Figure 23-28 Comparison of tetrafuoroethane isomers 134 and 134a

The most symmetrical arrangement of atoms does not have a letter after the refrigerant number, as in HFC-134. The second most symmetrical arrangement arrangement is followed by the letter "a" as in HFC-134a. If there is a third isomer, the third most symmetrical is followed by a "b." Tetrafluoroethane has only two isomers: HFC-134 and HFC-134a, shown in Figure 23-28.

Zeotropic and Azeotropic Refrigerant Numbers

Zeotropic refrigerants all receive a 400 series number. The numbers following the 4 indicate the order that the refrigerant number was assigned by ASHRAE. The uppercase letter after the number tells which percentage mix of the particular chemicals is used. For example R-401A was the first blend assigned a number and the first percentage mix of the chemicals in R-401A. R-401B is composed of the same chemicals, but with a different percentage of each chemical.

Azeotropic refrigerants all receive a 500 series number. Like zeotropes, the following two numbers identify the order in which the refrigerant was approved. Unlike zeotropes, azeotropes have no letter after the number because there is only one percentage mix where the components will behave like an azeotrope. For example, R-507 was the seventh azeotropic refrigerant to receive a number.

23.20 COMPATIBILITY

Refrigerants, like any chemical, can affect materials in detrimental ways. The effect of the refrigerant on the materials used in a system must be known. Preferably, the refrigerant should have no chemical or physical effect on the materials that the refrigeration system is built of. The refrigerant must not react with or deteriorate materials it comes in contact with during the operation. These include metallic compressor parts, gaskets, O-rings, seals, motor insulation and windings, piping, and condenser and evaporator heat transfer surfaces.

Refrigerants will often cause swelling in plastics and elastomers. Petroleum based refrigerants may dissolve some petroleum based plastics. When designing plastic insulation, O-rings, and seals, this becomes important. However, this has seldom been any concern to the refrigeration technician. With the introduction of new HFC refrigerants, the effect of a refrigerant on elastomers is suddenly of great concern. These new compounds are generally more chemically reactive than the older refrigerants they are designed to replace. This makes retrofitting an old system with new refrigerant difficult without technical information about the materials used inside the system. Systems should not be field retrofitted without the advice and consent of the equipment manufacturer.

Most refrigerants, including halogenated refrigerants, have no affect on any type of metal. There are some notable exceptions. Ammonia, still in wide use, chemically acts upon copper, brass, tin, and zinc. Therefore, all these metals are restricted from use with an ammonia system. Also, while pure ammonia is essentially inert to aluminum, ammonia and water mixtures will eat aluminum away. Aluminum is not a recommended metal for use with ammonia because of this.

Halogenated refrigerants are generally acceptable with most any common metal; but they should not be used with aluminum alloys containing more than 2% magnesium or zinc since both magnesium and zinc are reactive with a combination of halogenated refrigerants and water. HFC-410a is reactive with abraded aluminum. Abraded aluminum is aluminum that has been roughed up or ground up into pieces.

23.21 CONTAMINANTS IN REFRIGERANT

The only two chemicals that should be inside a refrigeration system are refrigerant and refrigeration oil. However, contaminants are often introduced through poor installation and service practices or through compressor failure. Contaminants that are frequently found in refrigerant include water vapor, acid, non-condensables, carbon, and particulates. When a refrigerant is recycled, many of these impurities can be removed. In order to resell the refrigerant it must be reclaimed by a certified source and brought back to the original level of purity indicated by ARI Standard 700-2006, which gives maximum allowable contamination levels for both new and reclaimed fluorocarbon refrigerants.

Water is undesirable in all but a very few refrigeration systems; notably, those that use water as either a refrigerant or an absorbent in an absorption cycle machine. Water may cause numerous problems, among them:

- Freezing up at the metering device can cause a loss of system performance.
- Water can promote oxidation in the system.
- Water may hydrolyze the refrigerant and form powerful acids that will corrode the system.

Water is a great catalyst for chemical reaction; it accelerates many chemical reactions, such as oxidation. Since chemical reactions are very undesirable in a refrigeration system, water is most unwelcome. Most of the metallic parts inside a refrigeration system are not made to withstand corrosion since they are, in theory, exposed only to refrigerant and oil. Neither of these substances will corrode the metals used in the system. Water will corrode most any type of metal. Since nonresistant metals are used, a little water in the system can wreak havoc. While water will not cause any direct chemical reaction with halogenated refrigerants, water will break down halogenated refrigerants in the presence of extreme heat. The temperatures on the discharge side of a compressor can be high enough to begin this process. Since halogenated refrigerants contain chlorine and fluorine, hydrochloric and hydrofluoric acids can form. These acids will eat away the metals in the system and attack the insulation of motor windings in hermetic compressors. Water can also be present in refrigerant cylinders. Using only clean, new refrigerant from a reliable source can effectively prevent this particular hazard.

TECH TIP

Noncondensables in a refrigerant cylinder or in a system will increase the pressure above the normal saturation pressure. A refrigerant cylinder with noncondensables will have a higher pressure than is indicated on a pressure-temperature chart for its temperature.

23.22 REFRIGERATION OILS AND THEIR APPLICATIONS

Refrigerants need to be chemically compatible with the oil used in the system. Chemical reactions occurring between the system refrigerant the oil are undesirable. Refrigeration oils and refrigerant must also be physically compatible. Most refrigeration systems depend on the refrigerant to carry the oil back to the compressor. In the best of all possible worlds, all the oil would remain in the compressor. However, in the real world it is impossible to keep all the oil in the compressor. Once the oil leaves the compressor, the only way to get it back to the compressor is for the refrigerant to bring it back.

For this to happen, the oil must be miscible with the refrigerant. Miscibility means that the oil will dissolve in the refrigerant in any proportion.

Mineral Oil

For years the primary oil in refrigeration systems has been mineral oil. Most CFCs and HCFCs are compatible with mineral oil. One of the primary challenges posed by HFC refrigerants is their incompatibility with mineral oil. Mineral oil is not the least bit miscible with HFC refrigerants. This means that once the oil has left the compressor, it does not return. Early work with HFC refrigerants and mineral oil showed that the oil tended to drop out at the first available opportunity, in the condenser. Normally, oil is more apt to drop out in the evaporator where the low temperatures thicken up the oil and make it more prone to separate. This tendency of oil to drop out in the condenser was dubbed "reverse solubility." This necessitated the development of new oils.

Polyalkylene Glycol

The first oil used with R-134a automotive systems was polyalkylene glycol, PAG. Polyalkylene glycol is a cousin of the polyethylene glycol used as antifreeze in cars. Anyone who has handled the glycol used for auto antifreeze knows that it is extremely slick, and seems impossible to clean off. PAG oils are like a thick antifreeze. Glycol based oils offer some challenges. They are chemically incompatible with CFCs, HCFCs, and mineral oil. Early attempts to convert R-12 systems to R-134a were frequently plagued by the formation of a sticky goo due to the incompatibility of PAG with both mineral oil and CFC refrigerant. PAG works well in new systems, but it proved too problematic for retrofit.

Like its antifreeze cousin, the glycol oils are very friendly with water. PAG sucks it up like a sponge. This is not desirable for a refrigeration system. Materials like the glycols, which have an affinity for water, are called hygroscopic. PAG oil must be packaged in metal containers because it can literally suck water out of the air through plastic containers. PAG containers should not sit around on the shelf after they are opened. PAG is best purchased in small quantities that are only opened immediately before use.

Polyol Ester

Polyol ester is the predominant oil of choice today. It is compatible with both old and new refrigerants, and is also somewhat compatible with mineral oil. Ester oils are fairly aggressive solvents, making material compatability an issue. Ester based oils can sometimes be used in retrofit situations, but they can be incompatible with the plastics and varnishes used in older systems. Polyol ester is also hygroscopic. Like PAG, it is shipped in metal containers. Also like PAG, it should be purchased in small quantities and only opened immediately before use.

CFCs	HCFCs	HFCs	Blends with HFCs and HCFCs
Mineral oil	Mineral oil	Polyalkylene glycol	Alkyl benzene
Alkyl benzene	Alkyl benzene	Polyol ester	Polyol ester
Polyol ester	Polyol ester		

Figure 23-29 Refrigerant and oil compatability

Alkyl Benzene

Alkyl benzene is an older synthetic oil. It was designed to be used where mineral oil is used. Alkyl benzene can be used with zeotropic blends which contain a mixture of HCFCs and HFCs. Material compatability is not as big an issue with alkylbenzene because it was developed for older systems. Figure 23-29 shows refrigerant and oil compatibility.

23.23 REPLACEMENT REFRIGERANTS

All replacement refrigerants must be evaluated and approved by the EPA. Substitutes are reviewed on the basis of ozone depletion potential, global warming potential, toxicity, flammability, and exposure potential. Lists of acceptable and unacceptable substitutes are updated several times each year.

The EPA lists alternative refrigerants as suitable for retrofit, new application, or unacceptable. Alternatives listed as retrofit refrigerants can be used to replace the refrigerant in an existing system. This does not mean that they will work with no system alterations, but they can be made to work in an existing system. Refrigerants listed as new alternatives will only work in new applications that accomplish the same thing. Sometimes these new alternatives are completely different approaches to cooling. One example is evaporative cooling, which is listed as an alternative for many types of systems. Evaporative cooling is a cooling system that reduces air temperature by evaporating water. Obviously an evaporative system is a completely different type of system from a traditional mechanical refrigeration system. It is only a replacement in the sense that it accomplishes roughly the same thing as a mechanical refrigeration system if humidity control is not an issue.

Retrofit refrigerants fall into two distinct categories: interim and long term. Interim replacements normally contain HCFCs, which are scheduled for eventual extinction. They are an improvement over CFCs as far as ozone depletion is concerned, but they still have an ozone depletion potential. Long term replacements do not contain any ozone depleting substances. Most long term replacements are HFCs.

There are some refrigerants that are specifically designed to replace CFCs in new equipment. HFC-134a replaces CFC-12 in new equipment, but is not generally considered a retrofit refrigerant. HCFC-123 replaces CFC-11 in new chillers. HCFC-123 is used as a retrofit for CFC-11 chillers, but it certainly is not a drop-in. These chillers are normally reworked, including replacing the impellers on the centrifugal compressors. HFC-407a is a very close replacement for HCFC-22 in retrofit situations. HFC-410A is the replacement for HCFC-22 in new equipment. It has pressures 40–60% higher than R-22, so it cannot be used as a retrofit. It is a replacement only in the sense that it is used in the same general types of cooling applications that HCFC-22 is used in.

23.24 DOT 39 NON-REFILLABLE CYLINDERS

The three basic types of refrigerant cylinders are:

- Non-refillable refrigerant cylinders.
- Refillable refrigerant cylinders.
- Recovery cylinders.

All three types of cylinders are shown in Figure 23-30.

Non-Refillable Cylinders (Disposable)

As the name suggests, the non-refillable refrigerant cylinder is only filled one time, by the refrigerant manufacturer, Figure 23-31. The regulations for these cylinders are specified in section 39 of CFR 49. It should never be refilled by anyone with anything, not even the refrigerant manufacturer. Disposable cylinders come with check valves built in that make refilling the cylinders nearly impossible because the check valves prevent flow back into the cylinder, Figure 23-32.

Figure 23-30 Refrigerant cylinders
(Courtesy National Refrigerants, Inc.)

Figure 23-31 Non-refillable refrigerant cylinder

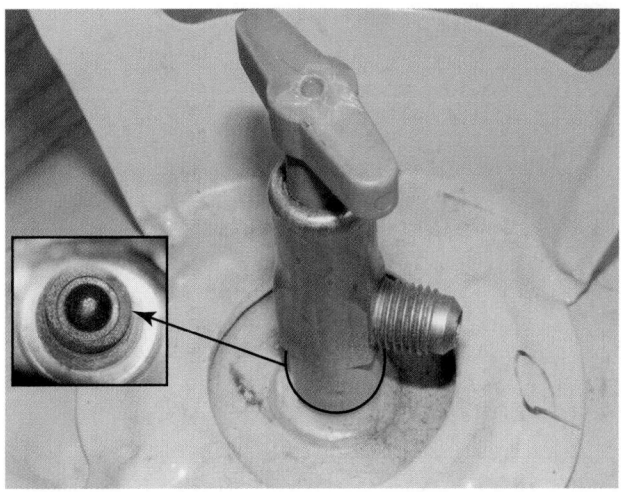

Figure 23-32 Non-refillable cylinders have a check valve in the stem to prevent flow back into the cylinder

Figure 23-33 The penalty for refilling and transporting a non-refillable cylinder is a $500,000 fine and/or 5 years imprisonment

These cylinders are non-refillable for a reason; they are not built to last as long as recovery cylinders and cannot withstand the same rigors as an approved recovery cylinder. The number one reason for not refilling disposable cylinders is to keep all your body parts firmly attached. The number two reason not to refill a disposable cylinder is that the potential penalty for refilling and transporting a non-refillable cylinder is now up to a $500,000 fine and spending 5 years in prison, Figure 23-33. This regulation is a Department of Transportation rule. It is designed to keep the highways safe, and it is enforced.

To prevent disaster, disposable cylinders should not be stored or used in temperatures exceeding 125°F. All refrigerant cylinders are rated for a maximum recommended service pressure. Most DOT 39 disposable cylinders have a service pressure of 260 psig. Disposable cylinders for use with R-410A have a service pressure of 400 psig. These pressures correspond to a

temperature of 120°F for saturated refrigerant. At the maximum recommended cylinder temperature of 125°F, these pressures increase to 278 psig and 447 psig, respectively. They are tested at the factory at 125% of their rated service pressure and they are supposed to have a minimum burst pressure of 250% of their rated service pressure. Figure 23-34 lists the service pressure, test pressure, and burst pressure for both types of DOT 39 disposable cylinders.

DOT 39 disposable cylinders have a frangible disk built into them to prevent pressures from reaching the bursting point of the cylinder, Figure 23-35. These disks look like knockouts in electrical boxes. A restriction on the other side

Refrigerant	Service pressure	Test pressure	Burst pressure
R-410A	400 psig	500 psig	1,000 psig
All others R-134a, R-22, etc.	260 psig	325 psig	650 psig

Figure 23-34 Pressure ratings of DOT 39 cylinders

Figure 23-35 Frangible disk on non-refillable DOT 39 cylinder

Figure 23-36 Flow limiting orifice on the inside of the cylinder underneath the frangible disk

of the disk limits the amount of flow out of the hole to prevent turning the cylinder into a missile, Figure 23-36.

SAFETY TIP

The frangible disk cannot protect the cylinder against all hazards. Heating the cylinder with a torch, or leaving the cylinder in the weather for extended periods of time, can create new weak spots that can lead to a violent cylinder rupture.

23.25 REFILLABLE REFRIGERANT CYLINDERS

The name says it all: refillable cylinders are intended to be refilled. However, only the owners of the cylinders or their agent may refill them. Refillable cylinders are large cylinders with water capacities of 123 lb or more; 125 lb of R-22 can be purchased in a large cylinder as shown in Figure 23-37. The customer generally pays a deposit on this cylinder when purchasing the refrigerant. When the cylinder is empty it is re-

Figure 23-37 123 lb water capacity refillable refrigerant cylinder
(Image Courtesy of Manchester Tank)

turned to the wholesaler. It is important to note that the refrigerant company still owns the cylinder. This means that the field service technician is not authorized to refill it.

23.26 RECOVERY CYLINDERS

The primary differences between a refillable cylinder and a recovery cylinder are size and ownership. Recovery cylinders are normally available in water capacities of 27 lb and 47 lb. Refillable cylinders and recovery cylinders are regulated by the DOT in Code of Federal Regulations 49 covering transport of hazardous materials. This is an extensive set of rules covering many things. Refrigerant cylinders are a very small part of this regulation. The primary hazard refrigerant cylinders pose is rupture.

Cylinder Markings

Cylinders are marked with the particular DOT specifications for that cylinder. The numbers and letters immediately following the letters DOT describe how the cylinder is made while the last group of numbers describes the cylinder service pressure. For example, a DOT-4BA-350 recovery cylinder is a welded or brazed steel cylinder with a recommended service pressure of 350 psig, Figure 23-38. This is the most

Figure 23-38 This specification shows that the service pressure for this recovery cylinder is 350 psig

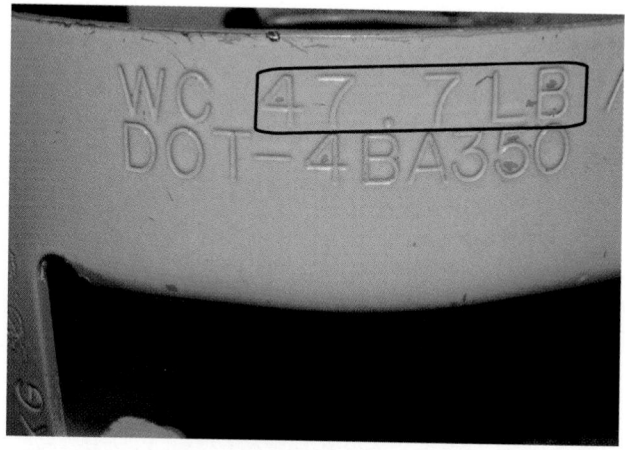

Figure 23-40 This recovery cylinder can hold 47.7 lbs of water

common specification for refrigerant recovery cylinders. There are also some DOT-4BA-260 and DOT 4BA-400 cylinders in use. These cylinders have recommended service pressures of 260 psig, and 400 psig, respectively.

Safety Relief Valve

Recovery cylinders have an automatic pressure relief valve built in that opens at 150% of the rated cylinder service pressure, Figure 23-39. The outlet of the relief valve should never be plugged or obstructed by anything. These valves reset once the pressure in the cylinder has dropped to a safe level.

Other crucial markings are the

- Water capacity.
- Tare weight.
- Date of manufacture.
- First retest date.
- Most recent test date.
- Last allowable retest date.

The water capacity is the weight of the water to completely fill the cylinder, Figure 23-40. The tare weight is the weight of the empty cylinder, Figure 23-41. These pieces of information are used to calculate how much refrigerant the cylinder can safely hold. This topic will be covered in detail in Unit 26, "Refrigerant Management and the EPA."

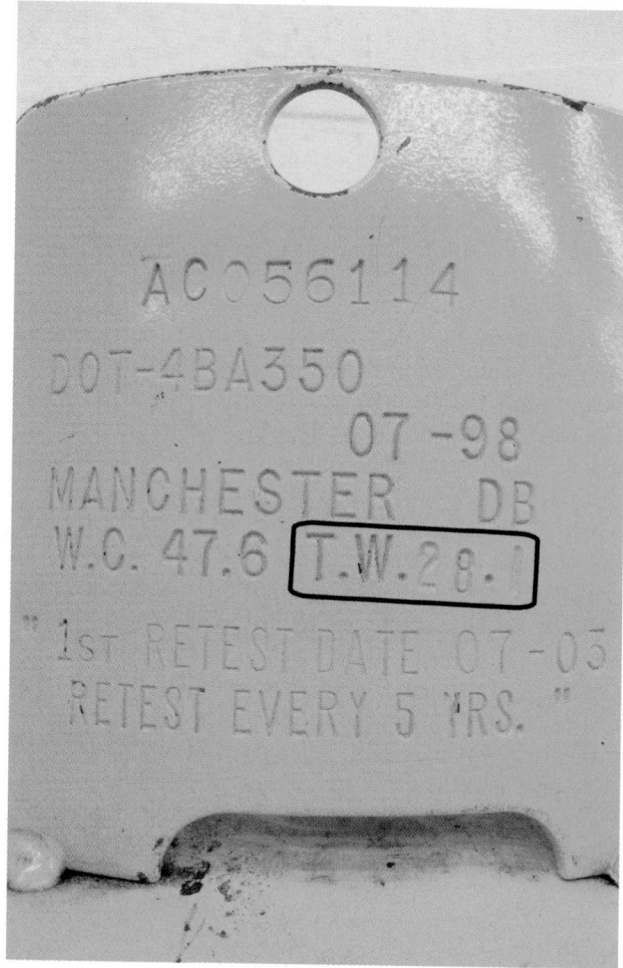

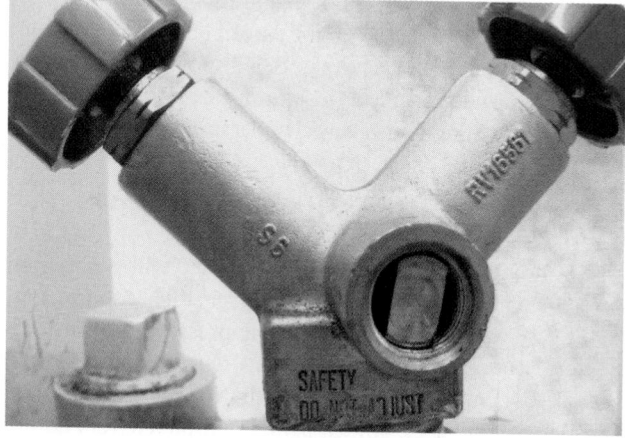

Figure 23-39 Safety relief valve on recovery cylinder

Figure 23-41 This recovery cylinder weighs 28.1 lb when empty

Figure 23-43 This 5 + 5 cylinder was manufactured in March 1997, retested in March 2002, and the last permissible refill date was March 2007

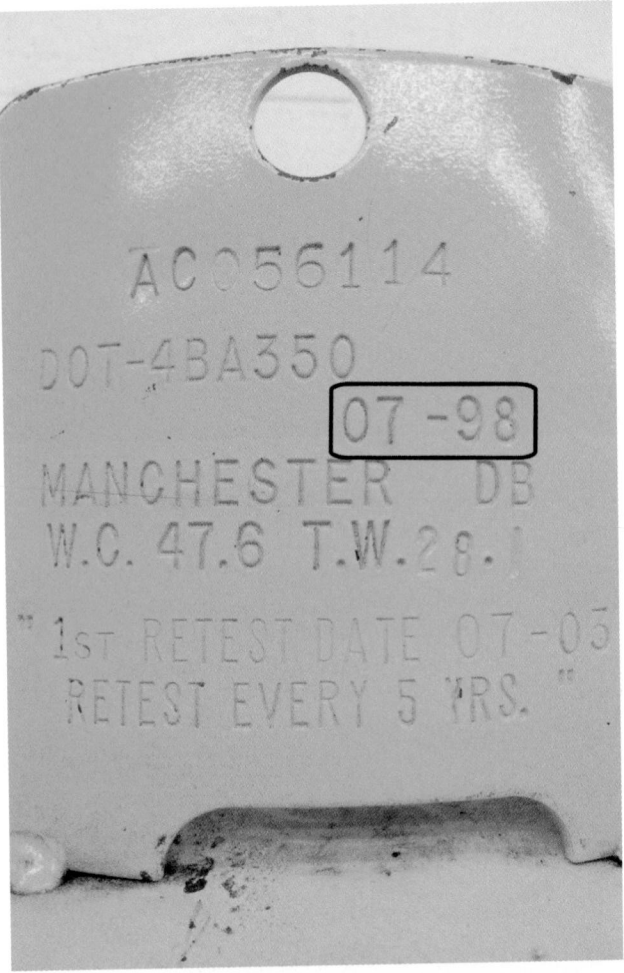

Figure 23-42 This recovery cylinder was manufactured July 1998

Cylinders with a service pressure under 300 psig must be tested every 10 years. Cylinders with a service pressure of 300 psig or more must be tested every 5 years. The date of manufacture and the first retest date are on every cylinder, Figure 23-42. The first retest date gives the month and year that a cylinder must be requalified. If the first requalification date has not yet arrived, the cylinder should be still on its first 5 years. Note that the 5 years starts when the cylinder is made, not when it is purchased. A cylinder that was made 2 years ago can only be used for another 3 years before getting requalified, even if it has been sitting on the shelf in the store. If the first retest date has already passed, the cylinder should not be used unless it was retested. If it was retested, the date that it was retested should be stamped on the cylinder. If the date was less than 5 years ago, the cylinder should be safe to use.

Some cylinders also have a last permissible use date, Figure 23-43. These are commonly known as 5 + 5 cylinders. They can only be requalified one time. These cylinders may not be used past the last permissible use date.

Cylinder Color

ARI Guideline K addresses suggested colors for refrigerant containers, Figure 23-44. Guideline K specifies that recovery

CFCs
R 11
R 12
R 13
R 13B1
R 113
R 114
R 500
R 502
R 503
HCFCs
R 22
R 123
R 124
R 401A
R 401B
R 402A
R 402B
R 403B
R 408A
R 409A
R 414B
R 416A
HFCs
R 23
R 134a
R 404A
R 407C
R 410A
R 417A
R 422A
R 422B
R 422D
R 507
R 508B

Figure 23-44 The suggested refrigerant cylinder colors in Guideline K

cylinders all be painted gray with a yellow top regardless of the type of refrigerant in the cylinder, Figure 23-45. Of course these cylinders must be labeled with the type of refrigerant they contain since cylinder color cannot be relied upon to identify them. The only thing the technician knows for sure by the color is that refrigerant in a gray and yellow cylinder is not new.

23.27 CYLINDER FILL LEVEL

The contents of any pressurized cylinder will increase in pressure if heated. As long as the cylinder still has some gas in it, the gas will compress and the rise in pressure will normally be slow enough that the built in safety devices can relieve the pressure when it exceeds 150% of the cylinder service pressure. However, if the cylinder is filled completely with liquid, a relatively small rise in temperature can create a very quick rise in pressure. This is because liquid is not compressible. A

Figure 23-45 Recovery cylinders are gray with a yellow top (*Courtesy National Refrigerants, Inc.*)

cylinder that is filled with liquid can go from 100 psig to over 1,000 psig simply by warming up 10°F, Figure 23-46. This can cause a violent explosion. Neither the relief disk on disposable cylinders nor the relief valve on recovery cylinders can relieve pressure quickly enough if a cylinder full of liquid should rise in temperature by 10°F in a few minutes. This type of dramatic pressure increase due to liquid expansion is called hydrostatic pressure.

To prevent disaster, cylinders should never be filled more than 80% full of liquid by volume and they should not be stored or used in temperatures exceeding 125°F. All refrigerant cylinders have a maximum recommended service pressure. This provides a good idea of how much pressure is too much. Do not pressurize recovery cylinders above their rated service pressure. More detail on safely filling recovery cylinders is provided in Unit 26, "Refrigerant Management and the EPA."

23.28 CHARACTERISTICS AND APPLICATIONS FOR REFRIGERANTS

The following information provides descriptions and tables for the properties of common refrigerants. The refrigerants will be arranged by common application.

Refrigerants Primarily Used in Air Conditioning

R-22—Monochlorodifluoromethane

Chemical family	HCFC—$CHCl_2F$
Formulation	Compound
Safety Rating	A1
Oil compatibility	Mineral oil, alkyl benzene, polyol ester
ODP	0.034
GWP	1,700

R-22 has been the refrigerant used in nearly all air conditioning systems manufactured for several decades, from window units up to 25 ton commercial DX systems. It was used extensively in commercial refrigeration after the phase out of CFCs, however, low temperature systems using R-22 often experience high compressor temperatures. It has a low ozone depletion potential and a moderate global warming potential. Because R-22 is an HCFC, it cannot be used in new equipment beginning January 1, 2010. It will no longer be manufactured or imported beginning January 1, 2020. The price of R-22 has risen dramatically in recent years as its production is being phased out.

R-407C—23% Pentafluoroethane, 25% Difluoromethane, 52% Tetrafluoroethane

Chemical family	HFC
Formulation	Zeotrope
	23% R-125, 25% R-32, 52% R-134a
Safety rating	A1/A1
Oil compatibility	Polyol ester, poly alkylene glycol
ODP	0
GWP	1,700

HFC-407C is a high glide zeotrope with a glide around 10°F. It is intended as a long term replacement for HCFC-22. Its operating pressures are very close to those of HCFC-22. Its operating efficiency is less than HCFC-22. HFC-407C can be used as a retrofit refrigerant in many systems with a change in refrigeration oil. It must leave the cylinder as a liquid because it is zeotropic.

R-410A—50% Pentafluoroethane, 50% Difluoromethane

Chemical family	HFC
Formulation	Zeotrope
	50% R-125, 50% R-32
Safety rating	A1/A1
Oil compatibility	Polyol ester, poly alkylene glycol
ODP	0
GWP	2,000

HFC-410A is a low glide zeotrope with a glide of 1°F or less. It has no ozone depletion and a moderate global warming potential. HFC-410A is the refrigerant that is replacing HCFC-22 in new air conditioning applications. However, its pressure is 40–60% higher than HCFC-22, so it cannot be used to replace HCFC-22 in existing systems. The operating efficiency of HFC-410A tends to be higher than similar

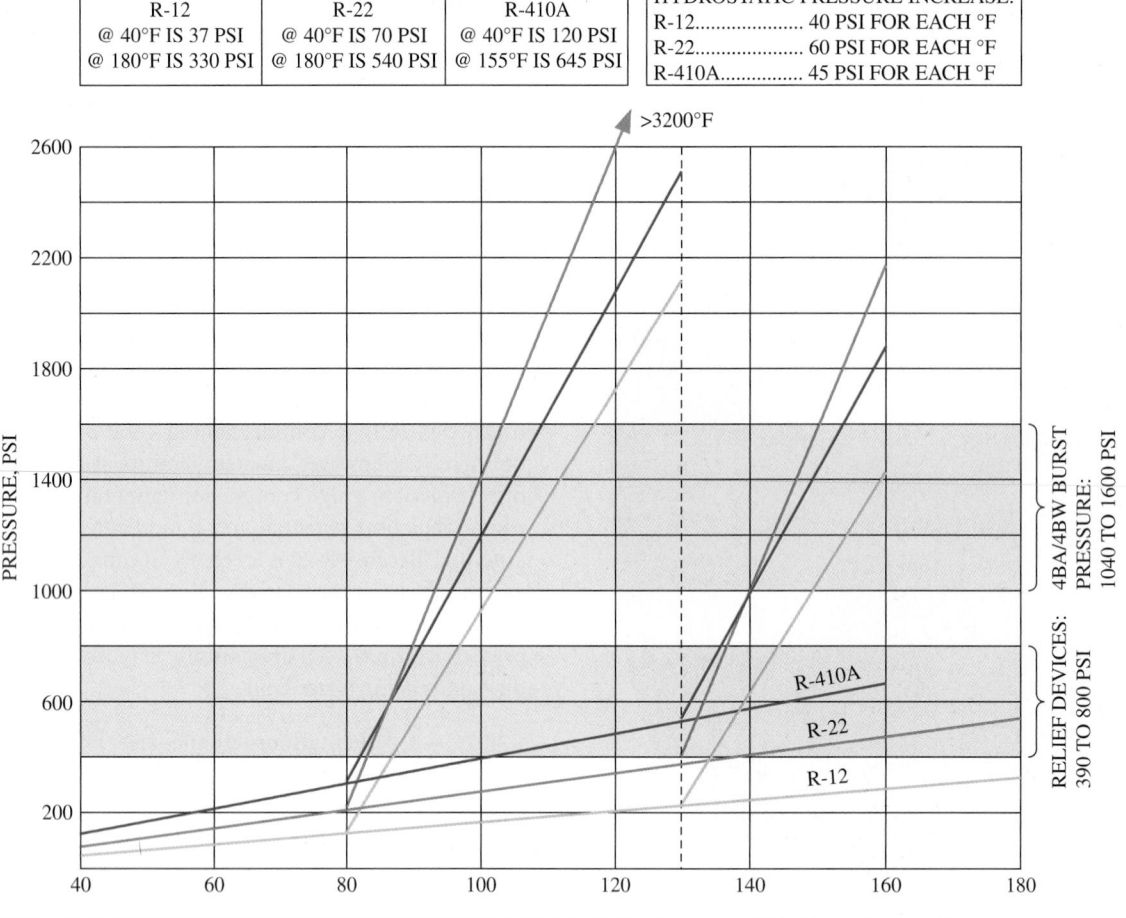

R-12	R-22	R-410A
@ 40°F IS 37 PSI	@ 40°F IS 70 PSI	@ 40°F IS 120 PSI
@ 180°F IS 330 PSI	@ 180°F IS 540 PSI	@ 155°F IS 645 PSI

HYDROSTATIC PRESSURE INCREASE:
R-12..................... 40 PSI FOR EACH °F
R-22..................... 60 PSI FOR EACH °F
R-410A................ 45 PSI FOR EACH °F

Figure 23-46 This chart shows the rapid rise in cylinder pressure when completely filled with liquid
(Courtesy of RSES)

HCFC-22 systems. HFC-410A requires service tools designed for it because of its high pressures. Since it is zeotropic, HFC-410A must leave the cylinder as a liquid.

SAFETY TIP

In the air conditioning refrigeration industry there are no distinctions between the service valve connections for the different refrigerants used. This differs from the automotive industry where different refrigerants have different sized access ports to prevent the accidental use of an improper gauge set on an unapproved refrigerant. In air conditioning it is strictly up to the technician to make certain before attaching the gauge set to a system that it is the proper gauge set. This is significant when working around systems that may contain R-410a because it has significantly higher pressure than most refrigerants used in the industry. Although the gauges will not explode, they can be overstressed to the point that they will no longer work properly.

Refrigerants Primarily Used in Commercial Refrigeration

R-404A—44% Pentafluoroethane, 52% Trifluoroethane, 4% Tetrafluoroethane

Chemical family	HFC
Formulation	Zeotrope
	44% R-125, 52% R-143a, 4% R-134a
Safety rating	A1/A1
Oil compatibility	Polyol ester, poly alkylene glycol
ODP	0
GWP	3,800

HFC-404A is a long term replacement for the CFC-502 in new systems. HFC-404A is a low glide zeotrope with a glide of 2°F or less. It has no ozone depletion and a moderately high global warming potential. It is primarily used in medium and low temperature systems, including commercial freezers, ice machines, and transportation refrigeration. HFC-404A is becoming the refrigerant of choice in low temperature commercial refrigeration applications. Since it is zeotropic, it must be removed from the cylinder as a liquid.

R-507—50% Pentafluoroethane, 50% Trifluoroethane

Chemical family	HFC
Formulation	Azeotrope
	50% R-125, 50% R-143a
Safety rating	A1
Oil compatibility	Polyol ester, poly alkylene glycol
ODP	0
GWP	3,900

HFC-507 is a true azeotrope designed to replace CFC-502 in new commercial refrigeration applications. As an azeotrope, it may be removed from the cylinder as either a gas or a liquid.

Refrigerants Primarily Used in Domestic Refrigeration

R-12—Dichlorodifluoromethane

Chemical family	CFC—CCl_2F_2
Formulation	Compound
Safety rating	A1
Oil compatibility	Mineral oil, alkyl benzene, polyol ester
ODP	0.82
GWP	10,600

CFC-12 was widely used for years in domestic refrigerators, automobiles, medium temperature commercial refrigeration, and ice machines. It has both a high ozone depletion potential and a high global warming potential. It has been illegal to manufacture or import CFC-12 since January 1, 1996. Because of its widespread use, some systems are still in operation that use CFC-12.

R-134a—1,1,1,2-tetrafluoroethane

Chemical family	HFC—CH_2FCF_3
Formulation	Compound
Safety rating	A1
Oil compatibility	Polyol ester, poly alkylene glycol
ODP	0
GWP	1,300

This is a chlorine-free fluorinated refrigerant designed to replace R-12 in new appliances. It is generally not considered a retrofit refrigerant. It has an ODP of 0.0, and a GWP of 1,300. It is suitable for use in domestic refrigerators, automotive air conditioning, and medium- and high-temperature commercial applications. It is a suitable replacement for R-12 wherever the evaporation temperature is –10°F or higher.

Refrigerants Primarily Used in Large Industrial Systems

R-11—Trichlorofluoromethane

Chemical family	CFC—CCl_3F
Formulation	Compound
Safety rating	A1
Oil compatibility	Mineral oil, alkyl benzene, polyol ester
ODP	1
GWP	4600

CFC-11 was widely used in low pressure centrifugal chillers. It has a high ozone depletion potential and a moderately high global warming potential. It has been illegal to manufacture or import CFC-11 since January 1, 1996. Because of its widespread use and the high cost of large centrifugal chillers, some systems are still in operation that use CFC-11.

R-123—2,2-dichloro-1,1,1-trifluoroethane

Chemical family	HCFC—$CHCl_2CF_3$
Formulation	Compound
Safety rating	B1
Oil compatibility	Mineral oil, alkyl benzene, polyol ester
ODP	0.012
GWP	120

This refrigerant was designed to replace R-11 in low pressure chillers. The pressure-temperature curves show close performance characteristics between these two refrigerants. R-123 has a safety group classification of B1, making it objectionable from the standpoint of toxicity. As a result, some service companies refuse to use it. As yet no new universally acceptable refrigerant has been developed to replace R-11. R-123 has a small ODP and a small GWP. Because R-123 is an HCFC, it will no longer be manufactured or imported beginning January 1, 2030.

R-717—Ammonia

Chemical family	NH_3
Formulation	Compound
Safety rating	B2
Oil compatibility	Mineral oil
ODP	0
GWP	0

Ammonia is one of the oldest refrigerants in use today. It has a much higher latent heat of evaporation than the other common refrigerants. This means that smaller piping can be used. It is corrosive to copper, but not to iron, steel, or aluminum. It therefore requires an all-iron, steel, or aluminum system including the compressor, condenser, evaporator, controls, and piping. It is not destructive to the ozone layer. Its greatest defect is its toxicity and flammability. It has a safety rating of B2.

Due to ammonia's safety hazards it is not found in appliances or normal comfort cooling applications. Typically it is used in large commercial or industrial applications where its operating efficiencies (lower horsepower per ton) are important and where plant engineers are available to operate the system. Examples would be dairies, ice cream plants, and large cold storage facilities.

Due to its toxicity, an operator must take special precautions to limit the quantity inhaled. Leaks are detected by use of litmus paper which changes color in the presence of ammonia, or a sulfur candle which creates smoke in contact with ammonia. Technicians must also take care to avoid ammonia contact with the skin.

SERVICE TIP

In addition to gloves and safety glasses that technicians should use with all refrigerants, there must be a self-contained breathing apparatus available for each worker in the area when working around systems that contain ammonia refrigerant. It is not possible to simply hold your breath and run from an area if an ammonia leak occurs. Part of the problem is the reaction the lungs have when a small quantity of ammonia is inhaled. Even a small amount of concentrated ammonia can damage lungs. Exposure to concentrated ammonia can temporarily blind you. The only way to prevent these problems is to have the appropriate equipment ready and available for emergency use.

UNIT 23—SUMMARY

Refrigerant is the fluid used in a refrigeration system to transfer heat. It does this by absorbing heat while evaporating at a low pressure and temperature and condensing at a high pressure and temperature. Refrigerants may be classified by many characteristics including:

Operating Pressure
Very high pressure.
High pressure.
Low pressure.

Chemical Composition
CFCs.
HCFCs.
HFCs.

Formulation
Compounds.
Zeotropes.
Azeotropes.

Toxicity
A: lower toxicity.
B: higher toxicity.

Flammability
1: Nonflammable.
2: Somewhat flammable.
3: Highly flammable.

Ozone Depletion Potential
0 ODP: No ozone depletion.
1 ODP: High ozone depletion (CFC-11).

Global Warming Potential
0 GWP: No global warming potential.
4,000 or greater: High global warming potential.

The majority of modern halogenated refrigerants are built around the hydrocarbon molecules methane and ethane.

Halogens replace some or all of the hydrogen atoms in the hydrocarbon molecules. CFCs and HCFCs have ozone depletion potential because they contain chlorine. HFCs have no ozone depletion potential because they contain no chlorine.

Refrigerant is available in disposable and refillable cylinders. Disposable cylinders should not be refilled by anyone with anything. Refillable cylinders are returned and refilled by the refrigerant manufacturer, but should not be refilled by field technicians. Recovery cylinders are used in the field to recover refrigerant. They should not be refilled more than 80% full by volume because liquid expansion can cause hydrostatic pressures that can rupture the cylinders if they are filled completely with liquid.

UNIT 23—REVIEW QUESTIONS

1. Define refrigerant.
2. What organization has established the number designation for refrigerants?
3. What are the chemical components of CFC refrigerant?
4. What are the chemical components of HCFC refrigerant?
5. What are the chemical components of HFC refrigerant?
6. What is ozone?
7. Which chemical family of refrigerants has the highest ozone depleton potential?
8. What is the primary safety concern when working with R-410A?
9. Define the term "glide" when referring to zeotropic refrigerants.
10. Explain the ASHRAE refrigerant safety designation regarding refrigerant toxicity and flammability.
11. What is the difference between a disposable refrigerant cylinder and a refillable refrigerant cylinder?
12. What is the difference between a compound and a zeotrope?
13. What is the difference between a zeotrope and an azeotrope?
14. What contaminants can be found in refrigerant?
15. State two reasons ammonia has limited use.
16. What refrigerant is being used in small appliances in place of R-12?
17. What refrigerant is being used in new air conditioning systems in place of R-22?
18. When working with ammonia, what safety equipment must be available?
19. How can the presence of a noncondensable material in a refrigerant cylinder be detected?
20. Describe the difference between latent heat and sensible heat and explain why these concepts are important for a refrigerant.
21. What condition is the refrigerant inside most refrigerant cylinders: superheated vapor, subcooled liquid, or a saturated liquid-vapor mix?
22. What determines the pressure of a refrigerant cylinder?
23. How can the pressure of a refrigerant be accurately predicted?
24. What is the difference between a low pressure refrigerant and a high pressure refrigerant?
25. Which type of refrigerants are listed as Class I ozone depleting substances by the EPA?

26. What chemical family is the basic building block for most modern refrigerants?

27. What is a halogenated refrigerant?

28. What effects does water have when introduced in a system with refrigerant?

29. What differences are there between handling zeotropes and azeotropes?

30. Explain the difference between a bubble point and a dew point.

31. What is fractionation and how does it affect the way zeotropic refrigerants are handled?

32. What is the difference between a high-glide blend and a low-glide blend?

33. Why do CFCs deplete the ozone layer?

34. What is the ozone layer?

35. What benefit is the ozone layer to us?

36. Why are HCFCs not as harmful to the atmosphere as CFCs?

37. What is the difference between ozone depletion and global warming?

38. What gas is used as the standard for comparison when assigning a refrigerants global warming potential?

39. What has been used for years as a refrigeration lubricant with CFCs and HCFCs?

40. What lubricants can be used with HFCs?

41. Why should a refrigeration lubricant be miscible with the system refrigerant?

42. What is a hygroscopic lubricant?

UNIT 24

Refrigerant System Piping

OBJECTIVES

After completing this unit you will be able to:

- explain the importance of minimizing pressure drop through the lines.
- explain the importance of maintaining minimum gas velocities in the lines.
- calculate the pressure drop in a liquid line due to vertical lift.
- list the system modifications required for long line applications of residential air conditioning systems.
- list some of the differences between air conditioning and commercial refrigeration piping.
- size refrigeration lines using line sizing charts.

24.1 INTRODUCTION

How does a technician determine what size lines to run when installing a refrigeration system? One common method is to measure the pipe stub-outs on the unit and use that size. If installations are restricted to "standard" installations, this method will often work. However, there are many variables that affect the size of refrigerant lines that cannot be determined without knowing the details of a particular installation. The penalty for incorrectly sizing the refrigerant lines can range from poor system performance to multiple compressor failures. It is in your best interest to know how to size refrigerant lines correctly. Refrigerant line sizing can be important from a service standpoint also since it affects system performance. Understanding line sizing concepts will help you solve those elusive problems that other mechanics cannot.

24.2 GOOD REFRIGERANT PIPING PRACTICES

There are good piping practices that should be followed when sizing and installing a refrigerant piping system:

- Keep it clean. Cleanliness is a key factor in the actual installation. Dirt, metal filings, sludge, and moisture will cause breakdown in the system and must be avoided. Neat, clean work will avoid many service difficulties.
- Pressure drop through all sections of piping should be kept to an absolute minimum to maximize system capacity and efficiency. Use as few fittings as possible. Fewer fittings mean less chance for leaks, and more importantly, less needless pressure drop.

- Each section of the piping system must also be sized to ensure enough velocity for proper oil return. In those installations where oil return and pressure drop are in conflict, proper oil return takes precedence.
- Be careful in making every connection. Use the right material and follow the method recommended by the equipment manufacturer. The lines should be purged with nitrogen during brazing to eliminate the formation of copper oxide inside the lines.
- Pitch horizontal lines in the direction of refrigerant flow, Figure 24-1. To aid in forcing oil to travel through lines that contain vapor (suction line, hot gas line), horizontal lines should be pitched in the direction of refrigerant flow. To help the oil flow in the right direction, this pitch should be a minimum of $1/2$ in for each 10 ft of run. Pitch also helps to prevent backflow of the oil during shutdown. In piping systems where sufficient return gas velocity can be ensured at all times, it is satisfactory to run the horizontal suction lines dead level. This may be desirable where headroom is at a premium or where a sloping run will interfere with other piping.

TECH TIP

Selecting the correct refrigerant lines can be very complex involving many factors. One factor, however, that should be considered the least is the cost of the materials. Copper line sets are frequently undersized for cost savings. However, undersizing a system's refrigerant lines significantly reduces the system's performance. Reduced performance means extended operation, and higher operating costs. The money saved on the initial installation is quickly spent on power bills.

PITCH HORIZONTAL LINES $1/2$ IN PER 10 FT AWAY FROM THE COMPRESSOR

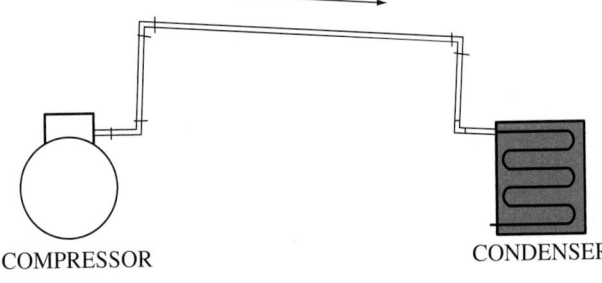

Figure 24-1 Lines should be sloped at least $1/2$ in per 10 ft of run in the direction of refrigerant flow

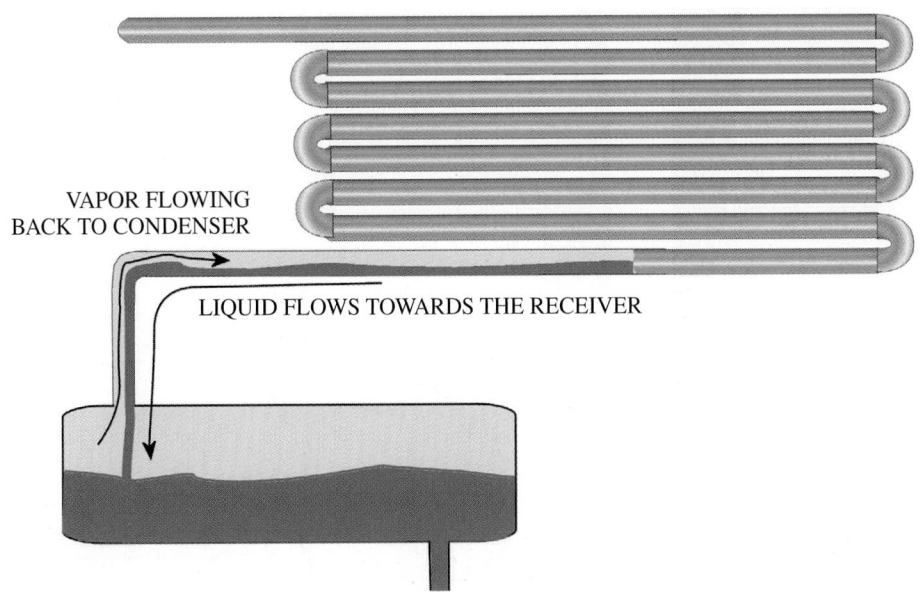

VAPOR FLOWING
BACK TO CONDENSER

LIQUID FLOWS TOWARDS THE RECEIVER

Figure 24-7 The condensate line should be large enough to allow free drainage of liquid from the condenser to the receiver

Long, large diameter liquid lines can add a considerable amount of charge to the system. Figure 24-8 shows the amount of refrigerant contained in each foot of liquid line for different diameters of tubing. Line lengths that cause the system charge to exceed the maximum charge limit of the compressor should be avoided. To limit the amount of refrigerant in the system, most residential air conditioning system manufacturers use $^3/_8$ in liquid lines for split systems using remote condensing units. However, the size of the liquid line will vary with tonnage and line length on commercial systems. Do not change the liquid line size from the original specifications because incorrectly sized liquid lines can seriously reduce system capacity and reduce the equipment life.

TECH TIP

The liquid line is typically not insulated; however, when it runs a great distance through a hot attic, it is advisable to insulate it from the extreme attic heat. In addition, insulating the liquid line will aid in performance of a heat pump. Finally, insulating the liquid line can reduce the noise caused by changeover of heat pumps.

24.10 PRE-EXPANSION FLASH GAS

Liquid leaving the condenser is subcooled, but it is still generally at a higher temperature than the surrounding air. Flash gas generally is not a problem with short liquid lines in normal ambient conditions. However, liquid lines can experience flash gas from pressure drop through the line, pressure drop due to vertical lift, or from passing through very high temperature areas. Refrigerant leaving the condenser remains a liquid only as long as its boiling point (condensing temperature) is higher than its actual temperature. Vaporization

of some of the liquid can occur before it passes through the metering device if a drop in pressure causes the boiling point to drop below the refrigerant's actual temperature. The vapor formed is called pre-expansion flash gas. Flash gas within the liquid line is undesirable, since it displaces liquid at the port of the expansion valve, greatly reducing capacity. Known as gas binding, it also affects the capacity of capillary tubes, as the ability of the tubes to carry vapor is considerably less than the ability to carry liquid.

Running a liquid line across a metal roof is an example of a situation that will cause pre-expansion flash gas. When the roof is heated by the sun, the roof can easily be hotter than the liquid line. Refrigerant lines should be raised at least 18 in above such a roof to minimize the effects of the sun, Figure 24-9.

A method of spotting flash gas is to compare the temperature of the liquid line where a solid stream of liquid exists to the temperature of the liquid line at a point where flash gas is suspected, Figure 24-10. A typical location for the second thermometer would be at the entrance to a TEV valve. If there is a noticeable temperature drop at point 2, flash gas could be

Ounces of R-22 per foot of line		
Line OD (in)	Liquid line (oz)	Suction line (oz)
¼	0.22	
3/8	0.58	
½	1.14	
5/8	1.86	0.04
¾		0.06
7/8		0.08
1 1/8		0.15
1 3/8		0.22

Figure 24-8 Amount of refrigerant charge per foot of line

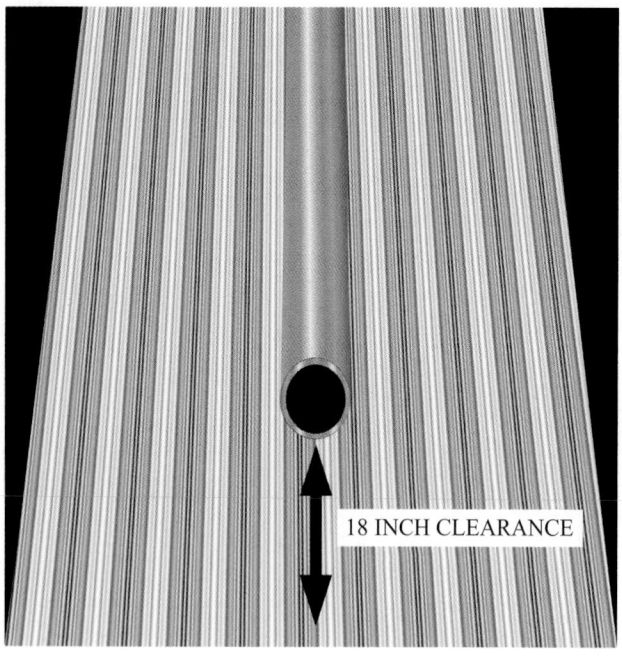

Figure 24-9 Liquid lines should be supported at least 18 in above metal roofs to prevent excessive temperatures that can cause flash gas in the liquid line

Figure 24-10 The 30°F temperature drop in this liquid line can indicate the presence of flash gas or a restriction in the liquid line

present. An exception would be where the presence of gas binding and low liquid flow would cause the liquid line to be warm at the TEV valve and mask the presence of the flash gas.

SERVICE TIP

Liquid line sight glasses are used in some applications as an indicator of flash gas. Many technicians install the liquid line sight glass near the condenser. However, the sight glass's usefulness is significantly diminished if it is in the liquid line near the condenser. At that location it simply tells you there is or is not flash gas there; however, flash gas can be forming in front of your metering device and go undetected. The best location for the sight glass is near the evaporator.

24.11 PRESSURE DROP DUE TO VERTICAL LIFT

Static loss refers to the pressure difference that exists between the bottom and the top of a liquid filled pipe due to the weight of liquid in the line. Static loss is a frequent cause of the creation of pre-expansion flash gas. Friction and static losses are present in all liquid lines, even properly sized lines. It is important to understand how much pressure loss there will be in the liquid line and offset that by subcooling.

Standing columns of liquid exert a force on the bottom of the column due to their weight. Refrigerants are no different. For example, a standing column of liquid R-22 at 100°F and 210 psig exerts a pressure of approximately 0.50 psi for every foot

of height of the column due to its weight. R-410A exerts 0.43 psi per foot of height. The pressure at the bottom of a 10 ft column of R-22 is 5 psi greater than the pressure at the top of the column. Conversely, for every 10 ft that R-22 is lifted in a vertical riser, the pressure at the top of the column is reduced by 5 psi. Figure 24-11 shows the effect of vertical lift in liquid lines.

Take the case of an R-22 system with a 30 foot lift, a 6 psi pressure drop in the liquid line, a condensing temperature of 105°F, and 3°F of subcooling. Considering the 3°F of subcooling, the liquid leaves the condenser at 102°F, 211 psig. If the liquid line riser has a 30 ft lift, the pressure at the top of the riser would be 15 psi less due to the weight of the refrigerant. The final pressure would be:

$$211 \text{ psig} - 15 \text{ psig} = 196 \text{ psig}$$
$$196 \text{ psig} - 6 \text{ psig line loss} = 190 \text{ psig}$$

This will produce a boiling point of 98°F. Since the liquid left the condenser at 102°F, enough liquid will vaporize to

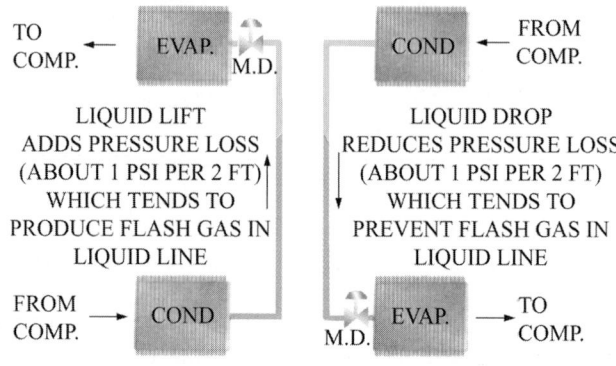

Figure 24-11 Liquid line static head with lift or drop conditions

cool the remaining liquid to 98°F. To avoid the formation of flash gas in this riser, liquid subcooling leaving the condenser of 8°F or more is required to compensate for lift and pressure drop in the line. This can be accomplished by the use of a liquid-to-suction-line heat exchanger.

Again, assume that the same conditions are applied to an air conditioning unit with 15°F of subcooling. The pressure loss in the liquid line could be much greater before flash gas is formed. Instead of leaving the condenser at 102°F as it did with only 8°F of subcooling, the liquid would leave at 90°F. The saturation pressure for 90°F R-22 is 168 psig. The pressure loss due to vertical lift could be as high as $211 - 6 - 168 = 37$ psi. The vertical lift could increase to 74 ft before flash gas would occur ($74 \times 0.5 = 37$).

This demonstrates the value of a proper amount of subcooling. It not only provides latitude for the designer when laying out the liquid line, but the proper amount of subcooling provides the maximum system capacity at the lowest operating cost.

This also highlights the importance of avoiding vertical lifts in the liquid line. Where possible, avoid installations with large vertical distances between the condensing unit and the evaporator. An example of a problematic installation would be a condensing unit on grade and the air handler in the attic of a multistory dwelling. Flash gas, reduced capacity, and increased operating cost are all likely to be problems.

If you cannot avoid this situation, provide enough liquid subcooling to overcome the pressure loss. Extra subcooling can be obtained by using a suction-to-liquid heat exchanger or stacking the liquid and suction lines together and insulating both lines inside a common wrap to promote heat exchange from the liquid to the suction line.

24.12 SUCTION LINE

Oil circulates throughout the system and must be returned to the compressor to prevent damage to the compressor. The most critical line in performing this function is the suction line. For example, observe the behavior of two common refrigerants used in refrigeration and air conditioning, R-22 and R-410A. In liquid form, these refrigerants will mix with oil and carry it along the piping with ease. Therefore, few, if any, oil problems exist in the liquid line. However, in their gaseous state the refrigerants are poor carriers of oil.

Oil in the suction line is at a lower temperature than the rest of the system, and therefore has higher viscosity, which slows down the flow over pipe surfaces. Also, the refrigerant is in vapor form and has only a mechanical effect on the oil. The vapor does not absorb the oil.

Minimum suction gas velocity is normally between 500–750 FPM for horizontal runs and 1,000–1,500 FPM for vertical runs. This is the minimum velocity needed to bring back the oil to the compressor. If there is a conflict between the size needed to achieve the minimum velocity required for oil return and the size needed to achieve a low pressure drop, size the suction line to achieve the minimum velocity for oil return. Be sure to check the velocity and size of both the

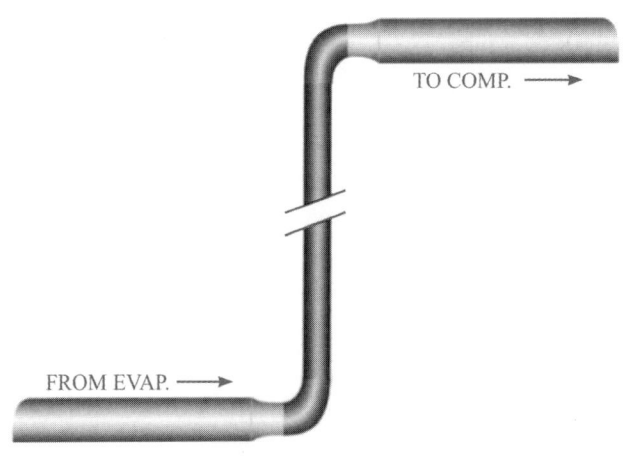

Figure 24-12 Reduced size suction gas pipe riser

horizontal and vertical sections of pipe since the minimum velocity for a vertical rise is greater than for a horizontal run. Frequently the best size for the horizontal run will be larger than the best size for the vertical riser, Figure 24-12. It is good practice in these cases to make the vertical piping smaller than the horizontal piping. This keeps pressure drop to a minimum and still maintains the minimum required velocity for oil return. The suction line, therefore, must be carefully designed to ensure a uniform return of dry refrigerant gas as well as sufficient oil to the compressor.

The maximum recommended saturation temperature drop in the suction line is 2°F. The equivalent pressure drop is different for different refrigerants. The suction pressure drop is important because it has a great effect on the compressor compression ratio. Reducing the suction pressure to the compressor increases the compression ratio. Any increase in this ratio reduces the capacity of the compressor to pump refrigerant vapor and increases the power required.

For example, for R-22 at 0°F, a 10°F temperature drop produces a 17 psi pressure drop. With a 100°F saturation condenser, the compression ratio at 0°F

$$(195.9 + 14.7)/(23.9 + 14.7) = 5.45$$

It becomes

$$(195 + 14.7)/(16.5 + 14.7) = 6.75 \text{ at } -10°F.$$

24.13 EQUIVALENT LENGTH OF FITTINGS

There is some pressure loss through every fitting and device in the refrigeration line. This pressure loss must be taken into account when sizing lines. The most common way of accounting for the pressure loss through fittings and devices in refrigeration lines is to compare the loss through each fitting as equivalent to the loss through a length of pipe. Tables give the equivalent length for different sizes and types of fittings. Figure 24-13 gives the equivalent length for common fittings and valves. Note that the equivalent length increases as the pipe size increases.

Copper pipe size (in OD)	90° elbow	45° elbow	Tee	Gate valve	Globe valve	Angle valve
1/2	0.8	0.4	2.5	0.26	7.0	4.0
3/4	1.0	0.6	2.5	0.3	12.0	6.5
7/8	1.45	0.8	3.6	0.36	17.2	9.5
1 1/8	1.85	1.0	4.6	0.48	22.5	12.0
1 3/8	2.4	1.3	6.4	0.65	32.0	16.0
1 5/8	2.9	1.6	7.2	0.72	36.0	19.5
2 1/8	3.6	2.0	9.6	0.96	48.0	22.5
2 5/8	4.5	2.4	11.2	1.1	56.0	28.0
3 1/8	1.0	2.9	12.8	1.4	72.0	32.0
3 5/8	1.0	3.4	16.0	1.6	80.0	40.0
4 1/8	1.0	4.0	18.6	1.7	100.0	48.0

Figure 24-13 Equivalent length of copper fittings and valves in feet of copper tubing of same size

When looking up line lengths in sizing tables, the length that should be used is the line's total equivalent length. The total equivalent length is the sum of the line's actual length plus the equivalent length of all the fittings and devices in the refrigerant line. It is common for the equivalent length of all the fittings and devices in the line to add up to 50% of the line length.

24.14 AIR CONDITIONING PIPING PRACTICES

What is considered good piping practice for one type of system may be considered poor practice for another type of equipment. In general, the piping recommendations for air conditioning equipment are somewhat different from the piping recommendations for commercial refrigeration. Most air conditioning manufacturers do not recommend oil traps, double risers, or expansion loops in their refrigeration lines. In general, air conditioning piping should be kept as straight and simple as possible. Most air conditioning manufacturers recommend that refrigerant lines not be run underground. Lengths of underground lines create a large, cool trap to condense significant quantities of refrigerant on the off cycle. This refrigerant is then delivered to the compressor as a liquid slug on startup.

24.15 PREVENTING LIQUID SLUGGING

Slugging is a momentary return of a quantity of liquid to an operating compressor. A slug can be either refrigerant or oil. To learn how to prevent liquid slugging, it is first necessary to understand what happens in a simple system when the compressor stops operating after its cooling requirements are satisfied. The evaporator is still filled with refrigerant—part liquid and part vapor. There will also be some oil present. The liquid refrigerant and oil may drain by gravity to points where, when the compressor starts running again, the liquid will be drawn into the compressor and cause liquid slugging.

The piping design must prevent liquid refrigerant or oil from draining to the compressor during shutdown. When the compressor is above the evaporator, this is not a problem. When the compressor is located in an area where the ambient temperature is cooler than the condenser and/or evaporator, off cycle refrigeration migration can be a problem. Traps in the discharge piping may be required as well as suction line accumulators and crankcase heaters. It is best to avoid such problematic conditions where possible rather than to try to design fixes for them after the fact.

TECH TIP

Soft refrigeration copper comes in coils, and when properly unrolled it is relatively straight. However, if the copper is simply pulled from the center like a spring, it will have a series of loops. The loops are not significantly deep; however, each loop can collect a small amount of refrigerant oil. When the amount of oil in the loops gets large enough, it will begin moving from the first loop to the second, where it picks up that oil and moves to the next. This moving slug of oil then can pass into the compressor and slug it. It moves much in the same way as the last bit of juice is sucked through a child's curlicue straw.

The greater the system refrigerant charge, the more likely it is that compressor failures may be experienced. Common sense dictates close coupled systems with clean, simple piping layouts and minimal refrigerant charges.

Some evaporator coils are designed to feed refrigerant at their top and take suction off the bottom. For top fed coils, a riser to at least the top of the evaporator must be placed in the suction line if the compressor is below the evaporator, as in Figure 24-14. This inverted loop is to prevent liquid draining from the evaporator into the compressor during shutdown. A hard shutoff expansion valve will also help prevent refrigerant

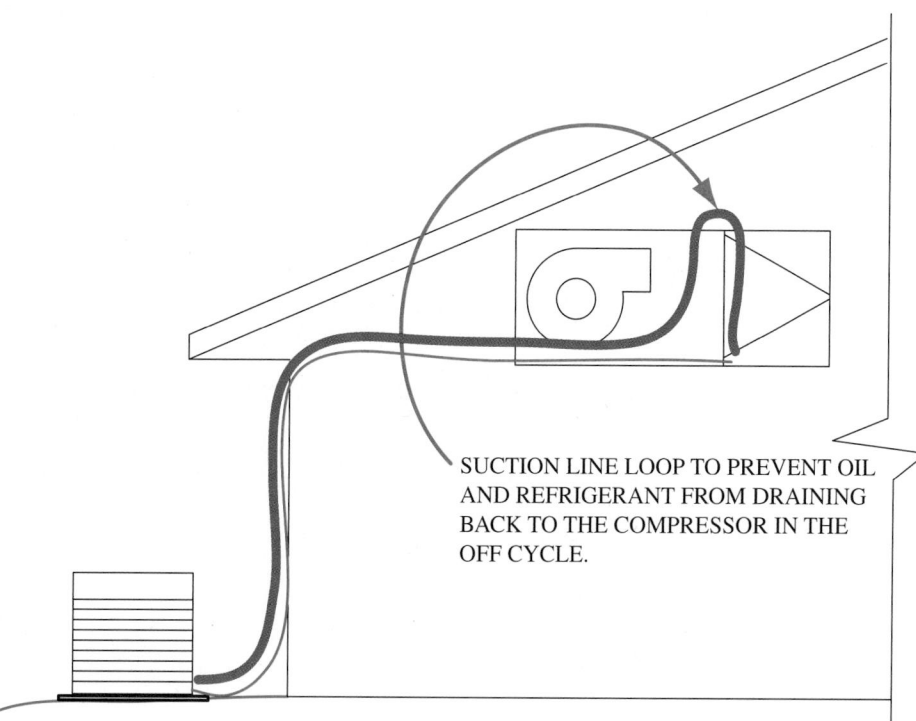

SUCTION LINE LOOP TO PREVENT OIL AND REFRIGERANT FROM DRAINING BACK TO THE COMPRESSOR IN THE OFF CYCLE.

flow back to the compressor on the off cycle. The sump at the bottom of the riser promotes free drainage of liquid refrigerant away from the thermostatic expansion valve bulb, thus permitting the bulb to sense suction gas superheat instead of evaporating liquid refrigerant. No loop is required for coils that feed at the bottom and take the suction off the top.

24.16 SIZING LINES FOR RESIDENTIAL AIR CONDITIONING

The importance of following the equipment manufacturer's instructions when sizing and installing refrigeration lines cannot be overstressed. Differences in equipment design and application can require different approaches to line sizing.

However, there are several design issues that most all residential air conditioning systems have in common.

Refrigeration lines have a practical limit in terms of both length and size. For safety reasons, hermetic compressors have a system charge limit, Figure 24-15. The charge limit is the maximum amount of refrigerant that the entire system can have in it for safe compressor operation. Extremely long or oversized lines can increase the amount of refrigerant in the system past the safe charge limit of the hermetic compressors used in residential equipment. The "soak out" limit is the maximum charge the oil in the compressor can absorb and not experience liquid slugging on startup.

Further, the compressor has a limited amount of oil. Extra long or oversized lines can hold so much oil that the compressor becomes low on oil. Adding oil to hermetic

Compressor model number	Compressor Btu/hr capacity @ ARI	Refrigerant oil charge (Zerol 150T) (pt)	Maximum system r-22 charge permissible with lubricant Zerol 150T supplied with the compressor (lb)	Compressor soak-out refrigerant charge limits (lb) (without crankcase heater energized 12 to 16 Hr)
H2NG094	87,700	7	15	10.0
H2NG104	101,800	7	17	10.0
H2NG124	119,400	7	20	10.0
H2NG144	144,100	8	24	15.0
H2NG184	183,200	16	30	20.0
H2NG204	212,400	16	35	20.0
H2NG244	252,900	16	40	20.0
H2NG294	287,300	16	45	20.0

Figure 24-15 Hermetic compressor charge limit

Unit nominal size (Btuh)	Acceptable vapor line diameter OD (in)	Cooling capacity loss (%) total equivalent line length (ft.)										
		Standard application				Long line application requires accessories						
		25	50	80	80+	100	125	150	175	200	225	250
18,000 R-22 AC	5/8	0	1	1	1	2	3	3	4	5	5	6
	3/4	0	0	0	0	0	1	1	1	1	2	2
24,000 R-22 AC	5/8	0	1	3	3	3	5	6	7	8	9	10
	3/4	0	0	0	0	1	1	1	2	2	3	3
	7/8	0	0	0	0	0	0	0	0	1	1	1
30,000 R-22 AC	5/8	1	3	5	5	6	8	10	11	13	15	17
	3/4	0	1	1	1	2	3	3	4	5	5	6
	7/8	0	0	0	0	1	1	1	2	2	2	3
36,000 R-22 AC	3/4	0	1	2	2	3	4	5	6	7	8	9
	7/8	0	0	1	1	1	2	2	3	3	4	4
42,000 R-22 AC	3/4	1	2	3	3	4	5	7	8	9	10	11
	7/8	0	1	1	1	2	2	3	4	4	5	5
	1 1/8	0	0	0	0	0	0	0	1	1	1	1
48,000 R-22 AC	3/4	1	2	4	4	5	7	8	10	11	13	14
	7/8	0	1	2	2	2	3	4	5	5	6	7
	1 1/8	0	0	0	0	0	0	1	1	1	1	1
60,000 R-22 AC	7/8	1	2	3	3	4	5	7	8	9	10	11
	1 1/8	0	0	1	1	1	1	2	2	2	3	3

Figure 24-16 Vapor line sizing and cooling capacity losses—R-22 air conditioner applications

compressors is not a viable option because the crankcase of most hermetic compressors is not large enough to hold any extra oil. Residential air conditioning equipment manufacturers specify the correct line size for their equipment in the installation instructions. Typically, the size for lines less than 50 ft is the same as the condenser stubout. Lines longer than 50 ft or having a vertical lift more than 20 ft generally require special installation considerations. Figure 24-16 shows one manufacturer's recommendations for line sizes in residential long line applications.

24.17 LONG LINE AIR CONDITIONING APPLICATIONS

Another difference between air conditioning and commercial refrigeration is the definition of a long line set. For residential air conditioning, refrigerant line lengths exceeding 80 ft or having a vertical rise of 20 ft are considered "long." A 100 ft line set would not be considered particularly long in a commercial refrigeration system. Consequences of using a long line set include:

- Additional refrigerant charge is required.
- Refrigerant migration control is needed.
- Oil return can become a problem.
- Significant system capacity losses are inevitable.
- Metering device adjustments are required.

System modifications that may be required to alleviate problems caused by a long line set include:

- Adding a liquid line solenoid at the outdoor unit. The liquid solenoid closes, preventing refrigerant flow from the condenser to the evaporator during the off cycle.
- Using a hard shutoff thermal expansion valve at the evaporator. The hard shutoff expansion valve prevents migration from the evaporator to the compressor during the off cycle.
- Adding a compressor crankcase heater. The crankcase heater is used to reduce migration to the compressor crankcase during the off cycle by keeping the oil warm.
- Adding a compressor hard start kit. The hard start kit is required to get start the compressor against the pressure difference that is created by installing the solenoid and hard shutoff expansion valve. It will also help the compressor start against the pressure created by a standing column of liquid in the liquid line.

At least one major equipment manufacturer recommends using only a $3/8$ in liquid line regardless of the length. The system subcooling will have to be high enough to offset the loss through the liquid line. Even with these modifications, the system capacity will be reduced. System capacity reduction from a long line set can be up to 17%, Figure 24-16.

24.18 COMMERCIAL REFRIGERATION PIPING PRACTICES

The refrigerant lines for commercial refrigeration systems are typically longer than the lines in air conditioning systems. Commercial refrigeration systems frequently have multiple components installed on a common piping system, something which is unusual in air conditioning systems. Underground lines are avoided in air conditioning applications, but are unavoidable in large supermarket installations. Finally, the evaporator saturation temperatures in commercial refrigeration systems are considerably lower than in air conditioning. These differences create unique challenges for commercial refrigeration piping. Oil traps, double risers, and expansion loops are all typical components of a commercial refrigeration system piping layout.

24.19 OIL TRAPS

Some manufacturers recommend oil traps on vertical risers to ensure oil return up the riser. The oil trap, often called an oil lift, is located at the bottom of a riser. The free oil droplets and oil on the side of the riser are blown upward by the velocity of the refrigerant. But the higher the oil is pushed, the slower it travels. Given enough height, some of the oil will stop moving upward begin to fall back down. The oil lift will fill with oil. The refrigerant velocity through the trap will increase due to the reduced area for the gas to flow through. This increased velocity helps the vapor entraining the oil carry it up the riser. An inverted trap should be used at the top of the line to keep the oil from draining back down once it has made it up the riser. Figure 24-17 shows how to pipe a vertical suction riser with an oil lift at the bottom and an inverted trap at the top.

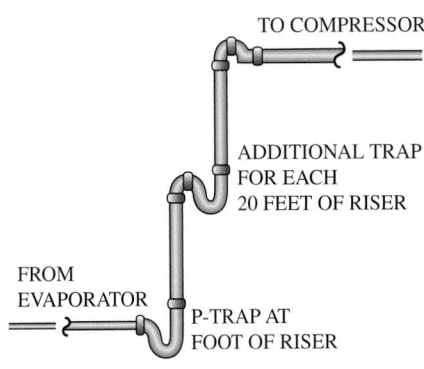

Figure 24-18 Multiple oil traps should be installed every 20 ft in high suction risers
(© 2008 Heatcraft Refrigeration Products LLC.)

Where the vertical rise is over 10 ft (3 m) on either suction or discharge lines, it is recommended that line traps be installed approximately every 20 ft so that the storage and lifting of oil can be done in smaller stages, as illustrated in Figure 24-18.

SERVICE TIP

It is important to note that not all manufacturers consider oil traps and double risers good piping practice. Instead, they stress sizing for proper velocity and leaving off the traps. They point out that the extra restriction added by the traps increases the pressure drop through the line. Always follow the manufacturer's recommendations for the particular equipment being installed.

24.20 VERTICAL RISERS IN MODULATING SYSTEMS

Riser sizes for both suction and hot gas lines are critical to permit carrying the oil upward with the force of the flowing gas. Vertical risers require a higher velocity than horizontal lines. The minimum velocity for a vertical riser is typically twice the minimum velocity of a horizontal line the same size. The increased velocity for vertical risers is often accomplished by using a smaller size for the riser than for the rest of the system. Vertical drops (flow down) will return the oil by gravity and are not critical as to size or velocity.

As system capacity reduces, so does the velocity of the refrigerant traveling through the lines. If the compressor is equipped with capacity control, the vertical riser can be sized to return the oil when the system is running at its minimum capacity. Short risers on systems with capacity control will usually be sized smaller than the remainder of the suction line, Figure 24-12. This helps keep the velocity up without adding too much pressure drop to the overall system. Although this smaller pipe has a higher pressure drop, its

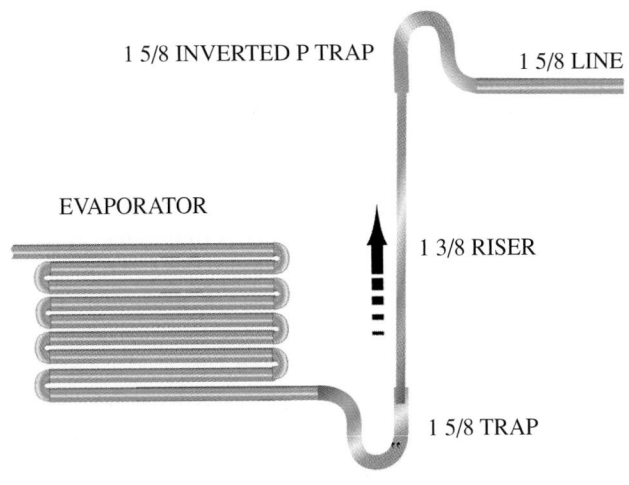

Figure 24-17 Suction risers should have an oil trap at the bottom and an inverted trap at the top

Figure 24-19 Double suction riser

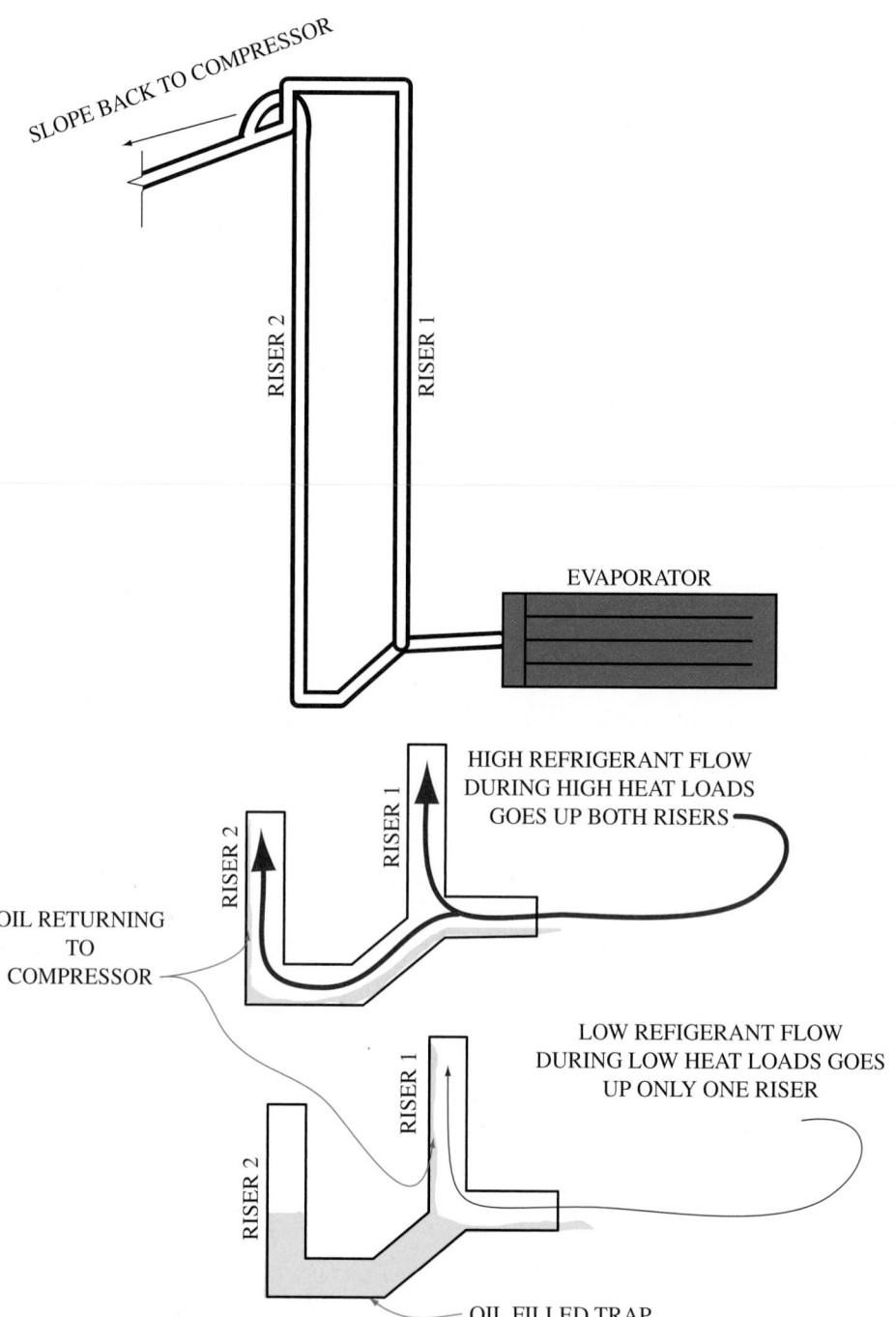

short length adds a relatively small amount to the overall suction line pressure drop.

An alternative to sizing the riser for minimum capacity is to provide a double riser in the suction line, as illustrated in Figure 24-19. If a double riser is used, additional oil is required in the system to fill the trap during periods when the overall capacity of the system is reduced, and only one riser is used. When full capacity is resumed, this extra oil can return to the compressor and overload the oil capacity of the crankcase, causing oil slugging. It is, therefore, desirable to avoid the use of double risers wherever possible.

The smaller riser should be sized for a minimum velocity of 1,000–1,500 FPM at the system's minimum capacity. The larger riser should be sized to carry the remaining system capacity at a minimum velocity of 1,000–1,500 FPM. Referring to Figure 24-19, riser 1 is used to carry the suction gas at minimum load. Riser 1 plus riser 2 are used to carry the suction gas at maximum load. The area of riser 1 plus the area of riser 2 is made equal to the area of the main suction line.

Both risers will carry refrigerant and oil when maximum cooling is required. On part load, as the amount of refrigerant being evaporated decreases, the gas velocity will also decrease to a point where it will not carry oil up through the larger riser. Oil will collect in the trap and force the refrigerant to flow up the smaller riser which is sized for the minimum system capacity, Figure 24-19. As the system load increases and more refrigerant is passed through the evaporator, this increased pressure will break the oil seal in the trap and carry oil upward through both risers.

SERVICE TIP

Small high speed compressors have relatively small crankcase capacities. If double risers with oil seals are to be utilized, it may be necessary to add an auxiliary oil receiver. Be sure the system has sufficient oil to permit proper compression lubrication at full and minimum capacities.

24.21 OFF CYCLE PROTECTION

When a remote condenser is being used and it is located higher than the compressor, the hot gas discharge line should not be piped directly up from the compressor. This makes the compressor head an oil and refrigerant trap.

Some oil is always in this line because it is being pushed along with the refrigerant vapor. A vertical riser directly from the compressor would allow oil to drain back to the compressor when it stops. Liquid refrigerant can be formed in the hot gas line in the winter. In cold weather, once the compressor cycles off, the hot gas line can be cooled to a temperature below the dew point of the refrigerant. This can result in liquid refrigerant being formed in the hot gas line. Either oil or liquid refrigerant can break valves on a reciprocating compressor on startup.

To prevent this, a discharge loop can be placed in the hot gas line with an optional check valve, Figure 24-20. Modest quantities of oil and liquid refrigerant can accumulate in this trap when the compressor shuts down and will be dissipated on startup without damage to the compressor.

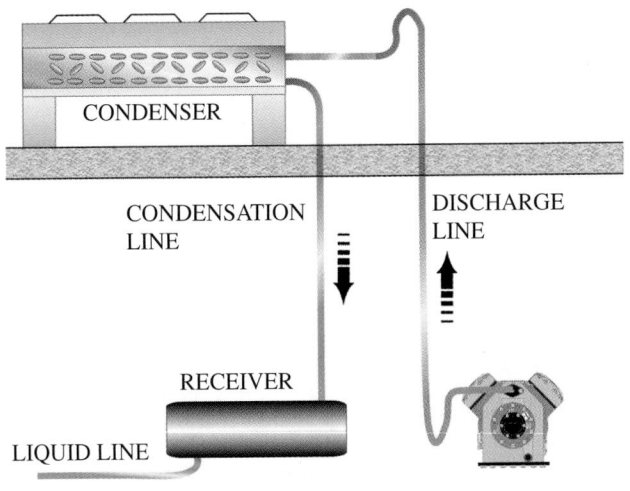

Figure 24-20 Discharge line risers should have a trap at the bottom to prevent liquid accumulation in the compressor head

Figure 24-21 This discharge check valve keeps liquid refrigerant from draining down on top of the compressor head during the off cycle

A discharge check valve is essential for systems with large quantities of refrigerant and a condenser that is located above the compressor. Figure 24-21 shows a discharge check valve on a transport refrigeration unit.

24.22 OIL RETURN IN PARALLEL COMPRESSOR SYSTEMS

Parallel compressors are often used to provide systems that can produce different levels of cooling capacity based on system need. When demand is heavy, all of the compressors will be operating; but as the load decreases, one or more of the system compressors can be cycled off.

TECH TIP

Keeping the oil level balanced between parallel compressors can be a problem. Oil level control systems are used with multiple compressors systems to ensure proper oil level in each of the compressors. If the oil level is too low, compressor lubrication can be lost and the compressor can be damaged or destroyed. If the oil level is too high, the crankshaft will be pushed through the oil. This will cause excessively high current draw, which can damage or destroy the compressor motor.

In parallel compressors one of the main problems is returning the oil back to the crankcases of each of the compressors. Without consideration for oil return and equilization, some compressors will end up with too much oil while others have too little oil. Maintaining the oil level in each compressor crankcase is important for reliable operation. The compressors should be mounted on the same level; normally they are mounted on a rack. A compressor rack is a frame constructed from structural steel, angle iron, or square tubing.

Figure 24-22 Typical oil equilibration piping for multiple compressors
(Courtesy of Bitzer US Inc.)

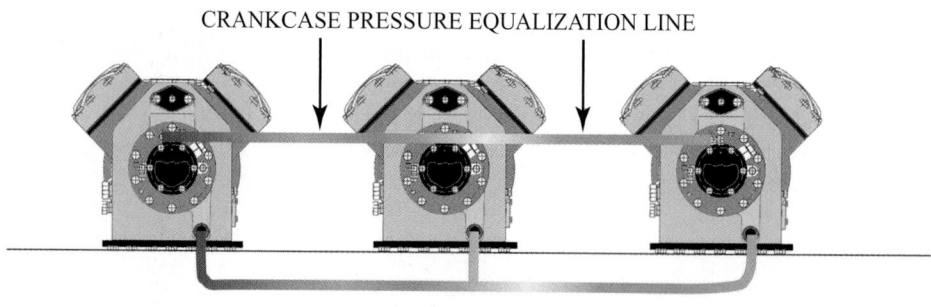

CRANKCASE PRESSURE EQUALIZATION LINE

OIL LEVEL EQUALIZATION LINE

Figure 24-22 shows an oil equalization piping system for multiple compressors. Two separate pipe systems are required to provide for oil level distribution. One pipe is connected into the bottom of the compressor. This pipe is called the oil level equalization line. Another pipe is attached to the upper portion of the compressor crankcase, and it is called the crankcase pressure equalization line. The lines are to be installed as follows:

- The crankcase oil equalization lines are screwed into the bottom ports of the crankcase. The line must be the same diameter as the bottom ports. These lines tie into a crankcase equalization manifold. The manifold should be mounted below the crankcase to prevent any vapors from entering the manifold. If vapor were to enter the manifold, it would prevent the oil from being equally distributed to the compressors' crankcases.
- The crankcase pressure equalization line is attached between the compressor and a manifold. The manifold must be higher than the top of the crankcases. This is

to prevent any liquid (oil) from entering the manifold which would also prevent equal distribution of oil to each crankcase.

There should be isolation valves on each of the equalization lines next to each compressor. This is to allow each compressor to be isolated for servicing. The manifold method is the preferred method of oil return because it can transfer oil from one crankcase to the other in case one crankcase has too much oil.

24.23 OIL LEVEL CONTROL

Oil level controls can also be used to return oil back to the compressor. Figure 24-23 shows piping for an oil control system using an oil separator and oil level controls. This is done by first piping the hot gas line to an oil separator. The outlet of the oil separator is piped to an oil receiver. In the receiver any liquid refrigerant is vaporized. It is vaporized because

Figure 24-23 Typical oil control system for multiple compressors

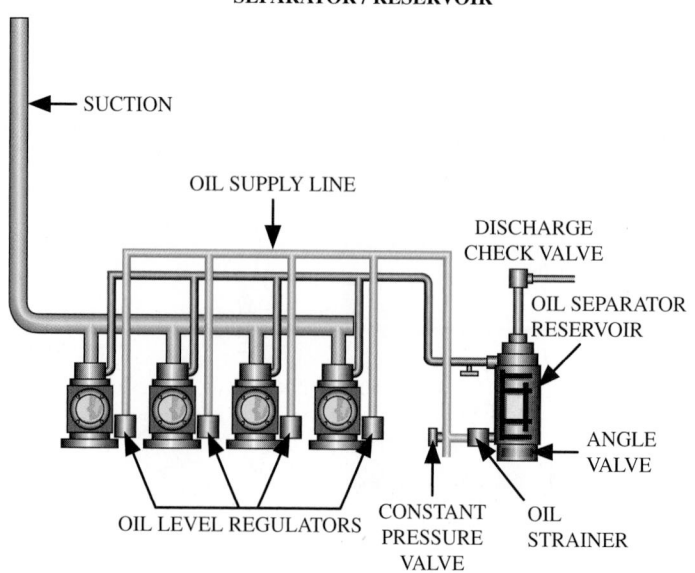

OIL SYSTEM WITH TEMPRITE
SEPARATOR / RESERVOIR

SUCTION

OIL SUPPLY LINE

DISCHARGE
CHECK VALVE

OIL SEPARATOR
RESERVOIR

ANGLE
VALVE

OIL LEVEL REGULATORS

CONSTANT
PRESSURE
VALVE

OIL
STRAINER

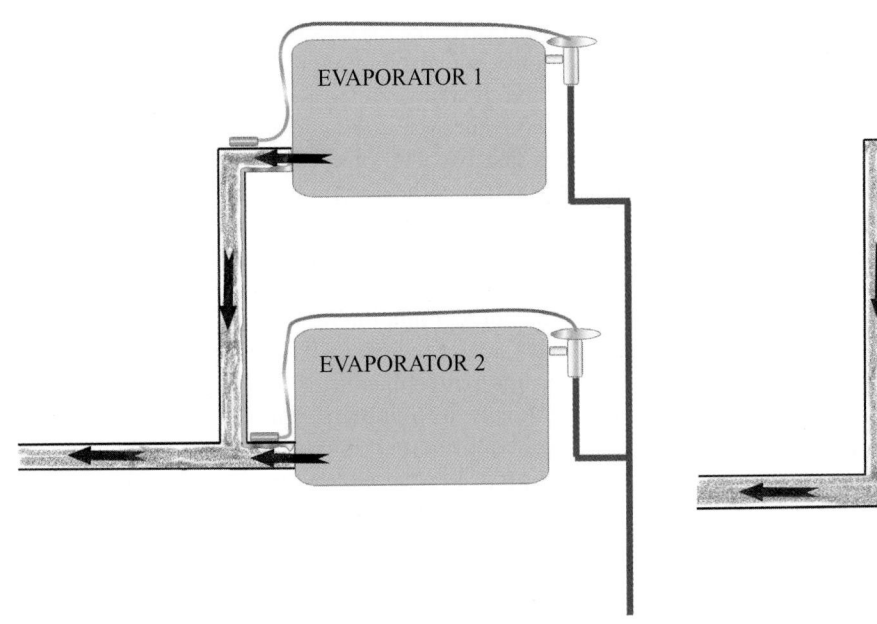

Figure 24-24 Liquid can drain from the top evaporator to the bottom evaporator with incorrectly piped evaporators

Figure 24-25 Properly piped evaporators prevent liquid from draining into the lower evaporator

there is a line connecting the receiver to the suction line. This lowers the pressure in the receiver. A pressure differential check valve maintains the pressure in the receiver to a point slightly higher than what the pressure is in the crankcase. This slightly higher pressure allows oil to flow from the receiver to the crankcase level controls. As the oil level drops in the crankcase, the level controls open and allow oil to flow into the crankcase.

This oil level control cannot lower the oil level in a compressor crankcase if the oil level becomes excessively high.

24.24 PIPING FOR MULTIPLE EVAPORATORS

Systems with multiple evaporators have a common liquid line and a common suction line. The evaporators are individually piped to these common lines. Care must be taken to ensure that flow from one evaporator does not affect the operation of other evaporators. When evaporators are stacked vertically, oil and liquid can drain out of the top evaporator into the bottom evaporator, as in Figure 24-24. This can affect the expansion valve bulb, causing the valve to throttle and starve the bottom evaporator. The suction lines should be piped as shown in Figure 24-25 so that liquid cannot drain from the top evaporator into the bottom evaporator.

Evaporator pressure regulators are required when multiple evaporators with different temperatures are piped to a common suction line. Each evaporator will have a pressure that corresponds to its saturation temperature. This means that evaporators with different pressures will all be piped into the same suction line. Evaporator pressure regulators keep the pressure in each evaporator from dropping below the correct operating pressure for that evaporator. The common suction line must be at or below the pressure of the lowest temperature evaporator. Figure 24-26 shows a multiple

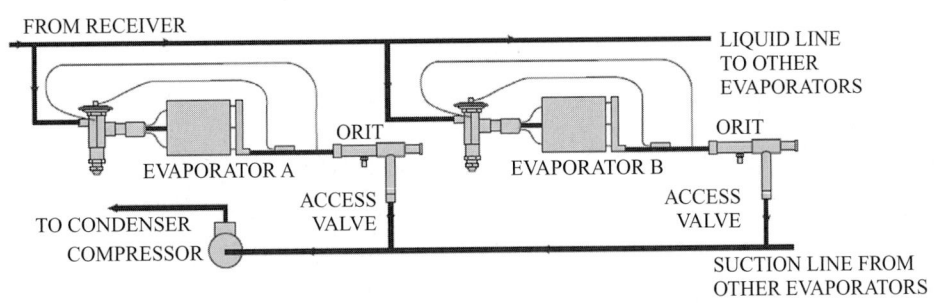

Figure 24-26 Multiple evaporators operating at different temperatures using a common suction line
(Courtesy of Sporlan Division-Parker Hannifin Corporation.)

Refrigerant Line Sizes   Capacity in Tons of Refrigeration

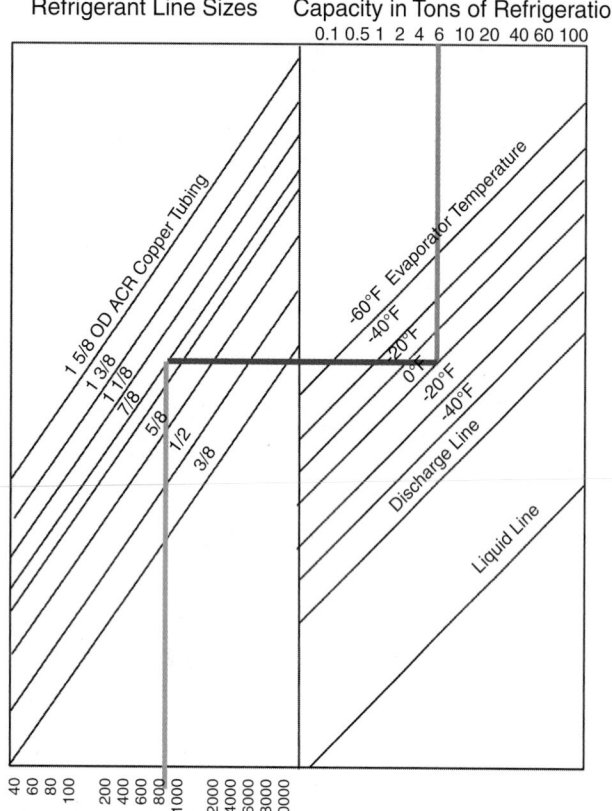

Refrigerant Velocity in feet per minute

Figure 24-27 Nomographs like this are used to determine the velocity of refrigerant through refrigeration lines

evaporator system with evaporator pressure regulators at the end of each evaporator.

24.25 COMMERCIAL REFRIGERATION LINE SIZING

Charts called nomographs are used to size refrigerant lines in commercial refrigeration and commercial air conditioning applications. Each refrigerant has two nomographs: one for pressure drop and one for velocity. Typically the line size required to meet the maximum pressure drop requirements is selected and the refrigerant velocity is checked to see that it falls between the minimum and maximum recommended velocities. The five factors needed to use a nomograph are the type of refrigerant, the length of the line in equivalent feet, the capacity of the unit, the condenser temperature, and the allowable pressure drop.

Figure 24-27 shows a simplified velocity nomograph. To use the nomograph, find the system capacity at the top right-hand side of the chart. There are diagonal lines representing different temperature suction lines, the discharge line, and finally the liquid line. Follow the vertical capacity line straight down until it intersects the diagonal line representing the pipe being sized, see the red line in Figure 24-27. On the left side of the chart are diagonal lines representing different sizes of pipe. Go horizontally across from the intersection until this line intersects the pipe size being checked, see the blue line in Figure 24-27. Drop straight down to the answer at the bottom left side of the chart, see the green line in Figure 24-27. In the case of pressure drop nomographs, this will be the pressure drop per 100 ft of pipe. In the case of the velocity nomograph, this will be the refrigerant velocity in feet per minute.

24.26 QUICK LINE SELECTION TABLES

Some commercial refrigeration equipment manufacturers publish quick refrigeration line sizing tables. These tables make assumptions about the type of refrigerant, condenser temperature, evaporator temperature, and line length. They are produced by application engineers who take the assumptions being used for a particular chart and use line sizing nomographs to determine the correct line size. These are accurate as long as the assumptions made fit your particular application. Figure 24-28 shows a typical quick sizing chart. This chart is for a system using R404a with a condensing temperature of 105°F, and evaporator temperatures ranging from –10°F up to 50°F.

Suction Line Pressure Drop for Refrigerant R 404A (Sized for 2°F saturation temperature drop)

Tons	-10° - 9°F Evap Saturation 1.9 psig pressure drop					10° - 29°F Evap Saturation 2.6 psig pressure drop					30° - 50°F Evap Saturation 3.4 psig pressure drop				
	Equivalent Length in feet														
	25	50	75	100	150	25	50	75	100	150	25	50	75	100	150
1.5	3/4	5/8	3/4	3/4	3/4	5/8	3/4	3/4	7/8	7/8	5/8	5/8	3/4	3/4	3/4
2	5/8	3/4	7/8	7/8	7/8	3/4	3/4	7/8	7/8	11/8	5/8	3/4	7/8	7/8	7/8
2.5	3/4	3/4	7/8	7/8	11/8	3/4	7/8	7/8	11/8	11/8	3/4	3/4	7/8	7/8	11/8
3	3/4	7/8	7/8	7/8	11/8	3/4	7/8	11/8	11/8	11/8	3/4	7/8	7/8	7/8	11/8
3.5	3/4	7/8	7/8	11/8	11/8	7/8	11/8	11/8	11/8	13/8	3/4	7/8	7/8	11/8	11/8
4	3/4	7/8	11/8	11/8	11/8	7/8	11/8	11/8	11/8	13/8	3/4	7/8	11/8	11/8	11/8
5	7/8	7/8	11/8	11/8	13/8	7/8	11/8	11/8	13/8	13/8	7/8	7/8	11/8	11/8	13/8
7.5	11/8	11/8	11/8	11/8	13/8	11/8	13/8	13/8	13/8	13/8	11/8	11/8	11/8	11/8	13/8

Figure 24-28 Liquid line selection using a nomograph for pressure drop

Refrigerant line type	Type of insulation	
	Thermal*	Vapor barrier
Liquid line	Sometimes on heat pumps in cold climates and on AC's in very hot attics	
Vapor line	Always	Always
Hot gas line	Sometimes on heat pumps	
Condensate line	Sometimes on rooftop installations	

*Sometimes refrigerant lines are insulated to reduce the transmission of sound from the lines to the occupied area.

Figure 24-29 Refrigerant lines and insulation

Notice that the line sizes increase in diameter as the line lengths increase.

24.27 REFRIGERANT LINE INSULATION

It is always good practice to insulate the suction line since it is usually lower in temperature than the surrounding air and can condense moisture. Insulation should be applied and thoroughly sealed with a good moisture barrier to prevent condensation on the outside of the pipe or in the insulation. On most systems, the suction line is the only line that is insulated. However, there are times when the liquid and hot gas lines need to be insulated too. The insulation needs of the piping are summarized in Figure 24-29.

All refrigerant line insulation should be closed cell to reduce the adsorption of water. Closed cell means that the material is made of millions of tiny gas pockets that are each completely sealed. This keeps the material from wicking up moisture and also allows it to act like a moisture barrier. Two types of pipe insulation are commonly used: buna-N elastomeric rubber and polyolefin. The elastomeric rubber is soft and very flexible. Its flexibility makes it difficult to cut, even with a razor knife. The polyolefin insulation is somewhat flexible, but is considerably more rigid than the rubber product. It is easier to cut, but does not conform to bends as well as the rubber product. Both are available in wall thicknesses ranging between $\frac{3}{8}$ in to $1\frac{1}{2}$; in and comp in unsplit or split form, Figure 24-30.

For new lines, the unsplit insulation is slid over the end of the tubing before the tubing is connected, Figure 24-31. This form of pipe insulation typically has a fine white powder lubricant on the inside to make it easier to apply. Try to avoid getting the powder inside the pipe while pulling the insulation over it.

The split insulation can be applied after the pipe is in place. Some has self adhesive strips to join the insulation, other types must be glued with a special cement made for the pipe insulation. In addition, the ends of the insulation should be glued together where they join.

Figure 24-30 Refrigerant line insulation is available in split and unsplit forms
(Courtesy of K-Flex USA L.L.C)

Figure 24-31 Unsplit pipe insulation is placed on the copper tubing before it is connected to the system

Suction Line Insulation

Insulation on the suction line is an absolute requirement. Suction line insulation eliminates condensation on the line and helps improve system efficiency by preventing the suction line from picking up heat from the surrounding air. Water condensing on the suction line can drip and can cause damage to ceilings, floors, furnishings, and electronics. Insulating the suction line helps keep the suction gas temperature as low as possible. Hermetic and semi-hermetic motor compressor assemblies are suction gas cooled. Lower return gas temperature is better for cooling the motor and keeping the discharge temperature down.

Heat Pump Gas Line Insulation

Some types of insulation that are acceptable for suction line insulation are not able to withstand the high temperatures of the gas line on a heat pump when it is operating in heat. Generally speaking, lines on heat pumps are usually insulated with elastomeric rubber insulation; polyolefin insulation material is not used for heat pumps. Make sure that insulation used on the large gas line of a heat pump system is rated for heat pump duty.

TECH TIP

The joints in the insulation on suction lines must be sealed. Often technicians have the misconception that the insulation is simply there to aid in system efficiency. That is only partially true. Because the refrigerant line is below the dew point, moisture can condense on the line. If the insulation vapor barrier is not sealed, water can collect around the copper and draw in through gaps and openings at the joints. The water can then run down the refrigerant line set and weep out, causing water stains and mold growth in the wall cavities. It is important that the seams of the refrigerant line insulation be sealed properly.

Liquid Line Insulation

Normally, no insulation is used on the liquid line because the liquid line is usually warmer than its surroundings. Allowing the liquid line to lose heat to the air actually improves performance by increasing subcooling. However, when the liquid line runs through a hot space such as an attic, insulation of the liquid line may be required to prevent boiling from occurring prior to the expansion valve.

Insulation on the liquid line of a computer room air conditioning system is desirable. The liquid can get quite cold in winter and lines running through humidified space to the air conditioning unit will sweat and drip if not covered.

Sometimes the liquid line can be insulated together with the suction line to promote heat exchange between the two lines for long line applications. The extra subcooling the liquid line receives from the suction line helps to prevent flash gas in the liquid line.

Hot Gas Line Insulation

In package units and condensing units with short hot gas lines between compressor and condenser, no insulation should be used on the hot gas line.

On remote condensers, insulating the hot gas line is advisable. If the unit is expected to operate in low outside temperatures, it is possible to reach the condensing temperature of the discharge refrigerant before the refrigerant reaches the condenser. This can cause liquid slugs to fall backward down the hot gas line into the superheated vapor from the compressor. Violent expansion of the slug vaporizing can cause "steam hammer," resulting in noise and vibration, even to the point of line breakage. Insulating the hot gas line would prevent this action.

When hot gas lines are run indoors in machinery rooms, they should be insulated or otherwise protected to prevent accidental burns to operating personnel.

Be sure to use an insulation that can withstand high temperatures if a hot gas line is insulated.

24.28 PIPING SUPPORTS

All piping must be properly supported, Figure 24-32. The supports must allow for the expansion and contraction of the pipe. The recommended allowance is $\frac{3}{4}$ in of movement per 100 ft of pipe. Hangers should be spaced according to the pipe size being supported. Figure 24-33 shows

Figure 24-32 Proper support for piping

OD pipe diameter (in)	5/8	7/8	1 1/8	1 3/8	1 5/8	2 1/8	2 5/8
Maximum span (ft)	5	6	7	8	9	10	11

Figure 24-33 Maximum spacing between supports for type L copper tubing

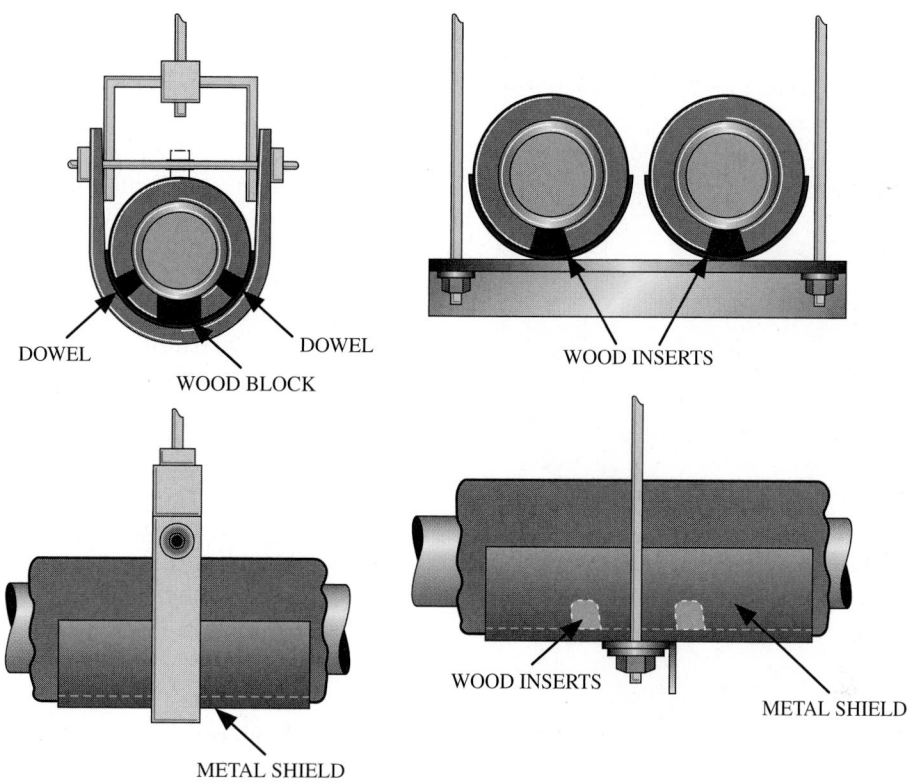

Figure 24-34 Wood pieces are inserted into the insulation to support the pipe at each pipe hanger

the recommended distances between supports for common sizes of copper pipe.

Piping should always be supported near a bend in the piping, preferably on the longest straight connection to the bend. The hanger must have sufficient width not to crush the insulation on insulated pipe. Extra rigidity must be incorporated into the insulation at the pipe clamp because the insulation will compress under the weight of the pipe. Sheet metal saddles or wood block inserts (on large piping) will serve this purpose, Figure 24-34.

24.29 VIBRATION DAMPENERS

It is usually desirable to isolate vibrating equipment to reduce noise and to prevent damage to the piping or other equipment. With soft copper tubing, loops or a coil of tubing can be connected to the moving part. For hard copper tubing a similar dampening effect can be produced by running the suction and discharge lines 15 times the pipe diameter in each of two or three directions before securing the pipe hanger. This will provide some give to the piping without undue strain. Flexible connectors at the compressor can help isolate the refrigerant piping from compressor vibrations and movement, Figure 24-35.

For larger equipment, rubber-in-sheath or spring vibration eliminator mounts and flexible piping connections can be provided for the compressor to supply the necessary isolation. Concrete inertia blocks are sometimes incorporated into the base. Piping and electrical lines must be securely anchored beyond the isolators to be effective.

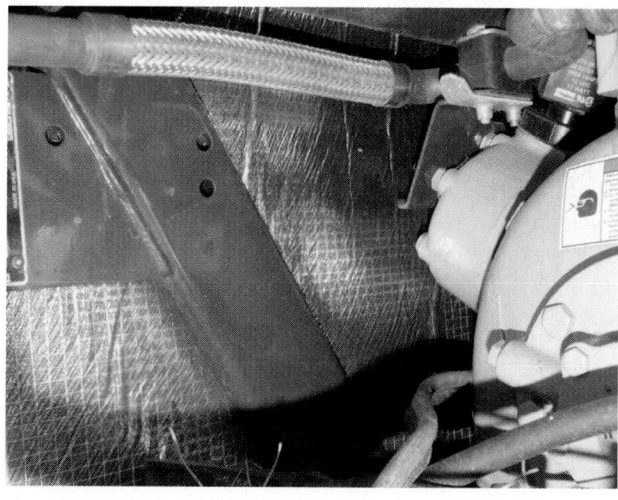

Figure 24-35 This refrigeration piping on this system is isolated from the vibration of this compressor by flexible connectors at the compressor

INTERNAL HOT GAS MUFFLER

Figure 24-36 This hermetic compressor has a built in discharge muffler to dampen discharge gas pulsations

24.30 HOT GAS MUFFLER

The pulsations from a compressor, usually a reciprocating type, can cause serious vibrations and noise in the hot gas line. This can be most noticeable where a remote air cooled condenser requires a long vertical hot gas line. Usually the larger the compressor, the more noticeable the pulsations, although this is dependent on speed and number of cylinders.

The best way to solve this problem is to install a hot gas muffler in the compressor discharge line, as shown in Figure 24-36. The hot gas muffler should be placed in a vertical position, so that it does not trap oil, as close to the compressor as possible, and securely mounted to the compressor. This usually destroys the resonance that the compressor has built up in the hot gas line. If this does not help, it may be necessary to enlarge the discharge line and relocate it, to destroy the resonance pattern.

UNIT 24—SUMMARY

The sizing of the refrigerant lines is important for many reasons. If the lines sizes are too small, the system will lose efficiency. If the line sizes are too large, the system may destroy itself due to slugging or oil starvation.

Pressure drop through the refrigerant lines kills system efficiency. The typical maximum pressure drop through any line is equivalent to a 2°F saturation temperature drop. Refrigeration vapor lines must also be sized to create a high enough velocity for the refrigerant vapor to carry the oil back to the compressor. Typical minimum horizontal line velocities are 500–750 FPM. Typical minimum riser velocities are 1,000–1,500 FPM. Minimizing pressure drop and ensuring oil return are sometimes in conflict. Larger lines minimize pressure drop, but smaller lines increase velocity to ensure oil return. Oil return should always take precedence.

Proper insulation of the various types of refrigerant lines will improve efficiency and system efficiency is critical for customer satisfaction. A properly insulated piping system can also eliminate operational problems. Piping support is necessary to eliminate potential problems including undesirable vibration. Vibration can cause both noise complaints and pipe failures.

WORK ORDERS

Service Ticket 2401

Customer Complaint: Compressor Keeps Cutting Out on the Low Oil Safety

System Type: Low Temperature Walk-in

You arrive at the small butcher shop to find the walk-in warm and the compressor off on oil safety. In talking to the owner you learn that the compressor is on top of the walk-in and the condenser is located on the roof. You also learn that the box had been set to hold the temperature at 40°F up until last month when it was converted to a low temperature walk-in with a 0°F setting.

When you inspect the walk-in and compressor you see that the last technician had made all of the necessary changes and additions to the compressor and evaporator including adding a defrost control.

Knowing that the compressor oil had to be in the system, you suspect that the evaporator is oil logged. You start the compressor and note that the oil level quickly rises in the compressor oil sight glass. After a few minutes the oil level is stable at $\frac{1}{2}$ the oil sight glass. The system has the correct amount of oil.

When you examined the new evaporator you noted that the tech used the original piping. A quick check of the evaporator and compressor technical specification indicates that the low temperature application has resulted in a lower refrigerant velocity in the suction line. You have determined that the refrigerant line is too large. The flow in the suction line is below 500 FPM.

Because the compressor is only a short distance above the evaporator, you can easily change the suction line with a smaller line to increase the velocity.

Once you have replaced the suction line the walk-in runs properly.

Service Ticket 2402

Customer Complaint: Poor Cooling

System Type: Residential Split System in Third Story Apartment, Condenser on Ground

A customer complains that their air conditioning system cannot cool the apartment on a hot day. They note that their neighbor two stories below has the same size apartment and the same type of unit, and it never has a problem. The lines run up three stories to get from the condenser on the ground to the evaporator in the attic.

The technician notices that even though the system has a vertical rise of 30 ft, the system has not been modified for a long line application. The technician changes the fixed restriction metering device to a hard shutoff expansion valve, adds a liquid line solenoid at the condenser, adds a hard start kit, and charges the unit until the subcooling is high enough to overcome the pressure drop from the high vertical lift.

The system cools better, but it still must run longer than the downstairs neighbor's unit because of the added heat load of the upstairs apartment and the reduction in system capacity even after the modifications.

Service Ticket 2403

Customer Complaint: Multiple Compressor Failures

System Type: Residential Split System on Ground Level with Lines Run Underground

A technician is asked to look at a system that has experienced multiple compressor failures. The house has a concrete slab floor and an exposed beam vaulted ceiling. The air conditioner blower coil sits in the middle of the house and the refrigerant lines run under the slab for about half of the length of the house. The compressor failures are always mechanical.

The technician decides that the compressors are probably dying from liquid slugs due to the long line set run underground. However, there is no alternate path for the lines due to the house construction. The technician suggests treating the system like a long line application and also adding a suction accumulator to protect the new compressor. The additions of a liquid line solenoid at the condenser and a hard shut off valve on the evaporator reduce the migration during the off cycle. The accumulator keeps the occasional slug from reaching the compressor. A hard start kit is also added to help the compressor start against pressure. Two years after the modifications the new compressor is still operating without incident.

Service Ticket 2404

Customer Complaint: Higher Than Expected Power Bills

System Type: New High Efficiency Residential Split System Changeout

A customer has just purchased a new 2 ton 16 SEER high efficiency air conditioner to replace their 25-year-old system. To the customer's surprise, it costs about the same to operate as the old unit. The installing contractor changed both the indoor and outdoor sections, but used the existing line set. The original line set had a $\frac{1}{4}$ in liquid line and a $\frac{5}{8}$ in suction line. The technician notices that the new system has line stub-outs for a $\frac{3}{8}$ in liquid line and a $\frac{7}{8}$ in suction line. The installers used sweat reducers to connect the system up to the old line set. The technician checks the manufacturer's literature, and it specifies a $\frac{3}{8}$ in liquid line and a $\frac{7}{8}$ in suction line. The technician notices that the liquid line is warm leaving the condenser and cool before it enters the evaporator. The technician explains that the small size of the old line set is causing enough pressure drop to create flash gas in the liquid line and reduce the system capacity, which causes it to run longer. The system operates correctly after replacing the old lines with the correct size liquid and suction lines.

UNIT 24—REVIEW QUESTIONS

1. What are the two major functions of refrigerant piping?
2. What effect does oil have on a system's coils?
3. What problems are caused by oversized suction lines?
4. What problems are caused by undersized suction lines?
5. What can be done to prevent refrigerant from being drained or migrating back to the compressor during the off cycle?
6. Why is it important to keep the oil level balanced between parallel compressors?
7. What is liquid slugging?
8. How is the maximum pressure drop for a suction line determined?
9. Which piping pressure drop has the greatest effect on the compressor's compression ratio?
10. What are some differences between piping practices for air conditioning systems and piping practices for commercial refrigeration systems?
11. Why are suction risers sized differently for systems with capacity control than for systems without capacity control?
12. Why are oil lifts needed in tall vertical refrigerant risers?
13. What is the most common range for minimum velocities in a horizontal line carrying refrigerant vapor?
14. What is the most common range for minimum velocities in a riser carrying refrigerant vapor?
15. Why is refrigerant oil flow through the liquid line not a problem?

16. What two factors affect the hot gas line size?

17. What are the two common reasons the suction line is insulated?

18. Why may the liquid line need to be insulated?

19. Why might the hot gas line need to be insulated?

20. How can flash gas be spotted in a liquid line?

21. What would be the pressure drop due to the weight of refrigerant in a 30 ft tall liquid line containing R-410A refrigerant at 100°F?

22. If the condenser pressure of the above system is 300 psig, how much subcooling will be required to offset the pressure drop created by the vertical lift?

23. According to Figure 24-36, what would be the recommended support spacing for $2\frac{1}{8}$ type L copper pipe?

24. Use Figure 24-30 to determine the refrigerant velocity through a $\frac{7}{8}$ in suction line on a walk-in cooler with a capacity of 2 tons, an evaporator saturation temperature of 20°F, and a condenser saturation temperature of 100°F.

25. Use Figure 24-13 to determine the total equivalent length of a 50 ft section of $1\frac{3}{8}$ in line with four 90° elbows and one angle valve.

26. An engineer wishes to select a suction line that will have a maximum pressure drop that is equivalent to a 2°F saturation temperature drop. What would the pressure drop be for an R-134a system operating with a 0°F saturation temperature?

27. What pressure drop should the engineer use on the nomograph if the equivalent length for the suction line in the above system is 75 ft?

28. What is considered a long line application for residential air conditioning?

29. List the system modifications that need to be made for a long line residential air conditioning application.

30. What is the minimum recommended velocity for a $2\frac{5}{8}$ in suction riser in a low temperature system using R-22?

UNIT 25

Accessing Sealed Refrigeration Systems

OBJECTIVES

After completing this unit you will be able to:

- describe the different types of refrigeration service valves.
- explain the operation of gauge manifold valves.
- explain how to properly install and remove a gauge manifold set on manual service valves.
- explain the operation of split system installation valves.
- explain how to properly install and remove a gauge manifold set on Schrader valves.
- describe how to gain access to systems without service valves.

25.1 INTRODUCTION

One of the last things a service technician should do when troubleshooting a system is attach a set of gauges to the system. Each time a sealed system is accessed there is a chance that some contaminants can be introduced to the system, or refrigerant can be lost. However, there are times when a refrigeration system's operating conditions cannot be accurately assessed without accessing the system's refrigerant piping to determine the pressures. Knowing the temperature difference across the coils, the amperage, and the airflow all give the technician vital information; but sometimes without the system operating pressures a final determination of a problem cannot be accurately made.

It is important to attach and remove a gauge manifold set properly. Understanding how to properly manipulate system access valves and install gauge manifolds is vital to the personal safety of the service technician. Improper technique can damage the system or injure the technician. Proper techniques should always be practiced so that they become a habit performed the same way each time.

SAFETY TIP

The proper personal protective equipment, PPE, for installing refrigeration gauges and manipulating valves includes safety glasses and gloves. When liquid refrigerant escapes into the atmosphere it boils at extremely cold temperatures. Liquid refrigerant sprayed in the eyes can cause blindness, sprayed on the skin can cause frostbite.

25.2 FACTORY INSTALLED SERVICE VALVES

With the implementation of the Clean Air Act, all manufacturers are required to install factory-installed service valves on Type II and Type III equipment. Type I equipment is only required to have a process stub. Commercial refrigeration and air conditioning systems have had factory-installed service valves for years.

SERVICE TIP

You must put service valve caps back on all access ports. This is an EPA refrigerant management requirement. Failure to do so is a violation of EPA rules and regulations. Many service access valve caps have O-rings to seal the system. Be sure these O-rings are in place before installing the cap to ensure a proper seal. Caps that have a metal-to-metal seal must be tightened one-eighth turn with a wrench after they have been finger tightened.

Factory installed service valves may be a manually operated stem shut-off valve, as in Figure 25-1, or a Schrader type valve. Schrader valves are spring-loaded valves similar to the valves used on car tires. They have a core that threads down

Figure 25-1 Manual two-way service valve

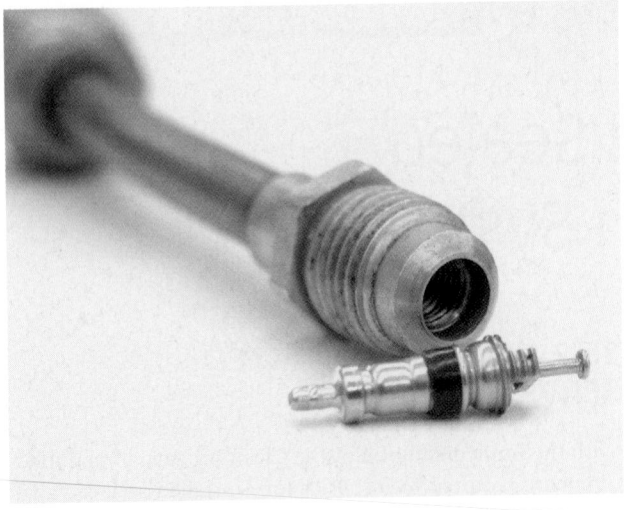

Figure 25-2 Schrader valve and core

Figure 25-3 Schrader valves should always have their cap on when not in use

into them, Figure 25-2. Refrigerant is allowed to flow into and out of the valve when the core is depressed. To prevent leaks, Schrader valves should always have their valve caps on when not in use, Figure 25-3.

Residential split system equipment service valves are usually located on the suction line and liquid line, Figure 25-4. The valve on the suction line is used to read the low side system pressure and the valve on the liquid line is used to read the high side system pressure. Most air conditioning systems use front-seating split system shut-off valves, as shown in Figure 25-5(b). These valves are used to hold the system refrigerant in during shipping. The gauges connect to the Schrader valve that is built into them. These valves are normally opened when the unit is installed, and then seldom used after that. It is not necessary to turn them to read pressure because the Schrader valve in them reads line pressure regardless of the valve position.

SAFETY TIP

A few residential split systems use manual stem valves as shown in Figure 25-5(a). The gauge connection on these valves is not a Schrader valve. These valves must be opened to read pressure. More importantly, they must be closed before removing the gauges.

On heat pump systems, both lines are on the high side during the heating cycle. To allow technicians to read low side pressures in heat, heat pump systems use a third valve that is always connected to the low side of the system regardless of the cycle, Figure 25-6. Residential packaged units typically have a low side and high side Schrader valve mounted on the outside of the equipment, Figure 25-7.

Commercial refrigeration systems typically have three manual stem service valves. A suction service valve and a discharge service valve are located on the compressor. A service valve called the king valve is mounted on the outlet of the receiver. These service valves are equipped with a gauge service port. Operating refrigerant pressures may be observed on the service gauge manifold when hoses are connected to these ports and the valves are cracked open.

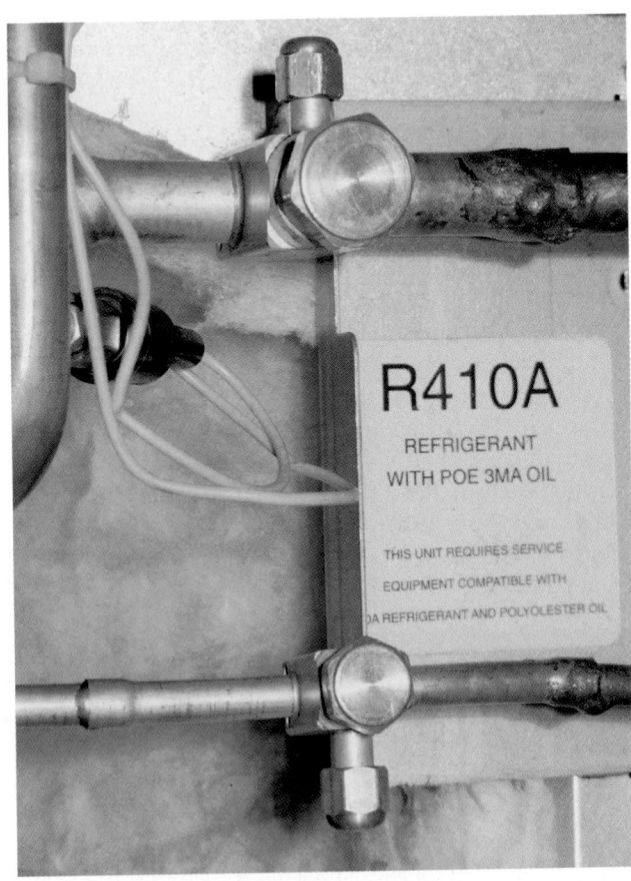

Figure 25-4 Residential split system installation valves

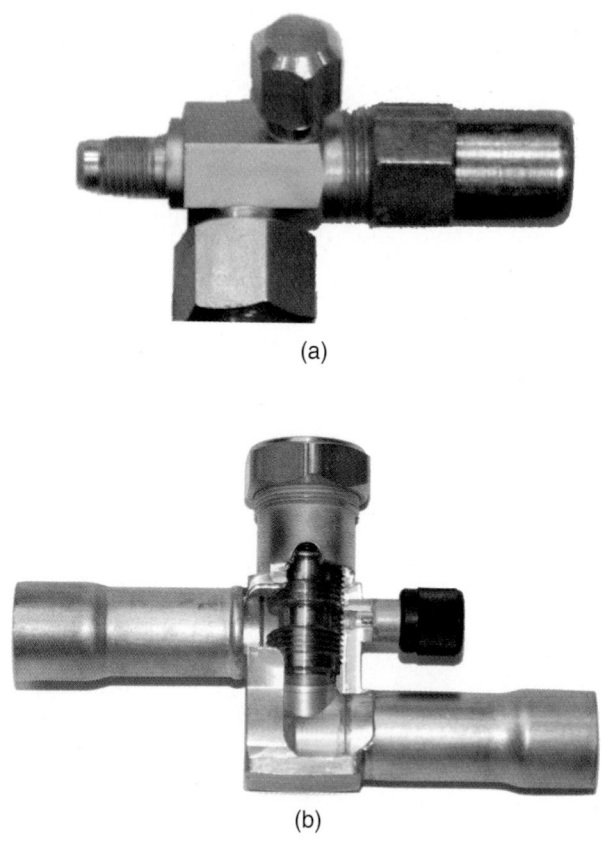

(a)

(b)

Figure 25-5 Service valves
(b Courtesy Rheem Manufacturing)

Figure 25-6 The arrow points to the port that is always on the low side of the system regardless of the operating cycle

25.3 MANUAL STEM SERVICE VALVES

Manual service valves have three ports and two seats. The three ports include a middle port that connects to the compressor or system, a line port that connects to the refrigerant line, and a service port that is used for servicing the system, Figure 25-8. The refrigerant has two paths it can take through the valve. It can flow between the middle port to the line port, the middle port to the service port, or between all ports. There is not a closed position on these valves because one of the two exit ports will always be open. Instead, the terms back seated and front seated are used to describe the valve positions.

The valve is back seated when the stem is turned all the way out counterclockwise. This position is called back seated because the valve is seated on the back port of the valve. In this position the service port is closed but the middle port is open to the line port, Figure 25-9. Service valves should always be placed in the back seated position before installing or removing gauges.

The valve is front seated when the stem is turned all the way in clockwise. This position is called front seated because the valve is seated on the front port of the valve. In this position the line port is closed but the middle port

is open to the service port, Figure 25-10. The front seat position can be used to isolate refrigeration system components.

SAFETY TIP

Be sure that internal pressure in the compressor is relieved by recovery and vacuum procedures before attempting to remove an isolated compressor from the system. Pressure remains in the compressor even after the service valves are front seated.

If the stem is positioned anywhere in between the back seat and front seat positions, all three ports will be open. Turning the valve one-half turn off of a fully seated position is called cracking the valve. When checking pressures, the valves are usually in the back seat cracked position, Figure 25-11.

The stems on manual service valves should only be turned with a valve stem wrench, Figure 25-12. The corners of the valve stems round off easily when they are turned with adjustable wrenches or pliers. Once a stem is rounded it cannot be turned with the correct wrench, Figure 25-13.

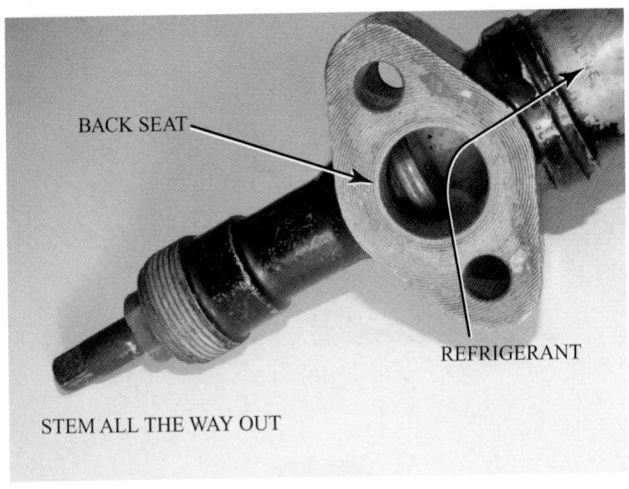

Figure 25-9 Two-way service valve in the back-seated position

Figure 25-7 High side and low side Schrader valves on a packaged unit

The cap for the valve stem and the cap for the service port should always be replaced after using manual service valves.

25.4 SCHRADER VALVES

Schrader valves provide a convenient method of checking system pressures or servicing the system where it is not economical or convenient to use manual stem service valves. The

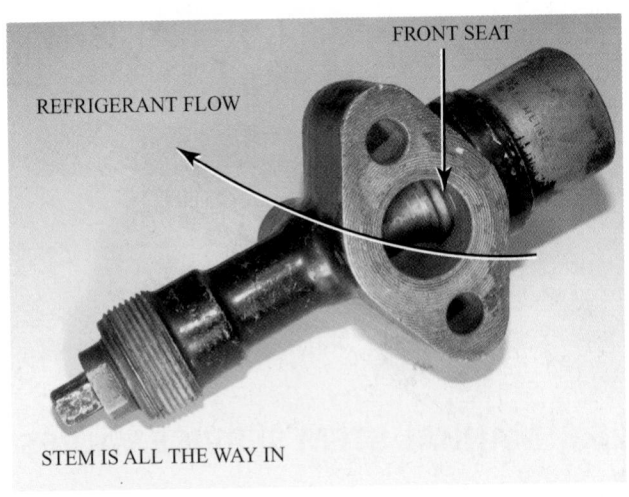

Figure 25-10 Two-way service valve in the front-seated position

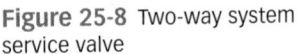

Figure 25-8 Two-way system service valve

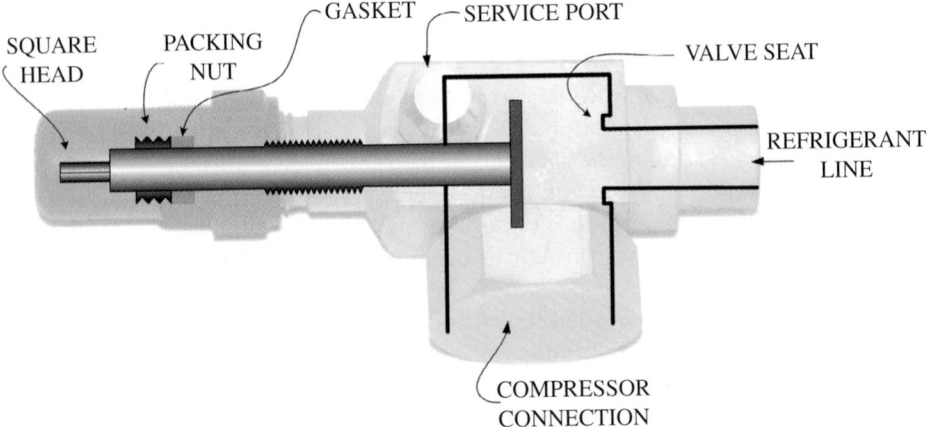

Figure 25-11 When a two-way service valve is cracked, the valve is just off of the seat, creating a small opening, or crack

Figure 25-12 Square stem service valve and valve wrench

Figure 25-13 This valve stem has been ruined by a careless technician using the wrong tool

Schrader valve core, shown in Figure 25-14, is a spring loaded device for positive seating. The valve is like those used on automobile tires, but the cores used in refrigeration valves are not the same as the cores used in car tires. The rubber used in tire valves is not compatible with refrigerants and would dissolve if used on a refrigeration system.

The stem must be depressed to force the valve seat open against spring pressure. Refrigerant hoses with built in core depressors must be used with Schrader valves. When a hose with a core depressor is connected to a Schrader valve, the valve core is pushed in and the valve opens, Figure 25-15. Ideally, the seal in the gauge hose will seat just as the depressor is pushed in and very little refrigerant will escape. Flow through a Schrader valve is limited because the core takes up most of the space in the center of the valve. This leaves only a small passage for refrigerant to go through, Figure 25-16.

If a valve core leaks, it can be replaced by using a core-removal tool to unscrew it. Some tools, such as the one in Figure 25-17, allow this to be done while the system is under pressure. All Schrader valves should have a leak-proof cap on them when not in use. The cap can prevent refrigerant loss even if the valve core does leak.

Figure 25-14 Schrader valve core

Figure 25-15 The core depressor on the refrigerant hose pushes in the Schrader valve core when the hose is connected

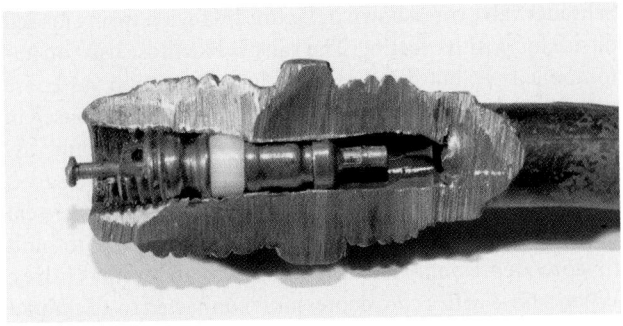

Figure 25-16 This cutaway shows how a Schrader valve works

Figure 25-18 The condensing unit is shipped with the valve closed to hold in the system refrigerant

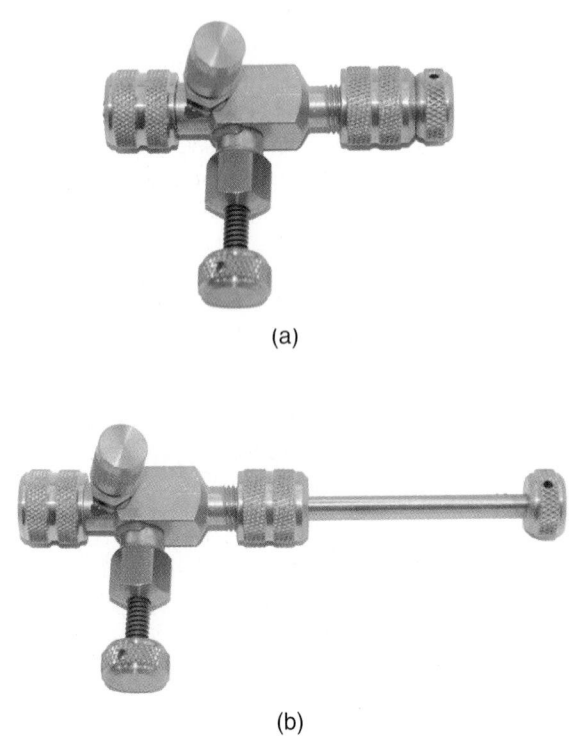

(a)

(b)

Figure 25-17 This tool can be used to change the core in a Schrader valve without losing the refrigerant in the system

service port is always open to the line port regardless of the position of the valve.

These valves are used primarily for holding the system charge during shipping. The systems are shipped with the valve run all the way down clockwise, Figure 25-18. After connecting the refrigerant lines and indoor coil, the system is evacuated through the service port. The valve is turned counterclockwise to open it and allow the trapped refrigerant to flow throughout the system. Typically the valve is never used again because it does not control refrigerant flow to the service port.

SAFETY TIP

Be careful when opening split system installation valves. The only thing that keeps the plug in the valve is a small lock-ring at the top of the valve. Stop turning when the valve plug approaches the lock-ring. The valve does not need to be tightened in the counterclockwise, or upposition. Overtightening the valve can cause the lock-ring to pop out and the plug will fly out under system pressure, with all the system refrigerant behind it.

25.5 SPLIT SYSTEM INSTALLATION VALVES

Most new residential split systems come equipped with unit installation valves, as shown previously in Figure 25-4. These valves are used to hold the refrigerant charge in the outdoor unit while it is shipped. These valves have three ports: the port to the unit, the line port, and the Schrader valve service port. Even though they have three ports, they do not behave like standard manual service valves. No ports are closed in the back seat position; the Schrader valve

25.6 GAUGE MANIFOLD SET

Technicians use the gauge manifold to diagnose trouble in refrigeration systems. Gauges allow the operator to watch both gauges simultaneously during evacuation or charging operations, and save time on almost any work that must be done on the system. The most common gauge manifold test sets contains two shut-off valves, three external connections, and two pressure gauges. The gauges and the flexible hoses that connect to the manifold to connect it to the system are color coded; blue is the low side of the system, red is the high side. The left-hand gauge is called a compound or suction pressure gauge. The right-hand gauge is called the high pressure or discharge pressure gauge. The hoses have $\frac{1}{4}$-inside diameter and are designed to seal on a $\frac{1}{4}$-inch male flare end. Typically one end is straight and connects to the manifold and the other end is angled to allow easier connection to service valves.

More advanced gauge manifolds are available that have four hose connections and four shut-off valves, Figure 25-19. Besides the low side and high side connections, there are two center connections, each with its own shut-off valve. Typically one of the middle connections allows the use of a $\frac{3}{8}$-inch hose for faster evacuation.

The most advanced gauge manifolds use digital gauges rather than analog bourdon tube gauges, Figure 25-20. These provide more accurate pressure measurement, built in saturation temperature charts for several refrigerants, and system analysis.

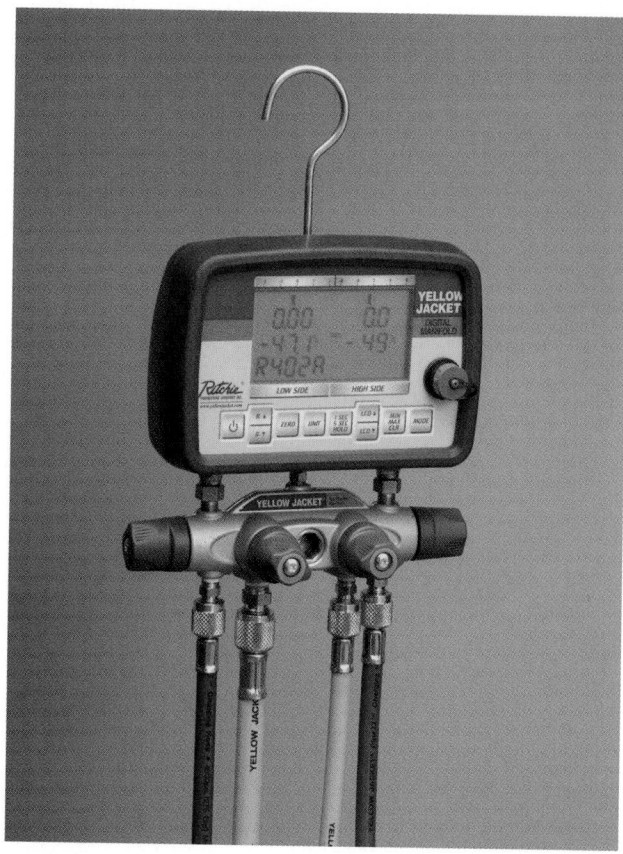

Figure 25-20 Digital manifold gauge set
(Courtesy of Ritchie Engineering Company, Inc.—Yellow Jacket® Products)

All gauge manifold sets are test instruments and should be handled carefully.

- Never drop or abuse the gauge manifold.
- Keep ports or charging lines capped when not in use.
- Never use any fluid other than clean oil and refrigerant.

SAFETY TIP

There are two major groupings of gauge manifold sets. One group is designed to be used with R-12, R-22, R-134A, R-408, R-407, and R-404. The other groups of gauge manifold sets are designed to be used with R-410A only. Do not use gauges designed for the lower pressured refrigerants on the very high pressure R-410A system.

25.7 REFRIGERATION GAUGES

Mechanical gauges require a physical device to translate pressure changes into movement that can be used to move a dial. Three types of devices are used in mechanical gauges: diaphragm, bellows, and Bourdon tube. Diaphragm gauges are generally used for lower pressures within a

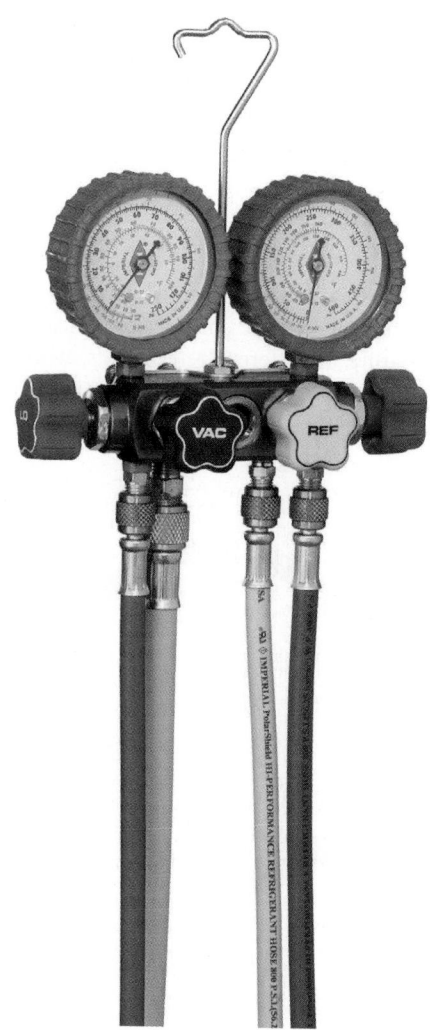

Figure 25-19 Four valve manifold gauge set
(Courtesy Imperial)

Figure 25-21 Example of a bellows style refrigeration gauge
(Courtesy of REFCO Manufacturing Ltd.)

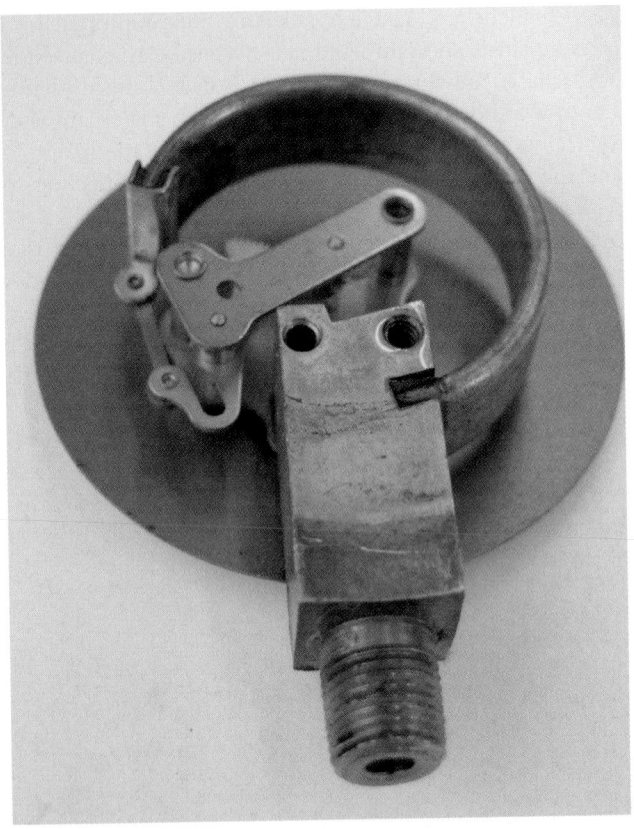

Figure 25-22 Bourdon tube

limited range and are usually not used in refrigeration. Bellows gauges are used in refrigeration gauges, but they are not as common as Bourdon tube gauges. The bellows expand with an increase in pressure and contract with a decrease in pressure. Figure 25-21 shows a bellows gauge used in refrigeration.

Most refrigeration gauges use a Bourdon tube as the operating element. The Bourdon tube is a flattened metal tube which is sealed at one end, curved and soldered to the gauge fitting at the other end, Figure 25-22. Figure 25-23 illustrates how a Bourdon tube operates. The blue shaded section shows the tube at rest at atmospheric pressure. A rise in pressure inside the tube tends to make the Bourdon tube mechanism straighten. The position the Bourdon tube will move to when pressure is applied is shown in Figure 25-23 in the dotted outline. This movement will pull on the link, which will turn the gear sector counterclockwise. The pointer shaft will move clockwise to move the needle. On a decrease in pressure, the Bourdon tube moves clockwise toward its original position and the pointer moves counterclockwise to indicate a decrease in pressure.

Pressure Gauges

The high pressure gauge has a single continuous scale. Gauge sets made for refrigerants such as R-134a and R-22 are usually calibrated (marked off) to read 0 to 500 psi. Figure 25-24 shows a high pressure gauge. The scale is usually

marked in 5 lb increments. On most gauges the outer scale is the pressure scale and the inner scales indicate the saturation temperature of different refrigerants at the indicated pressure. For example, if the gauge pointer indicated 200 psi

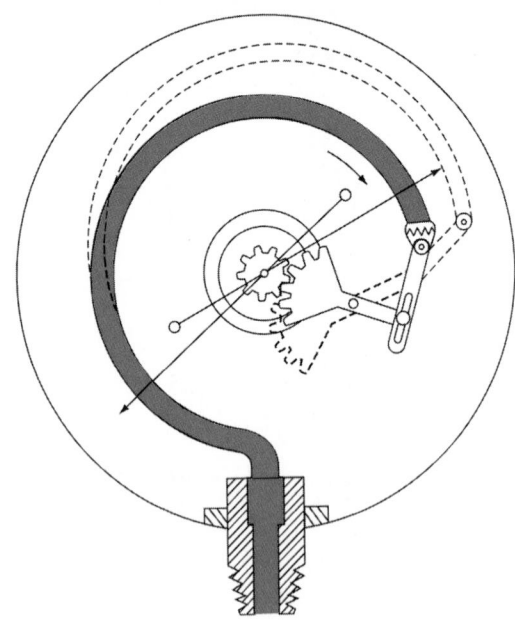

Figure 25-23 The dashed line shows how the Bourdon tube responds to a pressure increase

Figure 25-24 High side pressure gauge for most common refrigerants except R-410a
(Courtesy of Yellow Jacket Division, Ritchie Engineering Company)

pressure for R-22, the saturation temperature of the refrigerant would be approximately 101°F.

Pressure gauges made for R-410a have a higher pressure range because of the higher pressures of R-410 systems. R-410a pressure gauges can typically read pressures up to 800 psig. On an R-410a pressure gauge, each mark on the pressure scale represents 10 psig pressure. Figure 25-25 shows a high pressure gauge for R410a systems.

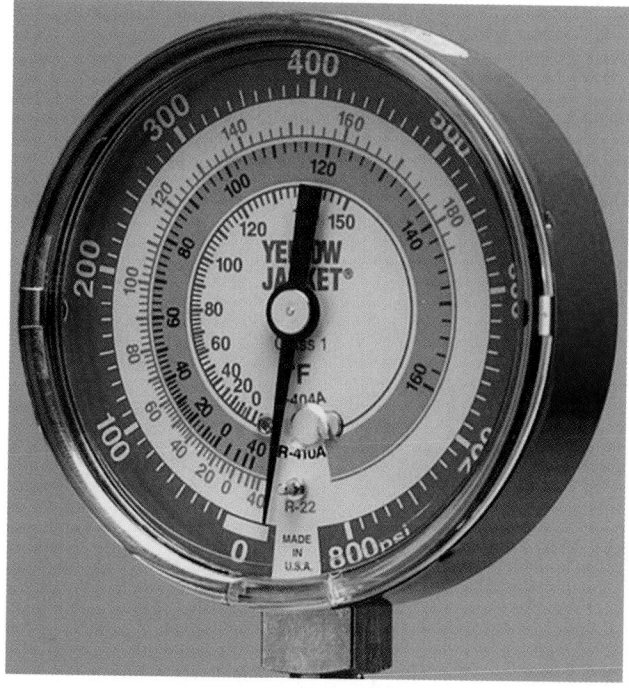

Figure 25-25 High side pressure gauge for R-410a
(Courtesy of Ritchie Engineering Company, Inc.—Yellow Jacket® Products)

Compound Gauges

The low side gauge is a compound gauge that measures both pressure and vacuum, Figure 25-26. Gauge sets made for refrigerants such as R-134a and R-22 are usually calibrated from 0 to 30 in of mercury vacuum and from 0 to 120 psig pressure. On a typical compound gauge each mark on the vacuum scale represents 2 in Hg vacuum and each mark on the pressure scale represents 1 psig pressure.

It is common for the standing pressure on the low side of a system to exceed the normal range of the compound gauge. The retard range protects the gauges from damage when a pressure above their normal range of operation is connected to them. Gauges for R-134a and R-22 typically have a retard range of up to 350 psig.

Compound gauges made for R-410a have a higher pressure range because of the higher operating pressures of R-410a systems. R-410a gauges can typically read pressures up to 350 psig and have a retard range up to 500 psig. On an R-410a compound gauge, each mark on the pressure scale represents 5 psig pressure. Each mark on the vacuum scale represents 5 in Hg vacuum. On the gauge shown in Figure 25-27, each mark on the vacuum scale represents 10 in Hg vacuum.

Like the high pressure gauge, the compound gauge also has scales calibrated to read saturation temperatures of various refrigerants such as R-134a, R-22, and R-410A. With these scales it is not necessary to refer to pressure-temperature tables or curves to calculate pressure-temperature relationships. Figure 25-27 shows a compound gauge for an R-410A system.

Gauge Accuracy

Gauges are classified by their percentage accuracy. Class 1 gauges are accurate to ± 1% of the reading throughout their range. This means that 100 psig can read anywhere between

Figure 25-26 Compound gauge for most common refrigerants except R-410a
(Courtesy of Yellow Jacket Division, Ritchie Engineering Company)

Figure 25-27 Compound gauge for R-410a
(Courtesy of Ritchie Engineering Company, Inc.—Yellow Jacket® Products)

Class 3-2-3 gauges are accurate to 3% for the first third of their scale, 2% for the middle third, and 3% for the final third of their scale.

Gauge Size

Gauges are available in different sizes. The most common sizes are $2\frac{1}{2}$", $3\frac{1}{8}$", and 4" in diameter. Figure 25-28 shows all three common sizes of gauges. Larger gauges are easier to read than smaller gauges. Their larger circumference allows for more accurate increments making them more accurate as well. This is especially important for gauges that are used over a wider range of pressure, like gauges designed for use with R-410a.

SERVICE TIP

Refrigeration gauges have a small adjustment screw that allows the gauge to be zeroed. The gauge is adjusted to zero with the hoses open to atmospheric pressure. However, it is possible for a gauge to zero out but not read other pressures accurately. From time to time the technician should attach the gauges to a new cylinder of refrigerant at a known temperature and compare the pressure reading to the temperature-pressure chart so that the gauge can be checked for accuracy. Gauges that are zeroed and are still inaccurate should be replaced.

99 and 101. Class 1 gauges are the most accurate mechanical gauges used in refrigeration. Class 1.6 and class 2 gauges are accurate to 1.6% and 2%, respectively. Class 2-3-2 gauges are accurate to 2% for the first third of their scale, 3% for the middle third, and 2% for the final third of their scale.

25.8 GAUGE MANIFOLD VALVES

The valves on a gauge manifold are used to control the flow of refrigerant from either side of the manifold to the center. Figure 25-29 shows a cutaway view of a gauge manifold. It is

Figure 25-28 Comparison of $2\frac{1}{2}$ in, $3\frac{1}{8}$ in, and 4 in mechanical gauges
(Courtesy of Ritchie Engineering Company, Inc.—Yellow Jacket® Products)

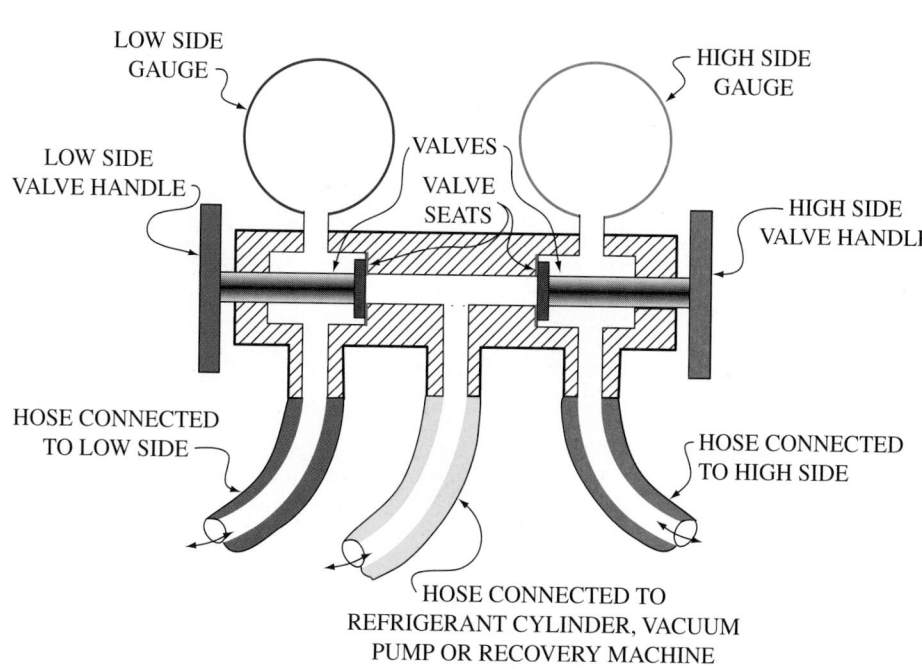

Figure 25-29 Cutaway of a gauge manifold

LOW SIDE GAUGE

HIGH SIDE GAUGE

VALVES

VALVE SEATS

LOW SIDE VALVE HANDLE

HIGH SIDE VALVE HANDLE

HOSE CONNECTED TO LOW SIDE

HOSE CONNECTED TO HIGH SIDE

HOSE CONNECTED TO REFRIGERANT CYLINDER, VACUUM PUMP OR RECOVERY MACHINE

not necessary to open the valves on the gauge set to read pressure. The parts above and below each valve are interconnected so the gauges will read pressure at all times when connected to the system. The valves open or close the path from each side to the middle port. When both valves are closed (front seated) the center or utility port is isolated, Figure 25-30(a).

Slightly opening a valve is called cracking the valve. Cracking open the low side valve connects the low side and

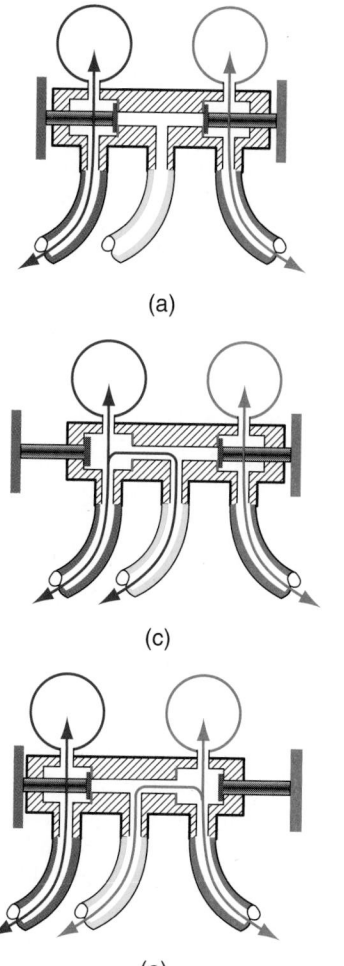
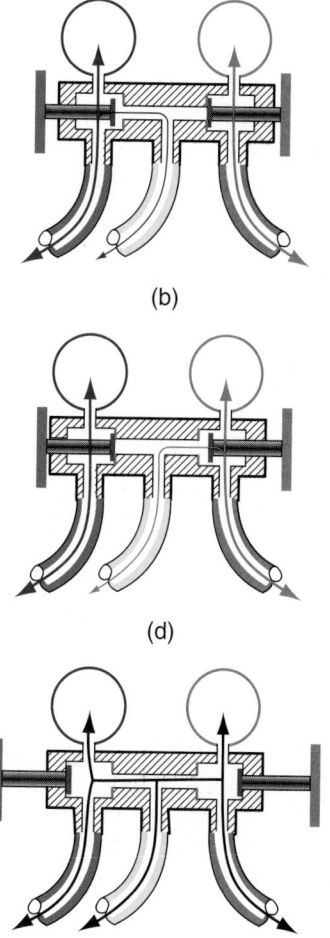

Figure 25-30 Gauge manifold valve positions

(a)

(b)

(c)

(d)

(e)

(f)

center hoses, Figure 25-30(b). Some refrigerant can now flow from the center hose to the system. Fully opening the low side valve opens the low side port to the center port for full flow or refrigerant or for evacuating the system, Figure 25-30(c).

With the low side valve closed, cracking open the high side valve will allow some refrigerant to flow from the high side to the center hose, Figure 25-30(d). Fully opening the high side valve opens the high side port to the center port to remove refrigerant from the system or for system evacuation, Figure 25-30(e).

Opening both the low and high side valves opens both the low and high side ports to the center port. This valve position is used for system evacuation, Figure 25-30(f).

25.9 REFRIGERATION HOSES

The refrigeration hoses are an important part of a gauge manifold set. They are what actually connects the gauges to the system. Charging and vacuum hoses are available in sizes of $\frac{1}{4}$", $\frac{3}{8}$", $\frac{1}{2}$", and $\frac{5}{8}$" inside diameter. The most common size is $\frac{1}{4}$". Refrigeration hoses are available in many colors, Figure 25-31. Many gauge sets use hoses that are color coded to the gauges: red for the high side, blue for the low side, and yellow for the center hose. Many four-port gauge manifolds have a $\frac{3}{8}$" port for vacuum and come equipped with a $\frac{3}{8}$" hose. Typical charging hoses have a straight end that connects to the manifold and an angled end that connects to the system. The angled end contains the core depressor for Schrader valves, Figure 25-32.

Refrigeration hoses are not simply a single tube; they are built in layers. Figure 25-33 illustrates the construction of a refrigeration hose. The rubber seen on the outside simply provides physical protection for the inner layers. The woven fabric layer just under the outer rubber layer provides strength. Some refrigeration hoses have two more inner layers, while others have only a single inner layer. The innermost layer actually contains the refrigerant. Hoses with two inner layers have extra permeation protection.

Hoses designed for use with refrigerants that operate at lower pressures than R-410a typically have a working pressure of 500 psig and a minimum burst pressure of 2,500 psig. Hoses designed for use with R-410a typically have a working pressure of 800 psig and a minimum burst pressure of 4,000 psig.

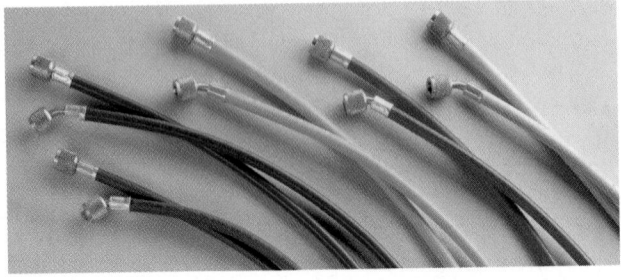

Figure 25-31 Refrigeration hoses are available in many colors
(Courtesy of Ritchie Engineering Company, Inc.—Yellow Jacket® Products)

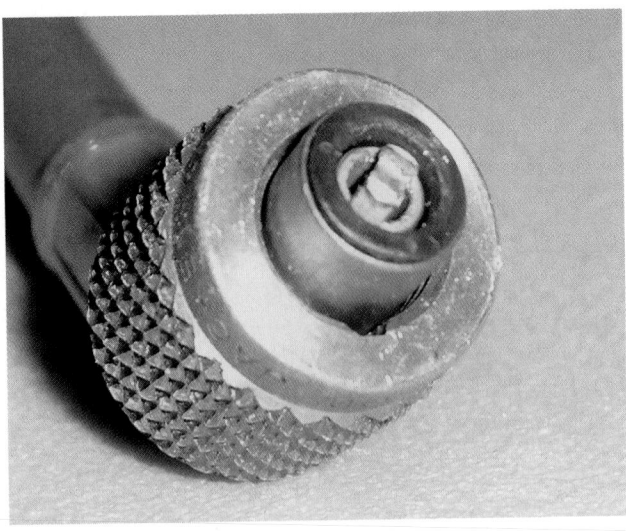

Figure 25-32 The angled end contains a core depressor for Schrader valves

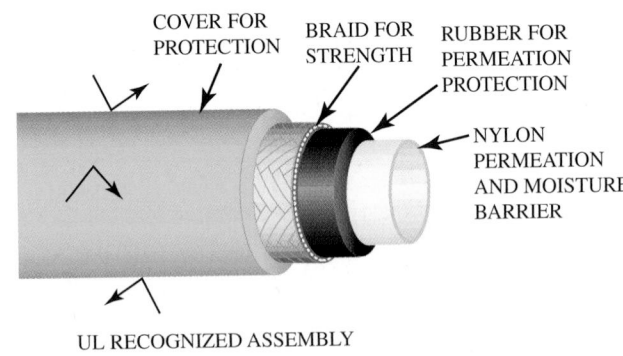

COVER FOR PROTECTION   BRAID FOR STRENGTH   RUBBER FOR PERMEATION PROTECTION

NYLON PERMEATION AND MOISTURE BARRIER

UL RECOGNIZED ASSEMBLY

Figure 25-33 Diagram of refrigeration hose construction
(Courtesy of Ritchie Engineering Company, Inc.—Yellow Jacket® Products)

25.10 CONNECTING A GAUGE MANIFOLD SET ON MANUAL SERVICE VALVES

Locate the suction service valve. It is usually located on the compressor where the suction line attaches. Check to make sure the service valve stem is back seated. This will ensure that no pressure is currently applied to the gauge port of the service valve. Remove the gauge port flare cap and attach the hose connected to the compound side of your gauges to the gauge port. Locate the discharge service valve. It is also located on the compressor, but it is the valve connected to the smaller discharge line leaving the compressor. Check to be sure the valve stem is back seated. Remove the gauge port cap and attach the hose connected to the high side of the manifold to the gauge access port on the discharge service valve.

The gauge manifolds and connecting lines should be purged to avoid system contamination from air and moisture.

To purge a unit that does not operate in a vacuum, crack both the suction and discharge service valves. Open the gauge manifold valves one at a time and bleed refrigerant out the middle line until all the air is out. This usually just takes a few seconds. This will purge the gauge manifold and the connecting lines. Many technicians simply loosen the hoses at the manifold connections and purge each hose. However, this does not purge the manifold or middle line.

SAFETY TIP

Contact with the gases being purged should be avoided. Oil and liquid refrigerant will sometimes escape during the purging process. Liquid refrigerant can cause frostbite.

The high side is used to purge both sides of the manifold on systems whose low side is likely to be in a vacuum. To purge from the high side only, connect the lines as before, but crack only the high side service valve. Open the low side and high side manifold valves at the same time and loosen the hose connection at the low side service valve. This will purge everything but the middle hose. It can then be purged separately by loosening the middle hose at the plug connection. This procedure will work on any system with manual service valves, but is only necessary when the low side is likely to be in a vacuum.

Some technicians purge the hoses and gauges from a separate refrigerant tank. This has the advantage of not losing any of the system charge. It has the disadvantage of requiring a drum of refrigerant even if you are just checking the pressures. To use this method, connect your gauges as before; except, connect the middle leg to the refrigerant drum. Do not open the service valves. Crack the tank valve and open both manifold valves. Loosen the refrigerant hoses at both the suction and discharge service valves and purge each individually. After both hoses are purged, close the valve on the refrigerant cylinder and close the manifold valves.

25.11 REMOVING A GAUGE MANIFOLD SET FROM MANUAL SERVICE VALVES

The simplest way to remove the gauge set is to back seat both the service valves. This should prevent any further escape of refrigerant into the gauges. There is still a considerable amount of refrigerant in the gauges and hoses that needs to be carefully released. Generally it is easier to release the refrigerant through the middle leg. Disconnect the middle hose at the plug connection and direct it into an empty can or other safe area. Slowly open each manifold valve, one at a time, until all the refrigerant has been released from the gauges.

There is a way to remove the gauges and avoid losing quite as much refrigerant. Leave the unit running. Instead of back seating both service valves, back seat only the discharge

service valve. Crack open both manifold valves. This will allow the high pressure gas in the discharge side of the manifold to pass into the low side of the refrigeration system. The pressure on the gauges will then be equal to the low side operating pressure. This is the lowest pressure any part of the system will ever have on it. After the pressures in the gauge manifold have come down to the operating low side pressure, back seat the suction service valve. The pressure trapped in the gauges can now be bled off through the middle hose; however, now the trapped pressure is significantly lower.

SAFETY TIP

If an error or equipment failure causes an unexpected release of refrigerant, keep your hands and body out of the refrigerant spray. Do not try to replace a hose or valve cap on a valve that has refrigerant escaping. Liquid R-410a is approximately –60°F at atmospheric pressure. It does not take long to get a nasty frostbite burn at that temperature.

25.12 CONNECTING A GAUGE MANIFOLD SET TO SCHRADER VALVES

Schrader valves automatically open when a hose with a core depressor is connected to them. The service technician normally does not have control over when the valve opens and closes. When hoses are connected the valve opens; when hoses are removed the valve closes. Frequently the valve will open before the seal is made and release refrigerant. If the Schrader valve is on the liquid line, the liquid that comes out will be extremely cold as it flashes off at atmospheric pressure. Occasionally the hose will seat before the core is depressed, and no pressure will be read. Some manufacturers' hoses have adjustable core depressors that can help either of these situations, Figure 25-34.

One way of minimizing the risk to the technician is to install the gauges on the Schrader valves with the system off. This reduces the pressures available at the high side valve when the hose is connected and reduces the chance of liquid refrigerant escaping. Connecting with the system off also makes purging the gauges easier. The gauges may be purged by opening the valves one at a time and releasing the air through the center hose.

Tools are available that give the technician more control over the valve. With control over when the valves open and close, gauges may be safely connected to Schrader valves with the unit in operation. A valve core removal tool like the one shown in Figure 25-17 allows gauges to be connected before opening the valve. Then the tool is used to remove the core, opening the system to the gauges. This also has the advantage of improving flow through the valve. This type of core removal tool can be used to change a Schrader valve core without recovering the system refrigerant.

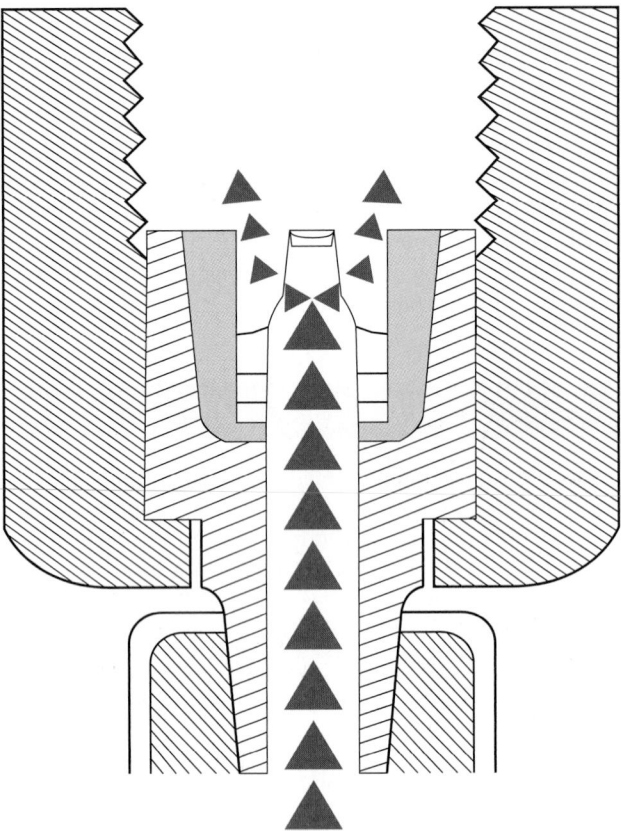

Figure 25-34 Adjustable core depressor
(Courtesy of Ritchie Engineering Company, Inc.—Yellow Jacket® Products)

A simpler tool, the thumbscrew core depressor, also allows the connection of gauges before the valve is opened, Figure 25-35. Turning in the thumbscrew depresses the valve core and opens the valve. This process is reversed to remove the gauges. The thumbscrew is turned out, allowing the valve to close. After the valve is closed, the gauges are removed.

25.13 REMOVING A GAUGE MANIFOLD SET FROM SCHRADER VALVES

When a hose is disconnected from a Schrader valve, the refrigerant that is trapped in the hose and gauges comes back out. This can be a surprising amount of refrigerant when the high side is connected to the liquid line. Positive shut-off hoses can drastically reduce the amount of refrigerant released when the gauges are disconnected. Positive shut-off devices include check valves on the end of refrigerant hoses, manually operated ball valves on the ends of hoses, and adapters that can be used with standard hoses. Available adapters include check valves, mechanisms like the quick couplings used on air hoses, and ball valves, Figure 25-36.

The check valves built into the end of a hose keep refrigerant from flowing backward out of the hose, Figure 25-37. Refrigerant will be trapped in the hoses after the gauges have been disconnected using a positive shut-off valve. Most of the trapped refrigerant can be put back in the system if the proper removal procedure is followed.

Using a positive shut-off hose, disconnect the high side with the unit still operating. Now crack both the gauge manifold valves to allow the trapped high pressure refrigerant into the low side. Last, disconnect the low side with the unit still operating. The remaining amount of refrigerant in the hoses can be safely and legally vented. Note that the gauges must be purged when they are connected, or part of what is going back into the system will be air and contaminants.

Three simple steps will reduce your exposure to refrigerant spray if positive shut-off hoses or adapters are not used. First, wear gloves and safety glasses. It is always a good idea to wear gloves and safety glasses when handling refrigerant, but

Figure 25-35 Thumbscrew core depressor valve
(Courtesy of Ritchie Engineering Company, Inc.—Yellow Jacket® Products)

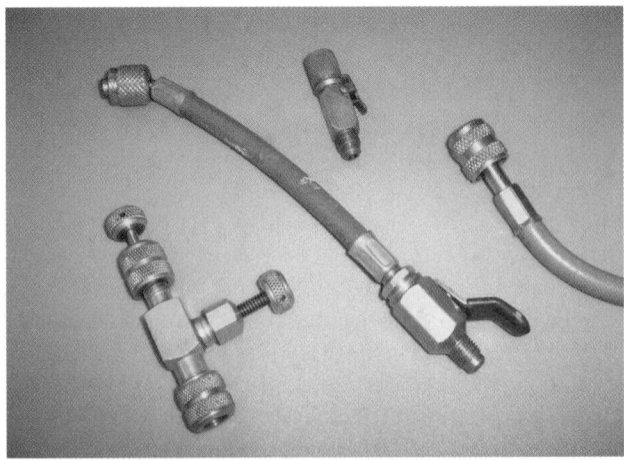

Figure 25-36 Positive shut-off adapters make connecting to Schrader valves easier

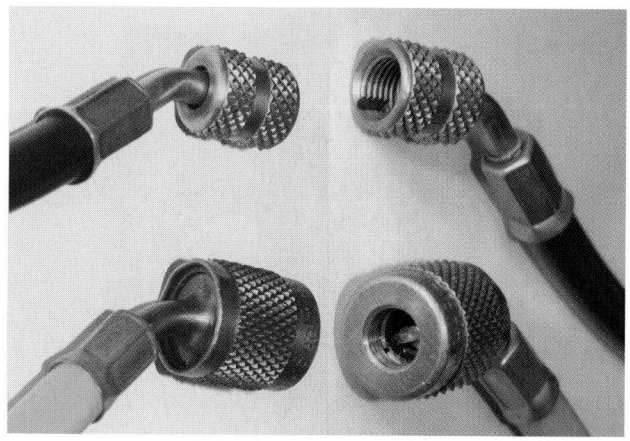

Figure 25-37 The hoses at the top of the picture have a standard Schrader core depressors. The hoses on the bottom of the picture have automatic check valves built in that keep the refrigerant in the hose from coming back out when the hose is removed

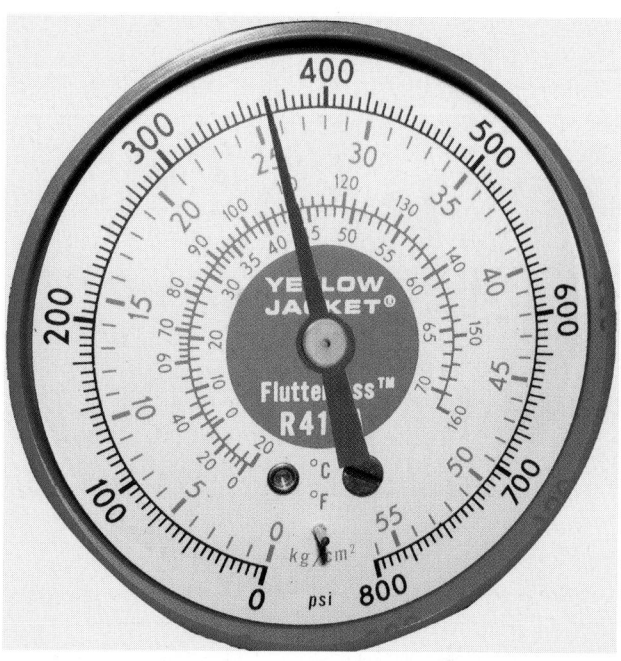

Figure 25-39 This gauge is reading 365 psig with a saturation temperature of 110°F for R-410a

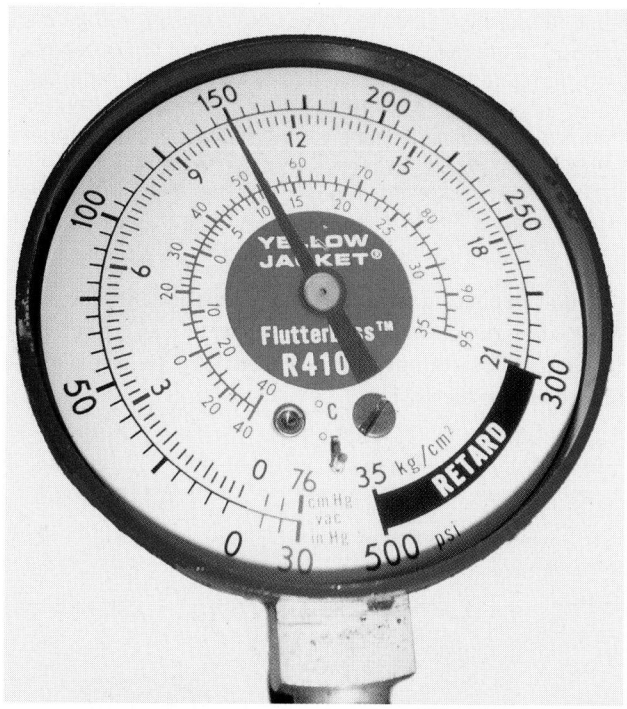

Figure 25-38 This gauge is reading 150 psig with a saturation temperature of 53°F for R-410a

it is especially important when using Schrader valves. Disconnect the low side with the system operating because the low side pressure is lower with the unit on. Turn the system off and let the system sit for several minutes before disconnecting the high side, because the high side pressure is lower with the unit off.

25.14 READING REFRIGERANT SATURATION TEMPERATURES

Refrigeration gauges not only read system pressure, they also show the refrigerant saturation temperature of common refrigerants. The saturation temperature of a refrigerant may be determined by observing the colored scale for that particular refrigerant. The gauge in Figure 25-38 is showing 150 psig for an R-410A system. The needle also points toward its corresponding saturation temperature, 53°F. The high pressure gauge shown in Figure 25-39 indicates a pressure of 365 psig and a corresponding temperature for R-410A of 110°F.

25.15 ACCESSING SEALED SYSTEMS

Most small appliances like refrigerators or window units do not have any valves installed at the factory. Instead, the systems are evacuated and charged at the factory through process tubes. A process tube, or process stub, is a copper tube connected to the system for the sole purpose of evacuating and charging the unit at the factory. The process tubes can be on the compressor or on one of the system lines, Figure 25-40. After the system is evacuated and charged at the factory, the process tube is pinched off and brazed shut.

The only way to gain access to these refrigeration systems is to use a valve that pierces a hole in the tubing. It is better to avoid entering a sealed system unless it is absolutely necessary because poking a hole in a sealed system can create problems. The technician could literally be installing a

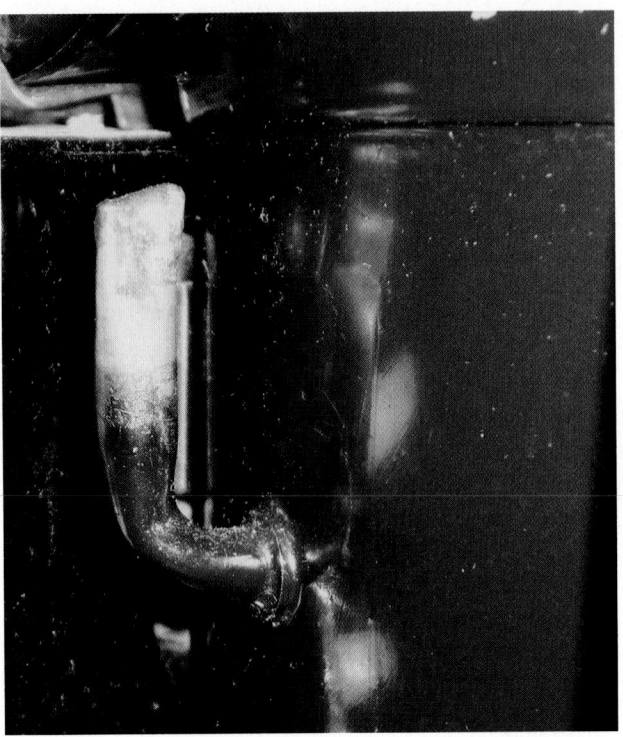

Figure 25-40 Process tube on hermetic compressor

leak. Small systems sometimes only hold a few ounces and putting gauges on them can remove enough refrigerant to make the system undercharged. It is definitely not a good idea to install piercing valves on small sealed systems just to perform a routine check. However, when the refrigeration system must be accessed, a piercing valve or piercing pliers are required.

SAFETY TIP

You must wear eye protection and gloves any time you access a refrigeration system. Liquid refrigerant accidentally released from a pressurized system can be at an extremely low temperature that can cause blindness and skin burns. Never position your face or head in a direct line with an access port as you are attaching or removing hoses.

25.16 PIERCING VALVES

One of the easiest devices available for sealed system access is the saddle piercing valve, or tap-a-line. These piercing valves are clamped to the tubing, sealed by a bushing gasket, and then they pierce the tube with a tapered needle. Most contain some sort of shut-off control. The technician should keep in mind that these valves should be used to gain temporary access to a hermetically sealed system for checking system operating pressures or for pressurizing for leak testing. The piercing valve

Figure 25-41 Bolt on piercing valve

shown in Figure 25-41 allows quick access to system pressures to immediately start diagnosing the refrigeration problem.

SAFETY TIP

Before brazing a Schrader valve onto a existing refrigerant line, all of the refrigerant in the system must be recovered. Any refrigerant that is allowed to enter the torch flame will produce a noxious gas. Breathing this gas can be dangerous, and could even cause lung damage. Remove the Schrader core before brazing to keep it from becoming damaged.

Bolt on piercing valves are bolted on the line, then the piercing needle is run down to pierce the copper tubing, Figure 25-42. Refrigerant flows through the hole pierced by the needle to the service port on the valve.

Figure 25-42 The needle pierces the copper tubing to gain access to the refrigeration system

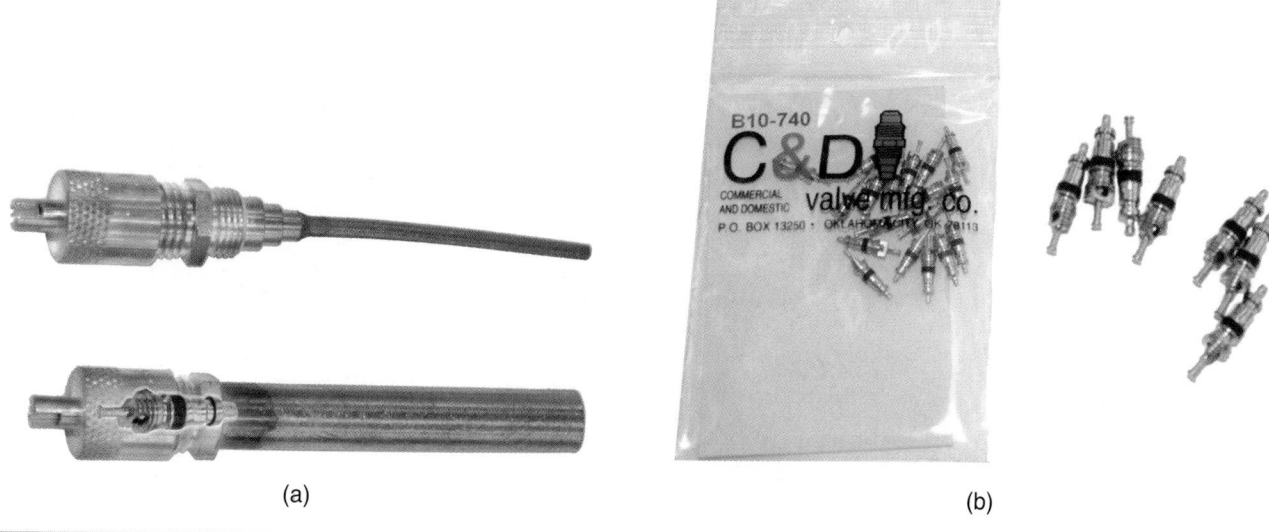

Figure 25-43 (a) Pigtail-type Schrader valve; (b) Schrader valve replacement cores

Bolt on piercing valves should be removed once the source of the sealed system malfunction has been located. The only way to do this is to recover the refrigerant from the system through the piecing valve. After the refrigerant has been recovered, a permanent valve may be brazed on. One way to do this is to install the piercing valve on a process tube. After the refrigerant is recovered, the process tube can be cut and a permanent valve brazed onto the process tube. Figure 25-43 shows Schrader valves made for field application.

Braze-on piercing valves are available, such as the one in Figure 25-44. They function like a Schrader valve after the tubing is pierced. Braze-on piercing valves can be used for initial access and left on the system. One safety concern with braze-on piercing valves is that they are brazed on while the system is still under pressure. Brazing on a system with pressure still in it is generally considered unsafe. If the tubing is overheated, it can rupture, allowing refrigerant and oil under pressure to blast out unexpectedly. The oil spray can ignite and create a flame thrower effect.

Another tool for accessing sealed systems is a set of piercing pliers, Figure 25-45. These can pierce the tubing and allow temporary access for system diagnosis and refrigerant recovery. Since the pliers obviously must be removed, they can only be used if the technician plans to recover the system refrigerant.

After piercing the system and recovering the refrigerant, a Schrader valve can be installed. Schrader valves are available for field installation in a variety of forms as seen in Figure 25-43. The core should be removed from the valve before brazing to avoid melting the plastic seals.

Figure 25-44 Steps in installing a braze-on piercing valve. Braze-on piercing valves can be used as both a means of gaining access to a sealed system as well as a permanent valve.

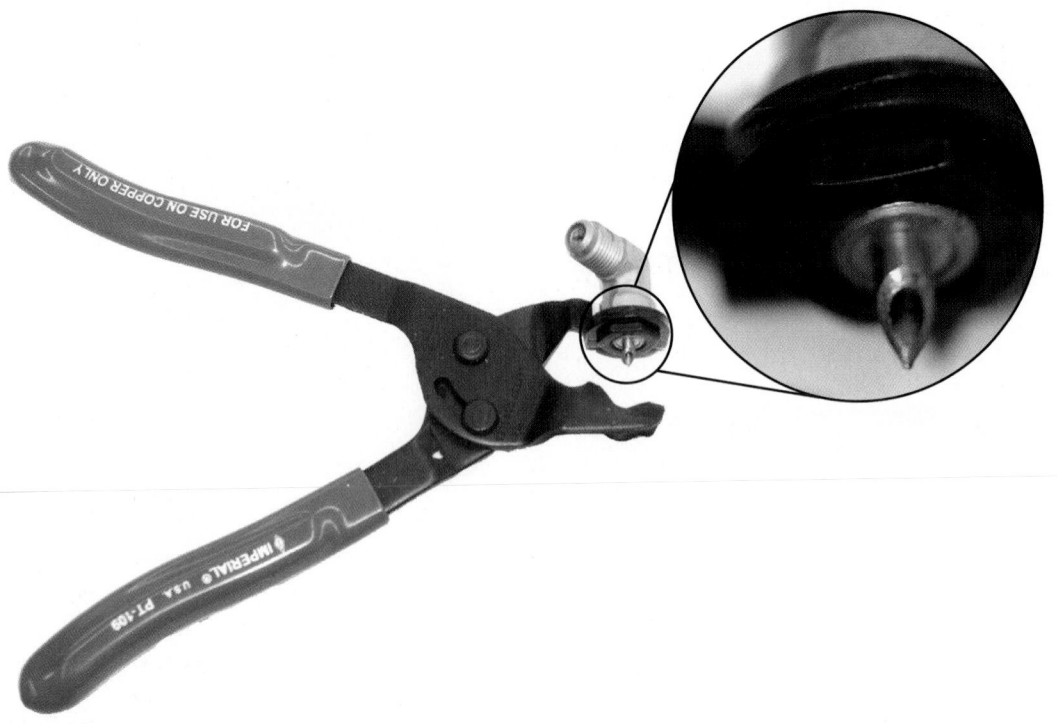

Figure 25-45 These piercing pliers can be used to gain access to sealed systems

UNIT 25—SUMMARY

Service valves are used to gain access to the refrigeration system. Type II and Type III systems all have service valves installed at the factory, Type I systems have process tubes. Commercial refrigeration systems typically use manual stem service valves on the suction and discharge sides of the compressor and on the liquid receiver. The normal operating position of a manual stem service valve is back seated. In the back seated position the service port is closed. System pressures can be read in the back seat cracked position. In the back seat cracked position, the valve is turned one-half turn off of the back seated position. Schrader valves are similar to the valves on car tires. They are found on most residential air conditioning systems. Schrader valves automatically open when a hose with a core depressor is connected and close when the close is removed.

Type I systems must be accessed using piercing valves. Bolt-on piercing valves should be used for system diagnosis and refrigerant recovery, but should not be left on the system. Braze-on piercing valves can be used for access and may be left on the system. Care should be taken when installing a braze-on piercing valve because of the inherent danger of brazing on a system under pressure.

Gauge manifolds are used to read system pressure. They consist of a compound gauge to read low side pressures, a high pressure gauge to read high side pressure, a manifold and valves to control refrigerant flow through the gauges, and hoses to connect to the system. Gauges are available in a high pressure range suitable for R-410a, and in a lower pressure range suitable for everything else. Positive shut-off hoses or adapters help technicians control the flow of refrigerant in and out of the gauges, especially when using Schrader valves. The saturation temperature of common refrigerants can be read on the gauges by looking at the colored scales.

WORK ORDERS

Service Ticket 2501

Customer Complaint: Air Conditioner Freezes Up

Equipment: Packaged Terminal Air Conditioner (PTAC) Using R-22 Refrigerant

A service technician for the Rest Easy Motel chain is asked to look at a PTAC in one of the rooms because it cools poorly and freezes over. Like most PTACs, this one has no service valves of any kind. The technician knows that the two most common causes of air conditioning evaporators freezing over are poor airflow and refrigerant undercharge. The technician decides to check the airflow first. The air filter is missing and the evaporator is very dirty. This is most likely causing reduced airflow over the evaporator. After cleaning the coil, the unit airflow is noticeably improved and the evaporator no longer freezes. The technician elects not to install a piercing valve and keep the system sealed. Instead, the system operation is checked by checking the system amp draw, airflow, and temperature drop across the evaporator coil.

Service Ticket 2502

Customer Complaint: Unit Operates but Does Not Cool

Equipment: Packaged Terminal Air Conditioner (PTAC) Using R-22 Refrigerant

A service technician for the Rest Easy Motel chain is asked to look a PTAC in one of the rooms because it operates but does not cool. Like most PTACs, this one has no service valves of any kind. The system operation is checked by checking the system amp draw, airflow, and temperature drop across the evaporator coil. The amp draw of the compressor is less than half of the normal RLA rating. The coil appears clean, the airflow is normal, but the supply air is the same temperature as the return air; no cooling is taking place. The technician decides to install a bolt-on piercing valve on the low side process tube. The reading on the low side with the compressor operating is 150 psig. The technician believes the compressor is bad, but decides to install a piercing valve on the high side process tube to be certain. The pressure on the high side with the compressor operating is also 150 psig. The compressor is condemned, the system refrigerant is recovered, the bolt on piercing valves are removed, Schrader valves are brazed in, a new compressor and liquid line filter are installed, the system is evacuated to 500 microns, and a charge is weighed in.

Service Ticket 2503

Customer Complaint: Unit Does Not Cool Adequately

Equipment: Commercial Refrigeration Unit on Walk in Cooler with R-134a

A technician is called to look at a walk in cooler whose capacity has noticeably declined. A check of the system pressures at the suction and discharge service valves reveals that the suction pressure is very low and the high side pressure is just slightly low. Both the system superheat and subcooling are high. The technician looks for system restrictions and finds a sweating liquid line filter drier. The technician determines that the filter drier is restricted and decides to change the filter drier, but does not want to recover all of the refrigerant. Instead, the king valve is front seated and the system is operated until the filter drier no longer sweats and the pressure on the line leaving the king valve is 0 psig. The technician turns off the unit and waits to make sure the pressure does not go above 0 psig. The old filter drier is replaced with a new filter drier, the system is evacuated from the suction service and king valves to 500 microns, the king valve is back seated, and the system is returned to service.

Service Ticket 2504

Job: Check Oil for Acidity on Semi-Hermetic Compressor

Equipment: Commercial Refrigeration System with Semi-Hermetic Compressor

A-1 Refrigeration changed the compressor is a commercial refrigeration system last week. A technician is sent to collect a small oil sample and perform an oil acid test on the oil to see if the oil is contaminated. The technician does not want to recover all the system refrigerant, but knows that the refrigerant pressure must be taken off of the compressor before opening the oil plug, so the technician decides to isolate the compressor using the suction and discharge service valves. First the system is operated long enough to warm up the crankcase and boil out any residual refrigerant from the oil. The system is turned off and locked out. Then gauges are installed on the compressor and both the service valves are front seated. The compressor is now isolated from the rest of the system. A recovery system is used to recover the small amount of refrigerant in the compressor. The crankcase plug is removed, a small oil sample taken, the plug replaced, and the oil is tested. The oil is clean, so the technician pulls a 500 micron vacuum on the compressor through the suction and discharge service valves. The service valves are back seated and the system is put back in operation.

UNIT 25—REVIEW QUESTIONS

1. What do technicians use the gauge manifold for?
2. What are the colors used on a gauge manifold set and what do they indicate?
3. What is the term for slightly opening a valve?
4. List three cautions when handling a gauge manifold set.
5. Why is the low side gauge called a compound gauge?
6. How does a Bourdon tube work in a gauge?
7. What must always be put on a Schrader valve port when not in use?
8. Why is it not always a good idea to install a gauge set and check system pressure?
9. What type of units are required to have service valves?
10. What type of units are only required to have process stubs?
11. Explain the difference between the back seated position and the front seated position on manual stem service valves.
12. When using manual stem service valves, describe how to position both the service valves and the gauge manifold valves when reading system pressures.
13. Why are positive shut-off hoses helpful when using Schrader valves?
14. What is the purpose of the saddle or piercing valve?

15. How can refrigeration gauges show the saturation temperature of the refrigerant in the system?

16. What is the retard range on compound gauges for?

17. What is the normal pressure range for the compound and high pressure gauges made for use on R-410a systems?

18. What is the normal pressure range for the compound and high pressure gauges made for use on R-134a and R-22 systems?

19. What personal protective equipment (PPE) should be worn when using gauge manifolds?

20. What can be done to reduce the risk of exposure to liquid refrigerant spray?

21. What is the difference between the two ends of a refrigeration hose?

22. What service valves are normally found on a commercial refrigeration system?

23. Why do split system heat pumps have three service valves?

24. Describe how to remove a gauge manifold set from a system and put most of the trapped refrigerant back into the system.

25. Describe how to purge a gauge manifold set using only the high side service valve.

26. Describe how to purge a gauge manifold set when connecting to Schrader valves.

27. What tool is used to turn the stems on manual stem service valves?

28. Describe how split system installation valves are used.

29. Why are bolt-on piercing valves not supposed to remain on systems permanently?

30. What is a process tube?

UNIT 26

Refrigerant Management and the EPA

OBJECTIVES

After completing this unit you will be able to:

- discuss the significance of the Montreal Protocol.
- outline the major provisions of Title VI, Section 608 of the 1990 Clean Air Act.
- determine the EPA specified recovery level for a given refrigerant and system.
- discuss the requirements for EPA certification.
- explain the different types of refrigerant recovery.
- discuss proper refrigerant recovery technique.
- discuss the difference between recovered, recycled, and reclaimed refrigerant.
- list types of refrigerant leak detection.
- discuss proper refrigerant leak detection technique.

26.1 INTRODUCTION

Understanding the laws and regulations designed to reduce the environmental impact of refrigerants is now a crucial part of an air conditioning technician's responsibility. Technicians must now pass a certification exam to demonstrate their understanding of these regulations before they are allowed to handle refrigerant. Reducing refrigerant emissions through good service practices, leak detection, and refrigerant recovery is a big part of any HVAC/R technician's job.

26.2 THE MONTREAL PROTOCOL

The problems of ozone depletion and global warming affect the whole earth's atmosphere and cannot be addressed by the unilateral action of one country. In 1985, the United Nations sponsored a treaty called the Vienna Convention for the Protection of the Ozone Layer seeking international cooperation to address concerns about ozone depletion. The participants agreed to study the problem, share information, and work toward a solution. In 1987, 29 signatories to the Vienna Convention developed the Montreal Protocol which established target dates for the phaseout of ozone depleting substances. To date, 191 countries have signed the Montreal Protocol.

26.3 1990 CLEAN AIR ACT

The United States Congress passed an extensive revision to the Clean Air Act in 1990. The legislation addresses many aspects of air pollution and air quality, including stratospheric ozone depletion. The Clean Air Act is divided into six major sections, called Titles. The last section, Title VI, covers Stratospheric Ozone Protection. There are 18 sections in Title VI, each dealing with specific aspects of the effort to address ozone depletion. These sections are numbered by the title and section. Section 608 is the eighth section of Title VI.

The Clean Air Act establishes the goals to be achieved and sets target dates. It does not set forth specific practices and procedures; those are left to the EPA to establish and enforce. The legislation gives the EPA the authority to regulate ozone depleting chemicals and their replacements, including refrigerant. Currently, the maximum possible fine for violation of the Clean Air Act is $32,500 per incident per day. Note that multiple violations can add up to a substantial amount of money.

26.4 SECTION 608

Section 608 of Title VI establishes regulations to reduce emissions of ozone depleting substances from everything except motor vehicle air conditioners, which are covered in section 609. Residential air conditioning, commercial and industrial refrigeration, and even transport refrigeration are covered in section 608. Regulations in section 608 establish:

- A prohibition on venting ozone depleting refrigerants.
- Technician certification.
- Restrictions on the sale of ozone depleting refrigerants.
- Reclaimed refrigerant standards.
- Certification of recycling and recovery equipment.
- Refrigerant recovery levels.
- Repair of substantial leaks in equipment with a charge greater than 50 pounds.
- Safe disposal of appliances containing ozone-depleting refrigerant.
- Record keeping.

26.5 VENTING PROHIBITION

Effective July 1, 1992, individuals are prohibited from knowingly venting ozone-depleting refrigerants into the atmosphere while maintaining, servicing, repairing, or disposing of air conditioning or refrigeration equipment or appliances. Four types of releases are permitted under the prohibition:

1. "De minimus" quantities of refrigerant released in the course of making good faith attempts to recapture and recycle or safely dispose of refrigerant. "De minimus" is latin for the minimum, or a little. There is no specific

quantity set as "de minimus." Instead, de minimus is defined as the amount released while following the manufacturer's instructions for the recovery device being used.

2. Refrigerants emitted in the course of normal operation of air conditioning and refrigeration equipment. Normal operating releases would include releases due to mechanical purging and small leaks. However, EPA requires the repair of substantial leaks in large equipment.

3. Releases of CFCs or HCFCs that are not used as refrigerants. For instance, mixtures of nitrogen and R-22 that are used as holding charges or as leak test gases may be released, because in these cases, the ozone-depleting compound is not used as a refrigerant. However, a technician may not avoid recovering refrigerant by adding nitrogen to a charged system; before nitrogen is added, the system must be evacuated to the EPA specified recovery level. Otherwise, the CFC or HCFC vented along with the nitrogen will be considered a refrigerant. Similarly, pure CFCs or HCFCs released from appliances will be presumed to be refrigerants, and their release will be considered a violation of the prohibition on venting.

4. Small releases of refrigerant that result from purging hoses or from connecting or disconnecting hoses to charge or service appliances will not be considered violations of the prohibition on venting. However, recovery and recycling equipment manufactured after November 15, 1993, must be equipped with low-loss fittings.

26.6 TECHNICIAN CERTIFICATION

Since November 14, 1994 anyone who performs maintenance, service, repair, or disposal that could be reasonably expected to release refrigerants into the atmosphere must be certified. Examples of actions that require certification include connecting gauges, adding or removing refrigerant, or opening a sealed refrigeration system. Technicians performing jobs that do not involve the refrigeration system, such as hanging ductwork or wiring units, are not required to be certified. Four types of certification have been developed to address different types of equipment. They are

- Type I for servicing small appliances.
- Type II for servicing high pressure and very high pressure appliances.
- Type III, low pressure appliances.
- Universal, for servicing all types of appliances except motor vehicle air conditioners.

Type I: Small Appliances

A small appliance is defined as a product that is fully manufactured, charged, and hermetically sealed in a factory with 5 lb or less of refrigerant. Examples of small appliances include domestic refrigerators and freezers, window air conditioners,

packaged terminal air conditioners and heat pumps, dehumidifiers, under-the-counter ice makers, vending machines, and drinking water coolers. Technicians working on small appliances must have either Type I or Universal Certification.

Type II: High Pressure Appliances

High pressure appliances use an ozone depleting refrigerant with a boiling point at atmospheric pressure between −58°F and 50°F. This category covers the widest of variety of appliances including residential air conditioning, commercial air conditioning, commercial refrigeration, and transportation refrigeration.

Type II: Very High Pressure Appliances

Very high pressure appliances use an ozone depleting refrigerant with a boiling point at atmospheric pressure below −58°F. Very high pressure appliances are typically cryogenic scientific equipment operating at extremely low temperatures. These appliances represent a very small portion of the refrigeration industry.

Technicians working on either high pressure or very high pressure appliances must have either Type II or universal certification.

MVAC-like Appliances

An MVAC-like appliance is an air conditioner in a non-road vehicle. These systems are generally identical to those found in cars and trucks, but the vehicles do not operate on the public road system, such as agricultural and construction vehicles. A farm tractor with an air conditioned cab is an example of an MVAC-like appliance, Figure 26-1. Technicians working on MVAC-like appliances may be certified under either section 608 or section 609.

Figure 26-1 Large agricultural machinery, like this cotton picker with an air conditioned cab, is classified as an MVAC-like appliance *(Compliments of John Deere)*

Type III: Low Pressure Appliances

Low pressure appliances use an ozone depleting refrigerant with a boiling point at atmospheric pressure above 50°F. The low side pressure on these systems usually operates in a vacuum. Large chillers are the only common type of low pressure systems. Technicians working on Type III low pressure appliances must have either Type III or Universal Certification.

Technician Certification Exam

To become certified, technicians are required to pass an EPA-approved test given by an EPA-approved certifying organization. There are four parts to the exam:

- Core.
- Type I.
- Type II.
- Type III.

Each section has 25 questions. Sections are scored individually and each section is passed or failed as a section. Technicians must correctly answer 18 questions to receive credit for a section. Technicians must pass the Core and at least one other section to become certified. The number of sections passed determines their certification. A universal certification is issued to people who pass all four sections.

TECH TIP

Although universal certification implies that technicians are certified to work on anything, universal certification does not cover MVAC systems, motor vehicle air conditioning systems. A section 609 certification is required to work on motor vehicle air conditioning systems.

26.7 REFRIGERANT SALES RESTRICTION

Since November 14, 1994, the sale of refrigerant in any size container has been restricted to certified technicians. The sales restriction covers refrigerant containing parts as well as refrigerant in cylinders or drums.

What Is Not Covered

Fully assembled appliances containing refrigerant such as household refrigerators, window air conditioners, and packaged air conditioners are not included in the sales restriction. HFC refrigerants are also not covered. Uncertified people may purchase HFC refrigerant like R-134a. Precharged split systems may also be purchased by uncertified individuals providing all of the components are sold at one time. Components of precharged systems are still subject to the sales restriction if sold individually.

TECH TIP

While it is legal for uncertified individuals to purchase an entire precharged split-system, they may not install the system. Connecting the refrigerant lines requires a certified technician.

26.8 RECOVER, RECYCLE, RECLAIM

Refrigerant that has been removed from a system contains impurities. What is done with refrigerant removed from a system depends upon the level of cleaning the refrigerant undergoes and whether or not the refrigerant will change ownership. The EPA uses three terms to describe the condition of refrigerant which has been removed from a system: recovered, recycled, and reclaimed. Although these terms all have a similar meaning in general use, they have very specific meanings when used to describe refrigerant in the context of EPA regulations.

Recovered Refrigerant

Recovered refrigerant has been removed in any condition from an appliance and stored in an external container without necessarily testing or processing it in any way. Recovered refrigerant may not change ownership. Recovered refrigerant may not be removed from one owner's system and then charged into a system owned by someone else. Recovered refrigerant may be charged into the system it came from or another system of the same owner.

Recycled Refrigerant

Recycled refrigerant has been removed from an appliance and cleaned for reuse without meeting all of the requirements for reclamation. In general, recycled refrigerant is refrigerant that is cleaned using oil separation and single or multiple passes through replaceable core filter-driers, which reduce moisture, acidity, and particulate matter. Although recycled refrigerant is safer than recovered refrigerant, it has the same basic restrictions. It may not be removed from one owner's system and then charged into a system owned by someone else. Recycled refrigerant may be charged into the system it came from or another system of the same owner.

Reclaimed Refrigerant

Reclaimed refrigerant has been reprocessed to at least the purity specified in the ARI Standard 700-2007, Specifications for Fluorocarbon Refrigerants. Its purity has been verified using the analytical methodology prescribed in the Standard. Refrigerant reclamation requires specialized machinery not available at a particular job site.

Reclaiming is done by an EPA approved refrigerant reclaimer at a reprocessing facility. Recovered refrigerant is sent to either a general reclaimer or back to the refrigerant manufacturer for reclaiming. Reclaimed refrigerant may be used anywhere new refrigerant may be used. It may change ownership.

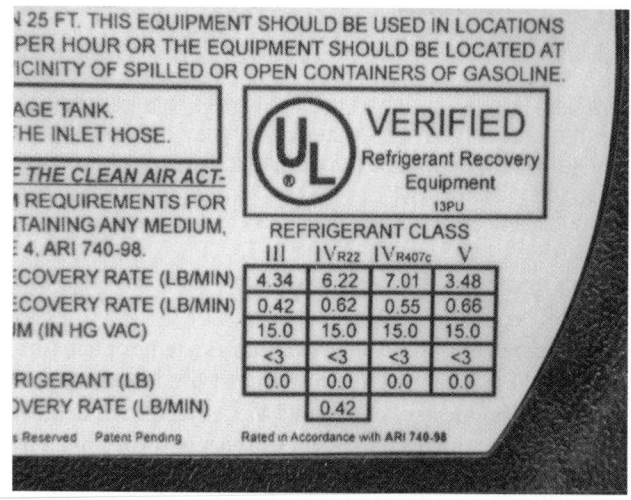

Figure 26-2 Recovery equipment should be certified by ARI or UL

26.9 RECOVERY EQUIPMENT CERTIFICATION

Refrigerant recovery and recycling equipment manufactured on or after November 15, 1993, must be tested by an EPA-approved testing organization to ensure that it meets EPA requirements. Third-party testing is not required for equipment manufactured before November 15, 1993. Currently, the EPA has approved both the Air-Conditioning and Refrigeration Institute (ARI) and Underwriters Laboratories (UL) to certify recycling and recovery equipment. Certified equipment can be identified by a label reading: "This equipment has been certified by ARI/UL to meet EPA's minimum requirements for recycling and/ or recovery equipment . . .," Figure 26-2. The intended use for the recovery equipment is listed at the end of this statement.

The standards vary depending on the size and type of air conditioning or refrigeration equipment being serviced. Recovery equipment for use with Type I small appliances must be able to recover 90% of the refrigerant in the small appliance when the small appliance compressor is operating and 80% of the refrigerant in the small appliance when the compressor is not operating. Figure 26-3 shows the recovery levels for equipment intended for use with Type II air conditioning and refrigeration systems. Recovery equipment for Type III, low pressure systems, must be able to lower the pressure in the system to an absolute pressure of 25 mm of mercury. This is approximately 29 in of mercury vacuum.

Equipment Grandfathering

Equipment manufactured before November 15, 1993, including homemade equipment, may be grandfathered if it meets the standards shown in Figure 26-3.

Companies Must Own Refrigerant Recovery Equipment

The EPA requires people servicing or disposing of air conditioning and refrigeration equipment to certify to the appropriate EPA Regional Office that they have acquired recovery or recycling equipment and that they are complying with the applicable requirements of this rule. This certification must be signed by the owner of the recovery equipment or another responsible officer of the company and sent to the appropriate EPA Regional Office. Figure 26-4 shows a sample form. Although owners of recycling and recovery equipment are required to list the number of trucks based at their shops, they do not need to have a piece of recycling or recovery equipment for every truck. Owners do not have to send in a new form each time they add recycling or recovery equipment to their inventory.

26.10 FACTORS AFFECTING RECOVERY REQUIREMENTS

Technicians need to know when they have finished recovering the refrigerant from a system. Removing all the refrigerant would require evacuating the system until achieving a perfect vacuum of 29.92 in Hg. Fortunately the EPA recognized that this would be impractical, and in most cases, impossible. The EPA uses the term "evacuate" when talking about the use of

Type of appliance	Refrigerant examples	Manufactured before 11/15/1993	Manufactured on or after 11/15/1993
Very high pressure	R-13, R-503	0 psig	0 psig
R-22 < 200 lb	R-22	0 psig	0 psig
R-22 ≥ 200 lb	R-22	4 in Hg vacuum	10 in Hg vacuum
Other high pressure < 200 lb	R-12, R-502	4 in Hg vacuum	10 in Hg vacuum
Other high pressure ≥ 200 lb	R-12, R-502	4 in Hg vacuum	15 in Hg vacuum
Low pressure appliance	R-11, R-123	25 in Hg vacuum	25 mm Hg absolute pressure

Figure 26-3 Type 2 and type 3 recovery levels

Form Approved
OMB No. 2060-0256
Expires: 07/31/2010

Figure 26-4 Form for registering refrigerant recovery
(Environmental Protection Agency)

☙EPA

ENVIRONMENTAL PROTECTION AGENCY
REFRIGERANT RECOVERY OR RECYCLING DEVICE
ACQUISITION CERTIFICATION FORM

EPA regulations require establishments that service or dispose of refrigeration or air-conditioning equipment to certify that they have acquired recovery or recycling devices that meet EPA standards for such devices. To certify that you have acquired equipment, please complete this form according to the instructions and **mail it to the appropriate EPA Regional Office. BOTH THE INSTRUCTIONS AND MAILING ADDRESSES CAN BE FOUND ON THE REVERSE SIDE OF THIS FORM.**

PART 1: ESTABLISHMENT INFORMATION

Name of Establishment

Street

(Area Code) Telephone Number

City   State   Zip Code

Number of Service Vehicles Based at Establishment

County

PART 2: REGULATORY CLASSIFICATION

Identify the type of work performed by the establishment. **Check all boxes that apply.**

☐ Type A - Service small appliances
☐ Type B - Service refrigeration or air-conditioning equipment other that small appliances
☐ Type C- Dispose of small appliances
☐ Type D - Dispose of refrigeration or air-conditioning equipment other than small appliances

PART 3: DEVICE IDENTIFICATION

	Name of Device(s) Manufacturer	Model Number	Year	Serial Number (if any)	Check Box if Self-Contained
1.					☐
2.					☐
3.					☐
4.					☐
5.					☐

PART 4: CERTIFICATION SIGNATURE

I certify that the establishment in Part 1 has acquired the refrigerant recovery or recycling device(s) listed in Part 2, that the establishment is complying with Section 608 regulations, and that the information gives is true and correct.

Signature of Owner/Responsible Officer   Date   Name (Please Print)   Title

EPA FORM 7610-31

recovery equipment, and "evacuate to the atmosphere" when describing the use of vacuum pumps. The recommended evacuation levels are based on the following factors.

Type of System

- Type I.
- Type II.
- Type III.

Date Recovery Machine Was Manufactured

- Manufactured before 11-15-93.
- Manufactured on or after 11-15-93.

Type of Refrigerant

- HCFC 22.
- Very high pressure refrigerant.
- Other high pressure CFCs and HCFCs.
- HFCs.

Amount of Refrigerant in System

- Under 200 lb.
- 200 lb or more.

The recovery levels for each of these specific circumstances are discussed in the following sections. Knowing these evacuation levels is extremely important; every section of the EPA certification exam will ask several questions about refrigerant evacuation (recovery) levels.

26.11 RECOVERY LEVEL EXCEPTIONS

Two exceptions to the EPA mandated recovery levels are permitted: opening systems for minor repairs and evacuating leaky systems.

Major and Minor Repairs

Systems can be opened for minor repairs after recovering the refrigerant to a level of 0 psig instead of the EPA mandated evacuation level for that particular system. A minor repair is one that does not involve the compressor, condenser, evaporator, or auxiliary heat exchange coil. Work on any of these components is considered a major repair, and requires the full EPA mandated evacuation. An example of a minor repair would be replacing a filter or a valve in a refrigerant line.

SERVICE TIP

The practical usefulness of the minor repair exclusion is limited. The EPA does not allow the system to be evacuated to the atmosphere after performing the minor repair. This means that the technician is not allowed to pull a deep vacuum on the part of the system that was opened before placing the system back into service. It is poor refrigeration practice to open systems and not pull a vacuum on them afterwards.

Leaky systems may also be evacuated to 0 psig instead of the EPA mandated recovery level for the system. The system must be evacuated to the lowest practical level, but that level can be no higher than 0 psig. Trying to evacuate a system with a leak below 0 psig can result in sucking air into the system and mixing it with the recovered refrigerant.

26.12 RECOVERY MACHINES: OLD VERSUS NEW

The age of the recovery machine affects the required recovery level in most cases. Specifically, if the recovery equipment was manufactured before November 15, 1993, then the required evacuation levels are not as stringent as the vacuum levels required of machines made on or after November 15, 1993. Older recovery equipment is not required to have low-loss fittings, but equipment manufactured on or after November 15, 1993 must have low-loss fittings on the refrigerant hoses.

TECH TIP

The Clean Air Act was passed in 1990 and specified that it would take effect beginning in 1992. The law did not flesh out all the specific details involved in recovering refrigerant, but simply said that it had to be done. Well 1992 came and went and the EPA had not completed work on the details, so there was no way to know exactly what would be required, other than the refrigerant could no longer be released to the atmosphere when installing, servicing, or disposing refrigeration equipment. So equipment manufacturers had to design, manufacture, and sell machines that could not possibly be built to any standard, since there was not a standard. These early machines were bulky, expensive, and generally not able to meet the standards that the EPA later published. In fairness to the contractors who purchased these early noncertified machines, the EPA published a less stringent set of recovery levels when they published their first set of regulations. This is why technicians now have two sets of refrigerant recovery levels to memorize.

26.13 TYPE I EQUIPMENT RECOVERY LEVELS

When using a recovery device manufactured before November 15, 1993, the recovery level for Type I systems is 80% regardless of the appliance compressor condition. When using a recovery device manufactured on or after November 15, 1993, recovery levels for Type I systems are established based on the condition of their compressor.

- 90% for appliances with operational compressors.
- 80% for appliances with nonoperational compressors

These recovery levels are valid for both system dependent (passive) and self contained (active) recovery devices. Self contained (active) recovery devices may also be certified by achieving a vacuum level of 4 in Hg.

SERVICE TIP

The Type I recovery requirements are unique because they specify what percentage of the system's refrigerant charge must be recovered instead of a vacuum level. The percentage charge that a recovery device can capture is tested using a very specific EPA prescribed test stand following the device manufacturer's instructions. If the recovery device successfully recovers the desired amount of refrigerant on the EPA test device, it is assumed that the same device will perform similarly in the field when used according to the manufacturer's instructions. It is important to read and follow the instructions provided with the recovery device. Field technicians are not required to prove that they successfully recovered 80% of the system's charge; they only have to demonstrate that they followed instructions using an EPA approved device.

26.14 TYPE II EQUIPMENT RECOVERY LEVELS

Remembering Type II recovery levels can be quite a challenge, but there are a few organizational tricks that will help.

Very High Pressure Refrigerants

The recovery level for systems using a very high pressure refrigerant is 0 psig. Neither the age of the recovery machine nor the amount of refrigerant in the system has any effect on this level.

HCFC-22

The recovery level for systems that hold less than 200 lb of R-22 is 0 psig, regardless of when the recovery machine was manufactured. It is important to note that this means 200 lb by weight, not the pressure reading.

The recovery level for a system holding 200 lb or more of R-22 is established by when the recovery machine was manufactured. The recovery level for machines made before November 15, 1993 is 4 in Hg vacuum. The recovery level for machines made on or after November 15, 1993 is 10 in Hg vacuum.

> ### SERVICE TIP
>
> There are very few systems that hold 200 lb of R-22. Typical residential systems hold less than 10 lb, and even 25 ton commercial systems only hold around 50 lb.

Other High Pressure Refrigerants

High pressure refrigerants other than R-22 require lower recovery levels than R-22. For systems holding less than 200 lb of refrigerant other than R-22, the recovery level is 4 in Hg vacuum when using a recovery machine made before November 15, 1993 and 10 in Hg vacuum when using a recovery machine made on or after November 15, 1993.

The final set of recovery levels is for systems using 200 lb or more of a high pressure refrigerant other than R-22. The recovery level when using a recovery machine manufactured before November 15, 1993 is 4 in Hg vacuum. The recovery level when using a recovery machine manufactured on or after November 15, 1993 is 15 in Hg vacuum.

Old Recovery Machines

The recovery level for high pressure refrigerants when using a recovery machine manufactured before November 15, 1993

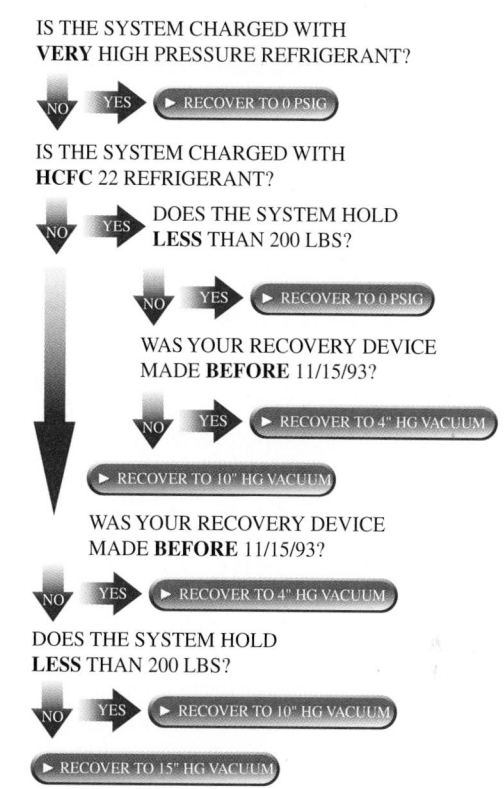

Figure 26-5 Decision flow chart for Type II refrigerant recovery levels

is never more than 4 in Hg vacuum. This simplifies remembering the recovery level when using an older recovery machine. For very high pressure refrigerants and R-22 systems holding less than 200 lb of refrigerant, the recovery level is 0 psig. For every other high pressure refrigerant situation when using a recovery machine manufactured before November 15, 1993, the recovery level is 4 in Hg vacuum.

Decision Flow Chart

Figure 26-5 is a decision flow chart that helps organize Type II recovery levels.

26.15 TYPE III EQUIPMENT RECOVERY LEVELS

Type III recovery levels are easy to remember: the target number is always 25. When using a recovery device that was manufactured before November 15, 1993, the required evacuation level is 25 in Hg vacuum. When using a recovery device manufactured on or after November 15, 1993, the required recovery level is 25 mm Hg absolute pressure. The amount of refrigerant in the system is irrelevant for Type III systems. An easy way to remember the evacuation levels for Type III low pressure systems is to remember that inches is the old way to measure and millimeters is the new way.

TECH TIP

Although 25 in vacuum and 25 mm absolute look similar, they represent very different evacuation levels. Atmospheric pressure is normally about 29.92 in Hg. A vacuum level of 25 in Hg vacuum means that 25 of the original 29.92 inches have been removed, leaving an absolute pressure of about 4.92 in Hg. This method of measuring vacuum measures how much pressure has been removed from the system. The 25 mm absolute pressure required for newer recovery machines measures how much pressure remains after evacuating the system. Since 25 mm is approximately 1 in, a pressure of 25 mm absolute is roughly equivalent to 29 in Hg vacuum, about 1 in shy of a perfect vacuum.

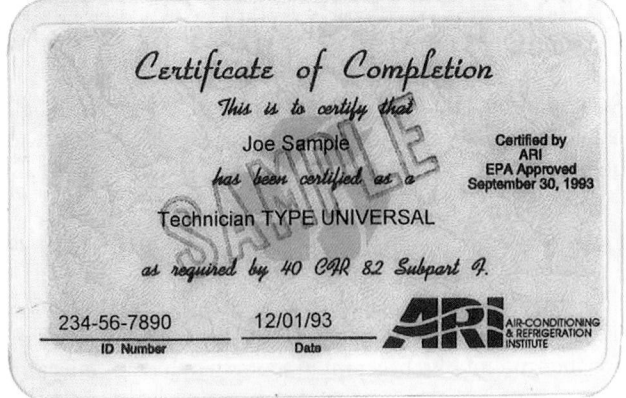

Figure 26-6 EPA certification card

26.16 SAFE DISPOSAL

Equipment that is typically dismantled onsite before disposal must have the refrigerant recovered in accordance with EPA's requirements for servicing before being dismantled. Examples of equiment requiring refrigerant recovery in the field before disposal include commercial refrigeration equipment, central residential air conditioning, chillers, and industrial process refrigeration. However, equipment that typically enters the waste stream with the charge intact, such as household refrigerators and room air conditioners, is subject to special safe disposal requirements.

The final person in the disposal chain, such as the scrap metal recycler or landfill owner, is responsible for ensuring that refrigerant is recovered from the equipment before disposal. However, technicians "upstream" can remove the refrigerant and provide documentation to the final person if this is more cost-effective. The final person in the disposal chain must have documentation showing who removed the refigerant if they accept appliances that no longer hold a refrigerant charge. The documentation must include a signed statement listing the name and address of the person who recovered the refrigerant and the date that the refrigerant was recovered.

The equipment used to recover refrigerant from appliances prior to final disposal must meet the same performance standards as equipment used for servicing, but it does not need to be tested by a laboratory. Technician certification is not required for individuals removing refrigerant from appliances in the waste stream.

26.17 RECORD KEEPING

Technicians, service companies, equipment owners, wholesalers, and refrigerant reclaimers are all required to keep some form of documentation. Technicians must keep proof of their certification, Figure 26-6. Employers are also required to keep copies of their employee's certification. Technicians servicing appliances that contain 50 or more pounds of refrigerant must provide the equipment owner with an invoice that indicates the amount of refrigerant added to the appliance. Owners of equipment that contains 50 or more pounds of re-

frigerant must keep servicing records documenting the date and type of service, as well as the quantity of refrigerant added, Figure 26-7. Owners of equipment that contains less than 50 lb of refrigerant are not required to keep records of refrigerant use. Wholesalers who sell CFC and HCFC refrigerants must retain invoices that indicate the name of the purchaser, the date of sale, and the quantity of refrigerant purchased. Reclaimers must maintain records of the names and addresses of people sending them material for reclamation and the quantity of material sent to them for reclamation.

26.18 HAZARDOUS WASTE

Recycled or reclaimed refrigerants are not considered hazardous under federal law. Used oils contaminated with CFCs are not treated as hazardous on the condition that the oil:

- Is not mixed with other waste.
- Has been subjected to CFC recycling or reclamation.
- Is not mixed with used oils from other sources.

26.19 RECOVERY EQUIPMENT

Recovery equipment is classified as either system dependent or self contained. System dependent recovery equipment depends on the system from which the refrigerant is being recovered to help remove the refrigerant. Self contained recovery equipment does not rely on the system because the recovery equipment has its own means of moving the refrigerant, typically a compressor.

System Dependent Recovery Devices

System dependent recovery devices may be used for recovering refrigerant from systems containing up to 15 lb of refrigerant. A system dependent recovery device depends on the system from which the refrigerant is being recovered to help move the refrigerant. The most common system dependent recovery device is basically a big plastic bag, Figure 26-8. As refrigerant enters it, its volume expands so that the pressure

System data	Commercial air conditioning equipment					
	Refrigerant type			HCFC 22		
	Refrigerant amount			60 lb		
				Leak rate calculations		
Date	*Service description*	*Amount recovered*	*Amount added*	*% charge*	*Annual adjustment*	*Annual leak rate*
1-1-2007	Unit placed in service					
6-30-2008	Added refrigerant		1.5 lb	1.5/60 = 2.5%	365/(365 + 182) = 0.0667	2.5% × 0.667 = 1.7%
12-10-2008	Replaced liquid drier	59 lb	60 lb	1/60 = 1.7%	365/163 = 2.2	1.7% × 2.2 = 3.8%
5-30-2009	Added refrigerant		1.5 lb	1.5/60 = 2.5%	365/172 = 2.12	2.5% × 2.12 = 5%

Figure 26-7 A refrigerant data log is used to document the amount of refrigerant added to systems containing 50 or more pounds of refrigerant

in the bag does not rise above 0 psig. The EPA refers to these bags as nonpressurized containers.

Whirlpool developed the bags for use with refrigerators. These bags will only hold about 1 lb of refrigerant. To use the bag on a refrigerator with an operating compressor, use the following steps:

- Connect the bag to the high side of the system.
- Let the refrigerant flow into the bag with the unit off for approximately 15 min.

- Start the compressor and let it operate for another 5 min.
- Remove the bag and cap it.

Figure 26-9 shows the correct connection for an appliance with an operational compressor.

To use the bag on a refrigerator with a compressor that will not operate:

- Connect the bag to BOTH the high side and low side of the system.

Figure 26-8 Nonpressurized refrigerant container
(Photographs used with permission from Whirlpool Corporation.)

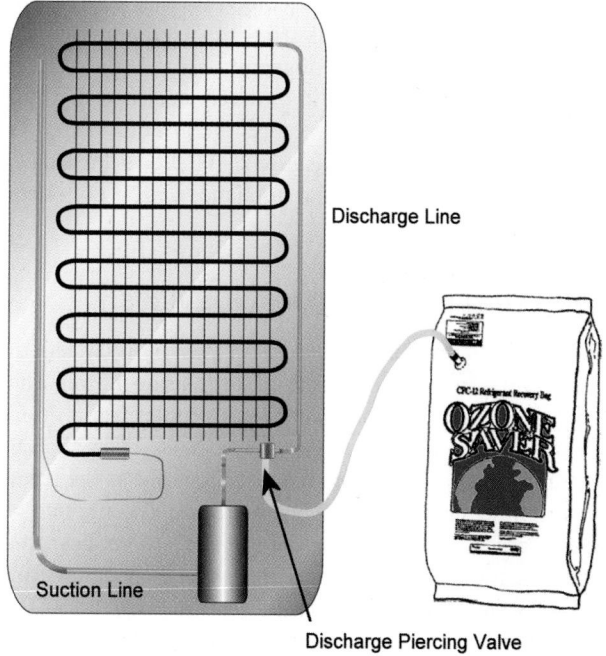

Figure 26-9 Connection of a system dependent recovery device to a small appliance with an operational compressor

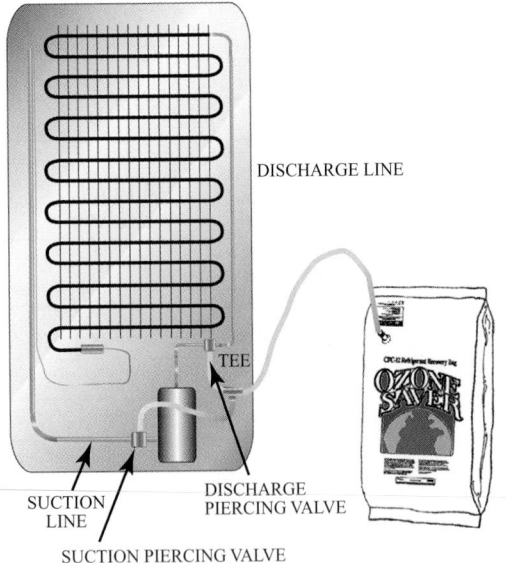

DISCHARGE LINE

TEE

SUCTION LINE

DISCHARGE PIERCING VALVE

SUCTION PIERCING VALVE

Figure 26-10 Connection of a system dependent recovery device to a small appliance with a nonoperational compressor

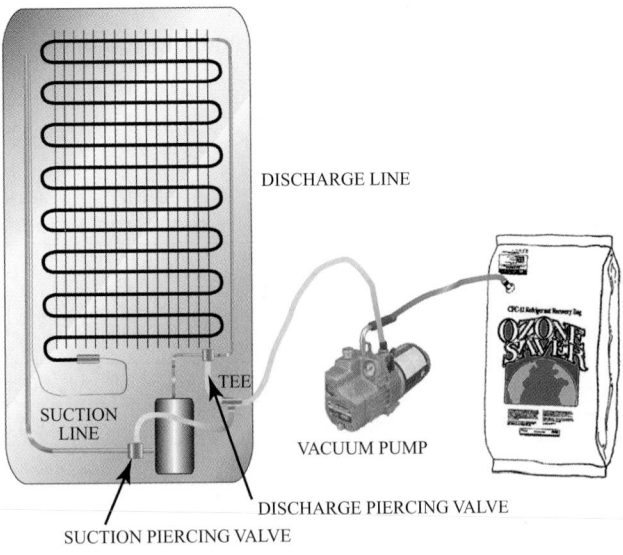

DISCHARGE LINE

TEE

SUCTION LINE

VACUUM PUMP

DISCHARGE PIERCING VALVE

SUCTION PIERCING VALVE

Figure 26-11 Connection of a system dependent recovery device using a vacuum pump

- Let the refrigerant flow into the bag with the unit off for approximately 15 min.
- Hit the compressor three times. (You read it right, hit the compressor.)
- Heat the compressor with a hair dryer or heat gun for another 12 min.
- Remove the bag and cap it.

Figure 26-10 shows the correct connection for an appliance with a nonoperational compressor.

A vacuum pump can also be used with a nonpressurized container (bag). Connect the vacuum pump to both sides of the system and connect the discharge of the vacuum pump to the bag. This requires some ingenuity because the vacuum pump is not designed to have its outlet connected to anything. The vacuum pump will pull the refrigerant out of the system and place it in the bag. Figure 26-11 shows the use of a vacuum pump and bag on an appliance with a nonoperational compressor.

Self Contained Recovery Devices

Self contained recovery devices do not rely on the system the refrigerant is being recovered from for their operation. They typically are small, specialized condensing units, Figure 26-12. They have a compressor, a condenser, and valves that are used to control the refrigerant flow in and out of the recovery machine, Figure 26-13. Most modern self contained recovery machines use oilless compressors to reduce cross contamination between refrigerants when changing from one refrigerant to another. Many also have purge cycles that will pump the refrigerant trapped in their condenser into the recovery cylinder after recovering the system refrigerant. A small amount of refrigerant is left between the outlet of the compressor and the outlet of the recovery machine. It is not

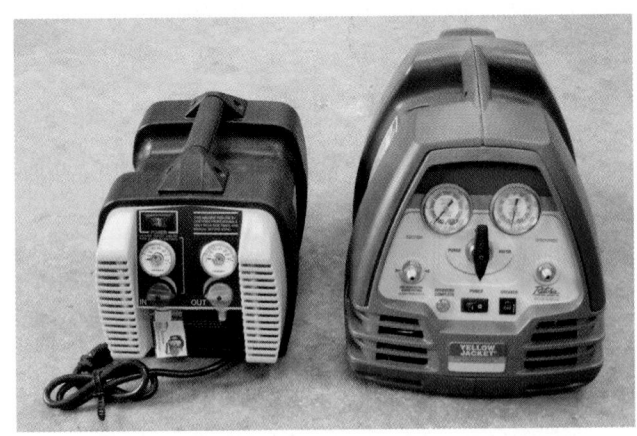

Figure 26-12 Self contained recovery devices

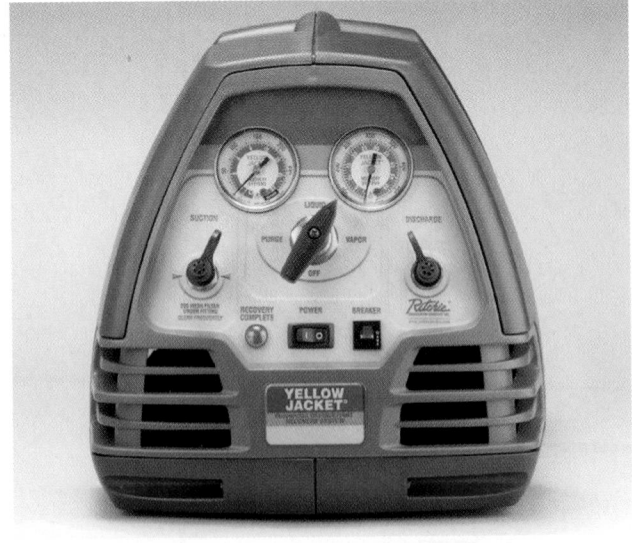

Figure 26-13 Most self contained recovery devices consist of a compressor, a condenser, and control valves
(Courtesy of Ritchie Engineering Company, Inc.—YELLOW JACKET Products)

a violation to release this small quantity of refrigerant in order to recover another type of refrigerant.

Water Cooled Recovery Machines

A very few recovery machines are water-cooled. The water source for water-cooled recovery machines is city water (tap water).

26.20 LOW LOSS FITTINGS

Low loss fittings reduce the amount of refrigerant released when hoses are connected and disconnected by keeping refrigerant from leaving the hose when it is disconnected. The majority of the refrigerant released when disconnecting a hose from a Schrader valve is actually coming out of the hose, not the valve. This can be a significant amount of refrigerant when the hose is filled with liquid. All hoses used with recovery equipment built after November 15, 1993 are required to have low loss fittings. These can be automatically closing check valves, like the one in Figure 26-14; or they can be manually controlled valves, like the one shown in Figure 26-15.

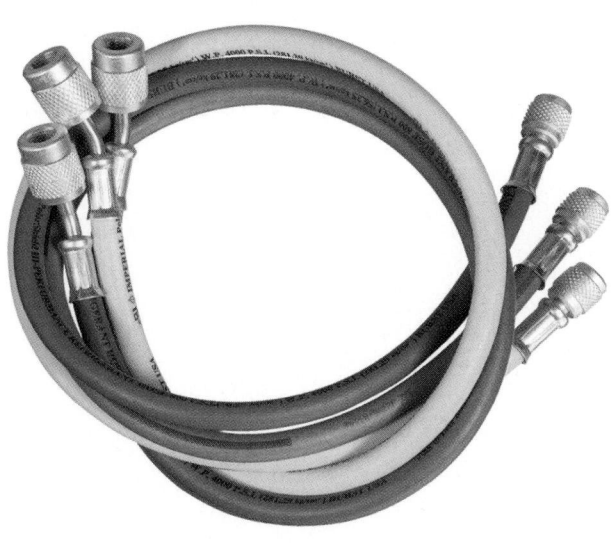

Figure 26-14 Hoses with low loss fittings

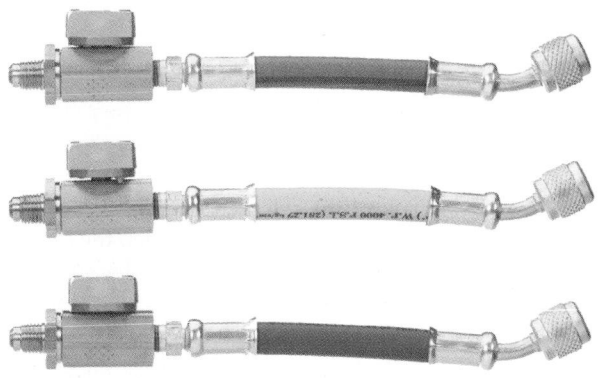

Figure 26-15 Short hose sections with manual shut off valves

26.21 RECOVERY CYLINDERS

Non-refillable cylinders should not be used for refrigerant recovery. Recovery cylinders are normally available in water capacities of 27 and 47 lb. Refillable cylinders and recovery cylinders are regulated by the DOT in Code of Federal Regulations 49 covering the transport of hazardous materials. Figure 26-16 shows a typical refrigerant recovery cylinder.

Cylinder Markings

Cylinders are marked with the particular DOT specifications for that cylinder, Figure 26-17. Some crucial cylinder markings are:

- DOT specification.
- Water capacity.
- Tare weight.
- Date of manufacture.
- First retest date.
- Most recent test date.
- Last allowable retest date.

The numbers and letters immediately following the letters DOT describe how the cylinder is made while the last group of numbers describes the cylinder service pressure. For example, a DOT-4BA-350 recovery cylinder is a welded or brazed steel cylinder with a recommended service

Figure 26-16 Refrigerant recovery cylinder
(Courtesy National Refrigerants, Inc.)

Figure 26-17 The cylinder specifications are stamped into the collar of the cylinder

Figure 26-19 The weight of the water to completely fill this cylinder is 47.6 lb

pressure of 350 psig, Figure 26-18. This is the most common specification for refrigerant recovery cylinders. DOT 4BA-400 cylinders are used for refrigerant R-410A recovery because of its high pressures. These cylinders have recommended service pressures of 400 psig.

The water capacity is the weight of the water to completely fill the cylinder, Figure 26-19. The tare weight is the weight of the empty cylinder, Figure 26-20. The tare weight and water capacity are used to calculate how much refrigerant the cylinder can safely hold.

Cylinders with a service pressure under 300 psig must be tested every 10 years. Cylinders with a service pressure of

Figure 26-20 This cylinder weighs 28.1 lb empty

Figure 26-18 This cylinder has a service pressure of 350 psig

300 psig or more must be tested every 5 years. The date of manufacture and the first retest date are on every cylinder, Figure 26-21. The first retest date gives the month and year that a cylinder must be requalified. If the first requalification date has not yet arrived, the cylinder should still be on its first five years. Note that the 5 years starts when the cylinder is made, not when it is purchased. A cylinder that was made 2 years ago can only be used for another 3 years before getting requalified, even if it has been sitting on the shelf in the store. If the first retest date has already passed, the cylinder should not be used unless it was retested. If it was retested,

Figure 26-21 This cylinder was manufactured in July, 1998

the date that it was retested should be stamped on the cylinder. If the date was less than 5 years ago, the cylinder should be safe to use.

Some cylinders also have a last permissible use date. These are commonly known as 5 + 5 cylinders. They can only be requalified one time. These cylinders may not be used past the last permissible use date, Figure 26-22.

Cylinder Color

ARI Guidline K specifies that recovery cylinders all be painted gray with a yellow top regardless of the type of refrigerant in the cylinder, Figure 26-14. Of course these cylinders must be labeled with the type of refrigerant they contain, since cylinder color cannot be relied upon to

Figure 26-22 The last date that this cylinder may be used is 10 years after its date of manufacture

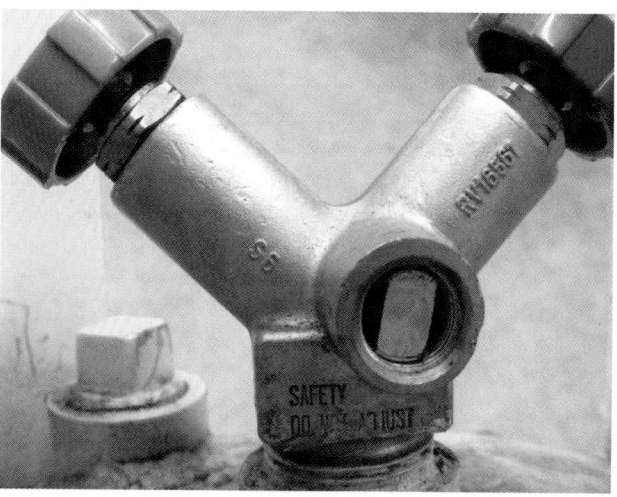

Figure 26-23 Recovery cylinder safety relief valve

identify them. The only thing the technician knows for sure by the color is that refrigerant in a gray and yellow cylinder is not new.

Safety Relief Valve

Recovery cylinders have an automatic pressure relief valve built in which opens at 150% of the rated cylinder service pressure, Figure 26-23. The outlet of the relief valve should never be plugged or obstructed by anything. These valves reset once the pressure in the cylinder has dropped to a safe level.

26.22 CYLINDER FILL LEVEL

Cylinders should never be filled more than 80% full of liquid by volume and they should not be stored or used in temperatures exceeding 125°F. All refrigerant cylinders have a maximum recommended service pressure. Do not pressurize recovery cylinders above their rated service pressure.

However, do not rely on pressure to determine the safe fill level. It is possible to fill a cylinder completely up with liquid and remain below the cylinder service pressure. Remember that for saturated mixtures of liquid and gas, the pressure is established by the refrigerant temperature, not the amount of refrigerant in the cylinder. It does not matter if the cylinder is 25% full or 95% full, the pressure will be the same so long as the temperature is the same. In practice the cylinder pressure gradually rises as recovery proceeds. This is because the warm refrigerant leaving the recovery machine tends to heat up the cylinder and all the refrigerant in it, raising the cylinder temperature and pressure. If the cylinder is cooled, its pressure will drop. Pressure absolutely cannot be relied upon to tell when a cylinder is full. Most recovery machines have high pressure safety switches. Remember these are safety switches, not fill level detectors. In short, do not simply fill the cylinder up until the high

Refrigerant	Density @77°	Specific gravity @77°	11.9 WC 80% Fill	26.1 WC 80% Fill	47.6 WC 80% Fill
12	81.84	1.31	12.47	27.35	49.88
22	76.92	1.23	11.71	25.68	46.84
134a	75.31	1.21	11.52	25.26	46.08
500	72.16	1.16	11.04	24.22	44.17
502	75.95	1.22	11.61	25.47	46.46
401a	74.5	1.19	11.33	24.85	45.32
404	65.17	1.04	9.90	21.72	39.60
407	71.12	1.14	10.85	23.80	43.41
408	66.31	1.06	10.09	22.13	40.36
409	75.91	1.22	11.61	25.47	46.46
410a	67.66	1.08	10.28	22.55	41.13

Figure 26-24 Safe fill level for common refrigerants and cylinder capacities

pressure safety device shuts off the recovery machine! Remember that when a safety shuts something off, it generally indicates that there is a problem.

The weight of the cylinder is the most commonly used method for determining when a cylinder is full. All DOT approved cylinders have their tare weight and water capacity stamped on them. If a cylinder was refilled with water, the maximum safe fill level could be determined by taking 80% of the water capacity and adding it to the tare weight. Before blends, all commonly used refrigerants were denser than water. Most of the 400 series refrigerants are less dense, and cylinders cannot safely hold as much of these refrigerants. In general a cylinder will only hold 75–80% as much 400 series refrigerant in the same size cylinder as the older refrigerants used. For example, 30 lb disposable cylinders have been common for years. All refrigerants came in the same size cylinders with the same net weight. This does not mean that all these different refrigerants filled the cylinders up equally, but none of them overfilled the cylinders at this level. The familiar 30 lb cylinder can safely hold only 25 lb of R-410a refrigerant. The cylinder is 80% full by volume, but it weighs less because the refrigerant is less dense than the older refrigerants. Therefore, it is necessary to calculate the net weight for each specific type of refrigerant to know exactly how much refrigerant a recovery cylinder can safely hold. The formula is

$$\text{tare weight} + (0.8 \times \text{water capacity} \times \text{specific gravity of the refrigerant at } 77°F)$$

- Tare weight is the weight of the empty cylinder. It is usually stamped as Tare or TW on the cylinder.
- Water capacity, stamped WC, is what the water would weigh if the cylinder was completely filled with water.
- The specific gravity of the refrigerant compares the weight of the refrigerant to the weight of water. This number must be looked up for each refrigerant.

Most refrigerant manufacturers do not give a specific gravity, but list the refrigerant's density instead. To calculate the specific gravity divide the refrigerant saturated liquid density at 77°F by 62.4, the density of water. The formula using the refrigerant density instead of specific gravity is

$$\text{tare weight} + (0.8 \times \text{water capacity} \times (\text{refrigerant density}/62.4))$$

This formula uses the saturated liquid density of the refrigerant at 77°F, and 62.4, the density of water.

Of course this only has to be calculated one time for each cylinder. Figure 26-24 gives the safe fill level for the two most common sizes of recovery cylinders for several refrigerants.

Some recovery machines use float switches that cut the recovery machine off when the cylinder is 80% full, Figure 26-25. Others use temperature sensing devices that sense

Figure 26-25 Some recovery cylinders have a float that shuts off the recovery unit when the cylinder is 80% full

the liquid level in the cylinder. Both of these are good safety devices, but they should not be used to determine fill level. Floats and switches are mechanical devices and can fail. It is important to always have a good idea how much room is in the cylinder and how much refrigerant will be recovered before starting.

26.23 RECOVERY TECHNIQUES

Remembering a few simple ideas will speed up refrigerant recovery.

- If possible, operate the system before beginning refrigerant recovery.
- Use the large diameter, short length hoses.
- Recover liquid first.
- Begin recovery at the lowest available access point.
- Heat the system from which refrigerant is being recovered.
- Cool the cylinder the refrigerant is going into.
- Recover from both sides of the system during vapor recovery.

Operate the System

If possible, operate the system before beginning refrigerant recovery. Refrigerant settles into the oil in the compressor. It takes a long time for recovery machines to vaporize this refrigerant out of the oil. Operating the compressor will pull the refrigerant out of the oil quicker.

Minimize Resistance Through Hoses and Connections

Short, large diameter connection hoses will reduce the restriction that the recovery equipment must pull the refrigerant through. Reducing the restriction will increase the speed of recovery and decrease the time required to recover the refrigerant.

Recover Liquid First

Remove as much liquid from the system as possible before proceeding with vapor recovery. Liquid recovery is faster than vapor recovery because a pound of vapor takes up hundreds of times more space than a pound of liquid. Vapor recovery requires the liquid to vaporize, dropping its temperature and pressure. Liquid is removed either from the king valve on the liquid receiver, or from the liquid service valve at the end of the condenser.

Let Gravity Help

When working on a system that has a difference in height between components, try to start your recovery at the lowest available access point. Rather than trying to pull liquid up hill against gravity, let gravity push the liquid down. For example, liquid recovery is normally done from the king valve on

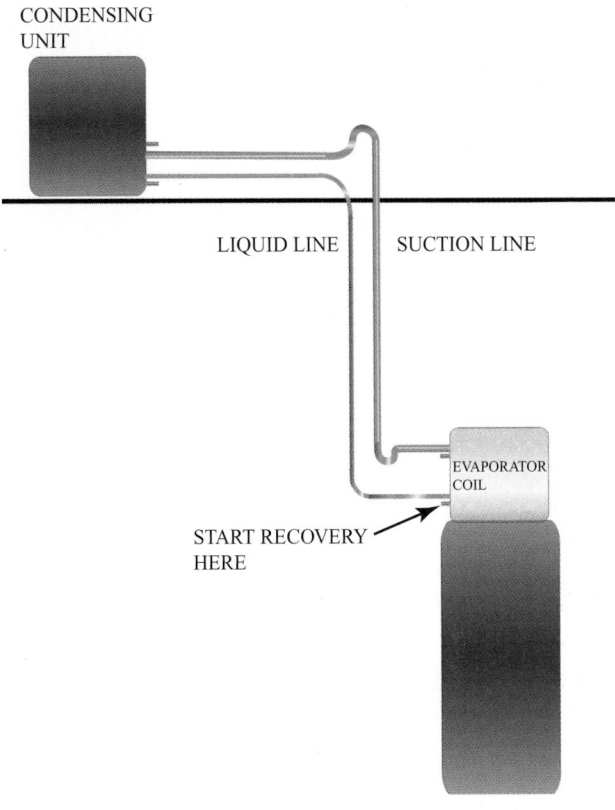

Figure 26-26 Begin recovery at the liquid line entering the evaporation when the condenser is located above the evoporator

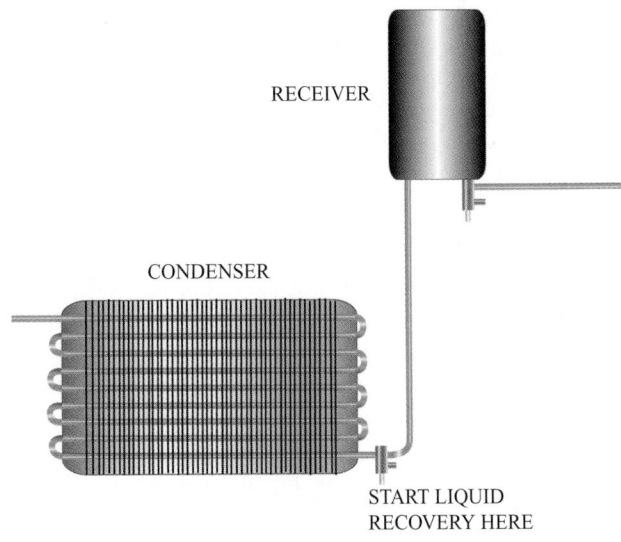

Figure 26-27 Begin recovery at the outlet of the condenser when the condenser is located below the receiver

the liquid receiver, but when the condensing unit is located above the evaporator, liquid recovery should start at the liquid line at the evaporator instead, Figure 26-26. Similarly, if the receiver is located above the condenser, start liquid recovery at the outlet of the condenser, Figure 26-27.

Figure 26-28 The frost line on this accumulator indicates there is still liquid sitting in the bottom

Figure 26-29 Cooling the recovery cylinder in ice can speed system recovery by keeping the cylinder pressure low

Heat the System

One of the basic principles behind the refrigeration cycle is that pressure and temperature move up and down together. Heating the system both before and during recovery will increase the refrigerant pressure and the refrigerant will come out faster. Pay particular attention to spots where liquid can puddle, such as the compressor, liquid receiver, filter-driers, or accumulator, Figure 26-28. To prevent excessive pressures, the system should not be heated with torches or steam, but with warm air or water.

Cool the Cylinder

The refrigerant recovery cylinder should be cooled in addition to heating the system. Cooling the cylinder will decrease its pressure and speed the recovery process. Cylinders can be cooled with ice, chemicals, or by active cooling, Figure 26-29. Active cooling involves connecting the recovery machine inlet to the vapor port on the cylinder and connecting the recovery machine outlet to the liquid valve on the cylinder, Figure 26-30. This turns the cylinder into an evaporator, cooling off the liquid and dropping its pressure. Some recovery units have this ability built in. They always connect to the cylinder with two hoses instead of one, Figure 26-31.

Recovering from Both Sides of the System

Vapor recovery is required to completely evacuate a system down to the EPA specified level. The recovery machine

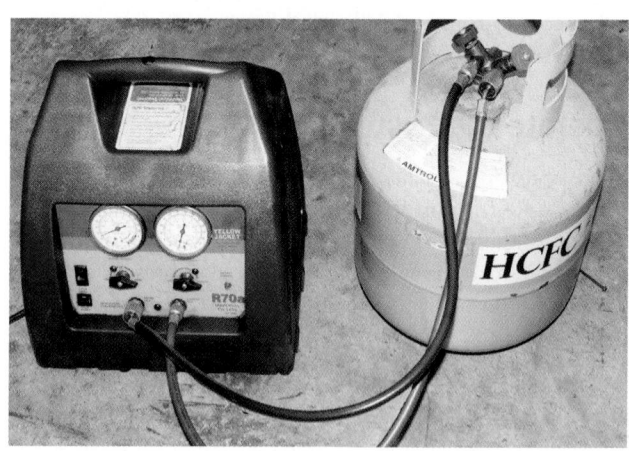

Figure 26-30 Recovery unit connected to cylinder to perform active cooling on the cylinder

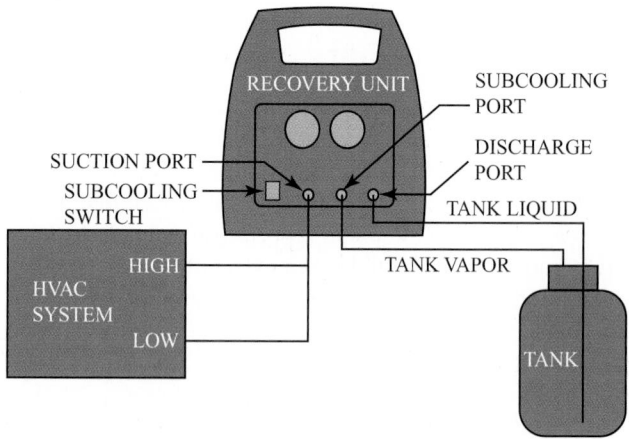

Figure 26-31 Recovery unit with subcooling connection for maintaining a low recovery cylinder temperature and pressure
(Courtesy of Ritchie Engineering Company, Inc.—YELLOW JACKET Products)

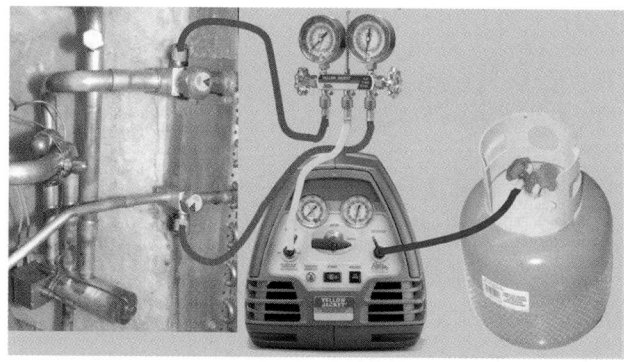

Figure 26-32 Recovery from both sides of the system when performing vapor refrigerant recovery

should be recovering from both sides of the system simultaneously during vapor recovery, Figure 26-32. Attempting vapor recovery through just one port requires some of the gas to travel through either the metering device or the compressor, drastically increasing the time required.

Wait Before Opening System

After recovering refrigerant to the required level, wait to be sure that the pressure in the system does not rise above the prescribed level. Any refrigerant that is pooled up in pockets like the compressor crankcase, receiver, filter-drier, or traps will vaporize and raise the pressure in the system as it heats up. Heating the system at these locations can help combat this. It generally saves time to evacuate beyond the required level because a slight pressure rise is almost guaranteed.

26.24 TYPE I REFRIGERANT RECOVERY

Some recovery techniques are unique to Type I appliances. Most Type I appliances do not have any type of service valves. The technician will have to add some type of service aperture before any refrigerant can be recovered. The EPA requires all Type I appliances to have a process stub or other "equally effective service aperture." That is what most Type I systems have: a short piece of copper tubing that has been pinched closed on the end and brazed up, Figure 26-33. The only way this can be used is to pierce it with a piercing valve or piercing pliers. Bolt on valves are more convenient and are relatively easy to use, but they frequently leak, Figure 26-34. They should not be left on the system for permanent access because of the relatively high probability of future leaks. Braze on piercing valves are brazed to the line prior to piercing the tubing, and are therefore less likely to leak, Figure 26-35. They can be used for both recovery and permanent access. However, using braze on piercing valves raises a safety issue. Most equipment manufacturers caution

against brazing on a system under pressure, but that is exactly what must be done to install a braze on piercing valve. Another option for gaining system access is to use a set of piercing pliers, Figure 26-36. Piercing pliers allow refrigerant recovery from Type I appliances without leaving a valve on the system.

Figure 26-33 Process stub on a compressor

Figure 26-34 Bolt on piercing valve installed on a system

Figure 26-35 Braze on piercing valve installed on a system

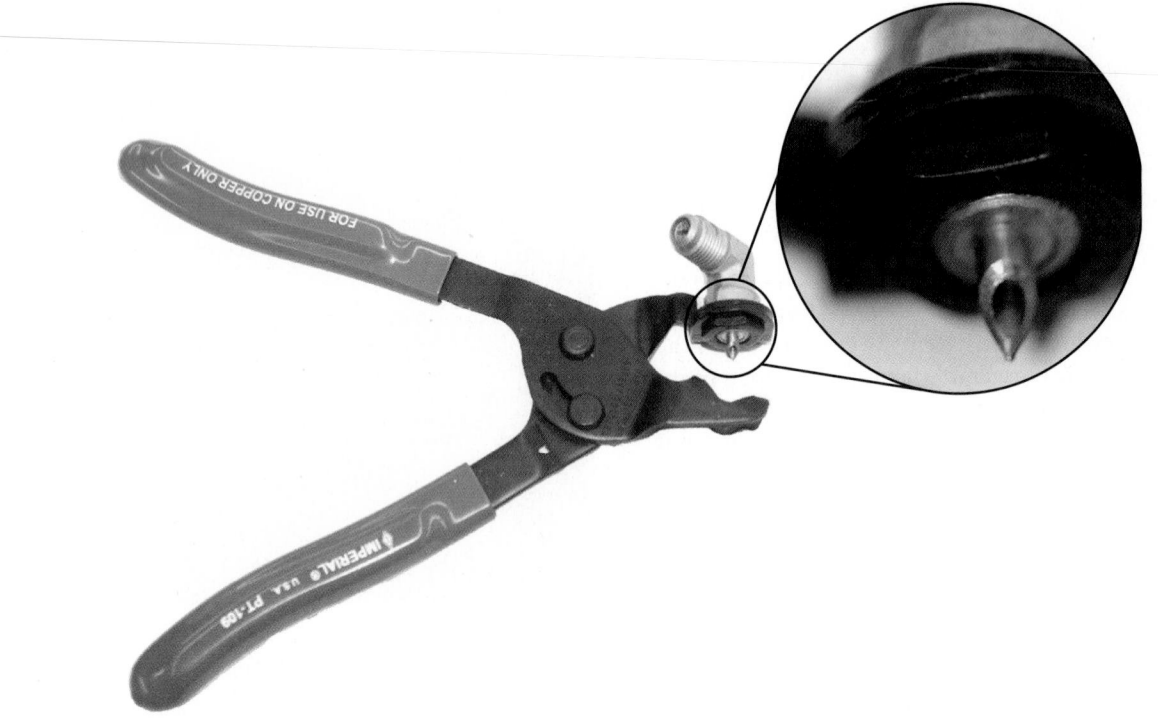

Figure 26-36 Piercing pliers

Schraeder valves work for permanent access valves, but can only be installed on a system that has already been evacuated, Figure 26-37. You should always check Schrader valves for leaks when working on systems using Schrader valves and replace leaky cores when necessary. Replace the valve caps after completing work on the system to avoid leaks.

Refrigerants That Should Not Be Recovered

Always check an appliance's data plate for the type and amount of refrigerant before beginning recovery. This is especially true for small appliances. Some refrigerators built before 1950 contain poisonous chemicals such as sulfur dioxide, methyl chloride, and ammonia, Figure 26-38. None of

these noxious chemicals are covered under the refrigerant recovery rules. However, for safety reasons, they should not be casually released to the air. Refer these systems to someone who is trained in handling them.

26.25 TYPE II REFRIGERANT RECOVERY

Type II systems cover the widest variety of applications, so the recovery techniques and equipment used for different Type II applications also varies widely. However, the order of preference for speed of recovery from a Type II system is usually:

- Recover into the receiver, also known as pumping a system down.

Figure 26-37 Schrader access valve on process stub of small appliance

- Push-pull.
- Liquid recovery.
- Vapor recovery.

Recover Into the Receiver

On systems with liquid receivers and king valves, time can be saved by pumping the system down into the receiver using the system compressor. Although the EPA uses the phrase "recover the refrigerant into the receiver," this is more commonly known as "pumping the system down" in the field. Pumping all of the refrigerant into the receiver traps all the refrigerant between the discharge valve on the compressor and the king valve on the receiver, Figure 26-39. This is accomplished by front seating the king valve and operating the system until the pressure on the low side of the system is at the EPA required recovery level, Figure 26-40. It is much faster to move the refrigerant into the receiver or the condenser than it is to recover all of it. Pumping a system down is only an option if the system compressor operates and the part of the system to be serviced is on the low side of the system or on the liquid line after the king valve. It will not work for repairing anything between the compressor discharge valve and the liquid receiver king valve.

Many systems that do not have receivers can still be pumped down. Most air conditioning systems have liquid line service valves and condensers large enough to hold an entire system charge, Figure 26-41. Residential air conditioners are normally shipped with an entire system charge trapped in the

Figure 26-38 These old "monitor top" refrigerators contain SO_2; this refrigerant should not be recovered
(Science Museum/Science & Society Picture Library)

condenser. However, if the system has lines over 50 ft, or if it has been overcharged, the condenser may not hold the entire system charge. The compressor discharge pressure should be monitored while pumping down a system. It will become very high if the condenser fills with liquid and there is no more room for vapor. This can cause loud noises from inside the compressor when the internal pressure relief valve opens.

Push-Pull Recovery

Many recovery machine manufacturers rate the maximum speed of their recovery unit using the push-pull recovery method. The push-pull recovery method pushes the gas discharged from the recovery machine into one part of the refrigerant system while pulling liquid out of the system.

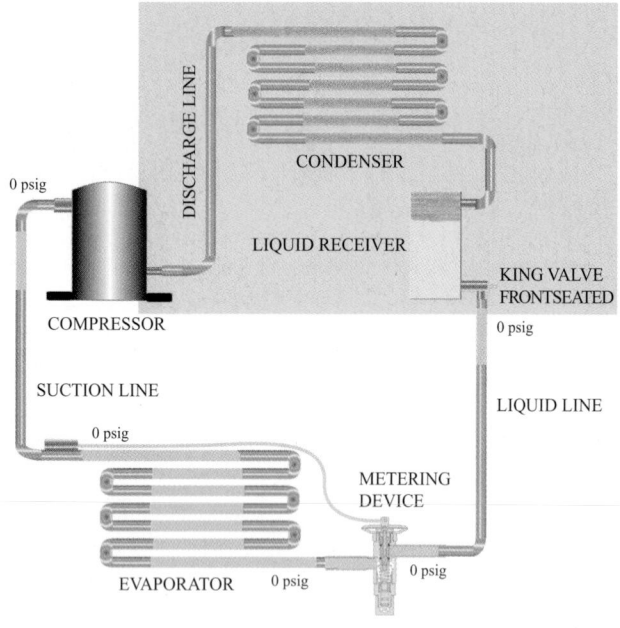

Figure 26-39 All the refrigerant is trapped between the compressor discharge valve and the king valve when the system is pumped down

Figure 26-40 Front seating the king valve keeps refrigerants from leaving the liquid receiver

In push-pull mode either the liquid line service valve or the king valve is connected to the liquid valve on the recovery cylinder. The vapor valve on the recovery cylinder is connected to the suction side, or inlet, of the recovery machine. The discharge, or outlet, of the recovery machine is connected to the discharge service valve on the compressor. Figure 26-42 shows the correct connections for push-pull liquid refrigerant recovery.

When the recovery machine runs, it will pressurize the condenser by pushing gas into the condenser. The pressure of the recovery cylinder will be reduced because the recovery machine is pulling gas from it. At the same time, pulling gas off of the recovery cylinder forces some of the liquid in the cylinder to boil. This reduces its temperature and pressure.

Figure 26-41 The liquid line service valve on residential split systems can be used to pump the system down

The result is an increased pressure difference between the system and the recovery cylinder. This produces the fastest rate of recovery because the liquid leaves the refrigeration system quickly without having to boil. Not having to boil the liquid in the system keeps the system temperature and pressure higher, helping to maintain the high pressure difference.

One limitation of the push-pull setup is that all the system charge cannot be recovered this way. After recovering liquid, the recovery machine will have to be reconnected to finish by recovering vapor.

Liquid Recovery Without Push-Pull

Push-pull works well for systems with large amounts of liquid sitting in a receiver. However, it is much less effective with smaller residential air conditioning equipment and heat pumps.

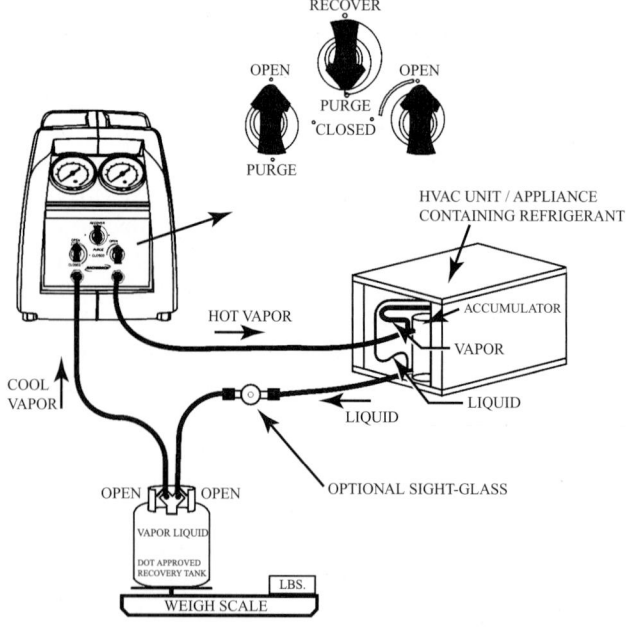

Figure 26-42 Liquid recovery using the push-pull method
(Courtesy of Bacharach, Inc.)

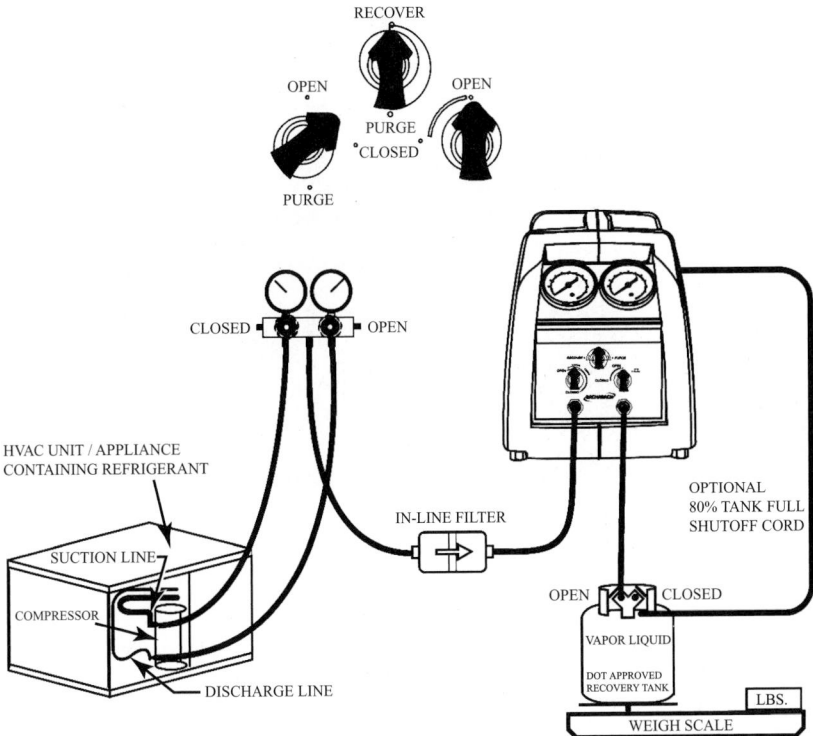

Figure 26-43 Recovery unit connected for direct liquid refrigerant recovery *(Courtesy of Bacharach, Inc.)*

Most recovery units today have a setting for recovering liquid directly. They do this by having a built in restriction that acts like a metering device to flash off the liquid before it reaches the recovery unit's compressor. This setting can be used to start the recovery process with liquid and switch over to vapor without moving hoses.

First, check the weight of the recovery cylinder to make sure it has room for the refrigerant in the system. Use the procedure outlined in Section 26.22 to determine the total weight of the cylinder and refrigerant when filled to the maximum safe fill level of 80%. Weigh the cylinder. Subtract the actual cylinder weight from the maximum safe fill level weight; the difference is the amount of room in the cylinder. The amount of room left in the cylinder should exceed the amount of charge listed on the equipment data plate.

Figure 26-43 shows a typical setup for recovering liquid refrigerant from a residential split system. The gauges are connected as they normally are, with the high side manifold hose connected to the liquid line service valve and the low side manifold hose connected to the suction service valve. The center manifold hose connects to the inlet of the recovery unit and the outlet of the recovery unit connects to the vapor port on the recovery cylinder.

All hoses should be purged of air before proceeding with recovery. The high side manifold gauge valve should be opened, the recovery inlet valve set for liquid recovery, the recovery outlet valve opened, and the refrigerant cylinder vapor valve opened, Figure 26-44. Operate the recovery unit and watch the pressures in the system and on the recovery unit gauges. An operating recovery system should not be left unattended. Most of the liquid will have been removed when the system pressure is substantially less than the saturation

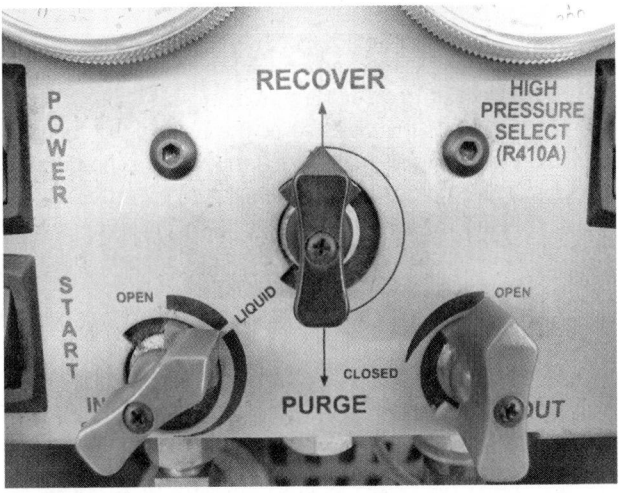

Figure 26-44 The recovery unit's valves are positioned for liquid recovery

pressure corresponding to the system temperature. The gauges and hose connections will feel cold as liquid flashes off coming through them. When all the liquid has been recovered, those parts that were cold will begin to warm up. After all the liquid has been removed, switch to vapor recovery to finish.

Vapor Refrigerant Recovery

To switch from direct liquid recovery to vapor, put the recovery inlet valve to vapor, Figure 26-45. This lets the vapor flow into the recovery unit unrestricted and speeds vapor recovery.

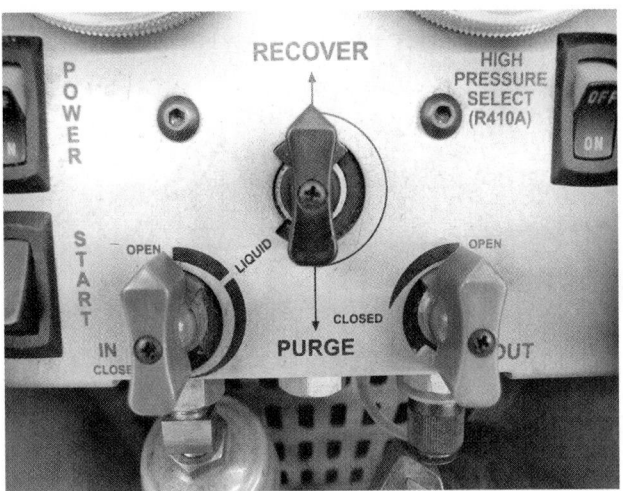

Figure 26-45 The recovery unit's valves are positioned for vapor recovery

Figure 26-47 The recovery unit valves are positioned to purge its condenser of refrigerant

Open both manifold valves so that the recovery unit pulls from both sides of the system. Any remaining cold pockets in the system should be heated using a heat gun. Monitor the system pressures and let the recovery go a little past the EPA mandated recovery level. For example, if the system holds less than 200 lb of R-22, the recovery level is 0 psig. Recover down to 5–10 in Hg vacuum instead of stopping at 0 psig. After achieving a vacuum slightly lower than the target vacuum, close the manifold valves and shut off the recovery machine, Figure 26-46. Wait to see if the system pressures are going to stay under the EPA mandated level. It is normal for the pressure in the system to rise a little, that is why it is a good idea to recover past the required level. If the system pressure is stable and at or below the EPA mandated level, the recovery is complete. Put the recovery machine valves in the purge position and operate the recovery machine until it has moved the refrigerant trapped in it into the recovery cylinder, Figure 26-47.

Figure 26-46 Recovering to 5 in Hg vacuum will help ensure that the system pressure will stay at or below 0 psig when the recovery unit is shut off

This normally only takes a few minutes. Close all valves before breaking down the recovery setup.

26.26 VERY HIGH PRESSURE RECOVERY

Very high pressure refrigerants have saturated pressures in a range of 250–700 psig at room temperature. They are used in low-temperature systems and cascade systems. Cascade systems are actually a combination of two refrigeration cycles. The evaporator of one is used to cool the condenser of the other. The system operating at the highest temperatures uses a "normal" high pressure refrigerant such as R-404A. The system with the ultra-low evaporator temperature uses a very high pressure refrigerant, such as R-508. Technicians should be aware of which system they are recovering from when working on cascade systems. A recovery system that is certified for R-404A is not suitable for recovering R-508.

Recovery machines and cylinders for very high pressure refrigerants are designed for the extreme pressures of these refrigerants. Never use a recovery machine that is not specifically designed for very high pressure refrigerant. It is a violation of EPA regulations to use a recovery unit that is not ARI/UL certified for the type of refrigerant being serviced. Figure 26-48 shows a recovery unit specifically certified for very high pressure refrigerant.

SAFETY TIP

Always check the ARI/UL rating on the recovery device before using it, especially with very high pressure refrigerants. Using a "standard" recovery unit on a system with very high pressure refrigerant is extremely dangerous because the components in the device are not designed to withstand the extreme pressures of very high pressure refrigerant.

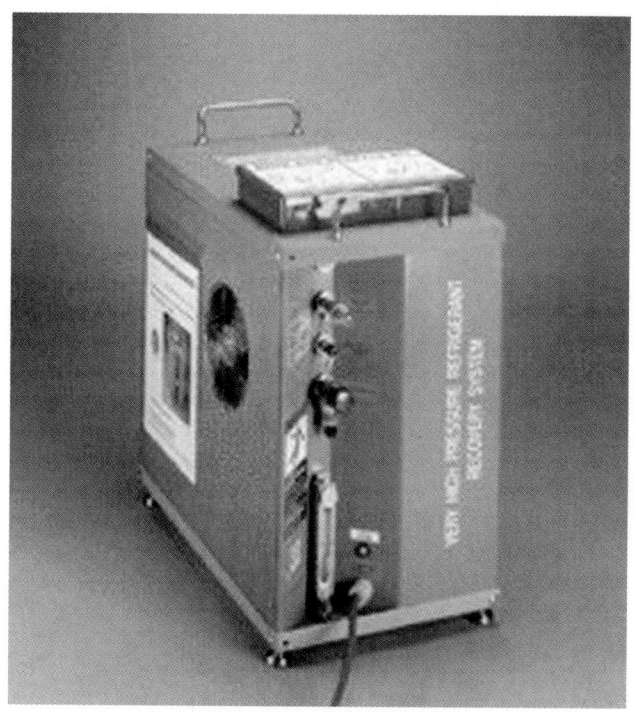

Figure 26-48 Very high pressure recovery unit
(Courtesy of Redi Controls, Inc. Refrigerant Mizer Model RS-503/13-C3)

26.27 CHILLERS AND WATER COOLED SYSTEMS

Recovering vapor from a system that still has liquid refrigerant in it forces the liquid to boil to replace the vapor. The liquid temperature and pressure drop as a result. Recovering vapor refrigerant from water cooled systems or chillers can drop the temperature and pressure of the refrigerant to the point that water in the chiller tubes or condenser shells begins to freeze. Freezing the water in tubes or shells can cause extensive damage to the system when the ice expands. Always recover liquid first from any system with water in either side to prevent damaging the system! Liquid does not have to boil to make vapor

during liquid recovery, so the system pressure and temperature will not drop as rapidly. Another trick is to circulate the water while recovering the refrigerant. Running water is far less likely to freeze. It is possible to remove all the water from small systems, but this is normally not practical in larger systems.

26.28 TYPE III REFRIGERANT RECOVERY

The vast majority of Type III systems are chillers, so the procedures in the previous section on chillers also apply to these systems.

Evaporator Operates in Vacuum

The fact that the evaporator on a low pressure chiller operates in a vacuum presents some unique problems. The recovery levels for low pressure systems are very low: 25 in Hg of vacuum for recovery machines built before November 15, 1993 and 25 mm absolute pressure for recovery machines built on or after November 15, 1993.

Purge Unit

All low pressure systems have purge units. These units purge the system of air that sucks into the low side during system operation because of system leaks in the low side, Figure 26-49. Air sucks in rather than refrigerant leaking out because the air pressure in the room exceeds the pressure in the evaporator, which is in a vacuum. Since air is a noncondensable, it travels to the condenser and stops there. A buildup of noncondensables increases the system high side pressure and reduces its efficiency. A purge unit gets rid of the gas at the top of the condenser where noncondensables collect. The purge unit on a system that is relatively leak free will not operate very much because noncondensables are not collecting in the system. On the other hand, a leaky system will have a lot of purge operation because noncondensables will constantly be entering the system through the leaks on the low side.

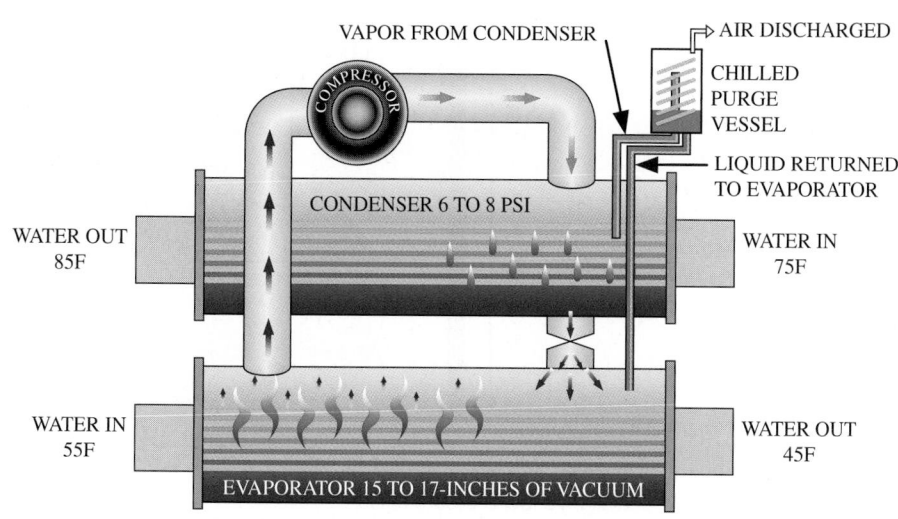

Figure 26-49 Purge unit on low pressure chiller
(Courtesy of Reftec International Inc. 800-214-4883.)

Figure 26-50 Circulating warm water in a low pressure chiller to raise the evaporator pressure to 0 psig
(Courtesy of Reftec International Inc. 800-214-4883.)

Minor Repair Exclusion

The minor repair exclusion can be used with low pressure systems. However, instead of recovering refrigerant to reach 0 psig, the low side pressure must be raised to 0 psig before opening the system for service for a minor repair since the low side is normally in a vacuum.

Raising the Low Side Pressure

One common low pressure refrigerant, CFC-11, has a boiling point of 75°F. This means that the system pressure will be below 0 psig any time the system temperature is below 75°F. If the low side of a low pressure system is opened, it will suck in air. This will lead to increased purge operation when the system is put back into operation. Purge operation should be minimized since some refrigerant is always lost when operating the purge unit.

There are two common methods used for raising the pressure of the evaporator on a low pressure chiller: adding nitrogen until the pressure comes up to 0 psig or circulating warm water through the chiller tubes. Adding nitrogen is better for the system than letting a bunch of air suck in because the air will contain oxygen and water as well as nitrogen. Since both these contaminants can harm the system, they are to be avoided. However, adding nitrogen is discouraged by the EPA because it increases the purge operation and increased purge operation amounts to increased refrigerant release. The EPA endorses circulating warm water through the chiller bundle to raise the evaporator pressure. The increase in temperature will cause a corresponding increase in pressure in the chiller, Figure 26-50.

SAFETY TIP

Be careful while circulating water in low-pressure chillers! The heat from the pump motors can heat the refrigerant in the chiller enough to build pressures over 15 psig, the point where the rupture disk opens. All the system refrigerant can be lost if the rupture disk breaks. This is an expensive accident for a system that holds thousands of dollars worth of refrigerant.

Rupture Disk

All low pressure chillers have a rupture disk on the evaporator which opens at 15 psig and vents all the refrigerant out of the evaporator, Figure 26-51. This is a physical safety device that

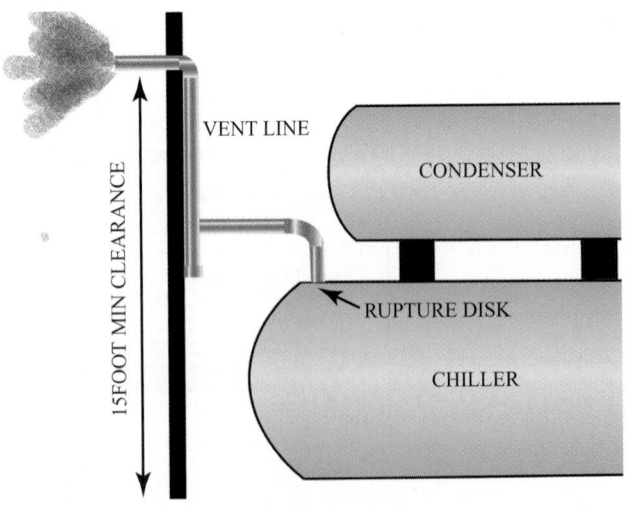

Figure 26-51 Refrigerant escaping through a broken rupture disk on a low pressure chiller

26.39 TIMELINE

The timeline below shows where we have been and where we are going in recognizing and addressing the problem of stratospheric ozone depletion.

1974	Molina-Rowland propose the ozone depletion theory
1985	Vienna Convention begins global co-operation to study ozone depletion
1987	Montreal Protocol proposes concrete steps to regulate ozone depleting substances
1990	US passes Clean Air Act amendments
July 1, 1992	Venting ban on ozone depleting refrigerants from stationary equipment
May 14, 1993	Final ruling outlining required practices
July 13, 1993	Evacuation requirements published in May ruling take effect
November 15 1993	Refrigerant recovery machines must be certified
November 14, 1994	Technicians must be certified
November 14, 1994	CFC and HCFC refrigerant sold only to certified technicians
November 15, 1995	Venting ban on HFC refrigrants
January 1, 1996	CFCs may not be manufactured or imported
Jan 1, 2010	No more manufacture of new systems containing R-22
Jan 1, 2020	No more manufacture or importing of R-22 and R-142b
January 2030	No more manufacture or importing of any HCFC refrigerant

26.40 CERTIFICATION OUTLINE

The EPA provides an outline of the topics covered in the different sections of the certification exam. This outline is provided below along with the section of text which covers each specific piece of information.

CORE

Ozone Depletion
Destruction of ozone by chlorine *23.16*
Presence of chlorine in CFC and HCFC refrigerants *23.6, 23.8–23.10*
Identification of CFC, HCFC, and HFC refrigerants *23.6, 23.8–23.10*
CFCs have higher ODP than HCFCs, which have higher ODP than HFCs *23.16*
Health and environmental effects of ozone depletion *23.16*
Evidence of ozone depletion and role of CFCs and HCFCs *23.16*

Clean Air Act and Montreal Protocol
CFC phaseout date *23.9*
Venting prohibition at servicing *26.5*

Venting prohibition at disposal *26.5, 26.16*
Venting prohibition on substitute refrigerants in November, 1995 *23.11*
Maximum penalty under CAA *26.3*
Montreal Protocol *26.2*

Section 608 Regulations
Definition/identification of high and low-pressure refrigerants *23.5*
Definition of system-dependent vs. self-contained recovery/recycling equipment *26.19*
Identification of equipment covered by the rule *26.4*
Need for third-party certification of recycling and recovery equipment *26.9*
Standard for reclaimed refrigerant, ARI 700 *23.22*

Substitute Refrigerants and Oils
Absence of "drop-in" replacements *23.23*
Incompatibility of substitute refrigerants with mineral oil *23.22*
Fractionation problem in blends *23.13*

Refrigeration
Refrigerant states and pressures at different points of refrigeration cycle *17.2*
Refrigeration gauges (color codes, ranges of different types, proper use) *25.6*

Three Rs
Definition of recover *26.8*
Definition of recycle *26.8*
Definition of reclaim *26.8*

Recovery Techniques
Need to avoid mixing refrigerants *26.23*
Factors affecting speed of recovery *26.23*

Dehydration Evacuation
Need to evacuate system to eliminate air and moisture at the end of service *27.1–27.4*

Safety
Risks of exposure to refrigerant *23.15*
Personal protective equipment *23.15*
Reusable cylinders vs. disposable cylinders *23.24–23.26*
Risks of filling cylinders more than 80% full *23.27*
Use of nitrogen rather than oxygen or compressed air for leak detection *26.33*
Use of pressure regulator and relief valve with nitrogen *26.34*

Shipping
Labels required for refrigerant cylinders *26.32*

TYPE 1 (Small Appliances)

Recovery Requirements
Definition of "small appliance" *26.6*
Evacuation requirements using equipment made before November 15, 1993 *26.13*
Evacuation requirements using recovery equipment made after November 15, 1993 *26.13*

Recovery Techniques

Identify refrigerants and detecting noncondensables *23.21*

Recovering refrigerant using a system-dependent recovery device *26.19*

Recover from both high and low side with inoperative compressors *26.19*

Run system compressor when using a system-dependent recovery device *26.19*

Should remove solderless access fittings at conclusion of service *26.25*

R-134a as likely substitute for R-12 *23.23, 23.28*

Safety

Decomposition products of refrigerants at high temperatures (HCl, HFl, etc.) *23.15*

TYPE 2 (High-Pressure)

Leak Detection

Signs of leakage in high-pressure systems *27.24–27-27, 26.38*

Need to leak test before charging or recharging equipment *26.35*

Order of preference for leak test gases *26.34*

Leak Repair Requirements

Allowable annual leak rate for commercial and industrial process refrigeration *26.33*

Allowable annual leak rate for other appliances *26.33*

Recovery Techniques

Recovering liquid at beginning of recovery process speeds up process *26.23*

Other methods for speeding recovery *26.23*

Methods for reducing cross-contamination and emissions *26.23*

Need to wait a few minutes after reaching required recovery *26.23*

Recovery Requirements

Evacuation requirements for high-pressure appliances in each of the following situations:

    Disposal *26.14, 26.16*

    Major vs. non-major repairs *26.11*

    Leaky vs. non-leaky appliances *26.11, 26.30*

    Appliance (or component) containing less vs. more than 200 lb *26.14*

    Recovery/recycling equipment built before vs. after November 15, 1993 *26.12*

    Definition of "major" repairs *26.11*

    System-dependent prohibition on systems exceeding 15 lb of refrigerant *26.19*

Refrigeration

How to identify refrigerant in appliances *27.15*

Pressure-temperature relationships of common high-pressure refrigerants *23.3*

Components of high-pressure appliances *17.4, 17.12*

Safety

Shouldn't energize hermetic compressors under vacuum. *19.6*

Equipment room requirements under ASHRAE Standard 15 *23.15*

TYPE 3 (Low-pressure)

Leak Detection

Order of preference of leak test pressurization methods *26.28*

Signs of leakage into a low-pressure system (e.g., excessive purging) *26.28*

Maximum leak test pressure for low-pressure centrifugal chillers *26.28*

Leak Repair Requirements

Allowable annual leak rate for commercial and industrial process refrigeration *26.33*

Allowable annual leak rate for other appliances exceeding 50 lb of refrigerant *26.33*

Recovery Techniques

Recovering liquid at beginning of recovery process speeds up process *26.23, 26.27*

Need to recover vapor in addition to liquid *26.23*

Need to heat oil to 130°F before removing it to minimize refrigerant release *26.28*

Circulate water in chiller during refrigerant evacuation to prevent freezing *26.27*

High-pressure cutout level of recovery devices used with low-pressure appliances *26.29*

Recharging Techniques

Need to introduce vapor before liquid to prevent freezing of water in the tubes *27.17*

Need to charge centrifugals through evaporator charging valve *27.17*

Recovery Requirements

Evacuation requirements for low-pressure appliances in each of the following situations:

    Disposal *26.15, 26.16*

    Major vs. non-major repairs *26.11*

    Leaky vs. non-leaky appliances *26.24*

    Appliance (or component) containing less vs. more than 200 lb *26.15*

    Recovery/recycling equipment built before vs. after November 15, 1993 *26.15*

    Definitions of "major" and "non-major" repairs *26.11*

    Allowable methods for pressurizing a low-pressure system for minor repair *26.28*

    Need to wait a few minutes after reaching required recovery level *26.23*

Refrigeration

Purpose of purge unit in low-pressure systems *26.28*

Pressure-temperature relationships of low-pressure refrigerants *23.3*

Safety

Equipment room requirements under ASHRAE Standard 15 *23.15*

Need to have equipment room refrigerant sensor for R-123 *23.15*

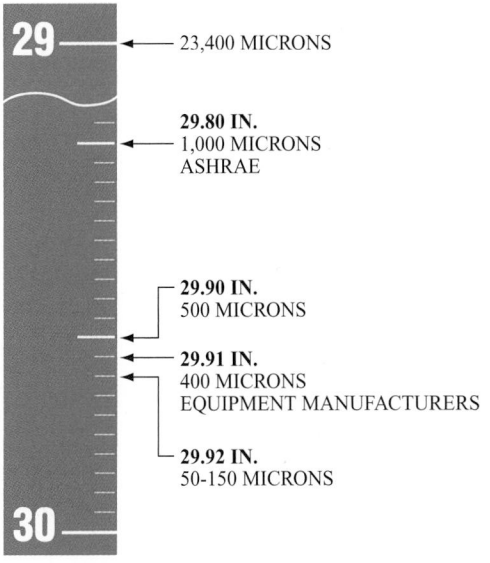

Figure 27-5 Atmospheric pressure is equal to 760,000 microns; the pressure remaining in a 500 micron vacuum is only enough pressure to support a column of mercury 500 microns high *(Courtesy of Ritchie Engineering Company, Inc.—YELLOW JACKET Products.)*

| Water Vapor Volume | | |
Saturation Temperature (°F)	Saturation Pressure (Microns)	Volume ft³ per Ounce
10	1760	566
20	2740	354
30	4180	225
40	6230	153
50	9170	106
60	13250	75
70	18740	54
80	26260	40

Figure 27-6 Volume of an ounce of vaporized water at different vacuum levels

system can be evacuated in a few minutes. It normally does not take long to remove air and noncondensables since they are already a gas. Achieving a deep vacuum on a system that is dry takes much less time than on a system that is contaminated with moisture. However, removing air and noncondensables is only one reason for evacuating a refrigeration system. Evacuating a system is also one of the principle means of dehydrating it.

27.7 SYSTEM DEHYDRATION

Dehydration is the process of removing moisture from a refrigeration system. Moisture in a system may exist as liquid or vapor. Water vapor is removed quickly along with the noncondensables. However, the water in liquid form must be vaporized before it can be removed. The amount of gas created when even a small amount of water is vaporized is quite large. Vaporizing an ounce of water at an absolute pressure of 1,000 microns of mercury creates over 500 ft³ of water vapor, Figure 27-6. It would take a 5 CFM vacuum pump an hour and 40 min to remove this much vapor!

Water in Compressor Oil

The time estimate in the above example assumes that the water is able to vaporize easily. However, water that collects below the refrigerant oil in the compressor crankcase can be more difficult to remove. Striking the compressor and applying heat to the compressor crankcase can help remove water from underneath mineral oil. A filter drier is the only reliable way to remove water from hygroscopic refrigerant

oil like polyol ester. Even a deep evacuation will normally not remove water that has been absorbed into polyol ester lubricant.

Sublimation

When systems are assembled in below freezing conditions it is possible to have ice inside the system. Frozen water can be evaporated through sublimation. Sublimation is the process of turning a solid into a gas without passing through the liquid stage. The vapor that comes off of dry ice is an example of sublimation, Figure 27-7. It is possible to dehydrate a system with ice inside it, but it is a very slow process. Heating any part of the system that is below freezing will speed up evacuation and dehydration if it has any moisture in it.

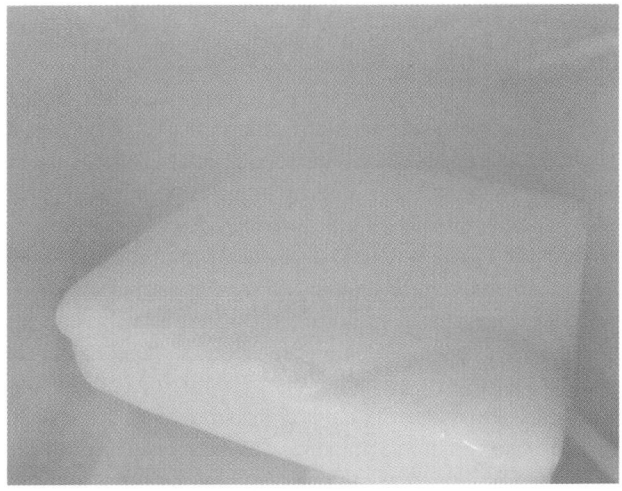

Figure 27-7 The vapor coming off of dry ice (solid carbon dioxide) is an example of sublimation

Temperature°F	Millimeters Hg absoulte pressure	Microns Hg absolute pressure	Inches Hg absolute pressure	Inches Hg vacuum
−70	0.02	20	0.0008	29.9192
−60	0.03	30	0.0012	29.9188
−50	0.07	70	0.0028	29.9172
−40	0.13	130	0.0051	29.9149
−30	0.23	230	0.0091	29.9109
−20	0.4	400	0.0157	29.9043
−10	0.68	680	0.0268	29.8932
0	1.1	1,100	0.0433	29.8767
10	1.76	1,760	0.0693	29.8507
20	2.74	2,740	0.1079	29.8121
30	4.18	4,180	0.1646	29.7554
40	6.23	6,230	0.2453	29.6747
50	9.17	9,170	0.3610	29.5590
60	13.25	13,250	0.5216	29.3984
70	18.74	18,740	0.7378	29.1822
80	26.26	26,260	1.0338	28.8862

Figure 27-8 Water will evaporate at temperatures below freezing in a vacuum

Speeding up Dehydration

During evacuation, the vacuum level in a system that has moisture in it will appear to get stuck between 1,500–5,000 microns absolute pressure. This is because the vaporizing water continually replaces the gas that is removed by the vacuum pump, preventing the pressure from dropping. If a system is suspected of having liquid water anywhere in it, every effort should be made to remove the water from the system prior to evacuation. Following good refrigeration practices will prevent water from getting into in the system in the first place. Heating any part of the system that is suspected of having moisture in it will speed up evacuation and dehydration by helping the water vaporize quickly.

Desired Evacuation Level

The lower the final system evacuation level is the better. Lower evacuation levels give more assurance of a dry system. However, the actual evacuation level required to vaporize all the water in the system is dependent on temperature. Lower system temperatures require lower levels of evacuation to ensure a dry system. Figure 27-8 shows that at an absolute pressure of 400 microns, water will vaporize as low as −20°F. A system pressure as high as 1,100 microns will vaporize water at 0°F. The most common benchmark for a good vacuum is a system pressure no higher than 500 microns of mercury absolute. Generally, a system is considered to be dehydrated if the system can hold a pressure of 500 microns Hg absolute or lower. Components with refrigeration oil cannot be evacuated lower than 200 microns absolute pressure because the oil starts to produce a vapor pressure at 200 microns absolute pressure.

Outgasing

Under deep vacuum, many materials release a small number of molecules that create a slight vapor pressure. Vacuum levels below 500 microns are difficult to maintain due to outgasing of connection hoses and materials in the refrigeration system. Refrigeration hoses do this more when they are new. Although many vacuum pumps are available that can pull down below 50 microns absolute pressure, it is not practical to evacuate most system components to this level in the field due to outgasing.

Keeping Water Out of System

It saves a great deal of time to follow good refrigeration practices when assembling systems. This includes keeping system components and piping plugged or capped while awaiting assembly and storing components with a charge of dry nitrogen to discourage the entry of air and moisture, Figure 27-9. One

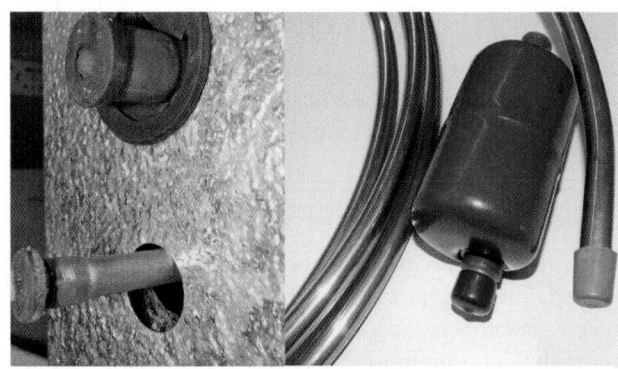

Figure 27-9 Refrigeration components should be sealed when not in use to keep out air and moisture

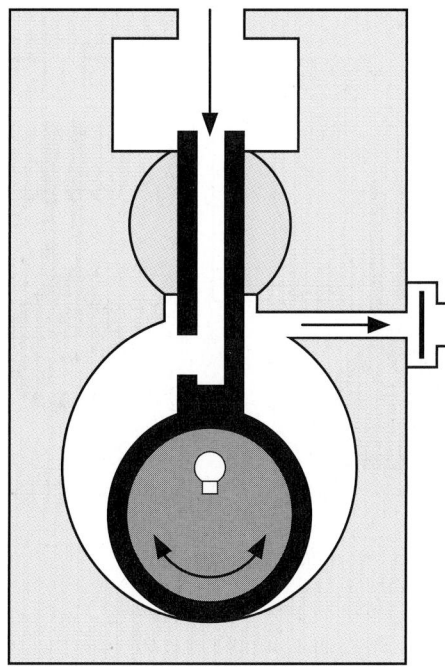

Figure 27-10 Diagram of rolling piston vacuum pump
(Courtesy of RSES)

Figure 27-11 Diagram of rotary vane vacuum pump
(Courtesy of RSES)

of the principle components of air is moisture; letting in air automatically lets in moisture as well. Allowing air in on a hot, humid day allows a significant amount of moisture in. If the component is stored on a cool location, water that came in as water vapor on a warm day may condense to droplets of liquid water, which will significantly increase the time required for system dehydration. It is far easier to keep moisture out of a system in the first place than it is to remove it.

27.8 VACUUM PUMPS

Two general designs of vacuum pumps are available: rolling piston, Figure 27-10, and rotary vane, Figure 27-11. Reciprocating piston type pumps are not used as vacuum pumps. They are incapable of producing a deep vacuum because of the clearance necessary between the piston head and valve plate. The rolling piston or the rotary vane designs are more suited for deep vacuum because neither requires any clearance volume. The rolling piston type is capable of lower pressures and is more rugged. However, they are also much heavier and more expensive, Figure 27-12. Most refrigeration vacuum pumps are rotary vane type pumps, Figure 27-13. These have the advantage of being lightweight and relatively inexpensive.

Vacuum pumps are produced in single stage and two stage models. Single stage pumps discharge directly to the atmosphere, Figure 27-14. Two stage pumps have a first stage that discharges into the suction side of the second stage,

Figure 27-12 Rolling piston vacuum pump

Figure 27-13 Rotary vane vacuum pump
(Courtesy Yellow Jacket Division, Ritchie Engineering Company)

Figure 27-14 Single stage vacuum pump
(Courtesy of RSES)

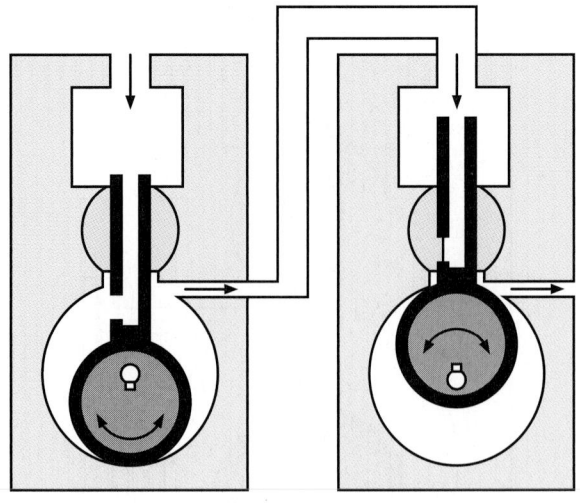

Figure 27-15 Two stage vacuum pump
(Courtesy of RSES)

Figure 27-15. Two stage pumps generally have the best record in the refrigeration industry. They are capable of producing consistently lower pressures and are generally more efficient when removing water vapor.

Gas Ballast Valve

A problem with two stage pumps is that there is a slight compression of the discharge gas coming out of the first stage and entering the second stage. This can tend to condense the water vapor being removed from the system and leave it in the vacuum pump oil. To prevent this problem, the discharge of the first stage can be directed out to the atmosphere instead of into the second stage through a valve known as a gas ballast valve, Figure 27-16. This limits

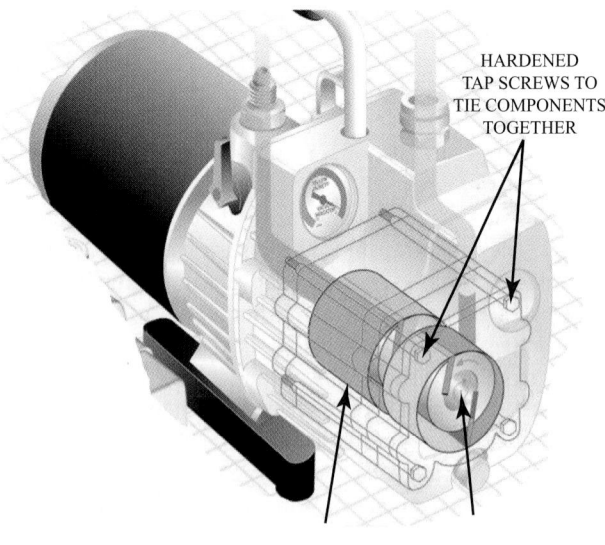

HARDENED TAP SCREWS TO TIE COMPONENTS TOGETHER

Figure 27-16 The gas ballast valve keeps water from condensing in the second stage by releasing the discharge of the first stage to atmospheric pressure
(Courtesy of Ritchie Engineering Company, Inc.— YELLOW JACKET Products)

Figure 27-17 The ballast valve is opened when starting the vacuum pump, and closed after the vacuum has pulled down to 20 in Hg

the vacuum that the pump can produce since admission of outside air will raise the absolute pressure of the second stage. The gas ballast valve is typically only open during initial pulldown. The ballast valve is closed once the system pressure has dropped to 20 in Hg vacuum, Figure 27-17.

Vacuum Pump Ratings

Vacuum pumps have two ratings, a volume capacity and a blank off pressure. The volume rating tells how fast the pump can move gas at ideal conditions. Rotary vane vacuum pumps intended for refrigeration use are available with capacities from 1 CFM up to 11 CFM. The CFM rating tells how many cubic feet of gas the pump can move in 1 min at ideal conditions. Figure 27-18 shows the suggested maximum system size for different CFM vacuum pumps.

The blank off pressure tells the lowest pressure the vacuum pump can produce. For refrigeration use, the vacuum pump blank off pressure should be no higher than 50 microns. The blank off pressure is more important to pulling a good vacuum than the CFM rating. Once the initial outrush of gas has been accomplished, the speed of evacuation has more

to do with the pressure difference between the system and the vacuum pump. The lower the pump's blank off pressure, the greater this final pressure difference will be. A 1 CFM pump with a 15 micron blank off pressure will evacuate most systems more quickly than a 10 CFM pump with a 100 micron blank off pressure.

27.9 VACUUM PUMP OIL

The oil in a vacuum pump acts as a seal as well as a lubricant for the pump. A vacuum pump cannot pull a vacuum any lower than the vapor pressure of its oil. Oil that is not intended for use in vacuum pumps has a much higher vapor pressure than vacuum pump oil, and will limit the amount of vacuum the pump can produce. Likewise, dirty oil will do the same thing. All the gases pulled out of a system by the vacuum pump pass through the vacuum pump oil. Refrigerant, water, and acids will dissolve in the oil as they pass through. Contaminants dissolved in the oil will produce a vapor pressure and limit the pump's ability to pull a good vacuum. Clean vacuum pump oil is typically clear, Figure 27-19. Vacuum pump oil that is contaminated with a large amount of water is milky or cloudy in appearance, Figure 27-20. Leaving dirty oil in a vacuum pump also exposes its internal parts to potentially corrosive chemicals, reducing its useful life. To maintain peak performance and prolong equipment life, most vacuum pump manufacturers recommend replacing the oil in the pump after each evacuation. The amount of volatile contaminants in the oil can be tested with a vacuum gauge. A vacuum pump should be able to pull down to 50 microns when connected directly to a vacuum gauge if it is in good shape and the oil is clean.

System size in tons	Pump CFM capacity
1–10	1.5
10–15	2.0
15–30	4.0
30–45	6.0
45–60	8.0
60 and above	11.0

Figure 27-18 Recommended vacuum pump capacity

Figure 27-19 The oil sight glass in a vacuum pump should show clear, clean oil

Figure 27-20 Cloudy or milky vacuum pump oil is contaminated with water

Figure 27-22 The needle thickness is equal to the space occupied by 1 in Hg vacuum on the compound gauge

27.10 VACUUM GAUGES

The compound gauge used on most gauge manifolds has a vacuum scale that reads from 0 psig down to 30 in Hg vacuum, Figure 27-21. However, mechanical gauges cannot accurately indicate the difference between a poor vacuum and a great vacuum. The needle on the gauge is typically wider than the space occupied by 1 in Hg vacuum, Figure 27-22. A high vacuum gauge is required to accurately read the vacuum on a system. The industry has developed electronic instruments to measure high vacuums.

In general, electronic vacuum gauges are heat sensing devices. The element that is connected to the system generates heat. The rate at which the heat is carried off changes as the surrounding gases and vapors are removed. The output of the sensing element changes as the heat dissipation rate changes. This output is indicated on a meter that is calibrated in microns of mercury absolute. The sensors used in these instruments are typically either a thermocouple or thermistor, Figure 27-23. Three general styles of electronic vacuum gauges are available:

- Vacuum gauges with an analog scale and needle, Figure 27-24.
- Vacuum gauges with a digital numeric display, Figure 27-25.
- Vacuum gauges with lights or segments that indicate general vacuum levels, Figure 27-26.

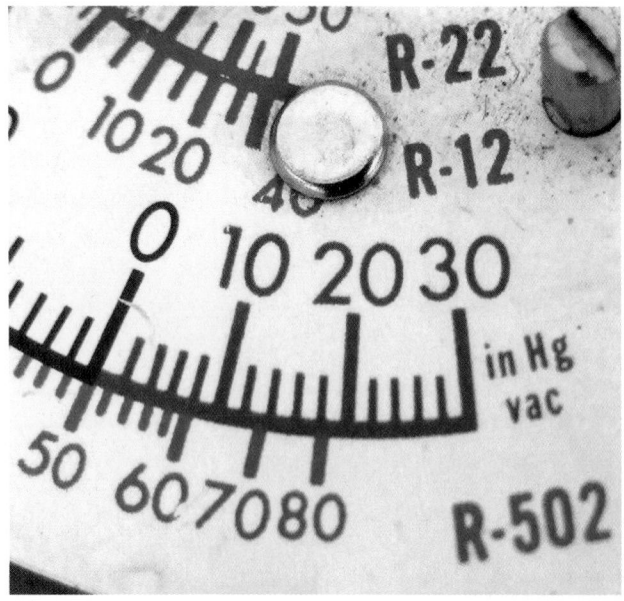

Figure 27-21 The vacuum scale on compound gauges is calibrated in Hg vacuum

Figure 27-23 Thermistor sensor used with electronic vacuum gauge

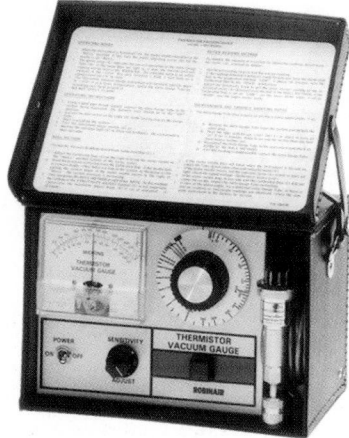

Figure 27-24 Analog electronic vacuum gauge
(Courtesy Robinair SPX/OTC)

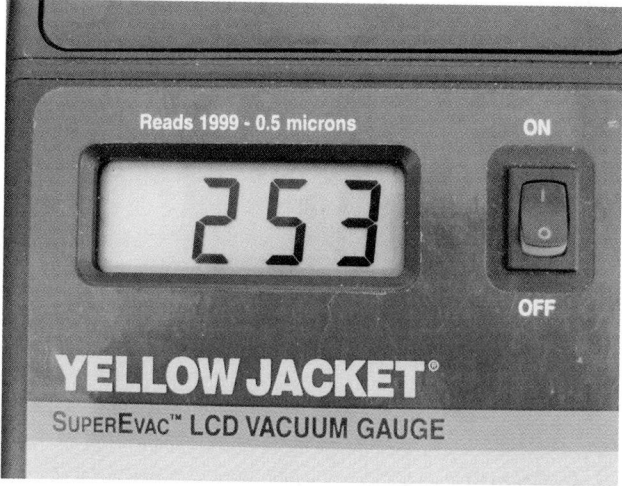

Figure 27-25 Electronic vacuum gauge with digital readout

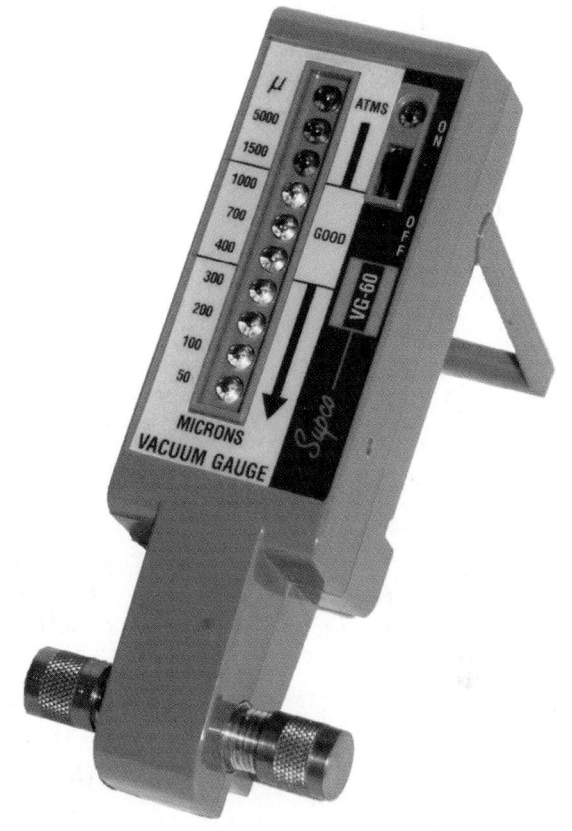

Figure 27-26 Segmented digital vacuum gauge
(Courtesy Robinair SPX/OTC)

Next, connect the gauge to a vacuum pump using as little connection hose as possible. Operate the pump. The vacuum gauge should read no higher than 50 microns. This is also a means of testing the pump. A pump with dirty oil will not pull down to its normal blank off pressure. These two tests help demonstrate that both your vacuum gauge and pump can perform their jobs.

Cleaning the Vacuum Sensor

Most vacuum sensors will not read accurately if they become dirty or contaminated with refrigeration oil. They may normally be restored to proper working condition by cleaning them using alcohol. After cleaning, turn the gauge upside down and allow the vacuum sensor to dry for 20–30 min before using the gauge.

27.11 MAINTAINING VACUUM GAUGE ACCURACY

Vacuum Gauge Calibration

Most analog vacuum gauges require calibrating before using. To calibrate the gauge, turn it on while the sensor is reading atmospheric pressure. Adjust the calibration screw until the needle indicates atmospheric pressure, Figure 27-27.

Most digital vacuum gauges sold today do not require calibration when used. However, a quick way to check the accuracy of a vacuum gauge is to turn it on while it is exposed to atmospheric pressure. The gauge should not indicate a vacuum, but should read atmospheric pressure. Segmented gauges typically have a segment at the top that indicates atmospheric pressure, Figure 27-28. Gauges with digital numeric displays typically show a single "1" to indicate atmospheric pressure, Figure 27-29.

SERVICE TIP

Do not attempt to clean the vacuum sensor by sticking Q-tips, wires, small screwdrivers, or any other crude device into the sensor. The chance of destroying the sensor this way is far greater than the chance of improving it by sticking something into it.

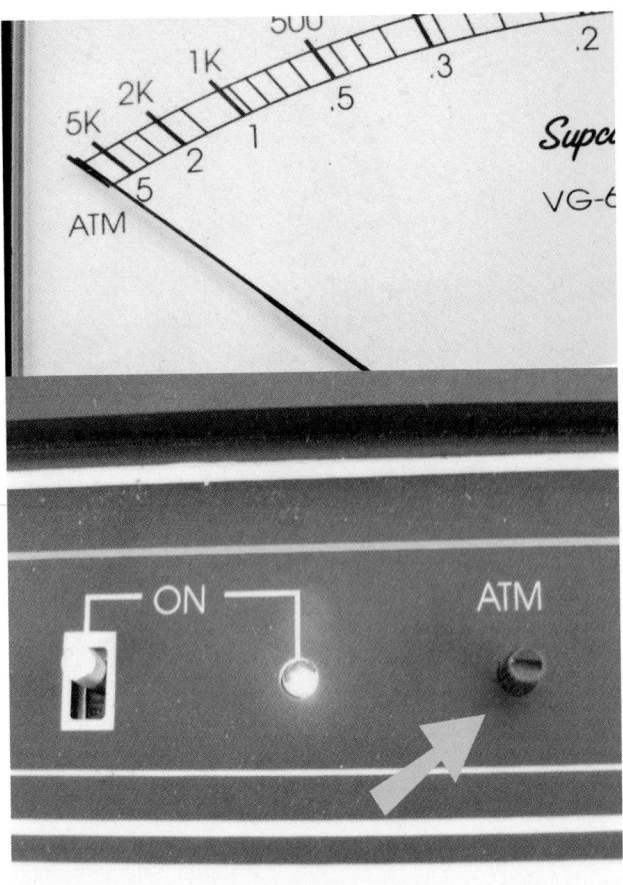

Figure 27-27 Analog vacuum gauges should be calibrated to atmospheric pressure before use

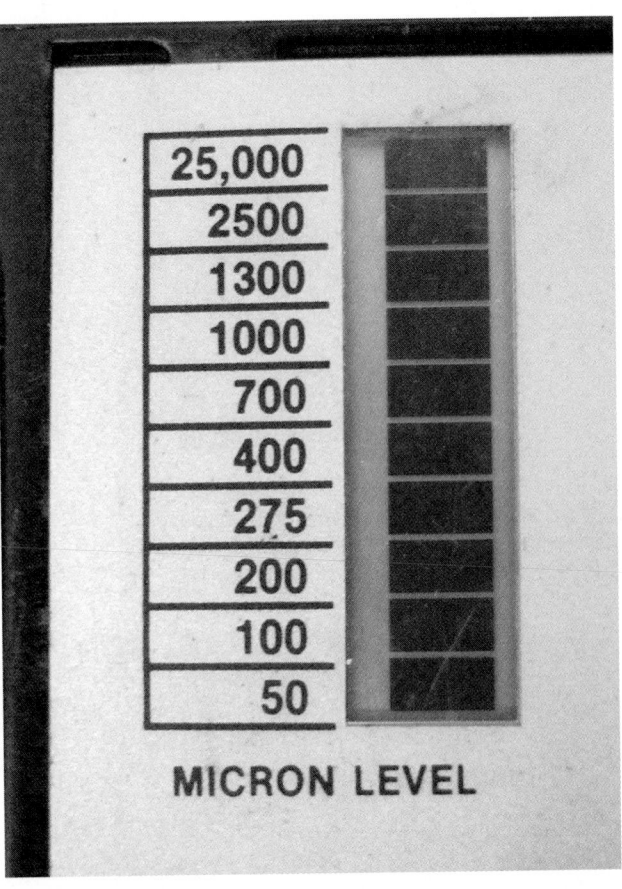

Figure 27-28 Segmented vacuum gauge showing atmospheric pressure

Maximum Pressure

Never expose the vacuum sensor to pressures higher than it is rated for. Check with the vacuum gauge manufacturer to determine the sensor's maximum pressure rating. Some vacuum sensors are designed to withstand pressures as high as 400 psig, but the sensors used with some vacuum gauges are not able to withstand high pressures. To avoid damaging these sensors, a shut off valve should be used between the sensor and the system so that the sensor may be isolated from the system before it is pressurized. This may be accomplished by connecting the vacuum gauge to the $\frac{1}{4}$ in center port on a four port manifold gauge set, Figure 27-30.

27.12 CONNECTING VACUUM GAUGES

The best place to connect a vacuum gauge is directly to the system being evacuated. The vacuum in the system will not be quite as low as the vacuum in the pump. Measuring at the system ensures accuracy. In order to connect a vacuum gauge directly to the system, either a third system access port is

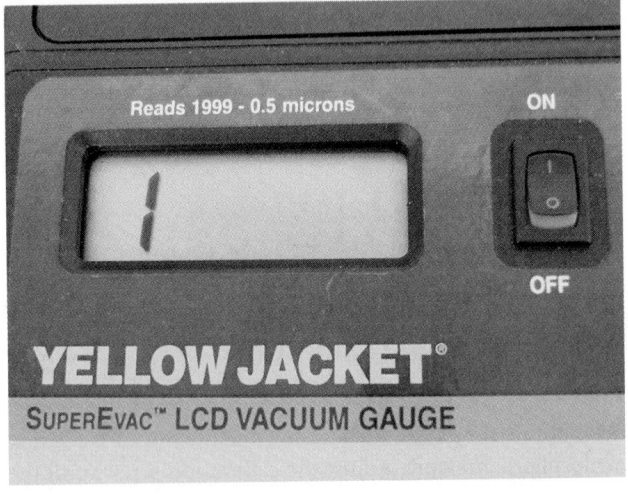

Figure 27-29 Digital vacuum gauge showing atmospheric pressure

necessary, or an adapter that allows connection of both the vacuum sensor and a charging hose to a single port can be used. A short hose or coupler is usually necessary to connect the vacuum sensor to the valve port because the connection on most vacuum gauge sensors is exactly the same as most

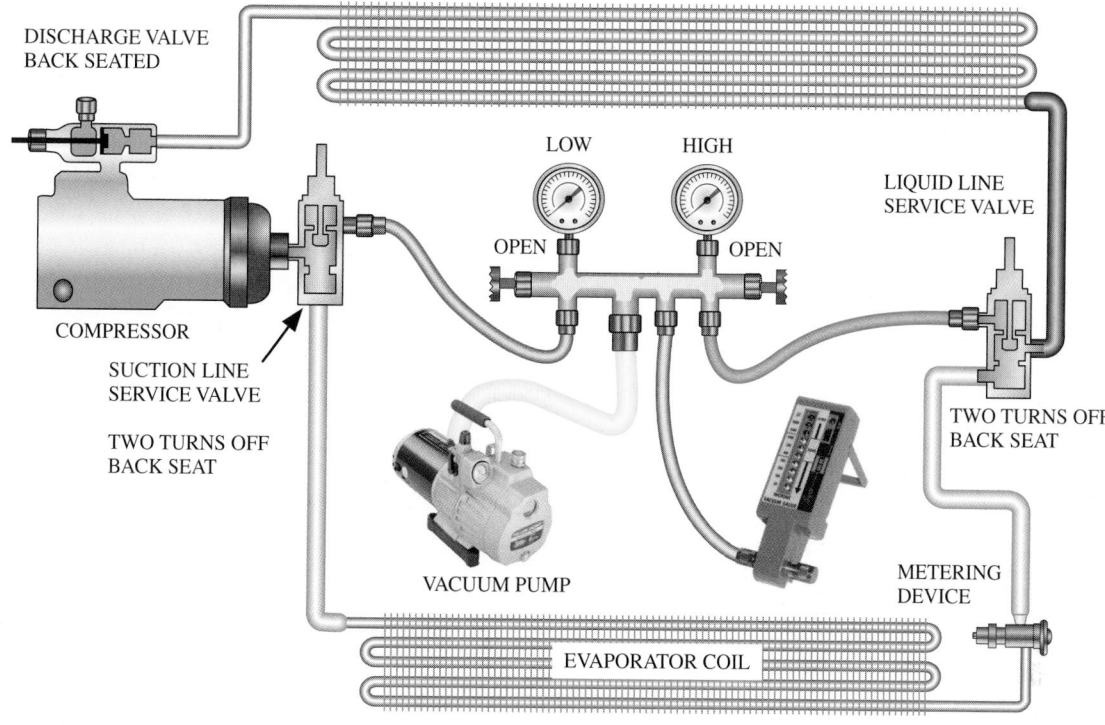

Figure 27-30 The $\frac{1}{4}$ in center port on a four port manifold can be used to connect a vacuum gauge

service valve ports, $\frac{1}{4}$ in male flare. The ideal connection is a short metal coupler, Figure 27-31.

Commercial refrigeration systems frequently have three service ports: one on the suction side of the compressor, one on the discharge side of the compressor, and one on the liquid receiver. The vacuum gauge can be connected to the discharge service valve port while the vacuum is drawn from both the suction service valve and the king valve, Figure 27-32. Heat pumps typically have a third access port that is always on the suction side of the compressor. The vacuum can be drawn through the common suction port and the liquid line port while the vacuum gauge is connected to the large gas line port, Figure 27-33.

Blank Off Valves

Many systems have only two service ports. The blank off test valve shown in Figure 27-34 allows connection of both the vacuum sensor and charging hose directly to the system. The built in shut off valves allow the vacuum sensor to be isolated from the system before it is charged.

Vacuum Manifolds

Another way to connect the vacuum gauge to the system is to use a vacuum manifold. A vacuum manifold is a device for connecting a vacuum sensor to both the system and the vacuum pump. Manifolds like the ones shown in Figure 27-35 attach to the vacuum pump and allow the connection of two $\frac{3}{8}$ in vacuum hoses as well as connection of the vacuum gauge. One problem with a vacuum manifold that connects to the vacuum pump is that the vacuum is being read at the pump instead of at the system.

Schrader Valves

Most residential systems have Schrader valves for service ports. The core in a Schrader valve is a significant restriction and increases the amount of time required to evacuate and

Figure 27-31 The vacuum gauge can be connected directly to the system using a short metal coupler or metal hose if the system has more than two gauge ports

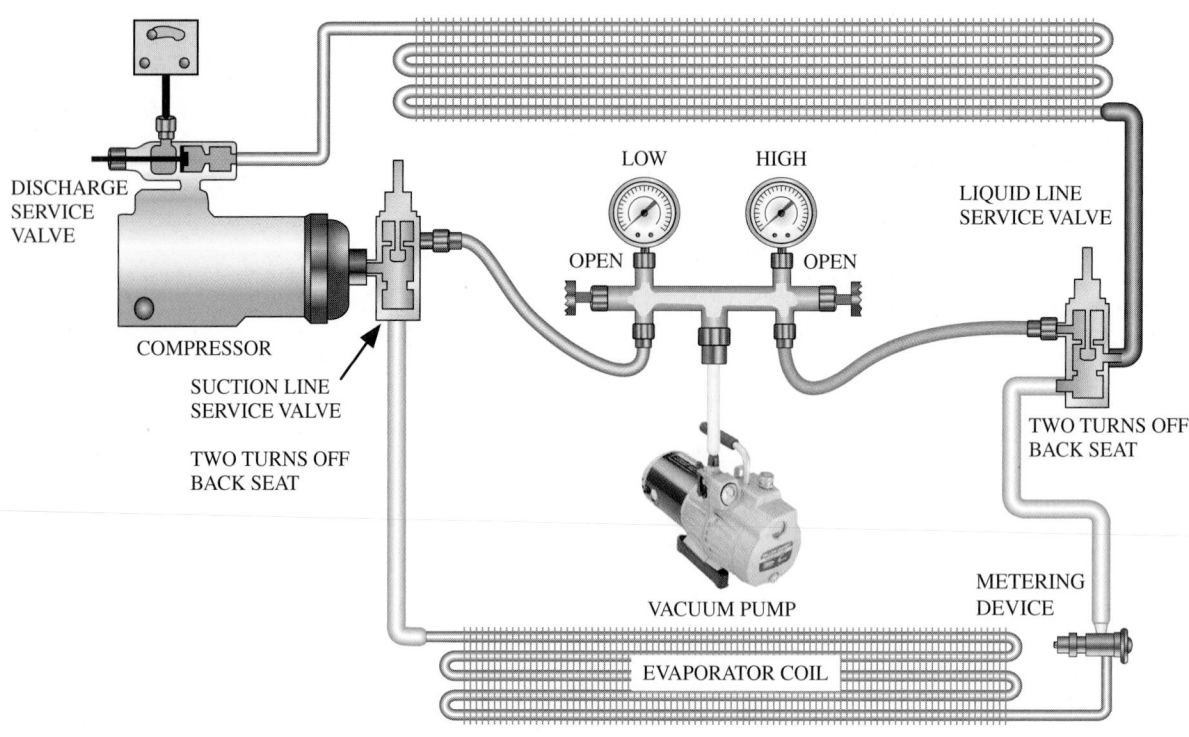

Figure 27-32 The vacuum gauge can be connected to the discharge service value on commercial systems that hare king valves

Figure 27-33 The vacuum gauge can be connected to the vapor line port on heat pump systems that have a common suction port

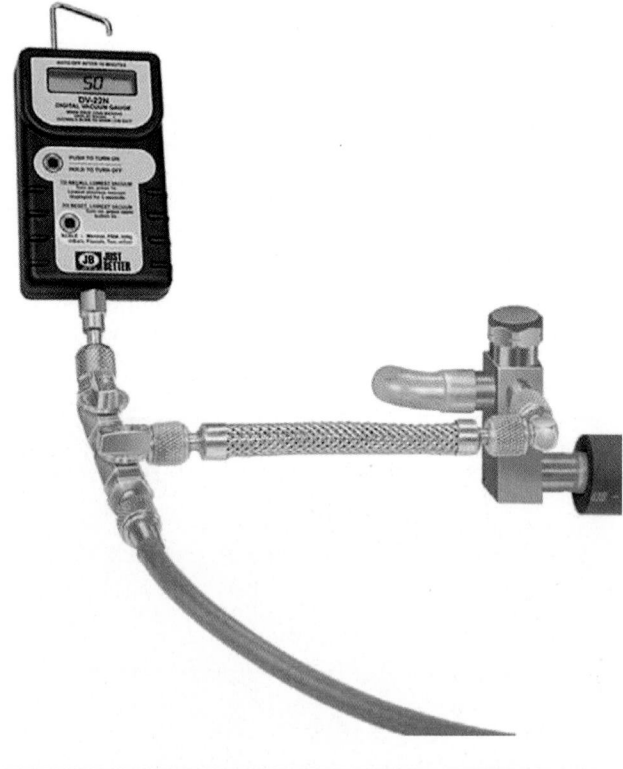

Figure 27-34 A blank off valve can be used to allow connection of the vacuum sensor and charging hose to a single system service port from http://jbind.com/tools/UserFiles/Image/instdv29.pdf from JB Industries web site jbind.com
(2008 JB Industries, Inc.)

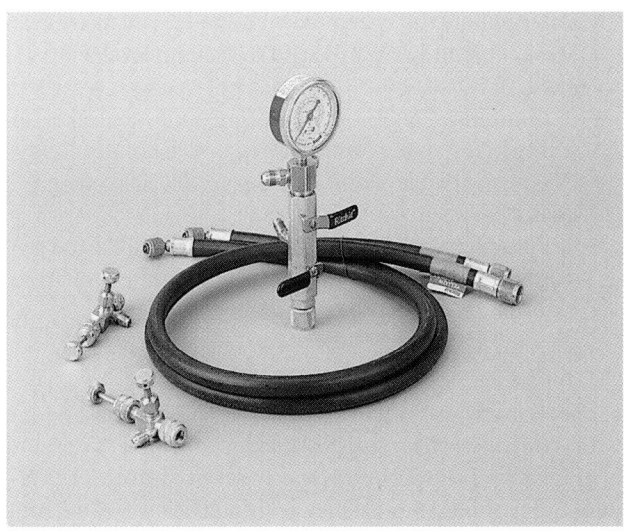

Figure 27-35 A vacuum manifold can be used to allow connection of multiple hoses and a vacuum gauge at the vacuum pump
(Courtesy of Ritchie Engineering Company, Inc.— YELLOW JACKET Products.)

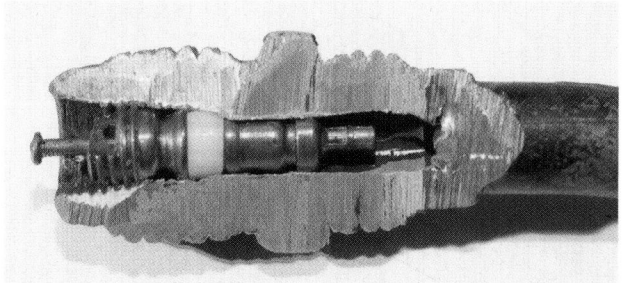

Figure 27-36 Schrader valve cores offer a great deal of restriction to evacuation and charging

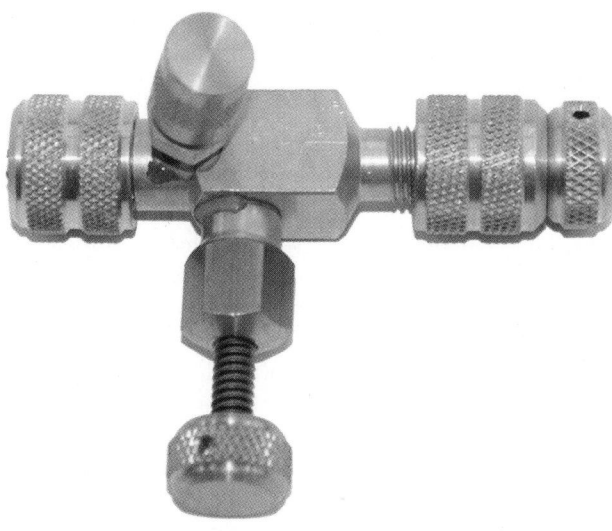

Figure 27-37 A valve core tool with a side port can be used to remove the valve core during evacuation and charging

charge a system. Figure 27-36 shows a cutaway of a Schrader valve with a core in it. Valve core removal tools with side ports, like the one shown in Figure 27-37, can be used to remove Schrader cores during evacuation and charging, and then replace them when charging is complete. This can cut the evacuation time in half.

Care should be used when removing and replacing valve cores during routine service because Schrader valves are not designed to have their cores removed and replaced frequently. It is possible to damage the Schrader valve, making it necessary to recover the system refrigerant and replace the damaged Schrader valve.

27.13 DEEP EVACUATION

The deep vacuum method is the most positive method of ensuring a system free of air and water. The equipment required includes a vacuum pump with a blank off pressure no higher than 50 microns, a reliable electronic vacuum gauge, a gauge manifold or vacuum manifold, and all connecting hoses. Hoses should be as short as possible and connections should be kept to a minimum. Use $3/8$ in or larger hoses whenever possible, Figure 27-38.

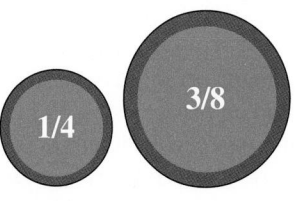

Figure 27-38 The cross sectional area of a $3/8$ in hose is over twice that of a standard $1/4$ in hose, allowing faster evacuation and charging

---

SERVICE TIP

Most manifold gauge sets have an internal opening and hoses with $1/4$ in diameter. Larger gauges and hoses are available that have a $3/8$ in interior diameter. The larger the interior diameter and the shorter the hose, the faster a system can be evacuated. As the pressure in the system drops, the rate of withdrawal is significantly hampered when working with the smaller diameter hoses. For most residential and light commercial applications this time is not a major problem. However, for larger commercial installations it can become a significant factor in the overall job time. Many manufacturers of gauges provide these larger diameter hoses and frequently they are black in color and less flexible than the normal gauge hoses.

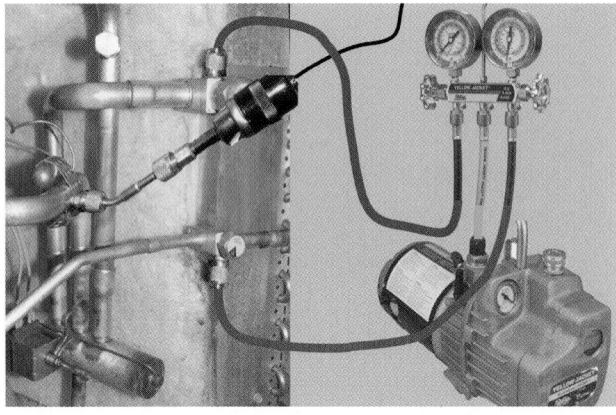

Figure 27-39 Vacuum pump and vacuum gauge connections using standard three-port manifold and a third system gauge port

The actual physical connection used depends very much upon the tools and equipment. The vacuum gauge can be connected directly to the system and the vacuum pump connected to the middle port of a standard three port manifold gauge on systems with three access valves, as in Figure 27-32 and Figure 27-33. Figure 27-39 shows a connection using a standard three-port manifold and a blank off test valve installed on the system low side service port with the vacuum gauge connected to it. Figure 27-30 shows a connection using a four port manifold with the vacuum gauge connected to the $\frac{1}{4}$ in center port and the vacuum pump connected to the $\frac{3}{8}$ in center port.

These are only a few of the possible connection strategies. Regardless of how the vacuum pump and gauge are connected, the technician should keep in mind a few overall concepts.

- There should be no pressure in the system before connecting a vacuum pump. If there is still refrigerant in the system it must first be recovered before attempting to pull a vacuum. If the system is pressurized with nitrogen, release the nitrogen before beginning evacuation.
- The vacuum level must be measured with an accurate vacuum gauge. Mechanical gauges are not accurate enough to determine when a system has been properly evacuated.
- The vacuum integrity of the connections should be checked before evacuating the system.
- The system should be evacuated from both the low side and the high side simultaneously.
- The system should be able to be isolated from the vacuum pump upon completion of the vacuum.
- The vacuum gauge should be able to read the system pressure during a blank off period at the end of the vacuum.
- The vacuum gauge should be able to be isolated from system pressure during charging.

- After pulling the system down to under 500 microns, valve it off and wait to see if the vacuum level will hold.
- A continuous, rapid rise in pressure indicates leaks either in the system or in the evacuation connections.
- A slow rise that levels off between 1,500–5,000 microns indicates system contamination.
- If the system leaks, the leaks must be identified and repaired. If the system is contaminated, further evacuation should correct the problem.

Whenever possible, check the vacuum integrity of your connections before evacuating the system. This can be done with manual service valves by making all connections and opening all valves except the system service valves. The vacuum pump should be able to quickly pull below 500 microns on the vacuum setup. If it cannot, then you are wasting your time trying to pull the system under 500 microns. To improve vacuum integrity, use as few mechanical connections as possible and use short, low permeation hoses.

How Long Should It Take to Pull a Deep Vacuum?

The simple answer is that there is no specified period of time that is required for a deep vacuum. A deep vacuum is done when the system pressure will hold below 500 microns Hg absolute pressure, Figure 27-40. A deep vacuum can be pulled on small, dry systems in minutes. The lines and evaporator coil on new installations of residential air conditioning split systems can typically be thoroughly evacuated to under 500 microns in 30 minutes. However, the same system with water contamination may take several hours. Time is not a replacement for a vacuum gauge.

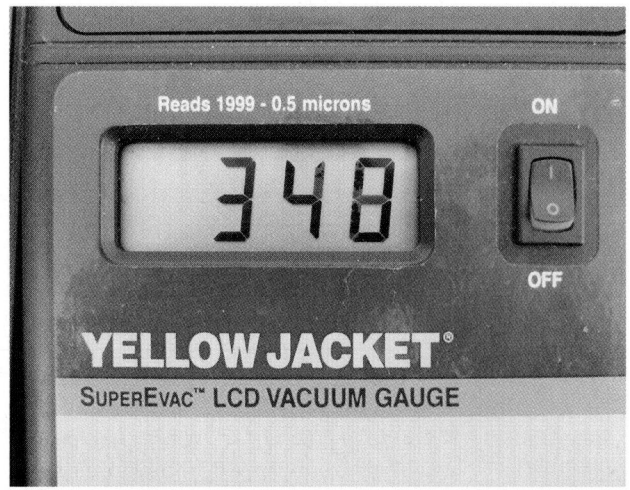

Figure 27-40 The system should be evacuated to under 500 microns for a deep vacuum

Pulling a vacuum all weekend is not an assurance that the system is properly evacuated. If the system leaks, no amount of time will work.

27.14 MULTIPLE EVACUATION

A multiple evacuation is an alternative to the deep vacuum procedure. Multiple evacuations can be faster than a single deep evacuation. The multiple evacuation procedure typically does not require a deep vacuum gauge. Multiple evacuation, sometimes called triple evacuation, is really several short vacuums in succession that are broken in between with dry nitrogen. The nitrogen absorbs and/or dislodges moisture in the system, making it easier to remove on subsequent evacuations. The number of evacuations, the amount of nitrogen introduced between evacuations, and the time period given for the nitrogen to "blot up" the moisture varies. There is really no scientific way of knowing how to adjust any of these factors for a particular system. The most common multiple evacuation is the triple evacuation, in which three successive vacuums are used.

Figure 27-41 shows a typical connection for multiple evacuation using a four port manifold. If there is nothing in the system, it is advisable to put some dry nitrogen in

before the first vacuum. This will yield one extra "blotting" period. Dry nitrogen is nitrogen that is free of water. Some nitrogen is pumped into the tank using water and is, therefore, wet. Be sure when purchasing nitrogen to request anhydrous nitrogen. Of course it is imperative to use a nitrogen regulator and pressure relief valve when pressurizing the system. Nitrogen tanks hold pressures as high as 2,000 psig and no refrigeration system will stand up to that kind of pressure. Recommendations on what pressure to use for the blotting period vary from 2 psig to full test system pressures. For safety, never exceed the low side system test pressure when adding the nitrogen. Let the nitrogen stand in the system for 10–15 min. Blotting times of up to 1 hour are sometimes recommended. However, if you are going to invest that kind of time, you might as well pull a deep vacuum. Obviously, longer waiting periods will generally yield better results.

Connect the vacuum pump to the center port of your gauges, open both manifold gauge valves, and pull a vacuum from both sides of the system. Let the pump pull for as long as the compound gauge will give you a visible drop in pressure. In any case, do not shut off the vacuum pump until the compound gauge has bottomed out, Figure 27-42. If an electronic vacuum gauge is used, watch how quickly the system pulls down. There may be no advantage in using the multiple evacuation method if

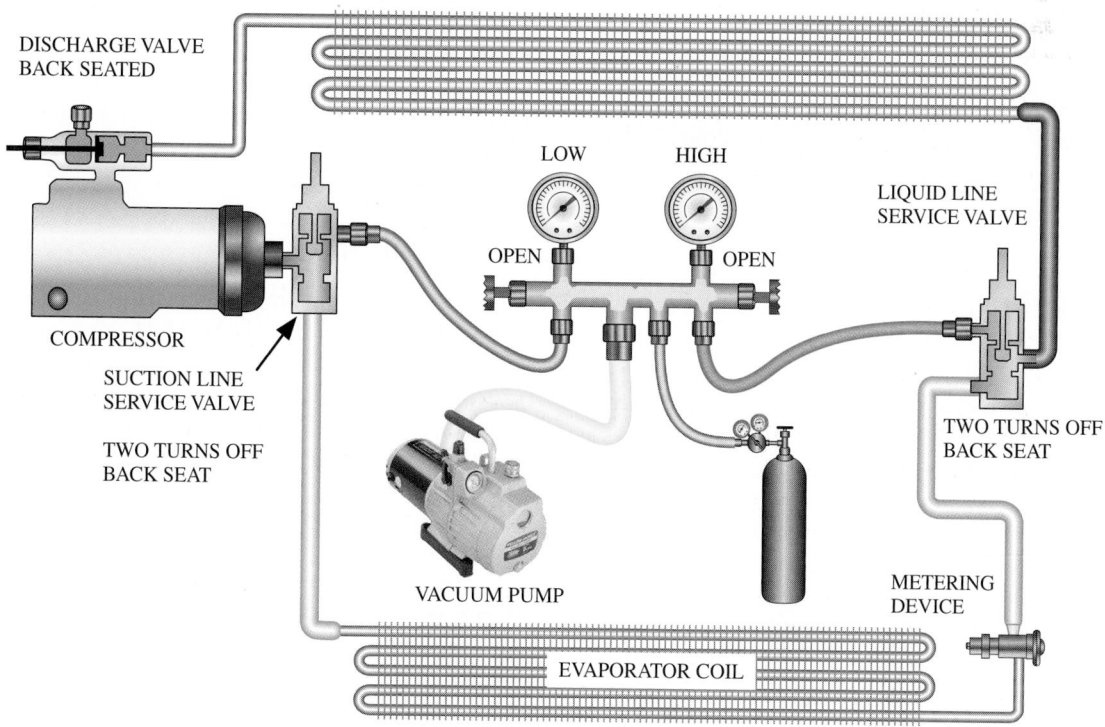

Figure 27-41 Connection for multiple evacuation

Figure 27-42 The compound gauge should peg out at 30 in Hg vacuum with each evacuation on a multiple evacuation

it is possible to achieve a deep vacuum quickly. Pulling a system down three times to 500 microns is really not any better than pulling it down once if the vacuum holds under 500 microns.

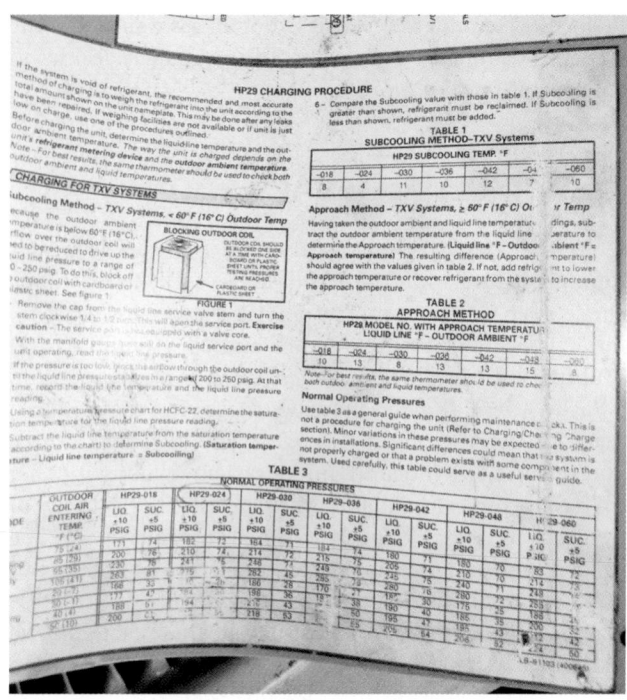

Figure 27-43 Most manufacturers provide charging information inside the unit service panel

---

SERVICE TIP

Electronic vacuum gauges are generally not used for multiple evacuations, but using one can easily demonstrate the effectiveness of multiple evacuation. Note the speed with which the unit pulls down on each successive evacuation. Generally, the system pulls down faster with each sweep.

27.15 DETERMINING SYSTEM CHARGE

Whether the system is a new one or an existing one that has been repaired, the final step in putting the system in operation is to charge it with refrigerant. The amount of refrigerant charge is more critical in some systems than in others. Systems that have a receiver and thermostatic expansion valve are less critical since extra refrigerant can be stored in the receiver, and the expansion valve feeds the refrigerant into the evaporator as required to match the load.

Any excess refrigerant in systems that do not have a receiver will be stored in some part of the system where it reduces the effectiveness of that part and reduces the capacity of the system. If the system is short of refrigerant, the metering device is not supplied with a solid stream of

liquid refrigerant and the evaporator will be starved for refrigerant, reducing the capacity of the system. If the system is overcharged, excessive pressures and floodback to the compressor may damage the compressor. The equipment installation instructions will provide the installer with the correct charging procedure for that piece of equipment. Many equipment manufacturers provide charging information on the equipment access panels, Figure 27-43.

Packaged Units

One way to determine the proper charge is to read it on the name plate as shown in Figure 27-44. Most manufacturers specify the type and amount of charge on the system data plate. For any one-piece system such as appliances, window units, or packaged air conditioning systems, the amount on the data plate will be the correct charge.

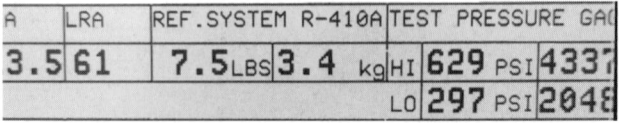

A	LRA	REF. SYSTEM R-410A		TEST PRESSURE GA
3.5	61	7.5 LBS	3.4 kg	HI 629 PSI 4337
				LO 297 PSI 2048

Figure 27-44 The type and amount of refrigerant is shown on the equipment data plate

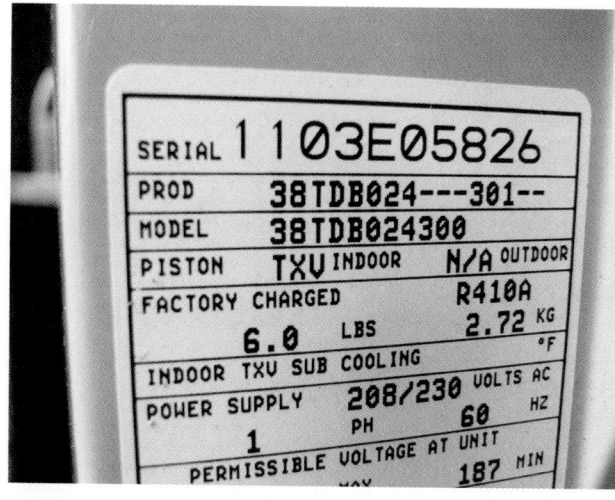

Figure 27-45 The factory charge for this split system condensing unit is shown on the data plate

Split Systems

The amount of charge required for a split system is affected by the length of the refrigerant lines. The length of the refrigerant lines is determined by the conditions of the installation. This is why the correct system charge will be different from one split system to another, even for identical equipment. The condensing unit on a split system has a factory charge amount on the data plate, Figure 27-45. Typically this amount includes enough refrigerant for the condensing unit, the evaporator coil, and some predetermined length of refrigerant line. The assumed line length varies from 15–30 ft, depending upon the manufacturer. The assumed line length used for any particular piece of equipment can be found in the installation instructions, Figure 27-46, or on the inside of the service access panel, Figure 27-47.

The system charge must be adjusted if the actual line length varies from the assumed line length. Most manufacturers only compensate for the liquid line and not the suction line because the amount or refrigerant in the suction line is so slight. Figure 27-48 shows how much refrigerant to add or subtract for every foot of difference in line length. This remains the same regardless of the type of equipment because it is based on the physical volume of the different size liquid lines. For example, a system with a factory charge of 56 ounces

of R-410A, an assumed line length of 15 ft, and a 35 ft long $\frac{3}{8}$ in liquid line:

$$56 \text{ ounces} + (35 - 15) \times 0.6 \text{ oz/ft} = 56 \text{ oz} + 12 \text{ oz}$$
$$= 68 \text{ oz total system charge}$$

Repairing Existing Equipment

When the system charge has been recovered in order to repair an existing system, the total system charge should be weighed in after evacuating the entire system.

New Installations

For new split system installations, only the additional amount of charge needs to be determined and added because the condensing unit comes precharged. In the above example, only 12 oz needs to be added for a new installation. The procedure for charging a new split system would be:

- Install refrigeration lines and evaporator coil.
- Evacuate the lines and coil below 500 microns.
- Determine the amount of charge adjustment needed for the extra line length.
- Weigh the charge adjustment into the evacuated lines.
- Open the charging valves on the condensing unit.

SERVICE TIP

Too often technicians in the HVAC/R field are of the opinion that if a little refrigerant is good a lot is better and too much is just about right. Refrigerant is not a magical fluid that adds cooling capacity to a system. The cooling capacity of a system that is overcharged is significantly decreased. The only time a system will operate with its designed peak performance is when the charge is at the manufacturer specified level. It is not an acceptable practice to add just a little more in case the system leaks.

27.16 CHARGING BY WEIGHT

The most difficult aspect of refrigerant charging is not putting refrigerant into a system, but knowing when to stop putting it in. There are so many variables to take into account that charging to a particular operating condition can be difficult. The easiest way to have confidence in the charge

REFRIGERANT CHARGE PER LINE SET LENGTHS	
LIQUID LINE SET DIAMETER	OUNCES PER 5 FEET (GRAMS PER 1.52 METER) ADJUST FROM 15 FT. (4.57M) LINE SET*
3/8 IN. (9.5MM)	3 OUNCES PER 5 FEET (85 GRAMS PER 1.52 METER)

*ADD THE AMOUNT SHOWN IF LINE LENGTH IS GREATER THAN 15' (4.57M), SUBTRACT THE AMOUNT SHOWN IF LESS THAN 15'.

Figure 27-46 Details on adjusting the charge for line length inside the system service panels
(Courtesy of Lennox Industries Inc.)

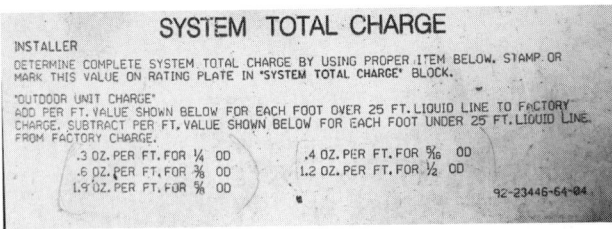

Figure 27-47 Many manufacturers provide details on adjusting the charge for line length inside the system service panels

Liquid line size	R-22 or R-410 A (oz/ft)
$1/4$	0.4
$3/8$	0.6
$1/2$	0.8
$5/8$	1.0

Figure 26-48 Liquid line allowance table

is to weigh in the correct amount of refrigerant into a fully evacuated system using an accurate scale. Scales such as the one shown in Figure 27-49 can be used to accurately weigh the refrigerant into the system. An electronic scale with the ability to be zeroed with the refrigerant cylinder on the scale is preferred.

Figure 27-49 Electronic Charging Scales like this one can be used to weigh in a refrigerant charge

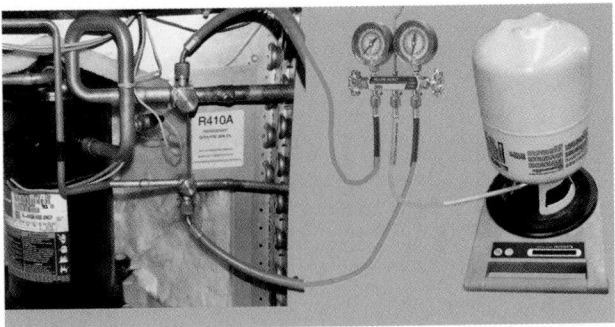

Figure 27-50 Connections for weighing liquid refrigerant into the high side of a system

Most fully evacuated systems will take in the entire charge in liquid form in one shot. Figure 27-50 shows the setup for weighing liquid into the high side of an evacuated system. To weigh in a system charge after evacuating a system:

- The system should be off and evacuated with the manifold gauges connected to the high and low sides of the system and the manifold valves closed.
- Connect the refrigerant cylinder to the middle hose on the gauges.
- Purge the center hose with vapor from the cylinder while it is in the upright position.
- Do not attempt to purge the other hoses, they are in a vacuum and do not need purging.
- Invert the cylinder and place it on the scale with the cylinder valve opened.
- Zero the scale with the cylinder on it.
- Open the high side manifold valve to allow liquid refrigerant to flow from the cylinder into the system.
- The position of the hoses should not be changed during charging because this can change the weight felt by the scale.
- Close the high side manifold valve when the desired charge is reached.

27.17 LIQUID CHARGING

Liquid charging is always much faster than vapor charging. This is because liquid is far more dense than vapor, and because taking liquid out of the refrigerant cylinder does not affect the cylinder pressure. The primary disadvantage of liquid charging is that it is easy to overcharge a system when adding liquid refrigerant. Liquid is normally charged into the system in either of two ways: into the high side with the system off, or by pulling liquid into the liquid line with the system operating and the king valve front seated.

Liquid Charging—System Off

On smaller systems, liquid charging is usually done with the compressor off. Prior to charging, the system must be leak tested and evacuated. Figure 27-50 shows connections for liquid charging in to the high side with the system off. When the charging is started, the system is under vacuum and the refrigerant cylinder is under pressure, so the refrigerant is pushed into the system due to the difference in pressure. After the system has been evacuated, liquid is introduced into the high side with the system off. Since the compressor can be damaged by liquid in the suction line, liquid is normally not charged into the low side of a system.

The system pressure rises as the refrigerant enters the system. Sometimes the system pressure and cylinder pressure will equalize before the full amount of refrigerant has been charged into the system. When this occurs, the charge may have to be completed as a vapor charge with the system operating.

Liquid Charging—System Operating

On larger systems, a king valve located between the condenser and the metering device offers a convenient means of charging the system on the high side, with the compressor running. When the king valve is front seated, Figure 27-51, flow from the receiver is shut off. As the system operates the pressure in the liquid line leaving the receiver starts to drop. When the pressure in the refrigerant cylinder exceeds the pressure in the liquid line, refrigerant is drawn into the system from the cylinder, Figure 27-52. This same technique may be used for most residential split systems by front seating the liquid line charging valve, Figure 27-53.

This will not work for all systems that have liquid receivers and king valves! To work properly, the liquid line must be isolated from the liquid receiver and open to the gauge port when the liquid receiver valve is front seated,

Figure 27-51 The king valve stem is turned in all the way clockwise to front seat it

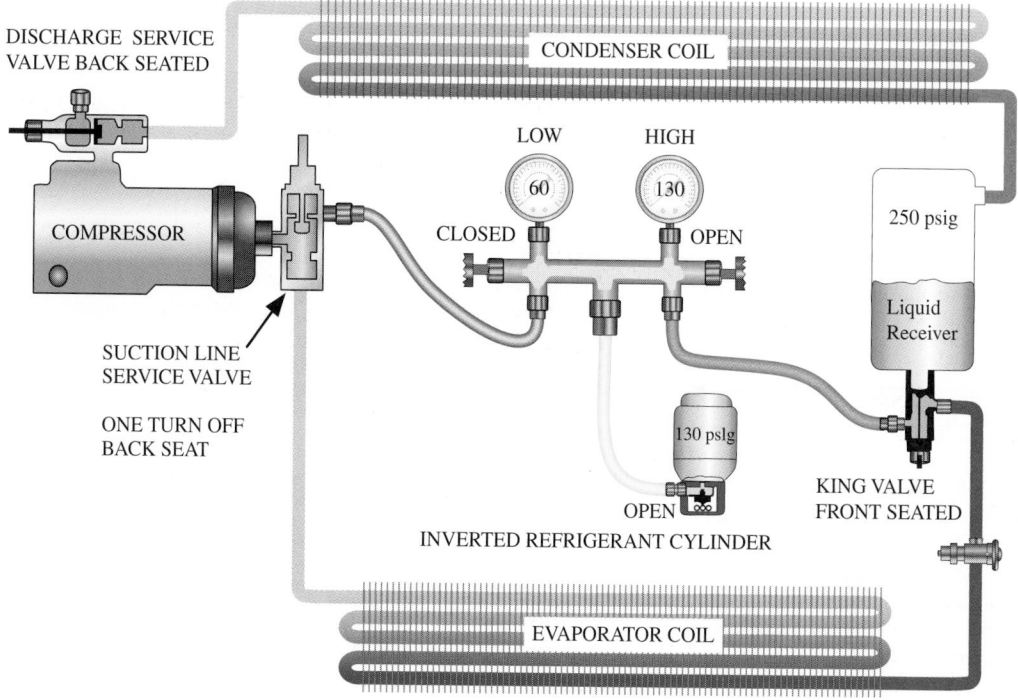

Figure 27-52 With the king valve front seated and the compressor operating, liquid refrigerant will be drawn into the liquid line

DISCHARGE SERVICE VALVE BACK SEATED

CONDENSER COIL

LOW

HIGH

60

130

COMPRESSOR

CLOSED

OPEN

250 psig

Liquid Receiver

SUCTION LINE SERVICE VALVE

ONE TURN OFF BACK SEAT

130 pslg

OPEN

INVERTED REFRIGERANT CYLINDER

KING VALVE FRONT SEATED

EVAPORATOR COIL

Figure 27-53 The liquid line service valve on split system air conditioning system can also be used to liquid charge with the compressor operating

Figure 27-54 King valves that have the gauge port open to the line port when the vavle is front seated can be used for liquid charging with the system operating

Figure 27-55 King valves that have the gauge port open to the receiver port when the valve is front seated should NOT be used for liquid charging with the system operating

Figure 27-54. Many receiver valves isolate the liquid line and leave the gauge port open to the receiver when the valve is front seated, Figure 27-55. These systems are not candidates for this method! If the liquid line is isolated from the receiver and the gauge port is open to the receiver, high side pressures from the compressor will be forced into the charging cylinder through the liquid receiver. This condition is very dangerous!

SERVICE TIP

On large systems, liquid charging with the compressor operating and the king valve front seated may cause cause compressor overheating and/or low pressure system shutdown. A system that is normally fed by a $\frac{5}{8}$ in liquid line with over 200 psig of pressure cannot be adequately fed by a $\frac{1}{4}$ in line with normal cylinder pressure. The result is that the system operates with a starved evaporator and a low suction pressure during the charging process. Liquid charging with the system operating should be limited to short durations of time in order to avoid system problems.

Liquid Charging Chillers

Low pressure chillers are charged through the evaporator charging valve. Liquid should not be charged into evacuated chillers or units with water cooled condensers. When liquid is charged into an evacuated unit, the liquid boils at

SERVICE TIP

It is easy to overcharge a small system using this charging method. When adding liquid refrigerant with the system operating, the gauges will show both low side and high side pressures, but these pressures tell the technician nothing about the amount of charge in the system. The amount of refrigerant added should always be checked with a scale to guard against overcharging.

a very low temperature because of the low pressure. This can freeze the water sitting in tubes in evaporators and condensers, causing significant damage to the system. To avoid this, charge the system with vapor until the system pressure is at a saturation pressure equal to 36°F. Liquid may then be safely introduced into the system without fear of freezing the water.

SERVICE TIP

On systems that require large quantities of liquid refrigerant to meet the basic charge requirement, liquid can be pumped into the system by using a cylinder heating band. These bands are thermostatically controlled and sense the cylinder pressure with a pressure sensitive switch that is connected to the refrigerant charging line. Cylinder heaters can significantly reduce the charging time.

27.18 VAPOR CHARGING

Vapor charging is used to add small amounts of refrigerant slowly because vapor takes up a great deal more space per pound than liquid. When a partial charge is required, vapor charging is usually employed. Figure 27-56 shows a typical connection for vapor charging. The center hose of the gauge manifold is connected to the valve on the refrigerant cylinder with the cylinder in the upright position. The center hose is purged using refrigerant from the cylinder. If the system was evacuated prior to charging, only the center hose needs purging. However, if vapor is being added to a system that already has some charge in it, all gauge hoses should be purged.

SERVICE TIP

Before attempting to vapor charge a system, make sure that the refrigerant to be charged is not a 400 series zeotropic refrigerant, such as R-410A. Zeotropic refrigerants should not be removed from the cylinder as a vapor because they will fractionate and the mixture of refrigerants will be incorrect. Worse, the refrigerant remaining in the cylinder is no longer the correct mixture after fractionation.

Small Appliances

The recommended charging procedure for small appliances whose total system charge is less than a pound is to evacuate the system and introduce vapor into the appliance until the static equalized pressure in the appliance equals the factory specification. This is the most accurate charging method for appliances whose total charge is only a few ounces. This is done after evacuating the appliance with the appliance off.

Refrigerant Cylinder Pressure Drop

The refrigerant cylinder pressure decreases as vapor is drawn off of it, even if there is still plenty of refrigerant left in the cylinder. As the vapor leaves the cylinder, it creates a low-pressure area above the liquid due to the void left by the exiting refrigerant. The liquid in the cylinder boils to fill this void with more vapor. This process continues as long as vapor is being removed from the cylinder. The heat required to vaporize the liquid comes from the liquid refrigerant and the tank itself and leaves with the refrigerant. The result is an ever-decreasing refrigerant temperature. Since the pressure

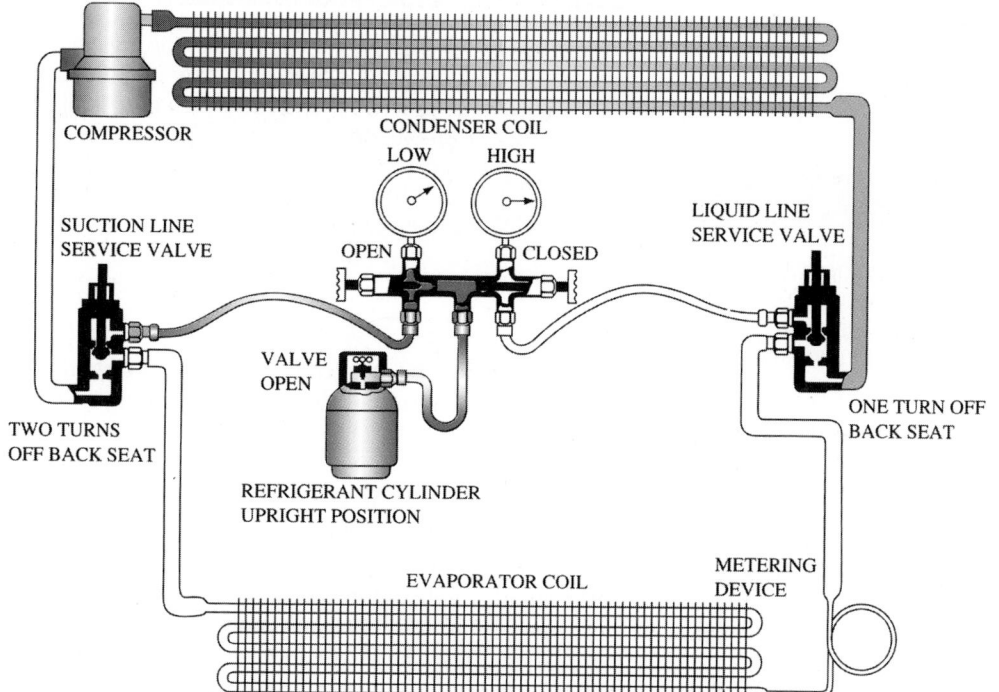

Figure 27-56 Connections for vapor charging a system

Figure 27-57 The frost line on this cylinder shows the liquid level; the liquid temperature has dropped because of vapor being removed from the cylinder

of a saturated refrigerant is determined by its temperature, a drop in temperature also means a drop in pressure. The charging process gradually grinds to a halt because of the drop in cylinder pressure. The frost line on the bottom of the cylinder in Figure 27-57 shows the liquid level of the cylinder. It has been cooled by drawing vapor out of the cylinder.

Heating the Refrigerant Cylinder

Heating the refrigerant cylinder will raise the refrigerant temperature and pressure, allowing the charging process to continue. Refrigerant travels from one container to another simply because of pressure difference. A full cylinder of refrigerant with a pressure of 50 psig will not even charge a refrigerator if the pressure in the refrigerator is 50 psig or higher. Remember, the pressure of a saturated refrigerant is controlled by its temperature, and not its volume. To get the refrigerant to travel from the refrigerant cylinder into the system, there will have to be a temperature difference if both the unit and the cylinder are in a saturated state. Therefore, heating the refrigerant cylinder is often required during vapor charging.

SAFETY TIP

It is possible to increase the cylinder temperature and pressure to a point where it can rupture and release an awesome amount of energy with one great explosion. Therefore, when a refrigerant cylinder must be heated, these precautions should be taken:

Wait until some of the refrigerant has been removed from a full cylinder before doing any heating.

Never use a concentrated heat form, such as a torch, to heat the cylinder. Warm water or air are effective and safe alternatives.

Limit the maximum temperature exposure of the cylinder to below 125°F.

Never obstruct or tamper with the safety relief device on the cylinder.

Vapor Charging with Unit Operating

Most vapor charging is done with the compressor operating while charging is taking place. The pressure difference between the tank pressure and the system evaporator pressure will be greater if vapor is introduced into the low side while the compressor is operating, Figure 27-56. This will delay the problem of cylinder pressure drop since the evaporator pressure is lower while the system is operating. If the amount of refrigerant being added is relatively small, operating the compressor and charging vapor into the suction side of the system generally provides enough temperature and pressure difference to complete the charging job. If large quantities of refrigerant are needed, however, the refrigerant cylinder will still have to be heated.

27.19 CHARGING ZEOTROPIC REFRIGERANTS

Refrigerants that fractionate, such as R-410A, must be charged as liquid to prevent the separation of the refrigerant. Weighing a liquid charge into an evacuated system is the same with zeotropes as with regular refrigerant since the refrigerant leaves the cylinder as a liquid. Adding small amounts with the system operating is different because the refrigerant should not leave the cylinder as a vapor. These refrigerants must come out of the cylinder as a liquid but must be a vapor before entering the compressor. To accomplish this safely, the refrigerant must be metered either by the gauge manifold hand valve or by an external charging device.

SERVICE TIP

Most refrigerant cylinders have arrows showing the correct cylinder position for charging. Early R-410A cylinders used a dip tube, so the cylinder delivered liquid in the upright position. Most cylinders used today do not have the dip tube, so they need to be inverted to deliver liquid. Check the arrows on the side of the cylinder to be sure which position the cylinder should be in to deliver liquid.

Zeotropes can be metered in with the unit operating by slightly cracking open the low side manifold valve and then closing it, Figure 27-58. This allows small amounts of liquid into the low side hose, but gives the liquid time to evaporate before reaching the compressor. Be patient. The liquid must flash off to vapor before entering the compressor. Allowing too much liquid in at once can damage the compressor because liquid is not compressible! Charging devices like the one shown in Figure 27-59 increase the safety of low side liquid charging. They are essentially a restriction that acts as a metering device.

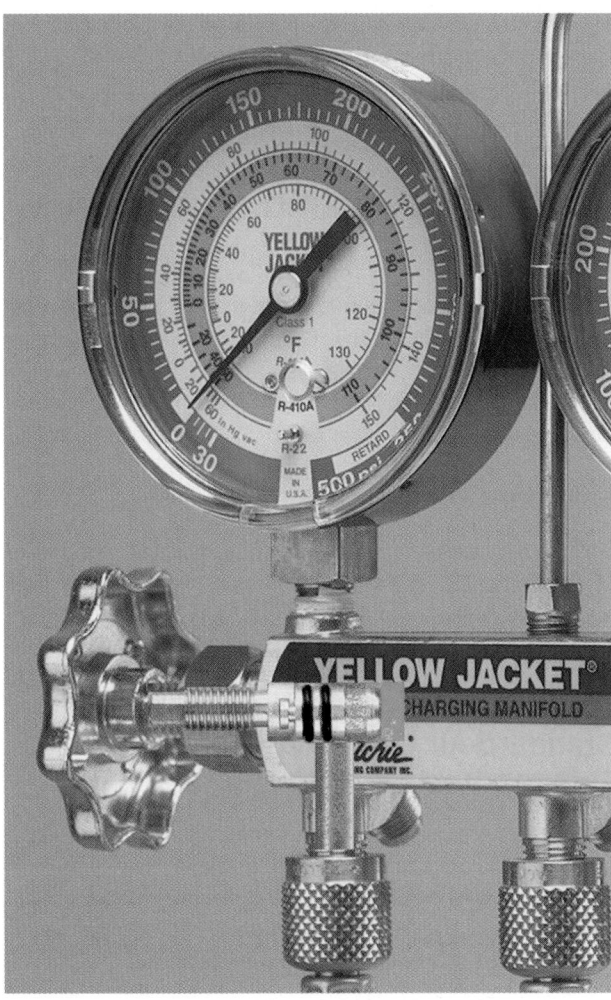

Figure 27-58 Liquid refrigerant can be metered in through the manifold gauges by cracking the hand valve on the suction side of the gauges
(Courtesy of Ritchie Engineering Company, Inc.— YELLOW JACKET Products.)

Figure 27-59 This device can be used in the charging line to flash off the liquid refrigerant
(Courtesy of Stride Tool Inc.)

Some gauge manifold sets have sight glasses that make it easy to monitor the condition of the refrigerant, Figure 27-60. For gauges that do not have this, a liquid line sight glass that has $^1/_4$ in flare fittings on both ends can be installed in the low side refrigerant hose.

Figure 27-60 The refrigerant condition may be monitored using the sight glass in this manifold
(Courtesy Imperial)

27.20 FACTORS AFFECTING SYSTEM PRESSURES

Checking the charge on an operating system involves checking some aspect of system performance. The major difficulty in checking system refrigerant charge by measuring any single aspect of its performance is that there are so many variables that can affect system performance. Getting all variables that affect system performance to conform to the manufacturer's specifications at one time can be quite challenging. Understanding how each of these variables affects system performance is crucial for the technician trying to measure system performance. Some of the most common variables that can affect system performance include the following.

Outdoor Ambient Temperature for Air Cooled Units

The high side pressure on air cooled systems is largely determined by the outdoor ambient temperature and the amount of air flowing over the condenser. Increased ambient temperature causes increased high side pressure.

Condenser Airflow for Air Cooled Units

The airflow across the condenser also affects the high side pressure. Less condenser airflow means less cooling, causing higher condenser temperatures and pressures.

Inlet Water Temperature for Water Cooled Units

The high side pressure on water cooled systems is largely determined by the condenser inlet water temperature and the water flow. Increased water temperature causes increased high side pressure, lower water temperature causes lower head pressures.

Condenser Water Flow for Water Cooled Units

Condenser water flow has a very large impact on high side pressures in water cooled units. Reduced water flow means less cooling, causing higher condenser temperatures and pressures. Increased water flow has just the opposite effect.

Return Air Wet Bulb for Air Conditioners

Return air wet bulb temperature has a big effect on evaporator temperature and pressure in air conditioning systems. Increased wet bulb temperatures mean increased load on the evaporator, which increases the evaporator temperature and pressure. Low wet bulb temperatures mean reduced evaporator load and reduced evaporator temperature and pressure.

Evaporator Airflow for Air Conditioners

The airflow across the evaporator in an air conditioning system is critical. Low airflow means low load and lower evaporator temperature and pressure. Reduced airflow also reduces the system sensible cooling (temperature change) while increasing the system latent cooling (removal of water). Increased airflow increases the load on the evaporator, and higher evaporator temperature and pressure. Increased airflow increases the system sensible cooling while decreasing the system latent cooling.

Returning Water temperature for Chillers

Returning water temperature has a big effect on evaporator temperature and pressure in a chiller. Increased water temperatures mean increased load on the evaporator, which increases the evaporator temperature and pressure. Lower water temperatures mean reduced evaporator load and reduced evaporator temperature and pressure.

Chilled Water Flow for Chillers

The water flow through the evaporator in a chiller is critical. Low water flow means low load and lower evaporator temperature

and pressure. Reduced water flow can be a hazard for chillers because the water can freeze if its temperature is allowed to drop too low. Increased water flow increases the load on the evaporator, and increases evaporator temperature and pressure.

27.21 STANDARD INDUSTRY DESIGN AND OPERATION

There are system operating characteristics that have become industry standards through common use. These generic standards should never replace manufacturer information, but understanding what is normal can help a technician understand how all these variables interact with each other.

Standard Design Conditions

The primary rating condition for AHRI listed air conditioning equipment is 95°F outdoor ambient, and 80°F dry bulb and 67° wet bulb indoor temperature. Air conditioning equipment is rated at this condition. Logically, that means this is the ideal operating condition for an air conditioning system.

Standard Air Cooled Condenser Temperature

For many years equipment manufacturers have been designing equipment to operate with a 125°F condenser temperature at the AHRI design condition of 95°F. A reasonably accurate approximation of condenser temperature for older equipment is to add 30°F to the outdoor ambient temperature.

High Efficiency Air Cooled Condenser Temperature

Most equipment manufactured today is not designed to operate with a 125°F condenser. Instead, 115°F at 95°F is more common. For newer equipment, condenser temperature can be approximated by adding 20°F to the ambient temperature. It should be noted that there is really an entire range of efficiencies, so the term "approximate" is apt. Some systems now operate as low as 10°F above the ambient temperature.

Water Cooled Condenser Temperature

Water cooled condensers typically operate at lower head pressures than air cooled condensers. Standard design for water cooled condensers is 105°F condenser temperature with 85°F entering water temperature and 95°F leaving water temperature. This provides two important pieces of information; the difference between the leaving water temperature and the condenser temperature is approximately 10°F. The temperature rise across the condenser is also approximately 10°F. The condenser temperature of a water cooled condenser can be approximated by adding 10°F to the leaving water temperature. Its performance can be quickly checked by looking for a 10°F temperature rise in the condenser water temperature.

Evaporator Temperature in Air Conditioners

The common design for air conditioning evaporators has been a 40°F evaporator when the air flowing across the evaporator is 80°F and 67°F wet bulb (50% relative humidity). Evaporator temperature can be approximated by subtracting 40°F from the return air temperature. However, this does not account for changes in humidity that will affect the evaporator temperature. Higher wet bulb temperatures will produce higher evaporator temperatures, while lower wet bulb temperatures will produce lower evaporator temperatures. The dew point temperature at 80°F db, 67°F wb is 60°F. A more accurate approximation would be to subtract 20°F from the dew point of the return air.

High Efficiency Evaporator Temperatures

New equipment designed for higher efficiency typically operates at a slightly higher evaporator temperature. Many systems are now designed for 45°F evaporators at the 80°F db, 67° wb condition. This would make the evaporator temperature 35°F colder than the return air temperature, or 15°F colder than the return air dew point temperature.

Evaporator Airflow

Standard airflow across an air conditioning coil is 400 CFM per ton. This is a very commonly applied standard. Many installations tweak this to get the desired amount of sensible and latent cooling from a unit, but practically everyone's unit will work with 400 CFM per ton moving across the evaporator coil.

Evaporator Temperature Drop

The temperature drop across an air conditioning evaporator is typically around 15°F at the ARI design of 80°F db, 67° wb. As the wet bulb temperature drops, the temperature difference increases to a maximum of approximately 20°F. Higher wet bulb temperatures decrease the temperature drop to a minimum of around 10°F.

Thermostatic Expansion Valve Superheat

Expansion valve superheat settings vary with the design and temperature range of the system. In general, the lower the evaporator temperature, the lower the valve superheat setting. Low temperature systems often operate with a valve superheat of 3–5°F; medium temperature systems with a valve superheat of 5–9°F; high temperature systems and air conditioning systems with a valve of superheat of 9–12°F.

Fixed Restriction Superheat

The system superheat of fixed restriction systems varies widely with system operating conditions. At AHRI design conditions, most fixed restriction systems operate with a superheat similar to expansion valve systems, around 10°F. However, their superheat increases significantly as the outdoor ambient decreases. Subtracting the ambient temperature from 105 gives an approximation of superheat for a fixed restriction system operating with return air at AHRI design conditions, 80°F db, 67° wb.

Subcooling

The subcooling on most correctly operating refrigeration systems is between 5°F and 15°F. All systems should have some subcooling. Most split systems will have problems with flash gas in the liquid line if they operate at less than 5°F subcooling. Subcooling values exceeding 15°F can be symptomatic of systems that are either overcharged or have a restriction in the liquid line.

27.22 MANUFACTURER CHARGING CHARTS

Some manufacturers provide charging charts, charging calculators, or performance charts for checking the charge while the system is in operation. Some of these performance charts are intended to be used for both checking and adjusting the charge while others are intended only to check system operation.

Figure 27-61 shows a performance chart for an R-410A packaged unit that correlates suction pressure, discharge

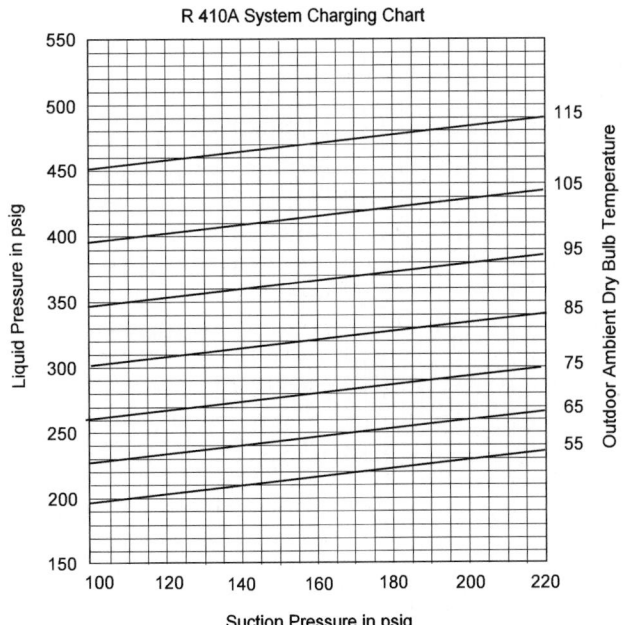

Figure 27-61 Typical manufacturer's charging chart correlating suction pressure, liquid pressure, and outdoor ambient temperature

Pressure at Suction Service Port (psig)

CAUTION: BEFORE FINAL REFRIGERANT CHECK, INDOOR RETURN AIR TEMPERATURE SHOULD BE AT COMFORT CONDITIONS FOR MOST ACCURATE RESULTS.

INSTRUCTIONS:
1. CONNECT PRESSURE GAUGES TO SUCTION AND LIQUID PORTS ON UNIT.
2. MEASURE AIR TEMPERATURE TO OUTDOOR COIL.
3. PLACE AN "X" ON THE APPROPRIATE CHART WHERE THE SUCTION AND LIQUID PRESSURES CROSS.
4. IF "X" IS BELOW AMBIENT TEMPERATURE LINE, ADD CHARGE AND REPEAT STEP 3.
5. IF "X" IS ABOVE AMBIENT TEMPERATURE LINE, RECOVER EXCESS CHARGE AND REPEAT STEP 3.

Figure 27-62 This chart is only accurate if the house is at comfort conditions

pressure, and outdoor ambient temperature. Note that this chart requires the indoor temperature to be at comfort conditions, Figure 27-62. If the indoor temperature is outside of comfort conditions, the chart will not be accurate. The liquid pressure is read on the right side of the chart, the suction pressure is read across the bottom of the chart. Find the intersection of the liquid and suction pressures. This intersection should fall on or near the diagonal line for the outdoor ambient temperature. If the intersection falls above the ambient temperature line, the system is overcharged. If the intersection falls below the ambient temperature line, the system is undercharged.

Figure 27-63 shows examples of undercharged, overcharged, and correctly charged systems operating at an outdoor ambient of 85°F. The dark blue lines represent a correctly charged system with a liquid pressure of 310 psig and a suction pressure of 140 psig. They intersect exactly on the light blue 85°F diagonal ambient temperature line. The red lines show an example of an overcharged system at the same ambient temperature, 85°F. The liquid pressure of 340 psig and the suction pressure of 160 psig intersect above the light blue 85°F diagonal ambient temperature line, indicating an

overcharge. The green lines show an example of an undercharged system at the same ambient temperature, 85°F. The liquid pressure of 290 psig and the suction pressure of 130 psig intersect below the light blue 85°F diagonal ambient temperature line, indicating an undercharge.

27.23 CHARGING FOR PROPER SUPERHEAT

The superheat method is a very accurate means of checking the refrigerant charge. A change in refrigerant charge of 1% can change the superheat 3°F. Superheat charging charts are commonly used for systems with fixed restriction metering devices. This is not as simple as stating a single superheat because the superheat of systems with fixed restrictions fluctuates with operating conditions. Fixed restrictions cannot adjust to varying load conditions, but a change in pressure drop produces a change in refrigerant flow, which produces a change in superheat. Warmer condenser ambient temperatures reduce system superheat by increasing refrigerant flow; cooler condenser ambient temperatures increase system superheat by decreasing refrigerant flow. Return air wet bulb temperature has just the opposite effect. Warmer return air wet bulb temperatures will increase superheat; cooler return air wet bulb temperatures reduce superheat. Figure 27-64 graphically shows how system operating

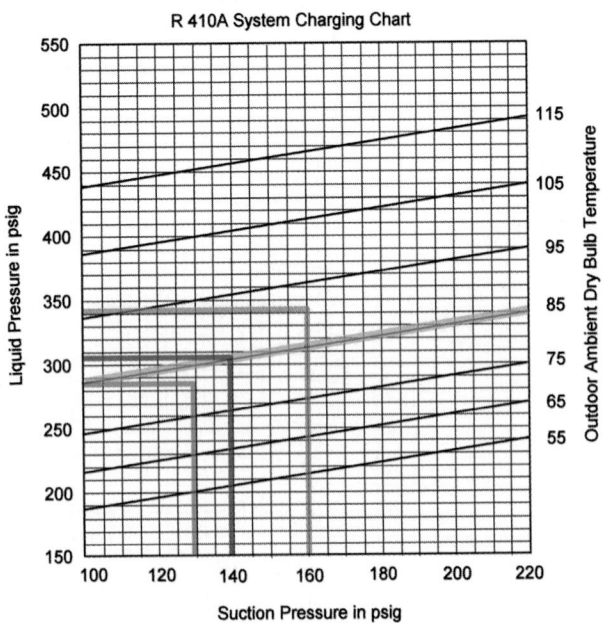

Figure 27-63 The red line shows an example of an overcharge, the blue line shows an example of a correct charge, and the green line shows an example of an undercharge

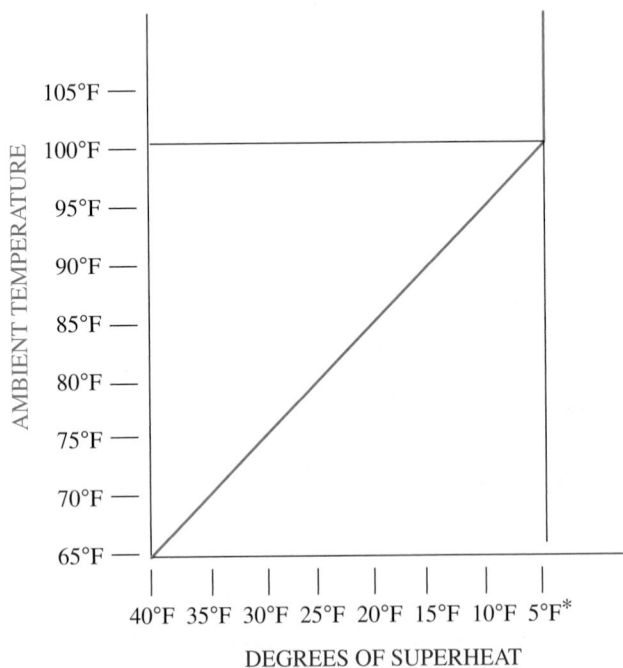

*Superheat should never be less than 5°F

Figure 27-64 The degree of superheat required for a correct charge change in direct proportion to the ambient temperature; the higher the temperature, the lower the degrees of superheat; the lower the temperature, the higher the degrees of superheat

INDOOR WB						OUTDOOR DB°F						
°F[1]	55	60	65	70	75	80	85	90	95	100	105	110
50	9	7										
52	12	10	6									
54	14	12	10	7								
56	17	15	14	10	6							
58	20	18	16	13	9	5						
60	23	21	19	16	12	8	6					
62	26	24	22	19	16	12	8	5				
64	29	27	24	21	18	15	11	9	6			
66	32	31	30	24	23	18	15	11	9	6		
68	35	33	30	27	24	21	19	16	14	12	9	6
70		35	33	30	28	25	22	20	18	15	13	11
72			35	33	30	28	26	24	20	20	17	15
74					34	31	30	27	25	23	22	20
76						35	33	31	29	27	26	25

Figure 27-65 This superheat charging chart gives the correct operating superheat based on both ambient temperature and indoor wet bulb temperature
(Courtesy of Johnson Controls)

conditions affect the superheat of systems with fixed restriction metering devices.

Charging charts like the one shown in Figure 27-65 give the correct system superheat for any operating condition. This can be used to check the system charge at any particular operating condition by comparing the actual system superheat to the superheat specified by the charging chart.

Both the outdoor ambient temperature and the indoor wet bulb temperature must be known to use the chart in Figure 27-65. Figure 27-66 shows an example with an indoor wet bulb of 66°F and an outdoor ambient of 90°F. Read across from the indoor wet bulb temperature on the left (66°F) until you reach the column under the outdoor ambient temperature (90°F). The required superheat at this condition is 11°F.

The superheat of an overcharged system will be lower than specified by the charging chart. This is because liquid will be traveling further through the evaporator before it is all boiled off, leaving less evaporator coil to superheat the refrigerant. In this example, a superheat of 7°F would indicate an overcharge. The superheat of an undercharged system will be higher than specified on the chart. This is because the liquid will be completely boiled off early in the evaporator, leaving more of the evaporator to superheat the refrigerant. In this example, a superheat of 15°F would indicate an undercharge.

Make sure to read all the fine print on any charging chart. Manufacturers attempt to make the charging charts as easy to use as possible while still providing accurate information. Most charts assume something. Typical assumptions would include system airflow, indoor temperature, or indoor humidity. Any condition that is assumed for the sake of simplicity is usually listed somewhere on the chart. Rather than asking for indoor wet bulb, some superheat charts ask for a regular dry bulb temperature both inside and outside, Figure 27-67. They assume the relative humidity to be 50%. These charts will not be accurate if the relative humidity is very far off of 50%. Other superheat charging charts only specify an outdoor ambient temperature, Figure 27-68. These charts are assuming an indoor temperature, usually the AHRI design condition of 80°F, 50% relative humidity. These charts are only accurate at this one indoor operating condition.

INDOOR WB						OUTDOOR DB°F						
°F[1]	55	60	65	70	75	80	85	90	95	100	105	110
50	9	7										
52	12	10	6									
54	14	12	10	7								
56	17	15	14	10	6							
58	20	18	16	13	9	5						
60	23	21	19	16	12	8	6					
62	26	24	22	19	16	12	8	5				
64	29	27	24	21	18	15	11	9	6			
66	32	31	30	24	23	18	15	11	9	6		
68	35	33	30	27	24	21	19	16	14	12	9	6
70		35	33	30	28	25	22	20	18	15	13	11
72			35	33	30	28	26	24	20	20	17	15
74					34	31	30	27	25	23	22	20
76						35	33	31	29	27	26	25

Figure 27-66 The correct superheat is found by locating the intersection of the outdoor ambient temperature column and the indoor wet bulb temperature row
(Courtesy of Johnson Controls)

Figure 27-67 The superheat charging chart uses both outdoor and indoor dry bulb temperature

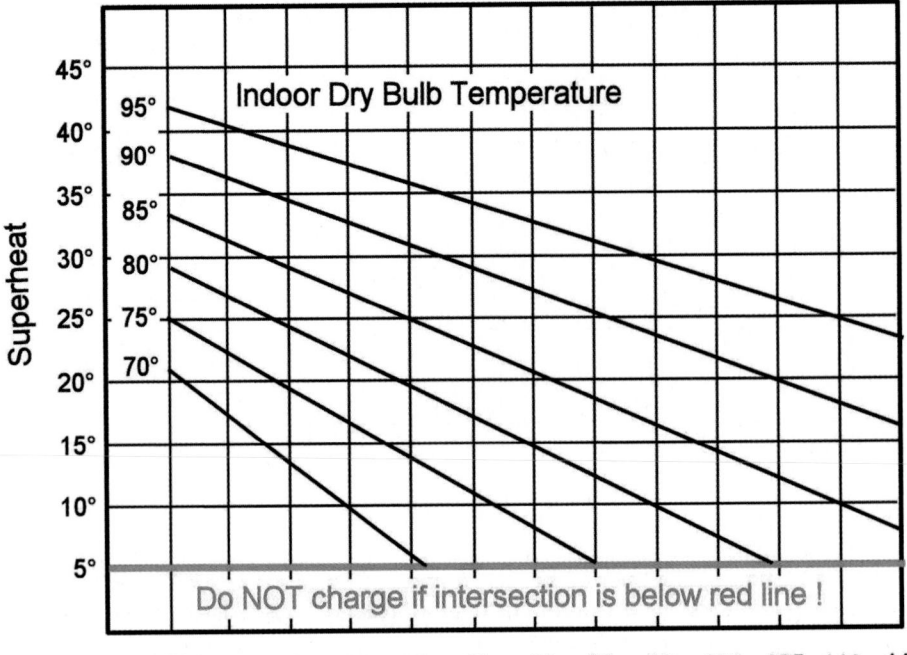

Chart is based on 400 CFM per ton airflow and 50% indoor relative humidity

---

SERVICE TIP

Be sure to check all system variables, especially the evaporator airflow. Other system variables can cause the superheat to be incorrect. Lower than normal evaporator airflow or a dirty evaporator will cause a low superheat. Higher evaporator airflow can cause a high superheat.

27.24 CHECKING SYSTEM SUPERHEAT

Two measurements are required to check system superheat: the suction line temperature and pressure near the compressor. It is important to use a fast reading, accurate thermometer or an electronic temperature probe to take the suction line temperature. Clamp on thermocouple probes like the one shown in Figure 27-69 work well.

Run the system for 10–30 min to allow the temperatures and pressures to stabilize. Also, record the indoor wet bulb and outdoor ambient temperatures, since these are required in using the manufacturer's charts. Then read the pressure and temperature of the suction line.

Use a pressure-temperature chart like the one in Figure 27-70 to determine the saturation temperature that matches the suction pressure. Subtract the saturation temperature from the actual vapor line temperature to obtain the superheat.

Compare it with the manufacturer's recommendation. Most manufacturers allow a variation of ±3°F. Add more charge if the system superheat is more than 3° higher than specified; recover charge if the superheat is more than 3°F lower than specified.

The system must operate for at least 10 min after any charge adjustment. Then repeat the test procedure to be certain that the charge is within the proper range.

An R-410a system operating with a suction pressure of 118 psig and a suction line temperature of 51°F has a superheat of 11°F. Using the charging chart in Figure 27-65 and the pressure-temperature chart in Figure 27-70, if these readings are obtained with 90°F ambient and 66°F wet bulb, this system is charged correctly.

SYSTEM SUPERHEAT

OUTDOOR AMBIENT TEMPERATURE	SYSTEM SUPERHEAT
65°F	45°F–50°F
75°F	30°F–40°F
85°F	20°F–30°F
95°F	8°F–12°F
105°F	3°F–5°F

Figure 27-68 Some superheat charts only require outdoor ambient temperature; they assume an indoor temperature and humidity

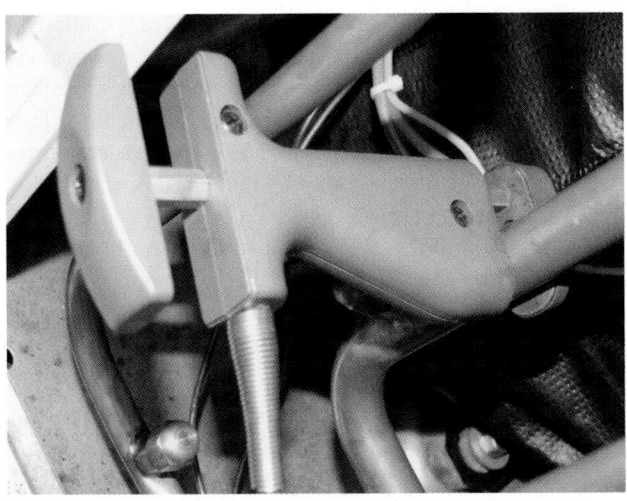

Figure 27-69 Clamp style thermocouple temperature testers work well for checking superheat and subcooling

27.25 CHARGING FOR PROPER SUBCOOLING

Thermostatic expansion valves will regulate the refrigerant flow over a wide range of load and charge conditions. Because thermostatic expansion valves try to maintain a constant superheat, the superheat method is not the best method for testing the charge in an expansion valve system.

Some manufacturers recommend using subcooling to check the charge on expansion valve systems. Normally under full load conditions, the refrigerant in an air conditioner will be subcooled 5°F to 15°F leaving the condenser. Figure 27-71 shows a typical subcooling charging chart. The example in Figure 27-72 shows a system operating with an ambient temperature of 95°F and a return air wet bulb temperature of 67°F. Read across from the outdoor ambient temperature (95°F) until you reach the column with the indoor wet bulb temperature (67°F). The subcooling is shown in parentheses. In this example the required subcooling is 5°F.

An undercharged system will have less subcooling than specified because there is less liquid sitting at the bottom of the condenser. An overcharged system will have a higher subcooling because there will be extra refrigerant sitting in the condenser.

Figure 27-70 Standard pressure-temperature chart for saturated refrigerant

(Courtesy of Arkema Inc.)

VAPOR PRESSURE, PSIG

Temp (°F)	11	12	22	113	114	500	502	134a	123
-50	28.9	15.4	6.2	–	27.1	12.8	0.2	18.7	29.2
-45	28.7	13.3	2.7	–	26.6	10.3	1.9	16.9	29.0
-40	28.4	11.0	0.5	–	26.0	7.6	4.1	14.8	28.9
-35	28.1	8.4	2.6	–	25.4	4.6	6.5	12.5	28.7
-30	27.8	5.5	4.9	29.3	24.6	1.2	9.2	9.8	28.4
-25	27.4	2.3	7.4	29.2	23.8	1.2	12.1	6.9	28.1
-20	27.0	0.6	10.1	29.1	22.9	3.2	15.3	3.7	27.8
-15	26.5	2.4	13.2	28.9	21.8	5.4	18.8	0.1	27.4
-10	26.0	4.5	16.5	28.7	20.6	7.8	22.6	1.9	27.0
-5	25.4	6.7	20.0	28.5	19.3	10.4	26.7	4.1	26.5
0	24.7	9.1	23.9	28.2	17.8	13.3	31.1	6.5	25.9
5	23.9	11.8	28.2	27.9	16.2	16.4	35.9	9.1	25.3
10	23.1	14.6	32.8	27.6	14.4	19.7	41.0	11.9	24.6
15	22.1	17.7	37.7	27.2	12.4	23.3	46.5	15.0	23.7
20	21.1	21.0	43.0	26.8	10.2	27.2	52.5	18.4	22.8
25	19.9	24.6	48.7	26.3	7.8	31.5	58.8	22.1	21.8
30	18.6	28.4	54.9	25.8	5.2	36.0	65.6	26.0	20.7
35	17.2	32.5	61.5	25.2	2.3	40.8	72.8	30.3	19.5
40	15.6	36.9	68.5	24.5	0.4	46.0	80.5	35.0	18.1
45	13.9	41.6	76.0	23.8	2.0	51.6	88.7	40.0	16.6
50	12.0	46.7	84.0	22.9	3.8	57.5	97.4	45.4	15.0
55	10.0	52.0	92.5	22.2	5.8	63.9	106.6	51.1	13.1
60	7.8	57.7	101.6	21.0	7.9	70.6	116.4	57.3	11.2
65	5.4	63.7	111.2	19.9	10.1	77.8	126.7	63.9	9.0
70	2.7	70.2	121.4	18.7	12.6	85.4	137.6	71.0	6.6
75	0.0	76.9	132.2	17.3	15.2	93.4	149.1	78.6	4.0
80	1.5	84.1	143.6	15.8	18.0	101.9	161.2	86.6	1.2
85	3.2	91.7	155.7	14.3	20.9	111.0	174.0	95.1	0.9
90	4.9	99.7	168.4	12.5	24.1	120.5	187.4	104.2	2.5
95	6.8	108.2	181.8	10.6	27.5	130.5	201.4	113.8	4.2
100	8.8	117.1	195.9	8.6	31.1	141.1	216.2	124.1	6.1
105	10.9	126.5	210.7	6.4	35.0	152.2	231.7	134.9	8.1
110	13.2	136.4	226.3	4.0	39.1	164.0	247.9	146.3	10.3
115	15.6	146.7	242.7	1.4	43.4	176.3	264.9	158.4	12.6
120	18.3	157.6	259.9	0.7	48.0	189.2	282.7	171.1	15.1
125	21.0	169.0	277.9	2.2	52.8	202.8	301.4	184.5	17.7
130	24.0	180.9	296.8	3.7	58.0	217.0	320.8	198.7	20.6
135	27.1	193.5	316.5	5.4	63.4	231.9	341.2	213.6	23.6
140	30.4	206.5	337.2	7.2	69.0	247.4	362.6	229.3	26.8
145	34.0	220.2	358.8	9.2	75.0	263.7	385.0	245.7	30.2
150	37.7	234.5	381.5	11.2	81.3	280.7	408.4	263.0	33.8

Bold Numbers - Inches Hg. Below 1 ATM

PRESSURE/TEMPERATURE CHART

Temp. Deg. F	R-408A (FX-10) Liquid Pressure	R-404A (FX-70) Liquid Pressure	R-409A (FX-56) Liquid Pressure	R-409A (FX-56) Vapor Pressure	R-407C Liquid Pressure	R-407C Vapor Pressure	R-410A Liquid Pressure
-50	1.6	0.6	12.4	17.2	2.9	11.4	3.5
-45	1.1	2.7	9.7	15.2	0.4	8.5	8.5
-40	3.3	5.0	6.8	13.1	2.5	5.2	11.6
-35	5.6	7.6	3.5	10.7	4.8	1.5	14.9
-30	8.2	10.4	0.0	8.1	7.3	1.3	18.5
-25	11.0	13.4	2.0	5.1	10.1	3.6	22.5
-20	14.1	16.8	4.1	1.9	13.1	6.1	26.9
-15	17.5	20.5	6.5	0.8	16.5	8.8	31.7
-10	21.2	24.5	9.0	2.8	20.1	11.9	36.8
-5	25.2	28.8	11.8	4.9	24.0	15.2	42.5
0	29.5	33.5	14.8	7.2	28.3	18.9	48.6
5	34.2	38.6	18.1	9.7	33.0	22.9	55.2
10	39.3	44.0	21.7	12.5	38.0	27.3	62.3
15	44.8	49.9	25.5	15.4	43.5	32.0	70.0
20	50.7	56.2	29.6	18.7	49.3	37.2	78.3
25	57.0	63.0	34.0	22.2	55.7	42.7	87.3
30	63.7	70.3	38.7	26.0	62.5	48.7	96.8
35	71.0	78.1	43.8	30.1	69.8	55.2	107.0
40	78.7	86.4	49.2	34.5	77.6	62.1	118.0
45	87.0	95.2	54.9	39.2	86.0	69.5	129.7
50	95.8	104.7	61.0	44.3	94.9	77.5	142.2
55	105.1	114.7	67.6	49.8	104.5	86.0	155.2
60	115.1	125.3	74.5	55.6	114.6	95.1	169.6
65	125.6	136.6	81.8	61.9	125.4	104.8	184.6
70	136.8	148.6	89.5	68.6	136.9	115.2	200.6
75	148.7	161.2	97.7	75.8	149.1	126.2	217.4
80	161.2	174.6	106.4	83.4	162.1	137.8	235.3
85	174.4	188.8	115.5	91.5	175.8	150.2	254.1
90	188.4	203.7	125.2	100.2	190.2	163.4	274.1
95	203.1	219.4	135.3	109.4	205.5	177.4	295.1
100	218.7	235.9	146.0	119.2	221.6	192.1	317.2
105	235.0	253.4	157.2	129.6	238.5	207.8	340.5
110	252.1	271.7	169.0	140.6	256.4	224.4	365.0
115	270.2	290.9	181.4	152.3	275.1	241.9	390.7
120	289.1	311.1	194.4	164.7	294.7	260.5	417.7
125	308.9	332.3	208.0	177.8	315.2	280.1	445.9
130	329.7	354.5	222.3	191.6	336.7	300.9	475.6
135	351.5	377.8	237.2	206.3	359.3	322.9	506.5
140	374.3	402.2	252.9	221.8	382.6	346.2	539.0
145	398.1	427.7	269.3	238.2	407.0	370.8	572.8
150	423.0	454.4	286.4	255.5	432.4	396.9	608.1

Bold Numbers - Inches Hg. Below 1 ATM

COOLING MODE				
OUTDOOR AMBIENT	**INDOOR WET BULB (°F)**			
	57	62	67	72
DB (°F)	LIQUID PRESSURE (SUBCOOLING)			
65	136 (3)	138 (4)	140 (4)	143 (4)
70	150 (4)	152 (5)	154 (5)	157 (5)
75	163 (5)	165 (5)	167 (5)	170 (6)
80	178 (5)	180 (5)	182 (5)	185 (6)
85	192 (5)	194 (5)	196 (5)	199 (6)
90	208 (5)	210 (5)	212 (5)	215 (6)
95	223 (5)	225 (5)	227 (5)	230 (6)
100	240 (5)	242 (5)	244 (5)	247 (6)
105	256 (5)	258 (5)	260 (5)	263 (6)
110	274 (5)	276 (5)	278 (5)	281 (6)
115	291 (4)	293 (4)	295 (5)	298 (6)
120	310 (4)	312 (4)	314 (5)	317 (5)
125	328 (3)	330 (3)	332 (4)	335 (4)

Figure 27-71 Typical subcooling chart for checking refrigerant charge

COOLING MODE				
OUTDOOR AMBIENT	**INDOOR WET BULB (°F)**			
	57	62	67	72
DB (°F)	LIQUID PRESSURE (SUBCOOLING)			
65	136 (3)	138 (4)	140 (4)	143 (4)
70	150 (4)	152 (5)	164 (5)	157 (5)
75	163 (5)	165 (5)	167 (5)	170 (6)
80	178 (5)	180 (5)	182 (5)	185 (6)
85	192 (5)	194 (5)	196 (5)	199 (6)
90	208 (5)	210 (5)	212 (5)	215 (6)
95	223 (5)	225 (5)	227 (5)	230 (6)
100	240 (5)	242 (5)	244 (5)	247 (6)
105	256 (5)	258 (5)	260 (5)	263 (6)
110	274 (5)	276 (5)	278 (5)	281 (6)
115	291 (4)	293 (4)	295 (5)	298 (6)
120	310 (4)	312 (4)	314 (5)	317 (5)
125	328 (3)	330 (3)	332 (4)	335 (4)

Figure 27-72 The correct system subcooling is found in parentheses at the intersection of the ambient temperature row and the indoor wet bulb column

27.26 CHECKING SYSTEM SUBCOOLING

Two measurements are required to check system subcooling: the liquid line temperature and pressure leaving the condenser. It is important to use a fast reading, accurate thermometer or an electronic temperature probe to take the suction line temperature. Clamp on thermocouple temperature probes like the one shown in Figure 27-69 work well.

Run the system for 10–30 min to allow the temperatures and pressures to stabilize, then read the pressure and temperature of the liquid line.

Use a pressure-temperature chart like the one in Figure 27-70 to determine the saturation temperature that matches the liquid pressure. Subtract the actual liquid temperature from the saturation temperature on the chart to obtain the subcooling. Compare it with the manufacturer's

recommendation. Most manufacturers allow a variation of ±1°F. Add more charge if the system subcooling is more than 1°F lower than specified; recover charge if the superheat is more than 1°F higher than specified. The system must operate for at least 10 min after any charge adjustment. Then repeat the test procedure to be certain that the charge is within the proper range.

An R-22 system operating with a liquid pressure of 227 psig and a liquid line temperature of 106°F has a subcooling of 5°F. Using the chart in Figure 27-72, if this system is operating with a 95°F ambient temperature and a 67°F wet bulb temperature, the system is charged correctly.

27.27 LIQUID-AMBIENT APPROACH CHARGING METHOD

The liquid line is always a little warmer than the outdoor ambient temperature. The approach charging method examines the temperature difference between the liquid line and outdoor ambient. To calculate the approach, measure the liquid line temperature and outdoor ambient temperature and subtract the outdoor ambient temperature from the liquid line temperature. It is a good idea to either use the same thermometer to take both readings, or to compare the two thermometers used at ambient temperature to make sure they correspond. Just a few degrees of difference can give a different diagnosis. Compare the measured temperature difference to the manufacturer's specification, Figure 27-73. If the temperature difference is higher than specified, the system is undercharged. If the temperature difference is lower than expected, the system is overcharged.

27.28 WATER COOLED SYSTEMS

The first checks to make on any water cooled system are water temperature and flow. The pressures of a water cooled system operating with too little water flow will be higher than normal, making the system look as if it is overcharged. The pressures of a water cooled system operating with water that is too cold will be lower than expected, making the system appear to be undercharged. The manufacturer's performance data for water cooled systems typically specify

Model no.	Approach temperature liquid line–outdoor ambient °F(°C)
10ACB12	7 (3.9)
10ACB18	5 (2.8)
10ACB24	9 (5)
10ACB30	10 (5.6)
10ACB36	12 (6.7)
10ACB42	14 (8)
10ACB48	13 (7.2)
10ACB60	12 (6.7)
10ACB62	12 (6.7)

Figure 27-73 Approach method

ENTERING WATER	FLOW GPM	COOLING PERFORMANCE DATA				HEATING PERFORMANCE DATA			
		WATER TEMP RISE	SUCTION PRESSURE	DISCHARGE PRESSURE	AIR TEMP DROP	WATER TEMP DROP	SUCTION PRESSURE	DISCHARGE PRESSURE	AIR TEMP RISE
35°F	7	NR	NR	NR	NR	5 - 6	38 - 44	163 - 207	19 - 24
	9	NR	NR	NR	NR	4 - 5	40 - 46	165 - 210	19 - 25
45°F	7	13 - 16	66 - 76	122 - 155	21 - 27	6 - 7	47 - 54	176 - 225	22 - 28
	9	10 - 13	66 - 75	118 - 150	21 - 27	5 - 6	48 - 55	178 - 227	22 - 29
55°F	7	13 - 16	67 - 77	133 - 170	21 - 27	7 - 9	55 - 64	192 - 245	25 - 32
	9	10 - 13	66 - 76	129 - 164	21 - 27	6 - 7	57 - 66	194 - 247	26 - 32
65°F	7	12 - 15	70 - 81	156 - 199	21 - 26	8 - 10	68 - 78	213 - 271	29 - 37
	9	10 - 12	70 - 80	151 - 192	21 - 26	7 - 8	69 - 80	215 - 273	30 - 38
75°F	7	12 - 15	72 - 82	172 - 219	20 - 26	9 - 11	74 - 85	223 - 283	32 - 40
	9	10 - 12	71 - 82	166 - 212	20 - 26	7 - 9	76 - 87	225 - 286	32 - 41
85°F	7	12 - 15	73 - 85	200 - 255	19 - 25	10 - 12	83 - 95	236 - 301	34 - 43
	9	9 - 12	73 - 84	194 - 248	19 - 25	8 - 10	84 - 97	238 - 303	34 - 44
95°F	7	11 - 14	75 - 86	227 - 289	19 - 24	NR	NR	NR	NR
	9	9 - 12	75 - 86	220 - 280	19 - 24	NR	NR	NR	NR

NOTE: CHART VALUES ARE ACCURATE ONLY FOR SYSTEMS OPERATING WITHIN DESIGN AIRFLOW LIMITS

Figure 27-74 System operating data for water source system

the condenser water flow, inlet water temperature range, and condenser water temperature rise, Figure 27-74. Operating pressure ranges for both the suction and discharge pressures are normally provided as well.

27.29 OIL CHARGING

Very rarely does oil need to be added to a refrigeration system. Unlike engine oil, refrigeration oil does not need to be changed regularly. The initial charge of refrigeration oil should last for the life of the system. A refrigeration system is a closed system, free of air and other contaminants. Further, the temperatures inside a refrigeration system are designed to stay under the temperature at which the oil begins to break down. Leaks seldom release enough oil to warrant adding any. A very small amount of oil sprayed out with refrigerant vapor makes a large, oily spot which may appear to be evidence of a large oil leak. When the compressor is low on oil, the oil is usually just somewhere else in the system. However, there are times when it is necessary to remove or add refrigeration oil.

Checking Oil Level

On compressors that have a crankcase sight glass as in Figures 27-75 and 27-76, the correct oil level can be accurately observed and the quantity adjusted to the level indicated in the sight glass. It is important, however, to observe the oil level

Figure 27-75 The sightglass is used to check the level of the compressor crankcase oil

after the system has been in operation. Refrigerant will dissolve in the oil during system shutdown and raise the apparent oil level. This refrigerant boils out when the system starts, carrying some of the oil with it. Most of this oil returns after the system has operated long enough for the pressures to stabilize, but some oil remains in the system all the time. The typical level in an oil sight glass starts out above the normal

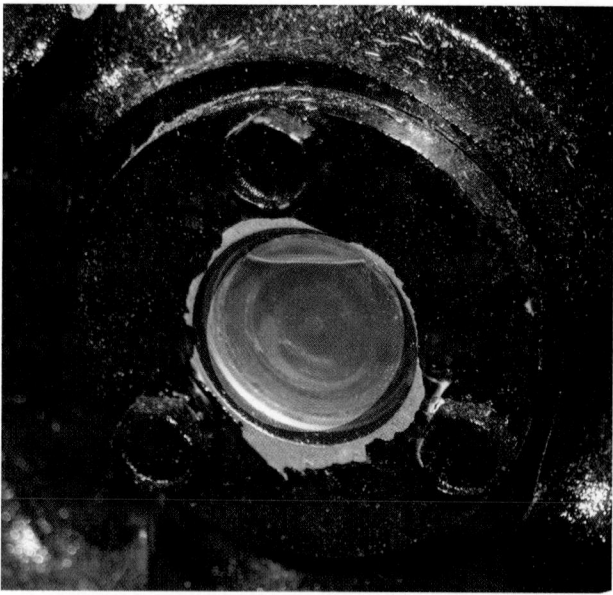

Figure 27-76 Dissolved refrigerant raises the oil level during the off cycle
(Courtesy Hampden Engineering Corporation)

oil level, drops to the bottom of the sight glass shortly after startup, and then gradually rises to the normal operating level, Figure 27-77. If the oil level is low after the system pressures have stabilized and the compressor crankcase is warm, the system may be low on oil.

Changing Compressor Oil

Oil is a scavenger and it will end up collecting most of the crud in a system. One of the fastest ways to clean a system that has experienced multiple compressor failures is to check and change the compressor oil. Occasionally refrigeration oil needs to be changed to make a refrigerant retrofit possible because the new refrigerant does not work well with the old refrigeration oil. Changing refrigeration oil for any reason is only really possible in systems with semi-hermetic or open compressors.

Hermetic Compressors

It is not practical to remove oil from a hermetic compressor. Hermetic compressors do not have crankcase ports. The only way to remove the oil is to remove the compressor, turn it upside down, and pour the oil out. It is also not possible to check the oil level on hermetic compressors because there is no oil sight glass. It is possible to add oil to a system with a hermetic compressor using a hand pump to force oil into the suction line. However, the technician cannot accurately measure the effect of adding the oil and has no reasonable way of removing the oil once it is in the system.

Figure 27-77 The oil level starts out too high, drops too low shortly after startup, and settles at the correct operating level after several minutes of operation

Semi-Hermetic and Open Compressors

Adding or removing oil is more reasonable with semi-hermetic and open compressors. Small semi-hermetic compressors have a crankcase plug above the normal crankcase oil level that may be used for removing or adding oil, Figure 27-78.

Figure 27-78 Crankcase plug in small semi-hermetic air coded compressor

Evacuating the Crankcase

Remember that the compressor crankcase is under pressure! The pressure must be removed from the compressor crankcase before removing any crankcase plugs. This may be accomplished by having the compressor pump itself down. Connect a set of gauge manifolds to the suction and discharge service valves on the compressor. Front seat the suction service valve, energize the compressors, and operate the compressor until the crankcase pressure is below the mandated EPA recovery level for the refrigerant in the system. Deenergize the compressor after it has pumped down and front seat the discharge service valve. Make sure the compressor cannot be turned back on.

The refrigerant will need to be recovered from systems that cannot or should not pump themselves down. Some compressor manufacturers do not want the compressor operating in a vacuum, even for a short period of time. Figure 27-79 shows the connections and valve positions necessary to recover refrigerant from the compressor. Make sure the compressor is off and cannot be turned on. Connect a set of gauge manifolds to the suction and discharge service valves on the compressor. Front seat both the suction and discharge service valves and recover the refrigerant to the EPA specified level for the refrigerant in the system. Note that the under 200 lb rule may be used because the part that is isolated contains less than 200 lb.

Removing Oil

An adapter like the one shown in Figure 27-80 can be used to remove oil from small semi-hermetic compressors. It provides a dip tube to the bottom of the crankcase. Once the adapter is in place, a few pounds of nitrogen introduced through the suction service valve will push the oil out the dip tube in the adapter.

Larger semi-hermetic and open compressors have crankcase drain plugs. Opening this plug allows oil to flow out of the compressor crankcase, Figure 27-81.

Adding Oil

The oil can be poured into the compressor crankcase after evacuating and opening the compressor crankcase. After the oil is added, the compressor will need to be evacuated. This should not take long because only the compressor crankcase is being evacuated. After evacuating the compressor, the suction and discharge service valves are back seated, allowing the system refrigerant back into the compressor.

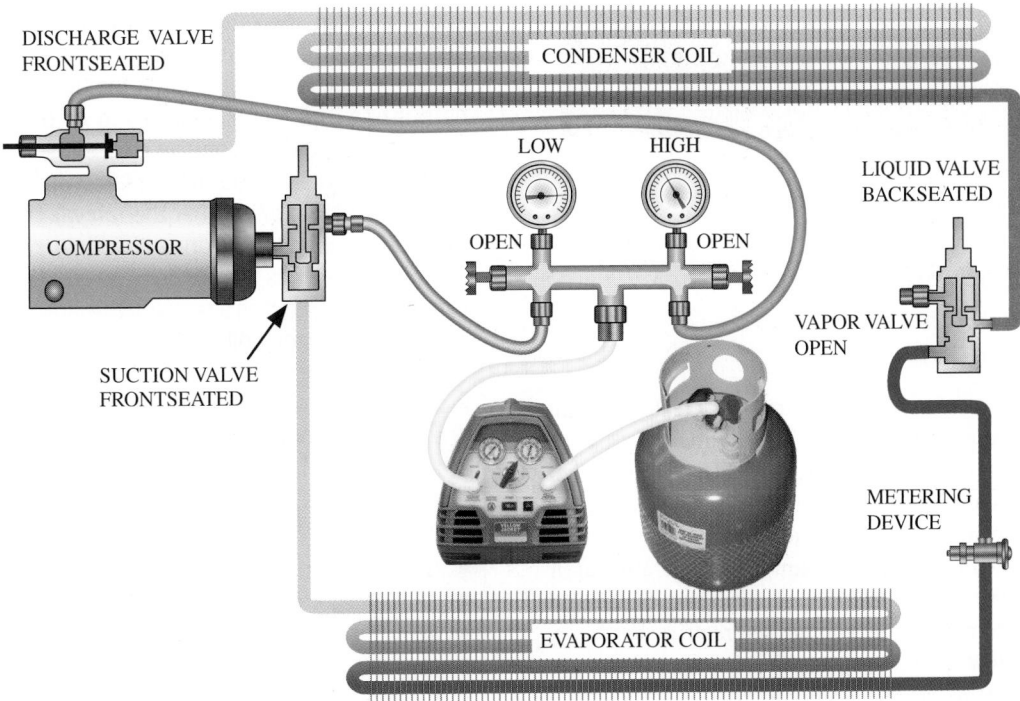

Figure 27-79 Connections for recovering refrigerant from compressor

Figure 27-80 This adapter allows removal of refrigerant from the crankcase plug on small, air cooled, semi-hermetic compressors
(2008 JB Industries, Inc.)

FILL PORT

SIGHT GLASS

06GA500004

DRAIN PORT

Figure 27-81 Crankcase drain plug on large compressor

Adding Oil Without Opening the Compressor Crankcase Using a Vacuum

In the evacuation method, the compressor creates a slight vacuum that is used to suck oil in. The oil line must have a manual valve to control flow through the oil line. One end of the oil hose is connected to the suction service valve, the other is submerged in the oil container. Purge the air from the oil line by blowing a small amount of refrigerant vapor through it into the oil. Front seat the suction service valve and operate the compressor long enough to create a slight vacuum. Oil may now be added by opening the control valve in the oil line. Close the oil control valve when the oil level in the compressor crankcase sight glass is at the minimum fill level, Figure 27-81. Back seat the suction service valve and remove the oil charging hose.

UNIT 27—SUMMARY

The only two chemicals that should be circulating in a refrigeration system are refrigerant and oil. Evacuating a system ensures that the system is free of noncondensables and moisture before charging. Deep vacuums are measured in microns of mercury absolute using electronic vacuum gauges. The lower the number the better the vacuum; a deep vacuum should hold under 500 microns. A system that has been evacuated is normally charged with liquid into the high side of the system with the system off. The amount of refrigerant added is measured by an electronic scale. The amount and type of refrigerant used in a system can be found by looking at the data plate. This amount must be adjusted for line length on split systems. Common forms of charging charts provided by manufacturers include charts that correlate operating conditions to system pressure, superheat, or subcooling. Superheat charts are used with fixed restriction systems while subcooling charts are used with thermostatic expansion valve systems.

WORK ORDERS

Service Ticket 2701

Customer Complaint: System Not Cooling Properly

Equipment Type: R-22 Residential Split System

The technician arrives at the residence. The customer states that the system has not been cooling very well for the last few weeks. The technician asks to go in and look at the indoor unit and finds that the fan is running and that there is very little air coming out of the vents. The technician notes that there is a TEV on the evaporator and finds that the outdoor coil is clean and the condenser discharge air temperature is cool.

The technician suspects that the evaporator coil may be freezing. The technician asks to go back in the residence so that the evaporative coil can be defrosted. The technician turns the thermostat fan switch to *on* and the system switch to *off* so that the fan will blow air across the coil to defrost it. During the defrost process, the technician watches the condensate drain to be sure that it does not overflow as a result of the large volume of water from the frozen coil.

Once the evaporator coil has been thawed, the technician returns to the outdoor unit to check the charge. The technician puts on his safety glasses and gloves, and attaches the refrigerant manifold gauge set to the system. The technician obtains the following pressures and temperatures:

- Suction line pressure is 50 psi
- Suction line temperature is 60°F
- Ambient air temperature is 85°F
- the high side pressure is 170 psi

The unit superheat chart calls for a superheat of 20°F, but the actual superheat is 32°F (50 psig = 28°F saturation 60°F − 28°F = 32°F). The technician determines that the system is low on refrigerant because the superheat is high. A leak is found on the Schrader valve. The technician uses a core removing and replacement tool to change out the Schrader core without having to remove the charge.

The charge is adjusted so that the proper superheat temperature is obtained. The technician notes the number of pounds of refrigerant that were added to the system. This information is put on the service ticket and recorded on the refrigerant log. The system is now operating satisfactorily.

Service Ticket 2702

Customer Complaint: System Is Tripping Main Circuit Breaker

Equipment Type: R-22 Residential Split System

The service technician checks to make sure the thermostat and compressor disconnect are turned off. Then the technician checks to make certain the breaker is good and turns power on to the disconnect. Leaving the disconnect off, the technician checks and determines the compressor is grounded. The technician reports to the customer that the compressor is bad, and the customer wants the compressor replaced.

The technician checks the price book and provides the customer with a cost estimate for the job. The customer accepts the estimate, and the technician calls the office and has the parts department send a replacement compressor.

While the compressor is being delivered, the technician puts on safety glasses and gloves and proceeds to recover the refrigerant. After the refrigerant is recovered to the proper level, the technician replaces the compressor and installs the liquid and suction line driers. A leak test is then performed to verify a tight system.

With a leak-free system, the technician then evacuates and dehydrates the system to 500 microns. After determining the system is tight and dry, the refrigerant charging process is started. To ensure the efficiency and longevity of the system, this process should be performed to the manufacturer's specifications.

The manufacturer's specifications dictate an approach charging method. Using the manufacturer's supplied chart, the technician reaches the appropriate temperature difference between the outdoor ambient temperature and the liquid line temperature, thus completing the charging process.

After cleaning up all of the packaging and other scrap material from the worksite, the customer is provided with a service ticket.

Service Ticket 2703

Customer Complaint: Poor Cooling and High Operating Cost

Equipment Type: R-22 Split System, New Condensing Unit Replacement

A customer complains that his new air conditioner does not seem to cool as well as his old one and it costs more to operate. The technician checks the system pressures

and finds that the high side pressure is 50 psig higher than the manufacturer's specification. The compressor is very hot, the compressor amp draw is high, and the system superheat is 30°F, but the unit calls for 15°F. The technician recognizes that this is not a simple case of overcharge because of the high superheat. The technician asks the homeowner for more information about the installation and the homeowner confesses that a friend of his changed the unit out one day during an extended lunch break. The technician suspects that the system has noncondensables from not being thoroughly evacuated. All the refrigerant is recovered into a separate cylinder. The system is evacuated to under 500 microns and a new charge of clean refrigerant is weighed in. The technician runs the system until all the pressures and temperatures stabilize, then checks the system pressures and superheat. The system now is operating at the required 15°F superheat with a normal condensing pressure. The compressor is running cooler and the amp draw is down under the data plate current rating.

Service Ticket 2704

Customer Complaint: Poor Cooling and High Operating Cost

Equipment Type: R-22 Split System, New Condensing Unit Replacement

A customer complains that her new air conditioner does not seem to cool as well as her old one and it costs more to operate despite the fact that the new system is a 14 SEER unit and the old one was a 10 SEER unit. The technician checks the system charge and finds that it is operating with a low suction pressure, a high superheat, and a high subcooling. The technician tries to adjust the charge, but it seems impossible. To get the superheat down to the recommended level, the high side has to be higher than the charging chart specifies for the ambient temperature. The technician decides to look at the indoor coil to look for clues and notices that the indoor coil is old. The technician uses a web-capable cell phone to look for an AHRI match between the new condensing unit and the old coil and discovers the two pieces of equipment are not matched. The technician explains that SEER ratings apply to matched systems, not individual components. Since the condenser and evaporator are not an AHRI match, they will not work well together. The technician suggests that the customer have a coil installed that is an ARI match to solve the problem.

Service Ticket 2705

Work to be Performed: New System Startup

Equipment Type: R-410A Split System Air Conditioner

A technician is called to perform a new system startup on an R-410A split system. The technician notices that the manufacturer lists the factory charge as adequate for 15 ft, but the lines on this system are 30 ft. The technician suspects that the system will need a small amount of charge to adjust for the extra line length, but decides to check the system operation before adding refrigerant. The technician gets the following readings while checking the system charge: 130 psig suction pressure, 60°F suction line temperature, 340 psig liquid pressure, 102°F liquid line temperature. The technician's first impression is that everything looks good. However, the manufacturer calls for an 8°F subcooling and the unit is operating with only 3°F of subcooling (340 = 105°F saturation). The technician throttles a small amount of liquid refrigerant into the low side with the system running, waits for 10 min, then rechecks the figures. The pressures have not changed, but the liquid line is now 100°F, making the subcooling 5°F. The technician throttles in another small amount of liquid, waits, and rechecks the system. The pressures have remained stable, but the liquid line temperature has dropped to 97°F, providing the correct subcooling.

UNIT 27—REVIEW QUESTIONS

1. What chemicals should be inside a refrigeration system?
2. How are vacuum pumps rated?
3. What is the purpose of evacuating a refrigeration system?
4. Explain what microns are and how they are used to measure vacuum.
5. What happens if noncondensables are left in the system?
6. What happens if moisture is left in the system?
7. Why does the presence of liquid water in a system slow down the evacuation process?
8. What is considered a good vacuum level for a deep vacuum?
9. Why are systems with fixed restriction metering devices critical to charge?
10. How does an overcharge of refrigerant affect system efficiency?
11. Why must refrigerants that fractionate, such as R-410A, be charged as a liquid?
12. How does an undercharge affect the superheat of a fixed restriction system?
13. How does an overcharge affect the superheat of a fixed restriction system?
14. How does an undercharge affect the subcooling of a thermostatic expansion valve system?
15. How does an overcharge affect the subcooling of a thermostatic expansion valve system?
16. What is the best method for charging a large system that holds 50 lb of refrigerant?
17. What is the best method of charging a small appliance that holds less than a pound of refrigerant?
18. Using Figure 27-65, what would be the proper superheat for a system with an ambient temperature of 95°F and a return air wet bulb of 70°F ?

19. Using the information in question 18, you measure a suction pressure of 130 psig for an R-410A system. What should the suction line temperature be?
20. Using the information from questions 18 and 19, what charge adjustment should be made if the suction line measures 55°F?
21. Using Figure 27-71, what would be the proper subcooling for a system with an ambient temperature of 115°F and a return air wet bulb of 62°F ?
22. Using the information from question 21, what should the liquid line temperature be if the liquid pressure is 293 psig for an R-22 system?
23. Using the information from questions 21 and 22, what charge adjustment needs to be made if the liquid line temperature is 110°F?
24. Why should a system be leak tested after it has been repaired and before it is evacuated?
25. Outline the procedure for adding oil to a semi-hermetic compressor without opening the compressor.
26. How often should the refrigeration oil in a compressor be changed?
27. Using Figure 27-73, what should the liquid line temperature be for a system operating at an ambient temperature of 97°F?
28. Using the information from question 27, what charge adjustment needs to be made if the liquid line temperature is 110°F?
29. Using Figure 27-61, the suction pressure is 140 psig, the liquid pressure is 370 psig, and the ambient temperature is 105°F. What charge adjustment needs to be made?
30. Using Figure 27-61, the suction pressure is 155 psig, the liquid pressure is 360 psig, and the ambient temperature is 95°F. What charge adjustment needs to be made?
31. List the variables that affect system pressures.
32. Give an example of a condition that can make a system appear overcharged even though the charge is correct.
33. Give an example of a condition that can make a system appear undercharged even though the charge is correct.
34. What is the standard AHRI design condition used for rating unitary air conditioning equipment?
35. Who is the most reliable source of information regarding the charge for any particular piece of equipment?
36. A new split system air conditioning system is being installed. The actual line length is 48 ft. The factory charge for the condensing unit is 94 oz. The installation instructions state that the factory charge assumes a line length of 20 ft and gives the per foot adjustment as 0.6 oz/ft. How much refrigerant should be added to the system after the lines and coil have been evacuated?
37. The compressor in an existing split system air conditioning system is being replaced. The actual line length is 35 ft. The factory charge for the condensing unit is 100 oz. The installation instructions state that the factory charge assumes a line length of 15 ft and gives the per foot adjustment as 0.6 oz/ft. How much refrigerant should be added to the system after the system has been evacuated?

HVAC/R Electrical Systems and Components

UNIT 28

Basic Electricity

OBJECTIVES

After completing this unit, you will be able to:

- explain how the structure of the atom affects electricity.
- discuss the difference between a conductor and an insulator.
- explain the difference between direct current and alternating current.
- list the characteristics of electric current that are commonly measured and the units used to measure them.
- explain the relationship of potential, current, and resistance in an electrical circuit.
- discuss the three elements required to make an electrical circuit.
- explain the difference between series, parallel, and series parallel circuits.
- use Ohm's law and/or the power formula to calculate values for volts, amps, ohms, and watts.

28.1 INTRODUCTION

Electricity and electrical problems are the most common issues HVAC/R technicians encounter. Installation and service both require an understanding of the basic electrical characteristics. A fundamental knowledge of electricity is required to truly understand all the electrical components in an air conditioning system. Understanding electrical circuit

characteristics and how to measure them allows technicians to test and analyze circuits in air conditioning systems. Therefore, it is essential that technicians have a good understanding of basic electrical theory.

28.2 STRUCTURE OF THE ATOM

It is necessary to understand the structure of the atom to understand electricity. The smallest piece of an element that can exist and still retain the same chemical properties is the atom. Atoms are made of small particles called protons, neutrons, and electrons. Protons are positively charged, electrons are negatively charged, and neutrons have no charge. In the center of the atom is a nucleus composed of protons and neutrons. Clouds of negatively charged electrons are arranged in energy levels around this nucleus, Figure 28-1. Usually, the number of electrons and protons are equal, so the atom is neither negatively charged nor positively charged. The negatively charged electrons are held in the atom by their attraction to the positively charged nucleus. The electrons are arranged in energy levels, with fewer electrons in the energy level closest to the nucleus and more electrons in the energy level farthest away from the nucleus. Each energy level has a maximum number of electrons that it will hold. The maximum number of electrons in each energy level is 2 in the first, 8 in the second, 18 in the third, and 32 in the fourth. As atoms become larger with more electrons, some electrons end up further away from the nucleus. The electrons that are farther

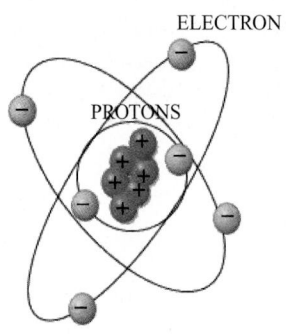

Figure 28-1 A simple carbon atom has a nucleus of positively charged protons surrounded by negatively charged electrons *(NOAA)*

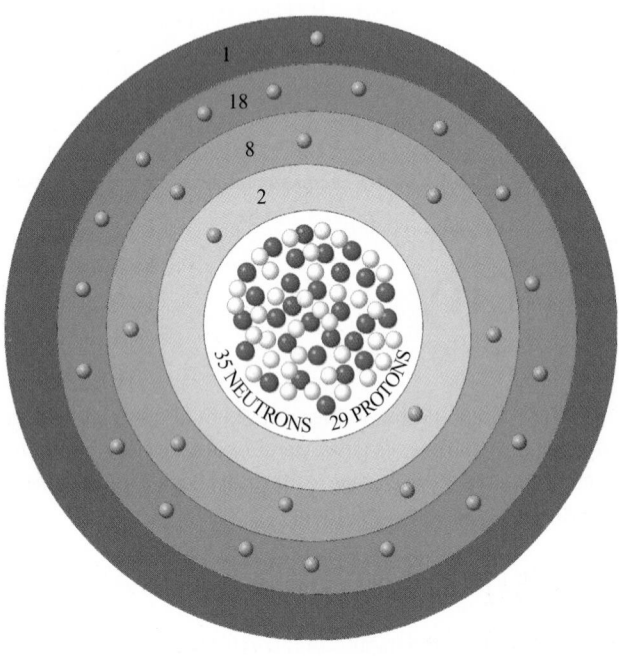

Figure 28-2 The first three electron energy levels of a copper atom are full, but the outer level has only one electron

away from the nucleus are not as tightly bound to the atom because the attraction is weaker. When just a few electrons are in an outer orbit, they can escape the bonds of their atom. Electrons that have escaped their atomic bonds are called free electrons. Figure 28-2 shows a copper atom. The first three

energy levels are filled, leaving one electron in the outermost energy level.

28.3 FLOW OF ELECTRONS

Electricity is the flow of electrons. Electrical flow is not like pouring electrons in one end of a wire and dumping them out the other. Rather, electricity is more like a string of dominoes. One bumps the next and the energy flows from one end to the other, but no individual domino moves very far. With electricity, an electron moves from one atom to another and causes an electron to leave that atom. This electron then moves to a neighboring atom, which causes it to lose an electron. This chain reaction carries through the wire to provide an electrical current, Figure 28-3. Energy is required to start and maintain this chain reaction and get all the free electrons moving in the same direction.

28.4 CONDUCTORS AND INSULATORS

Electrons can flow through some materials more easily than other materials. Atoms that have just a few electrons on their outer energy level make good conductors because those electrons can more easily become free electrons, Figure 28-2. Materials with a large number of free electrons make good electrical conductors. Most metals are good conductors because they have a large number of free electrons that are not bound to any particular atom. Gold, silver, copper, and aluminum are all excellent electrical conductors. This list is arranged in order of the metal's ability to conduct electricity with gold being the best conductor. Gold and silver are both commonly used as electrical conductors in electronic circuits where the amount of material is small, Figure 28-4. Copper is used most often in wiring because of its lower cost than gold and silver and its superiority to aluminum in conductance, Figure 28-5.

Insulators have far fewer free electrons, so they resist the flow of electrons. The outer energy level of an insulator is typically full, making it more difficult for electrons to escape. Ceramic, rubber, and plastic are examples of insulators. Thermoplastics are commonly used for the insulator on wires because a very thin layer of thermoplastic can resist hundreds of volts. A thicker insulation layer is required to contain higher voltages. The voltage feeding spark plugs in car engines is several thousand volts. Spark plug wires have a much thicker insulation jacket than house wiring because

Figure 28-3 Electron flow occurs as a chain reaction

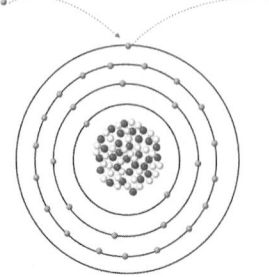
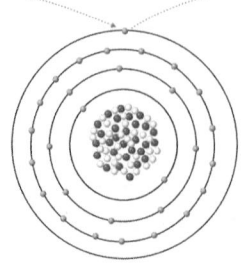
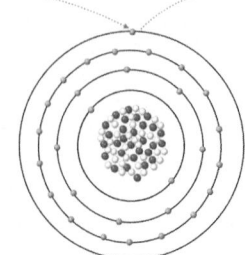

Figure 28-4 The contacts on the edge connector of this circuit board are made of gold

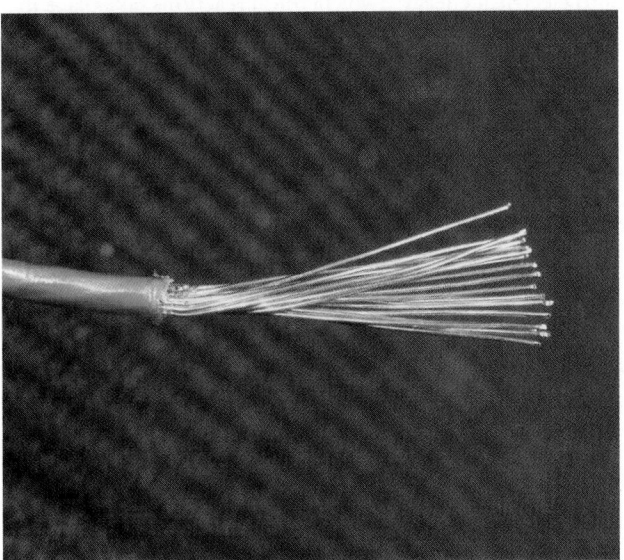

Figure 28-5 This wire is made of copper

Figure 28-6 The insulation on the wire on the left is designed for up to 600 V; the insulation on the wire on the right is designed for thousands of volts

they need to contain higher voltages. Figure 28-6 shows a comparison of the insulation on a power wire and on a spark plug wire. Ceramic insulators are used in high voltage applications that also require physical strength. The insulators on high voltage power distribution lines are ceramic.

28.5 SEMICONDUCTORS

The revolution in electronic circuits is based on the discovery and advancement of semiconductors. Semiconductors can behave like a conductor or like an insulator. This behavior allows them to be used like an electronically controlled switch. Silicon, carbon, and germanium can form uniform crystals because they have four electrons in their outer shell. Silicon is the most commonly used semiconductor material. The addition of trace amounts of another chemical into the crystalline structure is called doping. Doping alters the semiconductor's electrical properties. Doping can produce either a positive or negative charge in the semiconductor material, depending on the chemical used. N-type, negative semiconductors are doped with phosphorus and arsenic; P-type, positive semiconductors are doped with boron and gallium. The N-type and P-type materials are joined together to make semiconductor devices like diodes, transistors, and rectifiers.

28.6 STATIC ELECTRICITY

Static versus Dynamic

Electricity can be classified as either static or dynamic. Something that is static is stationary; something that is dynamic is in motion. Static electricity is the result of a standing charge, while dynamic electricity is in motion. Dynamic electricity has a current created by flowing electrons.

Static Charges

Objects can be neutral, positively charged, or negatively charged. If the number of electrons and protons in an object are equal, it will be neutral and will not have an electrical charge. If an object picks up additional electrons, it will become negatively charged because electrons have a negative charge. If an object loses electrons, it will become positively charged. Static electrical charges are the result of friction where electrons are literally rubbed off from one object to another, creating one positive and one negative charge.

Examples of Static Electricity

If the difference in charge between the two objects is great enough, electrons will jump from the negatively charged object to the positively charged object. Lightning is probably the most common type of static electricity, Figure 28-7. Lightning occurs during a storm when cloud particles acquire large amounts of electric charge as they rub across the ground. Meanwhile, the ground has built up an opposite

Figure 28-7 Lightning is a powerful example of static electricity
(NOAA Photo Library, NOAA Central Library; OAR/ERL/National Severe Storms Library (NSSL))

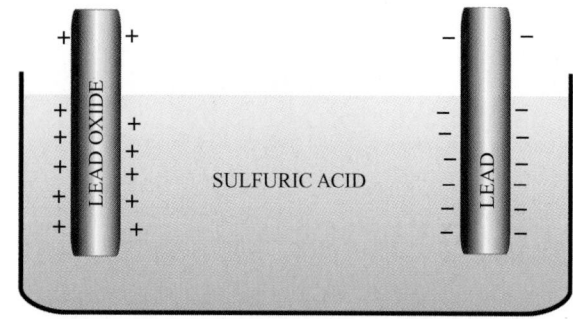

Figure 28-8 In a lead-acid battery, the reaction between the lead and sulfuric acid produces a negative charge while the reaction between the lead oxide and the sulfuric acid produces a positive charge

electric charge. A lightning bolt is created when the difference in charge becomes strong enough and the clouds get close enough to the ground for the electrons to jump. A smaller charge is acquired in dry weather by a person by walking along a thick rug, collecting negative charges from the rug by friction. A spark jumps from the person to an object when they reach to touch it because of the static charge they have built up.

SERVICE TIP

There are many printed circuit boards currently being used in the HVAC/R field containing electronic chips that control the functions of the system. These electronic chips can be damaged by an accidental discharge of static electricity. Always discharge yourself by touching the equipment frame when working around equipment with electronic components.

Static electricity has few practical uses; however, one rather common device uses static electricity to filter the air. Air is passed through a plastic media which is charged by static electricity from the movement of the air. The static charge is used to attract and trap the particles in the airstream. The process is very effective in removing fine dust particles and pollen from the air.

28.7 PRODUCING DYNAMIC ELECTRICITY

Other forms of energy that can be used to generate electricity include heat, light, chemical, mechanical, and magnetic. They generate electricity by moving free electrons. The two most common forms of energy used to generate electricity are chemical energy and magnetic energy.

Batteries

Batteries generate electricity by turning chemical energy into electrical energy. Two chemical reactions take place in a battery: one gives off free electrons and the other absorbs free electrons. A car battery is an example of a typical wet cell battery. Lead and lead-oxide are immersed in acid. The negative terminal is connected to the lead because the reaction between the lead and the acid creates free electrons. The positive terminal is connected to the lead oxide because the reaction between it and the acid absorbs free electrons, Figure 28-8. Electrons will flow from the negative terminal to the positive terminal when a path is created between them.

SAFETY TIP

Never create a path from one battery terminal to the other using only a conductor. The large current flow created has enough energy to melt the wire or cause the battery to explode! Any path between the two battery terminals should contain a load. A load has the ability to resist current flow and turn the electrical energy into useful work.

Generators

Generators use magnetic and mechanical energy to create electricity. When a magnetic field is placed near a conductor, the free electrons in the conductor line up with the magnetic field. Moving the magnetic field pulls the free electrons with it, creating electron movement and current flow in the conductor, Figure 28-9. Generators use this principle to transform magnetic and mechanical energy into electrical energy.

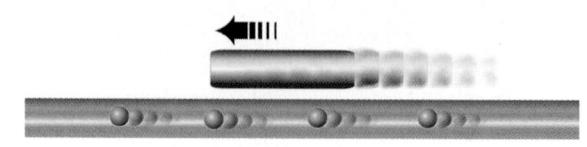

Figure 28-9 Free electrons in a conductor are pulled by the magnetic field moving past the conductor

28.8 CURRENT, VOLTAGE, WATTAGE, AND RESISTANCE

Electric Current—Amps

The coulomb is the measure of electrical charge. One coulomb is equal to the charge of 6.241506×10^{18} electrons. Coulombs are seldom used in practical measurement. Instead, the rate of electrical current flow is measured when testing electrical equipment. The rate of electrical current flow is measured in amperes, abbreviated amps. Electrical current is flowing at the rate of one amp when one coulomb of electrons passes by in a second. Amperes are represented in equations and formulas by the letter I for Intensity because amperes are a measure of the intensity of the electric current.

Electric Potential—Volts

The ability to make current flow is called electromotive force or potential. Potential difference provides the electrical pressure that makes current flow possible. Current flows through a conductor because of a difference in potential from one end of the conductor to the other. Voltage is a measure of the potential difference. Without a difference in voltage from one end of the wire to the other, there will be no current flow. Voltage is represented in equations and formulas by the letter E for Electromotive force.

Electric Work—Watts

The ability of electricity to do work depends on two factors: voltage and current. The watt is a measure of the rate at which electrical work is done. Wattage depends upon both voltage and current. A watt is defined as one ampere of current flowing at a potential difference of 1 V. Wattage can be calculated using the formula volts × amps = watts. Wattage is not truly a quantity, but a rate. Wattage does not measure the amount of work accomplished; it measures the rate at which work is accomplished. Wattage is a rate because it is calculated using amps, a measure of electrical current flow. Remember that flows are always measured as a rate. Watts are sometimes represented in equations and formulas by the letter P for Power and sometimes by the letter W for Watt.

Wattage is a reasonable measure for small appliances and light bulbs, but if you are heating a house you need something that works better for large measurement. Kilowatts, abbreviated kW, are used to specify the energy use of heating and air conditioning equipment. A kilowatt is equal to 1,000 W. The formula is simply watts/1,000 = kilowatts. Kilowatts are represented in equations and formulas by the letters kW for kiloWatt.

Watts and kilowatts are really both rates, not quantities. Electrical quantity is measured in kilowatt hours. Power companies use kilowatt hours to measure the amount of electrical work you did during the month. This is calculated by measuring kilowatt use over time. Kilowatt hours are represented in equations and formulas by the letters kWh for kiloWatt hours.

Resistance—Ohms

To some extent, all conductors and electrical devices resist current flow. The ratio of voltage to current is the resistance and it is stated in ohms. Ohms are represented in formulas and equations as R for resistance or the Greek letter omega, Ω, for ohms. The resistance of a conductor is affected by the physical properties of the material, the cross sectional area of the conductor, and the length of the conductor. Smaller diameter wires have a higher resistance than larger diameter wires. Long conductors have a higher resistance than shorter conductors.

> ### TECH TIP
>
> The resistance of most conductors increases as they rise in temperature. The low ohm reading of a cold light bulb increases almost instantly as it heats up and begins to glow, giving off light. This change in resistance occurs with any conductor as it is heated. Hot conductors have higher resistance than cold conductors. The increase in resistance as a conductor heats up is what controls the current in an electric furnace. It can, however, cause problems when the main power leads supplying power to a unit begin to heat up. This reduces the current to the unit which can cause it to malfunction. Of course, if too much current is drawn through a conductor, it can overheat and burn out.

28.9 DIRECT CURRENT

Direct current, DC, is a continuous flow of electrons in one direction, Figure 28-10. All batteries supply DC current. In the HVAC/R trade, DC current is used primarily for operating cordless tools. Direct current is also used in special applications like the control systems in transportation refrigeration equipment, the cells in electronic air cleaners, or operating electronic circuits.

28.10 ALTERNATING CURRENT

Unlike DC current which flows continuously in one direction, alternating current alternates its direction of flow through the conductor. It flows in one direction and then the

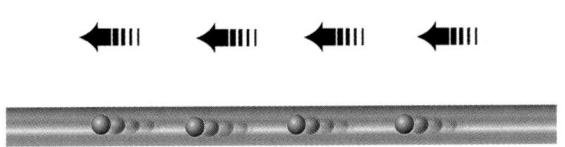

Figure 28-10 Electrons flow in only one direction with direct current

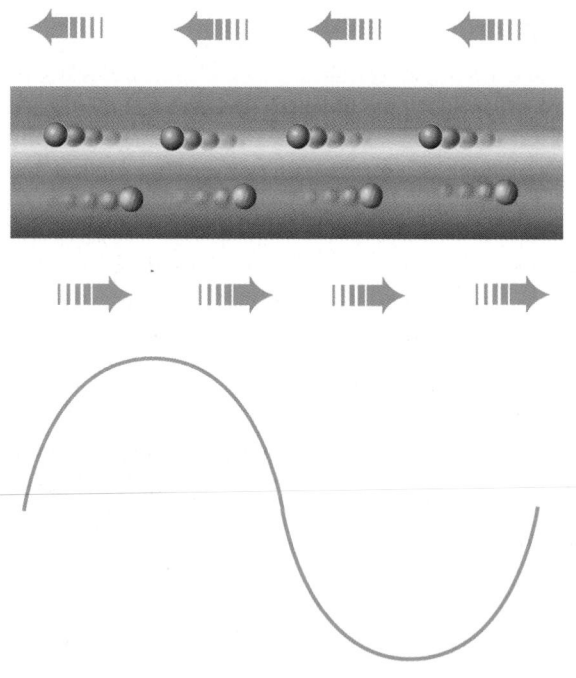

Figure 28-11 In alternating current, the direction of electron flow reverses at regular intervals

other at regular intervals, Figure 28-11. The AC waveform is a shaped like a sine wave. Half the time the current is positive and half the time it is negative. The period of time required for the voltage to peak in both directions and return to 0 V is called a cycle. Figure 28-12 shows one cycle of alternating current.

Frequency

The frequency of AC current is the number of cycles per second. Frequency is measured in *Hertz* (Hz): 1 Hz is equivalent to one cycle per second. In the U.S., 60 Hz power is standard. In Canada and many other parts of the world, the standard is 50 Hz.

Phase

The number of these waveforms occurring at the same time is called the phase. AC is available in single phase and three phase. A single phase AC circuit requires only two wires. A three phase circuit requires three wires: one for each phase. Three phase power is advantageous for operating electric motors and for transferring large amounts of current. Residences use single phase AC power while commercial and industrial buildings typically are supplied with three phase power.

Voltage

The voltage used in an AC circuit changes constantly. The average voltage supplied is 0 because the two halves of the sine wave cancel each other out. Therefore AC voltages are stated in effective voltage. The DC voltage that would produce the same heating effect in an electric heater is established as the effective AC voltage.

The effective voltage of a pure sine wave is 0.707 times peak voltage. For example, an AC current with a peak voltage of 170 V is rated at 120 V because it produces the same amount of heat in an electric heater as a DC voltage of 120 volts. This is shown mathematically as: 170 peak volts × 0.707 = 120 effective volts, Figure 28-13.

TECH TIP

A mathematical formula called the "root mean square" is used to calculate the effective voltage. The instantaneous voltage is measured many times each cycle. Each of these values are squared, the average of the squares is found, and finally the square root of the average is the effective voltage. This can be reduced a simple factor of 0.707 for AC currents that are pure sine waves. The 0.707 factor is not accurate for other waveforms.

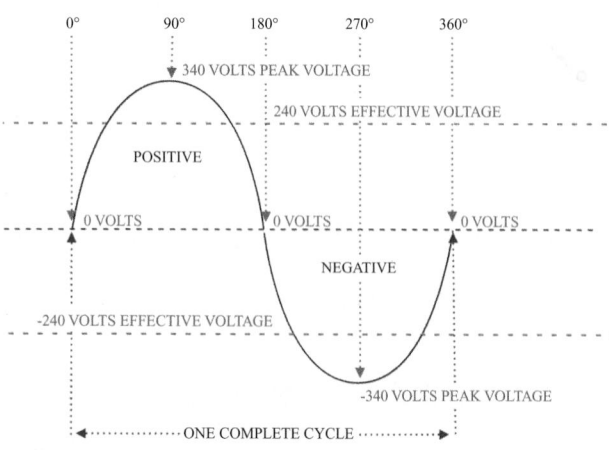

Figure 28-12 One complete cycle of alternating current

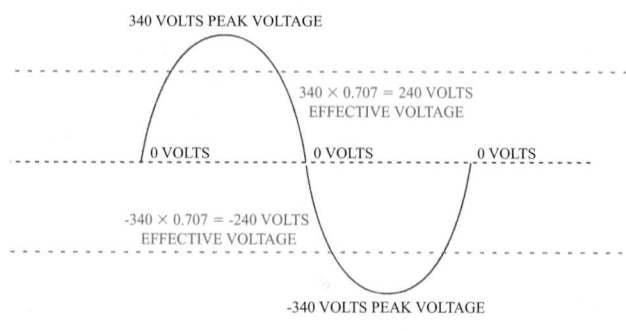

Figure 28-13 The effective voltage is 0.707 times the peak voltage

Reason for AC Current

Transmission of large amounts of power involves unavoidable line losses due to the resistance of the wires. The power lost in the line is calculated using the formula I^2R. Keeping the current, I, low is the key to reducing line loss. By utilizing high voltages, the power can be transmitted by using relatively low line current, thus minimizing the line losses. The voltage level of AC current can be more easily changed, or transformed, than DC current. This allows AC current to be transformed to extremely high voltages for transmisson across long distances and then transformed at the point of use back down to a safe voltage level.

28.11 GENERATING ALTERNATING CURRENT

AC current is produced by moving coils of wire through a magnetic field. The amount of voltage produced is proportional to how fast the coils of wire move and how strong the magnetic field is. AC current can be produced by either a generator or an alternator. A generator rotates coils of wire inside a magnetic field, while an alternator rotates a magnetic field inside coils of wire. Either way, free electrons in the coil of wire are pulled by the magnetic field, generating electricity. Figure 28-14 shows the operation of a simple AC generator consisting of a fixed magnetic field and a single loop of wire. As the loop turns clockwise through the magnetic field a flow of electrons is established in the wire. Alternating current is generated because the loop cuts the lines of force first in one direction and then in the other as it makes a complete revolution. Notice that the wire near the north pole is always negative and the wire near the south pole is always positive. However, the red half of the wire is near the north pole during the first half cycle, and near the south pole during the last half cycle. This means that the red wire is negative during the first half cycle and positive during the last half cycle.

28.12 ELECTRICAL CIRCUITS

There are three elements required for all electric circuits. A circuit must contain a power source, a path, and a load. The electrical power source can be provided by a battery or from the building's central electrical system, and the path is provided by the interconnecting wiring. The load is any electrical consuming device such as motors, relay coils, lamps, or resistance heaters. Electric loads convert electricity into useful work. Figure 28-15 shows a simple circuit consisting of a source, a path, and a load.

A complete circuit has continuity; it has a continuous path from the source to the load and back from the load to the source. A break anywhere in the circuit will keep current from flowing and prevent the load from operating, Figure 28-16. Switches can be added to a circuit to control when the circuit operates and when it does not operate. If the circuit path must pass through a switch, the switch can break the circuit and keep

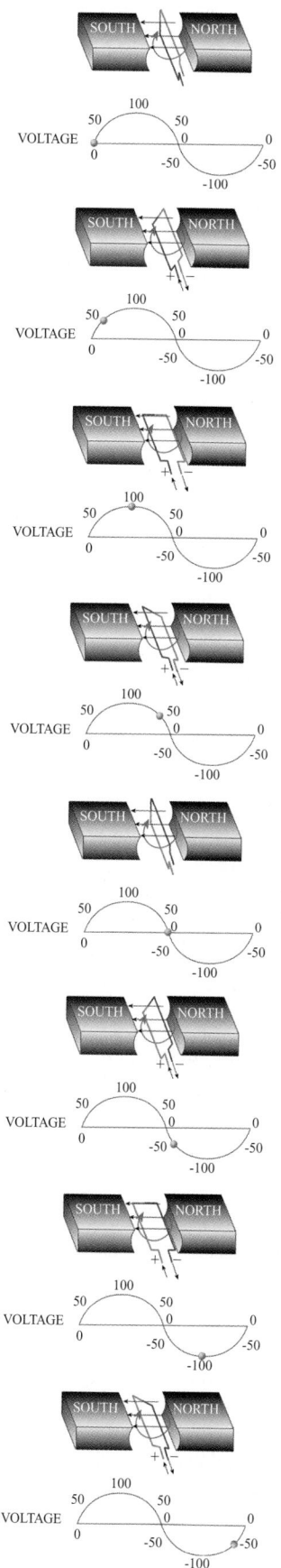

Figure 28-14 Operation of an AC generator

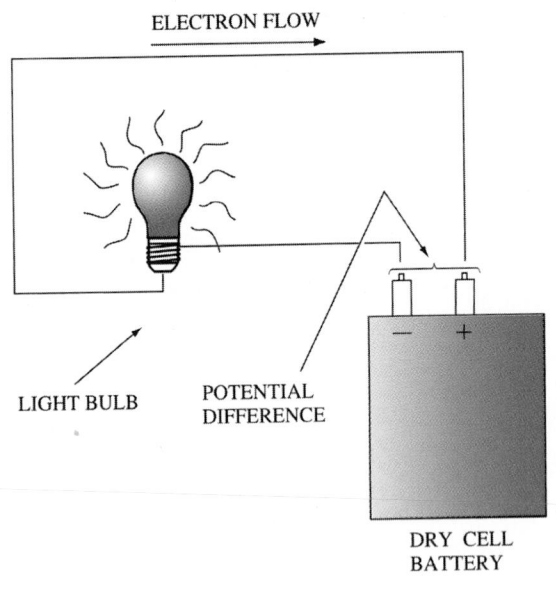

Figure 28-15 A simple electric circuit using a battery power source and a light bulb for the load

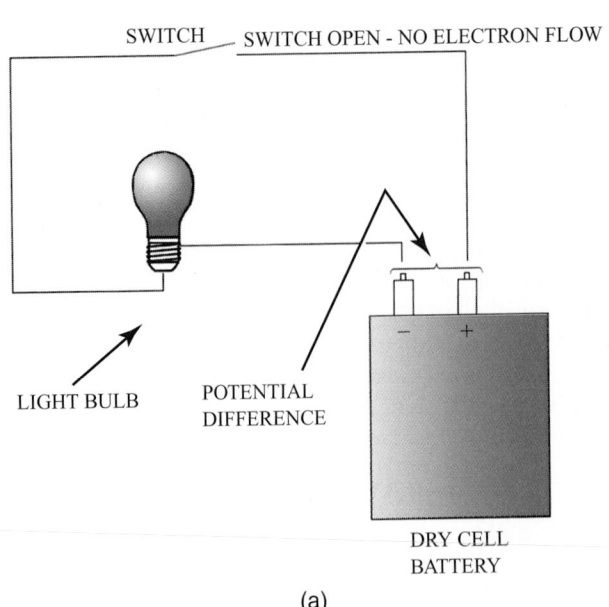

(a)

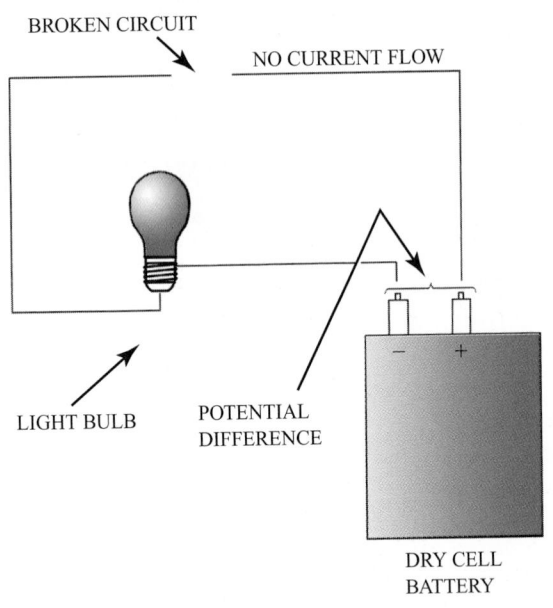

Figure 28-16 A break in the circuit stops electron flow

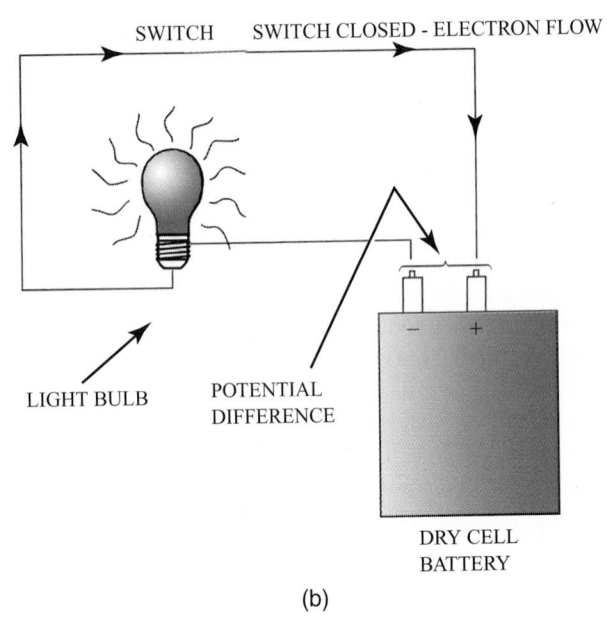

(b)

Figure 28-17 A switch is a controlled break, allowing the user to control the flow of electrons; (a) Switch open, no electron flow; (b) Switch closed, electron flow

the load from functioning, or make a complete circuit and allow the load to function, Figure 28-17. A switch is referred to as closed when it allows current flow. A switch is referred to as open when it is breaking current flow. These terms come from the operation of early knife blade switches, Figure 28-18.

An open circuit is a circuit without a complete path. Any break, or opening, in the circuit will keep it from operating. A short circuit is a circuit without a load. A short circuit has a power source and a complete path, but no load to do useful work. Without a load, current flow through the circuit is so high that both the source and the circuit conductors overheat.

TECH TIP

An electrical circuit that contains a source and path without a load is called a short circuit. A circuit that contains a source and load without a path is called an open circuit. Sometimes people refer to any circuit that does not function as having a short. This is an improper use of the term. An open circuit is one that does not work. A short circuit is one that will trip the power breaker or cause something to overheat and possibly catch fire.

OPEN - CIRCUIT IS BROKEN

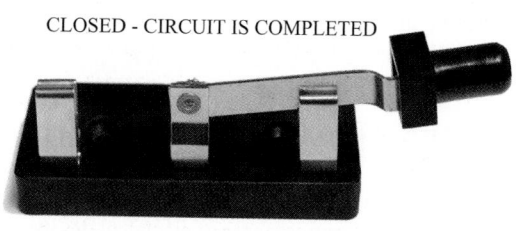

CLOSED - CIRCUIT IS COMPLETED

Figure 28-18 The terms "open" for off and "closed" for on describe the positions of a knife blade switch; they are used today when describing the position of all types of switches in electrical circuits

There are three types of path arrangements for circuits, as follows:

1. The series circuit, which allows only one path for the current to flow.
2. The parallel circuit, which has more than one path.
3. The series parallel circuit, which is a combination of series and parallel circuits.

28.13 SERIES CIRCUITS

In a series circuit, there is only one path for the current to follow. The power must pass through each electrical device in succession in that circuit to go from one side of the power supply to the other. An example of a series circuit is shown in Figure 28-19, where four lights are placed end-to-end in a single circuit.

The current in a series circuit is the same throughout the entire circuit because there is only one path for the electrons to take. Every device in a series circuit affects the current flow of the entire circuit. The voltage used by each device in the

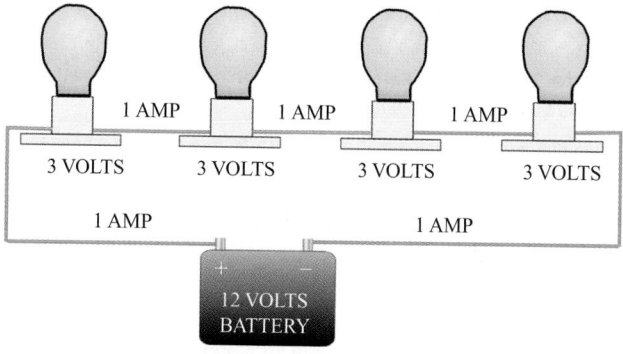

1 AMP   1 AMP   1 AMP

3 VOLTS   3 VOLTS   3 VOLTS   3 VOLTS

1 AMP   1 AMP

12 VOLTS
BATTERY

Figure 28-19 Four lights wired in series

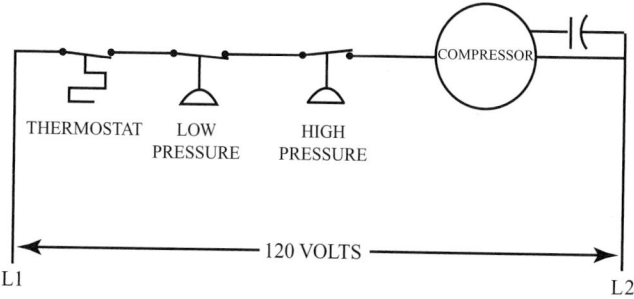

THERMOSTAT   LOW PRESSURE   HIGH PRESSURE   COMPRESSOR

120 VOLTS

L1   L2

Figure 28-20 Series circuit with three switches and one load

circuit is proportional to its resistance; devices with a higher resistance receive more voltage while devices with a lower resistance receive less voltage.

Loads are seldom wired in series with other loads in the HVAC/R industry. Usually there is one load controlled by a series of switches, as shown in Figure 28-20. In this diagram the 120 V power supply terminals are indicated with the symbols L1 and L2. The one load is a compressor motor. The switches placed in series with the compressor motor are used to control its operation. The thermostat is the operating control, and the other switches are all safety switches. The operating control is the switch that turns the circuit on and off during normal operation. Each safety switch checks for a specific operation condition that would be dangerous either to the equipment or to the user. If any one of the switches opens, the compressor will shut down. In a series circuit, all switches must be closed in order for current to flow through the circuit. The functions of the switches in this circuit are:

- A thermostat used as an operating control is placed in series with the compressor motor to start and stop the compressor in response to temperature.
- The low pressure switch senses compressor suction pressure and opens on a drop in pressure. It is set to cut out at a protective low pressure limit, but remains closed at normal operating pressures.
- The high pressure switch senses the compressor discharge pressure and opens on a rise in pressure. It is set to open at a protective high pressure limit, but remain closed at normal operating pressure.

28.14 PARALLEL CIRCUITS

A parallel circuit has more than one path for current flow. The voltage to each load is the same in a parallel circuit because each circuit has its own independent connection to the power source. The current for each load depends upon the resistance of that load. Loads with less resistance have more current flow; loads with more resistance have less current flow. Figure 28-21 illustrates a parallel circuit with three loads. Notice that the current for each load does not have to pass through any other loads because each load has its own individual path. If one load is broken or removed, the other loads will continue to operate because they have their own paths. In HVAC/R equipment, parallel circuits are used to supply the same voltage to each load. Each load has its own separate path for the current to flow.

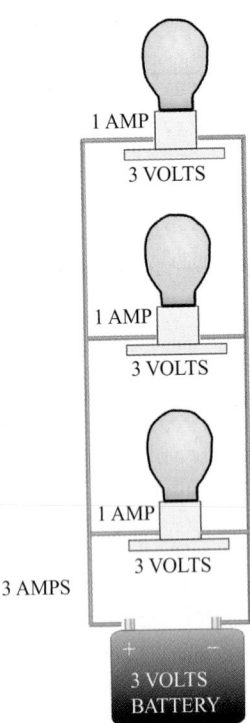

Figure 28-21 Parallel circuit with three loads in parallel

28.15 COMPARISON OF SERIES AND PARALLEL CIRCUITS

The characteristics of series and parallel circuits are opposite in every respect. In a series circuit, the *current stays the same* and the voltage changes with each load according to its resistance. In a parallel circuit, the *voltage stays the same*, but the current changes with each load. In series, the load with the *highest* resistance receives the most voltage. In parallel, the load with the *lowest* resistance receives the most current. In series, the overall circuit *resistance increases* as loads are added in series. In parallel, the overall circuit *resistance decreases* as loads are added in parallel. In series, the overall circuit *current decreases* as loads are added. In parallel the overall circuit *current increases* as loads are added.

Roads can be used to illustrate the difference between series and parallel circuits. A series circuit is like a single lane road with no passing lanes. There is only one way for all vehicles to get from one end of the road to the other and all vehicles can only travel as fast the slowest vehicle. Adding more distance to the road makes everyone's trip take even longer because there is more road to travel to get from one end to the other.

A parallel circuit is like a road with more than one lane. More vehicles can travel from one end of the road to the other at the same time because there is more than one path. Because there is more than one lane, all vehicles do not have to travel at the same speed. The speed in each lane is controlled by the conditions in that lane. Adding lanes increases the number of vehicles that can travel at one time and reduces the time it takes to move from one end of the road to the other.

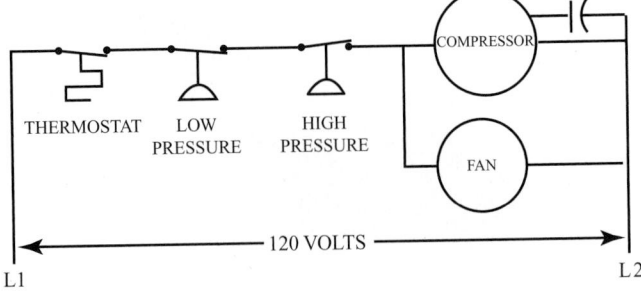

Figure 28-22 In this series parallel circuits the fan and compressor are in parallel with each other, but in series with switches

28.16 SERIES PARALLEL CIRCUITS

A series parallel circuit, as the name implies, combines both series and a parallel arrangements of electrical devices. A typical series parallel circuit is shown in Figure 28-22. Most equipment is wired with series parallel circuits. The most common use of series parallel circuits is to have several circuits in parallel with each other, with each circuit containing several devices in series. Typically each individual circuit in a series parallel arrangement has one load and one or more switches in series with the load. This allows full voltage to all loads while still maintaining control using the switches that are in series with the loads.

28.17 RELATIONSHIP OF VOLTAGE, RESISTANCE, AND CURRENT

It is useful for technicians to understand the relationship between voltage, resistance, and current. A change in one variable will affect the others. The balance shown in Figure 28-23 is a simple way to visualize the relationship between these three variables. Resistance and current are balanced on top of voltage. With voltage remaining the same, if resistance goes up, current will go down, Figure 28-24. On the other hand, if resistance goes down, current will go up, Figure 28-25. If the resistance remains the same, then voltage and current go up

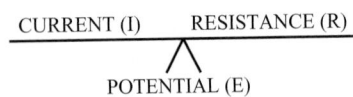

Figure 28-23 The relationship between current and resistance can be visualized as a balance

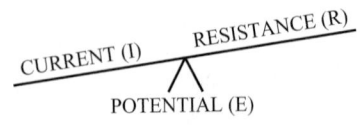

Figure 28-24 When the resistance increases, the current decreases

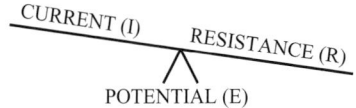

Figure 28-25 When the resistance decreases, the current increases

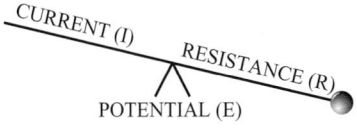

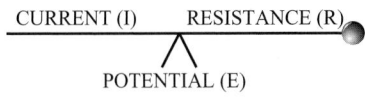

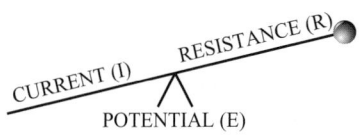

Figure 28-26 If the resistance stays the same, the voltage and current go up and down together

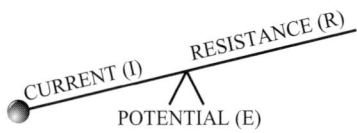

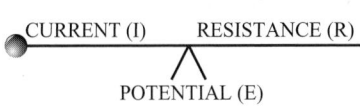

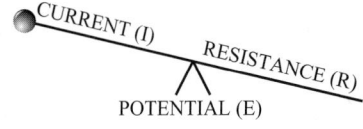

Figure 28-27 For the current to stay the same, the resistance and voltage must go up and down together

and down together, Figure 28-26. If current remains the same, then voltage and resistance must go up and down together, Figure 28-27.

28.18 OHM'S LAW

Ohm's law is the relationship between the voltage, current, and resistance in an electrical circuit. Ohm's law stated in simple terms is: 1 V applied across a resistance of 1 Ω will produce a current of 1 A. This can be written as the mathematical formula $E = IR$. If two of the values are known, the remaining value can be calculated. Figure 28-28 shows the three forms Ohm's law can take, depending upon the unknown value.

TECH TIP

It should be noted that Ohm's law does not apply to most AC circuits. The flow of current in AC circuits can be influenced by inductive reactance, and capacitive reactance. Magnetic coils of wire produce an induced voltage that opposes current changes in an AC circuit. This has the effect of reducing the current flow through the circuit. As a result, Ohm's law can not be applied to any AC circuit that contains a capacitor or magnetic coil. The only AC circuits that work correctly with Ohm's law are purely resistive circuits, such as electric heaters. The combined effect of resistance, inductive reactance, and capacitive reactance is called impedance. The Ohm's law formulas will work with AC circuits if the impedance is calculated and substituted in the formulas for resistance.

The following examples illustrate simple applications of Ohm's law.

EXAMPLE 28-1—SOLVING FOR CURRENT

The circuit in Figure 28-29 has a power source of 24 V and a load with a resistance of 8 Ω. Determine the amp draw of the circuit.

$$I = \frac{E}{R}$$

$$I = \frac{24 \text{ V}}{8 \text{ }\Omega}$$

$$I = 3 \text{ A}$$

Figure 28-28 Ohm's law formulas

Characteristic	Units	Written formula	Symbolic formula
Potential	Volts	voltage = current × resistance	$E = I \times R$
Current	Amps	amps = volts divided by ohms	$I = E/R$
Resistance	Ohms	ohms = volts divided by amps	$R = E/I$

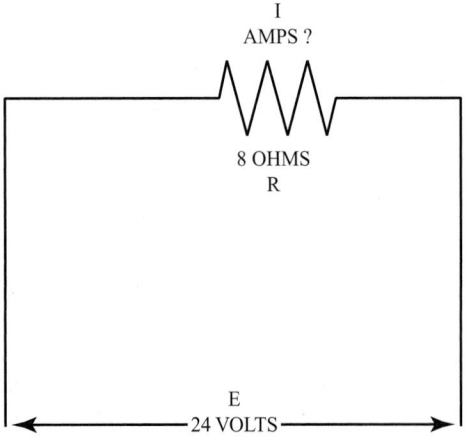

Figure 28-29 Calculating the current using Ohm's law with voltage and resistance known

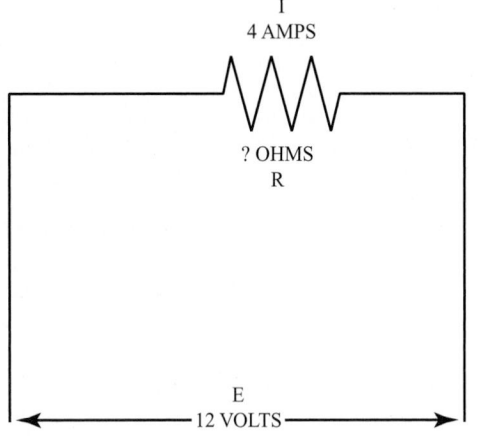

Figure 28-30 Calculating the resistance using Ohm's law with voltage and current known

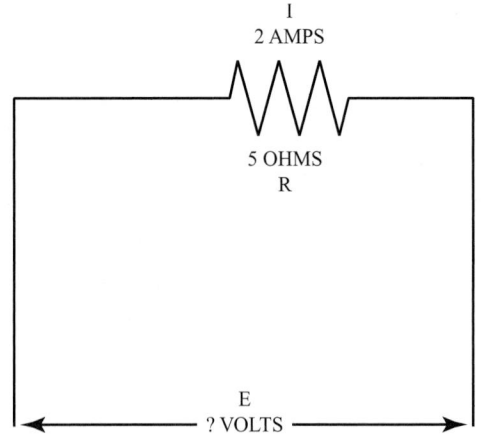

Figure 28-31 The total resistance of a series circuit is the sum of all the individual resistances

28.19 OHM'S LAW CALCULATIONS FOR A SERIES CIRCUIT

The calculations in the previous section used only one load. When a circuit has more than one load, the values can be different for each load in the circuit. The formulas used to calculate the total circuit resistance, current, and voltage depend upon whether the circuit is a series or parallel circuit.

Series Circuit Resistance

The total resistance of a series circuit is the sum of all the individual resistances. This is expressed in symbols as:

$$R_T = R_1 + R_2 + R_3 + R_4$$

For example, the total resistance of a circuit with resistances of 4 Ω, 5 Ω, and 6 Ω is found by adding the three resistances together: 4 Ω + 5 Ω + 6 Ω = 15 Ω total circuit resistance, Figure 28-32.

EXAMPLE 28-2—SOLVING FOR RESISTANCE

The resistor in Figure 28-30 is drawing a current of 4 A on 12 V. Determine the resistance of the resistor.

$$R = \frac{E}{I}$$

$$R = \frac{12\ V}{4\ A}$$

$$R = 3\ \Omega$$

EXAMPLE 28-3—SOLVING FOR VOLTAGE

In Figure 28-31, the 5 Ω resistor has a current draw of 2 A. Determine the voltage supplied to the circuit.

$$E = IR$$

$$E = 2\ A \times 5\ \Omega$$

$$E = 10\ V$$

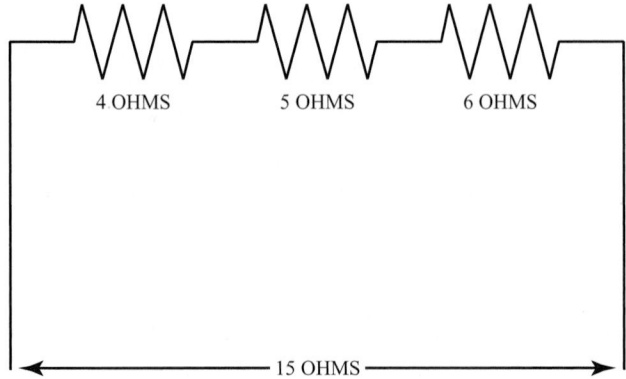

Figure 28-32 The total resistance of a series circuit is the sum of all the individual resistances

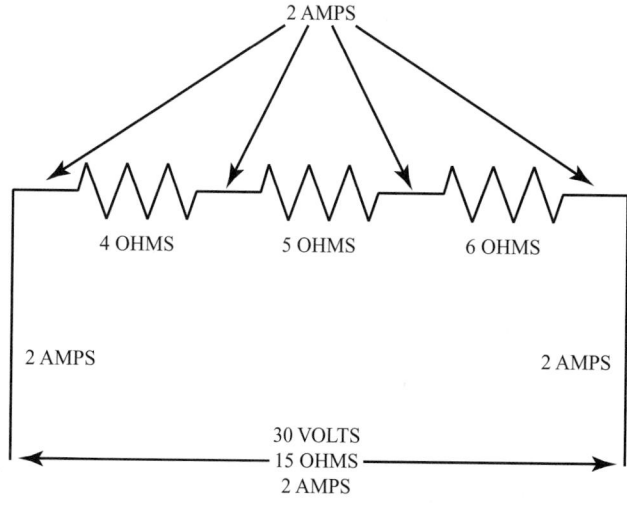

Figure 28-33 The current is the same throughout a series circuit

Series Circuit Current

The current flowing through a series circuit is the same for each load in the circuit. To determine the current in a series circuit, divide the total circuit resistance into the voltage applied to the circuit. For example, if 30 V is applied to a circuit with resistances of 4 Ω, 5 Ω, and 6 Ω, the circuit current is found by adding the resistances and dividing the sum into 30 V: 30/ (4 Ω + 5 Ω + 6 Ω) = 2 A. Since the current in a series circuit is the same throughout the circuit, the current for all of the resistances is 2 A, Figure 28-33. This is expressed in symbols as:

$$I_1 = I_2 = I_3 = I_4$$

Series Circuit Voltage

Although the current stays the same throughout a series circuit, the voltage across each load in a series circuit is proportional to its resistance. Loads with different resistances receive different voltages. The sum of the individual voltages equals the total voltage applied to the circuit. The voltage drop across each resistance can be calculated by multiplying the circuit current times the individual resistance. The series circuit with a current draw of 2 A and resistors of 4 Ω, 5 Ω, and 6 Ω would have volt-

age drops of 8 V, 10 V, and 12 V: 2 A × 4 Ω = 8 V, 2 A × 5 A = 10 V, 2 A × 6 Ω = 12 V. The sum of the individual voltages equals the applied circuit voltage: 8 V + 10 V + 12 V = 30 V, Figure 28-34. This is expressed in symbols as:

$$E_T = E_1 + E_2 + E_3 + E_4$$

28.20 CALCULATIONS FOR A PARALLEL CIRCUIT

Parallel Circuit Voltage

The voltage to each load in a parallel circuit is equal to the applied circuit voltage, Figure 28-35. This is expressed in symbols as:

$$E_T = E_1 = E_2 = E_3 \ldots$$

Parallel Circuit Current

The current draw for a parallel circuit is determined for each of its parts. Use the standard $I = E/R$ form of Ohm's law to determine the current draw through each individual resistance. For example, a parallel circuit with an applied voltage of 30 V and resistances of 3 Ω, 5 Ω, and 6 Ω would have individual current draws of 10 A, 6 A, and 5 A: 30 V/3 Ω = 10 A, 30 V/ 5 Ω = 6 A, 30 V/6 Ω = 5 A. The current consumed by the entire parallel system is the sum of the individual currents. 10 A + 6 A + 5 A = 21 A total circuit current, Figure 28-36. This is expressed in symbols as:

$$I_T = I_1 + I_2 + I_3 \ldots$$

Parallel Circuit Resistance

The resistance of a parallel circuit gets smaller as more resistances are added. This is because each load in parallel creates another current path, making it easier for electrons to flow. Another way to visualize this is to examine the relationship

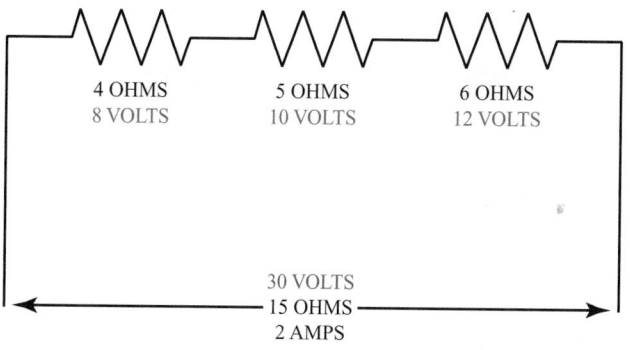

Figure 28-34 The voltage drop across each load in a series circuit is proportional to its resistance

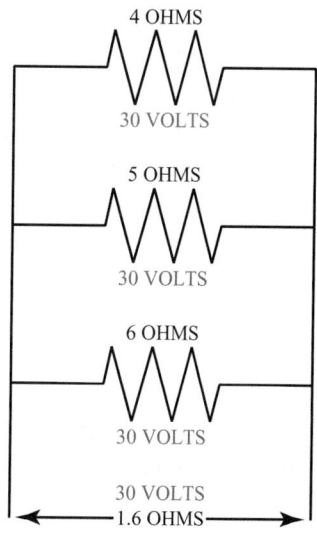

Figure 28-35 The voltage is the same to all loads in a parallel circuit

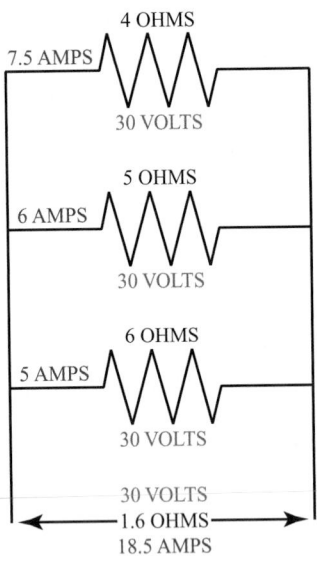

Figure 28-36 The total circuit current in a parallel circuit is the sum of the individual currents

between current and resistance. Since voltage = current × resistance, in order for the current to increase without increasing the voltage, there must be a decrease in resistance. For example, a 20 Ω resistor wired across 100 V would draw 5 A: 100 V ÷ 20 Ω = 5 A. Two 20 Ω resistors wired in parallel across 100 V would each draw 5 A. The total circuit current would be 10 A, 5 + 5. The total circuit resistance can be calculated using Ohm's law as 100 V ÷ 10 A = 10 Ω. In other words, the total resistance for two identical loads is *half* the resistance of one load by itself. Similarly, the total resistance of *any* parallel circuit containing several loads of identical value in parallel can be found by dividing the resistance value for one load by the number of loads, Figure 28-37.

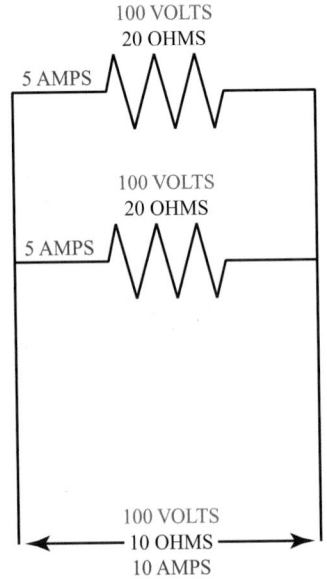

Figure 28-37 The total resistance of a parallel circuit with multiple identical resistances can be found by dividing the value of one resistor by the number of resistors

The formula is more complicated for parallel circuits with different value resistances. If there are only two resistances, the total resistance can be calculated by a formula called product over the sum:

$$R_T = \frac{(R_1 \times R_2)}{(R_1 + R_2)}$$

For example, to find the total resistance of a parallel circuit with one resistance of 12 Ω and one resistance of 10 Ω:

$$R_T = \frac{(R_1 \times R_2)}{(R_1 + R_2)}$$

$$R_T = \frac{(12\ \Omega \times 10\ \Omega)}{(12\ \Omega + 10\ \Omega)}$$

$$R_T = \frac{120}{22}$$

$$R_T = 5.4\ \Omega$$

If there are more than two resistances, use the following formula and solve for R_T.

$$\frac{1}{R_T} = \frac{1}{R_1} + \frac{1}{R_2} + \frac{1}{R_3}$$

Note that this formula is actually solving for the reciprocal of R_T. The answer must be inverted to find R_T. For example, a parallel circuit with resistances of 4 Ω, 5 Ω, and 6 Ω

$$\frac{1}{R_T} = \frac{1}{R_1} + \frac{1}{R_2} + \frac{1}{R_3}$$

$$\frac{1}{R_T} = \frac{1}{4} + \frac{1}{5} + \frac{1}{6}$$

$$\frac{1}{R_T} = \frac{15}{60} + \frac{12}{60} + \frac{10}{60}$$

$$\frac{1}{R_T} = \frac{37}{60}$$

$$R_T = \frac{60}{37} = 1.6\ \Omega$$

R_T will always be smaller than the smallest resistor in the problem. In the example $R_T = 1.6$ Ω which is smaller than 4 Ω, the lowest resistance in the problem.

TECH TIP

Finding a common denominator can get messy when the values are not simple numbers. An easy way to work parallel resistance problems is to use a calculator with a reciprocal key and memory. Enter each resistance followed by the reciprocal key "1/x." Then push the memory plus key "M+" to add the results of each process into memory. Last, push the memory recall key "MR" to display the sum and push the reciprocal key to show the answer.

UNIT 29

Electrical Power and Circuits

OBJECTIVES

After completing this unit you will be able to:

- identify the different types and categories of electricity and electrical power systems used in the HVAC/R industry.
- discuss the uses of single phase and three phase power.
- recognize the importance of properly sized wire for varying load requirements.
- explain how different circuits and components are utilized within an HVAC/R system.
- state the importance of overcurrent protection.

29.1 INTRODUCTION

The electrical power provided to residential and commercial customers is alternating current (AC) with a frequency of 60 cycles (Hertz). AC power flowing through an electrical circuit has unique characteristics that must be understood by the HVAC/R technician prior to installing or servicing equipment. It is also important to note that residential service will be very different from commercial service. Residential service requires lower voltage and single phase power. Commercial systems utilize higher voltages and three phase power. Therefore the electrical connections, the types of motors, and the electrical code requirements will not be the same.

This unit shows how resistance, inductance, capacitance, and impedance affect the operation of AC circuits. From this, the HVAC/R technician can understand the relationship of voltage to current in an AC circuit. Single phase and three phase power is also explained and the differences between the two made clear. Additionally there are examples of power distribution arrangements with the appropriate line voltage connections illustrated for both residential and commercial service. After reviewing this unit, the HVAC/R technician will have a good understanding of AC circuit behavior and power distribution.

29.2 ELECTRICAL POWER SYSTEMS

Power is supplied to a HVAC/R unit by the electrical power system. The power systems will have one or more electrical circuits that are used to deliver electrical power to the HVAC/R equipment. Electrical power systems have three essential requirements and one optional requirement:

- A source of power (could be a transformer).
- An electrical load device.

- An electric circuit: a path for the current to flow.
- (Optional) a switch to control the flow.

29.3 TYPES OF POWER SOURCES

There are two common types of power:

- Direct current (DC)
- Alternating current (AC)

Many electrical testing instruments operate on DC power. This is because the most common source of direct current is the battery. Batteries allow test instruments to be portable and convenient to use. DC power can also be used for control systems and on solid state modules for defrost and overcurrent protection. For these applications the DC power is often converted from AC power through a rectifier instead of using batteries.

Alternating current is the most common source of power for most HVAC/R systems. AC power is generated by all the power companies. In residences, 120 V AC is used to power most small appliances. Larger appliances such as electric stoves and residential air conditioning units use 240 V. The power company supplies residential users with 240 V over the incoming lines. A portion of it is tapped to supply the 120 V requirements. Commercial and industrial customers normally use higher voltages in single phase and three phase systems.

TECH TIP

In the United States the alternating current frequency supplied by power companies is normally 60 cycles. Many foreign countries supply power at 50 cycles. It is important to use equipment that is designed to operate at the proper frequency.

Transformers are used to increase or decrease incoming voltages to meet the requirements of the load. For control circuits, it is common to use a transformer to obtain 24 V from line voltages of 120 or 240 V. Most transformers that are used in the HVAC/R industry are 40 VA. These transformers have a maximum current output capacity of 1.6 A. Larger transformers are available that can produce higher output amperages at 24 V. These transformers may be needed when additional controls are added to a standard HVAC system. Additional controls might include humidifiers, duct air booster fans, and economizers.

29.4 ELECTRICAL LOADS

The second condition for an electrical power system is that it must have a load. A load is any electrical device that requires power to operate. The most common loads for HVAC/R systems are electric motors. Motors drive the compressors, fans, and pumps. Motors also drive dampers and zone valves. Many other electrical components require power, such as resistance heaters and solenoid valves.

29.5 ELECTRICAL CIRCUIT

The third condition for a power system is that there must be a path for the current to travel, Figure 29-1. Every electric circuit has at least two wires, often indicated as line terminals L1 and L2. For this illustration these would be the two prongs on the plug. In order for there to be a complete circuit, the path of the electricity flows through one wire of the electric circuit, passes through the load, and returns through the other wire of the electric circuit. In AC systems, the direction of power flow reverses 60 times per second.

29.6 SWITCHES

The fourth (optional) condition for the power system is the switch. The switch is a device to turn the load on and off. The switch may be manually operated such as turning on the lights when entering a dark room. Or the switch may be automatic such as a thermostat that turns a unit on and off in response to the surrounding temperature. Generally a switch will have two positions, open or closed. When the switch is open, no

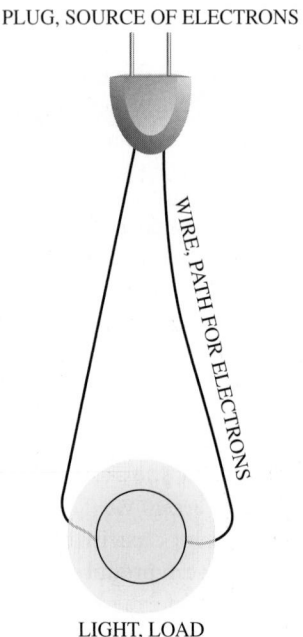

Figure 29-1 Principal components of a simple circuit

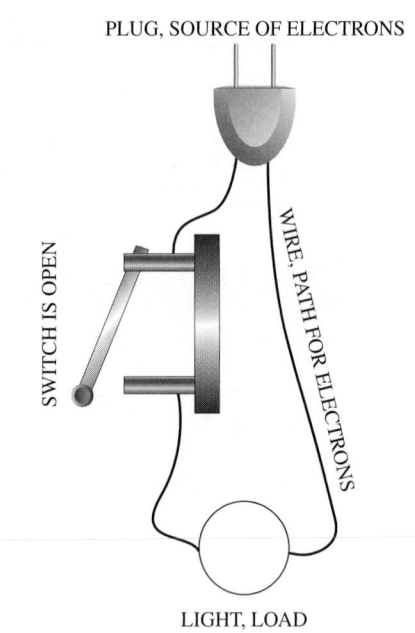

Figure 29-2 In an open circuit, no current flows

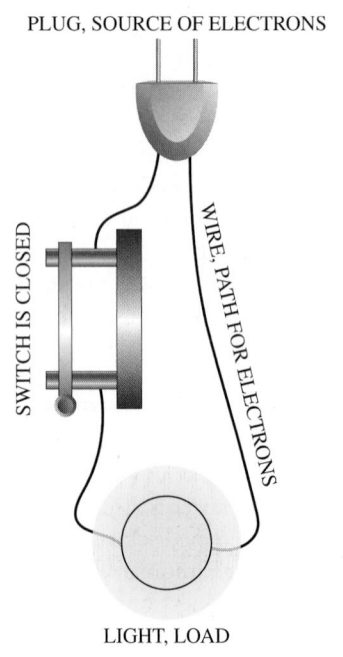

Figure 29-3 A closed circuit, with current flowing through the load

current flows, Figure 29-2. When the switch is closed, current flows and the load receives power, Figure 29-3.

29.7 RELAYS AND CONTACTORS

An automatic switch requires some method for opening and closing. This is often accomplished through the use of a relay. A relay is an electrically operated switch that uses an

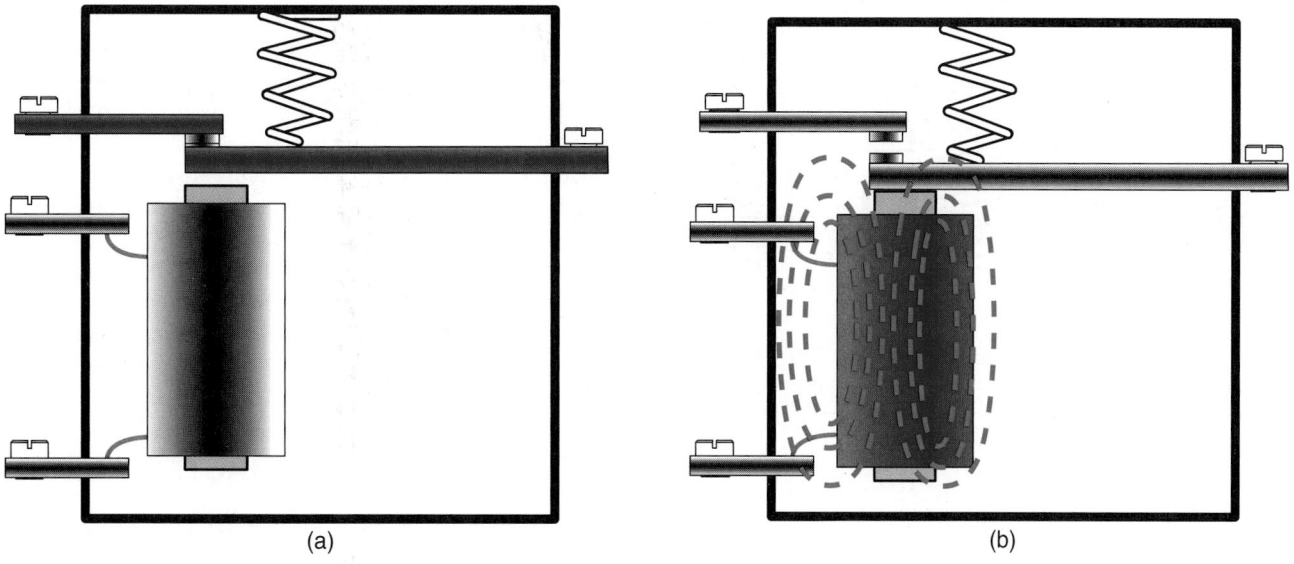

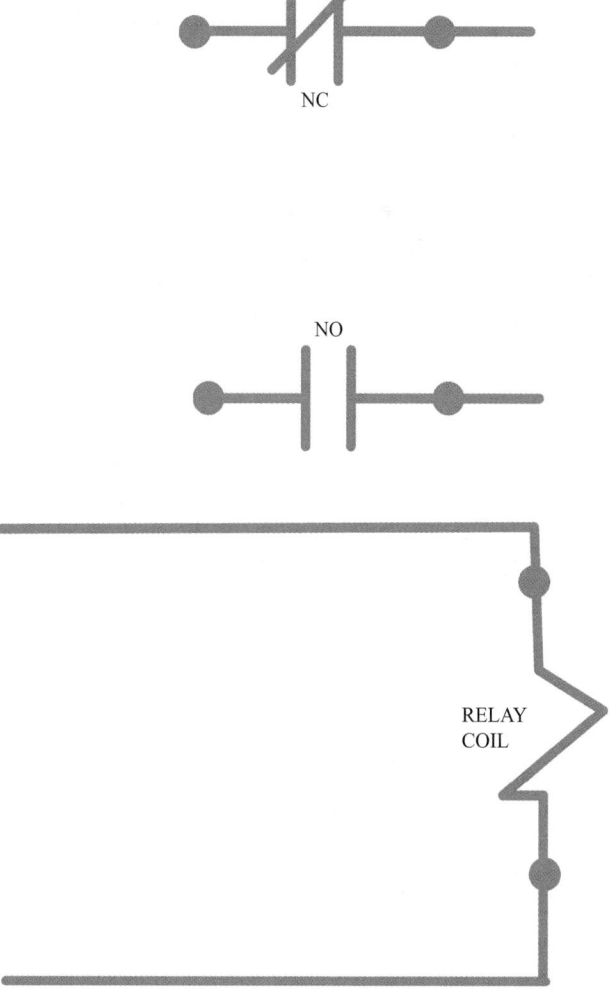

Figure 29-4 (a) The coil is deenergized and the contacts are held closed by spring force; (b) The coil is energized and the contacts are opened by the magnetic attraction of the coil

electromagnet to open or close a set of electrical contacts. Normally only a small amount of current is required to energize the electromagnet. This allows for a device with a high current rating such as an electric heater to be operated by a control relay operated by a low current signal. The control wires can be much smaller and separate from the large main supply lines required for the main load.

Relays can be designed for normally open (NO) switches or normally closed (NC) switches. The normal position of the switch is always the position of the switch when the relay coil is deenergized. Figure 29-4a shows a normally closed set of contacts with the relay coil deenergized. A spring is used to hold the contacts together. When the coil is energized (supplied with current), Figure 29-4b, a magnetic field is set up that attracts the lower contact toward the coil. This will separate the two contacts and open the circuit. As long as the current flows through the coil, the relay is energized, and the switch will remain open. The NC switch has a diagonal line through it as shown in Figure 29-5.

Relays and contactors have the same function except the contactor is larger, more rugged, and carries more current. The normally open contactor shown in Figure 29-6a has two sets of contacts for carrying more current. The normally open relay shown in Figure 29-6b only has one set of contacts. A motor starter is a contactor with motor overload protection added.

A good example of the use of a relay in a schematic diagram is shown in Figure 29-7. Very often the relay coil may operate at one voltage and the switches are located in another circuit operating at a different voltage. The coil is located in the low voltage circuit of the diagram and is controlled by the COOL switch. The low voltage is supplied through a transformer. The two contacts operated by the relay are located in the high voltage circuit of the diagram and can be identified as CC. Both of these contacts are normally open and are in series with the compressor (COMP).

Figure 29-5 Normally open and normally closed contact symbols

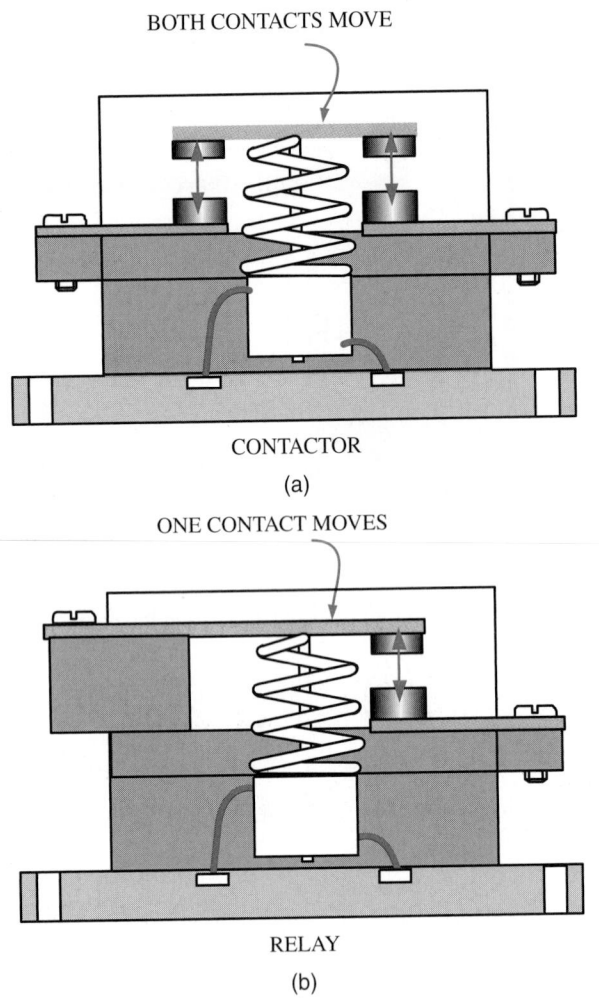

BOTH CONTACTS MOVE

CONTACTOR

(a)

ONE CONTACT MOVES

RELAY

(b)

Figure 29-6 (a) Contactor; note: contactors have two points on each circuit; (b) Relay; note: relays only have one set of points for each circuit

When the system calls for cooling (COOL), the relay in the low voltage circuit will be energized, thus closing the two CC contacts in the high voltage circuit. Power from the line terminals L1 and L2 will start the compressor and the outdoor fan. The indoor fan will operate on and off in the auto position. Its control relay (IBR) located in the low voltage circuit will close the normally open contact just below the normally closed contact for the indoor fan located in the high voltage circuit. The indoor fan can also be set to ON and run continuously. When the electric strip heat is on, the indoor fan will always run due to the normally closed contact.

29.8 TRANSDUCERS

Transducers are electrical or electromechanical devices that are often used to provide a control signal. They can be used to sense changes in pressure, temperature, light, sound, and vibration. They are most often semiconductors that convert

mechanical force into an electrical signal. The signal is used by a control device or microprocessor to stop, start, or adjust a system's operation. For example, a vibration sensor located on a large air handler would stop the motor when excessive vibration occurred. Another example would be a water depth gauge that would sense water pressure in a container. This signal could be used to stop or start a pump or turn a water valve on or off.

Because transducers are relatively low in cost and have high reliability, they are used frequently to provide remote sensing for HVAC/R equipment. Transducers have increased the life of systems and improved operating efficiencies by providing constant monitoring.

29.9 AC CIRCUIT CHARACTERISTICS

When current passes through a conductor, a magnetic field is produced. The coiling of the conductor concentrates the lines of force, Figure 29-8. The polarity at the ends of the coil will reverse as the current flow through the coil changes direction.

If an iron bar is placed inside the coil as in Figure 29-9, current flow through the coil will cause the lines of force to magnetize the core with polarity opposite to that of the coil. Because unlike poles attract and like poles repel, the iron bar or core attempts to center itself within the coil.

This principle is applied to the construction of relays and contactors. In the resting position, gravity keeps the contacts separated. Referring to Figure 29-10a, when current flows through the coil, the core is magnetized and tries to center itself in the coil. This raises the core and changes the position of the relay contacts, as shown in Figure 29-10b. A solenoid valve is another application of this same principle.

This induction principle is also applied to the construction of AC motors, Figure 29-11. The basic motor has two coils wrapped around stationary cores called stator poles. As AC current flows through the coils, the stator poles are magnetized. The stator field induces an opposing field in the rotor and the principle of attraction and repulsion causes the motor to run.

Another application of the induction principle is used in the construction of a transformer, Figure 29-12. Transformers are used to step down the line voltage to 24 V for the controls used in many HVAC/R units. Transformers contain a single iron core that is wrapped with two separate coiled conductors known as primary and secondary windings. When AC voltage is applied to the primary winding, the resulting lines of force are carried through the core. These lines create a current flowing through the secondary winding, inducing a voltage in that winding.

There are two types of transformers: step down transformers and step up transformers, Figure 29-13a, b. The amount of voltage induced in the secondary winding depends on the ratio of the number of turns in the primary winding to the number of turns in the secondary winding.

Figure 29-7 Ladder diagram showing the use of relays

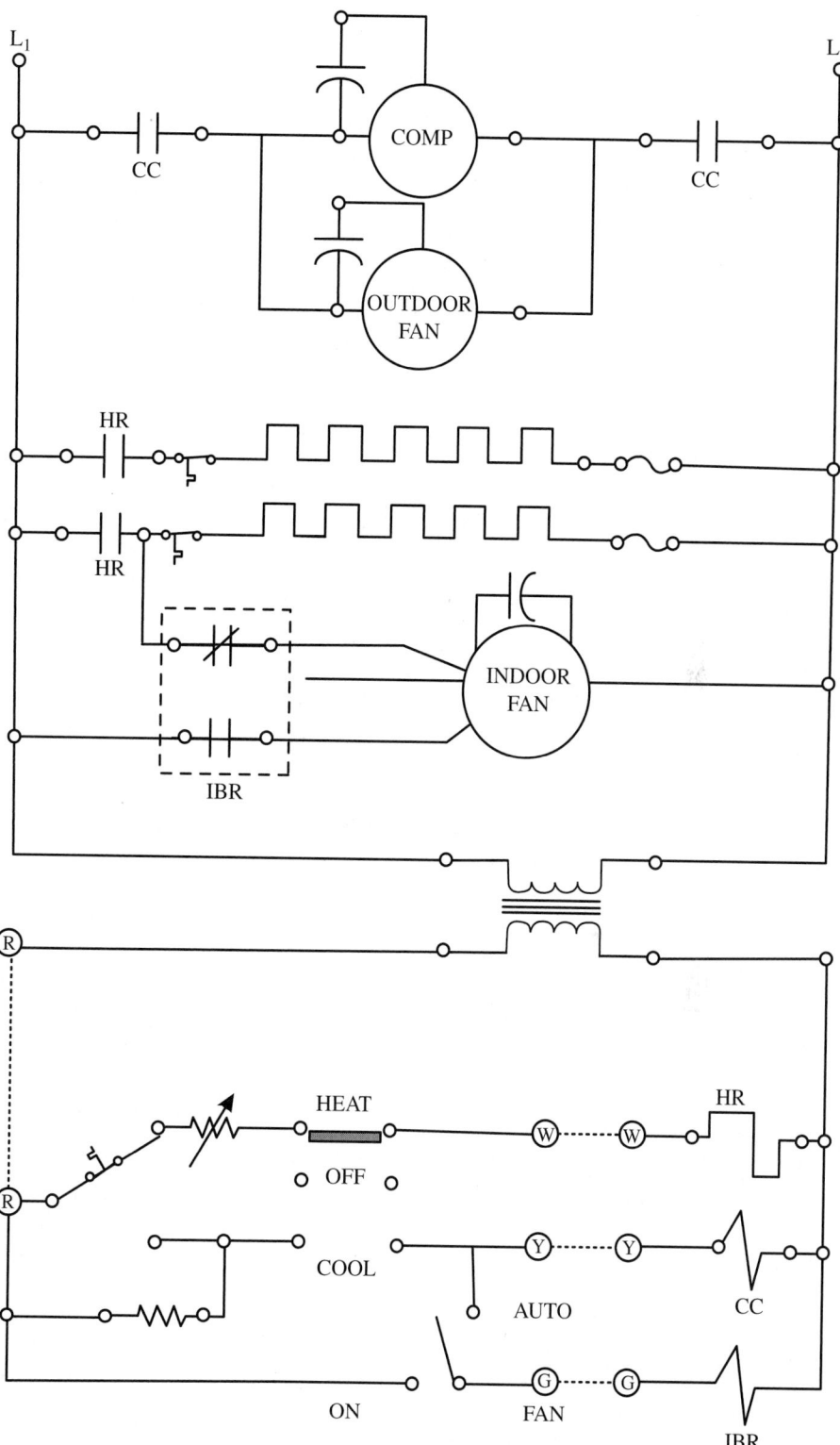

29.10 ALTERNATING CURRENT AND MAGNETIC INDUCTION

Magnetic induction, demonstrated in Figure 29-14, is used to generate voltage for commercial and residential use. Induction occurs when a conductor is placed in a magnetic field. As the conductor is moved through the field, a potential difference is created in the conductor. The size of this potential difference is dependent on the strength of the field and the speed of the conductor through the field. The direction of current flow is dependent on the position of the conductor in the field. As the conductor passes through the lines of flux at the north pole the

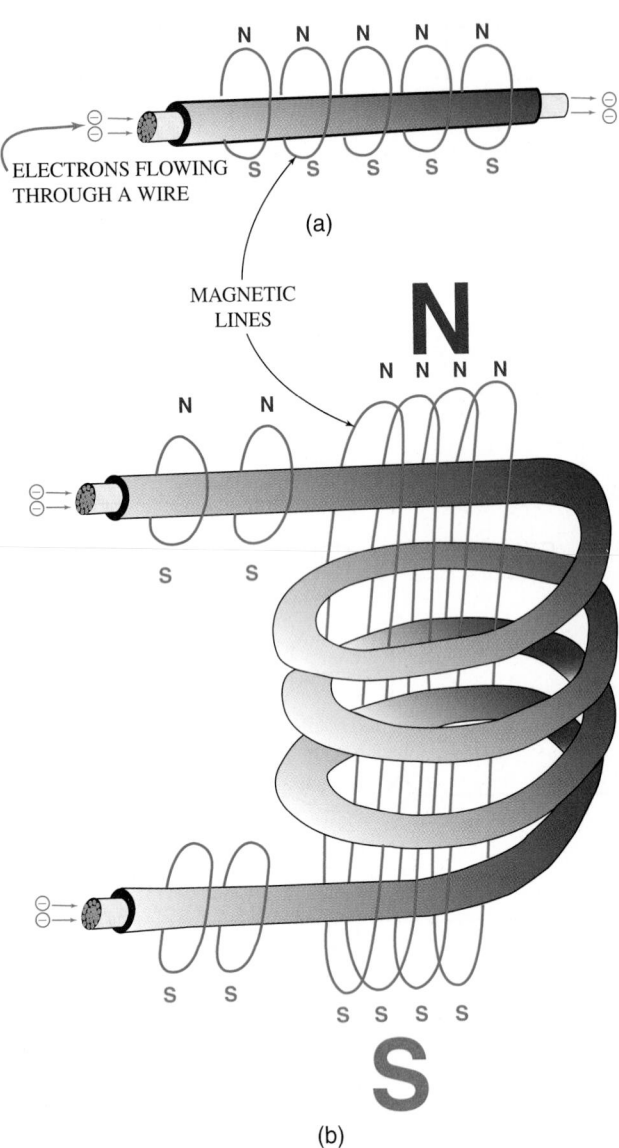

Figure 29-8 (a) Electrons flowing through a straight wire form a weak magnetic field around the wire; (b) When that same wire is coiled, the weak magnetic field around each wire combine to form a stronger magnetic field around the coil

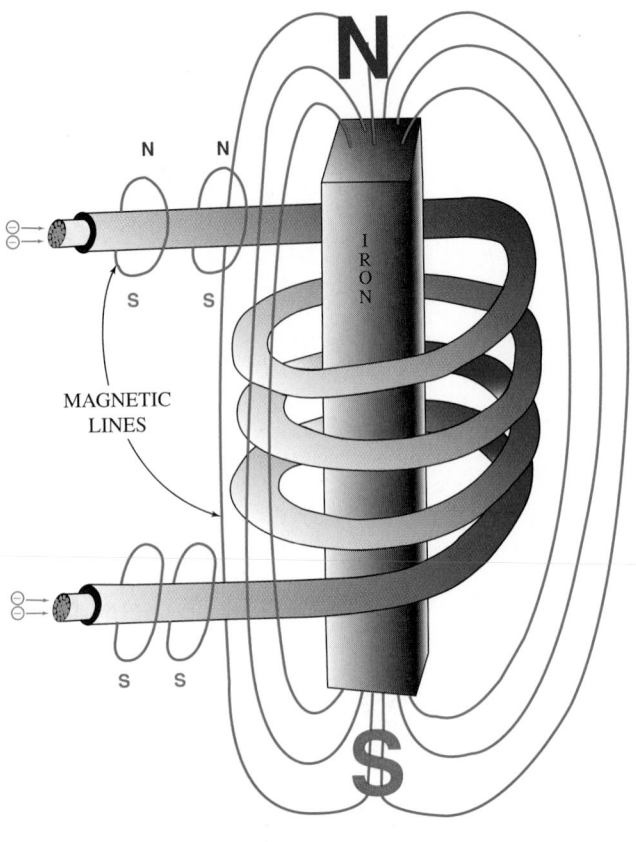

Figure 29-9 The addition of an iron core to the coil intensifies the magnetism and makes it stronger

TECH TIP

Sixty cycle current can create a low frequency hum in some motors and transformers. This hum is a result of the frequency of current that passes through the coil. Sometimes this noise can be very disturbing to the residents. Occasionally the sound is amplified because the motor or transformer is not tight on its mounting brackets. Secure the motor tightly to attempt to reduce the sound. If the sound can tracked to a vibrating sheet metal component, that component may be secured using a pop rivet or sheet metal screw to reduce the sound level.

current flows in one direction. This flow will be reversed as the conductor rotates and passes through lines of flux at the south pole. A conductor rotated through a permanent magnetic field will produce an alternating current.

Alternating current flow continuously reverses direction to produce a sinusoidal waveform that alternates polarity continuously at a fixed rate or frequency. The number of times per second the polarity is reversed is the frequency expressed in Hertz (Hz), or cycles per second. Alternating current is produced by rotating a coil within the magnetic field to produce an output voltage. Figure 29-15 is a diagram of a single cycle that is repeated 60 times per second (60 Hz), on a continuous basis. This is called single phase voltage.

Single phase power is commonly used for residential and small commercial systems. For larger motors, generally 5 hp and above, three phase power is normally used. This requires the addition of one more conductor to the generator as shown in Figure 29-16. The three conductors are positioned 120° from each other.

A diagram of the three phase waveforms is shown in Figure 29-17. They have the same shape, but they are 120° out of phase with each other.

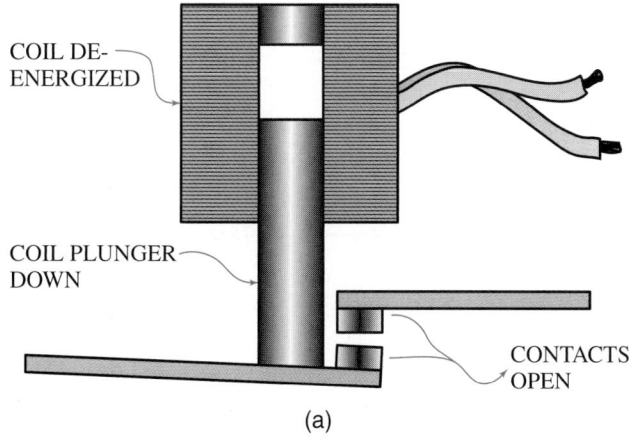

(a)

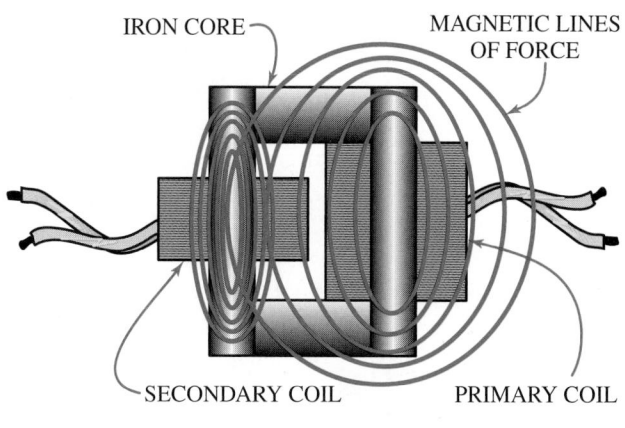

Figure 29-12 Power applied to primary coil induces a current in the secondary coil of a transformer

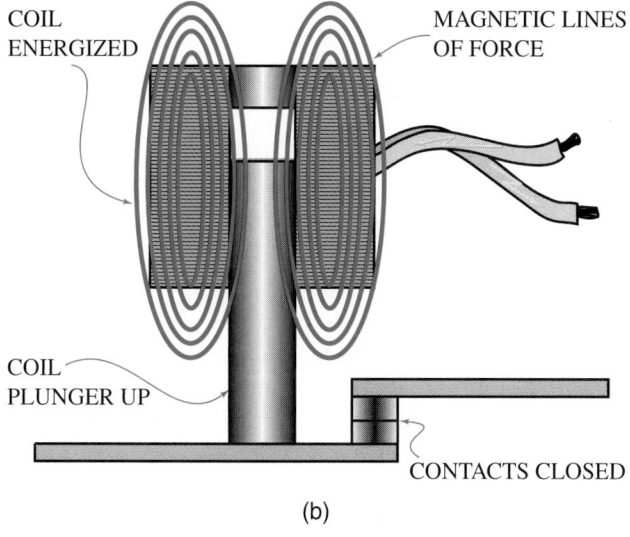

(b)

Figure 29-10 (a) Coil deenergized; (b) Coil energized

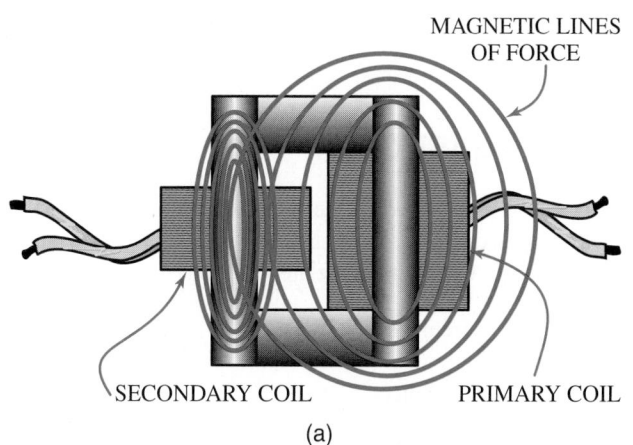

(a)

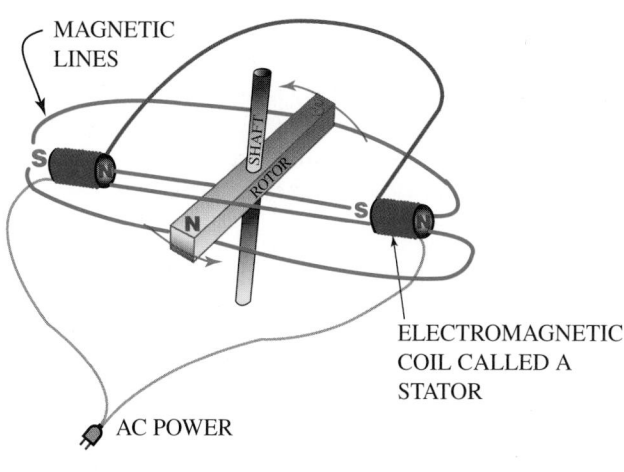

Figure 29-11 When AC power is applied to the coils of a motor, the rotor turns

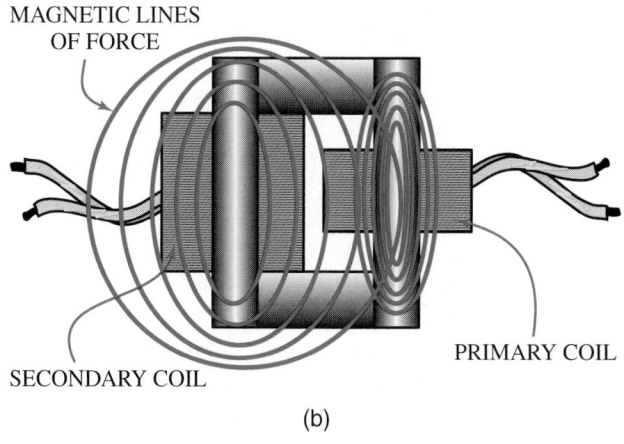

(b)

Figure 29-13 (a) Step down transformers have more windings on the primary coil; (b) Step up transformers have fewer windings on the primary coil

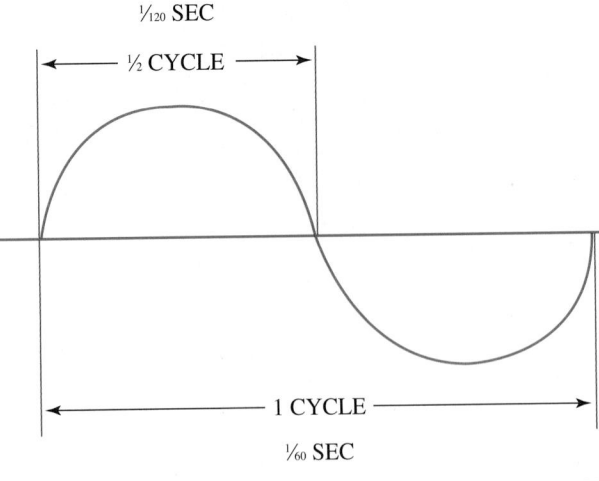

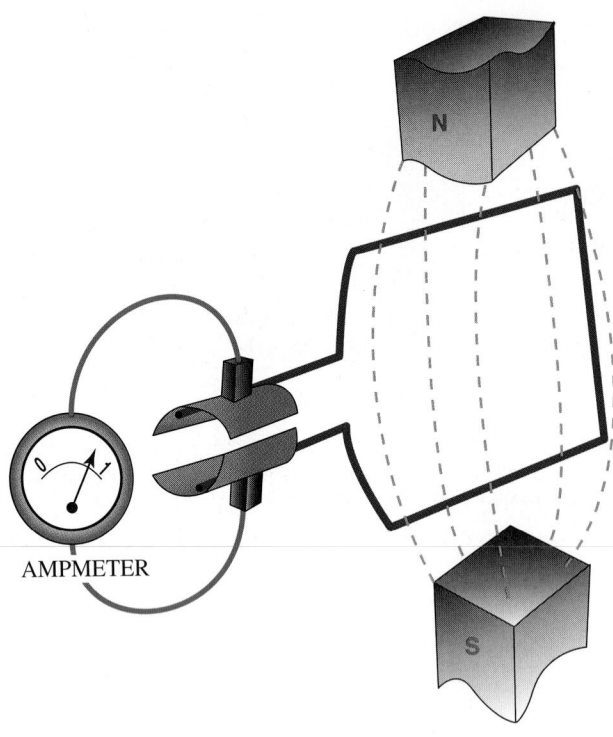

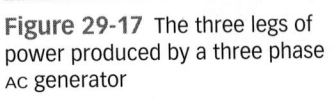

Figure 29-14 Current is induced in a coil of wire rotating in a magnetic field

Figure 29-15 One cycle of alternating current

29.11 PHASE SHIFT

In working with AC power, certain characteristics affect the power calculation, $E \times I$, which are known as phase shift factors. The phase shift factors relate to:

- Resistive circuits.
- Inductive circuits.
- Capacitive circuits

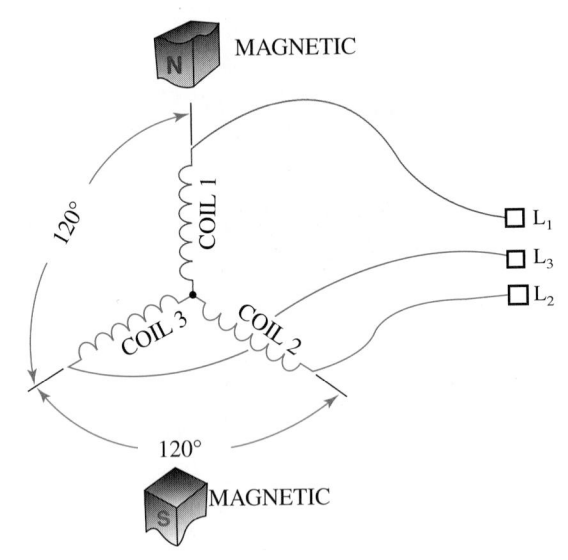

Figure 29-16 Three-phase alternating current is produced when three coils rotate inside of a magnetic field

29.12 RESISTIVE CIRCUITS

The resistive circuit, Figure 29-18, contains at least one resistive load, such as an electric heater or lamp. The current rises and falls with the voltage and the two are considered to be synchronized or "in phase." The maximum voltage occurs at the same time (or same phase angle) as the maximum amperage.

29.13 INDUCTIVE CIRCUITS

Motors, relays, transformers, and some other AC loads are constructed using coils of wire. These coils produce magnetism and are called inductive loads, Figure 29-19. The voltage and current in circuits containing inductive loads are phase shifted, or out of phase, sometimes as much as 90°.

Figure 29-17 The three legs of power produced by a three phase AC generator

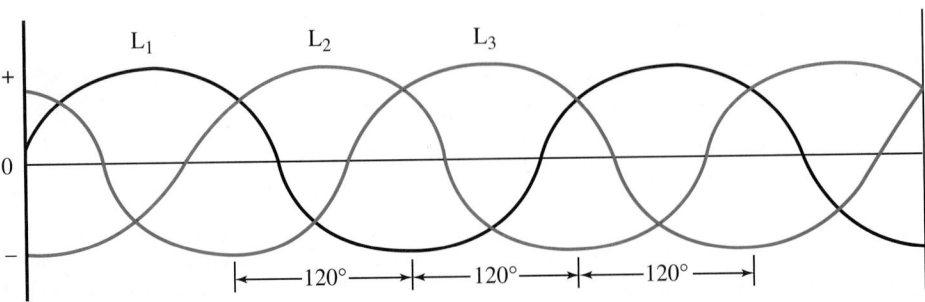

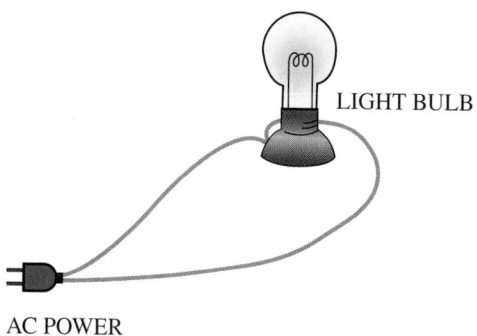

LIGHT BULB

AC POWER

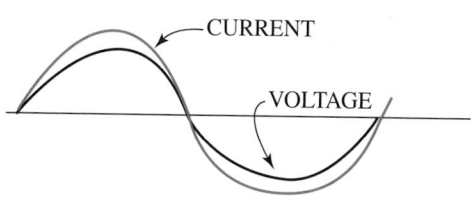

CURRENT

VOLTAGE

Figure 29-18 The AC voltage and current flow through resistance loads, like light bulbs, at the same time

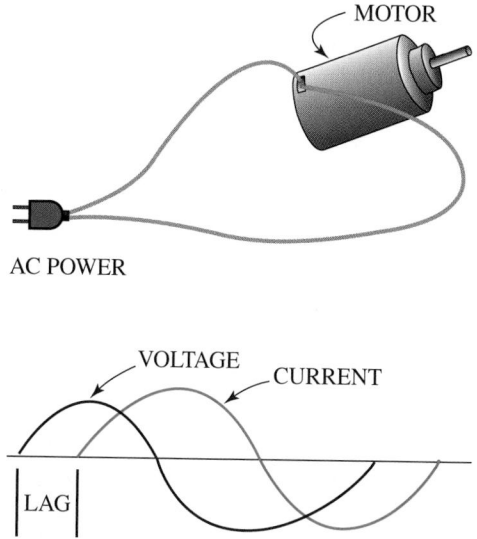

MOTOR

AC POWER

VOLTAGE

CURRENT

LAG

Figure 29-19 The AC voltage leads the current through inductive loads, like motors

In the inductive circuit the current lags, or is out of phase with the voltage, as shown in Figure 29-19. In this circuit, the current waveform peaks 90° after the voltage waveform. Because of this current lag, the measured power in an inductive circuit will always be less than the calculated power ($E \times I$). This is because measured power is an instantaneous reading, and at any particular time, one or the other or both voltage and current readings are not at their peak.

The term power factor (PF) is used to indicate this difference.

$$\text{power factor} = (\text{true power})/(\text{apparent power})$$

or

$$\text{power factor} = (\text{wattmeter reading})/(E \times I)$$

29.14 CAPACITIVE CIRCUITS

A capacitor is an electrical device that is used to change the phase relationship between the current and the voltage. This effect can be used to increase the starting power (torque) of an electric motor. A capacitor consists of a layer of insulation (a dielectric) placed between two plates of highly conductive metal, Figure 29-20. A capacitor is usually connected in series with the load, Figure 29-21. Obviously, no current can flow through the capacitor because of the dielectric. Initially, the current does flow through the series circuit, Figure 29-22. When the switch is closed, the supply voltage is applied across the capacitor. At that instant the electrons flow rapidly from the source to the 1st plate of the capacitor and from the 2nd plate of the capacitor to the source, causing a current to flow through the load. The capacitor quickly reaches peak current. It is described as charging during this period.

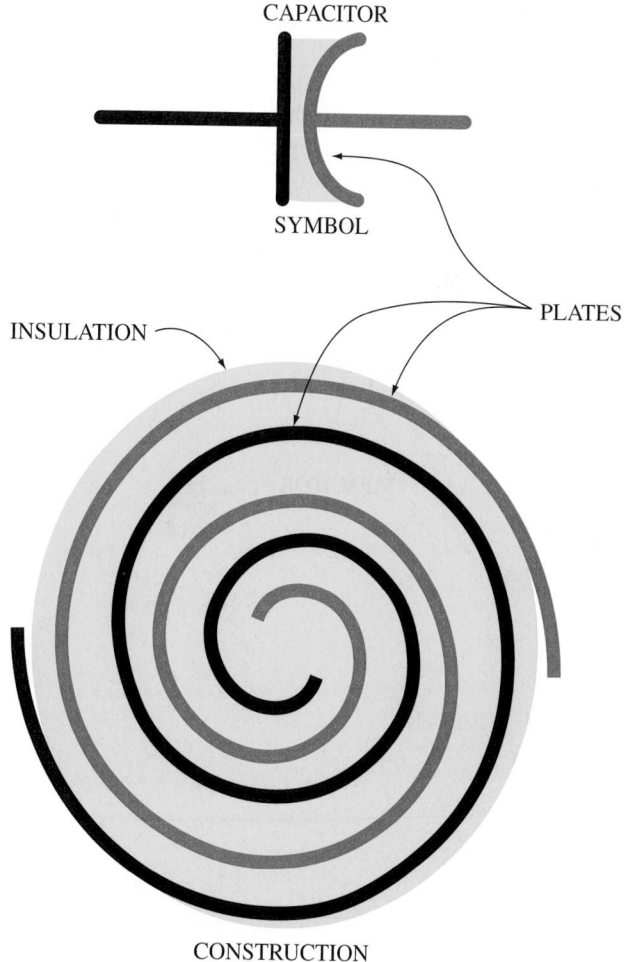

CAPACITOR

SYMBOL

INSULATION

PLATES

CONSTRUCTION

Figure 29-20 Capacitors are made up of two plates, thin metal foil, separated by an insulation paper and rolled up together

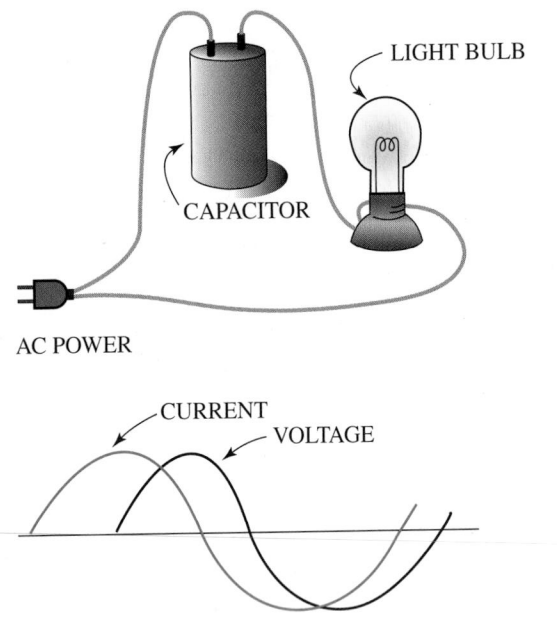

Figure 29-21 A capacitor causes a phase shift, so the current leads the voltage through a capacitance circuit

Following the initial rapid flow of electrons, the rate of current flow reduces, as shown in the downward movement of the current waveform, Figure 29-23. As electrons leave one plate and accumulate on the other, a potential difference (voltage) begins to develop across the capacitor. This difference is created by current flow and therefore lags the

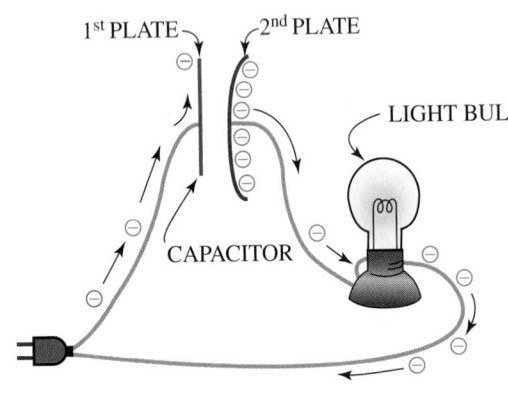

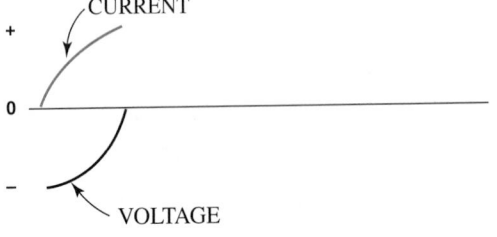

Figure 29-22 The capacitor charges when source voltage is applied. Elecrtrons flow rapidly from the source to the 1st plate of the capacitor and from the 2nd plate of the capacitor to the source, causing a current to flow through the load

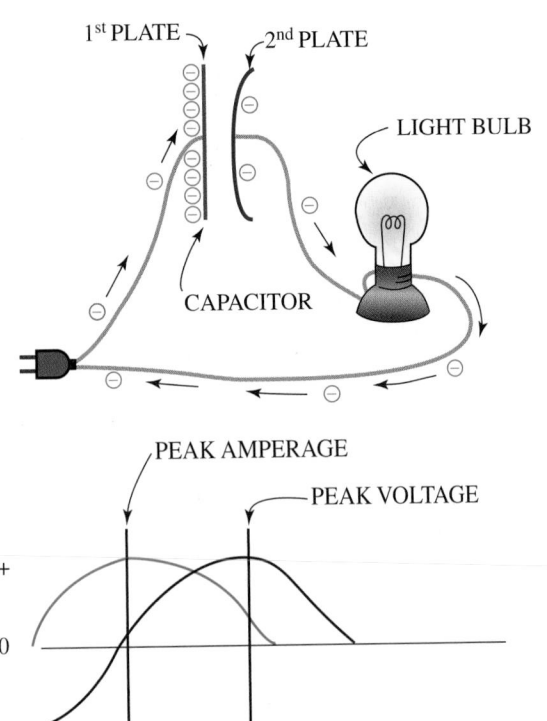

Figure 29-23 As the voltage on the first plate builds to its peak, most of the electrons have flowed off of the second plate

current. In this circuit, which contains a resistive load, current leads the voltage by 45°, Figure 29-23.

As the supply voltage waveform crosses the baseline, the polarity across the capacitor changes and electrons leave the 2nd plate. The capacitor discharges and the current flows through the load in the opposite direction, Figure 29-24. The capacitor continues in this manner as long as the source voltage is being applied.

TECH TIP

A capacitor provides a phase shift in order to help an induction electric motor to start. A start capacitor added to an electric motor gives it greater phase shift for greater starting torque. Too much phase shift from an excessively large start capacitor can actually reduce some of the starting torque. Engineers have done extensive studies to determine the most appropriate size of start capacitor to optimize the starting torque. Refer to the manufacturer's literature any time you are applying a start capacitor to an induction motor.

29.15 IMPEDANCE

Impedance is the opposition to the current flow in an AC circuit. Impedance is to an AC circuit what resistance is to a DC circuit; however, multiple impedances in a circuit cannot be added like resistances are added in direct current because the

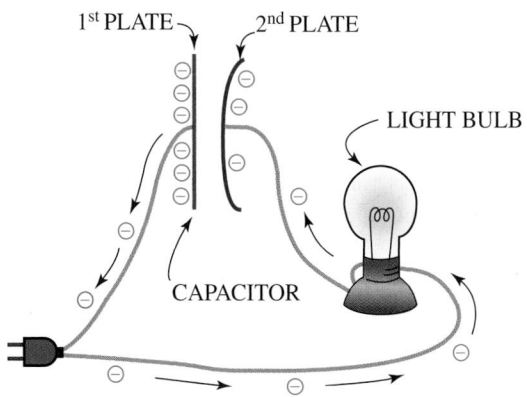

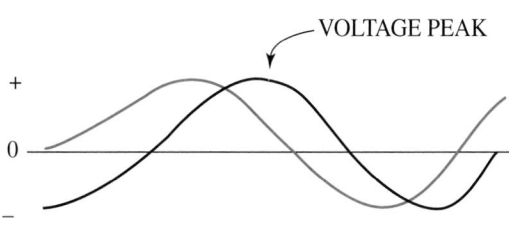

Figure 29-24 As the voltage peaks positive and starts back down toward zero, the electrons that were piled up on the first plate quickly flow off, forming a rush of current out of the capacitor

currents through inductive, capacitive, and resistance loads in an AC circuit are out of phase with each other.

TECH TIP

The word inductance means to cause or create. The electricity flowing through a coil of wire induces a magnetic field that causes another electric current to flow in a parallel coil. There is no electrical mechanical connection between the windings of an induction device such as a transformer. Each winding is completely separate. The only time the two windings are connected is when the transformer or motor has been overheated and the wiring insulation has broken down.

The following is an example of calculating impedance in an inductive circuit.

The formula that is used is:

$$Z = E/I$$

where
Z = impedance

EXAMPLE 29-1

What is the impedance of a single phase inductive circuit having a voltage of 240 V and a current flow of 10 A?

$$Z = \frac{240 \text{ V}}{10 \text{ A}} = 24 \text{ } \Omega$$

29.16 POWER DISTRIBUTION

Almost all of the electrical power used by consumers today is alternating current. It is supplied to substations at voltages as high as 120,000 V. There it is reduced to voltages between 4,800 V and 34,000 V for distribution to areas of commercial or residential users. Most power companies are now using 23,000 V or 34,999 V. Local transformers reduce the voltage levels to suit user requirements as shown in Figure 29-25.

TECH TIP

The primary reason that alternating current is used as the standard power source in commercial and residential buildings is that it is the most easily transformed from one voltage to another. Without the ability to transform power from the higher voltages used during transmission to the lower voltages used in our homes and businesses, cross country transmission lines would have to be made with extremely large diameter wires.

SERVICE TIP

Today, however, by using electronic switches, it is possible to more easily convert DC from one voltage to another and to convert power from DC to AC. A simple example of AC to DC conversion is a power inverter that uses an automobile's 12 V battery to produce 110 V of 60 cycle current. Power inverters are a great device to add to your service van because they allow you to run portable drill chargers and other electrical devices that normally must be plugged into a standard outlet.

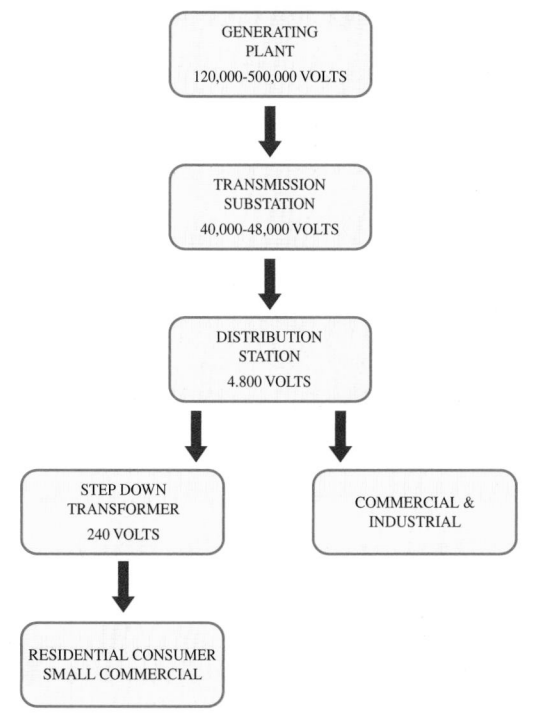

Figure 29-25 Votage reduction in the power distribution system

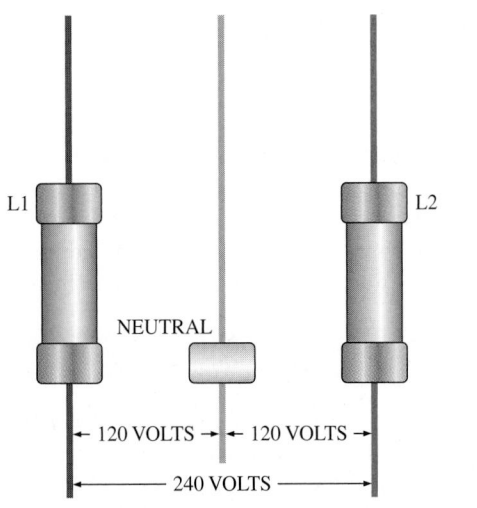

Figure 29-26 Line voltage for three wire 240 V single phase power supply

Four common low voltage systems are available to consumers:

- 240 V, single phase, 60 Hz systems.
- 240 V, three phase, 60 Hz systems.
- 208 V, three phase, 60 Hz systems.
- 480 V, three phase, 60 Hz systems.

29.17 ELECTRIC SERVICES

Single phase current is used for almost all residences. Any electrical appliance that operates on 120 V power is single phase equipment. The most common service supplied to residential and small commercial users is the 240 V, single phase, 60 Hz system. The system uses three wires, two hot wires and one grounded neutral. A schematic diagram of this 240 V system is shown in Figure 29-26. Electric utility companies use a transformer to produce this service, as shown in Figure 29-27.

All HVAC/R equipment is manufactured to operate satisfactorily on voltages of plus or minus 10% of the rated voltage unless otherwise specified. For example, if the equipment has a voltage rating of 240 V, the equipment should be able to operate at any voltage between 207 and 253 V. HVAC/R equipment has a tendency to operate more satisfactorily on maximum voltage than on minimum voltage.

The electric utility attempts to maintain a voltage at the load within this plus or minus ± 10% range. At peak load times, the line voltage may drop to near the permitted minimum. If you suspect any voltage problems, the line voltage at the HVAC/R load should be measured at these times.

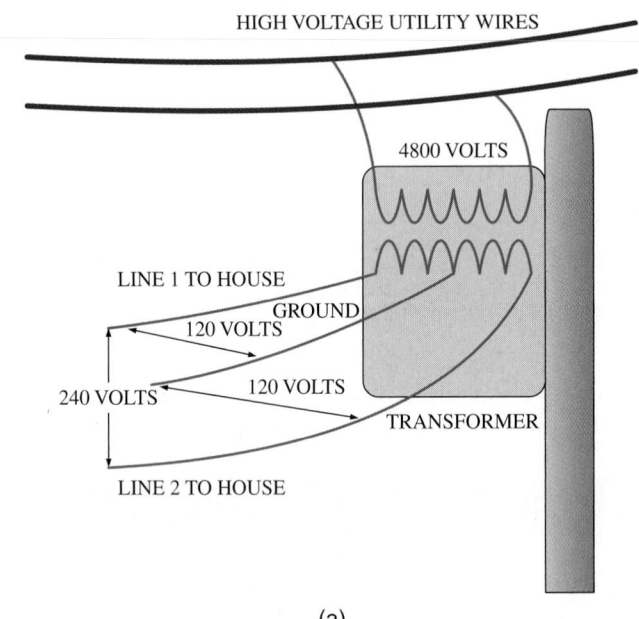

(a)

UNIT 12

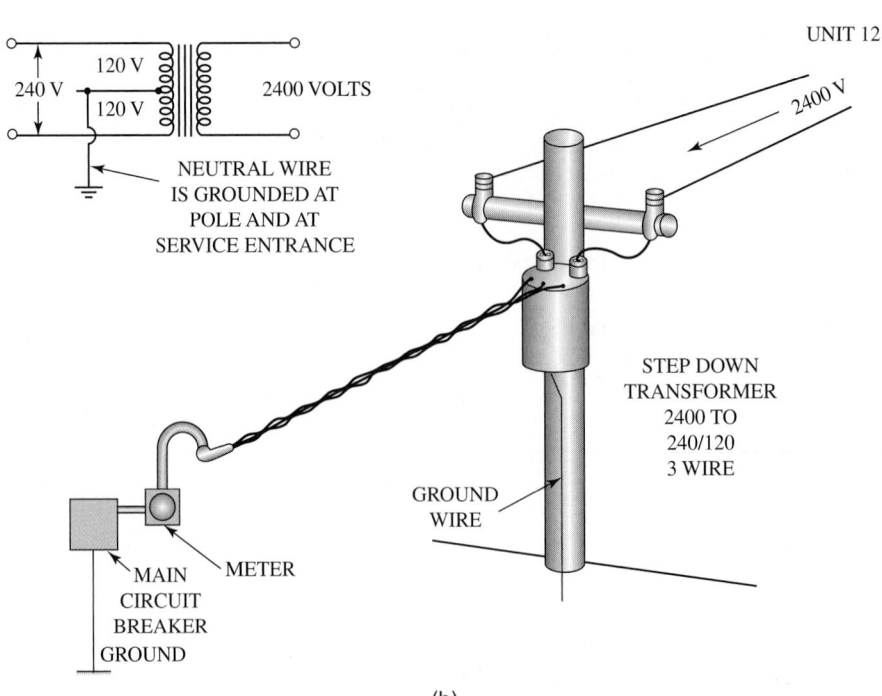

(b)

Figure 29-27 Step down transformer for a 240 V three wire single phase power supply

29.18 240 V, THREE PHASE, 60 HZ SYSTEMS

Three phase systems are commonly used for sizable commercial and industrial installations. These transformers have three hot legs of power and one neutral leg, as shown in Figure 29-28. This type of power supply is obtained from a delta transformer secondary hookup, as shown in Figure 29-29.

Three phase 240 V power is obtained by connecting to the three hot legs. Single phase 240 V power can be obtained by connecting to any two of the hot legs. Single phase 120 V power can be obtained by connecting to either of the adjacent hot legs and the midpoint neutral. Single phase 208 V power can be obtained by connecting to the nonadjacent hot leg and the ground. This is called the wild leg.

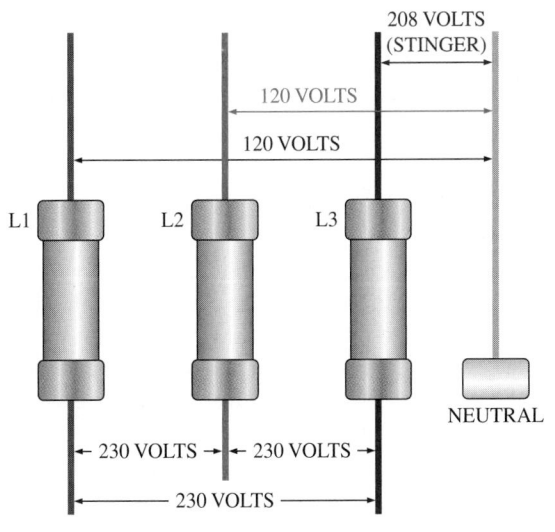

Figure 29-28 Line voltage for a four wire 240 V three phase power supply

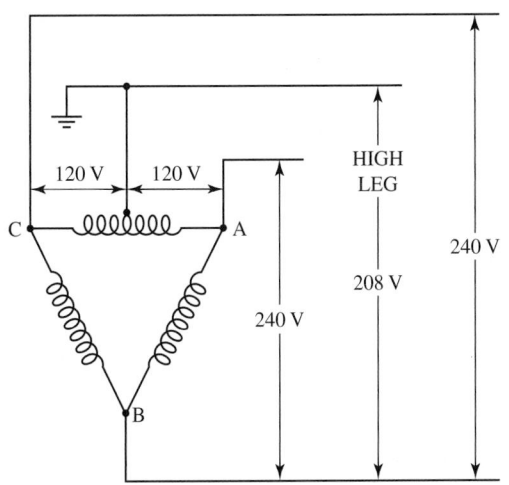

Figure 29-29 Line voltages for a four wire 240 V three phase system using a delta transformer secondary

29.19 208 V, THREE PHASE, 60 HZ SYSTEMS

These systems are common in schools, hospitals, and office buildings where 208 V three phase motors and 120 V single phase lighting and convenience circuits are required, as shown in Figure 29-30. From this type of system, 208 V three phase, 208 V single phase, and 120 V single phase services are available. The schematic for the transformer secondary hookup is shown in Figure 29-31.

SERVICE TIP

It is recommended that all motors used be rated for 208 V (not 230 V) for operation on 208 V systems.

29.20 480 V SYSTEMS

The 208 V/120 V three phase four wire wye connected system, shown in Figure 29-30 and Figure 29-31 , has been generally superseded in large buildings by the 480 V/277 V three phase four wire wye connected system, shown in Figure 29-32 and

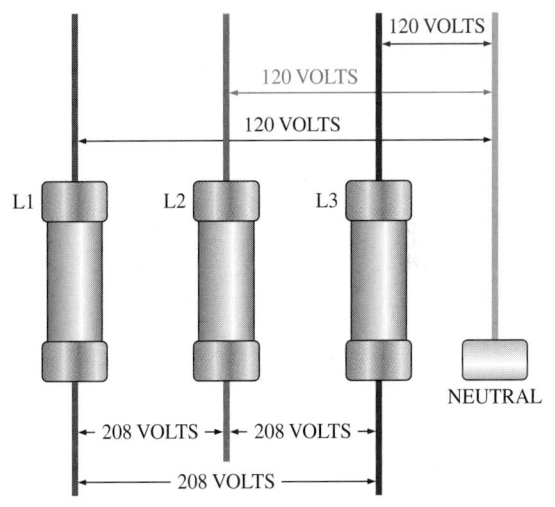

Figure 29-30 Line voltage for a four wire, 208 V three phase power supply

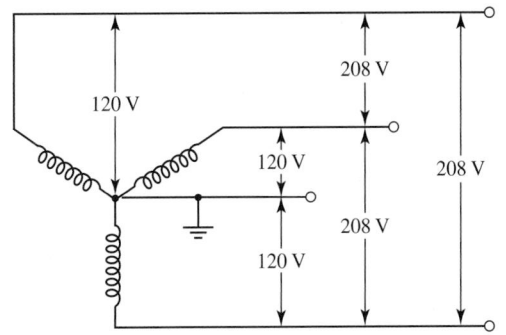

Figure 29-31 Line voltage for a four wire, 208 V three phase power supply using a wye transformer secondary

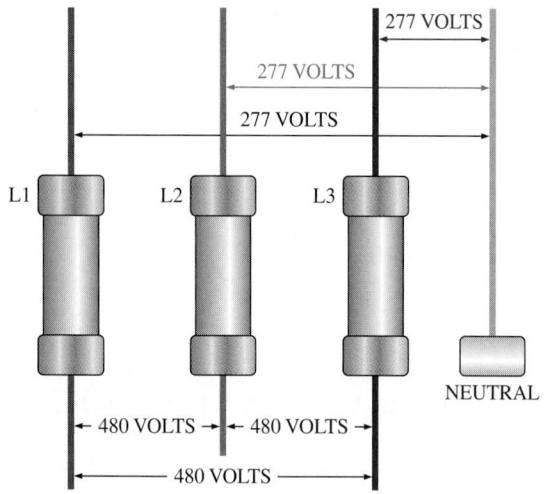

Figure 29-32 Line voltage for a four wire, 227 V/480 V three phase power supply

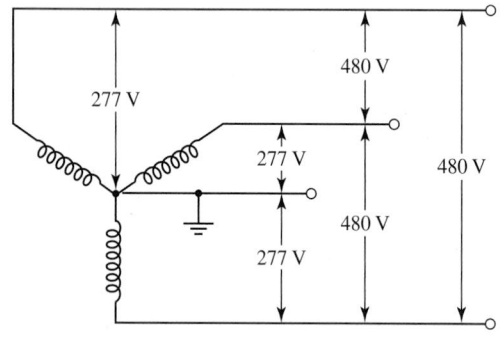

Figure 29-33 Line voltage for a four wire, 227 V/480 V three phase power supply, using a wye transformer secondary

Figure 29-33. This improvement was made possible by the development of 277 V fluorescent lighting. Standard 460 V three phase motors can be used on 480 V systems. Convenience outlet circuits at 120 V are provided for by 480 V/208 V or 480 V/120 V step down transformers. The higher supply voltage permits larger loads to be serviced by smaller wires. In addition, voltage drops are reduced.

TECH TIP

A 460 V three phase system will draw less current than a 208 V three phase system. For example, a 50 hp, 460 V, three phase, 60 Hz motor would have a full load of 57.5 A, while the same motor at 208 V would have a full load of 122 A.

29.21 SINGLE PHASE VERSUS THREE PHASE POWER

Three phase power is most often used by large HVAC/R equipment operators. The following are some of the reasons:

- Line current is reduced almost one-half for the same size motor load. This reduces the wire size and voltage

drop. In addition, the line current is reduced by one-third.
- There is less power loss to transformers in using it.
- Three phase motors are smaller, less expensive, more reliable, and more efficient than single phase. They do not require special capacitors to increase their starting torque.
- Some three phase motors have an ability to correct the phase shift caused by some other inductive loads. Large commercial consumers of electric power are often faced with a surcharge that is applied to their base electrical rate when their power consumption is out of phase. Three phase motors can reduce or eliminate this surcharge by correcting the phase angle.

Single phase power is used for most HVAC/R residential and light commercial systems. The following are some reasons:

- Single phase power is more readily available than three phase power.
- Because of the popularity of single phase power, a larger variety of equipment types and sizes are available.
- Single phase equipment is more readily available because it is often kept in stock at supply houses.

29.22 OVER CURRENT PROTECTION

The sizing of the electrical power wiring and over current protection are important for a number of reasons, with safety being the most important. If the wiring is not large enough to carry the current, it may overheat and cause a fire. It may also become hot enough to melt the insulation, allowing the wire to come in contact with part of the equipment case, which could cause an electrical shock to anyone touching the charged metal.

The fuse and/or circuit breaker sizing are important. Proper sizing will ensure that in case of an over current event the wiring is protected. This is very important because the wiring often runs through areas of homes and buildings that contain wood and other combustible building materials. If this wiring were to overheat, it could start a fire. All HVAC/R residential and most commercial units are located inside metal cabinets. As part of the UL certification process these cabinets are tested to guarantee that they will withstand an internal component fire. This is to confirm their safety should an over current event happen inside the unit.

Many HVAC/R units have name plates that list the minimum circuit ampacity and the maximum over current protection ratings. If the unit does not have this information, you may locate it in the National Electrical Code or calculate it using one of several similar equations.

29.23 SIZING POWER WIRING

The *minimum circuit ampacity* (MCA) is the amperage load that the conductor must be sized at as a minimum for the equipment load. MCA is calculated using the following equation:

$$MCA = (1.25 \times FLA_1) + FLA_2 + FLA_3 + FLA\ldots$$

where

MCA = the minimum circuit amperage capacity (ampacity)

1.25 = a constant that increases the FLA for the motor by 25%

FLA_1 = the full load amps (FLA) or rated load amps (RLA) of the largest motor

FLA_2 + FLA_3 + FLA . . . = the full load amps (FLA) or rated load amps (RLA) of the all the other motors.

For example, find the MCA for a rooftop unit that has the following data listed on its name plate: compressor FLA 22, two fans FLA 3.5 each.

$$MCA = (1.25 \times FLA_1) + FLA_2 + FLA_3 + FLA \ldots$$
$$MCA = (1.25 \times 22) + 3.5 + 3.5$$
$$MCA = 27.5 + 3.5 + 3.5$$
$$MCA = 34.5 \text{ A}$$

29.24 SIZING CIRCUIT PROTECTION AND DISCONNECTS

The maximum over current protection (MOCP) is the maximum amperage rating for fuses or circuit breakers that are used to protect the system. If wiring in the circuit passes too much current it will overheat and cause conductor failures or fires. Typically all equipment will have a listed maximum fuse or circuit breaker designation which should always be adhered to. Never use a larger fuse or breaker size than the one originally designated for the equipment. It is also important to note that a motor may be operating in an overloaded condition while the circuit itself is not and the fuse will not open the circuit. That is why each motor is also protected separately from the circuit from an overload within its own operating range.

SERVICE TIP

HVAC/R type fuses or circuit breakers must be used. These are often classified as "slow blow" because they will handle the momentary surge of current associated with motor starting. If standard circuit breakers or fuses are used, nuisance trips may result.

UNIT 29—SUMMARY

The HVAC/R unit is supplied by an electrical power system that includes a source of power, an electrical load device, an electric circuit, and a switch to control the electricity flow. Alternating current is the most common source of power used for most HVAC/R systems. The current flow reverses and changes direction at a regular interval referred to as frequency. The typical frequency is sixty times per second designated as 60 *Hertz* (Hz).

One important characteristic of AC power that needs to be understood is the relationship between the current and voltage

in a circuit referred to as *phase shift*. In a purely resistive crcuit the current rises and falls with the voltage and is considered to be "in phase". However the current lags the voltage in an inductive circuit and because of this phase shift the measured instantaneous power will be less than the calculated power. This difference is referred to as the *power factor*. In a capacitive circuit the phase shift is opposite and the currenct leads the voltage. Another important characteristic of an AC circuit, referred to as impedance, is the opposition to the current flow.

Power distribution systems can be single or three phase. Single phase power is typically used for most HVAC/R residential and light commercial systems. Single phase power is readily available and there is a large variety of single phase equipment to choose from. Three phase power is more commonly used in commercial applications. Three phase systems allow for reduced line current, less transformer power loss, and smaller more efficient motors. Since either of these systems may be encountered on the job site, the HVAC/R technician needs to understand both single phase and three phase circuits.

UNIT 29—REVIEW QUESTIONS

1. List the three essential requirements for an electrical power system.
2. What are the two types of power sources?
3. What is the most common source of power for most HVAC/R systems?
4. What is the purpose of transformers?
5. What is a *load*, and what is the most common load for HVAC/R systems?
6. Name three ways motors are used in HVAC/R equipment.
7. Describe the path of a complete electrical circuit.
8. What is the difference between a relay and a contactor?
9. Describe how contactors and relays operate.
10. What are transducers and what are they used for?
11. What are the two types of transformers?
12. Explain where single phase power and three phase power are normally used.
13. The phase shift factors that affect the power calculation $E \times I$ relate to what circuits?
14. What is the impedance of a single phase inductive circuit having a voltage of 120 V and a current flow of 5 A?
15. What are the four common low voltage systems available to consumers?
16. Why is three phase power most often used by large HVAC/R equipment operators?
17. Why is single phase power used for most HVAC/R residential and light commercial systems?
18. What can happen if electrical power wiring is not sized properly?
19. Find the minimum circuit ampacity (MCA) for a rooftop unit that has the following data listed on its name plate: compressor FLA 26, two fans FLA 3.0 each.
20. What can happen if an oversized fuse or circuit breaker is installed and the circuit is allowed to pass too much current?

UNIT 30

Electric Motors

OBJECTIVES

After completing this unit you will be able to:

- describe the operation of AC induction motors.
- explain the importance of torque, speed, and power usage for motors.
- explain how and why capacitors are often used for single phase motors.
- list the different types of single phase motors.
- describe the differences between single phase and three phase motors.
- list the different types of motor protection devices.
- test a motor circuit for proper operation.

TECH TIP

Manufacturers can produce motors with high starting torque, high running torque, or good running efficiency. It is impossible, however, to produce a single motor that has all three characteristics. The performance required of motors will determine what type of motor to use. Motors that frequently start but do not run for long periods of time would benefit from high starting torque. Motors that operate for long periods of time under heavy loads would benefit from having high running torque. Motors that operate for long periods of time under relatively light loads will benefit from good running efficiency. Manufacturers of equipment take these three factors into consideration when specifying which motor is to be used. For that reason it is recommended that you select a replacement motor within the same category as the one originally supplied with the equipment.

30.1 INTRODUCTION

Electric motors are the most important load device in the various types of HVAC/R units. They convert large portions of electrical energy to useful work. It is important, therefore, for the technician to understand how they operate and how they can be protected. It is also important to note that not all motors are exactly the same because different motors are designed for various types of service. Even though all motors are not the same they all share the important characteristics of torque, speed, and power usage.

30.2 AC INDUCTION MOTOR TORQUE

Torque is the twisting (or turning) force that must be developed by a motor to turn whatever it is driving. The power required for a motor to drive a fan, compressor, or any other piece of equipment is directly related to the torque and speed required. A greater amount of torque is required to start a motor than to run it. The starting torque requirements for a fan are low. The starting torque requirements for a reciprocating compressor are high. Providing extra starting torque is expensive. Therefore, to keep the cost down the motor is selected with the smallest torque that will adequately perform the work for which it is intended.

30.3 INDUCTION MOTOR PRINCIPLES

The two principal parts of a motor are the stator and the rotor. The stator is the stationary part and the rotor (often referred to as the armature) is the rotating part, as shown in Figure 30-1a,b. The stator core is built of slotted steel laminations. Coils of wire called windings are spaced in the stator slots. When current is applied to a stator coil a magnetic field is generated. Depending on the direction of current flow through the coil either a north or a south pole will be produced. Each winding can be considered a pole.

The rotor is a series of aluminum (or copper) bars mounted on a soft iron core. The core provides a path for the magnetic field of the rotor. The conductor bars are shorted together by an end ring permitting current to flow, as shown in Figure 30-2.

The current passing through the stator creates a powerful magnetic field, as shown in Figure 30-3. No current is actually supplied to the rotor. Instead the magnetic field of the stator induces current to flow through the rotor. This current induced in the rotor will also produce a magnetic field. However the current induced in the rotor is in the opposite direction from the stator current. This flow of current in the opposite direction creates and opposing magnetic field in the rotor which reacts with the stator field. The repulsion and

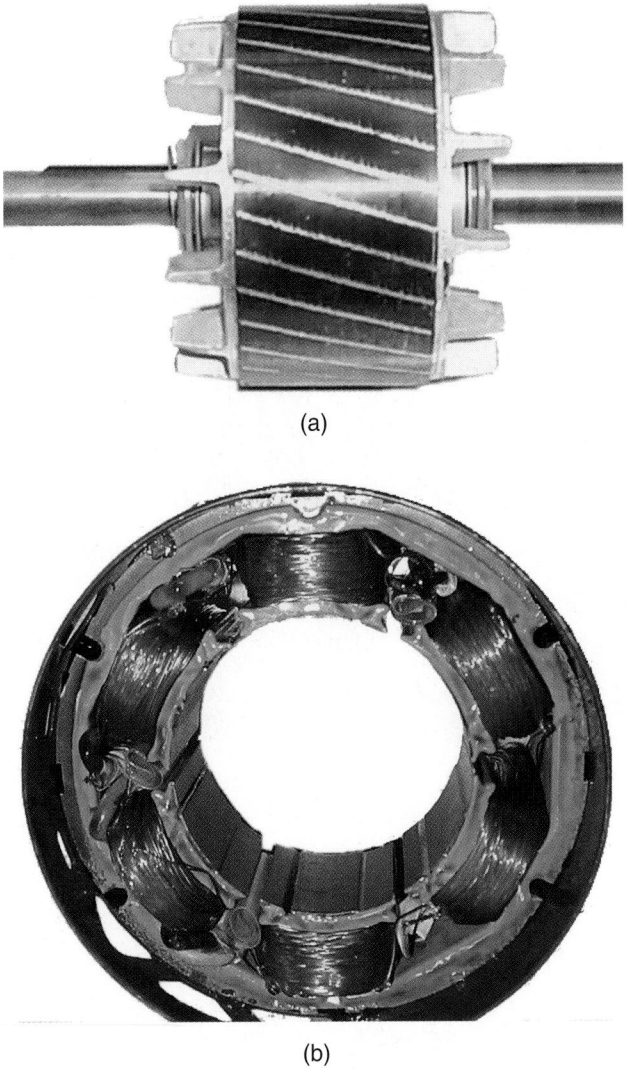

(a)

(b)

Figure 30-1 Parts of an electric motor: (a) Rotor; (b) Stator

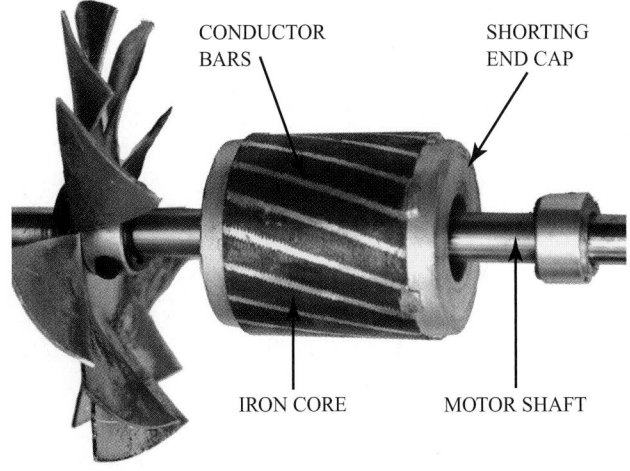

CONDUCTOR BARS   SHORTING END CAP

IRON CORE   MOTOR SHAFT

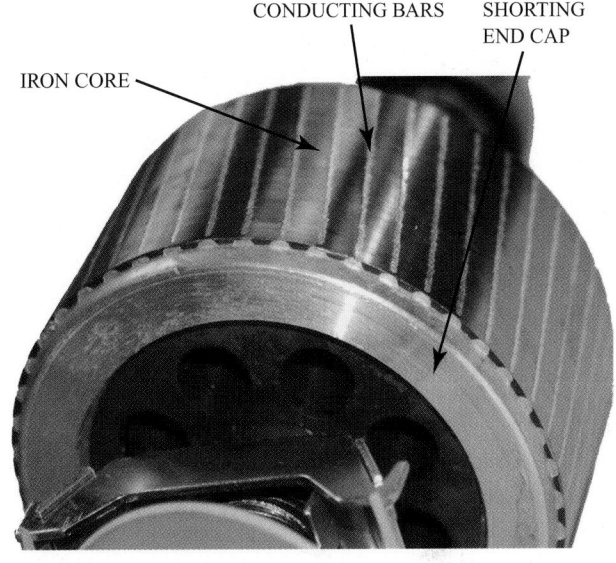

CONDUCTING BARS   SHORTING END CAP

IRON CORE

Figure 30-2 Squirrel cage type rotor
(Courtesy of Hampden Engineering Corporation)

attraction between the poles of the rotor and the stator cause the rotor to turn.

As shown in Figure 30-4, the like poles (north to north and south to south) in the stator coil repel the like poles in the rotor winding, causing rotation. In Figure 30-5, the rotor winding is shown with both north and south poles relatively near each other. The stator coil repels the like poles and attracts the opposite poles.

As the alternating current in the stator coils changes direction, the polarity of the stator coils also changes. The north pole coils now become south poles and vice versa. This is shown in Figure 30-6a,b. The current flow through the rotor also reverses direction so the polarity of the rotor changes along with the polarity of the stator. Even though the current is alternating, a continuous rotation is produced.

A problem can occur if the rotor is stopped in the position shown in Figure 30-7. In this position, regardless of polarity, no motion can occur. This position is sometimes described as dead center. To correct this condition, a start winding is added, as shown in Figure 30-8. The original winding is called a run winding. The two windings—the run winding and the start winding—are out of phase with each other and enough torque is created to start the rotor turning. Motors of this type are called split phase motors. Because of their low starting torque they are used only on fractional horsepower applications.

30.4 MOTOR SPEED

The speed of a motor is determined by the number of poles (stator coils) and the frequency (Hertz) of the alternating current. A greater number of poles results in slower motor speeds. Higher frequency produces faster motor speeds. Speed is measured in revolutions per minute (rpm). The maximum speed of a motor is known as the synchronous speed.

Figure 30-3 The induced magnetic field in the conductor bars is the same as the electromagnetic field; because like magnetic poles repel each other, the rotor is forced to spin as the fields repel each other *(Courtesy Hampden Engineering Corporation)*

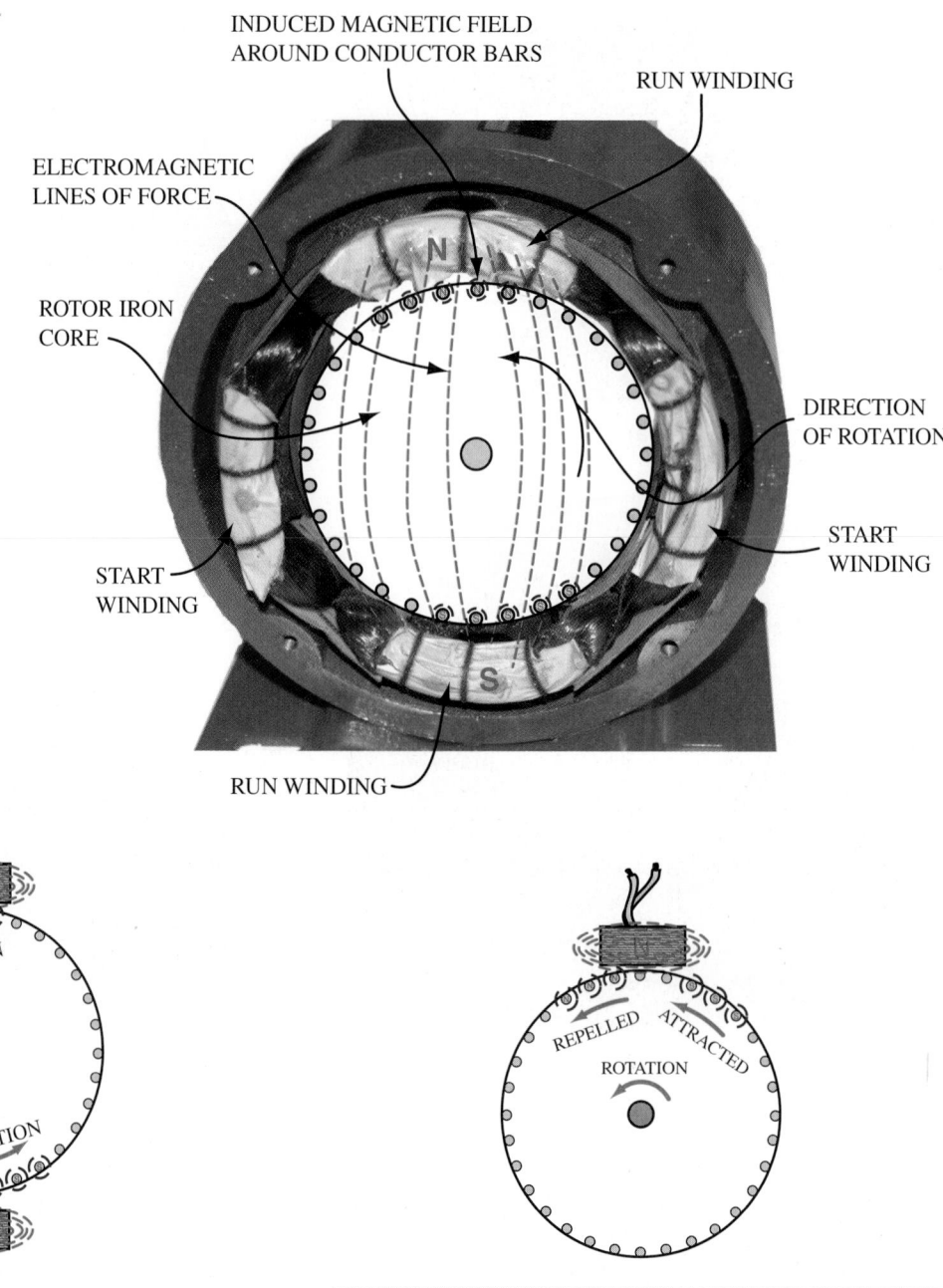

INDUCED MAGNETIC FIELD AROUND CONDUCTOR BARS

RUN WINDING

ELECTROMAGNETIC LINES OF FORCE

DIRECTION OF ROTATION

ROTOR IRON CORE

START WINDING

START WINDING

RUN WINDING

Figure 30-4 The magnetic field induced in the rotor causes it to rotate

Figure 30-5 On one side the like magnetic poles are being repelled, and on the other side the opposite poles are being attracted

CAUTION

The rpm of induction motors is totally dependent on the number of poles and the frequency of the alternating current. An induction motor will turn at the same rpm even though the voltage supplied to the motor is lowered. However, as the voltage is decreased, the current the motor draws increases. Motors that are operating at a low voltage will quickly overheat and may fail. It is for that reason that rheostat motor controllers should not be used on induction motors.

Motors are not 100% efficient. In actual performance there is some slippage, or inefficiency, in the motor operation. For motors used to power HVAC/R equipment, the actual speed is usually 95–97% of synchronous speed. Figure 30-9 shows two pole, four pole, six pole, and eight pole motors. The number of poles is used to calculate the synchronous motor speed.

The following is an example of calculating synchronous motor speed. The formula is:

$$\text{rpm} = \frac{\text{Hz} \times 60 \text{ sec/min}}{\frac{1}{2}p} \quad \text{or} \quad \frac{\text{Hz} \times 120}{p}$$

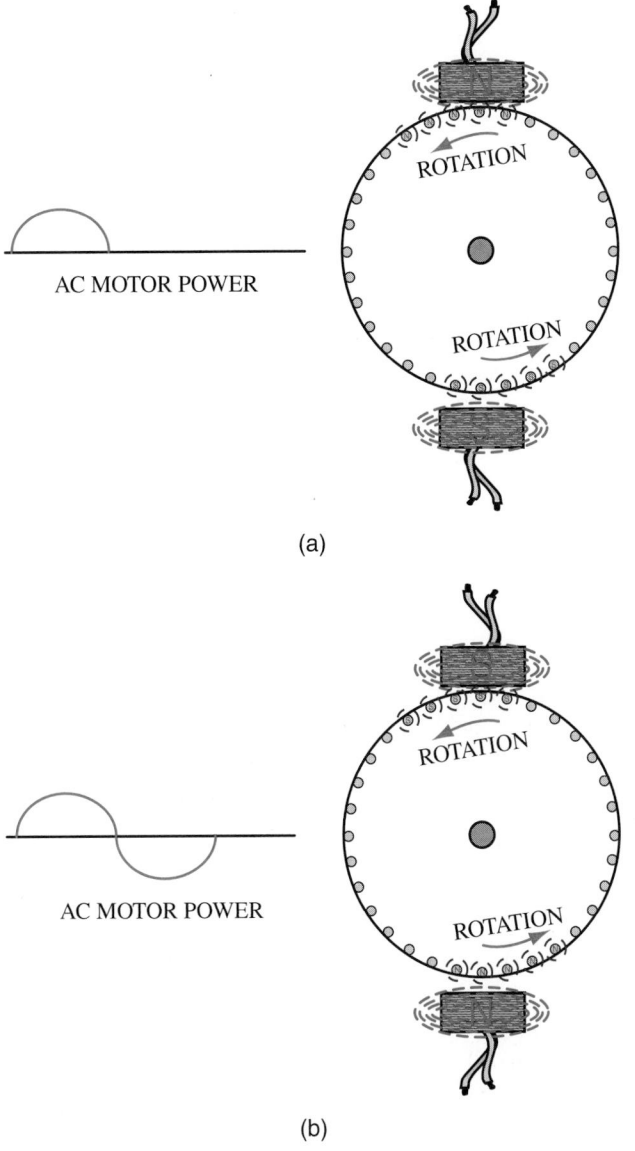

(a)

(b)

Figure 30-6 (a) In the first half of the AC power cycle, the rotor is pushed away from one side and attracted to the other; (b) In the second half of the AC power cycle, the current direction through the windings changes and the process is repeated, this is what keeps the motor spinning

where

> rpm = revolutions per minute
> Hz = frequency in cycles/sec
> p = number of poles

EXAMPLE 30-1

What is the speed of a four pole motor operating at a frequency of 60 Hz?

$$\text{rpm} = \frac{60 \times 120}{4}$$

$$\text{rpm} = \frac{7,200}{4}$$

$$= 1,800 \text{ revolutions per minute}$$

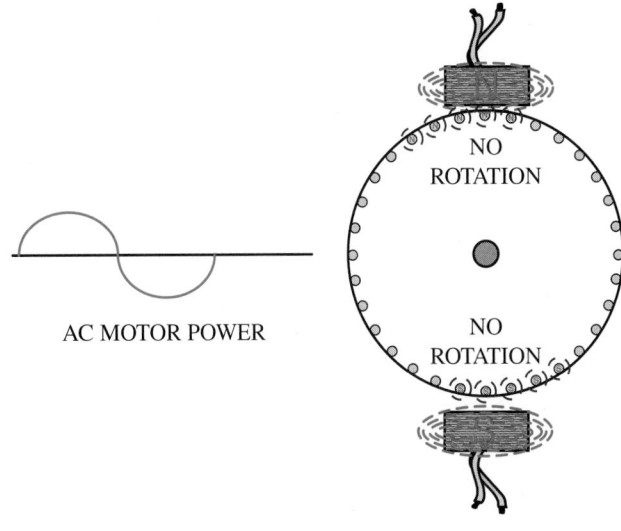

Figure 30-7 A motor cannot start rotating if the magnetic fields are at dead center

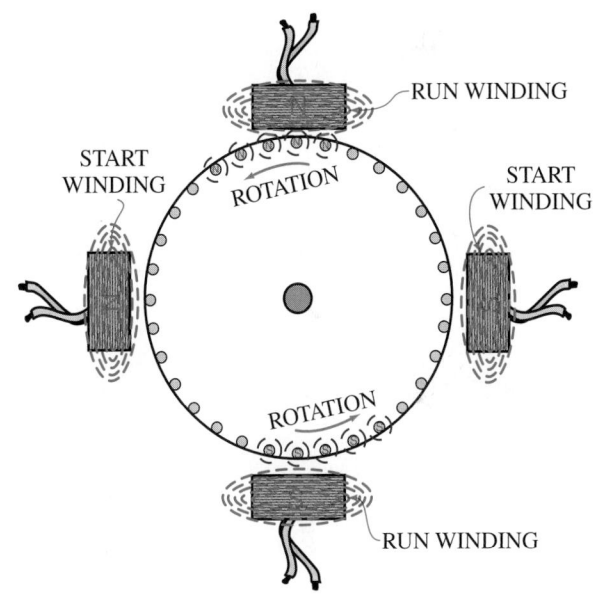

Figure 30-8 Start windings are offset from run windings to get the rotor out of dead center; start windings are often made of finer wire than run windings

30.5 CAPACITOR PRINCIPLES

A capacitor is made up of two conductors separated by an insulating material. The conductors are called plates and the insulating material is the dielectric. Referring to Figure 30-10, when voltage is applied, the current through the capacitor resistor circuit will lead the voltage. In order to provide strong starting torque for a split phase motor, a start capacitor is placed in series with the start winding. Figure 30-11 shows a capacitor in series with the start winding. When voltage is applied, the magnetism in the start winding will occur earlier than in the run winding and will provide the push needed to

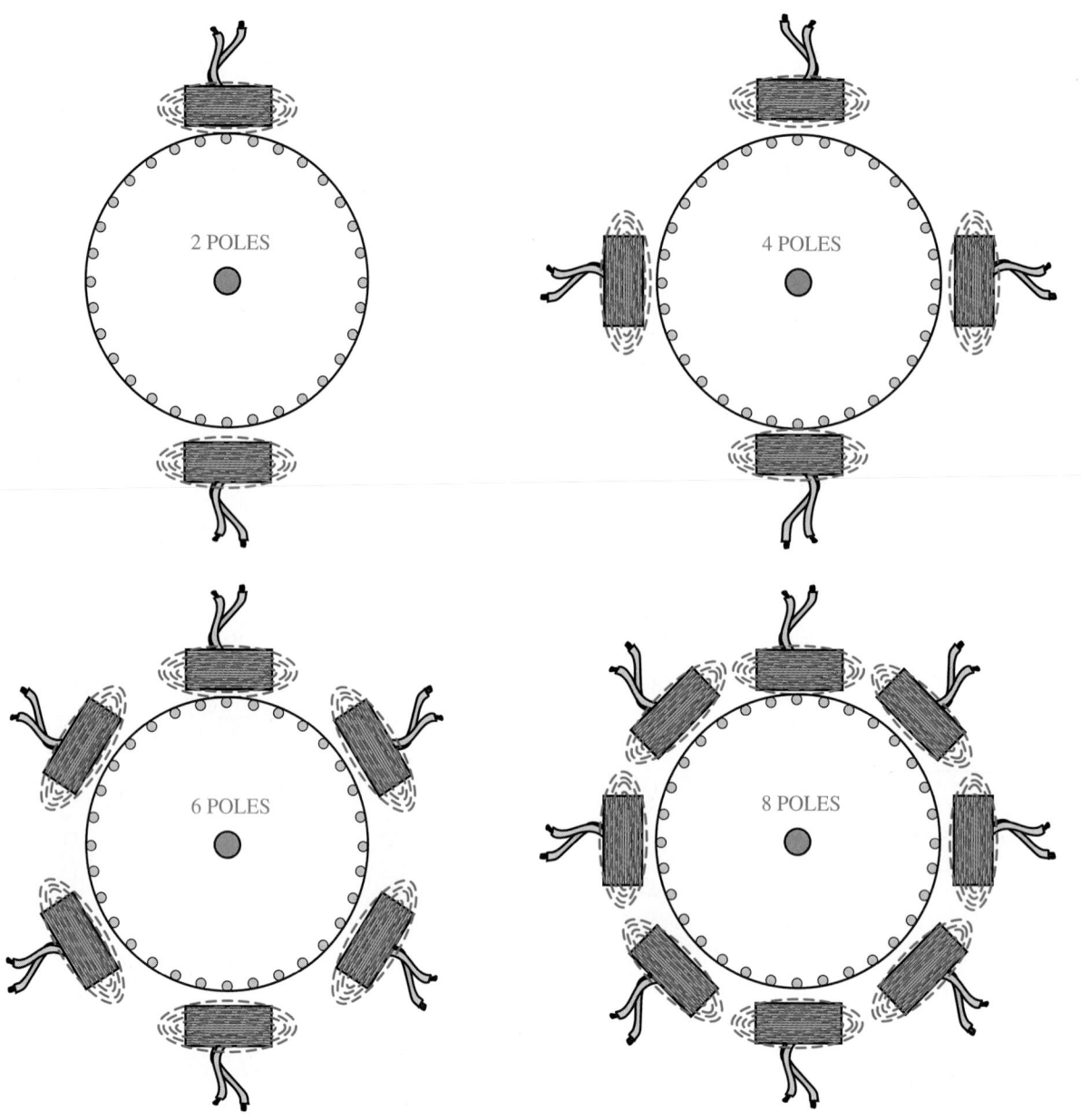

Figure 30-9 Synchronous speed depends on the number of poles

start the motor. Figure 30-12 shows the use of the phase shift to advance the magnetic field in the start winding.

When the current direction in the start winding reverses, the polarity of the start winding will also change. By this time, the rotor south magnetic pole has rotated to the point where it is repelled by the new stator south pole, causing continuous rotation.

A capacitor is rated by its capacity and voltage limit. The unit of capacity is the microfarad (mfd and μF are commonly used abbreviations). A high mfd rating is obtained by either using large plates or a small amount of insulation. A low mfd is obtained by using smaller plates or more insulation. The voltage stamped on the outside of the capacitor is the maximum voltage that can be connected safely across the capacitor. If this voltage is exceeded, the capacitor is likely to fail.

SERVICE TIP

There is often a misunderstanding that a capacitor provides the motor with higher voltage. This is because often on the side of the capacitor there is a much higher voltage listed than the voltage the system operates at. For example, 377 is a common voltage listing for capacitors. However, capacitors do not add voltage but merely shift the phase to increase the running efficiency or starting torque. Capacitors in motor circuits are subjected to higher voltages than the voltage powering the unit. The high voltage across the capacitor is the result of the charging and discharging of the capacitor in series with an inductive load.

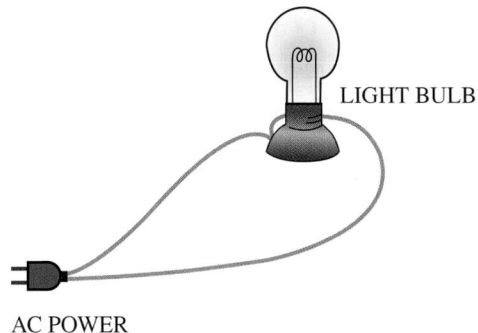

LIGHT BULB

AC POWER

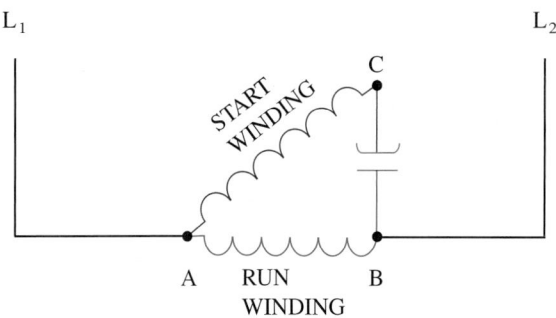

L₁ $\quad$ L₂

START WINDING

C

A $\quad$ RUN $\quad$ B
WINDING

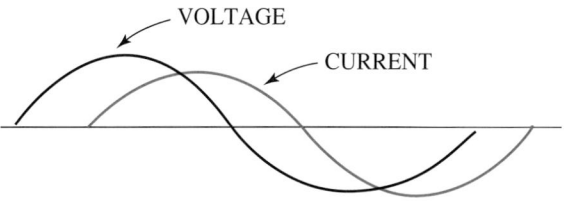

POWER FLOWING THROUGH RUN WINDING
FROM POINTS A TO B

VOLTAGE

CURRENT

(a)

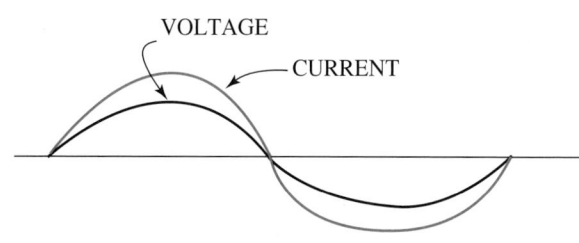

VOLTAGE

CURRENT

POWER FLOWING THROUGH START WINDING
AND CAPACITOR FROM POINTS A TO C TO B

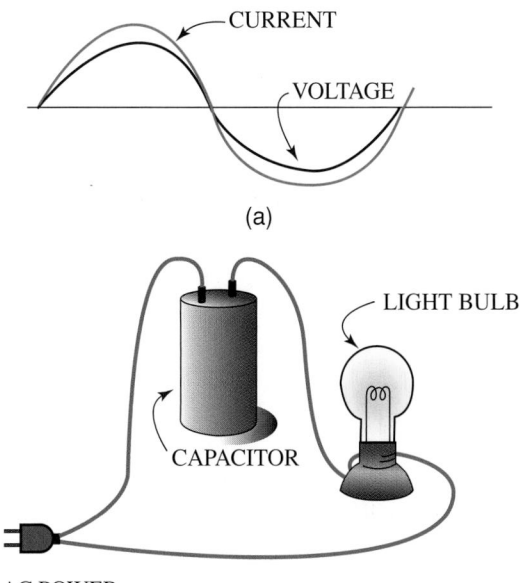

LIGHT BULB

CAPACITOR

AC POWER

Figure 30-11 The phase shift caused by the capacitor causes
the rotor to move, even if it is dead center

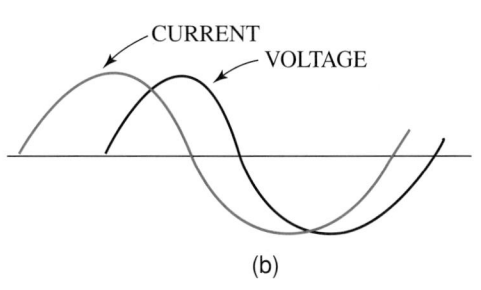

CURRENT

VOLTAGE

(b)

Figure 30-10 (a) The voltage and current flow through a
resistor, like the light bulb load in this circuit, at the same time;
(b) However, in the capacitor resistor circuit, the current leads
the voltage through the circuit

Capacitors are used to achieve the desired phase angle
shift and to obtain the required current through the series
load. Both of these qualities are obtained by selecting the
proper mfd rating.

Figure 30-13 shows the wiring of a start capacitor and
its relay, connected to a compressor motor. The start capacitor and the relay normally closed (NC) switch are in series
with the start winding. The start relay coil is connected in
parallel with the start winding. With this arrangement, the

starting torque of the motor is increased. The relay removes
the start capacitor from the circuit as soon as the motor is
running.

Referring to Figure 30-14, a run capacitor has been connected to the power and start terminals of the fan motor. The
run capacitor stays in the circuit all the time and increases the
efficiency of the motor. If the run capacitor should fail, the current draw of the motor would be increased and the motor
could overheat. Most PSC motors will not operate if the run
capacitor is defective.

Figure 30-15a shows the normal appearance of the run
capacitor. The run capacitor, which stays in the circuit continuously, is made of large plates and a large amount of insulation (dielectric) to dissipate the heat. The run capacitor
may also be round. The start capacitor does not stay in the
circuit long, and therefore does not have a heat dissipation
problem. It is typically made in rolled form, sandwiching
metal foil and insulating material, Figure 30-15b.

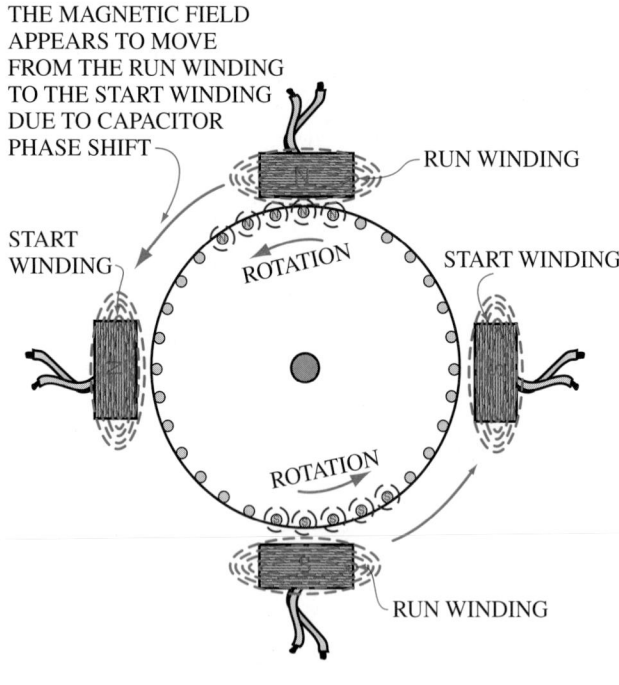

THE MAGNETIC FIELD APPEARS TO MOVE FROM THE RUN WINDING TO THE START WINDING DUE TO CAPACITOR PHASE SHIFT

RUN WINDING

START WINDING

START WINDING

ROTATION

ROTATION

RUN WINDING

Figure 30-12 Rotating magnetic field due to capacitor phase shift

30.6 SINGLE PHASE MOTORS

There are a number of different types of single phase motors. They differ from each other mainly by the amount of starting and running torque. The following types are the most commonly encountered:

- Permanent split capacitor (PSC).
- Capacitor start (CS).
- Capacitor start/capacitor run (CSR).
- Shaded pole.
- Split phase.

Permanent Split Capacitor (PSC) Motor

The permanent split capacitor (PSC) motor has a run capacitor in series with the start winding as shown in Figure 30-16. This capacitor stays connected at all times. It starts the motor and then is left in the circuit to improve the efficiency of the motor after it is running.

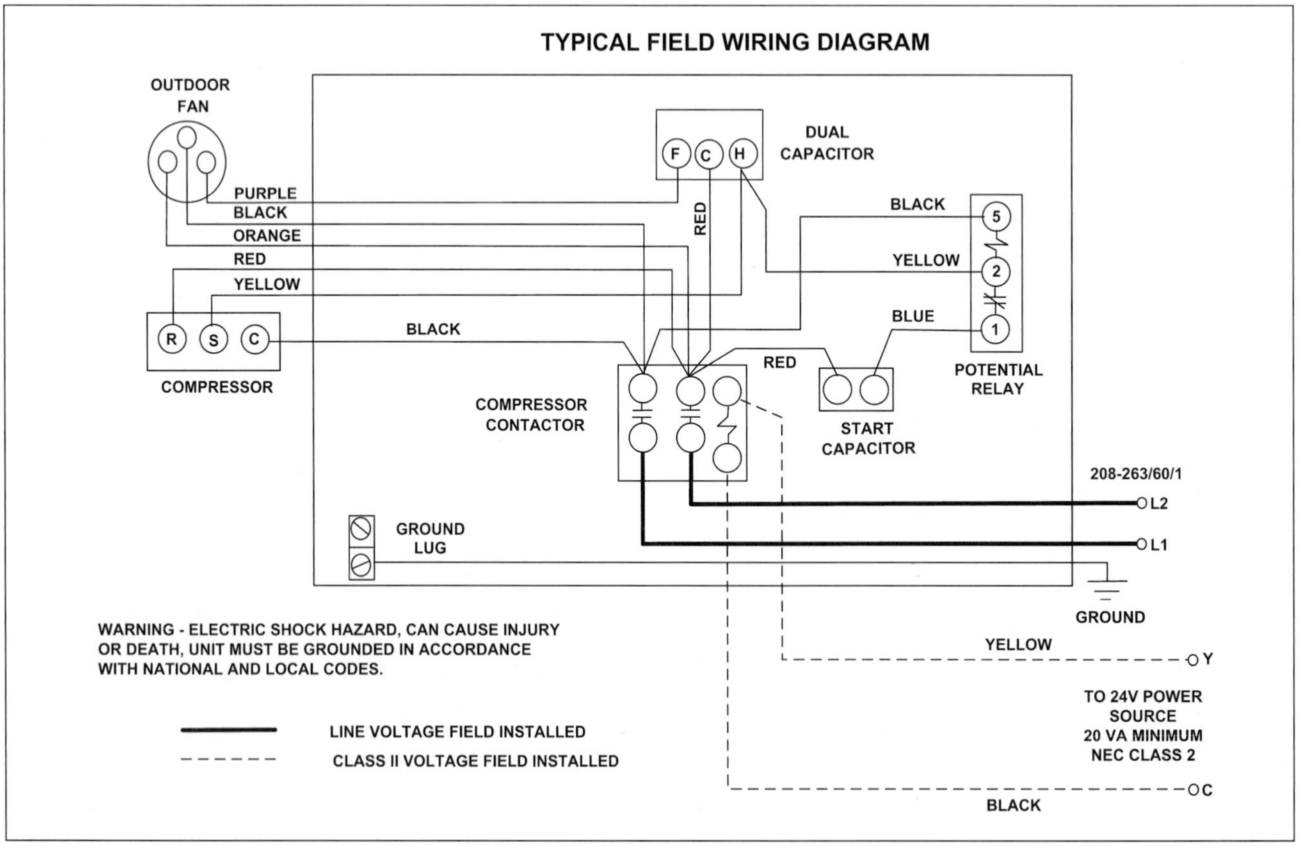

TYPICAL FIELD WIRING DIAGRAM

OUTDOOR FAN

DUAL CAPACITOR

F C H

RED

PURPLE
BLACK
ORANGE
RED
YELLOW

BLACK

BLACK

YELLOW

BLUE

5

2

1

R S C

RED

POTENTIAL RELAY

COMPRESSOR

COMPRESSOR CONTACTOR

START CAPACITOR

208-263/60/1

L2

GROUND LUG

L1

GROUND

WARNING - ELECTRIC SHOCK HAZARD, CAN CAUSE INJURY OR DEATH, UNIT MUST BE GROUNDED IN ACCORDANCE WITH NATIONAL AND LOCAL CODES.

YELLOW

Y

TO 24V POWER SOURCE 20 VA MINIMUM NEC CLASS 2

LINE VOLTAGE FIELD INSTALLED

- - - - - CLASS II VOLTAGE FIELD INSTALLED

BLACK

C

Figure 30-13 Start relay and start capacitor

(Courtesy of Lennox Industries, Inc.)

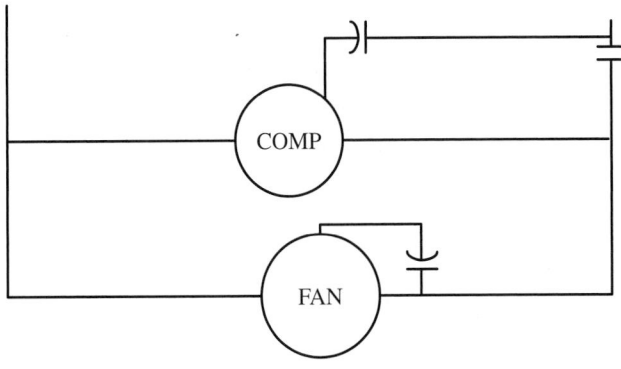

Figure 30-14 Run capacitor connected to the power and start terminals of the fan motor

The run winding has the number of turns of wire required to give the best motor performance at a given line voltage. The start winding has more turns of smaller wire, which gives it a higher resistance and lower current carrying capacity than the run winding.

The PSC motor will always have the common connection for the two windings attached to power. The run capacitor will be connected between the start winding and the run winding. The run capacitor therefore improves the performance of the motor both in starting and running.

> ### SERVICE TIP
>
> It is important that the proper size run capacitor be used with a PSC motor. If the capacitance changes more than 10% from the design capacitance, the motor windings will build up greater heat as they operate. If enough heat builds up, the motor can become damaged. It is therefore very important that the exact capacitor as specified by the manufacturer be installed on any PSC motor.

The PSC motor has moderate starting torque and good running efficiency. It is used to power fans and small compressors. The low mfd rating of the run capacitor results in a small phase angle shift, creating only a moderate starting torque.

Capacitor Start Induction Run (CSIR) Motor

A diagram of the capacitor start induction run (CSIR) motor is shown in Figure 30-17. This motor has a high starting torque, but is not as efficient as the PSC motor. The reason for its lower efficiency is that the capacitor is switched out of the circuit immediately after starting. This motor has a high mfd start capacitor.

There are two ways that the start capacitor can be removed from the circuit:

(a)

(b)

Figure 30-15 A comparison of the physical shape of start and run capacitors: (a) Run capacitor; (b) Start capacitor

- **Mechanical Switch**   This is a centrifugal switch attached to the motor shaft. When the motor reaches $\frac{2}{3}$ or $\frac{3}{4}$ of its rated speed, centrifugal force opens the switch, shown in Figure 30-17.

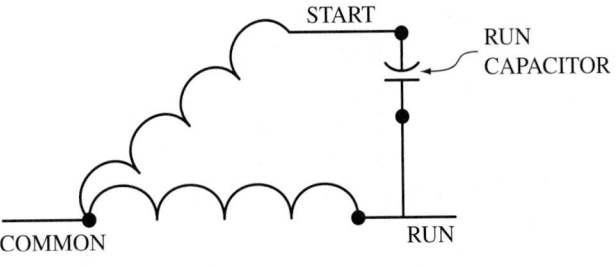

Figure 30-16 Permanent split capacitor (PSC) power

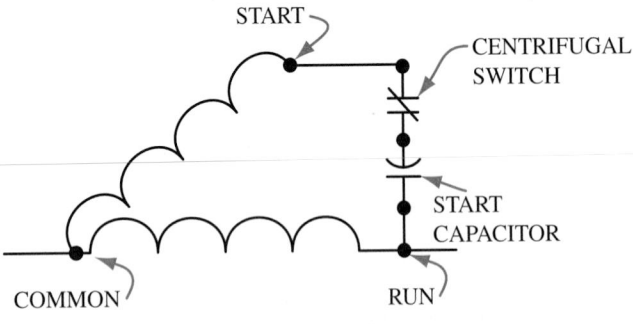

Figure 30-17 Capacitor start induction run (CSIR) motor

- **Electromagnetic Method** A potential relay is placed across the start winding. Its contacts are placed in series with the high mfd capacitor. When the motor is started, the capacitor produces a high starting torque. As the motor speed increases, the induced voltage across the start relay coil increases until it reaches a preset value higher than the line voltage. The relay coil is energized and the NC switch is opened, removing the start capacitor from the circuit.

Capacitor Start Capacitor Run (CSCR) Motor

The capacitor start capacitor run (CSCR) motor has both a start capacitor and a run capacitor, as shown in Figures 30-18 and 30-19. It has excellent starting and running torque, but is not as efficient as the PSC motor. It is used to drive most compressors.

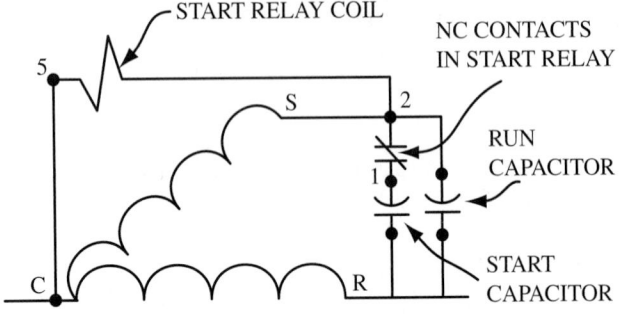

Figure 30-18 Capacitor start capacitor run (CSCR) motor

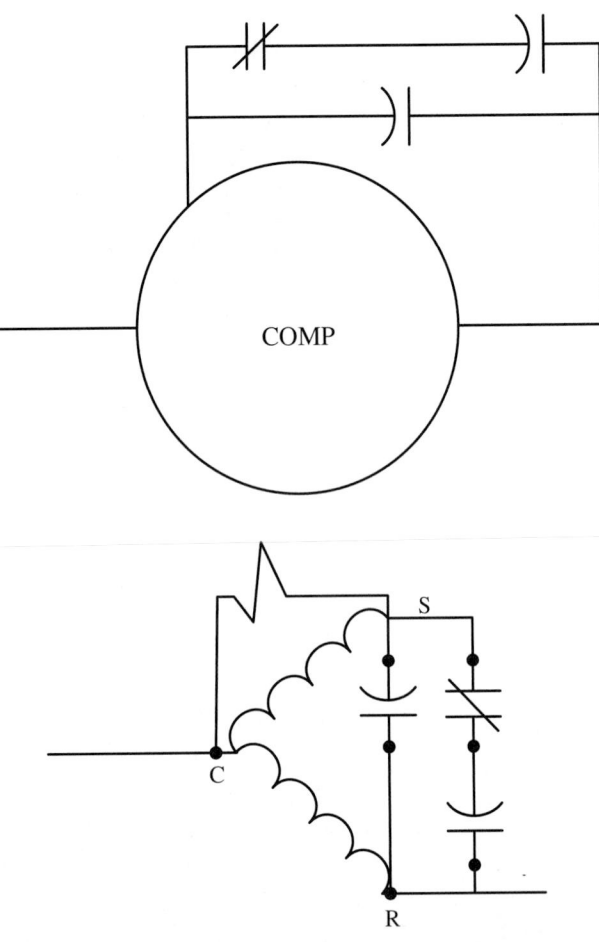

Figure 30-19 Capacitor start capacitor run motor diagrams

Start Kits

Start kits are available for the technician's use whenever it is necessary to improve the starting torque of a motor. When a motor keeps tripping out on overload, the addition of a start kit may solve the problem.

Where a high starting torque is required, a hard-start kit can be installed. Where low voltage or a voltage lag is experienced, a soft-starting kit can be used. A hard start kit contains a start capacitor and a start relay; a soft start assist uses a PTC device.

SERVICE TIP

Often start capacitors have bleed resistors connected between the two capacitor terminals. The purpose of this bleed resistor is to drain the capacitor's current during the motor's off cycle. This is done so that when the motor contactor starts the motor, there is not a capacitor discharge across the contactor's points. Such a discharge causes pitting of the contactor. Over a period of time this pitting will destroy the contacts. Bleed resistors are available from the supply house to be installed on start capacitors. If one is not installed, the contactor in the unit will become pitted and in some instances weld or stick together.

Positive Temperature Coefficient (PTC) Thermistor

A different soft-starting kit is available to be applied to PSC motors. This kit includes a positive temperature coefficient (PTC) thermistor. The PTC is a temperature sensitive device whose electrical resistance will increase as its temperature increases. This PTC is placed across the run and start terminals, parallel to the run capacitor of a PSC motor, as shown in Figure 30-20.

At room temperature, the PTC thermistor has a low resistance, about 25 or 50 Ω. When voltage is supplied, an initial surge of high current passes through the start winding. This is because the thermistor is effectively shorting out the capacitor. The surge causes an increased starting torque to start the motor. The temperature increase that results causes the PTC thermistor resistance to rise, removing the short from across the run capacitor. The motor then runs as a normal PSC motor.

Shaded Pole Motor

The shaded pole motor, as shown in the diagram in Figure 30-21, has a modified stator pole. A groove separates a small portion of the stator pole from the rest of the pole. A bank of metal is placed around the smaller section of the pole, which provides a phase shift needed to start the motor. Shaded pole motors have a low starting torque and their speed control under varying load conditions is poor. They offer a low cost motor for light duty applications such as running blowers on small air handling and heating units.

Split Phase

A split phase motor has very low starting torque and is used for applications that have easily started loads. This motor is seldom used in sizes larger than $\frac{1}{3}$ hp. The principle for operation is that two parallel connected motor windings are placed 90° apart. If the windings are identical, then the current through both will lag the voltage by the same phase angle. To generate a revolving magnetic field, one winding has a greater resistance and a lower reactance, so that the currents

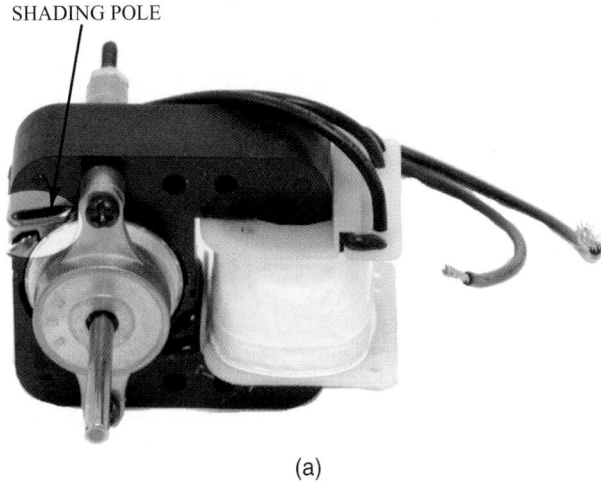

(a)

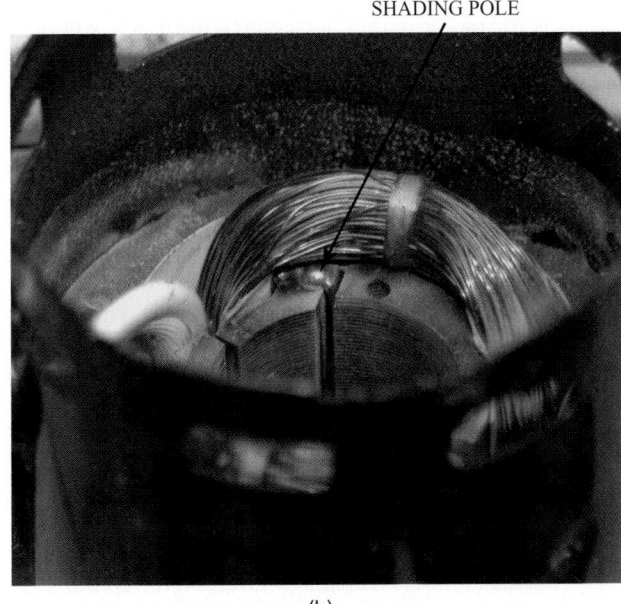

(b)

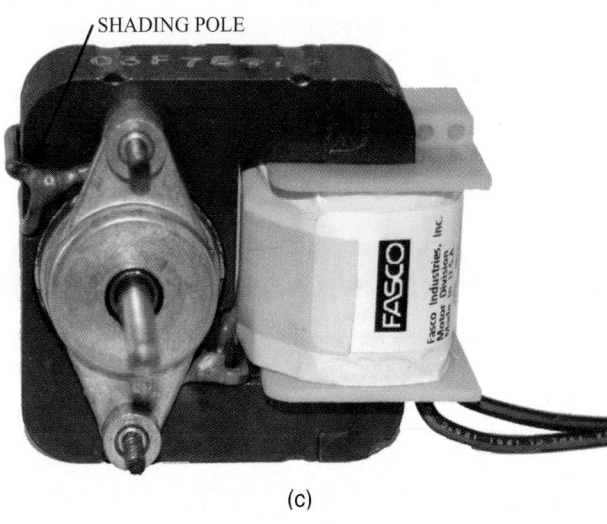

(c)

Figure 30-21 Shading pole on shaded pole motors

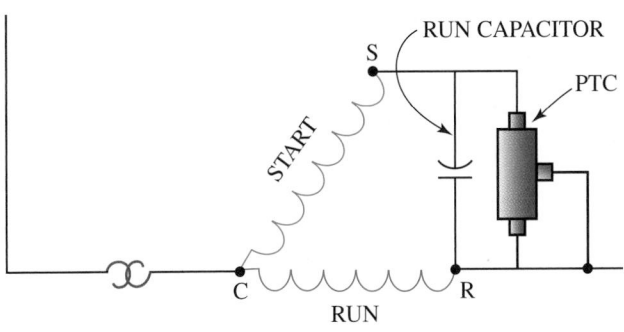

Figure 30-20 PTC start systems are sometimes referred to as soft start because they do not provide as much initial torque as a start capacitor and potential relay

through the two windings are shifted in time phase. The high resistance winding is called the starting or auxiliary winding and the low resistance winding is called the main winding. The starting winding is usually disconnected by a centrifugally operated switch when the motor reaches 70–80% of synchronous speed.

30.7 MULTIPLE SPEED BLOWER MOTORS

Blower motors have multiple speed settings often referred to as low, medium, and high; or low, medium-low, medium, medium-high, and high depending on the number of speed taps that the motor has. These speed taps do not actually change the motor's rpm. A motor's rpm is based on the number of poles and frequency. By changing the speed taps on a motor, the motor's effective horsepower is changed. By changing the motor output horsepower, the motor will turn at a different rate under different load conditions. For example, a $\frac{1}{3}$ hp motor rated at 1,750 rpm will turn at approximately 1,750 rpm when the motor is on the high setting. However, when the motor is on the medium setting, it may produce only $\frac{1}{4}$ hp. Although it is attempting to turn at the same speed of 1,750 rpm, it cannot because the load causes the motor to slow down, effectively reducing the rpm and CFM output of the blower. When the blower motor is on the low speed setting, it may produce only $\frac{1}{8}$ hp. This would result in an even lower rpm and blower CFM output.

30.8 THREE PHASE MOTORS

Three phase motors have the following advantages over single phase motors:

- They are easily reversible. The direction of rotation can be changed by interchanging any two supply voltage lines.
- There is less running torque pulsation because at least one phase is always producing an induced rotational effect on the rotor.
- They have higher starting torque because each winding is out of phase with the other windings and produces rotational torque.
- They have higher efficiency.

CAUTION

Do not attempt to run a three phase motor on single phase power. Although the motor may start, it will quickly overheat and damage the windings. The same thing will happen to a three phase motor if one of its legs of power is lost as the motor is being operated. For that reason, some large motors have single phase or lost leg motor protection systems, which will shut the motor down any time a single leg of power is lost to the motor.

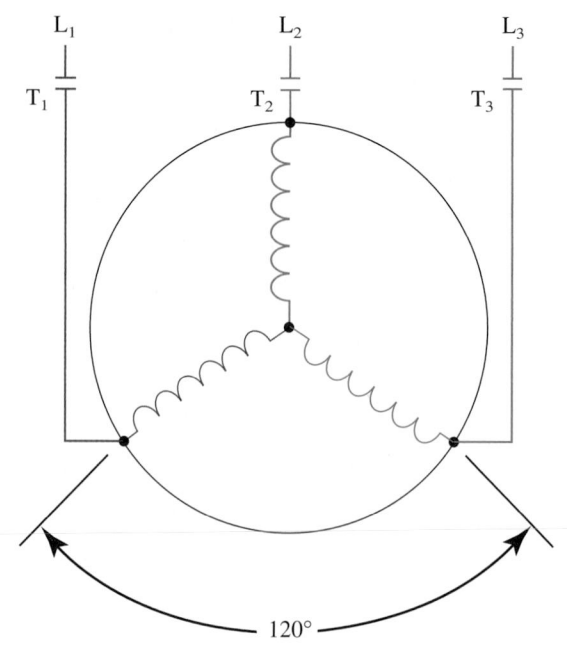

Figure 30-22 The three phase motor

The windings of a three phase motor are 120° apart, which facilitates starting. Figure 30-22 shows a schematic drawing of a three phase motor. No capacitors, no auxiliary windings, and no switching circuits are required. Three phase motors create their own starting torque.

Three phase motors are wired in either a delta configuration as shown in Figure 30-23 or a wye configuration as shown in Figure 30-24. The delta configuration is named because the circuit resembles the triangle shape of the Greek letter delta (Δ). The wye configuration resembles a capital letter Y. In the delta configuration, the line voltages equal the phase voltages, and the line currents are 1.732 times the phase currents. In the wye configuration, the line voltages equal 1.732 times the phase voltages, and the line currents equal the phase currents.

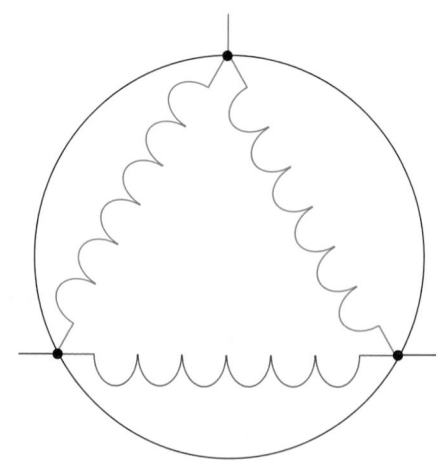

Figure 30-23 Delta three phase motor windings

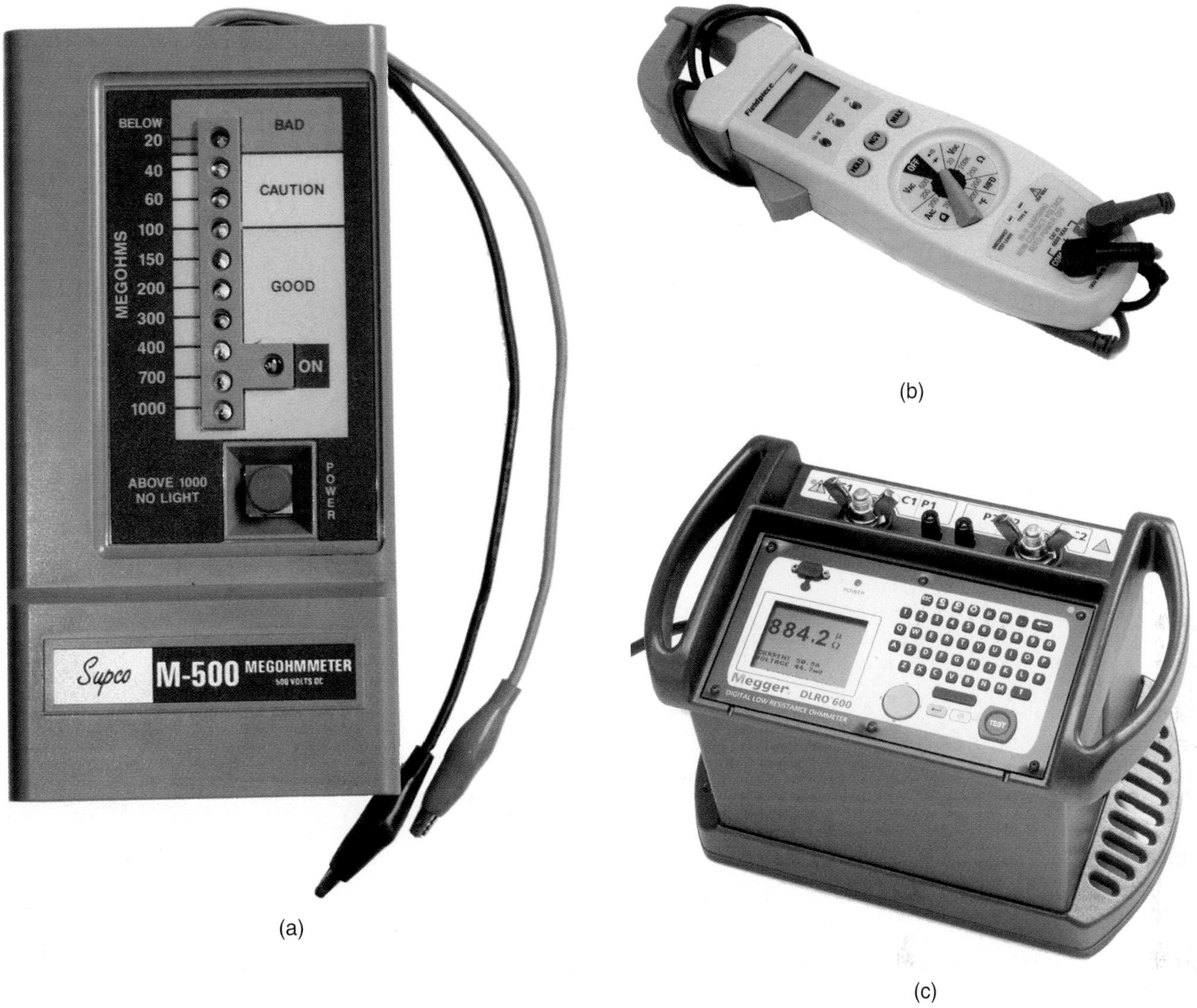

Figure 30-31 (a) Megohmmeter; (b) Clamp-on ammeter; (c) Digital megohmmeter
(Courtesy Megger®)

The first thing to do whenever testing any motor is to make sure that the power supply to the motor has been secured. The motor windings can be checked with a multimeter as shown in Figure 30-32. It may be necessary to remove a guard that encloses the terminals on a hermetic unit. The terminals should be marked C, S, and R.

CAUTION

Occasionally the terminal has been damaged and on a pressurized system the terminal can blow out. To avoid possible injury, unless the charge has been removed, use terminal points some distance away from the compressor when checking compressor motor resistance. Be sure that all accessories such as capacitors and relays are disconnected.

LEAD REMOVED

Figure 30-32 To test motor windings, first remove the leads

Figure 30-33 Method of determining run, start, and common motor terminals

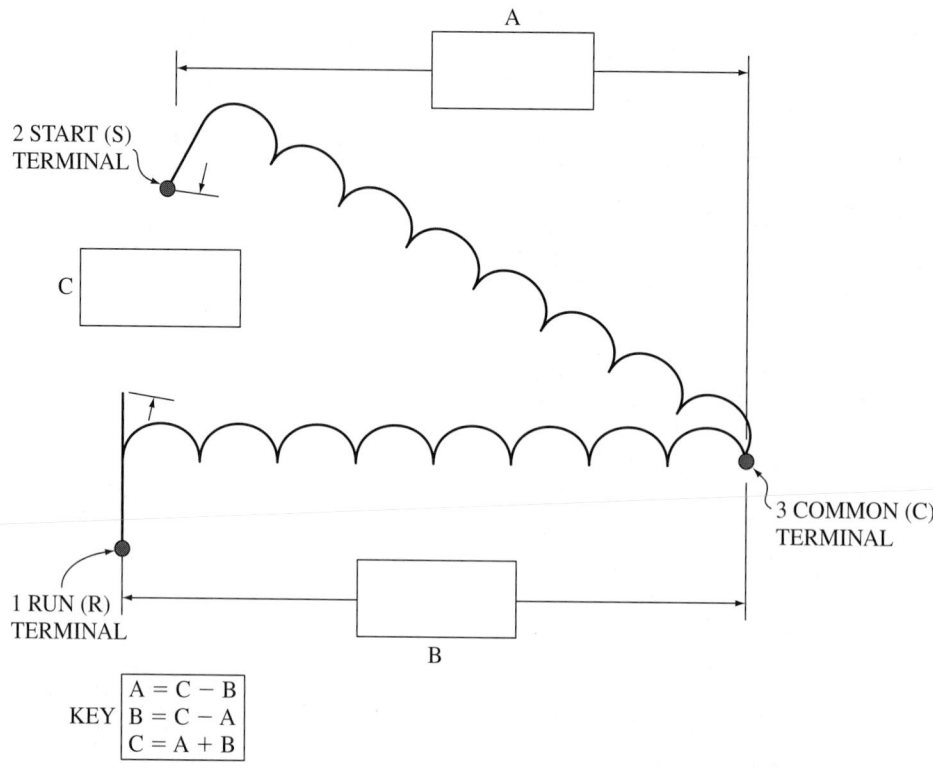

$$\text{KEY} \begin{array}{|l|} \hline A = C - B \\ B = C - A \\ C = A + B \\ \hline \end{array}$$

Use an ohmmeter to read the resistance in both the run and start winding. Be sure good contact is made with the proper terminals.

If the terminals are not marked, they can be identified by a simple test. First, measure the resistance between each pair of terminals. For example, assume that these readings are $5\frac{1}{2}$, 4, and $1\frac{1}{2}$ Ω. By diagramming them as shown in Figure 30-33, the terminals can be identified. In the example, the greatest reading is between 1 and 2. The common terminal is therefore 3, the one not being touched. So terminal 3 is C. Then, reading from C, the greatest resistance is to 2. Therefore, 2 is S. And, finally, since 2 is S and 3 is C, 1 must be R.

The motor is then tested for an open winding, a broken wire, or a shorted winding, as shown in Figure 30-34. To do this, a good low range ohmmeter (R × 1) is required. A zero resistance means a shorted winding. Low resistance means the winding is good. An infinity reading means it is an open winding. As a rule the start winding has a resistance three to five times the resistance of the run winding.

Large motors (5–10 hp and higher) have heavy copper windings to carry the motor current. They may therefore indicate a reading very close to a short when winding resistance is read, depending on the ohmmeter.

Figure 30-35a,b shows the motor being tested for a grounded winding. One lead is placed in contact with bare metal on the compressor casing. For this application the ohmmeter needs to be capable of measuring very high resistance (R × 100,000). For an ungrounded winding the resistance is generally 1–3 MΩ (megaohms). This applies to both single phase motors and three phase motors.

Figure 30-34 Method of testing open, shorted windings and broken wires

SERVICE TIP

The temperature of the compressor is important in testing for a partially grounded winding. If the compressor will run, it should be run for about 5 min before testing.

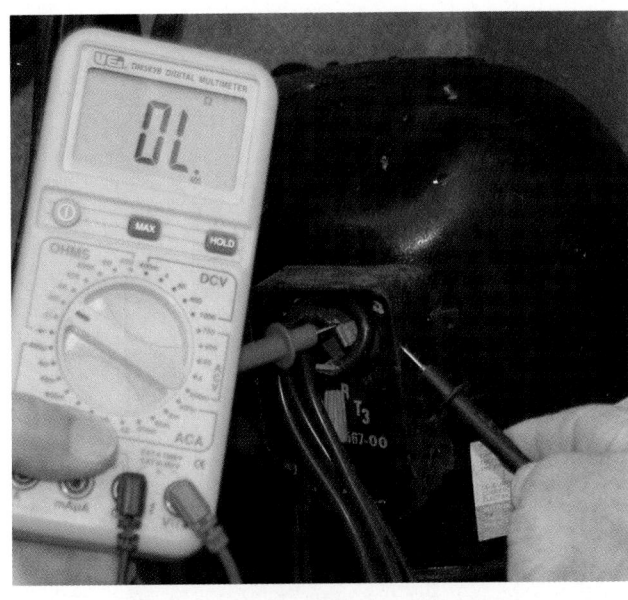

(a)

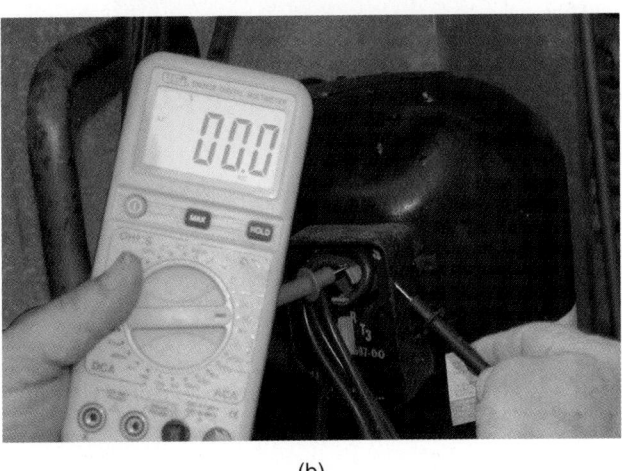

(b)

Figure 30-35 Testing for a grounded wiring: (a) Not grounded; (b) Grounded

30.15 INSULATION RESISTANCE TESTERS

Electrical insulation is classified by the temperature stability of the materials that are used for the winding. As an example, hermetic compressor windings generally are generally rated for class H (180°C or 356°F), Table 30-2. Windings of this type are composed of materials that have an acceptable thermal life expectancy at this temperature. Examples of insulating materials for his temperature range are silicone elastomers, mica, glass fibers, and polymers. The insulated windings will often have a varnish or polyester base top coat. When exposed to high temperatures over time, the insulation begins to break down. Hairline cracks can form in the top coat which can absorb dirt and moisture. Insulation testing helps to determine the level of insulation breakdown for motor windings over time. The motor is first tested when it is new and then at regular intervals during its useful life of operation.

Table 30-2 Motor Insulation Temperature Classification

Class	°C	°F
Class 90 (O)	90	194
Class 105 (A)	105	221
Class 130 (B)	130	266
Class 155 (F)	155	311
Class 180 (H)	180	356
Class 220	220	428
Over Class 220 (C)	> 220	> 428

These are special testers that are invaluable for testing leakage resistance from motor windings to ground. They are often used to periodically test semi-hermetic motor insulation. The meters can test leakage at high voltage (500 V for 208–240 V motors and 1,000 V for 480 V motors). They may be battery operated or use a hand cranked generator. They are often referred to as meggers. They may detect insulation faults, where an ordinary multimeter using a few volts DC would show a satisfactory reading.

SERVICE TIP

The wiring that is used for motor windings is insulated with a thin coat of varnish. As the motor is used and the windings are heated, this material will slowly carbonize. As it carbonizes, it will slightly change to a darker tan and eventually on to black. When it is completely carbonized, it does not provide any insulating capacity. As a motor heats up, this breakdown process can be accelerated to the extent that in extreme conditions it can carbonize almost immediately when overheated. A megger tests for the degree of breakdown in the insulation. This also provides an indication of the useful life that may remain with a motor or compressor.

SAFETY TIP

When testing for a grounded winding, one test lead is placed on the terminal and the other on the outer shell of the compressor. Be careful to make good contact with the motor shell. A coat of paint or a layer of dirt can hide a grounded winding. The copper refrigerant lines may also be used to check for grounds.

Figure 30-36 shows the terminals of the two types of three phase motors. The windings of a three phase motor all should have the same resistance. Remember when checking a three phase motor to be sure to reconnect it in the same manner as originally connected. Interchanging any two connections can reverse the rotation of the motor.

Figure 30-36 Two types of three phase motors wye and delta

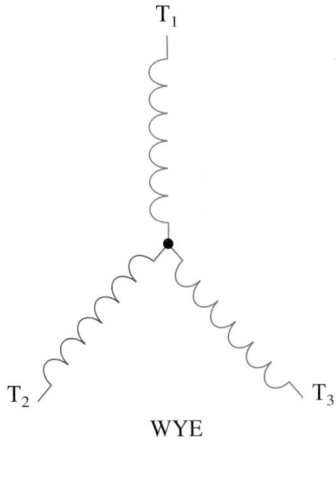

WYE

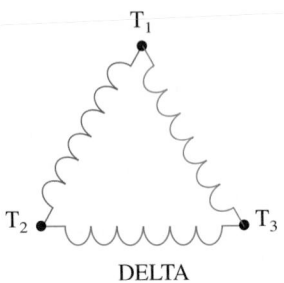

DELTA

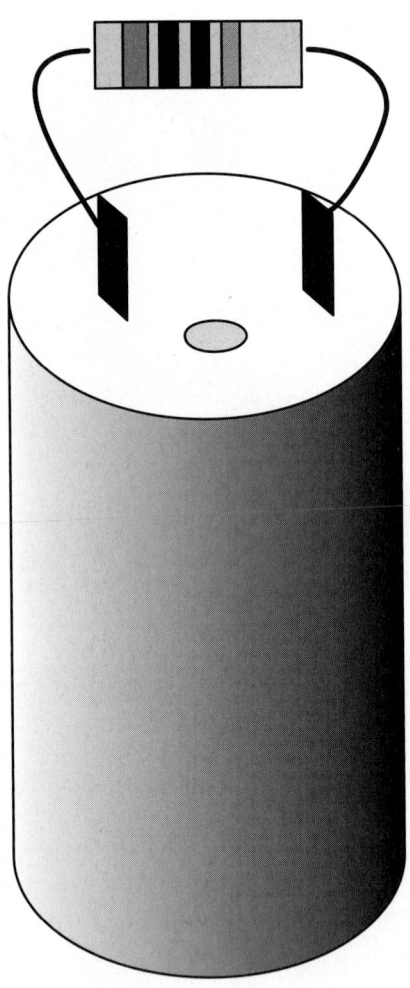

Figure 30-37 Using a bleed resistor on start capacitor

30.16 TESTING CAPACITORS

The first operation in testing a capacitor is to discharge it. Do not discharge it by shorting out the terminals. This can damage the capacitor. To avoid electrical shock, the technician should never place fingers across the terminals before properly discharging the capacitor.

The proper way to discharge a capacitor is to put it in a protective case and connect a 20,000 Ω, 2 W resistor across the terminals, as shown in Figure 30-37. Most start capacitors have a bleed resistor; however, it is good practice to make sure the charge has been bled off.

Capacitors can be roughly checked by using an ohmmeter. The ohmmeter used in testing capacitors should have at least an R × 100 scale. To test the capacitor, disconnect it from the wiring and place the ohmmeter leads on the terminals, as shown in Figure 30-38.

If the capacitor is not shorted, the needle will make a rapid swing toward zero and slowly return to infinity. If the capacitor has an internal short, the needle will stay at zero, indicating that the instrument will not take the charge. What you are actually doing is attempting to charge the capacitor using the battery in the ohmmeter (be sure the battery in the ohmmeter is good). An open capacitor will read high with no dip and no recovery.

The use of a capacitor analyzer is highly recommended. This instrument will read the mfd rating and detect any breakdown in the dielectric under load conditions. It will detect any capacitors that have failed to hold their ratings. It also is useful in measuring the rating of a capacitor that has an unreadable marking.

Some run capacitors have some sort of a mark, usually a red dot as shown in Figure 30-39, to indicate the terminal that should be connected to the run terminal. With this arrangement, an internal short circuit to the capacitor case will blow the system fuses without passing the current through the motor start winding.

Where two run capacitors are used on the same equipment, multiple run capacitors with a common terminal are used. One of these is illustrated on the left side of Figure 30-40. These two capacitors have different ratings as required by the equipment they serve. Testing is similar to the testing procedure for single run capacitors.

In Figure 30-40, the capacitor on the far right is a start capacitor with a bleed resistor across the terminals. The capacitor can be tested with this bleed resistor in place. The pop-out hole on the start capacitor allows insulation expansion if the capacitor is overheated. If the hole is ruptured, the capacitor must be replaced.

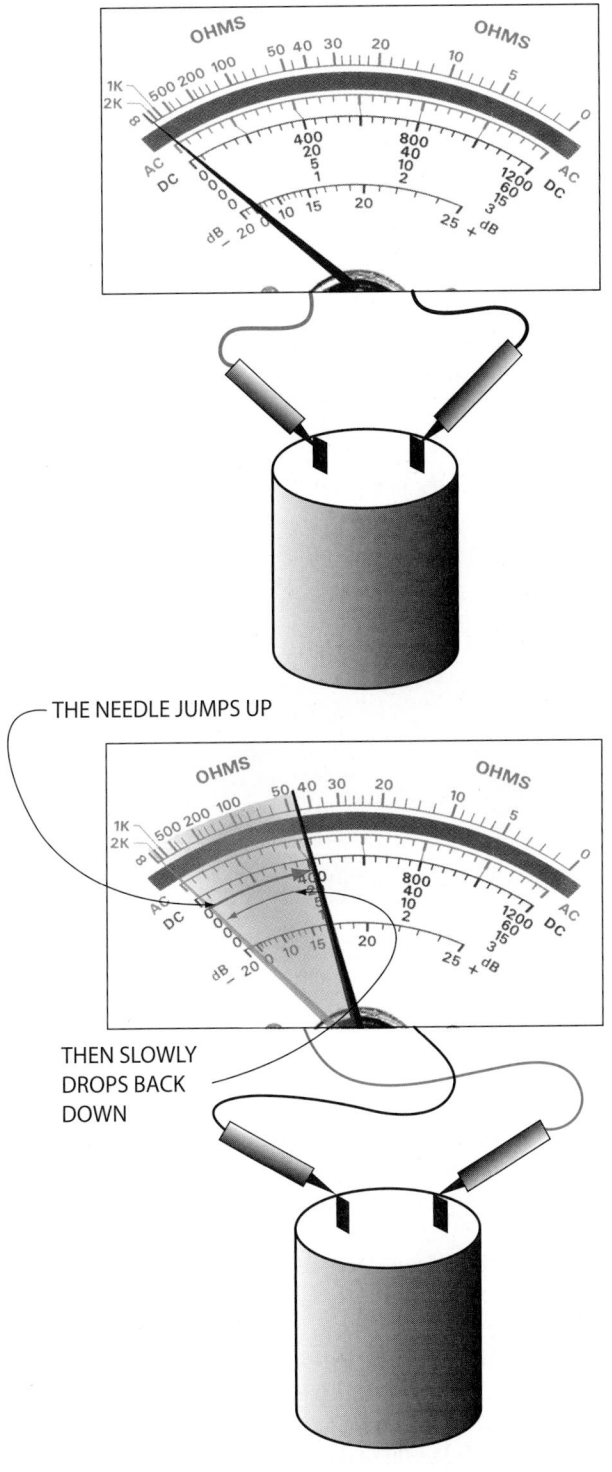

THE NEEDLE JUMPS UP

THEN SLOWLY
DROPS BACK
DOWN

Figure 30-38 Using an ohmmeter to test capacitors

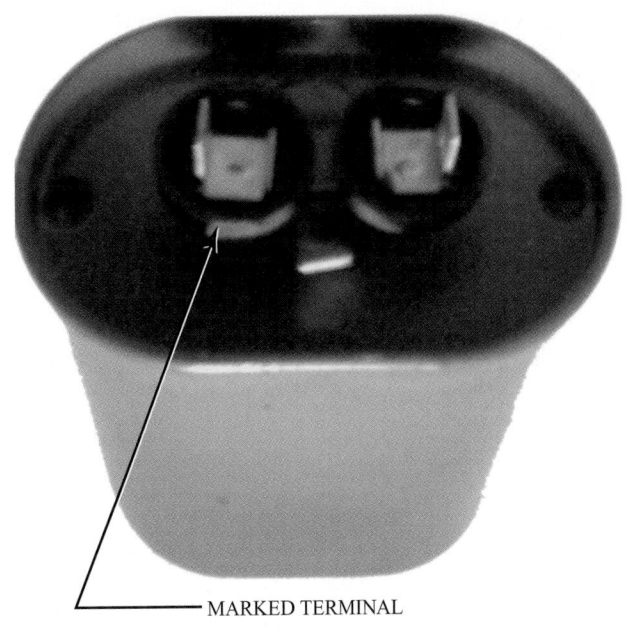

MARKED TERMINAL

Figure 30-39 The marked terminal on the run capacitor should be connected to the run terminal of the compressor

Figure 30-40 Multiple section or dual run capacitor and start capacitor

In replacing a capacitor, it is desirable to use an exact replacement. This means a capacitor with the same mfd rating and voltage limit rating. When this is not possible, substitutions can be made as long as the rules for substitutions are carefully followed.

Do not interchange start and run capacitors. Start capacitors are high capacity (100–800 mfd) electrolytic units that are intended for momentary use in starting motors. They are normally encased in plastic. Run capacitors have much lower capacitance ratings (2–40 mfd) but are made for continuous duty use. They are normally sealed in a metal can.

RELAY COIL TEST   RELAY CONTACT TEST

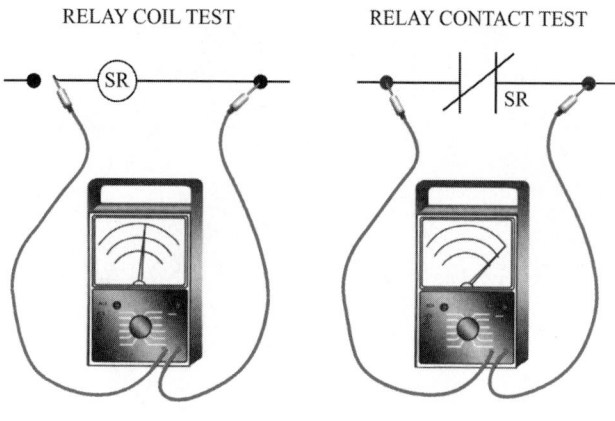

Figure 30-41 Using an ohmmeter to test a relay coil and its switch

30.17 TESTING START RELAYS

In replacing start relays, it is important to do the following:

- Always use the identical replacement. An improper substitution can damage the motor.
- The replacement must be mounted in the same position as the original and connected the same way. The method of testing the relay coil and contacts is shown in Figure 30-41.

CAUTION

Many start relay coils have higher resistance than average control circuit relays. Be sure to test the coil on the R × 100 scale before deciding that the relay is defective. Note that the pull-in/drop-out voltage of the relay is unique. Do not attempt to replace it with an ordinary, similar voltage relay.

When testing start relay contacts, the contacts should be closed and the ohmmeter will read zero resistance. Sometimes the contact sticks closed and under these conditions the start winding of the motor is often damaged. Sometimes the normally closed contacts will be badly burned and make a poor connection. If such is the case, replace the relay. Do not attempt to clean the contacts.

30.18 GE ECM™ MOTORS

ECM™ motors were developed by the General Electric Corporation (GE) in the mid-1980s, Figure 30-42. ECM™ stands for electronically commutated motor. They were originally used as blower motors, but today they are used for every motor need including combustion air blower motors, condenser fan motors, and compressor motors. These motors

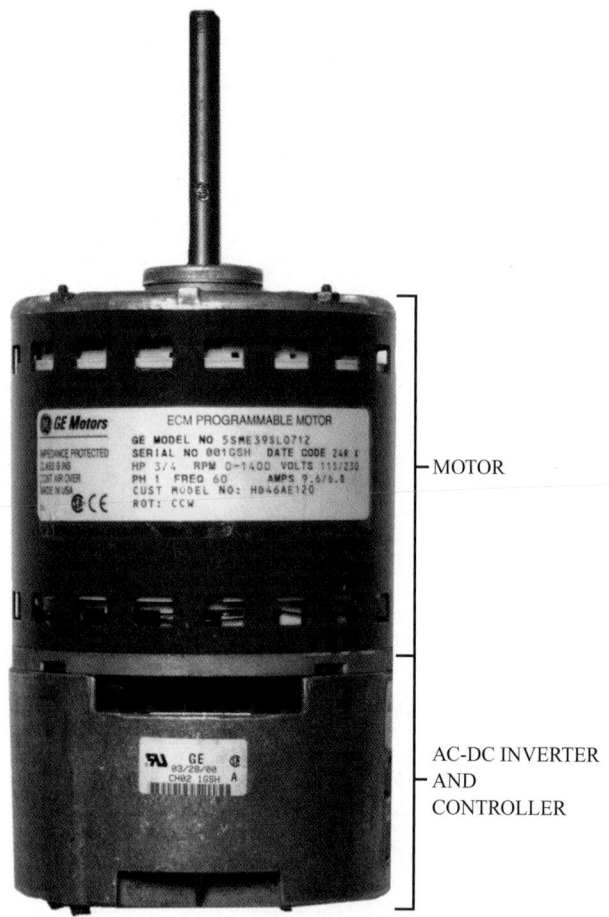

Figure 30-42 GE ECM™ motor

are ultrahigh efficiency, programmable, brushless DC motors, 120 V or 240 V AC input. They utilize a permanent magnet rotor and a built-in AC to DC inverter to produce the direct current that operates the motor, Figure 30-43.

ECM™ motors have a number of advantages including:

- **High Efficiency** ECM™ motors are approximately 70% efficient as compared to 45% or less efficiency for PSC motors.
- **Low Maintenance** ECM™ motors use ball bearings as opposed to sleeves, which are used on PSC motors, Figure 30-44. Ball bearings are permanently lubricated as compared to sleeved motors, which must be routinely lubricated.
- **Speed Control** ECM™ motors come preset for a specific cfm requirement. Because the rpm of DC motors is more easily adjusted, ECM™ motors can be field adjusted to a specific cfm and with the addition of a controller can be remotely controlled using a central energy management program, Figure 30-45.
- **Constant CFM** ECM™ motors are designed to provide a constant CFM over a wide range of static pressures. The ECM™ motor rpm will increase automatically to provide the designed airflow.

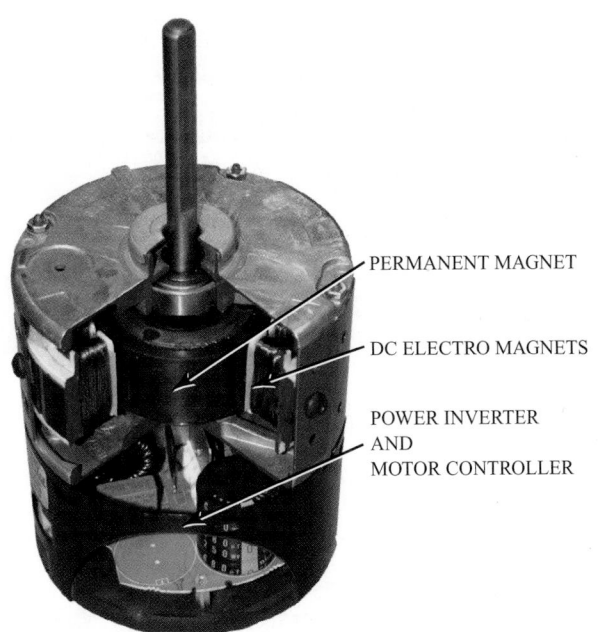

Figure 30-43 Cutaway of GE ECM™ motor

Figure 30-44 Cutaway of GE ECM™ motor showing ball bearings

- **Heat Load** ECM™ motors operate at almost ambient temperatures, as compared to PSC motors, which typically operate from 90° to 150° above ambient.
- **Soft Start** ECM™ motors are designed to start at a low rpm and gradually ramp up to the designed speed. This places less stress on the motor fan and other mechanical parts as compared to the almost instant starting of a PSC motor. Soft starting also decreases the sometimes-

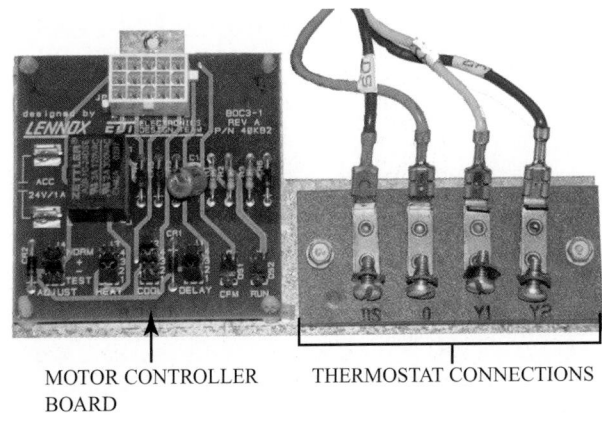

Figure 30-45 ECM™ motor controller PC board

noticeable blast of air from conventional blowers associated with PSC motor starting.

- **Flexibility in Size** Because the ECM™ motor's rpm can so easily be controlled without the loss of efficiency, it is possible for manufacturers to use a limited number of various horsepower rated ECM™ motors throughout their entire production line. This reduces inventory costs for the manufacturer and for the service company by reducing the number of replacement motors that they must carry on their service vehicles.

30.19 ECM MOTOR OPERATION

ECM motors consist of a motor and a control module, Figure 30-42. The rotor of the ECM motor is a permanent magnet and the stator is wound like a three phase motor, Figure 30-43. The module controls the speed and rotation of the motor by energizing the windings in sequence, creating a rotating magnetic field. The permanent magnets in the rotor follow this rotating magnetic field. No more than two windings are energized at one time, leaving one set de-energized. The module checks the speed and rotation of the motor by reading the voltage induced in the windings that are not energized. The motor periodically checks the work load on the motor by not energizing any windings and measuring how much the motor slows down in a fixed period of time. This allows the module to calculate what speed the motor must turn to provide the amount of airflow it is programmed for. The modules are programmed for the specific blower and unit the motor is matched with. ECM blower motors do not have a pre-set RPM; their speed is variable between 200 RPM to 1050 RPM, with a safety limit of 1500 RPM. The speed that a motor operates at is determined by its programming, the control signals it receives, and the resistance across the blower.

HVAC/R equipment uses blower control boards to control ECM motor operation, Figure 30-46, ECM motors are made for three types of controls: pulse width modulation, 24 volt thermostat signals, or a digital serial interface. With pulse width modulation, the control is not looking for the presence or absence of a particular voltage, but is measuring the length, or "width" of a series of voltage pulses. Longer pulses call for increased RPM; shorter pulses call for decreased RPM.

4 HEATING SPEEDS   4 COOLING SPEEDS

Figure 30-46 ECM™ motor control board showing speed jumpers

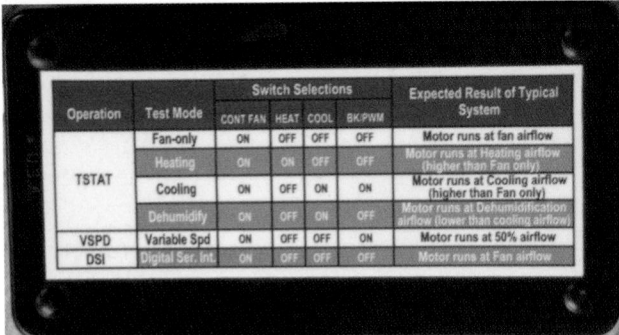

Operation	Test Mode	Switch Selections				Expected Result of Typical System
		CONT FAN	HEAT	COOL	BK-PWM	
TSTAT	Fan-only	ON	OFF	OFF	OFF	Motor runs at fan airflow
	Heating	ON	ON	OFF	OFF	Motor runs at Heating airflow (higher than Fan only)
	Cooling	ON	OFF	ON	ON	Motor runs at Cooling airflow (higher than Fan only)
	Dehumidify	ON	OFF	ON	OFF	Motor runs at Dehumidification airflow (lower than cooling airflow)
VSPD	Variable Spd	ON	OFF	OFF	ON	Motor runs at 50% airflow
DSI	Digital Ser. Int.	ON	OFF	OFF	OFF	Motor runs at Fan airflow

INSTRUCTION ON BACK OF MOTOR TESTER

MOTOR CONTROLLER PLUG   TEST SWITCHES

24 V AC POWER CLIPS

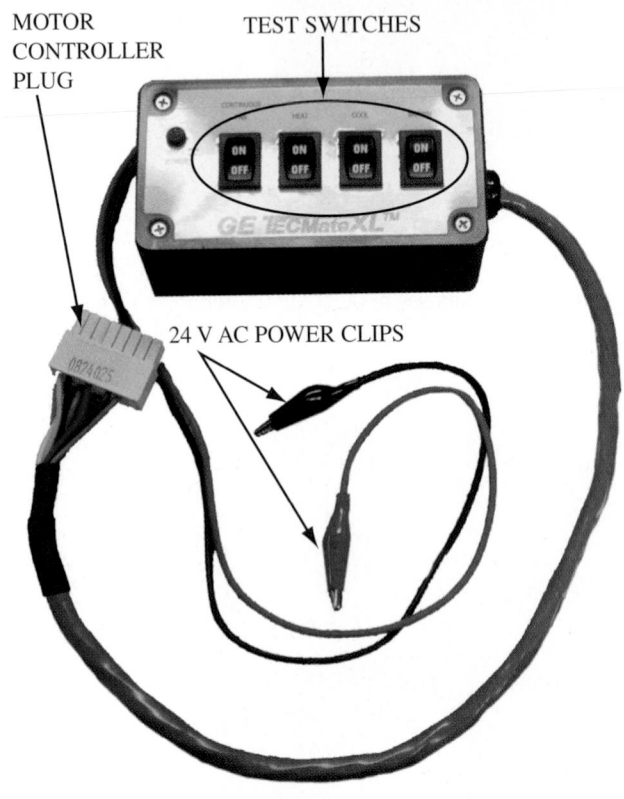

Figure 30-47 ECM™ motor tester

Thermostat control looks for 24 volts on pins that represent pre-programmed airflow requirements. Thermostat control is the most common. Digital serial controls are the newest of the three control methods. The unit communicates with the motor control using serial communication.

30.20 SERVICING ECM MOTORS

ECM motors have two electrical connections: a power connection and a control connection, Figure 30-48. Power is supplied to the power connection all the time, even when the motor is not running. Power to the unit should always be turned off when disconnecting or connecting the power plug. Plugging or unplugging the power plug with power on will cause a high current arc that can damage the motor module. The easiest way to check an ECM motor is to use a service tool that plugs into the control port to control the motor. Figure 30-47 shows a simple device that can be used to check the operation of an ECM motor. If the motor will operate using the tester, the problem is in the wiring harness or blower control board. If power is available at the power connector and the motor will not operate using the tester, the problem is most likely the motor control module. Control modules are replaceable without replacing the entire motor, Figure 30-49. The motor windings can be checked by removing the module from the motor and checking their resistance. They should ohm out like a three phase motor, with all the windings having the same resistance which should be less than 20 ohms. If the windings are good, the module is bad. Be certain to get the correct module because the modules are specific for the unit the blower is on.

30.21 SOLID STATE MOTOR CONTROLS

Motor control functions are typically operated through a combination of switches. As an example, if a thermostat calls for heat, a mercury switch can be used to close a set of contacts to energize the motor control relay which closes the motor starting contacts. Every time there is a switch (on/off), there is usually a set of contacts. These contacts can become worn and pitted over time and require maintenance. The opening and closing speed of contacts is also limited to the relay type, size, and configuration. A method of switching that does not require contacts is through the use of semiconductor materials.

Semiconductors

Some materials are good conductors of electricity while others are insulators. A semiconductor is a material that is neither a good conductor nor a good insulator. Semiconductor materials are often made from germanium and silicon. These materials due to their peculiar crystalline structure may under certain conditions act as conductors and under other conditions act as insulators. This ability to either conduct

ANODE   CATHODE

Figure 30-50 Diode showing anode and cathode

Silicon Rectifier

Using the principle of the diode, a simple full wave bridge rectifier can be configured to convert alternating current into direct current. Rectifiers are commonly used because many devices such as meters and control systems often require DC power. Power supplies for battery operated devices such as cell phones and laptop computers require AC to DC converters. Figure 30-51a shows the current flow to a direct current meter through diode rectifiers 3 and then 2. When the AC current reverses, the meter will still be operating on direct current with current flow through diode rectifiers 1 and 4, as shown in Figure 30-51b. Silicon rectifiers can be designed to operate throughout a wide range of current and voltage levels and are therefore used on many different types of applications. They are small, lightweight, and can be made shock resistant. Silicon rectifiers can have efficiencies as high as 99%.

Silicon Controlled Rectifier (SCR)

The silicon controlled rectifier (SCR) is similar to a diode in that it will block reverse current. The difference is that the SCR can also block forward current. More importantly, it can be switched electrically to allow forward current conduction by a pulse of current flowing through its gate, Figure 30-52. When the SCR is triggered by a gate pulse, conduction begins. The important application for an SCR is that it can be turned on and off like a switch without the need for electrical contacts. The speed of switching is also much faster than traditional contacts and the timing can be varied during operation. A TRIAC, shown in Figure 30-53, is a bidirectional device of two SCR's connected in parallel-opposed with a common gate. A positive voltage applied to the gate will "fire" the TRIAC in either direction.

Inverter

An inverter will change DC power into AC power. A basic SCR inverter is shown in Figure 30-54a. When the gate for SCR_1 is triggered, current I_1 will flow through the diode D_1 and through SCR_1. Current cannot flow through diode D_2 because it will block current flow in that direction. Once conduction begins it cannot be stopped by the gate. Special turn-off control circuitry must be used to stop the SCR conduction at the right time. In this case an inductor (L) and a capacitor (C) are used for this function. When conduction through SCR_1 stops, then SCR_2 is triggered and now current I_2 flows in the opposite direction to I_1 as shown in Figure 30-54b. Through the switching of SCR_1 and SCR_2, alternating current is produced. The frequency of the AC produced is controlled by the switching action of the SCR's.

AC POWER PLUG

CONTROLLER INTERFACE PORT

Figure 30-48 ECM™ motor connectors

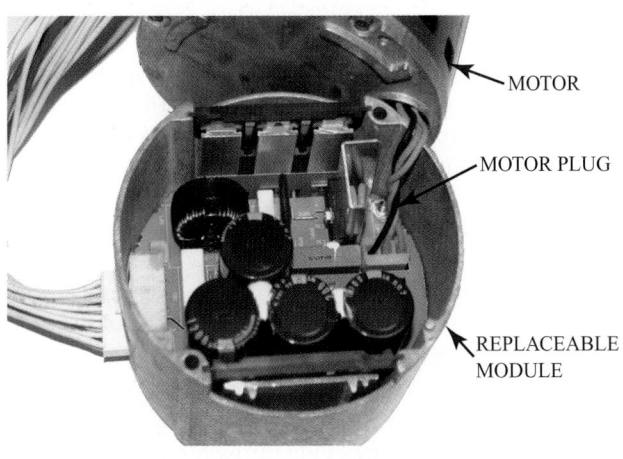

MOTOR

MOTOR PLUG

REPLACEABLE MODULE

Figure 30-49 ECM™ motor replaceable module

current or block current flow can be useful in a control circuit.

Diodes

A diode is a semiconductor that acts similar to a check valve, allowing for one way flow through an electrical circuit. A diode has an anode and a cathode, Figure 30-50. If the anode is connected to the positive terminal then the diode is forward biased and current will flow. If the anode is connected to the negative terminal then the diode is reverse biased and no current will flow. Diodes can vary from the size of a pinhead to larger sizes of 500 amperes or more.

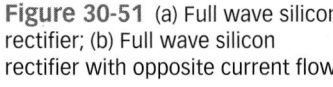

Figure 30-51 (a) Full wave silicon rectifier; (b) Full wave silicon rectifier with opposite current flow

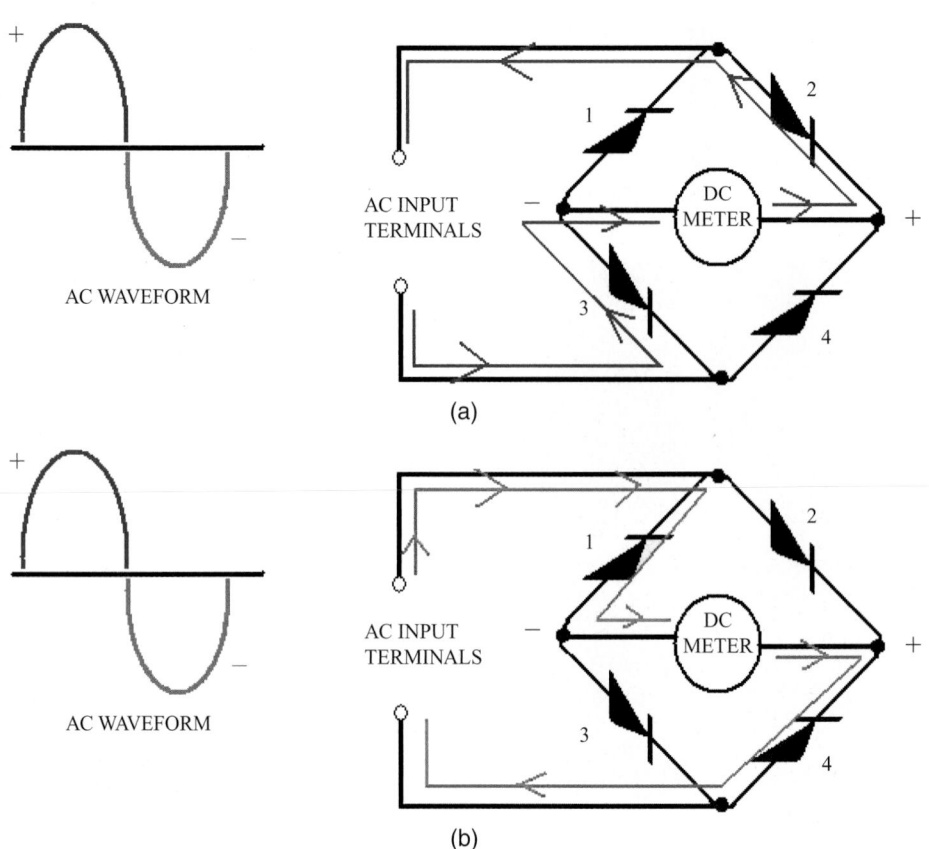

AC WAVEFORM

(a)

AC WAVEFORM

(b)

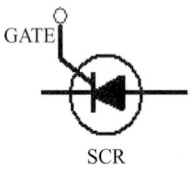

SCR

Figure 30-52 Silicon controlled rectifier with gate control

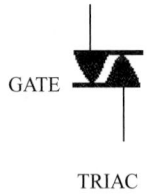

TRIAC

Figure 30-53 Triac bidirectional device

Variable Speed AC Motors

The speed of an AC motor is dependent on the number of stator poles and the frequency of the current. Multi-speed AC motors designed to operate on constant frequency (60 Hz) systems are provided with stator windings that can be reconnected to form different numbers of poles. A two-speed motor will have a winding that is switched to provide for either full speed or half speed. A four speed motor will have

two windings that each provide for two speeds when switched. This type of motor speed control is suitable for equipment that requires several definite speeds but not necessarily a continuously adjustable speed drive.

Variable Frequency Drive (VFD)

Variable frequency drives for AC motor speed control are becoming more commonplace for variable speed blower and compressor drives. In the past, solid state motor controls were not cost-effective for many applications. However with the increased focus on efficiency, variable speed drives can recover their initial cost over time through reduced electrical operating expenses.

The basic concept of a variable frequency drive is shown in Figure 30-55. A solid state rectifier is used to convert the line frequency AC into DC. The DC power is then converted back into adjustable frequency AC power through a solid state inverter. The reason for the VFD is to control the frequency of the AC power. Adjustment of the AC frequency will allow for motor speed control. This speed control is not a step type of control as delivered by changing the configuration of the stator poles. Instead, it is a fully variable speed control that may be continuously adjusted through the use of solid state devices. Typically this type of drive will generate a considerable amount of heat and some type of cooling will need to be employed during operation.

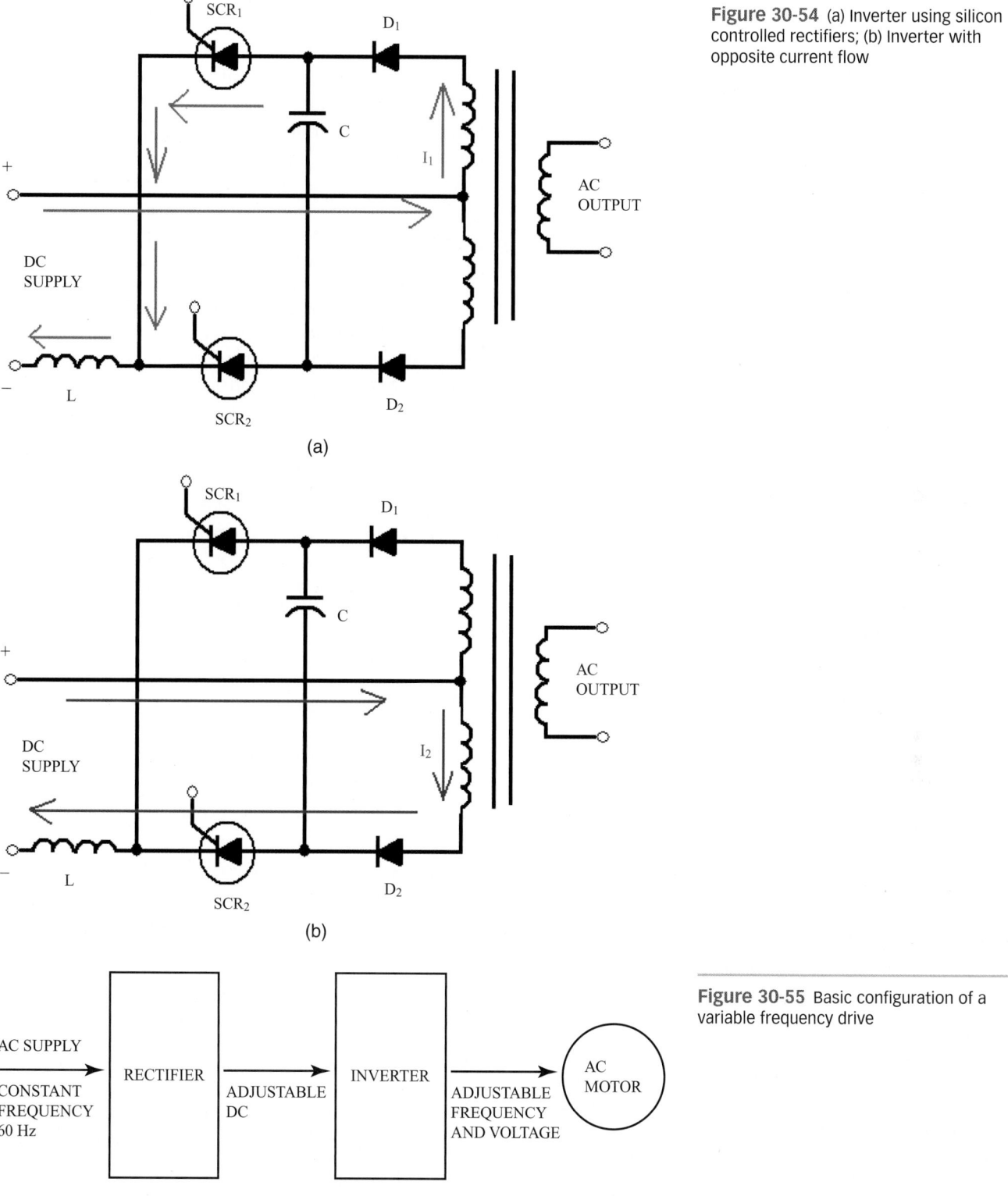

(a)

(b)

Figure 30-54 (a) Inverter using silicon controlled rectifiers; (b) Inverter with opposite current flow

Figure 30-55 Basic configuration of a variable frequency drive

UNIT 30—SUMMARY

Motors are used to power compressors and fans that are commonly found in air conditioning and refrigeration systems. Smaller residential units often use single phase motors. Many of these utilize start and run capacitors to increase starting torque and to provide better running characteristics. Larger systems often use three phase motors that do not require capacitors in their circuits. Three phase motors will draw less current for the same load range as single phase motors.

It is important to understand how to test a motor circuit. Wiring diagrams are generally supplied by the manufacturer of the unit. These are helpful when testing starting relays. Be sure to always discharge any capacitors before working on a circuit. New electronically commutated motors are growing in popularity because they offer the advantage of variable speeds with higher efficiencies as compared to conventional motors. Motor insulation should be tested on a regular basis with a megger to help determine the extent of insulation breakdown over time. The ability to properly maintain and troubleshoot electric motors is a basic requirement for HVAC/R technicians.

WORK ORDERS

Service Ticket 3201

Customer Complaint: No Air Flow

Equipment Type: Light Commercial Rooftop AC

The building contractor called the dispatcher to complain about the newly installed rooftop AC unit. The building was nearing completion and when the rooftop air conditioning unit was started, no air flowed from the supply registers. The technician arrived and found access to the roof and the unit. The technician removed the panel to access the supply fan and secured the panel so that it would not blow from the roof.

The fan was operating, however the technician immediately noticed that the fan was spinning in the wrong direction. This was a three phase motor. The technician secured the power going to the unit at the disconnect switch. The junction box for the motor leads was opened and the technician used a multimeter to check and make sure that the circuit was not energized. There was no measured power so the technician switched two of the three main power leads to the motor. After completing this, the disconnect switch was closed and the fan was now running in the proper direction and supplying air to the building.

Service Ticket 3202

Customer Complaint: Not Working

Equipment Type: Window Air Conditioning Unit

The customer brought a small window air conditioning unit into the refrigeration shop and explained that his son who was taking electrical classes had recently replaced a component and now the unit did not work at all. The technician working in the shop looked the unit over and noticed that it had a run capacitor mounted on the frame of a hermetic compressor and saw that it appeared new. Pulling a technical manual from the shelf, the technician looked up the specifications for the unit. The replaced capacitor was the wrong type. Most likely the motor became overheated and is now damaged. The technician told the customer that he would need to discharge the capacitor and then check the motor windings with an ohmmeter, however it is suspected that the unit is damaged beyond repair.

Service Ticket 3203

Routine Maintenance

Equipment Type: Light Commercial Walk-in Cooler Three Phase Motor

The technician was performing a monthly maintenance call at a small family owned grocery store. One of the items on the checklist was to test the insulation on the compressor motor. The power to the unit was shut off with the circuit breaker located in the electrical panel near to the unit. This was an older non-hermetic unit so the motor was separately coupled to the compressor. The technician used a multimeter to double-check that the circuit was deenergized at the motor controller before opening up the junction box. Satisfied the circuit was deenergized, the technician connected one end of the megger leads to bare metal on the motor frame and then the other end to one of the disconnected motor leads. The three windings were checked in this manner one at a time and the readings recorded. It was obvious in comparing the continually decreasing readings taken over time that the motor would soon need to be replaced. The technician explained to the owner that the motor would need to be replaced soon. Another option would be to consider replacing the old compressor with a newer more efficient semi-hermetic unit.

UNIT 30—REVIEW QUESTIONS

1. What is meant by motor torque?
2. What are two principal parts of a motor?
3. How is the speed of a motor determined?
4. How are capacitors rated?
5. What is a common application for capacitors in electric motors?
6. List the most common types of single phase motors.
7. What are the two ways that the start capacitor can be removed from the circuit?
8. What advantages do three phase motors have over single phase motors?
9. What is the most common cause of motor failure?
10. According to Table 30-1, what is the upper and lower limit of a motor with the voltage of 460 V?
11. What happens if there is single phasing of a three phase motor?
12. List the three types of protective devices that are used to protect the motor against excessive heat.
13. Where is the line duty device commonly located?
14. What is the advantage of manual reset?
15. What does an external supplemental overload device provide?
16. What is the first thing to do in testing any motor?
17. What are insulation resistance testers?
18. What is the proper way to discharge a capacitor?
19. Why is the use of a capacitor analyzer highly recommended?
20. In the principle of operation, what is one advantage of DC motors?

UNIT 31

Electrical Components and Wiring Diagrams

OBJECTIVES

After completing this unit you will be able to:

- interpret wiring diagrams.
- explain the benefits of the different types of electrical diagrams.
- describe how the different electrical components operate within the system.
- identify common electrical components and their symbols.
- draw a wiring schematic.
- explain load devices and the effect they have on a circuit.
- trace an electrical circuit.

31.1 INTRODUCTION

Most HVAC/R service work deals with electrical problems. These problems can be caused by component failure, improper installation, or misuse. It is, therefore, important that HVAC/R technicians have a thorough and complete understanding of electrical components and wiring diagrams so that they can properly install systems and diagnose problems. Manufacturers provide detailed wiring diagrams that guide the technician through installation and troubleshooting jobs provided that they can quickly and accurately read and interpret the diagrams. Once you have learned the basics as presented in this unit, extensive practice is required to thoroughly master electrical systems.

31.2 WIRING SYMBOLS

The wiring symbols used for HVAC/R diagrams are based on American National Standard Graphic Symbols for Electrical Wiring and Layout Diagrams, ANSI Y32.9. It is, however, important to note that some wiring diagrams may use nonstandard symbols. You must, therefore, check to see if there is a legend for the drawing showing how specific symbols are being used on this specific diagram. Never assume that the symbols are exactly as the standard shows them to be drawn.

31.3 ELECTRICAL CIRCUITS

All HVAC/R electrical systems are made up of electrical circuits. A basic electrical circuit, as shown in Figure 31-1, has three essential parts and one optional part as follows:

- A source of power.
- A load.
- A path for the current to follow.
- A control (optional).

As a result of these electrical components, electrical current is transformed into heat, light, sound, or mechanical motion. Although the control is optional, meaning that the circuit will operate without it, most systems have controls to regulate the supply of power to, or remove the power from, the load.

31.4 MAGNETISM

Since many electrical components operate using force termed magnetism, the technician should be familiar with some of its characteristics. Magnetism can be produced by electricity. Any time that current flows through a conductor it creates a magnetic field around it. To intensify the field, the conductor is coiled as shown in Figure 31-2. When this occurs, magnetic poles form at each end. The poles change polarity as the current alternates.

The magnetic force is further intensified by placing an iron rod in the center of the coil as shown in the Figure 31-2. When the current flows through the coil the rod tends to center itself in the coil. This principle can be used to operate a switch as shown in Figure 31-3. This arrangement is useful in the construction of relays, contactors, solenoid valves, and motors.

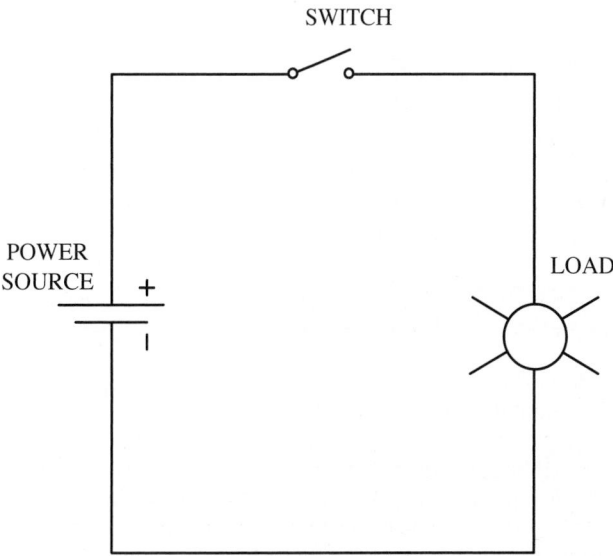

Figure 31-1 The basic components of an electric circuit

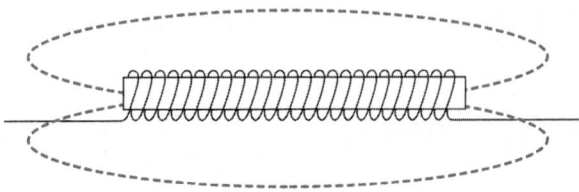

Figure 31-2 Electromagnetism produced by current flowing through a conductor

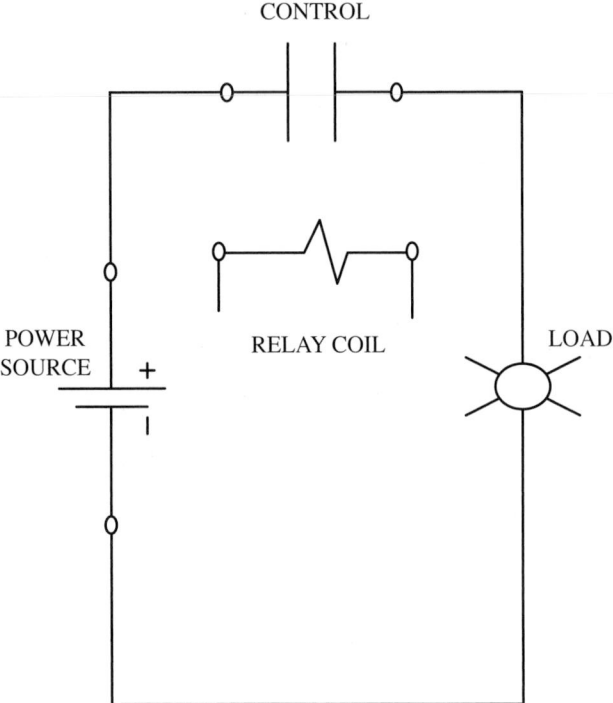

Figure 31-3 Electromechanical relay

Another characteristic of electromagnetism is its ability to induce a current flow in another conductor that passes through its magnetic field. This principle is known as induction. Induction is useful in the design of transformers, motors, and generators.

TECH TIP

Motors, transformers, generators, all have metal cores made of thin sheet metal strips. There are advantages to using thin sheet metal strips. It is far easier to manufacture thin sheets because they can be stamped where the thicker material would have to be cut. Sheet metal that is laminated together to form the metal core concentrates the magnetic field more intensely than a single solid piece of metal.

31.5 TRANSFORMERS

HVAC/R equipment often requires more than one voltage. One or more transformers are often used to step down the line voltage to supply load or control requirements. Occasionally a step up transformer may be used.

TECH TIP

There are several reasons that most HVAC/R equipment uses 24 V as the control voltage. First, under most state and local guidelines an electrician's license is not required to install and service these low voltage wires. Second, most codes do not require that these connections be made at electrical junction boxes. And third, under OSHA regulations, circuits that have less than 80 V fall under less stringent safety requirements.

Transformers are constructed using the induction characteristics of AC power. When current flows through a coil, a magnetic field is produced. When a second coil is placed in the field of the current carrying coil (primary), electric current can be transferred to the second coil (secondary), Figure 31-4. The process is made more efficient by wrapping the coils around a common metal core. The voltage transferred is directly in proportion to the ratio of the number of turns on the primary coil to the number of turns on the secondary coil. More than one secondary coil can be used if additional voltages or circuits are required.

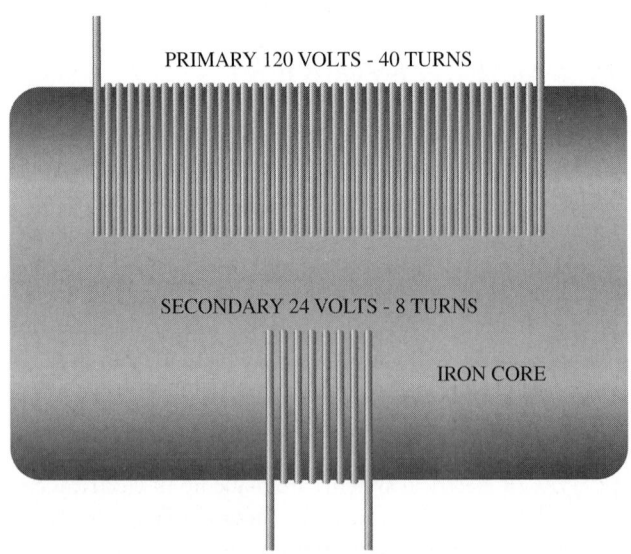

Figure 31-4 Primary and secondary voltages of a step down transformer

31.6 CIRCUIT LOADS

In this section, some common electrical devices that are parts of standard units will be described to show how they are connected in the system to perform their proper function. As an example, a schematic for a simplified packaged air conditioning unit is shown in Figure 31-5.

Where the power comes into the building, it enters a service entrance panel for distribution to the various electrical loads. Each electrical circuit that comes from this panel is electrically protected by either a fuse or a circuit breaker.

SERVICE TIP

There are many standardized symbols used to represent components in air conditioning and refrigeration wiring diagrams. Although most manufacturers use the Institute of Electrical and Electronics Engineers (IEEE) standard symbols, some manufacturers choose to use their own symbols for components. Be sure to refer to the drawing legend to determine what each symbol means.

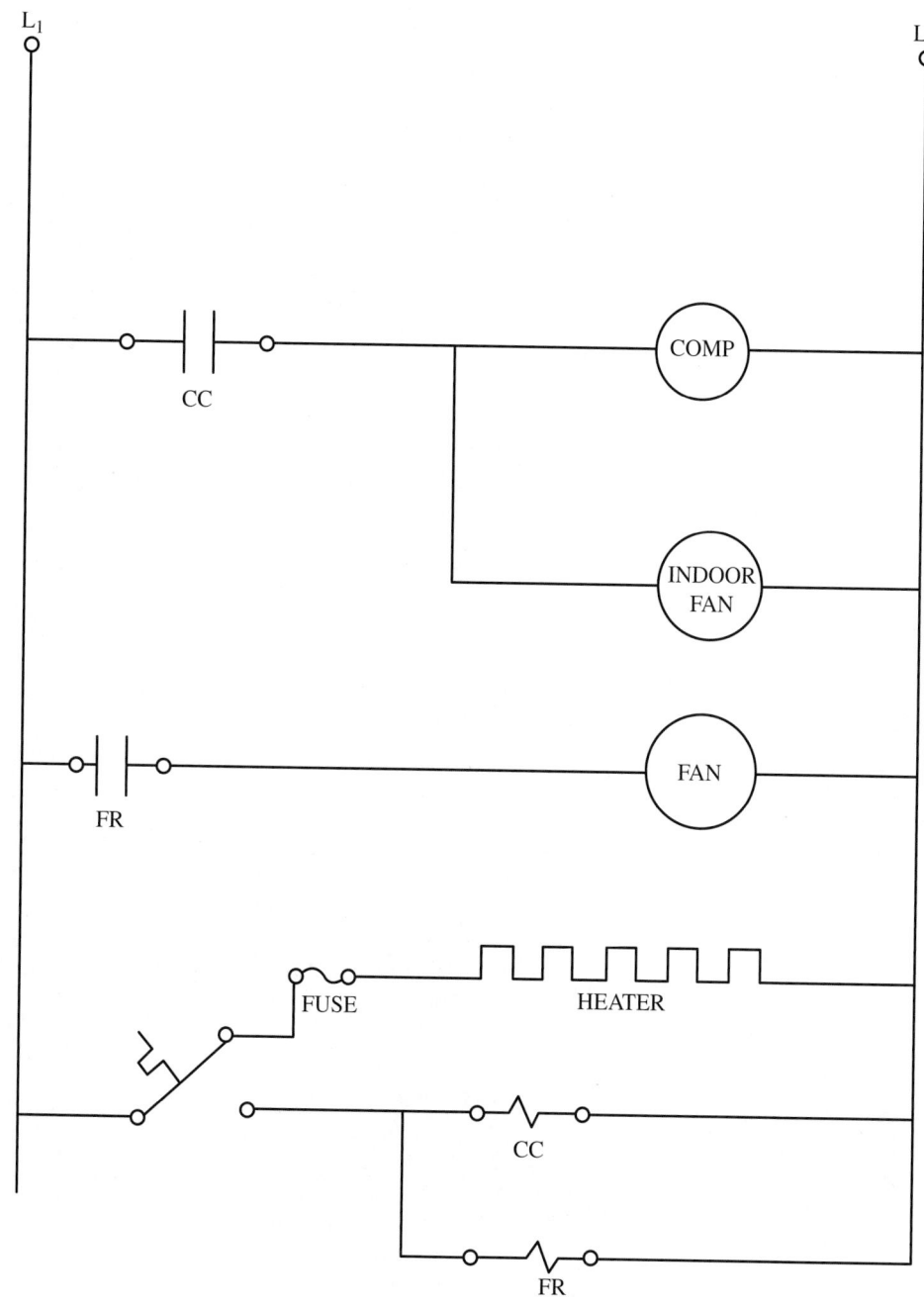

Figure 31-5 Packaged air conditioning wiring diagram

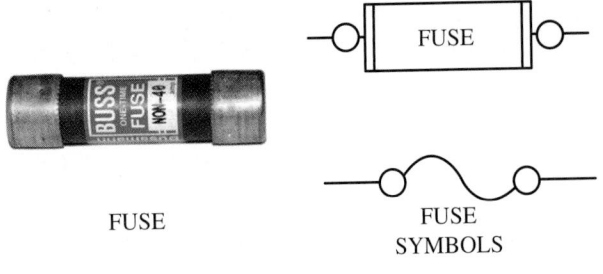

FUSE

FUSE
SYMBOLS

Figure 31-6 Symbol for fuses

A sample fuse and two commonly used fuse symbols are shown in Figure 31-6. A fuse is a special electrical conductor that is placed in series with a load and melts when excessive current flows through it, opening the circuit. Fuses are available in different types and sizes so that they can be selected to match the requirements of specific loads. If they are too small, they melt before they should. If they are too large, they do not offer the proper protection. Their selection follows the rules set forth in the electrical code or in the specifications accompanying the load.

Where fuses are used to protect motors in the circuit, a special type of fuse is used called a time delay fuse or dual element fuse. This type of fuse has a built-in delayed action that will tolerate momentary heavy starting current on motor power-up, but functions the rest of the time to protect the motor against excessive running current.

All residences have some type of electrical panel, where the electrical service enters the building and is distributed to the circuits in the building. Each circuit has some type of

protective device to automatically disconnect the power in case the circuit is overloaded. This protection can either be a fuse as described above or a circuit breaker. Note the symbols used to represent a circuit breaker in an electrical wiring diagram, Figure 31-7. The advantage of a circuit breaker over a fuse is that it can be manually reset at the electrical service panel after an overload, rather than replaced. Also, the circuit can be manually opened in case there is a need to perform service on the circuit.

In addition to the protective equipment in the entrance panel, electrical codes usually require that each circuit be protected at a distribution panel or subpanel. In addition, a service disconnect switch should be provided at the equipment being supplied current. An enclosed disconnect switch mounted on a brick wall above an outside unit is shown in Figure 31-8. This disconnect is conveniently located to provide an easy way to shut the power off from the unit for service.

Figure 31-8 Air conditioner disconnect

Figure 31-7 Circuit breaker symbols

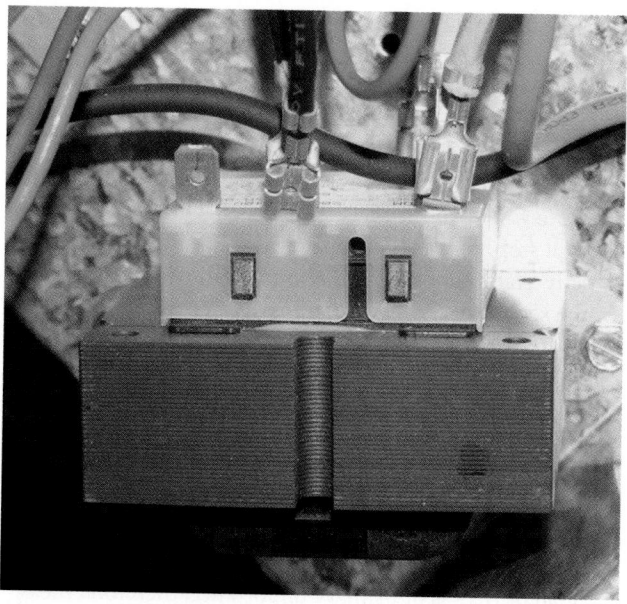

Figure 31-9 Control voltage transformer

Inside the unit itself the power supply is connected to a terminal strip where the power is distributed to the circuits within the unit. Some circuits such as fan motors and compressors use the full power source voltage. To produce the 24 V control voltage, a step down transformer is required as shown in Figure 31-9.

31.7 CIRCUIT CONTROLS

Some devices are classified as control devices and others are controlled devices. A control device is the device that tells the controlled device what to do. Control devices can be thought of as the brains of the operation because they make something happen.

Control Devices

Some examples of control devices are:

- Thermostat.
- Humidistat.
- Fan switch.
- Overload.
- Pressure switch.
- Defrost timer.
- Head pressure control.
- Low ambient control.

Controlled Devices

Controlled devices can be thought of as the workers in the operation because they do something. Some examples of controlled devices are:

- Fan motor.
- Damper.

- Compressor.
- Contactor.
- Pumps.
- Valves.
- Relays.
- Ventilator.

Something such as a change in temperature, pressure, humidity, or just the time elapsed causes the control device to send a signal to the controlled device causing it to respond. The signal sent may be 24 V, often referred to as low voltage or control voltage, or it may be line voltage or a digital signal. The control device uses a sensor of some type to start its action. In the case of a mechanical thermostat, the sensor can be a bimetal strip connected to a mercury bulb. But for an electronic thermostat, the sensor would most likely be a semiconductor connected to an integrated circuit.

Control devices can be automatic or manual. An automatic control device is one that works completely on its own without the need of an operator providing instructions. A thermostat is an example of an automatic control device. A manual control device is one that an operator or other person must activate or deactivate. The heat-cool-off selector switch on a thermostat is an example of a manual control.

Automatic Controls

- **Two Position Controls**   Two position controls may be used to start and stop controlled devices such as compressors, fans, or pumps based on the input from a sensor. These controls maintain temperature, air quality, or water level by simply starting and stopping their controlled device.
- **Proportional Controls**   Proportional controls are the ones that increase or decrease the output of a controlled device. Examples of proportionately controlled devices include variable air volume fan boxes, proportional control valves, or dampers. Proportional controls may send an analog or digital signal to the controlled device.
- **Proportional Integrated Controls**   Proportional integrated controls incorporate a basic level of integrated error correction to the proportional control logic. This is much like the marksman that fires a shot and sees that the wind drifted the bullet 3 in to the right. So the next time the marksman aims 3 in to the left of the target. This offset is programmed into controls so that the system operates as close as possible to the set point.
- **Proportional Integral Derivative Controls**   Proportional integral derivative controls learn how the system operates and make changes to the operating program as needed to maintain the most efficient operation. For example, some setback thermostats learn how long it takes to bring the heat up to the set

point or how long it takes to cool down to the set point. The next time the cycle is ready to start, the thermostat adjusts the starting time so that the temperature set point is reached at the correct time. Many building automation systems learn how the system responds to load changes and make corrections to maintain efficient control.

31.8 LOAD DEVICES AND THE CONTROL CIRCUIT

All load devices must have some type of control device placed in their circuit so that they can be controlled. Without a control device, which could be a switch, the load would run all the time. The level of control can range from the basic manual control to an advanced computer controlled system. The controlling device may control a device directly or indirectly.

An example of a direct control is a room thermostat. When the thermostat calls for cooling, the AC unit begins to run. The direct action of the control starts or stops the unit. An example of an indirect control device is the low pressure switch and thermostat arrangement on a walk-in cooler. In this case, when cooling is required, the thermostat sends a signal to energize and open the liquid line solenoid valve. The refrigeration compressor, however, is not controlled by the

thermostat and does not immediately start and begin to run. However, because the liquid line solenoid valve is now open, the suction pressure at the compressor inlet begins to rise. This rise in suction pressure eventually closes the low pressure switch and the compressor starts. As the space cools and the liquid line solenoid closes, the resulting drop in suction pressure will open the low pressure switch and the compressor will stop. In this type of system the thermostat does not directly start and stop the compressor. The low pressure switch serves this function as a result of the action caused by the thermostat on the liquid line solenoid valve.

31.9 ELECTRICAL LOAD DEVICES

The whole purpose of the electrical system is to supply power to the electrical devices in combination with a control sequence to produce a desired output. The proper operation of the load devices is of primary importance; therefore, the operation of some of the more common load devices will be examined to see how they fit into the wiring system.

The most useful type of diagram for observing the sequence of operation is the ladder diagram. In this diagram, the power is represented by vertical lines shown as L1 and L2. Figure 31-10 shows a ladder diagram. The electrical circuits are represented by horizontal lines, stretching between L1 and L2, each circuit containing a load device. The

Figure 31-10 Basic ladder diagram

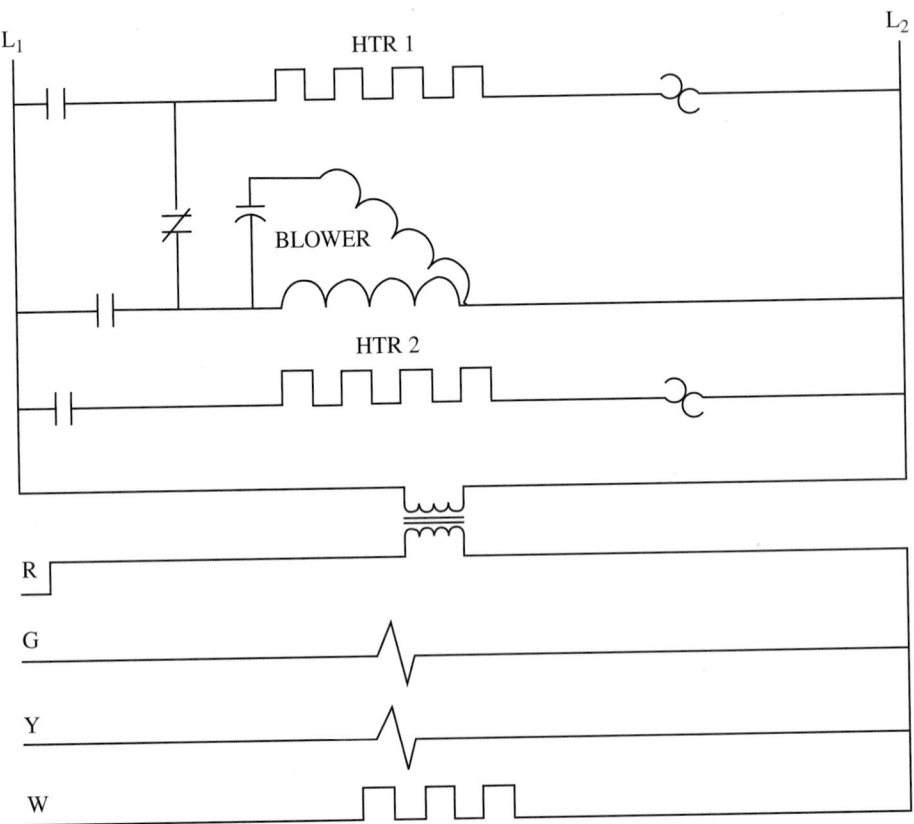

controls (switches) are added in series with the loads to turn the loads on or off as the proper operation of the system requires.

31.10 COMPRESSORS AND ELECTRIC MOTORS

The first major load that will be discussed is the compressor. Some of the symbols that are used to represent compressors in power supply diagrams are shown in Figure 31-11. The symbol at the top, consisting of a circle between two horizontal lines, represents a motor with two power line connections. The caption COMP within the circle indicates that the motor is a compressor motor. The two symbols in the center of Figure 31-11 indicate a motor that has both a start winding and run winding. The bottom symbol in Figure 31-11

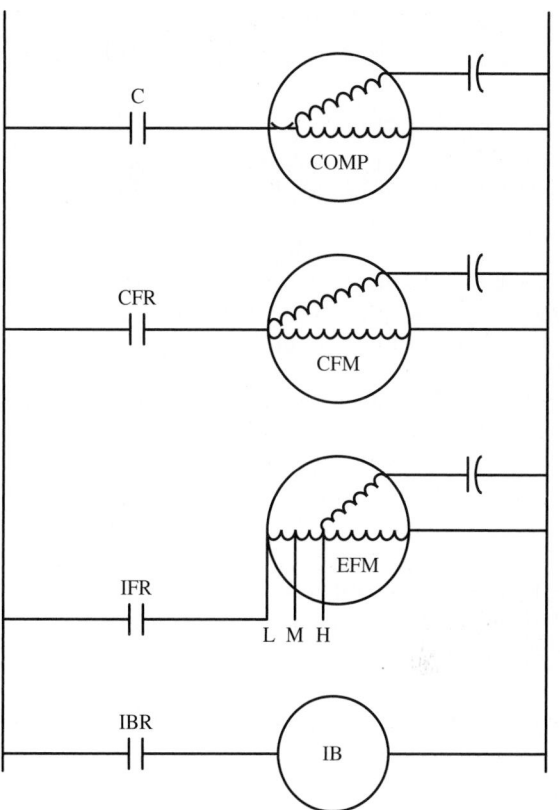

Figure 31-12 Basic ladder diagram with various motors shown

shows the three windings of a three phase compressor motor, and the three power connections required.

Figure 31-12 shows how the various motor symbols fit into the schematic wiring diagram. L1 and L2 represent the supply side of the power supply. The circuits for three types of motor loads have been connected to L1. The connections to L2 will be added later when the control devices are known.

31.11 WIRING DIAGRAMS

Wiring diagrams are a type of map, supplying complete information on how the electrical parts are connected for operation, control, and protection of the unit. Certain standards have been set for electrical symbols that represent electrical components, but they are not always followed by every manufacturer. Therefore the technician needs to be able to interpret the different types of symbols that manufacturers may use.

There are three types of basic wiring diagrams:

- External.
- Connection (or panel) pictorial.
- Schematic.

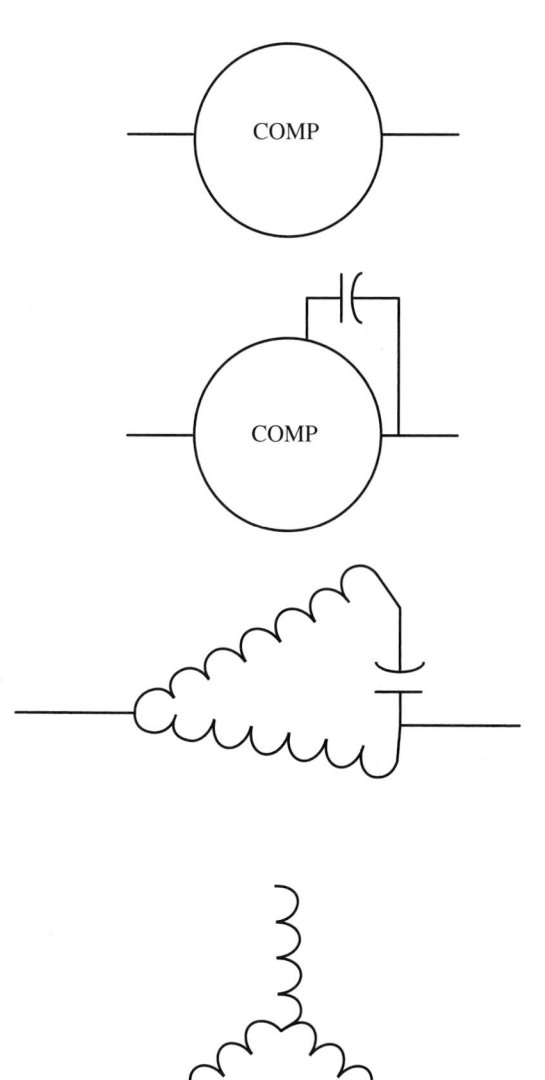

Figure 31-11 Compressor symbols

SERVICE TIP

Wiring diagrams for equipment may change as the manufacturer makes minor modifications to the equipment's components. Because wiring diagrams today are computer generated, it is easy for the manufacturer to make these minor changes without having to redraw the entire diagram. For this reason many of the manufacturer's diagrams may be slightly different from one another but look very similar. Make certain that you are using the correct diagram for the piece of equipment you are currently servicing by checking the model number on the diagram with the equipment model number.

External Diagram

The external diagram is supplied by many manufacturers along with installation instructions. These instructions show the type of electrical service required and how the unit must be connected. A diagram of this type would show the location(s) of terminals on the equipment, the type of external fusing needed, and the type of power that must be furnished for the unit to operate properly. This is an extremely important part of the job. If power is not properly applied, the unit will not function properly.

A typical external wiring diagram is shown in Figure 31-13. It is common practice for these diagrams to show both the external wiring supplied by others as well as the external wiring that is field installed by the installation crew or the electrician. The drawing may also specify wire sizes and the

Figure 31-13 Typical external wiring diagram used for unit installation

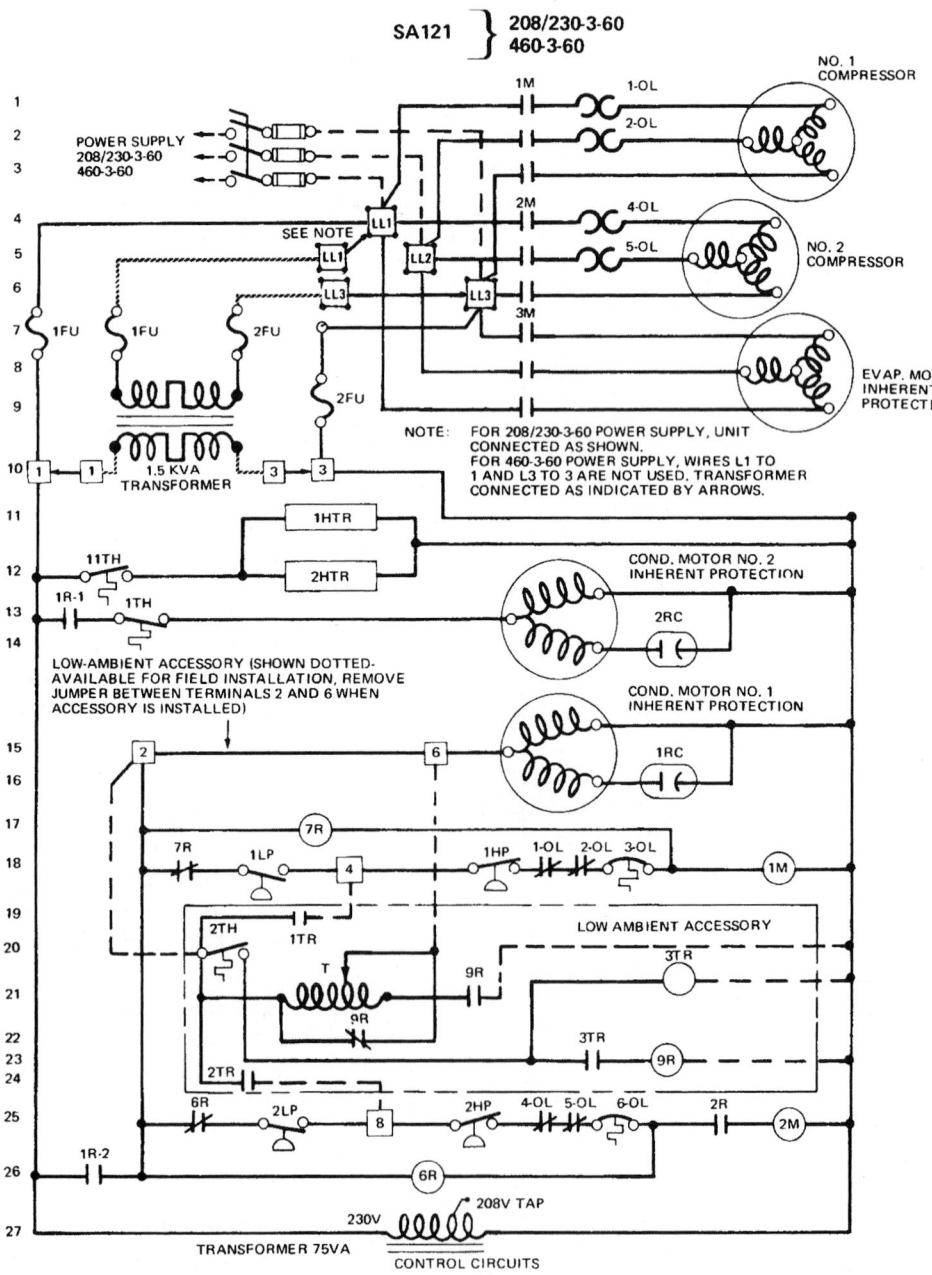

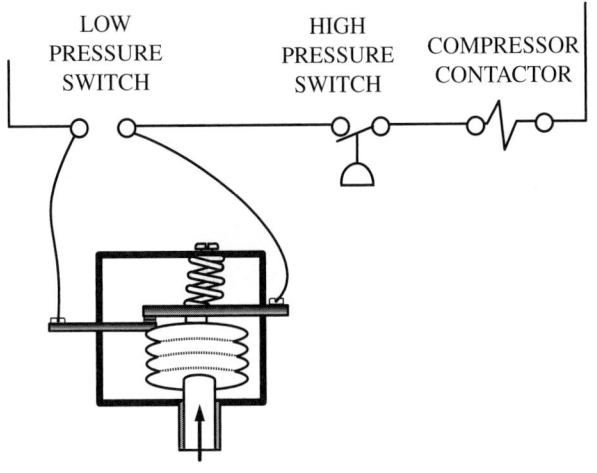

Figure 32-34 Low pressure switch (manual reset)

Combination High/Low Pressure Cutout

Some pressurestats are connected to both the low and high pressure sides of the system. These combination pressurestats are actually two separate devices built into a single device, Figure 32-35. The low and high pressure setting can be adjusted individually without affecting the other setting.

Oil Pressure Safety Switch

The oil safety switch is designed to protect against the loss of oil pressure. It is activated by pressure; however, it is operated by a pressure differential rather than by straight system pressure. A pressure reading at the oil pump discharge will be the sum of the actual oil pressure plus the crankcase pressure where the pump suction is located. The oil safety switch measures the pressure difference (net oil pressure) between the oil pump discharge pressure and compressor crankcase pressure and shuts down the compressor if the oil pump does not maintain a net oil pressure as prescribed by the compressor manufacturer.

For example, if a manufacturer indicated that a 15 psi net oil pressure was required, a compressor with a 40 psi crankcase (suction) pressure must have at least a 55 psi pump discharge pressure (net oil pressure = pump discharge pressure − crankcase pressure).

Oil Pressure Safety Switch Time Delay

Most refrigeration compressors have shaft driven oil pumps. Because of this, when the compressor starts, there is no oil pressure. Full oil pressure is not obtained until the compressor is up to speed. Therefore, a time delay device is built into the oil pressure safety switch to allow the compressor enough time to start.

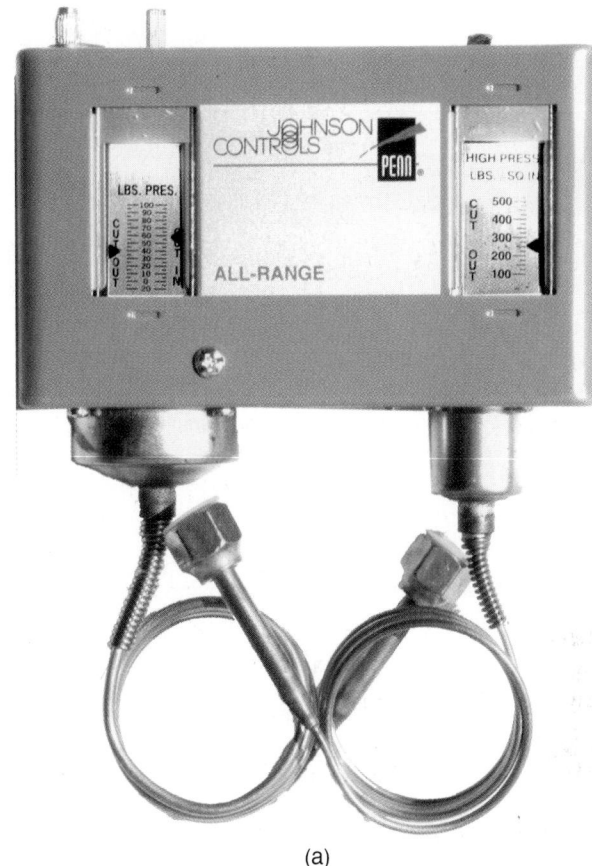

(a)

(b)

Figure 32-35 (a) Combination high and low pressure switch; (b) The high and low pressure sides of this control are separated inside the switch

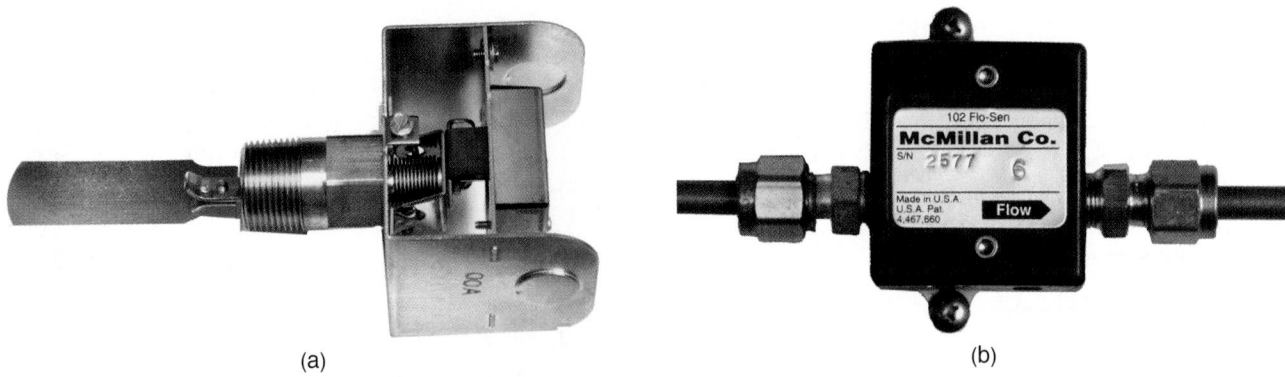

(a)   (b)

Figure 32-36 (a) Flow switch; (b) Electronic flow meter
(Courtesy Hampden Engineering Corporation)

One of the methods used to create this time delay is to include a heat activated bimetallic switch and a small resistance heater in the circuit. When the compressor is started, the oil pressure will be low and the normally closed pressure switch allows the resistance heater to become energized. As the oil pressure rises to normal shortly after the compressor starts, the pressure switch will open and deenergize the resistance heater and the compressor will continue to operate normally.

The compressor can never be run longer than a predetermined time on subnormal oil pressure. If the oil pressure does not build up to its normal level when starting the compressor, the pressure switch will remain closed. The energized resistance heater warps the bimetallic switch which opens the control circuit and stops the compressor. The time delay setting on most of these controls is adjustable from approximately 60 to 120 seconds. If oil pressure should drop below the cutin setting during the running cycle, the resistance heater is energized and, unless oil pressure returns to normal within the time delay period, the compressor will be shut down.

32.22 FLOW SWITCH SAFETY DEVICE

The sail switch, shown in Figure 32-36, is a protective device to prevent the operation of a unit when there is inadequate fluid flow. In an air system, the sail switch is placed in the duct to sense the flow of air. Unless there is an adequate supply of air over the coil, the unit is either not started or shut down. Switches of this type can also be placed in a waterline feed of a water cooled condenser. If there is an inadequate supply of water, or no water, the unit is prevented from running.

32.23 SAFETY RELIEF DEVICES

Pressure Relief Valve

Figure 32-37 shows a pressure relief valve that can be placed in the hot gas line, condenser, or liquid receiver as a high pressure safety control. These controls are required

by the installation codes on most water cooled systems. This valve automatically resets when normal pressures are reestablished.

Figure 32-37 Small welded pressure relief valve used in a receiver

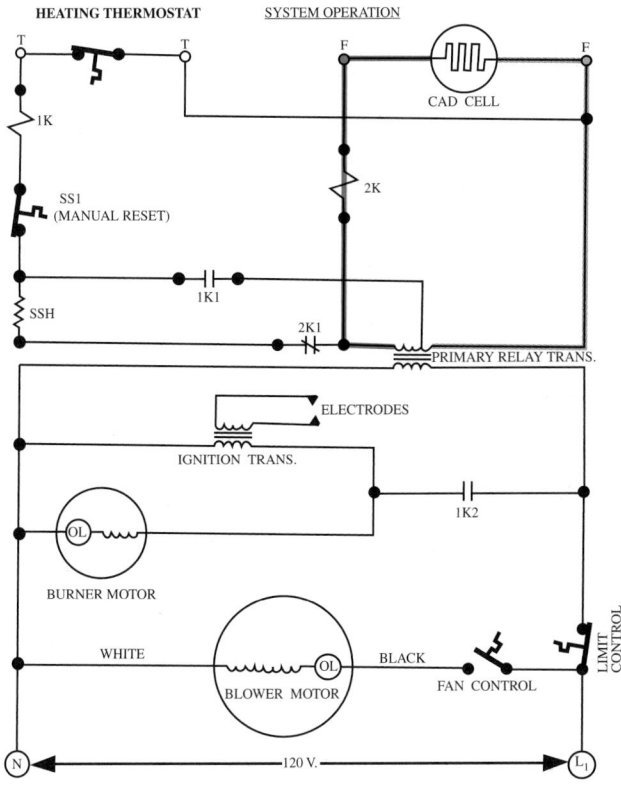

Figure 33-24 Cad cell circuit from an Amana oil furnace diagram edited
(Photograph used with permission from Whirlpool Corporation)

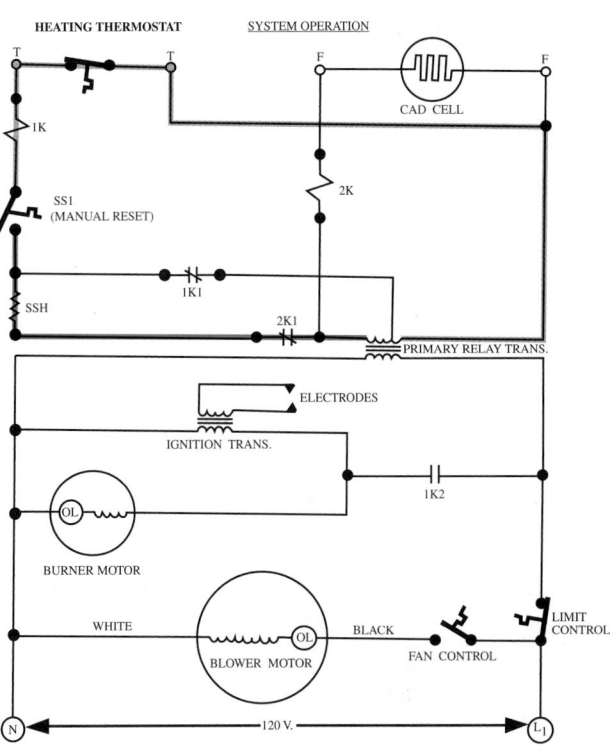

Figure 33-26 Safety switch opens, breaking the circuit to relay 1K from an Amana oil furnace diagram edited
(Photograph used with permission from Whirlpool Corporation)

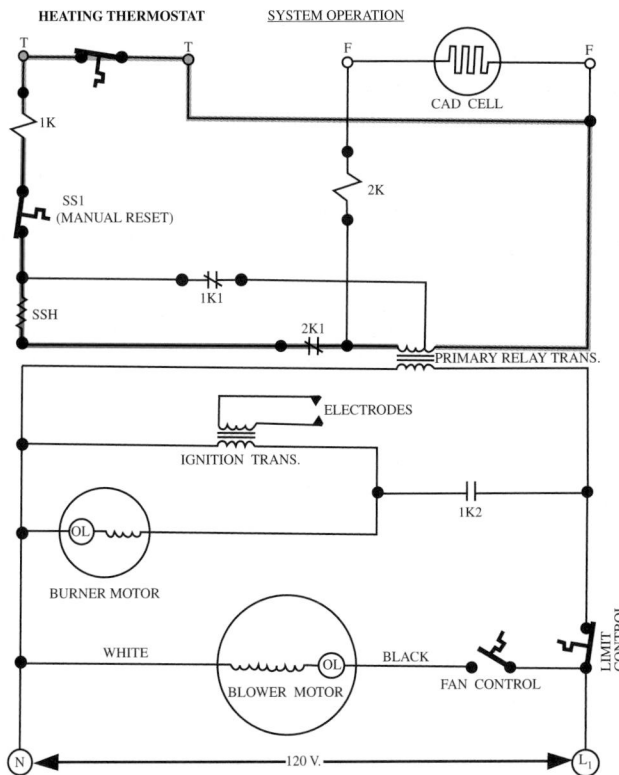

Figure 33-25 Safety heater circuit from an Amana oil furnace diagram edited
(Photograph used with permission from Whirlpool Corporation)

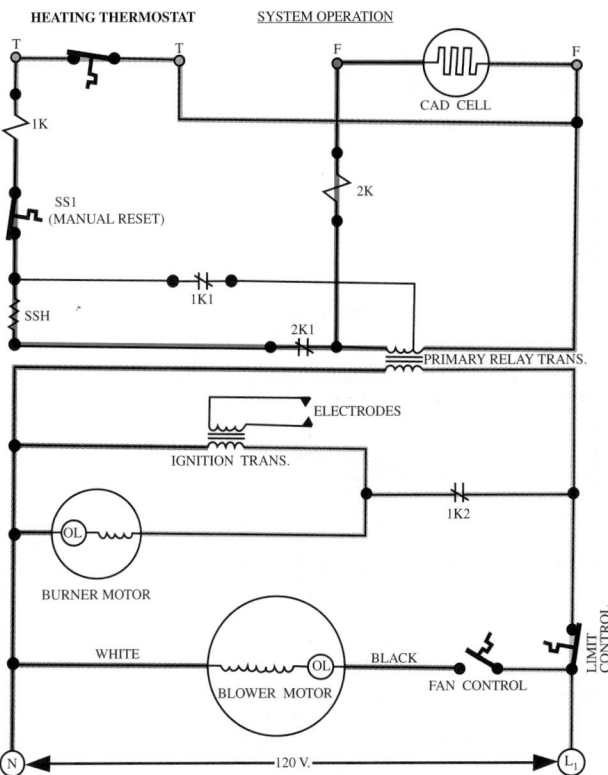

Figure 33-27 Relay 1K is energized from an Amana oil furnace diagram edited
(Photograph used with permission from Whirlpool Corporation)

Assuming the flames ignite, the cad cell changes to a low resistance and relay coil 2K is energized. This opens points 2K1, shutting off the safety heater, Figure 33-28. The furnace heats up until the fan control senses the temperature rise and closes to complete the circuit to the blower motor, Figure 33-29.

When the thermostat is satisfied, the circuit to relay coil 1K1 is opened and the burner shuts down. The blower continues to run until the fan control cools off, opens, and shuts off the blower. The limit control will open, break the circuit to the primary control, and shut off the burner should the furnace overheat.

Many modern primary controls now replace relay 2K with electronic components, but the operational logic remains the same.

33.9 CONDENSING UNIT DIAGRAMS

The basic condensing unit consists of a compressor, fan motor, capacitors, and contactor, Figure 33-30. With line voltage to the unit but no call for cooling, the line voltage stops at the contactor. Typically the common side of the transformer secondary is wired directly to one side of the contactor coil. The R side of the transformer secondary is controlled by the thermostat. When the thermostat is not calling for cooling, the R side of the transformer stops at the thermostat. The thermostat breaks the circuit, so there is no current flow. With no current flow there is no voltage drop through the coil, so the coil acts like a wire. This means that the common side of the transformer is available at

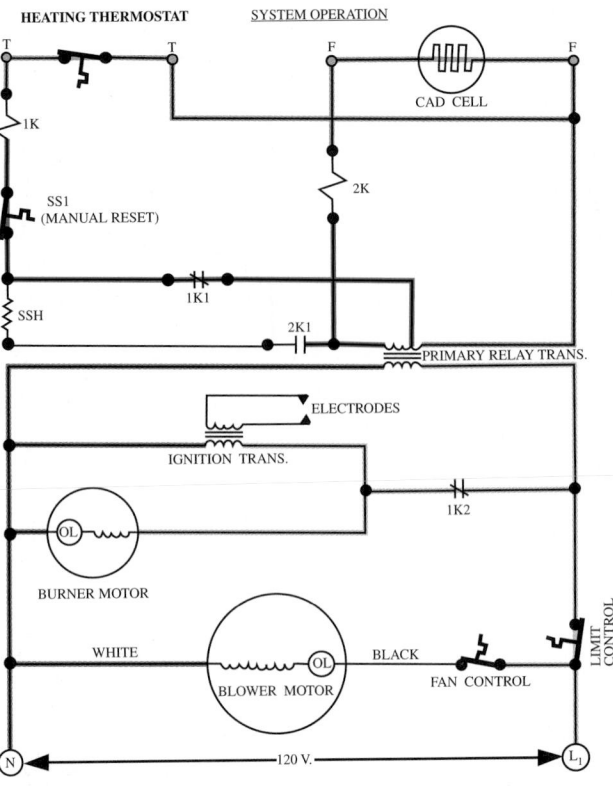

Figure 33-29 Fan control closes, operating the indoor fan from an Amana oil furnace diagram edited
(Photograph used with permission from Whirlpool Corporation)

both sides of the coil and at both control wires to the coil. On the diagram, both wires and both sides of the coil are shaded the same color. The contactor coil is not operating and no voltage is read at the contactor coil, Figure 33-31.

When the thermostat closes and calls for cooling, the R side of the transformer is connected to one side of the coil. Now a voltage drop of 24 V can be read across the contactor

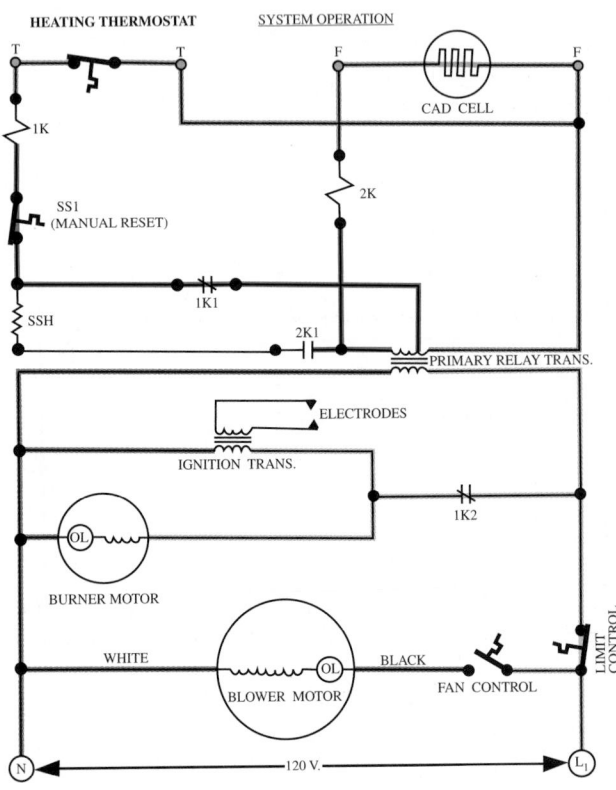

Figure 33-28 Relay 2K is energized from an Amana oil furnace diagram edited
(Photograph used with permission from Whirlpool Corporation)

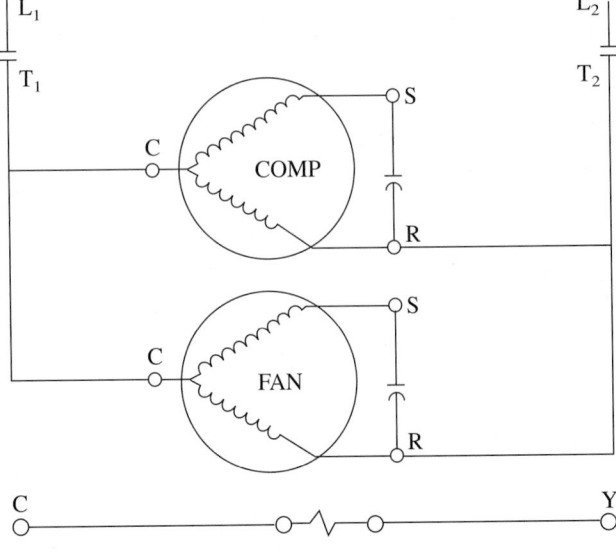

Figure 33-30 Ladder diagram of a condensing unit

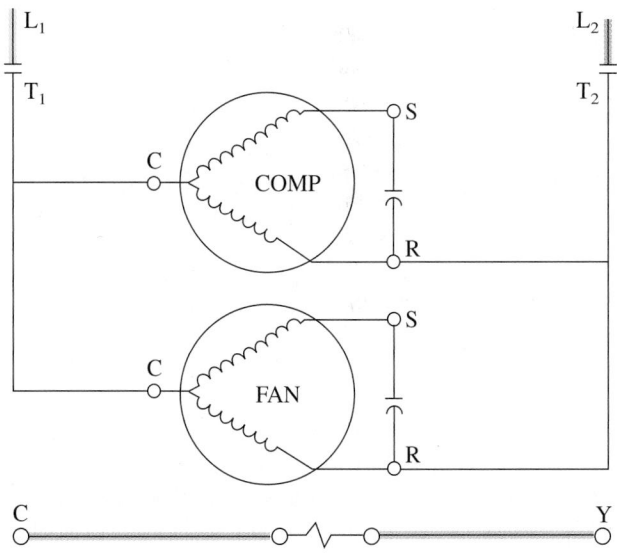

Figure 33-31 Ladder diagram of condensing unit with power on and system off

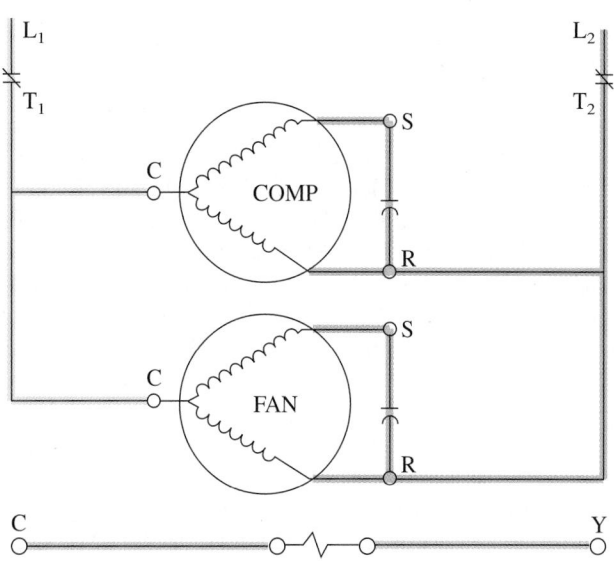

Figure 33-32 Ladder diagram of condensing unit with power on and system on

coil. This is indicated by the change in color. The contactor coil is energized.

Energizing the contactor coil closes the contactor's normally open points and the voltage from line 1 passes across the closed contacts through terminal 1 to the common leads of both the compressor and fan. The voltage from line 2 passes across the closed contacts to terminal 2

and onto the run terminals of the compressor and fan, Figure 33-32.

Figure 33-33 is of a wiring diagram for a condensing unit which uses a dual (three terminal) run capacitor. When line voltage is supplied to the unit, line voltage between L1 and L2 can be measured up to the contactor. A voltage measurement between the two terminals of the contactor would read

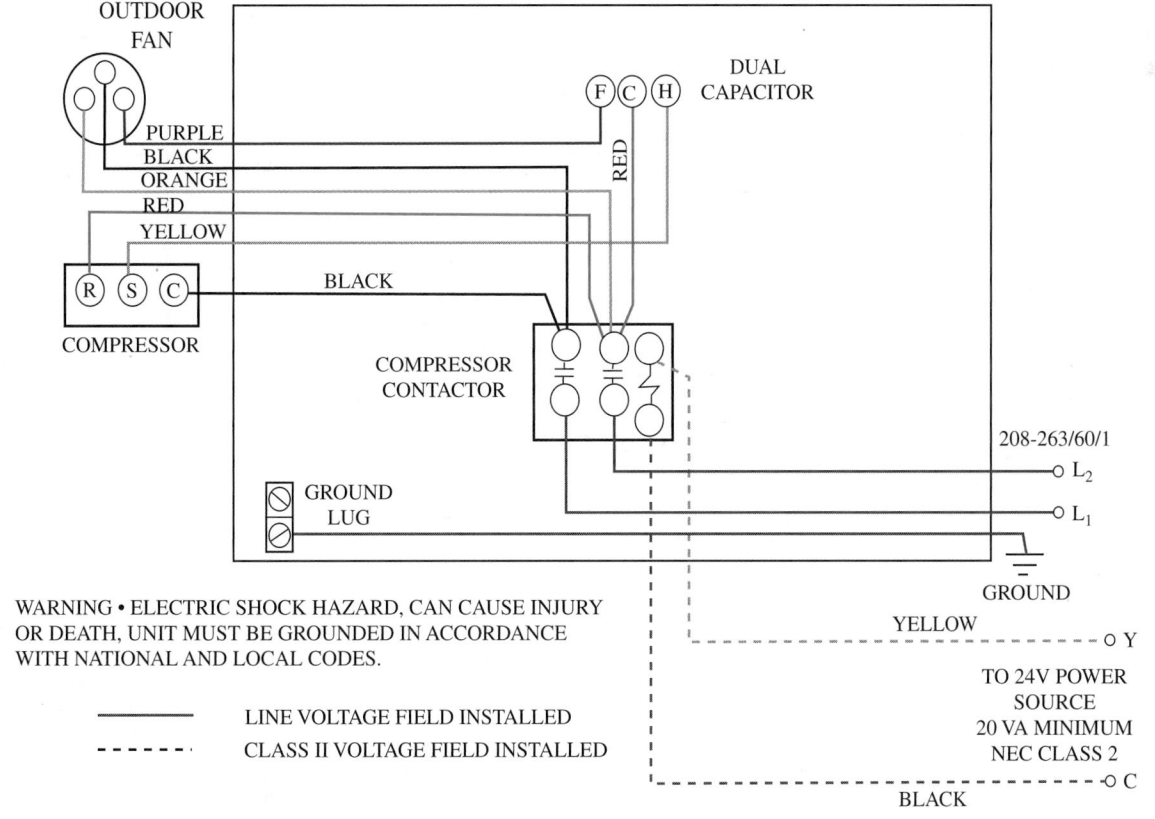

Figure 33-33 Schematic diagram for a dual capacitor unit
(Courtesy Lennox Industries Inc.)

208–240 V depending on the supply voltage. The control voltage would read 0 V.

With no call for cooling, there is no voltage drop across the contactor coil and the circuit to contactor coil is all the same color, shown in Figure 33-34. When the cooling contacts in the indoor thermostat close, the circuit is completed to the outdoor compressor contactor coil. This can be seen as a voltage drop or color change across the coil in Figure 33-35. The coil then closes the compressor contactor contacts and line 1 voltage passes across the contacts to the common terminals on the compressor and fan as shown in Figure 33-35. At the same time, line 2 voltage passes through the closed compressor contactor contacts to the dual capacitor and the start and run terminals on the compressor and outdoor fan.

Figure 33-36 is of a diagram similar to that shown in Figure 33-33, however, in this diagram the outdoor unit has a start capacitor and a potential relay. Figure 33-37 shows the diagram with power applied to the unit, and a call for cooling from the thermostat. Notice that power is shown in the same places as were shown in Figure 33-34. When this system is on and running, there is a voltage drop across the coil on the potential relay between terminals 5 and 2, as shown in Figure 33-38. This measured voltage is higher than the applied line voltage between L1 and L2. This higher voltage is the result of the back EMF created by the compressor motor as the compressor runs. It is this higher voltage, or potential, that causes the relay contacts located

between terminals 1 and 2 to open. This occurs within a fraction of a second as the compressor starts.

If the contacts in the potential relay do not open, the current flowing through the start capacitor would quickly cause the start capacitor to overheat and explode! Many potential relays must be mounted in the equipment so that the arrow marking up is in the correct direction, as shown on the relay in Figure 33-39.

33.10 GAS FURNACE DIAGRAM

Figure 33-40 is a ladder diagram of a basic standing pilot gas furnace with central air conditioning. With the system power on and the door switch closed, line 1 voltage can be read at the fan switch and at the line 1 terminal of the transformer, Figure 33-41. Line 2 voltage potential can be measured at all of the indoor blower motor terminals. It can be read at all of the terminals because without a current flow there is no voltage drop across the motor. Line 2 voltage can also be measured at the second power lead of the transformer. There is a voltage drop across the primary of the transformer because the transformer is energized any time the system is on and the blower compartment door switch is closed. The transformer provides power to the R terminal on the thermostat. Common on the transformer's potential voltage can be read on all sides of the cooling contactor, indoor fan relay, gas valves, and limit switch. This means that on the thermostat's sub base a voltage potential could be read from R to Y, R to G, and R to W.

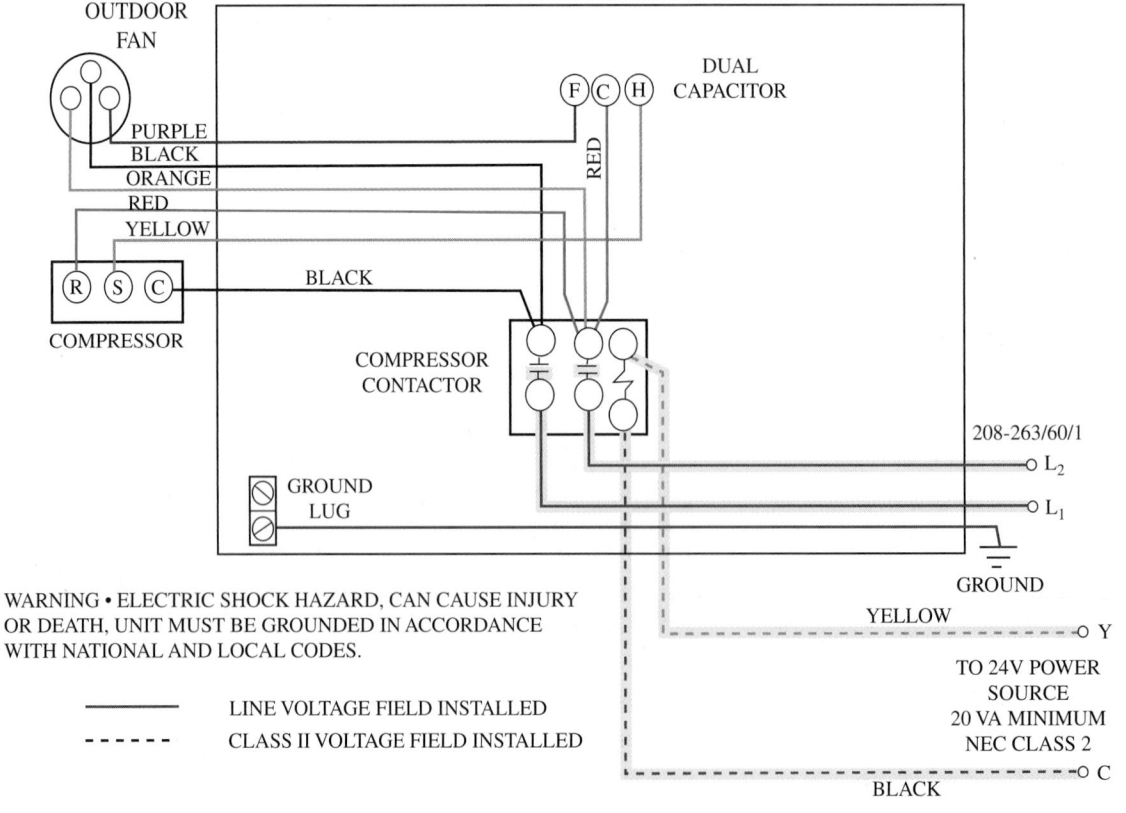

Figure 33-34 No cooling call, contactor coil not energized
(*Courtesy Lennox Industries Inc.*)

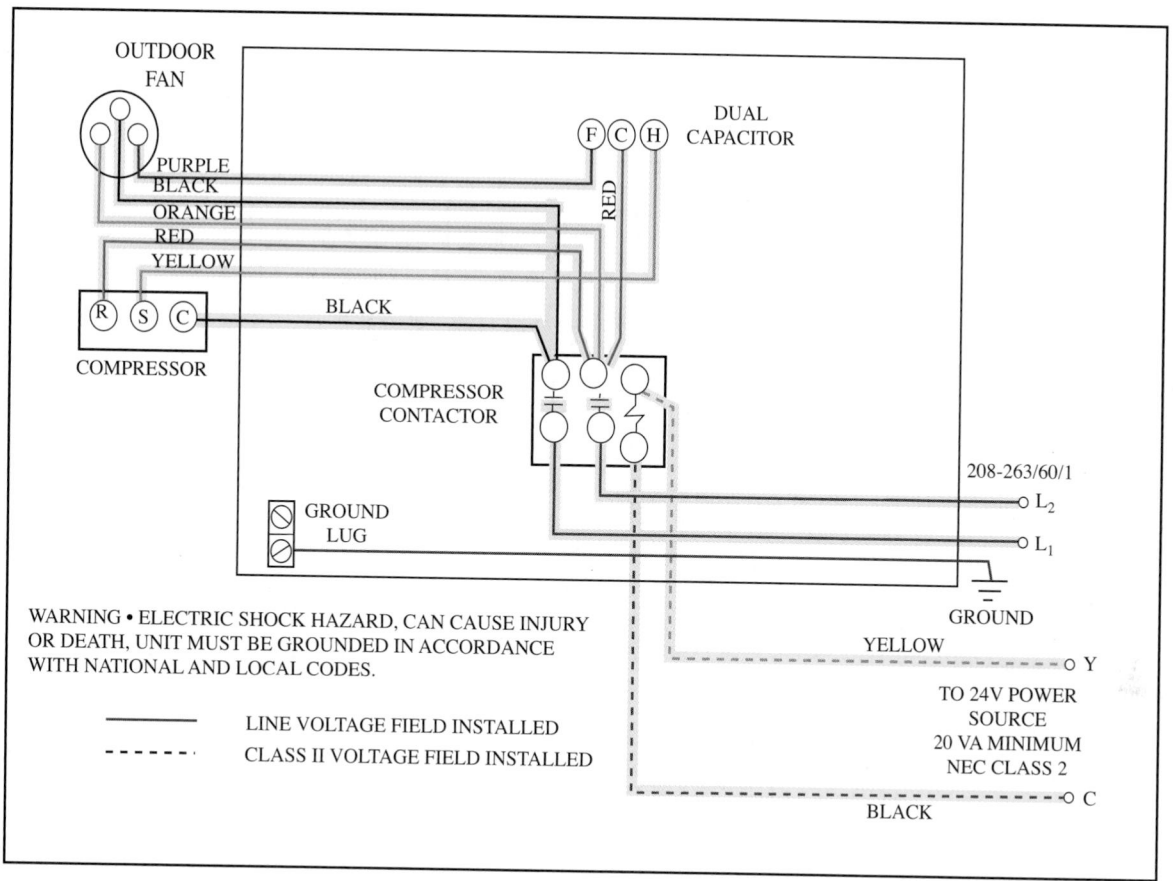

Figure 33-35 Call for cooling, coil energized
(Courtesy Lennox Industries Inc.)

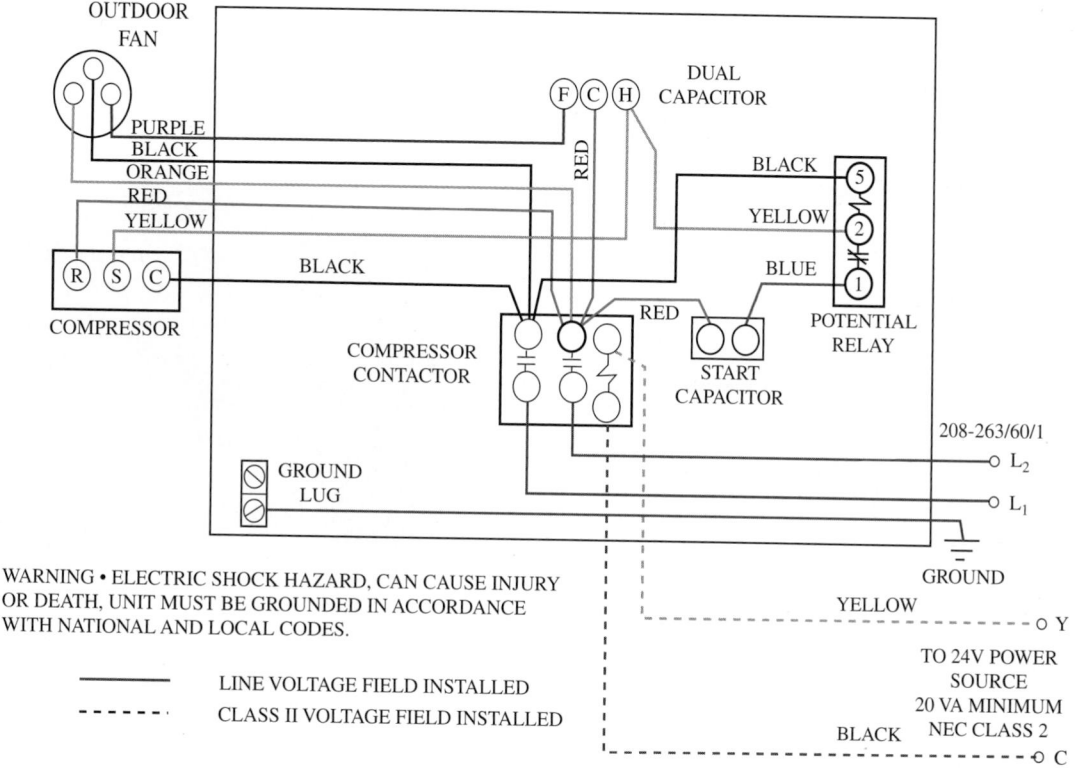

Figure 33-36 Schematic diagram for a dual capacitor condensing unit with a hard start kit
(Courtesy Lennox Industries Inc.)

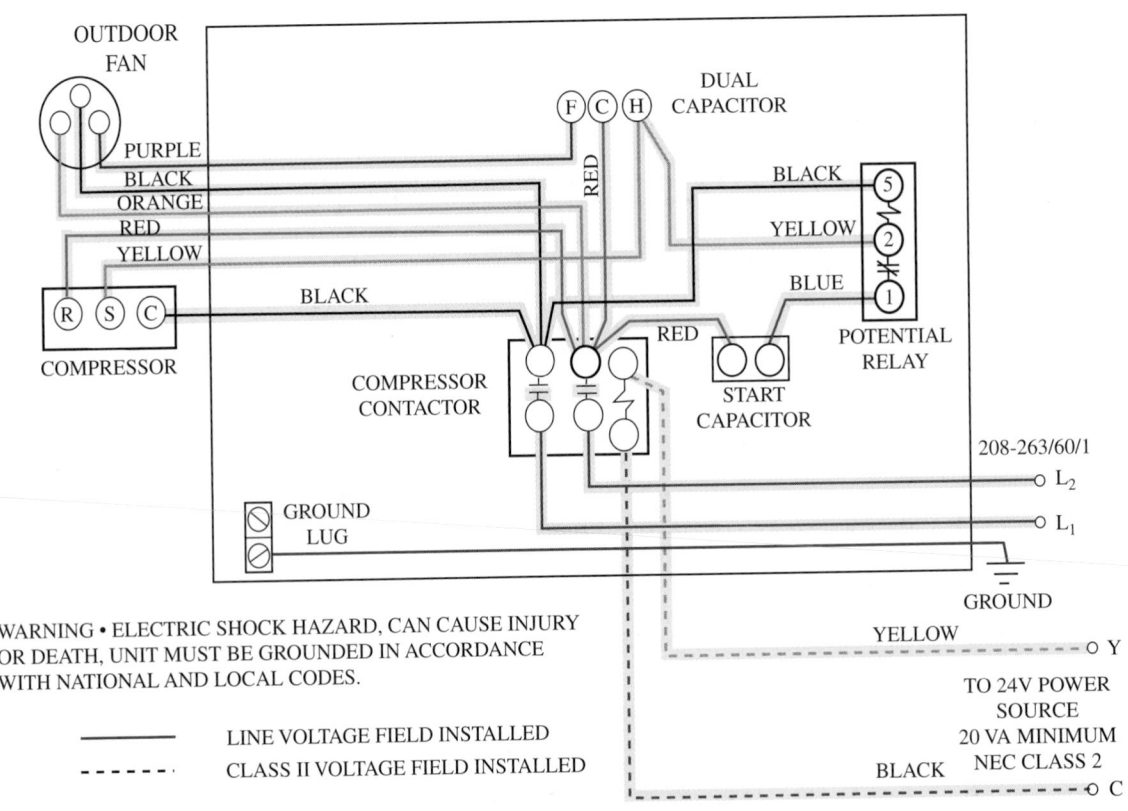

Figure 33-37 Operating unit with hard start kit, potential relay coil energized
(Courtesy Lennox Industries Inc.)

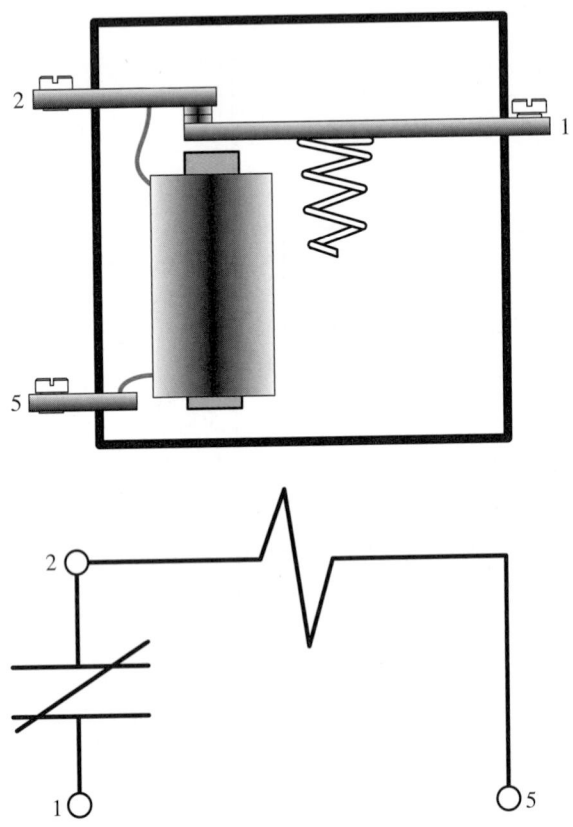

Figure 33-38 Potential relay diagram

When the system is in heating as illustrated in Figure 33-42, line 1 voltage can be read on the low, medium, high, and start leads of the indoor blower motor. There is a voltage drop across the motor from the common terminal to all three speed

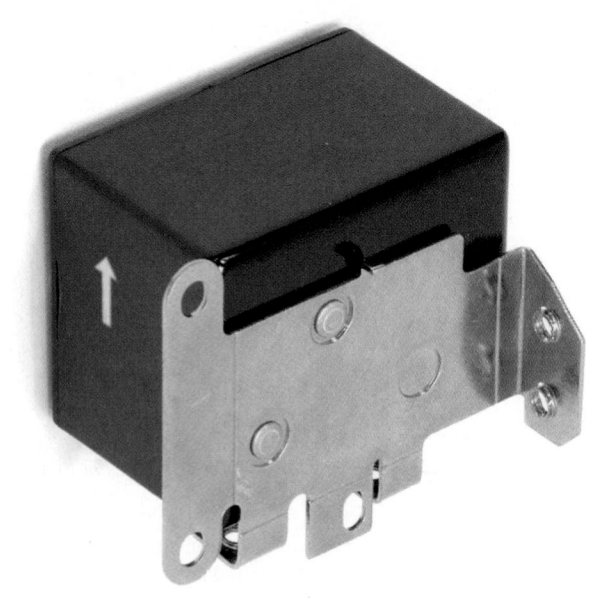

Figure 33-39 Many potential relays must be installed in the correct orientation to operate properly

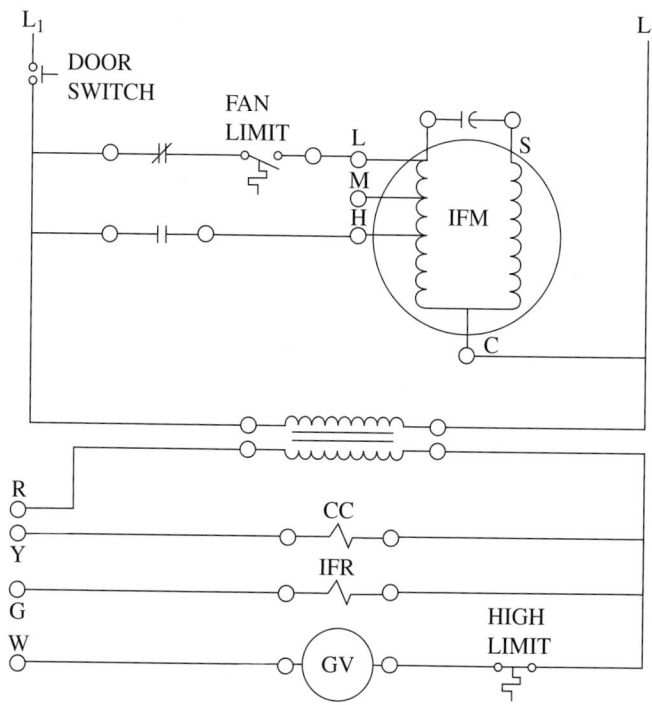

Figure 33-40 Standing pilot gas furnace ladder diagram

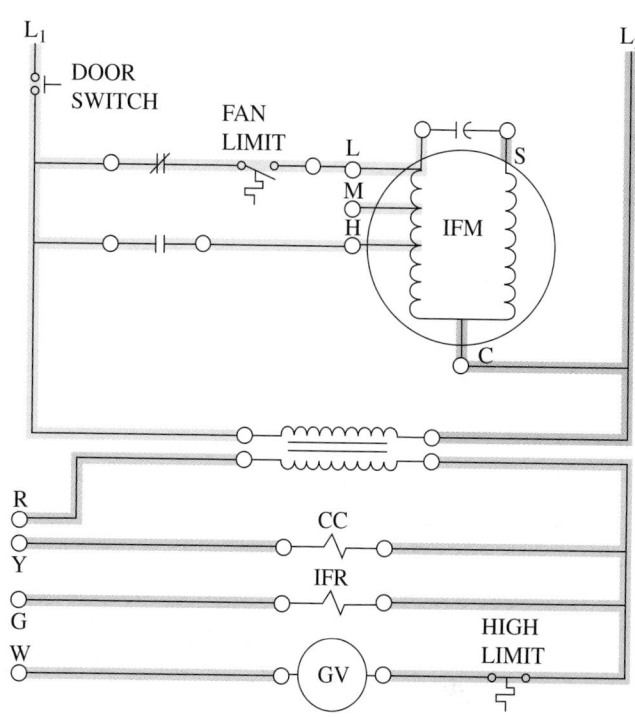

Figure 33-42 Gas furnace, operating in heating

terminals and the start terminal. A voltage drop can be measured across the primary windings of the control voltage transformer. A voltage drop can be measured across the gas valve but no voltage drop will occur across the cooling contactor or indoor blower relay because those circuits are not energized.

If the high limit switch opens, a voltage drop would occur across the high limit terminals and no voltage drop would be measured across the gas valve terminals. There would be no

voltage drop on the gas valve because there would not be a current flow through the open high limit. It is important to note that the fan switch would remain closed even though the gas valve is off so that the fan can continue to blow out the excessive heat from the furnace.

When this system is in cooling, Figure 33-43, the indoor blower relay contacts reverse so that the indoor blower motor is operating on high speed. The fan limit switch would remain

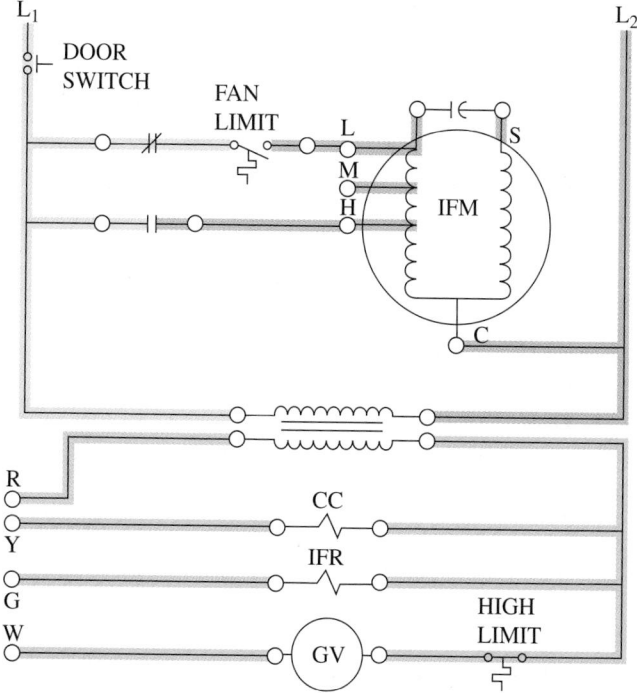

Figure 33-41 Gas furnace, power on but unit not operating

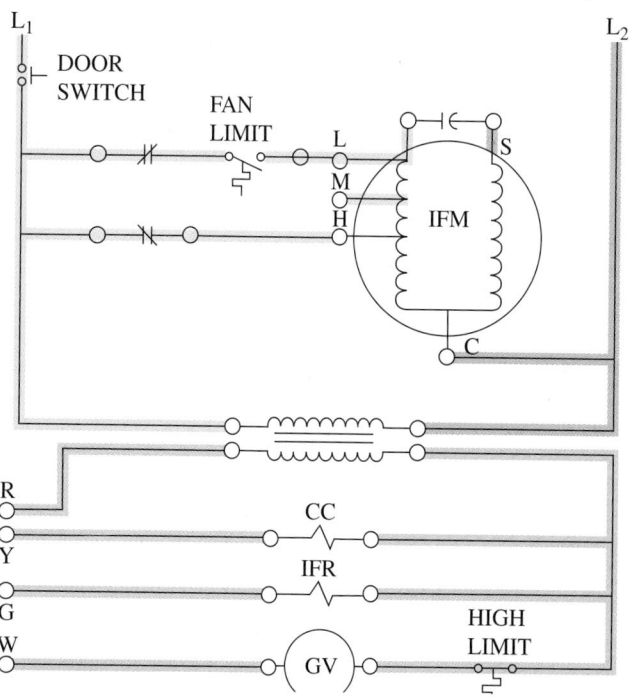

Figure 33-43 Gas furnace operating in cooling

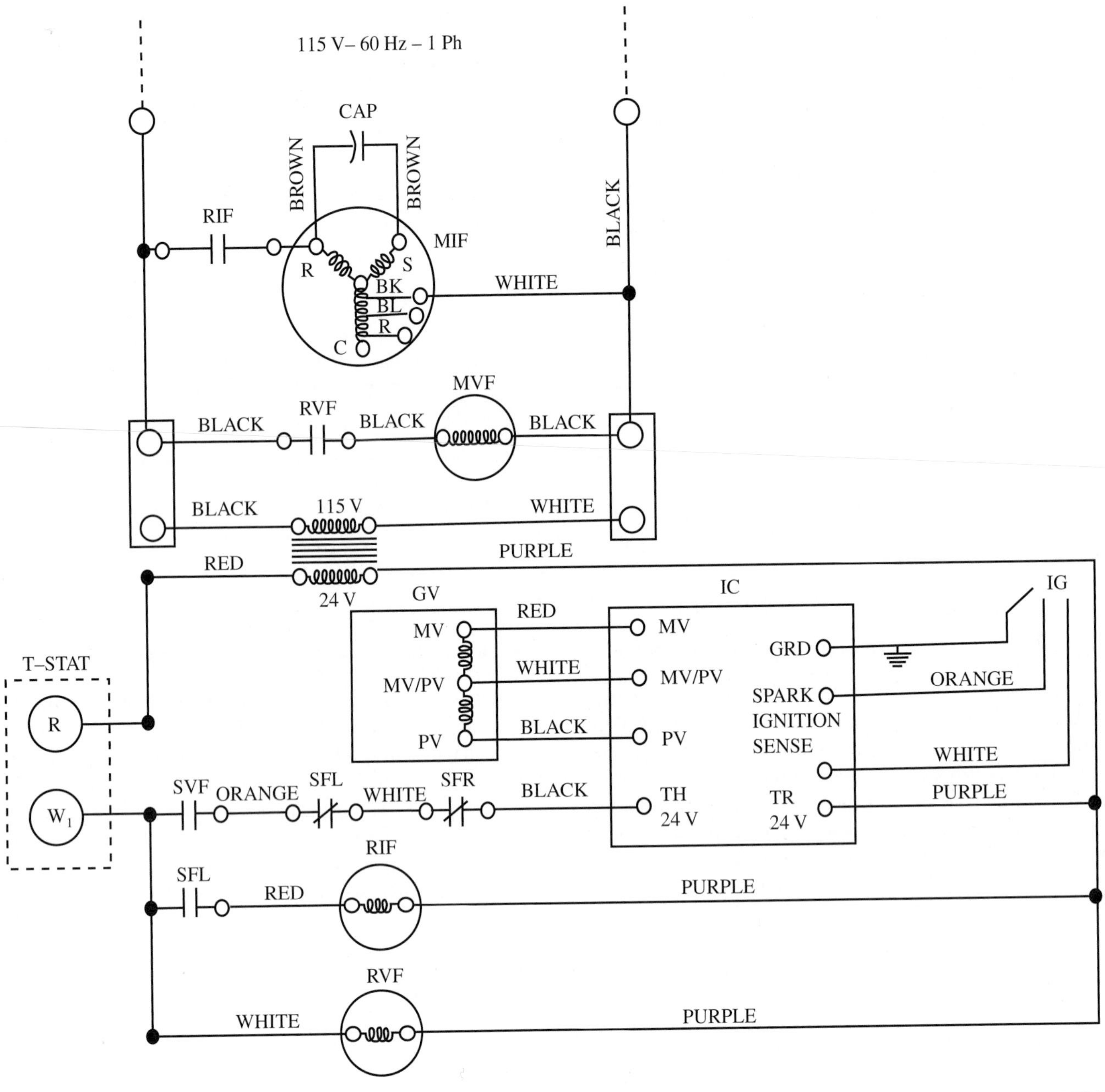

Figure 33-44 Ladder diagram of gas furnace with spark ignition

open since there is no fire in the furnace to cause that temperature switch to close. There would be a voltage drop measurable across the cooling contactor and indoor blower relay. There would not be a voltage drop measurable across the gas valve because the gas valve would not be energized.

Figure 33-44 shows a ladder diagram for a central gas furnace with a spark ignition. Figure 33-45 illustrates the various parts of the circuit that would be at line 1 and line 2 voltage potential. Note that there is a voltage drop that would be measured across the blower relay terminals RIF and the induction fan relay terminals RVF and the primary leads on the transformer. Most of the low voltage components are at the same potential. The only areas that would measure a potential

difference would be between the R and W_1 terminals in the thermostat.

Figure 33-46 shows those parts of the circuit that would have a potential voltage difference during the ignition phase of the furnace operation. This figure illustrates that only the induction fan motor and the transformer are energized on the line voltage side. The indoor blower motor does not become energized until after the furnace has had an opportunity to heat sufficiently. This delay in starting the indoor blower motor is done so that cold air is not blown into the residence on startup.

On the low voltage circuit there is not a voltage difference across R and W_1 because the thermostat contacts would

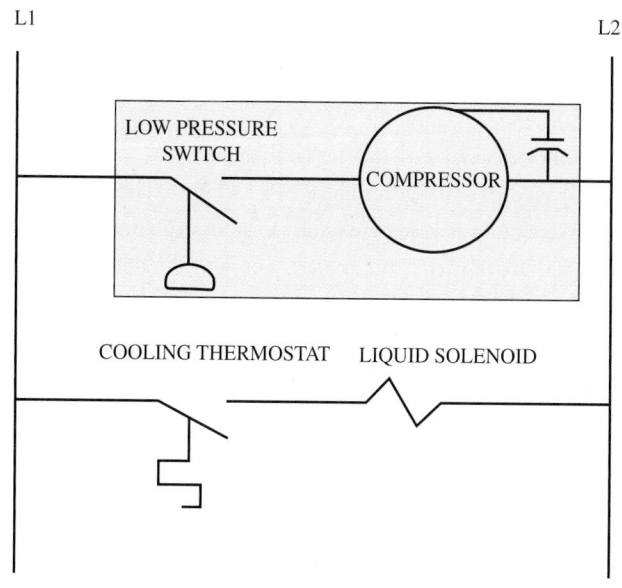

L1   L2

Figure 33-66 Pressure switch controlling the compressor

UNIT 33—SUMMARY

Reading and interpreting wiring diagrams is absolutely essential to success in the HVAC/R industry. Different types of wiring diagrams tell the technician the location of electrical components, the terminal designations on the components, the routing of the actual wires on the unit, the colors and/or labels of the wires used, where the field power wiring for the unit should be connected, and where the field control wiring needs to be connected. Most importantly, the schematic diagram shows the individual circuits and how the unit operates.

WORK ORDERS

Service Ticket 3301

Customer Complaint: Poor Cooling

Equipment: R-22 Packaged Air Conditioner

Diagram: Figure 33-21

A technician is called to look at a system that is not cooling properly. The compressor runs for a few minutes then cycles off, but both fans remain running. After consulting the diagram, the technician decides to check the low pressure switch and measures a voltage drop of 230 V, indicating that the pressure switch is open. The technician checks the suction pressure and finds it is 40 psig. Next, the technician checks the air filter and finds it very dirty. The filter is changed, the suction pressure rises, the pressure switch closes, and the compressor remains running.

Service Ticket 3302

Customer Complaint: Furnace Fan Operates Constantly

Equipment: Standing Pilot Gas Furnace

Diagram: Figure 33-44

A technician is called to look at a standing pilot furnace whose fan is running constantly. The diagram shows that the fan is controlled by both a fan relay and a fan switch. The technician checks the current of the high speed fan wire and finds 0 A. The amp draw of the low speed reads 3.5 A, indicating that the fan is operating on low speed. The technician checks the settings on the fan switch, turns off the power to the furnace, and checks the continuity of the fan switch. It reads 0 Ω, indicating that it is closed even though the furnace is not hot. The fan switch is replaced and the fan quits operating all the time.

Service Ticket 3303

Customer Complaint: Poor Cooling

Equipment: Air Source Heat Pump

Diagram: Figure 33-57

A technician is called to look at a heat pump that is not cooling well and notices that the outdoor fan is not operating. Consulting the diagram, the technician sees that the outdoor fan motor is controlled by the normally open CR relay contacts and the normally closed DFR contacts. A voltage measurement across the CR contacts reads 0 V, while a voltage reading across the DFR contacts reads 230 V. This reveals that the DFR normally closed contacts are open. Next, the technician checks the voltage at the defrost relay coil and reads 230 V, even though the unit is operating in cooling. Checking the air tubes of the defrost switch, the technician finds a wasp nest in the end of one tube. After cleaning out the wasps, the defrost relay coil is no longer energized and the normally closed points close, allowing the outdoor fan to operate.

Service Ticket 3304

Customer Complaint: Unit Blows Cold Air in Heating

Equipment: Air Source Heat Pump

Diagram: Figure 33-57

A service technician is called to look at an air source heat pump that is blowing very cold air during the heating season. The technician checks the diagram and sees the the reversing valve is energized in heat by the normally open RVR contacts. A voltage measurement at the reversing valve solenoid reads 230 V, indicating that the RVR relay is working correctly. The technician turns off the power to the unit and checks the resistance of the RVS. It reads infinite ohms, indicating a defective reversing valve solenoid coil. The reversing valve solenoid coil is replaced, the unit shifts into heat, and operates correctly.

Service Ticket 3305
Customer Complaint: Compressor Short Cycles
Equipment: Walk-in Cooler with Pump Down Circuit
Diagram: Figure 33-68

A technician is called to look at a walk-in cooler whose compressor runs for a minute, remains off for about a minute, and them comes back on. The box temperature is close to the thermostat setpoint, but the customer is concerned about the compressor constantly cycling on and off. The customer confides that he adjusted the differential on the low pressure switch from 20 psi to 5 psi thinking it would make the cooler operate at a lower temperature. The technician explains that the differential setting is now so low that the slight pressure rise that occurs naturally after the compressor shuts off is closing the switch before it should. The switch is set back to the correct setting and the compressor stops short cycling.

Service Ticket 3306
Customer Complaint: No Heat
Equipment: Oil Furnace
Diagram: Figure 33-27

A technician is called to look at an oil furnace that is not heating and observes that the burner does light, but it does not stay on for long and then the primary control locks out. The technician removes the cad cell and sees that it is covered with a fine layer of soot. The cad cell is cleaned and replaced and the furnace stays operating.

UNIT 33—REVIEW QUESTIONS

1. List the different types of electrical diagrams used by HVAC/R manufacturers.
2. Which diagram types are most useful for understanding the operation of the unit?
3. Describe the concept behind ladder diagrams.
4. What information does a point to point diagram give the technician?
5. What is the difference between a load and a control?
6. Why is there a potential of 24 V between the R terminal and the other terminals on a thermostat subbase?
7. What does a voltage reading across a set of contacts indicate?
8. What other diagrams are similar to point to point diagrams?
9. Why are relay coils and contacts not shown in the same place on a schematic diagram?
10. What information does a factual diagram give that a ladder diagram does not give?
11. How is field wiring distinguished from factory wiring on most diagrams?
12. What is the purpose of a component location diagram?
13. Why do most manufacturers supply more than one type of diagram with their equipment?
14. In Figure 33-57, what energizes the CR coil during the heat cycle?
15. In Figure 33-48, what switches must be closed to complete a circuit to the TH terminal of the ignition control?
16. In Figure 33-61, what controls the compressor?
17. In Figure 33-61, what does the VPS control?
18. In Figure 33-3, when is the reversing valve energized: the heating cycle or the cooling cycle?
19. In Figure 33-4, where does the power wiring connect to the unit?
20. In Figure 33-7, where does the W terminal on the thermostat connect?
21. In Figure 33-7, how does the high pressure switch, HPS, protect the compressor?
22. In Figure 33-6, where does the white wire on the airflow switch go?
23. In Figure 33-8, what type of wire should be used to wire the unit?
24. In Figure 33-8, how many wires should be run between the thermostat and the furnace?
25. In Figure 33-9, what do the field control wires on the T terminals connect to?
26. In Figure 33-9, what color wires connect to the limit side of the fan-limit switch?
27. In Figure 33-68, how does the thermostat control the operation of the compressor?
28. In Figure 33-40, what voltage operates the potential relay coil?
29. In Figure 33-40, what is the purpose of the potential relay?
30. List the heating operational sequence for the unit in Figure 33-52.

Residential and Light Commercial Systems

UNIT 34

Residential Air Conditioning

OBJECTIVES

After completing this unit you will be able to:

- explain the details of a unitary refrigeration system.
- install a room or window air conditioner.
- describe how a residential split air conditioning system is configured.
- explain why split systems were developed.
- discuss the proper arrangement and placement of equipment in a split system.
- describe how add-on coils can be used in a split system.
- explain why split system components need to be properly matched.

34.1 INTRODUCTION

Residential air conditioning systems are often made up of unitary air conditioning components. These are factory built and tested systems, complete as much as possible, with piping, controls, wiring, and refrigerant. Self-contained package units are usually simple to install, requiring only service connections and in some cases ductwork for field applications. The simplest of these is the window mounted room air conditioner.

Unitary air conditioning equipment consists of one or more factory made assemblies, which normally include an evaporator or cooling coil, a compressor and condenser combination, and possibly include a heating unit. When the air conditioner is connected to a remote condensing unit, such as in residential applications, the system is often referred to as a split system. A split system installation will require more fieldwork for the technician as compared to the installation of a simple package unit. The sizes of unitary equipment range from small fractional tonnage room coolers to large packaged rooftop units in the 100-ton category. Split system equipment up to 5 tons in capacity may be classified as either commercial or residential. There is a wide range of applications in both markets using the same product; however, above 5 tons the application becomes distinctly commercial, and product designs use different components.

34.2 ROOM AIR CONDITIONERS

Room air conditioners were primarily developed to provide a simplified means of adding air conditioning to an existing room. These units are considered semi-portable in that they can easily be moved from one room to another or from one building to another. They provide cooling, dehumidifying, filtering, and ventilation, and some units provide supplementary heating.

In numbers sold, room air conditioners such as the one shown in Figure 34-1 outsell all other types of unitary equipment. They are relatively low in cost, easy to install, and can be used in almost any type of structure, as shown in Figure 34-2.

The disadvantage of room air conditioners is that they may either block part of the window area and prevent the

Figure 34-1 Window air conditioning unit for cooling

Figure 34-2 Window air conditioning unit on Harry Elkins Widner building at Harvard University

window from being opened or require a special hole through the wall. Some people object to operating noise that they produce close to the occupants. They are best used to condition a single room; however, the spillover can supply some conditioning to adjacent areas.

TECH TIP

A common problem with window air conditioning units is the nuisance trips of the residence circuit breakers. Window units are often used in older homes where the electrical service is not adequate for the air conditioner load. It may be possible to rewire the residence for a single circuit to the air conditioner or it may be best to downsize the system to one that will not trip the circuit breaker. Downsizing the unit may provide less than desired levels of cooling on extremely hot days. However the constant shutting down of the oversized unit electrical service can result in the same lack of cooling. Additionally it may be possible to use more than one window unit in a room if the electrical outlets in that room are serviced by more than one circuit breaker.

34.3 CONSTRUCTION AND INSTALLATION OF ROOM AIR CONDITIONERS

There are basically two parts to the unit, as shown in Figure 34-3. One section goes inside the room where the evaporator fan draws in room air through the filter and cooling coil, delivering conditioned air back into the room. The other section extends outside the room where the condenser fan forces outside air through the condenser, exhausting the heat absorbed by the evaporator. One motor operates both the indoor blower and outdoor fan. The motor shaft extends through the separating partition and drives both fans. Condensate from the evaporator coil flows into the drain pan, which extends below the condenser fan. The condenser fan tip dips into condensate, splashing it onto the hot condenser where it evaporates and is blown into the outside air.

The window-mounted units are supplied with a kit of parts for installation. Sill brackets, window mounting strips, and sealing strips are set in place for installations in double hung windows, as shown in Figure 34-4. Side curtains fold out to fill up the extra window space, as shown in Figure 34-5. A sponge rubber seal is provided for the opening where the sash overlaps, and a sash bracket is installed to lock the lower sash in place, as shown in Figure 34-6.

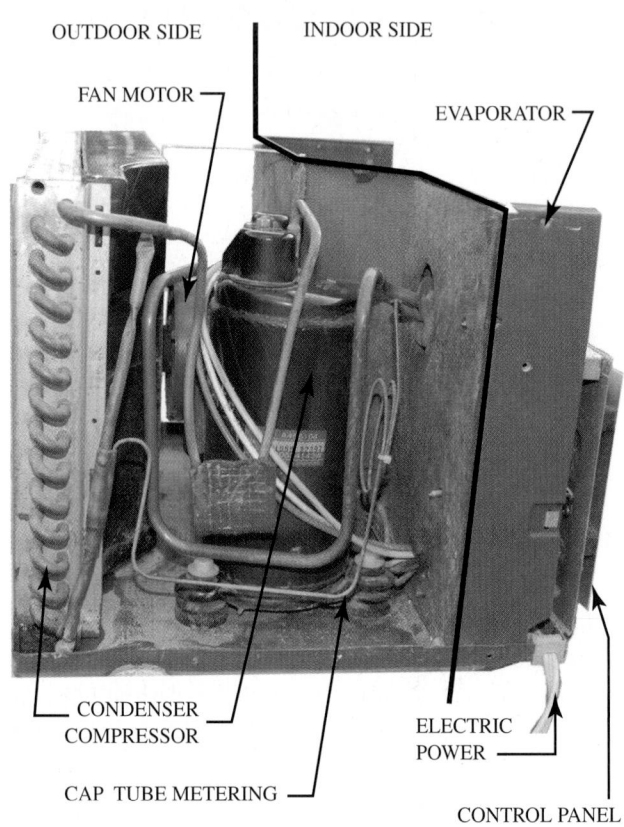

OUTDOOR SIDE INDOOR SIDE

FAN MOTOR

EVAPORATOR

CONDENSER
COMPRESSOR

ELECTRIC POWER

CAP TUBE METERING

CONTROL PANEL

Figure 34-3 Two basic parts of a window unit

UNIT 35

Residential Split System Air Conditioning Installations

OBJECTIVES

After completing this unit you will be able to:

- list the various installation components of a residential split system air conditioner.
- explain the installation process of the outdoor condensing unit.
- explain the installation process of the indoor evaporator and/or air handler.
- explain the methods used to select and install the refrigerant line sets.
- explain the electric wiring requirements of the system.
- explain the various methods used to check the airflow across an evaporator.
- explain the various methods used to check the refrigerant charge of the system.

35.1 INTRODUCTION

A popular style of air conditioning system used in many homes is the split system air conditioner. A typical split system consists of as few as two sections. There is an outdoor condensing unit and an indoor evaporator coil and air handler or an indoor evaporator coil and furnace. Many times these systems are connected to an existing forced air furnace, but they can also be installed as a stand alone system.

These systems must be assembled at the customer's home by a qualified technician. The installing technician must be proficient in the basic techniques used to run refrigerant lines, drain lines, and electric wiring. The technician must also possess the skills required to connect the system to the new or existing duct system.

35.2 PLANNING THE INSTALLATION

The success of any installation lies in its planning. Any equipment selection should be properly sized using the guidelines for load calculation as set forth in the Air Conditioning Contractors of America's (ACCA) Manual J. Proper planning allows for efficient and troublefree installation. Without proper planning, costly mistakes can and probably will occur, increasing the costs for the installing contractor.

Part of the planning procedure requires a technician to reference the manufacturer's installation manual and determine the installation requirements of the system. This will allow the technician to determine the refrigerant line sizes to run, the electrical requirements of the system, and any other manufacturer's recommendations required to properly install the system. The installing contractor should also review the local code requirements and make sure any code-related issues are covered.

A technician should also develop a list of materials needed for the installation. This will ensure that all the correct materials arrive on the job. Having to leave an installation to get more materials or the correct material costs valuable time on the job.

Proper planning also allows a technician to choose the proper location of the equipment. This is especially important when deciding where to install the outdoor condensing unit. A technician should always discuss and get the customer approval on the placement of the outdoor condensing unit. Installing it in the wrong location will cause problems for the contractor and the customer.

A technician should also develop a sequence of operation for the installation. This will allow for a more efficient installation process. A typical installation sequence is as follows:

- Determine the required Btu capacity of the system to be installed.
- Select the equipment and system components for the installation.
- If needed, configure the indoor section for an upflow, downflow, or horizontal installation.
- Set indoor coil in place.
- Install any needed ductwork.
- Set the outdoor pad in place and level.
- Set condensing unit in place.
- Install refrigerant lines.
- Leak test and evacuate/dehydrate refrigerant lines.
- Weigh in the correct amount of refrigerant according to the manufacturer's specifications.
- Run the required electrical wiring and connect up to the equipment.
- Install condensate drain line and pump (if needed).
- Start up system, confirm airflow, and check/adjust refrigerant charge.
- Clean up work area.
- Explain operation, warranty, and any required maintenance of the unit to the customer.

Equipment Sizing

Part of the installation process is choosing the right system components. The installing contractor must first determine the proper capacity of the equipment needed to satisfy the cooling and heating requirements of the structure. In order to determine the capacity needed, a heat gain calculation must be completed for the structure. For residential structures, the ACCA's Manual J is the industry standard. There are also many software programs available that will allow a contractor to perform this calculation.

It is important for a contractor to choose the right size system. Oversizing or undersizing a system can create problems for the contractor and the customer. An oversized system will not run long enough to properly dehumidify a structure. An undersized system will not be able to handle the load when the outdoor temperature is high.

Equipment Selection

Once the Btu requirements of a structure have been determined, the proper system components can then be selected. The outdoor condensing unit, such as the one shown in Figure 35-1, will be selected based on its Btu capacity for both sensible and latent cooling loads as outlined in ACCA Manual S, its seasonal energy efficiency ratio (SEER), and the type of condenser and voltage requirements. For residential systems a 208/230 single phase voltage, air cooled condenser is the standard and is used on most installations. The Btu capacity of the outdoor condensing unit will be chosen to match the Btu requirements of the structure. The SEER rating will be chosen based on the customer's requirements. The SEER is the operating efficiency rating of the condensing unit. The higher the SEER rating, the more efficient the condensing unit will operate. The installing contractor will normally offer their customer the option of choosing the SEER rating. Currently the minimum SEER rating available for new systems is 13.

Figure 35-2 A split system forced air furnace, evaporator coil, and condenser
(Courtesy of Sheridan Mechanical Services and http://www.myHVACparts.com.)

There are two types of installations for the indoor section of the system. One type is where the air conditioning system is connected to an existing forced air furnace, as shown in Figure 35-2. In this type of installation an evaporator coil and drain pan are attached to the existing furnace and the air conditioning system will use the same blower assembly and duct system as the forced air furnace. There are three different styles of evaporator coil and drain pan assemblies that can be used. One style is a cased coil assembly, which consists of an evaporator coil, metering device, drain pan, and housing. The complete assembly is designed to fit directly on top of a forced air furnace and the system's plenum (duct section) is connected to the top of this assembly. An uncased coil can also be used. This assembly consists of just an evaporator coil, metering device, and drain pan. It does not have its own housing. The assembly is designed to fit directly in the plenum of the duct system. The third option is a half cased coil, which is an evaporator coil, metering device, and drain pan contained in a housing covering only half of the coil.

The other type of indoor installation is where the air conditioner is a stand alone system, as shown in Figure 35-3. An air handler is used for this type of installation, consisting of an evaporator coil, metering device, drain pan, transformer, blower assembly, and housing. The air handler is connected to its own duct system. There are three configurations of air handlers: vertical upflow, vertical downflow, and horizontal.

The Btu capacity of the evaporator coil assembly or air handler selected may be different from the capacity of the outdoor condensing unit. Many applications require a larger evaporator to obtain a particular SEER rating or sensible heat ratio.

The metering device used for a particular installation may also need to be selected. The indoor unit may come

Figure 35-1 A typical outdoor condensing unit

Figure 35-3 A stand alone air conditioning system
(Courtesy of Goodman, © 2008 Goodman Manufacturing Company, C.P.)

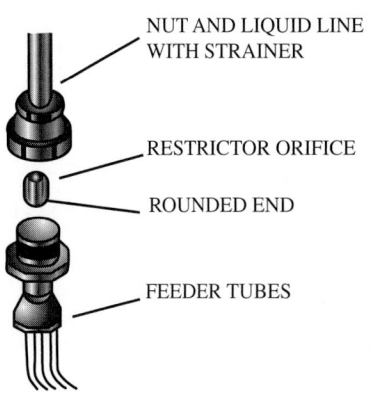

NUT AND LIQUID LINE
WITH STRAINER

RESTRICTOR ORIFICE

ROUNDED END

FEEDER TUBES

Figure 35-4 A fixed orifice used on a residential air conditioning system

Figure 35-5 A thermostatic expansion valve used on a residential air conditioning system

with a factory installed metering device; however, it may need to be changed out if it does not match the requirements of the system. Most manufacturers produce coils today with no metering device, allowing the installer to use the one that matches both the unit capacity needs and the refrigerant type being used, such as R-22 or R-410A. The metering device must match the Btu capacity of the condensing unit and indoor evaporator. There are two general types of metering devices used: the fixed orifice, as shown in Figure 35-4, and the thermostatic expansion valve (TEV), as shown in Figure 35-5.

Other Installation Components

There are several other installation components that must be chosen to complete an installation. The outdoor condensing unit will need an electrical disconnect switch, as shown in Figure 35-6. There are two types of disconnect boxes. One type contains only a switch and it may or may not have a fuse. The other type uses a circuit breaker for both the switch and electrical over current protection. An outdoor rated watertight flexible electrical cable, generally referred to as a whip, as shown in Figure 35-7, connects the system's disconnect to the condensing unit.

An outdoor pad must also be selected to set the condensing unit. This pad can either be a poured concrete slab or a prefabricated reinforced plastic pad, Figure 35-8. Most equipment manufacturers recommend that the equipment pad be 2 to 3 in larger on all sides than the condenser to reduce dirt spattering into the coils.

Appropriately sized refrigerant lines will also need to be selected. Copper ACR tubing is used. ACR tubing is processed for use on air conditioning and refrigeration systems. Its interior is processed to be clean and dehydrated and will not add any contaminants to a system. It is sized by its outside dimensions (OD) which differs from pipe used in the plumbing industry. Copper pipe used in the plumbing industry is sized by its inside diameter (ID).

Type L soft ACR tubing is sometimes used, as shown in Figure 35-9, and hard drawn ACR can also be used. Soft ACR tubing can be purchased in rolls of 50 ft lengths and cut to size on the job. Hard drawn ACR tubing can be purchased in 20 ft lengths and can also be cut to size on the job. To prevent condensation from forming on the suction line, it is typically

Figure 35-6 A disconnect switch for an outdoor condensing unit

Figure 35-7 A whip used on an outdoor condensing unit

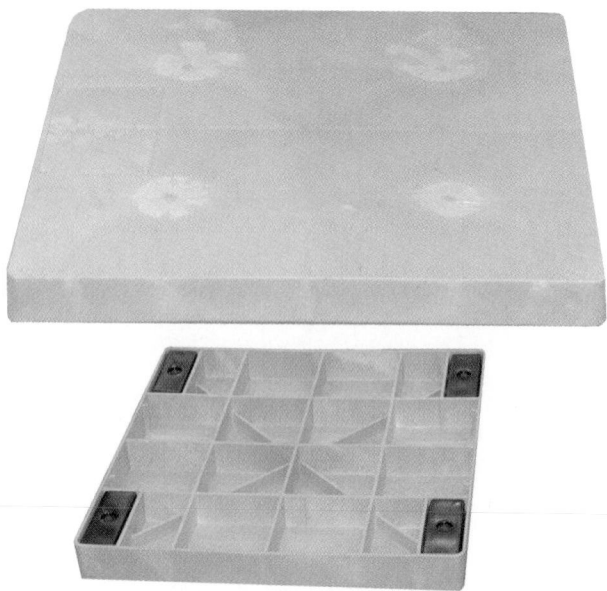

Figure 35-8 Prefabricated reinforced plastic pad
(Courtesy of DiversiTech Corporation)

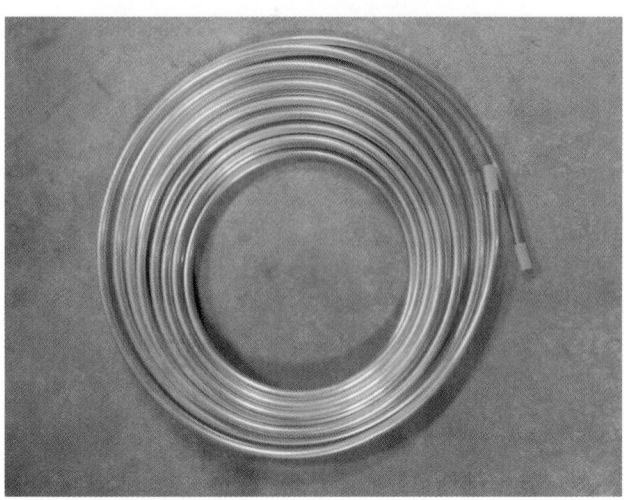

Figure 35-9 ACR tubing used for air conditioning and refrigeration systems

insulated with closed cell foam (Armaflex is often used). This insulation is sized based on the OD tubing size and the wall thickness required. Insulation is available with wall thicknesses of $^3/_8$ in, $^1/_2$ in, $^3/_4$ in, and 1 in. Insulation with a $^3/_8$ in, wall thickness is normally used on residential split system installations.

Wholesalers also sell ready-made line sets, consisting of an insulated suction line and a liquid line in various tubing diameters and lengths. These line sets are available in 15 ft,

25 ft, 35 ft, and 50 ft lengths with tubing diameters of $^5/_8$ in to 1 $^1/_8$ in for the insulated suction lines and $^3/_8$ in to $^1/_2$ in for the liquid lines.

A thermostat, shown in Figure 35-10, will also need to be selected. There are many different styles of thermostats. Thermostats are available as programmable and nonprogrammable as well as digital and mechanical. Different thermostats will have different features and capabilities depending on the system design. A contractor should consult with the customer as to the type of thermostat they prefer. A contractor will also need to select the wiring for the thermostat. Thermostat wiring is available in various gauge sizes and with different numbers of conductors. Residential installations will generally use a minimum of 18 gauge wire with either two, five, or eight

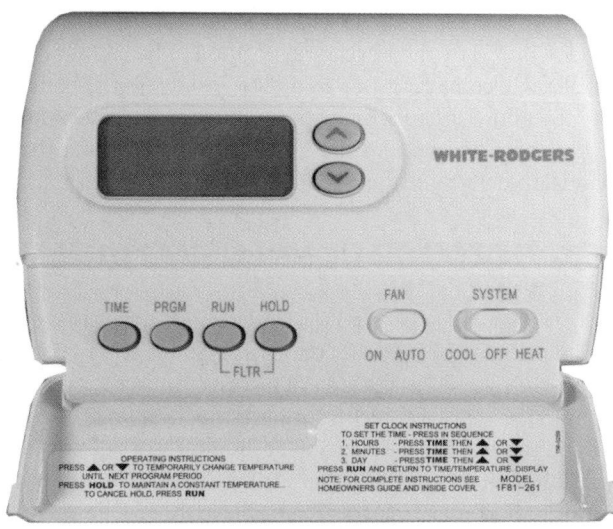

Figure 35-10 An HVAC thermostat

35.3 INSTALLING THE INDOOR EQUIPMENT

Normally the first part of the installation process is the installation of the indoor equipment. Depending on the type installed, the process will be slightly different. A cased coil, an uncased coil, and an air handler will all require different installation procedures.

Installing Cased Coils

When a cased coil, such as shown in Figure 35-12, is used on an installation it will generally sit on top of a forced air furnace or below the furnace on a downflow system. If the coil is used on an existing system, the supply air plenum will first need to be removed. Sometimes this also requires removing some other system components such as the furnace's vent piping.

conductors depending on the system and components to be installed. Some multistage heat pump applications may require as many as 12 wires.

Condensate tubing and fittings will also need to be selected. Normally the condensate drain lines used will be $\frac{3}{4}$ in Schedule 40 PVC. Be sure to check the local codes, as some may require $1\frac{1}{4}$ in drain lines after condensate leaves the unit. If there is not a convenient open drain close to the indoor assembly, a condensate pump, as shown in Figure 35-11, will also need to be selected to pump the condensate to an appropriate drain. The material used, as well as the location into which the condensate is drained, may be subject to local code.

Figure 35-11 A condensate pump used when no drain is close to the air conditioner's evaporator
(Courtesy of DiversiTech Corporation)

Figure 35-12 A cased evaporator coil

Once the supply air plenum is removed, the new cased coil is set on top of the furnace and is leveled to ensure proper drainage of the condensate. The coil does not need to be fastened to the furnace. A new supply air plenum is then fabricated and reinstalled between the top of the cased coil and the existing ductwork. All connections must be properly sealed to prevent air loss.

Installing an Uncased Coil

When an uncased coil, as shown in Figure 35-13, is used on an installation it will generally be installed inside the supply air plenum. One side of the supply air plenum will need to be removed or cut in order to allow the uncased coil to be slipped into the plenum.

To install the coil, first shut off power to the furnace and remove any system components in front of the side of the plenum on which the coil is to be installed. Next, lay out a pattern on the supply air plenum for the coil access opening and cut the opening. The access opening should allow the coil to sit close to the furnace, but should be at least 4 in above the furnace's heat exchanger. Once an opening is created, install a set of brackets to hold the coil assembly, making sure the brackets installed are level to allow for proper drainage of the coil's condensate. Next insert the coil into the plenum and place on the installed brackets. More than likely there will be open spacing between the coil and the inside walls of the plenum. These openings must be covered to prevent the supply air from bypassing the evaporator coil. Normally, a piece of sheet metal is installed between the coil and the inside walls of the plenum to cover this opening. Once the coil is set in place and leveled, a sheet metal patch will need to be fabricated to cover the opening on the side of the plenum. All joints must be sealed to prevent air leakage.

Installing an Air Handler

Since an air handler is a complete assembly its installation consists of setting the air handler in place and connecting the ductwork. A supply plenum will be connected to the discharge of the air handler and a return boot connected to its inlet.

Most air handlers can be installed in the vertical upflow, the downflow, or the horizontal position. Normally the air handler will come ready for an upflow installation. If used in the downflow or horizontal position, some modifications will need to be made to the unit. Consult the installation manual to determine these modifications.

35.4 OUTDOOR CONDENSING UNIT INSTALLATION

The location of an outdoor condensing unit is an important part of the overall installation. An incorrectly placed condensing unit can cause problems for both the installing contractor and the customer. The installer should always discuss the location of the condensing unit with the customer and verify the location chosen is not objectionable to them. Figure 35-14 shows the placement of an outdoor condensing unit. The following is a list of recommendations when deciding on the location of the outdoor condensing unit:

- Do not install a unit where the operating noise will be objectionable to the customer or their neighbors.
- Avoid locating the unit in direct sunlight.
- Do not locate where water, snow, or ice from the roof or eaves can fall directly onto the unit or where the roof overhang can cause recirculation of the air exhausted from the unit.

Figure 35-14 A typical placement of an outdoor condensing unit

Figure 35-13 An uncased evaporator coil

- Do not locate under decks or porches unless the clearance dimensions specified by the manufacturer are met.
- Locate the unit close to the building to minimize line length and to avoid installing underground piping.
- Locate the unit so that it can be readily serviced.
- Maintain required clearances around the unit for proper airflow.

Once the location has been chosen, the pad for the condensing unit can be set in place and leveled. The condensing unit can then be set in place on the pad. The condensing unit can be mounted and secured directly to the pad using a construction adhesive or tie down bolts (some local codes may require this). If construction adhesive is used, make sure not to block the drain holes located on the bottom of the condensing unit.

SAFETY TIP

Improperly lifting heavy objects can cause serious injury. A technician should always lift with the legs rather than the back; the leg muscles are much stronger than the back muscles. For added protection, wear a back support. Follow these recommended steps when lifting heavy objects:

- Move close to the object to be lifted.
- Squat down. Keep your back straight and your chin tucked in. Position one foot behind the other with the forward foot at the side of the object.
- Grip the object from underneath and wrap your hands around the object.
- Draw the object close to your body.
- Lift by slowly straightening your legs. Try to keep the weight centered over your legs as much as possible.

TECH TIP

Noise is recognized as an environmental pollutant. Outdoor air cooled condensing units are sound-producing mechanical devices, which some cities and towns regulate. Early attempts to create local ordinances prompted action on the part of the ARI in 1971 to establish a sound rating standard which local communities could adopt.

ARI Standard 270 applies to the outdoor sections of factory-made air conditioning and heat pump equipment (unitary air conditioners). Under the program, all participating manufacturers are required to rate the sound power levels of their equipment in accordance with the technical specifications contained in this standard. Test results are submitted by the manufacturers to ARI for review and evaluation. Units are sound rated with a single number, the sound rated number (SRN). Typical ratings are between 14 and 24.

35.5 INSTALLING THE REFRIGERANT LINES

To connect the indoor coil to the outdoor condensing unit, ACR tubing will need to be run and connected to each of these devices. One pipe run will be the vapor suction line and the other the liquid line of the system. These lines must be properly sized and installed to ensure the system operates in accordance with the manufacturer's specifications. Incorrectly sized or installed refrigerant lines can cause the system to operate outside its rated capacity or cause damage to the system's compressor.

Before installing the refrigerant lines, make sure the metering device installed in the indoor unit is correctly sized for the application. If a fixed orifice metering device is used, verify that it matches the rating for the outdoor condensing unit. Some new condensing units will come shipped with an appropriately sized fixed orifice, as shown in Figure 35-15. If the indoor unit's fixed orifice does not match the one that came with the condensing unit, it should be replaced with the one supplied by the condensing unit manufacturer. Many coils now ship with no metering device as one is added based upon capacity requirements and refrigerant type.

The overall length of the refrigerant line should be kept as short as possible. Do not exceed the maximum length as stated by manufacturer. Generally pipe runs can be up to 175 ft. If a line set exceeds a distance specified by the manufacturer, special modifications will need to be done to the system. Most manufacturers will have an installation bulletin detailing their requirements for these long line applications.

Figure 35-15 A fixed orifice shipped with a new condensing unit

The diameter of the refrigerant lines run must be properly sized; it is based on Btu capacity and the length of the refrigerant lines used on the system. Always follow the recommendations of the equipment manufacturer; the required line sizes will normally be given in the installation manual shipped with the equipment. When the condensing unit is installed above the evaporator unit, suction line size (if oversized) can affect the velocity of the refrigerant and the refrigerant's ability to carry oil.

TECH TIP

Do not base the line sizes on the stub connections at either the condensing unit or the indoor coil. These stub connections are based on an average installation and do not apply to every installation.

Suction lines should always be insulated to prevent water damage from condensation and to limit the refrigerant from becoming excessively superheated on the way back to the compressor. Liquid lines are normally not insulated except if there is a possibility that the liquid will gain excessive heat on its way to the metering device, such as if it is run through a hot attic.

Either soft or hard drawn ACR tubing can be used. Soft tubing is normally used, as it is easier to bend and form, as shown in Figure 35-16, making the installation of the tubing easier for the technician. When bending this tubing, use

Figure 35-17 Use a tube cutter for a clean and square cut

a tube bender to prevent kinking and to allow for a crisp bend. When elbows are required, use a long-radius instead of a short-radius. Long-radius elbows offer less resistance to flow.

Many times the ACR tubing used will need to be cut to length. Make sure to use the appropriate tubing cutters, as shown in Figure 35-17; they allow for a clean and square cut. Avoid using a hacksaw as it leaves too many burrs on the tube ends as well as filings that can contaminate the system. Always deburr the tubing ends after cutting them. Do not allow any of the burrs to fall into the copper tubing.

Instead of using fittings to join sections of tubing, many technicians will used a swaging tool to increase the diameter of one tube end, allowing the opposite end to be inserted into the enlarged end. This method allows for less soldered or brazed joints, leading to less chance of refrigerant leaks.

The tubing connections are joined using the brazing process. Always flow an inert gas, such as nitrogen, through the lines when brazing. This prevents the copper from oxidizing due to the heat. Oxidation will tend to flake off during operation, which will plug up filter-driers and metering devices.

The condensing unit will normally contain two isolation valves, as shown in Figure 35-18, each with a stub connection. One of these stub connections, is for the suction line and the other is for the liquid line connection. Each of these isolation valves will also have a Schrader port to allow a technician to attach the refrigeration manifolds. On new systems these isolation valves are initially front seated to hold a refrigerant charge contained in the condensing unit. When brazing the tubing to these stub connections, the core inside the Schrader must be removed. The valve contains a rubber packing which if overheated will be damaged. A core remover can be used to remove this Schrader core. A wet rag or a heat sink material must always be wrapped around the valves to prevent them from being overheated during brazing, Figure 35-19.

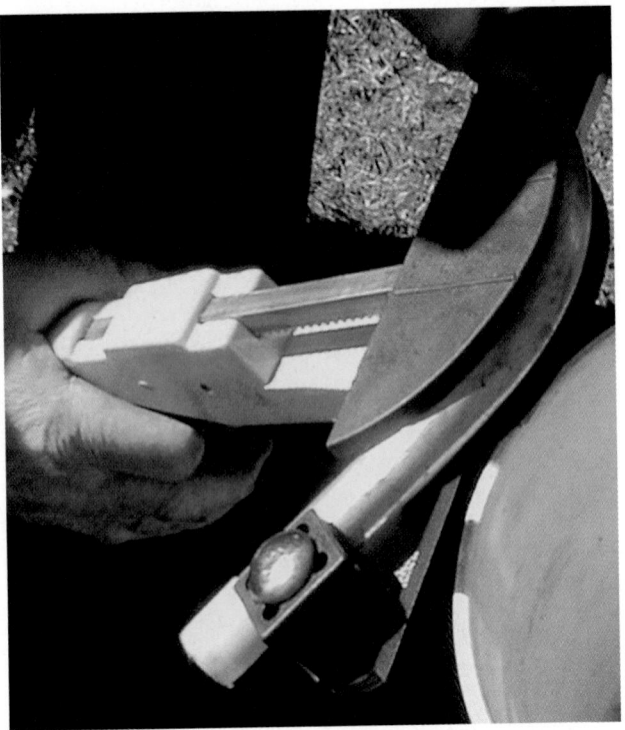

Figure 35-16 Soft ACR tubing is easier to bend and form

Figure 35-18 The isolation valves on an outdoor condensing unit

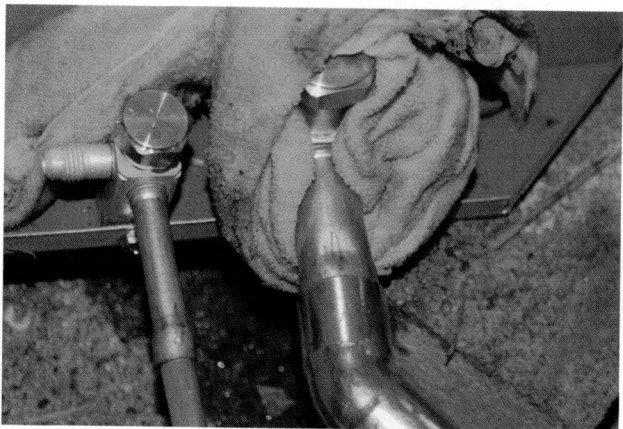

Figure 35-19 Wet rag wrapped around valves during brazing

When running the refrigerant lines, there should be support lines every 6 to 10 ft and within 2 ft of any bends. Insulated supports should be used to avoid any noise transmission and to avoid having the tubing come in direct contact with any water pipes or ductwork.

Normally, the refrigerant lines will need to run through some type of wall structure. When cutting through any wall, always check and recheck before cutting access holes—mistakes can be costly. When running refrigerant lines through a masonry wall, the pipe must be sleeved with a section of PVC tubing to prevent the deterioration of the copper tubing. This reduces the chance of a leak developing over time from the tubing rubbing on the masonry due to vibration. Always seal pipe penetrations with an appropriate sealant.

A liquid line filter-drier should always be a component included in the system. The best location for the filter-drier is indoors as close as possible to the metering device, although most installations have them outside near the condensing unit. The dessicant contained in the drier will

normally hold more moisture in a cooler environment. Some manufacturers install a liquid line drier at the factory. If this is the case, be sure not to add another one as this would result in two driers in series and this could cause a restriction.

Leak Testing

Once all the refrigerant lines are run and connected, the system needs to be leak checked. The lines and coil should be leak tested with dry nitrogen. Nitrogen makes a good initial leak test gas because it is inexpensive and legal to release to the air. Pressurize the lines and coil to between 100 psig and the system's low side test pressure. Never pressurize a system more than 150 psi. Make a note of the time and pressure. Use soap bubbles or an ultrasonic leak detector to check the line connections at both the inside and outside units. Also check any other mechanical or brazed joints in between. Finally, if the unit uses a field installed expansion valve, check all connections on the expansion valve. After making all these checks, recheck the pressure. The system has passed the initial leak test if the pressure is the same as when the system was first pressurized.

An alternative method for leak checking a system is to pressurize the system with a small amount of HCFC-22 and nitrogen. Add enough refrigerant to pressurize the system to 2 to 3 psig with the HCFC-22 and then add a nitrogen charge on top of the refrigerant. Pressurize the system again to a test pressure as recommended by the equipment manufacturer. Once the system is pressurized, an electronic leak detector can be used to locate the refrigerant leak. Only use this mixture with R-22 systems. Never mix R-22 with R-410A.

TECH TIP

Vacuum pumps are used in conjunction with a quality vacuum gauge to properly evacuate a refrigeration system before refrigerant is added to an empty system. Before opening a vacuum pump and gauge to a system, it is a good practice to perform a blank off test. A blank *off test* is when a vacuum pump only pulls a vacuum on the vacuum gauge and manifold.

Performing a blank off test before opening a vacuum pump and gauge to a system will allow a technician to verify that the vacuum pump and gauge are operating normally. It is better to identify a problem with either a vacuum pump or gauge before running on a system. Running a defective vacuum pump on a system is a waste of time; a sufficient vacuum level will not be obtained. Using a defective vacuum gauge will not allow a technician to determine if the appropriate micron level for complete evacuation is reached.

To perform a blank off test, turn off a valve between the system and the vacuum gauge, manifold and vacuum pump. Then run the vacuum pump until a 500 micron level is achieved. If a 500 micron level is achieved, a technician can safely assume that the vacuum pump and vacuum gauge are operating normally.

System Evacuation

Once the system is leak tested and is determined to be leak free, it needs to be evacuated. Release the nitrogen to the air and connect a vacuum pump and micron vacuum gauge. The system should be evacuated to a 500 micron level or the level recommended by the equipment manufacturer. Do not rely on a compound gauge, as they are not designed for deep vacuum detection.

Once a 500 micron level is achieved, shut off the pump and watch the micron gauge. A rise of 100–200 microns is normal. If the micron level rises above this but then levels out, try running the vacuum pump again because there may be some moisture left in the system. If the micron level rises and continues to rise, there is probably a leak in the system, which must be repaired. Once the line set and evaporator have been properly evacuated, the isolation valves on the condensing unit will need to be opened to allow the refrigerant to flow into the rest of the system if the new condensing unit has a precharge of refrigerant. Remove the valve stem caps from the isolation valves and turn the valve stem fully counterclockwise to open the valves.

If the new condensing unit does not have a precharge of refrigerant, weigh in the correct amount of refrigerant based on the system match and length of line set. Follow the manufacturer's recommendations, which is always the best way to charge a system.

35.6 FIELD WIRING

The installation of a residential split system air conditioner requires the installation of two dedicated line voltage and two low voltage electrical circuits. One dedicated line voltage circuit services the outdoor condensing unit through an (if required, fused) outside disconnect switch. The line voltage service to the outdoor condensing unit is normally a 208/240 V single-phase service rated at a specific amperage. The amperage rating needed will depend upon the size of the condensing unit installed. A separate low voltage circuit is also required from the furnace or air handler to the outdoor condensing unit. This is typically an 18 gauge 2 conductor service used for the control circuit of the system of a cooling only, single stage system. The other dedicated line voltage circuit is to the furnace or air handler. This is normally a 115 V or 230 V 15 A or 20 A circuit. The second low voltage circuit is for the system's thermostat connection. It is run from the furnace or air handler to the thermostat. Normally an 18 gauge, 4 wire conductor is used. Some installations will require a 5 conductor service if a 24 V digital thermostat is used. Newer multistage residential systems, which can have IAQ options, may require more wires. When connecting the low voltage wiring of the system, always refer to the manufacturer's wiring diagram for the proper connections.

Choosing an Overcurrent Protective Device

When installing residential air conditioning systems, the installing contractor must be sure the appropriate type of over current protection device is used with the outdoor condensing unit. There are three main types of over current protection devices:

- Fuse.
- Standard circuit breaker.
- HACR circuit breaker.

The type of over current device to use will normally be stated in the installation instructions or on the rating plate of the condensing unit, as shown in Figure 35-20. Some manufacturers will use the following wording on the data plate to state the type of overcurrent device to use:

- If the rating plate states MAX FUSE _____ AMPS, then a fuse with the proper rating must be placed in the circuit. Normally a fused disconnect will satisfy this requirement.
- If the rating plate states MAX FUSE or HACR CIRCUIT BREAKER _____ AMPS, then an HACR circuit breaker or fuse with the proper rating can be used.
- If the rating plate states MAX FUSE, HACR CIRCUIT BREAKER OR CIRCUIT BREAKER _____ AMPS or MAXIMUM OVERCURRENT PROTECTION DEVICE, then a fuse, HACR circuit breaker, or standard circuit breaker can be used.

The gauge of the electrical wire used also needs to be selected. The proper gauge must be selected to allow for the

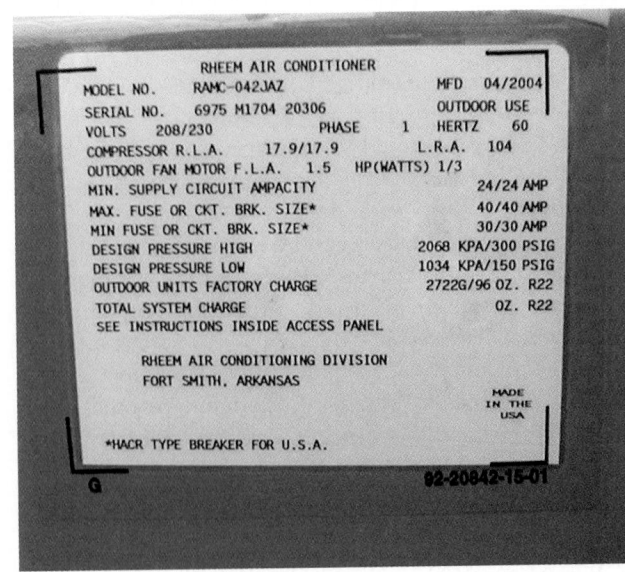

Figure 35-20 A rating plate of an outdoor condensing unit

proper amperage draw without the possibility of overheating the wire. When wiring equipment, always use the type and gauge of wire recommended by the equipment manufacturer and only make adjustments based on local or national codes. The value marked MINIMUM CIRCUIT AMPS is used to determine the proper wiring size to use. The wire size rating is based on a maximum ambient temperature of 86°F. If this is exceeded, the wire size must be rechecked after being derated for its new value.

TECH TIP

Only use fuses or circuit breakers that are HVAC/R rated. This type may be referred to as "slow-blow." These fuses and breakers can handle the momentary high current draw that occurs during compressor starting without blowing or tripping. The technician must be familiar with the appropriate National Electrical Codes, Local Codes and the Manufacturer Instructions.

35.7 INSTALLING THERMOSTATS

The placement of the thermostat is also important for the overall operation of the system. An incorrectly placed thermostat could cause the structure to be too cold or too warm. Following is a listing of some general requirements when mounting a thermostat:

- It should be installed on an inside wall and not on an outside wall or a wall exposed to any unconditioned space.
- It should be mounted 52 in to 60 in above the floor in an area with good air circulation.
- It should be mounted level.
- It should not be located in dead air spots.
- It should not be located near diffusers.
- It should not be located near any radiant heat sources, such as direct sunlight or in close proximity to floor and table lamps.
- It should not be located near any concealed pipe cooling ducts.
- It should not be mounted on a wall that separates conditioned and unconditioned space.

Normally 18 gauge wire is run from the thermostat to the indoor coil assembly. If the thermostat is located over 100 ft from the cooling equipment, number 16 gauge wire should be used. Remember, the smaller the number, the larger the wire size.

Wiring is normally color coded to simplify the connections between the thermostat and heating/cooling equipment. A typical color coding is shown below. Always check the manufacturer's instructions for the color coding of the low voltage system—not all manufacturers use this color coding.

- R   Red: transformer power (24 V).
- G   Green: fan control (The National Electrical Code allows the use of green as a current carrying wire only on voltages less than 50 V).
- Y   Yellow: compressor control.
- W   White: heating control.

35.8 INSTALLING THE CONDENSATE DRAIN PIPING

Since the evaporator will often operate at a temperature below the dew point temperature of the air drawn across it, water will be condensed from the air. The evaporator will have a drain pan located under its coil to collect this water. The water collected will need to be safely drained away from the evaporator. The installing technician needs to run a drain line from this pan to an open or vented drain. Laundry sink or basement floor drains are commonly used. Normally $^3/_4$ in Schedule 40 PVC is used as the drain line. However, other types of plastic pipe can be used such as CPVC (chlorinated polyvinyl chloride), PP (polypropylene), and ABS (acrylonitrile-butadiene styrene).

The drain pan on the evaporator will normally have both a primary and secondary drain. Pipe connections are normally $^3/_4$ in FPT (female pipe thread) connection. The primary drain is the lower of the two and a trap should be installed as close to the unit as possible if this location is under a negative pressure. The secondary drain is the upper connection and will allow water to drain from it, if the primary drain becomes clogged. Some applications do not require the use of a secondary drain; if it is unused it should be capped. These drain lines should be slightly pitched in the direction of flow and supported every 10 ft. A clean out should be provided, as shown in Figure 35-21, to allow service and maintenance technicians to clean the drain line as needed.

The secondary drain connection serves a great purpose if the evaporator is installed in an area where water overflow can cause severe damage to a customer's property. If the primary drain becomes clogged, water will safely drain down through the secondary drain line. When used, the secondary drain should not be connected to the primary drain and should not be trapped. It should be piped to a location that is separate from the primary drain and visible to the owner. The line should be tagged to notify the customer to call for service if water is seen draining from this pipe.

For attic or ceiling installations, it is advisable to install a drain pan under the fan coil to also prevent water damage caused by an overflowing condensate line. If a drain pan is installed under the fan coil, the secondary drain from the evaporator pan can be directed to this pan. This

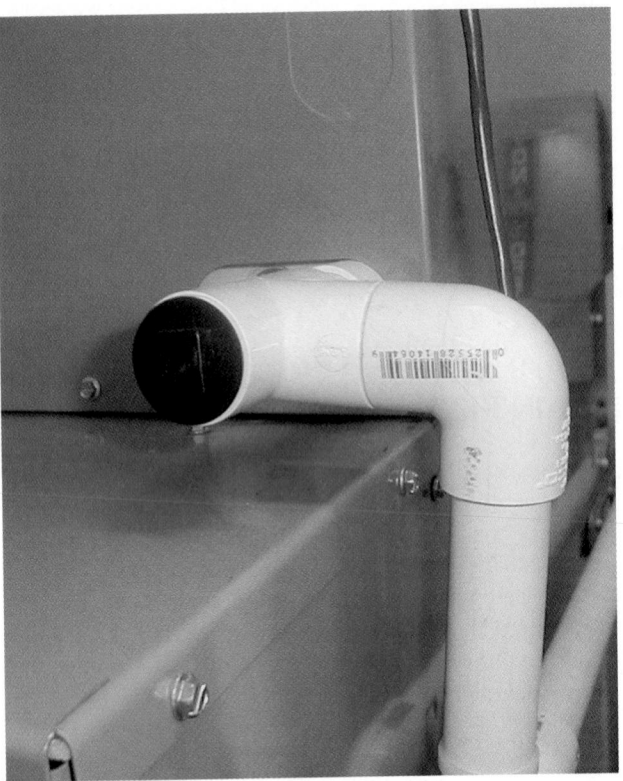

Figure 35-21 A clean-out for the primary drain line

pan must then be piped to a location that is both visible to the owner and will not cause any damage to the property. This line should then be tagged to notify the customer to call for service if water is seen draining from this pipe. Some units installed above finished ceilings have a safety switch located in the pan for shutdown in the event the pan is not draining properly. This limits expensive repairs due to water damage.

To cut and join PVC pipe as well as ABS and CPVC, the following procedure can be used:

- Use a plastic tubing cutter or a special cutter called a plastic tubing shear to cut the pipe. Avoid using a saw to cut this pipe. It will leave particles that could enter the pipe and cause a future clog.
- Deburr the pipe ends with a knife or file.
- Using an approved cleaning solvent, thoroughly clean the pipe ends and the inside of the fitting sockets.
- Apply a thin coat of primer to the tube end and the inside of the fitting sockets.
- Apply a thin coat of cement to the tube end and the inside of the fitting sockets.
- Immediately after applying the cement, push the pipe completely into the fitting sockets using a $1/4$ turn twisting motion until the pipe bottoms into the socket.

35.9 STARTUP AND SYSTEM CHECKOUT

Once all of the system components have been installed, the system needs to be started up and checked out per the instructions supplied in the installation manual. If the compressor has a crankcase heater, many manufacturers recommend that the heater be energized for a minimum of 24 hours before starting the system. This prevents liquid refrigerant from being in the compressor on startup.

The system's fan should be energized and the airflow across the evaporator should be measured. There should be approximately 400 CFM per ton of airflow across the evaporator. For example, a 3 ton residential air conditioning system should have approximately 1200 CFM of air flowing across its evaporator coil. However, airflow can be as low as 350 CFM per ton or as high as 450 CFM per ton to allow for changes to the sensible heat ratio to match specific requirements. If the airflow is too low, increase the fan motor speed per the manufacturer's instructions. If the airflow is too high, decrease the airflow per the manufacturer's instructions.

TECH TIP

There is a great deal of information available to technicians on the manufacturer's technical data sheets. All of this information is important and if you learn how to properly use it you will become more valuable to your company and your customers. Most manufacturers provide explanations as to what each column of data can be used for. If you have difficulty understanding any of the material, most manufacturers or their distributors will provide you with an in-depth explanation of the data and how it can be used. Also consult ACCA Manual S for detailed instruction of equipment selection.

Checking and Adjusting the Airflow

If too little or too much air is delivered across the evaporator coil, the system will not function properly. *Too much* air moving across an evaporator coil will result in poor humidity control. *Too little* airflow will result in an iced evaporator coil and possibly liquid flooding back to the compressor.

There are several ways a technician can measure the airflow across an evaporator. Two common methods are: measuring the temperature rise across the indoor system (this does require the air conditioning system to be attached to a forced air furnace or AHU), and measuring the static pressure drop across the evaporator.

TECH TIP

Measuring various types of temperatures is a common task for technicians. The thermometers used must be accurate in order for a technician to be able to properly work on air conditioning systems. Technicians should occasionally test the accuracy of their thermometers.

Testing a thermometer can easily be accomplished by placing it in a solution of crushed ice and water. Fill a bucket with crushed ice and add water so that ¾ of the ice is immersed in the water. It is best to have a solution that has more ice than water. Let the temperature of the solution stabilize—it should stabilize close to 32°F.

Once the temperature of the solution has stabilized, place the thermometer in the ice/water solution. Let the temperature measured on the thermometer stabilize and observe its reading. If the thermometer measures a temperature relatively close to 32°F, then it is relatively accurate. If not, the thermometer needs to be adjusted, repaired, or discarded.

Temperature Rise Method

When an air conditioning system is attached to a forced air furnace, the furnace can be used to calculate the airflow across the evaporator. By measuring the temperature rise across the furnace in the heating mode and with the fan operating at the same speed as it would during the cooling mode, the airflow across the device can be calculated.

To use this method, a technician would need to know the Btu output of the furnace and the temperature rise across the furnace (temperature rise = supply air − return air). To obtain the Btu output of a furnace, a technician would need to know the Btu input and its actual efficiency or AFUE rating. The following steps can be used to estimate airflow through a furnace and its evaporator coil.

Step 1. Obtain the Btu output of the furnace.
Step 2. Drill a hole in the return air duct near the furnace and insert a temperature probe into the hole. Drill another hole in the supply air duct, out of the line of sight of the heat exchanger, and place a temperature probe in the hole, as shown in Figure 35-22. Make sure the instruments used to measure the temperature at these two areas are calibrated to each other, meaning when exposed to the same temperature they read the same temperature.
Step 3. Turn the system on, call for heat, and operate the fan at the same speed that it would run at in the cooling mode. On some systems this is as easy as placing the fan selector switch to the ON position. On many systems the fan speed will be the same as it would during the cooling mode. On some newer systems, when the fan selector is switched to the ON position, the fan will operate at a continuous speed, which may not be the same speed as in the cooling mode. On

these systems, the technician may need to rewire the fan to allow it to operate at the same speed when in the cooling mode.
Step 4. Let the system run for 10 to 15 minutes so the temperatures can stabilize.
Step 5. Determine the temperature rise across the system by subtracting the return air temperature from the supply air.
Step 6. The airflow through the furnace as well as the air conditioning coil can then be calculated using the equation:

$$\text{CFM} = \frac{\text{Btu output}}{1.08 \times \Delta T} \qquad (35\text{-}1)$$

where

CFM = airflow volume measured in cubic feet of air per minute

Btu output = the rated heat output for the furnace measured in Btu/hr

1.08 = a constant for air under normal conditions at sea level (sometimes 1.1 is used for this value)

ΔT = the temperature difference between entering and exiting air, sometimes expressed as $(T_1 - T_2)$

For example, suppose a technician is working on a 3 ton air conditioning system with a forced air furnace with a Btu output of 80,000 Btu. When operating in the heating mode with the fan selector switch at the ON position (the fan will operate at the cooling speed), a technician measures a supply air temperature of 137°F and a return air temperature of 75°F. The temperature rise across the system would be 62°F (137°F − 75°F = 62°F). Then the airflow through the furnace and the evaporator coil can be calculated as:

$$\text{CFM} = \frac{\text{Btu output}}{1.08 \times \Delta T}$$

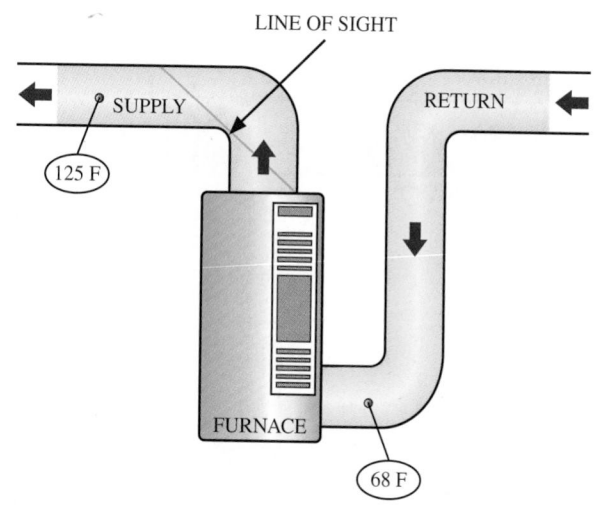

Figure 35-22 Measuring the temperature rise across a forced air furnace

$$CFM = \frac{80,000 \text{ Btu}}{1.08 \times 62°F}$$

$$CFM = 1,194.7$$

This will yield an estimated airflow value of 1,194.7 CFM across the evaporator coil. This is reasonably close to the desired value of 1,200 CFM, concluding that the airflow across the evaporator is sufficient.

Measuring the Static Pressure Drop Across an Evaporator

Another way a technician can measure the airflow across an evaporator is by measuring the static pressure drop across the evaporator coil. As air flows across an evaporator coil, it will drop some of its static pressure. As the volume of air flowing across the evaporator coil increases, so will its static pressure drop (loss). Equipment manufacturers publish specifications on the static pressure drop created by a volume (CFM) of air flowing across their evaporator coils. If the static pressure drop across an evaporator coil were measured, a technician can use the published specifications from a manufacturer to determine the actual airflow across the evaporator coil. Manufacturers will publish two different static pressure values: one for when the coil is dry and another for when the coil is wet. This is because there is a difference in the resistance to airflow across a dry and a wetted coil.

To calculate the pressure drop across an evaporator coil, a technician will need to measure the static pressure at the inlet and the outlet of the coil, as shown next. The pressures to be measured are relatively small, so a technician will need to use an incline manometer, which has a range approximately of 0.00 in wc. to 1.00 in wc.

The following steps can be used to measure the static pressure drop across an evaporator coil. Figure 35-23 shows a typical setup.

Step 1. Drill a $\frac{1}{4}$ in hole on either side of the evaporator coil. Always refer to the manufacturer's instructions for the recommended location of these holes. *Be extremely careful not to drill into the evaporator coil*—this will take a rather simple task and turn it into a nightmare for a technician.

Step 2. Insert a $\frac{1}{4}$ in tube into each hole far enough so that it will measure the static pressure on each side of the coil. Seal the insertion point of each tube and connect to a manometer as shown in Figure 35-23. Connect the inlet side of the evaporator coil to the lower end of the manometer, and connect the outlet side of the evaporator to the higher end of the manometer. Keep in mind it is critical that the inserted tubes be held so they are perpendicular to the flow of air to avoid having the measurement tainted by velocity pressure. Use of a pitot tube can prevent this possibility.

Step 3. Turn the indoor blower on and let it run for a few minutes so the airflow within the system can balance.

Step 4. Read the static pressure drop directly from the manometer.

Step 5. Using the information provided by the equipment manufacturer, read the amount of air flowing across the evaporator directly off the chart. Remember there will be a different value depending on whether the coil is dry or wet.

For example, a technician needs to determine the actual amount of air flowing across a dry 3 ton evaporator coil. The coil's model number is 036 and the measured static pressure drop is 0.18 in wc. Using the sample chart in Table 35-1 the airflow is determined to be 1,200 CFM. The conclusion is that the airflow is correct.

TECH TIP

Most manufacturers recommend that a system's airflow be set so that there is approximately 400 CFM per ton of air conditioning. In areas that have high relative humidity, a slightly slower fan speed can be used to aid in the humidification. In arid areas, the fan speed can be increased to provide more sensible cooling. As a rule of thumb, the fan speed should not be adjusted more than 10% above or below the manufacturer's recommendation. Excessively slow fan speeds can allow the evaporative coil to freeze up under light loads and excessively high fan speeds can put too large a load on the condenser under heavy load conditions.

Checking and Adjusting the Refrigerant Charge

There are several methods a technician can use to determine the correct refrigerant charge of a residential split system air conditioner. A technician should always first refer to the

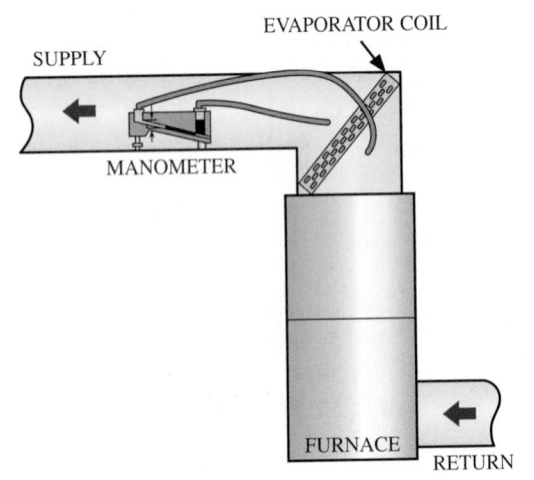

Figure 35-23 Measuring the static pressure drop across an evaporator coil

Table 35-1 Sample Performance Data Coil Static Pressure Drop (in. wc)

Unit model	Air quantity (CFM)													
	400	500	600	700	800	900	1,000	1,100	1,200	1,300	1,400	1,500	1,600	1,700
024	—	0.08	0.14	0.21	0.28	0.36	0.38	—	—	—	—	—	—	—
	—	0.07	0.11	0.15	0.20	0.25	0.30	—	—	—	—	—	—	—
030	—	—	—	0.12	0.17	0.22	0.28	0.34	0.42	0.50	—	—	—	—
	—	—	—	0.09	0.12	0.16	0.20	0.24	0.28	0.33	—	—	—	—
036	—	—	—	—	0.09	0.13	0.17	0.21	0.25	0.30	0.35	0.42	—	—
	—	—	—	—	0.07	0.10	0.12	0.15	0.18	0.21	0.25	0.28	—	—
042	—	—	—	—	—	—	0.10	0.13	0.17	0.20	0.24	0.28	0.32	0.36
	—	—	—	—	—	—	0.08	0.10	0.13	0.15	0.17	0.20	0.22	0.25
048	—	—	—	—	—	—	—	0.14	0.17	0.20	0.24	0.28	0.32	0.36
	—	—	—	—	—	—	—	0.11	0.13	0.15	0.17	0.20	0.22	0.25
060	—	—	—	—	—	—	—	0.12	0.16	0.18	0.22	0.26	0.30	0.34
	—	—	—	—	—	—	—	0.08	0.10	0.14	0.16	0.18	0.20	0.22

☐ Wet coil
▨ Dry coil

installation instructions and use the method recommended by the equipment manufacturer.

Many new residential condensing units are shipped from the factory with a refrigerant charge. The amount of refrigerant contained in the condensing unit will vary depending on its size and the manufacturer's engineering principles. Most manufacturers will ship their condensing units with enough refrigerant to properly operate a system with a 15 ft line set. This means if there is 15 ft of suction line and liquid line between the condensing unit and the evaporator, no additional refrigerant will need to be added to the system. Always check the installation instructions of the condensing unit as some manufacturers will add enough refrigerant for a different line length. If a system is installed with a line set greater than 15 ft (or the length stated in the installation instructions) the technician will need to add additional refrigerant to the system. The installation instructions will state the amount of refrigerant that needs to be added per foot of additional run of the liquid line used. Some manufacturers will also state the amount of additional refrigerant needed for the extended suction line, but this is normally a small amount and many times is omitted by the manufacturer.

For example, a new system is installed with a 25 ft line set, using a $\frac{3}{8}$ in liquid line. According to the manufacturer's instructions, the factory charge is adequate for a 15 ft line set. For each additional foot of $\frac{3}{8}$ in liquid run, there will need to be 0.6 oz of additional refrigerant added. As an example, if the length of the additional liquid line is 10 ft (25 ft − 15 ft = 10 ft)

then 6 oz (10 × 0.6 = 6 oz) of additional refrigerant will need to be added to the system.

For system using a non-TEV metering device, such as a fixed orifice, there is another means of determining if a system has an adequate refrigerant charge. This can be accomplished by measuring the superheat value of the refrigerant at the suction line leading into the condensing unit. The superheat value is not a constant value and varies at different indoor and outdoor ambient conditions. Manufacturers will publish a chart showing the required superheat value at various indoor and outdoor ambient conditions. If the actual measured superheat value is within ±5°F of the required superheat value, the system is properly charged. If the actual measured superheat value is more than 5°F higher than the required superheat value, refrigerant needs to be added to the system. If the actual measured superheat value is more than 5°F lower than the required superheat value, refrigerant needs to be removed from the system.

For systems using a TEV metering device, there is another means of determining whether the system has an adequate refrigerant charge. This can be accomplished by measuring the subcooling value of the refrigerant at the liquid line leaving the condensing unit. Generally a system is properly charged if the refrigerant is subcooled by 12–15°F at this location. Always check with the manufacturer of the system for their requirements. If the actual measured subcooling value is within ±3°F of the required subcooling value, the system is properly charged. If the actual measured subcooling value is more than 3°F lower than the required subcooling value, refrigerant needs to be added to the system. If the actual measured subcooling value is more than 3°F higher than the required subcooling value, refrigerant needs to be removed from the system.

When using either the subcooling or superheat methods of checking the refrigerant charge, allow the system to run approximately 15 minutes before measuring these values. This will allow the system's pressures and temperatures to stabilize so that an accurate reading can be obtained.

35.10 BEFORE YOU LEAVE THE JOB

Even after the installation is complete, the technician's job is not over. The work area should be completely cleaned. This includes wiping down the casing of the indoor and outdoor equipment as well as the thermostat. Any unused material needs to be removed from the property. If any of the customer's items were moved during the installation process, they would need to be returned to their original location.

The technician should show the customer the complete system and explain its operation. This includes how to operate the system's thermostat and where the system's electrical disconnects are located. The technician should also explain any required maintenance, such as changing the filter and cleaning the outdoor condensing unit, and explain the system's warranty in detail.

After explaining the operation of the system and explaining the system's warranty, the technician should ask the customer if they have any questions, place a company sticker on the unit, and thank them for using their company. If a "use and care" manual is provided by the manufacturer, it should be given to the customer.

TECH TIP

The actual total Btu capacity of an air conditioning system can be determined by measuring the airflow across the evaporator and the enthalpy difference of the air entering and leaving the evaporator. Then using the equation Btu capacity = $4.50 \times$ CFM $\times$ enthalpy difference (ΔH), the actual total Btu capacity can be determined.

The enthalpy difference of the air entering and leaving the system's evaporator can be determined by first measuring the wet bulb temperature of the air entering and leaving the evaporator. Then, using a psychometric chart, the enthalpy content of the air entering and leaving the evaporator can be determined.

For example, if the wet bulb temperature of the air entering the evaporator is 66°F, its enthalpy content will be 30.83 Btu/lb. And if the wet bulb temperature of the air leaving the evaporator is 57°F, its enthalpy content will be 24.48 Btu/lb. The enthalpy difference will then be 6.45 (30.83 − 24.48).

If the airflow across the evaporator were measured at 1,210 CFM, then using the equation Btu capacity = $4.50 \times$ CFM $\times$ enthalpy difference, the Btu capacity of the system would equal 35,120.25 Btu = ($4.50 \times$ 1,210 CFM $\times$ 6.45 Btu/lb.).

UNIT 35—SUMMARY

The success of any installation lies in its planning. Part of the planning procedure requires a technician to reference the manufacturer's installation manual and determine the installation requirements of the system. There are two types of installations for the indoor section: cased/uncased evaporator assemblies and air handlers. The location of an outdoor condensing unit is an important part of the overall installation process.

Before installing the refrigerant lines, make sure the metering device installed in the indoor unit is correctly sized for the application. Do not exceed the maximum line set length as stated by the manufacturer; generally pipe runs can be up to 175 ft. If the line set exceeds approximately 50 ft or a distance specified by the manufacturer, special modifications will need to be done to the system.

A standing pressure test is normally used to check for refrigerant leaks. Once the system is leak tested and is determined leak free, the system needs to be evacuated to a 500 micron level.

When installing residential air conditioning systems, the installing contractor must be sure the appropriate type of over current protection device is used with the outdoor condensing unit. The evaporator drain pan will normally have both a primary and a secondary drain. For attic or ceiling installations it is advisable to install an additional drain pan under the fan coil to prevent water damage caused by an overflowing condensate line. There should be approximately 400 CFM per ton of airflow across the evaporator.

The correct refrigerant charge of a system can be accomplished by weighing the correct additional amount of refrigerant, measuring the superheat value of the refrigerant at the inlet of the condensing unit, and measuring the subcooling value at the outlet of the condensing unit. For systems using a non-TEV metering device, the superheat method should be used to determine if a system has an adequate refrigerant charge. For systems using a TEV metering device, the subcooling method should be used to determine if a system has an adequate refrigerant charge.

After the installation is complete, the technician's job is not over. The work area should be completely cleaned and the system's operation and warranty explained to the customer.

WORK ORDERS

Service Ticket 3501

Customer Complaint: System Not Cooling Properly

Equipment Type: 3 Ton, 13 SEER R-22 Residential Split System AC

Last week a new 3 ton, 13 SEER, R-22 residential split system air conditioning system was connected to an existing 80,000 Btu output forced air furnace. This week the customer called complaining the system is not cooling properly. A technician is called out to check the system.

When the technician arrives on the job, the outdoor condensing unit and indoor blower are running. After further investigation the following conditions are observed:

- An outdoor ambient temperature of 95°F.
- Air filter is clean.
- Indoor blower is clean.
- Evaporator coil is clean.
- Condenser coil is clean.
- 208 V measured at the common and run terminals of the compressor.
- Suction pressure is 76 psig.
- Discharge pressure is 275 psig.
- A 70°F wet bulb temperature entering the evaporator.
- A suction line temperature at the inlet of the compressor of 63°F.
- With the heating system turned on and with the fan running at the cooling speed, a temperature rise of 61°F was measured.

The technician then decides the system is operating normally and discusses the system's operation with the customer.

Service Ticket 3502

Customer Complaint: System Not Cooling Properly

Equipment Type: 3 Ton, 14 SEER R-410A Residential Split System AC

Last week a new 3 ton, 14 SEER, R-410A residential split system air conditioning system with a fixed orifice was connected to an existing 80,000 Btu output forced air furnace. This week the customer called complaining the system is not cooling properly. A technician is called out to check the system.

When the technician arrives on the job, the outdoor condensing unit and indoor blower are running. After further investigation, the following conditions are observed:

- Air filter is clean.
- Condenser coil is clean.
- Return air temperature is 79°F DB and 64°F WB.
- System's supply air temperature is 69°F.
- Outdoor ambient temperature is 85°F.
- Suction pressure measured at the compressor is 105 psig.
- Suction line temperature at the inlet of the compressor is 65°F.
- Discharge pressure measured at the compressor is 330 psig.
- Discharge line temperature at the compressor is 195°F.
- Liquid line temperature at the outlet of the condenser is 99°F.
- Temperature rise across the furnace in the heating mode with the fan operating at the cooling speed is 65°F.

The technician then decides the system is operating with a low refrigerant charge and begins searching for the source of the leak.

Service Ticket 3503

Customer Complaint: System Not Cooling Properly When Outdoor Temperature Is High

Equipment Type: 2 Ton, 13 SEER R-22 Residential Split System AC

Last week a new 2 ton, 13 SEER, R-22 residential split system air conditioning system with a fixed orifice was connected to an existing 60,000 Btu output forced air furnace. This week the customer called complaining the system is not cooling properly when the outdoor temperature is high. A technician is called out to check the system.

When the technician arrives on the job, he discovers the outdoor condensing unit and indoor blower are running. After further investigation, the technician observes the following conditions:

- Outdoor ambient temperature is 95°F DB.
- Return air temperature is 70°F WB and 85°F DB.
- Evaporator coil is clean and free of frost or ice.
- Filter is clean.
- Suction pressure is 80 psig.
- Discharge pressure is 305 psig.
- Suction line temperature is 78°F.
- Liquid line temperature is 121°F.
- Supply air temperature at the outlet of the evaporator is 66°F DB

The technician then decides the system is operating with a high evaporator load, most likely due to an undersized air conditioning system.

UNIT 35—REVIEW QUESTIONS

1. Why is it important to properly plan the installation of a residential split system air conditioner?

2. What should a technician reference before installing a system?

3. What is the industry standard for determining the heat gain of a residential structure?

4. What happens if a system is oversized for its application?

5. What is the minimum SEER rating for new systems?

6. What is the name of the outdoor rated, watertight, flexible electrical cable connecting the system's disconnect to the condensing unit?

7. What gauge thermostat wire is typically used on residential systems?

8. Where should an outdoor condensing unit not be located?

9. Normally, what is the maximum length a line set can be run on many residential split system air conditioners?

10. How should a technician determine the diameter of the line set to use?

11. Why are sections of tubing that are to be fitted together sometimes swaged?

12. What micron level should be achieved when evacuating a system?

13. What are the three main types of over current protection devices that can be used on a condensing unit?

14. At what height should a thermostat be mounted above the floor?

15. What diameter condensate line is typically run from the drain pan of the evaporator?

16. What is the purpose of the secondary drain line?

17. What is the required airflow across the evaporator of a residential split system air conditioner?

18. What two methods can be used to measure the airflow across an evaporator?

19. For a system using a non-TEV metering device such as a fixed orifice, what method can be used to determine if the refrigerant charge is adequate?

20. When the installation is complete, what should a technician do before leaving the job?

UNIT 36
Troubleshooting Split Air Conditioning Systems

OBJECTIVES

After completing this unit you will be able to:

- troubleshoot split air conditioning system air distribution problems.
- adjust split air conditioning system airflow.
- troubleshoot split air conditioning system electrical problems.
- perform diagnostic tests on split air conditioning system electronic controls.
- read and interpret troubleshooting charts.
- troubleshoot split air conditioning system mechanical problems.

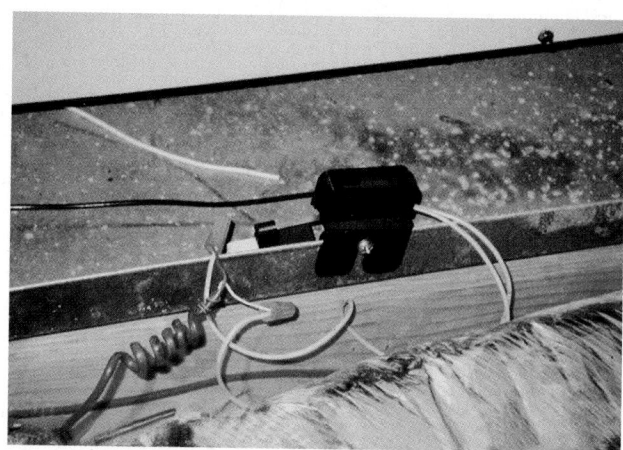

Figure 36-1 Float switch on condensate tray
(Courtesy of InspectAPedia.com)

36.1 INTRODUCTION

Troubleshooting a split air conditioning system correctly will result in the proper repair for the unit in a timely fashion. It is discouraging for the customer and the technician if multiple return visits are required to correct a malfunctioning unit. The trouble described by the customer may initially help you to determine which course of action needs to be taken. It will save you time to take a few minutes to discuss the symptoms with them. They may be able to provide you with valuable information which may lead you to the problem.

Most manufacturers supply troubleshooting charts for their equipment. After speaking with the customer, a good next step is to review these to assist in troubleshooting the system. A quick simple fix may not always be the correct answer. For example, the unit may be tripped out due to a stuck high water level switch on the evaporator condensate drip pan as shown in Figure 36-1.

Simply resetting the unit may bring it back on line, but if it trips out again you will be called to come back to the residence a second time. Before leaving the job, the drain pipe should be checked for an obstruction.

To avoid these types of situations, it is best to take the proper steps in evaluating the malfunction. Collect information about the problem. Read and calculate the system's vital signs such as suction and discharge pressures. Compare the measured values to the expected manufacturer's recommendations, Figure 36-2. Consult the manufacturer's troubleshooting aids if available along with any company specific troubleshooting guides.

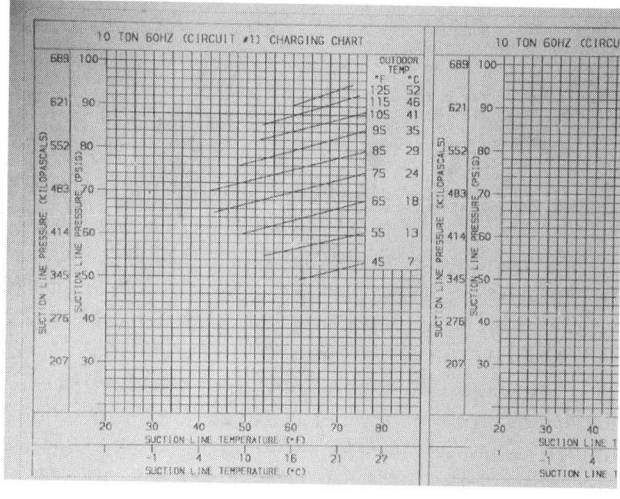

Figure 36-2 Refrigerant charging service data tag
(Courtesy of InspectAPedia.com)

SAFETY TIP

Electrical testing is generally a first step in any troubleshooting sequence. Make sure that you properly identify the power supply to the unit, Figure 36-3. Do not assume that the power is always shut off at the breaker. Sometimes breakers are mislabeled. Always use your meter to check for ground faults before energizing the unit to be serviced. At all times use your meter to check for voltage before physically disconnecting wires or opening control boxes.

Figure 36-3 Service control switch circuit breaker
(Courtesy of InspectAPedia.com)

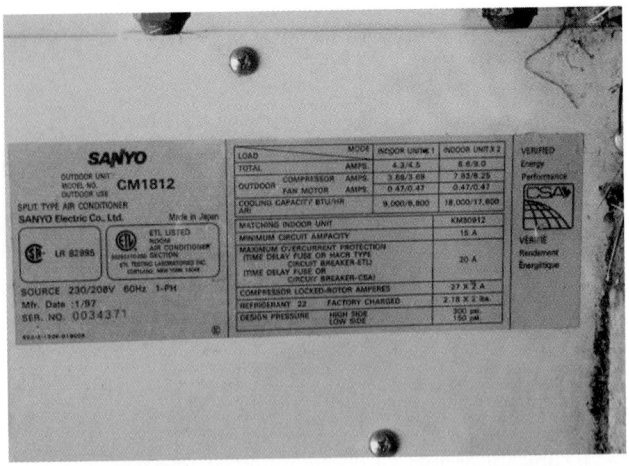

Figure 36-4 Split system data tag
(Courtesy of InspectAPedia.com)

36.2 SYSTEM FAMILIARIZATION

The split air conditioning system design may affect the way you troubleshoot the system. It is important to familiarize yourself with the system components and their location. Is the evaporator coil located in an indoor air handling unit or is it installed in conjunction with a furnace? Is the air handler a vertical upflow, vertical downflow, or horizontal unit and where is it located? Where are the system controls and switches located? What type of safety controls does the unit have? Check the capacity ratings for the system, Figure 36-4. A split system has a fan coil unit with a refrigeration coil located on the inside of the building and an outside mounted air cooled condensing unit, connected together with refrigerant piping. A typical split system with an air handling unit in the ceiling is shown in Figures 36-5 and 36-6.

Basically there are three types of problems. These are trouble with the air system, the electrical system, or mechanical components. Within these there is much overlap, so whatever the nature of the problem, it is good practice to follow a logical, structured, systematic approach. In this manner the correct solution is usually found in the shortest possible time.

36.3 AIR SYSTEM PROBLEMS

The primary problem that can occur in an air system is the reduction in airflow. Air handling systems do not suddenly increase in capacity, that is, increase the amount of air across the coil. On the other hand, the refrigeration system does not suddenly increase in heat transfer ability. First remove the panel to access the direct expansion (DX) coil in the air handler, Figure 36-7. (On many systems removing a panel would change the airflow across the coil and change the return and supply reading.) Take the temperatures of the return air (RA) as it enters and then the supply air (SA) as it leaves the coil. The difference between these two temperatures is referred to as the temperature drop or temperature difference of the air across the DX coil.

A sling psychrometer is used to measure the return air dry bulb and wet bulb temperatures needed to determine the relative humidity. Many electronic psychrometers are able to display relative humidity directly. A chart as shown in Figure 36-8 or one supplied by the DX coil manufacturer is then used to determine the expected temperature drop. As an example from the chart, return air at a condition of 68°F and 30% relative humidity should have a 24°F air temperature drop across the coil.

This measurement will help to determine if the problem is a result of improper airflow or a refrigeration system error. If the actual air temperature drop is greater than the required temperature drop, then the air quantity has been reduced. In this case, look for problems in the air handling system. This could be due to dirty air filters, a dirty evaporator coil, a problem with the blower, or an unusual restriction in the duct system.

Air Filters

Because this is the most common problem of air failure, check the filtering system first, Figure 36-9. Air filters of the throwaway type should be replaced at least once a month.

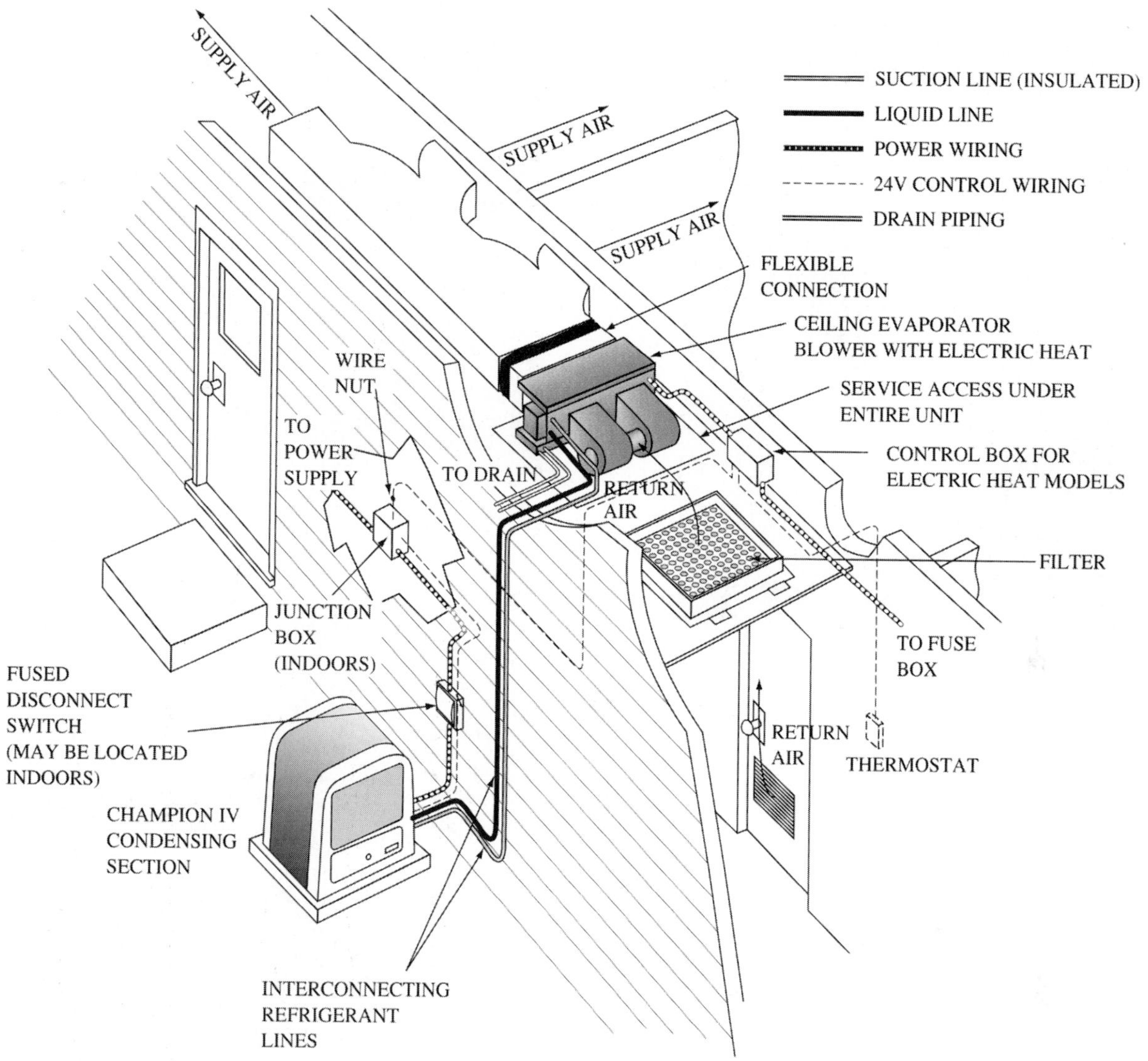

SUCTION LINE (INSULATED)
LIQUID LINE
POWER WIRING
24V CONTROL WIRING
DRAIN PIPING

SUPPLY AIR

SUPPLY AIR

SUPPLY AIR

FLEXIBLE
CONNECTION

CEILING EVAPORATOR
BLOWER WITH ELECTRIC HEAT

WIRE
NUT

SERVICE ACCESS UNDER
ENTIRE UNIT

TO
POWER
SUPPLY

TO DRAIN

CONTROL BOX FOR
ELECTRIC HEAT MODELS

RETURN
AIR

FILTER

JUNCTION
BOX
(INDOORS)

TO FUSE
BOX

FUSED
DISCONNECT
SWITCH
(MAY BE LOCATED
INDOORS)

RETURN
AIR   THERMOSTAT

CHAMPION IV
CONDENSING
SECTION

INTERCONNECTING
REFRIGERANT
LINES

Figure 36-5 Ceiling evaporator blower installation

Figure 36-6 Attic mounted air handler
(Courtesy of InspectAPedia.com)

Blower Motor and Drive

Check the blower motor and drive in the case of belt-driven blowers to make sure that both the blower motor and blower bearing are properly lubricated and operating freely. The blower drive belt must be in good condition and properly adjusted. Cracked or heavily glazed belts must be replaced. Heavy glazing can be caused by too much tension on the belt, driving the belt down into the pulleys. Proper adjustment requires the ability to depress the belt midway between the pulleys approximately 1 in for each 12 in between pulley centers.

The blower wheel should be clean. Dirt accumulation can sometimes fill in the area on a cupped blade allowing it to spin freely but substantially reducing the airflow, Figure 36-10. If the wheel is dirty or has mold build up, Figure 36-11, it must be removed and cleaned. Attempting to clean the wheel in place is never recommended. Do not try brushing only, because a poor cleaning job will cause an imbalance to occur on the wheel. Extreme vibration and

Figure 36-7 Air handler unit and coil
(Courtesy of InspectAPedia.com)

Figure 36-9 Dirty air filter
(Courtesy of InspectAPedia.com)

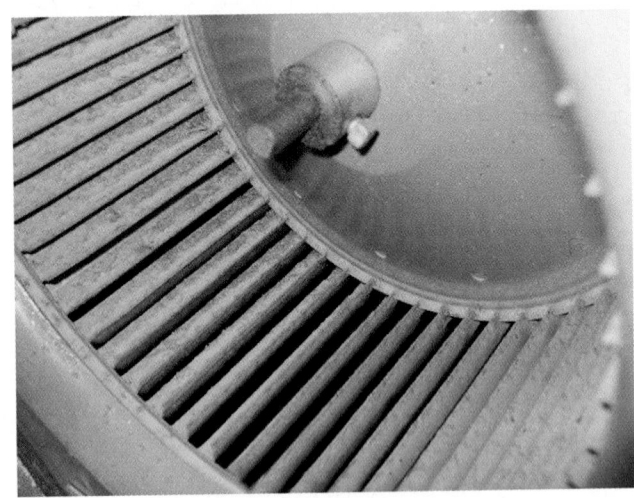

Figure 36-10 Dirty blower fan
(Courtesy of InspectAPedia.com)

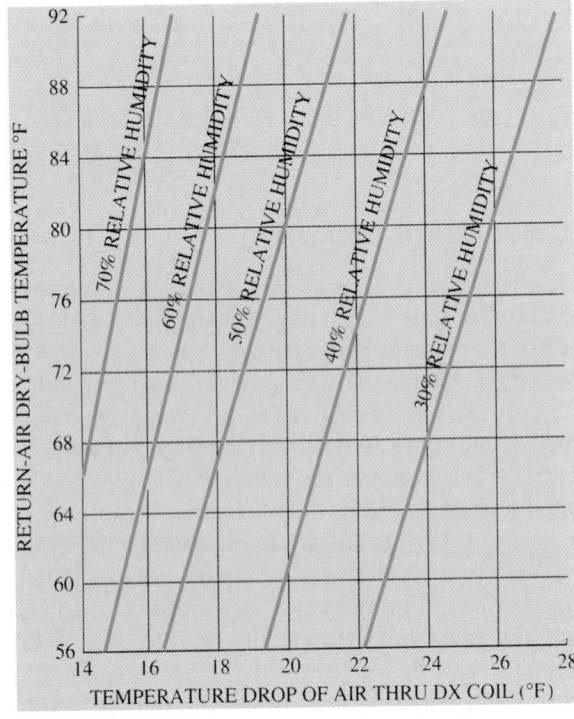

Figure 36-8 Air temperature drop for various return air conditions

Figure 36-11 Mold growth on blower fan
(Courtesy of InspectAPedia.com)

noise will result. This could cause deterioration of the wheel, damage to the belt, and damage to the motor.

Unusual Restrictions in Duct Systems

Placing furniture or carpeting over return grilles reduces the air available for the blower to handle, Figure 36-12. Shutting off the air to unused areas will reduce the air over the coil. Covering a return air grille to reduce the noise from the centrally located furnace or air handler may reduce the objectionable noise, but it also drastically affects the operation of the system by reducing air quantity.

The condition of the grill may also indicate potential problems. Water stains as shown in Figure 36-13 can be caused by improper humidity conditions. Soot stains as shown in Figure 36-14 may be a result of an improper functioning furnace exhaust leaking back into the air supply line.

Figure 36-14 Supply register soot stain
(Courtesy of InspectAPedia.com)

The collapse of the return air duct system will affect the entire duct system performance, Figure 36-15. Air leaks in the return duct will raise the return air temperature and reduce the temperature drop across the coil, Figure 36-16a,b. Look for pinched ducts as shown in Figure 36-17, sharp bends as shown in Figure 36-18, and unnecessary duct length as shown in Figure 36-19.

TECH TIP

Air distribution systems installed before the change in standards may have cloth or unapproved duct tape. These systems may need to be sealed properly in order for the central residential air conditioning system to function properly. The technician should give particular attention to the integrity of the sealing of all joints and the insulation and tape if externally wrapped.

Figure 36-12 Blocked register
(Courtesy of InspectAPedia.com)

Figure 36-13 Supply register water stain
(Courtesy of InspectAPedia.com)

Figure 36-15 Flex duct deterioration in hot attic
(Courtesy of InspectAPedia.com)

(a)

(b)

Figure 36-16 Leaky duct connections
(Courtesy of InspectAPedia.com)

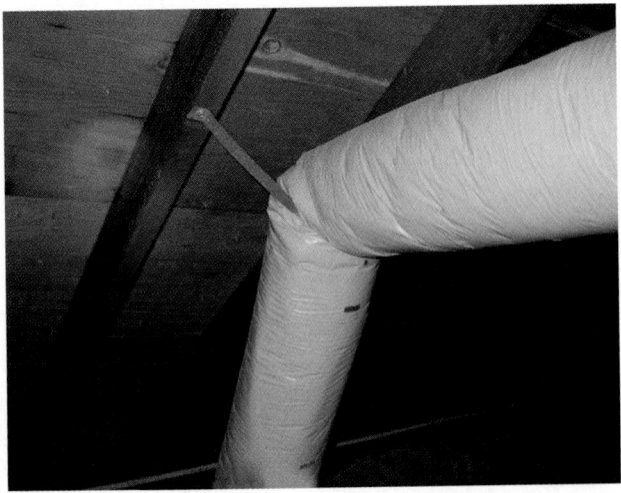

Figure 36-17 Pinched duct
(Courtesy of InspectAPedia.com)

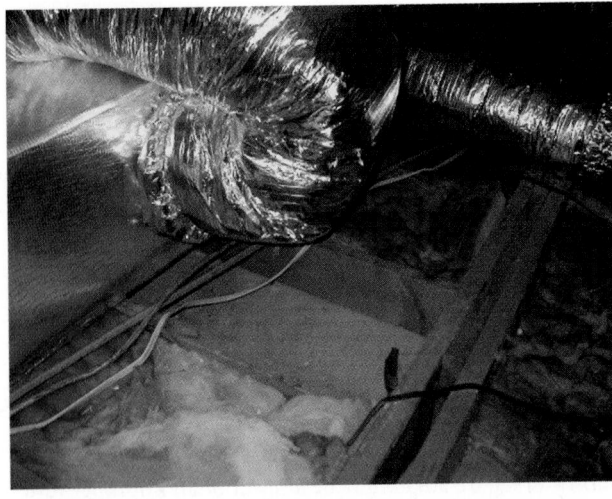

Figure 36-18 Duct sharp bend
(Courtesy of InspectAPedia.com)

Figure 36-19 Unnecessary duct length
(Courtesy of InspectAPedia.com)

Measure the difference in temperature between the return air at the grill compared to the return air temperature as it enters the unit. This difference should not exceed 2°F, as shown in Figure 36-20. If it does, the return duct needs to be insulated or there may be leak openings in the duct that need to be sealed.

SAFETY TIP

Some older fabric air handler vibration dampers are made from asbestos as shown in Figure 36-21a,b. Always follow the proper procedures for handling asbestos materials. Never rip or tear the asbestos and always wear an approved respirator.

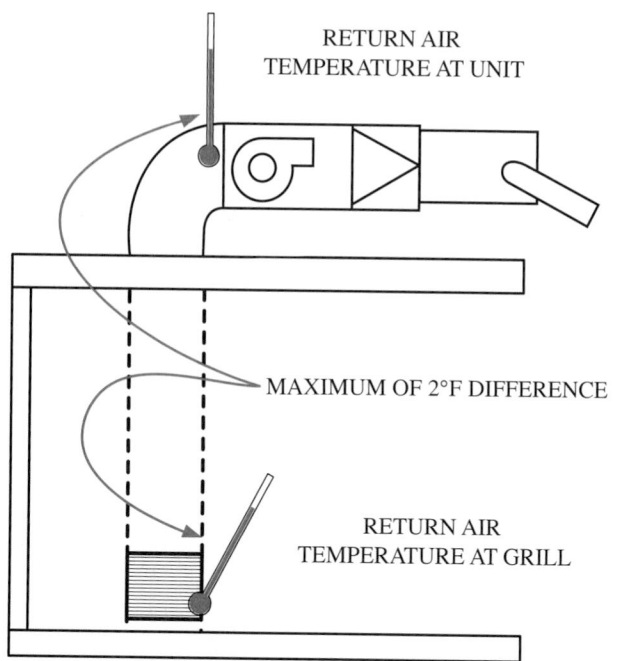

Figure 36-20 Checking return air system for leaks

Condensate Drain Pans

Condensate drain pans are located below the DX coil to collect any moisture that condenses from the air and drips off the coil. Depending on the humidity conditions, the amount of water drained away can be considerable. The condensate that collects will build up and overflow the pan if the drain becomes plugged or offers restricted flow. This is of particular concern with attic mounted units because the condensate will spill over and damage the ceiling. Some condensate drip pans have condensate pumps that will stop

and start automatically and are controlled by a float switch activated by the water level. Even if the condensate drain pan is empty, any signs of prior spill-over should be investigated further.

Adjusting the Airflow

Most manufacturers supply operating data on their equipment as shown in Table 36-1, indicating the total, sensible, and latent heat removal rating, at various outdoor dry bulb and indoor wet bulb temperatures at specific static pressures. For these same conditions, they supply the operating suction and discharge pressures of the equipment. This information is given so that the technician can match the actual conditions on the job with the performance conditions shown on the manufacturer's chart. Notice that in Table 36-2 a system with a low external static pressure of 0.30 would have an airflow of 625 CFM on low. But on a system with a higher external static pressure of 0.70, the blower would have to be set to high to obtain the same airflow.

S E R V I C E   T I P

Most manufacturers recommend that a system's airflow be set so there is approximately 400 CFM per ton of air conditioning. In areas that have high relative humidity, a slightly slower fan speed can be used to aid in the dehumidification. In arid areas, the fan speed can be increased to provide more sensible cooling. As a rule of thumb, the fan speed should not be adjusted more than 10% above or below the manufacturer's recommendations. Excessively slow fan speeds can allow the evaporator coil to freeze up under light loads and excessively high fan speeds can put too large a load on the condenser under heavy load conditions.

(a)

(b)

Figure 36-21 (a) Asbestos fabric in HVAC duct as vibration damper material; (b) Asbestos fabric air handler vibration damper *(Courtesy of InspectAPedia.com)*

Table 36-1 Typical Condenser Charging Data

RATINGS

NOTE - For Temperatures and Capacities not shown in tables, see bulletin - Cooling Unit Rating Table Correction Factor Data in Miscellaneous Engineering Data section.

Entering Wet Bulb Temperature	Total Air Volume		85°F (29°C)					95°F (35°C)					105°F (41°C)					115°F (46°C)				
			Total Cooling Capacity	Comp Motor kW Input	Sensible To Total Ratio (S/T) Dry Bulb			Total Cooling Capacity	Comp Motor kW Input	Sensible To Total Ratio (S/T) Dry Bulb			Total Cooling Capacity	Comp Motor kW Input	Sensible To Total Ratio (S/T) Dry Bulb			Total Cooling Capacity	Comp Motor kW Input	Sensible To Total Ratio (S/T) Dry Bulb		
	cfm	L/S	kBtuh	kW	75°F 24°C	80°F 27°C	85°F 29°C	kBtuh	kW	75°F 24°C	80°F 27°C	85°F 29°C	kBtuh	kW	75°F 24°C	80°F 27°C	85°F 29°C	kBtuh	kW	75°F 24°C	80°F 27°C	85°F 29°C

10ACC-018 — C33-18A COOLING CAPACITY

	cfm	L/S	kBtuh	kW	75°	80°	85°	kBtuh	kW	75°	80°	85°	kBtuh	kW	75°	80°	85°	kBtuh	kW	75°	80°	85°
63°F (17°C)	450	210	16.8	4.9	1.30	.73	.84	.95	15.9	4.7	1.39	.74	.86	.98	15.0	4.4	1.47	.76	.89	1.00	14.1	4.1	1.55	.78	.92	1.00
	650	305	18.3	5.4	1.34	.79	.93	1.00	17.3	5.1	1.43	.81	.96	1.00	16.3	4.8	1.52	.83	.99	1.00	15.3	4.5	1.61	.86	1.00	1.00
	850	400	19.3	5.7	1.36	.85	1.00	1.00	18.3	5.4	1.45	.87	1.00	1.00	17.4	5.1	1.56	.91	1.00	1.00	16.4	4.8	1.65	.94	1.00	1.00
67°F (19°C)	450	210	17.7	5.2	1.32	.59	.70	.81	16.8	4.9	1.41	.60	.72	.83	15.8	4.6	1.50	.61	.73	.85	14.9	4.4	1.59	.62	.75	.88
	650	305	19.3	5.7	1.36	.63	.77	.90	18.2	5.3	1.45	.64	.79	.93	17.2	5.0	1.55	.66	.81	.96	16.1	4.7	1.64	.67	.84	.99
	850	400	20.2	5.9	1.38	.67	.83	.97	19.1	5.6	1.48	.68	.85	.99	17.9	5.2	1.57	.70	.88	1.00	16.8	4.9	1.67	.72	.92	1.00
71°F (22°C)	450	210	18.4	5.4	1.34	.47	.58	.68	17.5	5.1	1.43	.47	.58	.69	16.6	4.9	1.53	.48	.59	.71	15.7	4.6	1.62	.48	.61	.73
	650	305	20.2	5.9	1.38	.49	.62	.74	19.1	5.6	1.48	.49	.63	.76	18.1	5.3	1.58	.50	.64	.78	17.0	5.0	1.68	.51	.66	.81
	850	400	21.2	6.2	1.39	.50	.65	.80	20.0	5.9	1.50	.51	.67	.83	18.9	5.5	1.61	.52	.69	.86	17.8	5.2	1.71	.53	.71	.89

(Courtesy of Lennox Industries, Inc.)

Table 36-2 Typical Cooling Unit Air Handler Performance Data

CB29M-21/26 Blower performance (208/230 V)

Air volume and motor watts at specific blower taps

External Static Pressure		Low			Medium			High		
in. w.g.	Pa	cfm	L/s	Watts	cfm	L/s	Watts	cfm	L/s	Watts
.00	0	700	330	245	895	420	310	1030	485	375
.05	10	690	325	240	875	415	305	1010	475	370
.10	25	680	320	235	865	410	300	990	470	365
.15	35	665	315	230	850	400	290	970	480	355
.20	50	655	310	225	830	390	285	955	450	350
.25	60	640	300	220	810	385	280	925	440	345
.30	75	625	295	220	795	375	270	900	425	335
.40	100	595	280	210	750	355	255	850	400	320
.50	125	555	260	195	700	330	240	800	380	305
.60	150	510	240	185	640	300	225	725	340	290
.70	175	395	185	165	—	—	—	620	295	265
.75	185	—	—	—	—	—	—	570	270	255

Note: All air data is measured external to unit with air filter in place. Electric heaters have no appreciable air resistance.

36.4 SPLIT SYSTEM ELECTRICAL PROBLEMS

Since the greatest numbers of malfunction problems are electrical, it is common practice to perform electrical troubleshooting (including controls) before mechanical troubleshooting. If the problem is mechanical, the electrical check will usually point the technician in that direction. If the system will not operate at all, it is probably an electrical problem that must be found and corrected.

TECH TIP

Before beginning any troubleshooting, you must locate the manufacturer's troubleshooting guide for the equipment you are working on, Table 36-3. Manufacturers have developed troubleshooting techniques that when followed will result in accurate and rapid location of the problem. These charts may seem complex and difficult to follow if you look at the entire chart. In order to properly use one of these charts, start at the beginning and follow each and every step. Do not simply jump ahead assuming that you know what the answer is. Do the test and report the results and then move to the next test as indicated by the manufacturer's guide.

Electrical Operating Sequence

The operating sequence is usually supplied by the manufacturer in the service instructions or it can be determined by the technician by studying the schematic wiring diagram. The functions of the operating and nonoperating equipment

Table 36-3 Toubleshooting chart – Cooling service

PROBLEM	CAUSE	REMEDY
Compressor and condenser fans will not start.	Power failure	Call power company
	Fuse blown or circuit breaker tripped	Replace fuse or reset circuit breaker
	Defective thermostat, contactor, transformer, or control relay.	Replace component.
	Insuficient line voltage.	Determine cause and correct.
	Incorrect or faulty wiring.	Check wiring diagram and rewire correctly.
	Termostat setting too high.	Lower thermostat setting below room temperature.
Compressor will not start but condenser fans run.	Faulty wiring or loose connections in compressor circuit.	Check wiring and repair or replace.
	Compressor motor burned out, seized, or internal overload open.	Determine cause. Replace compressor.
	Defective run/start capacitor, overload, or start relay.	Determine cause and replace.
	One leg of 3-phase power dead.	Replace fuse or reset circuit breaker.
Compressor cycles (other than normally satisfying thermostat).	Refrigerant overcharge or undercharge.	Recover refrigerant, evaculate system, and recharge to nameplate.
	Defective compressor	Replace and determine cause.
	Insuficient fine voltage.	Determine cause and correct.
	Blocked condenser.	Determine cause and correct.
	Defective run/start capacitor, overload, or start relay.	Determine cause and replace.
	Defective thermostat	Replace thermostat.
	Faulty condenser-fan motor or capacitor	Replace.
	Restriction in refrigerant system.	Locate restriction and remove.
Compressor makes excessive noise (Scroll only)	Compressor rotating in wrong direction	Reverse the 3-phase power leads as described in Start-Up section
Compressor operates continuously.	Dirty air filter	Replace filter.
	Unit undersized for load	Decrease load or increase unit size.
	Thermostat set too low.	Reset thermostat.
	Low refrigerant charge.	Locate leak, repair, and recharge.
	Leaking value in compressor.	Replace compressor.
	Air in system.	Recover refrigerant, evaculate system, and recharge.
	Condesor coil dirty or restricted.	Clean coil remove restriction. Excessive head pressure.
Excessive head pressure.	Dirty air filter.	Replace filter.
	Dirty condenser coil.	Clean coil.
	Refrigerant overcharged.	Remove excess refrigerant.
	Air in system.	Recover refrigerant, evaculate system, and recharge.
	Condenser air restricted or air short-cycling.	Determine cause and correct.
Head pressure too low.	Low refrigerant charge.	Check for leaks, repair, and recharge.
	Compressor values leaking.	Replace compressor.
	Restriction in liquid tube.	Remove restriction.
Excessive suction pressure.	High heat load.	Check for source and eliminate.
	Compressor values leaking.	Replace compressor.
	Refrigerant overcharged.	Recover excess refrigerant.
Suction pressure too low.	Dirty air filter.	Replace filter.
	Low refrigerant charge	Check for leaks, repair, and recharge.
	Metering device or low side restricted.	Remove source or restriction.
	Insuficient evaporator airflow.	Increase air quantity. Check filter and replace it necessary.
	Temperature too low in conditioned area.	Reset thermostat.
	Field-installed filter drier restricted.	Replace.
Compressor no. 2 will not run.	Unit in economizer mode.	Proper operation, no remedy necessary.

are determined by examination and testing. Necessary test instruments include: the volt ohm meter (VOM), the clamp-on ammeter, the capacitor tester, and the temperature analyzer.

The power circuit is the first to be examined, because power must be available to operate the loads. For example, on a refrigeration system with an air cooled condenser, the three principal loads that must be energized are the compressor motor, the condenser fan motor, and the evaporator fan motor. Before proceeding with anything else, the technician must be certain that the proper voltage is being supplied to the loads. The supply line voltage should be tested with a voltmeter and then compared to the manufacturer's recommended values.

If the voltage is correct, then the circuit will need to be tested further. Before energizing the circuit, always use your meter to check for ground faults. Once energized, the voltage for each load in the circuit can be tested. A clamp-on ammeter can be used to check the current draw for each load one at a time. The measured current should be compared to the current rating listed on the motor nameplate. As an example, if the current draw is too high, this may indicate a mechanical problem such as a stuck fan or seized compressor.

In troubleshooting, when a load is not working, the technician must determine whether the problem is in the load itself or in the switches that control the load. If the proper supply voltage is available but the compressor or fan motor does not run, then there may be a fault in the control circuit and the control circuit voltage should be tested. Generally the control circuit voltage will be much lower than the line voltage. Each load, compressor, or fan is generally controlled by a relay switch which is operated by an electromagnetic coil energized by the control circuit.

Use your meter to check for voltage before physically disconnecting wires or opening control boxes. Always test to determine if the fan or motor is tripped out on a safety switch before replacing components. When checking components with an ohmmeter, it is important that all power is disconnected and the component part is electrically isolated. Short circuits are usually due to faulty loads. If a faulty component is located, the job is still not complete. The technician should make a concerted effort to determine why or how the component failure occurred.

Installation and Service Instructions

The installation and service instructions supply a wide variety of information that the manufacturer believes is necessary to properly install and service the unit. This bulletin includes the wiring diagram, the sequence of operation, and any notes or cautions that need to be observed in using them.

Wiring Diagrams

Wiring diagrams usually consist of connection diagrams and schematic diagrams. The connection diagram shows the wires to the various electrical component terminals in their approximate location on the unit. This is the diagram that the

technician must use to locate the test points. The schematic diagram separates each circuit to clearly indicate the function of switches that control each load. This is the diagram the technician uses to determine the sequence of operation for the system.

TECH TIP

Wiring diagrams are often included inside the equipment panels. If the diagrams are not there, then contact the manufacturer. They are available from local suppliers and are often available from the manufacturers themselves through their websites. If you do not have a diagram, troubleshooting electrical circuits can be lengthy, time consuming, and inaccurate.

Troubleshooting Tables

The troubleshooting guide as shown in Figure 36-22 is helpful as a guide to corrective action. By a process of elimination, this guide offers a quick way to solve a service problem. The process of elimination permits the technician to examine each suggested remedy and disregard ones that do not apply or are impractical; leaving only the solution(s) that fits the problem.

Fault Isolation Diagrams

A fault isolation diagram, Figure 36-23, starts with a failure symptom and goes through a logical decision action process to isolate the failure.

Diagnostic Tests

Diagnostic tests, Figure 36-24, can be conducted on electronic circuit boards, at points indicated by the manufacturer, to check voltages or other essential information critical to the operation of the unit.

Some electronically controlled systems have automatic testing features, which indicate by code number a malfunction in the operation of the equipment as shown in Figure 36-25. Further tests are usually required to determine the action that is required.

36.5 SPLIT SYSTEM MECHANICAL PROBLEMS

When the measured temperature drop across the DX coil is less than required, this means that the heat removal capacity of the system has been reduced. This means that the amount of heat picked up in the coil plus the amount of motor heat added and the total rejected from the condenser is not the total heat quantity the unit is designed to handle. The problems associated with a system that starts and runs but does not

⚠ WARNING

DISCONNECT ALL POWER TO UNIT BEFORE SERVICING. CONTACTOR MAY BREAK ONLY ONE SIDE. FAILURE TO SHUT OFF POWER CAN CAUSE ELECTRICAL SHOCK RESULTING IN PERSONAL INJURY OR DEATH.

SYMPTOM	POSSIBLE CAUSE	REMEDY
Unit will not run	• Power off or loose electrical connection • Thermostat out of calibration - set too high • Defective contactor • Blown fuses • Transformer defective • High pressure control open (if provided)	• Check for correct voltage at contactor in condensing unit • Reset • Check for 24 volts at contactor coil - replace if contacts are open • Replace fuses • Check wiring-replace transformer • Reset-also see high head pressure remedy-The high pressure control opens at 450 PSIG
Outdoor fan runs, compressor doesn't	• Run or start capacitor defective • Start relay defective • Loose connection • Compressor stuck, grounded or open motor winding. Open internal overload • Low voltage condition	• Replace • Replace • Check for correct voltage at compressor check & tighten all connections • Wait at least 2 hours for overload to reset. • If still open, replace the compressor. • Add start kit components
Insufficient cooling	• Improperly sized unit • Improper indoor airflow • Incorrect refrigerant charge • Air, non-condensibles or moisture in system	• Recalculate load • Check - should be approximately 400 CFM per ton. • Charge per procedure attached to unit service panel • Recover refrigerant, evacuate & recharge, add filter drier
Compressor short cycles	• Incorrent voltage	• At compressor terminals, voltage must be ± 10% of

Figure 36-22 Typical troubleshooting table
(Courtesy of Lennox Industries, Inc.)

produce satisfactory cooling can be simply divided into two categories: refrigerant quantity and refrigerant flow rate.

To determine the problem, all the information listed in Table 36-4 must be measured. These results compared to normal operating results will generally identify the problem. The use of the word "normal" does not imply a fixed set of pressures and temperatures. These will vary with each make and model of the system. A few temperatures are fairly consistent throughout the industry and can be used for comparison. These are the DX coil operating temperature, the condensing unit condensing temperature, and the refrigerant subcooling.

SERVICE TIP

These vital signs must also be modified according to the seasonal energy efficiency ratio (SEER) of the unit. The reason for this is that the amount of evaporation and condensing surface designed into the unit is directly related to the efficiency rating. A larger condensing surface results in a lower condensing temperature and a higher SEER. A larger evaporating surface results in a higher suction pressure and a higher SEER. The energy efficiency ratio is calculated by dividing the net capacity of the unit in Btu/hr by the watts input. Every central split cooling system manufactured in the United States today must have a SEER of at least 13.

36.6 DX COIL OPERATING TEMPERATURE

Normal coil operating temperatures can be found by subtracting the design DX coil split from the average air temperature going through the coil. The DX coil split will vary with the system design. The term coil split is also often referred to as the temperature split or the approach temperature. It is the difference in temperature between the coil (condenser or evaporator) and the air passing across it.

The energy efficiency ratio (EER) is the output in Btu/hr divided by the power input measured in watts. It is less meaningful than SEER because it is a steady state rating and does not account for the time the unit operates before reaching its peak efficiency. However, the EER is still useful in determining coil operating temperatures. Systems in the EER range of 7.0 to 8.0 will have DX coil design splits in the range 25–30°F. Systems in the EER range of 8.0 to 9.0 will have DX coil design splits in the range 20–25°F. Systems with 9.0 + EER ratings will have DX coil design splits in the range 15–20°F.

The normal direct expansion (DX) coil operating temperature will be affected by the air passing across it. The air passing across the coil will have an inlet and an outlet temperature. The inlet air is the return air (RA) and can also be referred to as the entering air temperature (EAT). The outlet air is the supply air (SA) and can also be referred to as

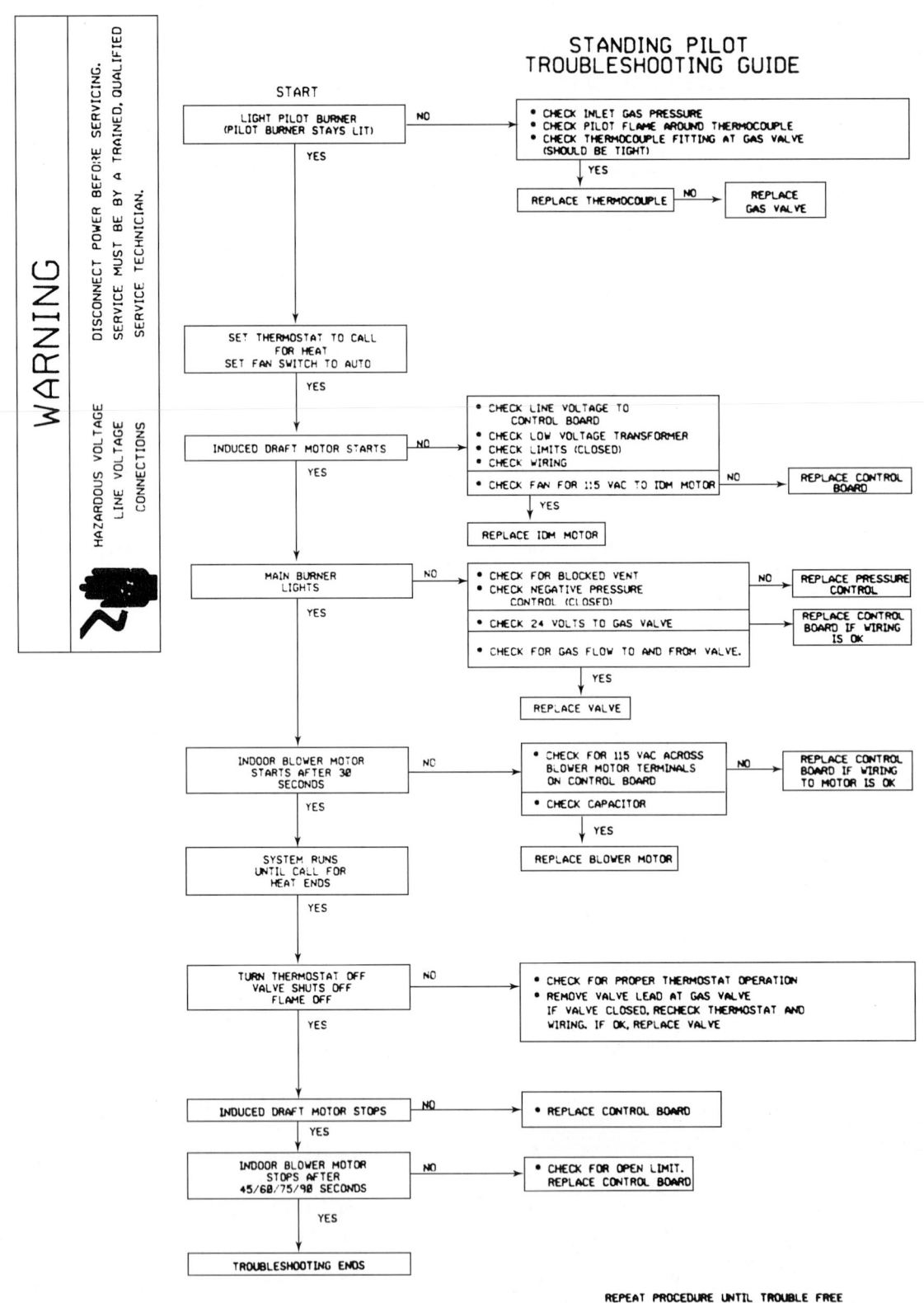

Figure 36-23 Typical fault isolation diagram
(Courtesy of Rheem Manufacturing)

CHECKOUT PROCEDURE

1- Disconnect power to unit.
2- Disconnect P49 from J49.
3- Connect voltage source as shown below.
4- Turn on power to unit. Blower should operate at low speed.

ECM LOW SPEED CHECKOUT

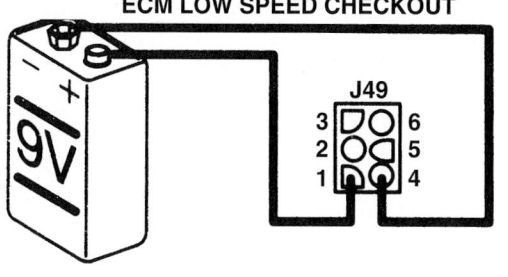

Figure 36-24 Typical diagnostic test
(Courtesy of Lennox Industries, Inc.)

the leaving air temperature (LAT). The EAT − LAT is equal to the temperature difference (TD or ΔT) of the air across the DX coil. The average temperature of the air passing across the coil can be calculated as TD ÷ 2. This calculated average temperature of the air can be used to calculate the normal DX coil operating temperature. The formula used for determining coil operating temperature is:

$$COT = \frac{(EAT + LAT)}{2} - DX\ coil\ split$$

where

COT = coil operating temperature
EAT = entering air temperature of the coil
LAT = leaving air temperature of the coil

For example, a unit having an entering air condition of 80°F DB and leaving air temperature of 60°F will have an operating coil temperature determined as in the following example.

EXAMPLE 36-1

For an EER rating of 7.0 to 8.0, the DX coil split is typically 25–30°F.

$$COT = \left(\frac{80°F + 60°F}{2}\right) - (25–30°F) = 40–45°F$$

Fault Codes

Figure 36-25 Fault codes

FAULT CODE	FAULT NAME IN PANEL	DESCRIPTION AND RECOMMENDED CORRECTIVE ACTION
1	OVERCURRENT	Output current is excessive. Check for excessive motor load, insufficient acceleration time (parameters 2202 ACCELER TIME 1, default 30 seconds), or faulty motor, motor cables or connections.
2	DC OVERVOLT	Intermediate circuit DC voltage is excessive. Check for static or transient over voltages in the input power supply, insufficient deceleration time (parameters 2203 DECELER TIME 1, default 30 seconds), or undersized brake chopper (if present).
3	DEV OVERTEMP	Drive heat sink is overheated. Temperature is at or above 115 C (239 F). Check for fan failure, obstructions in the airflow, dirt or dust coating on the heat sink, excessive ambient temperature, or excessive motor load.
4	SHORT CIRC	Fault current. Check for short-circuit in the motor cable(s) or motor or supply disturbances.
5	OVERLOAD	Inverter overload condition. The drive output current exceeds the ratings.
6	DC UNDERVOLT	Intermediate circuit DC voltage is not sufficient. Check for missing phase in the input power supply, blown fuse, or under voltage on main circuit.
7	AI1 LOSS	Analog input 1 loss. Analog input value is less than AI1 FLT LIMIT (3021). Check source and connection for analog input and parameter settings for AI1 FLT LIMIT (3021) and 3001 AI<MIN FUNCTION.
8	AI2 LOSS	Analog input 2 loss. Analog input value is less than AI2 FLT LIMIT (3022). Check source and connection for analog input and parameter settings for AI2 FLT LIMIT (3022) and 3001 AI<MIN FUNCTION.
9	MOT OVERTEMP	Motor is too hot, as estimated by the drive. Check for overloaded motor. Adjust the parameters used for the estimate (3005 through 3009). Check the temperature sensors and Group 35 parameters.
10	PANEL LOSS	Panel communication is lost and either drive is in local control mode (the control panel displays LOC), or drive is in remote control mode (REM) and is parameterized to accept start/stop, direction or reference from the control panel. To correct, check the communication lines and connections. Check parameter 3002 PANEL COMM ERROR, parameters in Group 10: Command Inputs and Group 11: Reference Select (if drive operation is REM).
11	ID RUN FAIL	The motor ID run was not completed successfully. Check motor connections.
12	MOTOR STALL	Motor or process stall. Motor is operating in the stall region. Check for excessive load or insufficient motor power. Check parameters 3010 through 3012.
13	RESERVED	Not used.
14	EXT FAULT 1	Digital input defined to report first external fault is active, See parameter 3003 EXTERNAL FAULT 1.
15	EXT FAULT 2	Digital input defined to report second external faults is active. See parameter 3004 EXTERNAL FAULT 1.
16	EARTH FAULT	The load on the input power system is out of balance. Check for faults in the motor or motor cable. Verify that motor cable does not exceed maximum specified length.
17	UNDERLOAD	Motor load is lower than expected. Check for disconnected load. Check parameters 3013 UNDERLOAD FUNCTION through 3015 UNDERLOAD CURVE.
18	THERM FAIL	Internal fault. The thermistor measuring the internal temperature of the drive is open or shorted. Contact your Carrier representative.
19	OPEX LINK	Internal fault. A communication-related problem has been detected between the OMIO and OINT boards. Contact your Carrier representative.
20	OPEX PWR	Internal fault. Low voltage condition detected on the OINT board. Contact your Carrier representative.
21	CURR MEAS	Internal fault. Current measurement is out of range. Contact your Carrier representative.
22	SUPPLY PHASE	Ripple voltage in the DC link is too high. Check for missing main phase or blown fuse.
23	RESERVED	Not used.
24	OVERSPEED	Motor speed is greater than 120% of the larger (in magnitude) of 2001 MINIMUM SPEED or 2002 MAXIMUM SPEED parameters. Check parameter settings for 2001 and 2002. Check adequacy of motor braking torque. Check applicability of torque control. Check brake chopper and resistor.
25	RESERVED	Not used.
26	DRIVE ID	Internal fault. Configuration block drive ID is not valid.
27	CONFIG FILE	Internal configuration file has an error. Contact your Carrier representative.

Table 36-4 Troubleshooting Chart for Refrigeration and Air Conditioning Systems, Showing Symptoms and Probable Causes

Probable cause	Low side (suction) pressure (psig)	D.X. coil superheat (°F)	High side (hot gas) pressure (psig)	Condenser liquid subcooling (°F)	Cond. unit amperage draw (A)
1 Insufficient or unbalanced load	Low	Low	Low	Normal	Low
2 Excessive load	High	High	High	Normal	High
3 Low ambient (cond. entering air °F)	Low	High	Low	Normal	Low
4 High ambient (cond. entering air °F)	High	High	High	Normal	High
5 Refrigerant undercharge	Low	High	Low	Low	Low
6 Refrigerant overcharge	High	Low	High	High	High
7 Liquid line restriction	Low	High	Low	High	Low
8 Plugged capillary tube	Low	High	Low	High	Low
9 Suction line restriction	Low	High	Low	Normal	Low
10 Hot gas line restriction	High	High	High	Normal	High
11 Inefficient compressor	High	High	Low	Low	Low

For an EER rating of 8.0 to 9.00 the DX coil split is typically 20–25°F.

$$COT = \left(\frac{80°F + 60°F}{2}\right) - (20-25°F) = 45-50°F$$

For an EER rating of 9.0+, the DX coil split is typically 15–20°F.

$$COT = \left(\frac{80°F + 60°F}{2}\right) - (15-20°F) = 50-55°F$$

This demonstrates that the operating coil temperature changes with the EER rating of the unit.

36.7 CONDENSING UNIT CONDENSING TEMPERATURE

The amount of surface in the condenser affects the condensing temperature the unit must develop to operate at rated capacity. The variation in the size of the condenser also affects the production cost and price of the unit. A smaller condenser will have a lower price but it will also have a lower efficiency (EER) rating. In the same EER ratings used for the DX coil, at 95°F outside ambient, the 7.0 to 8.0 EER category will operate in the 25–30°F condenser split range, the 8.0 to 9.0 EER category in the 20–25°F condenser split range, and the 9.0 + EER category in the 15–20°F condenser split range.

To calculate the DX coil operating temperature, the average air temperature across the coil was used to calculate the coil operating temperature. However, to calculate the

refrigerant condensing temperature in the condenser coil, only the entering air temperature will be required. The formula used for determining refrigerant condensing temperature is

$$RCT = EAT + \text{Condenser split}$$

where

RCT = refrigerant condensing temperature
EAT = entering air temperature of the condenser
condenser split = design temperature difference between the entering air temperature and the condensing temperatures of the hot high pressure vapor from the compressor

EXAMPLE 36-2

Using the formula with 95°F EAT, the refrigerant condensing temperature for the various EER systems would be:

For an EER rating of 7.0 to 8.0 the condenser split is typically 25–30°F:

$$RCT = 95°F + 25-30°F = 120-125°F$$

For an EER rating of 8.0 to 9.0 the condenser split is typically 20–25°F:

$$RCT = 95°F + 20-25°F = 115-120°F$$

For an EER rating of 9.0+ the condenser split is typically 15–20°F:

$$RCT = 95°F + 15-20°F = 110-115°F$$

This demonstrates that operating discharge pressures vary not only from changes in outdoor temperatures but with the different EER ratings.

TECH TIP

As an air conditioning system picks up heat, the temperature and pressure of the system increases on the suction side. If the air conditioning system cannot pick up heat in the evaporator, the suction pressure and temperature will go down. If the condenser is unable to reject the heat, the condenser temperature and pressure will go up. If the condenser is not receiving heat, its temperature and pressure will go down. Heat and temperature and pressure are all interrelated. If a system has lower than normal pressure and temperature, then heat is not being picked up. This may be caused by low airflow or low refrigerant charge. If a system has higher temperatures and pressures than normal, it is either picking up more heat than can be rejected by the condenser, or the condenser, is unable to reject the heat normally. The bottom line is that if you follow the temperature and pressure, you will follow the heat, which will enable you to diagnose refrigerant circuit problems.

36.8 REFRIGERANT SUBCOOLING

The amount of subcooling produced in the condenser is affected by the quantity of refrigerant in the system. The temperature of the air entering the condenser and the load on the DX coil also has an effect on the amount of subcooling produced. Typically it is desirable to have liquid subcooling of approximately 15–20°F.

If a refrigerant liquid line rises over 30 feet vertically, additional subcooling may be required to ensure that the metering device is receiving 100% liquid. The additional subcooling is required because of the pressure difference between the refrigerant at the condenser and pressure of the refrigerant at the metering device. This pressure drop is the result of the static head caused by the vertical lift of the refrigerant. Refer to the manufacturer's technical specifications to see what additional subcooling is required for unusually high vertical lifts.

36.9 INSUFFICIENT OR UNBALANCED LOAD

Insufficient air over the DX coil would be indicated by a greater than desired temperature drop through the coil. An unbalanced load on the DX coil would also give the opposite indication; some of the circuits of the DX coil would be overloaded, while others would be lightly loaded. This would result in a mixture of air off the coil that would cause a reduced temperature drop of the air mixture. The lightly loaded sections of the DX coil would allow liquid refrigerant to leave the coil and enter the suction manifold and suction line.

TECH TIP

The final step of installation that takes place at the residence is outside the control of the manufacturer. Many manufacturers have found that significant problems can exist in system installation, including the mismatching of equipment sizes. If you suspect that your refrigerant circuit problems are the result of mismatched equipment, call the equipment supplier or manufacturer and provide them the system component model numbers so they can inform you as to whether the system is mismatched in size and make recommendations to resolve the problems if a mismatched system exists.

In TEV systems, the liquid refrigerant passing the sensing bulb of the TEV would cause the valve to close down. This would reduce the operating temperature and capacity of the DX coil as well as lowering the suction pressure. This reduction would be very pronounced. The DX coil operating superheat would be very low, probably zero, because of the liquid leaving some of the sections of the DX coil.

Discharge pressure (high side) would be low due to the reduced load on the compressor, reduced amount of refrigerant vapor pumped, and reduced heat load on the condenser. Condenser liquid subcooling would be higher than normal because of the reduction in refrigerant demand by the TEV. The condensing unit amperage draw would be down due to the reduced load.

In systems using fixed metering devices, the unbalanced load would produce a lower temperature drop of the air through the DX coil because the amount of refrigerant supplied by the fixed metering device would not be reduced; therefore, the system pressure (boiling point) would be approximately the same.

The DX coil superheat would drop to zero with liquid refrigerant flooding into the suction line. Under extreme cases of imbalance, liquid returning to the compressor could cause compressor damage. The reduction in heat gathered in the DX coil and the decrease of refrigerant vapor to the compressor will lower the load on the compressor. The compressor discharge pressure will be reduced.

The flow rate of the refrigerant will only be slightly reduced because of the lower discharge pressure. The subcooling of the refrigerant will be in the normal range. The amperage draw of the condensing unit will be slightly lower because of the reduced load on the compressor and reduction in head pressure.

36.10 EXCESSIVE LOAD

In the case of excessive load, the opposite effect exists. The temperature drop of the air through the coil will be less, because the unit cannot cool the air as much as it should. Air is moving through the coil at too high a velocity. There is also the possibility that the temperature of the air entering the coil is higher than the return air from the conditioned area. This could be from air leaks in the return duct system drawing hot air from unconditioned areas.

The excessive load raises the suction pressure. The refrigerant is evaporating at a rate faster than the pumping rate of the compressor. If the system uses a TEV, the superheat will be normal to slightly high. The valve will operate at a higher flow rate to attempt to maintain superheat settings. If the system uses fixed metering devices, the superheat will be high. The fixed metering devices cannot feed enough refrigerant to keep the DX coil fully active.

The discharge pressure will be high. The compressor will pump more vapor because of the increase in suction pressure. The condenser must handle more heat and will develop a higher condensing temperature. A higher condensing temperature means a greater discharge pressure. The quantity of liquid in the system has not changed, nor is the refrigerant flow restricted. The liquid subcooling will be in the normal range. The amperage draw of the unit will be high because of the additional load on the compressor.

36.11 LOW AMBIENT (CONDENSER ENTERING AIR) TEMPERATURE

In this case, the condenser heat transfer rate is excessive, producing an excessively low discharge pressure. As a result, the suction pressure will be low because the amount of refrigerant through the metering device will be reduced. This reduction will reduce the amount of liquid refrigerant supplied to the DX coil. The coil will produce less vapor and the suction pressure drops.

SERVICE TIP

Often air conditioning and refrigerant equipment die at night. This is frequently caused because of the lower ambient temperatures experienced in the evening. Low ambient operation of refrigeration and air conditioning compressors can result in a liquid floodback or slugging of the compressor. If a system is to be operated on a regular basis during low ambient conditions, it should be equipped with a low ambient kit to protect the compressor.

The decrease in the refrigerant flow rate into the coil reduces the amount of active coil, and a higher superheat results. In addition, the reduced system capacity will decrease the amount of heat removed from the air. There will be a higher temperature and relative humidity in the conditioned area and the discharge pressure will be low. This starts a reduction in system capacity. The amount of subcooling of the liquid will be in the normal range. The quantity of liquid in the condenser will be higher, but the heat transfer rate of the evaporator is less. The amperage draw of the condensing unit will be less because the compressor is doing less work.

The amount of drop in the condenser ambient air temperature that the air conditioning system will tolerate depends on the type of pressure reducing device in the system. Systems using fixed metering devices will have a gradual reduction in capacity as the outside ambient drops from 95°F. This gradual reduction occurs down to 65°F. Systems that use a TEV will maintain higher capacity down to an ambient temperature of 47°F. Below these temperatures the capacity loss is drastic, and some means of maintaining discharge pressure must be employed to prevent the evaporator temperature from dropping below freezing. The most reliable means is control of air through the condenser via dampers in the airstream, the condenser fan cycling on and off, a variable speed condenser fan, or some combination of these components.

36.12 HIGH AMBIENT (CONDENSER ENTERING AIR) TEMPERATURE

When the outside air temperature rises on a hot day, then the temperature of the air entering the condenser will be higher. This also increases the condensing temperature and pressure of the refrigerant vapor. The suction pressure will also be high because the pumping efficiency of the compressor is reduced. There will also be less liquid line subcooling, which will increase the amount of flash gas across the metering device, further reducing the system efficiency. Due to the high ambient temperature, the discharge pressure will be high. There will be less liquid refrigerant in the condenser and reduced liquid subcooling. The system will run less efficiently and therefore will require more power so the amperage draw of the condensing unit will be high.

The amount of superheat produced in the coil will be different in a TEV system as compared to a system using a fixed metering device. In the TEV system the valve will maintain superheat close to the limits of its adjustment range even though the actual temperatures involved will be higher.

In a fixed metering device system, the amount of superheat produced in the coil is the reverse of the temperature of the air through the condenser. The flow rate through the fixed metering device is directly affected by discharge pressure. The higher air temperature will result in a higher discharge pressure and a higher flow rate. As a result of the higher flow rate, the amount of subcooling in the condenser is lower.

Table 36-5 shows the superheat that will be developed in a properly charged air conditioning system using a fixed metering device. Do not attempt to charge a fixed metering device system below 65°F, as system operating characteristics become very erratic.

36.13 REFRIGERANT UNDERCHARGE

A shortage of refrigerant in the system means less liquid refrigerant in the DX coil to pick up heat, and lower suction pressure. The smaller quantity of liquid supplied the DX coil means less active surface in the coil for vaporizing the liquid refrigerant,

Table 36-5 The Effects of Outdoor (Ambient) Temperature on Superheat

Outdoor air temperature entering condenser coil (°F)	Superheat (°F)
65	30
75	25
80	20
85	18
90	15
95	10
105 & above	05

and more surface to raise vapor temperature. The superheat will be high. There will be less vapor for the compressor to handle and less heat for the condenser to reject, leading to a lower condensing temperature and discharge pressure.

SERVICE TIP

The compressor in an air conditioning system is cooled primarily by the cool returning suction gas. Compressors that are low on charge can have a much higher operating temperature. The temperature can be high enough so that the motor windings begin to break down. As this occurs, the motor can ultimately short out, resulting in a compressor change out. If an air conditioning system has a leak it must be located so that a low refrigerant charge can be avoided.

The amount of subcooling will be below normal to zero, depending on the amount of undercharge. The system operation is usually not affected very seriously until the subcooling is zero and hot gas starts to leave the condenser together with the liquid refrigerant. The amperage draw of the condensing unit will be slightly less than normal.

36.14 REFRIGERANT OVERCHARGE TEV SYSTEMS

In systems using a TEV, the valve will attempt to control the refrigerant flow into the coil to maintain the superheat setting of the valve. However, the extra refrigerant will back up into the condenser, occupying some of the heat transfer area that would otherwise be available for condensing. As a result, the discharge pressure will be slightly higher than normal, the liquid subcooling will be high, and the unit amperage draw will be high. The suction pressure and DX coil superheat will be normal. Excessive overcharging will cause even higher discharge pressure, and hunting of the TEV.

SERVICE TIP

It is unacceptable to add a little extra refrigerant to a system just in case it may have a leak. If you suspect that a refrigeration system has a leak, do not overcharge the system but find the leak and fix it.

36.15 REFRIGERANT OVERCHARGE IN FIXED METERING DEVICE SYSTEMS

The amount of refrigerant in the fixed metering system has a direct effect on system performance. An overcharge has a greater effect than an undercharge, but both affect system performance, efficiency (EER), and operating cost.

As shown in Figure 36-26, at 100% of correct charge (55 oz), the unit developed a net capacity of 26,200 Btu/hr. When the amount of charge was varied 5% in either direction, the capacity dropped as the charge varied.

Figure 36-27 is a chart showing the amount of electrical energy the unit will demand because of pressure created by the amount of refrigerant in the system, with the only variable being the refrigerant charge. At 100% of charge (55 oz) the unit required 32 kW. As the charge was reduced, the wattage demand also dropped. When the unit was overcharged, the wattage required went up.

Figure 36-28 shows the efficiency of the unit (EER) based on the Btu/hr capacity of the system versus the wattage demand on the condensing unit. At the correct charge (55 oz) the EER was 8.49. As the refrigerant charge is either reduced or overcharged, the EER drops. From these charts, the only

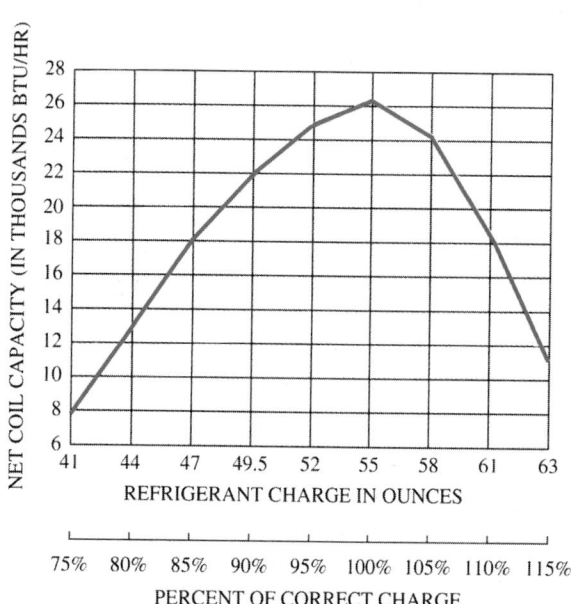

Figure 36-26 The effect of the refrigerant charge on the capacity of the unit

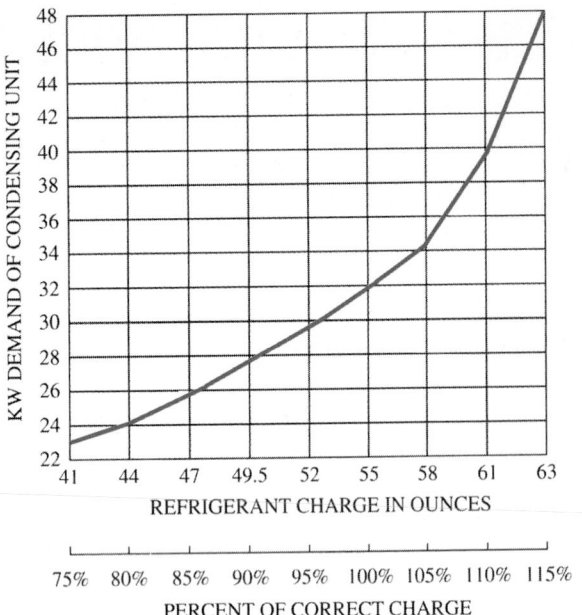

Figure 36-27 The effect of the refrigerant charge on the kW demand of the condensing unit

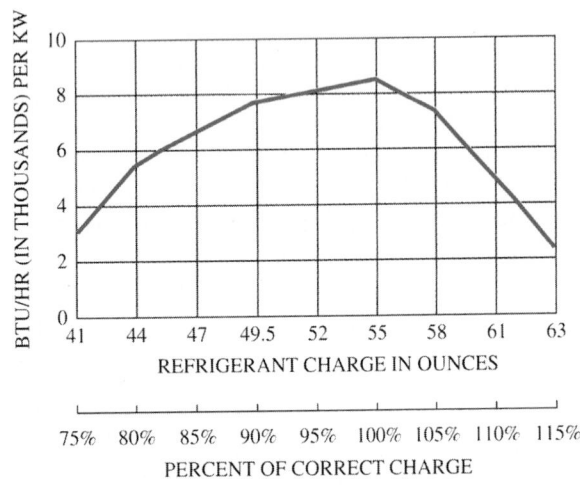

Figure 36-28 The effect of the refrigerant charge on the Btu/hr/kW ratio

conclusion is that the capillary tube systems must be charged to the correct charge with only a ±5% tolerance.

The effect of overcharge produces a high suction pressure because the refrigerant flow to the DX coil increases. Suction superheat will decrease because of the additional quantity to the DX coil. At approximately 8–10% of overcharge, the suction superheat becomes zero and liquid refrigerant will leave the DX coil. This will cause flooding of the compressor and greatly increases the chance of compressor failure. The discharge pressure will be high because of the extra refrigerant in the condenser. Liquid subcooling will also be high for the same reason. The amperage draw will increase

due to the greater amount of vapor pumped as well as the higher compressor discharge pressure.

36.16 LIQUID LINE RESTRICTION

A liquid line restriction could be caused by a plugged liquid line drier, a kink in the liquid line, or a solder joint filled with solder. A liquid line restriction reduces the amount of refrigerant to the metering device. The suction pressure will be low because of the reduced amount of refrigerant to the DX coil. The suction superheat will be high because of the reduced active portion of the coil, allowing more coil surface for increasing the vapor temperature as well as reducing the refrigerant boiling point. The discharge pressure will be low because of the reduced load on the compressor. Liquid subcooling will be high. The liquid refrigerant will accumulate in the condenser. It cannot flow out at the proper rate because of the restriction. As a result, the liquid will cool more than desired. The amperage draw of the condensing unit will be low.

SERVICE TIP

If the symptoms indicate that there is a liquid line restriction, it is sometimes easy to identify the liquid line drier as the problem. As the refrigerant flow is reduced through the drier due to the restriction, the pressure of the refrigerant will drop. This reduction in pressure across the drier will produce some flash gas similar to the situation that occurs across a capillary tube or TEV. The drier will be much colder on its outlet as compared to its inlet. A severely blocked drier may have frost accumulation on its outlet.

36.17 PLUGGED PRESSURE REDUCING DEVICE

Either a plugged fixed metering device or plugged feeder tube between the TEV valve distributor and the coil will cause part of the coil to be inactive. The system will then be operating with an undersized coil.

Plugged Fixed Bore or Capillary Tube Metering Devices

The suction pressure will be low because the coil capacity has been reduced. The reduced amount of vapor produced in the coil and resultant reduction in suction pressure will reduce compressor capacity, discharge pressure, and the flow rate of the remaining active capillary tubes. The suction superheat will be high. The discharge pressure will be low. The liquid subcooling will be high because the liquid refrigerant will accumulate in the condenser. The unit amperage draw will be low. The possibility of moisture in the system which freezes and plugs the capillary orifice should be considered.

Plugged TEV Feeder Tube

A plugged feeder tube reduces the capacity of the coil. The coil cannot provide enough vapor to satisfy the pumping capacity of the compressor and the suction pressure balances out at a low pressure. The remaining symptoms are similar to those of a plugged fixed metering device except that the superheat will be in the normal range. The TEV will adjust to the lower operating conditions and maintain the set superheat range.

36.18 SUCTION LINE RESTRICTION

A suction line restriction could be caused by a plugged suction line strainer, a kink in the suction line, or a solder joint filled with solder. It results in a high pressure drop between the DX coil and the compressor.

The suction pressure, as measured at the condensing unit end of the suction line, will be low. The superheat, as determined from the suction line temperature at the DX coil and the suction pressure (boiling point) at the condensing unit, will be extremely high. The discharge pressure will be low because of the reduced load on the compressor. The amperage draw of the condensing unit would be low because of the light load on the compressor.

Be aware that the symptoms listed above usually indicate a refrigerant shortage. A major difference is that with a suction line restriction, the subcooling will remain normal to slightly above normal. In an undercharged system, the amount of subcooling will be below normal to zero.

36.19 HOT GAS LINE RESTRICTION

For the condition of a gas line restriction, the discharge pressure measured at the compressor outlet will be high and measured at the condenser outlet will be low. The suction pressure will be high due to the reduced pumping capacity of the compressor. The DX coil superheat is high because the suction pressure is high. Liquid subcooling is in the high end of the normal range. The compressor amperage draw will be above normal.

If the discharge pressure is only measured at the condenser outlet, the symptoms can be easily misinterpreted. High suction pressure and low discharge pressure will usually be interpreted as a low capacity compressor. However, the high amperage draw of the compressor indicates it is operating against a high discharge pressure. This will point toward a restriction between the outlet of the compressor and the pressure measuring point.

36.20 LOW CAPACITY COMPRESSOR

The problem of a low capacity compressor is last on the list because it is the least likely problem. Determining the age of the unit may be of useful as an older compressor is more likely to have a reduced efficiency. When the compressor

will not pump the required amount of vapor, the suction pressure will balance out higher than normal. The DX coil superheat will be high. The discharge pressure measured at the compressor outlet will be low. Liquid subcooling will be low because not much heat will be in the condenser. The condensing will therefore be close to the entering air temperature. The amperage draw of the condensing unit will be extremely low, indicating that the compressor is doing very little work.

UNIT 36—SUMMARY

The referral to a troubleshooting chart will assist in locating the cause of the problem. As soon as the cause is verified, in most cases the remedy is self evident. For example, if a wiring connection is loose, it needs to be tightened. When a motor is burned out, it needs to be replaced. Where the replacement or service of specialized parts is required, usually the manufacturer provides detailed instructions for performing the work. When maintenance is required, such as cleaning a dirty coil or replacing worn out belts, these should be done following recommended standard procedures.

WORK ORDERS

Service Ticket 3601

Customer Complaint: Room Temperature Too High

Equipment Type: Residential Split AC System

A technician is called out to service a split AC system with an air handler and coil located in the attic. The technician arrives on the job, speaks to the customer, and discovers that the room temperature has been slowly rising during the past three to four weeks. The room temperature is higher than the thermostat setpoint, the air handler blower is running normally, and the outside condensing unit and compressor both appear to be running continuously.

The technician then measures the high and low side refrigerant system pressures and they are both low. The compressor amperage draw is also low. The technician suspects that there may be a refrigerant leak which has led to a shortage of refrigerant. Upon once again speaking with the customer the technician discovers that some landscaping had been done about three weeks ago. Investigating the outside lines that lead into the home, the technician finds that the liquid line had been disturbed and using a leak detector, a leak is located in the area of a brazed fitting. The refrigerant will need to be recovered, the leak repaired, and the system evacuated and recharged.

Service Ticket 3602

Customer Complaint: Low Register Airflow

Equipment Type: Residential Split AC System

A technician is called out to service a split AC system with an air handler and coil located in the attic. The technician arrives on the job, speaks to the customer, and learns that the air flow through the registers seems very low. Even without taking a measurement, it is easy to feel along the register and determine that not much air is being delivered. The customer also tells the technician that the system has just been started for the summer season about a week ago and that it has not worked well from that time.

The technician decides to first check the air handling unit in the attic, suspecting a clogged filter to be the problem. Upon investigating the unit, the technician discovers that squirrels had found an opening in the duct and built a nest in the path of the airflow during the winter months. The technician recommends that the customer contact an exterminator to remove the pests. Once this is done, the technician can come back and replace the filters and repair the duct.

Service Ticket 3603

Customer Complaint: Water Leaking from Ceiling

Equipment Type: Residential Split AC System

A technician is called out to service a split AC system with an air handler and coil located in the attic. The technician arrives on the job, and speaks to the customer, who says that there is water leaking from the attic and it has stained his ceiling. The customer believes that the water is coming from the AC unit.

The technician is not sure whether this may be a humidity related problem and first decides to check the air handling unit in the attic. The technician quickly discovers that the coil drain pan is overflowing and has caused the stain. A section of the drain piping is blocked and the technician cuts it out and replaces it. Once the blocked section is replaced, the water drains normally without backing up. The technician then recommends that the customer approve the installation of a float switch in the evaporator coil drain pan that will shut the unit down in the event of a similar occurrence in the future. This would reduce the chance of water ruining the ceiling again after the stain has been removed.

UNIT 36—REVIEW QUESTIONS

1. How is the temperature drop through a DX coil on a split AC system determined?

2. What is the most common problem of air failure on a split AC system?

3. If a split AC system does not operate at all, the problem is most likely what?

4. If the electrical load of a split AC system is not working, what must the technician try to determine?

5. What does an electrical connection diagram show?

6. List the measurements that need to be taken to determine the extent of a mechanical problem in a split AC system.

7. How are normal coil operating temperatures for a split AC system determined?

8. How does condenser size affect the EER?

9. What has the predominant effect on the amount of subcooling produced in the condenser of a split AC system?

10. What should be done if you suspect problems due to mismatched equipment sizes on a split AC system?

11. What type of temperature drop would you expect across the DX coil on a split AC system due to insufficient airflow?

12. What will happen to the suction pressure on a split AC system that is running with an excessive load?

13. Why do split AC systems often fail during the night?

14. A split AC system that uses a fixed metering device should not be charged if the ambient temperature falls below what level?

15. Capillary tube systems must be charged to within what tolerance?

16. What happens to the refrigerant superheat if a split AC system using a capillary tube is overcharged?

17. What happens to the amperage draw of a condensing unit on a split AC system if the liquid line is restricted?

18. How can one determine between a refrigerant shortage as compared to a suction line restriction on a split AC system?

19. How can you determine between an inefficient compressor as compared to a hot gas line restriction on a split AC system?

20. Is it acceptable to add a little extra refrigerant to a system just in case it may have a leak?

37.10 CERTIFICATION OF HEATING EQUIPMENT

All types of heating apparatus sold domestically have to be tested, certified, or listed by accredited testing agencies such as CSA International or Underwriters Laboratories, Inc. (UL). Gas appliances must meet standards set by a large number of governmental and independent agencies. Typically, the logos of the approving agencies can be found on the furnace name plate. Some of these agencies just establish standards, while others perform testing to certify that equipment meets these standards. Three of these agencies, AHRI, CSA, and UL, are involved in both setting standards and certifying equipment.

Governmental Agencies

- **United States Department of Energy (DOE)**   The primary governmental agency involved in gas furnace standards is the United States Department of Energy, DOE. One part of DOE's mission is to promote scientific and technological innovation in support of economic and energy security. DOE establishes the minimum AFUE that furnaces must meet. When developing their standards, DOE relies on research from two other governmental agencies: the National Institute of Standards and Technology, NIST, and the National Science Foundation, NSF.

- **National Institute of Standards and Technology (NIST)**   Founded in 1901, NIST is a nonregulatory federal agency within the US Commerce Department's Technology Administration. NIST's mission is to promote US innovation and industrial competitiveness by advancing measurement science, standards, and technology in ways that enhance economic security and improve our quality of life. NIST establishes measurement standards of all types.

- **National Science Foundation (NSF)**   The National Science Foundation is an independent federal agency created by Congress in 1950 "to promote the progress of science." NSF is the only federal agency whose mission includes support for all fields of fundamental science and engineering. NSF provides grants and oversight for basic science research.

Independent Agencies

- **American Gas Association (AGA)**   The AGA, founded in 1918, is the national trade association representing energy utilities that deliver natural gas. The AGA sets standards for gas appliance operation. By conforming to AGA guidelines, manufacturers can ensure that their equipment will operate properly on gas lines provided by AGA members.

- **Canadian Standards Association**   The Canadian Standards Association is a not-for-profit membership-based association serving business, industry, government, and consumers in Canada and the global marketplace. CSA America Inc., a division of CSA Group,

Figure 37-16 The CSA Blue Star Mark is for gas fueled products and indicates that a product complies with the requirements of applicable U.S. standards related to gas and electrical safety

is a standards development body in the United States for appliances and accessories fueled by natural gas, liquefied petroleum, and hydrogen gas. The CSA Technical Committees establish minimum construction and performance standards for gas heating equipment.

CSA also maintains testing facilities to certify gas fired heating equipment and electrical heating and air conditioning equipment. CSA will also do testing at the manufacturer's facility. The testing certifies that equipment meets standards set by organizations like ANSI, UL, CSA America, or the NSF. CSA Group acquired the Certification and Testing business from the AGA in 1997.

Gas furnaces and other comfort heating gas appliances tested and found to be in compliance bear the CSA Blue Star Mark and are listed in the CSA Certified Product Listings, Figure 37-16. Electrical products certified by CSA International to the applicable U.S. requirements are eligible to bear the CSA US Mark, as shown in Figure 37-17. This mark is accepted by

Figure 37-17 The CSA US Mark indicates that the product is in compliance with the requirements of the applicable United States standards

Figure 37-18 Underwriters' Laboratories (UL) seal
(Courtesy Underwriters' Laboratories)

regulatory authorities throughout the United States and is the equivalent of the UL mark.

- **Underwriters Laboratories (UL)** UL is an independent, not-for-profit, product safety certification organization that has been testing products and writing Standards for Safety for over a century. UL is involved in setting standards as well as testing. There are many UL standards relating to gas heating equipment.

UL gets involved in the approval and listing of heating and air conditioning equipment including large centrifugal machines of 100 tons and above. Local city codes and inspectors are guided by UL standards, and failure to comply with them may be costly to the manufacturer and installer. Most people are familiar with the UL mark, shown in Figure 37-18. UL maintains testing laboratories for certain types of products; however they often perform the necessary tests at the manufacturer's plant.

UNIT 37—SUMMARY

The three ingredients for combustion are fuel, oxygen, and heat. Complete combustion occurs when these are present in the correct quantities. The products of complete combustion of a fuel gas are carbon dioxide and water. Incomplete combustion occurs if any of the three ingredients are not present in the correct amount. Products of incomplete combustion include carbon monoxide and soot. Carbon monoxide is an extremely dangerous poisonous gas. It is odorless, tasteless, and lethal.

Gas fired heating equipment standards are set by a number of separate agencies including the American Gas Association, the American National Standards Institute, the Canadian Standards Association, the Department of Energy, the National Institute of Standards and Technology, the National Science Foundation, and Underwriters Laboratories. Testing and certifying equipment is performed by the Canadian Standards Association and Underwriters Laboratories. Annual Fuel Utilization Efficiency is a measure of gas furnace efficiency for the entire heating season. The minimum AFUE is 78% while the most efficient furnace available rates 97%.

WORK ORDERS

Service Ticket 3701

Customer Complaint: Furnace Does Not Heat the House

Equipment: Upflow Furnace Converted from Natural Gas to LP Gas

The furnace was recently installed. It was originally manufactured for natural gas and converted to LP by the installer. The service technician notices soot buildup on the heat exchanger. The flames are lazy and yellow, indicating incomplete combustion. There appear to be adequate combustion air openings and they are not obstructed. The manifold pressure reading is correct. The technician checks the gas burner orifices against the manufacturer's literature and finds that they are the original orifices sized for natural gas. Since a natural gas orifice is much larger than an LP gas orifice for the same capacity, the technician concludes that the oversized orifices are delivering too much gas, leading to incomplete combustion, soot formation, and poor heating. The orifices are changed to the correct size for LP gas and the soot buildup in the heat exchanger is removed.

Service Ticket 3702

Customer Complaint: Smoke Coming Out of Fireplace

Equipment: Upflow Gas Furnace Installed in a Hall Equipment Closet

The customer complains that if the furnace comes on when there is a fire in the fireplace, smoke starts coming out of the fireplace into the room. The technician looks in the equipment closet and finds that the combustion air grills have been covered in plastic and taped up. The homeowner says that they noticed cold air coming in through the grills and covered them up to keep the cold air out. The technician explains that the grills are there to provide combustion and ventilation air for the furnace. Without them, the furnace must draw in air from the rest of the house, creating a negative pressure in the house. This is why the fireplace smoke is coming out into the room. The customer is advised that this situation could be dangerous because it could lead to the furnace producing carbon monoxide and vent gas spilling into the house. The technician removes the plastic covering the grills and operates the furnace with a fire in the fireplace to verify that there is enough combustion air for both.

Service Ticket 3703

Customer Complaint: Furnace Comes on with a Boom!

Equipment Type: Horizontal Furnace Installed in Attic

The customer complains that the furnace sometimes lights with a load boom. It seems to happen more in colder weather. The technician observes that the burners are noisy and that the flames seem to be lifted away from the burner outlet. The air shutter adjustment is wide open. The technician reduces the primary air by closing the shutter until the flames start at the burner instead of away from it. The technician explains that the extra primary air was making the gas-air mixture hard to light. The delayed ignition caused gas to build up, resulting in a small explosion.

Service Ticket 3704

Customer Concern: Safety of Furnace

Equipment: Upflow Gas Furnace Installed in Equipment Closet

A customer has purchased a new house, which is heated by a gas furnace. They have always had electric heat and are concerned about the safety of gas appliances in general, and fire safety in particular. The technician agrees to do a thorough safety inspection and leaves the customer a gas safety bulletin the local gas utility produces. The technician explains that a key factor the customer can control is the combustion and ventilation air and shows the customer the combustion air grills, explaining that they should not be covered up or blocked. The technician also warns against using the equipment room as a closet and recommends that the customer purchase a carbon monoxide alarm.

UNIT 37—REVIEW QUESTIONS

1. Discuss the origin of natural gas.
2. List the three broad categories of fuel gases.
3. Complete this table of fuel gas characteristics.

Gas	Heat capacity	Specific gravity
Methane		
Ethane		
Propane		
Butane		

4. What are the products of complete combustion of a hydrocarbon gas?
5. What are the products of incomplete combustion of a hydrocarbon gas?
6. Why are LP gases considered more hazardous than natural gas?
7. Describe the two types of flames and their characteristics.
8. Describe the gas combustion process as it applies to a gas furnace.
9. Explain the causes of flue gas condensation and how it can be stopped.
10. Explain the cause of soot formation on the heat exchanger and how it can be stopped.
11. Explain how carbon monoxide is formed.
12. Discuss furnace combustion air requirements.
13. List agencies that establish standards for gas furnaces.
14. List agencies that perform testing to verify equipment performance.
15. Explain AFUE.
16. What is the minimum AFUE rating for a new furnace in the United States?
17. Which agencies set equipment standards and test equipment?
18. Which government agencies are involved in setting equipment standards?
19. What can be done to minimize the pollutants produced by a gas furnace?
20. What is the purpose of excess air in furnace combustion?

UNIT 38

Warm Air Furnaces

OBJECTIVES

After completing this unit you will be able to:

- define the four categories of gas fired furnaces.
- list the five furnace cabinet configurations.
- describe the operation of a standing pilot, natural draft furnace.
- describe the operation of an 80% mid-efficiency furnace.
- describe the operation of a 90% condensing furnace.
- discuss the evolution of the heat exchanger.
- discuss the operation of an atmospheric burner.
- explain why furnace efficiencies jump from 80% to 90%.

38.1 INTRODUCTION

Warm air furnaces have been the most common form of heat for decades. The furnace has evolved to meet the challenge posed by rising energy costs. Furnaces today are smaller, lighter weight, and more efficient. Understanding today's technologically advanced warm air furnaces is crucial for the successful technician.

A wide variety of warm air furnaces are available to meet many different applications. Factors to be considered when choosing a furnace include the fuel source, furnace location, efficiency, and venting. There are many furnaces to choose from because there are many options for each of these variables. In many cases, the contractor must choose between several possibilities because more than one type of furnace would work. Understanding all the choices will allow the installing contractor to make an informed, intelligent decision.

38.2 TYPES OF FURNACES

A gas furnace's operational characteristics place it into one of four categories based on its flue gas temperature and pressure.

- **Category I** An appliance that operates with a nonpositive vent static pressure and with a vent gas temperature greater than 140°F above the flue gas dew point, which avoids excessive condensate production in the vent.
- **Category II** An appliance that operates with a nonpositive vent static pressure and with a vent gas temperature less than 140°F above the flue gas dew point, which may cause excessive condensate production in the vent.

- **Category III** An appliance that operates with a positive vent static pressure and with a vent gas temperature greater than 140°F above the flue gas dew point, this avoids excessive condensate production in the vent. However, the positive pressure vent requires a sealed vent system.
- **Category IV** An appliance that operates with a positive vent static pressure and with a vent gas temperature less than 140°F above the flue gas dew point, which may cause excessive condensate production in the vent.

Category I furnaces are the most common. Category I furnaces can be further divided into natural draft and fan assisted. Most furnaces sold today are Category I, fan assisted. The draft inducer fan on most 80% furnaces does not produce a positive vent pressure because it is sized just large enough to overcome the resistance of the heat exchanger and because the temperature of the flue gas makes it lighter than air. Another benefit to induced draft furnaces is that the heat exchanger operates in a negative pressure. This ensures added safety to the consumer because if a hole develops in the heat exchanger, the surrounding air rushes into the heat exchanger, preventing harmful flue gases from escaping into the occupied space.

Category II and Category III furnaces are rare. Both of these require special vent materials, making their installation more costly. A special high temperature plastic vent material was developed for use with Category II and III furnaces. This venting material is no longer manufactured because of high failure rates and the resulting legal action.

Category IV furnaces are also common; they are the 90% condensing furnaces. Since the flue gas is relatively cool, PVC can be used as a vent material. PVC is easy to seal airtight and water will not bother it.

38.3 STYLES BASED ON INSTALLATION LOCATION

All furnaces are composed of two main sections: the heat exchanger compartment and the blower compartment. The arrangement of these two sections determines the general style of the furnace. Regardless of the style, the air always travels through the blower compartment first, before going to the heat exchanger. The reason is fairly simple; the fan motor would overheat otherwise. Furnaces can be categorized into five styles: upflow, lowboy, downflow or counterflow, horizontal, and multiposition.

For the most part, airflow through the furnace gives it its name. Air travels up in an upflow furnace, down in a downflow furnace, and horizontally in a horizontal furnace.

Figure 38-1 Upflow highboy furnace
(Courtesy of Bard Manufacturing Company)

The *upflow* furnace, Figure 38-1, is most popular. Its narrow width and depth allow for location in first floor closets and/or utility rooms. It can still be used in most basement applications for heating only or with cooling coils where headroom space permits. Blowers are usually direct drive multispeed or ECM. Return air can be either from the sides or from the bottom.

The *counter flow* or *down flow* furnace, Figure 38-2, is similar in design and style to the upflow, except that the air intake and fan are at the top and the air discharge is at the bottom. These are widely used where duct systems are set in concrete or in a crawl space beneath the floor. A fireproof base is required when the furnace is installed on a combustible floor. An extra safety limit control is also used.

Horizontal furnaces are installed in low areas such as crawl spaces, attics, or partial basements, Figure 38-3. It requires no floor space. Intake air enters at one end and is discharged out the other end. On older style furnaces, burners

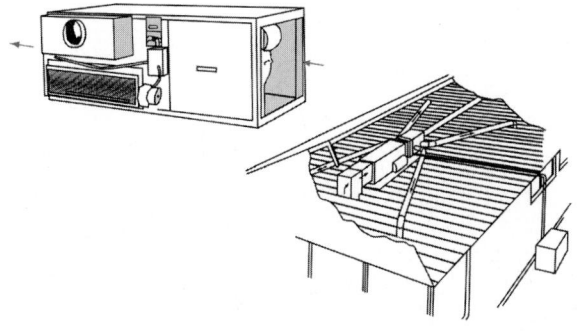

Figure 38-3 Horizontal furnace

are usually field-changeable for left-hand or right-hand application.

Lowboy furnaces, Figure 38-4, are built low in height to accommodate low ceilings. These furnaces are approximately 4 ft high, providing for easy installation in a low ceiling height basement. Lowboy furnaces have two sections side by side, like horizontal furnaces. But the air goes in the top of the furnace, makes a 180° turn as it goes through the furnace, and then leaves out the top of the furnace. Blowers are commonly belt driven. Many of these furnaces are sold for retrofitting older homes.

The installation technician can configure the fifth style, the multiposition furnace, on the job site to be an upflow, horizontal, and/or downflow furnace. The introduction of the multiposition furnace has allowed manufacturers and contractors to reduce the number of furnaces they must keep in inventory to meet local demand. The vent typically needs to be configured for the installation. Figure 38-5a,b shows a vent configured for upflow, downflow, and horizontal installation. Typical installations of the horizontal, counterflow, and upflow furnaces are shown in Figure 38-6.

Figure 38-4 Lowboy furnace
(Courtesy of Bard Manufacturing Company)

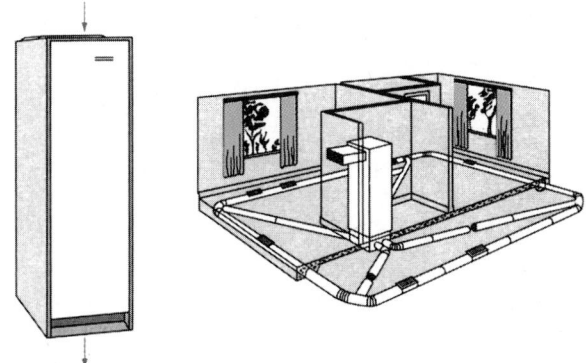

Figure 38-2 Counterflow furnace

(a)   (b)

Figure 38-5 Multiposition furnace

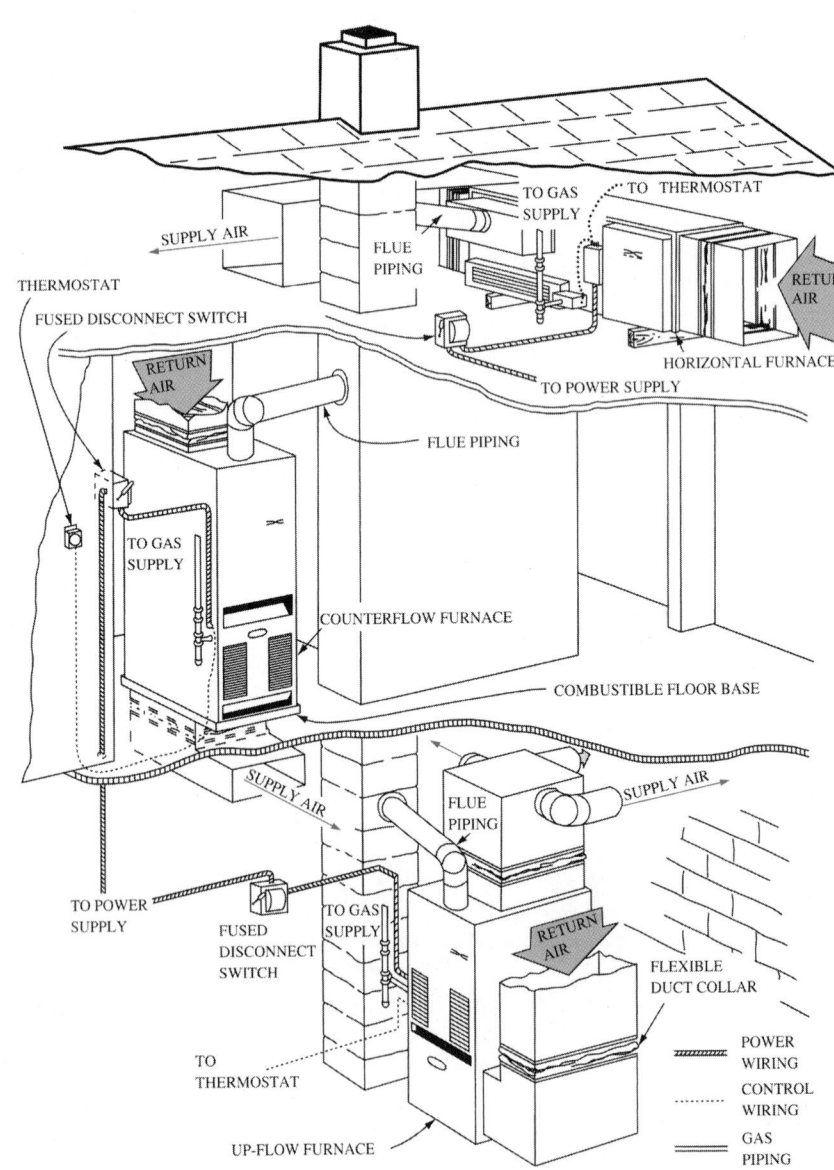

Figure 38-6 Composite diagram of three types of furnace installations: (1) Attic installation of a horizontal furnace; (2) First floor installation of a counterflow furnace; (3) Basement installation of a lowboy furnace

38.4 TYPE OF HEAT SOURCE

Furnaces may also be described in relation to the type of heat source: *fuel burning* furnaces and *electric* furnaces.

In fuel burning furnaces, fuel is burned in the combustion chamber. Circulating air passes over the outside surface of the heat exchanger. The products of combustion are vented to the atmosphere. Fuels used in these systems include:

1. Gas, both natural and LP.
2. Oil.

In an electric furnace, circulating air is directly heated by resistance type heating elements as the air passes through a metal sheath that encloses the resistance element.

38.5 GAS FORCED WARM AIR SYSTEMS

The furnace of today has evolved from the old pot bellied stove. Wood and coal burning stoves heated the room by a combination of convection and radiation. All objects in a direct line of sight from the stove were heated by radiation. However, if something blocked the path between the object and the stove, the intermediate object absorbed all the heat. Another problem with radiant heat is that it is uneven by nature. The amount of radiant heat transferred diminishes by the square of the distance between the source of the radiant heat and the object absorbing the heat. In simpler terms, the closer you get to the stove, the hotter you get. This means that certain areas of the room will be very warm while others will be chilly. Convection is also taking place. Cool air near the floor is heated by the stove, rises to the ceiling, loses its heat along the way, cools off and drops back down. This does help distribute the heat, but again, somewhat unevenly. The ceiling tends to stay about 20°F warmer than the floor. Unfortunately, most of the room's occupants are closer to the floor than the ceiling.

The first central furnaces were essentially pot bellied stoves inside a metal housing. Ductwork ran from the housing to all areas of the house, producing a more even distribution of heat. Since the stove was encased in a metal jacket, all radiant heat was converted to convection heat, eliminating the problem of hot and cold spots associated with radiant heat. These early furnaces did have a few problems of their own; for instance, the ductwork was enormous since the furnace was relying on natural convection to carry the heated air through the ducts to the house. If the ductwork was not gigantic, the restriction to flow did not allow the hot air to reach the house. Also, these furnaces lost more heat than they delivered. Since heat energy was used for venting the furnace as well as for air delivery, more heat went up the stack than was delivered into the house.

The next logical advance was the addition of a fan to force the air over the stove, which is now called a heat exchanger. This increased efficiency by wringing more heat out of the heat exchanger. It also reduced the size of the ductwork needed to deliver the air. Although this represented quite a step forward, the pot belly shape of the heat exchanger contributed to the problem of inefficiency. A large quantity of combustion gases never touched the sides of the heat exchanger due to its large round shape. If the combustion gas does not come in contact with the heat exchanger, its heat cannot be transferred. To increase heat transfer, the barrel type heat exchanger was squeezed, or flattened, to a rectangular box that was not very wide. This made it more difficult for flue gas to leave the heat exchanger without touching the sides, thus increasing efficiency. Typically several of these clamshell heat exchangers were combined together, each with its own burner. This became known as a sectionalized heat exchanger.

Furnaces remained about the same for decades and performed reliably with 60–65% efficiency. There was not much incentive to change them until the energy crisis of the 1970s. Suddenly, the same old furnace, which had operated economically for years, seemed to turn into a fuel-hogging monster. Of course what changed was the cost of the fuel. Changes increased furnace efficiency by about 20%. Through experimentation and some unfortunate experiences, an efficiency of less than 80% was determined to be the highest efficiency possible without condensing water out of the flue gas. Units that exceeded this efficiency had the unfortunate experience of condensing water in both the heat exchanger and the flue. This water was very corrosive due to its mild acidity, and these units often died untimely deaths of flue or heat exchanger failure.

The next major increase in efficiency took advantage of the early mistakes. By intentionally designing a furnace to condense water, efficiency could be increased. Now furnaces are available with efficiencies up to 96.6%. To do this, the point where condensation occurs has to be closely controlled and the condensing section of the furnace is typically made of stainless steel.

Furnace manufacturers now offer two types of furnaces:

- Mid-efficiency category I fan assisted.
- High efficiency category IV condensing type furnace.

The *mid-efficiency furnaces,* Figure 38-7, meet the minimum requirement of 78% AFUE (Annual Fuel Utilization Efficiency) and have a flue gas temperature at least 140°F above the dew point of the flue gas. The high efficiency furnaces have flue gas temperatures below the dew point and permit condensation within the furnace to pick up the extra latent heat. Since certain components are different, they will be described separately. Large numbers of the earlier standard furnaces, which use standing pilots and natural draft venting, are still in use and require service. They will also be described in this text, although they are no longer being manufactured.

(a)

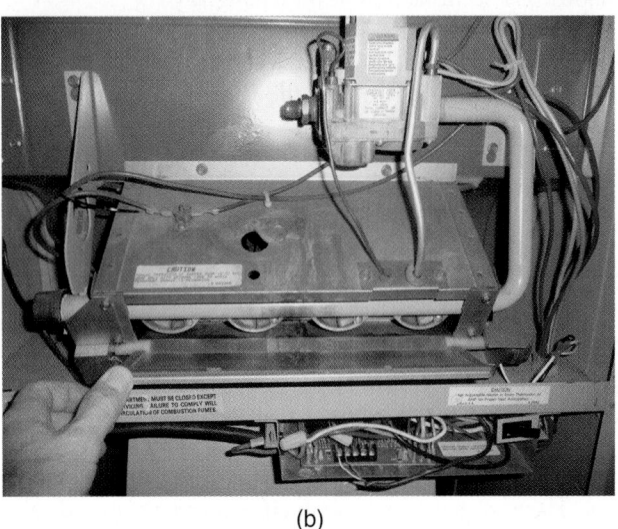

(b)

Figure 38-7 Mid-efficiency furnace

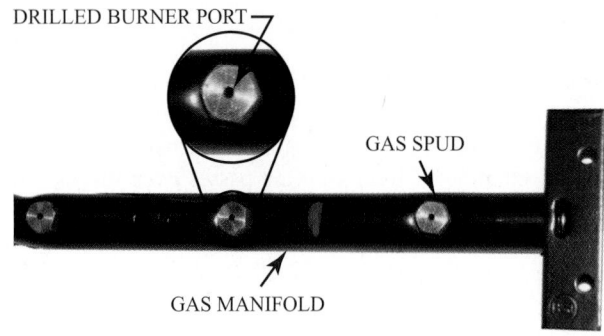

Figure 38-8 Burner bar

Figure 38-9 Spud with orifice number

38.6 MANIFOLD

The purpose of the manifold is to supply gas to all the burners. The manifold is usually a length of pipe connected to the gas valve on one end and closed on the other end. There is a small plug, called a spud, along the manifold at each burner outlet. The spuds thread into the manifold. Occasionally the manifold has a threaded plug that can be removed to check the manifold pressure, Figure 38-8.

38.7 ORIFICE

An orifice is a precisely drilled hole that meters the correct amount of gas into the burner. Along the manifold at each burner outlet there is a small plug called a spud. The spud is a small brass plug in which the orifice is drilled, Figure 38-9. Since the orifice size is what really matters, most people refer to the spud as the orifice. The specified sizes are very small and they must be drilled accurately. A slightly

larger hole lets in too much gas and overfires the burner. A hole that is not drilled straight can cause even more problems. The space between the orifice and the venturi on most atmospheric burners is open to the air. It has to be open so that primary air can be injected by the jet action of the gas emitting from the orifice. If the gas stream does not aim straight inward, it may hit the side of the venturi; or worse, the gas stream may miss the venturi altogether. This causes poor ignition and even explosions. While it is not impossible for a factory orifice to be drilled incorrectly, dirt, dust or other debris are more likely the cause of the gas stream to be deflected.

The size of the orifice is determined by three factors: the specific gravity of the gas, the heat content of the gas, and the required Btu/hr rating of the burner. The first two factors, specific gravity and heat content, are generally set by the gas type which is usually either natural gas or propane. The unit's Btu/hr rating divided by the number of burners determines the burner Btu/hr rating. For example: on a 40,000 Btu/hr furnace with a single burner, the orifice Btu/hr rating would be 40,000 Btu/hr However, if the same 40,000 Btu/hr furnace had two burners, each burner orifice would be rated at 20,000 Btu/hr Once you know what type of gas the burner uses and the Btu/hr required for each burner, you could look up the orifice size in an orifice chart, Table 38-1.

Table 38-1 Gas Orifice Capacity

Drill	Size	Natural Gas 3.5"	Propane 11"
70	.0280	1991	5476
69	.0292	2165	5956
68	.0310	2440	6713
1/32	.0313	2487	6843
67	.0320	2600	7153
66	.0330	2765	7607
65	.0350	3110	8557
64	.0360	3291	9053
63	.0370	3476	9563
62	.0380	3666	10087
61	.0390	3862	10625
60	.0400	4062	11176
59	.0410	4268	11742
58	.0420	4479	12322
57	.0430	4695	12916
56	.0465	5490	15104
3/64	.0469	5585	15365
55	.0520	6865	18888
54	.0550	7680	21131
53	.0595	8989	24730
1/16	.0625	9918	27286
52	.0635	10238	28167
51	.0670	11398	31357
50	.0700	12441	34228
49	.0730	13530	37225
48	.0760	14665	40347
5/64	.0781	15487	42608
47	.0785	15646	43045
46	.0810	16658	45831
45	.0820	17072	46969
44	.0860	18778	51663
43	.0890	20111	55331
42	.0935	22197	61067
3/32	.0938	22339	61460
41	.0960	23399	64377
40	.0980	24384	67087
39	.0995	25137	69156
38	.1015	26157	71964
37	.1040	27462	75553
36	.1065	28798	79229
7/64	.1094	30388	83603
35	.1100	30722	84522
34	.1110	31283	86066

38.8 BURNERS

The purpose of the gas burner is to properly mix the primary air and gas and to deliver this mixture in a manner that can be easily ignited and burned. There are two general types of burners, the atmospheric burner and the power burner. The atmospheric burner draws its air in from the surrounding atmosphere and requires air both at the point of gas entry and at the point of combustion. Power burners, on the other hand, normally get all their air at the point of gas entry. A power burner also draws its air from the surrounding atmosphere, but a blower forces it in mechanically. Many power burners pressurize both the air and the gas and are able to burn large quantities of gas quickly. The basic residential burner is the atmospheric burner. Even induced and forced draft units normally use atmospheric burners even though the "draft" through them is mechanically produced. First, we will discuss atmospheric burners.

Atmospheric Burners

The burner generally slides onto the spud, with the spud located in the middle of the burner face. The primary air openings are located all around it. In older furnaces, these air openings were fitted with adjustable shutters to control primary air entering the burner. Air shutters are no longer used on modern burners.

The gas shoots out of the orifice in a small, quick stream, which creates a negative pressure around it and draws in primary air through the primary air openings. The burner is shaped like an hourglass on the end. It has a large diameter at the face where the gas and air enter, a small diameter a short distance away, and returns to a large diameter at the burner's main body. This shape, called a venturi, causes the gas and air to swirl as they pass through the constricted opening, mixing them together. The orifice, primary air shutters, and venturi are crucially important because together they are responsible for mixing the gas and air in the correct proportions for complete combustion. Next, the gas travels through the venturi into the main burner body. Here, the gas-air mixture slows down and expands to fill the chamber. The mixture leaves through the burner ports.

There are several styles of ports from in-shot, one large hole, to drilled port, several small holes drilled in the burner. Figure 38-10a,b shows the two most common burners today, in-shot and slotted burners. In-shot burners produce a flame like a jet or rocket tail while drilled port burners produce lots of small, distinct flames. In-shot burners are generally the most efficient type of atmospheric burners, but they are also the noisiest.

Drilled port burners are usually quieter, but less efficient. In between these two types of atmospheric burners are slotted port and ribbon burners. Slotted port burners are usually made of stamped sheet metal and resemble drilled port, except that the slots are larger than the holes in a drilled port burner. Ribbon burners consist of several slots, which run the length of the burner. These produce long, thin,

(a)

(b)

Figure 38-10 Inshot (a) and slotted (b) atmospheric burners

ribbon flames. Virtually all furnaces today use in-shot burners because of their efficiency and because the flame from an in-shot burner fits the narrow heat exchangers used today. Regardless of the burner style, a good flame should have a bright blue inner cone surrounded by a darker blue outer cone. There should be no yellow in the flame; yellow indicates either too little air or too much gas in the mixture.

Power Burners

The other basic type of gas burner is the power burner. Power gas burners are seldom used on residential equipment, although a few units have used power burners. Power burners use a fan to force both the air and the gas into the combustion area. The air and gas can be mixed in the fan itself or after the fan inside a tube with angular vanes to create a vortex action and mix the air and gas. Generally, power burners are ignited by spark igniters or glow coils. Using power burners can achieve higher burning efficiencies than atmospheric because they have better control over the fuel-air ratio. Power burners are used on commercial multi-fuel furnaces. Nongaseous fuels, such as oil, require power burners for operation. The use of a power burner can make changeover from gas to oil easier.

38.9 HEAT EXCHANGERS

The job of the heat exchanger is to separate the combustion process from the air being heated, and as its name implies, exchange the heat from the combustion process to the air being circulated over the heat exchanger. To perform the job of gas separation, a heat exchanger needs only to be an airtight vessel with a hole in the bottom for the burners and one at the top for the flue gas to escape. So long as there are no holes in between these two openings, there is no problem. The second job, efficient heat transfer, is not as simple.

The earliest heat exchangers were basically barrels with a hole in the bottom and a hole in the top. They were adequate for gas separation, but were rather inefficient heat transfer apparatuses. Large quantities of the relatively unrestricted flue gas found their way up the vent without ever contacting the surface of the heat exchanger. This translates into lost heat.

By flattening the heat exchanger, more resistance to flow was created which forced more of the combustion products to touch the walls of the heat exchanger, increasing efficiency. Several of these flattened heat exchangers were used together to create one unit. These are commonly called sectionalized heat exchangers because they are built in sections, Figure 38-11. The vent opening on sectionalized exchangers is on the side at the top. Flue baffles were added at the top of the sectionalized heat exchangers, Figure 38-12. The baffles restrict the flow of combustion gases at a constriction near the top of the heat exchanger. This forces them to stay in the heat exchanger longer, thus, increasing heat transfer.

This concept was taken further with serpentine heat exchangers. The serpentine path and the narrow width helped

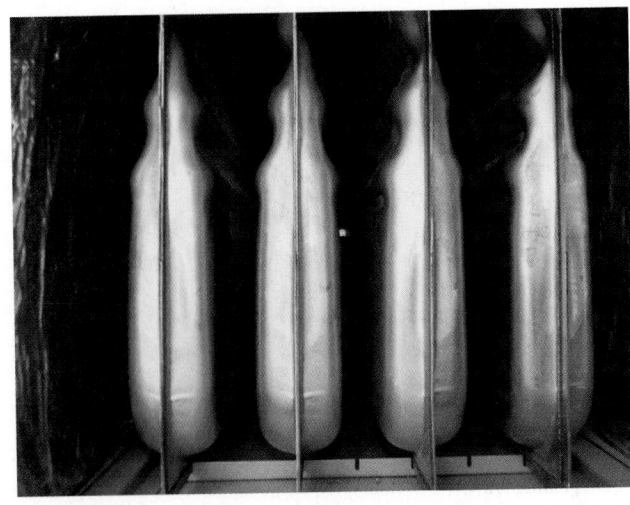

Figure 38-11 Sectionalized heat exchanger

Figure 38-12 Heat exchanger baffles

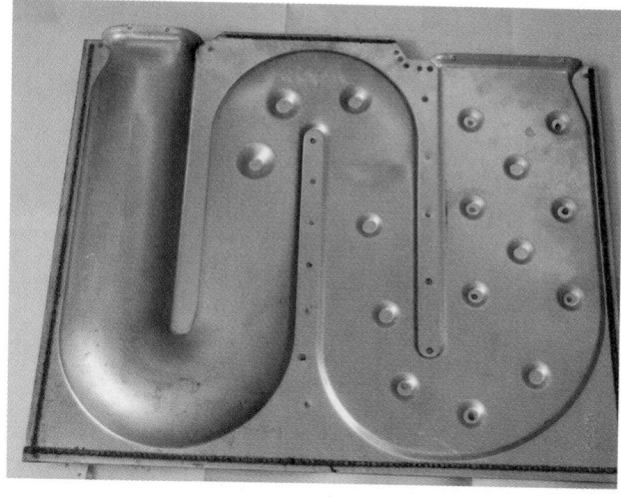

Figure 38-13 Serpentine heat exchanger section

squeeze more heat out of the combustion gas, Figure 38-13. These features also required an induced draft fan to draw the combustion gases through the heat exchanger. A fan pressure-breaking baffle was installed at the discharge of the induced draft blower, making the vent pressure negative so that the furnace could be vented with standard type b vent. Figure 38-13 shows a serpentine heat exchanger.

Furnace manufacturers began to use automotive exhaust tubing as the heat exchanger. By bending tailpipe material in a serpentine configuration, they managed to produce a heat exchanger which gave them 80% efficiency yet used considerably less material and energy to produce.

To get into the 90%+ range, you must condense. Most 90% furnaces are an 80% furnace with a stainless steel recuperative condensing coil. Most of these recuperative coils are built like a refrigeration coil, only from stainless steel. Some recuperative cells are just smaller stainless steel serpentine heat exchangers. Recuperative cells are installed ahead of the main heat exchanger in the airstream. Obviously, any unit employing such a coil must also provide a drain for the furnace. So far, the experience with this approach has been very good. If you plan ahead for condensation to take place, then it ceases to be a problem. These units have another common characteristic, PVC positive pressure vents. The flue gas leaving a 90% efficient furnace feels warm and wet to the hand. PVC can handle the temperature easily. The positive pressure is no problem so long as PVC is used because it is relatively simple to ensure a leakproof PVC vent. The positive pressure also allows more flexibility in vent location and design since the flue gas is being pushed out, not floating out. Most major manufacturers now offer a 90%+ condensing furnace as part of their product line and installation practices are similar from one to another.

Traditionally, burners were located at the bottom of the heat exchanger and flue gases escaped out the top because the furnace relied on natural convection to move the flue gas

through the heat exchanger. The addition of the induced draft blower made it possible to have the flames at the top of the heat exchanger and the exhaust gases leaving the bottom of the heat exchanger. The counter flow process where the combustion gas moves in the opposite direction from the air is more efficient. Many manufacturers use the counterflow heat exchanger design in their 90% efficiency models. Notice in Figure 38-7 that the burners are at the top where the hot air is leaving.

A key operating characteristic of any furnace is its temperature rise. Manufacturers give the acceptable temperature rise range on the data plates of their units. For a standard furnace, the temperature rise range is usually 30°F such as between 50°F and 80°F. However, the exact range will change depending on the unit's capacity. The range will always be listed on the unit data plate. That means that if 70°F air is entering the furnace, the air leaving it should be between 120°F and 150°F. The higher the efficiency of the furnace, generally, the lower the temperature rise. To increase efficiency, increase the airflow through the unit compared to a standard furnace with the same Btu/hr rating. Thus, since there is more air to absorb the heat, more heat will be absorbed. However, that also means that less heat will go into each cubic foot of air, so the temperature rise of the air will be less. High efficiency furnaces normally have a temperature rise of between 25°F and 65°F.

38.10 MID-EFFICIENCY FURNACES (80% AFUE)

Furnace manufacturers achieve an efficiency of 80% by eliminating the pilot light, improving heat exchanger efficiency, and adding an induced draft blower.

A drawing of the internal components of a mid-efficiency furnace is shown in Figure 38-14.

Figure 38-14 Internal view of the major components of a mid-efficiency gas furnace, with the component parts labeled
(Courtesy Lennox Industries, Inc.)

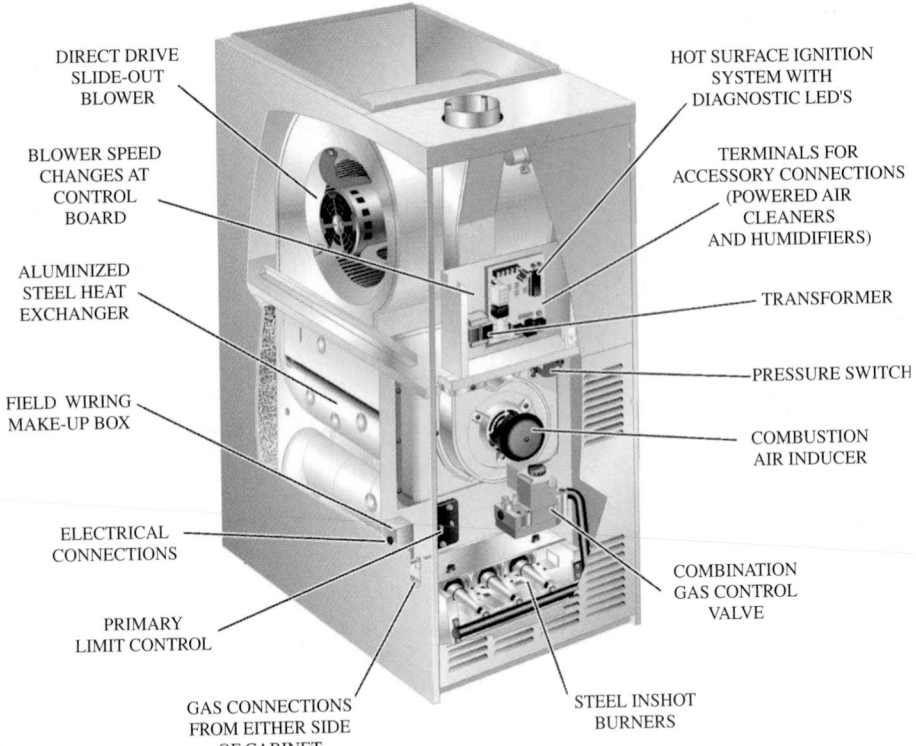

DIRECT DRIVE SLIDE-OUT BLOWER

BLOWER SPEED CHANGES AT CONTROL BOARD

ALUMINIZED STEEL HEAT EXCHANGER

FIELD WIRING MAKE-UP BOX

ELECTRICAL CONNECTIONS

PRIMARY LIMIT CONTROL

GAS CONNECTIONS FROM EITHER SIDE OF CABINET

HOT SURFACE IGNITION SYSTEM WITH DIAGNOSTIC LED'S

TERMINALS FOR ACCESSORY CONNECTIONS (POWERED AIR CLEANERS AND HUMIDIFIERS)

TRANSFORMER

PRESSURE SWITCH

COMBUSTION AIR INDUCER

COMBINATION GAS CONTROL VALVE

STEEL INSHOT BURNERS

INDUCTION BLOWER

Figure 38-15 An inducer-blower used to force the combustion gases through the furnace

The internal components of a mid-efficiency furnace include:

- The *inducer blower assembly,* with an induced draft blower to draw the flue gases through the heat exchanger and to the vent, as pictured in Figure 38-15. The inducer motor draws the exact amount of air needed through the combustion exchanger. The assembly is resiliently mounted to provide quiet operation.
- The *pressure switch,* which proves that the inducer fan is operating before the fuel can be ignited.
- The *gas control valve,* which delivers the fuel gas into the burner. The gas valve opens slowly to provide a controlled ignition. It also provides for 100% shutoff to ensure safe operation.
- The *burner assembly,* which provides for proper mixing of fuel and air, and ignites the fuel.
- The *blower door safety switch,* which disconnects the power supply to the unit whenever the front access panel is removed.
- The *control box,* which houses controls, including a microprocessor board that controls most furnace operations and functions. It provides a blower delay on startup and shutdown, while monitoring furnace performance. The technician can use this self-testing feature to identify a major component failure. The control board will check itself, then the inducer, silicon carbide ignition, low- and high-speed blower operation, and humidifier connections. Control boards often include a low amperage fuse that protects the

Service Ticket 3805

Customer Complaint: New Furnace Relocation

Equipment: Upflow/Horizontal flow Furnace

A homeowner has decided to install a furnace in the basement of his house. He purchases a furnace on sale from Furnace Mart and begins to install the furnace in the basement. After the job gets started, his wife inspects the furnace in the basement and does not like its location. She would prefer that the furnace be installed in the attic like the neighbor's.

The homeowner explains to his wife that he has already purchased the furnace and it is designed to be installed in the upflow position. His wife tells him to call a professional and find out if anything else can be done. At first the homeowner is reluctant but then after looking over the system he decides that maybe his wife is right. He is relieved after talking to a technician. It appears that the attic installation will work out just fine and the furnace he purchased can be adapted for this configuration. Although it costs the homeowner more money than if he installed the furnace himself, he feels reassured that the job was done professionally and with every safety requirement in mind.

UNIT 38—REVIEW QUESTIONS

1. List the four categories of gas fired furnaces based on flue gas temperature and pressure.
2. Explain the difference between a Category I furnace and a Category IV furnace.
3. List the five furnace cabinet configurations.
4. Why are standing pilot natural draft furnaces no longer manufactured?
5. What changes were made in furnace design to achieve 80% efficiency?
6. What is the difference between an 80% efficient furnace and a 90% efficient furnace?
7. Discuss the evolution of the heat exchanger.
8. Discuss the operation of an atmospheric burner.
9. Explain why furnace efficiencies jump from 80% to 90%.
10. What is the purpose of the orifice?
11. Why is it not a good idea to drill out orifices in the field?
12. What components are needed for a furnace to operate as a two stage furnace?
13. Why are some condensate pumps not approved for furnace condensate?
14. Can the furnace drain and the air conditioning drain be run with a common drain?
15. List the different types of gas burners.
16. Why do most furnaces today use burners?
17. What is the temperature rise of a furnace?
18. What part of the furnace does the air travel through first in all furnace cabinet configurations?
19. Why should technicians be familiar with standing pilot, natural draft furnaces since they are no longer manufactured?
20. Why are draft inducer fans necessary in today's furnaces?

UNIT 39

Gas Furnace Controls

OBJECTIVES

After completing this unit you will be able to:

- identify and name the different types of control components.
- describe the operation of flame safety devices.
- explain the function of gas pilots.
- explain the operation of a direct spark ignition system.
- describe how gas valves operate with thermostat and limit controls.
- read wiring diagrams and identify symbols.
- determine the maximum length of wire run to limit voltage drop.
- explain the operation of a control circuit.
- wire a control circuit.

39.1 INTRODUCTION

Controls can be used to accomplish a number of different tasks in a system. Most commonly they will function to operate a system within prescribed limits such as a thermostat control that starts a furnace when the temperature falls below the setpoint. Controls can also serve as safety devices, for example, to shut down a furnace if there is a flame failure. They can be designed with remote operation for convenience purposes, making it easier for the customer to change the operational settings. Additionally, controls can be designed to cycle the furnace on and off in such a manner as to operate the most efficiently.

A control system requires a source of power to operate, a load to utilize the power, and controllers to obtain the desired level of operation. The control system checks or regulates, within prescribed limits, the functions of an HVAC/R system. Controls have been developed to facilitate system operation, safety, personal convenience, and economy of equipment. On older models there may be dual control. One of the controls is called a fan switch and the other is called limit switch. Combined it is called a fan/limit switch.

39.2 TYPICAL CONTROL SYSTEM LAYOUT

A typical control system for a year round air conditioning system using gas for winter heating and refrigerated air for summer conditions is shown in Figure 39-1. A power type humidifier is included for winter and an electronic air cleaner for year round air filtration. A multispeed blower motor in the air handling unit is used to provide the best results in both the heating and cooling phases.

The operation of the system is under control of a room thermostat, which controls a gas valve in the heating phase and the condensing unit's operation in the cooling phase. The blower in the gas furnace must operate intermittently in the heating phase, depending on the furnace supply plenum temperature. A low voltage room thermostat is used to control a high voltage blower motor (120 V) and a higher voltage condensing unit (240 V). This is accomplished through the use of relays, contactors, or motor starters, depending on the load characteristics encountered.

In the control circuit shown in Figure 39-1, the power source is a transformer, which is part of a plate mounted relay/transformer assembly. The line voltage is reduced to the lower control voltage through the transformer. The other component of the assembly is a relay containing two sets of single pole double throw contacts. One set of contacts controls the speed of the blower motor. The other set controls the starting and stopping of the blower motor under the control of the furnace fan switch in the heating mode or directly when in the cooling mode.

39.3 CONTROL SYSTEM POWER SOURCE

While the source of power to operate a control system is usually electricity, some use electronic or pneumatic control, or a combination of all three. Here we will concentrate on electricity as the power source for residential and light commercial controls.

Heating control circuits can be designed to operate on either line voltage (115–120 V) or on low voltage, which is designated as a 24 V system. A low voltage control circuit is superior to a line voltage circuit because the wiring is simplified and safer, and low voltage thermostats provide closer temperature control than do line voltage thermostats.

The step down transformer or low voltage transformer that comes inside the furnace, Figure 39-2, is used in heating and air conditioning control systems. This transformer is used to reduce line voltage to operate the control components. Inside a simple step down transformer are two unconnected coils of insulated wire wound around a common iron core, as shown in Figure 39-3. To go from 120 V (primary) to 24 V (secondary), there are five primary turns to one secondary turn. For a 240 V primary the ratio would be 10:1, and so on. This, the induction ratio, is a direct proportion. Step up transformers would be just the reverse.

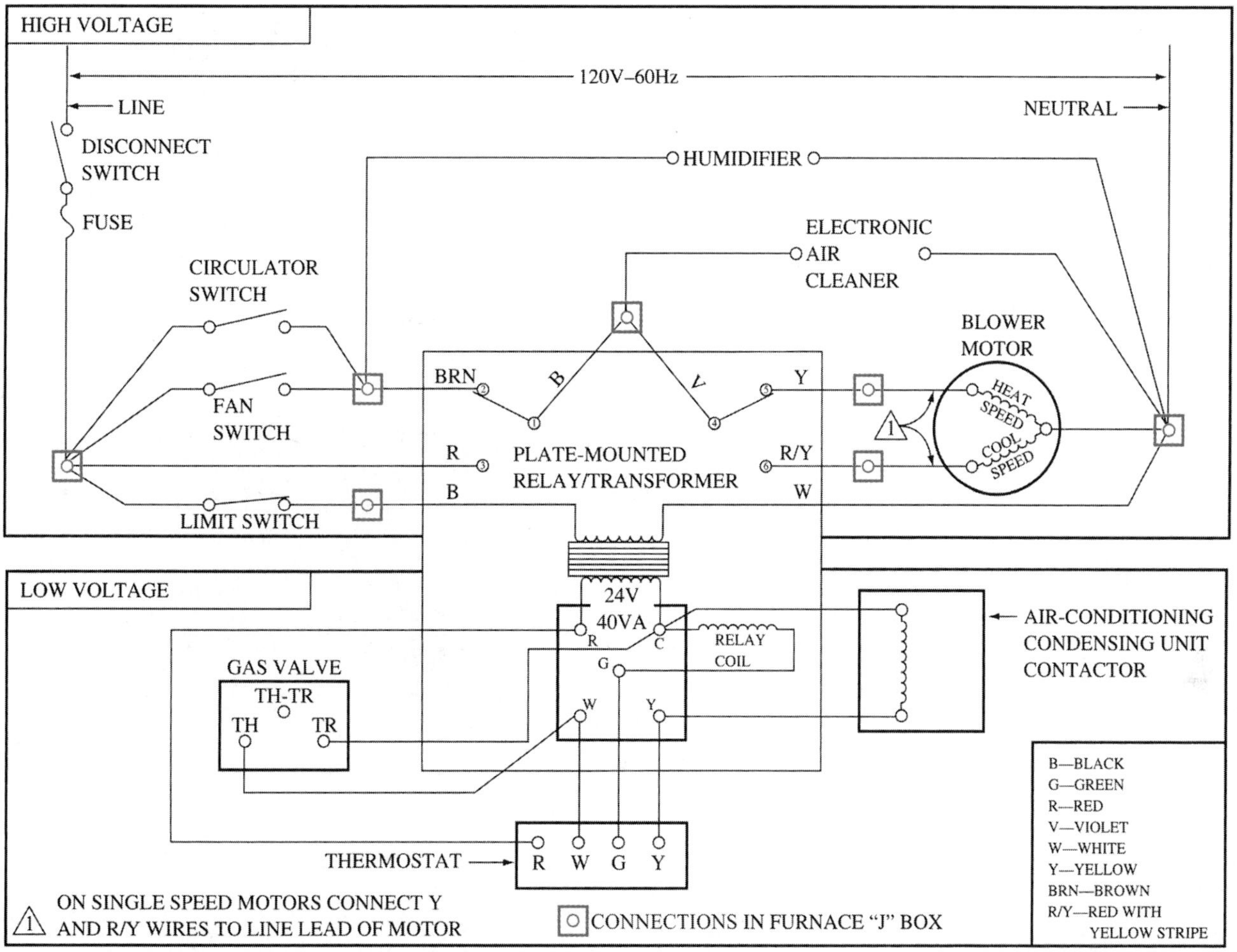

HIGH VOLTAGE

120V–60Hz

LINE

NEUTRAL

DISCONNECT
SWITCH

HUMIDIFIER

FUSE

ELECTRONIC
AIR
CLEANER

CIRCULATOR
SWITCH

BLOWER
MOTOR

BRN   B   V   Y

HEAT
SPEED

FAN
SWITCH

COOL
SPEED

R   PLATE-MOUNTED   R/Y
         RELAY/TRANSFORMER

B   W

LIMIT SWITCH

24V
40VA

LOW VOLTAGE

AIR-CONDITIONING
CONDENSING UNIT
CONTACTOR

R   C   RELAY
                  COIL

GAS VALVE

G

TH-TR

TH   TR   W   Y

B—BLACK
G—GREEN
R—RED
V—VIOLET
W—WHITE
Y—YELLOW
BRN—BROWN
R/Y—RED WITH
     YELLOW STRIPE

THERMOSTAT ──▶   R   W   G   Y

⚠ ON SINGLE SPEED MOTORS CONNECT Y
   AND R/Y WIRES TO LINE LEAD OF MOTOR

▢ CONNECTIONS IN FURNACE "J" BOX

Figure 39-1 Typical control system for an air conditioning system using gas heating and electric cooling

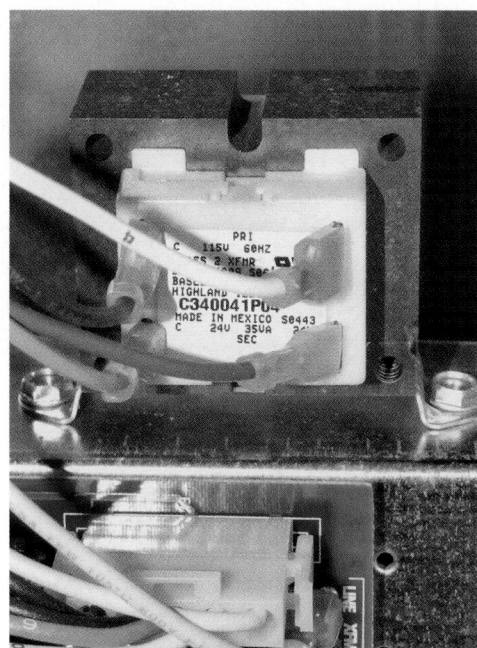

Figure 39-2 AC voltage transformer for low voltage controls

Transformers used in the HVAC/R field are rated by their secondary power output. The most common size transformer found in residential gas furnaces is 40 VA. The term VA (volt-amp) is used to express the watts of secondary power output. To convert VA to amps of output you divide the VA rating by the secondary voltage rating.

EXAMPLE 39-1

A given transformer has a primary voltage of 120 V and a secondary voltage of 24 V. Assuming that the transformer is rated at 40 VA, what is the secondary current?

Secondary (A) = 40 VA/24 V = 1.67 A

SERVICE TIP

A standard 40 VA furnace control transformer has a very limited amperage capacity. If additional components such as humidifiers, duct boosters, and dampers are added to a system's control circuit, it may be necessary to increase the size of the transformer used.

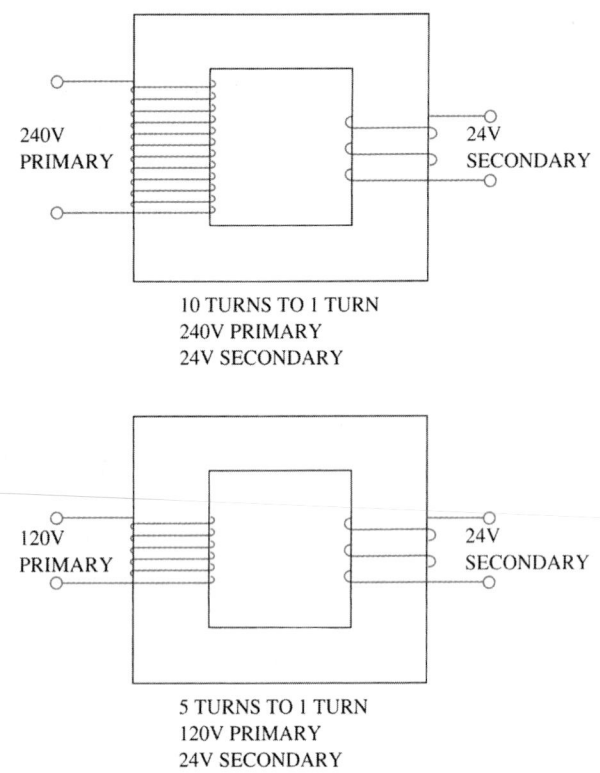

Figure 39-3 Construction of a step down transformer

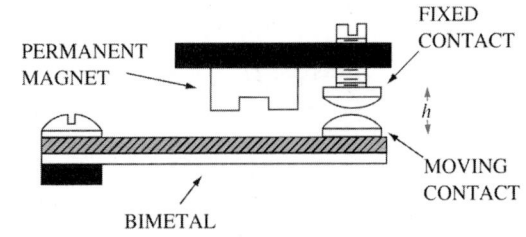

Figure 39-4 Snap action thermostat

(a)

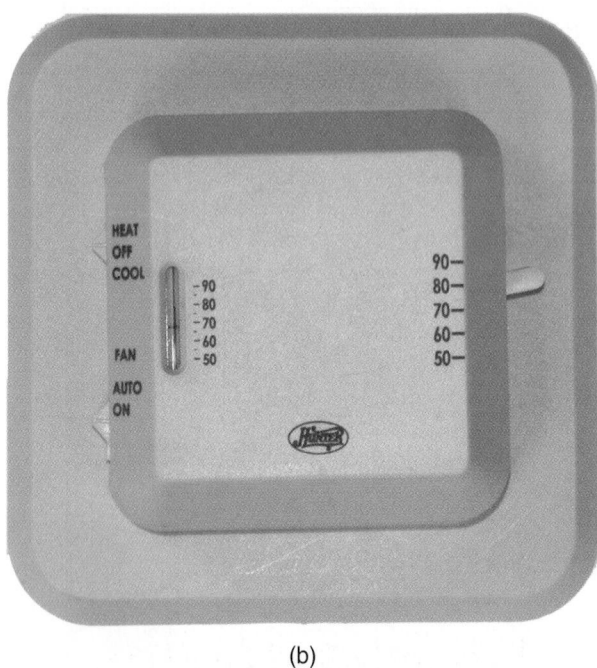

(b)

Figure 39-5 Low voltage thermostat used in a central system control circuits: (a) Heating only; (b) Heating and cooling

Transformers are available in a variety of voltages and capacities. The capacity refers to the amount of electrical current expressed in volt-amperes. A transformer for a control circuit must have a capacity rating sufficient to handle the current (amperage) requirements of the loads connected to the secondary. Ratings of 40 VA are needed for air conditioning because electrical devices containing a coil and iron, such as solenoid valves and relays, have a power factor of approximately 50%. Thus, for secondary circuits with such controls, the capacity of a transformer must be equal to or greater than twice the total name plate wattages of the connected loads.

The proper transformer rating for the electric control circuits will have been selected by the equipment manufacturer. If accessory equipment is added, however, the additional power draw must be considered. You may need to install a new larger VA transformer. This situation is common, for example, when cooling is added to an existing furnace and where the original transformer is too small. When replacing a defective transformer, make sure that the rating is equal to or greater than the original equipment.

39.4 THERMOSTATS

Snap action thermostats, Figure 39-4, are widely used. Low voltage thermostats, as shown in Figure 39-5a,b, are used in central system control circuits. First, the use of spiral shaped, lightweight bimetallic elements increases the effective length and thus the sensitivity to temperature change. Second, the use of sealed contacts eliminates the problem of dirt and dust. Although there are minor variations among different manufacturers, the contacts are always sealed in a glass tube.

A single action mercury bulb design is shown in Figure 39-6. As the bimetallic strip expands and curves, the mercury fluid moves to the left, completing an electric circuit between the two electrodes which carry only 24 V. The differential gap

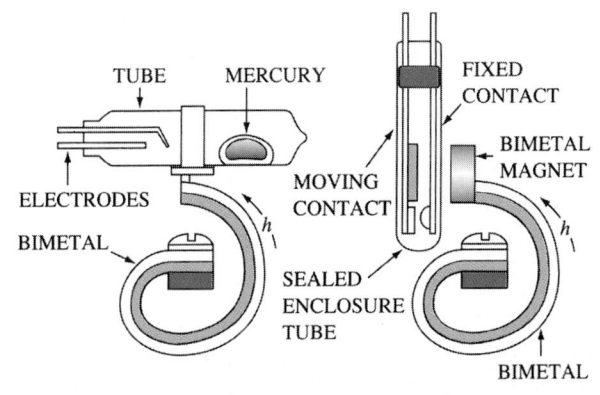

Figure 39-6 A single-action mercury-bulb thermometer on the left; A sealed tube with metal-to-metal contact on the right

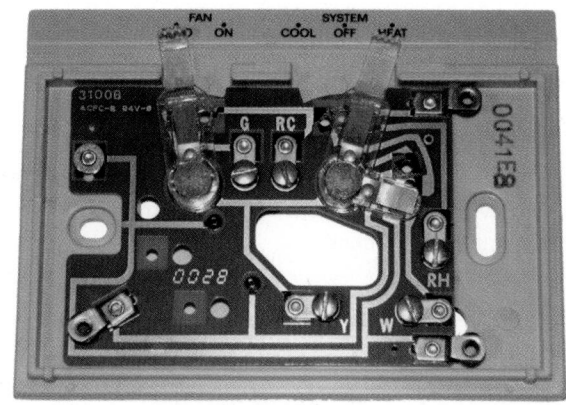

Figure 39-7 Subbase portion provides a mounting base for the thermostat and for system controls

between OFF and ON is very small: 0.75°F to 1°F from the setpoint. On the right is a sealed tube that has a metal to metal contact. The magnet provides the force that closes the contacts.

The subbase portion of the thermostat assembly, Figure 39-7, not only provides a mounting base for the thermostat, but is also used to control the system operation through a series of electrical switches. The system switch selects COOL, OFF, or HEAT. The blower operation is controlled by

the fan switch, which is a simple two position switch. When set on automatic, the fan will cycle with the furnace on heating or with the cooling in cool position. If in the ON position, the fan will run continuously.

More complex thermostats contain two adjustments that allow different control points for heating and cooling to be set. These thermostats may have an automatic changeover from heating to cooling. Figure 39-8 represents a two stage

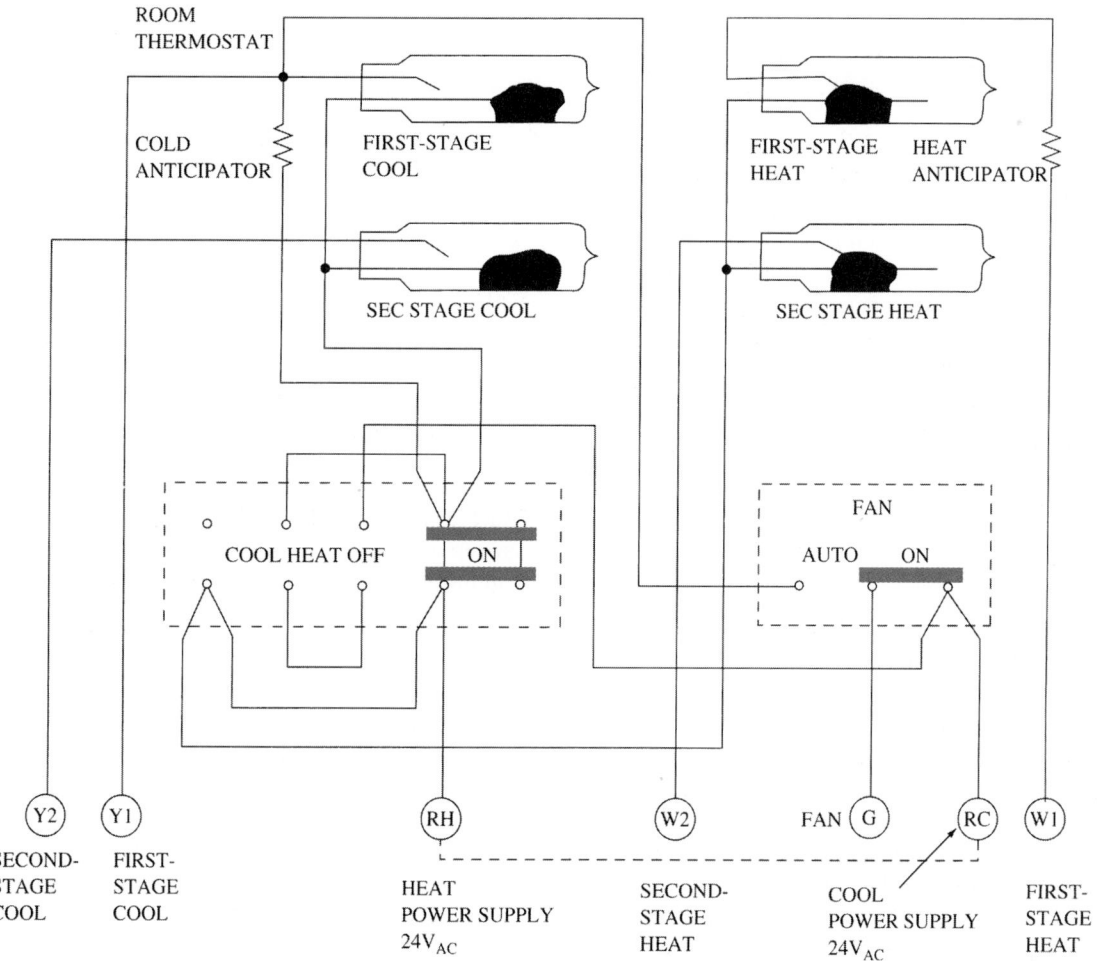

Figure 39-8 A two stage heating and two stage cooling schematic wiring diagram

cooling schematic wiring diagram. Two stage thermostats are common in heat pumps or commercial rooftop equipment, which use multiple compressors for cooling and two or more stages of heating. Note that seven electrical connections are required; however, RH and RC terminals are the same power source, so six wires are needed. With color coded low voltage wire, however, it is no problem to connect the thermostat to the mechanical equipment.

Electronic Thermostats

Electronic thermostats can be programmable or nonprogrammable. These thermostats often use thermistors or other integrated circuit sensors to sense temperature changes. Thermistor operation is based on the fact that the electrical resistance of a ceramic semiconductor changes as its temperature changes. Generally these thermostats have an LED display for enhanced readability.

Programmable electronic thermostats can be programmed to set back the temperature at predetermined times and days. This allows for additional energy savings by automatically reducing the demand for heating or cooling, for example at night or during the day when no one may be home. These can also provide additional information such as filter change reminders and system runtime data. Many of these thermostats provide for adjusting burner on-time and fan operation.

39.5 THERMOSTAT ANTICIPATORS

The sensitivity of room thermostats is affected by both system lag and operating differential. System lag is the amount of time required for the heating or cooling system to produce a temperature change that is felt at the thermostat. The operating differential of a thermostat is the change in room air temperature needed to open or close the thermostat contacts.

39.6 HEAT ANTICIPATION

Heat anticipators are used in low voltage thermostats to reduce the temperature swing caused by the systems. Heating anticipators are small electrical resistors that generate a little heat inside the thermostat when the heat is on. This "false heat" on the bimetal tricks the thermostat into thinking the room has reached the set temperature. The furnace burner goes off when the thermostat thinks the room is warm enough but the fan keeps running until the heat exchanger cools down. Without a heating anticipator, the room temperature would overshoot the set temperature, Figure 39-9a. Temperature swing is the difference between the temperature when the furnace comes on and goes off.

Although heating anticipators result in closer room temperature control and less overshooting of heating, they can shorten the heating cycle time, as shown in Figure 39-9b. If the heating anticipator is set too high, the furnace will short cycle, as shown in Figure 39-9c.

Some heating anticipators are fixed, while others are wire wound variable resistors wired in series with the load. They are rated in fractions of amperes. On the adjustable type, the installer will position the sliding arm to the proper load rating. A heating anticipator is shown in Figure 39-10. The initial setting should match the amp draw of the gas valve. But if on/off cycles are too long or too short, the system operation can be changed by adjusting the anticipator control lever to give a faster or slower response.

SERVICE TIP

Some customers are more sensitive to temperature change than others. These customers might have a complaint that the room gets too cold before the heat comes on. They might also complain that this occurs even when the temperature has been turned up slightly. What they are feeling is the temperature swing resulting from the heating anticipator being set too low. By raising the current setting on the heating anticipator, the heating cycle will shorten, and the temperature swing will decrease.

TECH TIP

The longer a furnace runs during its heating cycle, the more efficiently it operates. Setting the heating anticipator so that a larger temperature swing occurs will result in energy savings. Conversely, a short cycling heating system is less efficient to operate.

39.7 COOLING ANTICIPATION

The cooling anticipator is a fixed electric heating resistor. It is on when the AC is off. The small amount of heat produced by the cooling anticipator will force the AC to come on from time to time under light loads. Humidity will build up in a house when the AC is on but cycling because of a light load, such as at night. The cooling anticipator can cause the AC system to cycle four or more times an hour to provide dehumidification. This is particularly important in warm, humid climates.

39.8 HUMIDISTATS

Another type of controller found in residential comfort applications is the wall mounted humidistat, Figure 39-11. It is very similar to the low voltage thermostat, and it contains both a sensing element and a low voltage electric switch.

The sensing element consists of either an exceptionally thin moisture sensitive nylon ribbon or strands of human hair that react to changes in humidity. The movement of the sensing element is sufficient to make and break electrical

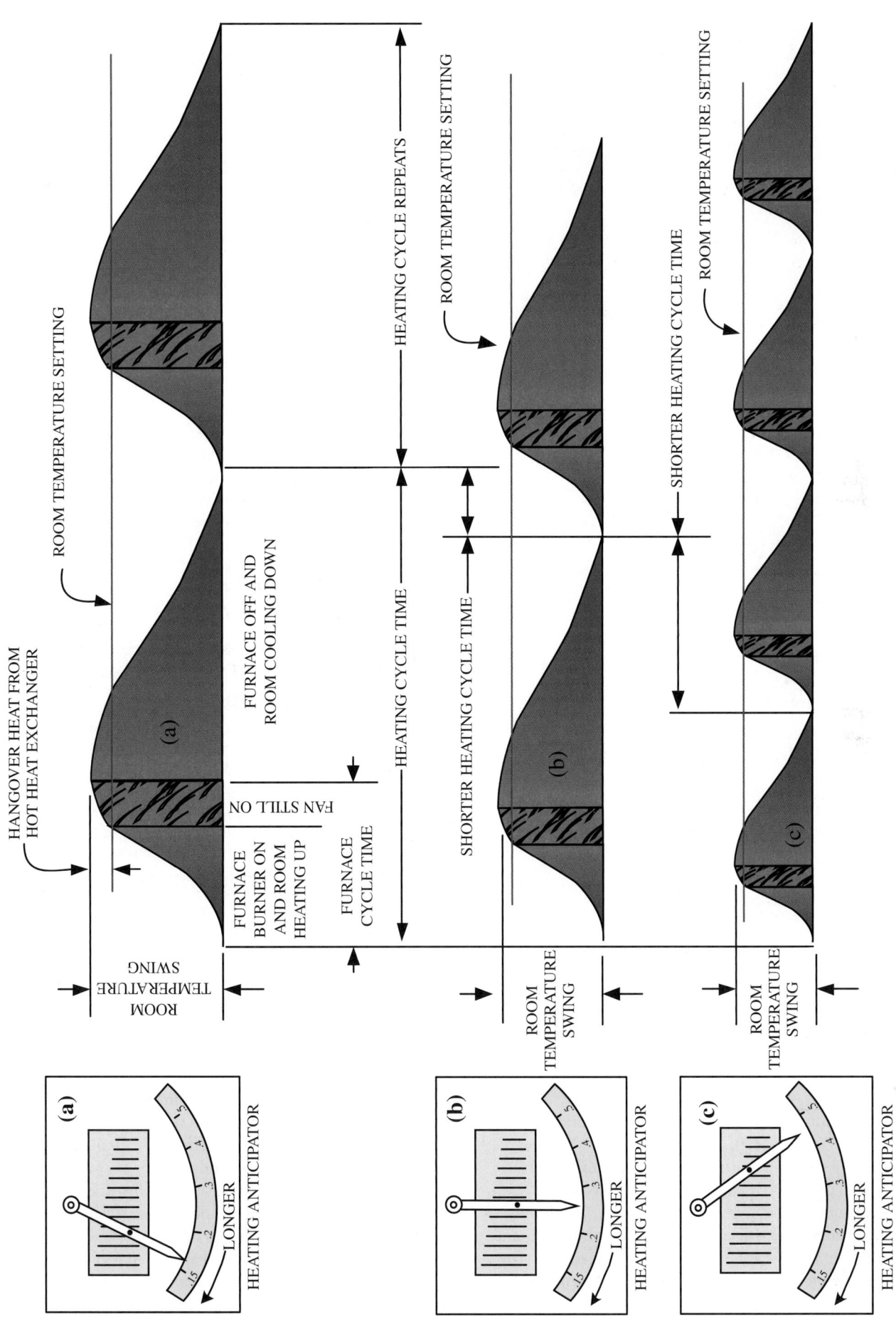

Figure 39-9 Effect of changing the heating anticipator on heating cycle times and temperature

Figure 39-10 An adjustable heating anticipator

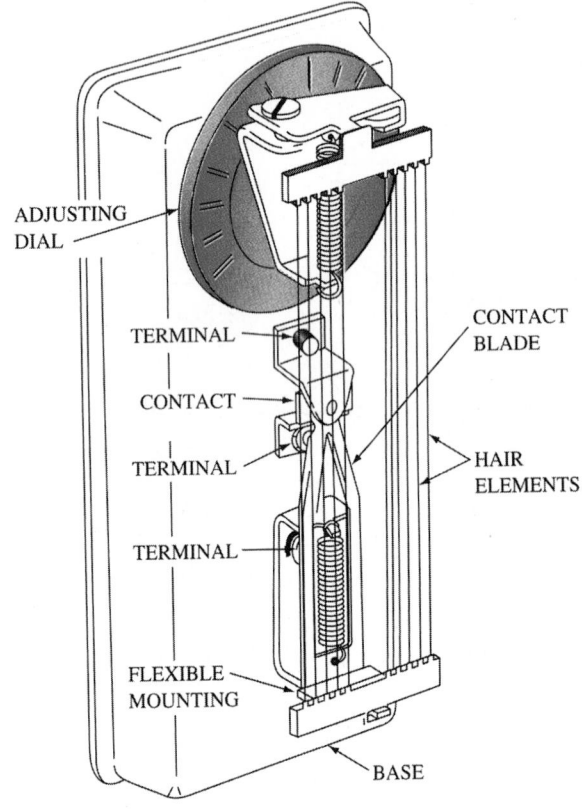

Figure 39-11 Construction of a wall mounted humidistat

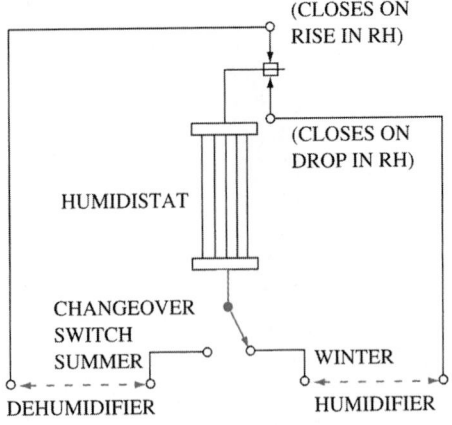

Figure 39-12 A simple schematic wiring diagram for year round control of humidity

The humidistat is not a precise controller. It may allow a change of 5% relative humidity before switching into action. Because people cannot detect or react to changes in relative humidity with the same sensitivity as room temperature, this swing is not noticed. More precise controls are available for specialized applications, such as computer rooms, libraries, and printing plants, where controllers such as wet bulb and dew point thermostats would be used.

SERVICE TIP

Adding humidity to a residence during the heating season will allow your customer to feel more comfortable at a lower thermostat setting. A large part of a person's comfort is the rate at which perspiration evaporates from their skin. As the relative humidity goes up, that rate of evaporation decreases; thus they feel warmer even at a lower actual room temperature. A humidistat can provide that control which will increase your customer's comfort and save them heating costs.

39.9 FAN AND LIMIT SWITCHES

Fan Switch

The fan switch controls the starting and stopping of the blower motor. The fan does not start when the burner starts. Instead, the fan switch closes and starts the blower when the air temperature inside the furnace plenum chamber has warmed up to the FAN ON setting. The fan switch remains closed when the burner stops, keeping the blower in operation until the air temperature inside the furnace cools down to the FAN OFF setting.

Newer programmable thermostats provide more fan options. The AUTO switch would be the setting for most homes. A single-speed fan turns on automatically with the air conditioner or furnace. A two-speed fan usually runs on high with the air conditioner, and on low or medium speed with the furnace. The thermostat fan operation switch is usually

contacts directly or when coupled with a mercury type switch. Humidistats for mounting on ductwork are also available.

A simple schematic wiring diagram for humidity control is shown in Figure 39-12. In winter the elements contract and close the contact to the humidifier. In summer the humidistat expands in response to a rise in the relative humidity and closes the contacts to the dehumidifier (cooling unit) circuit. A summer/winter changeover switch selects the appropriate operation.

preset at the factory for oil and gas applications. For electric heat, the setting must be changed so that the fan control is energized at the same time as the controls for the heating elements. This will keep the heating elements from burning out. The ON position allows the fan to run continuously for improved air circulation if desired. Some thermostats can be programmed to allow for the fan to continue running for a brief timed period after the furnace has shut off.

Limit Switch

The limit switch is a safety control. It prevents the furnace from overheating. As long as the plenum chamber temperature is below the setting of the limit switch, the switch remains closed. If the plenum chamber temperature rises to the switch setting, it opens to deenergize either the entire 24 V circuit or line voltage circuit and also close the automatic gas valve.

Combination Fan and Limit Switch

The combination fan and limit switch, Figure 39-13, is actually two switches in one. As a safety limit, some have fixed limit temperature settings; others are adjustable (approximately 180–200°F is the usual range). This allows a 50–60°F rise above normal operation before it opens. The fan control switch is also a temperature sensing device that is set to turn on the fan after the furnace has warmed up at least 15–20°F above room conditions, so that cold drafts are not experienced. It also stops the blower after the burner cuts off, so again there are no uncomfortable drafts. It is important to note that some systems employ constant fan operation and thus override this switch.

Other models may use spiral, flat bimetallic, or even liquid filled elements. Some forms of duct-mounted limit controls use a rod and tube or a liquid filled bulb to sense the air conditions.

39.10 GAS VALVES AND REGULATORS

Gas valves have the following functions:

- Manual control for ignition and normal operation.
- Pilot supply, adjustment, and safety shutoff.
- Pressure regulation of burner gas feed.
- On/off electric solenoid valve controlled by the room thermostat.

(a)

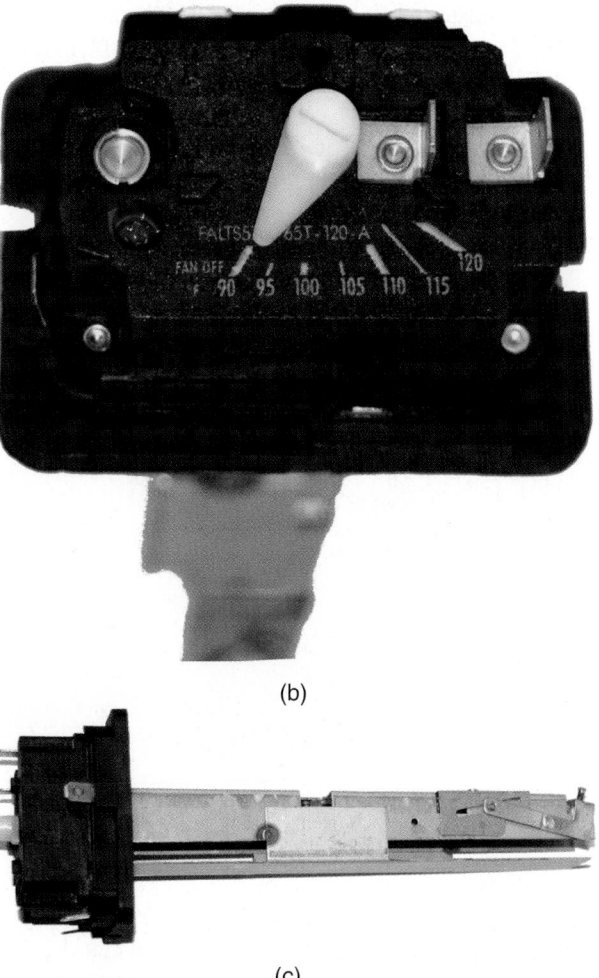

(b)

(c)

Figure 39-13 Combination fan and limit switch acts as a safety limit and temperature sensing device

Figure 39-14 Combination gas valve

At one time, the supplying of fuel gas to a heating unit was done by a combination of controls consisting of a gas pressure regulator and a solenoid valve. These controls were combined into a single valve assembly, Figure 39-14, to meet the standards for proper ignition, input control, and quiet cutoff of gas unit operation.

CAUTION

Unless you have received specific manufacturer's training on servicing gas valves, do not try to repair one that is not working. It is not safe for technicians to disassemble and reassemble gas valves and gas regulators. If it is determined that the problem is in the gas valve it should be replaced and not repaired.

39.11 COMBINATION GAS VALVE

The following methods describing pilot ignition and gas valve control apply chiefly to older residential furnaces that require service. Figure 39-15 shows a basic sketch of these functions for a natural gas valve. The schematic drawing of the valve shows the main diaphragm valve in the open condition that occurs during heat demand. When in this condition, the following assumptions can be made:

- The schematic applies to a gas heating appliance with the pilot flame burning.
- A thermocouple is connected to the automatic pilot magnet operator.
- The lighting operation was previously performed to open the automatic pilot valve.
- The main gas cock has been turned to the ON position after the pilot is lit.

UNITROL 7000ER SCHEMATIC

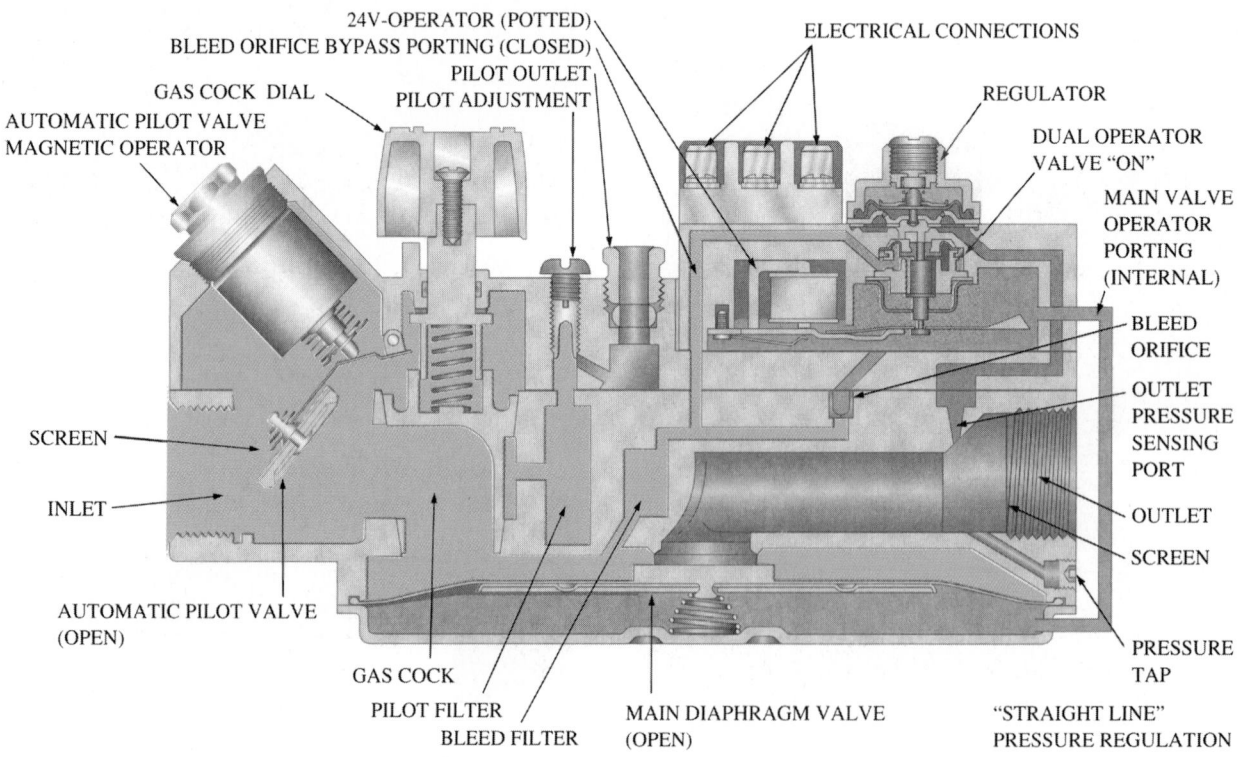

Figure 39-15 Cutaway of a combination gas valve in open position

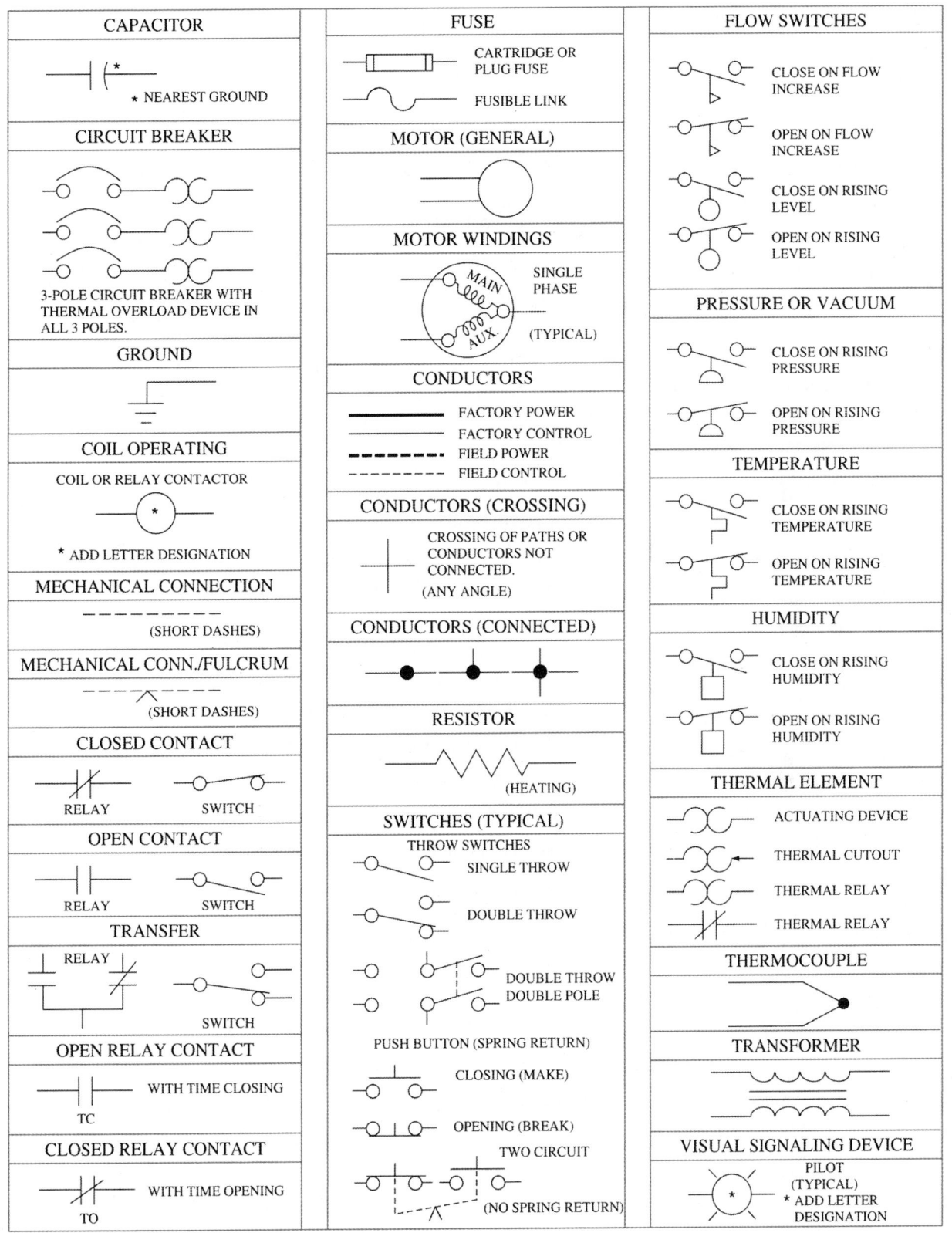

Figure 39-22 Electrical wiring symbols

Table 39-1 Legend for the Wiring Diagram

Relays		Switches		Miscellaneous	
R	Relay, General	DI	Defrost Initiation	C-HTR	Crankcase Heater
CR	Cooling Relay	DT	Defrost Termination	RES	Resistor
DR	Defrost Relay	DIT	Defrost Initiation Defrost Termination (dual function devices)	HTR	Heater
FR	Fan Relay			PC	Program Control
IFR	Indoor Fan Relay			OL	Overload
OFR	Outdoor Fan Relay	GP	Gas Pressure	L	Indicating Lamp
GR	Guardistor Relay	HP	Hight Pressure	⊕	Manual Reset Device
HR	Heating Relay	LP	Low Pressure	+	Automatic Reset Device
LR	Locking Relay (Lock-in or Lockout)	HLP	Combination High-Low Pressure		
PR	Protection Relay (Relay in series with protectective devices)	OP	Oil Pressure		
		RM	Reset, Manual		
VR	Voltage Relay	FS	Fan Switch		
TD	Time Delay Device	SS	System Switch		
THR	Thermal Relay (type)	HS	Humidity Switch (Humidistat)		
M	Contactor	TA	Thermostat, Ambient		
MA	Auxilary Contact	TC	Thermostat, Cooling		
		TH	Thermostat, Heating		
Nolenoids		TMA	Thermostat, Mixed Air		
S	Solenoid, General	CT	Thermostat, Compressor Motor		
CS	Capacity Solenoid	HT	High Temperature		
GS	Gas Solenoid	LT	Low Temperature		
RS	Reversing Solenoid	RT	Refrigerant Temperature		
		WT	Water Temperature		

technical sheet from the manufacturer's supply house. To help simplify the troubleshooting at the board level, identify four areas on the board: the input, output, board ground, and power supply. The input is probably an on/off signal from a thermostat or variable signal from a thermistor that indicates a change has occurred. The output is the signal coming out of the board to activate a relay or controlled device. Most solid state circuit boards rely on direct current to operate the electronic components, so they must be properly grounded. The power supply required could be high or low voltage, either 24 V AC or 5 V DC, or line voltage. If all four of these areas on the board are being provided as specified from the factory, there is a good chance the board has failed. It is not normally repaired in the field and should be replaced. Prior to replacement, however, verify there are no electrical shorts or wiring problems, that may have caused premature failure.

39.16 HEATING CIRCUIT

A simple schematic diagram for a typical gas fired upflow air furnace is shown in Figure 39-23. The wire conductors are represented by lines and the other components by symbols and letter designations. Note the very important legend that identifies these. Typically the schematic is the type of diagram used by service personnel to analyze the system.

Table 39-2 Maximum Length of Two Wire Run Based on Length and Current Capacity*

						Amperes							
Wire size	**5**	**10**	**15**	**20**	**25**	**30**	**35**	**40**	**45**	**50**	**55**	**70**	**80**
14	274	137	91										
12		218	145	109									
10			230	173	138	115							
8					220	182	156	138					
6								219	193	175	159		
4									309	278	253	199	
3										350	319	250	219
2											402	310	276
1												399	349
0												502	439
00													560

*To limit voltage drop to 3% at 240 V. For other voltages use the following multipliers:

110V	0.458	220 V	0.917
115 V	0.479	230 V	0.966
120 V	0.50	250 V	1.042
125 V	0.521		

For example, the maximum run for #10 wire carrying 30 amp at 120 V is 115 × 0.5 = 57 ft.

Note that if the required length of run is nearly equal to, or even somewhat more than, the maximum run shown for a given wire size, select the next larger wire. This will provide a margin of safety. The recommended limit on voltage drop is 3%. Something less than the maximum is preferable.

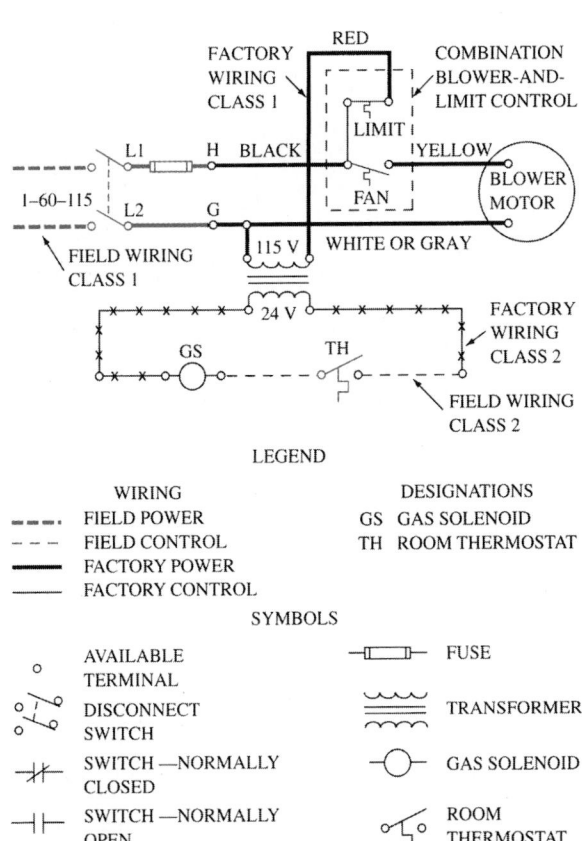

Figure 39-23 Heating circuit diagram for gas fired upflow furnace

Only five major electrical devices are in the diagram:

- The fan motor, which circulates the heated air.
- The 24 V automatic gas solenoid valve to control the flow of gas to the burner.
- The combination blower and limit control which controls fan operation and governs the flow of current to the low voltage control circuit.
- The step down transformer, which provides 24 V current to operate the automatic gas valve.
- The room thermostat, which directly controls the opening and closing of the automatic gas valve.

To build this same schematic diagram, begin with the power supply. The wires for the power supply are usually run by the installing technician. They must carry line voltage (single phase, 60 Hz, 120 V) to operate the blower motor and are represented by heavy broken lines to indicate field wiring, as shown in Figure 39-24. As a protection to the circuit, the power supply must be run through a fused disconnect switch. This is the main switch to the entire system.

In a gas fired heating system, the fan motor produces the heaviest load and is connected to the power supply, as shown in Figure 39-25. Since the fan motor is clearly identified on the diagram, it is not necessary to add it to the legend. Internal windings are not shown.

To test the system at this point, close the disconnect switch. The fan motor runs, since a simple circuit is completed from L_1 through the windings of the blower motor

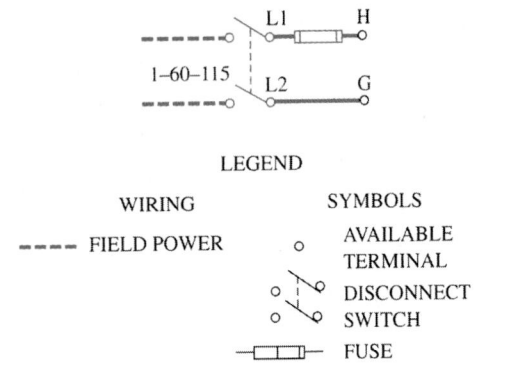

Figure 39-24 Diagram for a fused disconnect

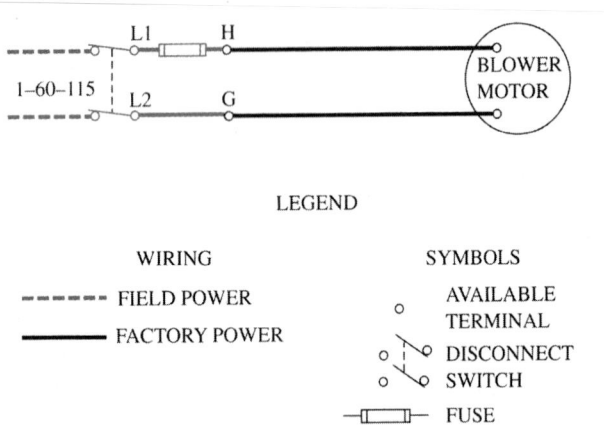

Figure 39-25 Diagram showing the fused disconnect wired to the blower motor

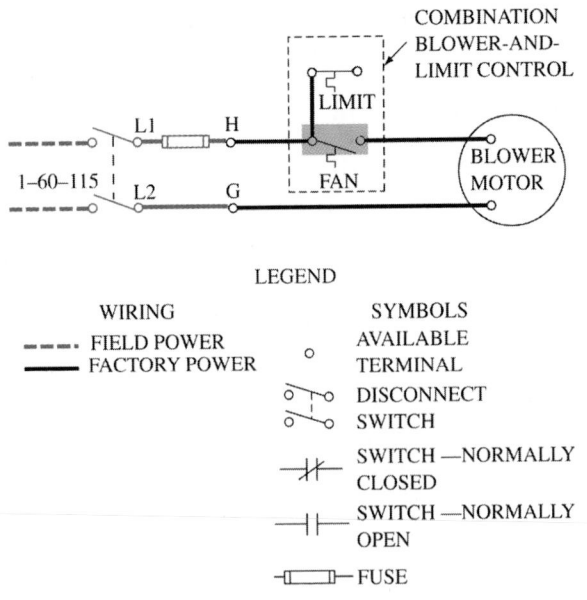

Figure 39-26 Wiring diagram showing the use of a fan limit control wired to a blower motor

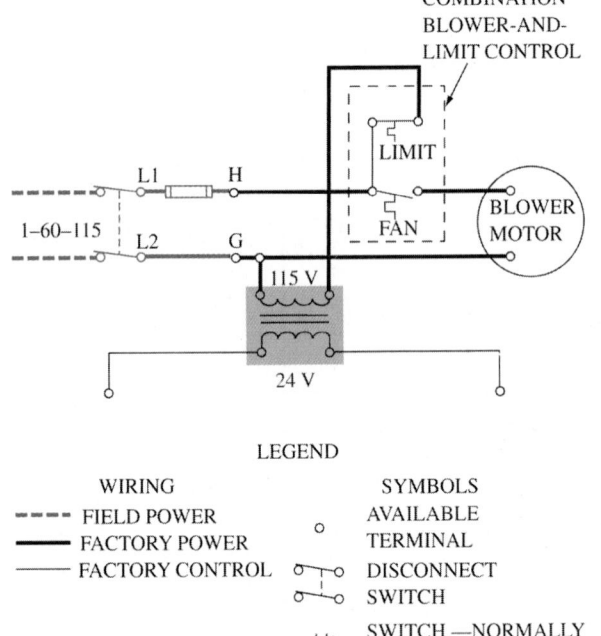

Figure 39-27 Schematic diagram showing the addition of a control circuit transformer

and back to neutral. Open the disconnect switch and continue the diagramming.

Since there must be automatic control of both the fan motor and the automatic gas solenoid valve, connect the combination fan and limit control, Figure 39-26. This control, as previously described, consists of a sensing element, which measures the temperature of the heated air inside the furnace, and two adjustable switches: a fan switch and a limit switch.

As illustrated, the combination fan and limit control are partially connected. The fan switch is wired into L1 in series with the blower motor windings. If the disconnect switch is closed now, the fan motor will not run because the fan switch in the fan motor circuit is open and will remain open until the temperature in the furnace warms up to the switch setting.

Small electrical devices, such as relays and solenoid valves, do very little work and require little current for operation. A step down transformer to reduce line voltage to 24 V is required and properly installed in the wiring diagram, as shown in Figure 39-27. One side is connected to neutral and the other side is connected to L1 through the limit switch. This places the limit switch in control of the entire 24 V circuit.

If the disconnect switch is closed, the blower motor still cannot run since the fan switch must remain open until the air temperature warms up. The transformer and the 24 V power source, however, are energized immediately from L1

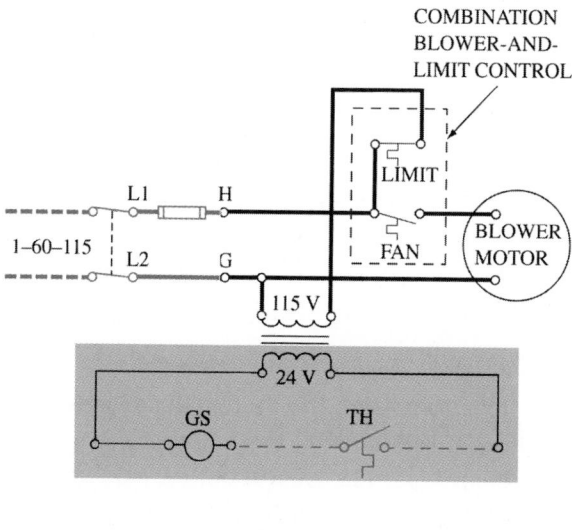

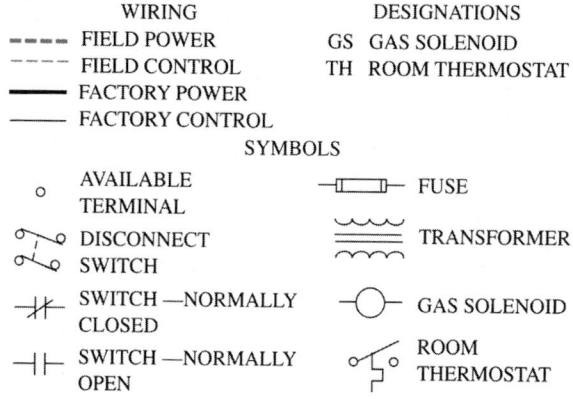

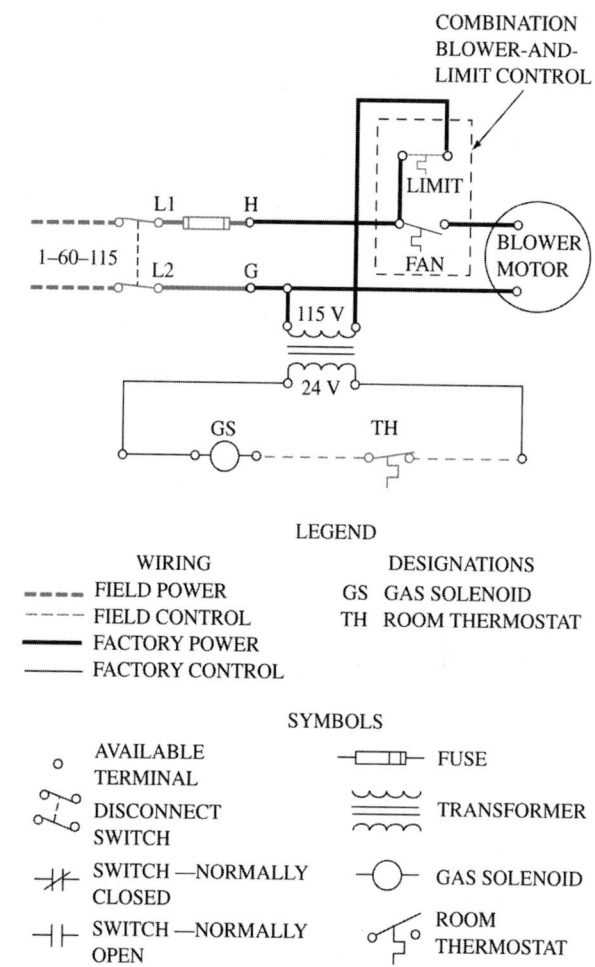

Figure 39-28 Schematic diagram of the low voltage circuit showing the thermostat operation of the gas valve

Figure 39-29 Schematic diagram showing the wiring of the limit control in series with the line voltage side of the transformer

through the closed limit switch and back to L2. Although there is now a source of 24 V current, nothing can be accomplished until there is a circuit across the 24 V supply.

The automatic gas solenoid valve and room thermostat are wired in series across the 24 V circuit, Figure 39-28, since the opening and closing of the gas solenoid valve is controlled by the thermostat. The gas valve is factory wired as indicated on the diagram by a lightly shaded unbroken line between terminals. Normally, the thermostat is located in a room away from the furnace and must be field wired, as indicated by the lightly shaded broken lines used to represent control circuit field wiring.

The circuit is now completely wired. Close the disconnect and limit switches and open the thermostat. The transformer and low voltage circuit are immediately energized from L1, through the closed limit switch back to neutral. With the thermostat open, the automatic gas valve remains closed. The fan motor cannot operate because the fan switch is open, and it will remain open until the air temperature in the furnace warms up to the FAN ON setting.

When the thermostat calls for heat, the automatic gas valve is energized, as shown in Figure 39-29, and the valve opens to admit gas to the burner. The fan switch would still be open so

that the fan motor cannot run until the air temperature in the furnace plenum chamber warms up to the FAN ON setting.

Thermostat and gas valve circuits are reopened when the room temperature setting is reached. Fan and blower contacts remain closed until the temperature of the heated air cools to the FAN OFF setting.

If at any time during furnace operation the plenum chamber overheats, the air temperature soon reaches the setting of the limit switch. This is an important safety switch, which opens at the overheating setting to deenergize the entire 24 V circuit. When this happens, the automatic gas valve closes, the burner is extinguished, and the thermostat is overridden. The fan switch remains closed and the blower continues to run as long as the heated air remains above the FAN OFF setting. The limit switch is manually reset by the service person after correcting the problem.

The operating sequence just completed proves that the wiring diagram is correct. The disconnect switch controls the entire electrical system; the blower motor operates independently of the burner, under the control of the fan switch. The automatic gas valve is cycled on and off by the room thermostat, under the control of the limit switch.

UNIT 39—SUMMARY

A control system requires a source of power to operate, a load to utilize the power, and controllers to obtain the desired level of operation. Generally the operation of the system is under the control of a room thermostat, which controls a gas valve in the heating phase and the condensing unit's operation in the cooling phase. The blower in the gas furnace must operate intermittently in the heating phase, depending on the furnace supply plenum temperature.

Heating control circuits are often designed to operate on low voltage because the wiring is simplified and safer. Furthermore, low voltage thermostats provide closer temperature control than do line voltage thermostats. A step down transformer is used to reduce line voltage to operate control components. Heat anticipators are used in low voltage thermostats to reduce the temperature swing caused by the systems.

Burner ignition methods are varied. A pilot is a small burner used to light the main burner when the gas valve opens. Standing pilots operate continuously while an electronic ignition system utilizes a spark electrode to ignite the gas pilot on a signal from the room thermostat. The direct spark ignition system uses an electrical flame sensor rod rather than a pilot. A hot surface ignition unit, rather than using a pilot, uses a silicon carbide material that when energized heats up to the gas ignition temperature.

WORK ORDERS

Service Ticket 3901

Customer Complaint: Furnace Fan Keeps Short Cycling

Equipment Type: 80,000 Btu Upflow Natural Gas Furnace

The technician analyzed the unit and discovered the fan was short cycling with the burners off. The technician discovered the fan switch differential was set too narrow (20%). The technician set the fan to come on at 140°F and cycle off at 90°F which is a 50°F differential. The technician ran the system through several cycles to ensure it is operating properly. The system is now operating as designed.

Service Ticket 3902

Customer Complaint: Pilot Light Comes on Briefly but the Burners Will Not Light

Equipment Type: 100,000 Btu Horizontal Gas Furnace

After talking to the customer, the technician decided to try running the system. After setting the thermostat to heat, the technician observed the spark igniter come on and light the pilot. After about 21 seconds, the pilot turned off without lighting the furnace. The technician determined the flame sensor was bad. After disconnecting the main power, the technician replaced the flame sensor. The technician turned the power back on and set the thermostat to heat. The spark igniter lit the pilot and in just a few seconds the burner lit and the system operated normally.

Service Ticket 3903

Customer Complaint: The System Runs Fine on Cooling But Not on Heat

Equipment Type: 125,000 Btu Upflow NG Furnace

The technician checked the system and found the system was not getting voltage between the common or C and W terminals. When the furnace is getting a heating signal, there will be no voltage read between R and W. It is probably less confusing to compare voltages to C common terminals in the furnace. The technician deenergized the system and performed a continuity check back to the thermostat and found that there was no continuity. The technician then checked for continuity between the R and W terminals on the thermostat with the thermostat set to call for heat. With no continuity between the thermostat terminals R and W, the technician replaced the thermostat. The technician returned power to the system and set the new thermostat to call for heat. The system operated normally in the heat settings. The technician cycled the thermostat a few times to ensure the system was operating as designed.

UNIT 39—REVIEW QUESTIONS

1. List the four areas of an electronic control board that should be identified when troubleshooting.

2. Identify the reasons a low voltage control circuit is more desirable than a line voltage control circuit.

3. A given transformer has a primary voltage of 240 V and a secondary voltage of 24 V. Assuming the transformer is rated at 40 VA, what is the secondary current?

4. What is the standard transformer VA rating for most HVAC systems?

5. Why are heat anticipators used in low voltage thermostats?

6. State the problem associated with setting a thermostat heat anticipator too high.

7. How is a humidistat similar to a low voltage switch?

8. Explain the reason why adding humidity to a residence increases customer comfort.

9. On a fan/limit switch what is the usual setting for the limit?

10. List the four functions of a furnace gas valve.

11. Describe how a main gas valve gets electrical power to open.

12. How many volts are generated in the spark ignition circuit?

13. Why is it necessary that the gas burning unit be grounded on DS1 system?

14. If a burner fails to light or the flame sensor fails to detect a flame, what happens to ensure the system is safe?

15. Identify the standardized electrical symbols for the following common controls: indoor fan relay, humidistat, manual reset, and crankcase heater.

16. If there is a 240 V circuit that will be carrying 30 A using #10 wire size, what is the maximum length of the two wire run that would limit the voltage drop to 3%?

17. In question 16, what would be the answer if the wire size is #12, the voltage is 120 V, and the amperage is 15 amps?

18. List the five major electrical devices in the heating circuit diagram in Figure 39-23.

19. Explain what a limit switch is, as well as its function and how it affects the control circuit.

20. State why the legend and the notes are an important part of an electrical diagram.

UNIT 40

Gas Furnace Installation, Startup, Checkout, and Operation

OBJECTIVES

After completing this unit you will be able to:

- explain the difference between natural gas and LP gas.
- use a gas meter to check the gas input of a gas furnace.
- use GAMA vent sizing tables to determine the correct vent size for a furnace.
- determine the correct size openings to provide combustion air for a furnace.
- determine furnace temperature rise.
- list acceptable ranges for flue gas CO_2 percent, O_2 percent, excess air percent, and net stack temperature.
- list safety precautions that should be practiced when starting a gas furnace.

40.1 INTRODUCTION

Modern gas furnaces are an efficient and safe way to provide whole house comfort. Increasingly, customers are choosing higher efficiency models to control heating costs. However, the full energy savings will only be realized if the furnace is installed correctly.

Design innovations in modern furnaces have produced more efficient, safer systems than those of just a few years ago. Some of these changes have changed the way furnaces are installed. Induced draft furnaces, two stage furnaces, condensing furnaces, and direct vent furnaces all require special installation techniques. These innovative furnaces will not perform as designed if installed incorrectly. Proper installation is also crucial for safe operation. Despite the many safety features incorporated into today's furnaces, they cannot always guarantee safe operation if the installation is unsafe.

40.2 NATURAL GAS

To check, test, and adjust a gas burning unit for the highest operating efficiency, the unit must have the proper gas input, the proper adjustment of the burners, the correct amount of combustion air, proper venting, and the correct amount of air for heat distribution.

To arrive at the correct gas input, two important factors must be known about the gas:

- Heat content in Btu/ft^3.
- Specific gravity.

Natural gas is a mixture of methane and ethane. Various sources have different heat contents in the range of 950–1150 Btu/ft^3. The specific gravity also varies between 0.56 and 0.72. These characteristics relate to sizing the piping and determining the amount of gas to be supplied to each burner.

Heating units are constructed to use gas pressure regulators set at an output of $3\frac{1}{2}$ in wc (water column, a pressure measurement). Burner designs will allow operation between 3 and 4 in wc manifold pressure. These pressures must not be exceeded. The actual operating pressure for any particular installation is determined by the gas heating value and the altitude. Table 40-1 shows a typical manifold pressure chart supplied with the installation instructions.

CAUTION

The diaphragm in a gas regulator is easily damaged with excessive pressure. Before pressure testing a gas piping system, the gas line should be removed from the gas valve and capped. This should be done even though there is a gas line shutoff so that the pipe joints from the shutoff to the gas valve can also be leak checked.

40.3 CHECKING THE GAS INPUT

Figure 40-1 shows the index or dial of a typical domestic gas meter. Included are two test dials, one for $\frac{1}{2}$ ft^3 per revolution and the other for 2 ft^3 per revolution. To determine if the correct amount of gas is being fed to the heating unit, it is only necessary to find the feed rate through the meter. For accuracy, all other appliances must be turned off. If the pilot lights of the other appliances including water heaters are turned off, be sure to relight them before leaving. Usually, the requirements of pilot lights are so small that they are ignored.

Table 40-1 Manifold Pressure Chart

Altitude range (ft)	Avg. gas heat value at altitude (Btu/cu ft)	Specific gravity of natural gas							
		0.58		0.60		0.62		0.64	
		Orifice no.	Mnfld press high/low	Orifice no.	Mnfld press high/low	Orifice no.	Mnfld press high/low	Orifice no.	Mnfld press high/low
U.S.A. and Canada 0 to 2000	900	43	3.5/1.5	43	3.6/1.5	43	3.8/1.6	42	3.2/1.3
	925	44	3.8/1.6	43	3.5/1.5	43	3.6/1.5	43	3.7/1.6
	950	44	3.6/1.5	44	3.8/1.6	43	3.4/1.4	43	3.5/1.5
	975	44	3.4/1.5	44	3.6/1.5	44	3.7/1.6	44	3.8/1.6
	1000	44	3.3/1.4	44	3.4/1.4	44	3.5/1.5	44	3.6/1.5
	1025	45	3.8/1.6	44	3.2/1.4	44	3.3/1.4	44	3.4/1.5
	1050	45	3.6/1.5					44	3.3/1.4
	1075	45	3.4/1.4	45	3.7/1.6	45	3.8/1.6		
	1100	45	3.3/1.4	45	3.5/1.5	45	3.7/1.5		
				45	3.4/1.4	45	3.5/1.5		
								45	3.8/1.6
								45	3.6/1.5
U.S.A Altitudes 2001 to 3000 or Canada Altitudes 2001 to 4500	800	43	3.8/1.6	42	3.2/1.4	42	3.3/1.4	42	3.5/1.5
	825	43	3.6/1.5	43	3.7/1.6	43	3.8/1.6	42	3.2/1.4
	850	43	3.4/1.4	43	3.5/1.5	43	3.6/1.5	43	3.7/1.6
	875	44	3.7/1.5	44	3.8/1.6	43	3.4/1.4	43	3.5/1.5
	900	44	3.5/1.5	44	3.6/1.5	44	3.7/1.6	44	3.8/1.6
	925	44	3.3/1.4	44	3.4/1.4	44	3.5/1.5	44	3.6/1.5
	950	45	3.7/1.6	44	3.2/1.4	44	3.3/1.4	44	3.4/1.4
	975	45	3.6/1.5					44	3.2/1.4
	1000	45	3.4/1.4	45	3.7/1.6	45	3.8/1.6		
				45	3.5/1.5	45	3.6/1.5		
								45	3.7/1.6
U.S.A. Only 3001 to 4000	775	43	3.7/1.6	42	3.2/1.3	42	3.3/1.4	42	3.4/1.4
	800	43	3.5/1.5	43	3.6/1.5	43	3.8/1.6	42	3.2/1.3
	825	44	3.8/1.6	43	3.4/1.4	43	3.5/1.5	43	3.7/1.5
	850	44	3.6/1.5	44	3.7/1.6	44	3.8/1.6	43	3.4/1.5
	875	44	3.4/1.4	44	3.5/1.5	44	3.6/1.5	44	3.7/1.6
	900	44	3.2/1.3	44	3.3/1.4	44	3.4/1.4	44	3.5/1.5
	925	45	3.7/1.5	45	3.8/1.6	44	3.2/1.4	44	3.3/1.4
	950	45	3.5/1.5	45	3.6/1.5				
						45	3.7/1.6	45	3.8/1.6

(Continued)

Table 40-1 Manifold Pressure Chart

	BTU								
U.S.A. Only	4001 to 5000	750	43	3.7/1.6	43	3.8/1.6	42	3.2/1.4	42	3.3/1.4
		775	43	3.5/1.5	43	3.6/1.5	43	3.7/1.6	43	3.8/1.6
		800	44	3.7/1.6	43	3.4/1.4	43	3.5/1.5	43	3.6/1.5
		825	44	3.5/1.5	44	3.6/1.5	44	3.7/1.6	43	3.4/1.4
		850	44	3.3/1.4	44	3.4/1.4	44	3.5/1.5	44	3.6/1.5
		875	**45**	**3.8/1.6**	44	3.2/1.4	44	3.3/1.4	44	3.4/1.5
		900	**45**	**3.6/1.5**					44	3.2/1.4
		925	**45**	**3.4/1.4**	**45**	**3.7/1.6**	**45**	**3.8/1.6**		
					45	**3.5/1.5**	**45**	**3.6/1.5**		
									45	**3.7/1.6**
U.S.A. Only	5001 to 6000	725	43	3.6/1.5	43	3.8/1.6	42	3.2/1.4	42	3.3/1.4
		750	43	3.4/1.4	43	3.5/1.5	43	3.6/1.5	43	3.8/1.6
		775	44	3.7/1.5	44	3.8/1.6	43	3.4/1.4	43	3.5/1.5
		800	44	3.4/1.5	44	3.6/1.5	44	3.7/1.6	44	3.8/1.6
		825	44	3.2/1.4	44	3.3/1.4	44	3.4/1.5	44	3.6/1.5
		850	**45**	**3.7/1.6**	**45**	**3.8/1.6**	44	3.2/1.4	44	3.4/1.4
		875	**45**	**3.5/1.5**	**45**	**3.6/1.5**				
		900	**45**	**3.3/1.4**	**45**	**3.4/1.4**	**45**	**3.7/1.6**	**45**	**3.8/1.6**
								45	**3.5/1.5**	**45**	**3.6/1.5**
U.S.A. Only	6001 to 7000	675	42	3.2/1.3	42	3.3/1.4	42	3.4/1.4	42	3.5/1.5
		700	43	3.6/1.5	43	3.7/1.6	43	3.8/1.6	42	3.3/1.4
		725	44	3.8/1.6	43	3.5/1.5	43	3.6/1.5	43	3.7/1.6
		750	44	3.6/1.5	44	3.7/1.6	44	3.8/1.6	43	3.5/1.5
		775	44	3.4/1.4	44	3.5/1.5	44	3.6/1.5	44	3.7/1.6
		800	**45**	**3.8/1.6**	44	3.3/1.4	44	3.4/1.4	44	3.5/1.5
		825	**45**	**3.6/1.5**					44	3.3/1.4
		850	**45**	**3.4/1.4**	**45**	**3.7/1.6**	**45**	**3.8/1.6**		
					45	**3.5/1.5**	**45**	**3.6/1.5**	**45**	**3.7/1.6**

Note: Orifice numbers shown in BOLD are factory installed.

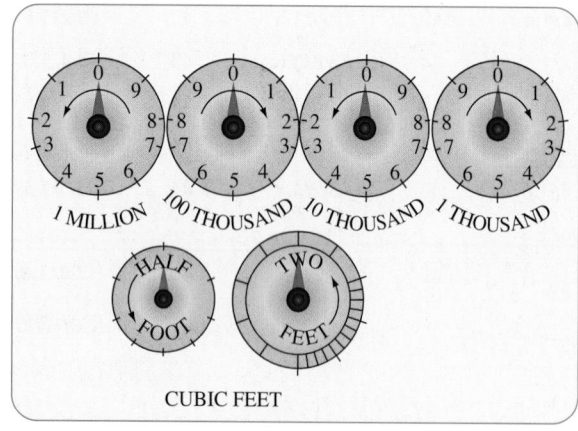

Figure 40-1 Typical domestic gas meter dials in ft^3

Gas flow through the meter is determined by the time it takes the test dials to turn one revolution. To determine this time, the following formula can be used:

$$\text{Time (sec/ft}^3) = \frac{\text{seconds per hour}}{\text{ft}^3/\text{hr of gas}}$$

To determine how long it would take for 142.8 ft^3/hr of gas to flow, the formula would be set up as follows:

$$\text{sec/ft}^3 = \frac{60 \times 60}{142.8} = \frac{3{,}600}{142.8}$$

It will require 25.2 seconds for 1 ft^3 of gas to go through the meter. Thus, the $\frac{1}{2}$ ft^3 dial would require 12.6 seconds per revolution, and the 2 ft^3 dial, 50.4 seconds per revolution. A stopwatch is recommended or a digital watch timing function.

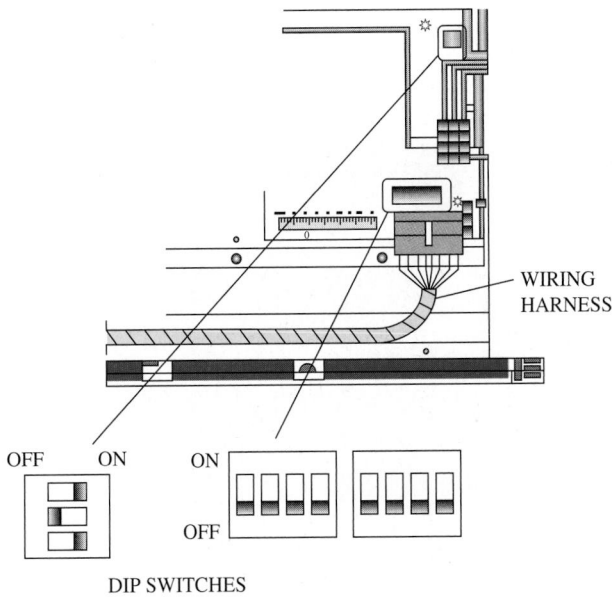

WIRING
HARNESS

OFF ON ON

OFF

DIP SWITCHES

Figure 40-14 ECM blower control jumper setting

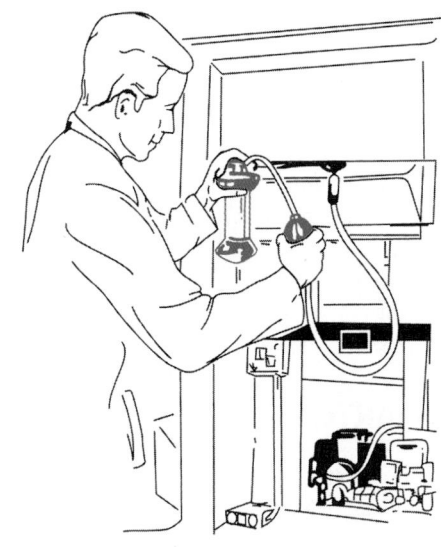

Figure 40-15 Testing the percent of CO_2 in the flue gas

No O_2 in the flue gas indicates incomplete combustion and possible production of carbon monoxide. Acceptable readings for safe operation range from 7%–9%. Readings above 9% indicate too much combustion air which is detrimental to efficiency.

TECH TIP

Checking a gas furnace fuel consumption as compared to heat output is a way of determining the actual operating efficiency of a particular system. This performance check is much like a driver confirming the fuel economy (miles per gallon) that their car is getting.

A means of recording such information is necessary so that it will become a permanent part of the unit operating and service history. This efficiency check sheet should include the information shown below.

Input

1. Type of gas: Nat. _____ Mixed _____ Mfg. _____
   Prop. _____ Bu. _____
2. Heat content (Btu/ft3) _____
3. Specific gravity of the gas: _____
4. Main burner orifice drill size: Found _____ Left _____
5. Manifold pressure (in wc): Found _____ Left _____
6. Meter test dial size: _____ ft^3 per rev.
7. Seconds required per rev. of test dial: Found _____
   Left _____

Primary Air Adjustment

1. Flame before adjustment: Sharp blue _____ Soft
   blue _____ Yellow tips _____
2. Flame after adjustment: Soft blue _____

Air Temperature Rise

1. Supply air temperature: First test _____ Second test
   _____ Left test
2. Return air temperature: First test _____ Second test
   _____ Left test _____
3. Air temperature rise: First test _____ Second test
   _____ Left test _____

CO_2 Percent

1. First test _____%
2. Second test _____%
3. Left test _____%

Stack Temperature Rise

1. Stack temperature: First test _____ Second test
   _____ Left test _____
2. Combustion air temperature: First test _____ Second
   test _____ Left test _____
3. Stack temperature rise: First test _____ Second test
   _____ Left test _____

Combustion Efficiency

1. Percent Efficiency _____   _____   _____

Gas-burning equipment of standard design should always be capable of 75–80% efficiency. Unless the unit is of a higher efficiency design (when the manufacturer's instructions and settings must be followed), an efficiency above 80% could adversely affect the draft of the unit as well as cause condensation of moisture in the chimney or flue pipe and on the surfaces of the heat exchanger. If the efficiency results are less than this range, the test should be repeated, checking and setting the proper input.

40.9 COMBUSTION EFFICIENCY

Three measurements are required to determine the combustion efficiency of a gas furnace:

- Ambient temperature (temperature around the furnace).
- Stack temperature (vent temperature).
- Oxygen percent in the flue gas.

The first two measurements are used to calculate the net stack temperature which is found by subtracting the ambient temperature from the stack temperature. Take the temperature before the draft diverter when taking the stack temperature on a natural draft furnace. The oxygen percentage is taken by drilling a small hole in the vent and taking a sample of the gas. This can be done with an aspirator connected to an hourglass shaped tester, Figure 40-16. The combustion efficiency is found using a slide rule provided with the combustion efficiency test kit.

All of these measurements can be made using an electronic combustion analyzer. The analyzer takes the sample, measures the oxygen percentage in the flue gas, measures the

Figure 40-17 Electronic combustion analyzer

net stack temperature, and calculates the combustion efficiency. The analyzer can also calculate the CO_2 and excess air percentages. Figure 40-17 shows a typical electronic combustion efficiency analyzer.

Acceptable readings for atmospheric gas burners are:

Oxygen percent	7%–9%
Carbon dioxide percent	7%–9%
Excess air percent	50%
Net stack temperature	325°F–500°F

40.10 STARTUP SAFETY

Technicians should always be conscious of the unique hazards posed by combustible gases when working with gas furnaces. Gas appliances are safe when installed and operated according to the manufacturer's instructions. However, technicians should not assume that everything is per the manufacturer's instructions. In fact, they should assume the opposite. It is reasonable to assume that a system which is not operating properly is either installed incorrectly or has a component that is not performing as designed. Either situation could create a hazard for the technician. There are a few precautions a technician can take that will reduce the chance of injury even if the furnace is potentially dangerous.

- Do not turn anything on until you have inspected the furnace! Check for the key safety items listed below. For example, turning on a system with a leak which has caused a buildup of gas could create an explosion.
- Check for the presence of gas in the area around the furnace. Use your nose or an electronic combustible gas sniffer to check for the presence of gas around the

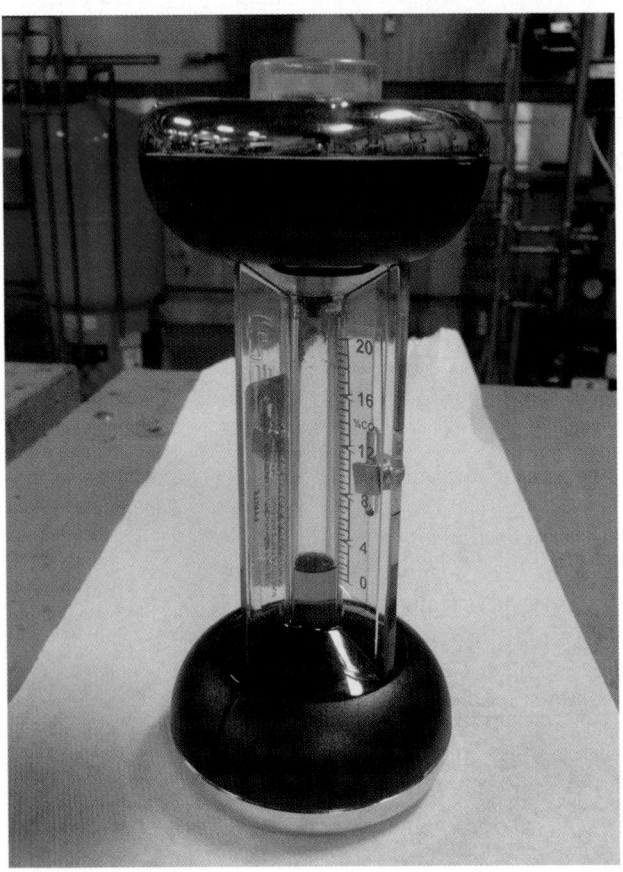

Figure 40-16 Combustion analyzer kit
(Courtesy of Dwyer Instruments, Inc.)

5. Heat exchanger complaints.
6. Cost of operation.
7. Noise.

41.8 GAS SYSTEM PROBLEMS

The possible causes for gas system problems are as shown in Table 41-1.

Many of the solutions to these problems are evident when the cause is determined. The following, however, includes further information regarding some of the remedies that can be tried. The category numbers refer to Table 41-1, gas symptoms problems.

1. **Control Transformer Burned Out**   An ohmmeter should be used to determine whether the primary or the secondary of the transformer is burned out. The cause is probably an overload in the secondary, which needs to be corrected before the transformer is replaced. If the overload cannot be reduced, a larger transformer must be used for the replacement.

2. **Pilot Outage**   One of the most common causes of pilot failure is improper impingement of the flame on the thermocouple; see Figure 41-9. This figure illustrates the proper size and location of the flame. Sometimes the pilot is extinguished by the gas burner during lighting. It is actually blown out by the burner flame. To correct this, it is often necessary to reposition the pilot to a more favorable location.

3. **Gas Valve Stuck Open or Closed**   A malfunctioning gas valve should be replaced.

4. **Improper Heat Anticipator Setting**   The anticipator should be set at the amount of current traveling in the control circuit when the unit is operating. The current can be measured using a multiplier coil and a clamp-on ammeter.

5. **Cycling on the Limit Control**   Occasionally a limit control will weaken and lower the operating range of the control. The normal range is to cut off between 140°F for a counterflow unit to 160–220°F on upright and horizontal units. If the control is cycling at a lower range, replace it.

6. **Fan Control Settings**   Almost all gas fired units operate best with fan control settings of 125–130°F fan ON and 100–105°F fan OFF. If the unit blows cold air on startup, the fan ON temperature can be changed to 145–150°F.

7. **Improper Burner Adjustment**   A properly adjusted burner will have approximately 40% of the combustion air mixing with 100% of the gas in the burner and 60% of the air mixing with the flame above the burner to complete the combustion process. Figure 41-10 shows a typical burner arrangement.

As the gas is emitted from the orifice, it expands and hits the proper place in the throat of the burner venturi. This produces maximum pull of primary air into the burner. Setting the burner for the correct flame condition will mean a minimum opening in the primary air control.

Figure 41-11a shows the size of the opening in an ordinary butterfly air control. When the burner and orifice are aligned properly and the burner is working correctly, a small opening in the primary air control will produce the soft blue flame that gives best overall unit performance Figure 41-11b.

An all blue sharp flame is one that is receiving too much primary air. This means that there is less radiant heat to heat the lower portion of the heat exchanger. Also, the excess air drives the flame products from the heat exchanger before good transfer of heat occurs from the flue product to the heat exchanger. Flue product temperatures rise and the unit efficiency drops. If the primary air is reduced too much, heavy yellow tips of improperly burning carbon are produced.

These are much lower temperatures and do not produce the heat. Unit efficiency therefore drops. The carbon can be released from the flame and collected in the heat exchanger to cause sooting and plugging of the flue passages. The proper setting of the primary air quantity is the beginning step in producing high unit operating efficiency. Improper setting of the primary air shutter can also con-

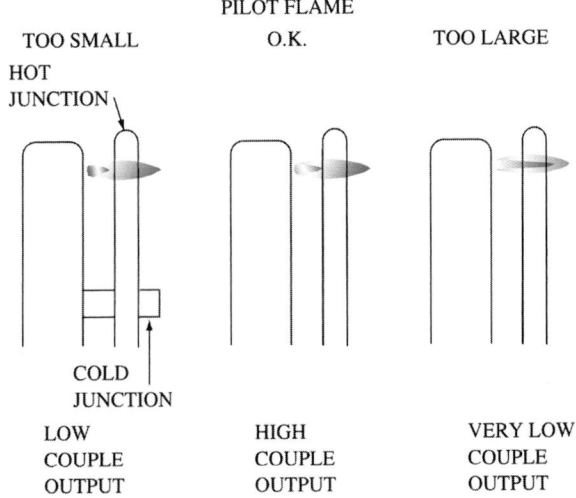

Figure 41-9 Proper size for a pilot flame

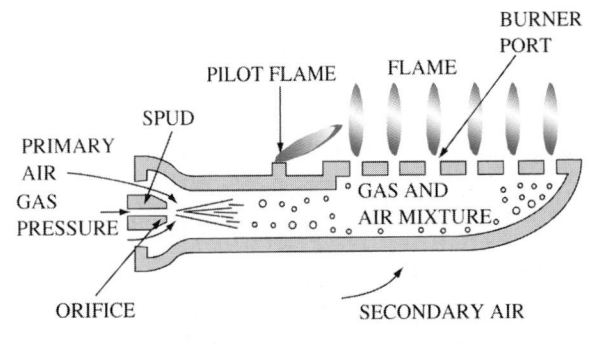

Figure 41-10 Primary and secondary air supply to the gas burner

Table 41-1 Gas Systems Problems

Problems	Possible causes*	Problems	Possible causes*
Will not start	Season switch open	Gas valve will not open	Transformer burned out
	Room thermostat set too low		Open circuit in thermostat
	Disconnect or door switch is open		Gas valve stuck open/closed
	Blown fuse		Defective safety pilot
	Limit control open	Gas valve short cycles	Improper heat anticipator setting
	Control transformer burned out (1)		Improper limit control setting
	Open circuit in thermostat		Dirty air filters
	Pilot outage (2)		Restriction in air supply
	Gas valve stuck open/closed (3)	Delayed ignition	Improper burner adjustment
	Safety pilot burned out		Improper input
	No fuel		Delayed valve opening
Runs, but short cycles	Improper heat anticipator setting (4)		Low line pressure
	Cycles on limit control (5)	Pilot outage	Pilot orifice burned out
	Gas input too low		Thermocouple burned out
Room temperature high	Thermostat setting too high		Safety pilot burned out
	Thermostat out of calibration		Low line pressure
	Improper heat anticipator setting		Drafts
Runs continuously	Short in thermostat circuit	Extinction pop	Improper air adjustment
	Gas valve stuck open		Improper burner adjustment
Blower cycles after thermostat is satisfied	Blower CFM adjustment fan control setting		Improper orifice alignment
			Poor valve cutoff
Blows cool air at start	Blower CFM adjustment fan control setting (6)	Burns inside burner	Improper air adjustment
			Improper input
Startup/cool down noise	Expansion noise in heat exchanger (11)		Extinction pipe
	Duct expansion		Leaking gas valve
	Oil-can effect (12)	Flame lift	Improper input
Noise from vibration	Blower wheel unbalanced or out of line		Improper air adjustment
	Pulleys unbalanced (10)		Cracked or leaking heat exchanger
	Defective blower belt	Flame rollout	Restriction in heat exchanger
	Bearings burned out		Improper venting
Odor	Burning rust on start		Improper combustion air supply (8)
	Improper venting	Yellow fire/carbon deposit	Improper air adjustment
	Motor running hot or burning out		Improper input
	Transformer burnout	Flashback	Improper input
	Cracked heat exchanger		Improper air adjustment
High fuel cost	Improper input		Improper venting (9)
	Improper burner adjustment (7)		Restriction in heat exchanger
	Improper unit sizing	Intermittent blower operation	Improper CFM adjustment
High electrical cost	Improper motor load		Improper fan control setting
	Defective motor	Heat exchanger burn out	Improper input
	Incorrect motor speed		Chemical atmosphere
No fuel	No line pressure		Improper position of burners
	Defective regulator	Resonance (pipe organ effect)	Resonance unit design
	Supply valve closed		

*The numbers listed to the right of some selected possible causes reference further explanation in the text.

tribute to pilot outage by producing extinction flashback, called *extinction pop*.

TECH TIP

Soot is most often caused by improper fuel air adjustments. However, if the flame impinges on internal metal parts of the furnace, then heat can be pulled out of the flame rapidly enough to retard proper combustion. Flame impingement can result in carbon forming. An example of carbon formed as the result of flame impingement can be seen if a copper wire is held in a match flame. Within moments black carbon will form around the copper wire as it withdraws the heat from the flame and retards the complete combustion process.

When the burner is operating, the gas/air mixture is blowing upward through the burner port at a given speed or velocity (determined by the burner design and type of gas). There is also a downward force or burning velocity, which is equalized by the gas/air outward velocity when burning is taking place. If, however, the burning velocity were to increase due to shutoff of the gas supply, the flame could approach the burner. Either the burner would absorb the heat below the combustion point and extinguish the flame or the flame would burn down through the burner port and ignite the mixture in the burner. This ignition produces the extinction pop.

Figure 41-12 shows what happens to the gas flame after the gas valve shuts off. At the moment of shutoff the gas/air mixture inside the burner is at a negative (below atmospheric) pressure. At full fire there is a full cone and a full tail of flame. Immediately after the gas valve closes, the burner pressure partially collapses. The full collapse of the fire down to the burner followed by extinction occurs when the burner absorbs the heat from the fire.

If the speed of gas burning is too high due to too much primary air, the flame does not collapse as rapidly as it should. The negative pressure is insufficient and there is an explosion of extinction pop within the burner when carry through occurs. This could cause a pressure wave over the pilot that blows the pilot out. A properly adjusted burner greatly reduces the chances of pilot outage.

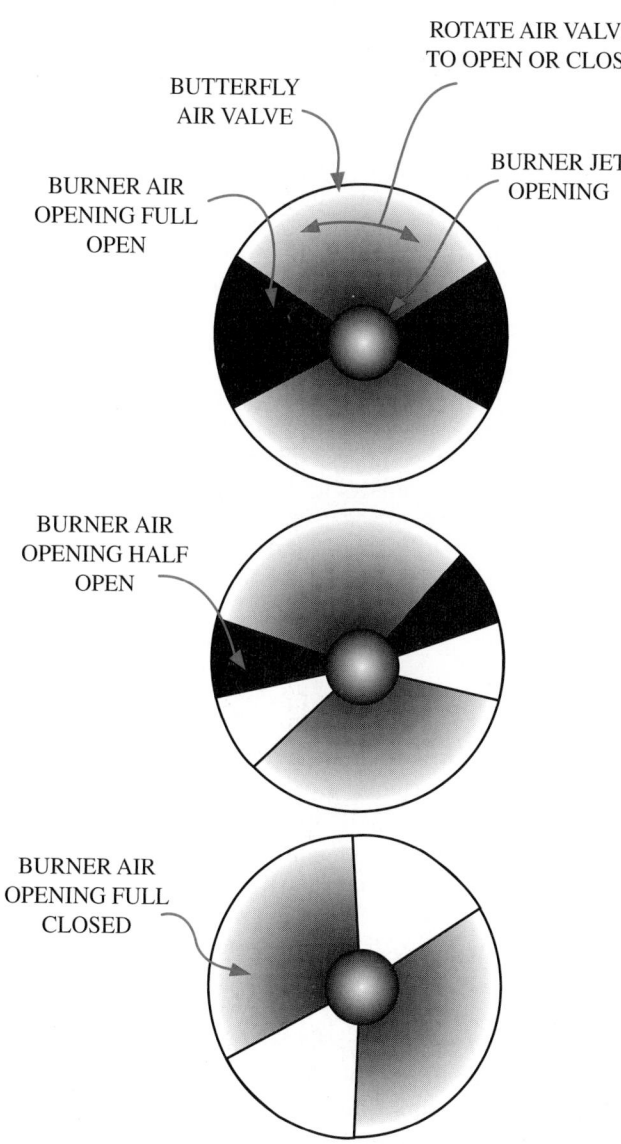

(a)

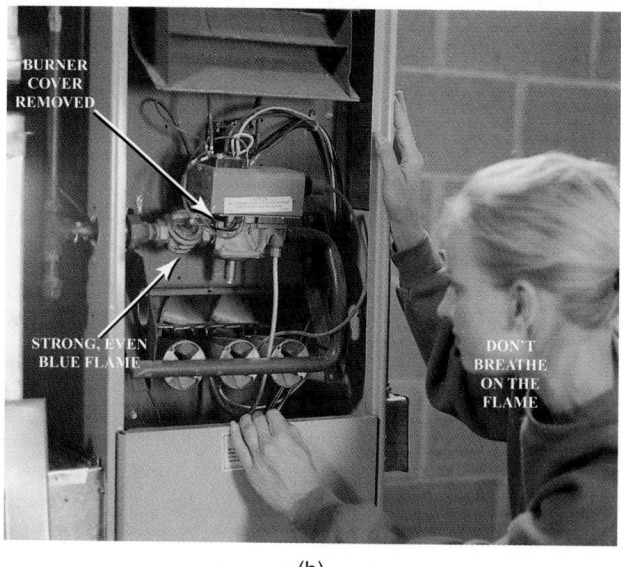

(b)

Figure 41-11 Primary air control opening size; (b) Soft blue flame with proper air control from The Family Handyman Fall Furnace Tune-up by Sam Satterwhite November 2000 http.www.rd.com/familyhandyman/context/182291
(Reprinted with permission from The Family Handyman Magazine, Home Service Publications, Inc., an affiliate of Reader's Digest Association, Inc., 2915 Commers Drivel, Suite 700, Eagan, MN 55121. ®Copyright 2000. All Rights Reserved.)

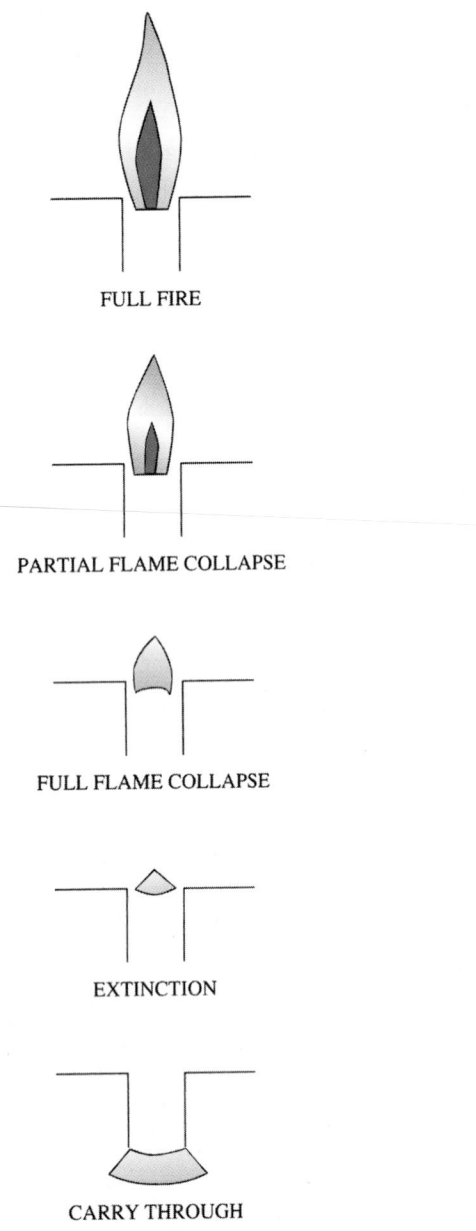

FULL FIRE

PARTIAL FLAME COLLAPSE

FULL FLAME COLLAPSE

EXTINCTION

CARRY THROUGH

Figure 41-12 Types of flame action at the gas burner

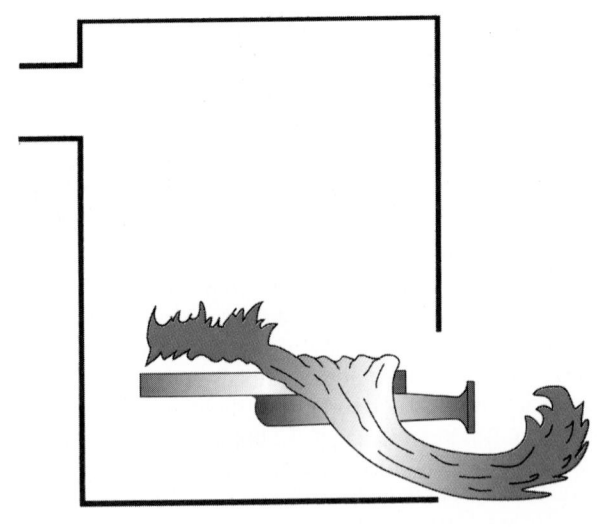

Figure 41-13 Rollout, due to insufficient secondary air

TECH TIP

The inside lining of a double walled vent pipe is made of aluminum. Aluminum is used because it heats up very quickly once the furnace starts. If heavier metal were used that warmed up slower, the water vapor in the vent gases would condense inside of the flue pipe until it heated up. This condensed water would then run down and corrode the furnace and/or heat exchanger. Even with an aluminum lined vent pipe some condensation occurs and in extremely cold climates enough water can be condensed to still run down to the furnace. Fortunately, in cold climates the furnace will run long enough to evaporate most of that moisture before it has a chance to cause damage. Traces of the moisture can be found around the furnace vent. Technicians may assume that water is from a leaking roof stack, however often it is just condensation.

---

8. **Improper Combustion Air Supply** Excess air is needed for proper combustion, even though changes in gas pressure, heat content of the gas, and barometric pressure may occur. Draft conditions also change with barometric pressure and wind conditions.

When a unit encounters insufficient combustion air, the flame tends to become hazy and erratic and may even roll over the edge of the burner and out the burner pouch opening. The flame will seek air. Figure 41-13 shows the effect of insufficient secondary air causing a floating flame.

9. **Improper Venting** The mixture of gas and air produces a mixture of water, carbon dioxide, nitrogen, and excess air. All of this has to be removed from the heat exchanger. This removal process is called venting.

There are two types of venting: active (power) venting and atmospheric or passive (gravity) venting. *Active venting* uses a mechanical device such as a motor driven blower to either draw flue products from the heat exchanger or to force combustion air into the heat exchanger. The most popular type is the draw type, where the blower is mounted on the flue outlet and creates negative pressure in the outlet of the heat exchanger to get the desired combustion efficiency. Because the pressure difference is caused by mechanical power, wind and/or atmospheric conditions have little effect on the venting performance.

In *atmospheric* or *passive venting*, hot flue gases pass from the heat exchanger into a flue pipe, chimney, or vent stack. The driving force for a passive vent is obtained from the hot gases rising in the surrounding cooler air. The amount of force depends on the temperature of the hot gases and the height of the gravity vent. The hotter the gases and/or the higher the vent, the greater the amount of driving force or pull that is produced. Also, the greater the pull, the more secondary air is drawn through the heat exchanger.

Enough air must be drawn through to provide complete combustion as well as complete venting of the flue products. If too much air is drawn out of the heat exchanger before the correct amount of heat extraction is done, this results in higher flue temperatures and reduced unit efficiency.

If the passive vent pipe were connected directly to the flue outlet, the amount of air drawn through the heat exchanger would vary with factors like the pull of the vent stack, the wind effect on the vent stack, and outside temperature. Control of the venting rate on the heat exchanger would be impossible. Further, under some atmospheric conditions it may be possible to have a higher pressure at the outlet of the vent than the combustion process can overcome. This can produce poor combustion with the production of CO as well as the usual products of CO_2 and H_2O.

To overcome the effect of atmospheric conditions, all units use an opening in the venting system called a draft diverter. Figure 41-14 shows four typical heating unit draft diverters. These all consist of an opening from the flue outlet of the heating unit, an opening into the vent pipe, and a relief opening to the surrounding atmosphere.

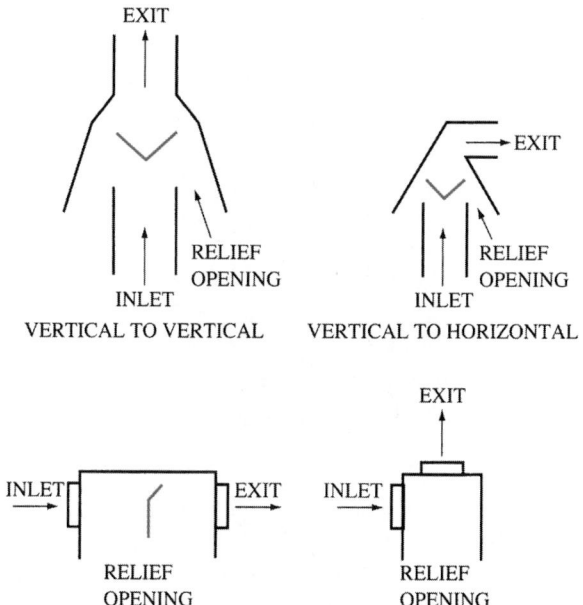

Figure 41-14 Typical gas appliance draft diverters

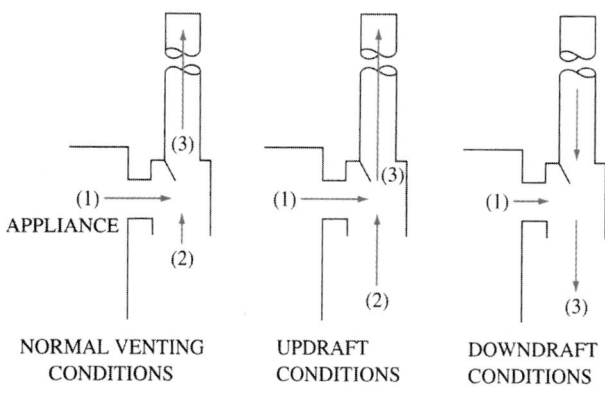

Figure 41-15 Operation of a draft diverter under various wind conditions

Figure 41-15 shows the operation of a typical draft diverter under no-wind conditions and with updraft and downdraft conditions. The amount of flue products, the dilution air entering the relief opening, and the amount of vent gases are indicated by the length of the arrows. With normal venting, some air is pulled into the draft diverter by the pull of the passive vent. The mixture of flue products and surrounding air (called dilution air) that blows up the vent is called vent gas. The action of the draft diverter is to break the effect of the vent by introducing surrounding air and neutralizing the pull at the flue outlet. The heat exchanger then operates at approximately equal pressure from burner opening to flue outlet. The amount of air for combustion is then controlled by the flue restrictors.

If the conditions surrounding the vent stack increase the stack pull, additional air is drawn into the draft diverter to compensate for the increased pull. There is little effect on the heat exchanger performance.

Under conditions where the vent stack pull is reduced or even reversed, creating a downdraft, all combustion flue products are forced into the surrounding area. In addition, the increased pressure in the flue outlet will reduce the flow through the heat exchanger. This can cause incomplete combustion and produce odors carried by the gases and moisture produced by the combustion process. Even though no odors may result, the large amount of moisture produced in the combustion process can accumulate in the occupied area and create adverse living conditions or possible structural damage.

To check for proper operation of the vent system, use a candle placed below the bottom edge of the diverter opening. With the unit operating and up to temperature, the candle flame should bend in the direction of the opening in the diverter. If the flame is neutral, the draft is on the weak side. Possibly the vent stack is not high enough or large enough. If the candle flame bends outward, a draft problem definitely exists that must be corrected. If the vent stack cannot be lengthened or enlarged, a forced draft unit must be installed to overcome the problem.

Figure 41-16 Aligning pulleys and checking belt tension

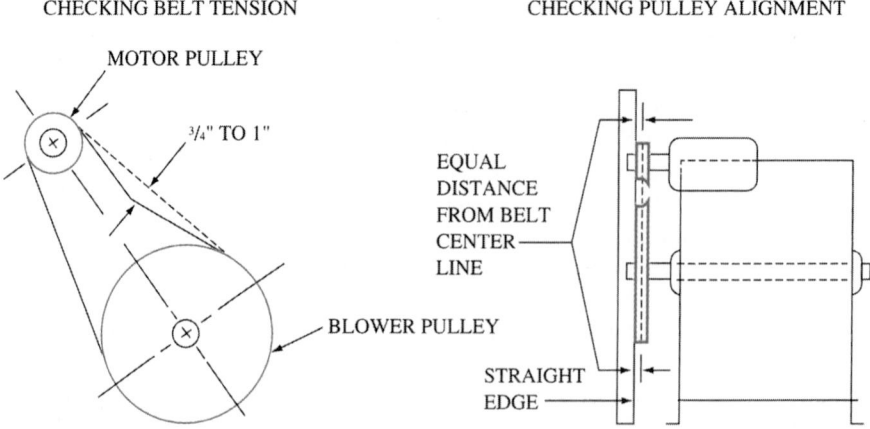

CHECKING BELT TENSION

MOTOR PULLEY

¾" TO 1"

BLOWER PULLEY

CHECKING PULLEY ALIGNMENT

EQUAL DISTANCE FROM BELT CENTER LINE

STRAIGHT EDGE

10. **Blower Drive** Belt driven blowers have a higher probability of vibration problems than direct drive blowers due to the additional parts involved. The most common problem is due to belt tension. It is commonly believed that the tighter the belt, the better the performance, but the opposite is true. The tighter the belt, the harder the motor has to work to get the belt in and out of the pulleys. The belt should therefore be as loose as possible without slipping on startup.

Figure 41-16 illustrates the test for proper belt tension. It should be possible to easily depress the belt midway between the motor shaft and blower shafts ¾ in to 1 in for each 12 in of distance between the shafts. Alignment of the motor and blower pulleys is important to keep vibration to a minimum as well as to reduce wear on the sides of the belt.

Finally, both motor pulley and blower pulley should be checked. They should be parallel to each other and perpendicular to the shaft. A warped pulley has a visible wobble that will create vibrations. Warped pulleys should be replaced.

11. **Expansion Noise in Heat Exchanger** Figure 41-17 shows a four section unit, each section composed of right-hand and left-hand drawn steel "clamshell" welded together. The sections are then welded into an assembly by fastening to the front mounting plate and rear retainer strap. Sometimes in the welding process stresses will be set up if the two metals are at different temperatures when the bond is made. This results in expansion noises, ticking, and popping as the heat exchanger heats and cools. Most of the time, these noises are muffled by the unit casing and duct system to a level where they are not objectionable.

In extreme cases, it is possible to reduce the noises by operating the unit with the blower disconnected, allowing the limit control to turn the unit off and on. This should be done through several cycles of the limit control. Cycling on this extreme heat will cause metal to stretch beyond the normal operation range and eliminate the sound. If this does not produce satisfactory results, the only cure is to change the heat exchanger.

12. **Oil-Can Effect** This effect is caused by the sudden movement of a flat metal surface where a forming stress has been left in the surface. This stress causes the metal to have a slightly concave or convex position rather than a flat plane surface.

Temperature change will cause a stress increase in the material until the metal rapidly changes position to the opposite of its original position. This change will produce a loud bang. Ductwork is very prone to this action and must be cross broken over any large panel areas. Unless this surface is cross broken, it is subject to the oil-can effect. The best correction is to remove the panel and cross break it to relieve temperature stresses.

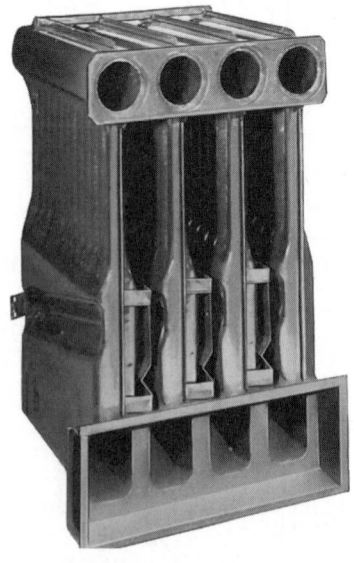

Figure 41-17 Clamshell gas heat exchanger
(Rheem Manufacturing Air Conditioning Division)

UNIT 41—SUMMARY

When troubleshooting a gas furnace, the technician's first responsibility is to perform a safety check. Look for visual signs of problems. After verifying that the system is safe to operate, proceed in a systematic manner. Use available resources such as troubleshooting flowcharts and diagnostic codes. Perform tests that can eliminate possible problem causes and narrow your search. Try to look for underlying causes, not just symptoms. For example: if a furnace is tripping out on the high limit, check for airflow problems. After isolating and repairing the problem, retest the system to ensure safe and proper operation.

——— WORK ORDERS

Service Ticket 4101

Customer Complaint: No Heat

Equipment: 80% Mid-Efficiency

A technician responds to a no heat call. The technician sets the thermostat to call for heat and the draft inducer fan starts, but nothing else happens. A check of the draft switch shows that it has not closed. A check of the pressure on the hose to the draft switch reads 0 in wc. The technician removes the tube to see if it is plugged and water comes out of the tube. Rechecking the draft, it now reads 0.25 in wc vacuum. The furnace now lights and operates.

Service Ticket 4102

Customer Complaint: No Heat

Equipment: 80% Mid-Efficiency

A technician responds to a no heat call. The technician sets the thermostat to call for heat and the draft inducer fan starts, but nothing else happens. A check of the draft switch shows that it has closed. A voltage check at the igniter shows that the igniter is receiving voltage, but is not operating. The technician checks the resistance out the igniter with an ohmmeter and it reads infinity. The technician replaces the igniter. The furnace now operates correctly.

Service Ticket 4103

Customer Complaint: Insufficient Heat

Equipment: 80% Two Stage Mid-Efficiency

A technician responds to an insufficient heat call. The technician sets the thermostat to call for high fire. The furnace lights and operates. The technician checks the voltage at the high fire solenoid on the gas valve and reads 24 V. Next, the gas pressure is checked. It reads 1.5 in wc at the manifold and 7 in wc at the gas valve inlet. The furnace data plate reads 1.5 in low fire manifold pressure, and 3.5 in high fire manifold pressure. The technician unsuccessfully tries to adjust the high fire manifold pressure. The gas valve is determined to be defective and is replaced. When the system is rechecked the high fire manifold pressure reads 3.5 in wc.

Service Ticket 4104

Customer Complaint: Furnace Sometimes Does Not Heat

Equipment: 90% Condensing Furnace Installed in Crawl Space

A technician is called to look at a 90% condensing furnace that works sometimes, and sometimes does not. The furnace is operating when the technician arrives. The customer says that he turns the heat off when he leaves for work and back on when he gets home. Occasionally on really cold days, the furnace will not come on. Yet it comes on later, usually after the outside temperature has warmed up a little. The furnace has a microprocessor control that stores fault history. The technician checks the fault history and sees that the furnace has shut down on draft safety several times. The technician notices that the drain from the condensate pump runs a long way through the crawl space and that the pump is equipped with an overflow kill switch. The technician concludes that water is freezing in the condensate pump discharge line causing the sump to fill and the kill switch to shut down the furnace. The technician replaces the soft plastic tubing used for the condensate pump discharge line with PVC, wraps the PVC with heat tape, and places pipe insulation over the new PVC condensate discharge line. Before leaving, the technician clears the fault codes so any faults that are stored will be after the drain fix. The mysterious cold weather shutdowns disappear. The technician checks the fault codes during the subsequent spring checkup and finds no fault codes.

Service Ticket 4105

Customer Complaint: No Heat

Equipment: Standing Pilot, Natural Draft Furnace

A technician responds to a no heat call on an old standard furnace. The technician notices the pilot light is not burning and attempts to light the pilot light. The pilot light will light, but it will not stay lit. The technician checks the millivoltage output of the thermocouple, reads 0 mV, and determines that the thermocouple is defective. The technician changes the thermocouple, lights the pilot light, and the furnace operates correctly.

Service Ticket 4106

Customer Complaint: No Heat

Equipment: Standing Pilot, Natural Draft Furnace

A technician responds to a no heat call on an old standard furnace. On a call for heat the main burners light.

After burning for several minutes the burners shut down. The indoor blower never comes on. The technician checks voltage to the blower motor and finds 0 V. The technician observes that the fan switch has rotated past the fan on cut in point and decides to check the fan switch next. Entering the fan switch is 120 V, but leaving is 0 volts. The technician concludes that the fan switch is defective. The flames had shut down on limit since the fan never came on. The fan switch is changed and the system rechecked. This time the fan comes on about three minutes after the burners light and the burners stay lit.

Service Ticket 4107

Customer Complaint: Carbon Monoxide Alarm

Equipment: 80% Mid-Efficiency Upflow Replacement Furnace

A technician is sent to look at a one year old mid-efficiency replacement furnace. The original installing contractor is no longer in business. The furnace is installed in the basement and connected to the old vent system. The technician observes that the old vent is a 7 in single wall vent and the flue collar on the new furnace is 4 in. Streaky rust stains appear on the bottom of every vent joint. The flames in one tube are visibly different from the others. The flames in that tube blow all around when the indoor blower comes on. The technician shuts down the furnace, removes the burner from that tube, and takes a closer look at the tube. There is a lot of rust and a hole at the back of the tube. The technician concludes that the heat exchanger has rusted out as a result of condensation in the oversized single wall vent. The technician recommends that the heat exchanger be replaced and a new correctly sized double wall vent run.

Service Ticket 4108

Customer Complaint: No Heat

Equipment: 90% Condensing Furnace with Combustion Air Piped In

A technician responds to a no heat call. The induced draft blower starts on a call for heat, but nothing else happens. The technician checks the draft switch and finds that it has not closed. Next, the vent pressure is checked and found to be −0.3 in wc in the combustion air pipe and +0.05 in wc in the vent pipe. The technician checks the ends of the air intake and vent pipes and notices leaves and grass in the end of the air intake pipe. Closer inspection reveals a bird's nest in the air intake. The technician removes the bird's nest and checks the vent screen at the furnace where a dead bird is found. The furnace operates correctly after removing the dead bird and bird's nest.

Service Ticket 4109

Customer Complaint: No Heat, Fan Runs Continuously

Equipment: 90% Condensing Furnace

A technician is sent to a no heat call on a mid-efficiency furnace. Upon arriving, the furnace fan and combustion blower motor are running even though the thermostat is turned off. The technician checks the voltage at the W terminal and finds 0 V. The diagnostic light is flashing a code that indicates the system shut down because of an open limit switch. The technician checks the resistance of the limit switch and it is indeed open, even though it is not hot. The technician replaces the limit switch and checks the air filter. The air filter is completely blocked. Because the filter is so dirty, the technician decides to check the underside of the recuperative coil. The condensing recuperative coil is checked after removing the blower; it is matted with dirt and animal hair. The coil is cleaned and the blower replaced. The technician explains that blocked airflow from the dirty filter and coil made the furnace cycle on the limit and eventually killed the limit switch. The customer is advised that the air filter needs changing regularly, at least once a month or the problems will repeat.

UNIT 41—REVIEW QUESTIONS

1. List the safety precautions to follow when working on gas furnaces.

2. List the general sequence of operation for an induced draft furnace.

3. Why should the door safety switch be checked before leaving the job?

4. List the seven categories of complaints with gas furnaces.

5. What is the purpose of the draft diverter on natural draft units?

   Use the chart in Figure 41-7 to diagnose the following problems and give probable cause(s).

6. The indoor blower on a furnace does not operate, but the induced draft blower does. After jumping terminals R and G, a voltage of 120 VAC is read between terminals N and A, but the blower still does not come on.

7. The indoor blower on a furnace is not operating in heat, but the induced draft blower does operate on heat. After jumping terminals R and G, the blower comes on and operates in high speed. The R to G jumper is removed and a jumper is placed between R and W. The burners light, but the indoor blower never comes on. No voltage is read between terminals N1 and ACC.

   Use the diagram in Figure 41-6 to answer the following questions.

8. A furnace does not come on when the thermostat calls for heat. The voltage between terminals W and C is 24 VAC. The voltage between the TH and C terminals is 0 VAC. List three switches that can cause these symptoms.

9. Assuming that the three switches in the previous question are not the problem, what other component could fail and cause these symptoms?

   Use the diagram in Figure 41-8 to answer the following questions.

10. The thermostat is set to bring on second stage heat. The induced draft motor and indoor blower motor both speed up, but the firing rate does not appear to increase. The temperature of the air leaving the furnace actually drops. The voltage between the C and M terminals on the gas valve is 24 VAC, but the voltage between the C and HI terminals is 0 VAC. What component could fail and cause these symptoms?

11. The thermostat is set to bring on second stage heat. The induced draft motor speeds up and the firing rate increases, but the indoor blower motor does not speed up. The temperature of the air leaving the furnace climbs. The voltage between terminal 1 on TB 25 and neutral terminal N reads 0 VAC. The voltage between terminal 2 on TB 25 and neutral terminal N reads 120 VAC. What component could fail and cause these symptoms?

   Use Table 41-1, gas systems problems, to answer the following questions.

12. What should be checked if the temperature rise on a furnace is too low?

13. What are some probable causes of noise and vibration?

14. What causes rollout of burner flames?

15. What are some possible causes of burner flashback?

16. What can cause the blower to come back on for a short time after cycling off?

17. What are some possible causes of delayed ignition?

18. What can cause soot accumulation on the heat exchanger?

19. On some furnaces little pops and pings can be heard before the blower comes on. What causes this noise?

20. A gas burner is noisy and the flames are lifting off the burner. What is the most likely cause?

UNIT 42

Oil Fired Heating Systems

OBJECTIVES

After completing this unit you will be able to:

- list the grades of fuel oil and compare their properties.
- discuss the types of nozzles available.
- explain the operation of a fuel oil burner.
- list the types of oil furnaces available.
- compare the efficiency ratings of different types of oil furnaces.
- explain the operation of oil furnace primary controls.
- describe oil tanks and piping system choices.

42.1 INTRODUCTION

Oil is the oldest fuel that is still widely used. Before gas furnaces and heat pumps, there were oil furnaces. Oil is still a popular form of heat in colder areas of the country. Oil furnaces typically have a higher heating capacity than either gas furnaces or heat pumps. Oil provides an economical fuel source for rural areas that are not served by natural gas because oil can be used anywhere a truck can go. When properly installed and maintained, an oil furnace burns just as cleanly as a gas furnace.

42.2 FUEL OILS

Fuel oils are mixtures of hydrocarbons made of long hydrocarbon chains derived from crude petroleum by distillation. Several different grades of fuel oil are available. Oil is divided into grades according to the oil characteristics; including viscosity, flash point, pour point, water and sediment content, carbon residue, and ash. The oil grades are classified according to their varying combinations of distillates and residuals. A distillate evaporates at relatively low temperatures. Light distillates are clear and will pour like water at normal room temperature. Residuals are what remain at the end of the distillation process. Residuals are black and tarry in appearance with the consistency of toothpaste at room temperature. Distillates are made of shorter carbon chains than residuals and have a lower heating capacity, but they are easier to store, pump, atomize, and burn. Oil grades range from 1 to 6, with 1 being 100% light distillates and 6 being nearly 100% residuals.

Oil Viscosity

Viscosity is a measure of how fast oil flows. A high viscosity number means that the oil is thicker and flows slowly, while a low viscosity number means that the oil is thinner and flows more readily. Oil's viscosity determines whether the fuel oil must be heated in order for it to flow. Table 42-1 shows the viscosity of several grades of fuel oil over a range of temperatures.

SERVICE TIP

All heating oil has a very distinctive odor. You must be very careful when working in residences not to contaminate the residence property with oil. Careless work habits can result in the home smelling of oil for days after a technician leaves. Often oil fired furnaces are located in basements, some of which do not have outside access. If it is necessary for you to access the system through the residence, you should wear paper shoe covers as you enter and leave the residence and each time you enter and leave the basement. In addition, you must clean your hands thoroughly before entering the residence to adjust the thermostat, set dampers or vents, and any other such service.

Oil Grades

Grades 1 and 2 are the grades of fuel oil primarily used for comfort heating applications. Both contain high quantities

Table 42-1 Properties of Fuel Oils

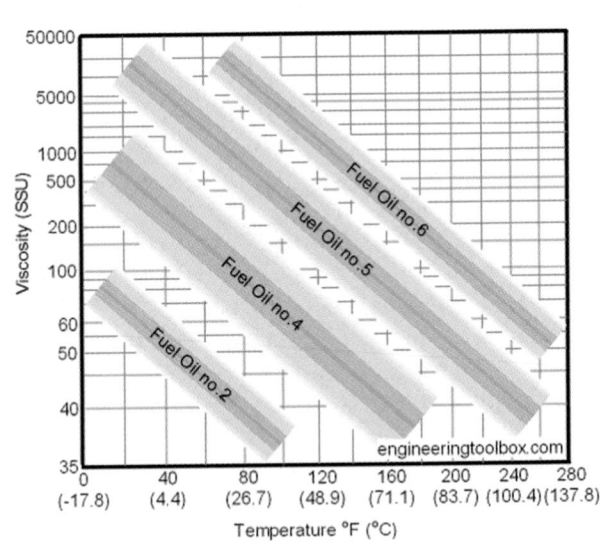

of carbon and hydrogen with traces of sulfur. The carbon content for these fuel oils ranges from 84–86% with a maximum of 1% sulfur. The sulfur content of fuel oils is kept as low as possible to reduce air pollution.

Number 1 grade fuel oil is considered premium quality. It is used in room space heaters, which do not use high pressure burners and depend on gravity flow, thus the need for the lower viscosity. Number 2 grade oil is the standard grade heating oil sold. Number 2 grade oil is used in equipment that has pressure atomizing, which includes most forced air furnaces and boilers. The heating value for numbers 1 and 2 grade oil falls in the range of 135,000–142,000 Btu/gal.

TECH TIP

It is often assumed that because heating oils are thicker than water they are heavier than water. This is not true. Oil floats on water. Although it is thicker than water it is less dense. Most heating oils range between 6.8–7.2 lb/gal as compared to water, which weighs 8.3 lb/gal.

42.3 TYPES OF OIL HEAT

Not long ago, oil heating systems were limited to boilers or rather large and inefficient warm air furnaces. Today, manufacturers specializing in oil products offer a much wider array of choices in oil heat. These designs include condensing furnaces with efficiencies reaching 95%, condensing unit heaters with 95% efficiency ratings, furnaces with firing rates as low as 50,000 Btu/hr, two stage residential furnaces, mid-efficiency noncondensing furnaces with efficiency ratings reaching 89%, and sealed combustion furnaces.

Most oil-fired boilers used for residential heating do not convert the water to steam but instead are specialized hot water heaters. The hot water can be used in a traditional hydronic heating system, or in a radiant heating system. In a radiant floor system, the hot water is circulated through pipes that are under the floor. Figure 42-1 shows a typical oil fired boiler.

Oil fired warm air furnaces heat the air using a heat exchanger, much like a gas furnace. One product that is unique to oil fired systems is the waste oil furnace. These are warm air furnaces that are specifically designed to burn waste oil. Waste oil burners are particularly attractive to companies that generate waste oil. Normally, the company would have to pay to dispose of the waste oil. By using waste oil as fuel, the company not only saves on disposal costs, but gets free heat in the bargain. Most modern recently manufactured oil burners are approved for use for B5 or lower grades of biofuels. However, older oil burners may need to be replaced or upgraded with all involved components to be compatible. Figure 42-2 shows a waste oil furnace.

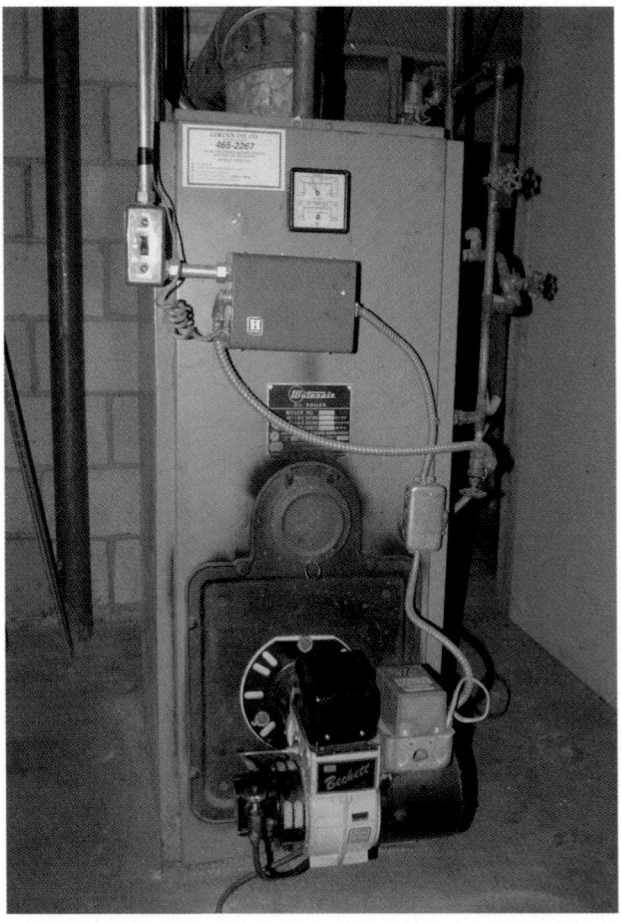

Figure 42-1 Oil fired boiler

42.4 TYPES OF FURNACES

Oil Furnace Configurations

Like gas furnaces, oil forced air furnaces are designed in five basic configurations.

- Upflow.
- Downflow (counterflow).
- Horizontal.
- Lowboy.
- Multi-position models.

These configurations describe the airflow through the furnace. Air travels up in an upflow furnace, down in a downflow furnace, and horizontally (left or right) in a horizontal furnace. Lowboy furnaces have two sections side by side as do horizontal furnaces; but the air goes in the top of the furnace, makes a 180° turn as it goes through the furnace, and then leaves out the top of the furnace. Lowboy furnaces are built low in height to accommodate areas where headroom is minimal. These furnaces are approximately 4 ft high, providing for easy installation in a low ceiling height basement. Blowers for lowboy furnaces are typically belt driven. A multi-position furnace can be used in more than one configuration.

Figure 42-2 Waste oil furnace
(*Photo Courtesy of Clean Burn*)

Oil Furnace Efficiencies

Oil furnaces are available in standard efficiency, mid-efficiency, and high efficiency condensing models. Older design oil furnaces had combustion efficiencies of around 60%. Added to this is the heat lost through the large amount of air required for combustion air and dilution air. Taking this additional heat loss into account, they perform no better than 50% efficiency overall. Most new "standard" oil furnaces now use flame retention burners. These operate with efficiencies closer to 80%, but the losses from combustion and dilution air are still present.

Many mid-efficiency furnaces, depending on their design and application, use high static burners that do not require barometric dampers, so the loss from dilution air is eliminated. The main determination for a barometric damper is the chimney. If the draft is excessive, the system may still require a barometric damper even with a high static burner. Some add sealed combustion, so all the combustion air comes from outside. These furnaces operate with efficiencies of 83–89%.

The combustion products from an oil furnace contain only half as much water as the combustion products from a gas furnace. Since this lowers the dew point, the combustion gases from an oil furnace can be cooled further before condensation starts to take place. Therefore mid-efficiency oil furnaces are less likely to condense water in this efficiency range as compared to gas furnaces although this is subject to the furnace application and the operating environment.

The high efficiency furnaces rated in the 90–95% efficiency range condense water out of the vent gases using a stainless steel recuperative secondary coil.

Both mid-efficiency and high-efficiency furnaces are available in two stage models that have a low and high firing rate. This improves the overall furnace efficiency by reducing the furnace cycling and extending the run times.

42.5 CONDENSING OIL FURNACES

Like condensing gas furnaces, the highest efficiency oil furnaces achieve their high efficiency by condensing water out of the combustion gases. This can be accomplished by adding a condensing recuperative secondary coil to cool the combustion

Figure 42-3 Category IV condensing duct furnace

gases with the return air. The combustion gases pass through this stainless steel recuperative secondary coil before traveling out the vent. Figure 42-3 shows a condensing duct furnace that has a two-pass stainless steel heat exchanger and can be configured to operate with natural gas, LPG, or #2 fuel oil.

Building a reliable condensing oil furnace can be somewhat of a challenge. This is because there is less latent heat to capture with only half as much water in the combustion gas of an oil furnace as compared to a natural gas furnace. Also, oil has considerably higher sulfur content, so the condensate is more acidic than the condensate from condensing gas furnaces. This means that the condensing recuperative secondary coil must be more resistant to corrosion. Despite these obstacles, there are over 300 furnaces listed by the Department of Energy as Energy Star furnaces. These furnaces have efficiencies in the range of 90–95%.

42.6 HEAT EXCHANGER

The typical oil fired heat exchanger, Figure 42-4, is a cylindrical shell of heavy gauge steel or cast iron in which combustion takes place. It offers additional surfaces for heat transfer from the products of combustion inside, to the air around the outside of the chamber. This type of heat exchanger is called a drum and radiator. The inside, containing the flame, is called the primary surface, and the outside is called the secondary surface.

Figure 42-4 Oil furnace heat exchanger

Some manufacturers add baffles, flanges, fins, or ribs to the surfaces to provide increased surface area to allow for faster heat transfer to the air passing over the surfaces.

The burner assembly is bolted to the heat exchanger. The firing assembly and blast tube extend into the primary surface in correct relationship to the combustion chamber or refractory. A flame inspection port is provided just above the upper edge of the refractory. This is used to observe proper ignition, flame shape, and flame size, and to measure over fire draft for startup and service operations.

> ### SAFETY TIP
>
> Never open the inspection port unless the power to the furnace is off, or there is a flame.

Recuperative Condensing Coil

High efficiency oil furnaces use stainless steel recuperative condensing secondary coils in the return air. After the combustion products travel through the standard heat exchanger, they pass through the recuperative heat exchanger where water is condensed from the combustion products. The remaining vent gas is vented through Schedule 40 PVC pipe.

42.7 REFRACTORY

High temperatures are required in the flame area of the heat exchanger to produce maximum burning efficiency of the oil/air mixture. To obtain this high temperature, a reflective material, called the refractory, is installed around the combustion area. It is an insulation type of material designed to reach white hot surface temperatures

(a)

(b)

Figure 42-5a,b Oil furnace refractory

quickly, with minimum deterioration. A refractory fire box is shown in Figure 42-5a,b. It should be noted that caution should be taken if a vacuum cleaner is to be used on this type.

> ### SAFETY TIP
>
> Occasionally the refractory fire box on an oil furnace can be flooded with oil. When this happens, the excess oil must be removed before the furnace can be restarted. With the oil burner assembly removed, use dry paper towels or rags to absorb the remaining oil before attempting to relight the furnace. Never attempt to relight a furnace with liquid oil in the bottom of the refractory fire box. If the oil in the refractory fire box is ignited, it is very difficult to extinguish.

> ### CAUTION
>
> Only CO_2 type extinguishers should be used on oil burner fires because they leave no residue. Dry chemical fire extinguishers will put out an oil fire, but the residue can cause an extensive and lengthy cleanup.

42.8 OIL BURNERS

The high pressure atomizing gun burner shown in Figure 42-6a,b is the type used on most residential and small commercial oil fired heating systems. Traditional high

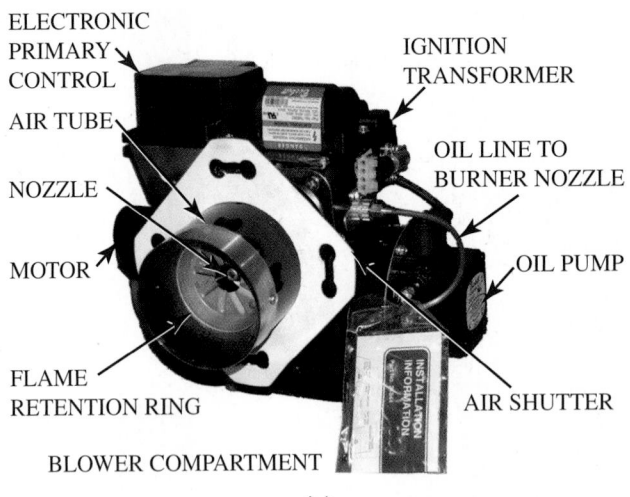

ELECTRONIC PRIMARY CONTROL

IGNITION TRANSFORMER

AIR TUBE

OIL LINE TO BURNER NOZZLE

NOZZLE

MOTOR

OIL PUMP

FLAME RETENTION RING

AIR SHUTTER

BLOWER COMPARTMENT

(a)

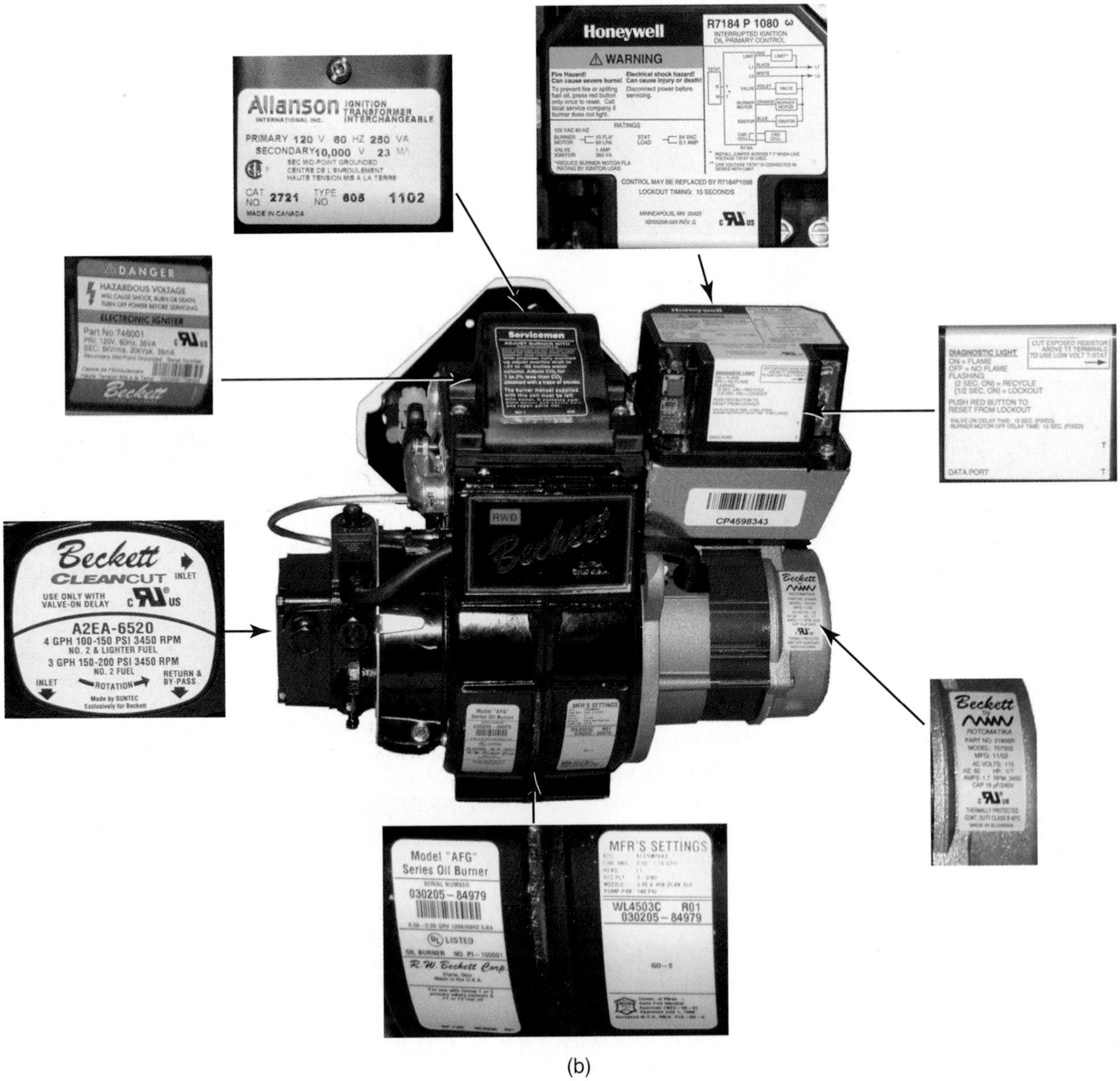

(b)

Figure 42-6 (a) High pressure atomizing gun type oil burner with parts identified; (b) Typical labels on the high pressure atomizing gun type oil burner

Figure 42-7 Oil burner flame

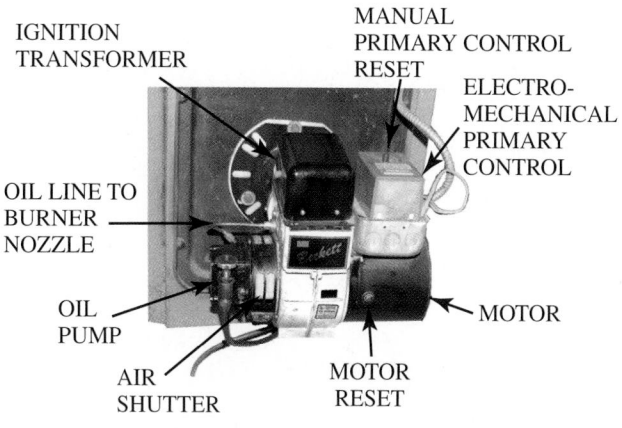

Figure 42-9 The air shutter shown at bottom left adjusts airflow for this old style oil burner

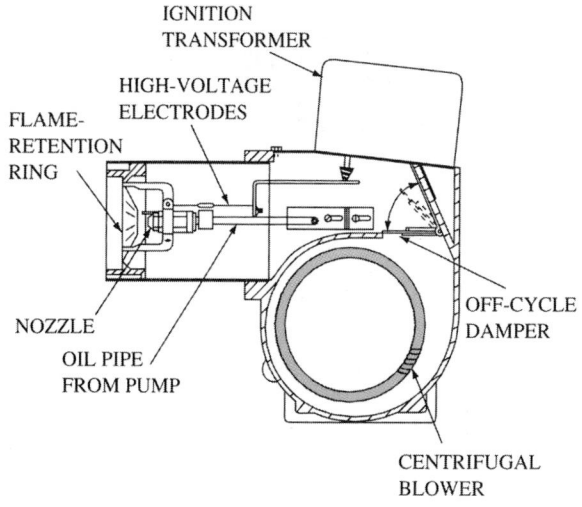

Figure 42-8 Cutaway view of the internal construction of an oil burner

pressure oil burners burn with a yellow flame, as shown in Figure 42-7. High pressure oil burners have the following components:

- Oil pump.
- Air blower.
- Electric motor.
- Ignition transformer.
- Blast tube, with nozzles and ignition system.
- Primary control.

The burner illustrated in Figure 42-8 shows a cutaway view of the internal construction of a burner assembly. The pump and blower are driven from a common motor shaft. The oil pump is a gear arrangement. The oil pump delivers more oil than the burner can use. The extra oil must either be bypassed internally in the pump or sent back to the tank through a separate oil return line. By placing a bypass plug in

the housing, the pump can operate as a single pipe or a two pipe system. The plug is removed for single pipe operation. Single pipe operation is used where the oil tank is above the burner and gravity oil feed to the burner is permitted. Generally the bypass plug must be installed for two pipe operation, however some newer pumps today do not require a bypass plug. Two pipe operation is needed when the oil tank is located below the fuel unit and a high lift and/or long run of fuel line exists. The pump supplies oil to the nozzle at 100–300 psi.

The burner blower includes a centrifugal wheel also mounted on the common motor shaft. It furnishes air through the blast tube which produces air fuel turbulence for proper mixing and combustion. The amount of air is controlled by sliding an air shutter or air band on the blower housing section, as shown in Figure 42-9.

Oil is pumped to the nozzle as shown in Figure 42-10a–c, which is mounted in an adapter. The orifice in the nozzle is factory bored to produce the correct firing rate, and must not be altered or changed in any way. The firing rate is approximately 0.75 gal/hr for each 100,000 Btu/hr output of the furnace. Under high pressure, the oil is atomized into fine droplets and mixes with the primary air.

The air deflector vane ring (turbulator) rotates or spins the atomized oil and air into the heat exchanger, Figure 42-11. Ignition is provided by a high voltage electric spark. The spark is provided by electrodes that are positioned so that the arc between them passes just above the oil and air mixture. However, the oil should not touch the electodes, just the spark from the electrodes. The spark can either operate all the time the burner is operating, or it can be shut off after the flame is proved. The 10,000 V AC for the spark is provided by the ignition transformer which is located on top of the burner housing.

The primary control governs the operation of the burner motor and ignition transformer. Safety is provided by a light sensitive cadmium sulfide cell, Figure 42-12a,b. The "cad cell" has a very high resistance in the dark, but a low resistance when exposed to light. The cad cell senses when there is no flame because it cannot see the light from the flame. When

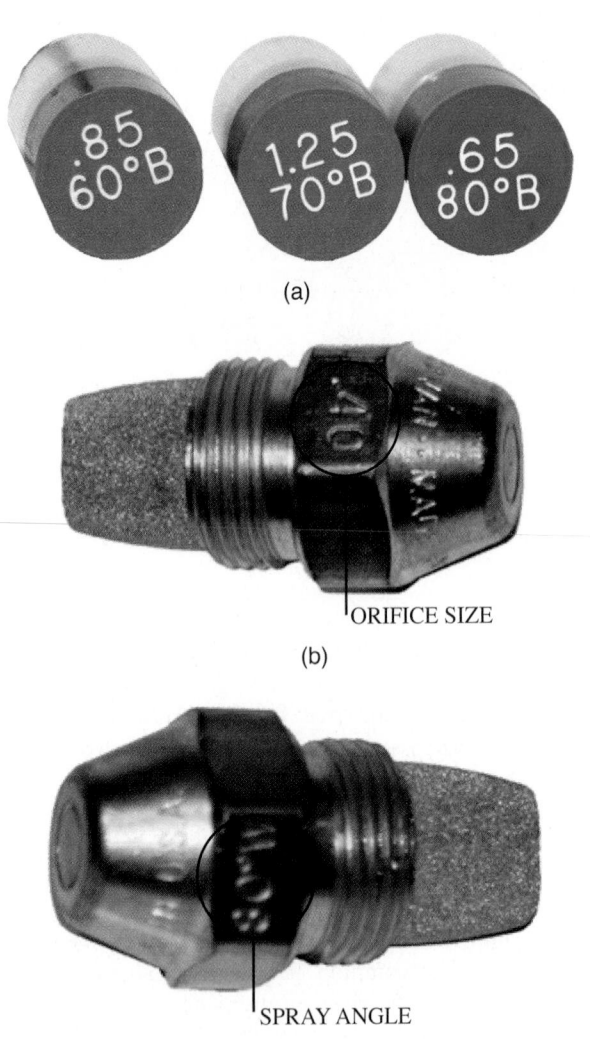

(a)

ORIFICE SIZE

(b)

SPRAY ANGLE

(c)

Figure 42-10 (a) Various sizes and types of nozzles; (b) Nozzle size is stamped on the nozzle; (c) Nozzle angle is stamped on the nozzle

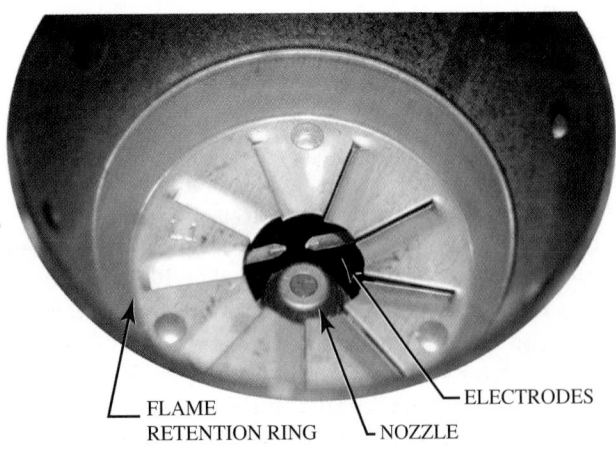

FLAME
RETENTION RING — NOZZLE — ELECTRODES

Figure 42-11 Oil furnace turbulator and electrodes

(a)

(b)

Figure 42-12 Cadmium sulfide (CAD) cell

the cad cell does not see the light of the flame, the primary control will stop the burner motor and ignition transformer, thus preventing oil from flowing into the heat exchanger. Most furnaces have a lockout system requiring the control to be reset manually before the burner can run again.

SAFETY TIP

Pushing the reset button multiple times can set up a potentially dangerous situation by soaking the combustion chamber with oil. Find out if the customer has already pushed the reset several times before trying to operate the furnace. Oil does not evaporate, so the oil will still be sitting in the combustion chamber even if the reset button was pushed several times the day before. If the furnace does light with a combustion chamber full of oil, the combustion chamber may not be able to contain the flames.

42.9 OIL BURNER NOZZLE

The nozzle is responsible for atomizing the fuel oil. Nozzles are described by their individual physical characteristics. These characteristics are the spray angle, the spray pattern, and the gallons per hour that pass through the nozzle at a given pressure.

The mist from a nozzle makes a cone shape, with the point of the cone at the tip of the nozzle. The spray angle describes the included angle of the sides of this cone. The spray patterns created by the nozzles tend to be listed as either solid, hollow, or semi-hollow cone. A solid cone spray pattern has a more or less uniform density of spray droplets throughout the cone shape. A hollow cone concentrates most of the droplets toward the outside of the cone, creating a hollow center in the cone. The semi-hollow core would be someplace between these two patterns.

The nozzle must be matched to the burner and combustion chamber. For example, a 30° spray pattern would be used for heat exchangers that are long and narrow while a 90° spray pattern would be used for a more square shape. The mix of oil and air is controlled by the spray pattern of the nozzle and the air pattern of the burner. The burner air pattern and the nozzle spray pattern must be compatible for proper mixing. The oil spray should not touch the sides of the combustion chamber or the ignition electrodes. Figure 42-13 shows the types of nozzles available.

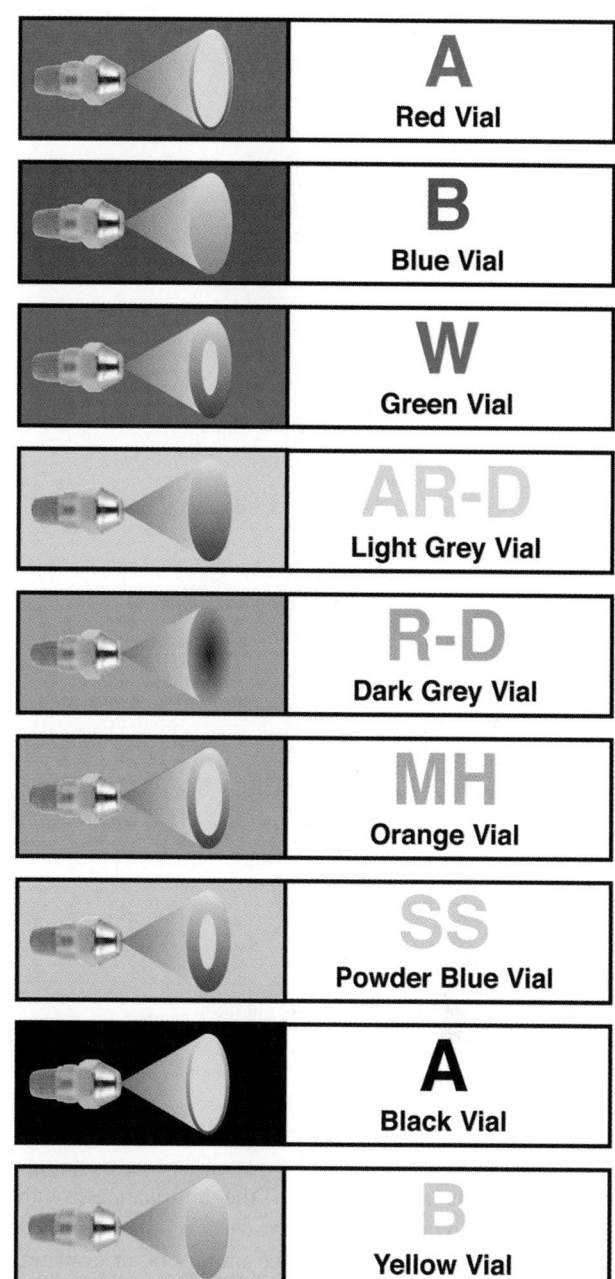

Figure 42-13 Nozzle sizing chart and spray patterns
(Courtesy of Delavan Spray Technologies)

TECH TIP

Although a nozzle appears to be a simple device, there are many different designs of nozzles. Having a nozzle that matches the burner design is crucial. Using a nozzle that does not match the burner could result in incomplete combustion and inefficient operation.

42.10 FLUE VENTING

Oil fired furnaces must have an ample supply of makeup air for combustion, and the methods of introducing makeup air for a gas furnace will also be adequate for oil equipment.

Masonry chimneys used for oil fired furnaces should be constructed as specified in the National Building Code of the National Board of Fire Underwriters. Prefabricated lightweight metal chimneys, Figure 42-14, are also available. These are rated for all flues, Class A and Class B. Class A flues are used for solid and liquid fuels while Class B flues are made specifically for gas fired equipment. Oil furnaces may also be vented using Type L vent, which is specifically made for oil furnaces.

The above roof dimension of the vent or chimney is the same for both gas and oil. Since oil fired furnaces operate on positive pressure from the burner blower, it is important to have a chimney that will develop a minimum draft of 0.01 to 0.02 in wc as measured at the burner flame inspection port. However, there are some newer residential units that can be designed to operate with a positive over fire draft.

Consistency or stability of draft is also more critical for an oil fired furnace, and the use of a barometric damper,

Figure 42-15 a–c, is required. The damper is usually installed in the horizontal vent pipe between the furnace and chimney. The damper has a movable weight so that it can be set to counterbalance the suction and to maintain reasonably constant flue operation. It is adjusted while the furnace is in operation and the chimney is hot. The over fire draft at the burner should be in accordance with the equipment installation instructions. It is used to control draft, but will not help if the draft is insufficient.

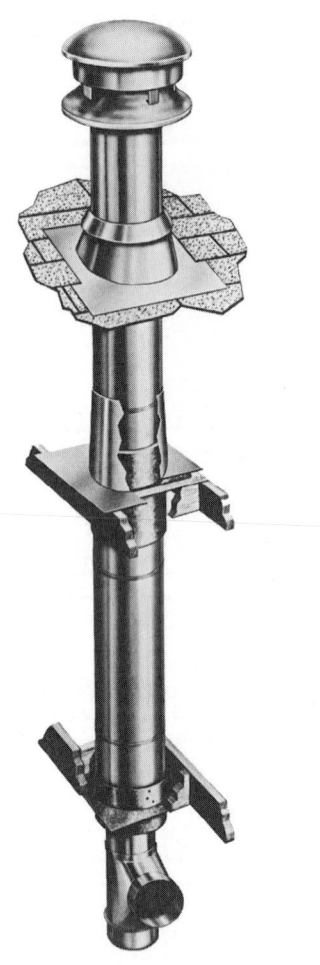

Figure 42-14 Factory built, all fuel chimney
(Courtesy of Selkirk Metalbestos)

High static burners may not require a barometric damper dependent on the chimney draft. If the draft is excessive, the system may still require a barometric damper. The elimination of a barometric damper reduces the amount of air drawn up the vent. Some furnaces use sealed combustion along with a high static burner. Air is drawn in from outside, so that no combustion or dilution air is required from inside.

Condensing furnaces use Schedule 40 PVC vents because of the low vent gas temperatures. Condensing furnaces require a condensate drain for the furnace and the vent.

42.11 CLEARANCES

Cabinet temperatures and flue pipe temperatures run warmer for oil burning equipment, so clearances from combustible material should be adjusted accordingly. One inch clearances are common for the sides and rear of the cabinet, compared to zero clearances for many gas units. Flue pipe clearances of 9 in or more are needed for oilfired furnaces, whereas only 6 in of clearance are needed for natural gas.

Front clearance is extremely important as space is needed to remove the burner assembly. Floor bases over combustible surfaces are generally increased for oil as compared to gas. For example, in horizontal oil furnaces installed in attics, the installer must pay particular attention to recommendations related to adjoining surfaces.

Clearances are an important part of the compliance and inspection procedures required by Underwriters Laboratories (UL) for securing their seal of approval. Also refer to the latest edition of the National Fire Protection Association (NFPA 31) Standard for the installation of oil burner equipment.

> ## CAUTION
>
> Many oil fired furnaces are located in open basement areas where they are subject to having items stored on, against, or near them. Such storage constitutes a major fire hazard and must be removed before you light the furnace. Caution the home owner or resident against such storage practices.

42.12 RATINGS AND EFFICIENCIES

In the past, the number of sizes available for oil burning furnaces was limited. Most furnace lines started big and got bigger. Offerings are more varied today, both in terms of size and efficiency. Table 42-2 lists some examples of models available from one manufacturer.

Table 42-2 Oil Furnace Models

Firing Rate	Efficiencies	Configurations
50,000	98%	Horizontal, unit heater
70,000	83%	Upflow
75,000	98%	Horizontal, unit heater
90,000	84%	Horizontal, upflow, downflow, lowboy
100,000	94%	Horizontal, unit heater
105,000	83%	Horizontal, upflow, downflow, lowboy
120,000	83%	Horizontal, upflow, downflow, lowboy
125,000	92%	Horizontal, unit heater
140,000	84%	Horizontal, upflow, downflow, lowboy
150,000	98%	Horizontal
200,000	94%	Horizontal
250,000	92%	Horizontal

(a)

(b)

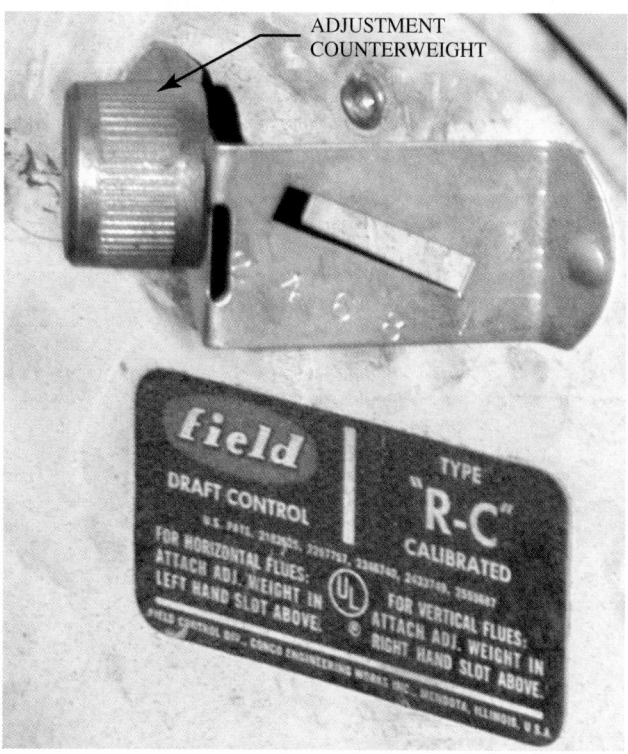

ADJUSTMENT
COUNTERWEIGHT

(c)

Figure 42-15 (a) Barometric damper, shut; (b) Barometric damper, open; (c) Damper adjustment counterweight

Figure 42-16 Fuel oil delivery truck

42.13 OIL STORAGE

Fuel oil is delivered to residences and small businesses by tanker trucks similar to the one shown in Figure 42-16. These trucks are equipped with pumps and flowmeters that register the amount of oil delivered. A printed receipt is then left with the resident.

The oil is stored at the residence in large tanks, Figure 42-17. These storage tanks are typically made of steel and contain 275–1000 gal of fuel oil. The 275 gal tanks are the most commonly used in residential settings. The tanks are nonpressurized and vented to the air. As the oil fills the tank, air leaves through the vent. As oil leaves the tank, air travels in through the vent to keep air pressure on the remaining oil in the tank.

There are two pipes connected to the top of the oil storage tank. One pipe is used for filling the tank with oil, and the other pipe is a vent. Figure 42-18a,b, shows the typical arrangement of these pipes outside the residence. The fill pipe has a cap that is easily unscrewed so that the fill nozzle from the truck can be attached to it, as shown in Figure 42-19. The vent pipe has an alarm whistle that stops sounding when the level of oil in the tank rises up to the fill level in the tank, as shown in Figure 42-20.

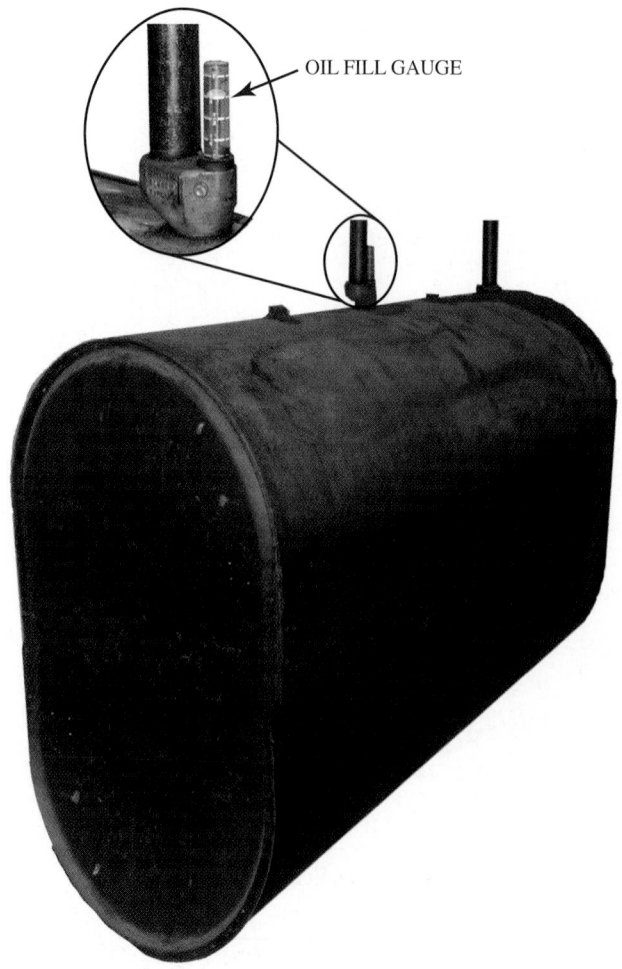

OIL FILL GAUGE

Figure 42-17 Oil storage tank and fill gauge

(a)

OIL FILL — — VENT/FILL ALARM

(b)

Figure 42-18 Residential fuel oil fill and alarm pipes: (a) Typical oil fill cap and vent; (b) Oil fill and vent pipes

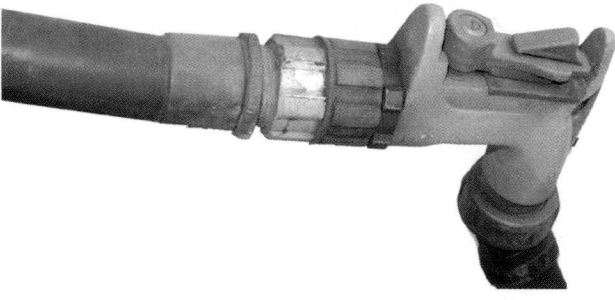

Figure 42-19 Fuel oil fill nozzle attached to oil fill pipe

Figure 42-21 Commercial fuel oil fill and alarm pipe sets

Figure 42-20 Fuel oil alarm cap showing internal screen

Some commercial installations may have more than one set of fill and alarm pipes, as shown in Figure 42-21. These fill and alarm pipes operate with the same system of indicating when the tank has been filled. An electronic alarm can be used to replace the mechanical air whistle on some systems, as shown in Figure 42-22.

42.14 PRIMARY OIL BURNER CONTROLS

A typical oil fired forced air furnace control system is shown in Figure 42-23. The fan and limit control performs the same function as on a gas furnace. The safety limit will open to stop the electrical current to the burner if the furnace temperature exceeds the limit setpoint, Figure 42-24. The fan switch is set to cycle the furnace blower on when the heat exchanger heats up to the fan switch ON setting and keeps the blower operating until the heat exchanger cools to the fan switch OFF setting. The space thermostat (24 V)

Figure 42-22 Electronic fill alarm

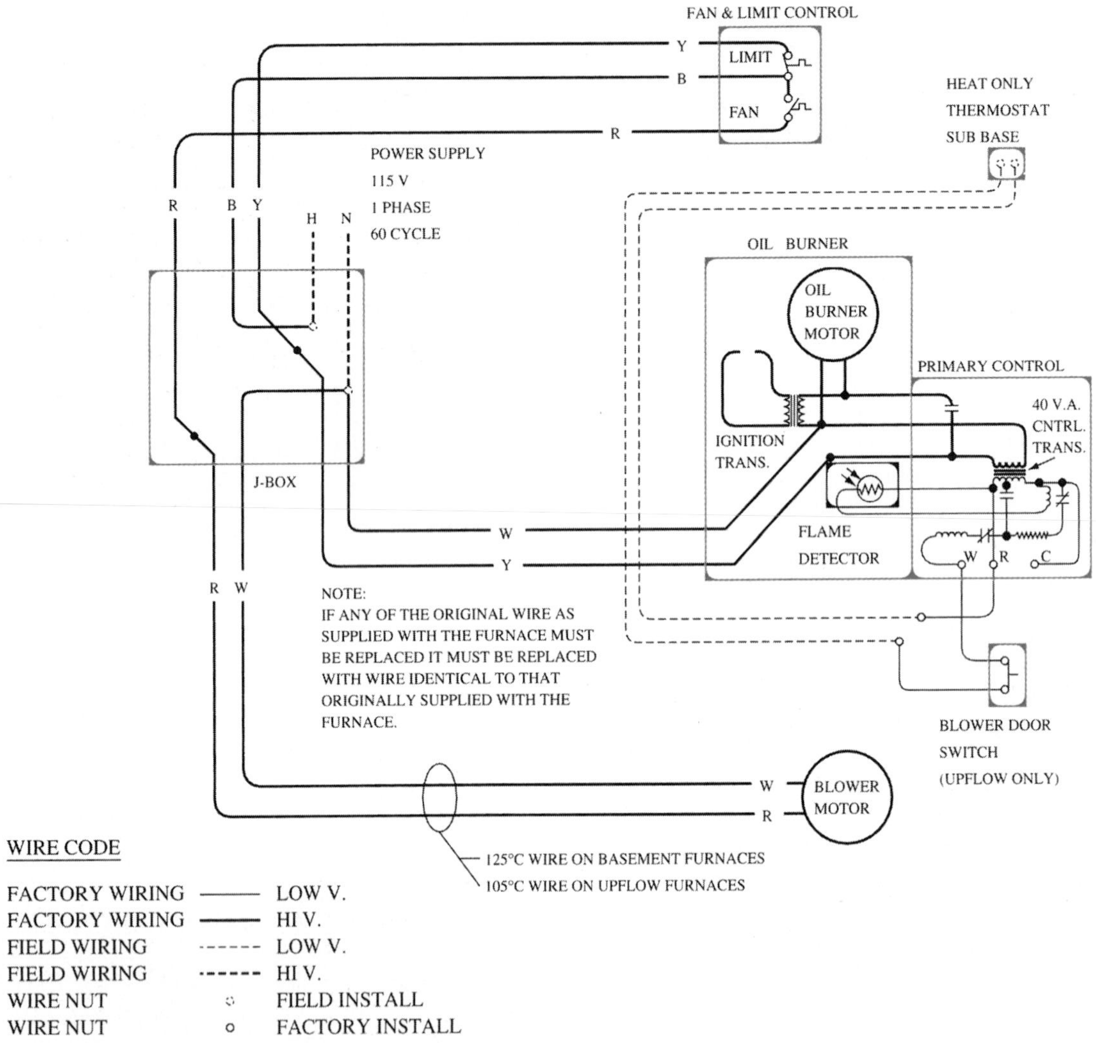

FAN & LIMIT CONTROL
LIMIT
FAN
Y
B
R
HEAT ONLY
THERMOSTAT
SUB BASE
POWER SUPPLY
115 V
1 PHASE
60 CYCLE
R B Y
H N
OIL BURNER
OIL
BURNER
MOTOR
PRIMARY CONTROL
40 V.A.
CNTRL.
TRANS.
IGNITION
TRANS.
FLAME
DETECTOR
W R C
J-BOX
W
Y
R W
NOTE:
IF ANY OF THE ORIGINAL WIRE AS SUPPLIED WITH THE FURNACE MUST BE REPLACED IT MUST BE REPLACED WITH WIRE IDENTICAL TO THAT ORIGINALLY SUPPLIED WITH THE FURNACE.
BLOWER DOOR
SWITCH
(UPFLOW ONLY)
BLOWER
MOTOR
W
R
125°C WIRE ON BASEMENT FURNACES
105°C WIRE ON UPFLOW FURNACES
WIRE CODE
FACTORY WIRING LOW V.
FACTORY WIRING HI V.
FIELD WIRING LOW V.
FIELD WIRING HI V.
WIRE NUT FIELD INSTALL
WIRE NUT FACTORY INSTALL

Figure 42-23 Typical oil burner control system wiring diagram

LO LIMIT
CIRC.
HIGH
LIMIT
SET HI
20° OR MORE
ABOVE LO

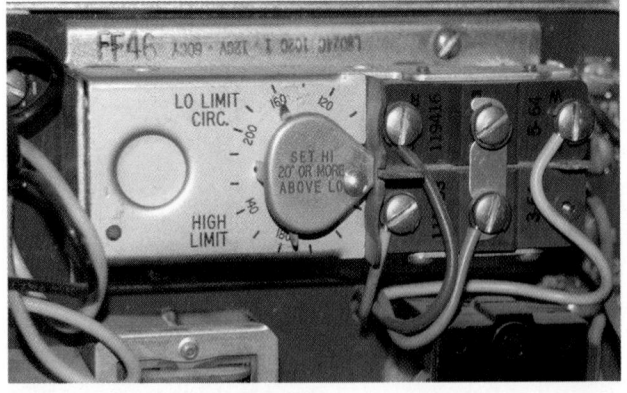

Figure 42-24 Oil burner temperature limit control

feeds directly to the burner low voltage secondary control circuit. This actuates the relay and flame detector circuit, feeding the primary line voltage to the burner motor and ignition transformer.

SAFETY TIP

The ignition circuit on an oil fired furnace uses approximately an 8,000–15,000 V arc to continuously ignite the oil. Accidentally touching the "live" ignition transformer contacts can result in a severe electrical shock.

Protector Relay Control

The original primary oil burner control, known as a stack relay, was mounted on the vent connector pipe. The bimetallic sensing element in the sensing tube would react to a rise in flue gas temperature and cause the relay to keep the oil burner operating. Figure 42-25 shows an example of this control with the cover in place and the sensing (stack) element protruding from the rear.

Figure 42-26 shows a typical control for the primary oil burner. The control has its own power source transformer as well as temperature actuation contacts and manual reset

Figure 42-25 Outer appearance of an oil burner stack mounted primary control

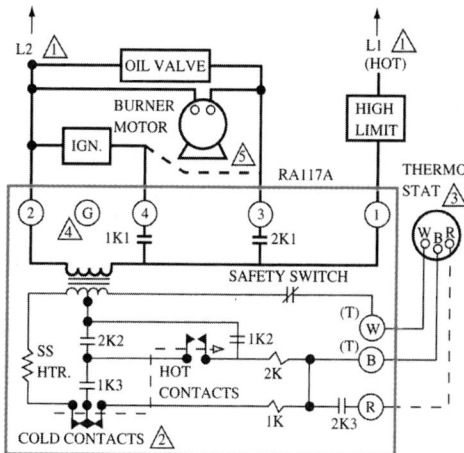

△1 POWER SUPPLY. PROVIDE DISCONNECT MEANS AND OVER-LOAD PROTECTION AS REQUIRED.

△2 CONTACTS BREAK IN SEQUENCE ON RISE IN TEMP.

△3 MAY BE CONTROLLED BY TWO-WIRE THERMOSTAT. CONNECT TO W AND B ONLY. TAPE LOOSE END OF RED WIRE, IF ANY.

△4 CONTROL CASE MUST BE CONNECTED TO EARTH GROUND. USE GREEN GROUNDING SCREW PROVIDED.

△5 TO REPLACE INTERMITTENT (FORMERLY CALLED CONSTANT) IGNITION DEVICE, WIRE IGNITION LEADWIRE TO TERMINAL 3 ON RA117A.

Figure 42-27 Wiring diagram of an oil burner primary control

safety switch. The operation of the control is by means of a slide clutch operating safety and holding contacts. The drive shaft at the top of the control provides the action for the slide clutch when moved by the expansion and contraction of the bimetallic element. Two relays are included, one to control the oil burner ignition transformer (relay 1A) and the other to control the oil burner motor (relay 2A). Low voltage thermostat terminals on the lower left and high voltage (120 V) on the lower right are separated by an insulated barrier. Figure 42-27 shows the internal wiring arrangement of the control as well as the burner motor and ignition transformer circuits, 120 V power supply, and 24 V thermostat circuit.

Following through the control circuit, the action of the cycle would be as follows: The thermostat, calling for heat, closes the circuit from the transformer through the safety switch,

Figure 42-26 Oil burner stack mounted primary control

through the thermostat, through relay coil 1K, through the right-hand cold contact, the left-hand cold contact, and the safety switch heater to the other side of the transformer.

Relay 1K pulls in closing contact 1K1, powering the ignition transformer; 1K2 energizes relay coil 2K and closing contact 1K3 to the center or common of the cold contacts.

When relay coil 2K is energized, it pulls in, closing contact 2K1, energizing the oil burner motor and oil valve (if used). Contact 2K2 removes the relays from the series circuit through the safety switch heater, reducing the amount of heat produced in the heater. If this action does not occur, the safety switch will open in a very short period of time, possibly 3–5 seconds. By removing the relay current from the safety switch circuit, the switch delay time is increased to 60–90 seconds.

The start of the oil burner produces hot flue gases from the heat exchanger over the bimetallic helix in the sensing tube. This rise in temperature forces the drive shaft forward, opening the left-hand cold contact and removing the safety switch heater from the circuit. A further rise in temperature (forward action of the drive shaft) closes the hot contact; this allows the oil burner motor and oil valve (if used) to continue to operate by passing relay contact 1K2.

Finally, the drive shaft moves forward enough to open the right-hand cold contact, dropping out relay 1K. This stops the ignition and keeps the oil burner operating through the hot contacts. If a flameout occurs or the burner shuts down from the action of the thermostat, the hot contact opens immediately upon a drop in flue gas temperature.

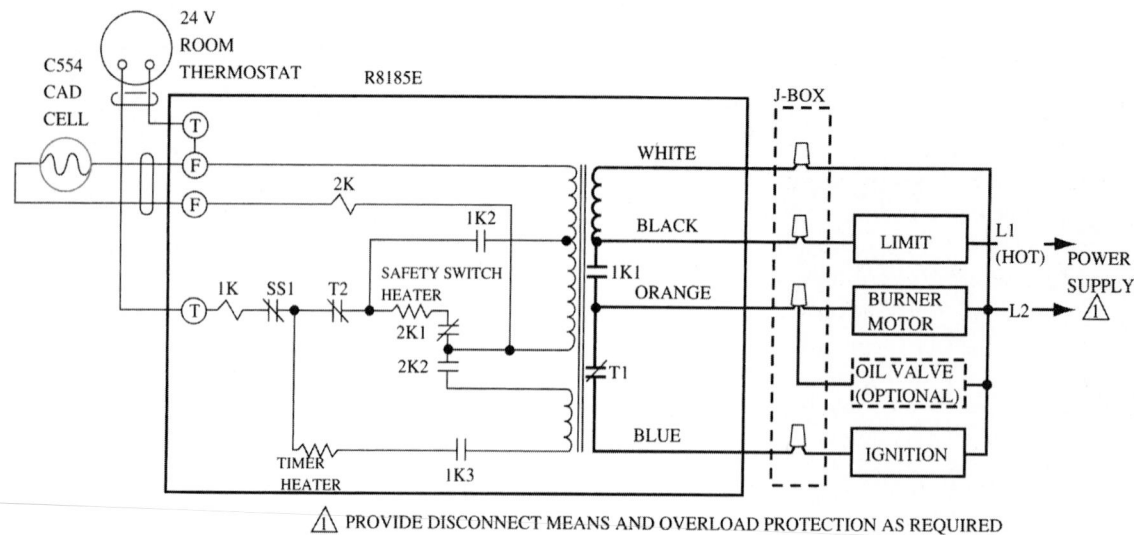

Figure 42-28 Oil burning wiring diagram, using a cad cell relay

Because contact 1K2 is open, the burner motor cannot operate until the cold contacts close, first the left side to energize the safety switch and then the right side to start the ignition oil burner motor cycle. By means of these lockout circuits, an explosive situation of spraying oil vapor into a white hot refractory can be prevented.

Flame Detector Relay Control

The stack mounted protector relay required extra wiring, as well as time and cost for manufacturing assembly or installation. To overcome this, a flame detection relay was developed. The cad cell is mounted directly in the oil burner housing and sees the light of the burner from the instant the flame is established. Two relays are used: 1K for control of the oil burner and ignition transformer, and 2K, the sensitive relay, controlled by the cadmium cell. Following the circuit action in the schematic in Figure 42-28, when the thermostat calls for heat and closes the contact between T and T, current flows from the transformer through the thermostat through relay coil 1K, safety switch, timer contact 2, the safety switch heater, and contact 2K1 to the other side of the transformer. This puts a higher voltage through the coil and safety switch heater. If the relay 1K fails to act, the safety switch will open in only a few seconds.

When relay 1K pulls in, however, contact 1K1 closes, energizing the oil burner motor, oil valve (if used), and the ignition transformer. Also, contact 1K2 closes, bypassing the safety switch heater, reducing its current draw, and increasing the safety switch action time. If no flame is established, the heater will continue to receive voltage and heat until the safety switch contact (SS1) opens and shuts down the system. The switch is manually reset.

When a flame is established, the light strikes the cadmium cell, and immediately reduces the resistance of the cell from over 10,000 Ω to about 1,500 Ω or less. The amount of current through relay coil 2K increases and the sensitive relay pulls in. This opens contact 2K1, which deenergizes the safety switch heater and energizes the timer heater through contact 1K3, which closed when relay 1K is pulled in. The timer heater now opens contact T1, shutting off the ignition transformer and the holding contact of the sensitive relay. This action will continue as long as burner operation is required.

If flame failure should occur, the cadmium cell resistance will increase, current flow through the sensitive relay will decrease, and the relay will drop out. This opens contact 2K2 which opens the circuit to relay 1K, and the burner shuts down.

The burner cannot come on until the timer heater has cooled sufficiently to close the ignition contact T1 and the relay 1K circuit contact T2. This ensures that the unit will have sufficient time to vent the furnace heat exchanger of unburned vapors as well as ensuring ignition at the next startup.

Most furnaces today still use the cad cell to sense the flame, but they now use electronic switching and circuitry rather than heaters and sensitive relays. The operating principle remains the same: the reduced resistance of the cad cell when it sees light. These controls typically lock out after an ignition failure and must be manually reset.

42.15 OIL SAFETY VALVES

Many fuel oil systems are installed so that the oil tank is at a higher elevation than the furnace. This makes getting the fuel to the burner easier. Unfortunately, it also makes it possible for any leaks in between the tank and the pump to leak oil continuously, especially when the furnace is off. In a worst case scenario, an entire tank of oil can leak out. The purpose of the oil safety valve is to prevent line leaks from draining the tank and causing environmental damage. Many state and local codes require oil safety valves. Refer to the latest edition of the National Fire Protection Association Standard (NFPA 31) for the installation of oil burner equipment.

The oil safety valve is mounted in the suction line to the oil pump as close to the tank as possible and no more than 3 ft above the fuel unit. The valve is normally closed and will only open if there is a vacuum on the outlet side of the valve. When the burner is off, if there is no vacuum, then the valve remains closed and oil flow is stopped. If the fuel lines are tight, a vacuum is created when the burner starts, allowing the oil to flow. However, air will be sucked into any leaks, reducing the vacuum on the line and keeping the valve closed. Since the valve remains closed, oil will not leak out. This not only prevents leaks, but also encourages customers to get the leaky lines repaired because the furnace will not fire. Without the oil safety valve, small leaks can be ignored because the unit will still operate and heat.

42.16 OIL VALVES

For oil to burn cleanly, it needs to be atomized and mixed with combustion air. Incomplete combustion will result if the oil is not delivered at the correct pressure or air is not available in sufficient quantity. Ideally, when the oil burner starts it should reach operating speed and have the correct amount of combustion air volume before oil is supplied and combustion is established. When the burner shuts off, the oil flow and combustion should shut off instantly. Both of these are accomplished by the oil valve. A delay type oil valve may be installed between the oil pump and the burner firing assembly. This type of valve, although wired to be energized at the same time as the oil burner motor (wired in parallel), has a delayed opening. This allows full operation of the burner blower and pump before oil flow is allowed. A thermistor is wired in series with the oil valve coil circuit. The thermistor has a high resistance when it is cold, limiting the current to the coil on startup. The voltage across the thermistor causes it to heat up, and its resistance drops as its temperature rises. The thermistor's reduced resistance causes an increase in the valve coil circuit. After 8–10 seconds, the current increases sufficiently to cause the magnetic coil pull to open the valve. The valve acts the same as any other type of solenoid valve on cutoff; it closes immediately upon deenergizing the valve and motor. Thus, instant cutoff of combustion occurs.

UNIT 42—SUMMARY

Today's oil heating systems are more efficient and adaptable than the large, inefficient furnaces from previous decades. Now oil furnaces are available in smaller, more efficient furnaces with efficiencies up to 95%. Two stage furnaces, condensing furnaces, sealed combustion furnaces, oil fired unit heaters, and furnaces designed to burn waste oil are some of the innovations in oil heat.

Fuel oil must be atomized to be burned. Because of this, oil furnaces have more parts and are somewhat more complex than gas furnaces. Oil burner components include an oil pump, a combustion air blower, a burner motor, a nozzle, an ignition transformer, electrodes, a primary control, and a cad cell. The oil is forced through a nozzle at high pressure, atomizing it. At the same time, air is forced into the combustion chamber where it mixes with the oil spray. The transformer delivers 10,000 V AC to the electrodes, which create a large electric arc that ignites the oil. The cad cell senses the light from the flames, resistance drops and allows the primary control to continue operation. Should the flames extinguish, the cad cell resistance increases, and the primary control shuts off the burner motor.

WORK ORDERS

Service Ticket 4201

Customer Complaint: Expensive Heating Bills

Equipment: Propane Unit Heater

Precision Auto, located in rural Wisconsin, has asked their local heating contractor if there is a less expensive way for them to heat their garage. They are using propane fired unit heaters which run a lot in the winter. The sales consultant suggests a waste oil fired furnace. The waste oil furnace can use old motor oil, making their fuel free. In addition to saving on heating bills, they will save on used oil disposal fees.

Service Ticket 4202

Customer Complaint: New Construction

Equipment: Central Hot Water Boiler

The architect for a new high rise being planned has asked for ideas on keeping heating costs controlled. She wants to use a large central boiler with hot water distributed throughout the building. She was considering a natural gas boiler, but the local gas company wants to put the complex on an interruptible service in exchange for favorable prices. The sales consultant suggests using a boiler fired with number 6 fuel oil. The equipment will require a heated storage tank and the oil will have to be preheated before combustion, but the price per Btu is much lower for the number 6 fuel oil.

Service Ticket 4203

Customer Complaint: Furnace Replacement

Equipment: Oil Fired Furnace

Dr. Greene has just purchased a house in the historic district which has an old oil fired furnace. He wants to replace the aging, inefficient furnace with a modern, energy efficient gas furnace. The sales consultant mentions that he does not have to switch to gas to get an efficient furnace and suggests a 95% efficient condensing oil furnace.

Service Ticket 4204

Customer Complaint: New Construction

Equipment: Mid-Efficiency Oil Fired Furnace

A developer has asked a contractor for ideas for efficient heating for the homes in her subdivision in rural Canada. The developer stresses that operating efficiency is important, but so is keeping costs controlled. The sales consultant suggests a mid-efficiency oil fired furnace as a good compromise between efficiency and cost. The consultant points out that a mid-efficiency oil fired furnace operates about 5% more efficiently than a mid-efficiency gas fired furnace.

UNIT 42—REVIEW QUESTIONS

1. List the grades of fuel oil and give a brief description of each type.
2. What is the difference between distillate oil and a residual oil?
3. How are nozzles rated?
4. What does oil viscosity mean?
5. Which grade of fuel oil has the highest viscosity?
6. Why can oil furnaces operate at efficiencies between 80% and 90% without condensing water in the heat exchanger or vent?
7. List the available oil furnace configurations.
8. Compare the efficiency of a mid-efficiency oil furnace to an older traditional oil furnace.
9. What is the advantage of a high static oil burner?
10. What are some of the challenges in building a condensing oil furnace?
11. How is an oil furnace heat exchanger shaped?
12. What is the purpose of the refractory?
13. What is the output pressure of a furnace oil pump?
14. What is the difference between a one pipe and a two pipe oil delivery system?
15. What is the purpose of the oil safety valve?
16. What is the purpose of the barometric damper?
17. What voltage does the ignition transformer provide to the electrodes?
18. How does a cad cell sense the flames?
19. What is the purpose of the oil valve in an oil burner?
20. What does the primary control do?
21. What can be done to prevent moisture from condensing on the inside of an oil storage tank that is located outdoors?
22. What are the two pipes at the top of an oil storage tank?
23. What is the heating value of number 2 fuel oil?
24. What type of venting is used for oil furnaces?

UNIT 43

Oil Furnace and Boiler Service

OBJECTIVES

After completing this unit you will be able to:

- list the operating sequence of a typical oil fired furnace.
- describe the procedure for purging the oil lines on a new furnace.
- list the operating characteristics required to determine combustion efficiency.
- explain the relationship between CO_2 flue gas percentage and combustion efficiency.
- list the items that should be checked as part of planned maintenance on an oil burner.

43.1 INTRODUCTION

Annual service is a must for oil burners. Oil must be atomized before burning because oil is a liquid fuel. The process of atomizing the oil, mixing the combustion air with the oil, and delivering the correct amount of both oil and air has many variables that all must be correct for the process to work. Some components, such as the nozzle and oil filter, need to be changed regularly. Operating characteristics such as the oil pressure, smoke spot readings, stack temperature, and CO_2 percentage need to be checked. Failure to perform the necessary annual maintenance will result in inefficient operation and dirty combustion.

43.2 OIL FURNACE WIRING DIAGRAM

Figure 43-1 shows a component location diagram for an oil furnace, while Figure 43-2 shows a connection diagram of the same furnace. The primary control is the main operating control of the furnace. It controls the oil burner motor, the ignition transformer, and provides flame safety. Flames are proved using a cad cell flame sensor that senses the light of the flame. Safety against the blower circulating vent gases is provided by a blower door switch in series with the low voltage circuit to the thermostat. Over temperature safety is provided by the limit. Power to the primary control passes through the limit control. If the furnace reaches the limit temperature, the limit will open to shut off the power to the primary control. This in turn will shut down the burner to prevent overheating the unit. The fan switch is in series with the blower motor to control the operation of the fan. After the burner lights and the furnace has warmed up, the fan control closes to operate the fan. Properly set, this control will close at 125–130°F to start the blower motor. The fan continues to run after the burner stops, and the fan switch opens at 95–100°F to stop the blower motor.

43.3 OPERATING SEQUENCE

The step by step operating sequence is:

1. The room thermostat closes to initiate a call for heat in the conditioned area.
2. If the blower door switch is closed, this causes current flow from the 40 VA transformer through the control circuits to the burner motor relay coil.
3. The relay contacts close allowing current flow from the H or hot side of the supply line through the limit switch to the burner motor and ignition transformer.
4. At the same time, two other 24 V control circuits exist. One circuit is through the cad cell and the safety relay coil. The second circuit is through the safety relay normally closed contacts and the safety heater.
5. The lack of a flame causes a high resistance in the cad cell which drops nearly all the voltage in its circuit, so the safety relay does not operate. The relay's normally closed contacts remain closed and the safety heater starts producing heat. Note that the safety heater is simply a time delay. The safety heater acts upon the safety switch contacts which are opened by the expansion of a bimetallic element. If the burner does not light, the heater will remain on and continue to produce heat until the bimetallic element expands to the point where the safety switch contacts open and the burner motor shuts down.
6. The ignition transformer establishes a spark across the electrodes located above the nozzle. The spark at this time is only $\frac{1}{8}$ in long, the distance between the electrode tips.
7. The burner motor, which is energized at the same time as the ignition transformer, also operates the combustion air blower. It reaches full load speed within 1 second. When the full amount of air is delivered by the blower, the ignition spark is blown forward into the oil spray and the oil is ignited. This occurs directly in front of the nozzle and quickly expands into a full burst of fire in the combustion chamber.
8. The electrical resistance of the cad cell located in the fire tube decreases when the light from the fire reaches the

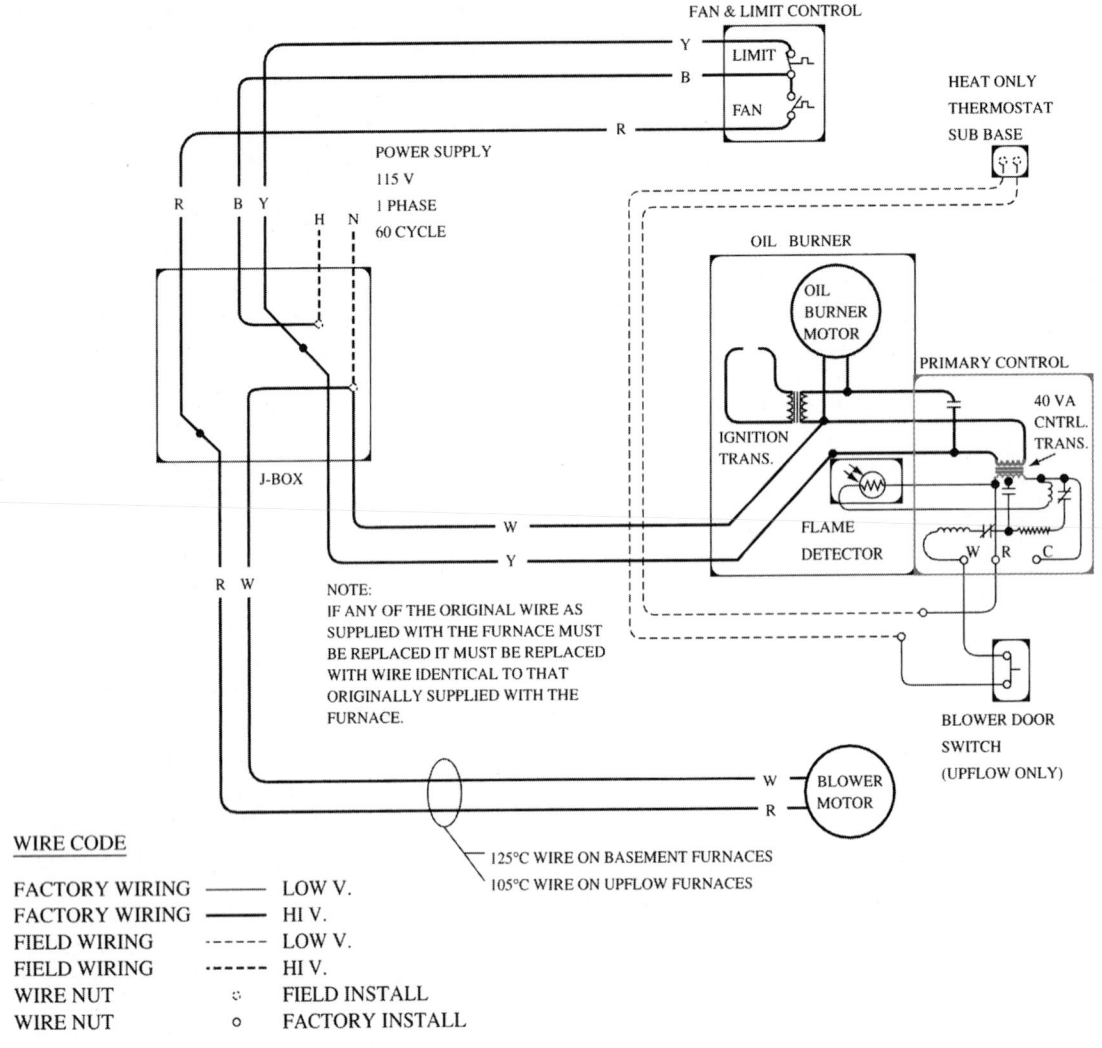

Figure 43-1 Wiring diagram for typical oil burner control system
(Courtesy of Lennox Industries Inc.)

cad cell. This decrease in resistance increases the current flow through the safety relay, allowing the safety relay to operate.

9. The normally closed contacts of the safety relay open to deenergize the safety heater and prevent the safety switch from opening.

10. The heat exchanger begins to heat up and when the temperature reaches approximately 130°F, the fan switch contacts close and the indoor blower comes on.

11. The conditioned space temperature will begin to rise and eventually reach the setpoint of the thermostat. At this point the thermostat opens the circuit to the primary control.

12. The primary control shuts off the burner motor and ignition transformer, shutting the flame down.

13. The indoor blower continues to run until the heat exchanger cools to approximately 100°F. At this point

the fan switch contacts open and the indoor blower turns off.

43.4 STARTUP

The initial system startup requires more than just turning on the burner. The first requirement is to purge the fuel system of air. This procedure is different for the single pipe system, where the fuel supply is above the burner; and the two pipe system, where the fuel supply is below the burner.

On the single pipe system where the oil supply is above the burner, it is only necessary to purge the air from the oil filter, fuel line, and fuel pump. The purge valve is located on the pump, Figure 43-3. It is only necessary to open this valve until the air in the system starts to flow out. Usually, this is one half to one turn of the valve counterclockwise. When the

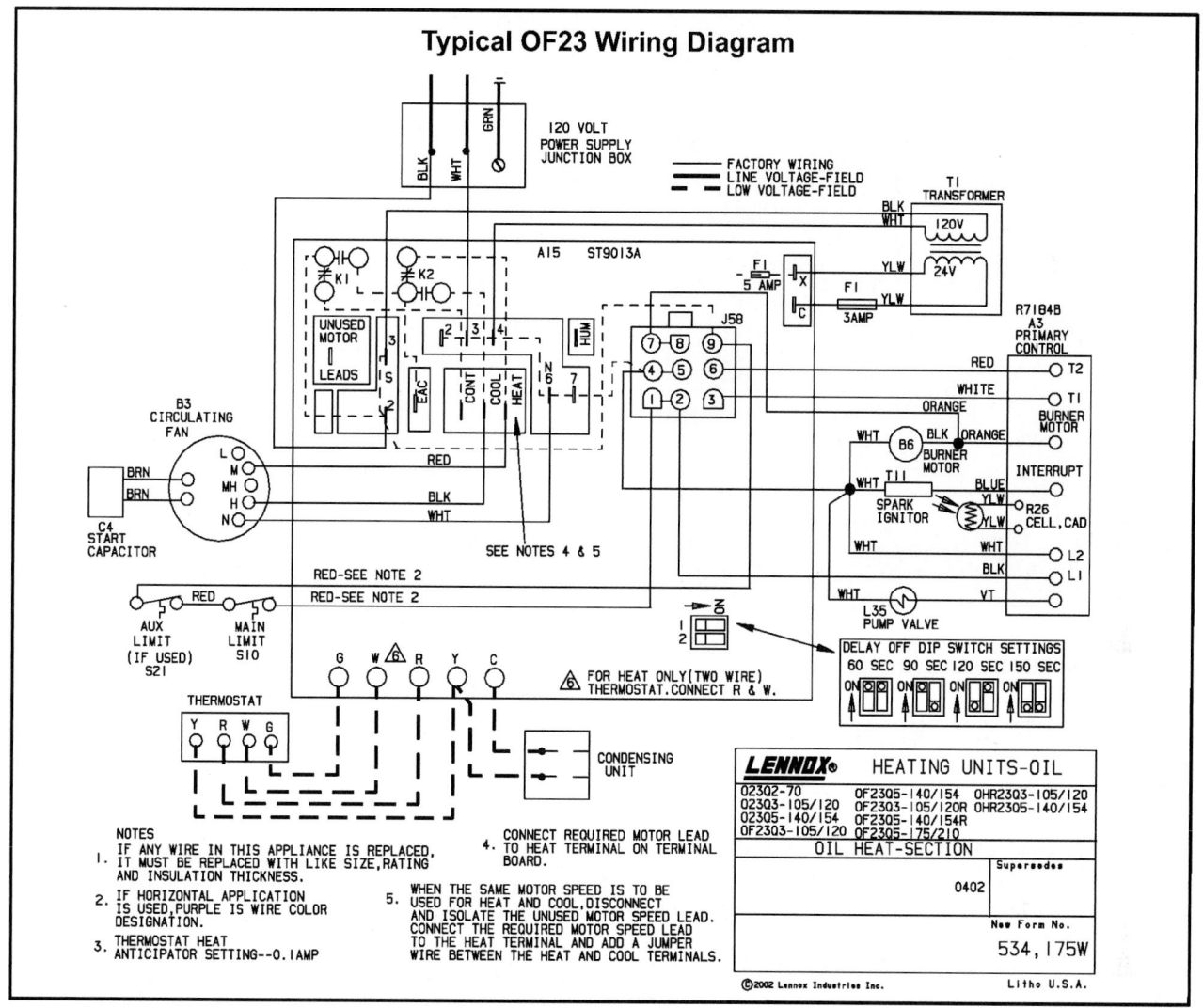

Figure 43-2 Wiring diagram for the Lennox OF23 system
(Courtesy of Lennox Industries Inc.)

air is out and oil starts to flow out, close the valve to prevent oil leakage.

SERVICE TIP

Use this tip during purging. Place a clear plastic hose on the air purge valve and put the other end of the hose in a container. Run the pump until the hose is full of oil with no air bubbles.

In a two pipe system the system is self purging. The pump will force the air down the oil return line and back into the tank. However, it may take longer than the cycle time of the safety switch to purge the system and the burner may shut down before a flame is established. It is then necessary to allow the safety switch to cool and reset before the burner can be started again. This must be repeated until the oil lines are completely purged of air and the fire is established.

SERVICE TIP

It is good practice when bleeding a two pipe system to have your pump gauge connected. This will ensure that no oil has reached the chamber and will also assist you in knowing when the oil has reached the fuel unit.

CAUTION

Repeated startup and shutdown of the burner can lead to a buildup of oil in the firebox. This oil can ignite all at once and cause a flareback which can damage the furnace and cause personal injury to someone standing close by. If you are trying to purge air from a two pipe system, make sure that excessive amounts of oil are not collecting in the firebox. If the air is not purged after more than a few attempts, check to see if there are other operational problems.

Figure 43-3 Furnace oil pump vent

43.5 EFFICIENCY TESTING

Checking the combustion efficiency is an important part of servicing an oil fired furnace. Efficiency testing is even more crucial for oil furnaces because there are more variables that may need to be adjusted in the field. The flame efficiency increases as the refractory temperature rises. The burner is operating at peak efficiency when the surface temperature of the refractory is white-hot. At this point efficiency tests can be taken. To reach these conditions, the burner should be allowed to operate at least 5 minutes.

Figure 43-4 shows the label on all new models listing the expected efficiency.

To use for future reference, a test sheet should be filled out recording the conditions to which the burner was adjusted. The following information should be included on the test sheet.

Data

Make of oil burner _____
Model No. _____ Serial No. _____
Nozzle: Size (gal/hr) _____ Type _____
Angle _____
Refractory: Shape _____

Operation

Over fire draft _____
Stack draft _____
Heat exchanger flow resistance _____
CO_2% _____
Net stack temperature _____
Efficiency _____
Smoke number _____

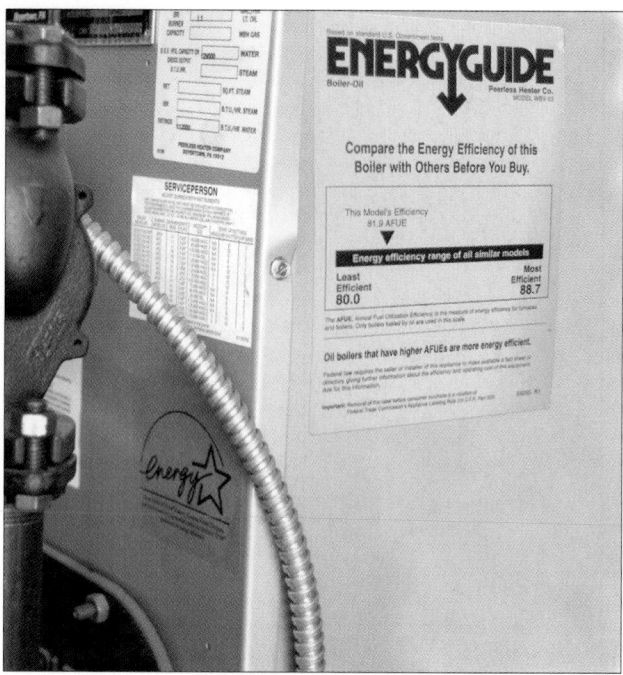

Figure 43-4 Energy efficiency sticker

Air temperature (supply plenum) _____
Air temperature (return plenum)_____
Air temperature (rise) _____

The make, model number, and serial number of the burner are required when referring to the manufacturer's recommendations. Recording the nozzle size, type, and spray angle will ensure the unit has been checked for proper input as well as spray angle for the shape of the refractory. A round or square refractory generally requires an 80° or 90° spray angle. A rectangular refractory generally requires a 45–60° spray angle, depending on the length of the refractory. With the unit operating and the refractory up to white-hot, operating tests can be made. Figure 43-5 shows a typical completed efficiency test sheet.

TECH TIP

Carbon or soot sublimes at a temperature slightly above 800°F. Subliming is the process of changing from a solid to a vapor without becoming a liquid. This means that the area of refractory material that is carbon free was at a temperature slightly above 800°F. The line where the carbon first begins to show is the beginning of the area that was below 800°F during system operation. If you observe a furnace firebox that has far less carbon-free refractory material, this may be an indication of a low flame temperature.

COMBUSTION EFFICIENCY TEST RESULTS

DATE *1-30-05*

NAME _____

ADDRESS *58 Woodward Rd*

TOWN *Milford*   PHONE: _____

	BEFORE	AFTER
SMOKE		*0*
CO_2		*8*
DRAFT		*104*
NET TEMP		*450*
EFFICIENCY		*77 1/4 %*
DRAFT O.F.		*102*
CO_2 O.F.		*—*
NOZZLE SIZE		*100*
NOZ. ANGLE		*80*
NOZ. PATTERN		*B*

OIL COMPANY, INC.

SER. TECH. *Rob*

DEALER COPY

Figure 43-5 Efficiency inspection tag

43.6 OVER FIRE DRAFT

The first test should be for over fire draft using a draft gauge such as those pictured in Figure 43-6 and Figure 43-7. Insert the test pipe for the gauge through the $\frac{1}{4}$ in hole in the observation port over the burner until the end of the pipe is beyond the inner edge of the combustion chamber. To accomplish this, it is sometimes necessary to substitute a longer piece of $\frac{1}{4}$ in copper tubing for the gauge probe pipe. This test should result in a minimum pressure of 0.02 in wc to −0.04 in wc to ensure the proper draft for best operation. If the manufacturer of the unit does not specify the over fire draft, it is best to start at a draft control setting of −0.04 in wc.

Some manufacturers specify stack draft for a setting. This means that the flow resistance of the heat exchanger must be taken into account for burner operation. By measuring both the over fire draft and stack draft on the new unit, the design draft resistance can be determined. To produce a negative pressure of a given amount over the fire, the stack draft must be a greater negative amount. The difference between the over fire draft and the stack draft will be the heat exchanger draft flow resistance. For example, if it is necessary

Figure 43-6 Draft gauge for measuring draft over the oil burner flame
(Courtesy of Bacharach, Inc.)

to have a stack draft of −0.06 in wc to produce an over fire draft of −0.04 in wc, the heat exchanger resistance would be 0.02 in wc. When checking the unit performance after a period of operation, if the heat exchanger flow resistance has doubled, it is necessary to mechanically clean the soot from the heat exchanger flue passages.

Figure 43-7 Stack draft gauge
(Courtesy of Bacharach, Inc.)

A negative pressure must be maintained on the heat exchanger to prevent the products of combustion from being forced into the occupied area. Not only do they carry free carbon or soot, but they also contain a high percentage of CO. This is especially true at startup. Therefore, a minimum over fire draft of –0.02 in wc is usually required for proper operation, with –0.04 in wc to be on the safe side.

The draft can be adjusted using the weight on the barometric damper. In general, the draft will be increased when the barometric damper closes, and decreased when the barometric damper opens. Particular attention should be paid to the over fire draft and the stack draft on a new installation. Make sure the weight is in the correct position with respect to a horizontal or vertical run. The damper weight should be adjusted to ensure the draft is in the range specified by the manufacturer.

Some units can operate with a positive pressure of over fire and it is important to be able to identify this type and make adjustments according to the manufacturer's specifications.

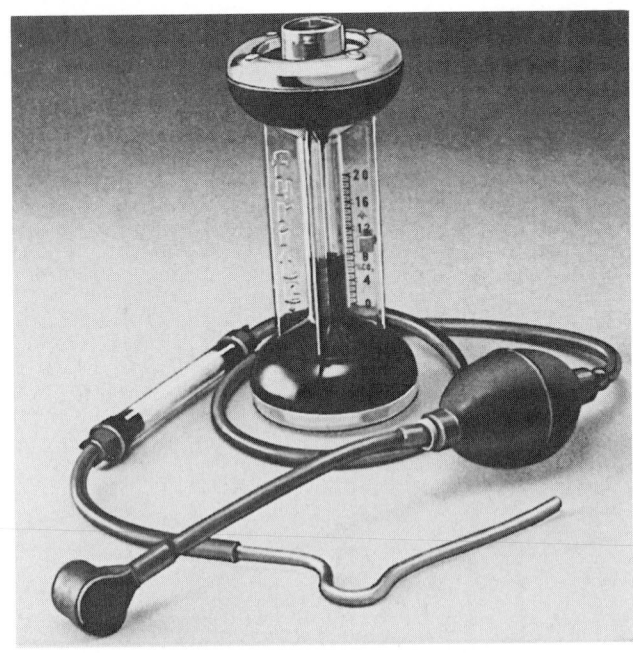

Figure 43-8 Carbon dioxide (CO_2) analyzer
(Courtesy of Bacharach, Inc.)

CAUTION

A carbon monoxide (CO) detector is a good recommendation for the homeowner to purchase and install near any combustion equipment, whether it is gas or oil. Carbon monoxide is often referred to as the silent killer because it can go unnoticed in a home for a long period of time if the home is not protected with a carbon monoxide monitor.

43.7 CO_2 RANGES

The theoretically perfect mix of fuel and air to burn completely with no fuel or air remaining is called stoichiometric combustion. The CO_2 percentage in the flue gas will be 15.5% at this point. The CO_2 percentage drops off from 15.5% if there is not enough air or if there is air remaining. For safety reasons, the correct air adjustment will always result in some amount of excess air. Therefore, the CO_2 percentage should be less than 15.5%. How much lower depends upon the burner design. In general, more efficient burners should be adjusted to produce higher CO_2 percentages than less efficient burners.

In order to obtain a good sample of flue gas, the CO_2 sample is taken at least 6 in upstream of the barometric draft damper and a distance twice the diameter of the flue pipe from an elbow. This will help to avoid the possibility of outside air mixing with the flue gas sample. Again, this may mean a longer sampling tube on the analyzer. Use a CO_2 analyzer such as the ones pictured in Figures 43-8 and 43-9 following the manufacturer's instructions.

Common operating CO_2 percentages for different types of burners are:

- **Old Style Gun Burners**   These burners have no special air handling parts other than an end cone and a stabilizer. A CO_2 reading of 7% to 9% should be obtained unless a CO_2 reading in this range results in more than

Figure 43-9 Electronic CO_2 tester

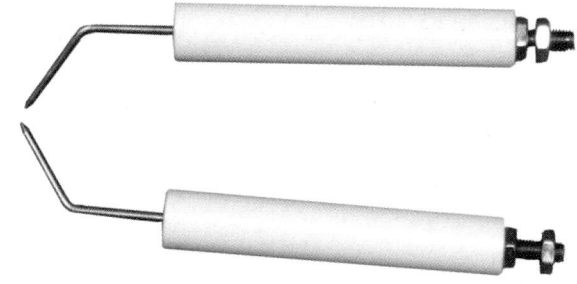

Figure 43-19 Oil furnace electrodes

Figure 43-20 Ignition transformer

Figure 43-22 Mitco ignition tester
(Courtesy of Mitco Manufacturing, Andrews S.C.)

SAFETY TIP

The output of the ignition transformer cannot be tested with a standard set of leads. A high voltage probe is required. Attempting to test the ignition transformer output with regular multimeter leads will destroy your meter and possibly injure you.

SERVICE TIP

Replacing the nozzle as part of your routine maintenance is important because over a season the nozzle bore will be worn slightly larger as the result of oil flow. As this wear occurs, the furnace efficiency is affected. Replacing the nozzle each season ensures that the furnace will operate properly.

14. Test the oil pump outlet for pressure.
15. Test the pump cutoff to verify a complete fuel shutoff. It should shut off at 80 psig or not drop off more than 20% of the pump's operating pressure.
16. Check the amperage draw of the oil burner motor. The amp reading should be under the name plate rating.
17. Test the cad cell primary control and cad cell flame detector eye.
18. Turn the fuel on and start the burner.

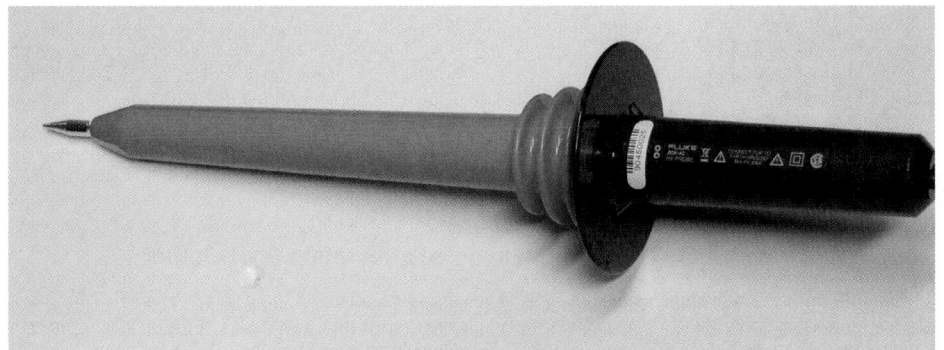

Figure 43-21 High voltage probe

UNIT 43—SUMMARY

Oil systems can burn cleanly if properly maintained. The fuel line filter and nozzle should be replaced annually. Operational characteristics that should be tested include the oil pump inlet vacuum, the oil pump outlet pressure, the stack temperature, the CO_2 flue gas percentage, and the burner motor amp draw. The combustion airflow should be adjusted to obtain a smoke spot number of less than 2 while still achieving the correct CO_2 range in the flue gas. The money spent on keeping the system operating correctly will be repaid in lower operating costs and longer equipment life.

┌── WORK ORDERS

Service Ticket 4301

New Furnace Startup

Equipment: Oil Furnace Using a Two Pipe Fuel Delivery System

Furnace Is Above the Oil Tank

A technician attempts to purge a new two pipe system by operating the system. After pushing the reset button twice, the technician inspects the combustion chamber for oil and finds none. Next, the technician installs a vacuum gauge on the suction side of the oil pump. With the pump running, the vacuum is only about 1 in Hg. The technician inspects the line for leaks and finds that the suction line connection is loose at the tank. The connection is tightened and the vacuum rechecked. This time the vacuum reads 10 in Hg. The furnace fires after pushing the reset button twice.

Service Ticket 4302

Annual Maintenance Equipment: Oil Fired Furnace with a Flame Retention Burner

A technician is called to perform an annual maintenance service on a flame retention burner. During the efficiency testing portion of the maintenance, the CO_2 reading is 9% and the smoke spot reading is 0. The technician remembers that while 9% is fine for an older style burner, it is too low for a flame retention burner. Leaving it this way would result in inefficient operation. After reducing the combustion air, the CO_2% increases to 12% and the smoke spot remains 0.

Service Ticket 4303

Customer Complaint: High Operating Cost

Equipment: Oil Furnace with Older Style Cast Iron Burner

A technician is asked to look at an older furnace whose owner is complaining about the operating cost. The technician operates the furnace and takes CO_2%, stack temperature, over fire draft, and stack draft measurements. The combustion efficiency seems appropriate for a furnace its age, but the over fire draft is low, only –0.01 in wc while the stack draft is fine, –0.04 in wc. The technician pulls the burner out and inspects the heat exchanger. The heat exchanger is covered with a thin layer of fine soot. The technician explains to the homeowner that the soot is acting like insulation, reducing the efficiency of the furnace by keeping the heat from transferring to the air flowing over the heat exchanger. After cleaning the heat exchanger, the over fire draft improves to 0.02 in wc.

Service Ticket 4304

Customer Complaint: Operating Cost

Equipment: Oil Furnace with Newer Style Gun Burner

A technician is called to check a furnace which is operating inefficiently. The customer says that a previous technician had done an annual maintenance service on the burner, but left no paperwork. The furnace is operating with a low smoke spot of 0 to 1, but the CO_2 percentage is only 7%, indicating too much combustion air. The owner asks the technician about the CO_2 analyzer and remarks that the other technician did not have one. After reducing the combustion air, the CO_2% increases to 10% and the smoke spot still reads between 0 and 1. The technician explains that it is possible to have too much combustion air, reducing efficiency.

Service Ticket 4305

Customer Complaint: Poor Heat, Smoky Vent Gases

Equipment: Newer Gun-Style Burner Oil Furnace

A technician is called to do an annual maintenance on an oil fired furnace. The customer mentions that the furnace is not heating as well as in previous years and that the vent gases are smoky. The technician inspects the heat exchanger and finds that it needs cleaning. The electrodes appear as if oil has been hitting them. The technician cleans the heat exchanger, replaces the nozzle, and cleans and adjusts the electrodes. The smoky flue gas clears up. The technician explains that the oil mist should not hit anything; if it does, incomplete combustion and smoke will result. The soot created acts like insulation, reducing the furnace efficiency even more. Changing the nozzle insures a good spray angle and proper atomization while adjusting the electrodes insures the oil will not hit them.

Service Ticket 4306

Replacement Unit Startup

Equipment: Flame Retention Style Burner

A new technician was sent to perform a system startup on a new oil furnace that has just been installed to replace an older furnace. While taking over fire draft readings, the technician notices that the readings are lower than the manufacturer's recommendations and that the barometric damper is staying wide open most of the time. After adjusting the weight on the barometric damper so that it stays shut more, the over fire draft increases to the manufacturer's recommended 0.02 in wc draft.

UNIT 43—REVIEW QUESTIONS

1. How does the refractory temperature affect the combustion efficiency?
2. What are normal on and off temperature ranges for the settings on the fan control?
3. Describe the procedure for purging a single pipe gravity feed system.
4. Describe the procedure for purging a two pipe system.
5. What pieces of information are necessary to determine combustion efficiency?
6. What can cause the heat exchanger flow resistance to increase after several years of operation?
7. Why must a negative pressure be maintained on the heat exchanger?
8. How is the door switch wired into the system in Figure 43-1?
9. What opens the contact on the safety switch in Figure 43-1?
10. Why does soot accumulation on the inside of the heat exchanger reduce system efficiency?
11. How does the cad cell operate to secure the burner in the event of a flame out?
12. What smoke spot number represents correct combustion?
13. How is net stack temperature calculated?
14. Discuss the relationship between the over fire draft and the stack draft.
15. What is the CO_2 percentage for a perfect stoichiometric mix of oil and air?
16. Why do we not try to adjust the CO_2 percentage to the perfect stoichiometric percentage?
17. Why does excess combustion air reduce combustion efficiency?
18. How should the output of an oil furnace ignition transformer be tested?
19. What components on an oil furnace should be changed annually?
20. What angle nozzle is usually used with a round combustion chamber?

UNIT 44

Residential Oil Heating Installation

OBJECTIVES

After completing this unit you will be able to:

- calculate the minimum required combustion air openings.
- discuss common applications for different oil furnace configurations.
- discuss oil tank installation.
- discuss factors in oil piping.
- calculate the equivalent length of a chimney connector.
- explain how a hydronic zone system works.

44.1 INTRODUCTION

Oil furnaces and boilers provide clean, reliable heat when properly sized and configured for the application, installed correctly, and maintained regularly. Shortchanging any of these three will lead to dirty, inefficient operation. Proper application, configuration, and installation are the first steps in providing a clean, reliable oil heating system that will serve the customer for many years.

44.2 EQUIPMENT SELECTION

Factors to be considered when selecting an oil furnace include

- Furnace location.
- Required heating capacity.
- Desired efficiency.
- Size of air conditioning equipment.

Location

The proposed furnace location will determine the furnace configuration. If the furnace is to be installed in an attic, a lowboy would not work. Table 44-1 summarizes the available oil furnace configurations and their typical applications.

Heating Capacity

The required heating capacity should be determined by using a recognized load calculation method, such as outlined in the ACCA Manual J. The furnace heating capacity should be the lowest standard capacity that is at least equal to the calculated required capacity. Since furnaces are only available in a few sizes, some over sizing is acceptable. Gross over sizing should

Table 44.1 Furnace Application

Configuration	Typical application
Lowboy	Basement, particularly basements with low head room
Upflow	Basement with good clearance; utility room or closet with duct in attic
Downflow	Utility room or closet with duct in crawl space
Horizontal	Attic or crawl space with duct in same space as furnace
Multipoise	Usually any of the above applications

be avoided because furnaces operate most efficiently with longer running cycles than with several short on and off cycles. Note that the heating capacity is listed as the output or bonnet capacity, not the firing rate.

A range of capacities can be achieved with the same burner by changing the nozzle. Table 44-2 shows the capacities available with one model furnace using the same burner and changing the nozzle size.

Efficiency

Oil furnaces are now available in efficiencies as high as 95% AFUE. The efficiencies and capacities available may be different from one configuration to another. The efficiency can impact the installation. If a condensing type furnace is chosen, the venting is different than for noncondensing models. Also, condensing furnaces require drains; noncondensing furnaces do not.

Table 44.2 Firing Capacity with Beckett AFG-F3 Burner

Firing rate (Btu/hr)	Firing rate (gph)	Nozzle
70,000	0.5	0.50 gph 70-W
91,000	0.65	0.65 gph 70-W
105,000	0.75	0.75 gph 70-B
119,000	0.85	0.85 gph 70-B
140,000	1.00	1.00 gph 70-W

Air Conditioning Requirements

If an air conditioner is to be installed with the oil furnace, the airflow capacity of the furnace must be adequate for the size of the air conditioner. Most manufacturers have furnaces that are considered heating-only furnaces. These furnaces do not have blower motors capable of moving the higher airflow required for air conditioning. If the furnace will be used to supply the airflow for an air conditioning system, make certain that the furnace airflow capacity meets the requirements of the air conditioning system.

44.3 LOCATING OIL TANKS

The oil tank may be located outside above ground, outside underground, or inside in a basement. Regardless of location, the installation of the fuel oil tank and connecting piping must conform to the standards of the National Fire Protection Association (NFPA) standard 31 and to local code requirements. Figure 44-1 shows a typical fuel oil storage tank.

Typically, most residential storage tanks are located in the basement. Regulations and space permitting, the oil tank can be located indoors as shown in Figure 44-2. The tank is required to be at least 5 ft from any flames or heat producing equipment. Note the use of a shutoff valve and a filter to catch impurities. This application uses a single pipe system because the burner is below the oil supply.

Figure 44-3 shows an installation with the oil tank buried in the ground. This installation uses both suction and return lines. In some instances a two stage fuel pump with a two pipe system is used if the oil supply is below the level of the burner. This is not a strict requirement as many residential applications with underground storage tanks operate with a single line and a single stage fuel unit.

If the oil tank is installed below ground, it is important to keep it filled with oil during periods when the ground is saturated with water. Otherwise, a high level of groundwater may force the oil tank to float upward. A heavy concrete cover over the tank may be advisable to help prevent the tank from floating. Copper piping may provide flexibility if ground movement should occur.

TECH TIP

Because of environmental concerns, many local and state governments have outlawed the installation of oil storage tanks below ground. Check the local building codes to see whether or not it is possible to install a tank underground. In some localities, existing underground tanks are not allowed to be replaced.

The suction produced by the fuel pump is measured in inches of mercury vacuum. Generally, 1 in of vacuum is required for each foot of vertical lift and for every 10 ft of horizontal supply piping. The vacuum required for lifting the oil due to the combined resistance of vertical lift and piping length should never be allowed to exceed 6 in Hg vacuum with a single stage single pipe, 12 in Hg with a single stage two-pipe, or 17 in Hg with a two stage two-pipe. If the vacuum at the pump exceeds these limits, entrained air in the oil will expand and cause capacity and noise problems.

If the oil tank is placed outdoors above ground, firm footings must be provided. The exposed tank and piping are also subject to condensation of water vapor and the possibility of freezing.

44.4 OIL WARM AIR FURNACE INSTALLATION

Oil furnace installations should follow the manufacturer's instructions and all state and local codes. NFPA 31, *Standard for the Installation of Oil Burning Equipment,* is an excellent resource and is referenced in many state codes.

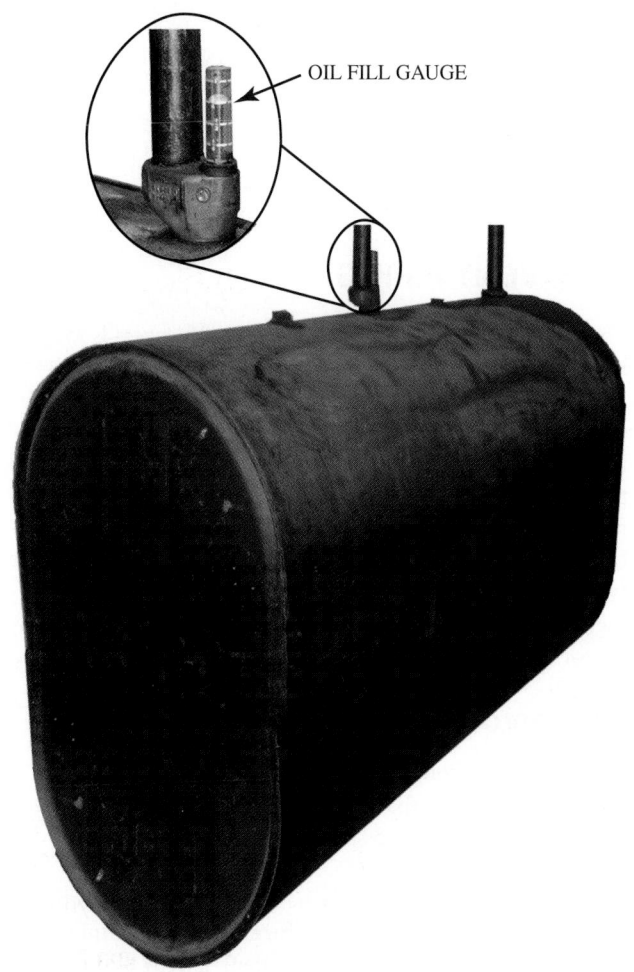

OIL FILL GAUGE

Figure 44-1 Oil storage tank and fill gauge

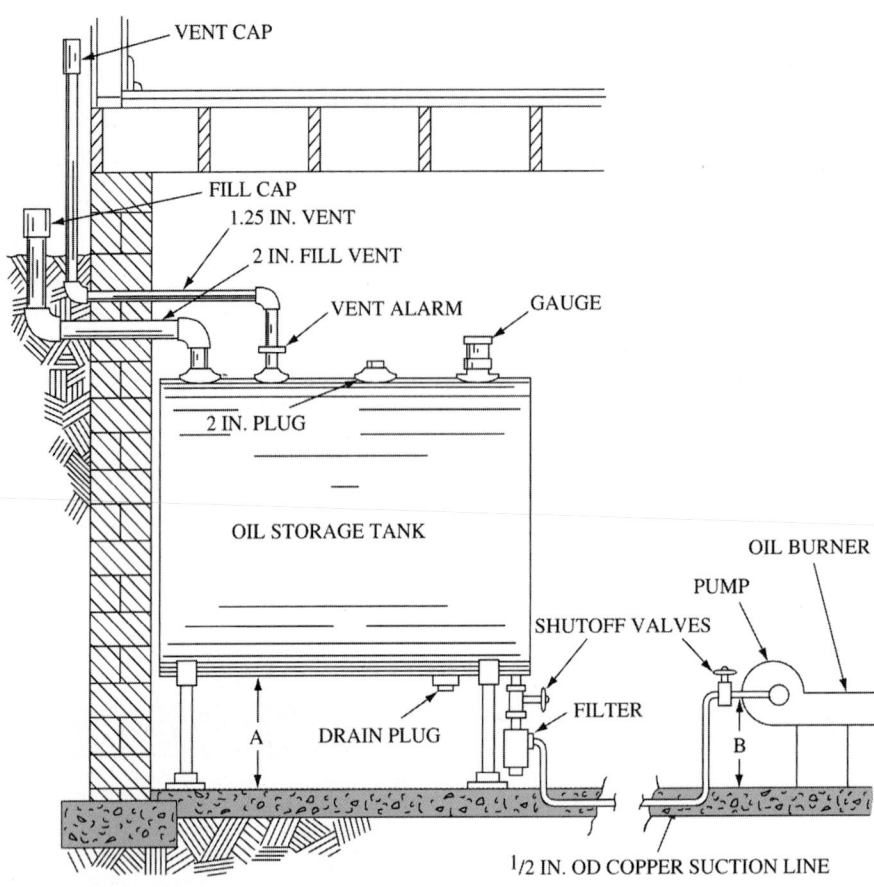

Figure 44-2 Indoor fuel oil storage tank

Furnace Location

Furnaces should not be installed under stairways. Oil furnaces can be heavy. When installing furnaces in the attic, make certain that the structural components of the house can support the furnace. Furnace clearances should be maintained according to the manufacturer's specifications. Remember to leave sufficient clearance around any panel that must be removed for service. This is usually at the front of the furnace. Although many codes specify a 24 in service clearance, do yourself a favor and leave at least 36 in. Generally speaking, the furnace return air must not be taken from the same room that the furnace is located in.

Combustion Air

Adequate combustion air is critical. Combustion air should be provided from the outside near the ceiling and floor. If the openings go directly outside, each opening should be at least 1 in² for every 5,000 Btu input. If the openings pass through vertical ducts, each opening should be at least 1 in² for every 4,000 Btu input. If the openings pass through horizontal ducts, each opening should be at least 1 in² for every 2,000 Btu input.

44.5   VENT PIPING

The most common venting practice for oil furnaces is to use a metal chimney connector and a masonry chimney, Figure 44-4. The connector is the pipe running from the furnace to the chimney. It should be kept as short as possible, with as few turns as possible, and it should have a rise of at least 0.25 in per foot of run. In basements and equipment rooms the connector may be either single wall metal or type L manufactured venting material. In attics and crawl spaces it must be type L. The connector should not pass through any floor, ceiling, or combustible walls and the entire length of the connector should be accessible for inspection and replacement.

Connector Size

If a single wall connector is used, the metal needs to be a much heavier gauge than the galvanized metal normally used for ductwork. Table 44-3 shows the minimum gauge for different connector sizes.

The connector must not be smaller in cross-sectional area than the flue collar on the furnace. The chimney connector should have a total equivalent length of no more than 75% of the chimney height. The total equivalent length is based on the actual length of the connector plus

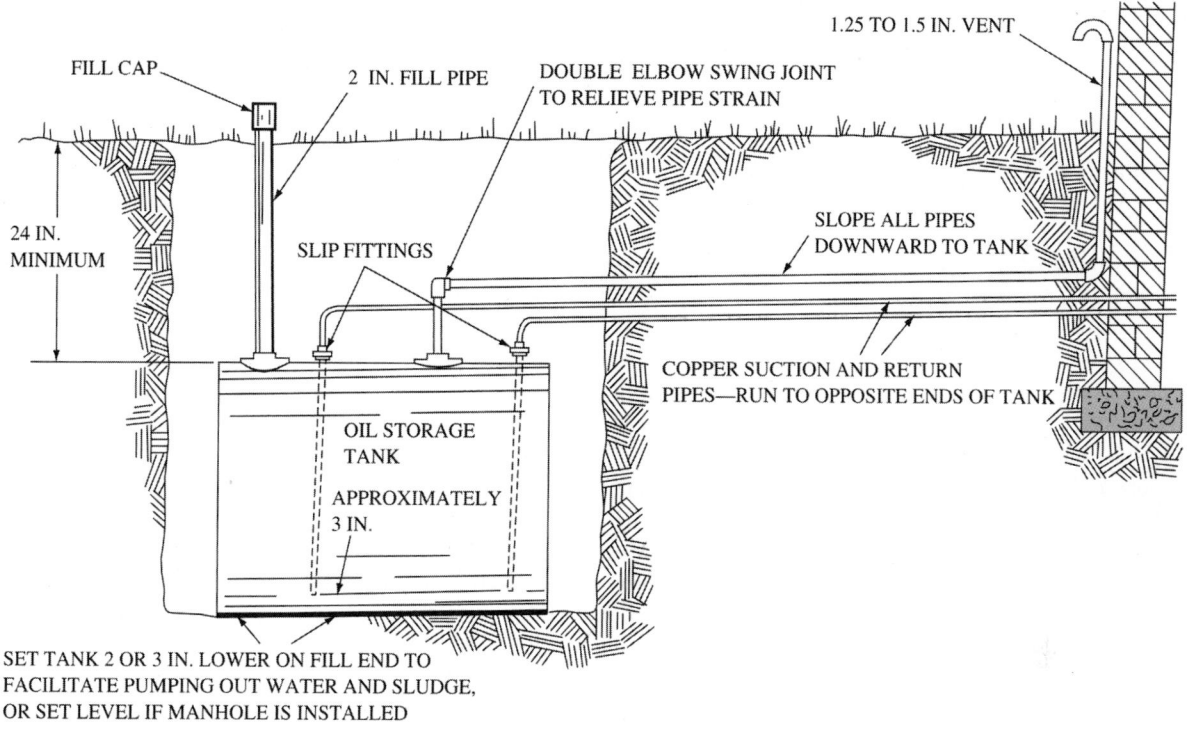

Figure 44-3 Underground fuel oil storage tank installation

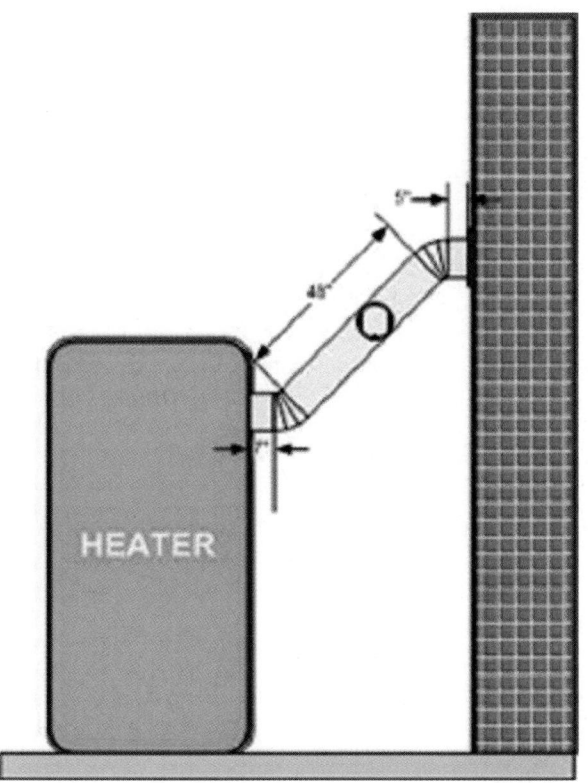

Figure 44-4 Oil furnace connected to masonry chimney
(From Advanced Residential Oilburners by George Lanthier,© 2007, by Permission of George Lanthier)

Table 44.3 Minimum Gauge for Single Wall Chimney Connector

Connector diameter	Minimum gauge
Less than 6 in	26
6–10 in	24

the equivalent length of any fittings. Table 44-4 shows the equivalent lengths for several common fittings.

The chimney height is based on the height measured from where the connector enters the chimney. For example: a 6 in connector that is 8 ft in actual length with two 90° ells has a total equivalent length of 8 + 11 + 11 = 30 ft. This must be no more than 75% of the chimney height above where the connector enters. Thus the chimney above the connector entrance must be 30 ÷ 0.75 = 40 ft. Unfortunately, this is higher than many residential chimneys. Replacing the 90° ells with 45° ells reduces the total equivalent length to 5 + 5 + 8 = 18 ft. By using the 45° ells, the chimney height above the connector entrance need only be 18 ÷ 0.75 = 24 ft.

Barometric Damper

Standard efficiency oil furnaces require a draft regulator, or barometric damper, in the chimney connector. Some sealed combustion furnaces do not use a barometric damper. Condensing furnaces also do not use a barometric damper.

Table 44.4 Connector Fitting Equivalent Lengths

Fitting	3 in	4 in	5 in	6 in	7 in	8 in	9 in	10 in
Tee	19	25	31	38	44	50	56	63
Wye	10	13	16	20	23	26	29	32
90° Ell	5	7	9	11	12	14	16	18
45° Ell	3	4	4	5	6	7	8	9

The draft regulator should be installed in the chimney connector as close to the furnace as possible and at least 18 in away from any combustible wall or ceiling. Older units may have a stack safety switch, and if that is the case, the draft regulator should be at least 18 in downstream from the stack switch, as in Figure 44-5.

The draft regulator should not be installed on the end of a bull-headed tee, but on the branch of a tee that is inline with the connector. Make sure the damper is oriented the way it was designed. A damper that is designed to be installed with the pivots horizontal to the ground will not work if it is installed on its side, Figure 44-6. The draft in the connector will need to be measured and the draft regulator adjusted during the initial startup.

Chimney

The chimney should be sized according to NFPA 211 and all local codes. The cross sectional area of the chimney should not be less than the cross sectional area of the connector. If a metal chimney liner is used, it should comply with UL 64. Oil furnaces should not be common vented with wood burning appliances, fireplaces, or gas burning appliances. They may be common vented with other oil fired appliances. If more than one oil fired appliance is vented into the same chimney, the cross sectional area of the chimney must be at least equal to the combined cross sectional areas of the connectors.

Type L Vent

The entire vent system can be constructed of type L venting material providing the furnace manufacturer approves the furnace for use with type L venting systems. Type L venting material should not be used with appliances with vent gas temperatures exceeding 550°F. Figure 44-7 Shows a Type L venting system connected to an oil fired furnace.

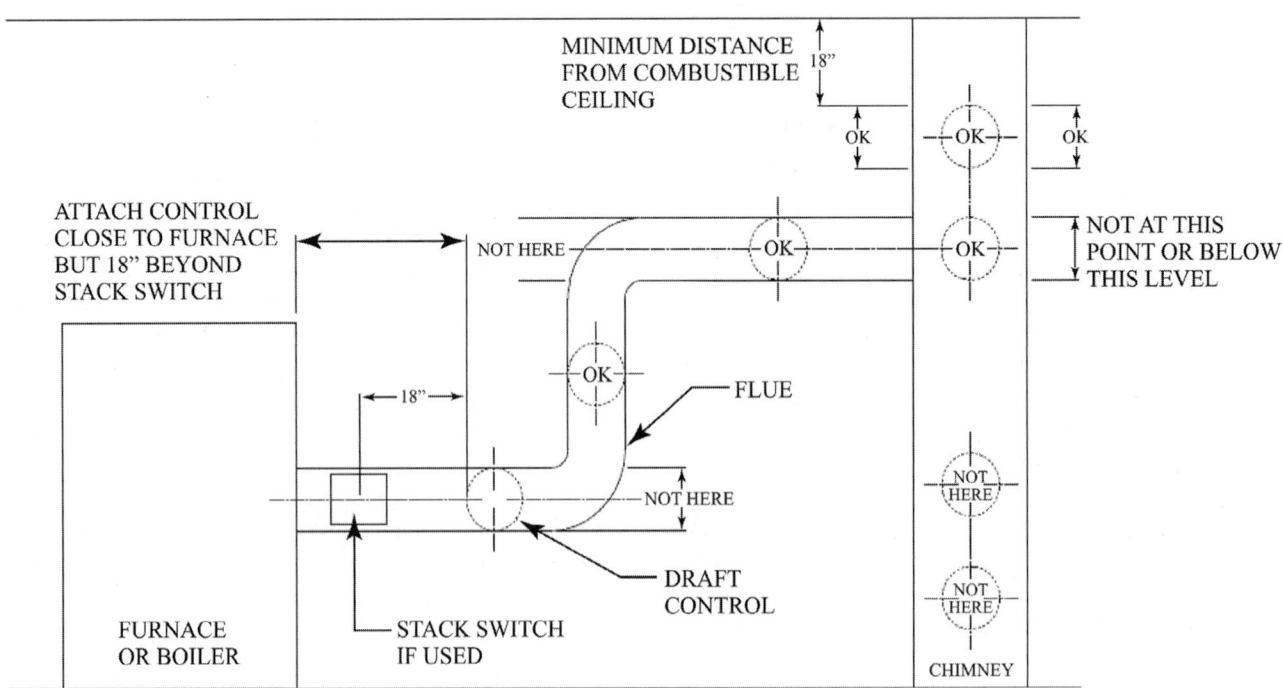

Figure 44-5 Draft gauge location
(Courtesy of Field Controls)

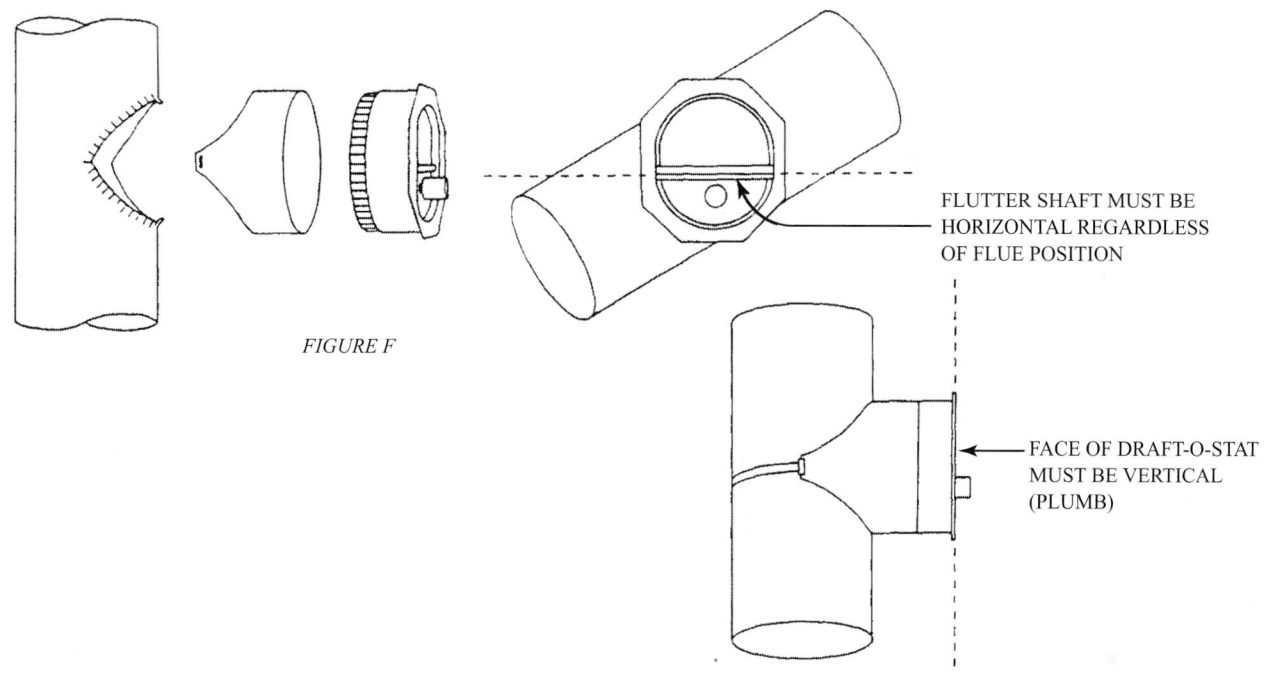

FLUTTER SHAFT MUST BE
HORIZONTAL REGARDLESS
OF FLUE POSITION

FIGURE F

FACE OF DRAFT-O-STAT
MUST BE VERTICAL
(PLUMB)

Figure 44-6 Draft regulator drawings from Figure F on page 6 of *Bard Oil Manual 2100–299B Rev A* Issue 04-07-98 File Tab 3
(Courtesy of Bard Mfg. Co. Inc.)

L-Vent Used as a Complete Interior Venting System

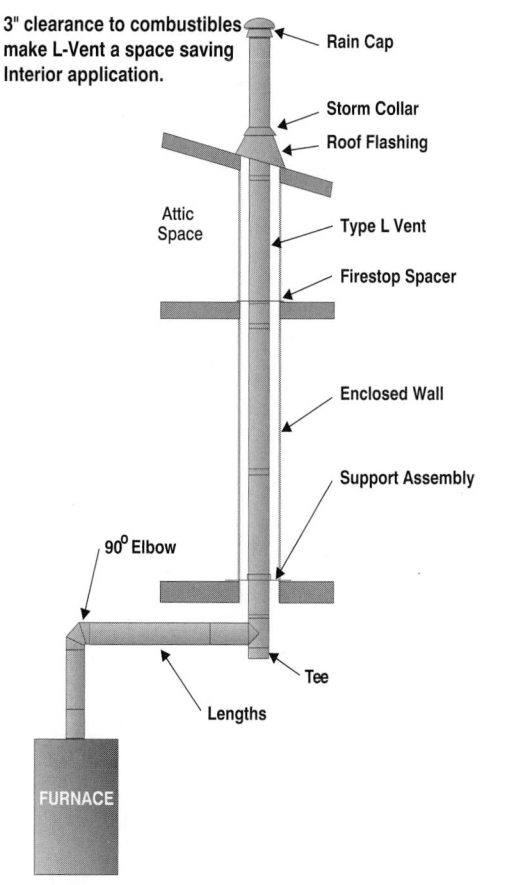

3" clearance to combustibles
make L-Vent a space saving
Interior application.

Rain Cap

Storm Collar

Roof Flashing

Attic
Space

Type L Vent

Firestop Spacer

Enclosed Wall

Support Assembly

90° Elbow

Tee

Lengths

FURNACE

Figure 44-7 Type L vent from left figure on page 7 of Type
L.pdf, as submitted
(Courtesy of Selkirk Corp.)

44.6 SYSTEM WIRING

The vast majority of oil furnaces and boilers operate on 115 V circuits. The wire conductors must be sized to carry the maximum circuit amperage of the furnace or boiler. The manufacturer's instructions typically specify the correct wire size, Table 44-5.

Three wires are typically connected for the power wiring: a hot wire, a neutral wire, and a ground wire. The ground wire is connected to the ground lug on the equipment cabinet. It is important that the polarity of the power wiring is connected correctly. The ground is important for safety. The connections to the hot wire and neutral must not be swapped. Some units with electronic control boards will not operate if the hot and neutral are swapped. Typically, the hot connection is black and the neutral is white.

SAFETY TIP

Many older furnaces were originally wired without a bonding safety ground to the cabinet. When replacing these furnaces, you should always run a new power wire with a hot, neutral, and ground so that the furnace can be properly grounded. Leaving the furnace cabinet ungrounded is dangerous.

Table 44-5 Wire sizing guide

Unit size	Volts—Hertz—phase	Operating voltage range		Max unit amps	Min wire gauge	Max wire length (ft)†	Max fuse or circuit breaker amps‡
		Max*	Min*				
105-12	115–60–1	132	104	12.2	14	26	15
120-20	115–60–1	132	104	15.7	14	26	20

*Permissible limits of voltage range at which unit will operate satisfactorily.
†Length shown is as measured one way along with path between unit and service panel for maximum 2% voltage drop.
‡Time-delay fuse is recommended.

Control Wiring

The control wiring for a heat only application consists of two wires. Typically the control wires connect to the two T terminals on the primary control and to the R and W terminals on the thermostat.

The control wiring for both a heating and cooling application consists of five wires. Two wires are used for heat and three more for the cooling and fan operation. Typically separate transformers are used for heating and cooling because the primary control has its own transformer.

SERVICE TIP

Most heating and cooling thermostats have connections for two 24 V inputs. These are normally labled RH, red for heating, and RC, red for cooling. Frequently the thermostats come with a jumper already installed between the two terminals because most systems only have one transformer. Oil heating systems with air conditioning typically have a separate cooling transformer, so the jumper should be removed.

47.7 HOT WATER

Besides providing the fuel for warm air furnaces, oil can also be used for heating domestic hot water or firing boilers. The combustion process and burners are essentially the same as in a warm air furnace. The heat is transferred to the water rather than to the air. Figure 44-8 shows a residential oil fired boiler. These residential boilers can range in efficiency from around 80–95% and are commonly used with hydronic heating systems.

A typical oil fired hydronic heating system is shown in Figure 44-9. Key components include an oil fired boiler, a circulation pump, an air separator, an expansion tank, radiant floor piping, a makeup water valve, a temperature-pressure relief valve, and a backflow prevention device required by code in many states.

TECH TIP

Radiant floor heating can heat effectively with water temperatures as low as 90–105°F. This allows lower boiler temperatures and increased operating efficiency.

44.8 ZONING

One advantage of hydronic heat is that installing a zoned heating system is relatively easy. Each heating zone has its own piping loop. Water flow to the zones is controlled by an electric zone valve, Figure 44-10. The zone valve is a normally closed electrically operated valve. A zone thermostat controls the zone valve, opening it when there is a call for heat. The zone valve has a set of contacts that close to energize the circulator pump, providing heat for the zone. The contacts for the valves are wired in parallel with each other so that any of the zone valves can energize the pump, Figure 44-11. This arrangement allows individual temperature control of multiple zones without complex controls and with relatively low installation cost.

There are many ways to pipe a zoned hydronic system. A major design challenge is to ensure steady water flow for even heat distribution. A simple method of achieving this is called reverse return. In reverse return piping, the zone with the shortest distance to the hot water supply has the longest distance to the return.

Figure 44-12 shows a typical piping system using zone valves. Balancing valves are used to compensate for different pressure drops and different load requirements. A balancing valve is placed in series with each zone, allowing the pressure drop though each zone to be adjusted.

44.9 STARTUP PROCEDURES

Some preliminary checks and steps are necessary before attempting to start the furnace. With the main power supply turned off, check to see:

- That the correct nozzle size has been selected for the desired input rate.
- All shipping supports are removed.

Figure 44-8 Residential oil fired boiler

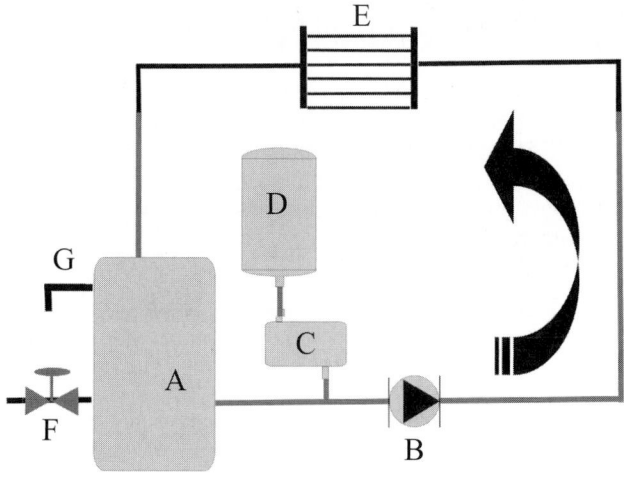

Figure 44-9 Basic hydronic system: (A) Oil fired boiler;
(B) Circulation pump; (C) Air separator; (D) Expansion tank;
(E) Radiant floor piping; (F) Makeup water valve; (G) Temperature-
pressure relief

Figure 44-10 Zone valve

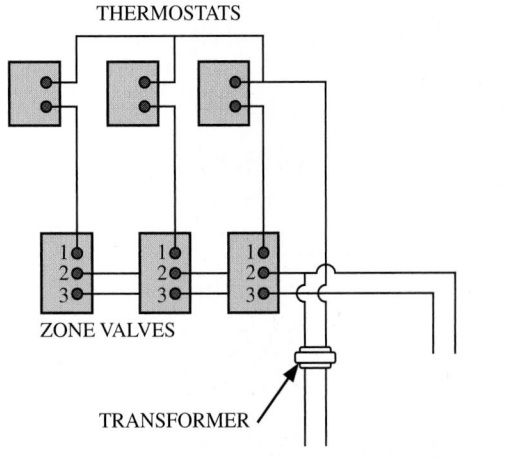

Figure 44-11 Zone valve wiring

- Power wiring is properly connected.
- Control wiring is properly connected.
- Blower access door is secured in place.
- Valve on the oil supply line is open.
- Reset button on the primary control is pushed down.
- Flame observation door and all cleanout access covers are closed.
- The thermostat is set to HEAT at a temperature higher than the room.

After all of the above items have been performed, set the disconnect switch to OFF and energize the circuit to the furnace. Check the voltage at the disconnect switch and verify that it is the correct voltage, usually 115 V.

Operational Check

To correctly adjust the burner, it will be necessary to measure the oil pump pressure, stack temperature, and carbon dioxide flue gas percentage.

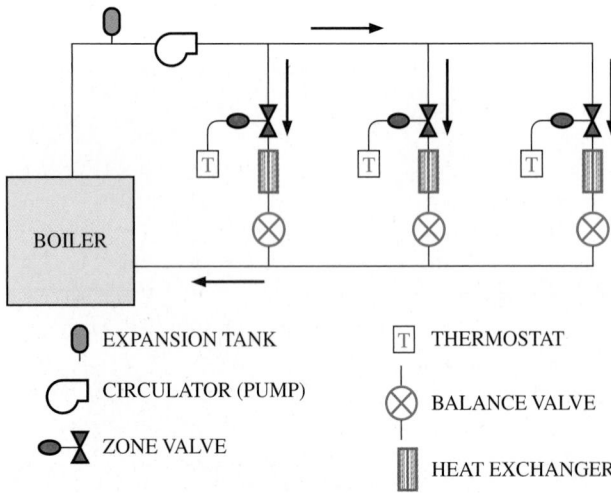

EXPANSION TANK

CIRCULATOR (PUMP)

ZONE VALVE

THERMOSTAT

BALANCE VALVE

HEAT EXCHANGER

Figure 44-12 Zoned hydronic system piping

All air should be purged from the fuel lines and a pressure gauge installed on the pressure port of the oil pump. The manufacturer's literature or a data plate on the oil burner can be used to identify the correct pump pressure. The most common pressure has been 100 psig for many years. However, most recent oil burners operate at higher pressures, 140–170 psig. Start the burner and compare the oil pump pressure to the recommended pressure. If the pressure is not correct, turn the adjusting screw clockwise to increase pressure or counterclockwise to decrease pressure.

The operation of the barometric damper should be checked. The manufacturer's instructions should list the recommended draft pressure between the damper and the furnace, –0.02 in WC is common. Adjust the weight on the barometric damper to achieve the correct draft.

The correct flame should have no smoke as measured by a smoke spot test. The CO_2 level should be 10–12.5%. If there is smoke in the flame or if the CO_2 level is outside of the 10–12.5% range, you need to adjust the air. To do this:

- Adjust the air inlet vane until you see a trace of smoke in the flame.
- Measure the CO_2 content of the flue gas.
- Open the air until you have lowered the CO_2 by 1–2%.
- The correct flame should have no smoke and the CO_2 level should be 10–12.5%.

The flue gas can also be checked for carbon monoxide to determine the combustion efficiency. To do this, measure the actual stack temperature and then subtract the equipment ambient temperature. The result will be the net stack temperature. The combustion efficiency can then be calculated using the CO_2 percentage, the net stack temperature, and a combustion efficiency slide rule. Ideally, the flue gas should have no carbon monoxide, however, trace amounts of up to 50 parts per million are acceptable. Other items to check are the temperature rise and blower current draw once the indoor blower comes on.

S E R V I C E   T I P

Pushing the safety reset several times on an existing furnace is not a safe practice because oil may already be sitting in the combustion chamber and every push delivers more oil. On a new installation, the lines are full of air. A two pipe system will purge itself, but it may take several pushes.

UNIT 44—SUMMARY

Proper installation and startup are required for oil fired appliances to burn cleanly and efficiently. There are several key components to ensure a successful installation. The furnace capacity needs to match the heating load. The proper oil tank must be installed along with the correct fuel line arrangement. There must be adequate combustion air supplied to the furnace as necessary. Always refer to both the NFPA and local codes for guidance. The correct exhaust vent and vent connector need to be installed at the proper locations and at the proper heights. Power and control wiring need to comply with the manufacturer's recommendations for voltage and current demand along with wire sizing requirements. Final installation will include combustion process measurements and adjustment.

WORK ORDERS

Service Ticket 4401

New Install: Unit Will Not Operate

Equipment: Oil Fired Furnace with Electronic Controls

A technician answers a service call to start a newly installed oil furnace. After making the necessary prestart checks, the technician tries to start the furnace and nothing happens. The technician investigates further and finds that there is a fault code flashing on the control board LED.

The technician refers to the installation manual that came with the furnace and finds that the flash pattern is listed as "incorrect power polarity." This leads the technician to check the power wire connections. The black power wire is connected to the white on the furnace, and the white power wire is connected to the black on the furnace. The technician swaps the wires and the furnace operates properly.

Service Ticket 4402

New Install: Unit Does Not Fire When Started

Equipment: Oil Fired Furnace with Two Pipe Fuel Supply, Tank Below Furnace

A technician is sent to start a newly installed oil fired furnace. Initially the furnace appears to start when it receives a call for heat, but it does not fire. After 2 minutes, the primary control shuts down on safety. Since this is a new installation and the furnace has not fired, the technician assumes that the lines have not been completely purged of air.

Sometimes with a two pipe fuel supply such as this, purging can be accomplished by restarting the furnace, thereby allowing the air to be pushed through the supply line into the return line and back to the tank. After pushing the reset button once, the furnace operates and the fires briefly, but goes out again. A second push of the reset button allows the furnace to start one more time. This time, after the furnace fires, it stays going.

Service Ticket 4403

Furnace Change-out: Reconnect Vent

Equipment: Oil Fired Furnace Vented into Masonry Chimney

A technician is sent to install the chimney connector to a new oil fired furnace that has just replaced an older

unit. The customer complained that the old furnace would sometimes admit smoke into the basement. The technician realized that this may have resulted from an improper vent connection.

The old furnace metal connecter was single wall and the draft regulator was connected to the end of a bullheaded tee. The technician decides to run a type L chimney connector and places the draft regulator on the branch end of an in-line tee. Also, the 90° ell and tee are replaced by two 45° ells. The draft regulator is adjusted and the over fire draft is measured to be 0.02 in WC. The draft in the chimney connector is measured to be 0.04 in WC. The system operates properly and there is no oil smell or smoke in the basement.

Service Ticket 4404

Changeout: Unit Does Not Operate

Equipment: Oil Fired Furnace with Electronic Controls

A technician has installed a new electronically controlled oil furnace to replace an aging furnace and used the same power wire configuration on the new furnace. The technician had not paid attention to the fact that the power line to the old furnace did not have an equipment ground.

After conducting the routine prestart checks, the furnace was started but nothing happened. The technician investigated further and found that the control board LED was flashing. The technician refers to the installation manual that came with the furnace and finds that the flash pattern is listed as "furnace not grounded." The technician quickly realizes what the mistake is and runs a new grounded power supply. With the unit grounded, the furnace starts and operates correctly.

Service Ticket 4405

New Hydronic System Has Cold Zone

Equipment: Oil Fired Boiler with Zoned Hydronic Radiant Floor Heat

A technician answers a service call for a recently installed hydronic heating system. The customer says that the problem is that one zone is colder than the others. This is especially true on cold days when all zones are calling for heat.

The first thing the technician checks is the zone valve and it is opening and hot water is passing through it. However, the return pipe from that zone is 15°F cooler than the other two zones. This low return temperature indicates poor water flow to that zone. The technician fully opens the balancing valve for the cold zone and partially closes the balancing valves for the other two zones. After 30 minutes of operation the return temperature of all zones is within 5°F. A check of the floor temperature in all three zones with an infrared thermometer shows that the floor temperatures are now around 90°F.

UNIT 44—REVIEW QUESTIONS

1. What factors should be considered when selecting an oil fired furnace?

2. What is the advantage of a multipoise furnace configuration?

3. What is the firing rate of a furnace with a 0.75 gph nozzle?

4. What is the heating capacity of an 80% efficient furnace with a 0.75 gph nozzle?

5. What would be the required vacuum for an oil furnace located 5 ft above the oil tank with a horizontal run of 20 ft?

6. What national standard is a good reference when installing oil furnaces?

7. What free air opening would be required for an oil furnace installed in a confined space if the air was coming through horizontal ducts and the furnace had a 0.65 gph nozzle?

8. Calculate the equivalent length of a 6 in diameter chimney connector with two 45° ells and 8 ft of pipe.

9. How high must the chimney be above the connector entrance for the connector in question 8 to operate properly?

10. What type of material must be used for a chimney connector in a crawl space?

11. Describe where the draft regulator should be installed in the chimney connector.

12. List the components required for an oil hydronic heating system.

13. What is the basic difference between an oil fired boiler and an oil fired furnace?

14. Describe how a hydronic zoned heating system works.

15. How is the circulator controlled in a hydronic system using zone valves?

16. What is the purpose of a balancing valve in a hydronic system?

17. Give a prestart checklist when checking a newly installed oil furnace.

18. What measurements should be taken when setting up a new oil furnace?

19. What national publication is a good reference for chimney construction?

20. What types of appliances may oil furnaces be common vented with?

UNIT 45

Troubleshooting Oil Heating Systems

OBJECTIVES

After completing this unit you will be able to:

- discuss common oil delivery problems.
- discuss common ignition system problems.
- discuss common primary control problems.
- explain how soot forms and what problems soot buildup can lead to.
- describe safety precautions which should be followed when checking a system with a tripped primary control.
- determine likely causes of oil heating system failures using a troubleshooting chart.

Figure 45-1 Oil burner motor reset button
(*Courtesy of InspectAPedia.com*)

45.1 INTRODUCTION

Oil furnaces use a liquid fuel that must be atomized before burning which provides for a unique set of problems when compared to gas furnaces. Operational troubles associated with oil furnaces can be related to the process of atomizing the fuel, mixing it with air, and igniting it with a high voltage spark. Though these are typical, in some cases the problems are much simpler. A thorough understanding of how all the furnace components operate will help you to identify and troubleshoot system malfunctions.

45.2 OIL BURNER PROBLEMS

Oil burner problems can be grouped by the main components of the oil burner:

- Oil burner motor problems.
- Oil pump problems.
- Nozzle problems.
- Ignition system problems.
- Primary control problems.

Burner Motor Problems

The burner motor is usually a split phase motor with a centrifugal switch and a manual reset type overload, Figure 45-1. Motor problems can include open, shorted, or grounded windings, a defective centrifugal switch, or even in rare occasions a defective overload. Regardless of the specific motor malady, the solution is generally motor replacement. It is usually not practical to repair motors in the field.

Symptoms that indicate problems with the burner motor include

- Burner motor not starting.
- Burner motor runs but trips out on overload.
- Burner motor runs but does not produce enough oil pressure.

Motor Will Not Start

If the motor will not start, begin by checking to see if the motor is receiving the correct voltage. If the motor has no measured voltage, then the problem is not with the motor. If the motor is receiving voltage and not operating, try pushing the manual reset for the motor overload. If the overload has tripped, the red button will be sticking out. Try pushing it to reset it. If the motor tries to start but cannot, either the motor is stuck or it is defective. Turn the power off and check to see if the motor is binding by spinning the combustion blower by hand. If it will spin easily, the motor is not bound. If the motor overload is not tripped, it is receiving voltage; if it is not bound but still will not run, then the motor is damaged. This may be traced to the windings or the centrifugal switch, however, rather than trying to repair it, the recommended remedy is to replace the motor.

If the fan will not spin, or is very difficult to turn, then the fuel pump is binding, the fan is hitting the housing, or the motor bearings are seizing. Disconnect the motor from the

Figure 45-2 Oil pump drive coupling

coupling that drives the oil pump, Figure 45-2. If the oil pump is the problem, the motor will now turn freely. If it does not turn freely then the motor bearings are most likely the problem and the motor should be replaced. Once the bearings become so dry that they seize, they cannot be fixed by lubricating them.

Motor Runs But Trips Out on Overload

If the motor runs but trips out on overload, check the motor's operating current and compare it to the full load amperage (FLA) marked on the motor. If the overload trips without the current exceeding the rated FLA, the overload is weak and the motor needs to be replaced. If the operating current exceeds the FLA, then look for items that might be binding the motor. Disconnect the coupling to the oil pump to see if the motor will operate with the correct operating current. If the oil pump is the problem, the motor will now turn freely. If the motor bearings are the problem, the motor should be replaced.

Burner Motor Runs But Does Not Produce Enough Oil Pressure

If the motor runs but the oil pressure is low, check the coupling that drives the oil pump. If the coupling is cracked or stripped out, the motor will run but the oil pump will turn slowly, or not at all. Replacing the coupling will correct this.

Oil Pump Problems

Oil pump problems include:

- Seized oil pump.
- Oil pump pressure not correct.
- Bypass plug incorrectly applied.
- Leaky shutoff.

Seized Oil Pump

If the oil pump will not turn, it is seized and should be replaced. If this is the case, then the quality of the oil should be checked. Water and sludge in the pump can cause it to seize. Cleaning the oil tank to remove accumulated debris and sludge is a good precautionary measure whenever an oil pump is replaced.

Oil Pump Pressure Not Correct

Check the inlet strainer screen if the pump will not maintain the correct pressure, Figure 45-3. If the system is a two pipe system, check to see that the bypass plug is installed. If the system is a one pipe system, check to see that the bypass plug has been removed. If the screen is clear and the pressure is still too low, try adjusting the pump's output pressure. Turn the adjustment screw clockwise to increase the pressure.

A leak in the suction line can also cause poor oil pressure by letting air in. Disconnect the nozzle line connector and direct its output to a container. Run the burner and observe the oil stream. The stream should be clear and steady. If air is being drawn in through a leak in the suction the oil stream will be frothy or bubbly. Finding and repairing the leak is necessary before proceeding. If none of the troubleshooting methods result in proper operation, then the pump is damaged and should be replaced.

Leaky Shutoff

When the burner motor stops, the oil pump should shut off tightly to prevent continued oil delivery into the combustion chamber. If the pump cutoff is working properly, the output pressure should not drop past 80 psig or not more than 20% below the operating pressure. If the pressure drops below these levels, the cutoff is leaking and the pump should be replaced.

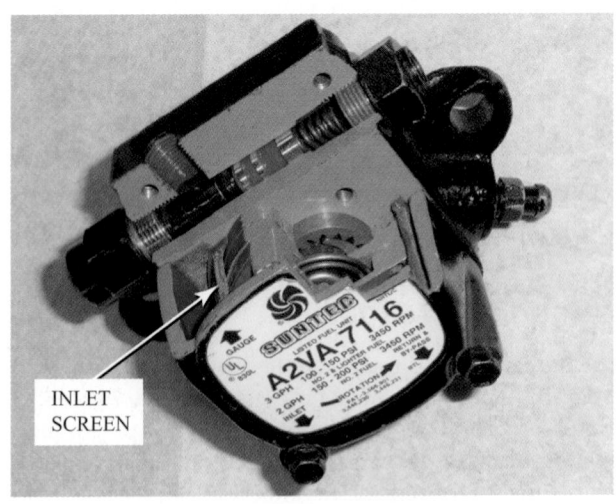

Figure 45-3 Oil pump inlet strainer

Nozzle Problems

The oil mist from the atomized spray cone should not come into contact with any part of the combustion chamber. If it does, the oil will not burn completely and sooty, inefficient combustion will result. Nozzles become worn over time and the atomization becomes less complete, resulting in incomplete combustion. The nozzle filter can become clogged over time and produce a poor spray pattern. Poor combustion that persists and cannot be adjusted can be a sign of a worn or dirty nozzle. Typically, the nozzle should be changed every year to ensure correct operation.

Ignition System Problems

Ignition problems can result in delayed ignition or no ignition. Ignition components include the ignition transformer, the electrodes, and the contacts that transfer electricity from the transformer to the electrodes. The transformer delivers 10,000 V AC to the electrodes, producing an arc between them.

This high voltage arc can be diminished by:

- Low transformer primary voltage.
- Improper electrode gap.
- Cracked or dirty porcelain insulators on the electrodes.
- Poor contact between the electrodes and the transformer.
- A weak transformer.

If the oil burner has been delivering oil and it has not been igniting, the first thing that needs to be done is to clean the excess oil out of the combustion chamber. Turn off the power and disconnect the control wires so that the burner will not try to light. Some furnaces have a cleanout port that can be used to gain access to the combustion chamber. If the furnace does not, it will be necessary to remove the burner assembly to allow for access. Carefully clean out any accumulated oil, but be careful not to damage the refractory.

The electrode setting should always be checked whenever there is an ignition problem. Generally speaking, the electrodes should be $1/8$ in apart, slightly ahead of the nozzle, and set at an angle specified by the burner manufacturer, Figure 45-4. Many manufacturers have plastic gauges that fit over the nozzle to assist in setting the electrodes. Also check the springs and contacts that transfer voltage from the transformer to the electrodes and the electrode porcelain insulators for cracks. If there is oil or carbon on the insulators it should be cleaned off.

When the furnace starts, the ignition spark should make a buzzing sound. If you do not hear the arc, check the transformer primary voltage. If the transformer is not getting the correct voltage, usually 115 V AC, then the primary control and wiring should be checked.

If the transformer is receiving the correct voltage, check the output of the transformer with a high voltage probe. Turn

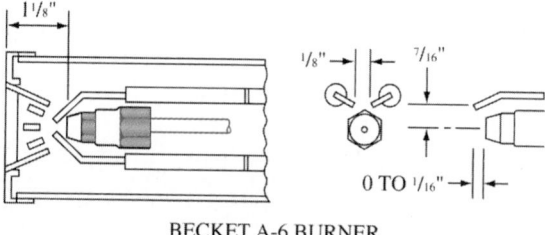

BECKET A-6 BURNER

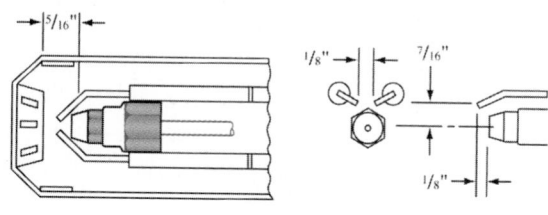

WAYNE MSR-6 BURNER

ABC/SUNRAY FC-134 BURNER

Figure 45-4 Oil burner electrode spacing dimensions *(Courtesy of Rheem Manufacturing Air Conditioning Division)*

the power off, swing the transformer up, turn the system on, and check the output terminals with a special probe made for the 10,000 V secondary winding. If the voltage is less than the transformer rating, usually 10,000 V, the transformer must be replaced.

Primary Control Problems

The burner should be operating if the primary control is receiving 120 V, the circuit is closed across the two T terminals, and the primary control has not tripped. An easy way to test the primary control is to jumper the T terminals, Figure 45-5. The burner should start and after lighting it should stay on. If the primary control trips out even though a flame is present, the problem could be in either the primary control or the cad cell.

After starting the burner, connect the leads to jumper the F terminals to test the cad cell. If the control still trips out, the primary control is bad. If the burner continues to fire, disconnect the cad cell and check its resistance. A good reading would be between 300 and 1,000 Ω. If the resistance is over 1,600 Ω, the cad cell is misaligned, dirty, or defective. Turn off the burner and recheck the cad cell resistance. It should rise to 100,000 Ω or more. While the burner is off, clean the cad cell and check its alignment. Start the burner again and

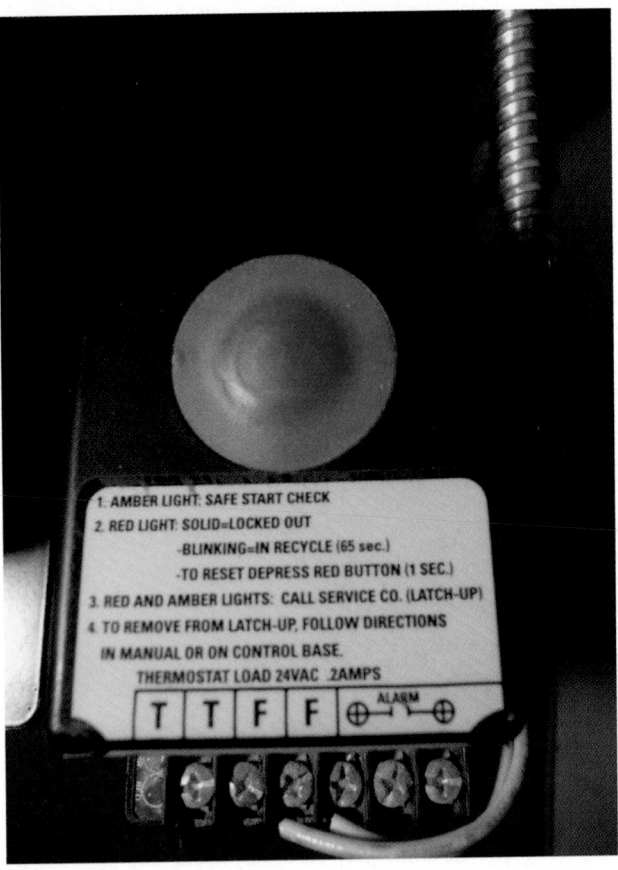

Figure 45-5 Primary control T terminals

recheck the cad cell resistance. If the cad cell still has too high a resistance, replace the cad cell.

45.3 OIL SYSTEM PROBLEMS

Not all problems are caused by the oil burner. The rest of the system from the tank to the vent can be the cause of system malfunctions.

Oil Tank Related Problems

A common oil furnace problem is the lack of fuel. Check to see that there is fuel in the tank before spending a lot of time chasing down nonexistent problems. If the tank is empty, the lines will need to be purged of air after the fuel tank is filled. If the oil tank was emptied, it is a good idea to change the fuel line filter, pump strainer, and nozzle. The last few gallons of oil are always the dirtiest and filling the tank stirs up the sediment on the bottom. A new filter will help protect against future problems.

Suction line leaks can cause two types of problems. On systems with oil safety valves, a suction leak may prevent the oil safety valve from opening and this will shut off all oil flow. Even without the safety valve, suction leaks can introduce air into the oil. A frothy oil and air mixture is delivered to the pump and uneven, dirty burning results.

If the vent on the oil tank is obstructed or plugged, the tank pressure can drop to the point that the fuel will not move.

Electrical Problems

Although oil furnaces are fairly simple to wire, they can still be wired incorrectly. If the furnace does not receive the proper voltage, nothing will operate. Modern furnaces with electronic control boards must be properly grounded and connected with the correct polarity. If the furnace is not grounded or the hot and neutral power wires are swapped, the furnace will not operate. This is usually indicated by a fault code from the diagnostic LED. On the control side, a bad thermostat or broken thermostat wire can cause the furnace to not operate.

Venting and Combustion Air Problems

Like any combustion appliance, oil furnaces need combustion air. In older leaky houses combustion air is usually assumed to enter through infiltration provided the furnace is located in an unconfined space. Newer houses should always have combustion air provided through grills or ducts. It is never wrong to bring in combustion air, even with older houses. A lack of combustion air will cause poor combustion and can lead to carbon monoxide poisoning.

The draft regulator should be adjusted to maintain the correct over fire draft, usually at least 0.02 in wc draft. The vent connector should be as short and straight as possible. Long chimney connectors with lots of sharp turns will lead to poor venting and poor combustion. If the draft regulator cannot maintain the draft at the proper setting, the chimney connector may be the problem.

If the over fire draft rises significantly after the indoor fan comes on, the heat exchanger is cracked. This is a dangerous situation which should be corrected immediately. The furnace must usually be replaced if the heat exchanger is cracked. Heat exchangers are normally only changed under warranty.

Soot

An oil furnace that is not properly installed and maintained will produce soot. Soot is unburned carbon and oil that occurs because of incomplete combustion. Soot can build to the point that heat exchangers and flues are clogged with soot. When this happens, an extensive cleaning of the heat exchanger, chimney connector, and chimney is required. Soot buildup can lead to a condition called puff-back. This occurs when the combustion products cannot leave the furnace. Usually the oil-air mixture is due to a blocked combustion chamber, leading to delayed ignition. When the oil does ignite, the small explosion produces a puff of soot and unburned oil forces its way out into the area around the furnace. This greasy black cloud leaves stains on surrounding areas. The way to prevent puff-back is to keep the furnace properly maintained so that soot buildup does not occur.

Fan Problems

If the burner runs, but the indoor fan never comes on, the problem could be with the fan motor, the fan switch, or the

UNIT 46

Electric Heat

OBJECTIVES

After completing this unit you will be able to:

- describe the different applications for electric heating.
- explain the purpose of sequencers used for electric heating elements.
- describe how the safety devices of electric furnaces operate.
- determine the best application for supplemental electric heating.
- explain the operation of a multistage thermostat for electric heating.

46.1 INTRODUCTION

The growth of electric heating began in the 1950s and first became popular in areas not served by natural gas pipelines. Throughout this same time period the electrical demand for air conditioning during the summer months was increasing. To help boost the winter demand, electric utilities and heating manufacturers began to encourage the use of electric heating. Special rates and promotional programs like "Live Better Electrically" and "Total Electric Home" were introduced in the 1960s, and the market developed rapidly.

Today, many systems provide both heating and cooling with a single air distribution system. Therefore most air handlers are configured to accept both cooling coils and heating elements. This has reduced the number of installations for straight stand alone electric furnaces and instead electric heat is often used in combination with a cooling system or heat pump.

46.2 WARM AIR ELECTRIC FURNACES

The typical residential electric furnace, Figure 46-1, consists of a cabinet, blower compartment, filter, and resistance heating section. Most manufacturers provide a place for a cooling coil. An electrical furnace has many advantages:

- It is more compact than the equivalent gas or oil furnace.
- Due to cooler surface temperature, it has "zero" clearance requirements on all sides. It may, therefore, be located in small spaces such as closets.

- Since there is no combustion process, there are no requirements for venting pipes, chimney, or make-up air. This reduces building costs and simplifies installation.
- Units may be mounted for upflow, downflow, or horizontal airflow applications, Figure 46-2.

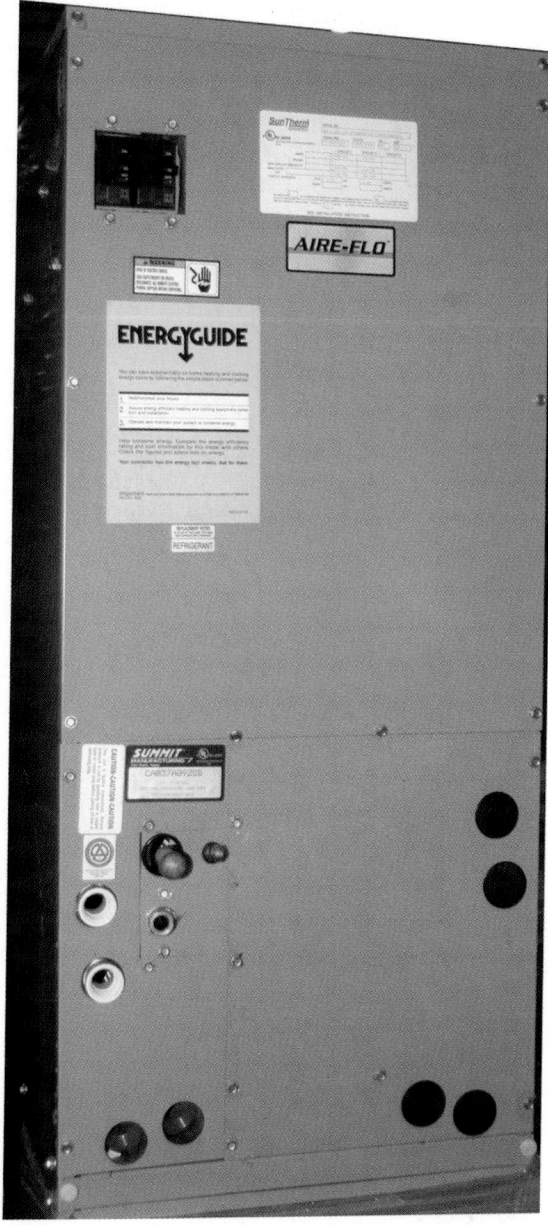

Figure 46-1 External view of an electric furnace

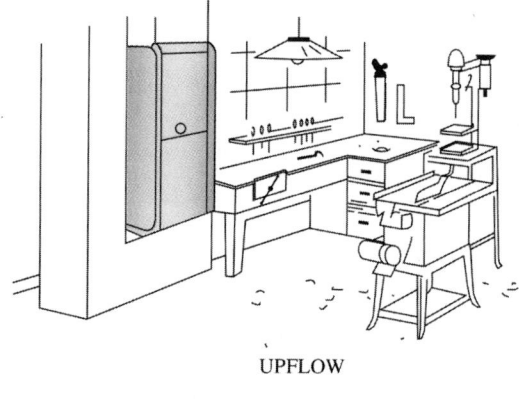

UPFLOW

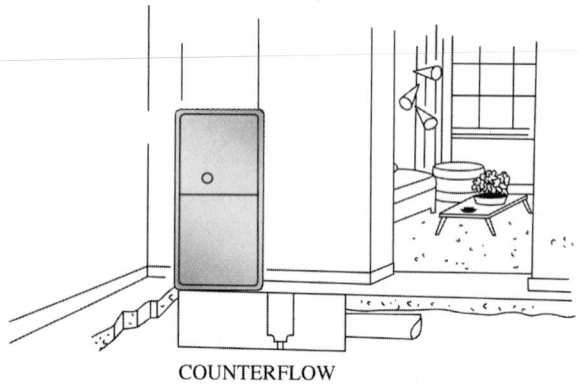

COUNTERFLOW

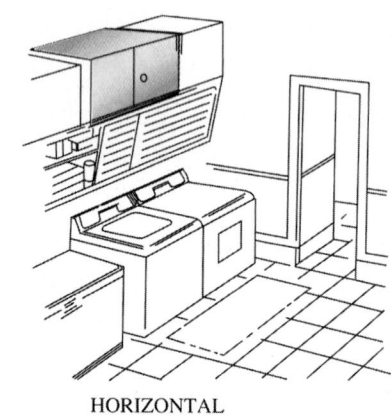

HORIZONTAL

Figure 46-2 Various types of electric furnaces

With electric heat there are no losses such as those experienced with oil and gas combustion processes. Therefore electric heat is considered to be close to 100% efficient.

The blower compartment is a housing that includes the filters and the blower fan for circulating the air through the system. Figure 46-3 shows a blower compartment with a centrifugal multispeed direct drive fan. Larger units use a belt driven fan. An electric furnace has less resistance to airflow as compared to an oil or gas furnace, and fan performance is more efficient.

The heating section consists of banks of resistance heater coils of nickel chrome wire held in place by ceramic insula-

tors, Figure 46-4. The heater normally operates on a 208 V to 240 V power source. The amount of heat produced by each heating element is affected by the supply voltage and the current flow which together determine the total wattage.

One watt of power produces an equivalent 3.412 Btu/hr of resistance heat. Electric power is measured in kilowatts (kW), with 1 kW being equal to 1,000 W. The term kilowatt-hour (kWh) is used to express the amount of energy used in one hour. The input for an electric furnace is given in kWh and the output is given in Btu/hr (also referred to as Btuh, but either way, it is Btu per hour). To find the heat output in Btu/hr, multiply the kW input by 3,412. Conversely, the input kW can be calculated by dividing the furnace Btu/hr output by 3,412.

The amount of heat produced by an electric furnace is a function of the supply voltage and the current flow.

$$Watts = Volts \times Amps$$

A furnace rated at 240 V with a current draw of 125 A would have a kW input of 240 V × 125 A = 30,000 W, which is 30 kW. Residential furnace output capacities normally range from 5 kW (17,060 Btu/hr) to 30 kW (102,360 Btu/hr).

A 30 kW, 240 V electric furnace has a current draw of 125 A, which for a 200 A entrance panel would leave only 75 A for other electrical uses. If the total heating demand is greater than this, then two electric furnaces would be used, with sequencing and zoning.

SAFETY TIP

All electrical work MUST conform to the requirements of local codes and ordinances and the National Electrical Code NFPA 70 current edition.

46.3 SEQUENCERS

Electric heating elements have a high current draw as they initially come on. The current draw drops slightly as the heating element gets hot. The initial high current draw is caused by the low temperature of the element. Electrical resistance increases as the temperature of the conductor increases. When the heating element begins to glow red, it draws less current.

The sequencer control is an important operation of the electrical furnace. When there is a call for heat, the electric sequencer contacts close and the circuit is energized. As the sequencer begins to heat up, the blower and first heater come on. In order to stage the elements, there is a time delay (in seconds) before each additional heater stage is energized.

Electric furnaces that have multiple heat strips are designed with a sequencer that allows each heat strip to come on individually or in small groups. Without a sequencer, the

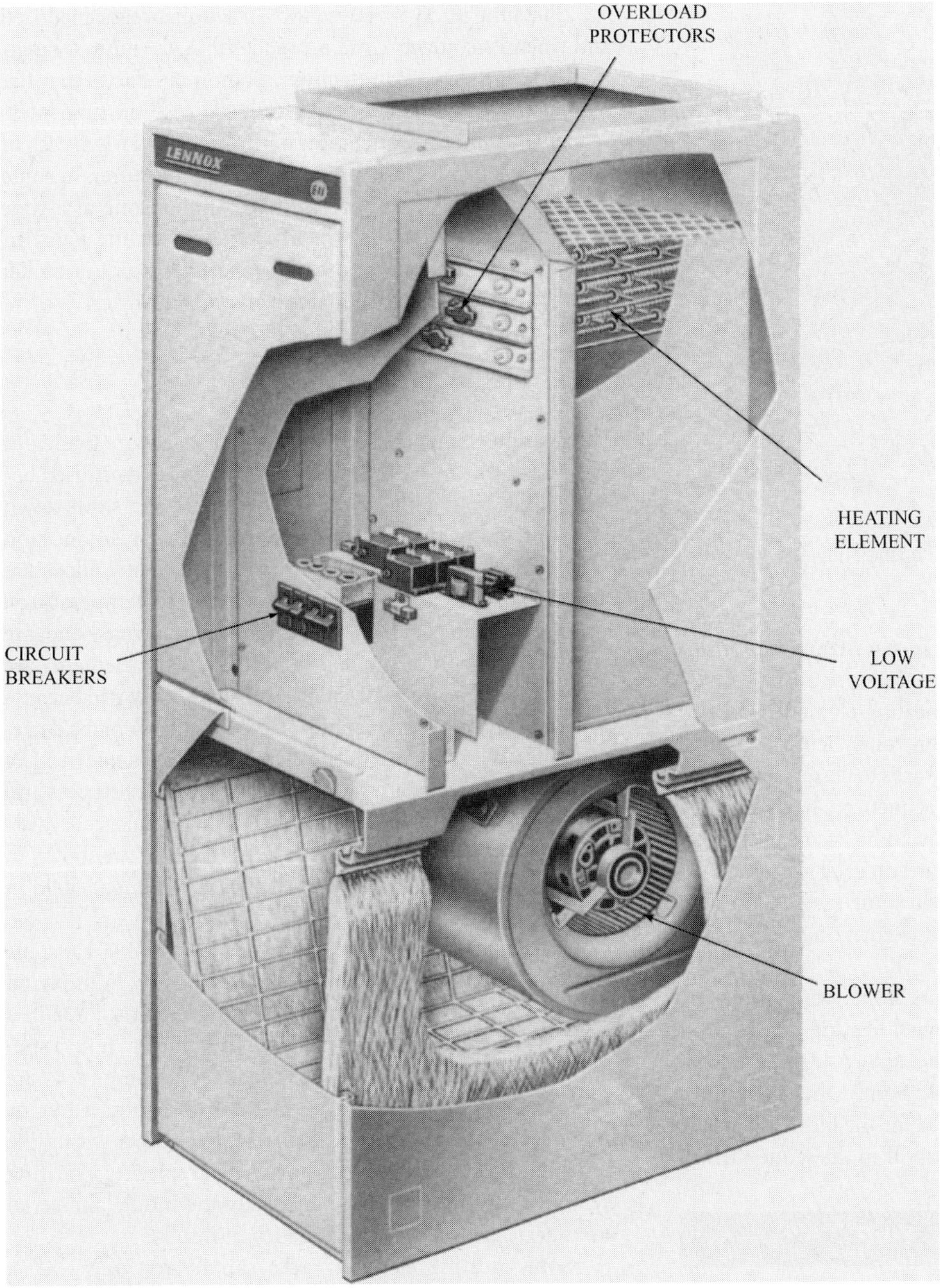

OVERLOAD
PROTECTORS
LENNOX
HEATING
ELEMENT
CIRCUIT
BREAKERS
LOW
VOLTAGE
BLOWER

Figure 46-3 Internal diagram of an electric furnace
(Courtesy of Lennox Industries, Inc.)

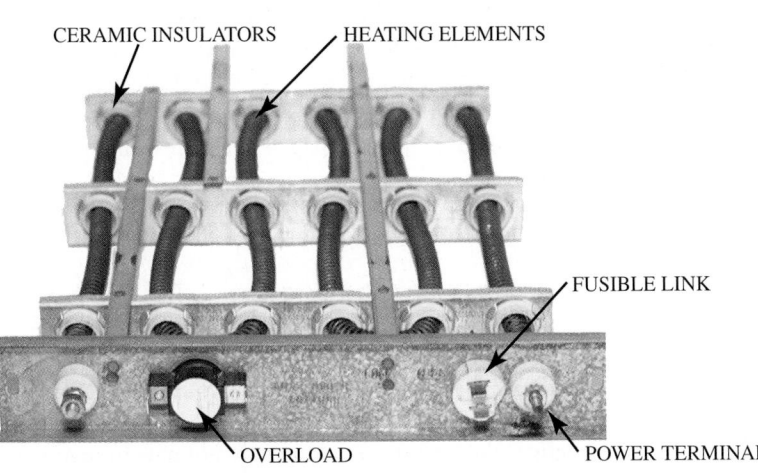

CERAMIC INSULATORS
HEATING ELEMENTS
FUSIBLE LINK
OVERLOAD
POWER TERMINAL

Figure 46-4 Electric heating element rack

Figure 46-5 White center pin shown pushes upward on contact

initial current draw for an electric furnace could be significant. Most systems use sequencers to sequence or stage on elements. A sequencer uses a small heating element wrapped around a bimetal strip or a PTC control. When the bimetal strip warms up enough, it snaps or warps to close a set of contacts to turn a heat strip on. Some sequencers have multiple contacts that are staged on. Staging can be accomplished by using a center pin that pushes upward on each successive set of sequencer contacts, Figure 46-5. In some cases where several heating elements are sequenced to turn on, multiple sequencers are used, Figure 46-6.

To prevent the heating elements from overheating, the unit blower must come on with the first heating element and it must remain on throughout the heating cycle until the last stage heating element has cycled off. Some sequencers have specific terminals that are designated for the blower. This set of contacts is the first on and the last off in the sequence.

SERVICE TIP

UL requires that the blower come on with or before the first heat element and must remain on until the last heating element has been deenergized.

Figure 46-6 Multiple sequencers

The time interval between when a sequencer is energized and when its contacts close is predetermined, within a range, by the sequencer's manufacturer. Some manufacturers offer sequencers with different time cycles. Likewise, the time interval between when a sequencer is deenergized and when each of the contacts drops out is preset by the manufacturer. In some cases, although the sequencers may come on one at a time sequentially, they may all go off at the same time together. Check with your supply house or the manufacturer to see what time cycle is required for the unit you are working on.

46.4 HEATING ELEMENTS

The heating elements used in electric furnaces are made out of a nickel chrome alloy. The nickel chrome alloy is used because it has both a high electrical resistance and slows down oxidation. Many metal alloys have an electrical resistance too low to be effective heating elements. Also, many alloys are susceptible to extreme oxidation at elevated temperatures. Heating elements appear to be long coil springs, and are bright in color until the coil is heated. As the elements are used, they will begin to discolor. Eventually, they will become dull black in color. The length of the heating element determines its kW capacity. Heating elements are available in 5 kW through 30 kW capacities for residential electric furnaces and may be as large as 60 kW or more for commercial electric furnaces. The typical kW options of a heating unit are shown in Figure 46-7. Figure 46-8 shows the heating elements held in place by ceramic spacers.

Electric heating elements are rated by their kW capacity. The kW capacity can be converted to Btu/hr by multiplying the kW value by 3.412. Electric heating elements come in a prewired rack. Each electric furnace is designed to hold a specific type and size of heating element rack. These racks are not interchangeable from manufacturer to manufacturer, or in many cases from one model furnace to another within the same manufacturer's product line. When replacing a heating element rack, be sure that you specify the model and serial number of the furnace the rack is to fit into.

Some heating element racks can be restrung with a replacement heating element, Figure 46-9. An advantage to restringing heating elements is that only a limited number of heating element sizes need to be stocked in your service van. However, replacing the heating element rack results in a significant time savings over restringing, and you are providing the customer with an entirely new part. Sometimes the ceramic insulators can be damaged during restringing, such as the one shown in Figure 46-10. A damaged insulator may fail some time after the installation job is complete.

46.5 APPLICATIONS

One common application of an electric furnace is to combine it with a split system heat pump. Whenever the outdoor temperature drops below the thermal balance point of the structure, the heat pump alone may not able to maintain a

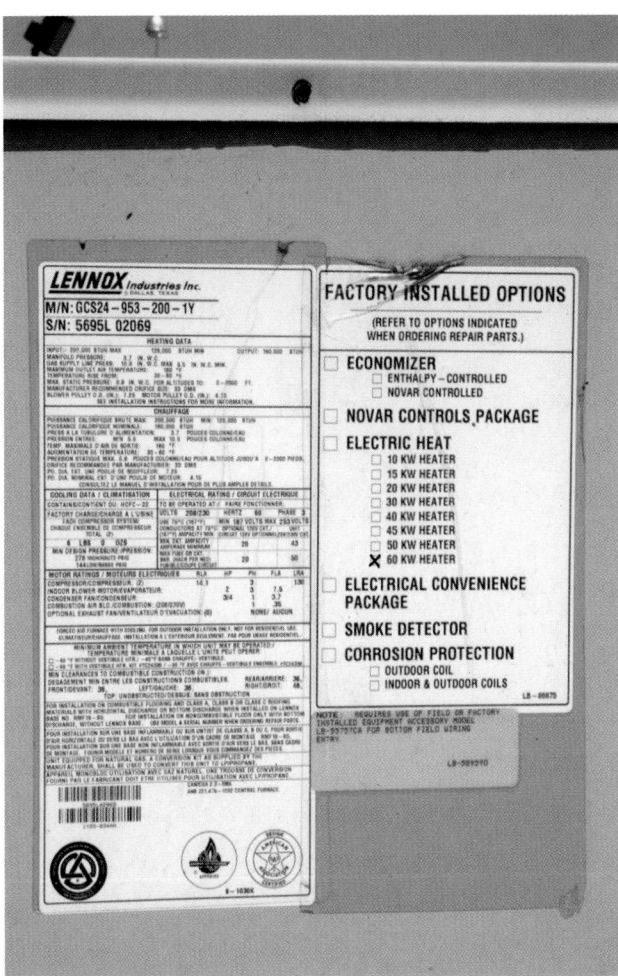

Figure 46-7 Name plate for 60 kW commercial heater

Figure 46-8 Heating element for 60 kW commercial heater

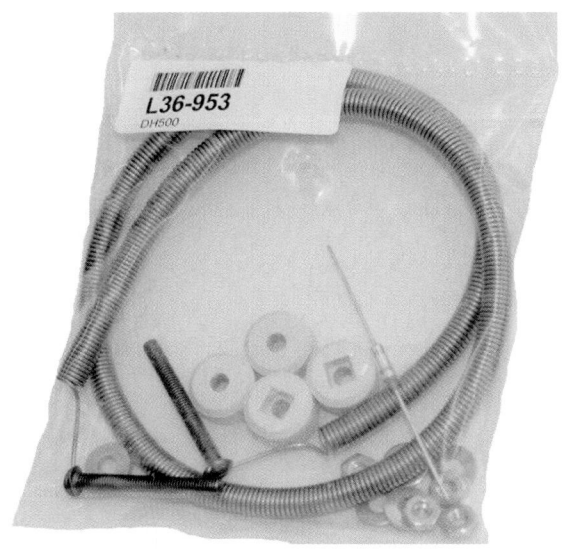

Figure 46-9 Electric heating element restringing kit

comfortable indoor temperature. This is when the electric furnace will supply the additional heat necessary to maintain the thermostat setpoint.

An example of an electric furnace and heat pump combination installation is shown in Figure 46-11. For these installations, the electric furnace acts as a fan coil unit. The refrigerated coil is installed in the furnace return air stream before the blower. The coil is connected by refrigerant tubing to the outdoor heat pump located on a slab outside the building. The thermostat is located in the conditioned space and controls the operation of the complete system to produce the heating or cooling as required.

An advantage of using an electric furnace as a supplemental heat source in a heat pump application is that this creates a draw through coil for the heat pump. This is the most efficient application for an indoor heat pump

Figure 46-10 Damaged ceramic insulator

Figure 46-11 Split system heat pump

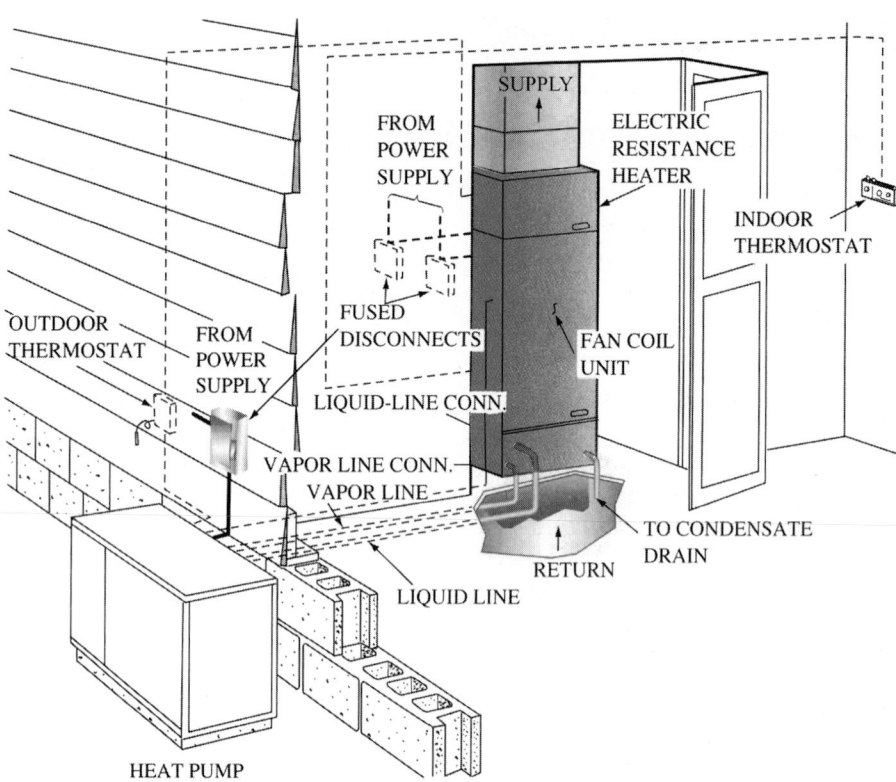

HEAT PUMP

coil. This is in contrast to gas or oil supplemental heating systems, where the coil must be located after the firebox to prevent condensation from forming on the heat exchanger.

Because of energy conservation concerns, some cities, counties, and states have ordinances or laws that prevent straight stand alone electric furnaces from being installed in new construction. This is because heat pumps are more efficient and under normal operating conditions will use less electricity. In those localities, heat pumps are used for primary heating in conjunction with electric furnaces that supply only supplemental heat.

46.6 ELECTRIC FURNACE CONTROLS

There are single stage and two stage thermostat systems, depending on the size of the unit. Figure 46-12 shows a thermostat that has a single stage for heating and a single stage for cooling. A fan control switch lever can be set to operate at low, medium, or high speed whenever the heating or cooling equipment cycles on.

Larger furnaces and some heat pumps use multistage thermostats. For electric furnaces the first stage would bring on at least 50% of the total capacity. The second stage of the thermostat would respond only when full heating capacity is needed. With this added control, wide variations in indoor

temperature are avoided. For heat pumps, the first stage brings on the heat pump and the next stage brings on the electric strips as needed.

Figure 46-13 shows a thermostat with two-stage heating and cooling and the system switch settings to control the thermostat operation are as follows:

- **OFF** Heating and cooling systems are off. If the fan switch is in the AUTO position, the cooling fan is also off.
- **COOL** Thermostat controls the cooling system. Heating system is off.
- **AUX. HEAT** Auxiliary heat is on. Cooling system is off.
- **HEAT PUMP** First stage heat is on. Cooling system is off.
- **2 STG. HEAT** First and second stage heat is on. Cooling system is off.

Electronic or digital thermostats use thermistors or other integrated circuit devices to sense temperature changes. The system and fan selections can be operated by a keyboard, Figure 46-14. The installer setup is used to customize the thermostat to specific systems. The fan can be configured to be operated in the heat mode either by the equipment or by the thermostat. The heating cycle rate can be adjusted for stage two heating. Fan operation can be extended to continue after the call for heating or cooling ends.

Figure 48-14 Sanded slip-on terminal with brass showing *(Courtesy of Spa Babes, Inc.)*

Some new blower motors do not have oil ports. These motors are supplied with a "lifetime" of lubrication sealed in the motor bushings. If one of these sealed motors has developed a bearing problem, it cannot be lubricated and must be replaced. Motors that have oil ports should be lubricated no more than once annually for heating furnaces, and no more than twice annually for heating/cooling furnaces. The oil used to lubricate a blower motor must be specifically labeled as electric motor lubrication oil. Figure 48-15 shows oil that is commonly used to lubricate electric motor bearings. General purpose or penetrating lubricants like Three in One or WD40® are not acceptable. Some of these oils have detergents or solvents that will actually damage the motor's bearings over time.

Do not overlubricate blower motors and follow any manufacturer's instructions, Figure 48-16. Most motors require just a few drops of lubricant in the oil fill ports located on each end. Excessive lubrication will result in oil running out of the bearing seals where it will deposit on the inside of the motor housing and windings as a thin film. The dust present in an air handler will collect as a layer on this oil film which then acts as an insulator and restricts airflow. In both cases, the motor will run hotter and the motor winding insulation will begin to break down. Over a relatively short period of time, this can cause the motor windings to short out.

If the motor has to be removed in order to lubricate the inner bearing, make certain that it is reinstalled with the oil fill ports facing up. Always make certain that the oil fill port plugs have been replaced before the motor is put back in service. Failing to cap these ports will allow dirt and dust to collect, which will be carried into the bearing the next time the motor is lubricated. This can cause damage to the motor bearings.

48.8 FURNACE EFFICIENCY AND CFM

Compared to most furnaces, it is easier to accurately determine the exact airflow through the air handler of an electric furnace. It is fairly simple to properly set the fan speed to provide the 400 CFM of airflow per ton that is recommended for

(a)   (b)

Figure 48-15 (a) Zip oiler; (b) Telescoping spout

most air conditioner air handlers. To calculate the actual CFM of an air handler, you must take the following readings:

- Total amperage draw of the heating elements. This amperage must be of the heating elements only; it should not include the blower.

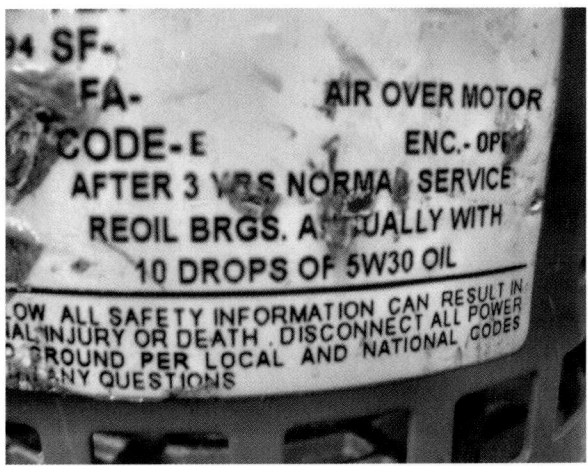

Figure 48-16 Oiling instructions on motor cover

- Voltage at the heating elements as the unit is operating.
- The return air temperature.
- The supply air temperature. Make certain that this temperature is not taken with a probe inserted in the supply plenum so that it would be in a direct line of sight with the heating elements. The radiant heat that the elements produce would give a false high reading.

Use the following formula:

$$CFM = \frac{V \times A \times 3.142}{\Delta T \times 1.08}$$

EXAMPLE 48-1

A unit with the following operating characteristics:

Voltage at strips	220 V
Amp draw of strips	27.8 A
Return air temperature	70°F
Supply air temperature	117°F

Temperature difference = 117°F − 70°F = 47°F

$$CFM = \frac{220 \times 27.8 \times 3.142}{47 \times 1.08} = \frac{19,216}{50.76} = 379 \text{ CFM}$$

48.9 TRANSFORMER

The transformer, Figure 48-17, in an electric furnace is subject to a greater load than most HVAC transformers because the system may have a number of sequencers, all of which have heat motors that use 24 V. It is important to check the secondary voltage supplied by a control voltage transformer while the system is operating to determine if the transformer can supply 24 V under load. When a transformer is overloaded or weak, the secondary voltage drops. A control voltage of 18 V or lower indicates a problem in the 24 V control system.

Figure 48-17 Control voltage transformer

Transformer problems are usually caused by control problems. A shorted relay sequencer heater will overload the transformer, causing it to fail. Simply replacing the transformer on a system with a shorted relay sequencer heater will only result in another failed transformer. The technician should check the resistance of all 24 V controls whenever replacing a transformer. Any control with a very low resistance across a relay coil should be replaced.

TECH TIP

Electric furnaces use 208–240 V as their primary power. Most replacement transformers have multiple power taps. Refer to the transformer's specifications to make certain that you are connecting the proper leads for the voltage your unit operates on. It is not an acceptable practice to simply assume that you are on a 240 V tap. If you do this on a 208 V system, the secondary voltage will be lower than 24 V. The voltage will be low under some circumstances where there are a number of current drawing devices on the secondary, such as humidifiers, multiple sequencers, and dampener motors. For example, under these heavy loads there may not be sufficient voltage and current to operate all of these devices.

48.10 BLOWER RELAY

The blower should come on when the first heating strip comes on and go off when the last heating strip goes off. How this is done depends on the furnace's control system. Electric furnaces that use separate sequencers for each heating strip typically use a second set of contacts on each sequencer to control the fan. All of these contacts are wired in parallel so that if any sequencer is closed, the fan operates. The blower relay on these furnaces is only used for continuous fan operation or for air conditioning.

Other furnaces use the blower relay to control the fan during heating. These usually require an electric heating thermostat. An electric heating thermostat energizes the G terminal during a call for heat to start the fan. The last sequencer to shut off has a set of contacts wired to control the blower on low speed. This keeps the blower operating when the thermostat is satisfied and the G terminal is no longer energizing the blower relay.

The all-in-one sequencers use a separate set of contacts to control the blower. These contacts will open and close at the same time as those controlling the first heating strip. On this type of system the first heating strip on is also the last one off, so the blower is operating any time any, one of the heating strips is on.

A blower that runs constantly on an electric furnace can be a sign of a sequencer with stuck contacts. This can be checked by measuring the furnace amperage draw. A high amperage draw with no call for heat is an indication of a stuck sequencer. The sequencer can be identified by checking the amperage draw leaving each sequencer until you find the one that is operating all the time. Check the relay sequencer heater voltage to be sure the problem is not in the control circuit.

TECH TIP

Occasionally during new construction metal debris can accidentally be left in a duct system. This debris can fall onto the heating elements because they are located at the top of the unit and are not protected by an evaporative coil the way that gas and oil burning systems are. Metal debris falling onto the heating elements will short a portion of the element to ground, turning it on.

UNIT 48—SUMMARY

The voltmeter and clamp-on ammeter are the service technician's most effective tools for tracking down problems in electric furnaces. They can be used to locate defective heating elements, open safety devices, and to check the airflow through the furnace.

Small resistances from poor connections can turn into large problems. Insufficient airflow can be at the root of many component failures in electric furnaces. Broken heating strips, open fusible links, and open thermal overloads are all caused by inadequate airflow.

WORK ORDERS

Service Ticket 4801

Customer Complaint: Poor Heating

Equipment: Electric Furnace Installed at the Local Animal Shelter

A service technician is called to inspect an electric furnace that is heating poorly. The furnace has three heating strips, each rated at 5 kW. The technician finds that only one heating strip is pulling current while the other two have no amperage draw. The technician checks the voltage at these two heating strips and measures a reading of 0 V. He then checks the fusible links and measures 240 V across one of them. Likewise, there is a reading of 240 V across the limit on the other strip.

The technician also notices that the airflow coming out of the registers is very low. Inspecting the air filter, the technician finds that it is packed with animal hair. The technician informs the manager of the animal shelter that the dirty filter reduced the airflow to the point that the heating elements overheated. This in turn

caused the fusible link and limit to fail. The technician replaces the fusible link, limit, and air filter and recommends to the manager that in the future the filter be changed once a week.

Service Ticket 4802

Customer Complaint: No Heat

Equipment: 15 kW Electric Furnace Installed in a Basement

A service technician answers a no heat call. Upon arrival, the technician finds that nothing is operating. An initial reading shows that the furnace has 240 V at the fuse block. The technician then measures the voltage at the R and C terminals on the furnace and reads 0 V.

In a hurry to get home, the technician diagnoses a bad transformer and quickly replaces it and then turns the furnace back on. The unit immediately starts, but no sooner has the technician packed up tools but a puff of smoke comes out of the transformer and the furnace stops. Unfortunately, upon checking the new transformer the technician finds that it is now failed too.

The technician realizes the unwise mistake that was made in jumping to an immediate conclusion. This time, skipping no steps, the technician begins by checking the 24 V circuits. The second relay sequencer heater is shorted, which led to the transformer failure. The technician replaces the sequencer and transformer and retests the system. This time the system runs and operates correctly.

Service Ticket 4803

Customer Complaint: High Bills

Equipment 15 kW Electric Furnace Installed in Crawlspace

A customer has called complaining of higher than normal electric bills. The technician arrives and the first obvious thing is that the furnace fan is running continuously. This is the case even with the fan switch set to AUTO and the system switch set to OFF.

The technician measures the furnace amperage draw at 23 A, which indicates that one of the heating strips is operating continuously. Using an ammeter, the technician identifies which set of heating strips is operating continuously. The technician then verifies which sequencer is controlling that set of heating strips.

The technician finds that there is no voltage to the relay sequencer heater. This is an indication that the sequencer contacts are not being held closed by the relay but instead must be stuck together. In this case the sequencer must be replaced. The technician makes the replacement, tests the furnace, and finds that it no longer runs continuously.

Service Ticket 4804

Customer Complaint: Furnace Will Not Run

Equipment: 20 kW Electric Furnace With an Electronic Setback Thermostat

A customer calls for help with an electric furnace. When the technician arrives at the residence, the customer explains the problem and provides some detail on the past history of the unit. This past spring the customer purchased and installed a new electronic setback thermostat from the home supply store down the street. The air conditioner worked fine through the spring and summer months. However, turning the furnace on this fall, nothing happened.

The technician inspects the thermostat wiring and everything appears to be connected tightly with no loose wires. While inspecting the furnace wiring diagram, the technician notices that the blower motor is controlled by the blower relay in the heat mode and the blower relay is energized by the G terminal. Realizing that this could be the problem, the technician asks the customer for the instructions that came with the thermostat. A section on configuring the thermostat for different systems is shown. The technician modifies the thermostat to bring the fan on in the heat mode and now the furnace operates correctly.

UNIT 48—REVIEW QUESTIONS

1. List three ways of checking the heating elements of an electric furnace.
2. Describe how a clamp-on ammeter can be used to check an electric furnace.
3. What would be the resistance reading of an open heating element?
4. A technician reads 240 V across the thermal overload to the first strip heater on an electric furnace. What does this mean?
5. List three ways of checking an overload in an electric furnace.
6. What should always be checked when replacing an overload?
7. What should always be checked when replacing a transformer?
8. What is the airflow through a furnace with the following readings:

   Voltage at the strips of 235 V
   Current draw of 39.5 A
   Return air temperature 72°F
   Supply air temperature 120°F

9. What type of oil should be used when lubricating the motor bearings?
10. Explain how a stuck heating sequencer can keep the fan operating continuously.
11. What is the correct remedy for a wire with one end which has overheated?
12. Why should relay slide-on posts not be sanded to clean off oxidation?
13. How can overlubricating a blower motor be detrimental?
14. What are the two general types of sequencers used on electric furnaces?
15. Describe two ways that electric furnaces control the blower motor.
16. What is the purpose of the white ceramic pieces on the strip heaters?
17. Why is a visual check of the heating strips on an electric furnace difficult to accomplish?
18. Why are terminal and wire resistance values critical in electric furnaces?
19. What are two types of safety that most electric furnaces utilize?
20. Why are the strips on an electric furnace staged to turn on in sequence instead of being energized all at one time?

UNIT 49

Types of Heat Pump Systems

OBJECTIVES

After completing this unit you will be able to:

- describe what a heat pump is.
- describe the cooling, heating, and defrost cycles.
- explain the operation of the reversing valve.
- explain the purpose of auxiliary heat.
- list the types of heat pump systems and configurations.
- discuss the operation of metering devices and check valves used in heat pumps.
- explain the purpose of suction accumulators and heating cycle charge compensators.
- explain the different types of efficiency ratings used for heat pumps.

49.1 INTRODUCTION

Heat pump systems lead all other forms of heat in terms of efficiency and low operating cost. The demand for heat pumps has increased because of the dramatic increase in the cost for all forms of energy. They must be installed correctly to take advantage of their energy saving technology. The least efficient system installed correctly will outperform a more efficient system which is poorly installed.

Heat pumps derive their name from the manner in which heat is delivered into the home: they are not "producing" heat, as in the case of fuel fired or electrical furnaces, but actually "pumping" heat from one area to another. Their efficiency is rated not by how efficiently they consume energy; but rather, by how efficiently they move it.

49.2 HEAT PUMPS

Like all refrigeration systems and air conditioners, heat pumps transfer heat from one place to another by changing the state of refrigerant. Basically all refrigeration systems are heat pumps; they transfer heat from a heat source at a low temperature to a heat sink at a higher temperature. What makes the heat pump unique is the ability to reverse the direction of refrigerant flow. In the summer it removes heat from the inside air and moves the heat to the outside air. In the winter it will remove heat from the outside air and move it to the inside air. Heat pumps are also called reverse cycle refrigeration systems.

A review of some basic physics principles will aid in your understanding of heat pumps. Five basic concepts will be discussed.

- Heat exists down to absolute zero, which is −460°F.
- Heat will only flow from a higher temperature region to a lower temperature region.
- Gases become warmer when compressed.
- Most matter can be in a solid (ice), liquid (water), or gas (steam) state.
- The temperature at which a material changes from a liquid to a gas or from a gas to a liquid depends on the pressure at which it is contained.

Concept 1: Heat in Cold Air

For many people, one of the biggest obstacles to overcome in understanding heat pump operation is accepting that heat exists even at very cold temperatures. Since heat is the form of energy which gives molecules their motion and all molecules are in motion, all molecules contain heat. The single exception to this is absolute zero. At absolute zero molecules do not move, and there is no heat.

Concept 2: Heat Flows From High to Low

Heat will only flow from a higher temperature to a lower temperature, period! The job of the heat pump is to make heat flow from a cooler area to a warmer area. To do this, the heat pump has a low side, which is colder than the cool area, and a high side, which is warmer than the warm area. Moving the heat from the low side to the high side is where the name "pump" comes from.

Concept 3: Compression Raises Temperature, Expansion Lowers Temperature

The high side is created by compressing, or squeezing, the gas. When a gas is compressed, the heat in the gas is concentrated and the temperature rises. This is done by a component called a compressor. Conversely, expanding a gas or liquid causes its pressure and temperature to drop. This is done by the expansion valve. The high side and low side of the system are created by the compressor and expansion valve. Note that the name of the component tells you what it does.

Concept 4: Change of State

Although it is possible to build a heat pump just by compressing and expanding gas, this type of system is not particularly efficient. The change in state of a refrigerant will more dramatically increase the efficiency of the heat pump. Liquids absorb hundreds of times more heat when they change state than when they change temperature. With this in mind, the refrigerant evaporates from a liquid to a gas in the evaporator and condenses from a gas to a liquid in the condenser. Again, note that the name indicates the component's purpose.

Concept 5: Saturation Temperature and Pressure

Fortunately, the temperature at which evaporation and condensation will take place is controlled by pressure. The increased pressure on the high side raises the condensing temperature, allowing the condenser to reject large amounts of heat while condensing the refrigerant. The decreased pressure on the low side lowers the evaporation temperature, allowing the evaporator to absorb large amounts of heat while the refrigerant evaporates.

Low Supply Air Temperatures

One obstacle to accepting heat pumps has been the relatively cool supply air temperatures that heat pumps produce. Customers who have been accustomed to traditional furnaces often object to the cooler supply air from the heat pump. Typical heat pump supply air temperatures range from 95°F to 110°F. Electric heat has a discharge temperature of 110−125°F and gas and oil heat supply air in the range of 120−140°F, Table 49-1.

Air at 95° blowing across your body in the winter does feel drafty. The solution to this problem is proper supply register placement. The air from the supply registers should not blow directly on the occupants. The heat pump is designed to heat your house, not you!

49.3 HISTORY OF HEAT PUMPS

The popularity of the heat pump rose with the increasing cost of electrical energy used for heating in residential and small commercial buildings. Heat pumps generally cost less to operate than fossil fuel furnaces and cost only about a third of what it cost to operate as electric strip heaters. The heat pump was actually developed by Lord Kelvin in 1852. The first practically applied heat pump was installed in Scotland in 1927. Between 1927 and 1950, heat pumps were installed in hundreds of residential and small commercial applications throughout Europe and the southern part of the United States. Many of these installations were merely air conditioning units converted to heat pumps by the addition of revers-

ing valves and applicable controls. These early heat pumps had high failure rates because they did not have defrost controls, crankcase heaters, or suction accumulators. Heat pumps acquired a bad reputation as a result of this high failure rate. Although improvements in design made heat pumps more reliable, the early high failure rates caused problems in the market for years. Further, the relatively low cost of energy during this same time period almost destroyed this market.

The demand for heat pumps has grown over the past several decades. The reason for this new interest in heat pumps is both economic and environmental in nature. Interest in heat pumps has increased in recent years because of growing interest in energy conservation, the rising cost of heating, and mounting concern over the pollution produced by power plants.

49.4 HEAT PUMP CYCLES

Basic Reverse Cycle Concept

In the conventional refrigeration cooling cycle, Figure 49-1, heat is absorbed by the indoor coil, the evaporator, and discharged to the outside by the outdoor coil, the condenser. To change from cooling to heating, the indoor and outdoor coils trade functions. The outdoor coil becomes the evaporator, and the indoor coil becomes the condenser. In the heating cycle, heat is absorbed by the outdoor coil, which is now the evaporator, and discharged to the inside by the indoor coil, which is now the condenser.

The heat pump cycle is shown in Figures 49-2 and 49-3. The coils are relabeled as indoor and outdoor because they are now dual purpose. This reduces confusion because the outdoor coil is the condenser in the cooling cycle and the evaporator in the heating cycle. The indoor coil is the evaporator in the cooling mode and the condenser in the heating cycle. The process is reversed by means of a four-way valve called a reversing valve, Figure 49-4.

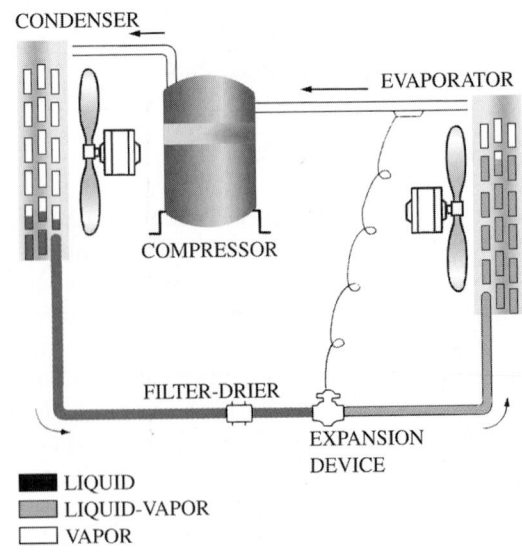

Figure 49-1 A conventional refrigeration cycle

Table 49-1 Supply Air Temperature Ranges for Various Heating Systems

Heating type	Discharge temperature
Electric strip heat	110–125°F
Gas heating	120–140°F
Heat pumps	95–115°F

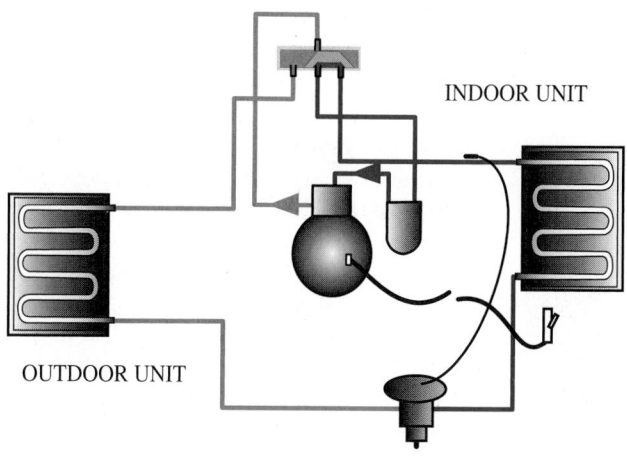

Figure 49-2 Heat pump system in cooling mode

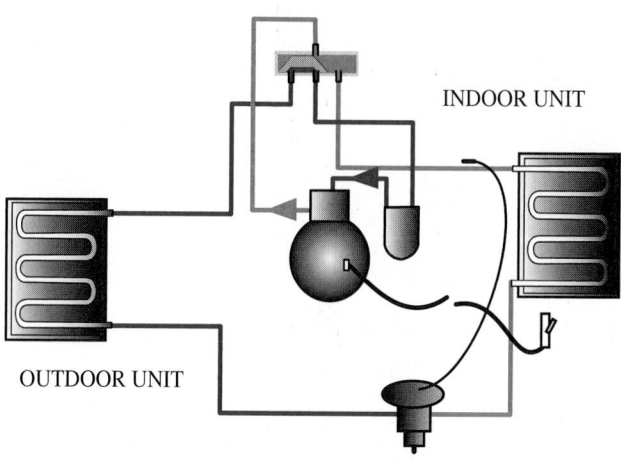

Figure 49-3 Heat pump system in heating mode

Figure 49-4 Heat pump reversing valve

TECH TIP

Remember to tell the owner that the outdoor section will run during the winter heating mode. Some customers may make unnecessary service calls because they believe that the outdoor section only operates in the cooling mode.

The Reversing Valve

The reversing valve is composed of three main parts: the pilot valve, the main valve, and the solenoid coil. The solenoid coil controls the pilot valve, which in turn controls the suction bleed to the main valve. The purpose of the main valve is to reverse the refrigerant route through the indoor and outdoor coils; thereby exchanging the functions of the condenser and evaporator coils.

The basic operation of a reversing valve can be compared to a solid cylinder sliding inside a hollow tube. Blowing in one end of the tube will shift the cylinder to the other end of the tube. This is how the cylinder inside the reversing valve is shifted, by pressure difference. By imposing the discharge pressure on one end of the reversing valve and the suction pressure on the other end of the valve, the pressure difference will shift the internal cylinder toward the side that is connected to the suction pressure.

The main valve body is constructed with the permanent suction in the middle of the valve on one side and the permanent discharge in the middle of the valve directly opposite the permanent suction port. The ports leading to the indoor and outdoor coils are located on either side of the permanent suction port. When at rest, the sliding cylinder always straddles two tube openings. One of these openings is always the permanent suction port which is connected to the low side of the system. The other opening will be either the indoor coil port or the outdoor coil port. This makes whichever coil is connected to the permanent suction via the sliding valve, the evaporator. The port that is not covered by the sliding valve is open to the permanent discharge port located opposite the permanent suction port. This makes whichever coil is connected to the uncovered port, the condenser, Figure 49-5.

The Metering Devices

Since both the indoor and outdoor coils must function as the evaporator, both coils need metering devices. However, only the metering device that feeds the coil acting as the evaporator should be in the refrigerant circuit. In some heat pump designs, check valves are connected in parallel with the metering devices to permit bypassing the metering devices when they are not needed in the circuit, Figure 49-6.

Recently, most manufacturers have been using metering devices that act as both a metering device and a check valve. Flow restrictors with pistons in them are popular in lower end models. These are like a check valve with a hole drilled through the ball in the check valve. In the forward direction, the piston seats and forces the refrigerant through the hole in the piston,

Figure 49-5 Internal view of heat pump reversing valve

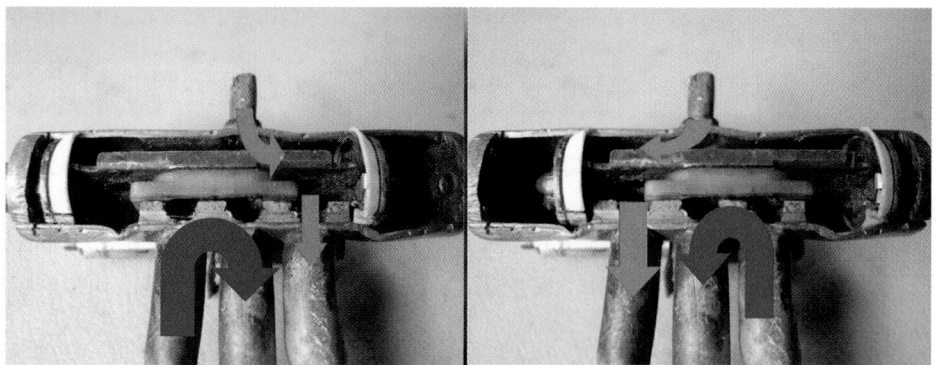

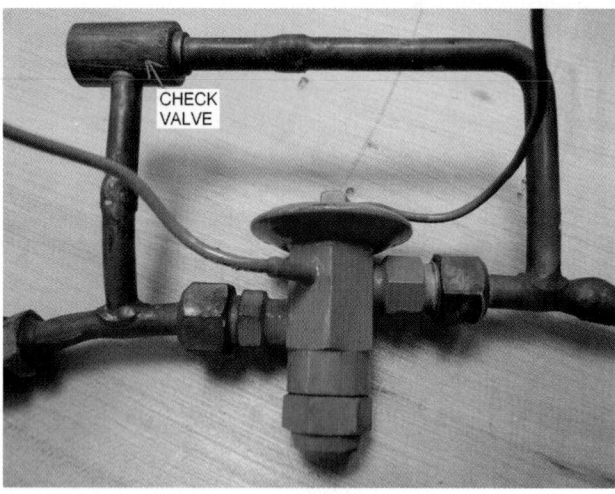

Figure 49-6 Check valve in parallel to TEV

Figure 49-7 Flow check orifice

creating a pressure drop. In the reverse direction, the piston lifts off the seat and refrigerant flows around the piston without a pressure drop. Figure 49-7 shows a flow check device in a heat pump and a close-up of the piston from a flow check device.

Bi-flow thermostatic expansion valves with a built-in check valve are now popular. In the forward direction the check valve seats and forces the refrigerant through the orifice in the expansion valve, creating a pressure drop. In the reverse direction, the ball lifts off the seat and refrigerant flows around the expansion valve without a pressure drop, Figure 49-8.

Another form of biflow thermostatic expansion valves are used on water source heat pumps. These valves meter in both directions. Using only one expansion valve is possible on packaged water source units because the two coils are so close together. This allows the manufacturers to build a unit with only one metering device and eliminates check valves completely, Figure 49-9.

The Cooling Cycle

During the cooling cycle, the high pressure/high temperature discharge gas is directed from the compressor to the outdoor coil (condenser), where it condenses to a high pressure, high temperature subcooled liquid. To avoid the restriction of the metering device connected to the outlet of the outdoor coil,

Figure 49-8 Biflow TEV on heat pump split system

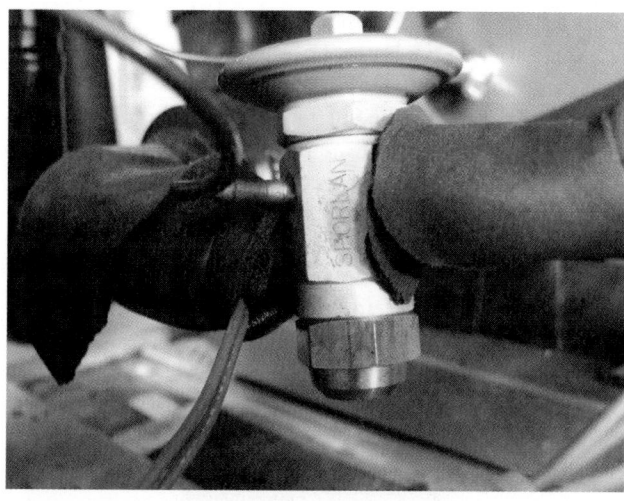

Figure 49-9 Biflow TEV on water source heat pump

a check valve is installed allowing the liquid to bypass the outdoor metering device. The liquid travels inside through the liquid line where the indoor check valve closes, forcing the refrigerant through the indoor metering device. The indoor metering device drops the refrigerant pressure and temperature so that heat can be absorbed in the indoor coil. The refrigerant vapor produced in the indoor coil now travels through the reversing valve to the suction accumulator and on to the compressor. The cooling cycle is complete.

The Heating Cycle

The refrigerant flow must be reversed for the heating cycle. Remember, the direction of refrigerant flow through the compressor is always the same; the direction of flow is changed by the reversing valve. In the heating cycle the reversing valve changes position, changing the direction of gas flow. The high pressure, high temperature gas from the compressor flows through the reversing valve to the indoor coil. The indoor coil now acts as a condenser, adding heat into the return air from the conditioned area. The hot vapor is condensed, and the temperature is reduced to produce a high pressure, high temperature subcooled liquid. The indoor check valve opens and allows the liquid refrigerant to flow around the indoor metering device. Continuing through the liquid line, the liquid refrigerant is forced through the outdoor coil metering device by the closing of the check valve connected in parallel with it. The low pressure, low temperature mixture of liquid and vapor refrigerant flows into the outdoor coil which is now the evaporator. The low refrigerant pressure keeps the refrigerant temperature lower than the outdoor temperature. Since the outdoor air is warmer than the refrigerant, heat is picked up from the outdoor air, evaporating the liquid refrigerant. This refrigerant vapor then flows through the vapor line, reversing valve, and accumulator to the compressor. The heating cycle is now complete.

The Defrost Cycle

It is important to keep the outdoor coil cleared of frost. The system efficiency drops when frost builds to the point that it blocks airflow. The defrost cycle is basically the same as the cooling cycle. The outdoor coil switches from being an evaporator to now being the condenser. This allows for hot vapor to pass through the outdoor coil to help defrost any frost buildup. However an adverse result from operating in this mode will be that the unit is air conditioning the house in the middle of winter! To offset this effect, the outdoor fan is deenergized and the auxiliary heat is energized during the defrost cycle. The auxiliary heat is energized to prevent 60°F air from blowing in the house.

The defrost cycle is controlled by a defrost control board. The unit cannot simply use temperature to control the defrost cycle or it would be constantly defrosting when the outdoor temperature was below freezing. A time control is used to prevent defrost any more often than the timing period. Most control boards have adjustable settings using a jumper, Figure 49-10. Common timing periods include 30, 45, 60, and 90 minutes. The unit will start a defrost cycle when the timing period is reached if the defrost thermostat is closed. The defrost cycle will continue until the defrost thermostat senses the coil is warm. The timer has a fail-safe termination time that will end the defrost cycle if the defrost thermostat does not. These boards are known as time initiated and temperature terminated.

While it is important to defrost the outdoor coil, the defrost cycle is very inefficient since the refrigeration cycle is working against the auxiliary heat. Time-temperature boards are very reliable, but they do initiate defrost cycles that are unnecessary. Many defrost schemes have been developed to reduce unnecessary defrost cycles in an attempt to improve efficiency. These are called "demand defrost controls" because they attempt to only initiate a defrost cycle when there is a need. The most commonly used demand defrost control measures the coil temperature and the ambient air temperature. The temperature difference between the coil and the outdoor air remains fairly

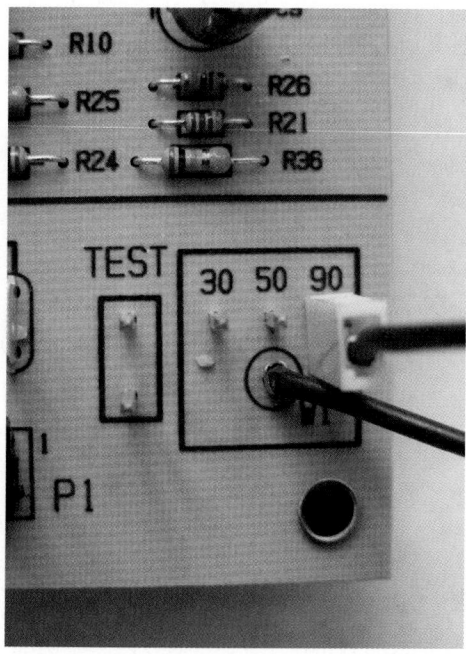

Figure 49-10 Time-temperature jumper on a defrost board

constant until the coil starts to frost. As the airflow decreases, the coil temperature decreases which increases the temperature difference between the air and the coil. Some demand defrost boards also use timers for failsafe termination.

TECH TIP

Tell your customer about the steam that will come off the outdoor unit during winter defrost cycles. Some owners may be startled when they see the steam coming from the outdoor coil. The owner may think this steam is smoke, and may believe the outdoor section is on fire. Prepare owners so that when they see this, they will be assured the system is running properly.

Refrigerant Storage

Since the heat pump operates year-round, it must be adaptable to a wide range of operating conditions. These varying conditions translate into significant variance in unit capacity. In simple terms, the heat pump is not always circulating the same amount of refrigerant so it needs a place for the unused refrigerant to collect. Liquid receivers do not serve this purpose for heat pumps because they have a definitive inlet and outlet and cannot be easily reversed.

Suction Line Accumulator

The suction line accumulator has become a standard component on heat pumps, Figure 49-11. For heat pumps, suction line accumulators have two distinct advantages over liquid receivers: they can be installed in the common suction line to the compressor where the flow does not reverse and they provide protection against liquid returning to the compressor.

One problem with the suction line accumulator is that it is designed to trap liquid. Since the oil returning to the compressor is a liquid, it naturally traps the oil as well as any liquid refrigerant. To return this oil to the compressor, the gas

must pass through a tube shaped like a J, Figure 49-12. There is a small hole in the bottom of the tube that slowly allows small amounts of oil and liquid refrigerant to return to the compressor through the suction line. This small hole can pose a problem because it can be easily plugged by contaminants. If this occurs, the refrigerant oil will gradually become trapped in the accumulator, resulting in a lack of lubrication for the compressor and eventual failure.

This problem most often occurs after a compressor burnout. Even if the accumulator does not become clogged after a compressor burnout, it can harbor a lot of contaminants

Figure 49-11 Suction accumulator for a heat pump

Figure 49-12 Accumulator

that the system would be better off without. Unfortunately, there is no way to clean an accumulator short of removing it. A few manufacturers actually recommend removal and cleaning or replacement of the suction accumulator when changing the compressor on a heat pump. The only special precaution for accumulator installation is to pay attention to the inlet and outlet of the accumulator. They are marked and MUST NOT BE REVERSED!

Heating Cycle Charge Compensator

A few manufacturers now use heating cycle charge compensator tanks, Figure 49-13. The compensator tank is basically an empty can with the gas line running straight through it. The gas line is not open to the tank, it just passes through the tank. Liquid refrigerant enters and leaves the tank through a single small line. This line is connected to the liquid line.

In the heating cycle, the gas line is cold, making the refrigerant in the compensator tank cold. Refrigerant in the liquid line migrates to the charge compensator tank because the refrigerant in the liquid line is at a higher temperature and pressure than the cooler liquid sitting in the compensator tank. This stores the extra refrigerant that is not circulated during the heating cycle, Figure 49-14.

During the cooling cycle, the gas line is hot, making the refrigerant in the compensator tank hot. The liquid refrigerant in the compensator tank leaves the tank and goes into the liquid line because the temperature and pressure of the

Figure 49-13 Heating cycle charge compensator tank

refrigerant in the tank are now higher than the temperature and pressure of the liquid line. This returns refrigerant to the cycle to be circulated during the cooling cycle, Figure 49-15.

49.5 AIR SOURCE SYSTEMS

Air source systems use air as both the heat source and the heat sink. In heating, the outdoor air is the heat source and the indoor air is the heat sink.

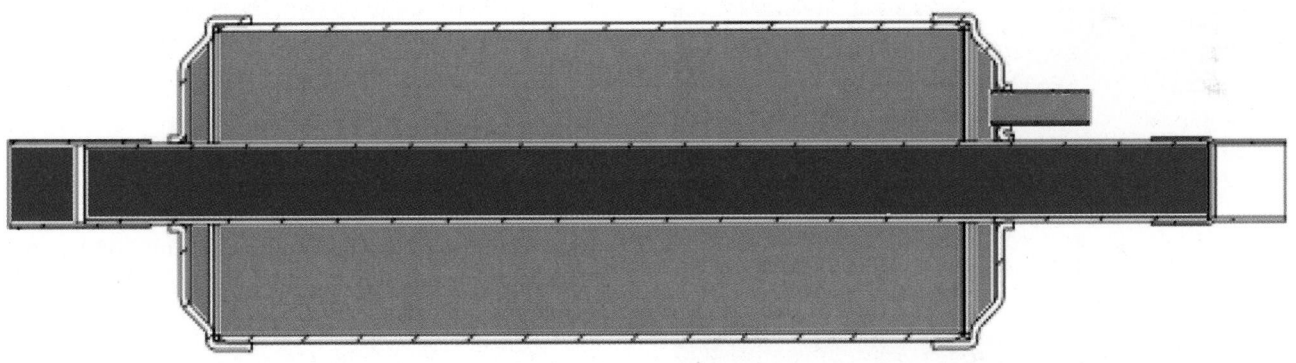

Figure 49-14 Compensator tank full during the heat cycle

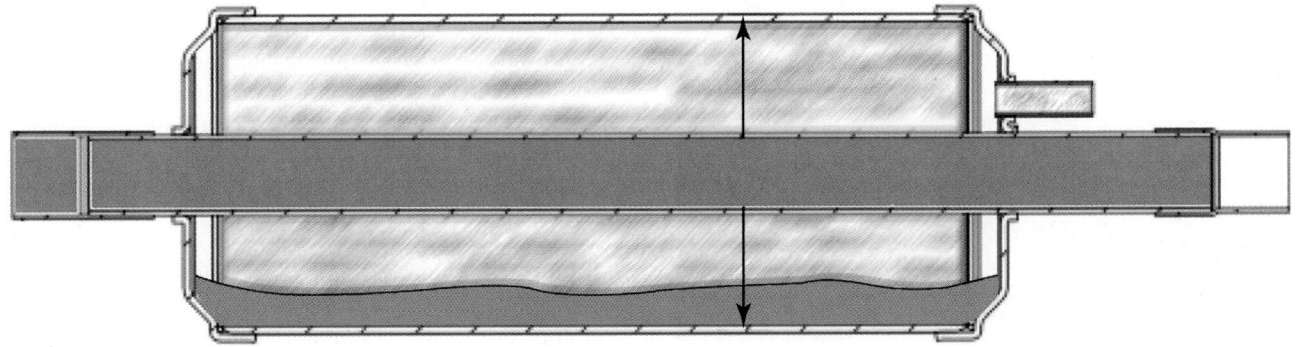

Figure 49-15 Compensator tank empty during the cooling cycle

Configuration

Air source heat pump systems are available as either packaged units, with all the components in one cabinet; or as split systems, with the compressor and condenser in one cabinet and the evaporator in another.

Packaged Units

Air source packaged units are available as side discharge, bottom discharge, or wall mount. Bottom discharge units are typically mounted on flat roofs on a curb. They are sometimes referred to as curb mount units. Side discharge duct connections can be arranged in two ways: over-under or side-by-side. Over-under units have the supply duct over the return duct, Figure 49-16. Side-by-side units have the return and supply ducts beside each other, Figure 49-17.

Figure 49-18 Convertible packaged unit

Some units are convertible from side discharge to bottom discharge. They accomplish this with removable panels on the bottom and sides of the unit where duct can connect. Typically these units arrive with both sets of panels in place. For bottom discharge, remove the bottom panels; for side discharge, remove the side panels, Figure 49-18.

Wall mount packaged units mount to the exterior wall of a building. The air moves though two large holes in the wall. The return air is drawn in at the bottom of the unit and the supply air leaves at the top. Many wall mount units are installed like giant room air conditioners, with no ductwork. The unit is bolted to the wall and two large grills cover the return and supply air openings. This is typical in trailers that serve as temporary offices or classrooms, Figure 49-19.

Split Systems

Split systems have two components: a condensing unit that is installed outside, and a blower coil that is installed inside, Figure 49-20. The condensing unit consists of a compressor, outside air coil, and outdoor fan, Figure 49-21. The blower coil contains the indoor fan and the indoor air coil, Figure 49-22.

The two components are connected by two refrigerant lines: a gas line and a liquid line. The liquid line always contains high pressure liquid, regardless of the cycle; however, the direction of the liquid changes. In cooling the liquid is traveling from outside to inside, in heating it is traveling from inside to outside. The gas line changes from a low pressure suction line in cooling, to a high pressure discharge line in heating. That is why it is called the gas line: the refrigerant in it is always gas.

Auxiliary Heat

Air source heat pumps work by removing heat from the outside air and delivering it to the inside. As the outside air temperature drops, the evaporator temperature and pressure must also drop in order to continue to absorb heat. This increases the compression ratio of the compressor and

Figure 49-16 Over-under package unit with panels removed

Figure 49-17 Side-by-side packaged unit

Figure 49-19 Wall mount unit

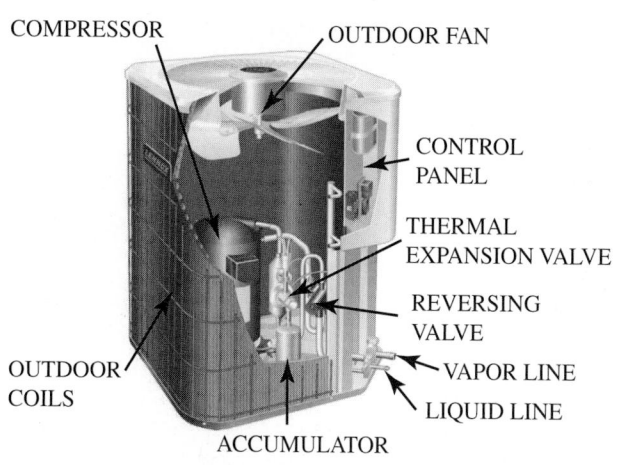

COMPRESSOR

OUTDOOR FAN

CONTROL
PANEL

THERMAL
EXPANSION VALVE

REVERSING
VALVE

VAPOR LINE

LIQUID LINE

OUTDOOR
COILS

ACCUMULATOR

Figure 49-21 Cutaway of a split system outdoor unit
(Courtesy Lennox Industries Inc.)

decreases its volumetric efficiency. In short, the system loses capacity. At the same time, the heat loss of the home actually increases at lower ambient temperatures. At some point, the heat pump's decreasing capacity will not be able to keep up with the structure's increasing load. The lowest temperature at which the heat pump can heat the structure is called the balance point. Below this temperature, extra heat will be required in order to maintain comfort conditions. This extra heat is called auxiliary or supplemental heat. Normally the auxiliary heat is not energized until the system reaches its balance point because auxiliary heat is more expensive to operate. In practice, the auxiliary heat is energized about 5°F above the balance point to ensure the system can handle the

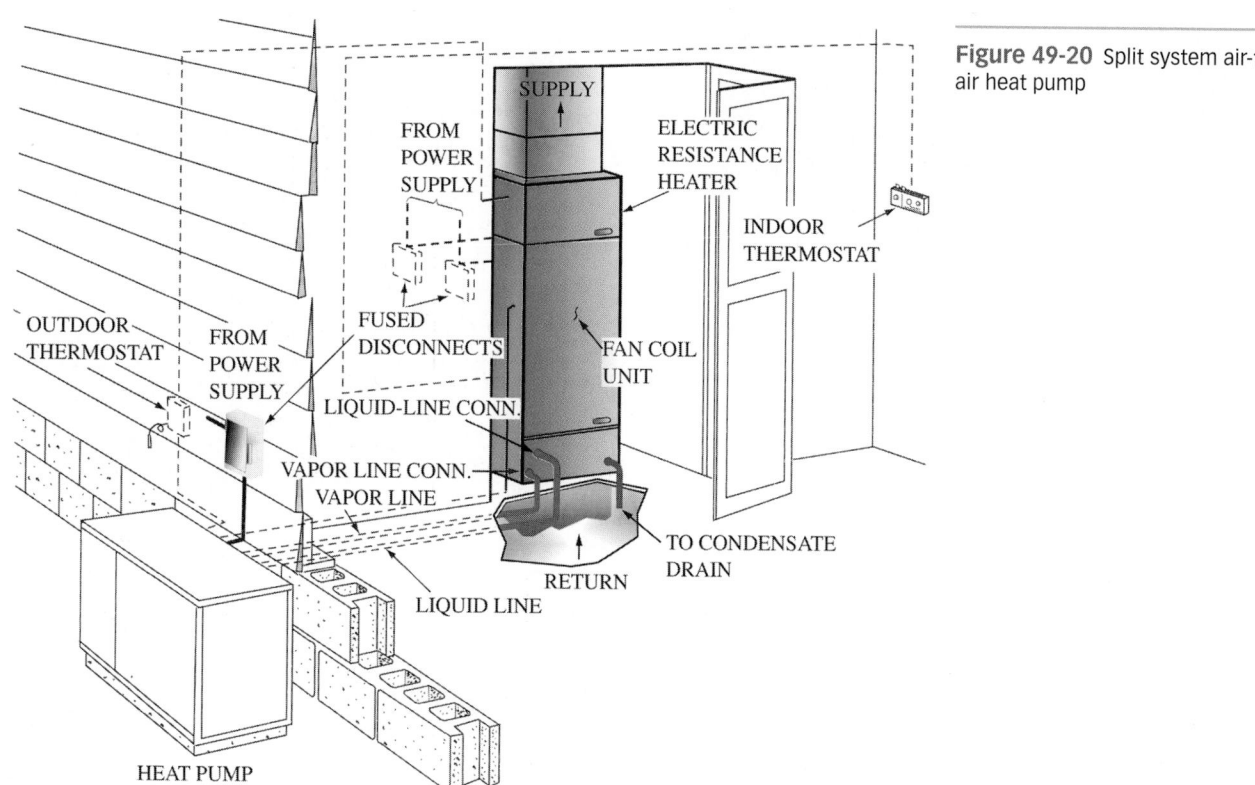

Figure 49-20 Split system air-to-air heat pump

SUPPLY

FROM
POWER
SUPPLY

ELECTRIC
RESISTANCE
HEATER

INDOOR
THERMOSTAT

OUTDOOR
THERMOSTAT

FROM
POWER
SUPPLY

FUSED
DISCONNECTS

FAN COIL
UNIT

LIQUID-LINE CONN.

VAPOR LINE CONN.
VAPOR LINE

TO CONDENSATE
DRAIN

RETURN

LIQUID LINE

HEAT PUMP

Figure 49-22 Heat pump blower and cooling coil indoor unit

Figure 49-23 Thermostat showing emergency heat setting

the compressor and outdoor fan at all. This setting is used when a problem exists with the refrigeration system and provides the customer with heat. This setting should be reserved for emergency use since the auxiliary heat is typically more expensive to operate than the heat pump.

Electric heat strips similar to those used in electric furnaces are most commonly used for supplemental heat, Figure 49-24.

demand. The auxiliary heat is also used to reheat the cool air the heat pump circulates in the defrost cycle.

The auxiliary heat is controlled by the second stage of a two-stage thermostat. The second stage closes approximately 1.5°F below the thermostat setpoint. If the heat pump cannot meet the heating demand, the second stage energizes to bring on the auxiliary heat. Some units also use outdoor thermostats set to 5°F above the balance point. These outdoor thermostats will not let the auxiliary heat come on until the temperature outside drops to their setpoint.

Besides the familiar HEAT, COOL, and OFF system settings, heat pump thermostats also have an emergency heat setting, Figure 49-23. Emergency heat energizes the auxiliary heat on first stage instead of second stage and does not energize

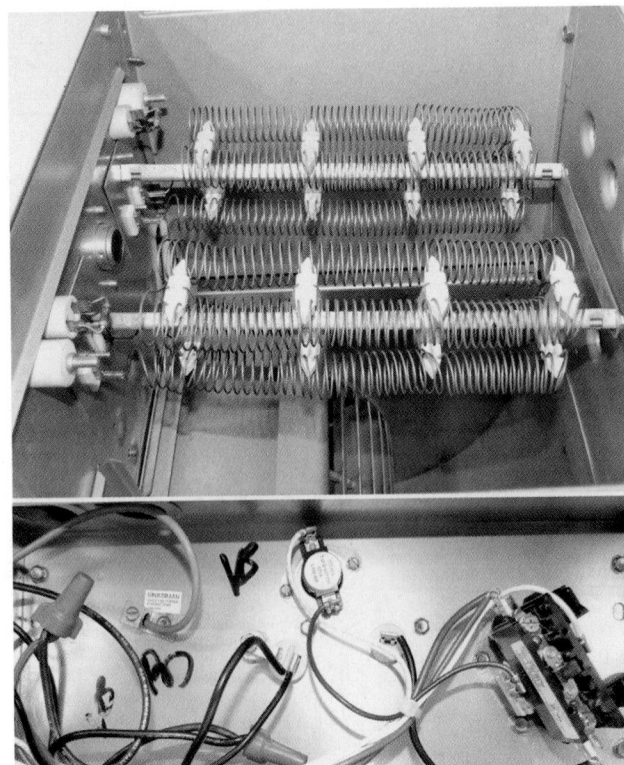

Figure 49-24 Electric strip heater

The strips are energized by the second stage of a two stage thermostat when the heat pump cannot maintain the house temperature. The strips are located after the coil in the airstream. Their heat is in addition to the heat produced by the heat pump; the heat pump continues to operate even after energizing the strips.

Gas or oil furnaces can also be used for supplemental heat in a dual fuel system. However, the indoor coil is installed after the furnace in the airstream, Figure 49-25. When a gas or oil furnace is used for supplemental heat, the heat pump shuts off when the furnace comes on because the hot air from the furnace passing over the indoor coil would cause extremely high head pressures in the heat pump.

49.6 WATER SOURCE HEAT PUMP SYSTEM

In heating, water source systems use water as their heat source and the indoor air as the heat sink. The operating concept of a water source heat pump is similar to an air source system: heat is transferred from one coil to another. Instead of two air coils, water-to-air heat pumps use one water coil and one air coil, Figure 49-26.

The water coil transfers heat from the refrigerant to the water and the air coil transfers heat from the refrigerant to the air. The refrigeration cycle for a water source heat pump is a little simpler because water source units have a much narrower operating temperature range than air source units. The water source unit's capacity is less variable because the water being supplied to it must be moderate in temperature. This means that water source units do not require suction line accumulators or charge compensators. Also, most water source packaged units use a single biflow thermostatic expansion valve, so there are no check valves or extra metering devices. Since the fluid circulating through the water source unit cannot be allowed to freeze, this type of heat pump does not need a defrost cycle.

Water source systems can be connected to an open or closed water loop. Open loops are open to the air and are supplied with water from a well. The water for an open loop is not recirculated, Figure 49-27a. Closed loops are pressurized loops of water buried in the ground that recirculate the same water, Figure 49-27b.

The construction of the water coil is efficient and compact, called tube in tube or coaxial. The water coil should be located in the heated area to prevent possible freeze-up if the outdoor ambient temperature should drop

Figure 49-25 Coil on furnace

Figure 49-26 Horizontal style water source heat pump with panels removed

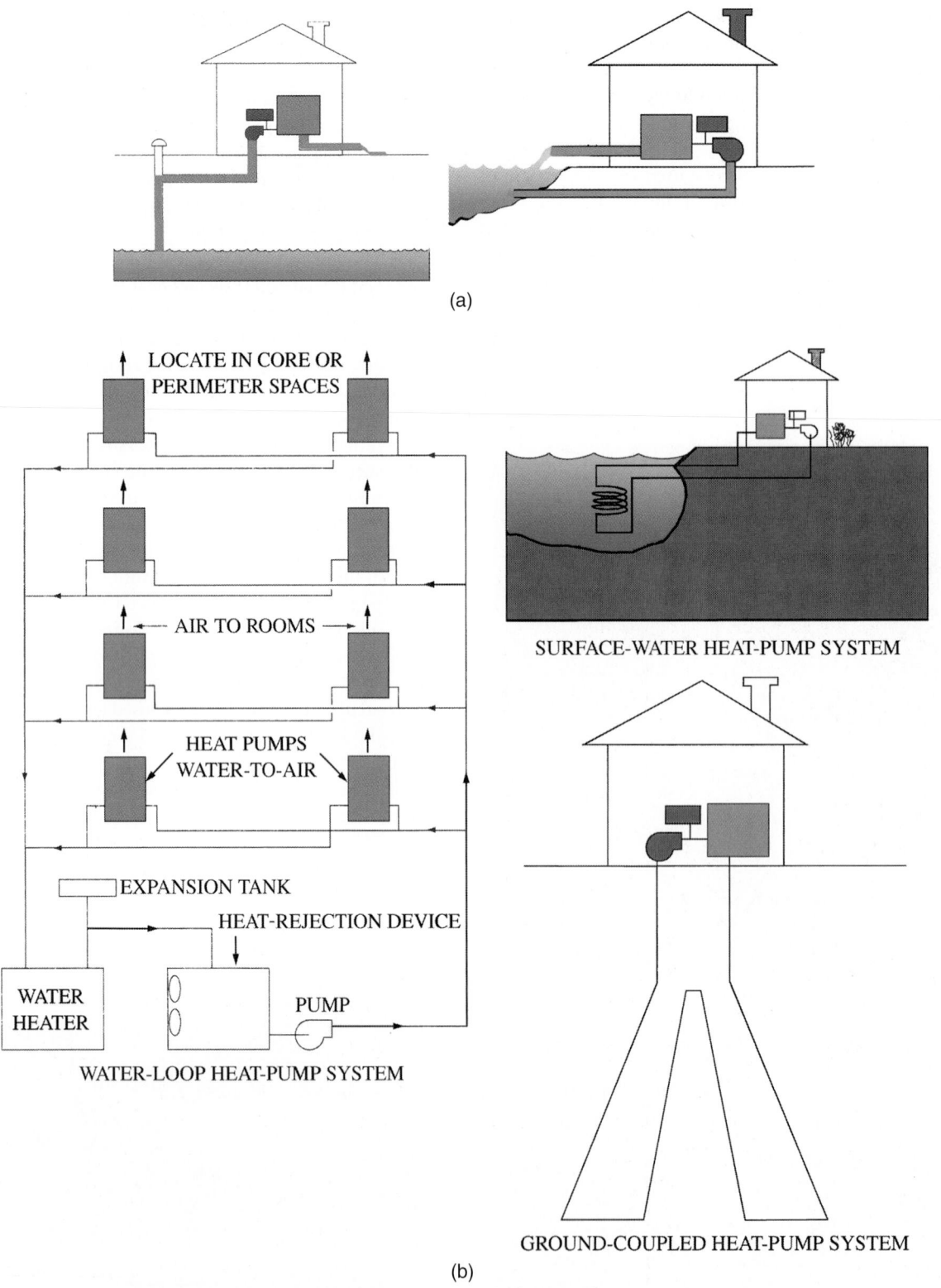

Figure 49-27 (a) Open loop system; (b) Closed loop system
(© American Society of Heating, Refrigerating, and Air-Conditioning Engineers, Ins., www.ashrae.org)

Figure 49-28 Cutaway view of a water coil

below 32°F. If the water-to-refrigerant heat exchanger is part of a packaged unit, it would be located in the conditioned area. These heat exchangers are made of copper, cupronickel, or stainless steel. Figure 49-28 shows a water-to-refrigerant coil and a cutaway of the coil. Water travels through the inner tube, and refrigerant flows through the outer tube.

Water source packaged units are available as either vertical or horizontal discharge. Many water source systems also have supplemental heat, but it is not as necessary for them because they do not lose capacity as the outdoor temperature drops and they do not have a defrost cycle. However, a unit sized correctly for cooling may still be undersized for heating and require additional heat.

49.7 AIR-TO-WATER SYSTEMS

Air-to-water systems use the air surrounding the unit as the heat source, and the water in the hot water system as the heat sink. Also called heat pump hot water heaters, these types of heat pump systems have been marketed in small unit sizes for water heating. This system is used to replace expensive electric water heating. They are mostly in the capacity range of 6,000 to 12,000 Btu/hr and may be incorporated into a package unit along with a hot water storage tank or as an add-on unit for existing storage tanks, Figure 49-29.

Larger units are available for commercial application to provide hot water and spot cooling. The unit becomes the primary heat source for domestic or small commercial hot

Figure 49-29 Heat pump hot water heater
(Copyright Climate Master, Inc. 2007. By permission.)

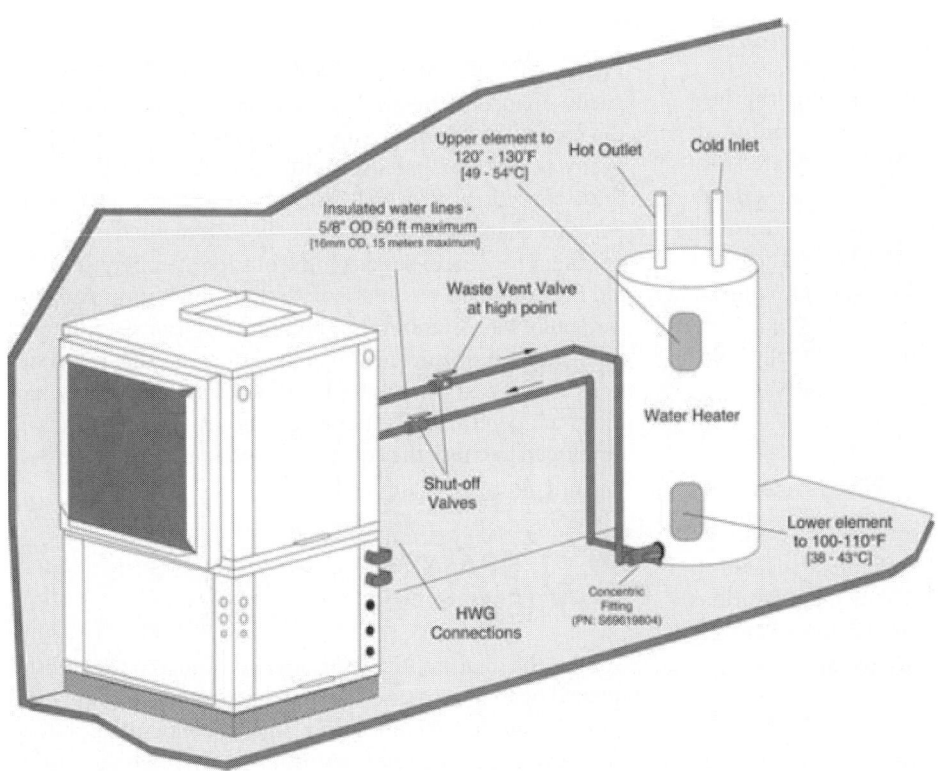

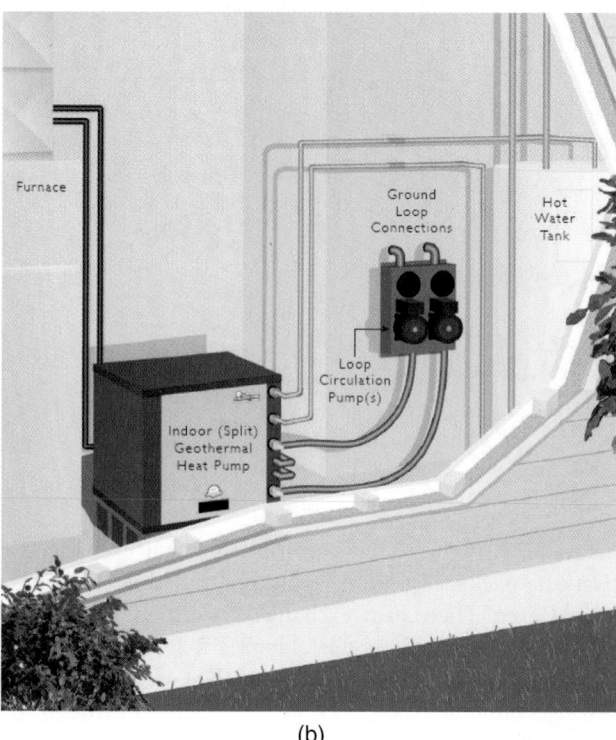

(a)   (b)

Figure 49-30 (a) Heat pump groundwater installation; (b) Geothermal heat pump
(From Climate Master Geothermal Heat Pump Comfort Systems Brochure RP001 Rev 17 April 2007D, page 9. Copyright Climate Master, Inc. 2007. By permission.)

water use, with the heat source of the water heater as backup. The higher efficiency rating or COP (coefficient of performance) of the air to water heat pump will usually supply hot water at a lower energy cost.

49.8 WATER-TO-WATER HEAT PUMPS

Water-to-water systems will use water as both the heat source and heat sink. They use two water coils and no air coils. They are very compact units. Water-to-water heat pumps are used with radiant floor heating systems. Radiant floor heating systems circulate hot water through tubing in the floor. Because radiant systems heat objects directly, they can provide comfort at lower room temperatures. Water-to-water heat pumps take heat out of geothermal ground loop and transfer it to the water circulating in the floor, Figure 49-30a,b.

49.9 HEAT PUMP EFFICIENCY RATINGS

Efficiency ratings are easily defined, but often misused to make a point. The next four sections will define the various efficiency ratings and how they are used to compare heating equipment. The following terms will be defined:

- Energy efficiency ratio (EER).
- Seasonal energy efficiency ratio (SEER).

- Coefficient of performance (COP).
- Heating seasonal performance factor (HSPF).

49.10 ENERGY EFFICIENCY RATIO: COOLING

Energy efficiency ratio or EER is the ratio of the cooling capacity divided by the watts for a given condition. Normally, the cooler the outdoor ambient, the greater the cooling capacity is. The compressor motor also draws less current at these conditions. The EER will change as the outdoor temperature changes, therefore using the EER method can be deceiving. The EER depends on the outdoor temperature. The old EER standard used 80°F dry bulb temperatures and 67°F wet bulb temperatures for indoor conditions as the test model. The problem encountered with this is that some systems are very efficient at 95°F but not at lower outdoor ambient temperatures. Therefore, the SEER test standard was developed to check the equipment operation across the normal operating outdoor conditions.

49.11 SEASONAL ENERGY EFFICIENCY RATIO: COOLING

SEER is the total amount of heat removed in a cooling season divided by total watts used during that cooling period. This is an elaborate test conducted by an independent laboratory. The test compresses time to simulate the full season operation of an air conditioning system. The Btu output and wattage is recorded. The final calculation is the SEER rating of the matched condenser and evaporator coil. The SEER rating is used to compare like capacity units for efficiency. The higher the SEER rating, the lower the operating costs. Unfortunately, the SEER rating is found on a temporary tag on the condensing unit and not on the name plate of the equipment. This paper tag may have a short life.

49.12 COEFFICIENT OF PERFORMANCE: HEATING

COP is the ratio of total heat output divided by heat input. COP excludes any supplementary resistance (electric) heat. Since the fan motor adds heat to the air it is included in this rating. COP is represented by the following formula:

$$COP = \frac{Btu \text{ heat output}}{Btu \text{ heat input}}$$

The COP for any electric heating system is near 1. In other words, the electric heat output in Btu is equal to the heat equivalent of the input wattage. Watts are converted into Btu by multiplying the watts by 3.4.

The COP rating for a heat pump is variable. The heat output for an air source heat pump will depend on the outdoor temperature. The cooler the outdoor temperature, the less heat in the air and the lower the heat capacity of the heat pump. As the temperature drops, the COP drops. The COP of a heat pump is always comparably higher than electric heat except at very low temperatures. The COP of an air source heat pump can be as low as one at very low temperatures and may approach four at ideal conditions. The higher the COP, the more efficient the operation and the lower the operating cost. Most air source heat pumps operate in a COP range of two to three.

Generally, the cost of operating an air source heat pump is one half to one third the cost of operating straight electric heat. The COP rating is not the best way to compare heat pump efficiency because the COP varies with the outdoor temperature. To truly compare two units on the basis of COP, you would need to know the COP of both units over the range of operating conditions, not just the system design condition.

49.13 HEATING SEASONAL PERFORMANCE FACTOR: HEATING

The HSPF is like a SEER for the heating season. It is designed to take varying operating conditions into account. HSPF is the total heat output of a heat pump, including supplementary electric heat during the heating season, divided by the total electric power in watts. It could be stated as the following formula:

$$HSPF = \frac{Total \text{ Btu heating season output}}{Total \text{ heating season watts}}$$

A heat pumps HSPF is always lower than its SEER. An independent laboratory determines the HSPF. The HSPF rating simulates the Btu values a heat pump will deliver during a heating season. This total Btu output is divided by the total watts used during the same time period. Unlike the COP rating, it is an effective way to compare heat pump efficiency ratings.

UNIT 49—SUMMARY

Heat pumps are available as air-to-air, water-to-air, air-to-water, and water-to-water units. Heat pump systems are the most efficient and economical heating systems available because they operate by moving heat instead of directly converting another form of energy into heat. The two coils in the heat pump act as either evaporators or condensers, depending upon the direction of the refrigerant flow. Heat pumps change the direction of refrigerant flow using a reversing valve.

Air source heat pumps lose capacity as the outdoor temperature drops. The temperature at which the heat pump capacity just equals the building heat loss is called the balance point. Below the balance point, auxiliary heat is needed to bridge the gap between the building heat loss and the heat pump capacity. Auxiliary heat can be an electric strip heater or a fuel fired furnace. The combination of a furnace and heat pump is called a dual fuel system.

WORK ORDERS

Service Ticket 4901

New Installation

Equipment: Wall Mounted Packaged Heat Pump

A sales consultant is asked to recommend a heating and cooling system for an add-on classroom trailer that is to be located outside the main building at the local high school. The building maintenance supervisor has requested that the installation be completed quickly and within a limited budget. There are a number of options that can be considered. One recommendation is for a split system air conditioning unit with a small gas fired furnace.

The building maintenance supervisor asks the sales consultant about the possibility of installing a heat pump system. The sales consultant acknowledges that these are being used more often but auxiliary electric heat will need to be included for the colder months. This will add to heating costs come winter. However a wall-mount packaged heat pump is the least costly alternative for installation. No ductwork will be needed because the building is one large room. The installation can be done in one or two days. Since the classroom trailer is not a permanent structure, this is considered to be the best solution for the building maintenance supervisor.

Service Ticket 4902

New Installation

Equipment: Water Source Heat Pump

Big Lake Power and Light is building a new office building that they would like to make a showcase for innovative energy conservation measures. A sales consultant is called in to help them decide which type of system would work best. The building is fairly large and there are a large number of different spaces. The best way to configure the space would be to set up a number of different heating zones.

The building is located in a rather cool climate which would certainly have an adverse effect on the efficiency of any heat pump system. However, the site is adjacent to a large lake which would allow for water source heat pumps connected together on a closed loop system. The lake water temperature at the location of the coils would remain fairly constant and provide enough heat for the building. In terms of energy conservation, this is exactly what the customer had in mind.

Service Ticket 4903

New Installation

Equipment: Air Source Split System Heat Pump

Dr. Studdart is Dean of the Technical Division of the local Technical College and has learned about ground loop systems from the air conditioning faculty. He is in the process of building a new home and this type of system for heating and cooling is intriguing to him. Dr. Studdart contacts a local company requesting a quote for the installation of a ground loop system. He is surprised when he finds how expensive it will be. The sales consultant explains that a ground coil requires considerable excavation and long lengths of piping.

Instead, the consultant suggests a very efficient air source split system heat pump with a SEER of 18 and an HSPF of 9. This is a much less costly alternative that still delivers impressive energy savings by using a two capacity compressor and ECM fan motors. Although it is not exactly what Dr. Studdart originally had in mind, it is certainly the most practical solution for his heating and cooling needs.

Service Ticket 4904

New Installation

Equipment: Water to Water Heat Pump

Tiles R Us is building a showroom to show off some of their tile floor products. They want to use radiant floor heating because they do not want the customers to perceive the flooring as cold. One method suggested by the sales consultant would be to use a gas furnace hydronic system. This would be the least complicated system for them to install. However, the owner of the showroom is concerned about rising energy costs and

would like to take advantage of heat pump energy savings if possible.

The sales consultant has noticed that space for a geothermal application is limited. However, a vertical loop which would reduce the amount of area that is disturbed when the loop is installed would probably work. The consultant would need to perform some additional calculations to make sure. If the numbers come out right, then the owner would still have a warm floor and the heat pump operating savings. The initial installation cost would be greater, so this would need to be calculated against the annual fuel savings to see if the decision would make economic sense.

UNIT 49—REVIEW QUESTIONS

1. List the types of heat pumps available by combinations of heat source and heat sink.

2. Why is a heat pump called a heat pump?

3. How is the refrigeration cycle reversed in a heat pump?

4. Why are accumulators and/or charge compensator tanks necessary in air source heat pumps?

5. What is auxiliary heat and why is it necessary?

6. Describe the operation of the reversing valve.

7. What is the difference between an EER and a SEER?

8. What is the difference between a COP and an HSPF?

9. List the configurations for air source packaged units.

10. Why are the coils in an air source heat pump referred to as the outdoor coil and indoor coil instead of the condenser and evaporator?

11. Explain why there is heat in the air even at cold temperatures.

12. List the physics principles that make heat pump operation possible.

13. Why do most heat pumps have two metering devices?

14. What keeps both metering devices from being in the refrigeration circuit at the same time?

15. What is a biflow thermostatic expansion valve?

16. What is the difference between the defrost cycle and the cooling cycle?

17. Show the function of the coils by writing Evaporator or Condenser in the appropriate box for the following table.

	Cooling	Heating
Outdoor coil		
Indoor coil		

18. Show the function of the metering devices by writing Active or Bypassed in the appropriate box for the following table.

	Cooling	Heating
Outdoor metering device		
Indoor metering device		

19. Where is the permanent suction line always located on a reversing valve?

20. Where is the permanent discharge line always located?

21. Why are water-to-air heat pumps more efficient than air-to-air heat pumps when operating at low outdoor temperatures?

22. What is the difference between a closed and open water loop for water source heat pumps?

23. What does the "Emergency Heat" setting on a heat pump thermostat do?

24. What is a dual-fuel heat pump?

25. What is the most common form of auxiliary heat?

26. Why don't most water source packaged heat pumps use check valves?

27. How does a flow-check piston type metering device work?

28. List the most common types of defrost controls used on air source heat pumps.

29. Explain how a time-temperature defrost board works.

Heat Pump Components

OBJECTIVES

After completing this unit you will be able to:

- explain how a heat pump thermostat differs from a conventional type.
- list the types of metering devices found in heat pump systems.
- explain the purpose of a biflow drier.
- describe how a reversing valve operates.
- explain the difference between a conventional thermostatic expansion valve, an electronically controlled electric expansion valve, and a thermal electric expansion valve.
- list the types of systems and operating conditions that require the use of suction line accumulators.
- explain the operation of an outdoor ambient thermostat and a holdback thermostat.

50.1 INTRODUCTION

The heat pump uses all of the components found on a conventional air conditioning system with the addition of many specialty components. The specialty components are used to direct the refrigerant flow in the heating, cooling, and defrost modes. They are used to protect the equipment from refrigerant and electrical related damage. The components are designed to enhance system efficiency, reliability, and performance.

The components will vary slightly from system to system depending on the design. A geothermal split system water-to-air heat pump will be configured somewhat differently than a geothermal water-to-water heat pump. Even so, the basic principles of operation remain the same although the individual specialty components may differ. It is important to understand why certain components are required for different systems and where they should be installed. For troubleshooting purposes, this is extremely important. If a well designed system is installed properly but is missing a critical key component, the unit may lose efficiency, run more or less frequently than it should, and even experience premature failure.

50.2 HEAT PUMP THERMOSTATS

The heat pump thermostat is specially designed for the heat pump system. There are a variety of heat pump thermostats. The correct thermostat must be selected for the system to operate correctly. Most air-to-air heat pump systems use a single stage cooling and two stage heating thermostat. Figure 50-1 shows a common heat pump thermostat. A two stage thermostat is required for the heating operation. The first stage of heat energizes the refrigeration circuit of the heat pump to operate. If the heat pump is not able to maintain the space temperature within a degree or two, the second stage of heat will be energized. The second stage of heat is usually electric heat. The second stage of heat is called supplemental heat or auxiliary heat. Less commonly, gas or oil heat can also be used as the auxiliary or second stage heat.

Another important feature of the heat pump thermostat is that it has the capability of bypassing the heat pump operation and operating totally on the auxiliary heat. The second stage of heat is known as auxiliary heat or emergency heat. There is a difference in how the terms are used. When the heat pump and second stage heat are operating together, the second stage of heat is known as supplemental heat. To operate the system in the emergency mode, switch the thermostat to the emergency heat position and adjust the thermostat to the desired heat setting. The heat pump refrigeration circuit system is deenergized or locked out and only the auxiliary heat is energized.

Nondigital heat pump thermostats may have two or more light indicators. On some models a light will indicate that the second stage of heat is energized. A different light will indicate that the emergency heat is operating. A third light may be used to indicate a system malfunction.

Figure 50-1 Heat pump thermostat

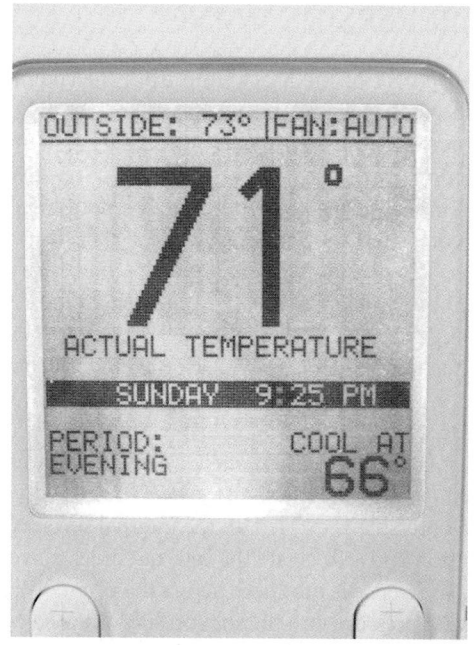

Figure 50-2 Digital thermostat display status

Digital thermostats will provide operating information within the display screen, Figure 50-2. Some messages may flash on and off such as built-in compressor protection which does not allow the compressor to restart too soon after a shutdown.

The customer should be instructed on how to use the heat pump thermostat. This will orient the customer on how to operate the system in the most efficient manner. This information will allow the customer to heat their building with emergency heat should a heat pump problem arise. Additionally, the operating instructions should be left with the homeowner.

50.3 BIFLOW FILTER DRIER

The biflow filter drier, Figure 50-3, is used in the refrigerant line that has refrigerant flowing in both directions. Depending on the refrigeration circuit design, sometimes

Figure 50-3 Heat pump biflow filter drier

the refrigerant flows through the liquid line in both directions. If a conventional filter-drier were installed in a flow-reversing refrigerant line, most of the contaminants collected in one direction of flow would be flushed back into the system when the reverse flow starts. The design of the biflow drier prevents this from happening. The purpose of the filter-drier is to remove suspended particles and moisture from the refrigeration system. The filter prevents contamination of the pressure reducing device. The biflow drier is similar to having two parallel filter-driers with internal check valves that prevent the loss of trapped contaminants. A double sided arrow is used to indicate the bidirectional flow of the refrigerant through the drier. These driers should be changed every time the system is exposed to the atmosphere. The suction line filter-drier is not considered to be a biflow drier because the refrigerant flow is always toward the compressor.

Some original equipment manufacturers (known as OEMs) prefer to install two standard filter-driers instead of the biflow drier. This design is shown in Figure 50-4. The drier is in the liquid line upstream of the pressure reducing device and the check valve prevents contaminants from flowing back into the refrigeration system. The advantages of this system over the biflow drier is that it provides more desiccant and filtering capacity and standard less expensive driers can be used for replacement.

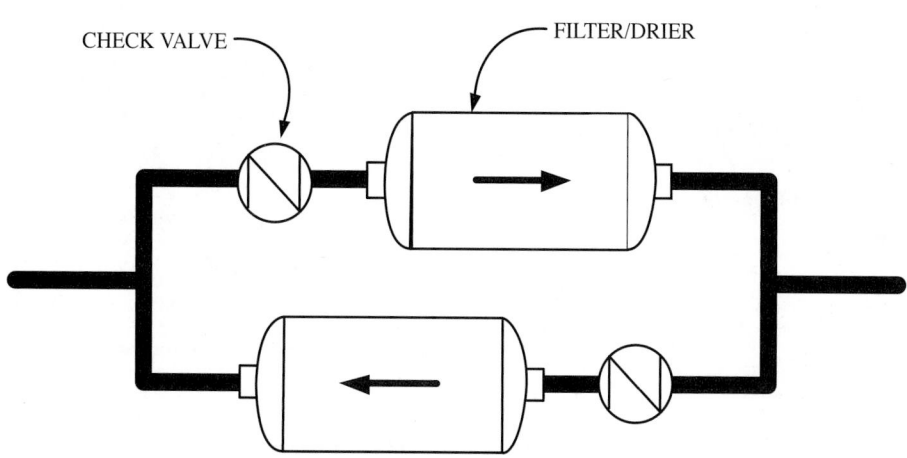

CHECK VALVE — FILTER/DRIER

Figure 50-4 Filter drier check valve setup for a heat pump liquid line

SERVICE TIP

Filter-driers can be used to clean up a system after a compressor burnout. Once the new compressor or condenser is in place, a less expensive model of filter-drier can be temporarily installed to trap the major contaminations in the system. A severe burnout may require more than one filter-drier change-out. Once the system has been cleaned up, a biflow filter-drier can be installed permanently.

50.4 REVERSING VALVE

The change-over of the heat pump from the cooling mode where the coil picks up heat (evaporator) to the heating mode where the coil gives up heat (condenser) is determined by the action of the reversing valve. A typical reversing valve is shown in Figure 50-5a,b. Internally, it is composed of two pistons connected to a sliding block or cylinder with two openings. The diagrams in Figures 50-6 and 50-7 show the position of the piston assembly in the heating mode and in the cooling mode.

The action of the piston is controlled by a solenoid valve that uses high pressure compressor discharge vapor to move the piston to the left or right, depending on whether the cooling or heating mode is needed. With the compressor discharge connected directly to the center of the piston chamber, equal pressure is exerted on the internal surfaces of each of the piston ends. To create the internal slider movement, a pressure difference is produced across the piston by bleeding the cylinder pressure into the suction side of the compressor. The bleeding action is controlled by the action of the two way solenoid valve.

In Figure 50-6 the solenoid valve is deenergized and the control plunger is relaxed in the bottom position. The bottom port vent line connected to the right end of the piston is closed. The top port vent line connected to the left end of the piston is open to the equalizing line. This allows the pressure to bleed off from the left end of the piston. This creates a pressure difference across the left side piston (usually 75 to 100 psig or greater) which causes it to travel to the extreme left. This movement repositions the slide valve to align the control port from the indoor coil with the control port leading to the compressor suction. This same movement also aligns the compressor discharge with the outdoor coil to allow for operation as a standard air conditioning system.

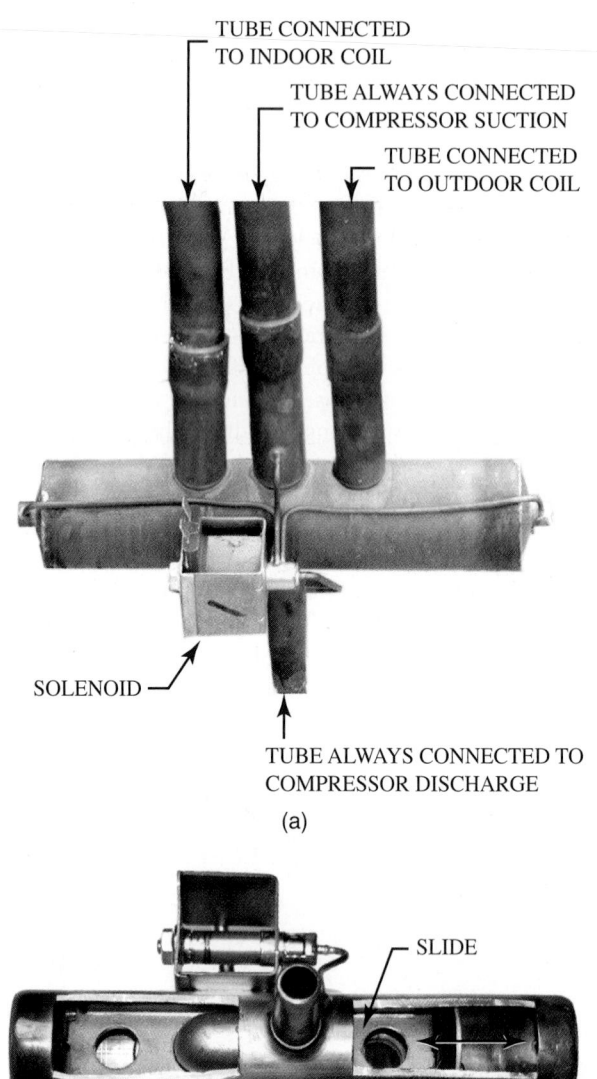

(a)

(b)

Figure 50-5 Heat pump reversing valve: (a) Outside view; (b) Cutaway view
(Courtesy Rheem Manufacturing)

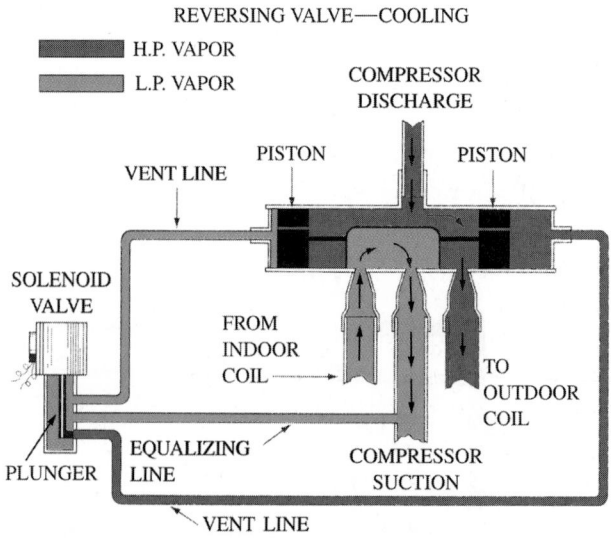

Figure 50-6 Reversing valve in cooling position

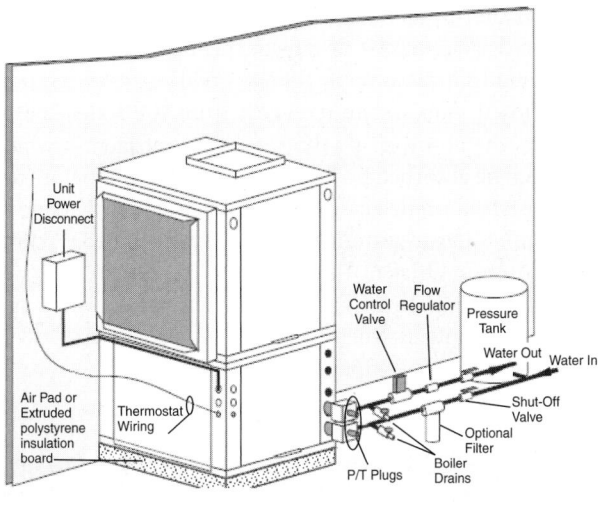

Figure 51-14 Water-to-air packaged heat pump open loop application
(From Climate Master Water System Design Guide, page 38, Figure 3-2. Copyright Climate Master, Inc. By permission.)

Figure 51-16 Coaxial coil
(From Climate Master Geothermal Applications All Products Technical Guide 10/01/06, page 32 (top left). Copyright Climate Master, Inc. 2006. By permission.)

51.9 WATER-TO-AIR CLOSED LOOP SYSTEM

A closed loop system involves indirect heat exchange as compared to an open loop system. This type of system is suitable where a pond or lake is located fairly close to the building, Figure 51-17. Most pond and lake water would not be suitable for an open loop system because it contains too many minerals and contaminants that would lead to scale build-up inside the direct expansion evaporator coil. Therefore this type of system requires a secondary refrigerant and would be classified as an indirect expansion type system.

Minimum pond sizes are roughly $\frac{1}{2}$ acre with at least an 8–10 ft depth. Coiled piping, typically polyethylene, is placed below the expected ice cap level in a series of loops or coils to increase the total surface area exposed to the water,

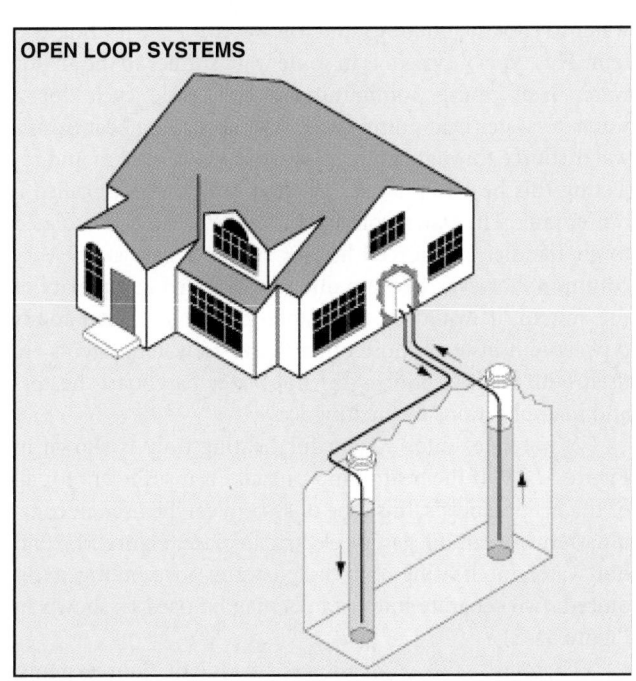

Figure 51-15 Open loop system
(Office of Energy Efficiency and Renewable Energy, U.S. Department of Energy)

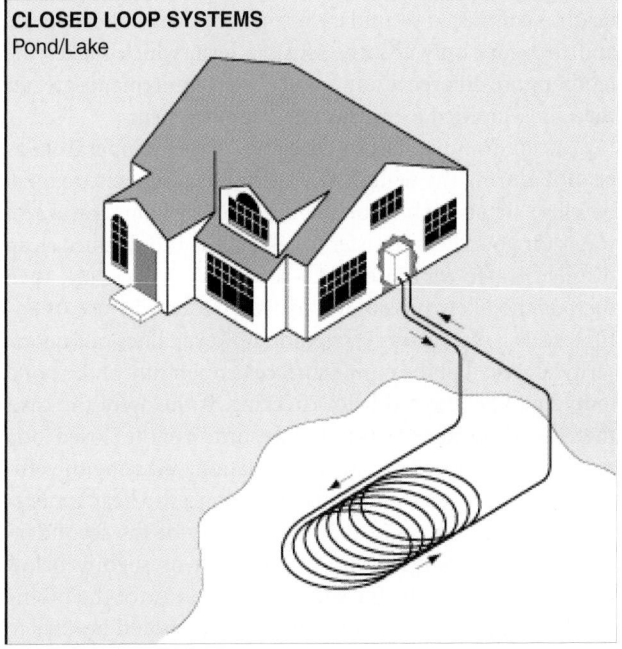

Figure 51-17 Pond closed loop system
(Office of Energy Efficiency and Renewable Energy, U.S. Department of Energy)

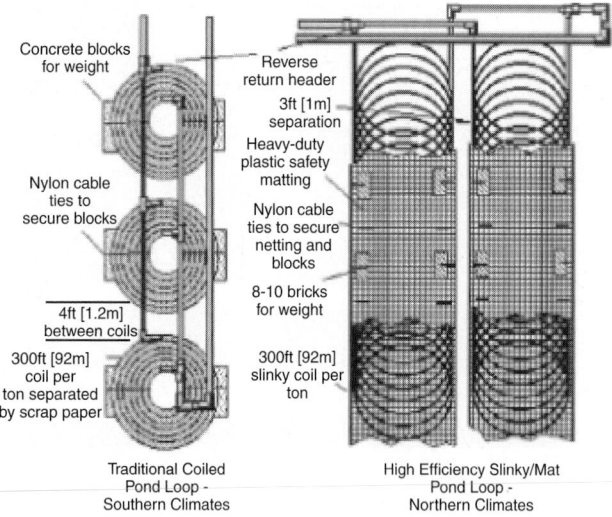

Figure 51-18 Piping arrangements for pond closed loop *(From Climate Master Water to Water System Design Guide, page 38, Figure 3-2. Copyright Climate Master, Inc. By permission.)*

Figure 51-18. A secondary refrigerant must be circulated through the piping to absorb heat from the pond water. Generally an antifreeze solution with varying percentages of propylene glycol, methanol, or ethanol is used.

The reason for the use of antifreeze is primarily one of heat transfer. The secondary refrigerant must be at a lower temperature than the pond water for heat transfer to occur. The greater the temperature difference, the better the heat transfer. In a direct expansion system, the primary refrigerant evaporates and expands, absorbing both sensible and latent heat. In contrast, a secondary refrigerant does not evaporate and therefore only absorbs sensible heat, which makes the temperature difference and surface area requirements greater than those needed for a direct expansion system.

As an example, assume the pond water temperature to be 40°F during the winter. The antifreeze temperature must be close to or slightly below the freezing temperature of water for good heat transfer to take place. If only pure clean distilled water were used as a secondary refrigerant, then there is the likely possibility for it to freeze. The use of antifreeze as a secondary refrigerant, however, does not necessarily suggest that the piping surface temperature of the pond loop could be lowered below freezing. If this were the case, then the pond water on the outside surface of the closed loop piping would freeze and act as insulation, reducing the efficiency of the system dramatically. Due to the heat transfer through the piping and the flow velocity of the secondary refrigerant, its temperature might be at or slightly below freezing while the outside surface temperature of the piping would still remain just above freezing. It should be easy to understand that this type of system requires close control of the secondary refrigerant loop temperature to operate properly and efficiently.

In a water-to-air open loop system, the heat from the water source is directly absorbed by the primary refrigerant and transferred to the air supply for the building. With a water-to-air closed loop system, the heat from the water source must first be absorbed by the secondary refrigerant which must then be absorbed by the primary refrigerant before being transferred to the air supply for the building. Therefore, in general, water-to-air open loop systems will be less complex and more efficient than water-to-air closed loop systems. However both of these systems have efficiency and operating advantages when compared with air-to-air systems that operate in cold temperature climates.

TECH TIP

Local codes and regulations must be checked carefully before installing a closed loop pond system. There may be restrictions with regard to the type of secondary refrigerants that can be used because there is always a potential for leakage from a damaged pipe into the pond water. Another consideration often overlooked is the thermal shock to the natural pond environment. There are many regulations today dealing with acceptable levels and restrictions on thermal pollution.

51.10 WATER-TO-WATER HEAT PUMP SYSTEM

A reversible water-to-water heat pump can provide chilled water to cool the building, and hot water for the heating system. This type of system is in some ways similar to the air-to-water heat pump configuration. The basic cycle for a water-to-water heat pump consists of absorbing heat from a water source through an open or closed loop system and rejecting this heat to a large insulated tank of water called a buffer tank. The water from the buffer tank can be circulated to air handlers for forced hot air systems. This is not very common, however, because due to the added complexity of the system, it would be preferable to install a water-to-air type system instead. More often, water-to water systems are used with radiant flooring or hot water baseboard heaters and in applications for melting ice.

A water-to-water system for heating only is shown in Figure 51-19. If the heat pump capacity is insufficient for all of the heating needs, this type of system can be used in combination with an oil, gas, or electric furnace, Figure 51-20. If hot water for heating and chilled water for cooling is required, two separate buffer tanks may be used as shown in Figure 51-21.

There are several advantages of radiant floor systems. Water transfers heat better than air. The amount of heat that can be carried by water in a small diameter length of piping will be equal to or greater than the same amount that can be

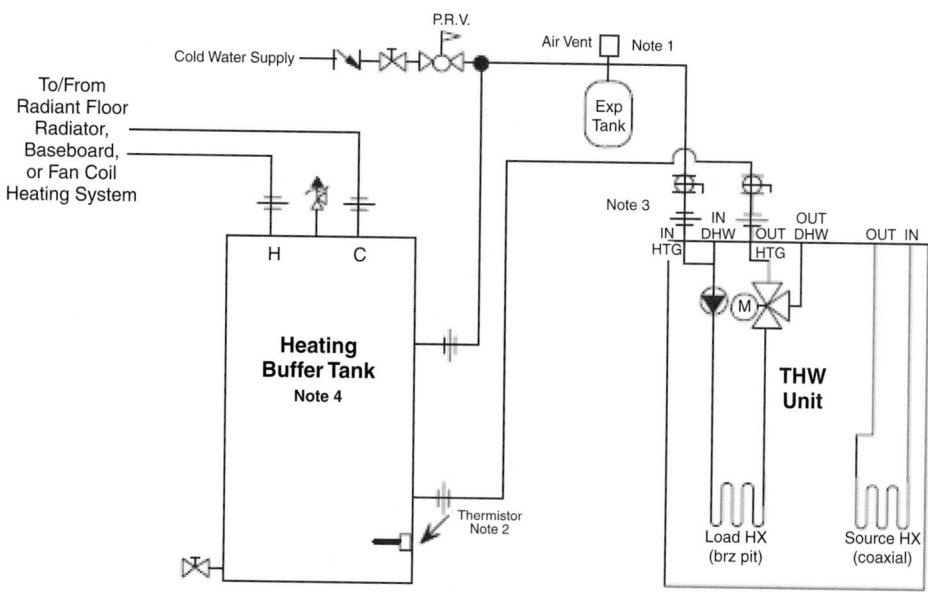

Figure 51-19 Buffer tank for heating applications only *(From Climate Master Water to Water System Design Guide, page 15, Figure 2-3. Copyright Climate Master, Inc. By permission.)*

carried with the air in a large duct, thereby saving space, Figure 51-22. More power would be used to circulate an equivalent amount of air required for heating as compared to water. Radiant floor systems provide heat at the floor level, heating objects in the space and not the air directly. Less of the heat will be wasted by rising as hot air to collect at the top of the ceiling, which reduces efficiency.

Water-to-Water Heat Pump Efficiencies

Water source heat pump efficiencies are often best determined by the COP. This can be seen from the water-to-water performance data from Table 51-4. The source EWT (entering water temperature) will have the most effect on the system performance. This is similar to the effect the outdoor air temperature has on air-to-air systems. However, as noted ear-

lier, the water source will generally have a fairly constant temperature so that performance is more consistent over the entire heating season.

The load EWT and LWT are the temperatures of the water entering and leaving the heat pump to be circulated through the heating loop (radiant floor, baseboard, etc.). The water leaving the heat pump is at a higher temperature as it enters the heating loop and comes back to the heat pump at a lower temperature after giving off heat to the space. Notice that the COP decreases as the required hot water temperature for the heating loop rises. It would be more efficient to maintain a radiant floor temperature from between 80°F to 100°F, which generally should be sufficient. However, many hot water baseboard heating systems require water temperatures of at least 120°F.

Also, notice that the COP increases at higher flow rates. Therefore, careful consideration should be given to the piping

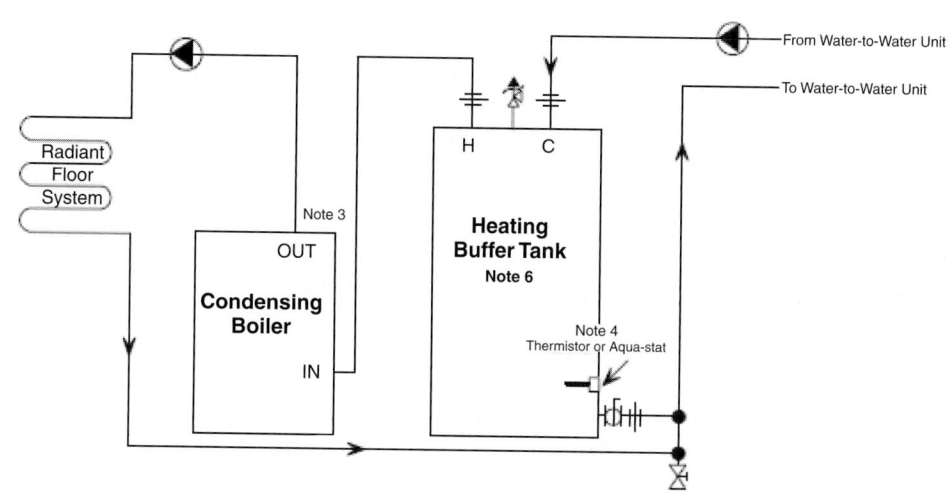

Figure 51-20 Buffer tank with backup heat *(From Climate Master Water to Water System Design Guide, page 20, Figure 2-8. Copyright Climate Master, Inc. By permission.)*

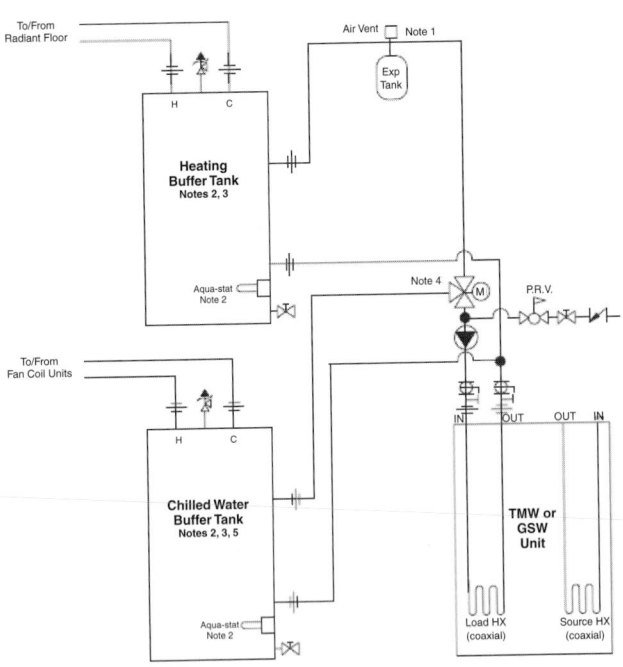

Figure 51-21 Buffer tank for heating and cooling applications
(From Climate Master Water to Water System Design Guide, page 17, Figure 2-5a. Copyright Climate Master, Inc. By permission.)

system layout and circulating pump requirements when sizing an appropriate system.

51.11 GROUND SOURCE HEAT PUMP SYSTEM

Ground source heat pumps are well suited for cold climates because the temperature of the earth below the frost line remains above freezing and relatively constant all year long. However, there are a number of factors to consider before recommending the installation of this type of system. The site must be evaluated with regard to geology, hydrology, and

Water Pipe

Air Duct

Figure 51-22 Thermal energy comparison of water vs. air
(From Climate Master Water to Water System Design Guide, page 1, Figure 1-1. Copyright Climate Master, Inc. By permission.)

land availability. This type of system will always be a closed system with a secondary refrigerant circulated through ground pipes. The secondary refrigerant will absorb heat from the soil and this is much less efficient than absorbing heat from water in a lake or pond.

A closed loop located in a body of water has the advantage of the natural circulation of water where the warm water rises and the cold water falls allowing for heat transfer through convection. In contrast, a ground loop has a limited ability to remove heat from the ground. As the ground surrounding the loop grows colder, it will take time for additional heat to travel through the soil by conduction. It is therefore essential that a large enough area is excavated for the ground loop to be effective as a heat sink. Horizontal ground loops are the most economical but can take up a lot of space, Figure 51-23a–c. Vertical ground loops take up less space but are more difficult to install as they need to be bored rather than dug with a backhoe or trenched with an excavator, Figure 51-24a,b.

The soil and rock that make up the area to be used for the ground loop need to be considered. Difficulties can be encountered in areas with an abundance of hard rock with little soil available to trench. Ground surface water can sometimes be desirable for the ground loop as long as it does not interfere with the installation process. A trench that fills with water after it is dug and the piping has been installed will provide for better heat transfer. There will be some natural circulation of the ground water that will improve the ground loop efficiency as long as the operating conditions are set so as not to freeze the water on the outer surface of the piping, which would then only reduce rather than increase heat transfer.

TECH TIP

A closed loop ground system is practical only when the geology, hydrology, and land availability meet the requirements for the system to be installed. This type of system will have an extensive ground loop through which a secondary refrigerant circulates. Always check with all local codes and environmental regulations prior to installing this type of system. In some areas, any leakage of the secondary refrigerant from the ground loop into the soil could be deemed unacceptable and subject to a possible fine.

Ground Source-to-Air Application

The ground source heat pump can be used in combination with gas, oil, or electric heat. Since the ground source closed loop will have a secondary refrigerant flowing through it, this system is very similar to a water-to-air closed loop application. Figure 51-25a shows an outdoor ground source heat pump used in combination with a furnace. Figure 51-25b

Table 51-4 Water-to-Water Heat Pump Performance Data

SOURCE				LOAD																					
Flow				Flow 15.0 gpm								Flow 22.6 gpm							Flow 30.0 gpm						
EWT °F	GPM	WPD		EWT °F	HC MBtuh	Power KW	HE MBtuh	LWT °F	COP	WPD		HC MBtuh	Power KW	HE MBtuh	LWT °F	COP	WPD		HC MBtuh	Power KW	HE MBtuh	LWT °F	COP	WPD	
		PSI	FT							PSI	FT						PSI	FT						PSI	FT
20	30.0	11.1	25.5	60	73.6	5.06	56.3	69.8	4.26	2.2	5.1	74.4	4.88	57.8	66.6	4.48	4.3	9.9	74.9	4.79	58.5	65.0	4.58	7.0	16.2
				80	69.9	6.33	48.3	89.3	3.24	1.8	4.2	70.5	6.08	49.7	86.2	3.39	3.6	8.3	70.7	5.96	50.4	84.7	3.48	5.9	13.6
				100	67.8	8.03	40.4	109.0	2.48	1.3	2.9	68.1	7.71	41.7	106.0	2.59	2.7	6.3	68.2	7.56	42.4	104.5	2.64	4.9	11.3
				120	67.3	10.16	32.6	129.0	1.94	0.9	2.1	67.3	9.77	33.9	126.0	2.02	2.2	5.1	67.3	9.59	34.6	124.5	2.06	4.0	9.3
	15.0	4.3	10.0	60	76.5	5.10	59.1	70.2	4.39	2.2	5.1	77.3	4.91	60.6	66.8	4.62	4.3	9.9	77.8	4.82	61.3	65.2	4.73	7.0	16.2
				80	72.7	6.38	50.9	89.7	3.34	1.8	4.2	73.2	6.13	52.3	86.5	3.50	3.6	8.3	73.5	6.01	53.0	84.9	3.58	5.9	13.6
				100	70.4	8.09	42.9	109.4	2.55	1.3	2.9	70.7	7.77	44.2	106.3	2.67	2.7	6.3	70.8	7.62	44.9	104.7	2.73	4.9	11.3
				120	69.9	10.23	35.0	129.3	2.00	0.9	2.1	69.9	9.84	36.3	126.2	2.08	2.2	5.1	69.9	9.66	36.9	124.7	2.12	4.0	9.3
30	22.6	7.0	16.2	60	81.0	5.15	63.4	70.8	4.61	2.2	5.1	81.9	4.95	65.0	67.2	4.84	4.3	9.9	82.4	4.86	65.8	65.5	4.96	7.0	16.2
				80	76.9	6.44	55.0	90.3	3.50	1.8	4.2	77.5	6.18	56.4	86.9	3.68	3.6	8.3	77.8	6.06	57.2	85.2	3.76	5.9	13.6
				100	74.6	8.16	46.8	109.9	2.68	1.3	2.9	74.9	7.84	48.1	106.6	2.80	2.7	6.3	75.0	7.69	48.8	105.0	2.86	4.9	11.3
				120	74.0	10.32	38.8	129.9	2.10	0.9	2.1	74.0	9.93	40.1	126.5	2.18	2.2	5.1	74.0	9.74	40.8	124.9	2.23	4.0	9.3
	30.0	10.3	23.8	60	84.6	5.17	67.0	71.3	4.80	2.2	5.1	85.6	4.97	68.6	67.6	5.04	4.3	9.9	86.1	4.88	69.4	65.7	5.16	7.0	16.2
				80	80.4	6.46	58.3	90.7	3.65	1.8	4.2	81.0	6.21	59.8	87.2	3.82	3.6	8.3	81.3	6.09	60.5	85.4	3.92	5.9	13.6
				100	77.9	8.19	50.0	110.4	2.79	1.3	2.9	78.2	7.87	51.4	106.9	2.91	2.7	6.3	78.4	7.72	52.1	105.2	2.98	4.9	11.3
				120	77.3	10.36	42.0	130.3	2.19	0.9	2.1	77.3	9.97	43.3	126.8	2.27	2.2	5.1	77.3	9.78	43.9	125.2	2.32	4.0	9.3
	15.0	3.7	8.6	60	88.2	5.24	70.3	71.8	4.93	2.2	5.1	88.5	4.97	71.6	67.8	5.23	4.3	9.9	88.7	4.84	72.2	65.9	5.37	7.0	16.2
				80	86.2	6.64	63.5	91.5	3.80	1.8	4.2	86.7	6.28	65.3	87.7	4.05	3.6	8.3	87.0	6.11	66.1	85.8	4.17	5.9	13.6
				100	83.7	8.42	54.9	111.2	2.91	1.3	2.9	84.3	7.98	57.1	107.5	3.10	2.7	6.3	84.6	7.77	58.1	105.6	3.19	4.9	11.3
				120	80.5	10.56	44.5	130.7	2.23	0.9	2.1	81.3	10.06	46.9	127.2	2.37	2.2	5.1	81.6	9.82	48.1	125.4	2.44	4.0	9.3
40	22.6	6.2	14.3	60	93.4	5.29	75.3	72.4	5.17	2.2	5.1	93.8	5.01	76.7	68.3	5.49	4.3	9.9	93.9	4.88	77.3	66.3	5.64	7.0	16.2
				80	91.3	6.70	68.4	92.2	3.99	1.8	4.2	91.8	6.34	70.2	88.1	4.25	3.6	8.3	92.1	6.17	71.1	86.1	4.38	5.9	13.6
				100	88.6	8.49	59.6	111.8	3.06	1.3	2.9	89.3	8.05	61.8	107.9	3.25	2.7	6.3	89.6	7.84	62.8	106.0	3.35	4.9	11.3
				120	85.3	10.65	48.9	131.4	2.35	0.9	2.1	86.1	10.15	51.4	127.6	2.49	2.2	5.1	86.4	9.91	52.6	125.8	2.56	4.0	9.3
	30.0	9.2	21.3	60	97.5	5.31	79.4	73.0	5.38	2.2	5.1	97.9	5.03	80.8	68.7	5.71	4.3	9.9	98.1	4.90	81.4	66.5	5.87	7.0	16.2
				80	95.4	6.73	72.4	92.7	4.16	1.8	4.2	95.9	6.36	74.2	88.5	4.42	3.6	8.3	96.2	6.19	75.1	86.4	4.56	5.9	13.6
				100	92.6	8.52	63.5	112.3	3.18	1.3	2.9	93.3	8.08	65.7	108.3	3.38	2.7	6.3	93.6	7.87	66.7	106.2	3.48	4.9	11.3
				120	89.1	10.70	52.6	131.9	2.44	0.9	2.1	89.9	10.19	55.1	128.0	2.59	2.2	5.1	90.3	9.95	56.4	126.0	2.66	4.0	9.3
	15.0	3.1	7.3	60	100.1	5.34	81.9	73.3	5.50	2.2	5.1	100.5	5.05	83.3	68.9	5.83	4.3	9.9	100.7	4.92	83.9	66.7	5.99	7.0	16.2
				80	97.9	6.76	74.8	93.0	4.24	1.8	4.2	98.4	6.39	76.6	88.7	4.51	3.6	8.3	98.7	6.22	77.5	86.6	4.65	5.9	13.6
				100	95.0	8.56	65.8	112.7	3.25	1.3	2.9	95.7	8.12	68.0	108.5	3.45	2.7	6.3	96.0	7.91	69.0	106.4	3.56	4.9	11.3
				120	91.4	10.75	54.7	132.2	2.49	0.9	2.1	92.3	10.24	57.3	128.2	2.64	2.2	5.1	92.7	9.99	58.6	126.2	2.72	4.0	9.3
50	22.6	5.6	12.8	60	106.0	5.38	87.6	74.1	5.77	2.2	5.1	106.4	5.10	89.0	69.4	6.12	4.3	9.9	106.6	4.97	89.7	67.1	6.29	7.0	16.2
				80	103.6	6.82	80.4	93.8	4.45	1.8	4.2	104.3	6.45	82.3	89.2	4.74	3.6	8.3	104.5	6.27	83.1	87.0	4.88	5.9	13.6
				100	100.6	8.64	71.1	113.4	3.41	1.3	2.9	101.3	8.19	73.4	109.0	3.63	2.7	6.3	101.7	7.98	74.5	106.8	3.74	4.9	11.3
				120	96.8	10.84	59.8	132.9	2.62	0.9	2.1	97.7	10.33	62.5	128.6	2.77	2.2	5.1	98.1	10.08	63.7	126.5	2.85	4.0	9.3
	30.0	8.5	19.7	60	110.7	5.40	92.3	74.8	6.00	2.2	5.1	111.2	5.12	93.7	69.8	6.37	4.3	9.9	111.4	4.99	94.4	67.4	6.55	7.0	16.2
				80	108.3	6.85	84.9	94.4	4.64	1.8	4.2	108.9	6.47	86.8	89.6	4.93	3.6	8.3	109.2	6.30	87.7	87.3	5.08	5.9	13.6
				100	105.1	8.68	75.5	114.0	3.55	1.3	2.9	105.9	8.23	77.8	109.4	3.77	2.7	6.3	106.3	8.01	78.9	107.1	3.89	4.9	11.3
				120	101.1	10.89	64.0	133.5	2.72	0.9	2.1	102.1	10.37	66.7	129.0	2.88	2.2	5.1	102.5	10.12	68.0	126.8	2.97	4.0	9.3

(From Climate Master Genesis GSW Water-to-Water, page 103. Copyright Climate Master, Inc. By permission.)

shows a similar application but with the compressor located inside the building. The installation of a coil on an existing furnace may help to reduce energy costs. The ground source heat pump will supplement the heat required for the building.

51.12 DUAL SOURCE HEAT PUMP

This type of system combines an air source heat pump with a ground source type. When the outside temperature drops in the evening, the ground source system will be able to take advantage of the constant temperature of the earth. However, due to the additional capacity supplied by the air source, a smaller ground loop would be required, which minimizes the initial installation cost. Dual-source heat pumps generally have higher efficiency ratings than air source heat pumps.

51.13 DUAL FUEL HEAT PUMP PACKAGED SYSTEM

A dual fuel heat pump combines both an air-to-air heat pump and a gas furnace into one packaged system, Figure 51-26. This type of unit will generally utilize a two stage compressor

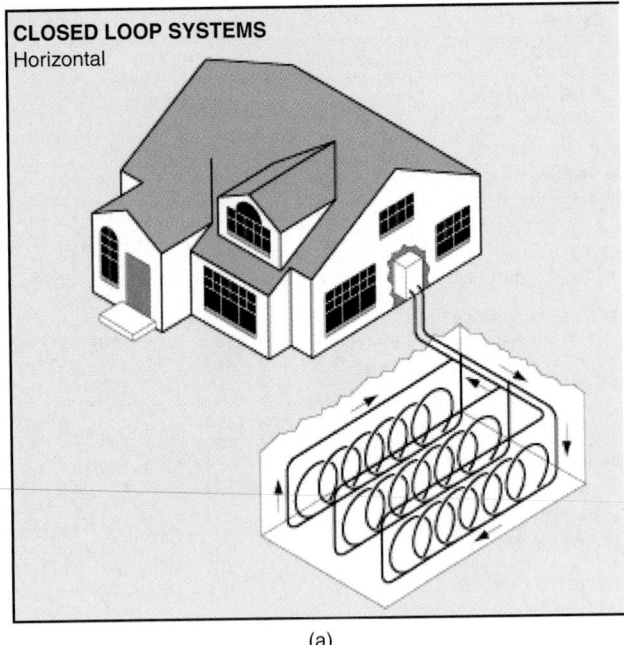

(a)

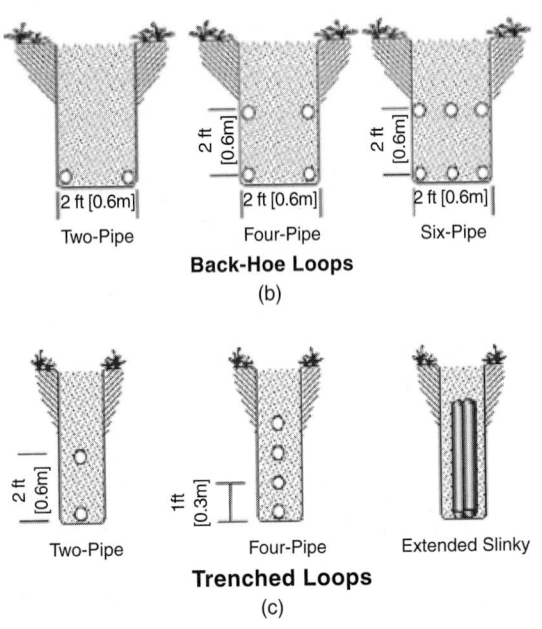

Back-Hoe Loops

(b)

Trenched Loops

(c)

Figure 51-23 (a) Horizontal closed loop; (b) Back hoe horizontal closed loop; (c) Trenched horizontal closed loop
(a, Office Energy Efficiency and Renewable Energy, U.S. Department of Energy; b, From Climate Master Water to Water System Design Guide, page 352, Figure 3-7. Copyright Climate Master, Inc. By permission.; c, From Climate Master Water to Water System Design Guide, page 52, Figure 3-7. Copyright Climate Master, Inc. By permission.)

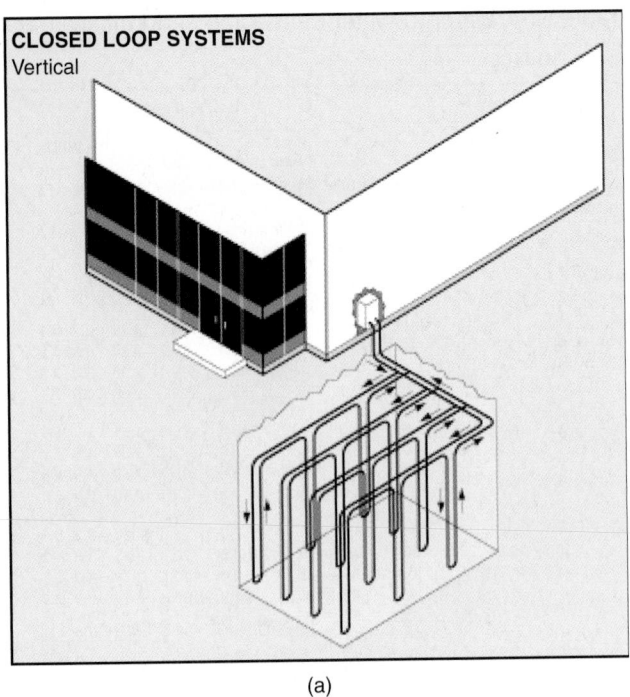

(a)

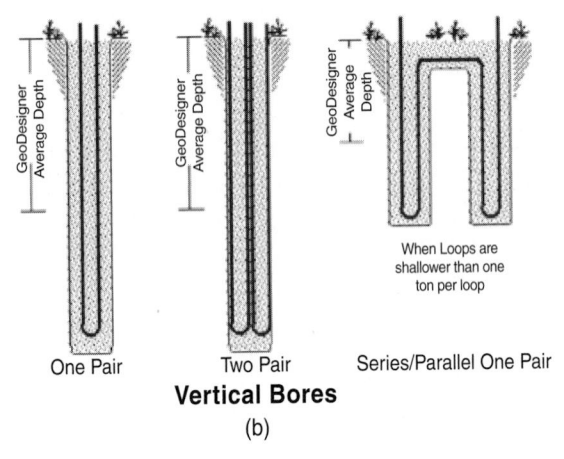

Vertical Bores

(b)

Figure 51-24 (a) Vertical closed loop; (b) Bored vertical closed loop
(From Climate Master Water to Water System Design Guide, page 52, Figure 3-7. Copyright Climate Master, Inc. By permission.)

and a variable speed blower motor and a dual fuel thermostat. The heat pump will provide for cooling in the summer season and heating during moderate winter conditions. As the temperature drops outside, generally below about 35°F, the system automatically switches to gas furnace heating. At this lower outside temperature, gas becomes the more economical heating source and also provides for greater heating capacity than the heat pump.

51.14 DOMESTIC HOT WATER

Many heat pump systems can be configured to supply hot domestic water with much higher efficiencies than comparable electric hot water heaters. The recovery rate for a heat pump hot water heater is also greater as compared to an

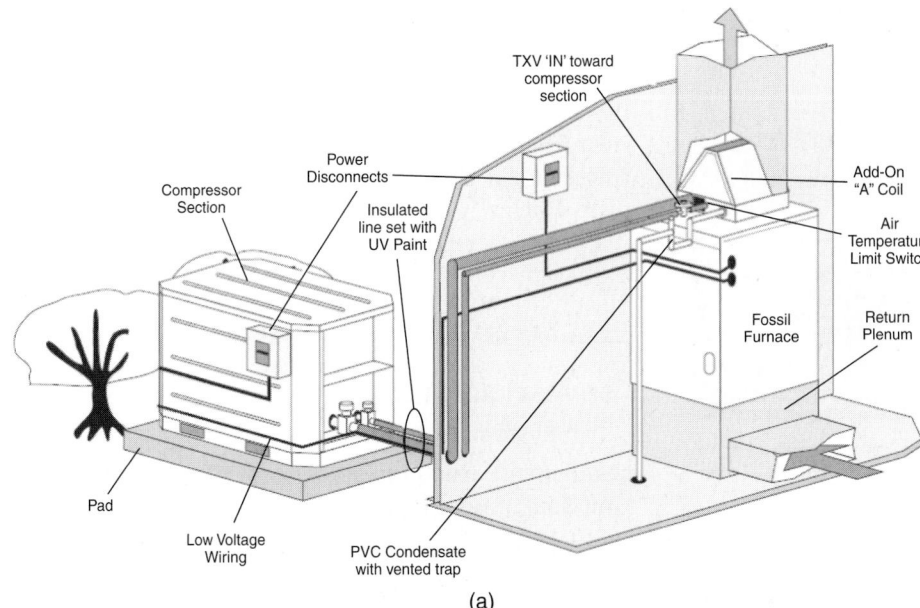

Figure 51-25 (a) Split ground source heat pump add-on coil for fossil fuel furnace with outdoor compressor; (b) Split ground source heat pump add-on coil for fossil fuel furnace with indoor compressor
(a, From Climate Master 97B0047N01 Rev 28 June 2007D, page 22, Figure 13b. Copyright Climate Master, Inc. 2007. By permission.; b, From Climate Master 97B0047N01 Rev 28 June 2007D, page 21, Figure 12b. Copyright Climate Master, Inc. 2002. By permission.)

(a)

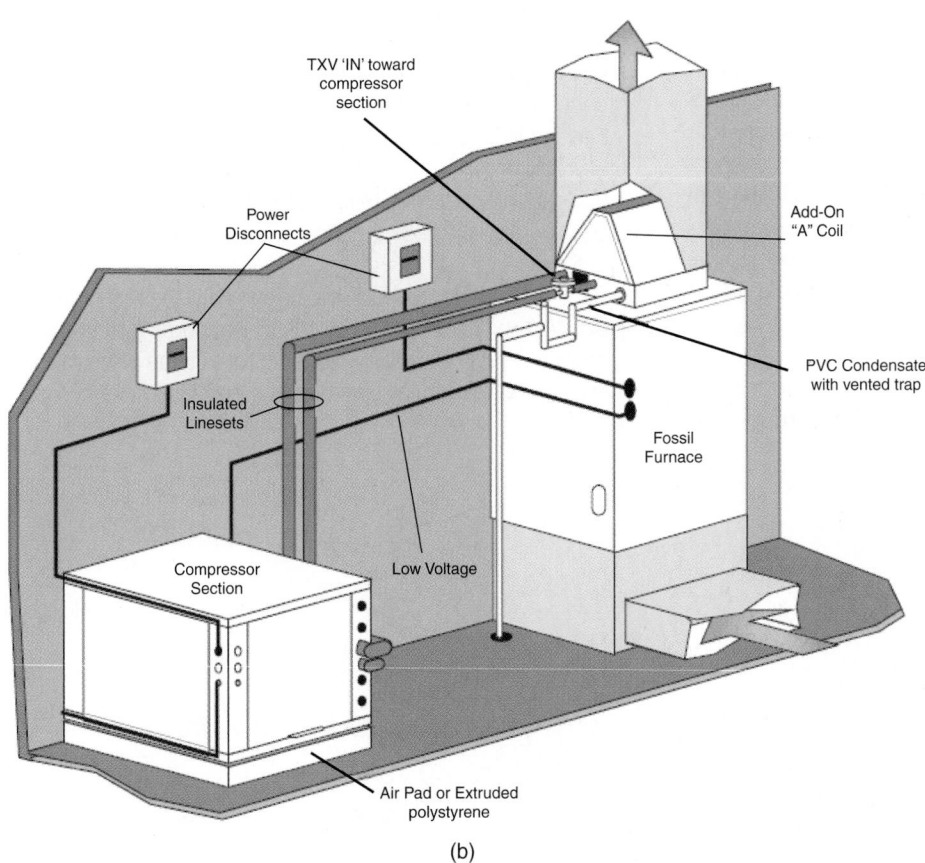

(b)

electric hot water heater. This means that water will heat faster. Water temperatures leaving the heater are generally no higher than 145°F.

Domestic hot water heating can be configured with outdoor split systems, Figure 51-27, and indoor package units,

Figure 51-28. Water source heat pumps typically use an indirect water-to-water heat exchanger, Figure 51-29a,b. This coil located inside the tank isolates the domestic (potable) water from the heating water. Some units have electric resistance heating elements for use as a backup.

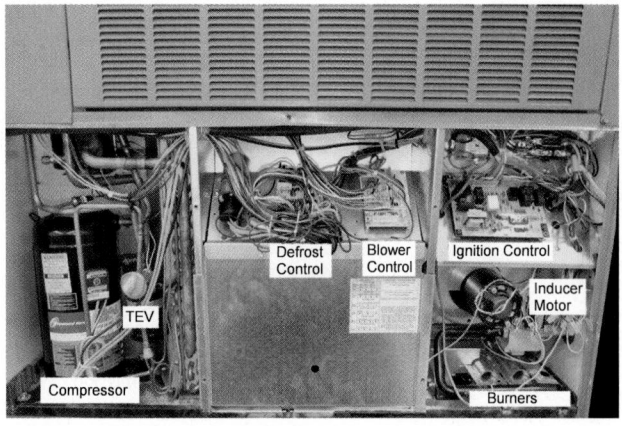

Figure 51-26 Dual fuel heat pump

UNIT 51—SUMMARY

The best system is the one that is properly designed, sized, and installed while meeting the needs of the specific application. A heat pump that is very efficient is not worthwhile if the building seems too cold and feels drafty. Air source heat pumps that are constantly icing up and defrosting will consume higher levels of energy. A radiant floor heating system will fall short of providing the proper level of heat if the water temperature is too low. Ground and water source heat pumps may require closed loops that must allow for the proper flow rates and controlled secondary refrigerant temperatures.

Properly designed and installed heat pump systems can save the customer money and provide four season heating and cooling needs. However if the heat pump is in-

correct for the selected application, the customer will be discouraged and unhappy with the system's performance. Heat pumps that have received bad reviews are generally those that are not well suited for the intended application right from the outset and this may be partly due to poor advice provided by a contractor with limited knowledge of these systems.

WORK ORDERS

Service Ticket 5101

Split System Retrofit

Equipment: Existing Split System to Be Replaced by Air Source Heat Pump

The sales representative met with the customer to discuss the options for upgrading her current heating and cooling system. During a recent service call the technician recommended that the outside air conditioning system be replaced as it was old and becoming expensive to maintain. However, the small gas furnace and cooling coil located in the basement was still in good operating condition. When she told the technician that the price of heating with gas was becoming increasingly expensive, he recommended a heat pump system. The technician had recently been installing heat pumps throughout the community and their performance was receiving favorable reviews.

The sales representative agreed with the technician's advice. The latest 14 SEER air-to-air heat pump systems the company had been carrying as a product line were much improved over earlier versions. The energy efficiency was

Figure 51-27 Domestic hot water split system with outside compressor
(From Climate Master 97B0047N01 Rev 28 June 2007D, page 26, Figure 18. Copyright Climate Master, Inc. By permission.)

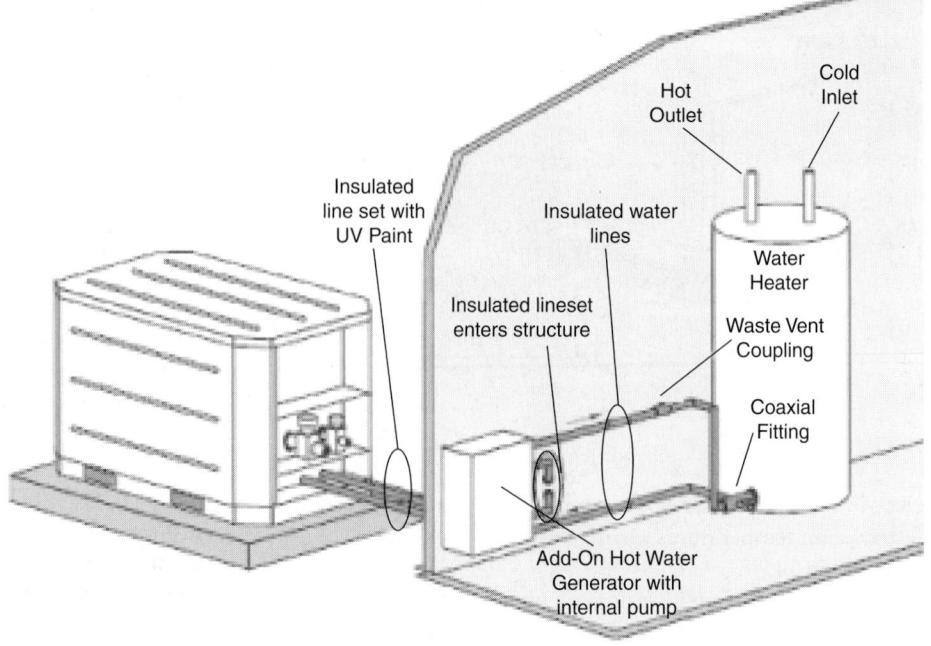

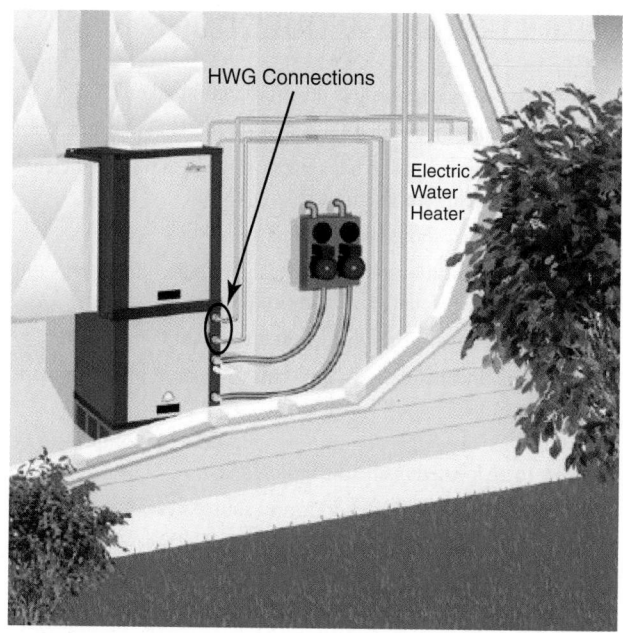

Figure 51-28 Domestic hot water packaged unit with inside compressor
(From Climate Master Geothermal Applications All Products Technical Guide 10/01/06, page 28, Figure 21. Copyright Climate Master, Inc. By permission.)

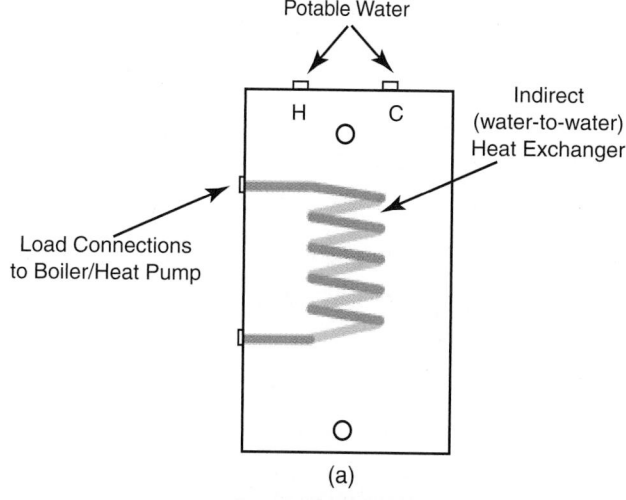

"Typical" indirect water heater rated for 180°F (82°C) or hotter water

(b)

Figure 51-29 (a) Indirect type water heater; (b) Indirect type water heater, internal view
(a, From Climate Master Water to Water System Design Guide, page 25, Figure 2-7. Copyright Climate Master, Inc. By permission.; b, From Climate Master Water to Water System Design Guide, page 25, Figure 2-9. Copyright Climate Master, Inc. By permission.)

very good and in this moderate climate the air-to-air system with on demand defrost worked exceptionally well. Rather than replace the gas furnace, it could remain in place and be used for auxiliary heat if necessary. The customer agreed to the retrofit and the existing outdoor unit was replaced with an air-to-air heat pump. The refrigerant circuit was piped inside to the existing coil in the gas furnace and commissioned for operation.

Service Ticket 5102

Customer Complaint: Low Water Temperature

Equipment: Water Source Heat Pump With Open Loop

The customer complained to the technician that the heat from the radiant floor was not sufficient. Dial thermometers had been installed in the lines leaving the heat pump and the customer noted that the water temperature had been gradually decreasing since the system had been installed more than a year ago.

Having never been to this residence before, the technician began to review the specifications for the system. The technician was surprised to find that the system was operating with an open loop from a small manmade pond located in the back yard. The water quality was obviously poor and no doubt has led to scale and deposits on the water side of the refrigeration coil. This would reduce the heat transfer and lead to a gradual decrease in amount of heat absorbed from the pond water. The technician also found that the auxiliary electric heat for the buffer tank was disconnected.

The customer explained that during the initial installation, the contractor recommended a closed loop but it was going to be much more expensive to install. It was the customer's decision to go with the open loop. A few months ago, when the auxiliary electric heat began running a majority of the time, the customer simply disconnected it.

The technician explained that it was not worthwhile to try to cut costs by trying to change the parameters for the application involved. It did no good to try to save a few dollars on the installation to only have a system that would not work properly. The technician politely told the customer that the technician would only be willing to work on the system if the customer would follow the suggestions for improvement. At the very least a closed loop system would need to be put into place if the existing system was to be used.

Service Ticket 5103

Customer Complaint: Frequent Cycling and High Operating Cost

Equipment: Mini-Split Heat Pump

The customer complained to the technician that the new mini-split system that was recently installed by a local discount supply house was frequently cycling, using more electricity than originally anticipated. Almost immediately the technician realized that the system was much larger than what would normally be required for a space of this size. The technician asked the customer who had determined the sizing requirements for the mini-split. The customer explained that the unit was a close-out model and on sale for a very reasonable price. As a further incentive, the discount supply house where the mini-split was purchased offered free installation.

The technician asked if the mini-split could be returned because it was oversized. The customer shook his head no, because this had been a sale item and no returns would be allowed. The technician said that someone from the supply house should have offered to help in sizing the unit to make sure it would meet the application. The technician recommended that the customer talk to someone at the discount supply house about this situation but could not offer any other solution than replacing the unit with an appropriately sized mini-split.

UNIT 51—REVIEW QUESTIONS

1. What type of heat pump is the most common and why?
2. What are the advantages of an air-to-water heat pump system?
3. What is the relationship between air-to-air heat pump efficiency and outside air temperature?
4. What is a dual source heat pump?
5. What site conditions should be taken into account when considering the installation of a ground source heat pump?
6. What are some of the advantages for radiant floor heating?
7. Why are the insulated water tanks for heat pump systems referred to as "buffer" tanks?
8. With what type of heat pump system would the compressor be able to be located inside the building?
9. Why are water source and ground source heat pump systems very adaptable for colder climates?
10. What will cause a mini-split heat pump to cycle?
11. Can heat be a form of pollution?
12. How is heat transferred in a heat pump ground loop?
13. What type of system requires a secondary refrigerant?
14. What happens if water freezes on the outside of a closed loop pond heat pump system?
15. The most efficient air-to-air heat pumps have an HSPF of what?
16. The Energy Star label is awarded to those air-to-air units with SEER values of——or greater and HSPFs of——or greater.
17. What is the difference between a direct and an indirect expansion system?
18. Why would an air source heat pump be more efficient than an air-to-air heat pump?
19. What are some disadvantages of the mini-split heat pump?
20. How must the outdoor unit on a heat pump be mounted in areas where snowfall accumulates?

The Unit Will Not Go into Defrost

The most common cause of this is a loose or poorly connected termination bulb of the defrost control. It is very important that the bulb be securely fastened with heat transfer compound on the joint, insulated, and sealed from moisture. Ice can build up at this location and loosen the bulb fastening. The second cause can be failure of the pressure switch due to dirt and/or insects in the pressure switch tube connections. There is always the possibility of failure of the timer control, but this is remote. Check the previous two items before replacing any parts.

The Unit Goes into Defrost with Very Little Frost on the Bottom of the Coil

The major cause of this action is a dirty outdoor coil. Its frost-free resistance is so high that it takes very little increase in pressure drop to start the defrost cycle. A thorough coil cleaning is in order.

The Unit Does Not Defrost the Entire Coil

This is an indication that the defrost cycle is interrupted before the cycle is completed. As noted earlier in Section 53-11, one correction to this problem is to adjust the automatic termination to extend the period of the defrost cycle and another is to reduce the amount of auxiliary heat used in the defrost cycle to an amount not more than the sensible capacity of the unit on the cooling cycle.

UNIT 53—SUMMARY

Service problems with heat pumps fall into three main categories: air circulation problems, refrigeration problems, and defrost problems. Air circulation problems for heat pumps are similar to those encountered with general air conditioning systems. However one significant difference is that heat pumps have higher airflow per ton than other heating systems and their air supply temperature is lower than other heating systems.

Refrigeration problems are generally categorized as refrigerant quantity or refrigerant flow problems. Heat pumps have a number of different components compared to conventional refrigeration systems, such as reversing valves, check valves, and bi-directional expansion devices. It is important for the technician to understand why these components are required and how they are installed and operated.

The heat pump defrost systems is essential to maintain proper operation during the heating mode. During this cycle the outdoor coil is subject to icing dependent on the outside air temperature and humidity. The defrost cycle needs to be initiated early enough to eliminate the formation of ice but not so often as to reduce the unit's efficiency.

WORK ORDERS

Service Ticket 5301

Complaint: Room Too Drafty

Equipment: Air Source Packaged Heat Pump

The technician answered a service call for a customer complaining that the home was too drafty and that cold air was blowing from the registers all of the time. The first thing that the technician checked was the thermostat setting. There were three settings available which were ON, OFF, and AUTO. The blower was set to the ON position which allowed it to run continuously whether the heat pump was operating or not.

The technician asked the customer about this and the customer explained that the thermostat had originally been set for the AUTO position but because it always seemed so drafty she had changed it to the ON position hoping to blow more air into the room.

The technician told her that this would not increase the heat and that the unit is designed to work best with the blower in the AUTO position. If it was not supplying enough heat, then there could be other reasons. The technician reviewed the original specifications for the unit and it seemed to be sized properly for the heating load. The air supply registers were also properly located so as not to induce unnecessary drafts.

However it had been unusually cold in the area during the past month and this type of a system would require additional auxiliary heat as the temperature had been dropping below freezing. The technician found that one of the electrical strips for the auxiliary heat had failed and so that was replaced. With the blower on AUTO and the electric auxiliary heat operational, the house was no longer drafty for the customer.

Service Ticket 5302

Complaint: High Energy Cost

Equipment: Split System Air Source Heat Pump, Air Handler in Basement

The customer told the technician that his electricity costs had been fairly stable since installing the heat pump five years ago. However, most recently the electricity cost had increased significantly and he was wondering if this was because the system was getting older and worn out.

The technician told him that should not be the case as long as regular maintenance is conducted, which the records indicated. He did mention however that some landscaping was done just a month or so back in the vicinity of the outdoor coil. Inspecting the manual for the unit, the technician found it had a pressure-time-temperature defrost system. This was a fairly elaborate system, however it was also generally very efficient in regulating the timing for the defrost cycle.

Removing the outside protective grill from the outdoor coil, the technician found it to be extremely dirty. It was covered with dust, leaves, and grass. Evidently the landscaping work had stirred up this debris which was drawn into the outdoor coil. The pressure drop of the air through the coil is the determining factor for initiating the defrost cycle for this type of unit. Due to the dirt buildup on the coil, less frost has to form to reach the required pressure drop to initiate the defrost cycle. The unit was defrosting far too often and wasting energy. The technician cleaned the outdoor coil and told the customer that the electrical bill should return to normal.

Service Ticket 5303

Complaint: Not Enough Heat

Equipment: Split System Air Source Heat Pump

The technician answered a service call for a customer complaining that the home was too cold and not getting enough heat. This had only been happening within the past few days and before that time the house was warm enough. The technician checked the thermostat settings and they seemed to be OK but the room temperature of 65°F was considerably lower than the setpoint of 70°F. The blower for the air handler in the basement appeared to be operating normally, however the temperature of the indoor coil was lower than expected and the auxiliary electric strip heaters were on.

The technician went outside and removed the protective grill from the outdoor coil and found it to be covered in ice. This most likely indicates a problem with the defrost cycle. The defrost system for this unit was the time-temperature type. The problem could be a loose or faulty defrost thermostat. A poor contact between the thermostat and the coil tube prevents the thermostat temperature from dropping below 26°F. However, the technician could not check this because the entire coil was covered in ice, including the thermostat.

The technician decided to initiate the defrost cycle manually while at the same time testing the defrost timer control board. After turning off the power, a jumper was placed across the outdoor thermostat connections DFT and R, see Figure 53-12a,b. Then turning the power back on, the heat pump immediately shifted into the defrost mode. This indicated that the defrost timer was working properly. After enough of the ice was clear, a visual inspection seemed to indicate that the outdoor thermostat sensor was mounted correctly with good contact. Therefore suspecting a faulty thermostat, the technician replaced it.

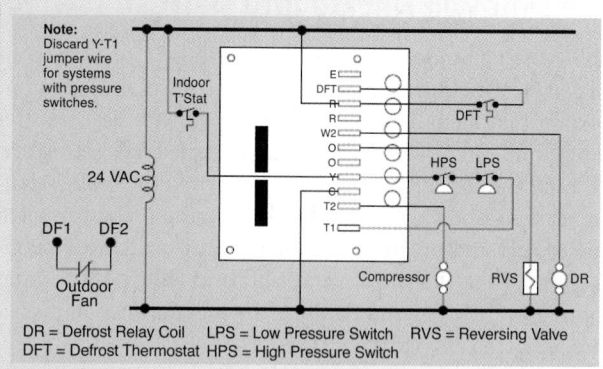

(a)

(b)

Figure 53-12 (a) Time-temperature defrost timer control board wiring diagram; (b) Time-temperature defrost timer control board
(ICM 302 Courtesy of ICM Controls Corp.)

UNIT 53—REVIEW QUESTIONS

1. When a heat pump system is in the heating mode and there is an increase in the temperature rise, what does this indicate?

2. How often should throwaway filters be checked?

3. Why should automotive oil never be used to lubricate blower motors?

4. What are the three major differences between an air conditioning and a heat pump system?

5. When changing a reversing valve, what position should the main piston and also the pilot valve sit?

6. Why must the pilot valve be positioned as described in Question #4?

7. When installing a new valve, it should be protected from getting too hot. What is the maximum temperature the valve body will tolerate?

8. What is the primary refrigeration problem in a heat pump system?

9. List four common problems with check valves on a heat pump system.

10. What are the indications a check valve has stuck closed on an outside coil?

11. Name the four most predominant defrost systems.

12. A temperature-differential defrost system will not go into defrost. This is the most common complaint on this control. Describe the correct solution to this problem.

13. A pressure-time-temperature defrost system goes into defrost with very little frost on the bottom of the coil. Describe the major cause and solution to this problem.

14. If the unit does not run, what is the first thing to check?

15. Basically the service problems with heat pumps fall into three main categories. What are they?

16. Why might customers complain about their heat pump systems being cold and drafty?

17. If the hot gas sensor located in the compressor discharge line shuts down the compressor, this may indicate what?

18. If the high pressure switch located in the compressor discharge line shuts down the compressor, this may indicate what?

19. How should the accumulator for a heat pump system be sized and why?

20. Why is it not recommended to energize the solenoid coil when it is not installed on the reversing valve?

System Design, Sizing, and Layout

UNIT 54

Basic Building Construction

OBJECTIVES

After completing this unit you will be able to:

- recognize the different materials used in basic construction and select the proper procedures and methods of construction for each.
- describe the different insulation R values of common building materials.
- relate the importance of fire dampers in construction.
- incorporate the different methods of construction necessary for a successful residential or commercial project.
- forecast what part of an HVAC/R system needs to be installed during each phase of construction.
- explain the importance of LEED Certification.

54.1 INTRODUCTION

The heating and air conditioning system becomes an integral part of the building. System components, ductwork, and piping must all must be supported by the structural members of the building. Wiring, ductwork, and piping must pass through floors, walls, and ceilings. An understanding of common building construction is necessary to ensure safe installations. Improperly supported equipment can pose a safety hazard. Cutting the wrong structural components of a building can compromise the integrity of the entire structure. Air conditioning technicians must have an understanding of basic building construction so that they can intelligently discuss aspects of the building construction that will affect the installation of the HVAC system with the general contractor.

54.2 BASIC RESIDENTIAL CONSTRUCTION

There are four major parts of a residential building:

- Foundation.
- Floor.
- Walls.
- Roof.

Foundation Types

The foundation supports the rest of the building. As seen in Figure 54-1, the foundation of a residential building is generally one of three construction types:

- Slab on grade.
- Crawl space.
- Basement.

All foundations, regardless of type, rest on a footing. The footing supports the weight of the building, spreading it over the entire area of the footing. The footing dimensions vary

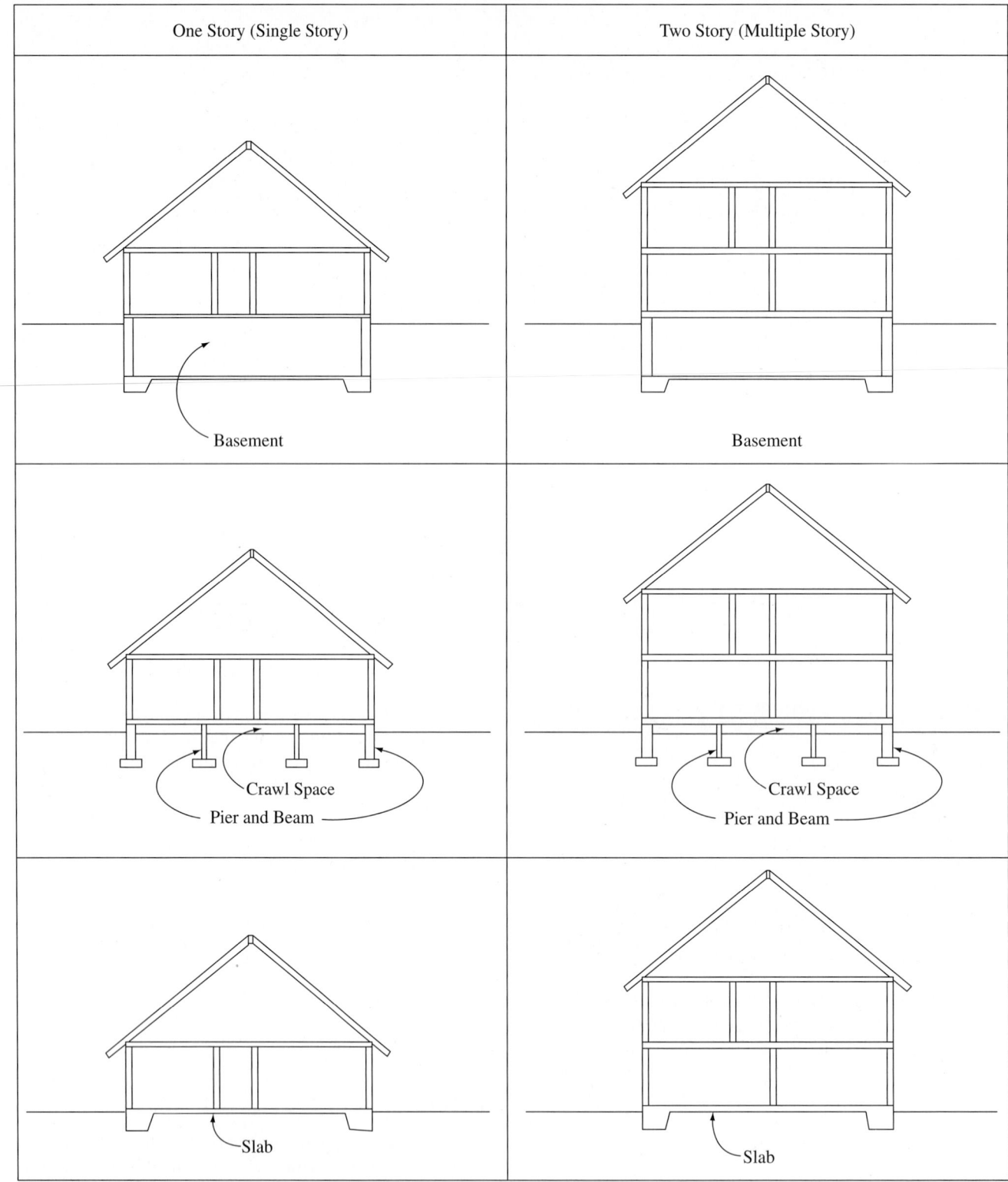

Figure 54-1 Basic house design and types of foundation used in residential construction

depending upon the type of soil and the local frost line. Figure 54-2 shows the cross section of a typical footing. Most footings are poured concrete reinforced with steel reinforcing rod. Figure 54-3 shows trenchwork and reinforcing prior to pouring the footing.

54.3 SLAB ON GRADE

Concrete slab on grade floors are poured on the ground with reinforcing. The reinforcing may be post tension cables, reinforcement rods, or wire mesh. These materials are used to

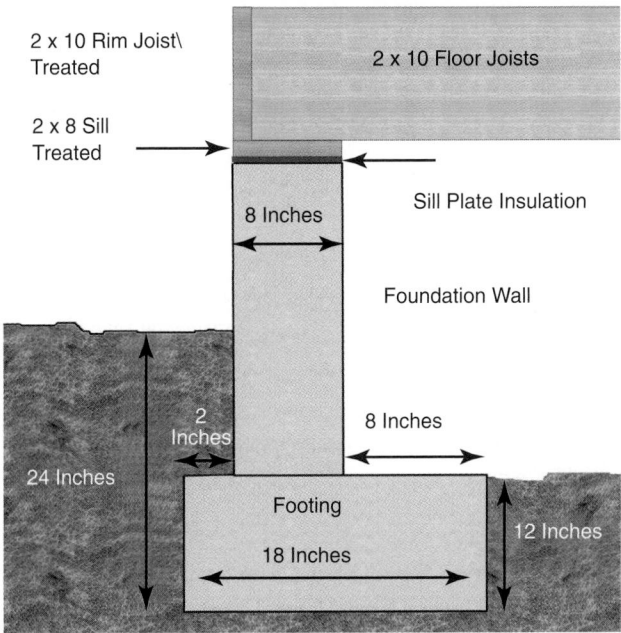

2 x 10 Rim Joist\ Treated

2 x 8 Sill Treated

2 x 10 Floor Joists

Sill Plate Insulation

8 Inches

Foundation Wall

8 Inches

2 Inches

24 Inches

Footing

18 Inches

12 Inches

Figure 54-2 Detail of typical footing and foundation wall

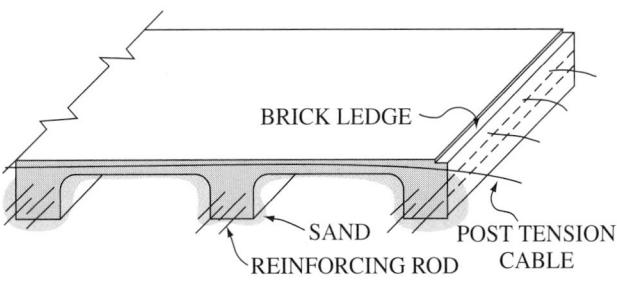

BRICK LEDGE

SAND

REINFORCING ROD

POST TENSION CABLE

Figure 54-4 The footing and support beams are formed along with the slab

help prevent cracking of the slab over time. Typical residential slabs are from 4–6 in thick and are poured continuously, incorporating the footing and cross beams where they are used, Figure 54-4. The concrete is deeper at the footing area and the footing reinforcing material is heavier than the reinforcing material used in the rest of the slab. Figure 54-5 shows a slab that is ready to pour.

Running Lines Under a Slab

Refrigerant lines, plumbing, and wiring must sometimes be located under a concrete slab. If refrigerant lines or

Figure 54-3 Footing is ready to pour
(Courtesy of Brewer Construction Inc.)

(a)

(b)

Figure 54-5 Site preparation for pouring a slab

condensate plumbing are to be placed below grade, they must be placed before the slab is poured. They should be installed inside a 3 to 4 in chase or conduit pipe. The conduit is buried in sand to protect it from sharp objects such as stones, Figure 54-6.

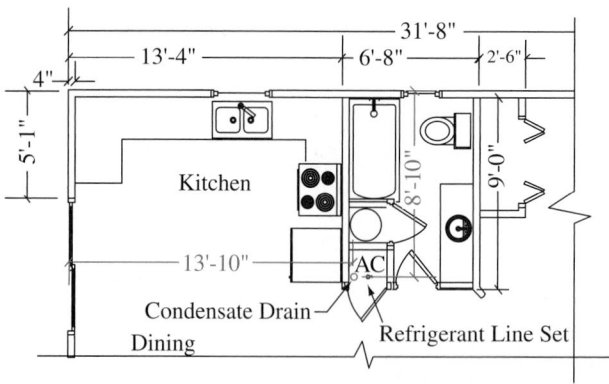

Figure 54-7 Locating refrigerant and condensate drain lines

CAUTION

Copper piping, including refrigerant lines, reacts to concrete. Therefore, copper tubing should not be buried directly in the concrete.

When installing refrigerant lines and condensate drain lines before a slab is poured, make certain that your dimensions are taken from the outside of the building to locate these pipes. It is often the case that dimensions are given from the inside wall. If the outside building dimensions are not given, you must look at the wall thickness as provided on the detailed wall section and add that dimension to your interior dimensions so that your pipes will come up in the appropriate location.

For example, the condensate drain in the center of Figure 54-7, the center of the drain is approximately 2 in inside the AC equipment room. The distance from the outside kitchen wall to the condensate drain is calculated by adding the wall thickness and the distance from the equipment room wall to the drain to the 13'-4" dimension on the plan. 13'-4" + 4" outside wall thickness + 2" distance from equipment wall to drain = 13'-10" The distance to be measured is 13'-10" from the outside kitchen wall.

However, this only locates one dimension. It is also necessary to determine the distance from the outside bathroom wall to the condensate line. This distance is calculated by adding the outside wall thickness to 9'-0" and then subtracting the inside wall and pipe distance inside the room.

9'-0" + 4" outside wall − 4" inside wall − 2" distance to drain = 8'-10".

The distance to the condensate pipe from the outside bathroom wall is 8'-10". Always double-check your dimensions before leaving the job site after roughing in these lines. Figure 54-8 shows lines being installed in a concrete slab.

54.4 CRAWL SPACE FOUNDATIONS

The foundation wall rests on the footing. The floor will be constructed and supported by the foundation wall along the perimeter of the house, and on beams supported by piers in the interior portion of the house, Figure 54-9. A crawl space is an unfinished space beneath the floor that is enclosed by the foundation wall. Crawl spaces get their name from their height. Typically, most crawl spaces are too low to walk in, necessitating crawling to move from one area to another. There is no floor, just dirt. The dirt should be covered with a vapor barrier, Figure 54-10.

The wiring, plumbing, air conditioning equipment, and ductwork are usually located in the crawl space of houses with crawl space construction.

TECH TIP

The vapor barrier is extremely important. Moisture accumulation under the house can create unhealthy conditions that promote mold and attack the wood members of the floor. The vapor barrier is also important for comfort. Houses with crawl spaces that lack vapor barriers can feel clammy in the summer, even at relatively cool temperatures because of the increased humidity entering the house through the crawl space.

Figure 54-6 Plumbing, including refrigerant, lines are buried in sand-filled trenches beneath the slab

(a)

(b)

Figure 54-8 All copper lines are protected with foam insulation so that they do not come in direct contact with the slab concrete

54.5 BASEMENTS

Residential construction sometimes includes a basement, as shown in the drawings in Figure 54-1. Basements have a floor, and are high enough to walk in. While the standard ceiling height of a normal room in a residence is 8 ft, basement ceilings may be lower. When the basement ceilings are less than 7 ft high, laying out and installing ductwork so it does not interfere with the use of the basement can be a problem. Basements are constructed in houses in many states and regions but may not be very common in other areas. Area soil conditions and the level of groundwater both affect the construction of residential basements.

Basement walls are typically constructed with poured concrete or cinderblock walls, Figure 54-11 (top, middle). They usually have concrete floors. However, in some arid (dry) climates such as Denver, Colorado, basements may have a wooden joist floor structure, Figure 54-11 (bottom). Properly designed and constructed basements provide a relatively low cost per square foot additional space to residences.

Moisture and poor ventilation are the two most common problems associated with basement areas. Without adequate dehumidification, high levels of moisture can contribute to the growth of mold and mildew. Proper ventilation can help control mold and mildew growth as well as provide better indoor air quality.

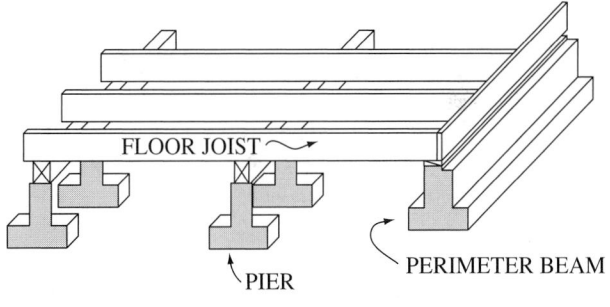

Figure 54-9 Pier and beam foundation for supporting floor joists

54.6 HOUSE FRAMING

Most residential construction uses wood as the primary structural material for walls, floors, ceilings, rafters, and decking material, Figure 54-12. Steel studs and beams can be used in some residential construction but are not in widespread use. Some residential structures are made of masonry materials like concrete blocks or poured concrete walls. Typical "brick" houses are actually brick veneer; the walls are still framed. The brick wall is not structural, but built in front of the frame wall and tied to it to hold the brick wall in place, Figure 54-13.

Before

After

Figure 54-10 Crawl space with a vapor barrier from Basement Systems picture on web page *http://www.basementsystems.com/crawlspace_products/crawlspace_vapor_barrier.php* *(CleanSpace Encapsulation System, Courtesy of Basement Systems)*

Figure 54-11 Types of basement wall and floor construction techniques used for residential homes

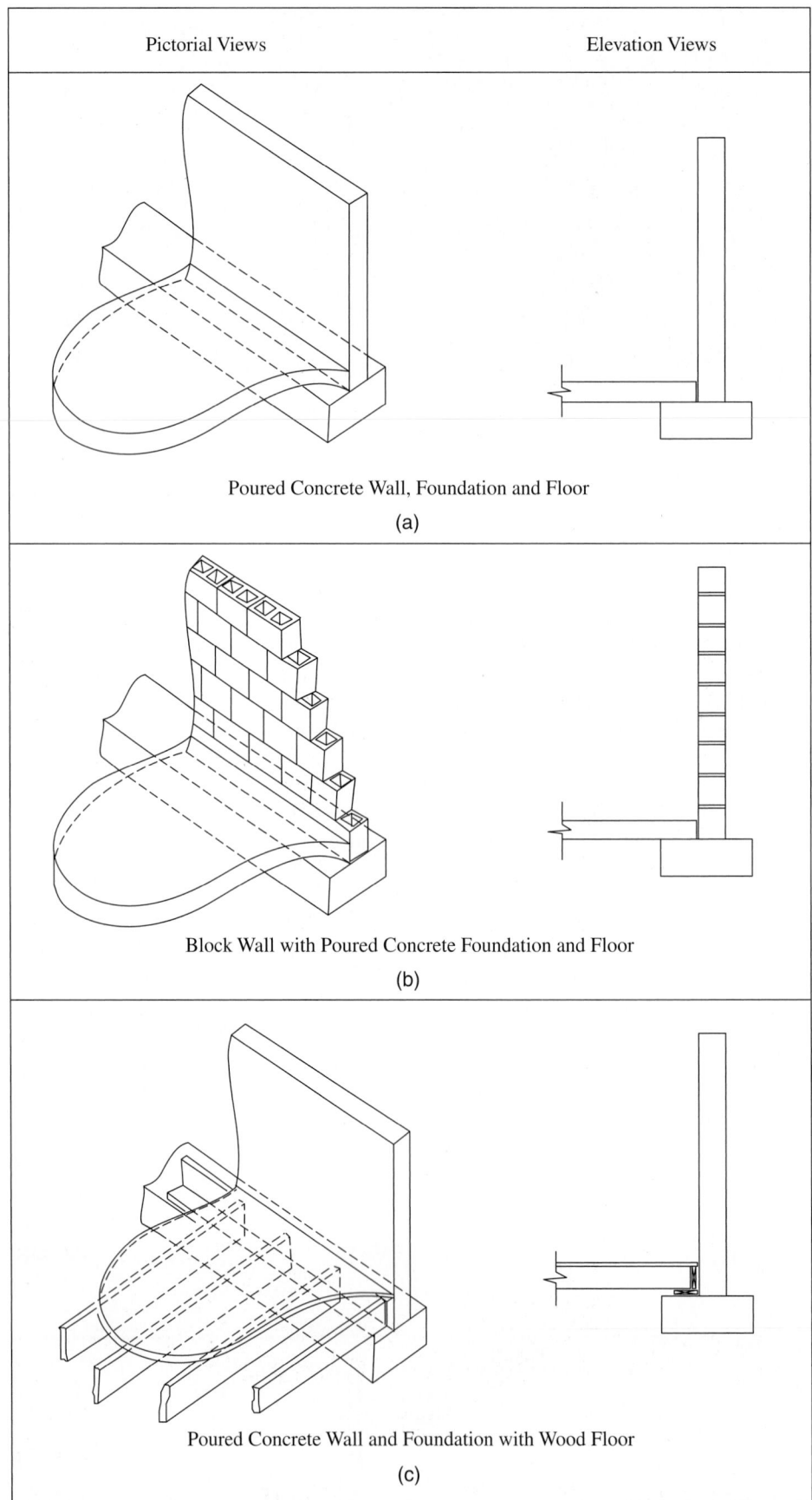

Pictorial Views   Elevation Views

Poured Concrete Wall, Foundation and Floor

(a)

Block Wall with Poured Concrete Foundation and Floor

(b)

Poured Concrete Wall and Foundation with Wood Floor

(c)

Figure 54-12 Typical framing is installed on 16 in centers; blocking is used at wall intersection to provide easier sheetrock installation

Nominal size	Actual dimensions
2 × 4	$1^1/_2 \times 3^1/_2$
2 × 6	$1^1/_2 \times 5^1/_2$
2 × 8	$1^1/_2 \times 7^1/_4$
2 × 10	$1^1/_2 \times 9^1/_4$
2 × 12	$1^1/_2 \times 11^1/_4$

Figure 54-14 Lumber dimensions in inches

Framing Members

Nearly all framing members in a traditional wood frame house are "2 by" lumber with a nominal 2 in thickness. It is rough cut at 2 in, but the actual thickness is closer to $1^1/_2$ in by the time the lumber is planed. The nominal dimensions and the actual dimensions for most common framing lumber are listed in Figure 54-14.

Figure 54-15 shows the framing members on a typical house. *Floor joists* support the floor. They rest upon the foundation wall and on beams supported by piers. Typically, floor joists are placed 16 in on center. This means that the measurement from the center of one framing member to the center of the next one is 16 in. Floor joists vary in size from 2 × 6 up to 2 × 12 depending upon the span, the type of wood used, and the floor load. The walls

are constructed of *studs*. Wall studs are usually 2 × 4 on 16 in centers. *Ceiling joists* lie on top of the walls and support the weight of the ceiling. Ceiling joists are usually 2 × 6 and are usually placed 16 in on center. *Rafters* rest on the exterior walls and support the roof. Rafters can be as small as 2 × 6 or as large as 2 × 12 depending upon the span, roof pitch, type of wood, and snow load.

54.7 WOOD FLOOR CONSTRUCTION

Floor construction for crawl space and basement foundations is similar. Crawl space foundations use piers and beams to support the floor joists; basement foundations can use either piers and beams or load bearing walls to support the floor joists. Floor joists are spaced either 16 or 24 in apart. These joists can be solid wood, wood trusses, or engineered wood I-beams. Figure 54-16 shows a floor system framed with dimensional lumber, Figure 54-17 shows floor joist framing using engineered wood I-beams, and Figure 54-18 shows a floor framed with open web wood trusses. When solid wood joists are used, any ductwork running perpendicular to the joists must be located below the joists. Open web trusses and engineered I-beams may allow the

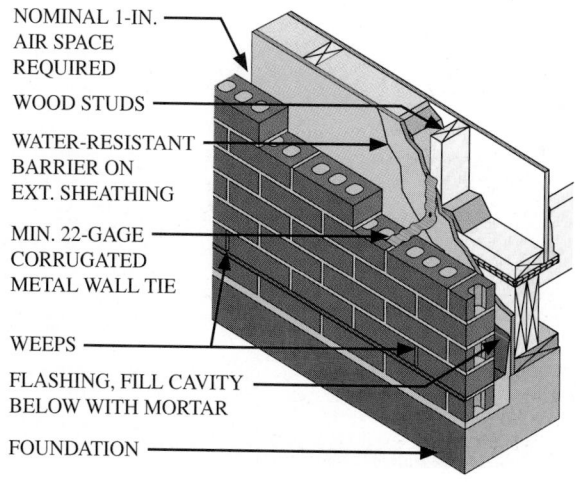

NOMINAL 1-IN. AIR SPACE REQUIRED

WOOD STUDS

WATER-RESISTANT BARRIER ON EXT. SHEATHING

MIN. 22-GAGE CORRUGATED METAL WALL TIE

WEEPS

FLASHING, FILL CAVITY BELOW WITH MORTAR

FOUNDATION

BRICK VENEER/WOOD STUD WALL

Figure 54-13 The brick veneer wall is tied to the frame structural wall

Figure 54-15 Common house framing
(Courtesy American Forest and Paper Association, Inc.)

Figure 54-16 Dimensional lumber floor joists

Figure 54-18 Open web floor joists

ductwork to pass through precut or fabricated openings. With permission from the construction manager and the manufacturer of the laminated beams being used, you may be allowed to cut holes on site that will allow the ducts to pass through, Figure 54-19.

(a)

Figure 54-17 Wood I-beam floor joists

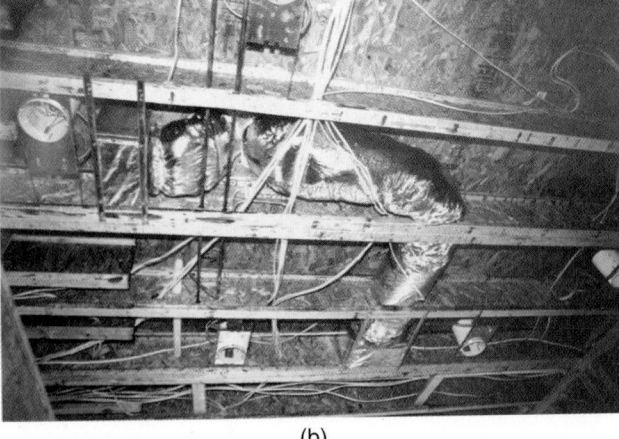

(b)

Figure 54-19 Vents going through two types of floor joists; (a) Truss; (b) Beam

SAFETY TIP

Do not cut a hole in any structural member without first obtaining permission from the manufacturer of the product and the job site foreman. Under no circumstances can a beam's structural surface be cut, shown in red in Figure 54-20. Cuts or gouges along these surfaces can cause the structure to prematurely fail.

Flooring Material

Wood floors consist of multiple layers: a subfloor, the underlayment, and the actual flooring surface. The subfloor is commonly plywood or OSB (oriented strand board) with tongue and groove edges along its length, Figure 54-21. The subfloor ranges in thickness from $\frac{5}{8}$ in to $1\frac{1}{8}$ in. When $\frac{5}{8}$ in material is used for subflooring, another layer of plywood or OSB is applied at right angles to the subfloor. This layer is called the underlayment. It normally has a smooth finish to facilitate applying the finished flooring materials. The total thickness typically must be at least 1 in. The $1\frac{1}{8}$ in flooring material does not need an extra layer of underlayment.

Subflooring and underlayment are often glued and nailed down. Sometimes screws are used in place of nails. Using mastic increases the overall floor strength and reduces future floor squeaks. Figure 54-22 shows how the plywood decking is offset, that is, each new length starts at a different place from the one next to it so that the seams between pieces of plywood do not occur next to each other. This increases the strength and durability of the floor.

54.8 WALL CONSTRUCTION

Figure 54-23a–d shows the typical wall sections for the four most common types of residential wood frame construction. You will note from the first floor construction level that each of the typical wall sections is similar.

Most residential walls are constructed with 2 × 4's located 16 in on center, Figure 54-12. In some cases 2 × 6's are used on the exterior walls. This allows for more insulation to both reduce the heat load and the sound level in the dwelling. In

Figure 54-21 Tongue and groove flooring material

some areas when 2 × 6's are used in the perimeter wall, they may be spaced 24 in on center. The 2 × 4's or 2 × 6's used for walls are located on a horizontal board called a base plate. If this base plate is located on a concrete floor, it must be pressure treated lumber. This is to reduce both wood rot and insect attacks. Two horizontal boards are placed on top of the stud wall. These are called the top plate. Typical wall heights for residential construction are 8 ft, 9 ft, and 10 ft, with 8 ft being the most common. Vapor barriers are frequently used in wall construction to control the flow of water vapor through the wall. The location and type of vapor barrier is in part determined by the climate. A vapor barrier is placed on the outside of the 2 × 4 wall in warm climates and on the inside in cold climates before the finished siding or masonry work is performed, as shown in Figure 54-24. House wraps have become popular for controlling infiltration through the wall. A house wrap is a large roll of material that can literally be wrapped around the exterior of the house before the exterior siding is installed, Figure 54-25. House wraps differ from vapor barriers in that they are specifically designed not to be a vapor barrier. They prevent air leaks through the wall without impeding the flow of water vapor.

54.9 CEILING AND ROOF CONSTRUCTION

Some builders use prefabricated roof trusses, as shown in Figure 54-26. These are almost always fabricated out of 2 × 4 materials with metal cleats connecting the joints. Contractors often favor such trussed roof systems because they are strong, durable, and easily assembled on the job site. They make it slightly more difficult for the air conditioning technician to locate a unit in an attic and make straight duct runs.

NEVER CUT THE EDGE OF A LOAD
SUPPORTING BOARD

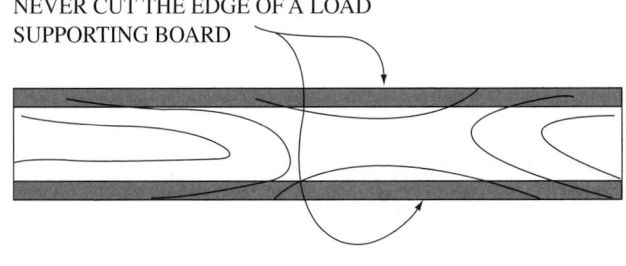

Figure 54-20 Cutting the edge of a horizontal supporting beam will significantly reduce the beam's strength

(a)   (b)

Figure 54-22 (a) Plywood decking is glued and nailed to the floor joists; (b) Plywood, joints

If trusses are not used, the ceiling rafters are typically 2×6 to 2×12 dimensional lumber depending on the room span, as shown in Figure 54-27. Roof rafters are typically 2×6's; however, depending on the height of the roof, width of the span, and possible snow load or northern climates, 2×8, 2×10, and even 2×12 may be used for rafters. The entire roof area will be covered by thick plywood roof decking material for composite roofs, asphalt shingles, and sheet metal roofs. When wood shingles are used, a lapped system will be installed across the top of the rafters as opposed to roof decking. An advantage of shingle construction is that with this lapped substructure the attic area will vent freely, which reduces the heat load on the residence during summer.

> ### SAFETY TIP
>
> A safety harness and lanyard is required under OSHA regulation for construction workers any time they will be working more than 6 ft above the floor.

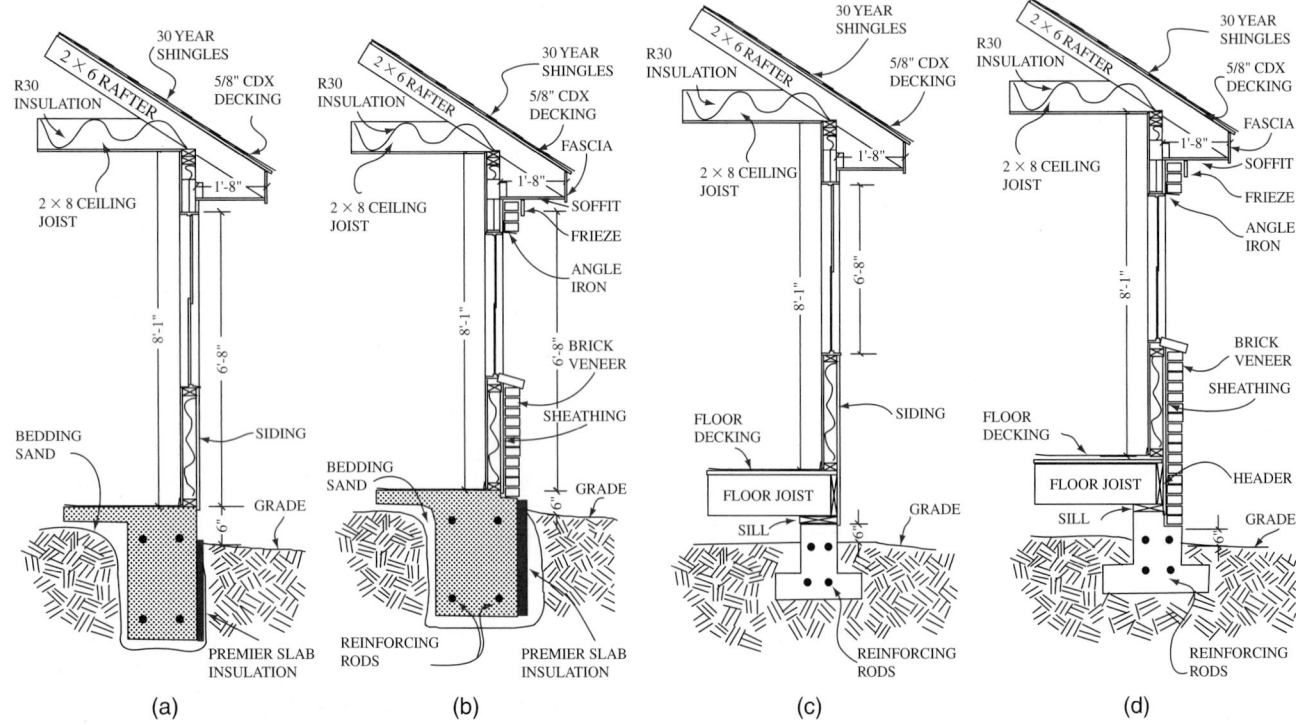

(a)   (b)   (c)   (d)

Figure 54-23 Typical wall sections: (a) Slab with siding; (b) Slab with brick veneer; (c) Pier and beam with siding; (d) Pier and beam with brick veneer

Figure 54-24 Vapor barrier is installed before brick veneer is applied

Figure 54-25 House wrapped with house wrap to reduce infiltration

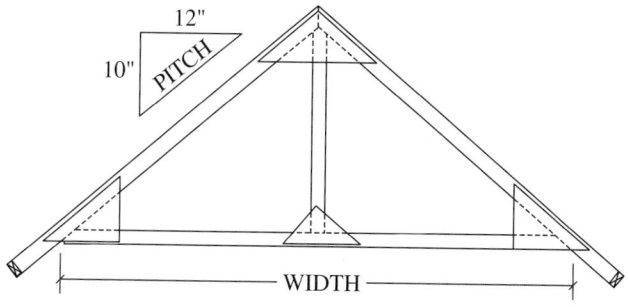

Figure 54-26 Prefabricated trusses are available in a variety of widths

54.10 INSULATION

There are four common types of insulation used in residential construction. They are:

- **Rock Wool**   Rock wool is a synthetic material fabricated from a mineral.
- **Fiberglass**   Fiberglass insulation is a spun glass. Fiberglass is available in rolls and bats with or without

Figure 54-27 Ceiling joists can be made from a variety of sizes of conventional lumber depending on the roof slope, load, and span; the flatter roof section here uses 2 × 6's but the steeper section uses 2 × 12's

an attached vapor barrier. Most fiberglass bat insulation is pink or yellow. Blown in fiberglass is usually white. The color of the insulation has no effect on the capacity of the insulation to resist heat.

- **Cellulose Insulation**   Cellulose insulation is a synthetically produced insulation product that uses recycled newspaper as its basic material. Cellulose insulation can either be blown loose or else a binder can be added so that it can be blown in wall cavities as a solid fill material.
- **Foam Insulation**   There are a number of foam insulations that can be used in residential construction as either a sheet or a product that is blown in on site.

SAFETY TIP

When working with insulation, wear a respirator to avoid breathing the fine insulation dust. Avoid touching insulation with unprotected skin. Wearing a long sleeved shirt, gloves, and a cap will reduce your exposure to insulation that can cause irritation to your skin.

For all insulation, the ability to resist the transfer of heat is directly related to its thickness. Some materials may have greater resistance per inch of material than others. However, compressing the insulation material significantly reduces its heat resistance. Squeezing a 6 in fiberglass batt into a $3\frac{1}{2}$ in wall space will not create a super insulated wall. Fiberglass batts designed for insulating standard $3\frac{1}{2}$ in walls are available in R-11 and R-13 densities.

Often the 2 × 4 top plates and bottom plates on a wall must have holes drilled in them in order for wires or plumbing to pass through. These holes must be sealed to prevent air infiltration. The holes are typically filled using expandable foam as shown in white in Figure 54-28. Any holes drilled horizontally in 2 × 4 wall studs are typically not sealed.

Figure 54-28 Wires that go through the top plate of a wall must be either caulked or filled with expanding foam

The ceiling is the area in a residence that loses and gains most of the heat. Since ceilings are so crucial for heat gain and loss, code requires that a much thicker layer of insulation be installed in the attic. Attic insulation can be blown, loose insulation, or bat insulation. Table 54-1 lists common insulating materials and their R values based on thickness.

54.11 WALLS AND CEILINGS

The most common material found on interior walls for residences is sheetrock. Sheetrock is a product that has paper on both sides of a powdered gypsum. Figure 54-29 shows a room before (a) and after (b) sheetrock installation. Sheetrock is not a structural material. If it is struck very hard the paper will become damaged and the gypsum can be pulverized. Once sheetrock has been damaged, the damaged portion must be removed and replaced with a new section of sheetrock. Sheetrock is relatively soft and can be easily pierced with a screwdriver.

Sheetrock is attached to the stud using either sheetrock nails or screws. The sheetrock joints are covered with a sheetrock compound and paper tape. The paper tape does not have adhesive. It is held in place by the sheetrock compound. Sheetrock is finished by sanding the

Table 54-1 R Values of Common Building Materials

Material	R per Inch
Batt and blanket rock wool	R3.7
Blown cellulose	R3.1–R3.7
Blown mineral wool—horizontal fill	R2.9–R2.2
Blown mineral fiber	R2.2–R2.9
Expanded polystyrene board (white bead board)	R4.0
Fiberglass batt, high density	R3.5–R4.3
Fiberglass batt, standard density	R2.9–R3.7
High density batt and blanket fiberglass	R4.3
Loose fill cellulose	R3.7
Loose fill fiberglass	R2.2
Loose fill rockwool	R2.9
Low density fiberglass batt and blanket	R3.1
Medium density fiberglass batt and blanket	R3.7
Mineral wool batt	R3.14–R3.80
Polystyrene board (blue or pink board)	R6.3–R5.6
Polyurethane board (open cell)	R5.50–R6.25
Rigid foam board	R3.7–R8
Spray-on polyurethane foam	R6.3–R5.6
Spray-on cellulosic fiber	R3.4–R2.9

WORK ORDERS

Service Ticket 5401

Equipment: New Split System Installation in House on Concrete Slab

In the site preparation phase, the general contractor is preparing a slab to be poured and needs any work under the slab to be completed. Refrigerant lines and condensate drain need to be installed.

The technician arrived at the job site, laid out location of furnace/AHU and also the location of condensing unit, and ran a 4 in PVC conduit under the future concrete slab. The technician then rolled out both the suction and liquid lines, insulated the suction line, and pulled them along with thermostat wire inside the conduit being careful not to kink the copper tube or tear the insulation. The technician checked to make sure there would be no place where concrete from the poured slab would contact any part of either line and made sure there was plenty of tubing length on each end to connect the furnace/AHU and the condensing unit. The technician made sure that the tubing caps remained in place on each end of the tubing so the system would be free of moisture and foreign matter. Before leaving, the technician took location dimensions of the line location and recorded this on the blueprints. The job is ready for slab inspection.

Service Ticket 5402

Equipment: New Split System Installation in House on Concrete Slab

In the framing phase the general contractor called and the framing is near completion. The ductwork and wiring need to be roughed in. The refrigerant lines were pulled during the slab preparation.

The technician roughs in the return air box in the hall and the supply air drops in the ceiling. The control wiring is run from the thermostat location in the hall to the air handler in the equipment closet. The control wiring between the air handler and the condenser was run with the refrigerant lines during slab preparation. The electrician pulls the power wire for the air handler inside and the condensing unit outside. The technician installed nail plates where appropriate. The technician called for a rough-in inspection.

Service Ticket 5403

Equipment: New Split System Installation in House on Concrete Slab

The general contractor notifies the technique that the house is dried in. It is time to set the equipment, run the ductwork, connect the refrigerant lines, and complete the wiring.

The technician set the air handling unit in the equipment closet and the condensing unit on the pad outside. The refrigerant lines are connected to the air handling unit. The condensate line is run from the air handling unit to the condensate stub provided during slab preparation. The electrician wired the power wire to the air handler and the condensing unit. The technician wired the low voltage thermostat wiring to the air handler and condensing unit.

The return and supply air plenums are installed, and the ductwork is run. The supply duct is run in the attic, and the return runs to a return box in the hall. Since the supply duct is in the attic, duct with an insulation value of R-8 is used. The return duct is insulated with R-6 because it is not exposed to attic conditions. All ductwork is properly connected, sealed, and supported to prevent air leaks and restrictions.

Service Ticket 5404

Equipment: New Split System Installation with Lines Under Concrete Slab

The home is complete and the new owner is ready to move in. The technician is called to do the initial system startup. The technician leak checks the lines and coil using nitrogen. Finding no leaks, the lines and coil are evacuated. While the system is being evacuated, the technician checks all electrical connections. With the disconnect remaining off, the voltage to the lugs at the top of the disconnect is checked and compared to the voltage on the system data plate. The thermostat is mounted and wired. The system is valved off when the vacuum reaches 400 microns. The vacuum holds for 10 minutes, rising slightly to 450 microns and leveling off. After determining the system is tight, clean, and dry, the technician releases the refrigerant from the condenser into the system. The technician then starts the unit and checks the voltage before and after starting the unit to check for voltage drop in the power wire. The information in the manufacturer's installation instructions is used to check the system charge. The technician records the system operating data on the startup form used by the company. The technician calls for final inspection when the system is performing per the manufacturer's specifications.

UNIT 54—REVIEW QUESTIONS

1. What is the standard ceiling height in a residence?
2. Name the two most common problems with basements.
3. Name the reinforcement materials used in concrete slabs.
4. Why should refrigerant lines or condensate plumbing be installed in a chase or conduit if they are to be under a poured concrete slab?

5. How is ductwork location affected by solid wood floor joists ?

6. Why is plywood decking offset, as seen in Figure 54-22b?

7. Why do contractors often favor a trussed roof system?

8. Name four common types of insulation used in residential construction.

9. Using Table 54-1, what would be the insulation R-factor of 4 in of medium density fiberglass batt and blanket material?

10. What is the most common material used for interior walls of residences?

11. What material is sometimes required by the fire code for studs?

12. What is a roof curb?

13. What consequences can result from failing to contact the roofing company before making a roof penetration on a bonded roof?

14. What is the space above the drop in ceiling in a commercial building used for in the HVAC/R industry?

15. What must be included in any duct that passes through a firewall?

16. What is the purpose of a fire damper?

17. Why is the cost of owning a "green" building often less than the cost of owning a conventionally constructed building?

18. What is the mission of the USGBC?

19. What does LEED certification mean?

UNIT 55

Drawings and Blueprint Reading

OBJECTIVES

After completing this unit you will be able to:

- identify mechanical, electrical, and architectural drawings.
- explain the difference between orthographic and pictorial drawings.
- interpret the different line types incorporated in a drawing.
- make a sketch of a floor plan to scale.
- explain the purpose of each of the various drawings that make up a typical set of drawings.

55.1 INTRODUCTION

It is very important that HVAC/R technicians be able to read drawings accurately. In the past there may have been a lead technician who told all the other technicians exactly what to do and where to put the various parts and pieces of equipment. Today most jobs require each technician to read and follow the drawings. The production schedule on most modern construction sites is so tight that you do not have a lot of time to stand around and look at the drawings. You must be able to quickly read the drawing; therefore, you need to practice this skill to become fast and proficient in reading and interpreting drawings.

55.2 TYPES OF DRAWINGS

Drawings are a universal language. For example, many highway signs require no accompanying text. An arrow pointing around the corner tells drivers that a curve is coming up. Mechanical, electrical, and architectural drawings are used extensively in the HVAC/R industry to provide the technician with a graphic representation of equipment, HVAC/R systems, and buildings. Mechanical drawings are used to illustrate equipment, systems, and components such as air handlers, refrigerant coils, component layout, relays, motors, valves, and other parts and pieces of HVAC/R systems. Electrical drawings are used to show how the components in a system are wired together, as in Figure 55-1. Figure 55-2 shows the symbols used for some common electrical components. Architectural drawings are used to represent buildings, houses, and other structures as well as systems within those structures

such as system location for electrical, duct layout, piping layout, and other substantial building parts as shown in Figure 55-3.

The term "blueprints" or simply "prints" date back to the early part of the twentieth century. At that time the only copying technique available was to lay the drawing on a chemically treated paper, expose the sheets to a bright light, then expose the treated sheet to ammonia fumes. This turned the sheet bright blue leaving the lines white. With the invention of large format copiers, the blueprinting process is seldom used today, but the term *blueprint* is often still used when referring to a set of architectural or mechanical drawings.

55.3 ALPHABET OF LINES

All drawings use a standard set of lines. This set of lines is collectively referred to as the alphabet of lines. Each of the lines has a specific purpose. Figure 55-4 shows how the various lines are used in drawings. The alphabet of lines can be understood even if the words on the drawings are done in another language.

The basic line types are:

- **Object Line** The object line is used to represent the visible lines or edges of an object.
- **Hidden Lines** Hidden lines are used to represent major components that would be obscured by the surface of the object.
- **Center Lines** Center lines are used to represent the center of an object that is round or symmetrical. They are also used to locate the center of holes.
- **Section Lines** Section lines are used to represent the edge of a cutaway surface.
- **Dimension Lines** Dimension lines are used in conjunction with numbers representing the size or length of an object.
- **Extension Lines** Extension lines are lines that extend from a point being dimensioned.
- **Cutting Plane Lines** Cutting plane lines are used to locate an imaginary cut on a surface to expose the parts inside of an object.
- **Break Lines** Break lines are used to show the removal of an area of an object to expose the inside of the object. They are frequently used on pictorial drawings to expose the internal workings of an object.

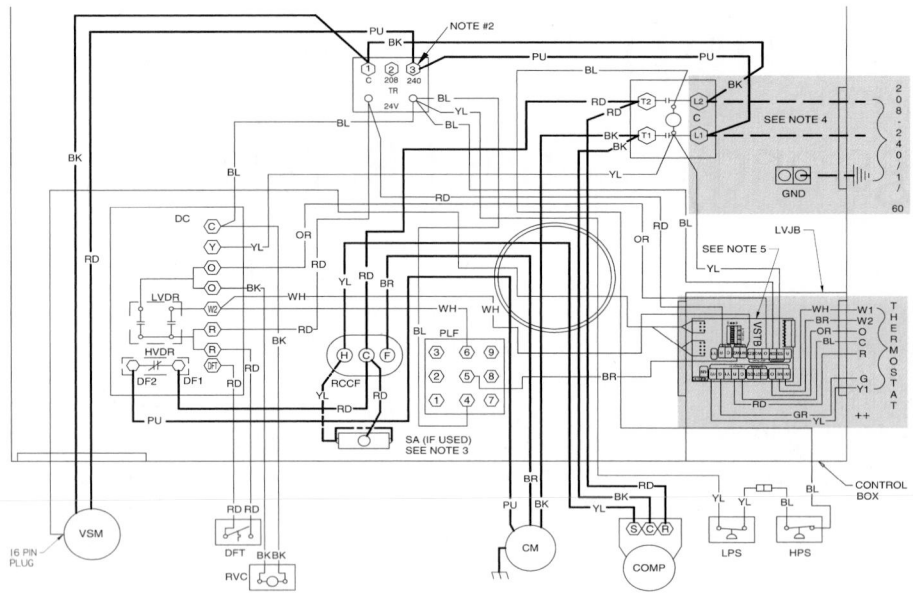

Figure 55-1 The block highlighted in yellow shows field power wiring connections, the green highlighted block shows field low voltage connections

- **Leaders and Arrows** Leaders and arrows are used to locate or identify items on a drawing.
- **Phantom Lines** Phantom lines show where a part will be placed or another position where a part can be moved.

55.4 MECHANICAL DRAWINGS

Mechanical drawings are divided into two major groups, orthographic drawings and pictorial drawings. Orthographic projections or simply projection drawings are typically made up of one or more views of the object, as it would appear if you were looking straight at it. These views are always shown in the orderly arrangement diagrammed in Figure 55-5. If an object to be pictured would look the same from the back and front views, the duplicate view would typically not be drawn. Most mechanical drawings use the front view, right side, and top views of the object to fully describe the object's shape and appearance. Figure 55-6 is an example of the three views used to illustrate one piece of electrical equipment, a grounding lug.

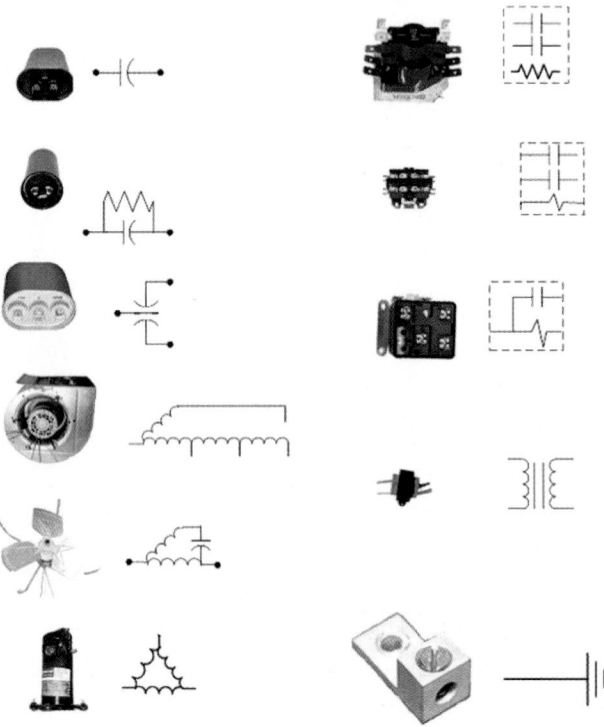

Figure 55-2 Standardized symbols are used to represent the various components found in electric circuit including resistors, capacitors, and inductors

Figure 55-3 Architectural drawings are called "blueprints" because of the printing process used to reproduce these large sheets

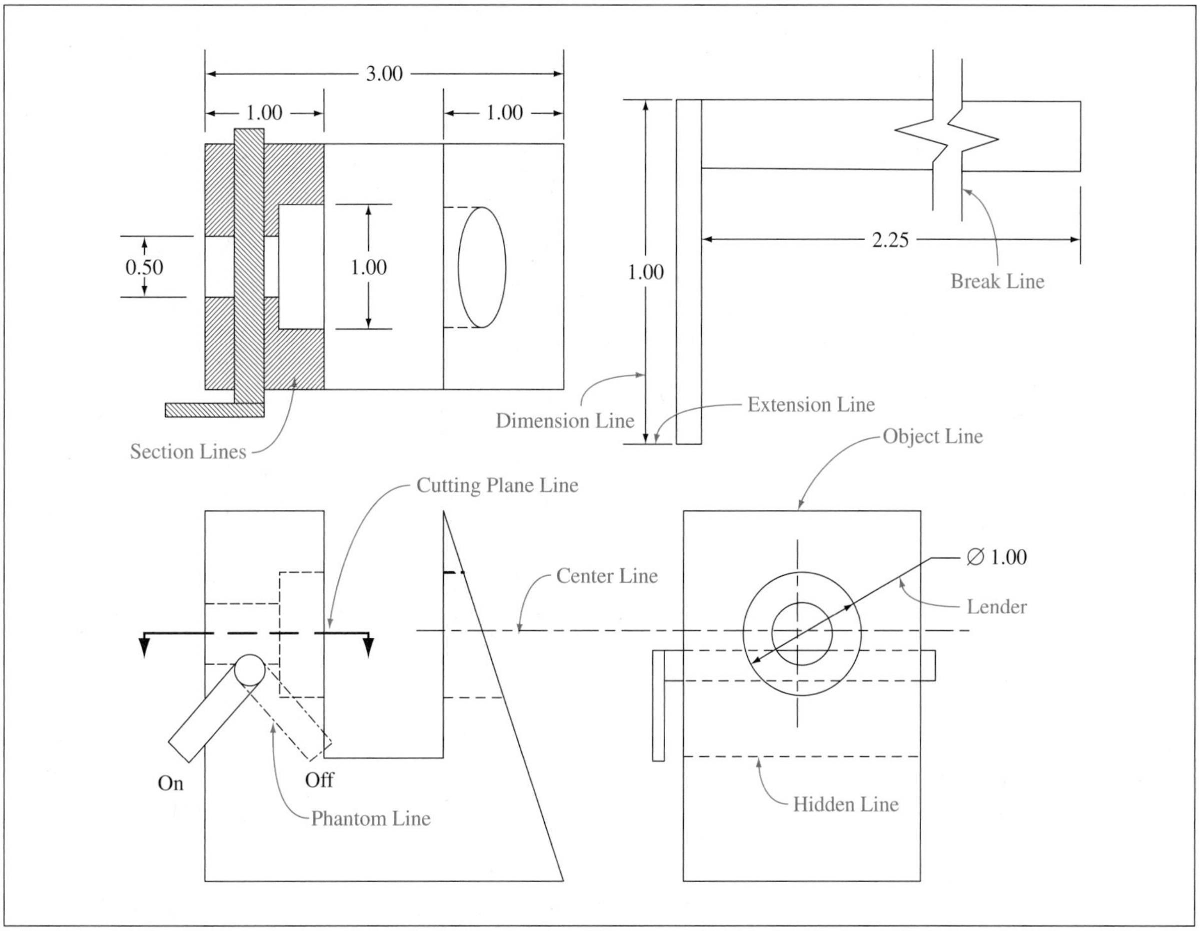

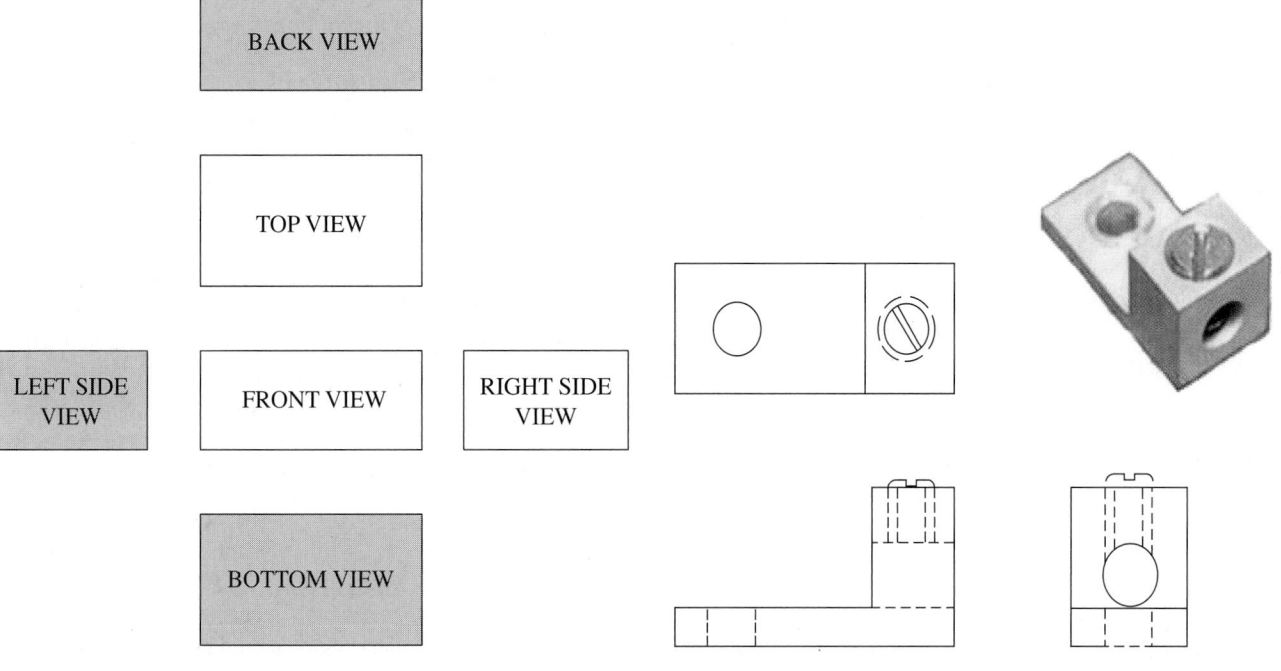

3.00
1.00
1.00
1.00
0.50
1.00

Section Lines

Dimension Line

2.25

Break Line

Extension Line

Object Line

Cutting Plane Line

Center Line

Ø 1.00

Lender

On   Off

Phantom Line

Hidden Line

Figure 55-4 The alphabet of lines used in an architectural drawing

BACK VIEW

TOP VIEW

LEFT SIDE
VIEW

FRONT VIEW

RIGHT SIDE
VIEW

BOTTOM VIEW

Figure 55-5 Orderly arrangement of views for mechanical lines

Figure 55-6 Three views used to illustrate a grounding lug

55.5 PICTORIAL DRAWINGS

Pictorial drawings are the most common mechanical drawings used in the HVAC/R industry. Pictorial drawings are used to draw a picture-like representation of the object, such as the connector in Figure 55-7. These drawings are made as if the draftsman were standing and looking at the unit. Pictorial drawings are often used to show the technician the location of the various components used to make up an air conditioning or heating unit. Pictorial drawings are the easiest drawings to use for identifying parts because they look like what they represent. Pictorial drawings are extensively used in manufacturers' sales literature because they are so easy to understand. A cutaway pictorial drawing like the one in Figure 55-8 may even show the arrangement of interior parts you would not be able to see in a photograph.

55.6 ARCHITECTURAL DRAWINGS

Architectural drawings are used to show the layout and structure of houses and buildings. These drawings are typically made as if the drafter is looking straight down at the building. Lines are used on an architectural drawing to represent the building's walls and other major mechanical and structural components located within the building. Figure 55-9 shows a small residential house. The doors, windows, bathroom fixtures, and major kitchen appliances are easily identifiable.

Multiple pages of drawings are often used to completely and clearly illustrate all of the different elements and systems used in the construction of a building, Figure 55-10. These drawings collectively are known as the building plans. Some of these drawing pages are combined in a set of plans for a single family home or residence. But in a set of drawings for a commercial building, there may be separate drawings for each of the major parts of the building. Figure 55-11 shows a comparison between plans for a single family residence and a commercial building. The plans on the right in Figure 55-11

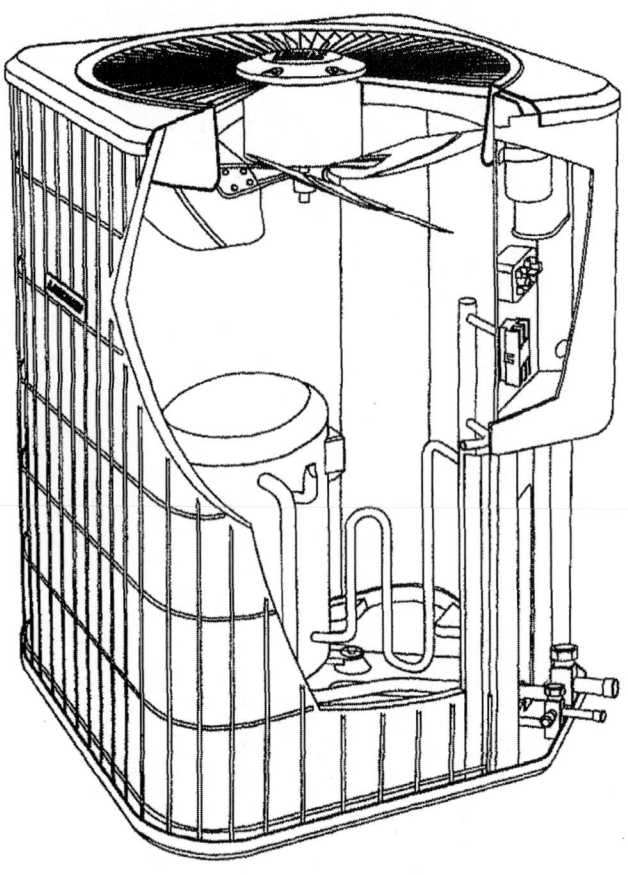

Figure 55-8 A cutaway pictorial drawing can show both internal and external appearances
(Courtesy of Lennox Industries, Inc.)

are for a single family residence; the plans on the left in Figure 55-11 are for a commercial building.

A set of drawings for a single family home may start with a pictorial drawing of the proposed house, Figure 55-12. Not all house plans have a pictorial drawing. A floor plan of the building shows the layout and gives the dimensions, Figure 55-13. Next there may be drawings for the electrical, Figure 55-14, plumbing, Figure 55-15, and HVAC, Figure 55-16. When combined, these three are often referred to as the mechanical drawings for a building.

Additional drawings may show different views of the house, called elevations. Figure 55-17 shows the left, right, front, and back elevations for a typical single family residence. Other drawings may show a plot or site plan of where and how the building is located on the land, Figure 55-18. Detailed drawings of building components, such as roof framing, windows, stairwells, kitchen cabinets, and roof details, may also be included in a set of detail drawings, Figure 55-19.

55.7 ARCHITECTURAL SYMBOLS

There are many standard symbols used in architectural drawings. Figure 55-20 shows the common architectural symbols and gives their description. Some symbols such as the symbol

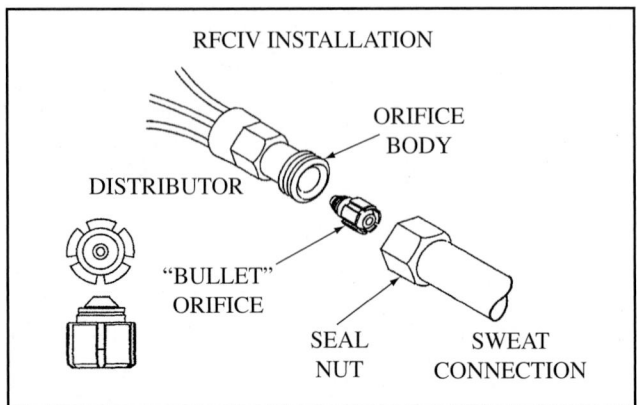

Figure 55-7 A pictorial drawing from a manufacturer show how an assembly fits together; this one includes top and side views of a part to help identify it

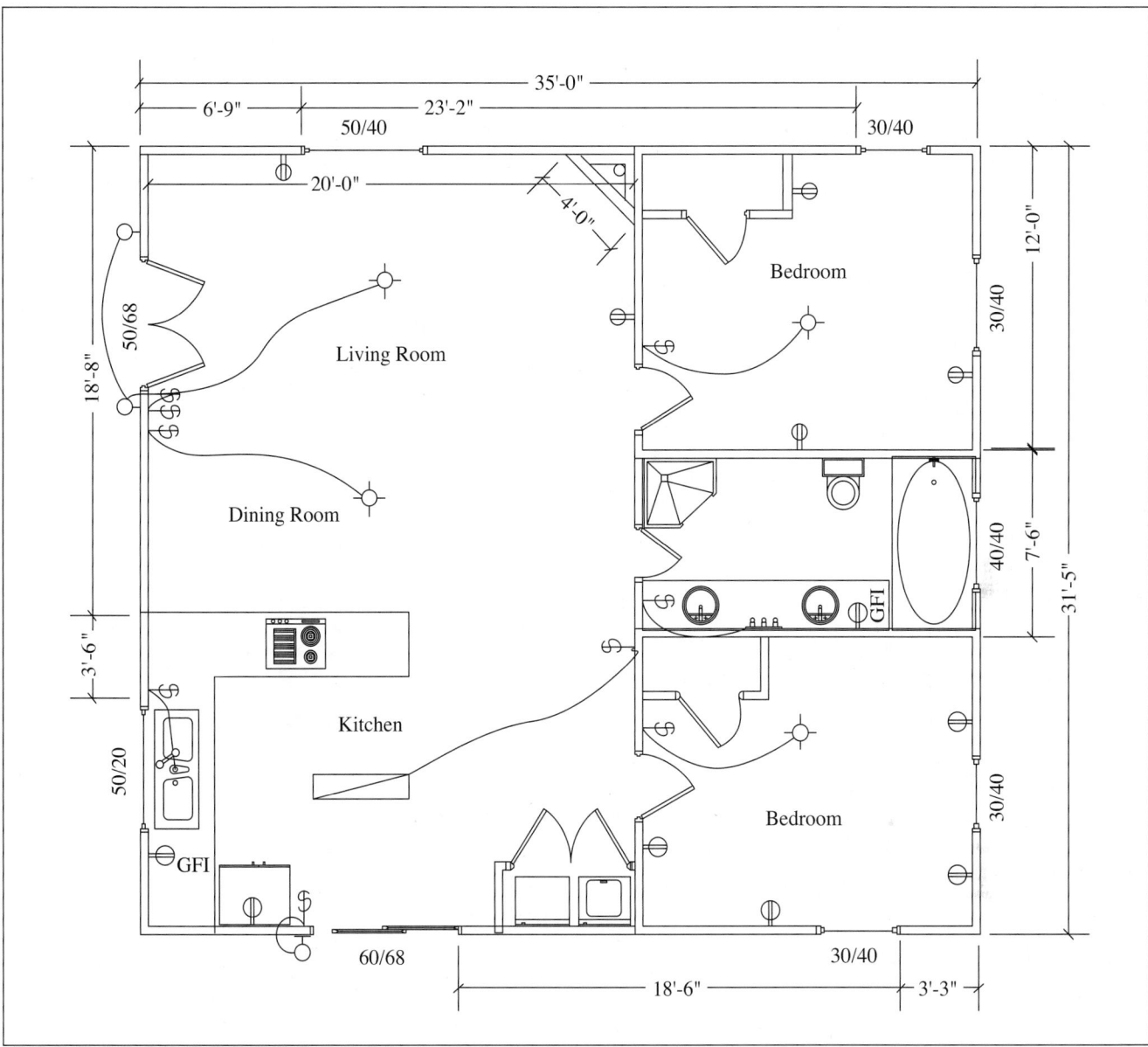

Figure 55-9 Simple floor plan of a small residential house

for a ceiling light can be used for a variety of different types of lights, as seen in (a) and (b) of Figure 55-21. Variations of the light symbol can be used to represent recessed lights, track lights, a ceiling fan with a light, and a vent fan with a light, as seen in (c) through (f) of Figure 55-21. In Figure 55-21, (g) shows the symbol for a standard light switch and (h) shows the symbol for a standard receptacle. Common variations of the light switch and outlet symbols are given in Figure 55-20. Most drawings will have a table showing the symbols and explaining their use because many symbols do not resemble the object they are representing. Examples are the register, vent fan, and shower nozzle, shown in (i)–(k) of Figure 55-21. In addition to the commonly used symbols, architects can invent their own symbols for items located on the drawings. The symbols table should include the standard

symbols and any created symbols the architect will be using for that drawing. For large commercial buildings there may be an entire page dedicated to symbols. Always refer to the symbols table when reading blueprints.

TECH TIP

The purpose and appearance of architectural electrical drawings and electrical schematics in air conditioning systems are very different. The electrical symbols used for architectural drawings are very different from the symbols used in HVAC electrical schematic diagrams.

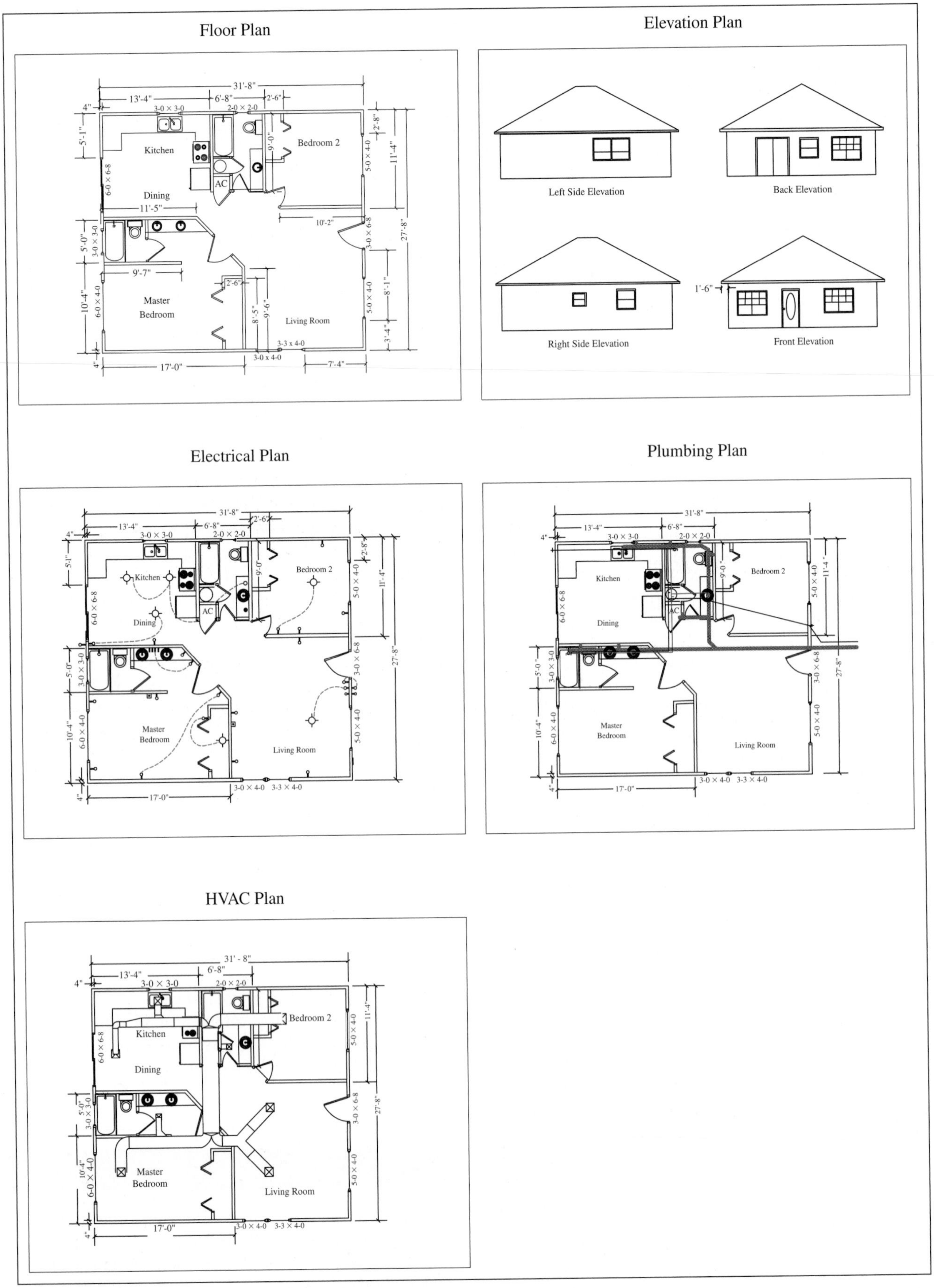

Figure 55-10 Typical drawings found in a set of plans used in the construction of a single family home

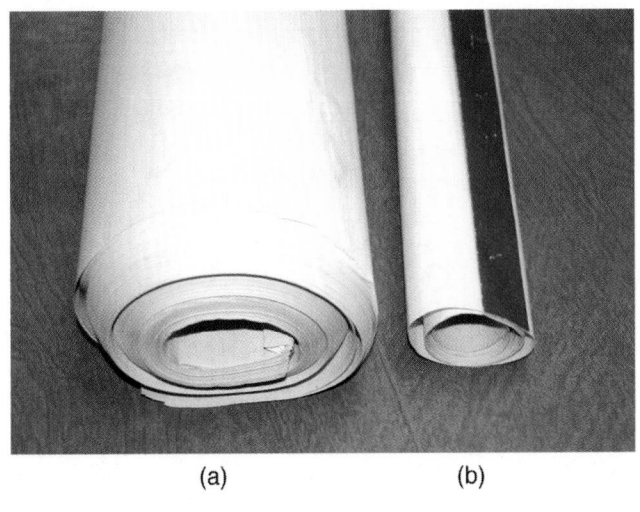

(a)   (b)

Figure 55-11 (a) Blueprints for a commercial building; (b) Blueprints for a residential home

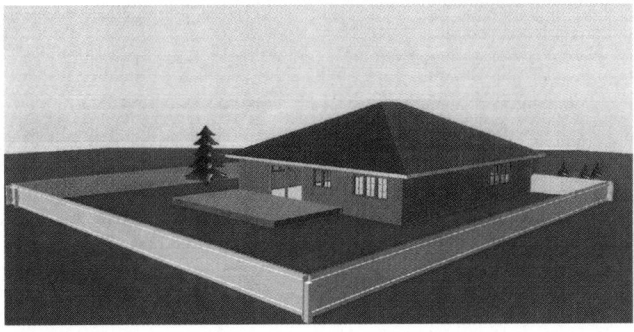

Figure 55-12 Computer-generated pictorial view

55.8 READING MECHANICAL DRAWINGS

Figure 55-22 shows a three view drawing of an air conditioning condensing unit. The vapor line or suction line in the top view has been shaded blue, and it can be seen on the right side view of the orthographic projection. The liquid line had been shaded red, and it can be seen on the top and left side views, and just as a sliver in the right side view. The discharge air grill on top of the unit has been shaded yellow, and it too can be seen in all three views. The grill only appears as a thin yellow line in the left side and right side views; its actual shape can only be seen in the top view. In an orthographic projection, not all of the parts of the unit can be seen clearly in each of the views. In the case of the liquid and suction lines, they are only both completely visible in the top view. Only the liquid line is shown in the left

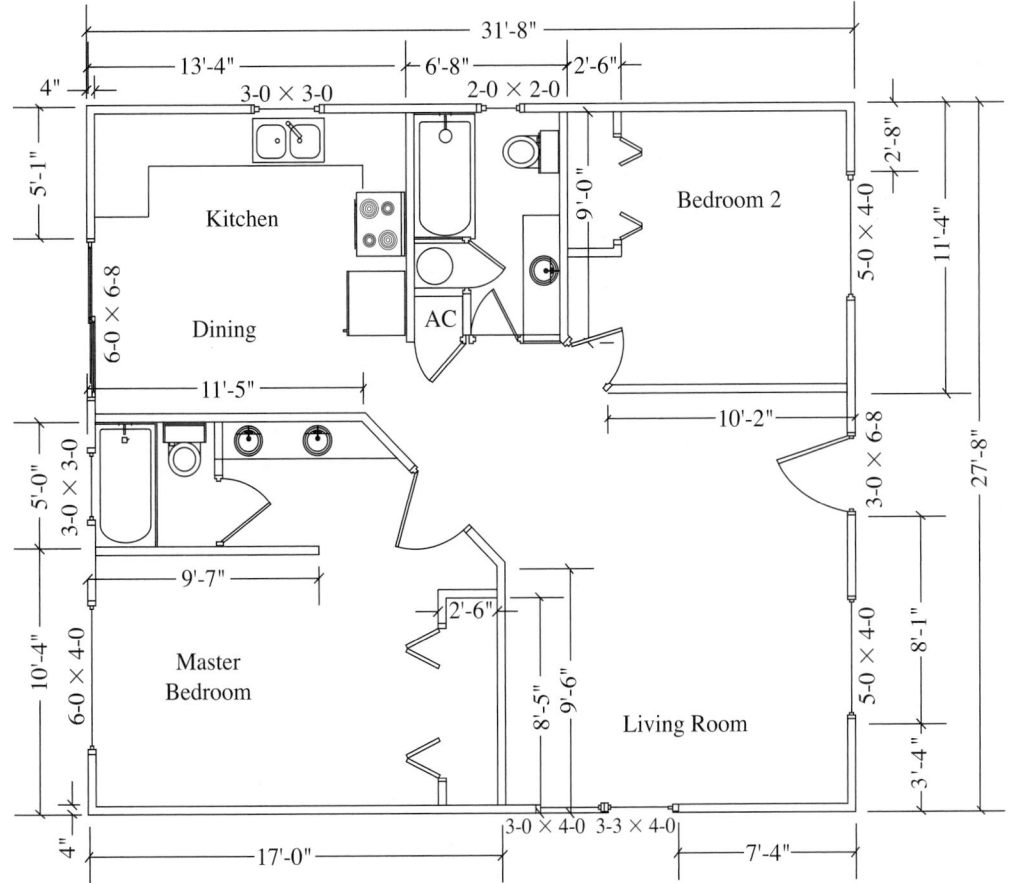

Figure 55-13 Blueprint showing the basic building dimensions and layout

Figure 55-14 Blueprint showing the house electrical plan

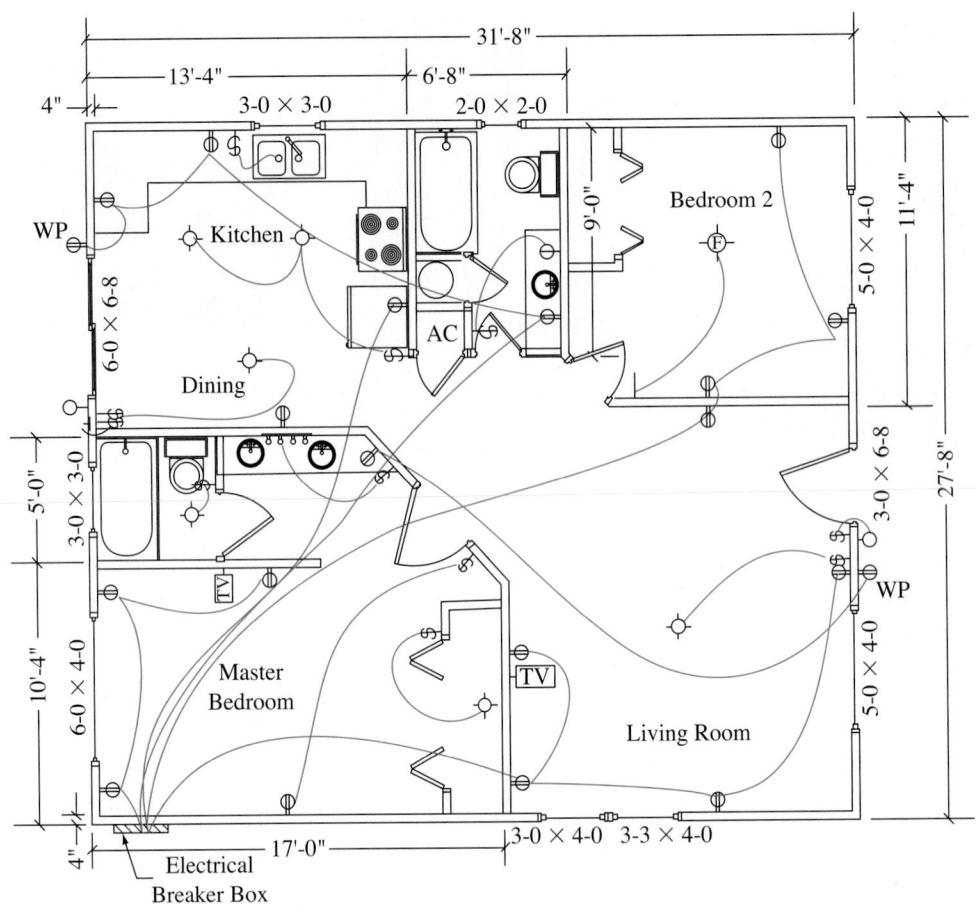

Figure 55-15 Blueprint showing the house plumbing plan

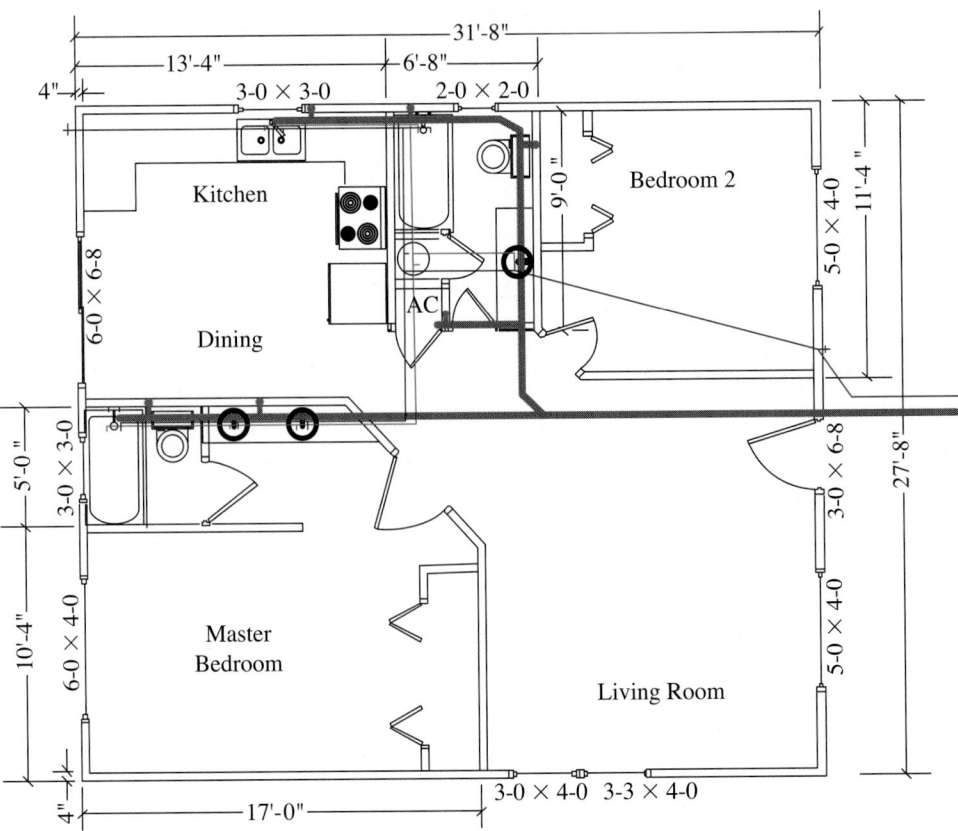

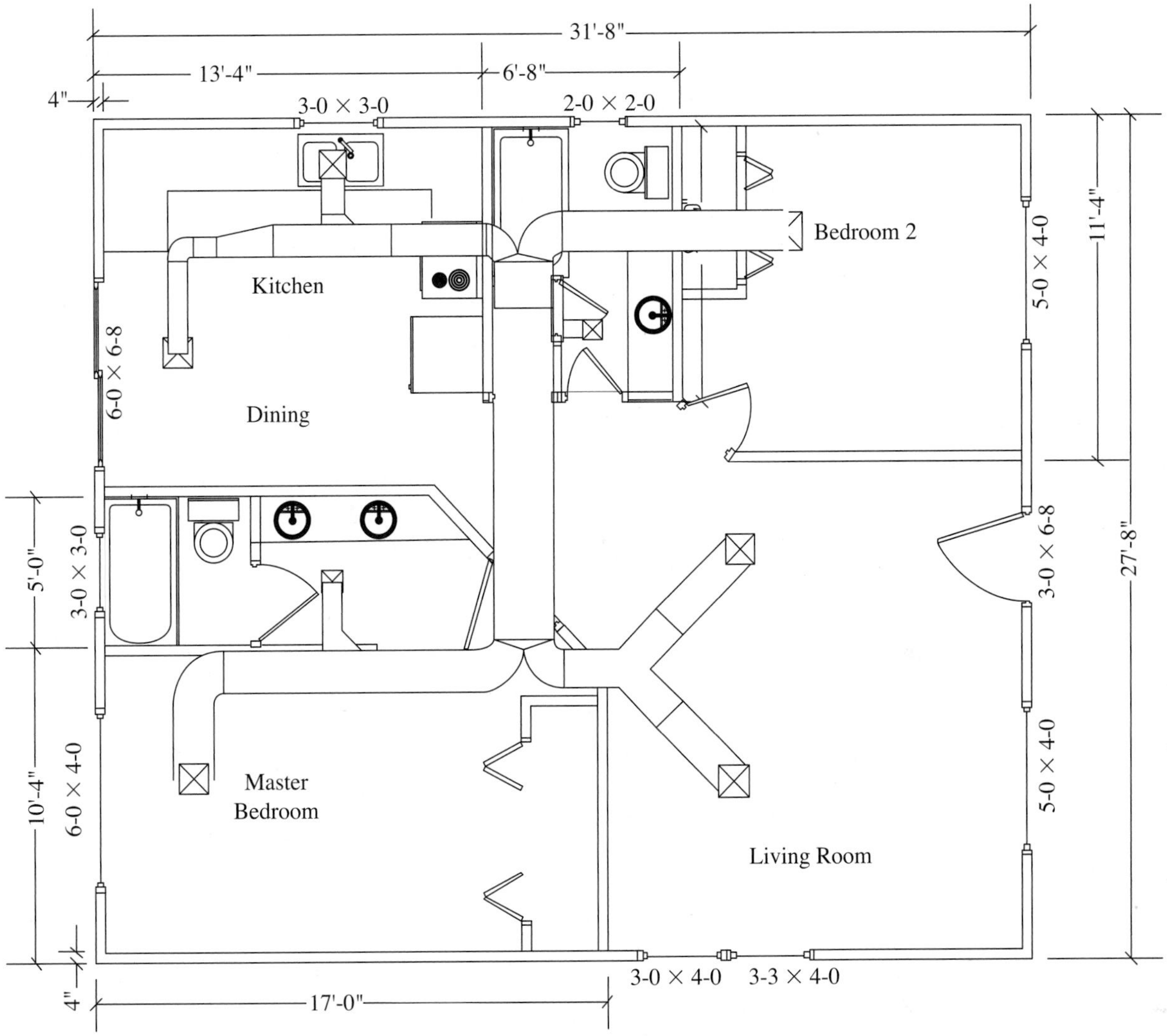

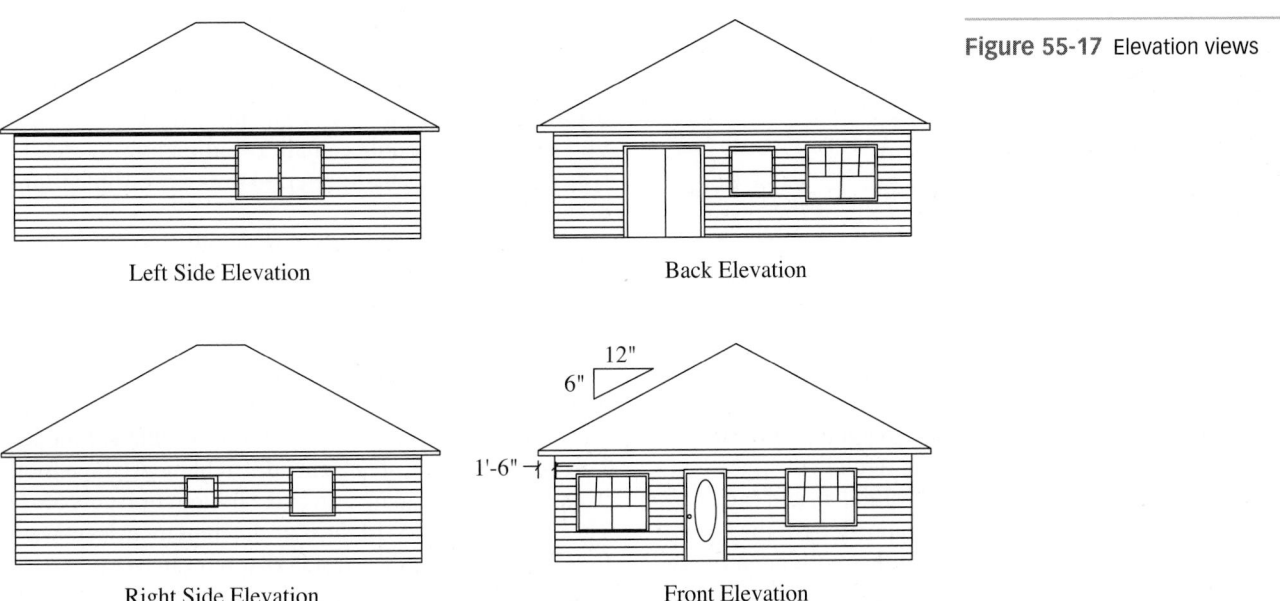

Figure 55-16 Blueprint showing the HVAC details

Figure 55-17 Elevation views

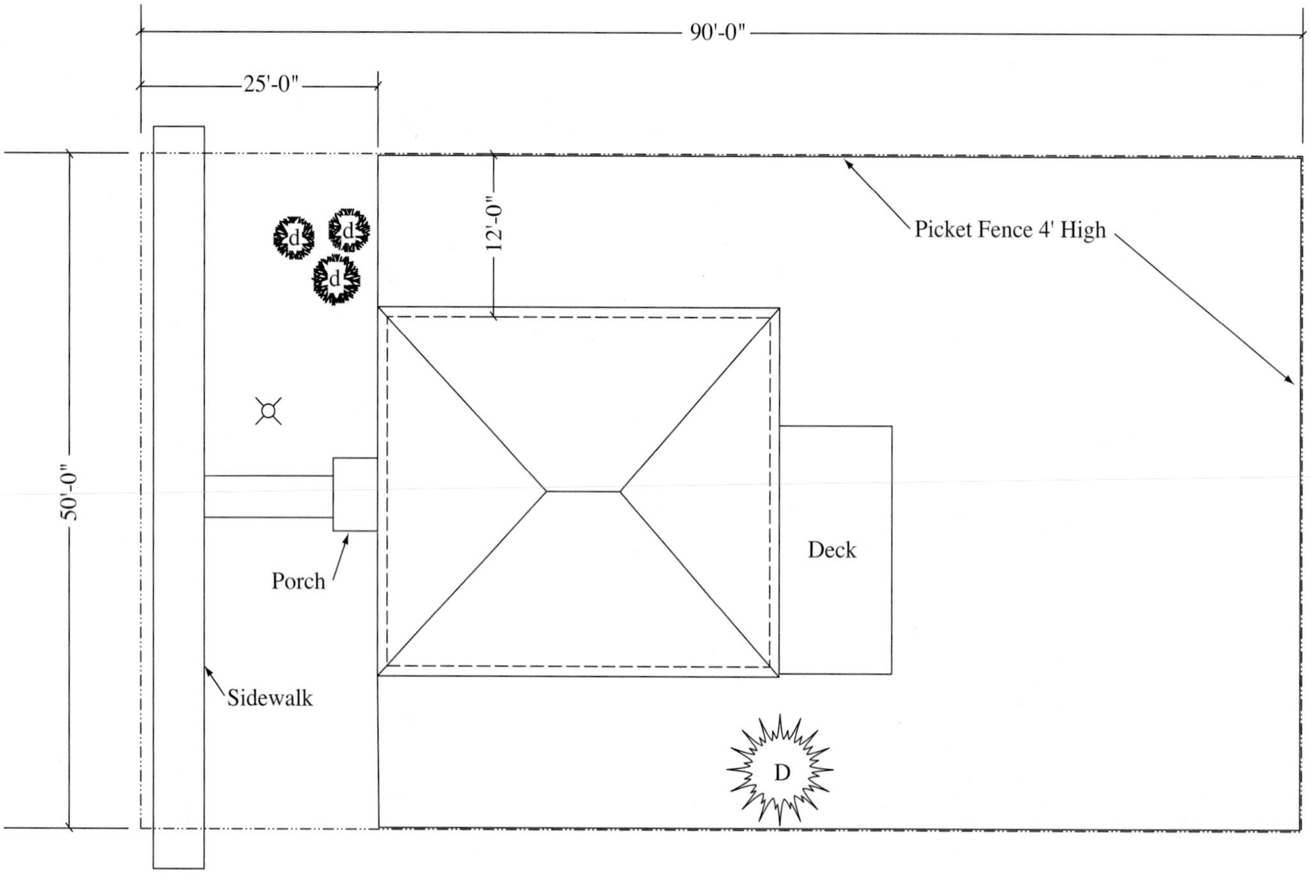

Figure 55-18 Plot plan

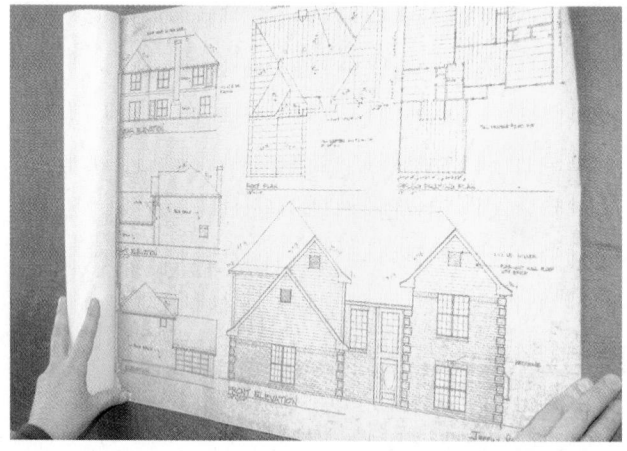

Figure 55-19 Detail drawings may give specific information about building components

side view because the suction line is behind it and cannot be seen. Only the suction line is seen in full in the right side view because the liquid line is mostly hidden, and can only be seen as a thin red line. The unseen portions of the liquid and suction lines could have been drawn as hidden lines, but that would not make this drawing clearer or easier to understand. Often items that are not required for the purpose of the drawing will not be shown if adding them would make the drawing less clear. In the actual drawings used in manufacturing this condenser, there would have been far more detail.

Each of the three primary views used in an orthographic projection can contain dimension information as in Figure 55-23. In the front view the width and height of the object are shown, in the right side the depth and height of the object are shown, and in the top view the width and depth of the object are shown. In an orthographic projection each view can only contain two dimensions, and this type of drawing is actually referred to as a two-dimensional drawing.

A pictorial drawing can contain all three dimensions, Figure 55-24. In this single view you can see the width, height, and depth of the object. For the purposes of installation, service, and identification, usually all of the overall dimensions of the system are given. Being able to reference dimensions is important because most manufacturers show one drawing to represent an entire line of different models. This one drawing must reference different model dimensions in a table, such as can be seen at the bottom of Figure 55-22. The overall height (A) of the nine different models shown in the table is given on the left side view but can be easily transferred to the right side view.

DESCRIPTION	SYMBOL
SINGLE-POLE SWITCH	S
THREE-WAY SWITCH	S³
FOUR-WAY SWITCH	S⁴
WATERPROOF SWITCH	S_WP
DOUBLE OUTLET	⊖
WATERPROOF OUTLET	⊖_WP
GROUND FAULT INTERRUPTOR (GFI)	⊖_GFI
240 VOLT OUTLET	⊖_240v
TRANSFORMER	T
JUNCTION BOX	J
POWER PANEL	▨
BRANCH CIRCUIT	∿
CEILING LIGHT	◇
RECESSED CEILING LIGHT	⊗ R
TRACK LIGHTS	◇—◇—◇—◇
WALL LIGHT	⊢◯
CEILING FAN WITH LIGHT	◇F
VENT FAN WITH LIGHT	⊞F
VENT FAN	F
TV CABLE JACK	⊢TV
THERMOSTAT	⊢T

Figure 55-20 Standard electrical symbols used in architectural drawings

55.9 READING ARCHITECTURAL DRAWINGS

It is a common practice to leave off the last dimension from a wall in the architectural drawing. The omission of such a single dimension is often done because it is not possible to make the slab or floor exactly the correct size during construction. Any difference in overall size would simply be added or subtracted from that room's size. However, the dimensions for all of the rooms are needed to calculate the Btu/hr heat loss and gain of the house.

Any dimension shown that is parallel to the front wall would be the width of the house, room, door, and so on,

and any dimension shown parallel to the left side wall would be the depth of the house, room, door, and so on. The front walls of the house in Figure 55-25 are shown as red, and the window and doors are shown as yellow. The walls on the left side are shown as blue and the windows are green.

The size of the living room is not given on the drawing. To determine the depth of the living room you would subtract the size of the master bedroom (17'-0") from the overall depth of the house (31'-8").

$$\begin{array}{r} 31'\text{-}8'' \\ -17'\text{-}0'' \\ \hline 14'\text{-}8'' \end{array}$$

The width of the living room is determined by subtracting the width of bedroom 2 (11'-4") from the total width of the house (27'-8").

$$\begin{array}{r} 27'\text{-}8'' \\ -11'\text{-}4'' \\ \hline 16'\text{-}4'' \end{array}$$

The living room is 16'-4" wide and 14'-8" deep.

55.10 ELECTRICAL DRAWINGS

Commonly used electrical symbols are shown in Figure 55-20. On drawings, a free flowing line is used to connect switches to lights and outlets in branch circuits. These branch circuit lines make it easy for the technician to determine which switches control which lights or devices. For example, in Figure 55-26, the red light switch next to the front door (on the right side of the plan) controls the red entryway light. In this section, we will examine all of the colored branch circuits in Figure 55-26.

All of the blue electrical outlets are connected to the same blue branch circuit. These plugs are located outside, in the kitchen, and in the bathrooms, where electrical shock hazards are highest. All electrical outlets located in these areas must be connected to a ground-fault circuit interrupter (GFCI). The initials GFI are often used to designate an outlet or switch that is attached to one of these safety devices.

In the living room the green switch is connected to the green light in the hall and to the green switch by the back door. These three-way switches allow the lights to be turned off and on at more than one location.

The main electrical panel for this house is shaded yellow. Commercial buildings often have more than one power panel. When more than one power panel is used, the panels are identified with a series of numbers and letters. In commercial installations, often, the separate electrical drawings will show the size and location of the circuit breakers that supply power to the individual building circuits. To make future maintenance easier, many builders will stencil the power panel and breaker number on the surface of every switch and outlet in the building.

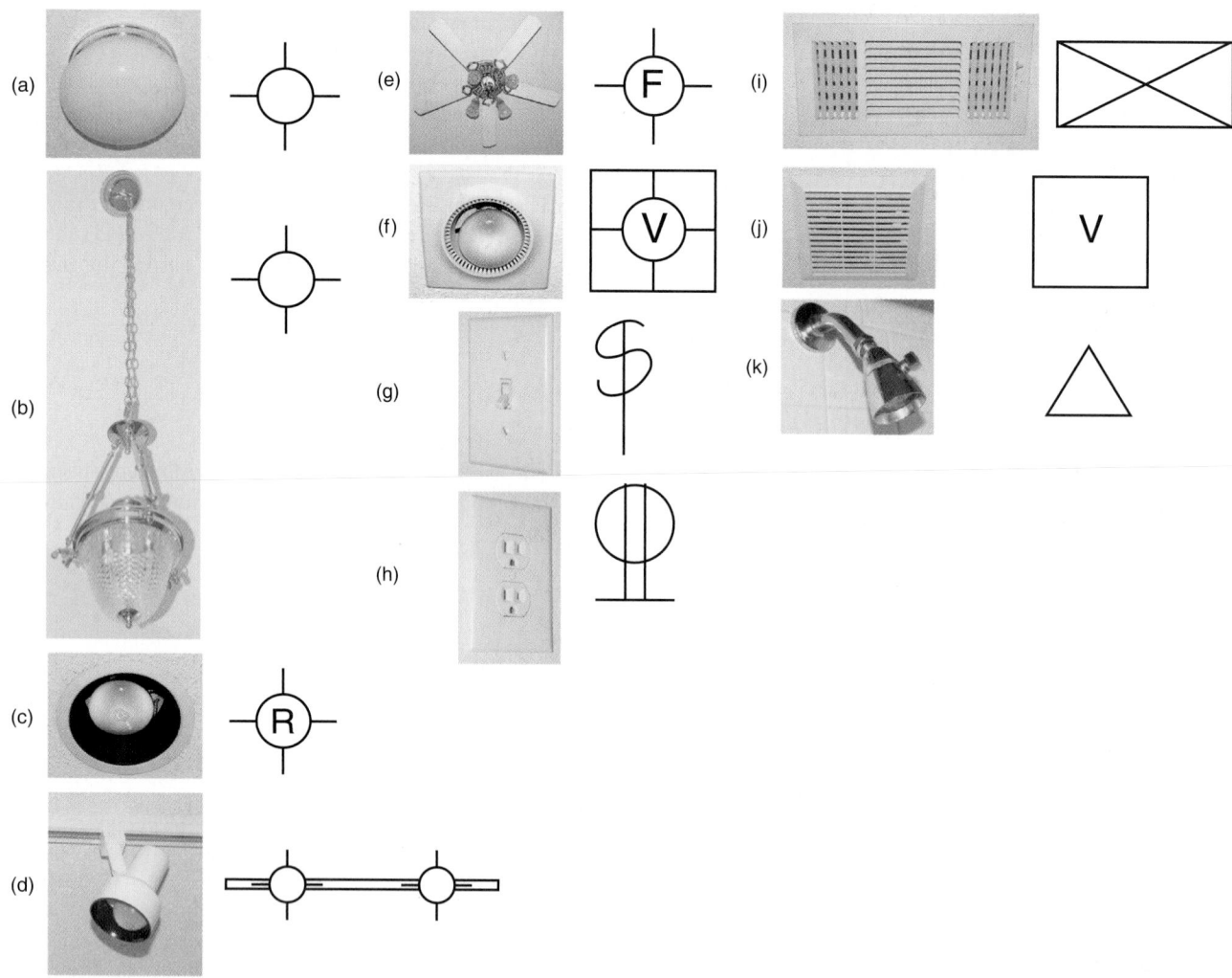

Figure 55-21 Examples of standard architectural symbols and the items they represent: (a) Ceiling light; (b) Ceiling light; (c) Recessed light; (d) Track light; (e) Ceiling fan with light; (f) Vent fan with light; (g) Light switch; (h) Electrical outlet; (i) Air register; (j) Vent fan; (k) Shower nozzle

---

TECH TIP

Architectural electrical drawings show where components are in the building and which components are on the same circuit. They do not actually show the electrician how to wire the circuit or show how the circuit works. Schematics in air conditioning show how each circuit operates and how to make field wiring connections.

55.11 HVAC SYSTEMS DRAWINGS

The placement of the indoor unit is often shown on the plan by a hidden line, such as in Figure 55-27. An arrow and note are used to identify the indoor furnace. In this case it is an upflow gas furnace with air conditioning

shown in the top center of the drawing. The sheet metal supply ducts are shown with the supply registers. When flex ducts are used, single lines are used to show the duct locations such as the red lines in Figure 55-28. Note the small blue loops with a short leader drawn around each duct run in Figure 55-28. These give the dimensions of each duct. Round ducts have a single dimension for the diameter, shown in blue numbers on Figure 55-28; while square or rectangular ducts will have two dimensions noting their width and height.

On residential drawings the supply registers may be drawn as rectangles. In some cases arrows are used to denote the direction of air distribution from the register. The size and location of residential ducts and supply registers, and even the return grills, are not always noted on the drawings. If they are not provided, you should prepare a drawing showing your proposed sizes and locations and present that drawing to the owner or job site foreman for approval before you begin work.

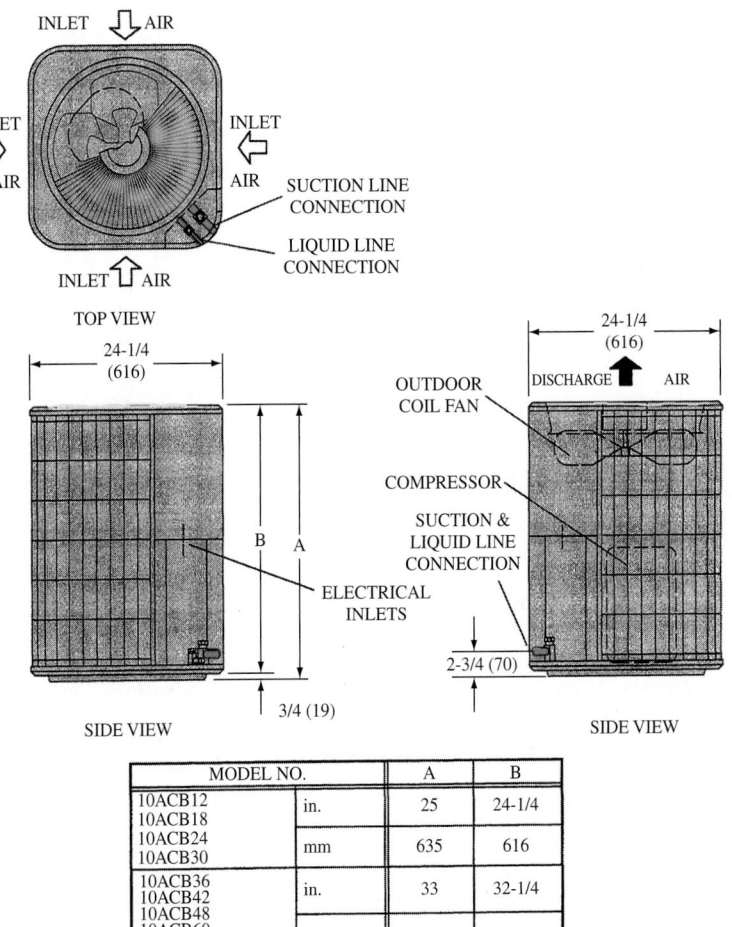

Figure 55-22 Identifying parts as shown in the three different primary views, top, left side, and right side; in this case, one drawing is enough to give dimensions for nine model numbers
(Courtesy of Lennox Industries, Inc)

MODEL NO.		A	B
10ACB12 10ACB18	in.	25	24-1/4
10ACB24 10ACB30	mm	635	616
10ACB36 10ACB42 10ACB48	in.	33	32-1/4
10ACB60 10ACB62	mm	838	819

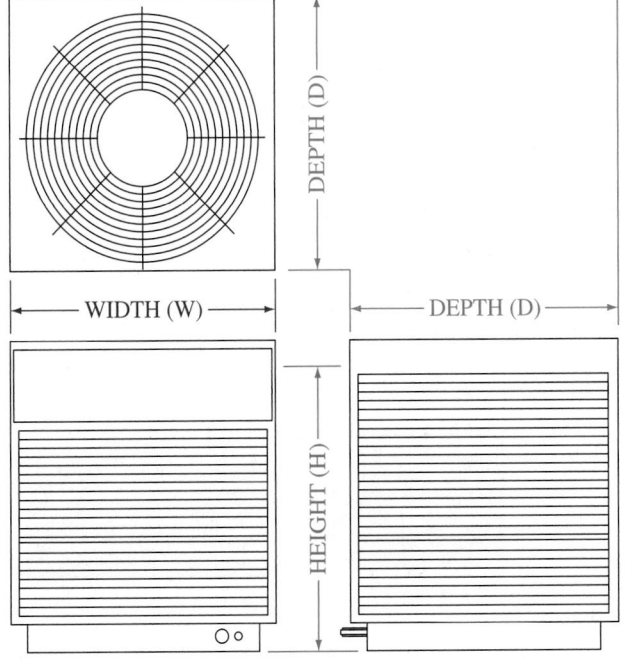

Figure 55-23 Dimension layout on orthographic drawing

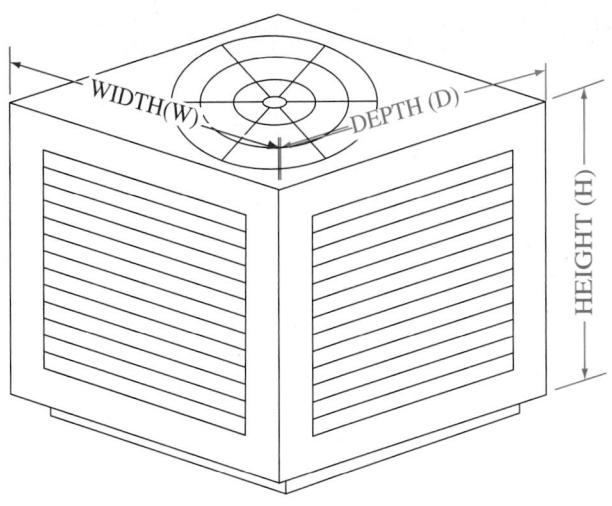

Figure 55-24 Dimension layout on a pictorial drawing

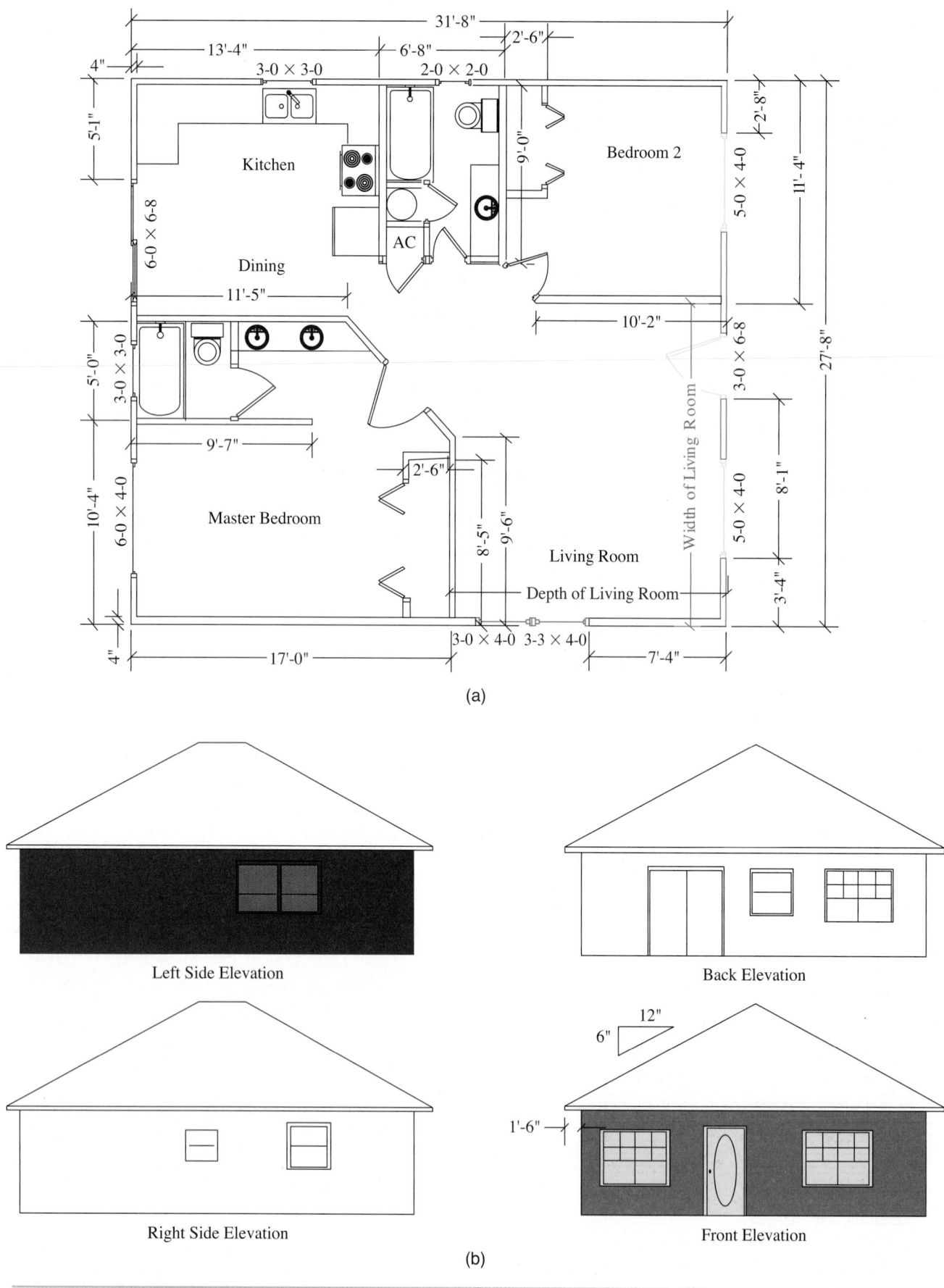

Figure 55-25 Walls represented in plan (a) are shown in the same color in elevations (b)

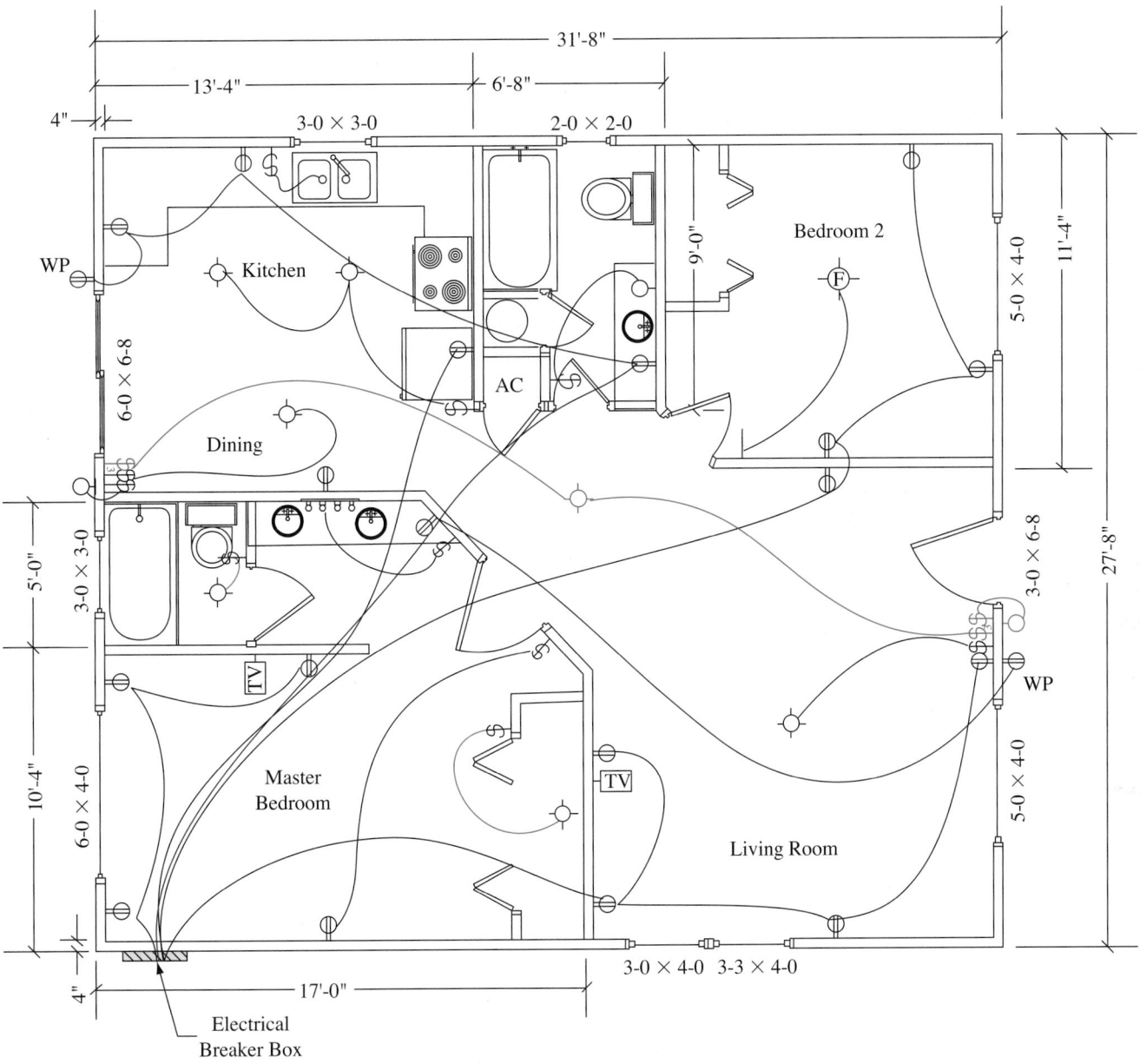

Figure 55-26 Electrical branch circuits

In commercial installations the unit location will always be shown on the drawing. Also, the drawings will contain the engineered duct layout. Duct sizes are presented as either a note with a leader or in the same way that they were in the residential drawing, using a loop and note. Some commercial rigid sheet metal systems use a short (approximately 10 ft long) section of flexible duct to connect the air diffuser to the end of the rigid duct. This is common practice in buildings that use dropped ceilings, because the exact location of the diffuser is dependent on the ceiling grid.

Commercial air distribution system plans usually will contain the CFM of air that will be supplied through the room diffuser. This CFM volume of air has been determined to be sufficient to meet that area's heat gain and heat loss requirements. The CFM values listed for each of the diffusers and grills will be used by the air balance technician to determine proper system setup during the initial testing and balancing process.

TECH TIP

As a general rule of thumb, 400 CFM is equal to one ton of air conditioning. So a diffuser supplying 800 CFM of air to an area would be providing two tons of air conditioning. A diffuser supplying 600 CFM of air would be producing $1\frac{1}{2}$ tons of air conditioning. This is a quick way of determining the amount of the cooling load requirements for a system.

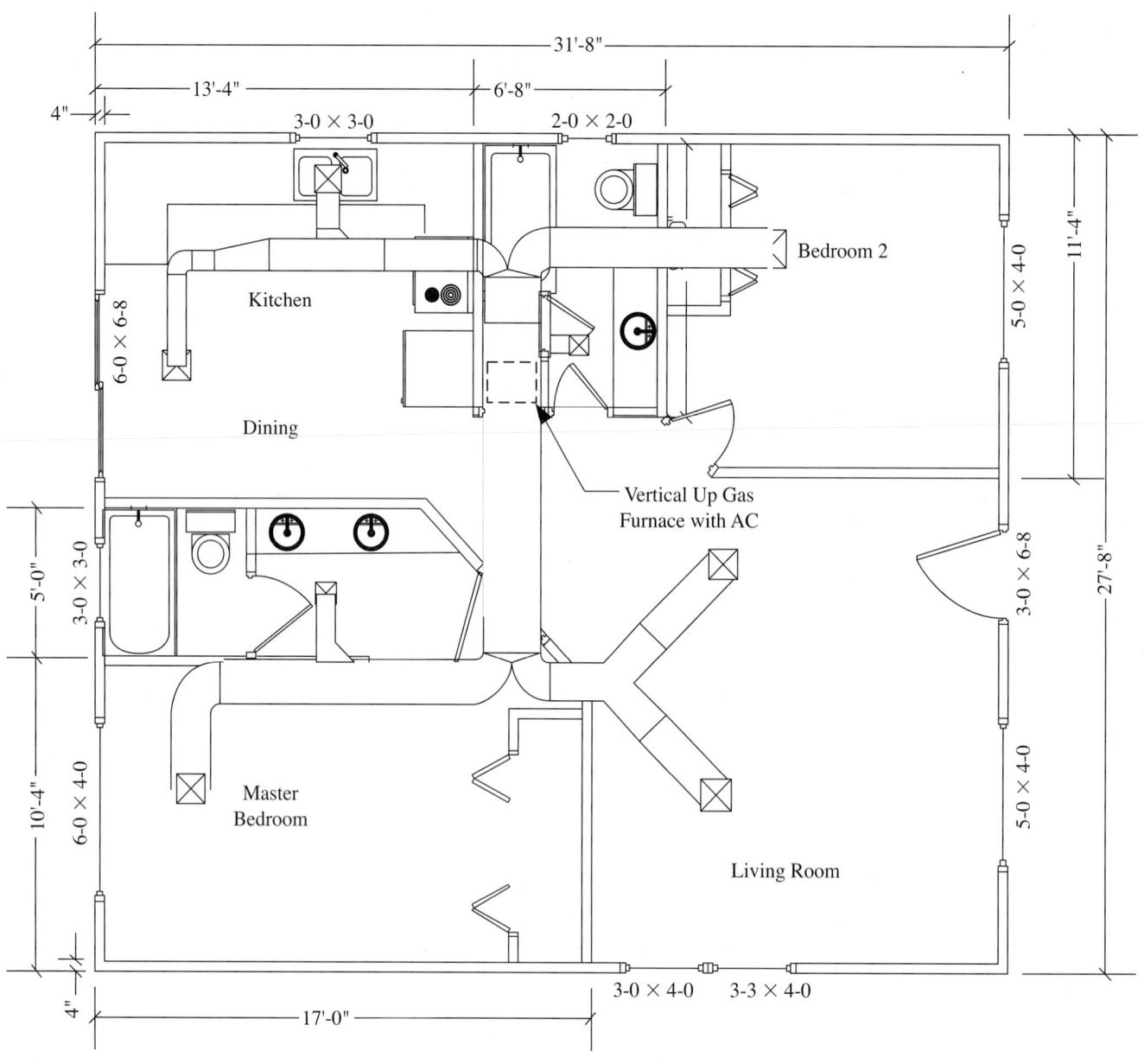

Figure 55-27 Mechanical drawing for duct layout for sheet metal duct

55.12 DETAILED DRAWINGS

Details are used to show the typical wall section and the insulation in the walls and ceiling, Figure 55-29. Other detailed drawings are used to show any special millwork for kitchen cabinets, bathroom cabinets, and built-in furniture. On commercial building sets of drawings, more detailed drawings are included. Drawings showing the size and configuration of fittings for natural gas and condensate drain lines are common. Others show roof flashing and the curb for rooftop units on commercial buildings. Many other detailed drawings are included as part of the set of drawings for commercial installations; however most do not relate to HVAC systems.

55.13 DRAWING SCALE

Of course, drawings must be made smaller than the actual building so they will fit on the drawing page. A scale is used to make the drawing smaller and maintain accuracy. On a scale an inch or foot is represented as shorter than it actually is. Special rulers called scales are marked so they can easily be used to make a drawing of the desired size, Figure 55-30. There are two commonly used scales; one is architectural, as shown in Figure 55-30 a,b, and the other is engineering, as shown in Figure 55-30 c,d. Most residential drawings are made using a scale where $\frac{1}{4}$ in on the drawing equals 1 ft in the building, so a large home will fit on a standard size sheet

UNIT 57

Duct Systems and Duct Design

OBJECTIVES

Upon completion of this unit you will be able to:

- describe the layout of the all major duct systems.
- discuss the different types of duct material and their uses.
- discuss how to determine the duct system design static pressure.
- explain the difference between design friction loss rate and the actual static pressure loss through a duct.
- explain how a duct's equivalent length is determined.

57.1 INTRODUCTION

Duct systems are the distribution network for conditioned air to be moved throughout a building. Duct systems are designed to provide conditioned air that matches the needs of the structure. Proper duct system design is critical to the energy efficiency of a building. Duct designers must use information such as: heat load calculations, cooling load calculations, equipment selection, and architectural design to produce specialized duct plans for each structure. Technicians need to understand duct systems and airflow to be able to troubleshoot and maintain an HVAC system. Factors that adversely affect system airflow will also have a negative impact on system efficiency and reliability.

57.2 AIR DISTRIBUTION SYSTEM COMPONENTS

Forced air systems are used to distribute conditioned air in residential and small commercial buildings. Air is conditioned and distributed through the duct system throughout the building. The basic components of a forced air system are the blower, the return air ductwork carrying air to the blower, and the supply air ductwork carrying air from the blower to the building.

Most systems have large boxes on both the return and supply ends of the blower called plenums, Figure 57-1. The plenum distributes the air to the ductwork attached to it. The duct design can be compared to a tree, the main ducts leaving the plenum are called trunk ducts, and the individual ducts running to each room are called branch ducts. The point where a branch duct comes off of a trunk duct is called a take off.

The duct openings to the conditioned space are covered by registers, diffusers, or grills. The return air openings are covered by return air grills. The supply air openings are covered by supply air registers. They direct the airflow into the room. These are sometimes called diffusers because they spread, or diffuse, the air.

Between the blower and the diffuser, the airstream must change direction and shape. This is accomplished with duct fittings. Turns are made with elbows, often called ells, Figure 57-2. A wye fitting is used to split one large duct into two smaller ducts, Figure 57-3. A change in the size of a rectangular duct is accomplished with a transition, Figure 57-4. A change in the size of a round duct is done with a reducer, Figure 57-5. When the register at the end of a round branch duct is rectangular, a fitting called a boot is used to allow the round duct to connect to the rectangular register, Figure 57-6.

Figure 57-1 The supply and return plenums are connected on either end of the indoor blower
(Courtesy of Stanfield Air Systems)

983

Figure 57-2 Elbows are used for turns in the ductwork

Figure 57-5 A reducer is used to change round duct from one size to another

Figure 57-3 A wye is used to split one large duct into two smaller ducts

Figure 57-6 A boot is used at the end of a round duct to allow connection of a rectangular register or grill

Figure 57-4 A transition is used to change rectangular duct from one size to another

The blower provides the pressure difference to move the air through the ductwork. The amount of air the blower can move and the amount of energy needed to move the air is controlled by the resistance to airflow from the ductwork and all the system components in the airstream. The duct offers resistance to airflow, creating a pressure drop as the air travels through it. Besides the ducts, every component that the air travels through adds pressure drop. This includes filters, humidifiers, heat exchangers, coils, registers, and grills. The amount of pressure left for moving air through the ductwork is the difference between the amount of pressure the fan can produce and the amount of pressure drop from all these system components. Figure 57-7 shows the components of a forced air system and the pressure drop created across each component.

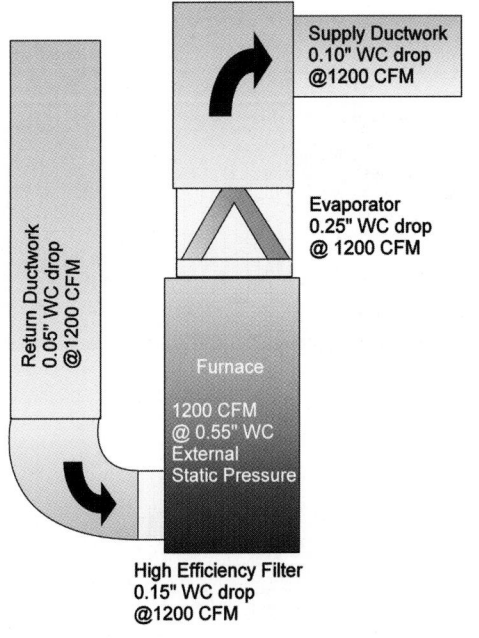

Figure 57-7 Basic components of a forced air system

57.3 DUCT LOCATION

The three most common areas to locate the duct system are in the attic, in the space between the joists in the ceiling or between floors, and under the building in either the basement or crawl space. The structure and layout of the building determine the available location for system components. The building's design affects the air handler location, which then controls the duct system layout. The duct location will determine the amount of duct insulation required. The building's designer may specify the layout, or may leave it up to the air conditioning contracting company.

For maximum system efficiency, the duct system should be located so that it is within the building's insulation envelope, Figure 57-8. In a residence with a full basement, the

Figure 57-8 Duct installed in joist space so it is inside the building envelope

basement is an excellent location for the trunk ducts and conditioning equipment. Equipment can also be located in a closet space or utility room. All enclosures must meet local fire and safety codes.

TECH TIP

A number of studies have shown that traditional duct installation practices can result in systems that have excessive air leaks. New codes require the use of UL 181 approved duct tapes and UL 181 approved mastics to reduce air leaks and improve system efficiencies.

It is not always possible to locate the ducts within the building's envelope. For slab construction, ducts and even equipment can be placed in the attic. However, an attic duct system is a particularly poor choice for an air conditioning system in a warm climate. Ducts located in unconditioned areas must be properly insulated, and an allowance must be made for heat loss included in the load calculation. Energy efficiency guidelines require that ducts located outside of the building's envelope have R8 insulation value. Ducts for perimeter (heating only) systems can be located in the slab.

Before beginning the duct system layout and design for any building, check with the local building department, county, or state code and/or regulatory agencies to determine the specific insulation requirements for the building's type and location.

57.4 EQUIPMENT TYPES

The design of the duct system is affected by the type of equipment selected. Forced air equipment is typically either packaged equipment or a split system. With packaged equipment, the entire system is located outside the structure and the ductwork is typically located in the basement or crawl space, Figure 57-9.

Split systems consist of an inside blower and an outside condensing unit. Split systems offer more flexibility in duct location because of the many possible blower locations. The blowers can be upflow, downflow, or horizontal. The name describes the direction of airflow. Five common split system duct configurations are:

- Upflow blower in the basement with all ducts in the basement, Figure 57-10.
- Upflow blower located in the house with supply ducts located in the attic and return in the house, Figure 57-11.
- Downflow blower in the house with supply ducts in the crawl space and return in the house, Figure 57-12.
- Horizontal blower in the crawl space with all ducts located in the crawl space, Figure 57-13.
- Horizontal blower located in the attic with all ducts located in the attic, Figure 57-14.

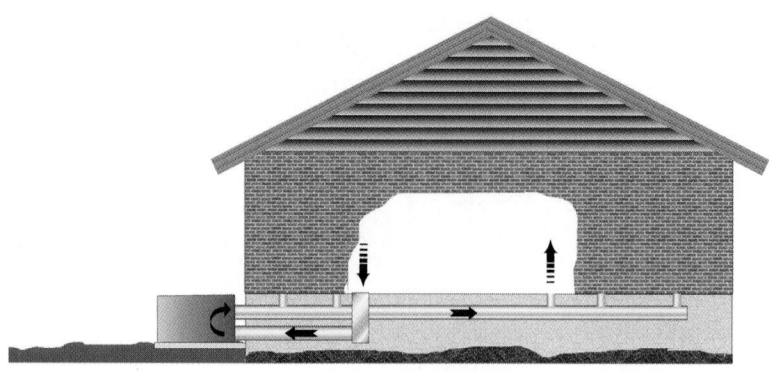

Figure 57-9 Packaged air conditioning unit with ductwork in crawl space

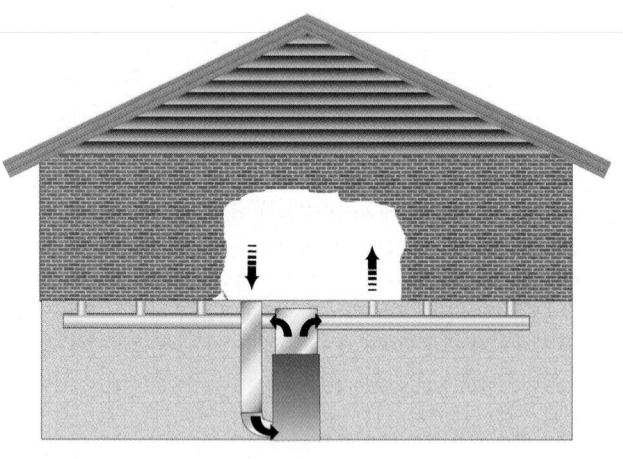

Figure 57-10 Upflow blower in the basement with all ducts in the basement

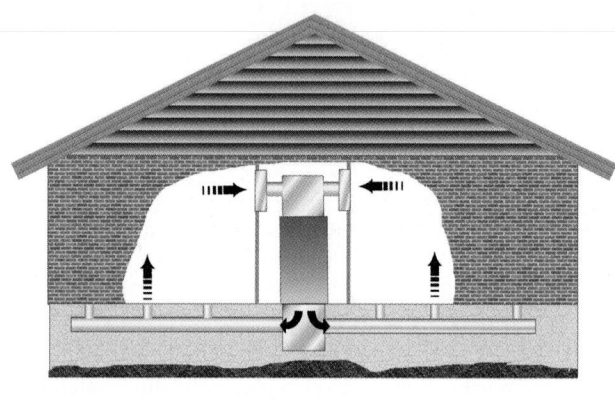

Figure 57-12 Downflow blower in the house with supply ducts in the crawl space and return in the house

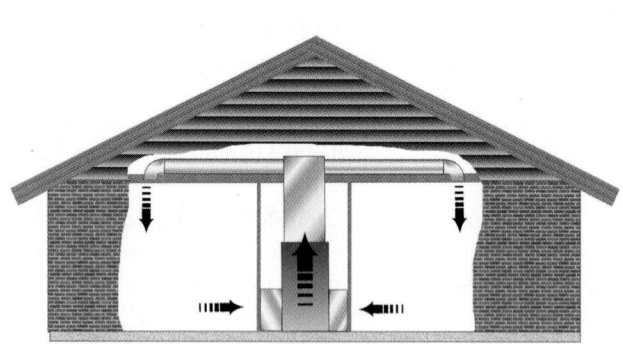

Figure 57-11 Upflow blower located in the house with supply ducts located in the attic and return in the house

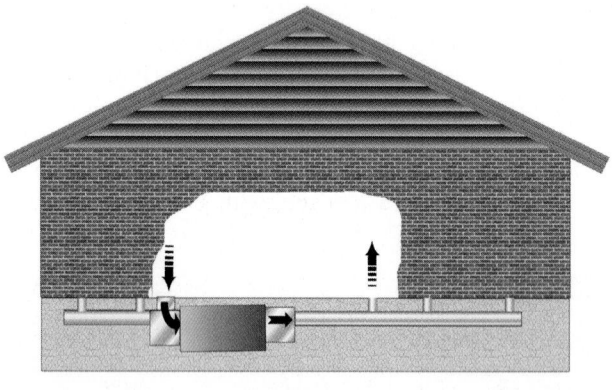

Figure 57-13 Horizontal blower in the crawl space with all ducts located in the crawl space

57.5 DUCT SYSTEM TYPES

The four most common duct configurations are radial, reducing radial, extended plenum, and reducing extended plenum. Two less common types are the perimeter loop system and the central plenum system.

Radial Duct Systems

Radial duct systems are designed so that all or almost all of the duct runs originate at the central plenum. In some cases a few of the duct runs may have wyes or duct triangles as a means of joining additional ducts to an initial run, Figure 57-15. Radial systems are most frequently installed

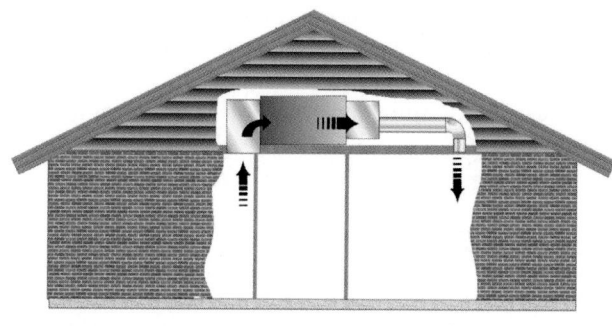

Figure 57-14 Horizontal blower located in the attic with all ducts located in the attic

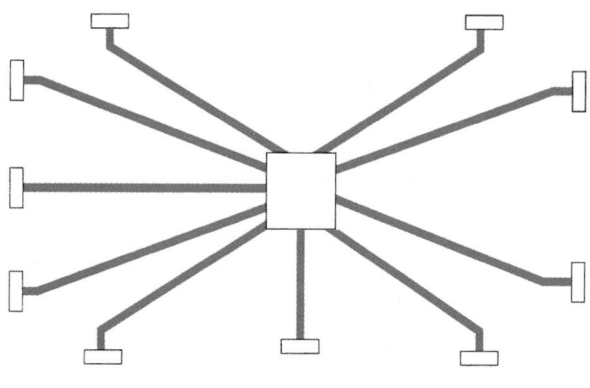

Figure 57-15 Radial duct system

in attics, but can also be installed in crawl spaces and basements. Radial systems are commonly used in small houses built on concrete slabs.

Reducing Radial Duct Systems

A reducing radial system uses several larger ducts leaving the main plenum which branch into smaller ducts as they get closer to their destination, Figure 57-16. This reduces the connections at the plenum, and reduces the overall amount of duct used.

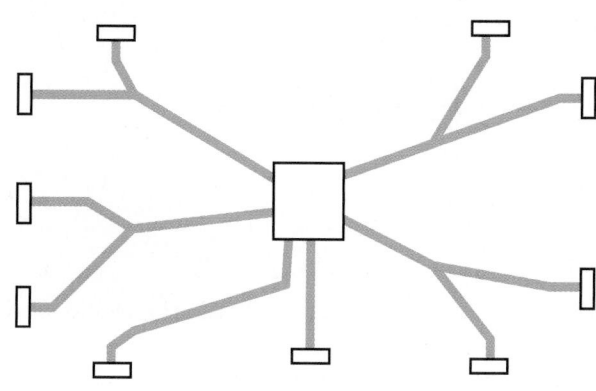

Figure 57-16 Reducing radial duct system

Extended Plenum

The extended plenum duct system uses a large trunk duct that travels the length of the building from the air handler. These systems are sometimes referred to as trunk duct systems, Figure 57-17. The trunk duct is considered an extension of the plenum. The trunk ducts in extended plenum systems do not reduce in size as they travel across the structure. Extended plenum systems can be located in the crawl space, attic, or basement.

Reducing Extended Plenum

The trunk ducts in the reducing extended plenum system reduce in size, Figure 57-18. Typical reducing plenum trunk ducts will reduce after every three to four take offs. Not only does this save material cost, it makes the duct system work better. The air velocity in the trunk drops as the volume of air traveling through the trunk drops. Reducing the size of the trunk duct restores the velocity of the air in the trunk duct. This helps keep the static pressure throughout the system more even, aiding in more even air distribution.

Perimeter Loop System

The perimeter loop duct system uses radial feeder ducts from the blower that attach to one trunk that is installed around the outer edge of the foundation. Each supply is tapped off this trunk to provide equal airflow throughout the structure, Figure 57-19. Perimeter loop systems are normally installed

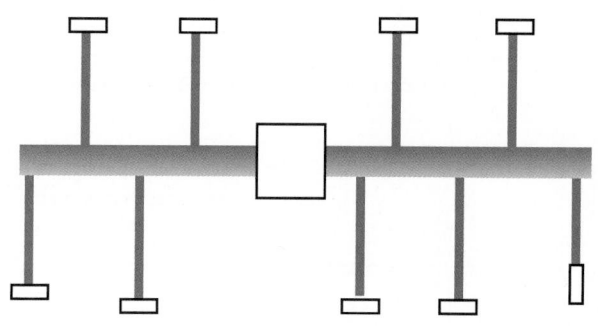

Figure 57-17 Extended plenum duct system

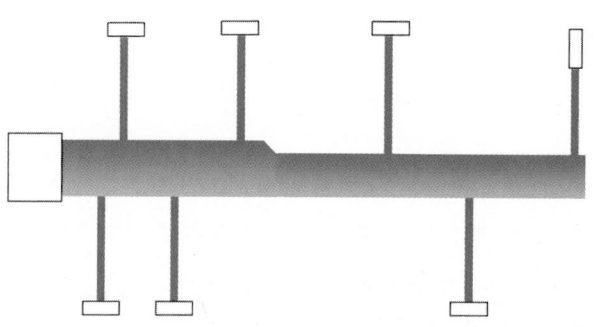

Figure 57-18 Reducing extended plenum duct system

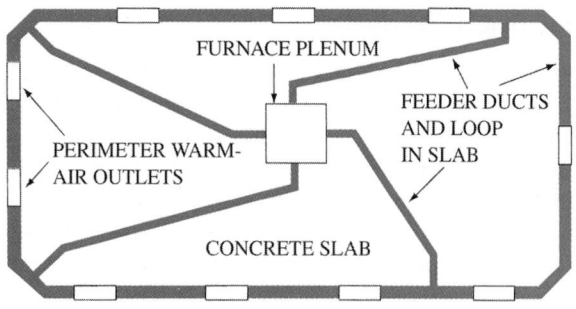

Figure 57-19 Perimeter loop duct system

in concrete foundations and have the added efficiency of heating the slab. The duct for a perimeter loop system must be placed before the slab is poured. These systems are generally used in single story, commercial office buildings built on slabs.

Central Plenum System

The central plenum duct system uses structural cavities as a pathway for supply or return air plenums. The basement, crawl space, or space between floor joists can all serve as the plenum. Air is blown into the cavity, and holes are cut through the floor into the plenum cavity wherever a register is needed, Figure 57-20. To ensure proper operation of a plenum system, the cavity must be airtight and configured in a way that the airflow is not compromised.

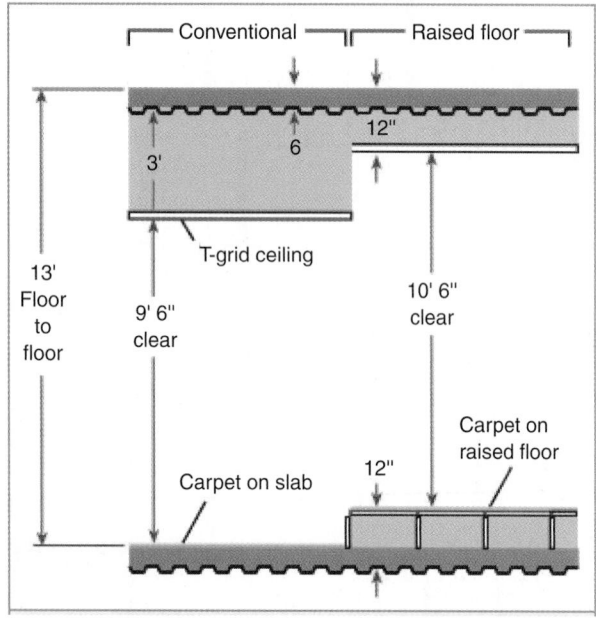

Figure 57-20 Supply air is delivered in channels under the floor and return air in the space above the ceiling
(Used with permission, © 2008 E Source Companies LLC.)

This system is used because of its low cost. This system may not meet mechanical codes in some jurisdictions. Indoor air quality is a major concern due to the nature of these cavities. Moisture, mold, and odors are often hard to control.

57.6 DUCT MATERIALS

Air ducts can be made from many different materials. The most common types of ductwork are galvanized steel sheet metal, spiral metal, fiberglass ductboard, flexible duct, and fabric duct.

Galvanized Sheet Metal

Sheet metal can be fabricated into most any shape imaginable by a skilled sheet metal worker. Galvanized sheet steel comes in large, flat sheets which are 4 ft wide and 8–10 ft long, Figure 57-21. Sheet metal offers the least amount of resistance to airflow of any duct material because of its smooth surface.

Many localities adopt the metal duct standards developed by the Sheet Metal and Air Conditioning Contractor's National Association (SMACNA). The thickness of the metal is called its gauge. A guideline for selecting metal thickness is shown in Figure 57-22.

For many years galvanized sheet steel was used exclusively for air conditioning ductwork because of its workability and durability. However, the material is expensive and costly to install, so other types of duct material have become popular. These include spiral metal duct, fiberglass ductboard, and flexible duct.

Figure 57-21 Sheet metal is supplied in large sheets which can be used to fabricate sheet metal ductwork

	Comfort heating or cooling			Comfort heating only
	Galvanized steel			
	Nominal thickness (in inches)	Equivalent galvanized sheet gauge no.	Approximate aluminum B & S gauge	Minimum weight tin plate pounds per base box
Round ducts and enclosed rectangular ducts				
14″ or less	0.016	30	26	135
Over 14″	0.019	28	24	—
Exposed rectangular ducts				
14″ or less	0.019	28	24	—
Over 14″	0.022	26	23	—

Figure 57-22 Gauges recommended for sheet metal ductwork

Spiral Metal Duct

Spiral duct is made from long strips of narrow metal and fabricated with spiral seams, Figure 57-23. Machines are available for making ducts on the job to fit required diameters and lengths. Spiral metal duct is used in commercial applications. It is frequently used where the ductwork will be exposed. It requires less support than other types of duct due to its inherent rigidity.

TECH TIP

The UL 181 standard covers factory made ducts and air connectors. All fiberduct and flexible duct should be UL approved and meet the UL 181 standard.

Figure 57-23 Spiral metal duct system

Fiberglass Ductboard

Fiberglass ductboard is a rigid material made of compressed fiberglass with an outer vapor barrier, Figure 57-24. It comes in 1 in, $1\frac{1}{2}$ in, and 2 in thicknesses. Fiberglass ductboard has the advantage of being an inherently good insulator for both heat and sound. This reduces the duct losses and provides sound absorbing qualities. Fiberglass ductboard is less expensive than metal and fabricating ductboard duct is generally easier than fabricating sheet metal duct. Ductboard is less durable than sheet metal duct and has a higher resistance to airflow than sheet metal because of its rougher interior surface.

Flexible Duct

The most common duct material used today in residential duct systems in undoubtedly flexible duct. Flexible duct has a spiral metal wire for support, a smooth plastic inner liner, an outer cover that serves as a vapor barrier, and fiberglass insulation sandwiched in between the inner liner and outer cover, Figure 57-25. The outer cover is typically vinyl or mylar. Flexible duct comes in 25 ft lengths compressed in a box which is about 3 ft long. When opened it expands lengthwise into ducts, Figure 57-26.

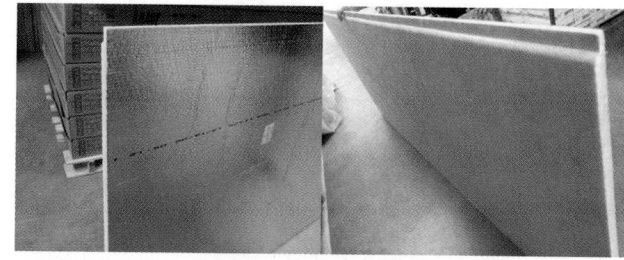

Figure 57-24 Fiberglass fiberduct comes in large sheets and can easily be fabricated into duct

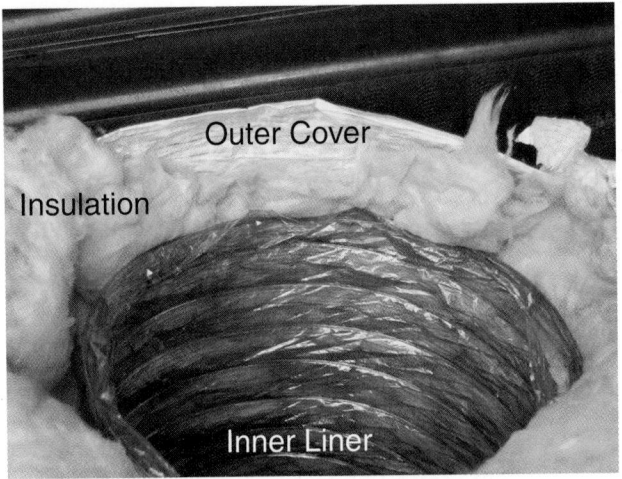

Figure 57-25 Flex duct is made of a helix wire for support, an inner liner, fiberglass insulation, and an outer vapor barrier

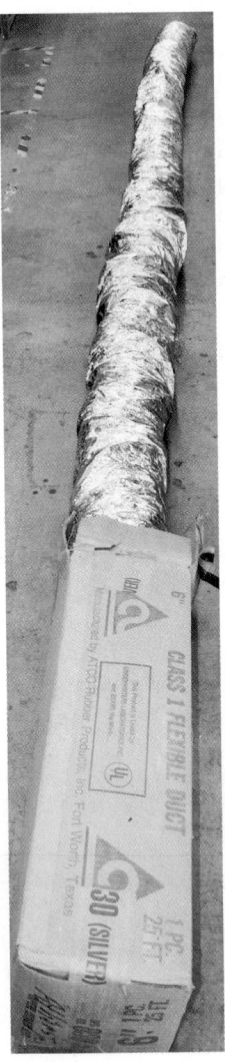

Figure 57-26 Flexible duct comes compressed in a box and expands when removed from the box

SERVICE TIP

It is very important to stretch flex duct before installing it. Leaving the duct slack can easily double the duct's resistance to airflow. Allowing extra length in the duct run is a particularly bad practice which may save time during installation, but will significantly reduce the airflow through the duct.

Flex duct is very popular because it is the least expensive duct material and the easiest to install. Unfortunately, it is also the easiest to install incorrectly. Common problems with flex duct include tight radius turns and improper support. Many poorly installed flex duct jobs have given the material a bad name. However, it is possible to install a good duct system with flex duct by following the manufacturer's installation instructions. Flex duct is very quiet because its soft sides absorb sound. However, the soft, undulating sides also have the highest resistance to airflow of all of the most commonly used duct materials.

57.7 SEALING DUCTWORK

The largest loss of efficiency in a ducted air system comes from air leaks. Unconditioned air leaking into the return air side of the system can add a considerable heat load. Conditioned air leaking out of the supply air side of the system is like literally throwing away energy. Sheet metal ductwork is most commonly sealed with mastic.

Mastic has a consistency similar to sheetrock mud and is spread or "painted" on, Figure 57-27. It is stiff, but still somewhat flexible after it dries. All duct sealants should be UL-181 approved. Duct tape was once the primary method of sealing metal duct, but tape use is less common today. If duct tape is used, it should be UL-181 approved. There is an abundance of inexpensive duct tape available

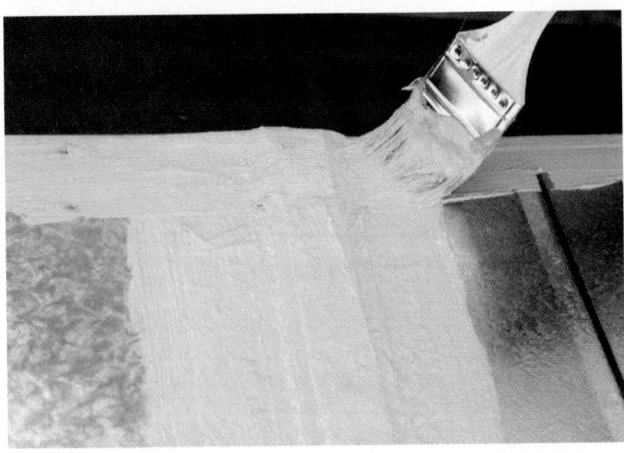

Figure 57-27 Applying mastic to sheet metal duct joints

that is not UL 181 approved; it should not be used for sealing ductwork.

Fiberglass ductboard is sealed with UL-181 aluminum foil tape. It is critical to use tape approved by the ductboard manufacturer and apply it according to the manufacturer's instructions. Some of this tape requires heating with an iron to set it. Flexible duct is sealed with both UL-181 tape and mastic. Flexible duct only requires sealing at the ends where it is connected.

TECH TIP

The UL 181A standard covers closure systems for rigid ducts while the UL 181B standard covers closure systems for flexible ducts and air connectors. Mastics, tapes, and sealants should meet either the UL 181A or the UL 181B standard, depending upon the type of duct.

57.8 INSULATING DUCTWORK

Fiberglass ductboard does not need to be insulated because it is made of fiberglass and has inherent thermal insulating properties. Flexible duct does not need to be insulated either, because fiberglass insulation is part of its construction. Sheet metal ducts do need to be insulated. Sheet metal ductwork can be insulated on the inside with duct liner, or on the outside with duct wrap.

Duct liner is applied to the inside of the duct. It is available in thicknesses from $1/2$ in to 2 in. In general, duct liner is made of a denser fiberglass material than duct wrap. Duct liner reduces the interior size of the ductwork, so the ducts must be made with larger dimensions to accommodate the use of duct liner.

The most common duct wrap is fiberglass with an outer vapor barrier. It is commonly available in 1.5 in and 2 in thicknesses. Many energy efficiency codes now require the 2 in thick duct wrap. The vapor barrier prevents condensation on the outside of the duct during air conditioning when the duct temperature may be below the dew point temperature of the area the duct is in. Condensation on the duct represents a significant loss of system efficiency and can cause property damage from dripping. The vapor barrier can be vinyl or paper and aluminum foil kraft back.

57.9 EQUIVALENT LENGTH

The amount of pressure lost through a duct is directly related to its equivalent length. Many runs in a normal residential house will be longer than 100 ft in equivalent length. Every time the air changes direction it loses some of its pressure. This loss in pressure is most commonly stated as equivalent to the pressure loss through a length of duct. An elbow with a large radius will have an equivalent length of approximately 10 ft. This means that the pressure lost when the air moves around this elbow is equivalent to the pressure lost when traveling through 10 ft of pipe. Figures 57-28 through 57-31 show the equivalent length for several common fittings when duct static and velocity are within the normal range of residential systems.

To find a duct's total equivalent length, add up the trunk duct length to the take off, the branch duct length, and the equivalent lengths of all the fittings used from the blower to the register. For example, take a branch duct run on an extended plenum system, Figure 57-32. The trunk duct leaving the plenum is equivalent to 35 ft; the branch take off from the trunk duct is another 35 ft. The torpedo boot on the end of the run adds 50 ft. The run has 150 ft of

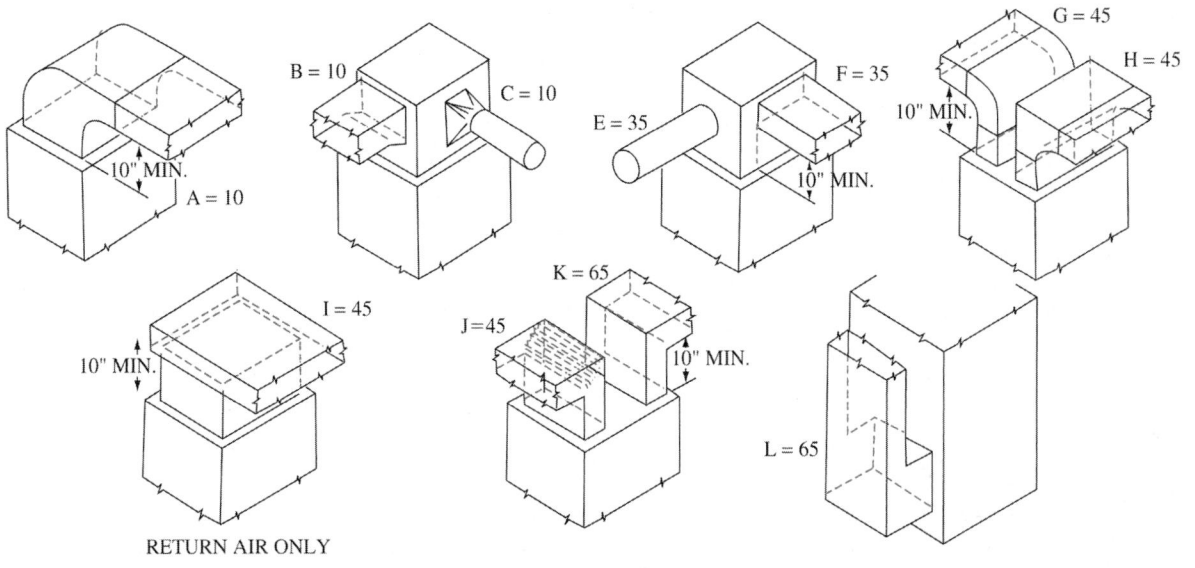

Figure 57-28 Equivalent lengths: supply and return air plenum fittings
(© American Society of Heating, Refrigerating, and Air-Conditioning Engineers, Inc., www.ashrae.org)

Figure 57-29 Equivalent lengths:
extended plenum fittings
*(© American Society of Heating, Refrigerating,
and Air-Conditioning Engineers, Inc.,
www.ashrae.org)*

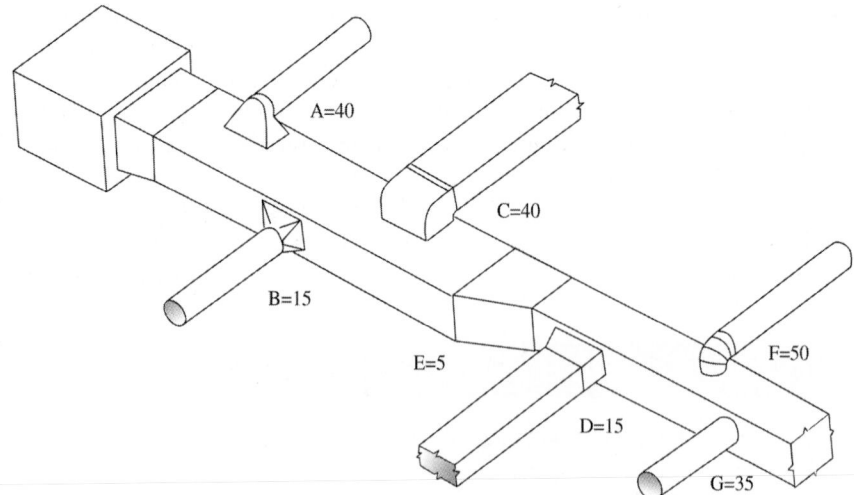

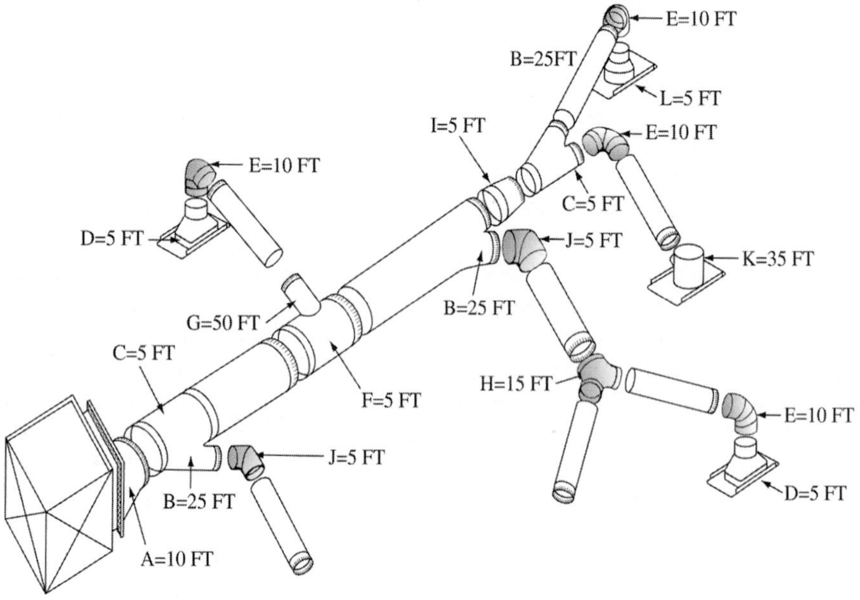

Figure 57-30 Equivalent length of
round supply system fittings
*(© American Society of Heating, Refrigerating,
and Air-Conditioning Engineers, Inc.,
www.ashrae.org)*

A = 30   B = 35   C = 60   D = 55   E = 70

F = 45   G = 30   H = 50   I = 5   J = 15

K = 30   L = 30   M = 5   N = 15   O = 5   P = 5

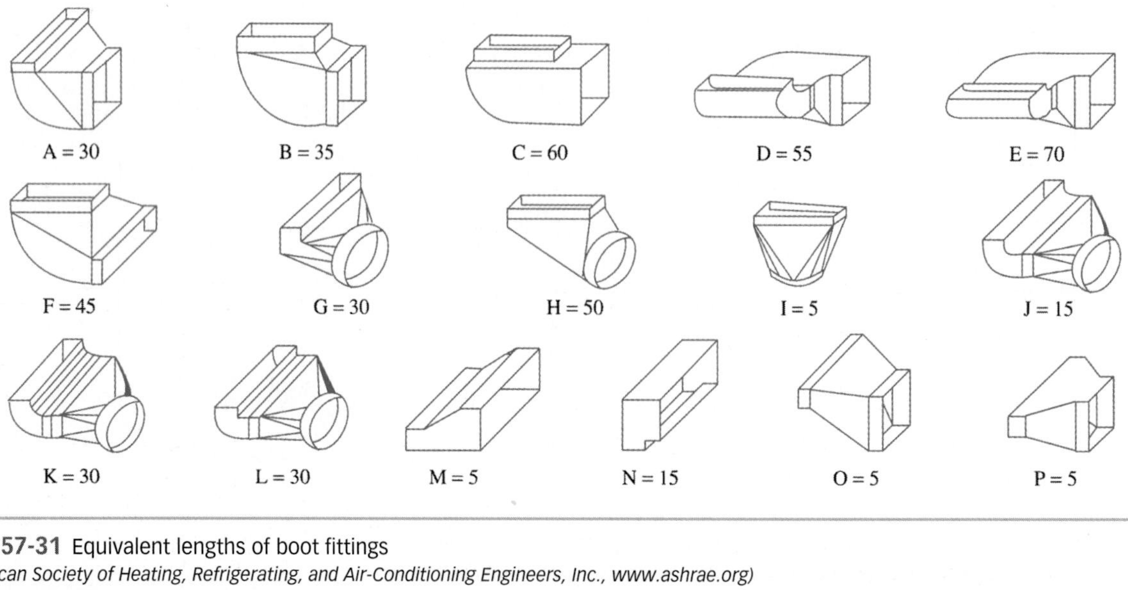

Figure 57-31 Equivalent lengths of boot fittings
(© American Society of Heating, Refrigerating, and Air-Conditioning Engineers, Inc., www.ashrae.org)

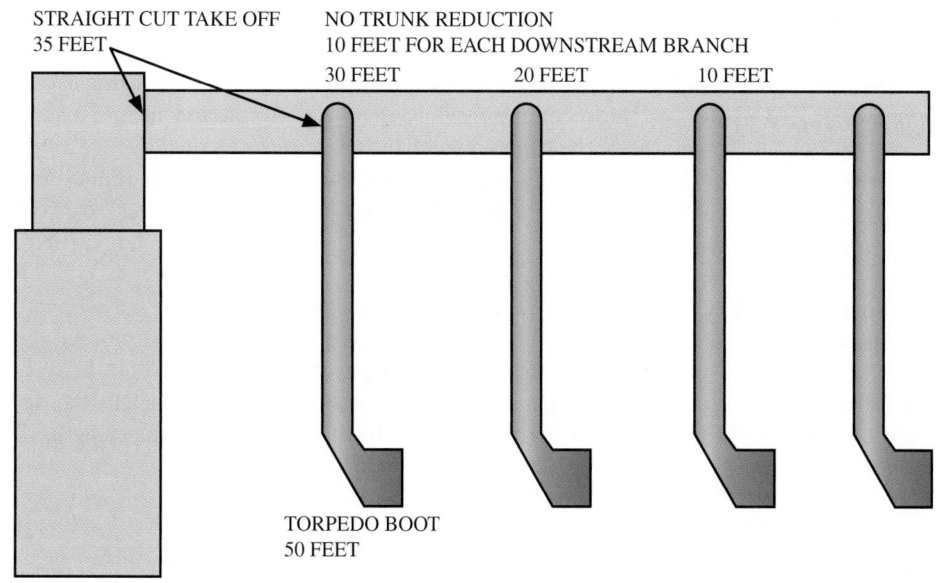

STRAIGHT CUT TAKE OFF
35 FEET

NO TRUNK REDUCTION
10 FEET FOR EACH DOWNSTREAM BRANCH

30 FEET   20 FEET   10 FEET

TORPEDO BOOT
50 FEET

Figure 57-32 Example of branch duct total equivalent length using inefficient fittings

equivalent length in fittings alone. After adding 10 feet for each downstream branch, 15 feet for the distance from the blower to the takeoff, and 20 feet for the distance from the takeoff to the boot, the total equivalent length is 30 + 15 + 20 + 150 = 215 ft.

This can be improved by using more efficient duct fittings. The trunk leaving the plenum can be reduced to 10 ft by using a tapered fitting. Similarly, the branch take-off can be reduced to 15 ft. The downstream branch factor has been eliminated by using a reducing trunk. Replacing the 90° boot with an elbow and straight boot changes the equivalent length of the boot from 30 ft to 15 ft. All of these

changes together reduce the equivalent length of fittings to 40 ft, making the total equivalent length 15 + 20 + 40 = 75 ft, Figure 57-33. Often, the added cost of using more efficient fittings is offset by being able to use a smaller duct at a higher friction rate.

The bottom line is that many duct runs exceed 100 equivalent feet. The design friction rate will have to be adjusted lower to keep the actual pressure drop through the run from exceeding the desired pressure loss through the run. This is done using the formula shown in section 56.10 or the length conversion scale on the ACCA duct calculator.

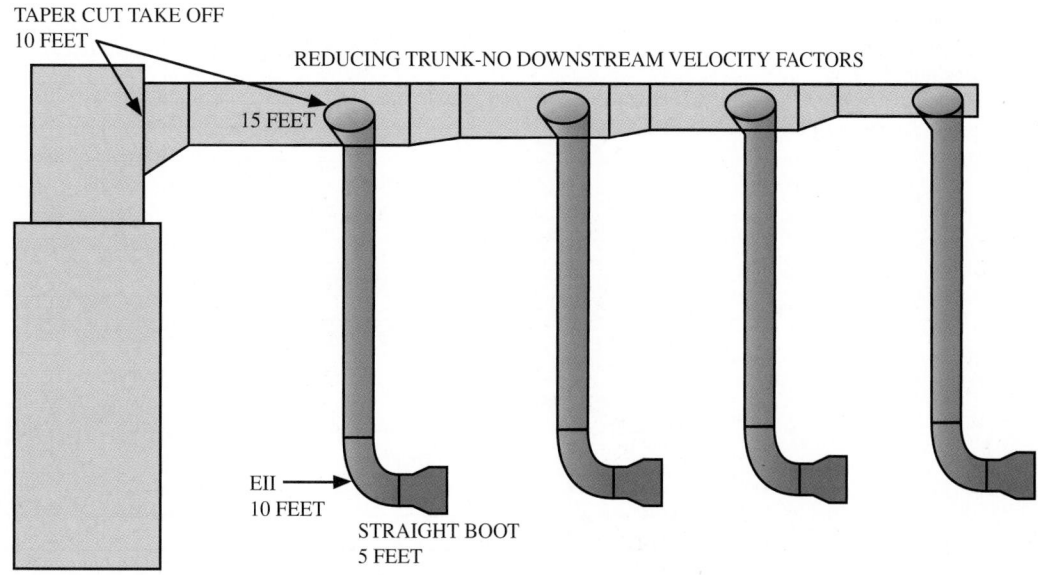

TAPER CUT TAKE OFF
10 FEET

REDUCING TRUNK-NO DOWNSTREAM VELOCITY FACTORS

15 FEET

EII
10 FEET

STRAIGHT BOOT
5 FEET

Figure 57-33 Example of branch duct total equivalent length using efficient fittings

57.10 USING A DUCT FRICTION LOSS CHART

Duct friction loss charts are used to design duct systems. Figures 57-34 through 57-37 show the standard scales:

- Air volume, vertical lines shown in red, Figure 57-34.
- Static pressure loss (friction loss), horizontal lines shown in blue, Figure 57-35.
- Duct size, diagonal lines shown in green, Figure 57-36.
- Air velocity, diagonal lines shown in yellow, Figure 57-37.

If any two values are known, all the other values can be determined from the chart. For example, 1,000 CFM moving through a 12 in duct will have a velocity of approximately 1,300 fpm and the rate of static loss will be just under 0.2 in wc per 100 equivalent feet of duct, point A on Figure 57-38. Most commonly, the design friction rate and airflow volume are the two known quantities. To select a duct size for a specific friction rate, find the intersection of the air volume and friction rate lines. To move 1,000 CFM at a friction rate of 0.1 in wc per 100 ft of duct will require a 14 in duct, point B on Figure 57-38.

It is important to recognize the difference between rate and absolute value. The friction rate chart does not tell the designer what the actual loss through a duct will be because that depends upon the duct length. Rather, it tells the designer what the loss will be for every 100 ft of duct length. To

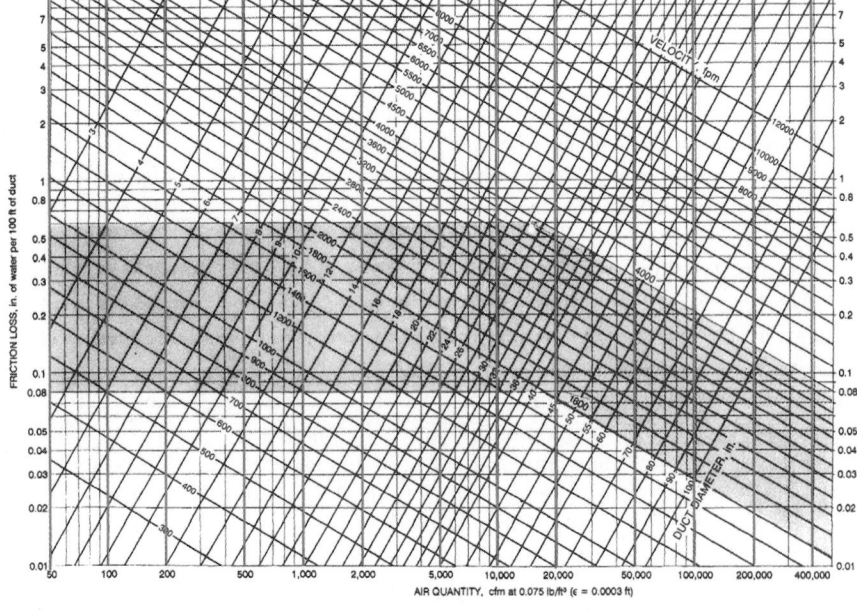

Figure 57-34 The air volume lines are highlighted in red on this duct friction chart
(© American Society of Heating, Refrigerating, and Air-Conditioning Engineers, Inc., www.ashrae.org)

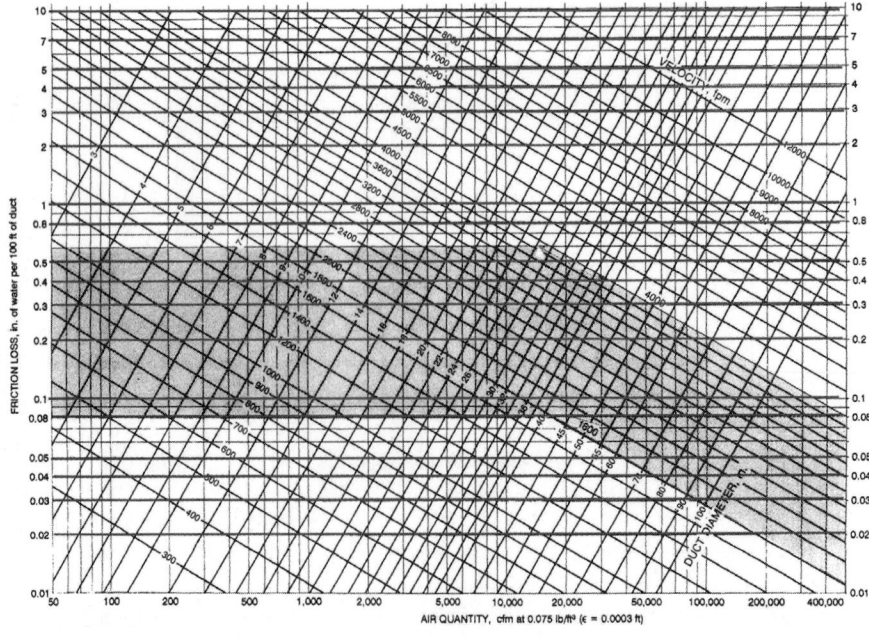

Figure 57-35 The friction loss lines are highlighted in blue on this duct friction chart
(© American Society of Heating, Refrigerating, and Air-Conditioning Engineers, Inc., www.ashrae.org)

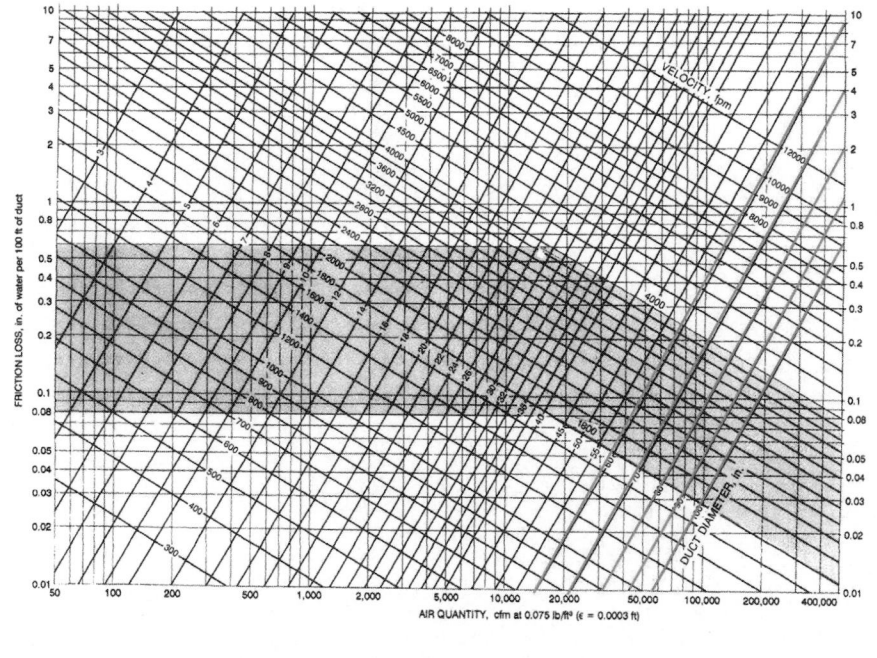

Figure 57-36 The duct size lines are highlighted in green on this duct friction chart

(© American Society of Heating, Refrigerating and Air-Conditioning Engineers, Inc., www.ashrae.org)

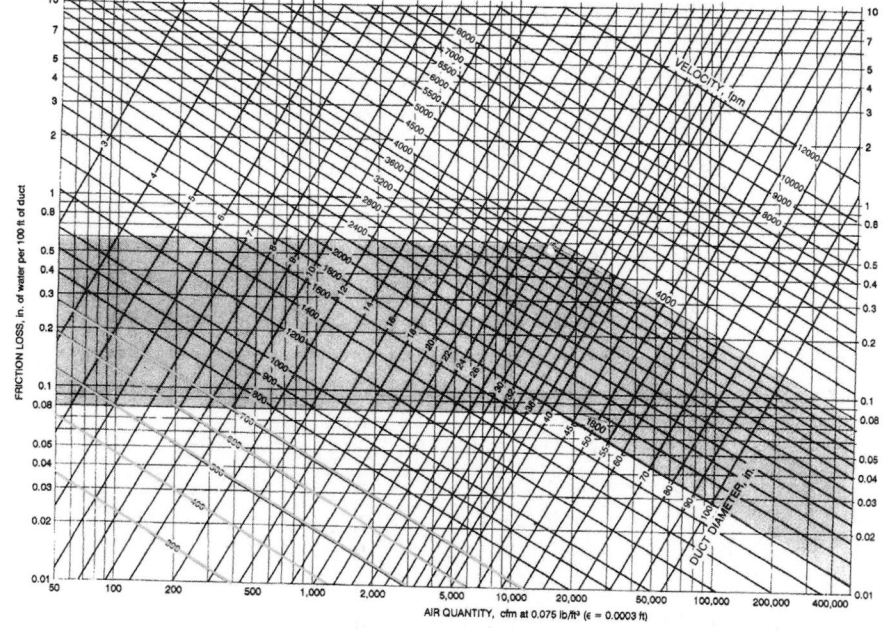

Figure 57-37 The air velocity lines are highlighted in yellow on this duct friction chart

(© American Society of Heating, Refrigerating, and Air-Conditioning Engineers, Inc., www.ashrae.org)

determine the actual static pressure loss for a given CFM with any length run

$$\text{Actual static loss} = (\text{total equivalent length}/100) \times \text{friction rate per 100 ft}$$

A 50 ft section of duct would be half as long as a 100 ft duct and would create only half the static pressure drop. Since a 100 ft length of 6 in duct loses 0.085 in wc static pressure while moving 100 CFM, it will lose half of that, 0.0425 in wc, to move 100 CFM through a 50 ft section. A 200 ft section of 6 in duct would lose twice the static pressure, 0.17 in wc, while moving 100 CFM. Since all duct runs are not the same length, they will not all deliver the same amount of air, even if they are all the same size duct. This is why it is inaccurate

to state that a 6 in duct will carry 100 CFM at a static pressure of 0.085 in without any reference to its length.

Most of the time the available static pressure is known and what the designer is looking for is what size duct will deliver the correct amount of air. In this case, the friction rate is adjusted so that the end result is equal to the design static pressure. The friction rate can be adjusted for different lengths of duct using the following formula:

$$\text{Adjusted friction rate} = \text{design friction rate} \times (100/\text{equivalent length})$$

For example, the adjusted friction rate using a system design friction rate of 0.10 in wc and a duct length of 50 ft

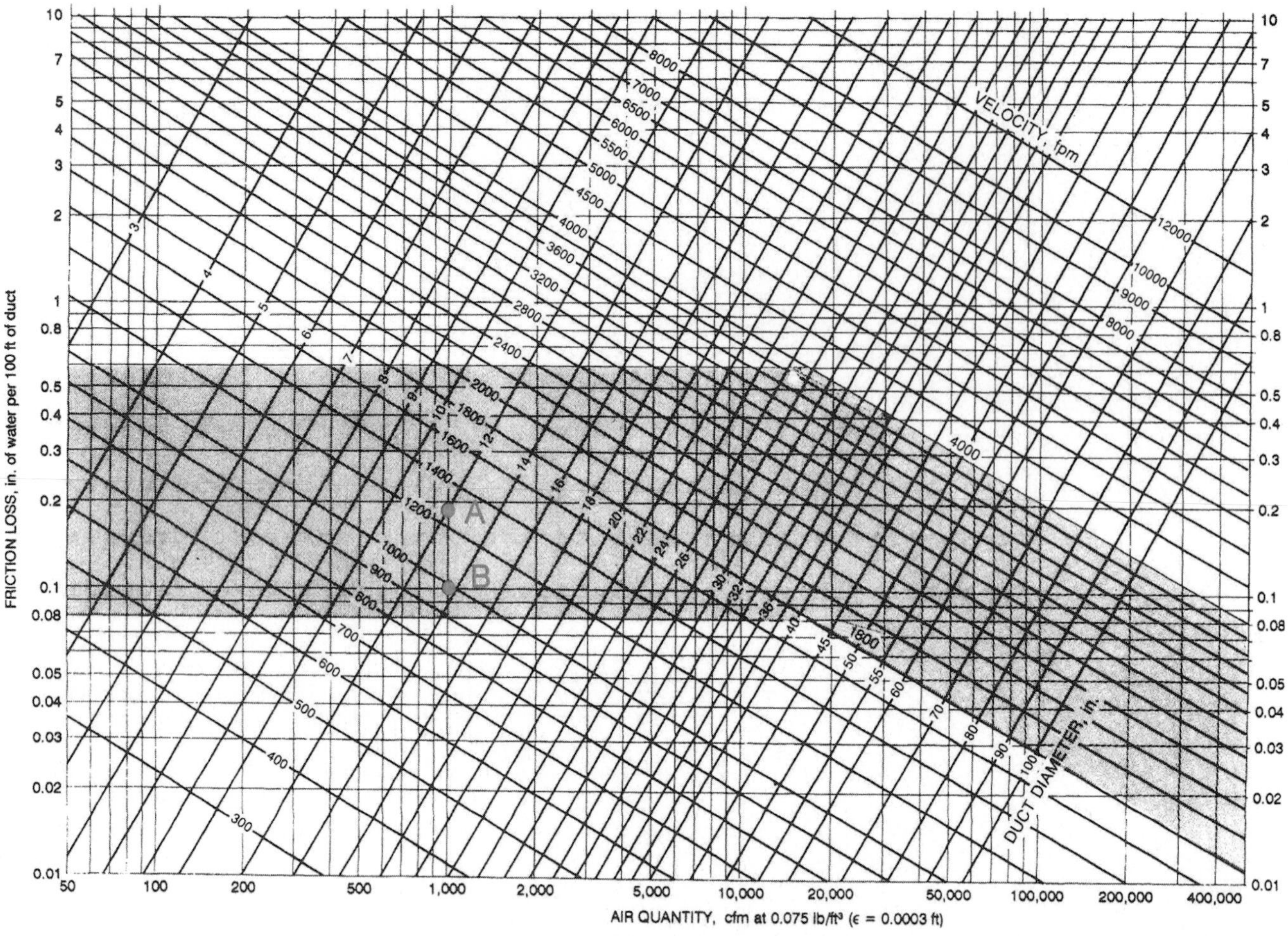

Figure 57-38 Friction chart examples
(© American Society of Heating, Refrigerating, and Air-Conditioning Engineers, Inc., www.ashrae.org)

would be 0.1 in wc × (100/50) = 0.2 in wc. At 0.2 in wc, the air will lose exactly 0.1 in wc static pressure traveling 50 ft. The adjusted friction rate for a 200 ft run would be 0.1 in wc × (100/200) = 0.05 in wc. At 0.05 in wc, the air will lose exactly 0.1 in wc by the time it travels 200 ft.

57.11 USING A DUCT CALCULATOR

Duct calculators are the most commonly used duct design tools. They take the place of friction charts and moderately complex calculations. All duct calculators have a few standard scales: round duct size, square to round conversion, friction rate per 100 ft, velocity, and volume. Lining up any two of these variables will allow you to look up the others. Most duct calculators are designed for smooth galvanized metal duct. Some of these will give conversion factors to accurately calculate other types of duct. The ACCA duct calculator offers a number of advantages over most other duct calculators. It gives friction rates for many different types of duct, converts velocity pressures to velocity, and has a convenient scale for determining the actual static pressure loss of a duct whose equivalent length is not 100 ft, Figure 57-39.

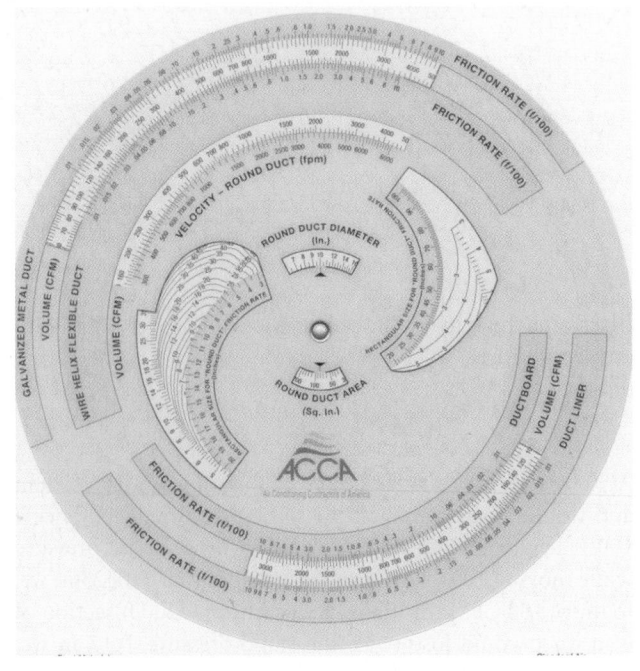

Figure 57-39 ACCA duct calculator
(ACCA Duct Calculator, copyright Air Conditioning Contractors of America)

Sample Calculations

Place the arrow on "6" in the round duct diameter window. Find 100 in the volume window. Directly across from 100 CFM in the galvanized metal friction rate window you should see 0.08 in wc, Figure 57-40. In the flexible duct friction rate window you should see approximately 0.15 in wc, Figure 57-41. These numbers represent the static loss per 100 ft of duct when 100 CFM is traveling through it. Now with the arrow in the round duct size window still pointing to "6,"

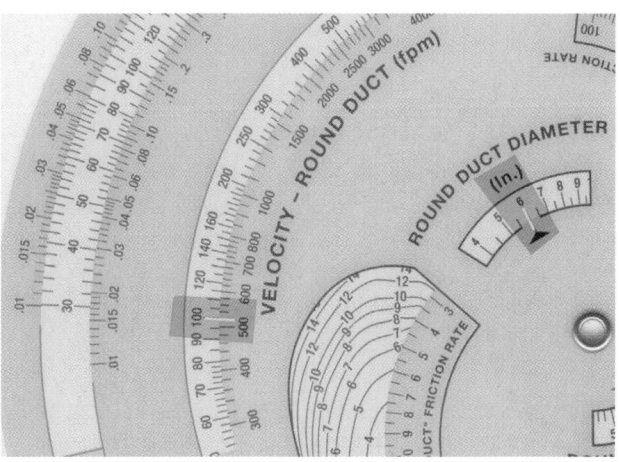

Figure 57-42 100 CFM of air traveling through a 6 in duct has a velocity of approximately 520 fpm
(From ACCA Duct Calculator, copyright Air Conditioning Contractors of America)

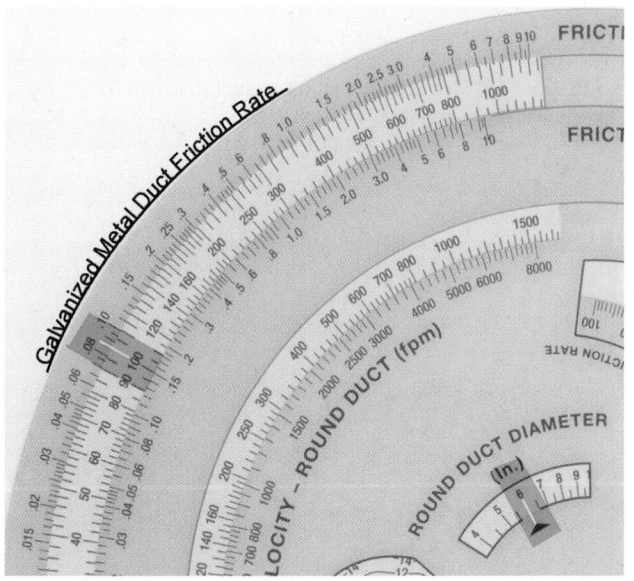

Figure 57-40 A 6 in metal duct carrying 100 CFM has a static pressure loss of 0.085 in wc per 100 ft
(From ACCA Duct Calculator, copyright Air Conditioning Contractors of America)

find 100 CFM in the volume window opposite the velocity window. Directly across from 100 CFM you should read approximately 520 fpm, Figure 57-42. This is the velocity of 100 CFM of air traveling through a 6 in duct.

Of course any two known values can be used to look up the others. To design for a particular static pressure, line up the static pressure across from the CFM and then look at the duct size to determine what size duct is needed. Another use is to design the system to maintain a particular duct velocity. The required duct size can be determined by lining up the design velocity across from the needed CFM.

The ACCA duct calculator has a handy conversion chart at the bottom on the side that says "Auxiliary Calculations." Using the earlier example of 100 CFM at 0.085 in wc, put the 100 ft arrow across from 0.085 in wc. Now look across from the 50 ft mark and see an adjusted static of 0.042 in wc. Without moving the duct calculator, look across from 200 ft and you should see 0.17 in wc, Figure 57-43. This scale can also be used to determine what design friction rate is needed

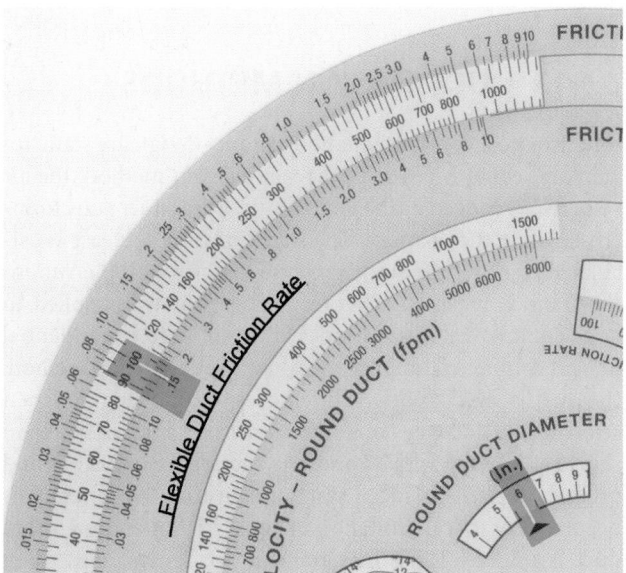

Figure 57-41 A 6 in flex duct carrying 100 CFM has a static pressure loss of 0.15 in wc per 100 ft
(From ACCA Duct Calculator, copyright Air Conditioning Contractors of America)

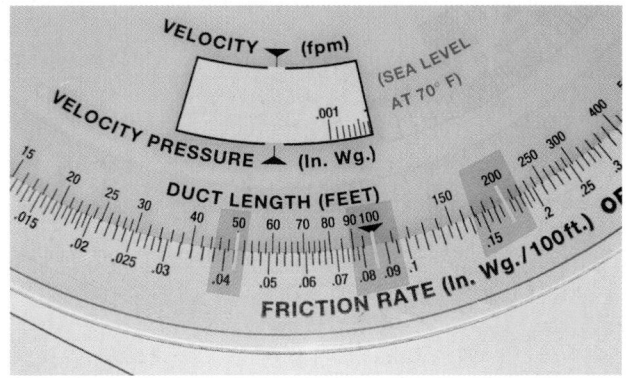

Figure 57-43 At a friction *rate* of 0.85 in wc, a 50 ft length of duct will lose 0.042 in wc; a 200 ft length will lose 0.17 in wc
(From ACCA Duct Calculator, copyright Air Conditioning Contractors of America)

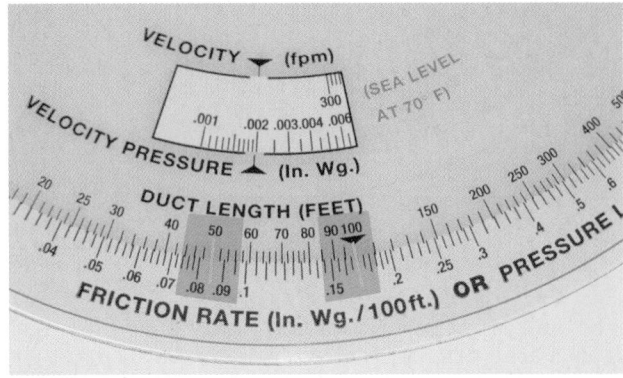

Figure 57-44 For a 50 ft section of duct to lose 0.085 in wc, the friction *rate* should be 0.17 in wc
(From ACCA Duct Calculator, copyright Air Conditioning Contractors of America)

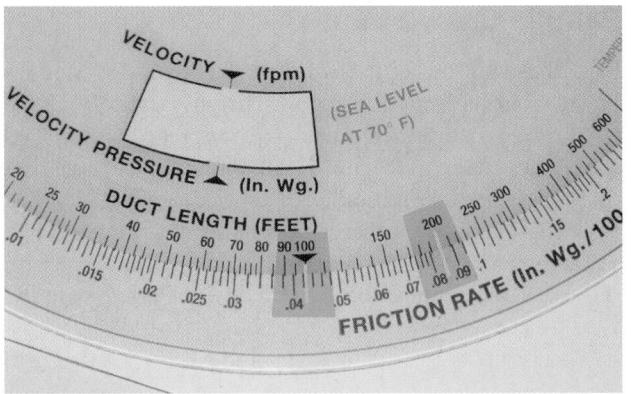

Figure 57-46 For a 200 ft section of duct to lose 0.085 in wc, the friction *rate* should be 0.042 in wc
(From ACCA Duct Calculator, copyright Air Conditioning Contractors of America)

to achieve a desired design static pressure drop for a duct run which is not 100 ft long. Suppose a system is to be designed with a supply duct static loss of 0.085 in wc. What friction rate would achieve 0.085 in wc pressure drop in a 50 ft duct? Note that in this case the end result is 0.085 in wc, not the rate per 100 ft. Line up the 0.085 in wc with 50 ft. Now look across from the arrow at 100 ft and you should see approximately 0.17 in wc, Figure 57-44. A 50 ft duct with a friction rate of 0.17 in wc will give exactly 0.085 in wc drop. Looking in the round duct diameter window you should see that a 5 in duct will handle 100 CFM at this friction rate, Figure 57-45. Now line 0.085 in wc up with the 200 ft mark. The arrow at the 100 ft mark indicates that we should use 0.042 in wc to design a 200 ft duct, Figure 57-46. Line up 0.042 in wc with 100 CFM and look in the round duct size window. You should see that a 7 in duct is required for this 200 ft duct, Figure 57-47. Notice that the 50 ft 5 in duct, the 100 ft 6 in duct, and the 200 ft 7 in duct will all deliver the same amount of air with a static pressure loss of 0.085 in.

To design a truly balanced system, the design friction rate for each run should be adjusted. This scale comes in *very* handy when designing duct systems.

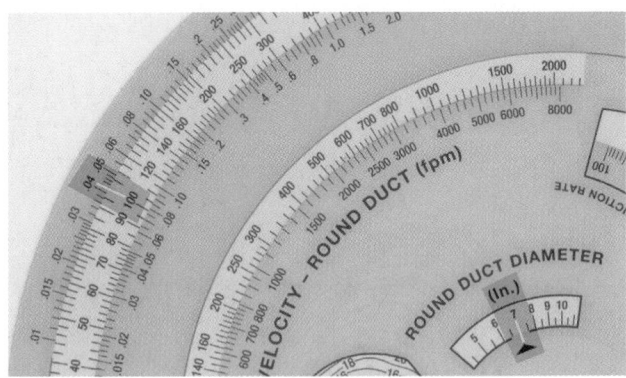

Figure 57-47 A 7 in duct can handle 100 CFM at a friction rate of 0.042 in wc
(From ACCA Duct Calculator, copyright Air Conditioning Contractors of America)

57.12 DUCT DESIGN METHODS

The two most common methods of duct design are static regain and equal friction. In the static regain method, the air velocity is reduced at the end of long trunk duct runs to increase the static pressure. The static pressure increase is calculated to offset the static pressure loss through the run, so the static is regained. This method is primarily applied to large commercial installations and is not used in residential or light commercial applications. In the equal friction method, the duct is sized to offset differences in duct length. When selecting the duct size, long runs use a lower friction rate than short runs. When applied properly, the equal friction method produces a well balanced system, delivering air where it is needed. A practical limitation of equal friction design is that duct is only available in certain physical sizes. This often forces the designer to choose a duct that is a little larger or smaller than the ideal duct size.

Two commonly used guides for duct design are the ASHRAE duct design method and the ACCA Manual D. The

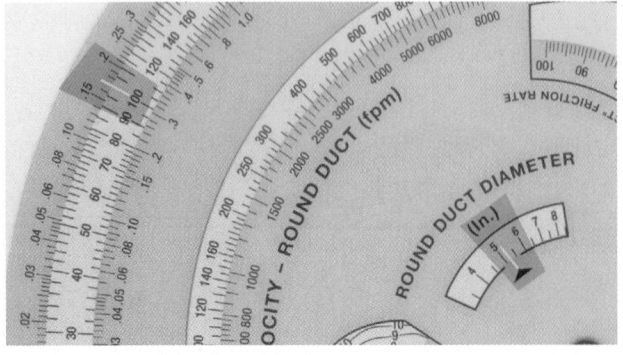

Figure 57-45 A 5 in duct can handle 100 CFM at a friction rate of 0.17 in wc
(From ACCA Duct Calculator, copyright Air Conditioning Contractors of America)

current Manual D method is a modified equal friction method because the friction rate is not adjusted for each run. Rather, all runs are designed at a friction rate that will work for the run with the highest equivalent length. This produces an inherently unbalanced system because all runs are treated the same, even though they have different equivalent lengths. Manually adjustable dampers are added to each branch duct to balance the system by taking airflow measurements and making adjustments to the dampers to adjust the airflow through each run. The disadvantage of this system is simply that the system must be operated and balanced after installation to perform well.

57.13   DUCT DESIGN GOALS

There are three basic goals when designing a duct system. In order of importance they are:

1. Allow the system to circulate enough air to operate properly.
2. Distribute the air proportionally to where the heat load is.
3. Keep airflow noise below objectionable levels.

Minimum Duct Restriction

The first goal is the most important. All heating and cooling equipment that circulates air has some minimum requirement for airflow. A duct system that will not allow the unit to deliver this minimum airflow will cause inefficient operation at best and equipment problems at worst. A fan's capacity is stated as the amount of air it can move against a particular pressure. This pressure is usually stated in inches of water column. Friction charts and/or duct calculators help determine the amount of static pressure drop a particular type and size of duct will offer to any given airflow. In general, as more air is pushed through the same size duct, the pressure drop through the duct increases. Duct calculators or friction charts show the amount of resistance a duct has to airflow. This is stated as static pressure loss per 100 ft of duct, measured in inches of water column. It is important to keep in mind that this is a friction *rate*, not an absolute quantity. In other words, a duct length is necessary to accurately determine what the static loss will be for a particular duct.

Required Information

To design a duct system that will allow the fan to move an adequate amount of air, the designer needs to know:

- **System CFM** The amount of air the system must move.
- **Maximum Available System Static** The maximum static pressure available for moving that quantity of air.
- **Duct Friction Rate** The airflow resistance of the duct material has to airflow.

System Airflow

Airflow is measured in cubic feet per minute, or CFM. As the term suggests, CFM measures the volume of air that is moved every minute. Systems can operate correctly over a range of airflows. The proper airflow requirement is found in the manufacturer's design and specification literature. If you do not have a specification sheet to work from, 400 CFM per ton of cooling works for most residential equipment. The ductwork should be designed to handle the higher of the heating or cooling system airflow. The cooling airflow is usually used because the required airflow for cooling exceeds the required airflow for heating in most situations. Cool air is heavier, and therefore harder to move.

In air conditioning, the airflow across the evaporator helps determine the amount of sensible cooling versus the amount of latent cooling accomplished. Reducing the airflow will increase the amount of moisture removed from the air but decrease the amount of sensible cooling accomplished. Conversely, increasing the airflow reduces the latent cooling but increases the sensible cooling. The amount of sensible and latent cooling required can be determined by using ACCA Manual J. It is important to recognize that duct sizing is done on the basis of sensible cooling capacity, not total cooling capacity. Sensible capacity is what is going to actually cool the room down, so the sensible heat load for each room is used to determine how much air that room requires.

Maximum Available System Static

The maximum static pressure the equipment can operate against is usually specified by the equipment manufacturer. Keep in mind that anything the air must travel over or through will create some static pressure drop. Examples of devices that produce a static pressure drop include evaporator coils, humidifiers, air filters, grills, and registers. The amount of static pressure loss for any of these devices depends upon the airflow rate. More airflow creates a higher static pressure loss. The maximum available static pressure for the duct system can be determined by subtracting all losses except ductwork from the maximum operating static pressure of the equipment at the design airflow.

For example, take a 2 ton system moving 800 CFM of air with a total available static pressure of 0.55 in wc, an evaporator coil with a static pressure drop of 0.25 in wc, a filter with a static pressure drop of 0.10 in wc, and supply registers and return grills with a static pressure drop of 0.05 in wc. All the fixed losses add up to 0.4 in wc, leaving 0.15 in wc of pressure for ductwork.

Limiting Air Noise

The design static pressure that has been determined is for the entire duct system. If the supply duct is designed at 0.15 in wc and the return duct at 0.15 in wc, the total duct static loss would be 0.3 in wc and the fan will not move enough air. The supply static and return static added together needs to equal 0.15 in wc.

One determining factor for design static for the supply and return ducts should be the velocity of the air as it travels

Figure 57-48 Airflow through metal duct at 600 fpm and 1,000 fpm velocities

@600 fpm duct velocity			@1000 fpm duct velocity		
	Friction rate			**Friction rate**	
Duct size	**(in wc)**	**CFM**	**Duct size**	**(in wc)**	**CFM**
6	0.11 (in wc)	120	6	0.3 (in wc)	290
8	0.085 (in wc)	220	8	0.2 (in wc)	350
10	0.07 (in wc)	330	10	0.15 (in wc)	550
12	0.055 (in wc)	480	12	0.12 (in wc)	780
14	0.045 (in wc)	650	14	0.10 (in wc)	1,050

through the duct. It is possible to select a duct size that will maintain a workable static pressure but end up with a velocity that creates an objectionable amount of noise. If air moves faster than 600 fpm it begins to make noise. Above 1,000 fpm, the customer will have to turn up the television when the air conditioning starts.

In general, as duct sizes increase, design static must decrease to maintain the same velocity. There are normally more supply registers than return air grills in most systems. This means that the return air ducts must handle more air than the supply ducts. Therefore, return air ducts are larger than supply air ducts. If return air ducts are sized exactly like supply air ducts, the return air ducts will often be noisy. Figure 57-48 shows the maximum design static for several sizes of duct at velocities of 600 fpm and 1,000 fpm.

A quick look at Figure 57-48 shows that if a designer sticks strictly to a 600 fpm maximum velocity, the main supply trunk ducts and all the return ductwork will be rather large. Any duct that ends in a supply register or a return grill should be limited to a 600 fpm velocity. However, the trunk ducts that supply the branch ducts can operate at higher velocity and noise levels because they do not open up into the living area. Still, 1,000 fpm is considered the outer limit for velocity in trunk ducts in residential systems.

57.14 DETERMINING BRANCH DUCT AIRFLOW

To have an even temperature throughout the house, the amount of air each room receives should be based on the heat load for each room. Typically, the airflow required for both heating and cooling is calculated and the higher value chosen.

Dividing the entire building heat load by the system CFM will tell how much Btu/hr is delivered for every CFM of airflow. For example, a house with a heating load of 30,000 Btu/hr and an airflow of 600 CFM would be have a heating airflow divisor of 30,000/600 = 50 Btu/CFM. If a room in this house had a heating load of 4,000 Btu/hr, the required airflow for heating that room would be 4,000/50 = 80 CFM.

To determine the cooling airflow divisor, divide the total calculated sensible cooling load by the amount of airflow the system will move to arrive at a capacity divisor. For example,

a house with a sensible cooling load of 16,000 Btu/hr and an airflow of 800 CFM would have a capacity divisor of 16,000/800 = 20 Btu/CFM. If a room in this house had a sensible cooling load of 2,400 Btu/hr, the required airflow for cooling that room would be 2,400/20 = 120 CFM.

TECH TIP

Airflow divisors are simply reciprocals of airflow factors, as used in ACCA Manual J. Using the example of 30,000 Btu and 600 CFM, the airflow factor would be calculated by dividing 600 CFM by 30,000 Btu/hr to get 0.02 CFM per Btu/hr. This number is then multiplied by the room load to get the required airflow. For example, 0.02 × 4,000 Btu/hr = 80 CFM. The airflow divisor has the advantage of being a "normal" number, rather than a tiny decimal number, which reduces rounding error and keeps the process simpler.

57.15 BRANCH DUCT SIZING

Three pieces of information are required to size each branch duct: the system design static pressure, the total equivalent length of each run, and the required airflow for each run. A friction chart or duct calculator can be used to determine what size duct will be required to deliver the correct amount of air at the design static. Line up the duct's total equivalent length, including fittings, with the adjusted design static on the scale for duct length adjustments. Now look at the static pressure indicated by the arrow at the 100 ft mark. This is the value that will be used to look up the duct size on the other side of the duct calculator. On the other side of the duct calculator, line up this adjusted static with the required CFM for the duct run. The arrow in the round duct window will indicate the size of round duct that will deliver the required amount of air at the design pressure loss for that duct run.

You have many of the same issues on the return side. Ideally, each return should handle the air from the supply registers in the portion of the house where the return is located. It is critical that the total amount of air handled by all the returns add up to the total system CFM. It is also important that air be able to move from one room to another easily. Air will not enter a room if the air that is already in the room cannot leave.

S E R V I C E   T I P

Undersized returns are a common problem found in duct systems today. A marginal duct system can often be dramatically improved by adding additional return air runs.

57.16 TRUNK DUCT SIZING

Each trunk duct should be able to carry the total volume of air for all its connected branches at the static pressure loss of the branch with the lowest adjusted static. For example, a trunk duct to supply the four branch ducts listed in Figure 57-49 would be sized for 400 CFM at a design static of 0.08 in wc.

The trunk duct is sized using a friction chart or duct calculator. In this example, a 10 in diameter duct would be the closest actual duct size, Figure 57-50.

Airflow (CFM)	Adjusted design static (in wc)
120	0.12
80	0.08
100	0.10
200	0.11

Figure 57-49 Trunk duct sizing example data

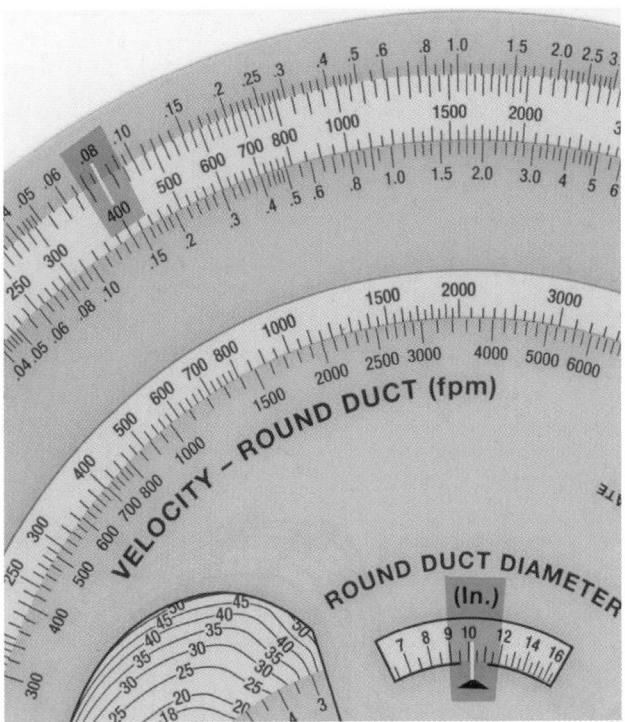

Figure 57-50 Duct selection for 400 CFM at 0.085 in wc
(From ACCA Duct Calculator, copyright Air Conditioning Contractors of America)

UNIT 57—SUMMARY

Duct systems distribute conditioned air through a building. The basic components consist of a blower, supply air ducts, and return air ducts. Duct systems are designed using load calculations, equipment performance specifications, and building plans.

Ductwork is commonly made of galvanized sheet metal, spiral metal, fiberglass ductboard, flexible duct, or fabric duct. Metal duct must be insulated; fiberglass ductboard and flexible duct do not require insulating because they are inherently insulated. Sheet metal duct and flexible duct are sealed with UL-181 duct tape and UL-181 mastic. Fiberglass ductboard is sealed with UL-181 foil tape.

All components in the airstream create static pressure loss, including the air filter, evaporator coil, electric heaters, humidifiers, supply registers, and return air grills. The static pressure available for moving air through the duct system is found by subtracting all losses other than duct losses from the blower total external static pressure at design airflow. The pressure lost as air travels through duct fittings is measured in equivalent feet of pipe. The total equivalent length of a duct run is found by adding the length of the trunk duct, branch duct, and the equivalent length of all the fittings. Duct is sized using a friction chart or duct calculator. Friction charts and duct calculators give the friction rate per 100 ft of duct. The actual pressure drop through any duct will also depend upon its total equivalent length.

UNIT 57—REVIEW QUESTIONS

1. What friction rate should be used to size a duct for a static pressure drop of 0.1 in wc if the duct has a total equivalent length of 150 ft?

2. What size metal duct should be used to deliver 170 CFM with a pressure drop of 0.15 in wc if the total equivalent length is 130 ft?

3. What friction rate should be used to size a duct for a static pressure drop of 0.1 in wc if the duct has a total equivalent length of 50 ft?

4. What size metal duct should be used to deliver 290 CFM with a pressure drop of 0.15 in wc if the total equivalent length is 80 ft?

5. What is the velocity of 500 CFM of air moving through a 10 in duct?

6. Why should all ductwork designs start with an accurate heat load study?

7. Explain the function of the following duct components:
   Ell
   Wye
   Transition
   Boot

8. What is the total available static pressure for the ductwork for a system with the following specifications:
   Blower: 0.55 in wc total external static at design airflow.
   Evaporator coil: 0.25 in wc static pressure drop at design airflow.

Filter: 0.1 in wc static pressure drop at design airflow.

Registers and grills: 0.05 in wc static pressure drop at design airflow.

9. Why should air velocity in branch ducts be limited to 600 fpm?

10. Why are duct friction charts designed for sheet metal ducts not accurate for fiberglass ductboard or flexible ducts?

11. What is the difference between duct liner and duct wrap?

12. What is the purpose of the vapor barrier on the outside of duct wrap?

13. Why do fiberglass ductboard and flex duct have higher friction loss rates than sheet metal?

14. What is the difference between a radial duct system and an extended plenum duct system?

15. What is the purpose of reducing the trunk duct size in a reducing extended plenum duct system?

16. What is a central plenum duct system?

17. Where are radial duct systems typically installed?

18. What is the maximum static pressure difference that most residential blowers are designed for?

19. What is the greatest loss of efficiency in most duct systems?

20. What are the UL 181, UL 181A, and UL 181B standards?

Duct Installation

OBJECTIVES

After completing this unit you will be able to:

- list the agencies that set standards for duct systems.
- explain the difference between a flexible duct and a flexible connector.
- list the materials used to construct duct systems.
- explain how to seal duct systems.
- describe how to join different types of duct.
- describe how to measure the amount of duct leakage.
- select a register using register selection engineering data.

58.1 INTRODUCTION

The most common materials used for duct construction include galvanized steel, fiberglass ductboard, and wire helix flexible duct. Regardless of the materials used, a correctly installed duct system should last as long as the house, should not leak, and should be insulated well enough to prevent duct loss and gain to unconditioned space.

58.2 STANDARDS

Approved methods of manufacturing, installing, and sealing ductwork are published by several national agencies that publish codes, standards, and guides. These standards are often referenced in state and local codes. Organizations publishing duct standards include:

- Underwriters Laboratories.
- National Fire Protection Association.
- Sheet Metal and Air Conditioning Contractors National Association.
- North American Insulation Manufacturers Association.
- Air Diffusion Council.
- Air Conditioning Contractors of America.

Underwriters Laboratories

Underwriters Laboratories Standards 181, 181A, and 181B are probably the most referenced duct standards. Any manufactured duct should comply with UL 181 standards. Standard 181 covers manufactured duct materials, such as fiberglass ductboard and wire helix flexible duct. Two classes of manufactured duct are listed according to their flammability: class 0 and class 1. Class 0 ducts have a flame spread index of 0. Class 1 ducts have a flame spread index not over 25 and a smoke developed index of not over 50. The flame spread index is a number relating to ASTM E 84 flammability testing. A rate of 100 is assigned to untreated bare wood while 0 is assigned cement board. The smoke developed index compares the amount of smoke produced compared to concrete, at 0, and red oak, at 100.

Many mechanical codes require that mastic and tape be UL 723 rated for metal duct. UL 723 tests materials for flame spread and smoke development. Materials that are UL 723 rated can be used on and in air plenums. UL Standard 181A addresses closure and sealing systems for manufactured rigid ducts, such as fiberglass ductboard. UL Standard 181 B addresses closure and sealing systems for flexible ductwork. Note that a tape may be UL rated, but not meet 181 standards. A tape that only displays the 723 rating and not the 181 rating is not intended for ductboard or flex. Figure 58-1 shows the marking on UL rated duct tape and mastic.

National Fire Protection Association

The NFPA publishes two standards that are widely referenced, 90A and 90B. Standard 90A covers the installation of ventilation and air conditioning while 90B covers the

Figure 58-1 Duct tape and mastic should be UL 181 approved

installation of warm air heating and air conditioning. Both standards discuss the types of materials that may be used for ductwork and discuss the application difference between flexible air duct and flexible air connector. Air ducts must either be made of rigid nonflammable materials, like sheet metal, or be tested and shown to meet the UL 181 standard. Flexible duct connectors are not certified to meet every provision of UL 181; therefore, their use is more limited.

Sheet Metal and Air Conditioning Contractors National Association

SMACNA publishes several duct and installation standards. The most commonly referenced is *HVAC Duct Construction Standards—Metal and Flexible*. It covers a lot of the nuts and bolts aspects of constructing and installing ductwork. Topics include duct joining, duct sealing, and duct hanging, among others.

North American Insulation Manufacturers Association

NAIMA represents the fiberglass industry. They publish a manual called *Fibrous Glass Residential Duct Construction Standard*. This standard covers both the standard for fiberglass ductboard materials and how the materials should be installed.

Air Diffusion Council

The ADC represents flexible duct manufacturers and publishes standards relating to flexible duct systems. The most referenced is the *Flexible Duct Performance and Installation Standards* which gives specific instructions for properly installing flexible wire helix duct.

Air Conditioning Contractors of America

ACCA publishes many manuals for designing and installing air conditioning systems. For duct installation, the *HVAC Quality Installation Specification* is the most relevant. This manual covers the components of a quality installation, including the duct system.

Figure 58-2 Snap lock seam on round galvanized duct

58.3 SHEET METAL DUCT

Galvanized sheet metal duct has been the gold standard of duct systems for years. No other duct material has a lower friction rate or is as durable as sheet metal. Unfortunately, nothing else comes close to the cost of sheet metal either. Sheet metal is still used, but its prominence in residential duct systems is waning because of its high cost.

Round Galvanized Duct

Round duct is shipped in bundles of duct with one piece tucked inside another. Each piece needs to have its longitudinal seam snapped together before use. Figure 58-2 shows a typical snap lock seam.

Snap lock round duct is typically available in sections of 3, 4, and 5 ft depending upon the material, gauge, and duct diameter. Table 58-1 shows the lengths available from one supplier.

Table 58-1 Duct Section Length in Feet

Diameter (in)	30 Ga.	28 Ga.	26 Ga.	24 Ga.	Aluminum	Stainless
4–10	5		5	5	4	4
12	5		5	5	4	4
14		3	5	5	4	4
16			3	3	4	4
18			3	3	4	4
20			3	3	4	4
24			3	3	4	4

Figure 58-3 The crimped end on a round piece of galvanized duct

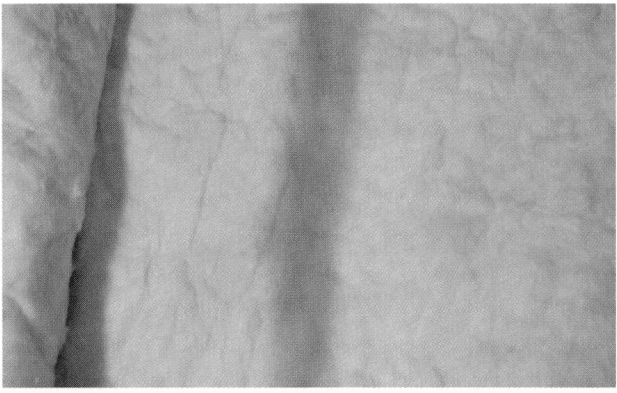

Figure 58-5 The stain on the duct wrap is caused by small dust particles escaping the leaky duct joint and getting caught in the duct insulation; it shows where the duct leaks air

One end of the duct is crimped, making its outside diameter slightly smaller than the regular duct diameter. A bead behind the crimp serves as a stop when inserting one duct into another, Figure 58-3. The crimps should be installed in the direction of airflow to reduce turbulence, Figure 58-4. All joints should be fastened with sheet metal screws or rivets. Ducts 10 in in diameter or smaller should have at least three equally spaced screws or rivets per joint. Larger ducts should have at least four equally spaced screws or rivets per joint. The quantity of screws may vary depending on the inspection authority in your area.

These joints are not airtight and need sealing. The outer insulation around the pipe does not help seal in the air. Take apart an older system with unsealed joints and there is a black line in the duct wrap where the joint was, Figure 58-5. This black ring is formed by tiny dirt particles that were caught in the fiberglass as air leaked out of the joint. Tape and/or mastic are required to make these joints airtight.

One method of sealing these joints is to use two wraps of UL 181A duct tape. The problem with this method is that little wrinkles are invariably left in the tape, and small amounts of air can escape through the wrinkles, Figure 58-6.

The preferred method is to use either mastic alone, or tape and mastic. Mastic works fine by itself provided that the cracks being sealed are not too large. Large cracks can be covered with UL 181A duct tape first, and then covered with mastic.

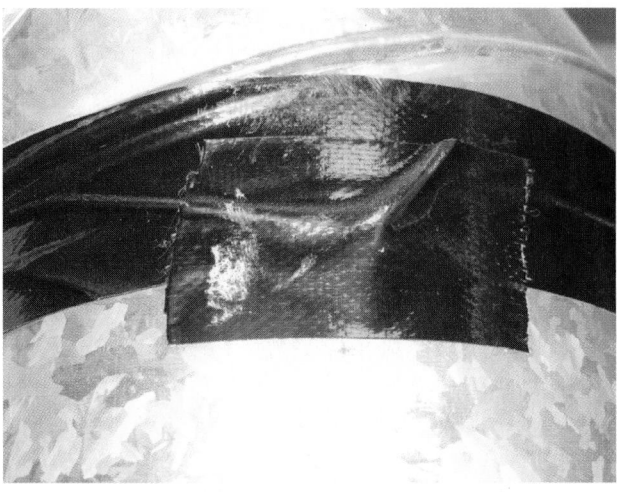

Figure 58-6 Wrinkles in duct tape can cause air leaks

Rectangular Galvanized Duct

Rectangular duct typically is made in two L-shaped pieces. Each piece has one duct width and one duct height, Figure 58-7. These pieces are normally joined by either a snap lock joint or a Pittsburgh joint. The 0.25 in edge of the snap lock snaps down into the seam. Typically it is hammered down using a sheet metal hammer, Figure 58-8. The $\frac{1}{4}$ in edge in a Pittsburgh seam fits into the seam and the edge of the seam is hammered over, Figure 58-9. The Pittsburgh joint is more airtight, but takes more material and time to produce.

Rectangular ducts are joined by S-locks and drive cleats. An S-lock is a piece of sheet metal in a flattened S-shape. One duct slides into the S-lock in one direction and the other duct slides into the S-lock from the other direction, Figure 58-10. S-locks are used on the larger duct dimension, usually the top and bottom. The shorter dimensions are joined by drive cleats. The duct edges are turned back and

Figure 58-4 Airflow should be toward the crimped end of the duct

Figure 58-7 Rectangular duct before assembly

Figure 58-9 Hammering Pittsburgh seam on rectangular duct

the drive cleat slips over the edges and pulls the duct together, Figure 58-11. These are driven down with a mallet; thus the name drive cleat. These joints are not airtight and need to be sealed, preferably with UL 181A mastic or UL 181A tape and mastic.

Hanging Metal Duct

One advantage of metal duct is that it has structural integrity, making it much easier to hang than flexible duct. Hangers should be spaced no further than 12 ft apart. Many materials

Figure 58-8 Hammering in snap lock seam on rectangular duct

Figure 58-10 The long sides of the duct are joined using S-locks

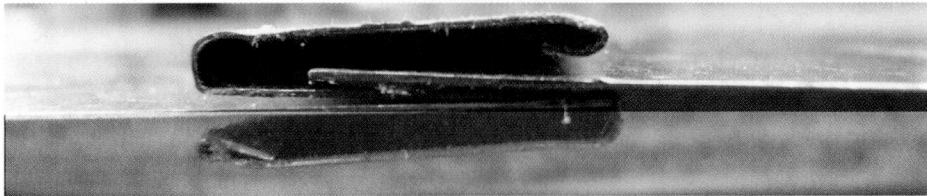

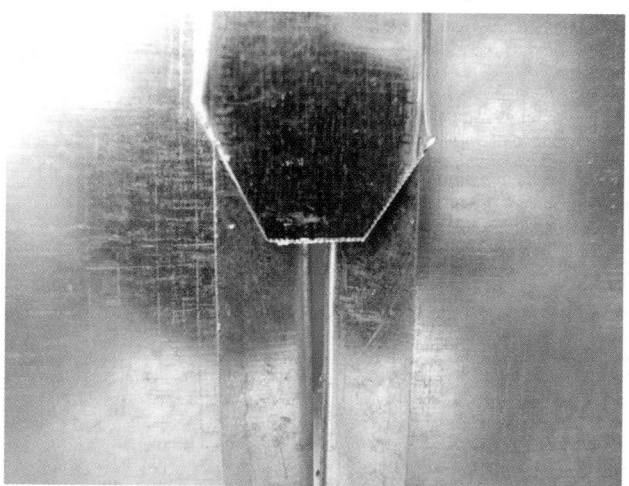

Figure 58-11 The short sides are joined with drive cleats

can be used as hangers including wire, plumbers strap, or sheet metal strips. Any screws that are run into the duct to fasten the hanger to the duct should be covered with mastic. When possible, long sections of metal duct are assembled on the ground and hung as a section. This makes it easier to assemble straight runs. Frequently these sections are also insulated before being hung. Attaching the duct one piece at a time while hanging the duct is much more difficult. Likewise, insulating while working around the hangers is more difficult than when the section of duct is on the ground and can be freely moved around. Figure 58-12 shows properly supported duct.

Take Offs

The first step in installing a take off is to cut a hole in the duct. The easiest, fastest, and cleanest method for cutting a round hole in the duct is to use an adjustable hole cutter,

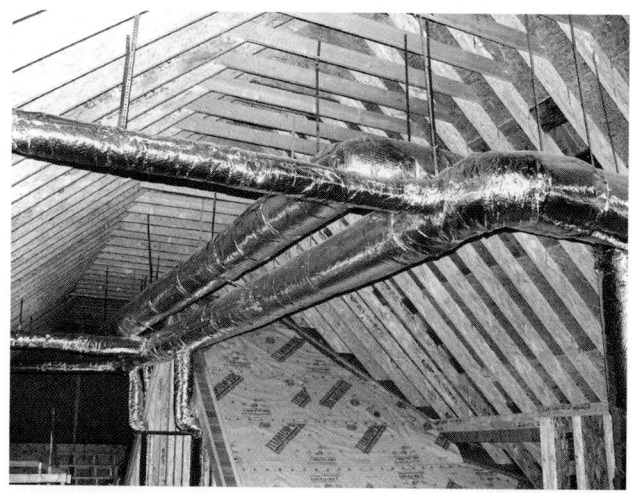

Figure 58-12 Properly supported and insulated galvanized duct system
(Courtesy of Stanfield Air Systems)

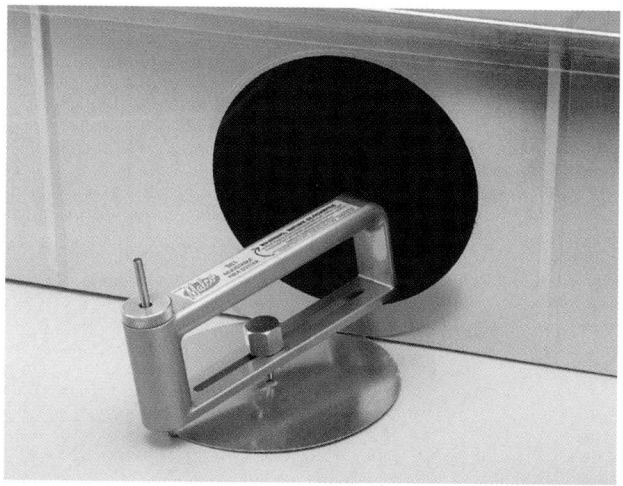

Figure 58-13 This hole was just cut using the adjustable hole cutter
(Courtesy of Malco Products, Inc.)

Figure 58-13. The hole cutter is set to the size of hole needed. A drill is attached to the hole cutter bit. First, drill a hole where the center of the hole will be. Next, place the pivot point in the hole and cut a full circle using the drill.

Holes can also be cut using aviation snips. Hold a short piece of pipe the size of the take off up to the duct and draw its perimeter on the duct. Cutting this hole out is harder than it might appear at first. It is generally not possible to simply cut along the line in a circle. When sheet metal is cut with snips, one side must bend out of the way to let the snips pass by. Neither side can bend out of the way on a piece of duct. Two solutions are (1) making a spiral cut from the center and (2) using a duct piercing tool to cut a line across the diameter of the hole and cutting out each semicircle.

For the spiral cut, a starter hole should be struck in the center using a duct piercing tool, Figure 58-14. Cut in an increasing spiral using either left hand or right hand aviation

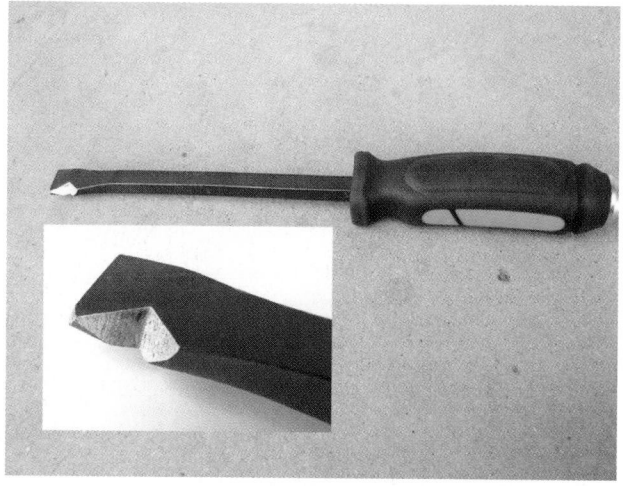

Figure 58-14 Duct piercing tool

Figure 58-15 Round holes can be cut using a spiral pattern

snips, Figure 58-15. Continue to follow the line once the spiral reaches it.

For the semicircle cut, use a duct piercing tool to cut across the diameter of the hole, Figure 58-16. Then use left or right aviation snips to cut out each semicircle, Figure 58-17.

Take offs are connected to metal duct using either dovetails or flanges. Dovetail fittings have tabs that are formed by a series of slits along the perimeter of the fitting, Figure 58-18. Every other tab is turned 90° to the fitting, Figure 58-19. The straight tabs are inserted into the hole, the technician reaches through the hole and bends the straight tabs over. Sheet metal screws are run though three or four evenly spaced tabs to securely hold the fitting in place. The intersection of the collar and ductwork is sealed with mastic. This is particularly important with dovetail fittings.

Flange fittings have a flange that fits on the outside of the duct. Some flange take offs have a self-adhesive pad that attaches the fitting to the duct and seals it, Figure 58-20. If the flange is not self sealing, mastic should be

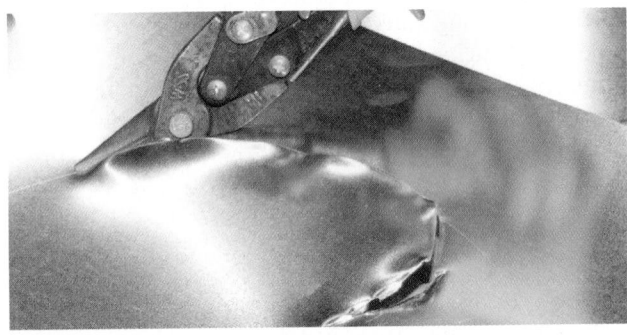

Figure 58-17 Once the diameter has been sliced, the circle can be cut in two semicircular sections

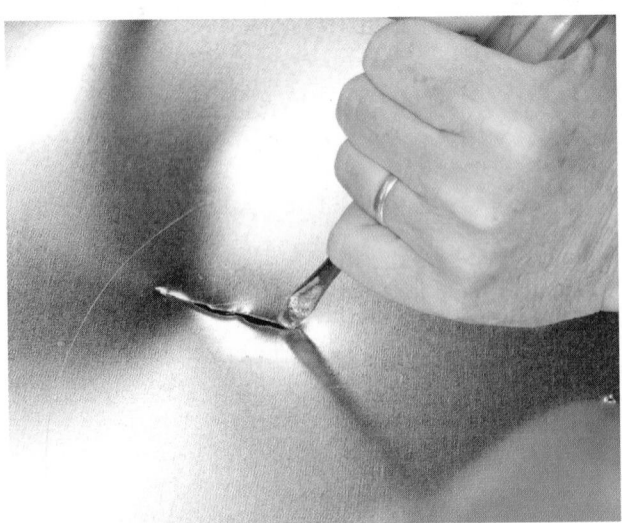

Figure 58-16 Slicing the diameter of a circle using a duct piercing tool

Figure 58-18 Traditional dovetail take off

Figure 58-19 The tabs of the dovetail fitting folded over

applied to the flange before placing the fitting against the outside of the duct. The fitting is held in place by three to four equally spaced sheet metal screws run through the flange.

58.4 DUCT INSULATION

One major disadvantage of metal duct compared to ductboard or flex is that metal duct must be insulated. Round duct is insulated with duct wrap. The most common type of duct wrap is made of fiberglass with an outer vapor barrier of vinyl, aluminum foil, or aluminum foil reinforced with kraftback paper. Duct wrap comes in 4 ft rolls. One side has 2 in of vapor barrier that is uninsulated. This edge laps over the edge of the insulation already on the duct, providing a continuous vapor barrier. When insulating duct, the duct wrap is pulled around the duct and lapped over itself. The insulation should be pulled tightly around the duct to eliminate gaps and sags in the insulation. But compressing insulation reduces its R value, so it should not be pulled so tightly that the fiberglass is flattened. The most common method for fastening the duct wrap is stapling it to itself. A clinch staple is used that goes through both layers of insulation and turns back, Figure 58-21. The insulation should be stapled every 6 in for the entire length. The exposed outer edge is taped with a UL 181A tape which matches the vapor barrier. When the job is done, no metal should be showing, no fiberglass should be showing, and the vapor barrier should cover the entire duct system, Figure 58-22.

The duct wrap should be cut in pieces that are large enough to wrap around the duct and have some overlap. For round duct, this is typically the duct circumference plus an adjustment for the thickness of the wrap plus some overlap. The adjustment is 9.5 in for 1.5 in thick wrap, 12 in for 2 in thick wrap, and 17 in for 3 in thick wrap. Table 58-2 shows the size that duct wrap should be cut for different diameter ducts and different thickness of duct wrap. For example, 2 in thick insulation for a 7 in diameter duct should be 34 in wide.

The same basic concept applies to rectangular duct, but the adjustments are not quite as large. The adjustments are 7 in for 1.5 in thick insulation, 8 in for 2 in thick insulation, and 11.5 in for 3 in thick insulation.

Duct Liner

Rectangular duct, plenums, and return air boxes may be lined with insulation rather than wrapped, Figure 58-23. Duct liner is also fiberglass, but it does not have a vapor barrier. Duct liner is glued to the inside of the duct and connected with mechanical fasteners that compress the insulation. The fasteners should start within 4 in of the end of the duct and continue every 18 in for the length of the duct. A new row of fasteners should be installed every 12 in across the width the duct.

Lining the duct makes a system quieter and is usually easier than wrapping the duct. Disadvantages of lining duct include increased resistance to air flow. One of the advantages of metal duct, low air resistance, is negated by lining it with

Figure 58-20 Flange take off with sticky pad

Figure 58-21 Clinch staples hold insulation together by turning outward in each direction

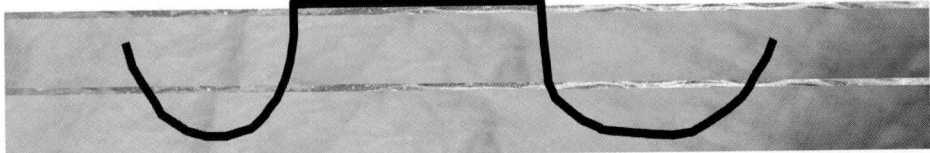

Figure 58-22 Properly insulated ductwork
(Courtesy of Stanfield Air Systems)

Figure 58-23 Galvanized duct insulated with fiberglass liner

Table 58-2 Duct Insulation Dimensions (in Inches)

Duct Dimensions		Insulation Thickness		
Duct diameter	Duct circumference	1.5 in (9.5 in adjustment)	2 in (12 in adjustment)	3 in (17 in adjustment)
5	16	25.5	28	33
6	19	28.5	31	36
7	22	31.5	34	39
8	25	34.5	37	42
9	28	37.5	40	45
10	31.5	41	43.5	48.5
11	35	44.5	47	52
12	38	47.5	50	55
14	44	53.5	56	61
16	50	59.5	62	67

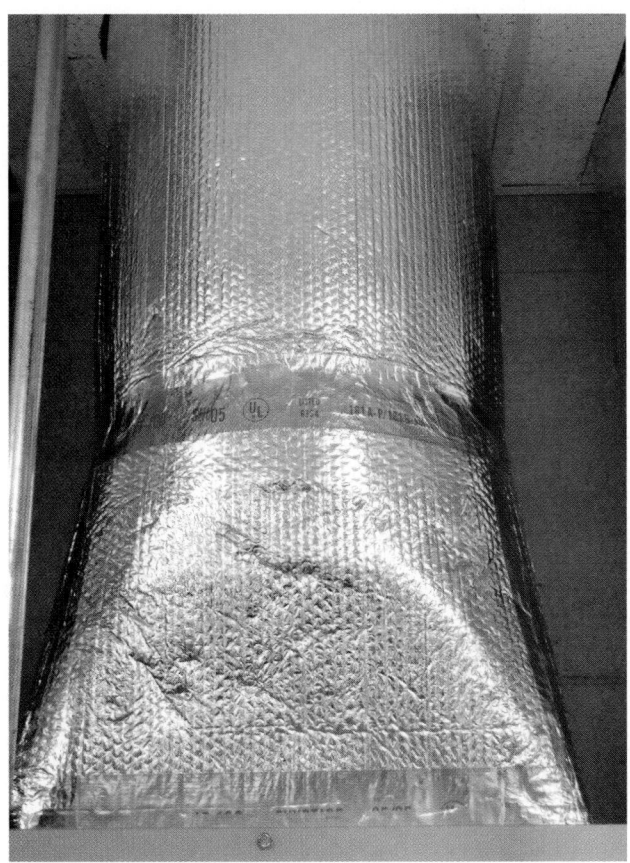

Figure 58-24 Duct insulated with bubble wrap

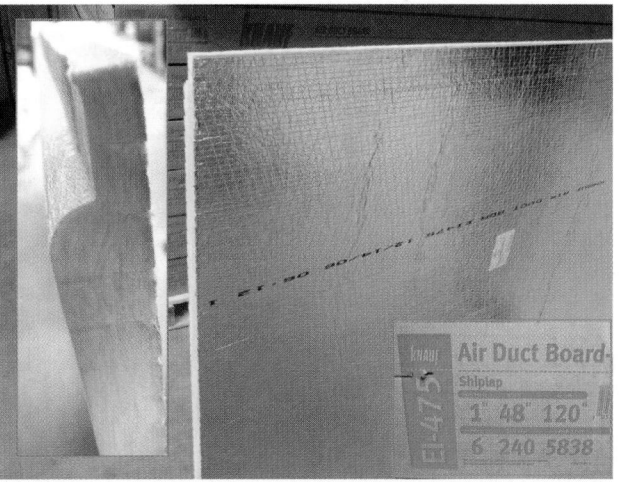

Figure 58-25 Fiberglass ductboard

fiberglass. Liner also tends to collect dust. After a period of years the liner will end up looking like a dirty filter because the fiberglass grabs and holds tiny dust particles. When a liner is used, the duct must be made larger to compensate for the space the liner takes up. When using 1 in liner, the duct must be 2 in larger in both dimensions to allow for the thickness of the duct liner.

Bubble Wrap

Bubble wrap is a new form of duct insulation. It is similar to the bubble packing material with outer layers of either metalized mylar or aluminum, Figure 58-24. Bubble wrap may be used as liner or as duct wrap. Bubble wrap is typically not applied directly to the duct. Spacers are applied to the duct and the bubble wrap is applied to the spacers. Installers like bubble wrap because it does not irritate their skin and cause itching like fiberglass does. However, it is a new product without the long track record of success that fiberglass has.

58.5 DUCTBOARD

One alternative to sheet metal duct is ductboard. Ductboard is a rigid fiberglass insulating board with an outer vapor barrier used to construct plenums and ductwork, Figure 58-25. The inner wall does not have a covering, but the fiberglass is matted and stiff, not fluffy like duct wrap. Quality ductboard

should be UL 181 rated, and the tapes used to fabricate it should be UL 181A rated. Compared to metal duct, ductboard has several advantages. It is relatively low in both material and installation cost, it does not need insulating because it is inherently thermally efficient, it is generally easier to fabricate, and it produces quieter systems.

Despite these advantages, many contractors still consider a ductboard duct system inferior to a metal duct system. It is less durable than metal, but holds up well if fabricated correctly. Unfortunately, the industry has seen a lot of ductboard that was not fabricated correctly and did not last long. Ductboard has a higher resistance to airflow because of its relatively rough interior surface. This surface also causes it to collect dirt. Small dust particles entrained in the air lodge in the surface of the ductboard; after several years of service the interior surface of most ductboard systems is black.

Fabrication

Ductwork is constructed by cutting grooves or slots in the fiberglass where each corner will be. The tools are hand tools with razor sharp knife blades that cut through the fiberglass to form the joints. Types of joints used are the V-groove, shiplap, and modified shiplap, Figure 58-26. Enough fiberglass is cut out to allow the ductboard to fold and form corners. The last edge is cut to form a flap. The ductboard is then folded at these corners. The two edges of the ductboard are mated and the flap is folded over and secured using staples and UL 181A duct tape, or just UL 181A duct tape. Pressure sensitive tape and heat activated tape are both available.

Pressure Sensitive Tape

The edge of the flap should be positioned in the middle of the tape with a minimum overlap of 1 in on each side. Pressure sensitive tape should be worked with a tool edge, not just not fingertip pressure. Rub tape firmly with a plastic sealing tool until the facing reinforcement shows through the tape.

Shiplap

Modified Shiplap

V-Groove

Figure 58-26 Types of ductboard joints
(Reprinted by permission of NAIMA)

Avoid excessive pressure on the sealing tool that could cause the tape to be punctured at staple locations, Figure 58-27.

Pressure sensitive tape should not be used below 50°F without heating. The duct must be preheated using an iron with the plate temperature set at approximately 400°F. Quickly position the tape on the preheated area and press in

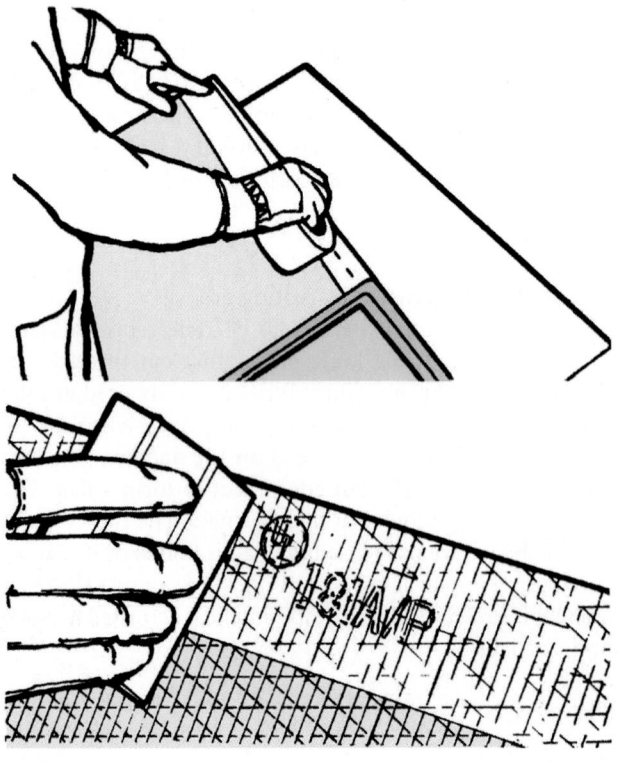

Figure 58-27 Applying pressure sensitive tape to a ductboard seam
(Reprinted by permission of NAIMA)

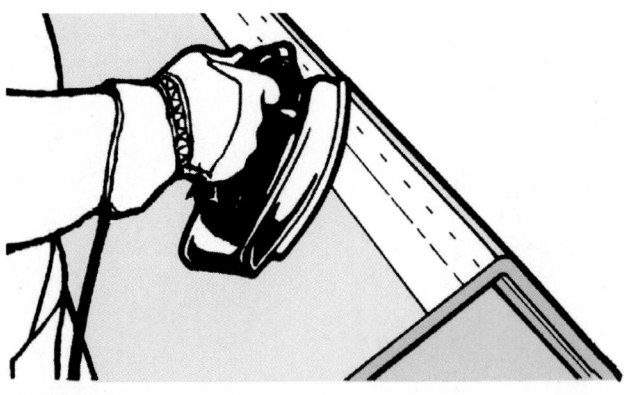

Figure 58-28 Pressure sensitive tape may need to be heated in cold weather for good adhesion
(Reprinted by permission of NAIMA)

place. Pass the iron two or three times over the taped area using a rapid ironing motion, Figure 58-28. Complete the bond by rubbing the tape firmly with the plastic sealing tool until the facing reinforcement shows through the tape clearly.

Heat Activated Tape

The edge of the flap should be positioned in the middle of the tape with a minimum overlap of 1 in on each side. The seaming iron should have a plate temperature of between 550°F and 600°F. Slowly pass the iron along the tape seam with sufficient pressure and dwell time to activate the adhesive, Figure 58-29. Heat indicator dots on the tape will darken to indicate when a satisfactory bond has been achieved, Figure 58-30. Use a second pass of the iron to complete the bond. Avoid puncturing the tape at staple locations with excessive pressure from the iron. Allow all joints and seams to cool below a 150°F (66°C) surface temperature before any stress is applied.

SAFETY TIP

Always work with gloves and exercise caution to prevent burn injuries from contact with the iron or with heated surfaces. Even momentary contact with a 600° surface can cause a painful burn.

Joining Ductboard Sections

Ductbord sections are joined to each other using a shiplap joint. The shiplap joint provides some structural rigidity to the joint. The sections are sealed using either pressure sensitive or heat activated tape, Figure 58-31.

Hanging Ductboard

Properly constructed, ductboard has good structural integrity. It is also lightweight, so hangers are not required to

Figure 58-29 Heat setting tape must be ironed before it will adhere
(Reprinted by permission of NAIMA)

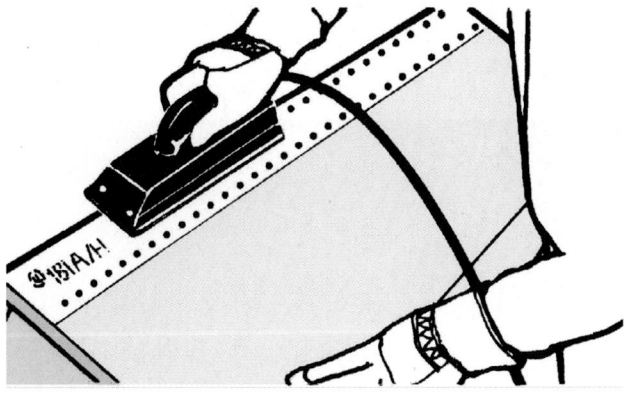

Figure 58-30 Heat indication dots appear when the tape has been heated sufficiently
(Reprinted by permission of NAIMA)

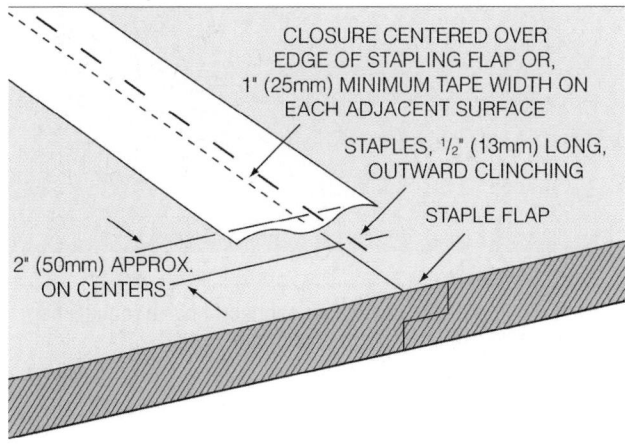

CLOSURE CENTERED OVER EDGE OF STAPLING FLAP OR, 1" (25mm) MINIMUM TAPE WIDTH ON EACH ADJACENT SURFACE

STAPLES, 1/2" (13mm) LONG, OUTWARD CLINCHING

STAPLE FLAP

2" (50mm) APPROX. ON CENTERS

Figure 58-31 Joining ductboard sections
(Reprinted by permission of NAIMA)

support a lot of weight. Duct hangers should be at least 1 in wide across the bottom. A common arrangement is to use an inverted 1 in metal channel that is suspended by wire, straps, or rods, Figure 58-32. Hangers should not be placed directly under joints between two pieces of duct to avoid stressing the

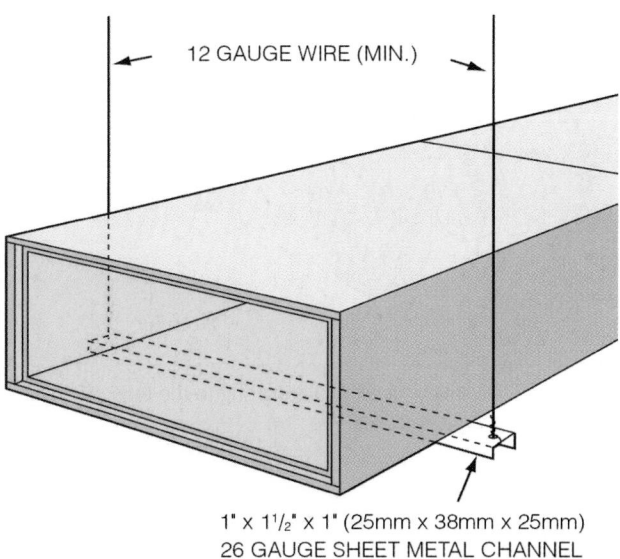

12 GAUGE WIRE (MIN.)

1" x 1 1/2" x 1" (25mm x 38mm x 25mm) 26 GAUGE SHEET METAL CHANNEL

Figure 58-32 Properly supported ductboard duct
(Reprinted by permission of NAIMA)

joints. Hangers should be placed every 6 ft for duct that is less than 12 in high, or every 8 ft for ducts that are 12 in high or larger. Duct should be suspended at least 1 in above ceiling insulation in attics. In crawl space applications it should be at least 4 in above the ground and 1 in below the floor insulation.

Take Offs

The most common use of ductboard is for plenums and trunk lines in systems that use flex duct for branch ducts. Take offs designed specifically for fiberduct should be used. Two types are available: spin-in collars and dovetail collars. The preferable method of cutting the hole is to use a hole cutter that is the same diameter as the collar. If using a spin-in, cut a 1 in slot on the outside of the hole, Figure 58-33. Cut a ring from a piece of ductboard to insulate the collar. Its inside diameter should be the same as the diameter of the sheet metal collar. The width of the ring should correspond to the R value of the flexible duct insulation: 1 in wide for R-4, 1.5 in wide for R-6, and 2 in wide for R-8. Slide the ring

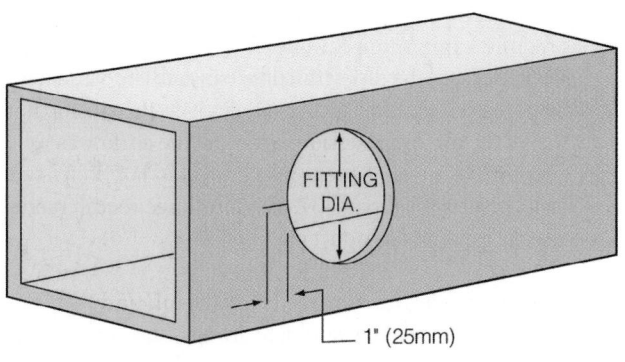

FITTING DIA.

1" (25mm)

Figure 58-33 Hole cut in duct for a spin-in takeoff fitting
(Reprinted by permission of NAIMA)

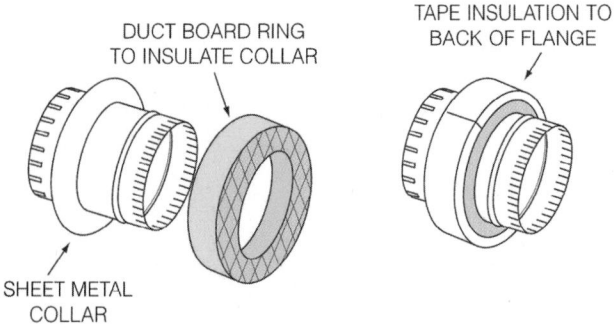

Figure 58-34 Applying an insulating ring to the take off collar *(Reprinted by permission of NAIMA)*

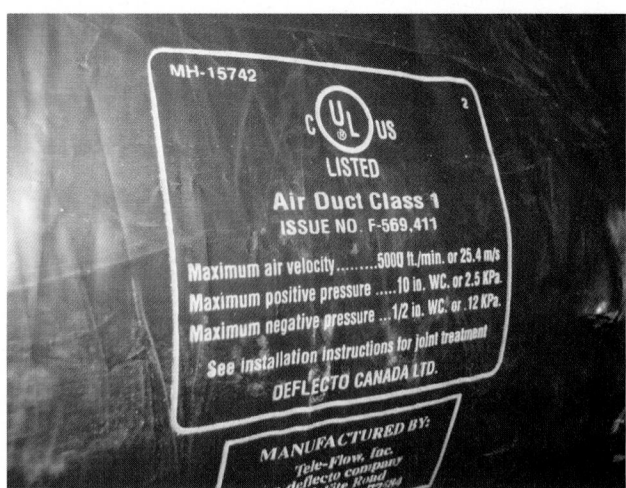

Figure 58-35 UL 181 flexible duct has a square or rectangle label and has no length restrictions

over the collar and tape it to the collar, Figure 58-34. Apply mastic to the back of the collar flange and insert the collar into the hole until the flange seats against the face of the duct-board. For spin-ins this is done by turning the collar clockwise and "threading" it into the hole. Dovetail collars will also go in more easily if they are turned while inserting them. Reach through the collar and bend the tabs on the dovetail over. The flex duct is connected to the take off as described in Section 58.6.

58.6 FLEX DUCT

Both the UL 181 standard and the NFPA 90 standard differentiate between flexible air duct and flexible air connectors. A flexible air duct must pass all 15 of the UL 181 tests while air connectors are not required to pass the flame penetration, puncture, or impact tests in standard UL 181. Ducts meeting the more stringent air duct classification can be used in any length while air connectors are limited to 14 ft. Air connectors are limited to temperature less than 250°F, are not allowed to pass through floors, and are not allowed to pass through walls that are required to have a fire rating.

The markings on the duct indicate whether it is rated as a flexible duct or a flexible connector. Flexible ducts have a square or rectangular shaped label, Figure 58-35 while flexible connectors have a circular label, Figure 58-36. These markings should appear every 10 ft on the duct. Flexible duct is available in insulation R values of 4.2, 6.0, and 8.0. Many codes require a minimum R value of 6.

Flexible duct is the easiest ducting to install. Unfortunately, it is also the easiest to install incorrectly. Poor craftsmanship not only makes the job unprofessional, it hurts the airflow as well. Flex duct that is kinked, flattened, or draped in lazy loops will not work correctly, Figure 58-37. The four basic requirements for correctly installing flex duct are:

- Connecting flex duct correctly to take offs and fittings.
- Stretching the duct to eliminate droops, sags, and crimps.
- Trimming the duct to the correct length.
- Supporting the duct every 5 ft with 2 in wide material.

Figure 58-36 UL 181 flexible air connector has a round label and cannot be used for lengths over 14 ft

Connecting Flex Duct

The basic method of connecting flex duct is to slide the inner core at least 2 in over a metal beaded connector, roll back the outer insulation, fasten the inner core, and then roll the insulation back in place and fasten it. Two approved methods are used for fastening the core and insulation: UL 181B duct tape or UL 181B mastic and straps.

When using duct tape, the inner core should be taped using at least two wraps of tape. Remember to leave enough

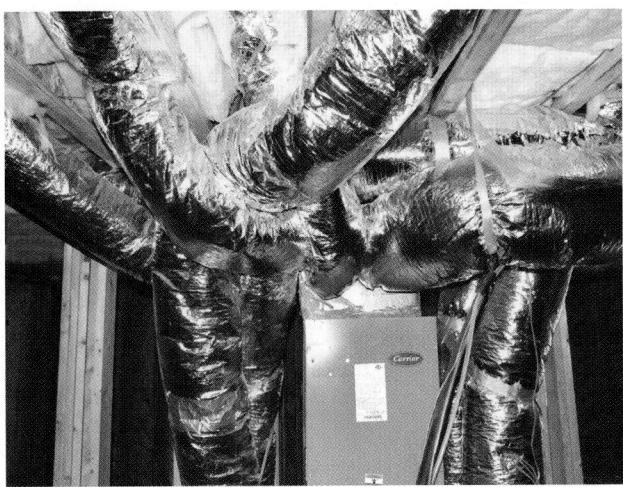

Figure 58-37 Incorrectly installed flexible duct system

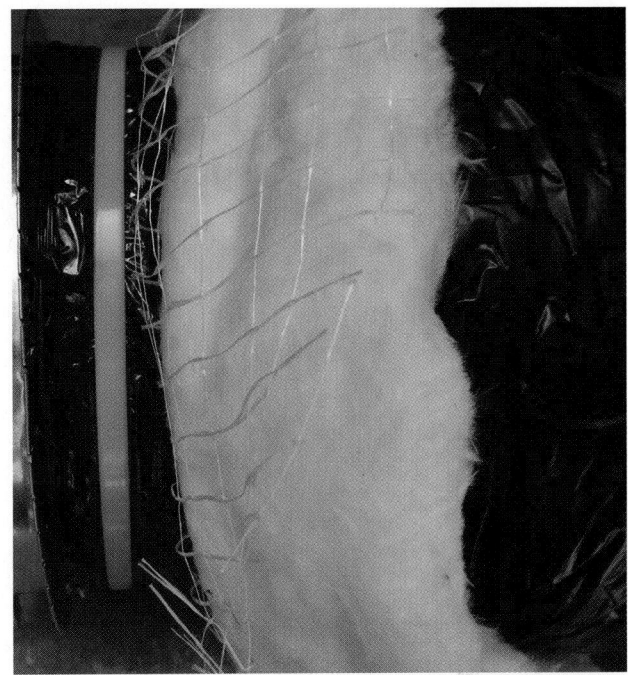

Figure 58-38 The inner core is slid over the bead of the fitting and strapped

metal exposed for the tape to grab. Slide the insulation back in place and tape the insulation in place with at least two wraps of tape.

When using mastic and clamps, UL 181B mastic must be applied to the metal connector before sliding the inner core on. Slide the inner core on past the bead and secure with a strap, Figure 58-38. Roll the insulation in place and secure it with a second strap, Figure 58-39. When the duct is installed vertically, three screws should be run into the metal behind the strap to avoid slipping.

Stretching Flex Duct

Flex duct by its very nature does not want to stay straight. It is necessary to pull it straight to eliminate sags. The maximum allowable sag between supports is 0.5 in/ft.

Trimming Flex Duct

Flex duct should be trimmed to the length needed and no more. Sloppy installers sometimes leave an extra foot or two on the run, knowing they cannot reuse that foot of duct. But leaving extra duct leads to sags, bends, and crimps that severely reduce airflow. Figure 58-40 shows the effect of leaving extra duct length. Figure 58-41 shows a duct that has been trimmed to the correct length.

Supporting Flex Duct

Flex duct is not heavy, but it needs more support than metal duct because it has no structural strength of its own. Flex duct should be supported every 5 ft with straps or hooks that are at least 2 in wide. Galvanized wire and plumbing strap are definitely not appropriate for supporting flex duct. Figure 58-42 shows what happens when flex is supported by

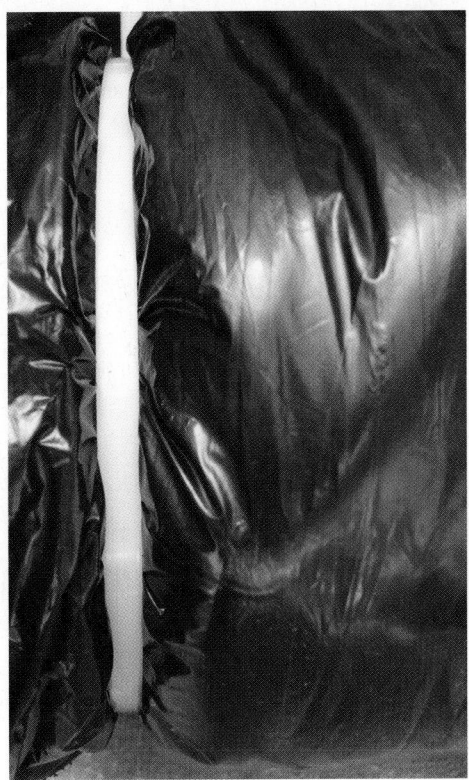

Figure 58-39 The insulation and outer jacket are pulled over the inner core and strapped

wire. Figure 58-43 shows a common abuse of flexible duct: squeezing and twisting it to fit through places that are simply not large enough for the duct. Figure 58-41 shows a properly supported flex run.

Figure 58-40 This run will have a high resistance to airflow

Figure 58-41 This flexible duct is properly applied; it is tight, straight, and well supported by wide supports

Figure 58-43 Not much air will make it through this duct

Figure 58-42 This flex duct is being pinched by the wire that is supporting it

58.7 DUCT SEALING

Sealing duct leaks is the fastest way to improve the efficiency of a ducted heating and cooling system. Older homes that have poorly sealed duct systems typically lose 25% or more of their system capacity due to duct leaks. Sealing the duct system during installation is relatively simple and does not take a lot of extra time or money. The money spent sealing the system will be recovered during the first year of operation. Figure 58-44 illustrates the effect of sealing and insulating ductwork.

The biggest leak source in many older systems is the use of building cavities for return air. It is virtually impossible to

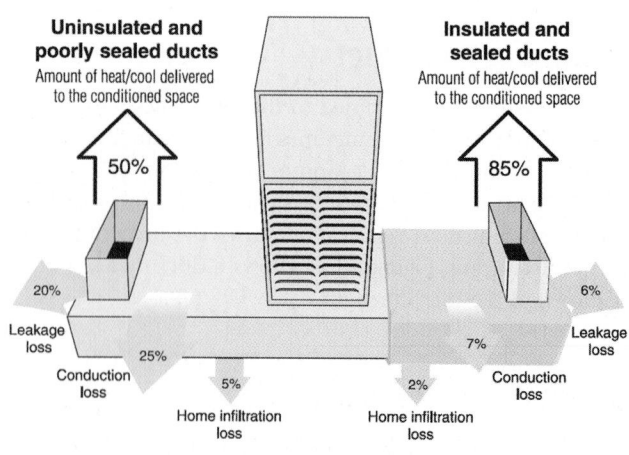

Uninsulated and poorly sealed ducts
Amount of heat/cool delivered to the conditioned space
50%
20%
Leakage loss
25%
Conduction loss
5%
Home infiltration loss

Insulated and sealed ducts
Amount of heat/cool delivered to the conditioned space
85%
6%
Leakage loss
7%
Conduction loss
2%
Home infiltration loss

Figure 58-44 Improper duct sealing and poor duct insulation lose a significant portion of a system's capacity and increase utility bills
(Office of Energy Efficiency and Renewable Energy, U.S. Department of Energy.)

seal these properly, resulting in large amounts of attic or crawl space air being drawn into the system. The best way to correct this is to avoid using building cavities for duct.

Besides building cavities, the largest source of leaks is around plenums and take offs. The holes are frequently not cut precisely and many times the only attempted seal is duct tape. Close to half the duct leakage in many systems is at the supply and return plenums.

The use of garden variety duct tape with no mastic is the next most often encountered problem. This type of tape is handy for many things, but sealing ductwork is not one of them. Any connecting and sealing products, including duct tape, should be UL 181 rated. Duct tape that has not passed the UL 181 tests will dry up and harden with age, losing its tackiness and sealing ability. Even the best duct tape is not a particularly effective solution for sealing around plenums and take offs; a UL 181 rated mastic is required. Mastic will work fine by itself on small cracks, but tape and mastic will be needed for larger cracks.

When sealing ducts, it is sometimes necessary to test to verify the results. The most common method is to use a duct blaster, Figure 58-45. All duct outlets are sealed and a duct blaster is used to pressurize the entire duct system to between 0.5 in wc and 1.0 in wc. After pressurizing the duct, the amount of airflow is measured. If the system was completely tight, the airflow would be 0. However, no system is that tight. The amount of air flowing is the amount leaking out of the ductwork. This measurement is used for comparison after tightening. After tightening the duct another measurement is taken. A comparison of the two measurements provides a quantitative measure of the effectiveness of the duct tightening.

Figure 58-45 A duct blaster is used to pressurize ducts to find leaks and verify duct system integrity
(Courtesy of The Energy Conservatory, Minneapolis, MN)

58.8 GRILL AND REGISTER SELECTION

Supply air registers or diffusers are responsible for distributing the air into the room. Without the correct diffuser, the room can still be uncomfortable even if the system and ductwork are sized correctly. The overall goal is to ensure even temperature throughout the room without creating noise and drafts. In general, the supply air should not blow directly on the people in the room. The primary factors to be considered when selecting supply air registers are the:

- Required CFM.
- Throw.
- Face velocity.
- Static pressure drop.

Throw

The throw is important because it determines how far into the room the conditioned air travels. The register throw is the distance from the register that the air will travel before it slows down to the terminal velocity listed in the engineering data. Table 58-3 shows the terminal velocity for common residential diffusers.

The desired throw is also determined by register location. Floor registers should have a throw of at least 6 ft to get the air up to head height. This is especially true for cooling applications with floor registers. If the throw is too little, the cold air will stay near the floor. However, the throw should be less than the ceiling height. Using a floor register with a 10 ft throw in a room with an 8 ft high ceiling will create drafts as the air bounces off the ceiling.

For high sidewall registers, the throw should be equal to 75–100% of the distance from the register to the opposite wall. Again, this is primarily a concern in cooling. Too small a throw will cause dumping, where the cold air falls to the floor. This causes drafts where the air is falling. Excessive throws cause bouncing off the wall and produce drafts.

Large throws should be avoided with low sidewall registers because the air does blow into the occupied zone. Low velocities and small throws will work with low sidewall in heating only. Low sidewall registers should not be used for air conditioning because it is impossible for them to get the air up at head height without blowing air into the area where people are.

Table 58-3 Terminal Velocity for Common Residential Diffusers

Register type and location	Terminal velocity (fpm)
Floor register	50
Sidewall register	75
Round ceiling diffuser	50
Square ceiling register	75–150

Round ceiling diffusers should be located near the center of the room. The throw should be approximately equal to the distance from the register to the walls. Throws exceeding this distance can usually be tolerated because the air tends to roll down the walls. Too small a throw will cause dumping and drafts in air conditioning. In heating, short throws will cause the warm air to remain high up around the ceiling.

Face Velocity

The velocity of the air at the face of the register determines the throw and the noise. Higher velocities give larger throws and also more noise. Lower velocities yield less noise and shorter throws. The main limitation of register face velocity is the noise created by the moving air. Table 58-4 shows recommended maximum face velocities for several different applications. Note that the quieter applications have lower recommended face velocities.

Static Pressure Drop

Since supply registers and grills add restriction to the free flow of air out of the ductwork, air pressure is required to force the air through them. This is referred to as the static pressure drop across the register. Ideally, it should be kept as low as is possible, but it must be accounted for when designing a duct system. The registers selected should have a static pressure drop at the design airflow that is equal to or less than the assumed register pressure drop used to design the duct system. Like the noise, the pressure drop increases as the velocity increases. Most residential registers have a static pressure drop between 0.03 to 0.05 in water column when the face velocity is between 500 and 750 fpm.

Noise Criteria

The industry uses a noise criteria (NC) system to designate the level of noise in the area where the registers will be used.

Table 58-4 Recommended Register Face Velocities

Type of location	Recommended face velocity (fpm)
Broadcasting studios	500
Residences	500–750
Apartments	500–750
Churches	500–750
Hotel bedrooms	500–750
Theaters (live)	500–1,000
Private offices, acoustically treated	500–1,000
Motion picture theaters	1,000–1,250
Private offices, not treated	1,000–1,250
General offices	1,250–1,500
Retail stores	1,500
Industrial buildings	1,500–2,000

Each NC curve is assigned a number, in 5 dB increments. The number corresponds to the decibel reading at approximately 1,500 Hz. NC 25 is characteristic of areas with very little background noise, and NC 50 for is characteristic of areas with so much background noise that people must be within a few feet of each other to talk. Most register manufacturers now include NC recommendations in their commercial register selection guides, Figure 58-46.

Engineering Data

The tables with the information on register performance are in the engineering data section of the manufacturer's literature.

Figure 58-46 Register selection table with integrated noise criteria information
(Data provided by Hart & Cooley, Inc. By permission.)

Square & Rectangular Ceiling Diffusers
SR/AR 4-Way

Face Velocity		500	600	700	800	900	1000	1200	1400	1600	1800	2000
Pressure Loss		.02	.02	.03	.04	.05	.06	.09	.12	.16	.20	.25
6 x 6	cfm	50	60	70	80	90	100	120	140	160	180	200
Ak .10	Throw X/Y	2-3/2-3	2-3/2-3	2-4/2-4	2-4/2-4	3-5/3-5	3-5/3-5	4-6/4-6	4-8/4-8	5-8/5-8	5-9/5-9	6-11/6-11
9 x 9	cfm	110	135	155	180	205	225	270	315	360	410	450
Ak .22	Throw X/Y	2-4/2-4	2-4/2-4	3-5/3-5	3-5/3-5	4-6/4-6	5-8/5-8	5-9/5-9	6-11/6-11	6-12/6-12	7-13/7-13	8-14/8-14
12 x 12	cfm	200	240	280	320	360	400	480	560	640	725	800
Ak .40	Throw X/Y	3-5/3-5	4-6/4-6	4-8/4-8	5-8/5-8	5-9/5-9	6-11/6-11	6-12/6-12	7-13/7-13	8-15/8-15	9-17/9-17	10-19/10-19
15 x 15	cfm	310	375	440	500	565	625	750	875	1000	1125	1250
Ak .62	Throw X/Y	4-6/4-6	4-8/4-8	5-9/5-9	6-11/6-11	6-11/6-11	6-12/6-12	8-15/8-15	10-18/10-18	10-19/10-19	12-21/12-21	13-23/13-23
18 x 18	cfm	450	540	630	720	810	900	1080	1260	1440	1620	1800
Ak .90	Throw X/Y	4-8/4-8	5-9/5-9	5-11/5-11	6-12/6-12	7-13/7-13	8-15/8-15	10-17/10-17	11-20/11-20	13-23/13-23	15-27/15-27	16-30/16-30
21 x 21	cfm	615	740	860	985	1110	1230	1475	1725	1970	2220	2460
Ak 1.23	Throw X/Y	5-9/5-9	6-11/6-11	7-13/7-13	8-14/8-14	9-15/9-15	9-17/9-17	11-21/11-21	13-25/13-25	15-29/15-29	17-31/17-31	19-35/19-35
24 x 24	cfm	800	960	1120	1275	1440	1600	1925	2240	2570	2890	3200
Ak 1.6	Throw X/Y	5-11/5-11	7-13/7-13	7-14/7-14	8-15/8-15	9-17/9-17	10-19/10-19	12-23/12-23	14-29/14-29	16-31/16-31	18-35/18-35	20-39/20-39
27 x 27	cfm	1010	1215	1420	1615	1820	2020	2430	2840	3240	3650	4040
Ak 2.02	Throw X/Y	6-12/6-12	7-13/7-13	8-15/8-15	10-18/10-18	10-19/10-19	12-22/12-22	14-27/14-27	16-32/16-32	18-35/18-35	20-38/20-38	23-42/23-42
33 x 33	cfm	1370	1650	1925	2200	2470	2750	3300	3850	4400	4950	5500
Ak 2.75	Throw X/Y	7-13/7-13	9-16/9-16	10-18/10-18	12-21/12-21	14-24/14-24	16-27/16-27	18-33/18-33	19-37/19-37	23-41/23-41	27-46/27-46	31-50/31-50

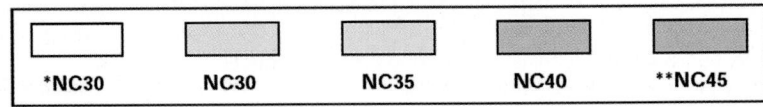

*NC30	NC30	NC35	NC40	**NC45

* less than or equal to   ** greater than or equal to

420/421 Floor Diffuser

Face Velocity		300	400	500	600	700	800	900	1000
Pressure Loss		.006	.010	.016	.022	.031	.040	.050	.062
2x10	cfm		35	45	50	60	70	75	85
Ak .085	Spread		3	5	5	6	7	8	9
	Throw		4	4.5	6	7	8	9	10
2x12	cfm	30	40	50	60	70	80	90	100
Ak .100	Spread	3	4	4.5	5.5	6.5	7	8	9
	Throw	3.5	4.5	5.5	7	8	9	10	11
2x14	cfm	35	45	60	70	80	90	105	115
Ak .115	Spread	3.5	4	5	7	7	8	9	10
	Throw	3.5	4.5	6	8	8	9.5	10.5	12
4x8	cfm	40	50	65	80	90	105	115	130
Ak .13	Spread	3	4	5	6.5	7.5	8.5	9.5	11
	Throw	4	4.5	6	7.5	8.5	10	11	13
4X10	cfm	50	70	85	100	120	135	155	170
Ak .170	Spread	4.5	5	6.5	7.5	9	10	11.5	13
	Throw	4	6	8	10	11	12.5	14	15.5
4x12	cfm	60	80	100	120	140	160	175	195
Ak .195	Spread	5	6.5	8	9.5	11.5	13	14.5	16
	Throw	4	5.5	7	8	9.5	11	12	13
4x14	cfm	70	90	115	140	160	185	205	230
Ak .230	Spread	5.5	7	8.5	10	12	13.5	15.5	17
	Throw	4.5	5.5	7	8.5	10	11.5	12.5	14
6x10	cfm	70	95	120	145	170	190	215	240
Ak .24	Spread	5.5	7	8	10	12	14	15	17
	Throw	4	5.5	7	8.5	10	11	12.5	14
6x12	cfm	85	115	140	170	200	230	255	285
Ak .285	Spread	6	7.5	9	11	13	15	17	19
	Throw	4.5	6	7.5	9	10	12	14	16
6x14	cfm	100	130	165	200	230	265	300	330
Ak .33	Spread	6.5	8	9	12	14	16.5	18	20
	Throw	4.5	6.5	8	9.5	11	13	15	17

Terminal velocity of 50 fpm.

Figure 58-47 Floor register selection data
(Data provided by Hart & Cooley, Inc. By permission.)

Figure 58-47 shows the engineering data for a series of residential floor registers. The register face velocities are listed across the top with the static pressure loss across the registers listed immediately underneath the velocities. The register sizes are on the left-hand side with the effective face area of the register listed under each size. In each box in the table are listed the CFM and throw for that size and face velocity. The easiest way to locate an acceptable register is to start with one criteria and look for the rest. This can be demonstrated by an example. Suppose a register is needed for an air volume of 100 CFM, a throw of 6 to 8 ft, a pressure drop of no more than 0.03 in wc, and a face velocity below 700 fpm. There are many register sizes that can handle 100 CFM, but only a few that will meet all our requirements. For example, the 2 × 12 will handle 100 CFM, but at a velocity of 1,000 fpm and a pressure drop of 0.062 in wc. At the other end of the table, a 6 × 14 will handle 100 CFM, but with a throw of only 4.5 ft. Under the 700 fpm velocity column, note that a 4 × 10 will handle 120 CFM at the maximum acceptable velocity. Move to the left to find 100 CFM listed under the 600 fpm velocity column. This selection matches our volume, velocity, and pressure drop requirements, but its throw is just a little more than we would like. A 4 × 10 would most likely work all right, but the 4 × 12 listed under it would match all our requirements. The 4 × 12 is the best choice, but the 4 × 10 is acceptable.

Return Air Grills

Return air grills primarily serve to hide what would otherwise be a large unsightly hole. They do not direct the air like supply registers do. A generally accepted rule for estimating the required return air grill size is that it should have 1 in² of gross area for every 2 CFM of air it handles. However, manufacturers' selection charts are the most accurate way to size return grills. The selection criteria for return air grills are:

- Air volume.
- Pressure drop.
- Face velocity.

Ideally, the pressure drop should be kept as low as is possible, but it must be accounted for when designing a duct system. The grille's static pressure drop at the design airflow should be equal to or less than the assumed pressure drop used to design the duct system. Just as in sizing supply registers, the pressure drop and noise both increase as the velocity increases. The face velocity should be kept under 600 fpm; faster velocities lead to noticeably increased air noise. Figure 58-48 shows a typical return air grill selection chart. The face velocities are listed across the top. The grill sizes are on the left-hand side with the effective face area of the grill listed under each size. In each box in the table are listed the CFM and static pressure drop for that size and face velocity. Suppose a return grill was needed to handle 400 CFM with a face velocity of less than 600 fpm and a static pressure drop of 0.05 in wc or less. Under the 600 fpm column a 16 × 10 will handle 400 CFM, but at a higher pressure drop than our design pressure drop. One row down, the 16 × 12 will handle 437 CFM with a pressure drop of 0.057 in wc by the time the volume is reduced to 400 CFM, the pressure drop will be very close to our design pressure drop and the face velocity will be a little under 500 fpm. Other sizes also meet our criteria; a 30 × 6 has a pressure drop of 0.053 in wc with a volume of 410 CFM.

Face velocity*		300	400	500	600	700
16 x 6	CFM	132	177	221	265	309
Ak 0.44	Ps.	0.019	0.034	0.054	0.078	0.106
16 x 8	CFM	176	234	293	352	410
Ak 0.59	Ps.	0.019	0.034	0.053	0.077	0.105
16 x 10	CFM	219	292	365	438	511
Ak 0.73	Ps.	0.019	0.034	0.053	0.076	0.104
16 x 12	CFM	262	349	437	524	612
Ak 0.87	Ps.	0.019	0.034	0.053	0.076	0.103
16 x 14	CFM	305	407	509	610	712
Ak 1.02	Ps.	0.019	0.034	0.052	0.075	0.102
16 x 16	CFM	348	464	580	696	812
Ak 1.16	Ps.	0.019	0.033	0.052	0.074	0.101
16 x 24	CFM	519	692	865	1038	1211
Ak 1.73	Ps.	0.018	0.033	0.051	0.071	0.097
16 x 25	CFM	540	720	900	1081	1261
Ak 1.80	Ps.	0.018	0.033	0.051	0.071	0.097

Figure 58-48 Return air grill selection chart
(Data provided by Hart & Cooley, Inc. By permission.)

Filter Grills

Filter grills should be sized larger than standard return air grills because the filter reduces the effective area of the grill and because a lower velocity across the filter is needed for it to be effective. Maximum face velocities of 300–400 fpm are recommended.

58.9 DUCT CLEANING

Duct cleaning standards and duct cleaning technician certifications are established by the National Air Duct Cleaners Association. A key point in discussing duct cleaning is that typically the entire system needs cleaning, not just the ducts. Blowers, coils, and filters should all be checked and cleaned whenever ductwork is cleaned. System components, including ducts, accumulate a fine layer of dust over time. In most systems there is more dust accumulation in the return than the supply. Mold can also sometimes grow in ductwork, but the presence of mold indicates a more serious problem than simply dirty ducts. The mold can be cleaned, but if the root cause is not addressed, the mold will return. Mold requires moisture to live; if mold is growing in the system, moisture is getting in. Finding and eliminating the source of moisture is necessary for long term mold remediation.

A visual inspection is necessary to determine the need for cleaning. A visual inspection after cleaning is necessary to assess the results. Duct systems should have inspection ports at major turns and after any obstruction such as coils or filters. Frequently these will have to be added the first time a system is cleaned. Tools are available that enable inspection of the duct system via remote video cameras, Figure 58-49. This enables the technician to see what must be cleaned, even if the area is around a corner. Video inspection systems also allow the customer to see the results of the job.

Most duct cleaning equipment is some form of specialized vacuum cleaner. Some systems are large units mounted on the back of a truck with large hoses connected to the ducts in the house, Figure 58-50. These systems move a large volume

Figure 58-50 Large truck-mounted duct cleaning equipment *(Courtesy of Heat Seal)*

of air and rely on air volume and velocity to remove debris from the duct. Other systems are much smaller and use a series of brushes along with inspection tools, Figure 58-51. Some systems use a percussive tool that flails around inside the duct to knock dirt loose. These systems will only work with metal ducts.

Metal ducts are the easiest to clean because they are not likely to be damaged by the cleaning equipment. Fiberduct and fiberglass lined duct can be cleaned with soft bristle brushes, but heavy agitation or stiff brushes can damage the fiberglass and do more harm than good. Flex duct can sometimes be cleaned with gentle brushes, but it may be more practical to replace it than clean it. Fabric duct systems, Figure 58-52, can literally be taken down and washed.

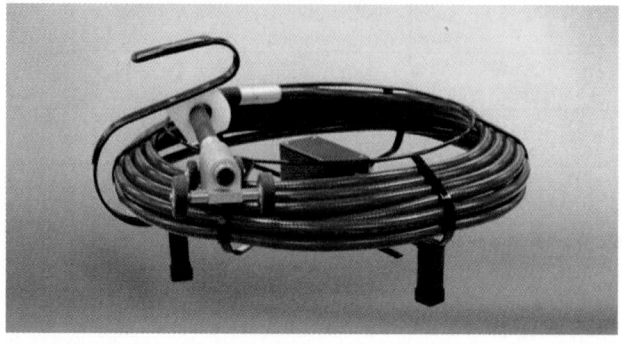

Figure 58-49 Video inspection tool for examining the inside of ductwork before and after cleaning *(Courtesy of Abatement Technologies, Inc.)*

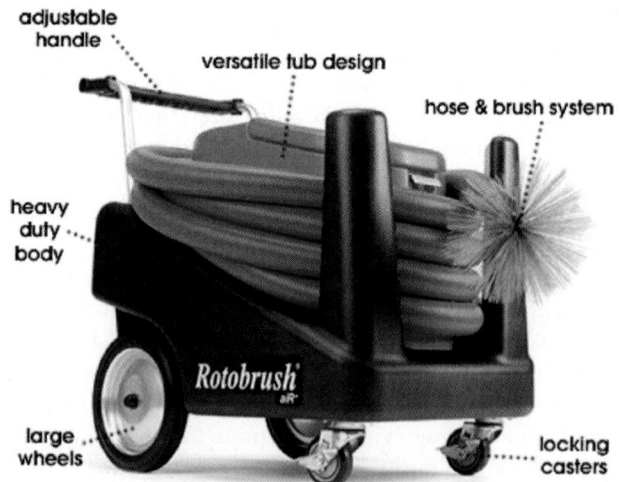

Figure 58-51 Small portable duct cleaning equipment
(Copyright © 2008 Rotobrush International LLC. All rights reserved and unauthorized use, reproduction or disclosure is prohibited. Rotobrush, Rotobrush air™, and Roto-Vision are registered trademarks of Rotobrush International LLC. I2 CAM is a trademark of Rotobrush International LLC.)

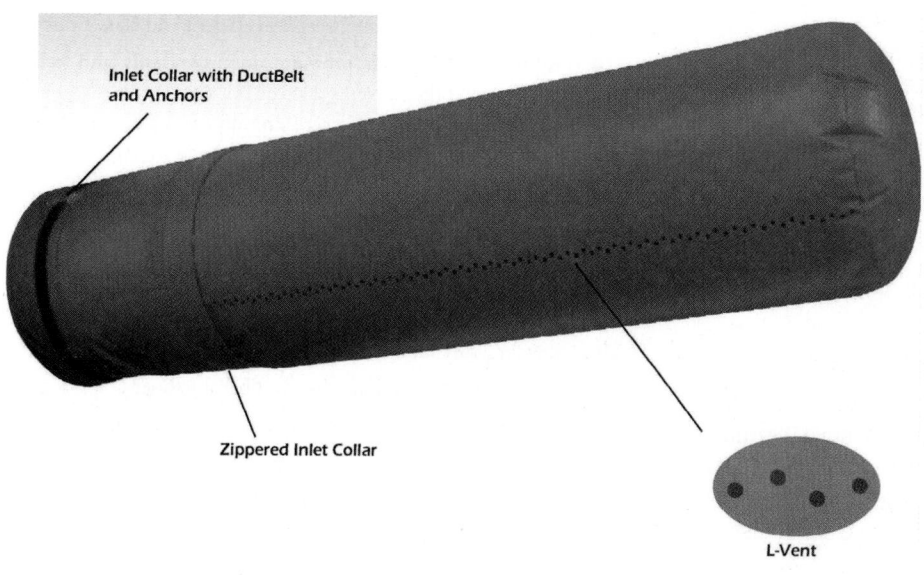

Figure 58-52 Fabric duct
(Courtesy of DuctSox Corp.)

Inlet Collar with DuctBelt
and Anchors

Zippered Inlet Collar

L-Vent

UNIT 58—SUMMARY

A properly designed and installed duct system

- Allows for proper airflow through the system.
- Delivers conditioned air throughout the structure according to the heat load.
- Does not leak.
- Is well insulated and thermally efficient.
- Is quiet.

This can be achieved using sheet metal, ductboard, flex duct, or any combination of these materials. The difference between a poor duct system and a good one is often just a matter of a few minutes and a little extra material. Sealing metal ducts, trimming flex ducts, or fabricating fiberboard ducts are not complicated tasks; they just take a little extra time and material.

── WORK ORDERS

Service Ticket 5801

Job: Duct Tightening

Equipment: 20 Year Old Split System Air Conditioner with All Metal Duct

A customer contracted for a duct tightening job because the local electric utility has a rebate for duct tightening. The contractor is required to reduce the duct leakage by at least 50%. The technician starts by measuring the duct leakage with a duct blaster. Next the old outer insulation around the plenum is removed. Many leaks are evident around both the supply and return plenums. The technician uses UL 181A tape and mastic to seal these leaks and

retests the system and finds that simply sealing the leaks around the plenums reduced the duct leakage by 30%. The technician goes on to check the rest of the system and wraps the plenum with new higher R value insulation.

Service Ticket 5802

Complaint: Poor Airflow in Office

Equipment: Commercial System Using a Metal Trunk and Flex Duct Drops

The vice president of customer assurance at APEX Industries moves into a newly renovated office and finds it stuffy. There is very little air coming out of the ceiling register. The technician who is called to fix the problem looks above the ceiling and notices that the flex run is too long and is almost doubled over. The flex is trimmed to an appropriate length and stretched so that the air has a straight shot. The register now has adequate airflow.

Service Ticket 5803

Complaint: Musty Odor When Unit Runs

Equipment: Split System in Crawl Space with Ductboard Trunk Line and Flex Runouts

A technician is called to look at a system that is blowing musty air into the house and notices that the fiberduct plenums are only attached to the 0.5 in flanges on the unit with duct tape. They are both leaky, but the return plenum has sagged and there is a gap on one side between the plenum and the unit. The technician also notices that there is no vapor barrier on the ground. The plenums are removed, 2 in wide sheet metal flanges are connected to the unit's 0.5 in flanges with sheet metal screws, and the plenums are reattached using three long sheet metal screws with large washers on each side of the plenums to attach them to the new metal flanges. The plenums are then sealed to the unit with UL 181A duct tape. The technician recommends that the customer install a vapor barrier over the exposed dirt in the crawl space.

Service Ticket 5804
Job: Duct Cleaning
Equipment: Metal Trunk Line and Runouts

A customer notices that the ductwork by his filter grill is very dirty on the inside and calls to have his ducts cleaned. The technician uses the video inspection tool to see the extent of the dirt, makes a tape of the inspection, and shows the customer. The ducts are cleaned using a portable duct cleaning machine with soft bristles on the trunk lines. The blower wheel and evaporator coil are also cleaned. The technician makes a new tape showing the ducts after cleaning and suggests that the customer consider installing a high efficiency air cleaner to keep the ducts clean.

Service Ticket 5805
Complaint: No Airflow in Bedroom
Equipment: Radial System with Lined Metal Plenum with Flex Runouts

A new system has no airflow in the master bedroom. The technician looks at the duct run to the bedroom and sees no obvious problems. After removing the flex duct from the plenum, the technician finds that the liner in the plenum was not entirely cut out. After cutting out the liner and reattaching the duct, the bedroom has good airflow.

UNIT 58—REVIEW QUESTIONS

1. What standard covers ductboard and methods of connecting and sealing ductboard?
2. What standard covers flexible duct and methods of connecting and sealing flexible duct?
3. What is the difference between class 0 duct and class 1 duct?
4. List the agencies that promote duct standards and briefly describe what they cover.
5. Explain the difference between a flexible duct and a flexible air connector.
6. List the materials commonly used to construct duct systems.
7. Describe how two pieces of round sheet metal pipe are joined.
8. Describe how sheet metal ductwork is sealed.
9. Describe how to join fiberboard duct.
10. How far apart should hangers for metal duct be placed?
11. How far apart should hangers for fiber ductboard be placed?
12. Describe the proper method of hanging flexible duct.
13. List four methods of insulating metal ductwork.
14. Using Table 58-2, what width should 2 in fiberglass duct insulation be to wrap an 8 in diameter round duct?
15. Describe how ductboard is formed into ducts.
16. List three types of take off fittings available for sheet metal duct.
17. Describe how to install a dovetail take off fitting on a ductboard trunk.
18. What are some of the limitations on the use of flexible air connectors?
19. Describe how rectangular sheet metal ducts are joined.
20. How do the staples that hold duct insulation together work?
21. What is the correct spacing for the mechanical fasteners used to hold duct liner in place?
22. Discuss some of the major problems that cause leaky duct systems in older homes.
23. How does a duct blaster measure the amount of duct leakage?
24. What is the recommended face velocity for a return air filter grill?
25. Explain what manufacturers mean by a register's throw.
26. List the factors to consider when choosing a supply register.
27. What are the noise criteria curves?
28. Using Figure 58-45, select a floor register that will provide an 8–10 ft throw for 150 CFM with a face velocity less than 700 fpm.
29. What are the two main types of duct cleaning equipment being used?
30. Why is a visual inspection necessary when cleaning ductwork?

UNIT 59

Zone Control Systems

OBJECTIVES

After completing this unit you will be able to:

- explain the purpose of zone control systems.
- list the methods used to control excess airflow in a zone system.
- explain the purpose of variable air volume control systems.
- describe the operation of a basic zone control system.
- list the components commonly used in a zone control system.
- explain the difference between a basic zone control system and a communicating zone control system.

59.1 INTRODUCTION

Zone control gives customers increased control over their comfort systems. Customers are no longer satisfied with systems that leave one part of their house hot while another part is cold. Zone systems allow control over different portions of the house without installing multiple units.

Many heating and air conditioning installations are installed in buildings where the floor plan is spread out, such as ranch style and split-level houses. On these jobs it is not practical to control comfort throughout the entire area using one thermostat. These layouts require zoning, because the loads differ from one area to another. For example, a basement area typically needs a significant amount of heat to stay warm in the winter, but needs virtually no cooling in the summer. The amount of air delivered to the basement needs to change between seasons. Zoning solves this problem.

59.2 PRINCIPLES OF ZONING

Zoning is a method of controlling the supply of conditioned air to each unique area to match the load requirements. This is done by separating the air supply to each unique area by the use of a zone damper in the ductwork and controlling each zone damper with an individual thermostat.

The first consideration when selecting a zoning system is to determine what areas of the building are to be zoned. This can range from a two zone system for a two-level house to a system that handles each room as a separate zone. Areas to be zoned are selected by building use, building load, or building orientation.

Building use zoning is based on separating the areas depending on how they are used. For example, bedrooms can be on one zone and living areas on another. This is common for residential zoning.

TECH TIP

Occupancy sensors, devices that detect movement of people in an area, can be used to enhance the efficient operation of zoned systems. Occupancy sensors will allow a zone to be activated only when it is occupied. The popularity of occupancy sensors has resulted in a decrease in their cost so that they now can be used for many more applications. In fact, occupancy sensors have already found their way into residences for light switches.

Building load and orientation zoning considers the areas of a building with unique heat loads. For example, the south side of a building would be on a separate zone from the north side. This type of zoning is common for commercial structures.

The following are some examples of zone controlled systems:

1. A three zone split level system is shown in Figure 59-1. Each level of this residence has a separate trunk duct from the supply air plenum with a zone damper installed. Each of these dampers is controlled from an individual thermostat located in that zone.
2. Zone control for a bi-level house is shown in Figure 59-2. This system has three zones: living area, bedrooms, and recreation room. The system uses a zone control panel, a 40 VA transformer, three zone dampers, and three thermostats.

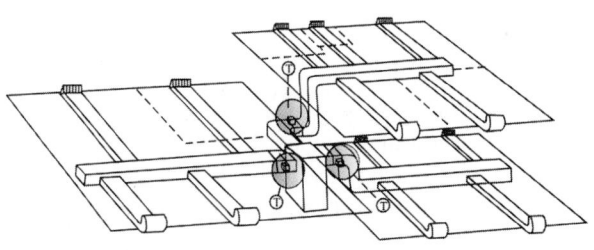

Figure 59-1 Three zone split level system

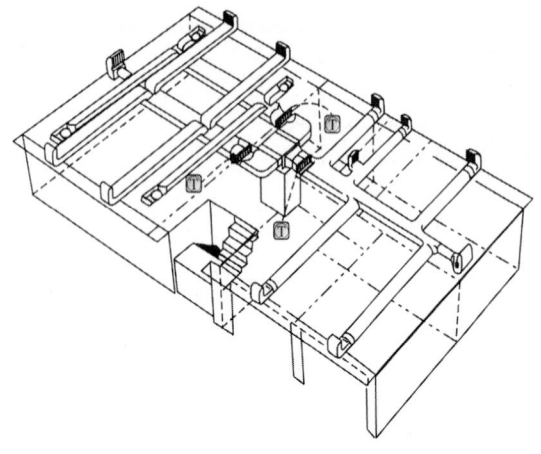

Figure 59-2 Zone control for a bi-level house

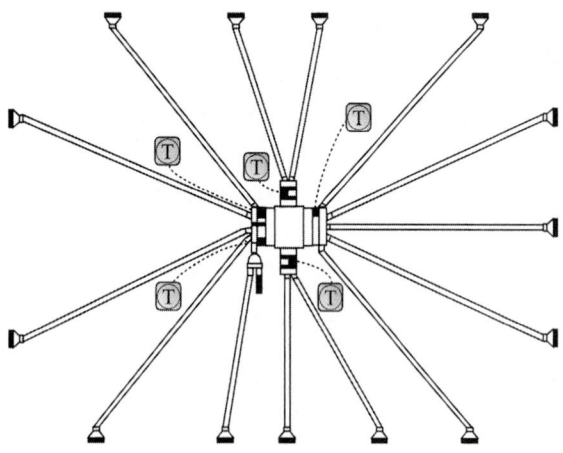

Figure 59-3 Five zone radial system

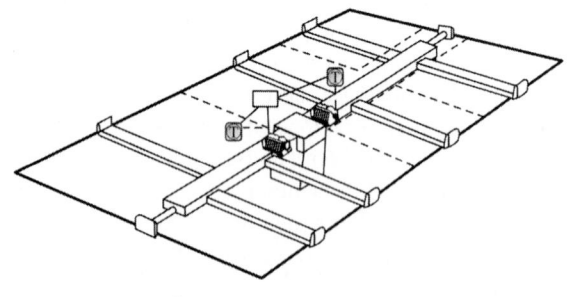

Figure 59-4 Two zone ranch style house

3. A room by room temperature control is shown in Figure 59-3 for a five zone radial system. These ducts can be located overhead or in the slab floor.
4. A two zone ranch house is shown in Figure 59-4. Each zone has a thermostat controlling a zone damper.
5. A four zone office building system is shown in Figure 59-5 using a zone control panel, four dampers and thermostats, and a 40 VA transformer.

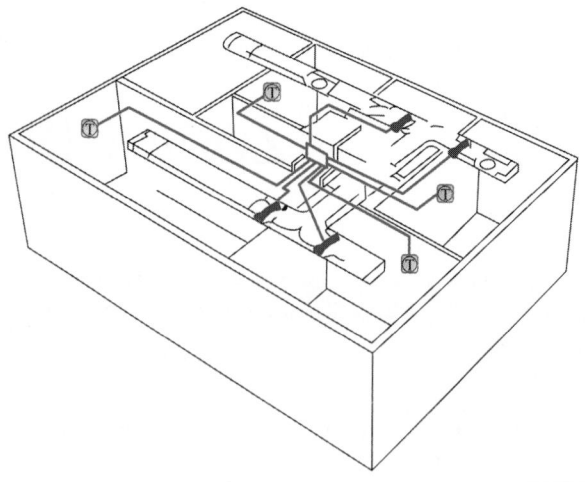

Figure 59-5 Four zone professional office system

6. A room by room comfort control layout is shown in Figure 59-6. In this illustration each outlet has an automatic square to round transition damper.

SERVICE TIP

Some homeowners will close off the vent to rooms that are not in use or commonly used such as spare bedrooms. If enough of the system's capacity is shut down as a result of this attempt to economize, it can actually cause major problems with the system itself. For example, reducing the airflow below the manufacturer's specifications can reduce the heat load on the evaporator. This can cause refrigerant floodback to the compressor, shortening its life. Another example is raising the discharge air temperature of a gas furnace by restricting the airflow through it. This causes the high limit to cycle the furnace off and on, reducing its efficiency. An attempt to economize in this manner may ultimately result in higher utility bills and shorter equipment life for the owner.

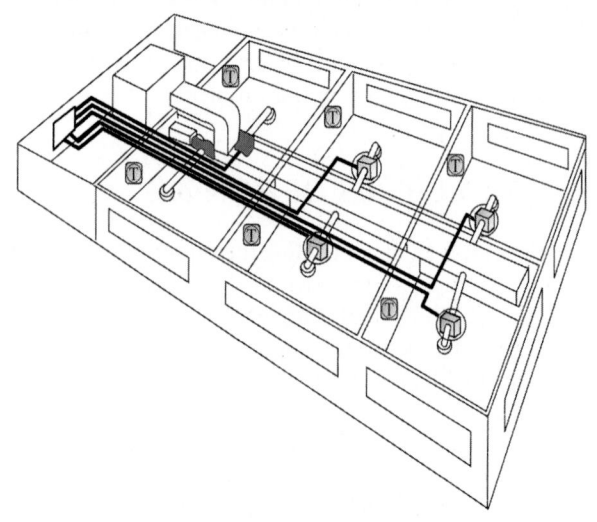

Figure 59-6 Individual room zone control system

59.3 RELIEVING EXCESS AIR PRESSURE

A problem that can occur on a system of thermostatically controlled zone dampers is forcing too much air through portions of the duct system. When some major zone dampers are closed off, the remaining zones must handle an excessive amount of air. This can cause reduced system airflow, air noise, drafts, and poor control in the operating zones. The solution to this condition is to provide some means of relieving this excessive air pressure.

There are a number of ways to accomplish this, including:

- Bypassing supply air to the return.
- Dumping excess air into an area whose temperature is not critical.
- Using dampers that allow some air to pass even when they are closed.
- Oversizing the ductwork so that a single zone can handle the system airflow.
- Variable air volume.

Air Bypass Method

The most commonly used method is to bypass supply air back into the return air duct as shown in Figure 59-7. This is usually accomplished by adding a barometric damper between the supply and return. When the pressure differential exceeds the setpoint of the damper, it opens to relieve the pressure. This ensures that the static pressure across the blower never exceeds the setpoint of the bypass damper. Keeping the system pressures and velocities under control eliminates air noise and objectionable drafts.

The disadvantage of this arrangement is that it does nothing to solve the problem of system load. The system is operating with only a partial load. With prolonged use on heating the high limit control may shut down the system. In cooling, the evaporator can freeze from lack of load. Plenum thermostats are used to address this problem.

A plenum, or discharge air thermostat, is frequently used to shut off the heating system when the discharge air starts to get too hot, Figure 59-8. Similarly, a low limit is used to shut down the compressor when the discharge air starts to get too cold. On systems that use thermistor sensors, a single discharge air sensor is used. The discharge thermostat solves the problem of equipment capacity exceeding the load, but it creates a new problem: short cycling. The discharge air temperature can change rapidly when only a single zone is open, causing the system to shut off before the demand in that zone is met. The system will come back on as soon as the required off time is satisfied. Thus, the system can short cycle trying to

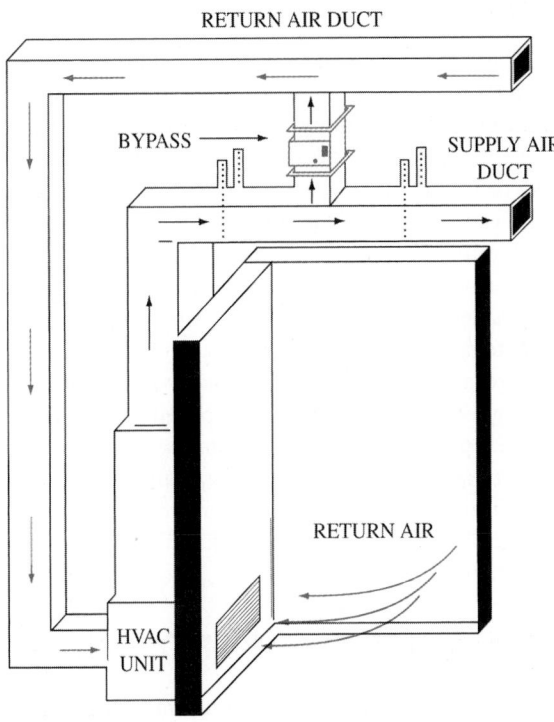

Figure 59-7 Relieving air pressure through bypassing air from the supply plenum back to the return

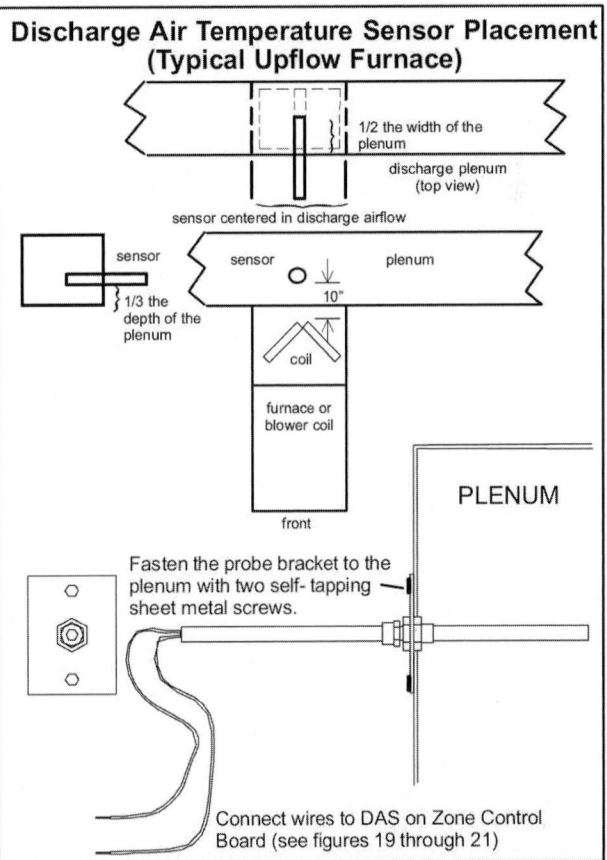

Figure 59-8 A discharge air sensor should be used when air is by passed, from figure 4 on page 5 of harmony3install.pdf
(Courtesy of Lennox Industries)

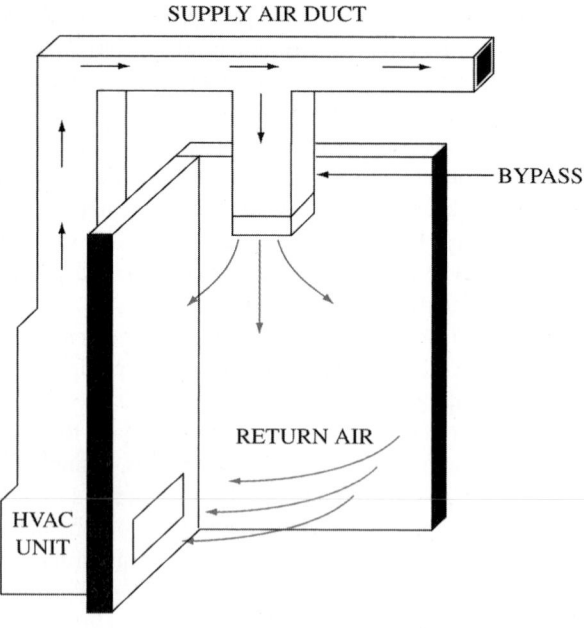

Figure 59-9 Duct arrangement for a "dump" zone

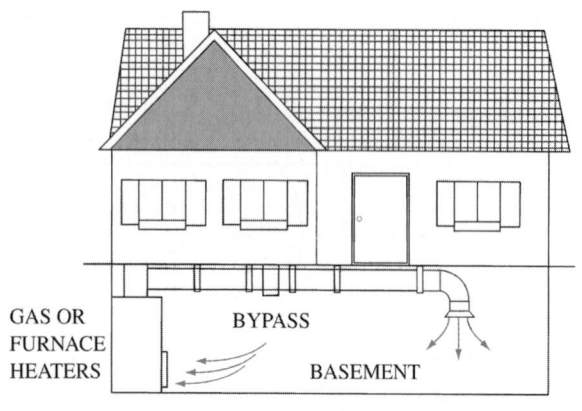

Figure 59-10 Relieving air pressure by dumping it into the basement

meet the demand of a zone whose load is much smaller than the system capacity.

Dump Zone

The pressure difference can be relieved by dumping excess air into a zone whose temperature is not critical, as shown in Figures 59-9 and 59-10. Again, a barometric damper can be used to accomplish this. If the dump zone is large enough, discharge air thermostats are usually not required. This solves both the air velocity problem and the system load problem, but can create a problem with the comfort in the dump zone. Using a dump zone can also have an impact on energy cost because the system is over conditioning an area that might not be conditioned at all if it were not a dump zone.

Damper Leakage Method

The damper leakage method essentially uses the entire building as a dump zone. Some air passes by all the dampers, but more is directed through the open damper. This system is simple; it does not involve any bypass dampers or discharge air thermostats.

This can be accomplished by adjusting standard dampers to still be slightly open in the closed position or using dampers that are slightly smaller than the duct they are in. Using this method, a small amount of air will be supplied all the time; even to the zones that are not calling.

The system performance of a damper leaking system is difficult to predict. If the loads in the zones are not close to the same, the system will not maintain the correct temperature in any zone except the zone with the highest load.

Oversized Duct

Another approach is to size each zone duct to handle 60–70% of the total system air volume. This keeps the equipment operating correctly and puts the air where the load is. It can create problems with the air distribution in the rooms. As the volume of air leaving the registers changes, so does the throw. If the registers are sized for the largest volume of air that will be moving through them, the throw will be too little when all the zones are open. On the other hand, if the registers are sized for a smaller amount of air, the registers will be noisy and drafty when the full system air volume is going to just one zone. This arrangement is really only practical on small jobs with two or three zones.

Variable Air Volume

A variable air volume system changes the amount of air the fan delivers to match the zone requirements, eliminating the need for bypassing or dumping air. When applying variable air volume zone systems, heating and cooling systems with staging or modulating capacity are used so that the system capacity can match the load on the system. In the past, this type of control was only available for commercial systems. With the advent of ECM variable speed motors, variable capacity residential equipment, and communicating controls these systems are now available for residential systems.

One example of a variable air volume residential system is the Carrier Infinity Zone controller used on a variable capacity heat pump. The control system uses only four wires: two for power and two for communications. The blower communicates zone airflow characteristics back to the system controller. Thus, the controller knows what the airflow and resistance of each zone is.

59.4 AUTOMATIC RELIEF DAMPERS

During relief operations, it is important to maintain at least the minimum airflow through the air handling unit; otherwise the coil performance will be unsatisfactory. The following formula can be used to determine the quantity of bypass air:

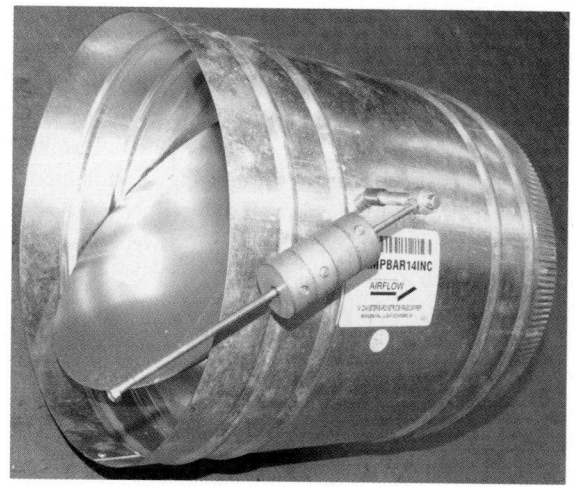

Figure 59-11 Static pressure relief damper

air handler (CFM) − smallest zone peak (CFM)
　　　　　　　　　 − leakage of all closed dampers (CFM)
　　　　　　　　　 = bypass airflow (CFM)

　　Automatic dampers are used when either bypassing or dumping is required to relieve excess air pressure. Two types of dampers are used for this: barometric dampers and motorized dampers.

Barometric Dampers

Barometric static pressure relief dampers, Figure 59-11, require no electrical connections. They are used on low pressure systems with static pressures usually below 0.5 in wc. They are held closed with either an adjustable weight or by spring pressure. When the pressure difference across the damper exceeds the weight or spring pressure, the damper opens. The amount of opening is regulated by the amount of air to be relieved. The advantage of these dampers is that they are self regulating and require no power or control signals. The disadvantage is that they must be adjusted for each installation to work correctly and they tend to leak a little all the time.

Motorized Dampers

Motorized static pressure relief dampers are electrically or electronically operated by a zone control in response to a signal from a remotely located duct pressurestat. These dampers have the advantage of closing tighter when bypass is not needed, and they generally do not require adjustment. They do require a more sophisticated control system and a static pressure sensor.

59.5 TYPES OF ZONE DAMPERS

Damper Styles

There are many shapes, sizes, and styles of zone dampers designed to fit various requirements. Each damper type has a specific application. Some different damper styles available are:

- Opposed blade damper for rectangular ducts.
- Single blade dampers for round duct.
- Retrofit dampers.
- Supply register dampers.
- Square ceiling diffuser dampers.
- Round ceiling diffuser dampers.
- Floor diffuser dampers.

Trunk Duct Dampers

Most zone systems control airflow in the trunk ducts. This has the advantage of minimizing damper cost since a single trunk damper controls the airflow to several branch ducts. This method also keeps air noise to a minimum by placing the dampers away from the point where the air enters the house. The disadvantage of trunk duct dampers is that multiple trunk lines are required. This is more of a concern for retrofit applications than for new construction. Figure 59-12 shows a damper used for a rectangular trunk duct, while Figure 59-13 shows a damper used for a round trunk duct.

Branch Duct Dampers

Another strategy is to put a damper in every branch duct. The advantage of this strategy is that multiple trunk ducts are not required. However, the system expense goes up rapidly

Figure 59-12 Zone damper for rectangular duct

Figure 59-13 Zone damper for a round duct

because of the cost of the extra dampers. The system need not have a zone for every room when using branch duct dampers; several dampers can be slaved together and controlled from one zone, Figure 59-14. The dampers used for branch ducts are smaller versions of dampers used for trunk ducts as shown in Figures 59-12 and 59-13.

Register and Diffuser Dampers

The damper can be built into the supply registers and diffusers. The advantage of this method is that changing the registers is usually easier than changing the ductwork. The disadvantages are the cost of buying a diffuser damper for every diffuser in the house and the noise created by throttling the air right where it enters the room.

Damper Control

The two methods of controlling zone dampers are two position control or modulating control. Some dampers may be used with either type of system, while others are designed exclusively for either two position control or modulating control.

The dampers in a two position control system are either open or closed; there is no partial opening or closing. Two position control is simpler, but generally does not provide as even a temperature control as modulating control. Dampers designed for two position control can be either motor driven in both directions, or they can be motor driven in one direction and returned in the other direction by a spring. Dampers that are motor driven in both directions can usually be applied to both two position and modulating systems, while spring return dampers are only applicable to two position systems. The motor on a spring return damper is usually stronger because it must overcome the spring as well as operate the damper.

Modulating controls can open and close the dampers in increments, rather than completely opening or closing the zone dampers. This type of control requires dampers that are powered in both directions. The zone control system for a modulating damper system is usually more complex. Modulating zone damper control can be used in conjunction with air bypass to produce variable air volume control to a system without changing the fan speed.

SERVICE TIP

Zone dampers must be located as close as possible to the plenum or supply trunk. If they are too close to the register, there is a possibility that air passing a partially opened damper will cause a whistling sound that can be heard in the room. If a sound can be heard and it is possible to move the damper further away, one method of eliminating the sound is to put one or more 90° turns in the duct after the damper and before the room register.

Figure 59-14 Several dampers can be wired to operate together as one zone
(Courtesy of EWC Controls, Inc.)

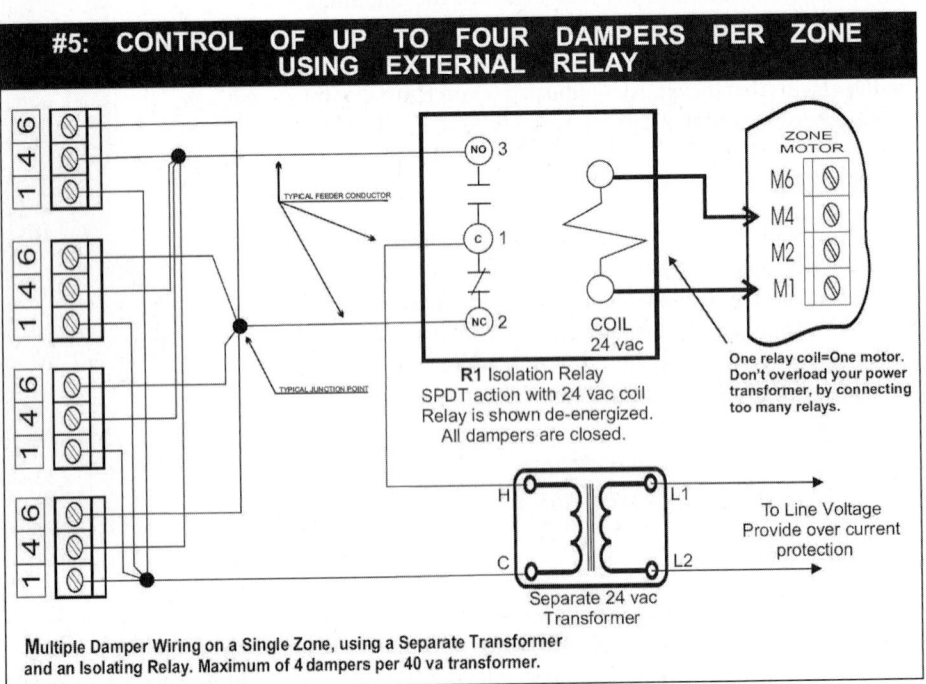

59.6 TYPES OF ZONING SYSTEMS

A number of manufacturers make control systems for installations requiring zoning. These systems differ in number of zones handled, types of applications, methods of control, and types of adjustments provided. The types of systems available generally fall into two categories: basic systems that stress simplicity and advanced systems that stress performance.

Basic Zone Control Systems

The most basic zone control systems are typically limited to a maximum of four zones, single stage heating and cooling, two position damper control, and require either bypassing or dumping to control the air pressure. These systems typically are designed to work with standard off the shelf thermostats. Wiring for these systems is usually letter for letter: R to R, G to G, and so on. The emphasis of these systems is simplicity. On many of these, one of the thermostats is considered the master, and the system selection is determined by its system setting. The system will cycle on by any of the thermostats, but only the master determines whether the system is in heating or cooling.

Added Features

Companies offering these basic types of zoning panels also offer systems with more features. Items like two stage heating or cooling, or dual fuel heat pump integration, can be included. These systems still use traditional 24 V thermostats, two position dampers, and bypass air, but they do have the ability to work with more efficient staged heating and cooling equipment.

Advanced Zone Systems

Other zoning systems stress a high level of technology to achieve enhanced performance and comfort. Typically these systems take advantage of equipment with variable speed ECM blower motors, modulating damper control, and staged capacity heating and cooling. Normally, the controls are proprietary, not common over-the-counter controls. Temperature is typically measured using thermistor sensors.

59.7 BASIC ZONE CONTROL SYSTEM

Ultrazone EWC-ST-3E Zone Control Panel

Ultrazone EWC-ST-3E zone control, Figure 59-15, is an example of a basic zone control system. The system is designed to work with standard heating and air conditioning equipment. Either mechanical or non-power-robbing electronic thermostats may be used. A single control is capable of controlling a two zone or three zone system. If a greater number of zones are required, controls may be interconnected for additional zones, Figure 59-16.

Figure 59-15 Basic three zone control panel
(Courtesy of EWC Controls, Inc.)

A thermostat and a damper are required for each zone. The zone dampers are controlled by the zone control panel and operate in two positions; dampers are either fully open or fully closed. The zone thermostats send a signal to the zone control and the control operates their respective dampers.

The zone 1 thermostat determines whether the system is operating in heating, cooling, or is off. The zone 1 thermostat must have an O terminal that is energized in cooling and a B terminal that is energized in heating. These signals tell the zone control whether the system will operate in heating or cooling. There will be either six wires connecting the panel to the zone 1 thermostat, or seven wires if the thermostat requires a common terminal connection. All other zone thermostats can be simple three or four wire thermostats.

Since the EWC-ST-3E zone control panel is designed for limited applications, there is no programming or mode switches. The panel has a single J1 jumper that determines fan operation in heat. With the jumper in place, the zone panel sends 24 V to the system's G terminal during heat. With the jumper cut, the panel does not send 24 V to the unit in heat, as in a gas furnace.

Control Panel Wiring

A typical wiring diagram for the EWC-ST-3E panel is shown in Figure 59-16. The system shown is for five zones. For only two or three zones, the slave panel would not be used. Note that there are six wires between the panel and the zone 1 thermostat and only three wires to the other two zone thermostats. All damper motors are wired with three wires. Also note that the panel requires a separate field supplied 24 volt, 40 VA transformer.

Figure 59-16 Two panels can be wired together for additional zones *(Courtesy of EWC Controls, Inc.)*

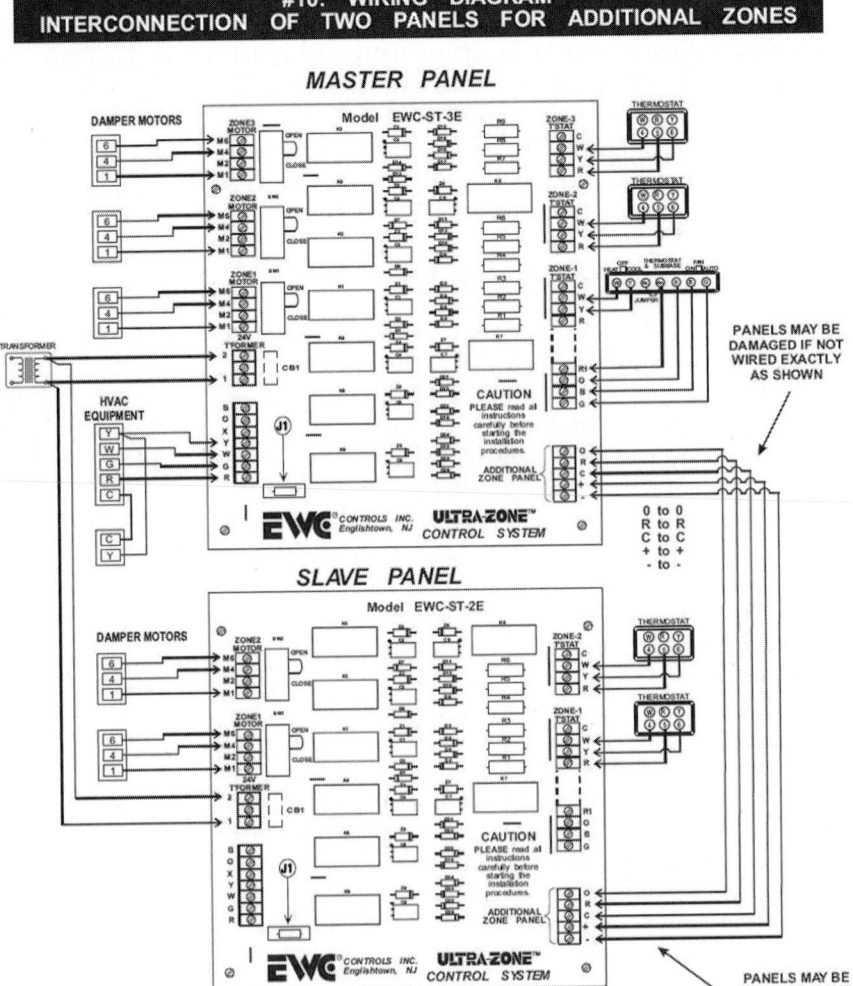

SERVICE TIP

A separate 24 V 40 V A transformer is required to be wired to terminals 1 and 2 of the terminal block labeled "T-Former." The transformer on the indoor unit should not be used to supply 24 V to the zone control panel. The additional load will overload the transformer causing transformer failure and erratic system operation.

59.8 BASIC ZONE CONTROL SYSTEM OPERATION

System switching from heating to cooling is provided through the zone 1 thermostat. This thermostat is normally placed in the zone that has the greatest usage. In a residential installation, the best location would probably be the living room.

The zone panel will respond to a call from any thermostat, provided the call is for the same mode that the zone 1 thermostat is in. If zone 1 is on cooling, a call for heat from another thermostat will have no effect. When any zone calls, its zone damper opens and zones not called are closed. The system is started if it is not already on. When all the zones are satisfied, all dampers go to a fully open position and the system cycles off. This permits the fan to dissipate any residual heat that may be left in the furnace and allows fan only operation.

59.9 ADVANCED ZONE CONTROL SYSTEMS

Lennox Harmony III Zone Control System

The Lennox Harmony III zone control system is designed to work with variable speed ECM motors to vary the airflow instead of bypassing air, Figure 59-17. The Harmony III system

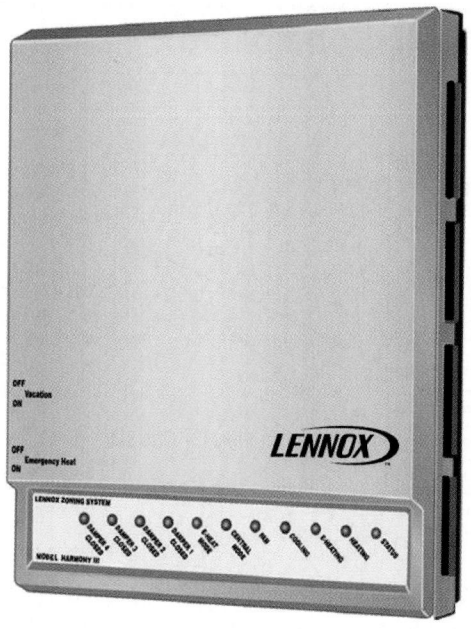

Figure 59-17 Zone control panel designed to work with ECM motors
(Courtesy of Lennox Industries)

is designed specifically to work with Lennox products that have ECM blowers. It uses two position dampers and standard electronic single stage thermostats. A discharge air sensor is used to monitor the temperature of the air in the supply

plenum. An outdoor air sensor is used to monitor outdoor temperature for the control of dual fuel heat pump systems. The system can have up to four zones, but only two zones can be used with single stage heating and cooling equipment. Figure 59-18 shows the components and connections for the Harmony III zone control system.

The installing technician must make modifications to the control board of the furnace or heat pump indoor blower control board. These include jumper settings, cutting wires, and setting the upper blower limit to match the system. Figures 59-19, 59-20 and 59-21 show the changes that must be made on a blower control board. Setting these incorrectly can result in improper operation or even blown fuses. Reading and following the installation instructions is crucial!

The Harmony III zone control board also has jumper settings that must be made. The most important are the jumpers that control the amount of air that goes into each zone; called the PIAB, (percent into adjustment band) jumpers. The adjustment band is the difference between the minimum and maximum CFM rating of the air handler. The zone control system allows the technician to direct an appropriate percentage of that air volume to each zone. Volume settings must be selected for zone 1 and at least one other zone. Unused zones must have their jumpers set on OFF. Figure 59-22 shows typical PIAB jumper settings for a two zone system.

Jumper settings range from 0–100%. The percentages tell how much of the difference between the maximum

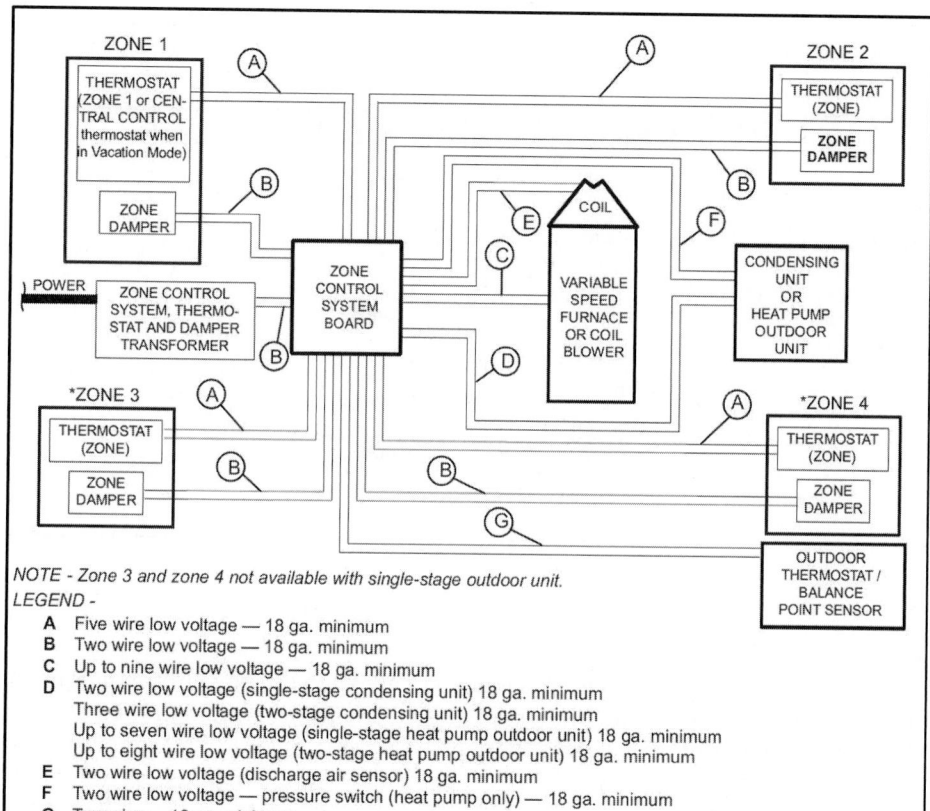

Figure 59-18 Harmony III wiring
(Courtesy of Lennox Industries)

Figure 59-19 Blower control changes in the Harmony III control panel *(Courtesy of Lennox Industries)*

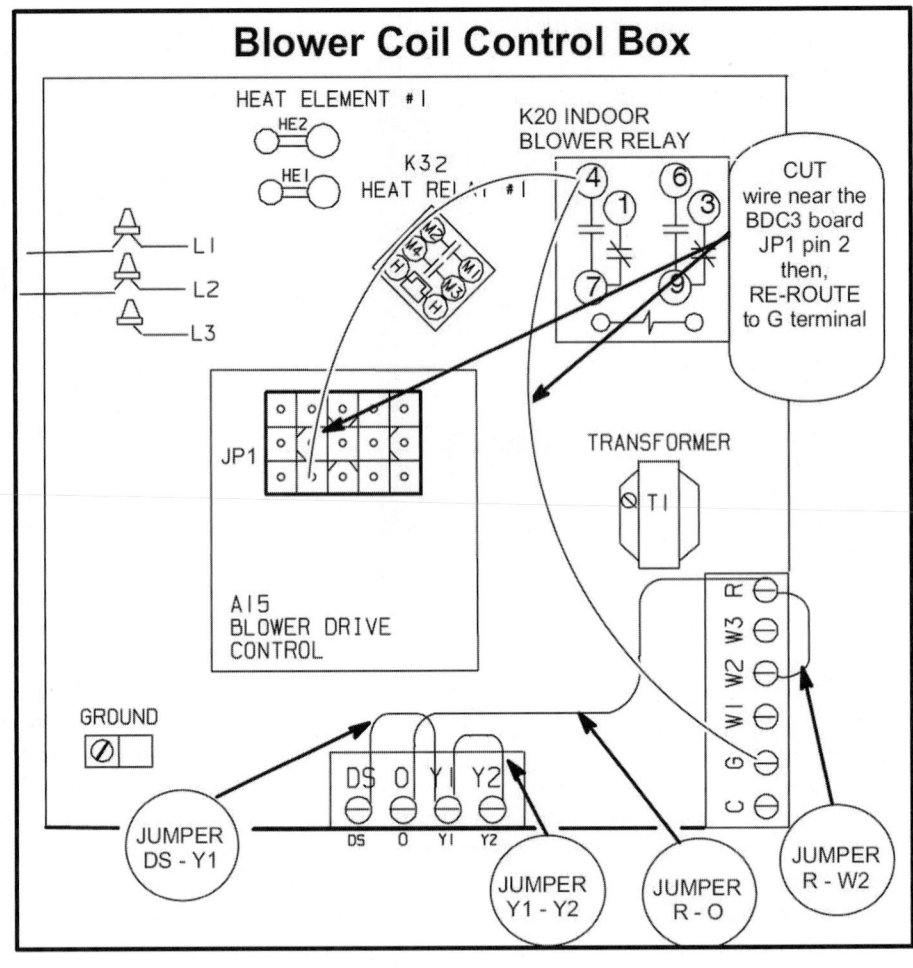

Figure 59-20 Cable modifications for the Harmony III control panel *(Courtesy of Lennox Industries)*

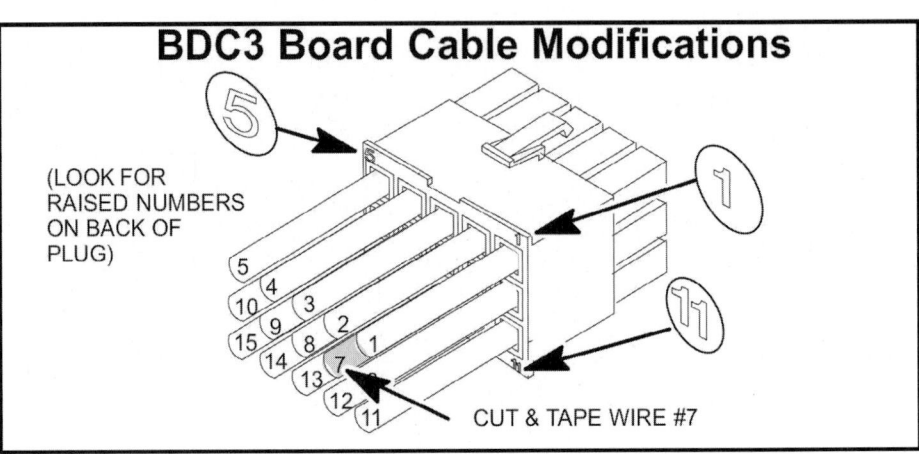

CFM and minimum CFM the fan will deliver. This amount is added to the minimum CFM for the total airflow. That is: zone jumper setting × (the CFM adjustment range of the motor) + the minimum motor CFM = CFM delivered. When jumpers are set at 100%, this corresponds to full air-

flow. When jumpers are set to 0%, this corresponds to the minimum air volume available according to the air handler installation instructions, not 0% of maximum air. For example, if an air handler has a minimum air volume of 800 CFM, and a maximum of 1,500 CFM, and the jumper

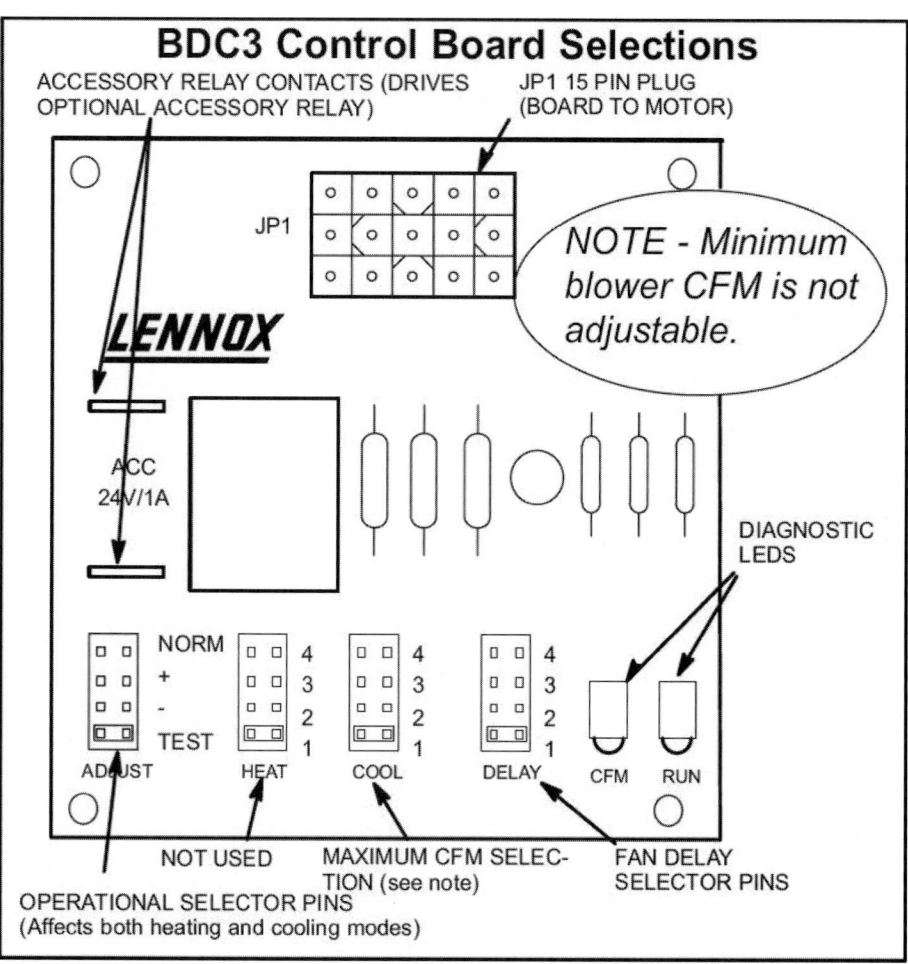

Figure 59-21 Control board selections for the Harmony III control panel
(Courtesy of Lennox Industries)

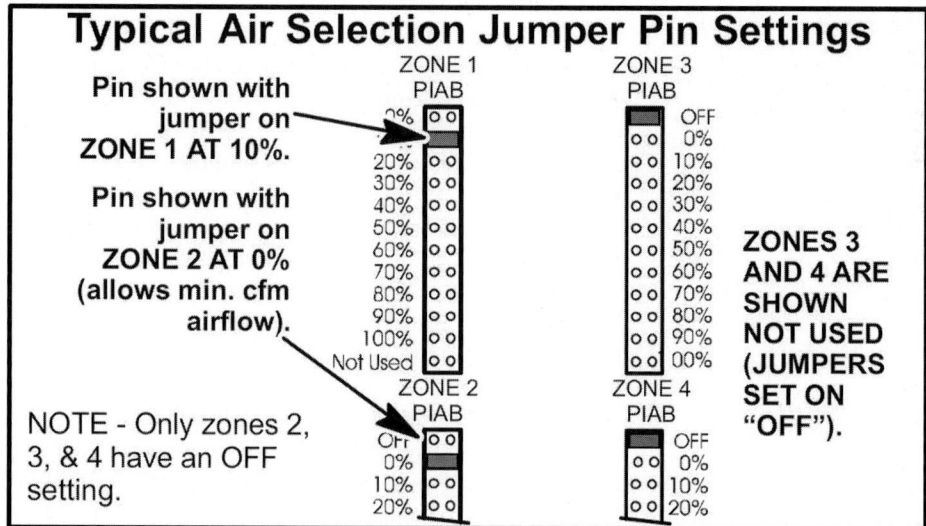

Figure 59-22 PIAB settings on the Harmony III control panel
(Courtesy of Lennox Industries)

is set to 0%, the air delivered will be 800 CFM. If the jumper is set to obtain 50%, the air handler will deliver 50% of the difference plus the minimum: $0.50 \times (1{,}500 - 800) + 800 = 1{,}150$ CFM. Setting the PIAB jumpers incorrectly will result in equipment problems and unsatisfactory performance.

59.10 ADVANCED ZONE CONTROL SYSTEM OPERATION

A major difference between the Harmony III and basic zone control systems is that there is no master zone that controls the system operation. Any zone may initiate a call for heating or cooling. The system can even switch between competing calls for heating and cooling from different zones. Calls are satisfied on a first come first served basis. If competing calls persist, the system will operate for 20 minutes in one mode, switch to the other for 20 minutes, and switch back until the calls are satisfied.

Another major difference is the fan operation and staging. On a call for cooling the first stage compressor will be energized and the fan will start at minimum speed and slowly ramp up to the speed indicated by the PIAB jumpers. The system must operate on first stage for 4 min before bringing on second stage cooling. Second stage cooling is energized if the discharge air sensor senses a temperature of 7°F or more above the temperature set by the staging jumper on the control board. If the discharge air temperature drops to 45°F or colder, the compressors are shut off to prevent the coil from freezing. Once the discharge air rises 10°F and the system is off for at least 5 min, the compressor will cycle back on.

In heat, the blower runs at minimum speed until the discharge air is above 100°F. Once the discharge air exceeds 100°F, the blower is ramped up to the setting of the PIAB jumpers. The furnace is cycled between low fire and high fire to maintain a discharge air temperature between the temperature of the heating staging jumper and 20°F above that setting. There is a minimum 3 min delay between high and low fire.

SERVICE TIP

Many of the electronically controlled systems have unique programming features. Refer to the operating instructions provided by the manufacturer for the specific piece of equipment you are working on when making changes in settings. In some cases it may be necessary to contact the equipment manufacturer directly for assistance in some programming features. Many controller manufacturers have toll free phone numbers for the technician's assistance with programming problems.

59.11 COMMUNICATING ZONE SYSTEMS

Carrier Infinity Zone System

The Infinity zone control is designed to work with Carrier's Infinity line of products. The Infinity zone system consists of several intelligent communicating components which includes:

- Infinity zone control (or user interface).
- Smart sensors.

- Damper control module.
- A variable speed furnace or fan coil.
- Two stage air conditioner or heat pump.
- Infinity packaged products.

The components continually communicate with each other via a four wire connection called the ABCD bus. Commands, operating conditions, and other data are passed continually between components over the ABCD bus. The communications allow for more intelligent system control. For example, the Infinity zone control knows the real time airflow through each zone because the blowers communicate this information back to the control. Figure 59-23 shows the ABCD bus connections between communicating components.

Unlike the other zone control systems discussed, the Infinity zone control is the component that would normally be considered the thermostat. The user interface that mounts on the wall is actually the system zone controller. The Infinity system does have a damper controller, but its job is simply to operate the dampers based on commands from the Infinity controller.

The Infinity zone control is also the user interface. It functions as a programmable thermostat as well as a system controller and zone controller. In a standard setup, the Infinity controller is used to program all the zones and enter the temperature settings for all zones. Temperature sensors that have no user interface are used in the other zones, Figure 59-24. Optional smart sensors can be used in place of the standard zone sensors. These allow users to change the temperature setting for a zone at the zone sensor rather than at the Infinity controller.

The wiring and connections for an Infinity zone control system are shown in Figure 59-25. The indoor unit, outdoor unit, zone control, and damper control are all connected with the four wires of the ABCD buss. The sensors are connected with two wires, and the damper motors with three wires.

All Infinity furnaces or fan coils are variable speed and multi-stage. The infinity system controls the fan speed and system capacity to match the demands of the system, so bypassing air is not required. The control can be used with furnaces, air conditioners, heat pumps, or dual fuel heat pumps.

New installations do not require jumpers or programming, the control recognizes the communicating components connected to the system and configures itself on initial power-up. First the control will locate all communicating components. Next, the system will open all dampers and perform a static pressure check. This process will take about $1\frac{1}{2}$ min to complete. When completed, a screen will appear displaying the static pressure (in inches) across the equipment at the expected highest delivered airflow. If the static pressure is over 1 in, a warning will appear, but equipment operation and the True Sense dirty filter detection operation will not be affected. After the static test, the

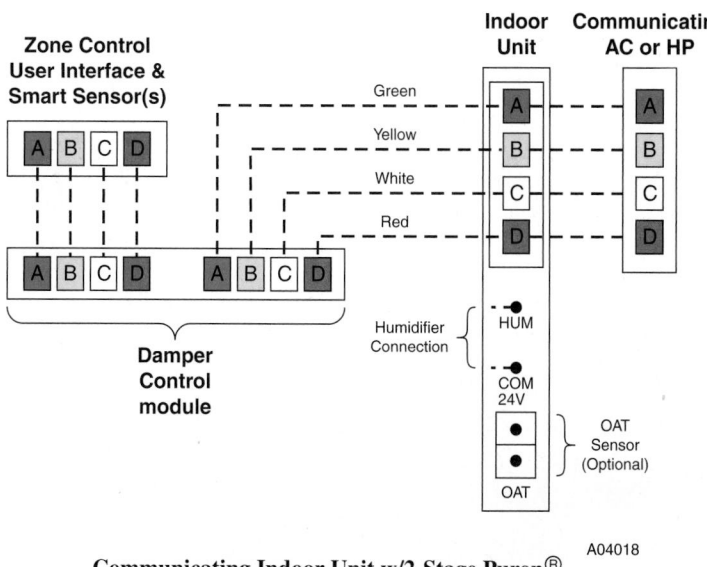

Communicating Indoor Unit w/2-Stage Puron®
Refrigerant Communicating Outdoor Unit

Figure 59-23 Four wire connections for the Infinity zone control system

control does a duct assessment. The duct assessment will measure the relative size of the ductwork, up to and through the dampers. These measurements are used to control the correct amount of airflow in the zoned system. Status messages will appear on the screen to indicate what the system is doing. The process will take approximately 1 min per zone. The duct assessment will override a call for heat or cool. A duct assessment will automatically occur each day at a user selectable time. The factory default time is 1:00 PM, but may be changed by entering the Zoning Setup menu.

During the duct assessment, the system will first open all zones and drive the blower to 175 CFM/ton of cooling (or the minimum indoor unit's airflow, whichever is greater). It will then take a static pressure measurement. The system will then close all zones and open one zone at a time, taking

a static pressure measurement for each zone. The system will then close all zones and take a pressure measurement, getting a value for the duct leakage up to and through the dampers. With these static pressure measurements, the system will calculate the relative size of each zone as well as the percent leakage through the dampers. At the end of the process, the display will show the relative size of each zone duct.

59.12 COMMUNICATING ZONE CONTROL SYSTEM OPERATION

The primary difference in operation between most other zone control systems and the Infinity zone control system is that the Infinity system is an intelligent communicating system. The zone controller is collecting real time operating data and making decisions about system operation based on this data. Other systems rely on mode switches, jumpers, or programs that are configured at the time of installation. These systems can only respond to on or off signals. The Infinity can determine when the air filter is stopped up based on changes in the fan. Staging of multiple stage equipment is done based on demand, rather than any predetermined temperature or zone arrangement. Air bypass is not required because the fan speed is varied based on the demand and the number of operating zones. The Infinity also responds to demands for dehumidification by reducing the fan speed and increasing the latent heat capacity of the evaporator coil. The Infinity controller has a service mode that displays the system history and any system faults, allowing technicians to see faults when diagnosing system problems. All of this is done by collecting real time operating data and making decisions.

Figure 59-24 Infinity remote room sensor

Figure 59-25 Wiring of complete Infinity zone control system

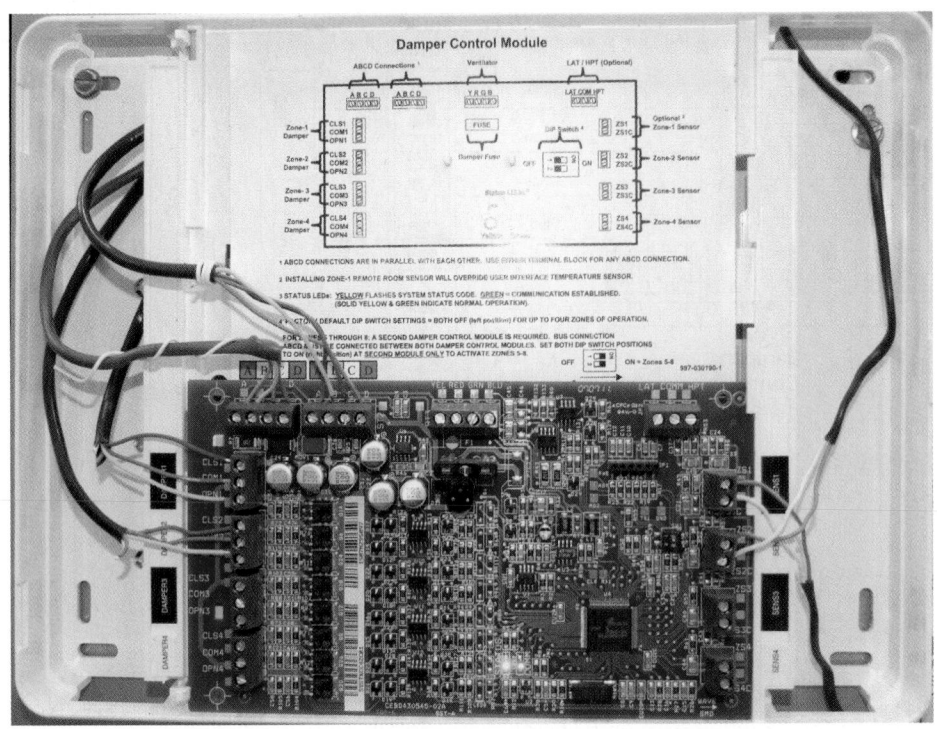

UNIT 59—SUMMARY

Residential zone systems have moved from a luxury reserved for only a few high end homes to a viable strategy for comfort and economy in a much broader range of applications. Many zoning products are available, from simple relay logic, two position systems with air bypass, to sophisticated communicating systems with variable air volume and capacity control. A zone system may be as simple as a two zone system for a two story house, or as complex as a zone for every area in the house with different temperature and setback schedules for each area. A decade ago technicians might seldom be required to work on a zone system; today a technician is almost certainly going to need to work on residential zone systems.

—— WORK ORDERS

Service Ticket 5901

Customer Complaint: Basement Too Cold in Summer

Equipment: Basic Zone Control Using two Position Dampers, Single Stage Heating and Cooling

A technician is called to look at a zoned system with three zones: one in the finished basement, one in the living areas, and one in the bedrooms. The basement is staying below 70°F even though the thermostat for that zone is set to 78°F. The technician notices that the system is operating and cold air is coming out of the basement diffusers. A visual check of the damper shows that it is open. However, a voltage check at the damper indicates that it is receiving a signal to close. The technician determines that the damper is stuck open and recommends replacing the damper.

Service Ticket 5902

Customer Complaint: No Heat

Equipment: Heat Pump with ECM Motor and an Advanced Zone Control

A technician is called to look at a zoned heat pump system that is not heating. The technician notices that all zones are calling for heat, but no air is coming out of the registers in one zone. Air is coming out of the other zones, but it is not warm. The temperature outside is above the heat pump balance point. A check of the outside unit reveals that it is not operating and the high pressure switch has tripped. The technician resets the pressure switch and the compressor comes on. Heat is now coming out of two zones, but one zone still has no airflow. The technician checks the damper and finds it closed even though it is receiving a signal to open. The technician concludes that the stuck damper caused an airflow problem when only that zone was calling, which led to the high pressure switch tripping. The tripped pressure switch then prevented the system from operating and heating the remaining zones. The technician recommends replacing the stuck damper.

Service Ticket 5903

Customer Complaint: Delay in System Starting

Equipment: Advanced Zone Control

A customer is concerned because the system waited for several minutes before it came on after she had adjusted the temperature. The customer had just returned home from running and heard the system cycle off. Because she was hot, she adjusted the temperature down several degrees to bring on the air conditioner. However, nothing happened. While the customer was on the phone with the service company, the system came on. The technician explained that the system has a built-in off cycle timer which makes the system stay off for 5 min any time the system cycles off. This is for the protection of the compressor.

Service Ticket 5904

Customer Complaint: Hot Air in Cooling Mode

Equipment: Basic Zone Control on Heat Pump

A technician is called to look at a newly installed system that is delivering hot air in the cooling mode. The technician notices that the heat pump is operating in the heating mode even though the master thermostat is set for cooling. A look at the diagram for the outdoor unit shows the reversing valve should energize in cooling with the O terminal. Checking the zone panel jumpers, the technician discovers that the reversing valve switchover jumper has been set to reverse in heat instead of cooling. The technician moves the jumper to the cooling position and the heat pump operates correctly.

Service Ticket 5905

Customer Complaint: No Airflow in the Bedroom Zone

Equipment: Advanced Zone Control System, Single Stage Heating and Cooling

A technician is called to look at a newly installed system. The zone serving the bedroom area is not delivering any air. The technician notices that there is no air delivery in the zone, even with the system switch is OFF and the fan switch is set to ON. A check of the zone damper shows it is closed. A voltage check shows voltage between the common and close terminals on the damper. At the zone control, a voltage check shows voltage between the common and open terminals. The technician looks at the wire colors and determines that the open and close signal wires to the zone damper have been reversed at the damper. The wires are swapped at the damper and the system operates correctly.

UNIT 59—REVIEW QUESTIONS

1. Why are zone control systems used?
2. List the components found in a basic zone control system.
3. What two general criteria are used to select zones for a building?
4. Explain the reason zone control systems need a method for handling excess air.
5. List the methods of handling the excess air in a zone system.
6. Discuss the disadvantages of air bypass.
7. Explain the concept of variable air volume in a zoning system.
8. Explain the difference between two position and modulating damper control.
9. Explain how a barometric damper operates.
10. List several types of zone dampers.
11. Explain the difference between a basic zone control system and an advanced zone control system.
12. The PIAB jumper on zone 1 of a Lennox Harmony III control is set at 40%. The minimum airflow is 900 CFM and the maximum is 1,800 CFM. How much air will this zone receive? Show all work.
13. Explain the purpose of using a dump zone in a zone control system and give an example.
14. What is the difference between a communicating zone control system and a basic zone control system?
15. What is the purpose of the master thermostat in the basic zone control system?
16. What is the purpose of discharge air sensors?
17. What is the purpose of the outdoor air sensor on a zone control system?
18. How are motorized dampers controlled when they are used as bypass dampers to relieve a pressure differential across the blower?
19. Describe the added features available on some basic zone control systems.
20. How is an Infinity zone control system configured?

UNIT 60

Testing and Balancing Air Systems

OBJECTIVES

After completing this unit you will be able to:

- explain why TAB (test and balance) is critical to the operation of an air condition system.
- explain why TAB is critical to energy consumption of an air condition system.
- list the organizations involved in the TAB industry.
- list the instruments used to perform TAB procedures.
- explain proper use of instruments used in TAB procedures.
- describe test and balance procedures.

60.1 INTRODUCTION

Test and balance, sometimes referred to as test, adjust, and balance or just TAB, is the adjustment of the air side and water side of an HVAC system to the operational specifications of the designer's original intent. In some cases these adjustments must be redone due to seasonal changes or changes in the structure. This unit will discuss the air side of an HVAC system.

Commercial projects recognized the need for TAB as early as the 1960s. Originally the installation contractor completed any test and balance that was needed at startup along with other commissioning activities. As commercial projects grew and indoor air quality became a more clearly defined issue, independent TAB contractors began to operate as a quality control check on the system and the project. The TAB industry has grown into a large part of the commercial HVAC industry. There are many measurements and adjustments that are specific to testing and balancing that are not normally performed in regular HVAC/R work. Technicians working for TAB contractors go through extensive training and certification which can take up to five years to complete.

The residential TAB market has seen large growth recently due to energy costs and increased health concerns related to residential indoor air quality. The largest energy consuming appliance in the home is the HVAC system, and most of these systems are estimated to have a 30% loss of efficiency due to improper air side design and instillation. Some states and the federal Department of Energy have adopted standards for the testing of HVAC residential systems and offered incentives to builders who will have their homes certified under the programs. At the local level many power companies offer TAB analysis for little or no cost to the consumer, in hopes of lowering energy consumption.

Health concerns have increased in the residential environment as home construction techniques and materials have improved. As homes have become increasingly tighter due to energy concerns, the infiltration of outside air has been reduced, causing indoor pollutants and stagnant air to affect those more susceptible to such pollutants, such as infants and the elderly. Many respiratory afflictions, such as asthma, are on the rise while at the same time, studies show indoor pollution rising as well. A combination of ventilation and filtration can be used to introduce filtered, fresh air into the house. TAB is seen as part of the solution because the airflow in a properly balanced system is more predictable and controllable. A home that is properly balanced will prevent air from stagnating and help to reduce pollutants by the conditioning and filtering of the indoor air.

60.2 TAB ORGANIZATIONS

In the test and balance industry there are several organizations committed to developing standards, procedures, training courses, and to certification of technicians and contractors. As in the rest of the HVAC industry, these organizations overlap on missions and compete in several ways. Associated Air Balance Council (AABC), National Environmental Balancing Bureau (NABB), and Testing Adjusting and Balancing Bureau (TABB) are the major organizations which specialize in test and balance of HVAC systems. Other groups are also involved in TAB but not exclusively. ASHRAE, the American Society of Heating and Air Conditioning Engineers, is a good example of one of these organizations.

The Associated Air Balance Council is the oldest of the three and started in 1960s. The AABC is an independent association, and its member's firms can have no affiliation with manufacturers or HVAC contractors. Member firms must also enroll their technicians in AABC training courses. These courses, combined with four years of industry experience, lead to technician certification. AABC publishes standards for the industry and a newsletter. Member firms are required to participate in a quality assurance program where the association receives feedback from the client on the work preformed.

The National Environmental Balancing Bureau was started in the 1970s. NEBB certifies firms and provides training at their Arizona facility. The training includes labs and practical exams. NEBB also publishes standards and manuals which cover all aspects of the TAB industry.

The Testing Adjusting and Balancing Bureau is the youngest of the three. TABB is an organization started in 2001 to work with the trade union SMACNA and SMACNA contractors. Due to this relationship, TABB cannot be considered an independent agency. TABB publishes standards, manuals and a newsletter, and all these publications are produced in partnership with SMACNA. TABB certifies technicians, supervisors, and contractors because TABB's approach is that everyone involved in the project be TABB trained from designer to installer. TABB produces industry training for designers, supervisors, and tradesmen. TABB training is offered to tradesman at the union hall during apprenticeship and as continuing education throughout their career. TABB takes a "Total Quality" approach instead of a "quality by inspection" approach. This is possible because of the relationship TABB has with all of the participants in the project.

Although each organization takes a different approach, the outcome of having a well installed and energy efficient system that provides conditioned air and comfort to the people using the space is met by using standards and methods developed by these associations. Although many smaller projects may not use independent firms or union contractors, TAB is a critical part of the commissioning of each installation and modification of all HVAC systems. Not testing and balancing every system adds to the energy cost for the owner and society, as well as possible medical costs for the occupants.

60.3 TAB TEST INSTRUMENTS

In smaller companies contractors may have the startup technician perform the required TAB tests. Measurements taken for TAB applications are temperature, pressure, velocity, rotating speed (rpm), and electrical. Many instruments used by service technicians are also used by TAB technicians, such as: digital thermometers, psychrometers, anemometers, manometers with a pitot tube, and digital multimeters. Other instruments used in TAB tests that would not be commonly found on a typical service van are: chronometric tachometers, digital or analog capture hoods, or air differential pressure gauges. These are specialized tools that TAB technicians may choose to use depending on the application.

TECH TIP

As with most test instruments on the market today, the accuracy of digital test equipment is better and the ease of use is often greatly improved over analog models. The sling psychrometer is the clearest example. The drawback to digital instruments is price and in some cases digital versions can run 10 times more than analog versions. This is why sling psychrometers are still in use today.

60.4 TEMPERATURE MEASUREMENTS

Temperature measurements are taken to compare return and supply air temperature in the conditioned space; entering and leaving air temperature at the furnace or evaporator coil. In some cases suction and discharge temperature are also measured by TAB technicians to confirm proper system refrigerant charge. Instruments used for these measurements are:

Glass tube thermometers,   Figure 60-1, are available in a number of ranges, scale graduations, and lengths. They have a useful range from –40° to over 220°F.

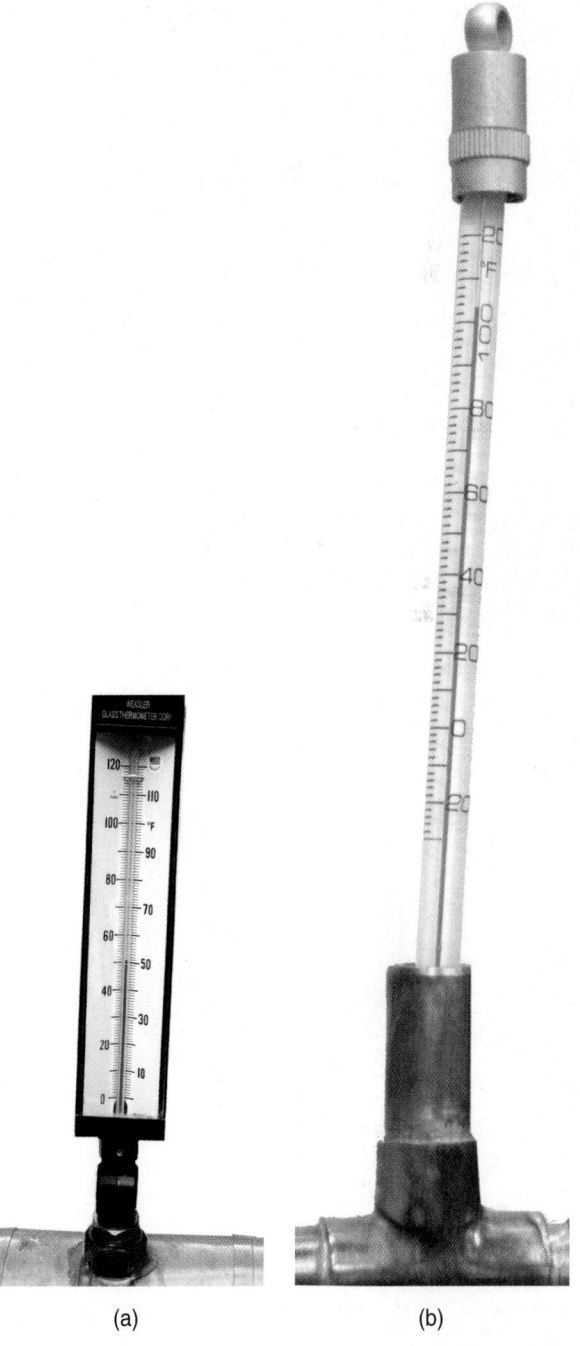

(a)   (b)

Figure 60-1 Glass tube thermometers: (a) In protective case; (b) With glass tube exposed

Dial thermometers are available in two general types: bimetal stem, Figure 60-2, and remote bulb with flexible capillary tube, Figure 60-3. Bimetal stem thermometers use a spiral formed bimetal inside the tube. As the bimetal expands and contracts it produces a twisting motion that moves the needle on the thermometer. The remote bulb model permits temperature measurements from a remote location. The bulb and capillary tube are liquid or gas

Figure 60-2 Bimetal dial thermometer reading air temperature leaving a supply air register

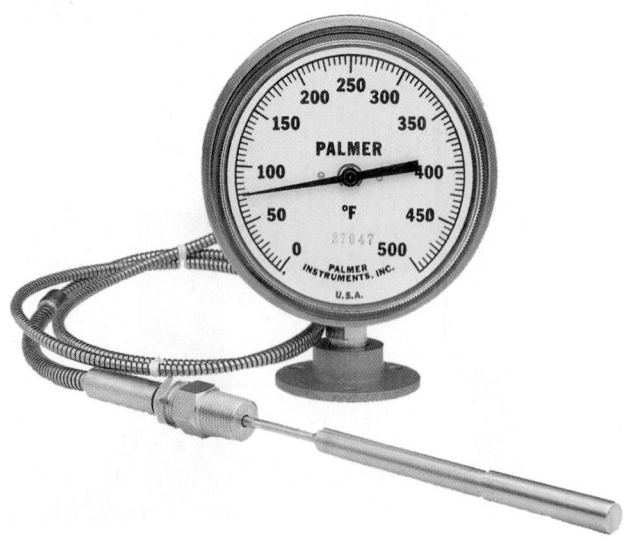

Figure 60-3 Remote bulb and capillary tube dial type thermometer
(Photo Courtesy of Palmer Wahl, Asheville, North Carolina)

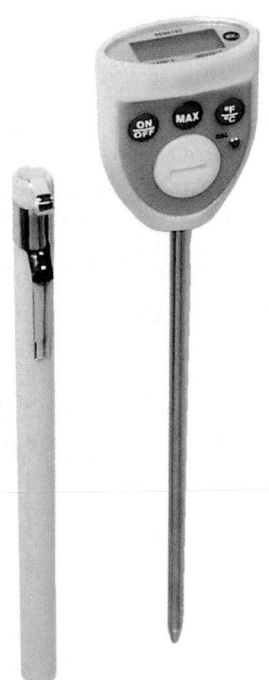

Figure 60-4 Digital pocket thermometer

filled, and the fluid expands or contracts to operate a Bourdon tube. Dial thermometers usually have a longer reading time lag than glass tube thermometers.

Digital pocket thermometers, Figure 60-4, are electronic, digital replacements for the typical dial type pocket thermometer. They are generally more durable and more accurate than mechanical stem type pocket thermometers.

Electronic thermometers have interchangeable probes to permit more accurate reading in selected ranges. There are three basic types of temperature sensing elements used: resistance temperature detectors (RTDs), thermistors, and thermocouples. The meters are built for use with a particular type of sensor. Thermometers with interchangeable probes and multiple connections are useful for reading temperatures at a number of locations. They can also be used to read the temperature difference between two probes for comparative temperature readings like superheat, subcooling, or delta T measurements, Figure 60-5.

Resistance temperature sensors are wound wire with known resistance values. The resistance of the wire increases as its temperature increases, producing a very accurate reading. RTD sensors typically have a very narrow operating range. They also have a longer time lag than the thermocouple type due to the time required for the wire's temperature to change.

Thermistor sensors also change resistance with temperature, except they use a semiconductor instead of wire. Most thermistors used for electronic thermometers decrease in resistance as their temperature increases. Thermistor sensors typically read faster than RTD sensors. Figure 60-6 shows an electronic thermometer that uses thermistor type sensors.

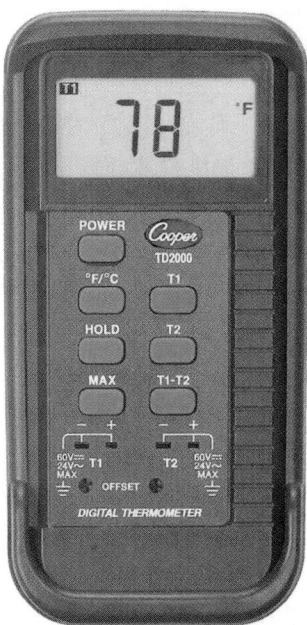

Figure 60-5 This dual input electronic thermometer can be used for comparative temperature measurements like superheat, subcooling, and delta T

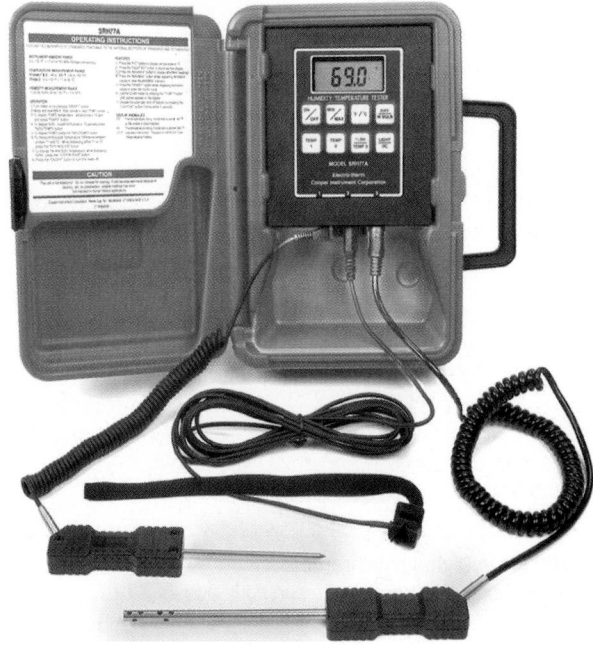

Figure 60-6 This electronic thermometer uses thermistor sensors
(Courtesy of Cooper-Atkins Corporation)

Thermocouple sensors produce a small DC voltage that is proportional to the temperature difference between the two ends of the thermocouple. Thermometers that use thermocouple sensing devices are calibrated to read this voltage as temperature and read temperature directly. There are two common types of thermocouple sensors: type J and type K. Figure 60-7 shows an electronic thermometer that uses thermocouple sensors.

Figure 60-7 Thermocouple thermometers

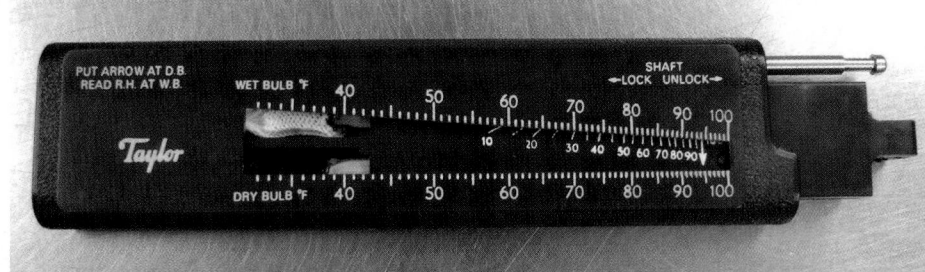

Figure 60-8 Sling psychrometer

SERVICE TIP

Electronic thermometers with dual inputs make reading differential temperature measurements such as superheat, subcooling, and delta T much easier. Most dual input electronic thermometers have a function that automatically displays the difference between the two temperature probes.

60.5 ENTHALPY MEASUREMENTS

Enthalpy measurements are calculated from wet bulb and dry bulb temperatures. Measurements are then plotted on a psychrometric chart to find the enthalpy of air in the measured space or to compare entering air enthalpy to leaving air enthalpy across an evaporator coil. Instruments used are, the sling psychrometer and the electronic hygrometer.

The *sling psychrometer* consists of two glass thermometers, one of which has a wick wetted by water surrounding the bulb. The frame that supports the two thermometers is hinged to permit revolving the wetted instrument in the air. The unit should be whirled at a rate of two revolutions per second for most accurate results. Readings are taken on both thermometers after the temperatures have stabilized. Readings indicate dry bulb and wet bulb temperatures, which can be plotted on a psychrometric chart to determine numerous properties of the air sampled. Figure 60-8 shows a sling psychrometer.

The *electronic hygrometer* is usually constructed with a thin film capacitance sensor. As the moisture content and temperature change, the resistance of the sensor changes proportionately. These instruments usually read directly in relative humidity. No wetted wick is necessary and the instrument can remain stationary when readings are taken. Figure 60-9 shows an electronic hygrometer.

60.6 PRESSURE MEASUREMENT

The pressure measurements that technicians take while testing and balancing systems range from the air pressure inside ductwork to the pressures in a refrigeration system. The instrument used to take the pressure reading depends largely upon the level of the pressure. Inclined manometers, magnehelic gauges, and digital manometers are used for small

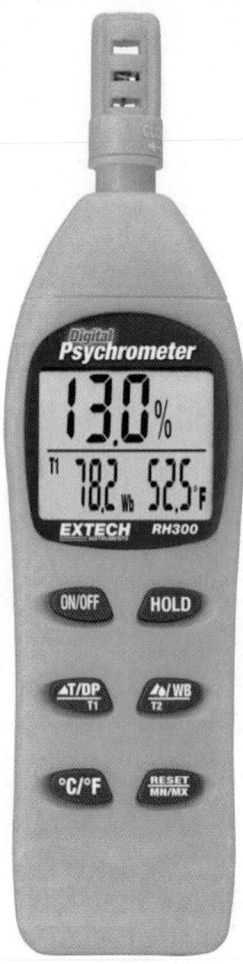

Figure 60-9 Digital psychrometer
(Courtesy of Extech Instruments Corporation)

pressures of less than 1 in wc such as the air pressure drop across a coil. Bourdon tube gauges are used for higher pressures measured in psig, such as the refrigerant pressure drop across a refrigeration system component.

Bourdon Tube Gauges

Calibrated pressure gauges typically use a Bourdon tube assembly for sensing pressure, Figure 60-10. The Bourdon tube may be constructed of stainless steel, copper, or bronze. The dials are available with pressure, vacuum, or compound gauges showing both pressure and vacuum. Gauges are used

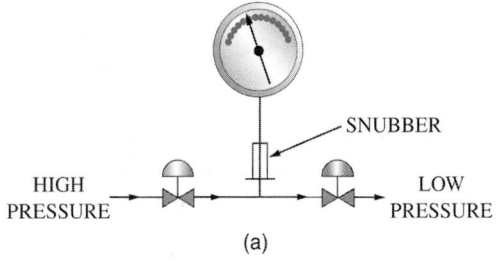

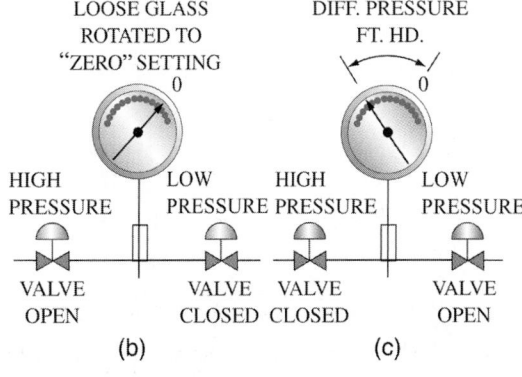

Figure 60-11 Single gauge for measuring differential pressures *(Courtesy of SMACNA)*

Figure 60-10 The most common type of gauge used for higher pressure is the Bourdon tube gauge

for checking pump pressures; coil, chiller, and condenser pressure drops; and pressure drops across orifice plates, valves, and other flow calibrated devices.

Most flow measurements require determining the pressure drop across a component. Pressure differential readings can be done with two separate gauges, or a single gauge with a rotating dial, or a special differential pressure gauge. When two gauges are used, it is essential that the gauges be calibrated to each other. This can be checked by comparing the two gauges when there is no flow and they are reading only static pressure. They should register the same pressure.

Figure 60-11 shows how a single gauge with a rotating dial is used. The gauge is installed with two valve connections. The high pressure line is opened to measure the high side pressure while the low pressure line valve remains closed. The gauge dial is then rotated to zero. The high pressure valve is closed and the low pressure line valve opened. The pressure reading will be the difference between the two pressures.

A differential pressure gauge uses two inputs and measures the difference between the two pressures.

Manometers

U tube manometers, Figure 60-12, are used for measuring gas pressure. When not connected, both ends of the U tube are open to the atmosphere. The tube is partly filled with liquid. Both tubes register zero when they are both open to the atmosphere. When one tube is attached to gas pressure, the side connected to gas pressure drops and the open side rises. The pressure is indicated by the difference in the height of the two columns. U tube manometers are recommended for measuring pressures above 1.0 in wc.

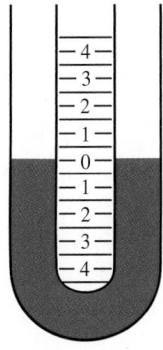

Figure 60-12 U tube manometer

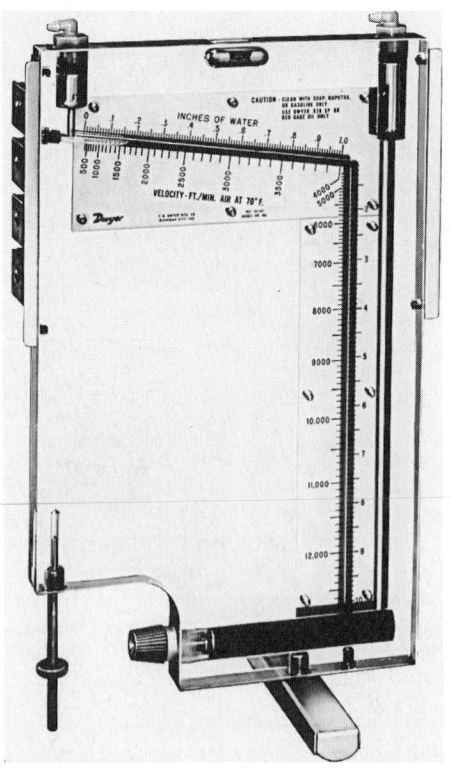

Figure 60-13 Inclined/vertical manometer
(Courtesy of Dwyer Instruments, Inc.)

Inclined Manometers

The inclined manometer, Figure 60-13, is useful for measuring static pressure, velocity pressure, and total pressure in a duct when connected to a pitot tube. The pitot tube is constructed with a tube in a tube design, Figure 60-14. When pointed against the airflow, the inner tube measures total air pressure and the outer tube measures static pressure. The difference between the two pressures is the velocity pressure, Figure 60-15. For air at temperatures close to normal room temperature, the air velocity can be calculated using the formula: 4005 × square root of velocity pressure. For example, an airstream with a velocity pressure of 0.16 in wc would have a velocity of: 4,005 × square root of 0.16 = 4,005 × 0.4 = 1,602 fpm. Charts are also available for converting velocity pressure to fpm (ft/min), Figure 60-16.

SERVICE TIP

Digital manometers are available that can read in the same pressure ranges as inclined manometers. These are much easier to transport and use than traditional inclined manometers.

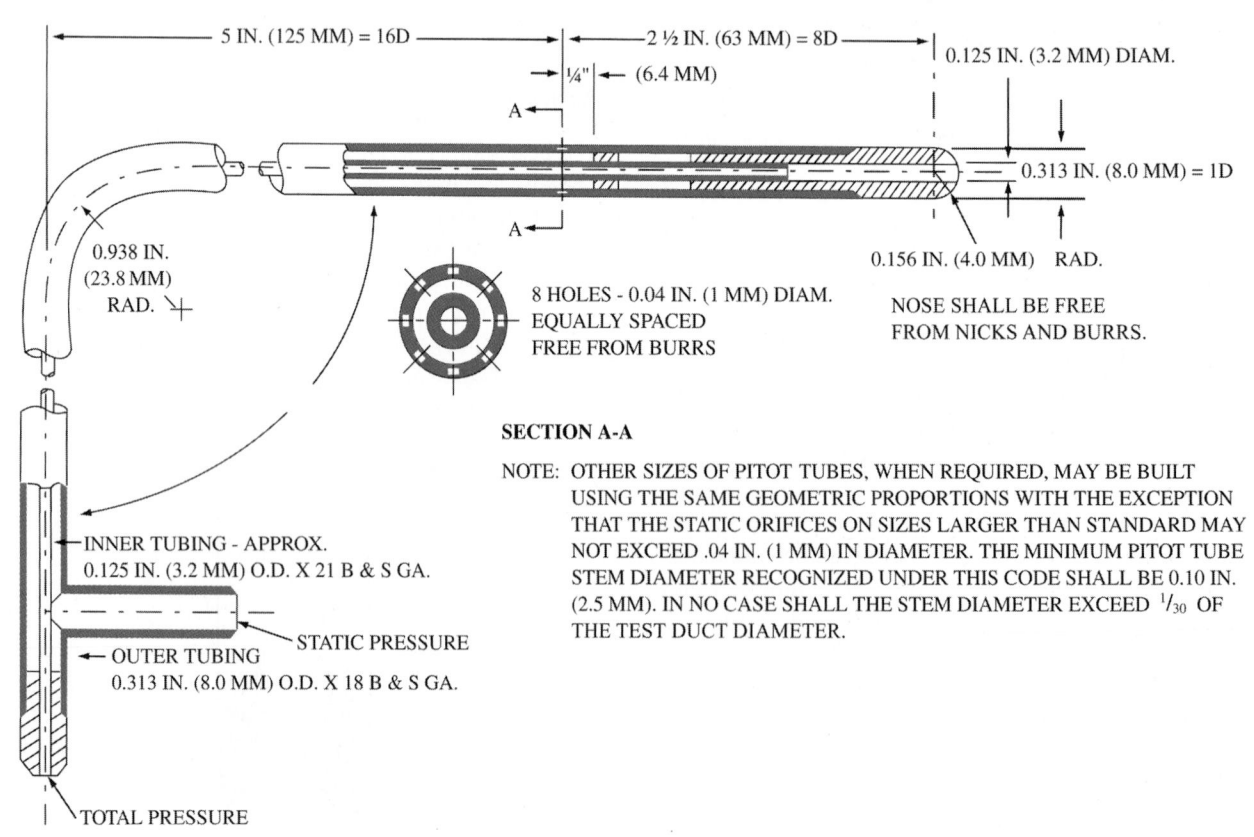

Figure 60-14 Detailed construction of a pilot tube
(Courtesy of SMACNA)

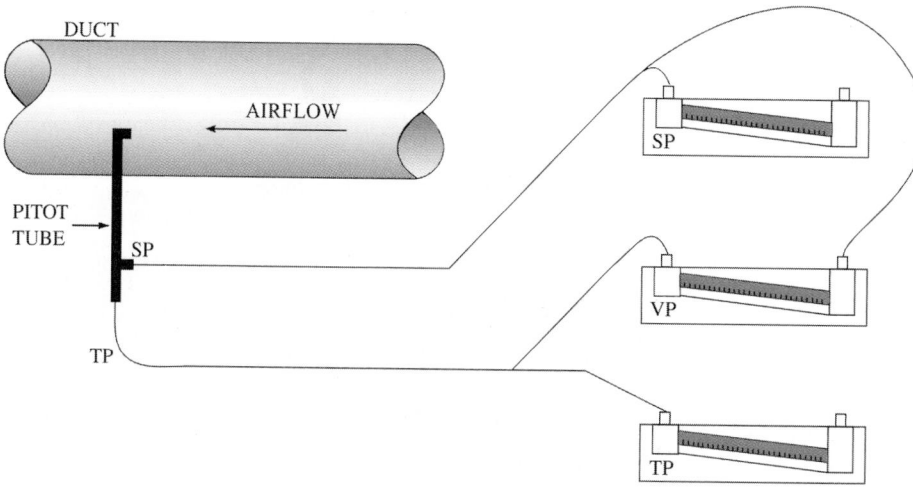

Figure 60-15 Standard manometer connection to a pilot tube
(Courtesy of SMACNA)

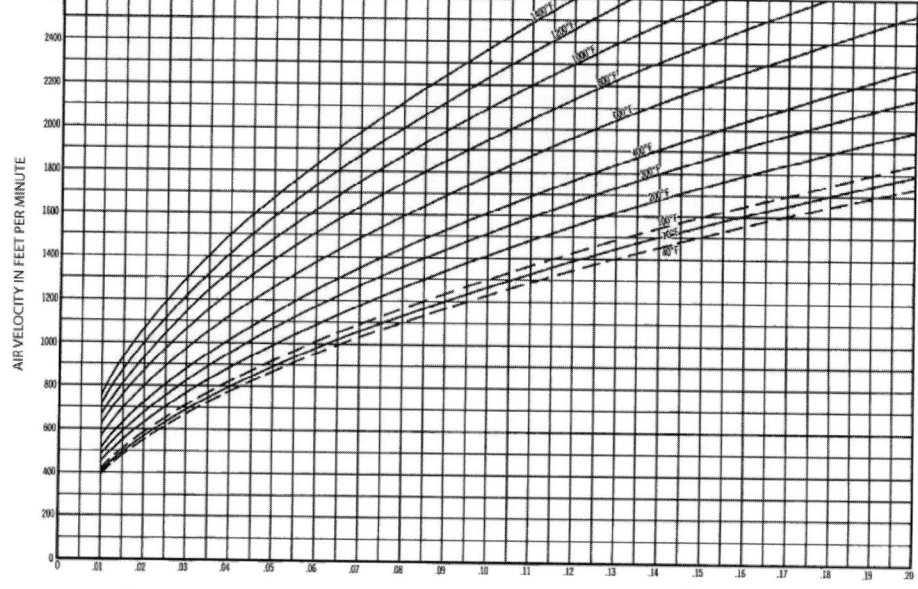

Figure 60-16 Chart for determining air velocity pressure
(Courtesy of Dwyer Instruments, Inc.)

60.7 AIRFLOW

Airflow measurements measure the rate of airflow. The two most common airflow measurements are air velocity, in feet per minute, and air volume, in cubic feet per minute. Feet per minute, fpm, measures how fast the air is traveling. Cubic feet per minute measures the volume of airflow. Having the correct air volume, CFM, is crucial to any air conditioning application.

Air Velocity

Air velocity is not the same through all parts of the duct. It tends to move faster toward the middle, and slower toward the outside of the duct. A procedure called traversing the duct is used to get an accurate velocity reading. Readings are taken at several positions in the duct to get the average air speed through the duct. The combination of the inclined manometer and pitot tube is used in measuring air volume in a duct by making a traverse, Figure 60-17.

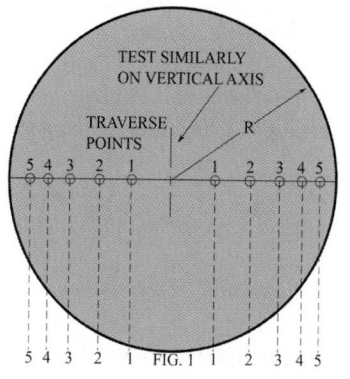

Figure 60-17 Round duct traverse
(Courtesy of SMACNA)

Air Volume

The air volume can be calculated in cubic feet per minute, CFM, using the velocity in feet per minute, fpm, and the cross-sectional area of the duct in square feet, ft^2. The formula is:

$$CFM = area \times velocity$$

For example, a 12 in $\times$ 24 in duct has a cross sectional area of 2 ft^2:

$$12 \times 24 = 288 \text{ in}^2$$
$$288 \text{ in}^2/144 \text{ in}^2/ft^2 = 2 \text{ ft}^2$$

If the velocity through this duct is 350 fpm, the air volume is 2 ft^2 $\times$ 350 fpm = 700 CFM.

Air Velocity/Volume Measuring Instruments

Inclined manometers and pitot tubes read airflow be reading the pressure in a duct. This will not work once the air has left the duct and is entering the room. Instruments are available that read fpm, CFM, or both directly without having to read a pressure in a duct. Some direct reading airflow instruments used are the rotating vane anemometer, the thermal anemometer, the velometer, and the flow hood.

The **rotating vane anemometer** consists of a lightweight air propelled wheel, geared to dials that record the linear feet of airflow passing through the instrument. Anemometers read feet of air. The instrument is placed in the airstream and readings are then taken for a measured amount of time. The anemometer reading is divided by the time to arrive at a velocity reading in feet per minute. Anemometers can be either analog or digital. The analog instrument is a direct reading with the choice of a number of different velocity scales. The digital instrument will automatically average the readings and display the velocity readout in fpm, Figure 60-18.

The **thermal anemometer** operates on the principle that the resistance of a heated wire will change with its temperature, Figure 60-19. The probe is placed in the airstream and the velocity is indicated on the scale of the instrument. Thermal anemometers can be used for measuring very low velocities of air, such as found in a room. They can also be used in a duct to determine air velocity.

A velometer reads the instantaneous speed of the air, not the averaged speed. A velometer is similar to the speedometer on a car, which tells how fast the car is going at that instant. Velometers are also available in both analog and digital form. Figure 60-20 shows an analog velometer. Many digital velometers can function as either a velometer or an anemometer.

The **flow hood** is useful in accurately determining the airflow volume in CFM from an outlet, Figure 60-21. It completely collects the air supply and directs it through a 1 ft^2 opening where a calibrated manometer provides the CFM

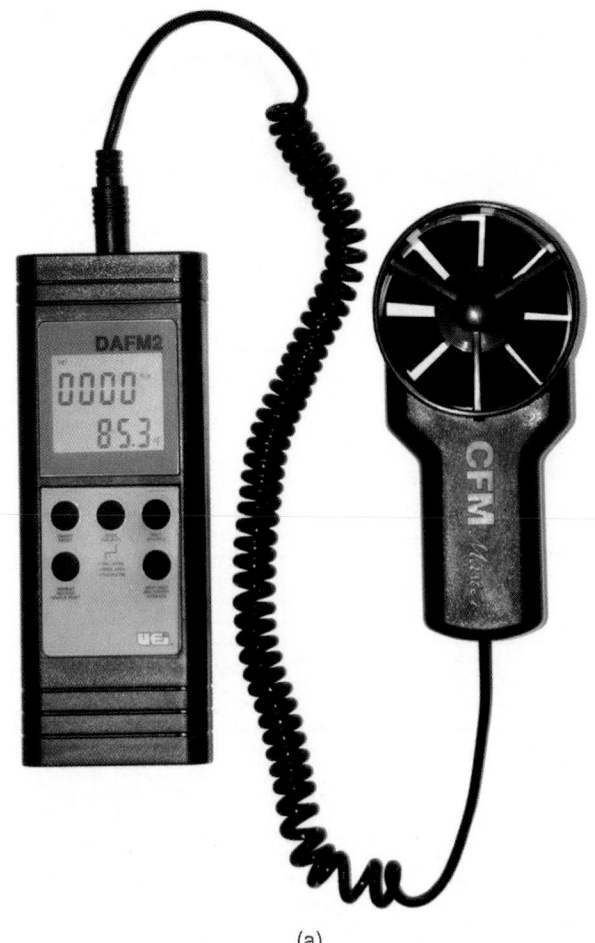

(a)

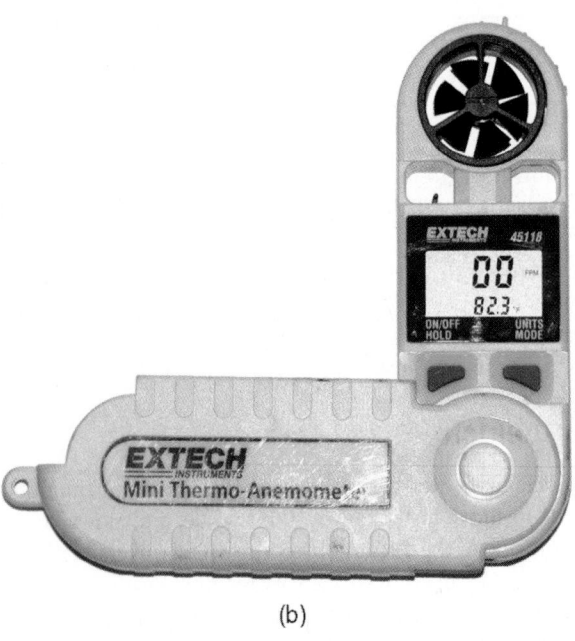

(b)

Figure 60-18 (a) Rotating vane anemometer; (b) Electronic rotating vane anemometer

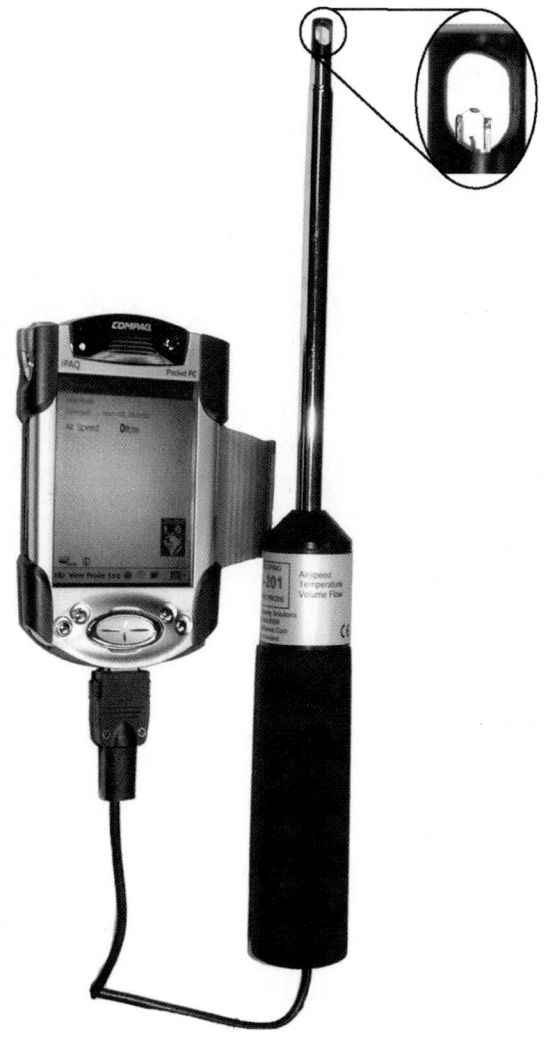

Figure 60-19 Thermal anemometer

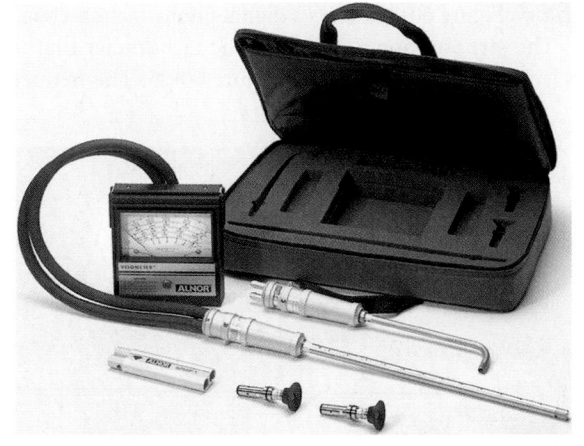

Figure 60-20 Velometer
(Courtesy of Alnor Instrument Company)

readout. Hoods should be selected to as nearly as possible fit the diffuser being measured and have a tight seal around the opening. Flowhoods are considered the most accurate measurement of airflow through registers and grilles.

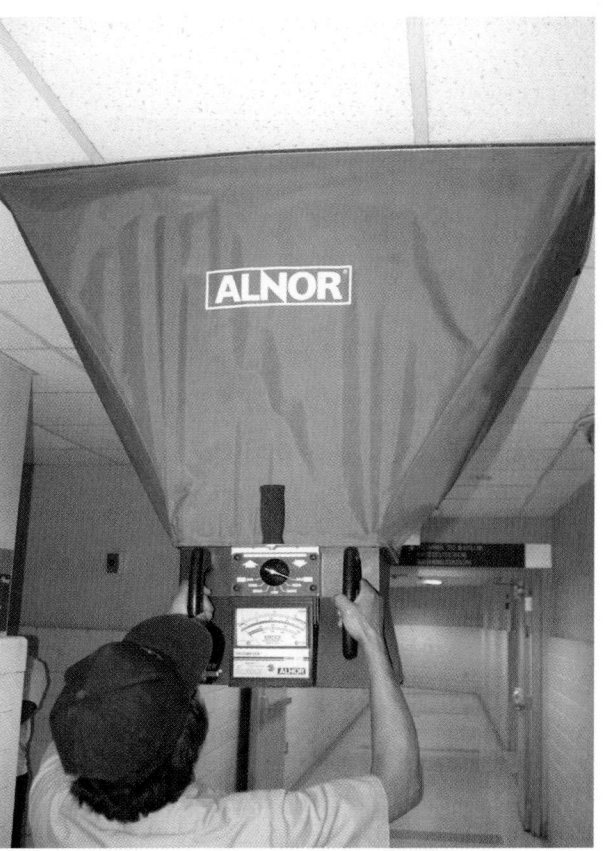

Figure 60-21 Flow measuring hood
(Courtesy of Alnor Instrument Company)

60.8 ELECTRICAL MEASUREMENTS

Electrical measurements are taken to determine voltages, current, and wattage used by electrical loads such as electric motors or electric furnaces. The wattage can be used to find variables such as Btu or rpm (revolution/minute) which are used in duct system performance equations. The instrument used may display units of measure such as volts, amps, or watts, and these units are converted by technicians as needed. Common electrical meters include the digital multimeter and the clamp-on ammeter.

The **digital multimeter** is useful for making electrical measurements in the field. Most meters have several scales including volts, ohms, and amperes. Multimeters typically read small currents inline, such as milliamps.

The **clamp-on ammeter** is used to read large currents. The clamp-on transformer jaws permit reading current flow without disconnecting the circuit. Care must be exercised when reading ampere flow to only clamp onto one wire at a time. Enclosing two wires may result in a zero reading. The amp draw of a blower motor can be used as a general indicator to show the amount of air that a blower is moving. The amp draw increases as the fan moves more air and decreases as the blower moves less air.

A **wattmeter** is needed to take accurate wattage readings in most alternating current circuits. Apparent power can be determined by multiplying the voltage and amperage, but the apparent power in an alternating current circuit is usually higher than the actual wattage because of the effects of inductive and capacitive reactance. Purely resistive alternating current circuits are an exception because they are not subject to inductive or capacitive reactance.

60.9 ROTATION MEASUREMENT

Rotation measuring of fans by TAB technicians may be required to determine fan revolutions per minute (rpm). The airflow rate produced by a fan is directly related to fan speed. Measuring the fan speed before and after any adjustments ensures the proper adjustment is made. Instruments used to measure rotation are the mechanical tachometer, digital photo-tachometer, the chronometric tachometer, and the stroboscope.

A **mechanical tachometer** requires contact to the center of the rotating shaft which is being measured, Figure 60-22. A rubber tip transfers the rotational motion to the tachometer which reads in revolutions per minute.

The **chronometric tachometer** combines a revolution counter and a stopwatch in one instrument, Figure 60-23.

(a)

RUBBER TIP IS HELD AGAINST
ROTATING MOTOR SHAFT.

(b)

Figure 60-22 Tachometer: (a) Front view; (b) Side view

Figure 60-23 Chronometric tachometer
(Reprinted with permission by Megger)

The spindle is placed in contact with the rotating shaft. This sets the meter hand to zero and starts the stopwatch. After a fixed amount of time, usually 6 s, the counting mechanism is automatically uncoupled, and the instrument can be removed from the shaft and read.

A **digital photo-tachometer** uses reflective tape on the outside on the rotating device. It calculates the speed by measuring the frequency of the reflective tape passing by the stationary position of the photo tachometer. The instrument is battery operated and uses a digital display to show the speed in rpm. Digital photo-tachometers can take measurements that contact tachometers cannot take because they do not require physical contact. Some models can save the readings in memory. Figure 60-24 shows a digital photo-tachometer.

The **stroboscope** is an electronic tachometer that uses an electronically flashing light, Figure 60-25. The frequency

Figure 60-24 Digital photo-tachometer
(Courtesy of Extech Instruments Corporation)

Figure 60-25 Stroboscope for measuring rotational speed

of the light flashes can be adjusted to equal the frequency of the rotating object. When the two are synchronized, the rotating object appears to be standing still. The rpm value can then be read on the stroboscope's dial.

60.10 USING TEMPERATURE RISE TO MEASURE SYSTEM AIRFLOW

One of the simplest ways to measure airflow is the *temperature rise method*. One advantage to this method is that the equipment used in the measurement is standard on

all service trucks. Using the temperature rise method on a heating system is straightforward because it is entirely a sensible heat process. All the heat that goes into the air changes the air temperature. Dry bulb temperature measurements are taken both of entering and leaving air and the *difference* of the two numbers gives the technician the TD or *temperature difference*.

Entering air temperature − leaving air temperature
= temperature difference

Temperature Rise Measurements

Find the furnace *output ratings* from the equipment information sheets. These should be listed in Btu/hr. The CFM can be calculated using the heat output in Btu/hr the temperature difference, and 1.08 which is the constant for *standard air*. The factor 1.08 is the mathematical combination of all the other factors in the formula: $1.08 = 60 \text{ min/hr} \times 0.075 \text{lb/ft}^3 \times 0.24 \text{ Btu/lb}$. To calculate CFM:

$$\text{CFM} = \frac{\text{furnace output in Btu/hr}}{(\text{TD} \times 1.08)}$$

Air Conditioning System Temperature Drop

The temperature difference across an air conditioning coil cannot be used to calculate airflow because all the system capacity does not go into changing the air temperature; some capacity is used to condense water on the evaporator coil. The system capacity and the amount of latent cooling versus sensible cooling varies depending upon the system operating conditions, making temperature drop calculations inaccurate.

Wet bulb temperatures can be used to find the enthalpy of the air entering and leaving the evaporator. These measurements can be used to calculate the total system capacity. However, since the system capacity is not fixed, but varies depending upon its operating conditions, the enthalpy change through the evaporator coil is not an accurate way to determine system airflow.

TECH TIP

TAB technicians are keenly aware of the impact that improper unit sizing has on occupants and society as a whole because their training is focused on efficiency and indoor air quality. Many times "rule of thumb" sizing is used by untrained workers to speed a project along. Problems with these systems often stick out like a "sore thumb" once TAB technicians take their measurements and apply formulas on those units that have been sized using a rule of thumb. Problems resulting from improper sizing can affect the reputation of the worker and the employer.

60.11 USING STATIC PRESURE DROP TO MEASURE SYSTEM AIRFLOW

The amount of air moved by any blower or air conditioning component containing a blower is dependent on the pressure that the blower is working against. The airflow a blower is moving in a system can be accurately determined by measuring the pressure drop across the blower and comparing that pressure to the manufacturer's specifications. To determine the amount of air a blower is moving:

1. Measure the total static pressure difference across the blower.
2. Compare the static pressure difference across the blower to the manufacturer's specifications to determine the system airflow.

Figure 60-26 shows how to measure the pressure drop across a blower.

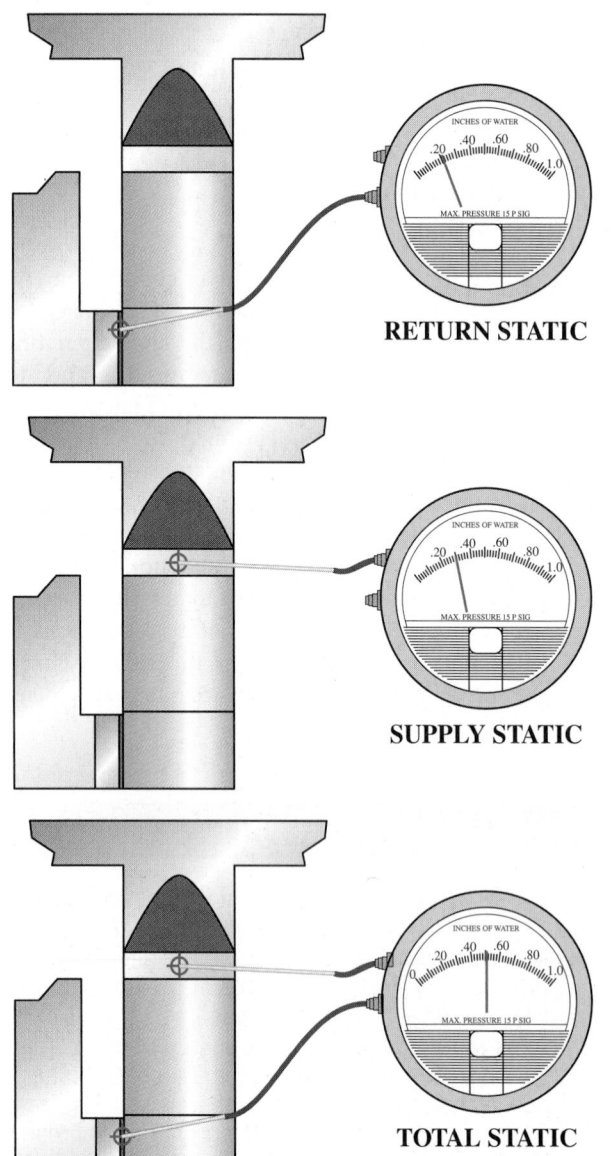

RETURN STATIC

SUPPLY STATIC

TOTAL STATIC

Figure 60-26 The static pressure difference across a blower can be used to determine the airflow through the blower

60.12 MEASURING AIRFLOW AT REGISTERS AND GRILLS

The easiest and most accurate method for measuring the airflow at registers and grills is with a flow hood. The flow hood is placed over the register or grill and all the air moving through the register or grill must pass through the flow hood. The CFM is read directly on the flow hood. Anemometers or velometers can be used by measuring the average airflow velocity and multiplying it by the free area of the register or grill. The actual opening in the grill is much smaller than the overall grill area. The specifications for the register or grill are necessary to determine the free area of the register or grill.

> ### SERVICE TIP
>
> A cone or pyramid with a known area can be fabricated and placed over the register. This eliminates the need to determine the free area. The airflow through the opening of the measurement cone is generally more even than at the face of the register, making it easier to take an average velocity reading

60.13 DUCT LEAK TESTING

The "T" in TAB is for testing, and this starts with a general inspection. If the testing is part of the commissioning of a new or modified system, then comparisons should be made between the designer's plans and the physical layout of the project. This comparison will point to possible problems before measurements are actually taken and could save the technician considerable time. If the testing is taking place on an existing system, then a review of designer plans may not be an option. In this case gathering manufacturer's data is the first step prior to inspection. System tonnage, blower CFM, and heat exchanger data should be noted by the technician on the paperwork for easy reference. Later this information will be included in the report submitted to the client along with the findings of the test.

The system should be started prior to testing to confirm airflow at the return and that the system is supplying airflow at the supply terminals. At this point the technician is simply concerned about the presence of airflow. In the balancing phase of TAB we will measure for quantity of airflow. Low or no flow can indicate duct or system problems. Once flow is confirmed, an amp draw reading should be taken before shutting the system down. If the amp draw is not in range of what the manufacturer requires, restrictions above design specifications or duct leaks may be present. Again this will give the TAB technician an indication that the system has apparent problems before starting the duct leak test.

Once these preliminary checks are made, the duct leak test can be done. Duct leakage is determined by blocking all duct outlets, pressurizing the duct, and measuring the amount of air that is required to maintain that pressure. As air leaks out, more air is let in to maintain the pressure in the duct system. In theory, no additional airflow should be required to maintain the pressure once the duct has been pressurized.

There are several ways to complete a leak test, but the standard method is the use of an orifice tube. The orifice is certified and designed for a specified flow curve. A pressure source is installed to pressurize the duct system. This is normally an axial fan with an inlet damper to control airflow and limit pressure to the duct system. Two manometers are used during these checks. One will be installed to measure pressure drop across the orifice, and the other will measure static pressure in the duct system at the farthest distance from the orifice. Pressure supplied to the duct system should not exceed maximum design ratings that are specific to each system. The technician should read the pressure drop across the orifice; then compute the flow rate using the flow curve data. The actual leakage rate can then be compared with the allowable leakage rate of the duct system. Most systems should have a loss rate no greater than 2%. A review of standards and local codes should be used to determine each project's maximum loss rate.

Once the inspection and leak tests are completed, then a report should be generated for the client. If the duct system is out of design tolerance, the system should be corrected to meet design conditions before attempting to balance the system. Most duct systems are installed in a nonconditioned space, so ducts that leak will increase energy costs and prevent the system from controlling humidity, temperature, and indoor air quality to the efficiency level that the system was designed to meet.

60.14 SYSTEM BALANCING

Balancing in its broadest meaning includes testing and adjusting a system to produce its design specifications. It is the final step in the HVAC project prior to occupancy and use by the owner. It is an important phase of the work, since many components from many sources have been assembled to perform a valuable service. Usually equipment adjustments and control settings are necessary to prepare for the desired operation.

General concepts and measurements should be understood before focusing on particular systems. It is easier to balance a heating system during cold weather and a cooling system during warm weather; however, this is not always possible. It is recommended that the first balance be made when the job is completed or before occupancy, and the final balance made during a period as near design temperature conditions as possible.

All duct systems should have balancing dampers installed at the trunk of the duct system. All branches should have the airflow adjusted at these dampers. Supply registers should be used as balance adjustment points only if a branch feeds more than one supply register. If supply registers are used as balancing dampers, they will produce excessive noise in the space. If a duct system has no balancing dampers installed at the trunk, the owner should be notified in writing that the system cannot be properly balanced without their installation.

The blower must be sized and adjusted to supply the needed output for the whole duct system. The blower is sized by the design engineer, but the blower rpm may need to be adjusted by the technician to meet actual demand. The TAB technician is expected to measure the CFM produced by blower and complete the adjustments necessary for the actual performance to match the design performance.

60.15 GENERAL AIR BALANCING PROCEDURE

First, collect complete information about the installation. This should include unit specifications, control systems details, job layout, and airflow quantities for each register and grille. Examine the entire installation. Look for problems that need to be corrected, such as leaky ductwork, missing parts, and incomplete wiring.

After gathering system data, the overall system airflow should be measured and compared to design specification. There is no point in adjusting the airflow to individual areas until the overall system airflow is correct. Open all dampers, operate the system and measure the overall system airflow in CFM. Compare the actual system airflow to the design airflow. If the actual delivered airflow is more than 5% out of specification, adjust the blower speed to achieve design airflow.

The next step is to compare the airflow delivered in the space to the airflow at the blower. Use a flowhood, velometer, or anemometer to measure the airflow at each supply register and return grill. The sum of all the CFM measurements at the individual return grills should be within 10% of the system CFM at the blower. Leaks in the return air ducts will cause the air entering the return grills to be less than the total amount of air the blower is moving. If the difference is greater than 10%, the return ducts should be checked for leaks. Similarly, the sum of all the CFM measurements at the individual supply registers should be within 10% of the system CFM at the blower. Leaks in the supply air ducts will cause the air leaving the supply air registers to be less than the total amount of air the blower is moving. If the difference is greater than 10%, the supply air ducts should be checked for leaks.

Once the total delivered airflow is within specification, the supply register measurements should be compared to design specifications for each area. Dampers can now be adjusted to achieve the correct airflow at each register. Since the adjustments are being made starting with all dampers open, start by partially closing the dampers to registers that are delivering too much air. Begin with the register that exceeds design specifications the most.

Physical adjustments to dampers change the overall system resistance, affecting the CFM throughout the duct system.

Ideally, measurements should be taken after each adjustment to see the effect of the adjustment on the entire system. However, this can be very time consuming. An alternative is to measure only the output of the zone you are adjusting until it is correct, and then retake the overall system CFM to ensure that the overall system airflow has not dropped as a result of the adjustment. Recheck all measurements periodically to see the overall effect of your adjustments. Using reliable equipment and taking accurate measurements can save large amounts of time.

Last, reset the thermostat to the proper room temperature. Instruct the owner on proper operation of the system. Record the information used in balancing the system, including the weather conditions on the day the job was balanced.

60.16 BALANCING A ZONED AIR SYSTEM INSTALLATION

The same procedure is used for balancing a zoned air system, except that zone dampers are adjusted to produce the correct airflow to each zone. The overall system airflow is established, the zone dampers are adjusted, and finally the dampers to individual runs are adjusted.

UNIT 60—SUMMARY

Testing and balance procedures are the final check to confirm that the operation of a heating and air conditioning system is within design specifications. A system that has not been tested and balanced can allow unhealthy conditions to develop in the conditioned space and could affect the long term health of the occupants.

Test and balance is considered the first step in improving energy efficiency of an air conditioning system.

Test and balance procedures are designed to balance airflow evenly in a structure, and this includes comparing design plans to actual measurements of duct system CFM along with all factors contributing to duct system CFM.

In addition to standard tools used by service technicians, TAB technicians may also use a chronometric tachometer, digital or analog capture hood, air differential pressure gauges, and recording thermometers to perform their work.

The TAB industry is supported by many organizations and associations that produce standards and certifications for contractors and technicians as well as publications for consumer information.

──── WORK ORDERS

The service tickets are all on a small single zone commercial air conditioning system with ducted return and supply air having the following specifications:

Design airflow: 4,000 CFM

Blower design pressure drop: 0.7 in wc

Design supply air static pressure: 0.5 in wc

Design return air static pressure: –0.2 in wc

Blower full load amp rating: 5.5 A

Service Ticket 6001

The technician measures the following system performance data:

Actual pressure drop across blower: 0.68 in wc

Measured airflow at blower: 4,050 CFM

Actual measured blower amp draw: 5.5 A

Total airflow at supply registers: 3,900 CFM

Total airflow at return grills: 3,000 CFM

From this data, the technician concludes that the total airflow is within specifications, but that the return air duct has one or more leaks.

Service Ticket 6002

The technician measures the following system performance data:

Actual pressure drop across blower: 1.2 in wc

Actual measured supply air static: 0.3 in wc

Actual measured return air static: –0.9 in wc

Measured airflow at blower: 3,100 CFM

Actual measured blower amp draw: 2.5 A

From this data the technician determines that the overall airflow is low due to airflow restrictions that are causing an excessive pressure drop across the blower and reducing the airflow. The technician examines the supply and return air static pressure readings and notices that the return air duct has a lower than normal static pressure reading. Static pressure readings across the HEPA filters show that the majority of the pressure drop is occurring at the filter. The filters appear clean. The technician looks up the application data for the filters. They are designed to have a static pressure drop of 1 in wc at their rated airflow. The technician informs the company that the filters will not work with the system.

Service Ticket 6003

The technician measures the following system performance data:

Actual pressure drop across blower: 0.5 in wc

Actual measured supply air static: 0.3 in wc

Actual measured return air static: –0.2 in wc

Measured airflow at blower: 3,000 CFM

Actual measured blower amp draw: 2.4 A

The technician notices that the pressure drop across the blower is lower than the design specification and that both the supply and return static pressures are lower than design. From this data the technician concludes that the blower speed should be increased to increase the system airflow.

UNIT 60—REVIEW QUESTIONS

1. List six types of measurements used to perform TAB procedures.

2. List five instruments are used in TAB procedures.

3. Outline the general test and balance procedure for system airflow.

4. Explain how to measure temperature rise.

5. Why is the temperature difference across an air conditioning coil not used to calculate airflow?

6. Explain how to measure airflow using temperature rise.

7. How do the test and balance procedures for a zoned system differ from a nonzoned system?

8. How is the CFM at a supply register determined using a velometer?

9. What does amp draw have to do with TAB procedures?

10. Why are the dampers on registers normally not used for balancing the system airflow?

11. Can a proper balance be performed on a duct system that does not have balancing dampers for each branch?

12. What can cause the total airflow leaving the supply registers to be much lower than the amount of air the blower is moving?

13. Why does a technician working for a TAB firm require specialized training?

14. How can TAB improve the health of the occupants?

15. Why is interest in TAB picking up in the residential market?

16. Can energy costs be affected by TAB of a system?

17. How are feet per minute measurements (fpm) different from cubic feet per minute measurements (CFM)?

18. Name two organizations that support the TAB industry by developing standards and offering certification.

19. How is a single pressure gauge with a rotating dial used to measure the pressure difference in a circulating water system?

20. Why would having a system tested and balanced be a good first step toward reducing energy cost?

UNIT 61

Fundamentals of Psychrometrics

OBJECTIVES

After completing this unit you will be able to:

- discuss the factors affecting human comfort.
- list the ways the body dissipates heat.
- explain the relationship between dry bulb, wet bulb, and dew point temperatures.
- plot points on the psychrometric chart given any two variables.
- locate all unknown air properties on a psychrometric chart from the intersection of two known air properties.
- calculate the mixed air temperature of two different temperature airstreams.

61.1 INTRODUCTION

When people think about the properties of air and comfort, they think first about temperature. However, temperature is not the only property of air that is important to air conditioning. The properties of air include weight, volume, temperature, water content, and heat content. Humidity is nearly as important to human comfort as temperature. All the properties of air are important for the operation of air conditioning equipment. The study of air and its properties is called psychrometrics.

61.2 CONDITIONS FOR COMFORT

Comfort is the feeling of physical contentment with the environment. The study of human comfort involves understanding how the area around a person affects the feeling of comfort and how the body adapts to changes in its environment. Many tests have been run to determine what conditions most people consider comfortable in the winter and the summer. The surrounding temperature, relative humidity, and air movement are all influencing factors. In the winter, cooler temperatures can be offset by higher relative humidity and less air movement. In the summer, higher temperatures can be offset by lower relative humidity and increased air movement.

Generalized Comfort Chart

The results of test data have been incorporated in comfort charts, one for summer conditions and one for winter conditions. Figure 61-1 shows the summer comfort conditions in

red and the winter comfort conditions in blue. Note that the temperature range for summer comfort is about 5°F higher than the winter temperature comfort range. This assumes the use of warmer clothing in the winter and lighter clothing in the summer.

Body Temperature Regulation

Normal internal human body temperature is 98.6°F, winter and summer. The proper functioning of the body is dependent on constantly maintaining this temperature. The body temperature of warm blooded animals, including humans, is closely controlled by producing more internal heat than necessary and regulating the release of that heat to the surroundings. The heat is produced by converting food energy into heat. There are four ways the body loses heat to the environment:

- Conduction, Figure 61-2.
- Convection of cool air, Figure 61-3.
- Radiation, Figure 61-4.
- Evaporation, Figure 61-5.

Conduction, radiation, and convention all require surrounding conditions that are cooler than the body temperature in order to dissipate heat. Conduction cools the body by the transfer of heat from the skin to the air surrounding and touching us. Convection accelerates the cooling process by movement of cool air over the body, increasing the transfer of heat from the body to the air. The wind chill effect often reported in the winter is due to convection. Cooling by radiation occurs when we get close to a large object that is colder than our body temperature. Heat loss through radiation can be demonstrated by standing next to a cold outside wall in the winter. Heat leaves the body and travels to the cold wall without the person actually touching the wall.

The body cannot be cooled by conduction, convection, and radiation whenever the surrounding temperature is warmer than body temperature. In fact, they begin transferring heat in. Evaporation is the only body cooling process that does not require cooler surroundings. Evaporation only requires that the body produce sweat and that the surrounding air be able to absorb water. Rapid evaporation of perspiration produces a cooling effect. This is why the humidity plays an important role in human comfort. People feel cooler in drier air because their perspiration can readily evaporate. They feel warmer in air with a higher relative humidity because the evaporation process is slower.

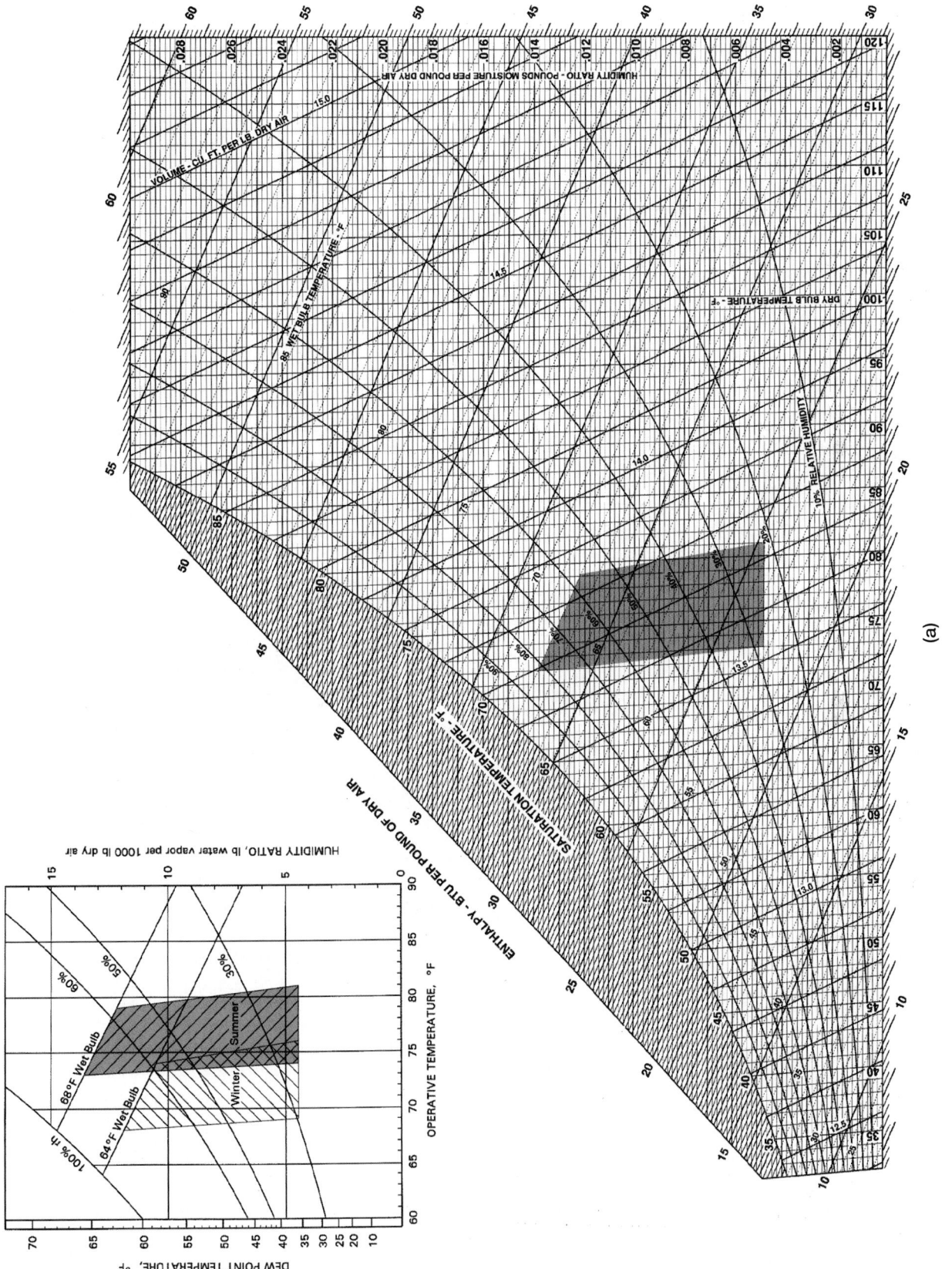

(a)

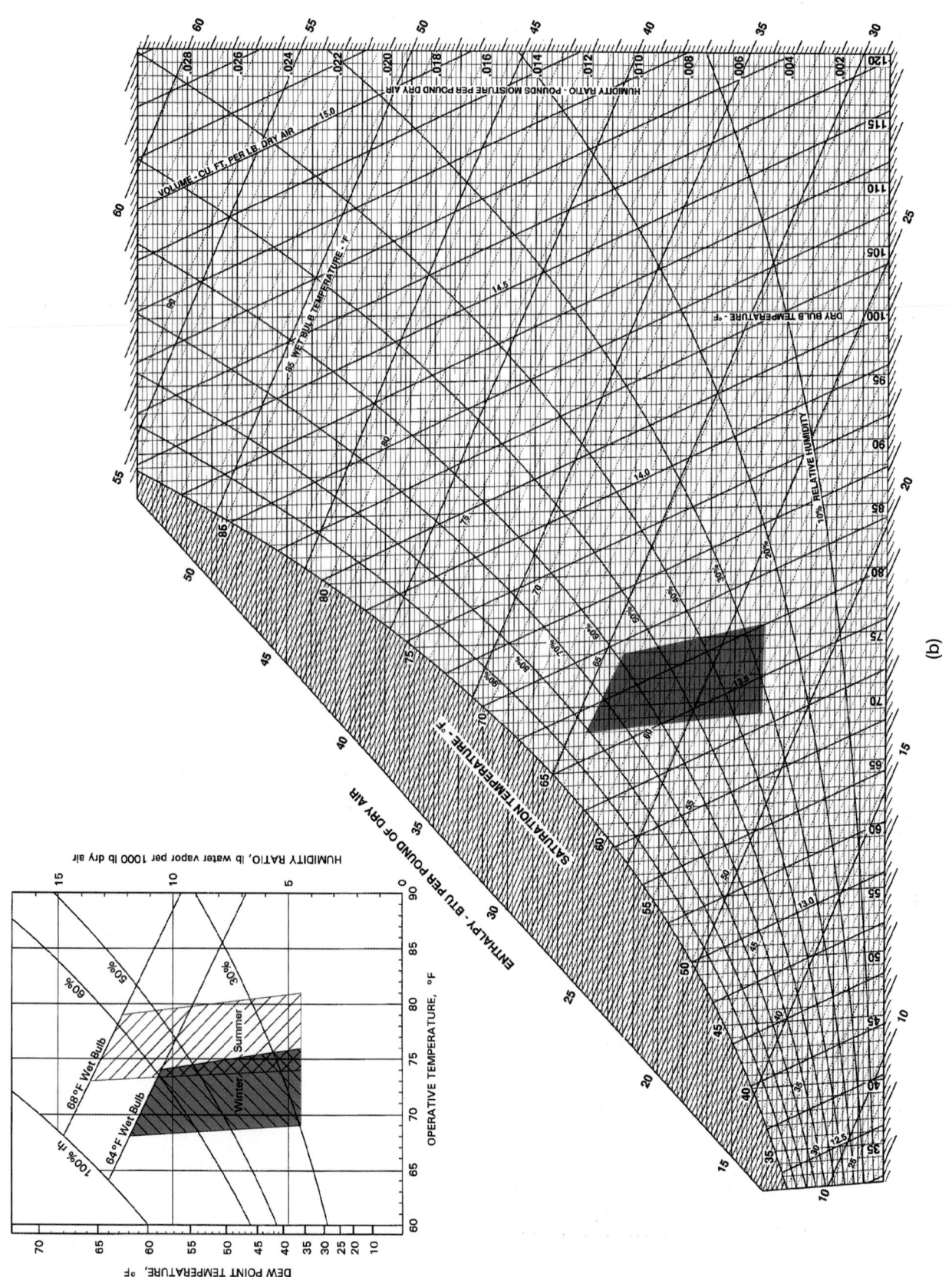

Figure 61-1 Generalized comfort conditions; summer conditions are shown in red and winter conditions are shown in blue

61.7 PSYCHROMETRIC CHART

The psychrometric chart is a graphical representation of air properties, Figure 61-15. Pschrometric charts are used by engineers to plot system performance when designing air conditioning systems. A system plot provides a visual picture of the changes taking place in the air passing through the air conditioner.

The psychrometric chart can show the following air properties:

- **Dry Bulb Temperature**   Measures the normal air temperature in degrees Fahrenheit and shown with vertical lines, Figure 61-16. The dry bulb temperatures are shown across the bottom of the psychrometric chart.
- **Wet Bulb Temperature**   Measures the wet bulb temperature in degrees Fahrenheit and shown with diagonal lines, Figure 61-17. The wet bulb temperatures are shown along the curved portion on the left-hand side of the psychrometric chart.
- **Enthalpy**   Measures the total heat content of the air in Btu per pound of air. The enthalpy lines are diagonal lines that are nearly parallel to the wet bulb temperature lines, Figure 61-18. The enthalpy values are shown on the left

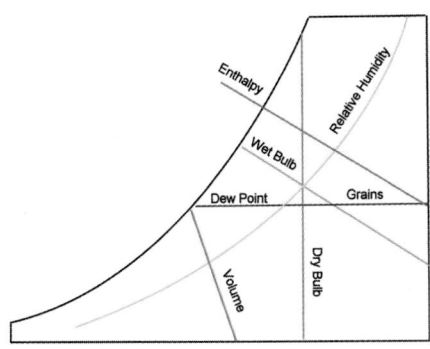

Figure 61-15 The lines on the psychrometric chart represent different air properties

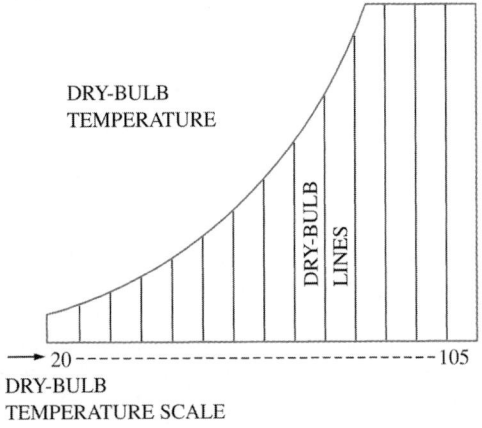

Figure 61-16 Dry bulb temperature lines on psychrometric chart

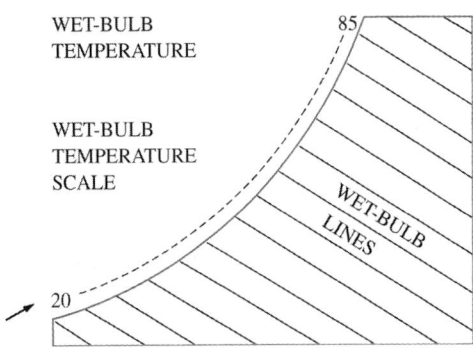

Figure 61-17 Wet bulb temperature lines on psychrometric chart

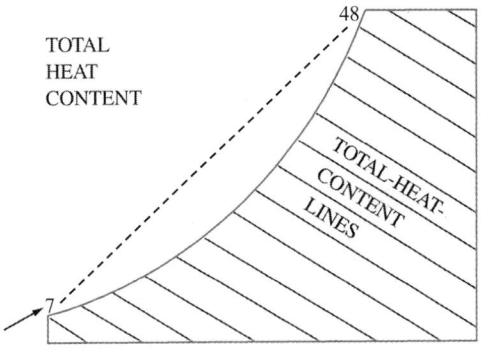

Figure 61-18 Enthalpy (total heat content) lines on psychrometric chart

along a straight line that is roughly parallel to the curved line. Instead of having a separate set of diagonal lines, some charts have the enthalpy values on both the left and right side of the chart. A straightedge is used between them to indicate the enthalpy line, see Figure 61-1.

- **Dew Point Temperature**   Measures the temperature where water will start to condense out of the air. It is measured in degrees Fahrenheit and shown with horizontal lines, Figure 61-19. The dew point temperatures are shown along the curved portion on the left-hand side of the psychrometric chart. They are the same numbers used for reading wet bulb temperature. However, the

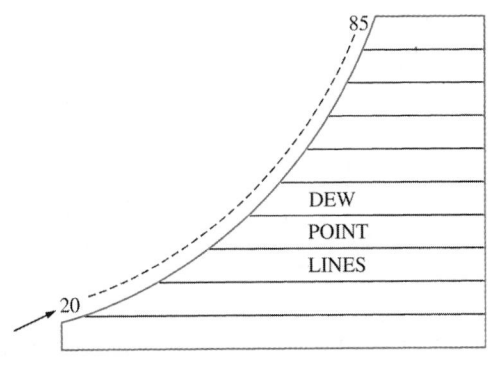

Figure 61-19 Dew point temperature lines on the psychrometric chart

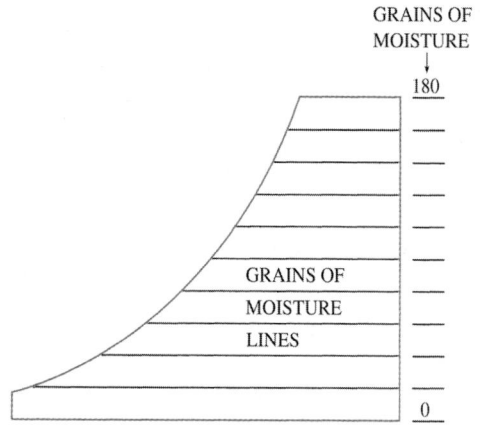

Figure 61-20 Grains of moisture line on the psychrometric chart

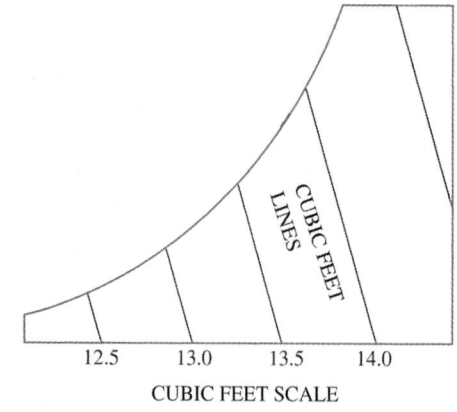

Figure 61-22 Specific volume lines on the psychrometric chart

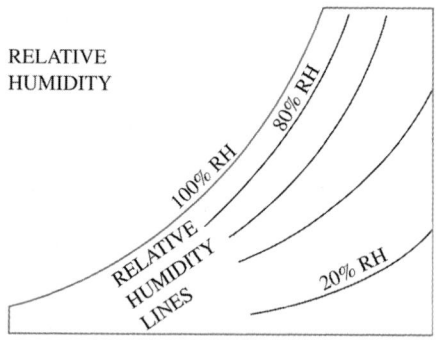

Figure 61-21 Relative humidity lines on the psychrometric chart

temperature and 67°F wet bulb temperature is shown by the red dot in Figure 61-23. Blue arrows from that point show the values of the other properties at that condition. Summarized, they are:

Dry bulb temperature	80°F (given)
Wet bulb temperature	67°F (given)
Dew point temperature	60°F
Relative humidity	50%
Enthalpy	31.4 Btu
Specific humidity	75 grains
Specific volume	13.8 ft^3

dew point lines are horizontal while the wet bulb lines are diagonal.

- **Specific Humidity**   Measures the weight of water vapor in the air in grains and is shown with horizontal lines, Figure 61-20. The specific humidity readings are shown on the right-hand side of the chart.
- **Relative Humidity**   Expresses the percentage of water vapor in the air compared to the amount of water vapor the air can hold. Relative humidity is shown by the sweeping curved lines, Figure 61-21. The values are written on the lines.
- **Specific Volume**   Measures the space in cubic feet occupied by each pound of air. The specific volume lines are diagonal lines with a less severe slope, Figure 61-22. The values are written on the lines.

61.8 PLOTTING POINTS ON THE PSYCHROMETRIC CHART

Any two air properties that use separate lines can be used to plot a point on the psychrometric chart. All the other properties can be determined once the intersection is found. For example, the intersection of 80°F dry bulb

61.9 SENSIBLE HEAT AND LATENT HEAT PROCESSES

Nearly all processes will involve a change in sensible heat, latent heat, or both. The exception would be a process whose beginning and ending points lie on the same diagonal enthalpy line. Processes that cause a horizontal shift from the start to the finish represent a sensible heat change because the air temperature is changing, Figure 61-24. Processes that cause a vertical shift from the start to the finish represent a latent heat change because the air temperature is remaining the same while the specific humidity is changing, Figure 61-25.

Many processes may cause both sensible and latent heat changes. It is possible to use the psychrometric chart to determine the amount of sensible heat change and latent heat change for an air conditioning process. Plot a third point to form a right triangle between the beginning and ending points of the process. The triangle should have one vertical leg and one horizontal leg. Look up the enthalpy of all three points. The sensible change will be the difference in enthalpy from end to end of the horizontal leg. The latent change will be the difference in enthalpy from end to end of the vertical leg, Figure 61-26.

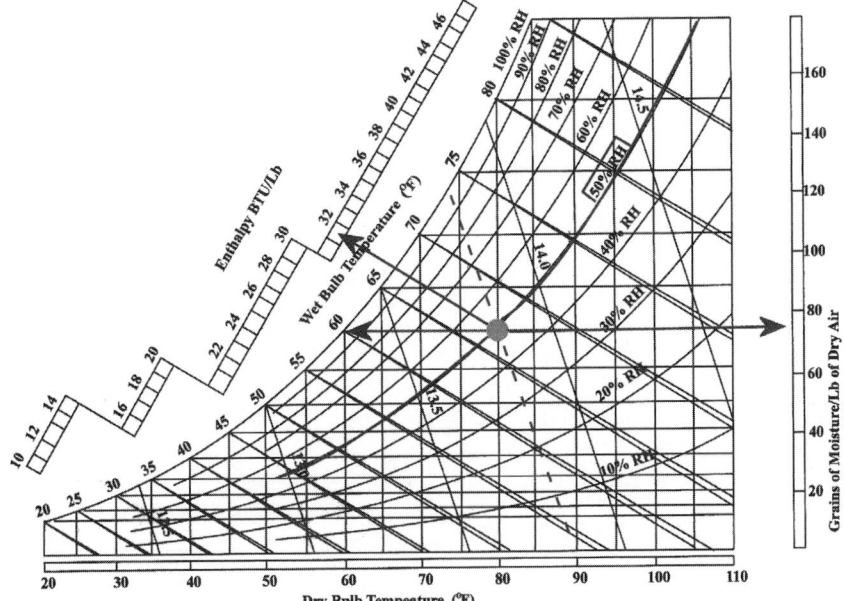

Figure 61-23 Psychrometric chart with 80°F dry bulb and 67°F wet bulb temperatures

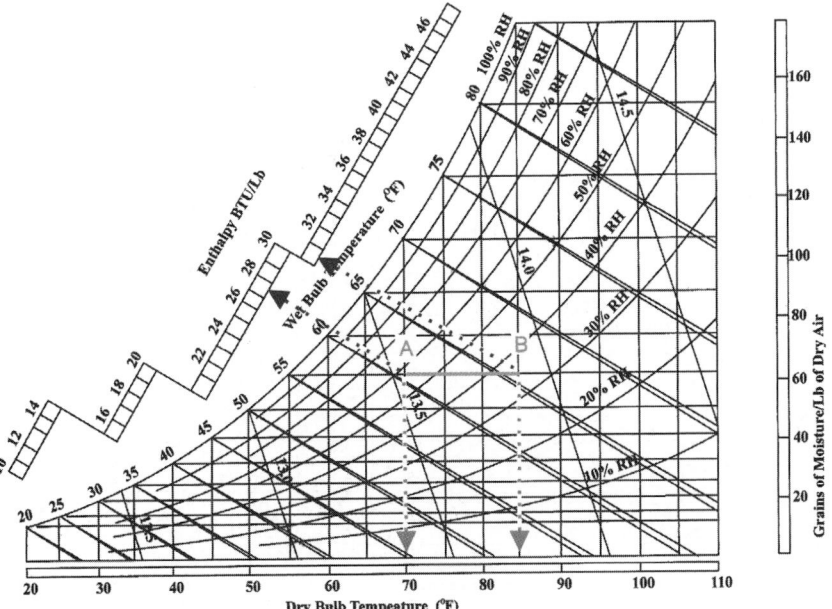

Figure 61-24 Green line between A and B shows a sensible heat change; the red arrows show the temperature change from 70°F to 80°F, the blue arrows show the enthalpy change from 27.5 Btu to 30.5 Btu

61.10 PLOTTING COMMON AIR CONDITIONING PROCESSES

The changes that take place in the properties of the air during an air conditioning process can be plotted. Examples of plotting common air conditioning processes are shown next.

Heating

Figure 61-27 shows the addition of sensible heat. The process is shown moving along a horizontal line to the right. The wet bulb temperature and enthalpy increase and the relative humidity decreases. The dew point temperature and the

water content do not change. This process involves only sensible heat change.

Cooling with a Dry Evaporator Coil

Figure 61-28 shows the reduction of sensible heat. This process represents cooling with a coil whose temperature is above the dew point of the entering air. The process is also shown moving along a horizontal line, but in the opposite direction. The wet bulb temperature and enthalpy decrease and the relative humidity increases. Again, there is no change in dew point or water content. This process involves only sensible heat change.

Figure 61-25 Green line between A and B shows a latent heat change; the red arrows show the specific humidity change from 43 grains to 62 grains, the blue arrows show the enthalpy change from 27.5 Btu to 30.5 Btu

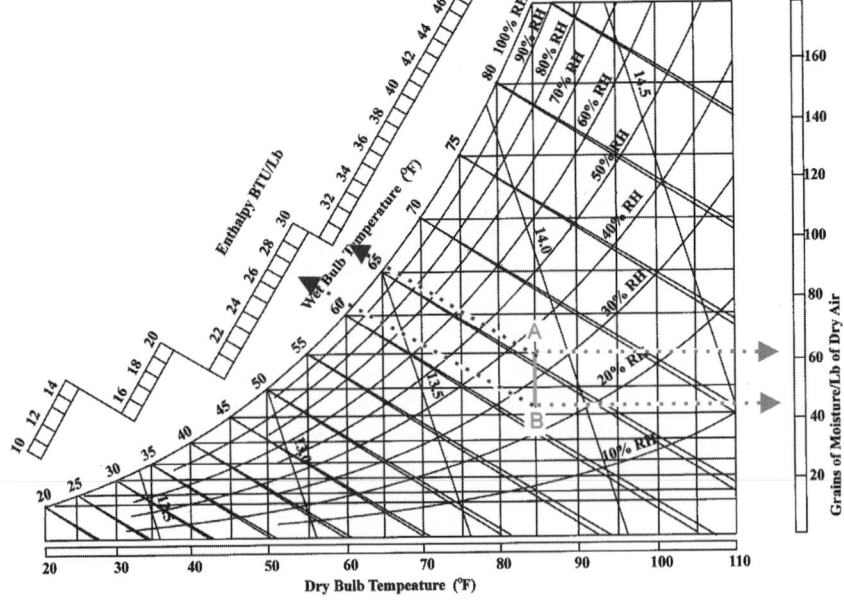

Figure 61-26 B to C shows the sensible change while A to C shows the latent change

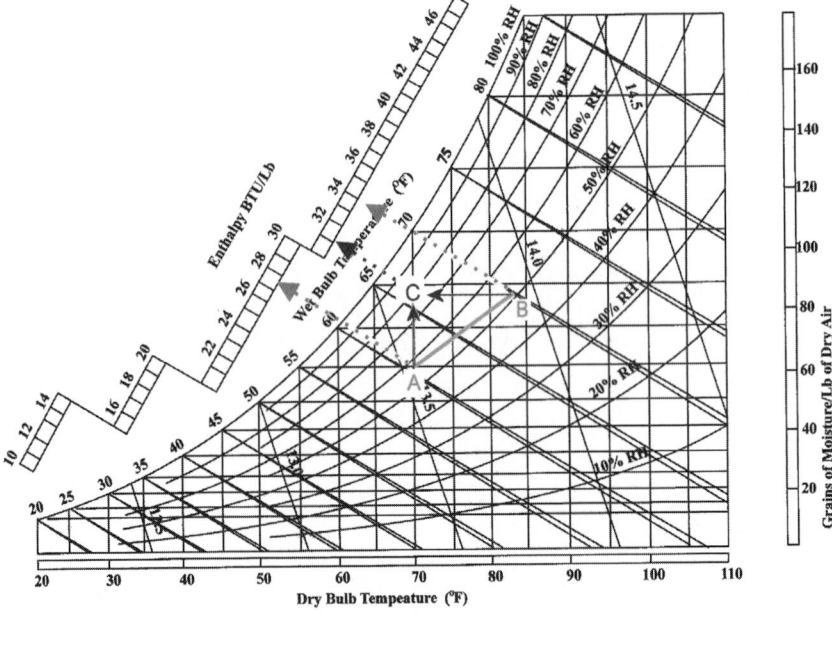

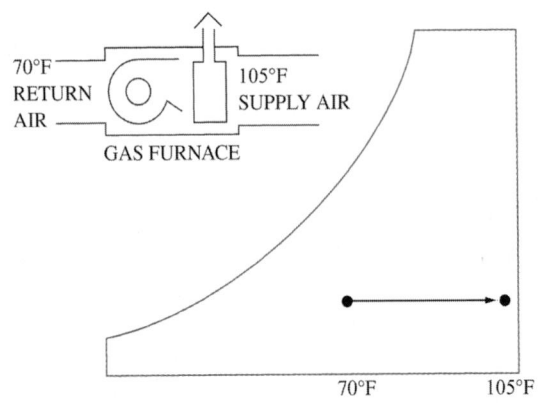

Figure 61-27 Plotting the addition of sensible heat by a furnace, on the psychrometric chart

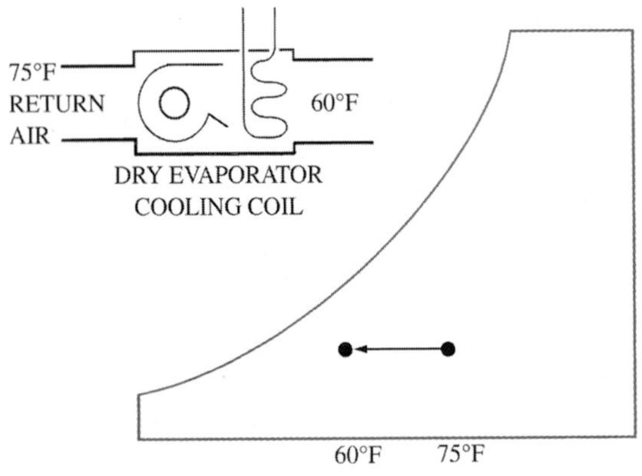

Figure 61-28 Plotting the temperature of air being cooled without dehumidification on the psychrometric chart

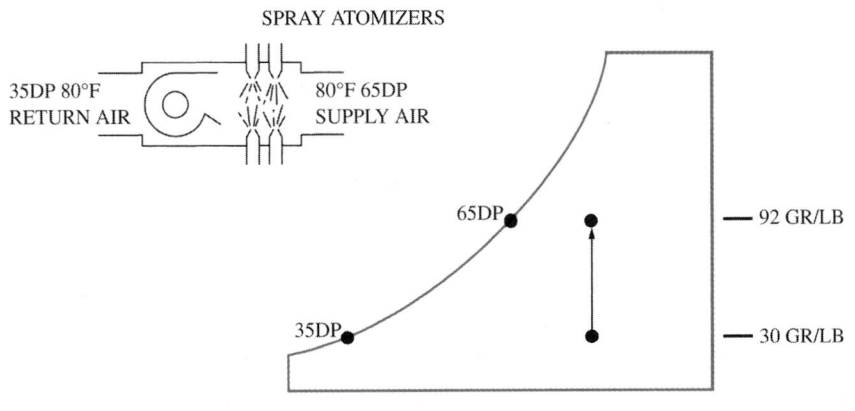

Figure 61-29 Plotting the addition of moisture to the air produced by a humidifier

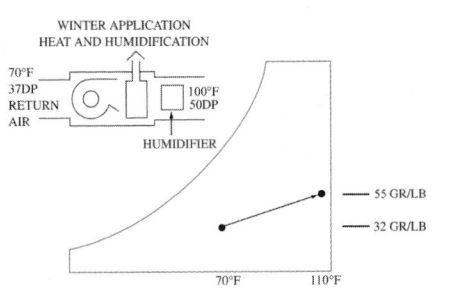

Figure 61-30 Heat and moisture added by a hot air furnace with a humidifier

Humidifying

Figure 61-29 shows the addition of water. This action is represented by a vertical line moving upward as the specific humidity increases. The only property that does not change is the dry bulb temperature, which is held constant. Heat is added as evidenced by the increase in enthalpy, but the heat is used to evaporate the water. The wet bulb temperature, dew point, and relative humidity all increase. This process involves only latent heat change.

Simultaneous Heating and Humidifying

Figure 61-30 shows the simultaneous addition of sensible heat and water. The line representing the operation moves upward to the right. The air picks up both heat and water as it moves through the conditioner. The enthalpy, wet bulb, specific humidity, and dew point temperature all increase. The relative humidity could increase, remain the same, or decrease, depending on how much water is added. In actual operation, the amount of heat and water added must match the heat and water lost by the structure to maintain the same temperature and humidity in the building. This process involves both sensible and latent heat change.

Cooling and Dehumidification

Figure 61-31 shows the reduction of both sensible heat and water. This is the traditional refrigerated air conditioning cycle. The line representing the operation moves downward to the left. The cooling coil both cools the air and condenses water as the air passes through it. The enthalpy, wet bulb, and dew point all decrease. The relative humidity increases, since the air is nearly saturated when it leaves the coil. This process involves both sensible and latent heat change.

Evaporative Cooling

Figure 61-32 shows the process of removal of sensible heat accompanied by a simultaneous increase in water. The process uses evaporation of water to cool the air. The process follows the wet bulb line in the chart. The dry bulb temperature decreases as the water in the air and the relative humidity increase. This process essentially converts sensible heat to latent heat; enthalpy is constant.

Figure 61-31 Cooling and dehumidification produced by an air conditioner, plotted on the psychrometric chart

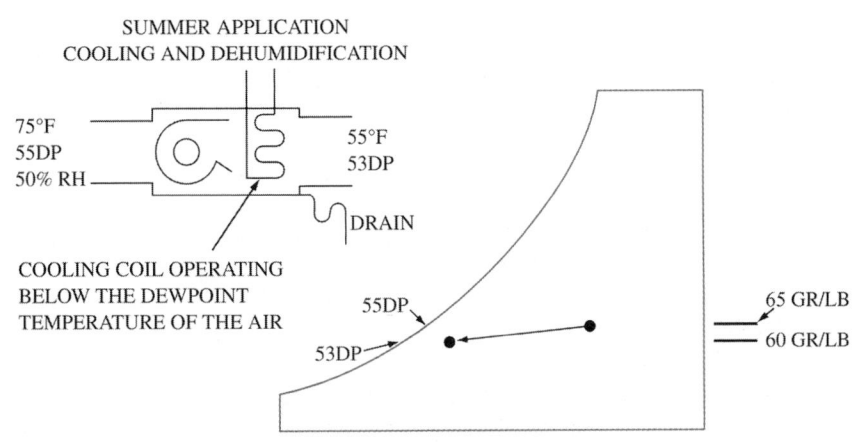

Figure 61-32 Cooling and humidification produced by an evaporative cooler plotted on the psychrometric chart

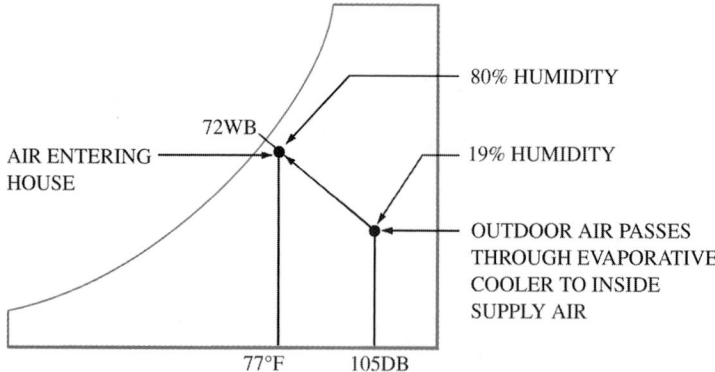

61.11 CALCULATING AIR CONDITIONING SYSTEM PERFORMANCE

The psychrometric chart can be useful in checking the performance of air conditioning equipment, as shown in the following example. Because the wet bulb and enthalpy lines nearly overlap, the wet bulb temperature is really all that is needed to determine the enthalpy. Four measurements are necessary to calculate the actual cooling capacity of an air conditioning system:

- Wet bulb temperature of the entering air.
- Wet bulb temperature of the leaving air.
- Dry bulb temperature of the leaving air.
- Airflow volume in CFM.
- Entering air dry bulb (only necessary if sensible and latent values are to be calculated).

The wet bulb temperatures are used to determine the enthalpy of the entering and leaving air. The difference in the enthalpy between the entering and leaving air will show the amount of heat lost from each pound of air. The dry bulb and wet bulb temperatures of the leaving air are used to determine the volume of each pound of air. The CFM and this volume are used to determine the pounds of air per minute. The total cooling capacity in Btu per minute is determined by multiplying the enthalpy difference in Btu times the pounds per minute of air. This value is multiplied by 60 to show the cooling capacity in Btu/hr. This can be summarized by the following formula:

Enthalpy change = enthalpy of air in − enthalpy of air out

Pounds/minute of air = CFM airflow/cubic feet per pound specific volume of air

Btu/hr = 60 × pounds of air/minute × Btu/lb enthalpy change

Example Calculation

An air conditioner is operating with a return air temperature of 80°F dry bulb, 69°F wet bulb. The supply air temperature is 63°F dry bulb and a 61°F wet bulb with an airflow of 850 CFM. Referring to Figure 61-33, the enthalpy of the return air is 33 Btu/lb, the enthalpy of the supply air is 28 Btu/lb. and

Figure 61-33 The enthalpy of the entering air is 33 Btu/lb and the enthalpy of the leaving air is 27 Btu/lb

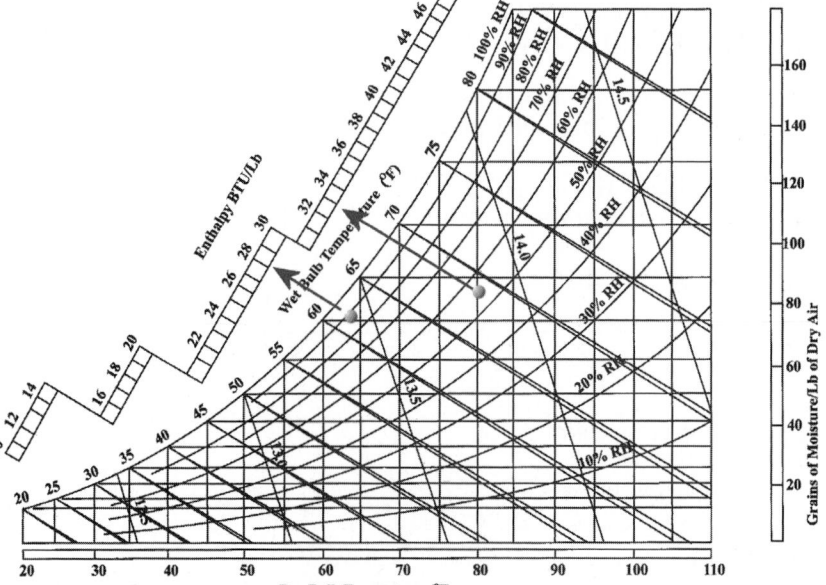

Pollutants can be produced naturally by the earth or may be dependent on some level of human intervention. Radon is a radioactive gas that is produced naturally by the earth. There are also certain elements or compounds that may mix and interact to produce a potentially harmful contaminant. Some household cleaners can oxidize rapidly and emit a strong, gaseous odor when contacting materials that are commonly found in buildings. Chlorine bleach and ammonia cleaner can react and form chlorine, a poisonous gas. Still other pollutants may result from certain processes taking place. For example, a copier may be producing ozone at a level that it is harmful to the operator and perhaps even the coworkers because it is not properly ventilated. Another example is the buildup of carbon dioxide and moisture from the building occupants' breathing. Both water and carbon dioxide can cause indoor air quality problems in high enough concentrations. Improper operation of a piece of heating equipment can be the source of deadly carbon monoxide from incomplete combustion. Many building materials contain formaldehyde and will produce formaldehyde gas when exposed to higher temperatures and humidity. This pollutant can be harmful even at relatively low levels. These are all examples of situations commonly encountered in the marketplace that an HVAC/R technician might encounter and have to resolve.

CAUTION

It should be emphasized that this is a basic introduction to the pollutants. It is not intended to be an all inclusive or exhaustive set of information. What is contained in this unit should help an HVAC/R technician become familiar with the concepts and to gain a basic understanding for what they might encounter. However, it should not be the only source of information and it is not intended to instruct technicians how to resolve every indoor air quality issue they will encounter.

62.4 CHEMICAL POLLUTANTS

Asbestos

Asbestos is a naturally occurring material mined from rocks that occurs in fiber bundles having unusual tensile strength and fire resistance. Asbestos has been banned for use in the US in certain products since the late 1980s, but it is frequently encountered in older buildings. It can be found in the older buildings in joint compounds, vinyl floor tiles, pipe and boiler insulation, fireproofing, caulks, shingles, and a variety of coatings. Asbestos becomes a potential indoor air quality problem when it is in a "friable" condition. Friable means that the fibers can easily be released into the air with minimal disturbance. Asbestos also becomes a serious issue when it might be disturbed for any cutting or sanding operations or any demolition. The HVAC/R technician should not disturb

or remove asbestos containing materials. In many cases, it is best to simply leave material alone that it is believed to be asbestos if it is in good condition and intact. Outside assistance will almost certainly be required if the project would require disturbing asbestos material. Asbestos cannot be positively identified without the services of an outside laboratory to do sampling.

SAFETY TIP

In all cases where asbestos-like material is encountered, the HVAC technician needs to take extra care and caution as the fibers can cause diseases of the lung including Asbestosis, Mesothelioma, and Lung Cancer. HVAC/R technicians should never enter a posted area for any reason when working in an environment where asbestos remediation is underway in a part of a building.

SERVICE TIP

When a material suspected of containing asbestos is believed to be the cause of an indoor air quality problem, the services of another professional should be retained. It is good to have a relationship with a local laboratory and properly qualified asbestos remediation contractor who can address asbestos if it is encountered in the area of operations where an HVAC/R technician works.

CAUTION

Under most circumstances it is illegal for technicians to remove asbestos from the jobsite. Asbestos removal must be carried out by licensed asbestos abatement companies. Removing asbestos without the proper equipment can be hazardous to your health and could result in fines for you and your company. If you suspect that an older installation has asbestos you must request that an approved laboratory test the material to see whether or not asbestos is present.

Lead

Lead is another pollutant that HVAC/R technicians will encounter as they work in older buildings. The HVAC/R technician will need to know how to address lead when it is encountered. While paint that contains lead is often a primary source of airborne contamination, lead can also be found in water and contaminated soils. Lead paint that is in good condition should remain intact. If the paint suspected of containing lead is found to be in poor condition, then it will need to be tested by a laboratory to confirm that it does indeed contain the pollutant and then it must be properly removed. The paint should not be scraped, sanded, or burnt off by untrained individuals. Lead poisoning can cause damage to many of the body's organs and lead dust can be easily brought home to spouses and children on clothes. Decontamination is part of the requirement for performing lead remediation work.

Radon

Radon is a gas that is produced from radium which is found in rocks and soil in the ground. A building that is constructed in close proximity to a source of this gas can become contaminated easily if the pollutant is not controlled. It should also be noted that radon has been found in water from wells and this can be a source for the pollutant to enter a building. Radon gas is colorless and odorless. Radon testing should be performed using methods that meet or exceed established testing industry standards. The standard remediation for radon gas is tightening the building envelope and capturing and removing the gases. This is usually done through ventilation. Radon gas that is not addressed and allowed to enter the living space can lead to lung cancer for building occupants.

Combustion

Combustion is a chemical reaction that occurs most commonly inside equipment that is installed in buildings. The by-products of combustion have the potential to cause significant indoor air quality issues when they do not vent properly or something causes the combustion process to go wrong. HVAC/R technicians may need to perform combustion analysis, draft testing, spillage testing, or building depressurization testing when investigating indoor air quality issues relating to combustion.

CO

Carbon monoxide is a colorless, odorless, and tasteless gas. CO can be produced in substantially harmful quantities when the combustion process becomes incomplete from lack of oxygen or low combustion temperatures. Incomplete combustion and CO may occur from a flame impingement, poor fuel-air mixture, incorrect flame pattern, or combustion air starvation.

Carbon monoxide inhibits the blood's ability to carry oxygen. Extremely low concentrations of CO have been associated with long term health effects especially in children, the elderly, and those who have their health compromised by other diseases or ailments. CO levels as low as 9 PPM (parts per million) are deemed as actionable by some credible industry standards. The technician should always exercise extra caution when working in or around combustion appliances to ensure that the levels do not exceed the OSHA permissible exposure limits of 50 parts per million for an 8 hr time weighted average.

The HVAC/R technician needs to understand that proper combustion is not only essential to aid them in pre-

venting an opportunity for an indoor air quality problem to occur, but it is also essential to enable the equipment to operate efficiently, meet manufacturer specifications, and remain clean and serviceable.

SERVICE TIP

The source of CO contamination may not be the appliances, but the garage. Cars produce large volumes of CO. CO produced by a car operating in an attached garage can be pulled into the house and distributed by the air conditioner or furnace. This is especially likely if the air conditioning equipment is located in a mechanical room adjoining the garage.

CO_2

Carbon dioxide is a normally occurring trace gas in the earth's atmosphere. It has been used as one means for measurement of indoor air quality relative to outdoor air quality. When measuring carbon dioxide, the HVAC/R technician needs to recognize that outdoor air will provide a baseline against which the indoor air can be evaluated. A technician addressing indoor air quality should recognize when the indoor air concentrations of CO_2 are higher than the outdoor concentrations. Demand controlled ventilation systems are available that operate when carbon dioxide levels exceed a certain operating setpoint in a building. Keeping inside levels close to the outdoor baseline is the goal. Since CO_2 concentration is addressed by outside air ventilation, it is not possible to reduce the CO_2 level inside any lower than the CO_2 level outside.

NO_2

Nitrogen dioxide is a gas that is poisonous when inhaled. It is a reddish brown color and has an odor. It can cause serious injury or death even at extremely low levels of exposure, especially to those individuals at risk such as children, the elderly, and those with respiratory diseases and ailments. Another closely related pollutant is nitric oxide. Together these two pollutants are commonly referred to as NO_x. These are both by-products of combustion and contribute to acid rain.

Environmental Tobacco Smoke

Environmental tobacco smoke is becoming less of an indoor air quality problem as more and more authorities having jurisdiction are restricting the use of tobacco products in public places. Where smoking does still occur it can become an indoor air quality issue that an HVAC/R technician may be asked to address. Since environmental tobacco smoke has an estimated 4,000 compounds in it, it is typically a challenge to address using a single method of remediation. Most often the best solution is a combination filtration and exhaust system.

Mercury

Mercury is a heavy metal. Mercury is also found in the air in particulate form around industrial plants that consume high sulfur content fuels. It can be found in buildings in a number of other forms such as in fluorescent light bulbs, batteries, thermostats, and thermometers. It is important that HVAC/R technicians who are addressing indoor air quality where mercury is found or suspected take special precautions to protect themselves from unnecessary exposure. Mercury must be disposed of properly to avoid cross contamination.

Volatile Organic Compounds

VOC's are a class of chemical compounds that give off gas due to their high vapor pressure under standard conditions. Indoor air quality is quite often compromised by these compounds which are found in a number of building materials. They come from paints, carpeting, manufactured woods, and laminates. There are several types of VOC's encountered, include aldehydes, ketones, and hydrocarbons.

- **Aldehydes**   Aldehydes are a class of organic chemical compounds. Formaldehyde is the most commonly encountered aldehyde. Varying forms of this chemical are used in pressboard materials like medium density fiberboard, plywood, particleboard, or oriented strand board (OSB). It is also used in the production of insulation, paints, coatings, glues, and certain fabric materials and is a by-product produced during combustion, especially from unvented fossil fuel burning appliances.

People are typically exposed to formaldehyde when they breathe air that contains formaldehyde fumes. Formaldehyde can cause burning and watery eyes and irritate nasal cavities and mucous membranes. Other reactions include chest tightness, difficulty breathing, and allergic reactions. The first line of defense against formaldehyde exposure is to use formaldehyde free products or low formaldehyde containing products. Ventilation is a common approach to reducing formaldehyde concentrations when the formaldehyde is coming from products inside the building.

- **Ketones**   Ketones are often used in paints and perfumes. The most commonly encountered ketone encountered in indoor air quality will likely be in paints. When an indoor air quality issue is raised due to odor from painting it is often related to the ketones in the paint. Selecting paint products that are low in VOC's will typically lower the amounts of ketones.
- **Mercaptans**   Mercaptans are often used as an odorant in natural gas for safety since the gas is odorless. Those who are chemically sensitive can react to even trace amounts in the parts per billion range of these odorants. It does not take a large dose to impact indoor air quality for these people. Mercaptans can enter the building through gas leaks and combustion products entering the building. To reduce mercaptan levels eliminate any unvented combustion appliances and make sure the vents on vented appliances are operating correctly.
- **Hydrocarbons**   Hydrocarbons are substances that contain only the elements hydrogen and carbon. They are often used as fuels. Many of our rubber products, asphalts, plastics, and fiber materials contain hydrocarbons in aromatic form. These hydrocarbons can cause indoor air quality issues in buildings.

Particulates

Particulates can arise from natural processes such as wind erosion, sea spray evaporation, volcanic eruption, and biological processes. However, natural sources usually create far less contamination than manmade activities. Some of the manmade activities that cause air contamination are power plant operation, industrial processing, various types of transportation, and agricultural activities.

A micron is a millionth of a meter or one thousandth of a millimeter. Figure 62-1 shows the relative size of some particulates in microns. By comparison, human hairs range in size from 25 to 300 microns. Particles smaller than 10 microns are not visible to the naked eye. Smaller particles such as smoke are visible only in high concentrations. Health authorities are concerned with particles that are 2 microns or less because they can be retained in the lungs. Note the size range of a few common pollutants: pollen, 10 to 100 microns; bacteria, 0.4 to 5.0 microns; tobacco smoke is a solid ranging in size from 0.1 to 0.3 microns; and viruses, 0.003 to 0.06 microns.

Pesticides

Pesticides as well as insecticides, rodenticides, herbicides, and fungicides are chemicals used for controlling certain plants, animals, and parasitic organisms. They are designed to kill plants and animals and can be extremely harmful or even fatal to humans. They are important to the technician addressing indoor air quality because the compounds can be carried in on the feet of occupants of the building and become airborne causing reactions by some individuals. These items may be in high enough concentration on surfaces of or around a building that they can actually be drawn in by natural infiltration entering the building through the cracks and crevices.

Ozone

O_3 is an oxidizing agent with a very pungent odor. It is harmful to humans and animals and will cause severe irritation of the mucous membranes in the airway. Ozone is produced by electrical discharge and certain types of ultraviolet radiation. Ozone is an excellent agent for breaking down certain hydrocarbon substances as well as deodorizing air and purifying water. However it must be used carefully. The levels of ozone present in a space must be checked throughout the process of sanitizing with proper testing equipment because ozone can cause damage or harm items it comes into contact with through rapid oxidation. Ozone should never be introduced into occupied living spaces as it will cause harm to humans and animals.

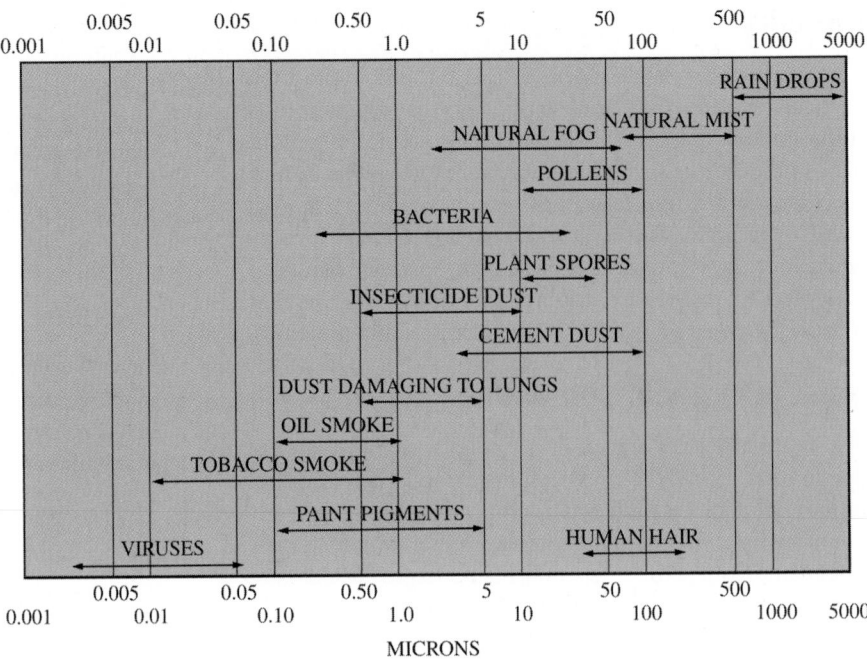

Figure 62-1 Sizes and characteristics of airborne solids and liquids

62.5 BIOLOGICAL POLLUTANTS

Pests

Pests have the potential to introduce biological contaminants into an indoor air environment. In the case of bats and mice, their fecal matter can be hazardous to humans. These droppings are often encountered when entering areas of buildings like ceilings, soffits, or attics. The droppings need to be carefully dealt with. The fecal material should not be inhaled or allowed to be dispersed as it could cause new or additional IAQ issues. Care should also be taken when performing pressure diagnostics on buildings using fan assisted pressurization devices. Creating a large negative pressure in the building can pull these contaminants into occupied space. Mice can carry food-borne bacteria such as salmonella, and deer mice in some parts of the country carry the hantavirus. The disease can spread when a person breathes in air or comes into contact with contaminated surfaces exposed to the saliva, urine, or feces from an infected mouse. From an indoor air quality perspective, one of the best ways to prevent infection in a building is to keep the building tight and not let anything in. If there is evidence of infestation from pests, then this needs to be properly addressed by trained professionals.

Bacteria

Bacteria are common in the indoor and outdoor environment and can be the cause of diseases in plants, humans, and animals. All bacteria are not harmful. For example, bacteria is used in pickling and fermenting processes. Bacteria are classified by their shape primarily as well as their need for oxygen and whether they are impacted by heat. The quantity of bacteria growing is largely impacted by the host it is living on or in as well as temperature, air movement, light, and moisture. Bacteria may

grow in soil, water, and food and in humans and animals to name a few potential hosts. Bacteria may often be found as a result of a water or moisture problem. These bacteria tend to live off of dead organic matter and will thrive in many of the materials commonly found in and around our buildings.

Fungi

Fungi are organisms that absorb their food from an external source. This group includes molds, mildew, yeasts, and mushrooms. An HVAC/R technician will have numerous encounters with items that fall into this category. Fungi generally thrive on organic materials although there are some that require a living host organism and are parasitic in nature. Much like bacteria, there are fungi that are good and bad. Fungi can cause disease in humans. From an indoor air quality perspective, it is often the airborne mold spores containing mycotoxins that need to be addressed.

It is important to recognize that most of these items occur everywhere. However, an HVAC/R technician should learn to recognize that the presence of fungi may be an indication of other problems. For example, *Stachybotrys chartarum* is a mold that thrives in materials containing cellulose that have been water damaged. If it is found, then there is a need to investigate where the water is coming from. The likelihood of finding water damage along with the source of the contaminant is extremely high.

Viruses

Viruses invade the human immune system and cause diseases. They produce toxins and are smaller than bacteria. Viruses are often very difficult to destroy. They are not something that an HVAC/R technician will normally be able to address. It should be noted however for future reference that there is ongoing research being performed that looks at how HVAC and IAQ equipment may be used to help in the control of certain viruses, particularly in highly controlled laboratory settings. High concentrations of ultraviolet light have been shown to be effective in killing virus in the air.

62.6 POLLUTANT PATHWAYS

In addition to understanding the pollutants that might be encountered, an HVAC/R technician needs to understand the pathways that allow the pollutants to enter and spread. The possible pollutant pathways through the building envelope or mechanical systems are extensive.

Outside to Inside

One of the more common pollutant paths occurs from outside the building to inside the building. For example, window or door openings, plumbing stacks, and chimney chases are obvious examples. Some common pathways would include a duct system (Figure 62-2), wall chase (Figure 62-3), plumbing chase (Figure 62-4), chimney stack (Figure 62-5), or an electrical penetration (Figure 62-6).

There are also less obvious examples, such as the space between the sill plate and foundation (Figure 62-7), foundation wall cracks (Figure 62-8), and voids in air barriers, vapor barriers, and thermal materials (Figure 62-9), attic hatches (Figure 62-10), and top plates (Figure 62-11). There are also substantial pathways through vent pipes and exhausts, fresh air intakes, and other openings made for mechanical devices such as attic fans. These can be pathways under some conditions but not under other conditions. Each of these is an outdoor to indoor connection. HVAC/R technicians often look first at the mechanical system as the source for indoor air quality problems since they do not typically focus much attention on the integrity of the building

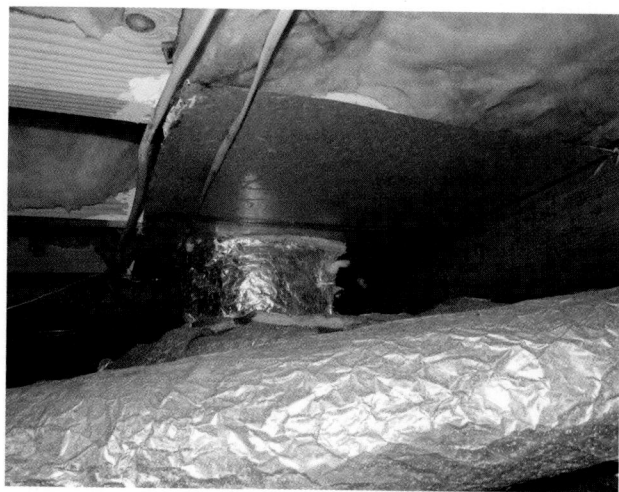

Figure 62-3 Panned floor joists can suck air from both the crawl space and the attic

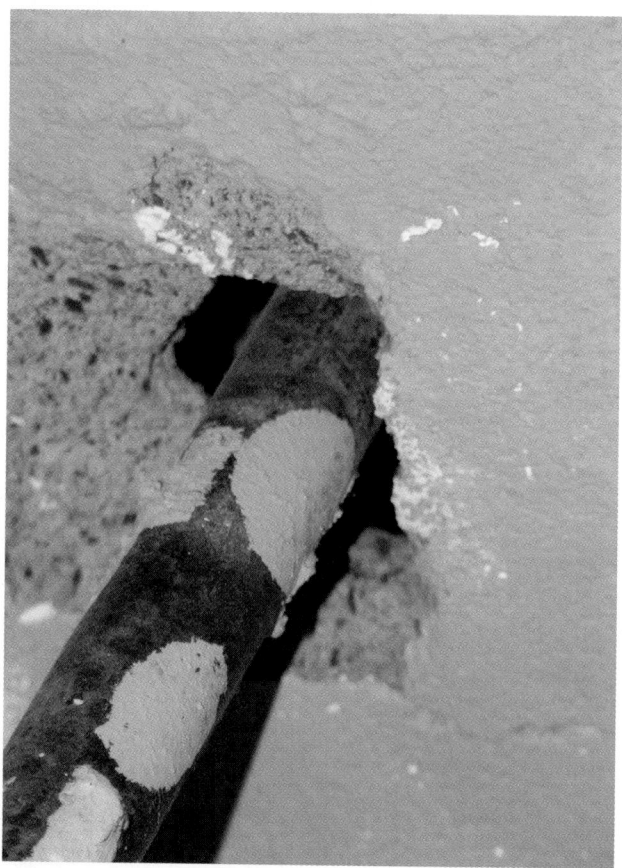

Figure 62-4 Leaks around plumbing can provide a path for pollutants

Figure 62-2 Leaks in return ductwork located in a crawl space can pull in contaminants from the crawl space

envelope. Technicians should know where and how to identify issues in the building envelope. They should also be able to measure the amount of building leakage to the outside and understand how this interacts with the building mechanical systems. Understanding how a building's construction and its systems interact is called building science.

Figure 62-5 Pollutants can be pulled in through a chimney

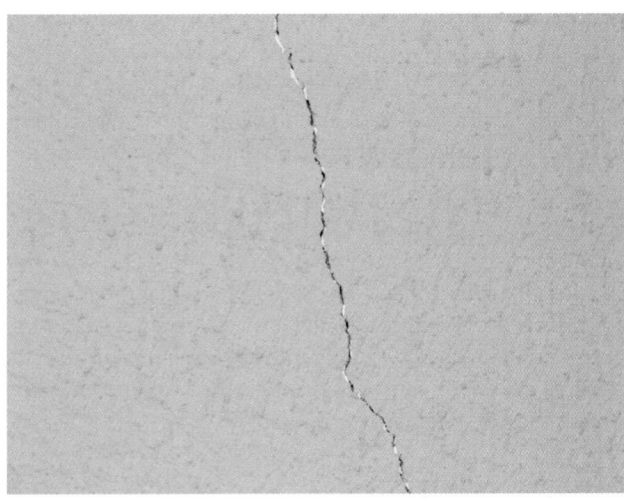

Figure 62-8 Cracks in the foundation wall can provide a pathway for pollutants to enter

Figure 62-6 The holes in framing for wires can provide a pathway for pollutants

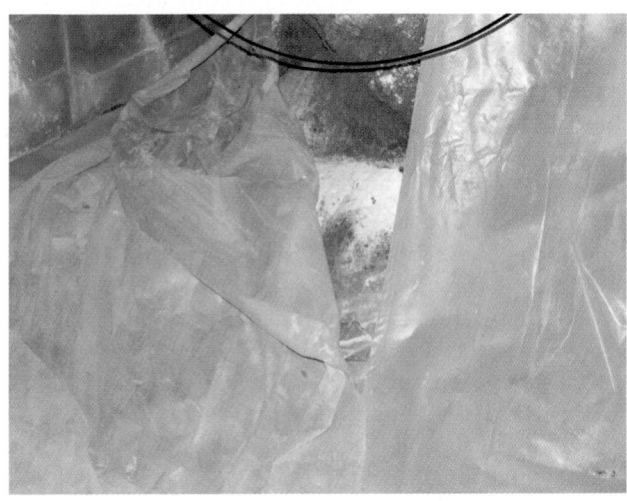

Figure 62-9 Gaps in crawl space vapor barriers can increase the pollutants inside the crawl space

Figure 62-7 The crack between the sill and the foundation can allow infiltration to carry pollutants inside

Figure 62-10 Air gaps around attic hatches can provide a way for infiltration to carry pollutants into the house from the attic

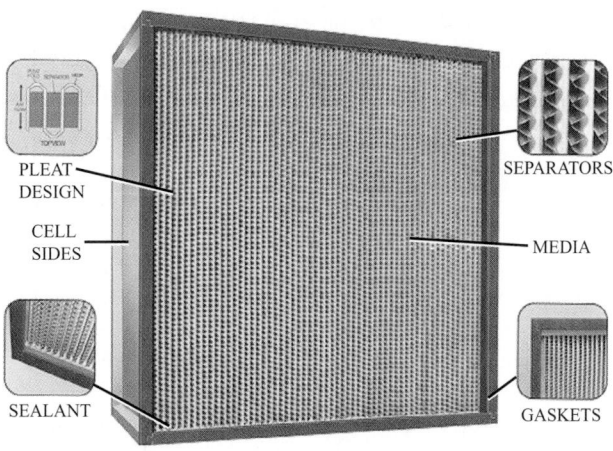

Figure 63-7 HEPA filter
(Courtesy of Camfil Farr)

the airflow the filter is rated to handle, and its resistance at the rated airflow.

Filter Efficiency

Many different methods have been devised to measure air filter efficiency. The two most commonly used methods are called the filter arrestance and the dust spot efficiency. The arrestance method measures the weight of the material captured by the filter and compares it to the weight of the test material that was released. A filter with an efficiency 50% arrestance captures half of the material passing through the filter when measured by weight. Special test dust with calibrated particle sizes is used for these tests. Although many filters are advertised by stating an average arrestance percentage, filter efficiency is not as simple as a single percentage.

All filters capture different size particles at different levels of efficiency. A filter that removes 99% of the particles larger than 10 microns, may only remove 1% of the particles smaller than 1 micron. But since large particles weigh more than small particles, the average arrestance efficiency can be quite high even though most of the particles pass through.

The dust spot efficiency test is designed to measure a filter's ability to remove very small particles that can easily pass through many filters and cause staining on walls and surfaces. The dust spot method uses atmospheric dust instead of calibrated test dust. Air is passed over test paper to achieve a stain from deposits of small particles in the air. This is done both before and after the filter. The efficiency is calculated by comparing the amount of "clean" downstream air required to create the same stain as the dirty upstream air.

Filter efficiency ratings are complicated by the fact that the efficiency of all filters changes as they become dirty. Most mechanical filters become more efficient as they fill with particles and the space for particles to pass through becomes smaller. For this reason, many manufacturers advertise a peak arrestance efficiency that is measured when the filter is ready to be changed.

Figure 63-5 Most residential air conditioning equipment is supplied with low efficiency 1 in panel filters

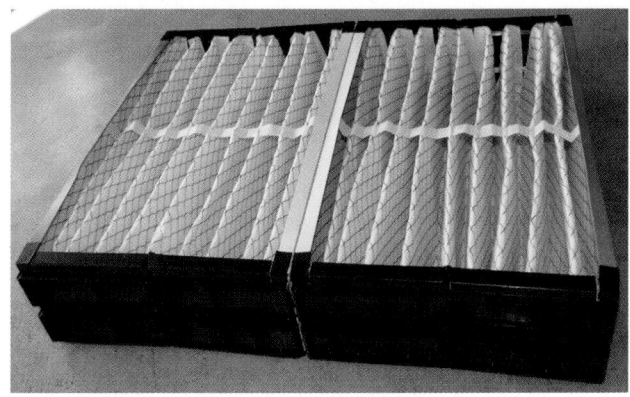

Figure 63-6 Medium efficiency pleated filter

63.4   AIR FILTER RATINGS

There are four important factors to be considered when choosing an air filter: the size of the contaminants the filter must remove, its efficiency at removing the contaminants,

Particle Size Ranges for MERV Testing		
Range	Minimum Size in Microns	Maximum Size in Microns
1	0.30	0.40
2	0.40	0.55
3	0.55	0.70
4	0.70	1.00
5	1.00	1.30
6	1.30	1.60
7	1.60	2.20
8	2.20	3.00
9	3.00	4.00
10	4.00	5.50
11	5.50	7.00
12	7.00	10.00

Figure 63-8 Particle size ranges for MERV testing

ASHRAE Standard 52.2-2007 addresses these problems by establishing a rating system that measures the arrestance of particles in 12 different ranges of size, Figure 63-8. The Minimum Efficiency Reporting Value, or MERV, looks at the efficiency of a filter over each range with different levels of filter loading. Filter loading is a term that describes the amount of material the filter has collected. The minimum efficiency for each range is then used to determine the filter's MERV rating. MERV ratings range from 1 for the lowest efficiency filters, to 20 for the highest efficiency filters. Figure 63-9 shows the specifications for the MERV ratings. As a filter's MERV rating increases, so does its pressure drop.

One advantage of the MERV rating is that a user can match the MERV rating to the size of contaminant that must be removed. Filters with a relatively low MERV rating can effectively remove pollen, but a high MERV rating is required to remove bacteria.

Composite average particle size removal efficiency (%) in size range (µm); ANSI/ANSHRAE Standard 52.2-2007				
MERV	0.3–1.0	1.0–3.0	3.0–10.0	Contaminants typically controlled / Typical application
1			<20	Particles >10.0 µm: pollens, dust mites, textile/carpet fibers — Minimum filtration: residential buildings
2			<20	
3			<20	
4			<20	
5			20–35	Particle 3–10.0 µm: mold, spores, cement dust — Most commercial and better residential buildings
6			35–50	
7			50–70	
8			>70	
9		<50	>85	Particles 1.0–3.0 µm: Legionella, lead dust, coal dust, auto emmissons — Superior residential and better commercial buildings
10		50–65	>85	
11		65–80	>85	
12		>80	>90	
13	<75	>90	>90	Particles 0.3–1.0 µm: all bacteria, most tobacco smoke, droplet nuclei, most smoke — Hospital inpatient and general surgery; superior commercial buildings
14	75–80	>90	>90	
15	85–95	>90	>90	
16	>95	>95	>95	
IEST Standards				
17	>99.97 on 0.30 µm particles, IEST Type A			Particles <0.3 µm (viruses, radom progeny, carbon dust) — Cleanrooms and pharmaceutical manufacturing
18	>99.99 on 0.30 µm particles, IEST Type C			
19	>99.999 on 0.30 µm particles, IEST Type D			
20	>99.9999 on 0.10–0.20 µm particles, IEST Type F			

Figure 63-9 MERV parameters

(© American Society of Heating, Refrigerating, and Air-Conditioning Engineers, Inc. www.ashrae.org)

Airflow

Filters have a maximum airflow rating. Exceeding the airflow rating of a filter will decrease its efficiency and increase the pressure drop across the filter. Operating a filter at decreased airflow levels will increase its efficiency and decrease its pressure drop. The recommended airflow is based on the filter face velocity, that is, the speed of the air passing through the filter. Increased airflow produces increased airspeed, which reduces the effectiveness of the filter.

Pressure Drop

Pressure drop is created across an air filter because of its resistance to airflow. This resistance ranges from 0.1 in wc for clean low efficiency filters, to over 1 in wc for some HEPA filters. Filter manufacturers specify the recommended final pressure drop for their filters. This is the maximum pressure the filter is designed to withstand. Typically, the final pressure is produced when the filter is holding its maximum capacity of dirt. The filter must be changed at this point. However, most filters should be changed before they reach this point. Most residential air conditioning equipment cannot operate correctly at pressure drops exceeding 0.5 in wc across the blower. All of that cannot be used for the filter, some of that pressure drop is used by coils, ductwork, and registers. Most of these systems will not move enough air if the pressure drop across the air filter starts to exceed 0.2 in wc. An air filter in a residential air conditioning system with a pressure drop of 0.5 in wc across it is letting very little air through.

The filter's airflow resistance can be measured with an inclined manometer, digital manometer, or magnehelic gauge. It is common practice on large commercial central systems to include a magnehelic gauge or inclined manometer to check the differential pressure across for the filter section, Figure 63-10. This instrument compares the air pressure on the upstream and downstream sides of the filter assembly. The gauge on the instrument indicates when the filters should be changed.

SERVICE TIP

There are 1 in pleated high efficiency filters for sale whose pressure drop when clean approaches the limit of most residential equipment. These filters cause airflow problems for many systems when they become just a little dirty. Always check a filter's airflow rating and pressure drop, not just its advertised efficiency. There are many filters for sale that simply will not work in most residential systems.

63.5 MECHANICAL FILTRATION

Mechanical air filters work by passing the air and contaminants through a media. The contaminants get stuck in the fibers and the air passes through. A number of materials have been used as the filtering media, including coarse glass fibers, animal hair, vegetable fibers, synthetic fibers, metallic wool, expanded metals and foils, crimped screens, random matted wire, and synthetic open cell foams, Figure 63-11. In general, finer fibers produce higher filter efficiency. Filter efficiency also increases as the fiber density increases. However, the air pressure drop across the filter also increases as the filter density increases. The efficiency of mechanical filters increases as the filter becomes dirty because it becomes more and more difficult for particles to pass through the filter. The pressure drop across the filter also increases as it gets dirty, reducing the airflow through the filter.

Filter Coatings

The efficiency of coarse fiber media is sometimes increased by coating the media with a viscous substance, such as oil, which acts as an adhesive to the airborne particles coming into contact with it. Another technique is to use materials with an electrostatic charge to attract particles. One problem with these strategies is that they lose their effectiveness as the filter becomes dirty.

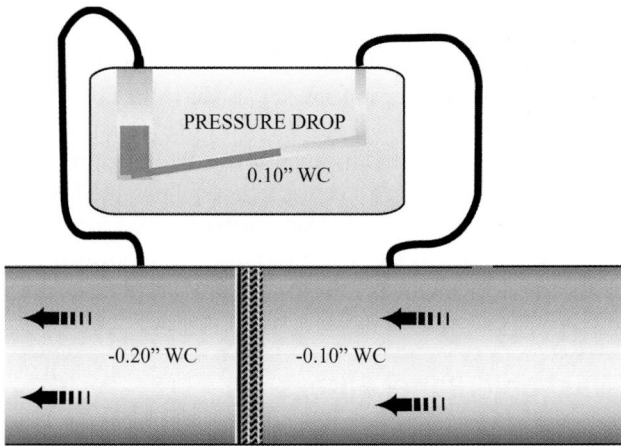

Figure 63-10 Inclined manometer reading pressure drop across air filter

Figure 63-11 Different filter media; from top left; expanded metal, polyester, foam, hog's hair, light density fiberglass, pleated high density fiberglass

Figure 63-12 Extended surface area filter
(Courtesy of Camfil Farr)

Extended Surface Area Filters

The area of the filter material exposed to the air can be extended to improve efficiency and minimize the pressure drop created by denser filter material. Extended area filters are made of random fiber mats or blankets of bonded glass fiber, wool felt, or synthetic materials. Pleating of the media provides a larger filter surface area compared to the face area. This allows for higher filtering efficiency at a reasonable pressure drop. Figure 63-12 shows an extended surface area filter. The efficiency of uncoated extended surface area filters is usually higher than the viscous coated coarse fiber filters. In addition to their effectiveness, the extended surface filters have a larger dust holding capacity for longer periods of use.

63.6 PANEL FILTERS

The low efficiency filters that come as standard equipment on forced air heating and cooling equipment are panel filters. Both disposable and washable panel filters are available. The dust holding capacity of panel filters is generally low because of the limited amount of media in them. They need frequent replacement or cleaning; typically every month. These filters protect the equipment, but do not do much for cleaning the air.

SERVICE TIP

Panel filters are directional; the airflow is intended to flow through the filter in only one direction. The direction is clearly marked on the side of the filter with an arrow, Figure 63-13. Look for the directional arrow when installing panel filters and install the arrow pointing toward the unit.

Figure 63-13 The directional arrow on panel filters should point toward the unit

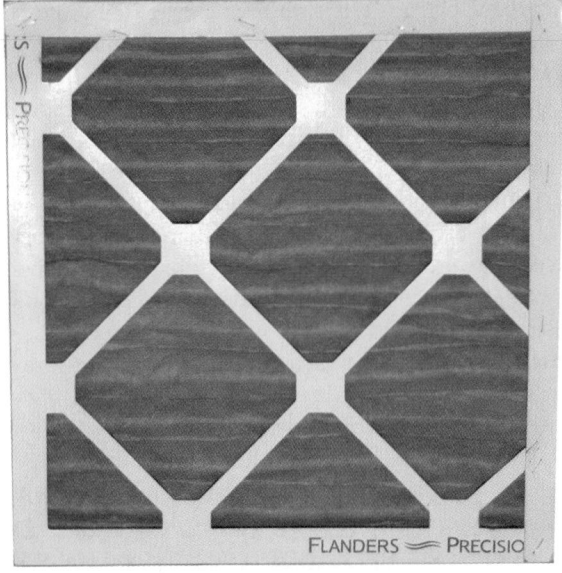

Figure 63-14 Throwaway filter

Disposable Panel Filters

Disposable panel filters consist of a cardboard frame with a grill to hold the filter material in place, Figure 63-14. The filter media material is made of glass fibers that are loosely woven on the entering air side and more densely packed and on the leaving air side. Some makes also have the fiber media coated with an adhesive substance in order to attract and hold dust and dirt. Filter thickness is usually 1 in for residential equipment and 2 in for commercial equipment. These filters typically have an initial clean resistance of 0.1 in wc with a face velocity of 300 fpm. The maximum face velocity is typically around 300 fpm and the maximum final pressure drop is typically between 0.3 to 0.5 in wc.

Washable Panel Filters

Permanent washable panel filters are also available. These filters may be removed, cleaned with detergent, dried, and reinstalled. They typically have a metal or plastic frame with a cleanable media, Figure 63-15. The media is typically expanded

Figure 63-15 Reusable filter

Figure 63-16 Hog's hair filter

metal or foam. Another washable filter is the hog's hair filter, Figure 63-16. It is made from hog's hair, bonded together in a mat. These filters have enough rigidity that they do not need a frame, but they do frequently have metal rods running through them to help stiffen them.

SERVICE TIP

Getting the homeowner to keep filters clean is not easy, and dirty filters are probably the main contributor to malfunctioning equipment. As the mechanical filter clogs with dirt, airflow is reduced to a point where the cooling coil will freeze, causing compressor failure. In a heating system, dirty filters can cause overheating and reduce the life of the heat exchanger or cause nuisance tripping of the limit switch. Operating costs increase with loss of efficiency.

63.7 RENEWABLE MEDIA FILTERS

Renewable media filters keep the structural components of the filter and replace the media when it becomes dirty. Two common types of renewable media filters are pleated filters

Figure 63-17 Pleated replaceable media filter

and moving curtain filters. Renewable media pleated filters use a frame and combs to support and separate the pleated material, Figure 63-17. When the material becomes dirty, the media is replaced, but the existing frame and combs are reused for the replacement media. Similar filters are available that hold the pleated filter material in a cardboard frame. For these, the entire cardboard box is replaced, Figure 63-18.

Renewable pleated filters are used in residential and light commercial applications. These filters are generally medium efficiency. The increased amount of media gives these filters a much higher dust holding ability. They do not require changing as often as the disposable panel filters. Most pleated 4 in and 5 in deep extended media filters will last between 6 months to a year between changes.

The moving curtain filter is an automatic moving curtain with the random fiber medium, treated with a viscous

Figure 63-18 Pleated boxed filter—Lennox Model X5430 MERV 16 replacement filter from http://www.iaqsource.com/product.php/lennox/x5430/?product-110868
(Courtesy of Lennox Industries)

Figure 63-19 Rolling curtain renewable media filter

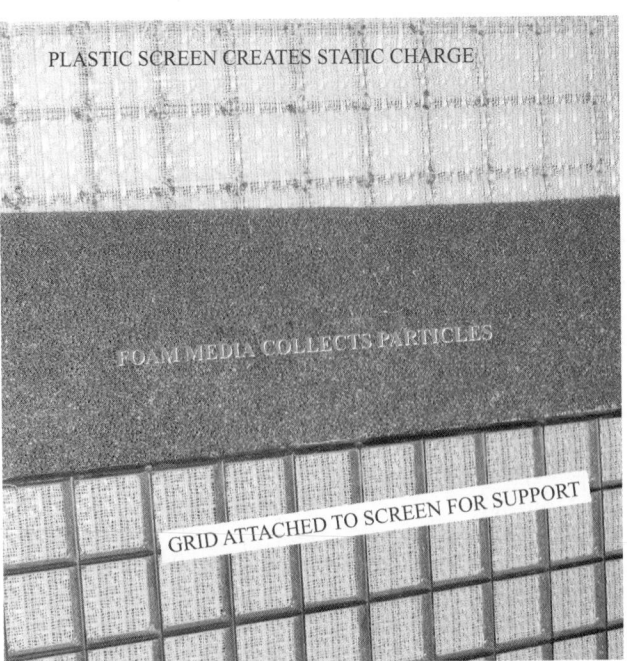

Figure 63-20 Composition of electrostatic air filter

material, and furnished in roll form. The material rolls down from the top of the unit. As the exposed area becomes saturated with dirt, a clean section is automatically rolled into place. The used portion is collected in a roll at the bottom and thrown away. A fresh roll is again placed at the top to the unit and the filtering continues.

Figure 63-19 shows a moving curtain renewable media filter. Moving curtain filters are used in commercial applications to remove lint and aerosols in textile mills, dry cleaners, and press rooms.

63.8 ELECTROSTATIC FILTERS

Did you ever notice how electronic components collect dust? The dust is attracted to them because of their electrostatic charge. Electrostatic filters make use of this principle to increase their efficiency. Some disposable filters are manufactured using materials that have an inherent electrostatic charge. However, this charge tends to dissipate as the filter gets dirty, and the filter efficiency declines. Another type of electrostatic filter uses materials that produce static electricity when air flows across the filter. A static electric charge is developed as the air flows over the material, charging the particles. They are then attracted to the media inside the filter. A filter media, such as foam or polyester fibers, is sandwiched in between the statically charged panels, Figure 63-20. These

filters typically have a relatively high initial air pressure drop which increases as they become dirty. These filters must be cleaned monthly to prevent airflow problems.

SERVICE TIP

It is very important to clean electrostatic filters often. It can be very difficult to clean one of these once it has become clogged with dirt. This is especially true of the filters that use a fuzzy appearing polyester media in the center. Once one of these becomes excessively dirty, it just becomes an expensive disposable filter.

63.9 ELECTRONIC AIR CLEANERS

The operating efficiency of electronic air cleaners varies with airflow. Each model may be used over a range of airflow quantities (CFM). The stated efficiency will be rated at a nominal CFM. The operating efficiency at other airflows within the filter's operating range will be listed separately. Higher airflow produces lower efficiency. Residential electronic air cleaners come in sizes of 800 CFM to 2,000 CFM. Static pressure drop will run about 0.20 in wc at the nominal airflow rating point. Ratings are published in accordance with the National Bureau of Standards Dust Spot Test and are certified under ARI standards. There are three types of units used for commercial service: ionizing plate, charged media nonionizing, and charged media ionizing.

Ionizing Plate Air Cleaners

Ionizing plate electronic air cleaners use high voltage DC current to ionize particles in the air and attract them to

Figure 63-21 The ionization section of an electrostatic air cleaner consists of ionizing wires alternating with grounded plates

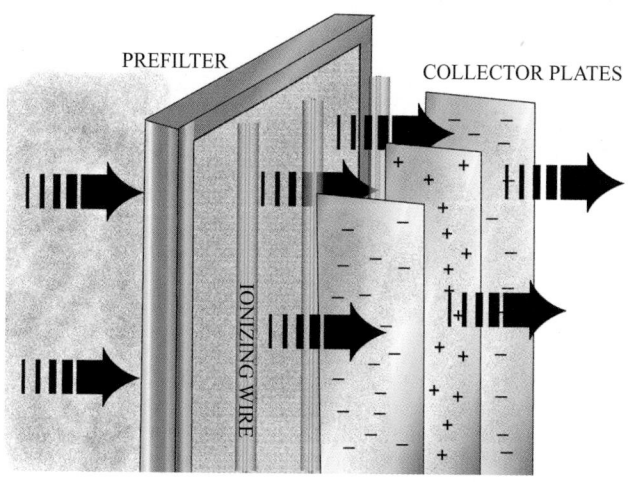

Figure 63-22 Operation of two stage electrostatic precipitation

Figure 63-23 The prefilter is seen on the left; the prefilter on the right has been removed

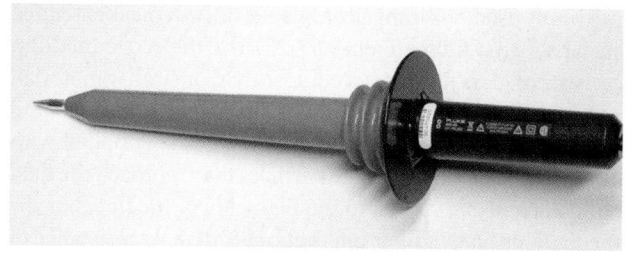

Figure 63-24 This high voltage probe and a standard digital multimeter can be used to read the high DC voltage on an electronic air cleaner circuit

oppositely charged plates. A series of thin wires is suspended between a group of grounded plates, Figure 63-21. A high voltage DC current produces an electric field between negatively charged thin wires with and grounded plates. The dust particles passing through receive a negative charge from the electrical field. This is called the ionizing section because it is ionizing the dust particles. The collection section is a series of plates located just behind the ionizing section. The ionized dust particles are attracted to the oppositely charged collection plates and fasten onto them, Figure 63-22. This process is called two stage electrostatic precipitation because it occurs in two stages and the dust particles precipitate out of the air.

The voltage is typically from 8,000 to 12,000 V DC. The plates are parallel to the airstream and offer little resistance to the airflow. For best results the airflow through the plates

should be evenly distributed. Conventional type prefilters are used ahead of the electronic air cleaners to screen out the larger particles in the air, Figure 63-23.

SAFETY TIP

Do not attempt to use a standard multimeter and lead set to measure the output voltage on an electronic air cleaner. The voltage is much higher than either the leads or meter are designed for. The voltage can be read using a special high voltage probe, Figure 63-24. This probe reduces the voltage to a level that can be safely read by a standard multimeter.

The collector plates must be periodically cleaned. Their efficiency declines as they get dirty. Most collector plates can be removed easily and can be placed in a dishwasher for cleaning. Due to the high voltage used by the electronic units, safety switches are provided that will turn off the power when the filter access door is opened. A few filters have built in cleaning mechanisms. They use water sprayed on the plates in place. Suitable drains are provided in the bottom of the filter compartment. Ionizing plate air cleaners should be cleaned two to four times a year.

SERVICE TIP

Electronic air cleaners do not make dirt disappear, they collect it. Cleaning the plates is essential. If the plates are allowed to get excessively dirty, arcing can occur between the plates. The arcing burns the dust to a fine white ash. This fine white powdery ash then escapes the air cleaner and can pack in the fins of the indoor coil. Adding an electronic air cleaner and not cleaning it is really worse than using low efficiency filters.

Charged Media Nonionizing Air Cleaners

The charged media nonionizing filters are very different in construction. These filters consist of a dielectric filtering medium, usually arranged in pleats, as in typical extended surface media filters, Figure 63-25. The dielectric medium consists of glass fiber mat, cellulose mat, or similar material, supported by a grid consisting of alternately grounded and charged members. The charged members are supplied with 12,000 V DC power. Airborne particles that approach the field are polarized and drawn to the filaments of the fibers of the media. This type of filter offers about 0.10 in wc resistance to the flow of air when clean, with a face velocity of 250 fpm.

Charged Media Ionizing Air Cleaners

The charged media ionizing electronic filters combine the effects of the other two designs. Dust is charged in a corona discharge ionizer and collected on a charged media filter mat. This construction increases the effectiveness of the filter but is more critical to operate successfully.

SERVICE TIP

The high voltage on an electronic air filter can cause discharges when the surface of the collector plate becomes excessively dirty or if a large particle or insect comes in contact with the collector plate. This electrical discharge or spark can be annoying to homeowners because of its sound and interference with television and radio reception. For installations where persistent arcing is a problem, the source of the arcing must be identified and controlled. It may mean more frequent cleaning of the collector plate or possibly the installation of a prefilter to catch or keep out larger particles or insects.

Undesirable Operating Conditions

Two operating conditions can cause problems with electronic air filters: (1) space charge and (2) ozone. The unit needs to be carefully built and installed so that charged dirt particles do not escape into the filtered space (space charge). If they do, they can darken the walls faster than if no cleaning arrangement was used. Figure 63-26 shows the effects of

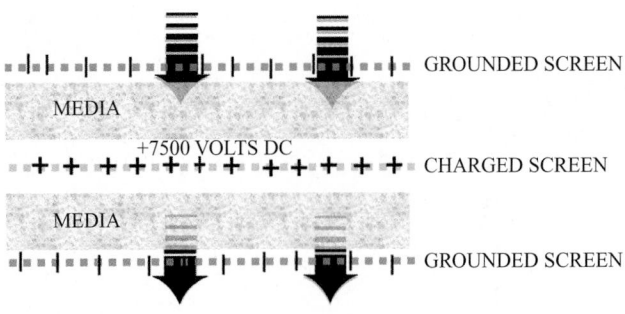

Figure 63-25 Nonionized charged media filter operation

Figure 63-26 Charged particles can cause staining if they escape the electronic air cleaner

small ionized particles escaping the air cleaner. Proper installation and application are key to preventing this condition. Moving air at speeds exceeding the filter's rating can allow charged particles to escape.

Electronic air cleaners produce a small amount of ozone because of their high voltage. Ozone is a poisonous gas. When the unit is operating correctly, the amount of ozone produced is well within the recommended safe limits. If the unit is continuously arcing, it may yield levels of ozone, which are annoying and even poisonous. High levels of ozone are indicated by a strong bleach-like odor.

63.10 ADVANCED HYBRID AIR CLEANERS

Several manufacturers now offer air cleaners that clean, sterilize, and deodorize the air. These filters offer some combination of HEPA media filter, ultraviolet light, charged media electronic air cleaner, and activated charcoal, Figure 63-27.

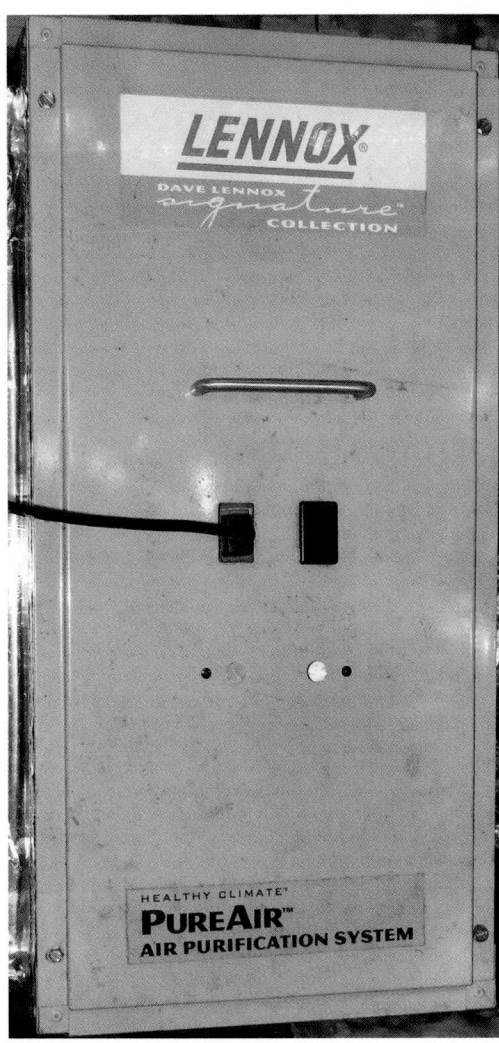

Figure 63-27 This high efficiency filter cleans and disinfects the air

The HEPA filter or electronic air cleaner removes the minute particles, the ultraviolet light or charged media sterilizes the air, and the activated charcoal removes odors. They are aimed at the high end residential market for customers who are concerned about the indoor air quality of their home.

63.11 FILTER INSTALLATION

Filters should be placed ahead of heating and cooling coils and other mechanical equipment to protect the system from dust.

Panel Filters

Panel filters have an arrow that indicates the direction of airflow. It should be pointed toward the unit, Figure 63-13. The published performance of filters is based on straight through unrestricted airflow. The filter size should be appropriate for the amount of air passing through it. For example, a panel filter rated for a maximum face velocity of 300 fpm should have a face area of 2.67 ft^2 for a 2 ton unit: 400 CFM/ton × 2 tons =

Figure 63-28 Filters can be installed on both sides of a furnace to increase the filter surface area

Figure 63-29 Medium efficiency 5 in filters require a filter box

800 CFMi 800 CFM/300 fpm = 2.67 ft^2, or 384 in^2. A 20 in × 20 in filter would work (400 in^2); a 16 in × 20 in would not (320 in^2). It is common to pull return air in from both sides of a unit if the airflow capacity requires more filter face area than can be accommodated easily by a single filter, Figure 63-28.

Extended Media Filters

Extended media filters require the installation of a filter box, Figure 63-29. This box can be mounted to the unit or in the return duct. A transition should be used if the duct size is

Figure 63-30 This airflow sensor turns the electronic air cleaner on when it senses airflow

smaller than the opening in the filter. In either case, sealing the filter box to the duct or the unit is important to maintain maximum filter efficiency. It does not make sense to install an efficient filter and leave air leaks around the filter that will allow dirty, unfiltered air to enter the system. Service access should be considered when installing the filter box. The filters that must come out are as long as the box. It will be difficult to change the filters if a 25 in wide filter box is installed with a 20 in service access. The filter airflow capacity should match the system airflow.

Electronic Air Cleaners

Electronic air cleaners are installed like extended media filters, except that they need a power supply. The air cleaner should operate whenever the blower runs, but it should not operate when the blower is off. Some air cleaners have an airflow sensor that detects airflow and automatically turns the filter on and off with airflow, Figure 63-30. Other air cleaners require a relay or sail switch to energize the filter when the fan runs.

63.12 ULTRAVIOLET (UV) LIGHTS

Ultraviolet lights (UV) are used to sterilize the surfaces inside duct systems. These lights have been popular for years in hospitals where 100% of the air entering an operating room has to be outside air. The air passes through a duct box containing a large number of ultraviolet lights where the air is sterilized before entering the operating room, Figure 63-31. Ultraviolet

Figure 63-31 This bio-wall unit can kill virus and bacteria in the air in one pass, from Sanuvox BioWall Brochure
(Courtesy of Sanuvox Technologies)

lights will kill mold, fungus, bacteria, and any other living organisms if the light is intense enough and the organisms are exposed to it for a long enough period of time.

In recent years, ultraviolet light sterilizing units have become available for the residential and light commercial market. Most of the lights used in residential applications are not strong enough to sterilize the air as it passes by. These lights are typically located in the plenum where they sterilize the coil, drain pan, or filter. Location of the UV light is critical because UV lights can only disinfect surfaces that the light can see. Typically more than one lamp is required to adequately cover the coil, Figure 63-32. Lights that are designed to keep the coil, drain pan, or filter clean operate all the time, even when the system is not running. Lights that attempt to sterilize the air come on during system operation. This is accomplished by tying their circuit into the fan blower relay circuit in the indoor equipment.

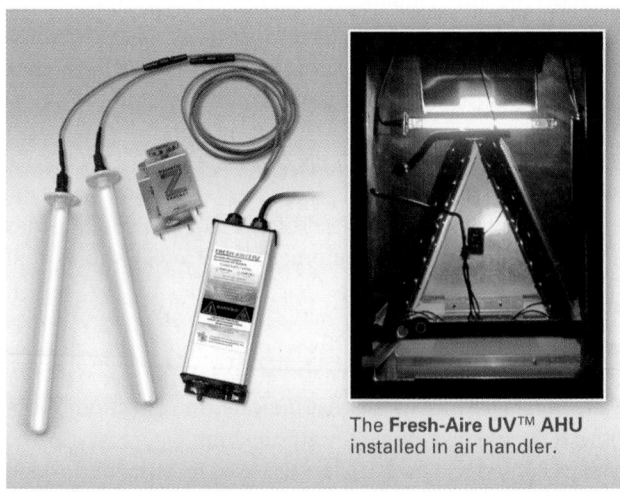

The **Fresh-Aire UV™ AHU** installed in air handler.

Figure 63-32 Residential application of UV light to keep the coil clean
(Courtesy of Triatomic Environmental)

The intensity of the ultraviolet radiation decreases with use, so the lamps in UV lights require replacement every year in most cases. The effectiveness of the UV light drops off as the lamp nears the end of its useful life. Some longer life lamps can go 2 to 3 years, but their UV output is typically only half of the original output by the end of 3 years.

SERVICE TIP

Some indoor coil drain pans are made of plastic materials that can be degraded by ultraviolet light. Before installing an ultraviolet light in a plenum or near a coil, make certain that the drain pan is UV resistant.

SAFETY TIP

Ultraviolet light at the levels required for air sterilization is dangerous to technicians. The ultraviolet light can result in severe skin burns like those caused by too much exposure to the sun. In addition, burns on the eyes can occur. The intensity of the sterilizing lights is such that it only requires a momentary exposure to cause damage. Ultraviolet light boxes must have an interlock circuit that prohibits the light from coming on when access panels are open.

63.13 WHY HUMIDIFICATION IS NEEDED

The heated air in homes and buildings becomes dry during the heating season. The relative humidity of the average heated house in the winter is lower than the relative humidity in the Sahara Desert! The outdoor air cannot hold as much moisture at the lower temperatures. When the cold winter air is heated, the increased volume increases the air's ability to hold moisture, but the amount of moisture actually in the air remains the same. As a result, the relative humidity drops drastically.

This super dry air sucks water out of everything it contacts, including people. This impacts comfort by making us feel colder and by drying out our mucous membranes. Other undesirable conditions that result from low relative humidity include increased static electricity and shrinking and cracking of wood furniture. Adding humidity to the air can also help save energy in the winter by promoting comfort at lower temperatures. It is desirable to maintain 30% to 60% relative humidity in the house. Figure 63-33 shows that many undesirable conditions that are detrimental to health are decreased between 30% and 60% relative humidity.

Air at 35°F and 100% relative humidity contains less water than air at 70°F and 30% relative humidity. Air at 35°F and 100% relative humidity contains 30 grains of moisture per pound of air. When air is heated to 70°F, it can hold

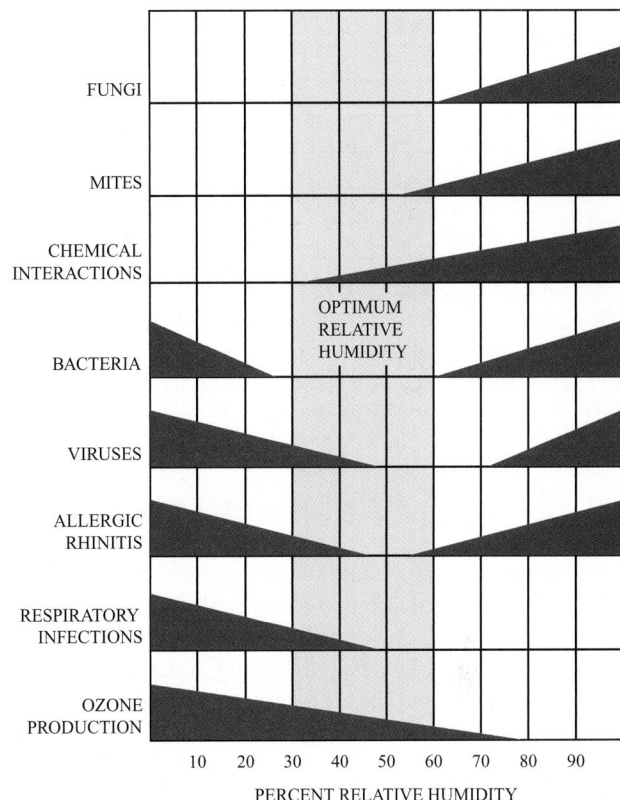

Figure 63-33 Maintaining the relative humidity between 30% and 60% has numerous health benefits

110 grains of moisture per pound. Thus, to maintain 50% relative humidity in a 70°F house, the grains of moisture per pound must be increased to 55 (110 × 0.5 = 55). One pound of air entering a house from the outside will require the addition of 25 grains of moisture (55 − 30 = 25). The amount of infiltration depends on the tightness of the windows and doors and other parts of the construction.

It is impractical in most buildings to maintain high relative humidity when the outside temperature is very low. Condensation forms on the inside of cold building surfaces when the surface temperature drops below the dew point of the air. This occurs first on the windows, but it can also occur inside the walls, contributing to rotting of walls from the inside out. For this reason, the recommended humidity level is lower for low outside temperatures than for higher outdoor temperatures. The amount of water that can be safely added to the air depends on:

1. Outside temperatures.
2. House construction.
3. Amount of relative humidity that the interior of the house will withstand without condensation problems.

Figure 63-34 shows the recommended humidity levels for different outdoor temperatures.

OUTDOOR TEMPERATURE	RECOMMENDED SETTING
-20°F	15%
-10°F	20%
0°F	25%
10°F	30%
20°F	40%
30°F	45%
40°F	50%

Figure 63-34 The recommended humidity setting is 50% at 40°F; the recommended setting decreases 5% for every 10°F decrease in outdoor temperature

63.14 TYPES OF HUMIDIFIERS

There are several types of humidifiers. Generally, the different types may be divided into two general classes: those that rely on heat in the air to evaporate the water and those that supply their own energy for evaporating the water. Humidifiers that require heat from the air for water evaporation include atomizing, evaporative, and bypass humidifiers. Vaporizing and steam humidifiers supply their own energy to evaporate the water.

The type of humidifier used depends upon the type of heating equipment and the amount of moisture needed. While all types of humidifiers will operate with furnaces, many types will not work well with heat pumps because the supply air is not hot enough to evaporate the water. Typically heat pumps require vaporizing, steam, or bypass humidifiers.

Humidifiers are typically wired to operate whenever the fan is operating during the heating cycle. They are usually controlled by a humidistat that senses the relative humidity of the return air. The wiring diagram shown in Figure 63-35 shows wiring with a single speed fan motor. Vaporizing and steam humidifiers can be wired to operate whenever there is a demand for more humidification. They can actually turn

on the indoor blower and operate even if the heat is not operating.

63.15 ATOMIZING HUMIDIFIERS

Atomizing humidifiers work by spraying an atomized water mist into the airstream. Heat in the air then evaporates these small atomized droplets. Atomizing humidifiers typically require a 100°F minimum air temperature to operate. The water is atomized by either a motor that slings the water around, or a spray nozzle that sprays a water mist directly into the duct. A motorized humidifier will not put more water into the air than it can evaporate, but these humidifiers can have a low capacity. Figure 63-36 shows a motorized atomizing humidifier.

The capacity of mister style humidifiers is only limited by the nozzle size. However, it is easy to spray more water into the duct than the air can evaporate, making a mess. Mister humidifiers typically use a temperature sensor wired in series with the water solenoid to prevent spraying water into the duct when the air is not hot enough to evaporate the water, Figure 63-37. The nozzle has a built-in filter to prevent the nozzle from clogging, Figure 63-38. The nozzle should be changed annually to ensure correct operation.

63.16 EVAPORATIVE HUMIDIFIERS

Evaporative humidifiers provide a wetted surface that adds moisture to the heated air. There are three types of evaporative humidifiers:

1. Plate.
2. Rotating drum.
3. Fan powered.

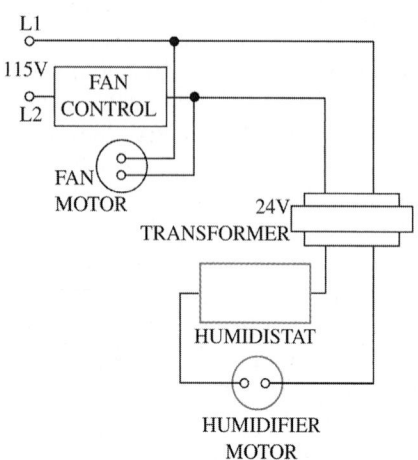

Figure 63-35 Wiring diagram for a humidifier with a single speed motor

Figure 63-36 Motorized atomized humidifiers can deliver 6–11 gal of water per day

Figure 63-37 The mister will not energize the water solenoid until its thermostat senses that the air is warm

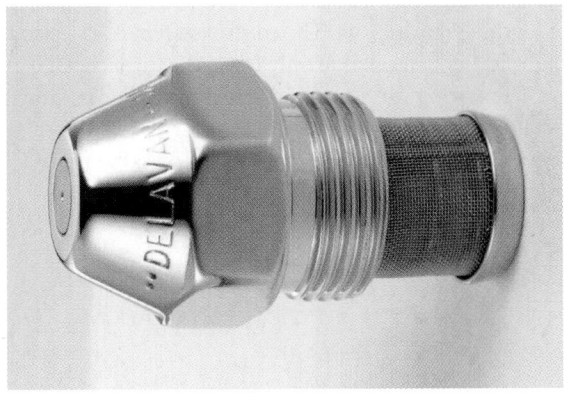

Figure 63-38 Typical humidifier nozzle manufactured by Delavan as shown at http://www.smarthome.com/3281N.65/ ThermoMist-Nozzle-Replacement-o-65GPH/p.aspx
(Courtesy of Delavan Spray Technologies)

Plate Humidifiers

The plate evaporative humidifier has a series of porous plates mounted in a rack, such as the one shown in Figure 63-39. The lower section of the plates extends down into water contained in the pan. A float valve regulates the supply of water to maintain a constant level in the pan. The pan and plates are mounted in the warm air plenum. Plate humidifiers have a relatively low capacity compared to other humidifiers. The plates become brittle as mineral deposits from the evaporated water build in the plates. Annual maintenance includes changing the plates and cleaning the water sump.

Figure 63-39 Plate type humidifier
(Skuttle Indoor Air Quality Products)

Rotating Drum Humidifiers

The rotating drum evaporative humidifier has a slowly revolving drum covered with a polyurethane pad partially submerged in water, as shown in Figure 63-40. As the drum rotates, it absorbs water. The water level in the pan is maintained by a float valve. The humidifier is mounted on the side of the return air plenum. Air from the supply plenum is ducted into the side of the humidifier. The air passes over the wetted surface, absorbs moisture, and then goes into the return air plenum. Annual maintenance

Figure 63-40 Rotating drum under-duct humidifier

includes changing the drum pad and cleaning the water sump.

Rotating Plate Humidifiers

The rotating plate evaporative humidifier is similar to the drum type in that the water absorbing material revolves; however, this type is normally mounted on the underside of the main warm air supply duct, Figure 63-41. Annual maintenance includes changing the plates and cleaning the water sump.

Bypass Evaporative Media Humidifier

The bypass style humidifier is mounted on either the supply or return air plenum. A duct is run from the humidifier to the other plenum, Figure 63-42. When the fan runs, air passes from the supply plenum, through the humidifier, into the return air plenum. A manual damper is installed to shut off the bypass air when the system is operated in cooling.

Air passes over a media pad inside the humidifier. Typically, the media is expanded metal, Figure 63-43. A humidistat is used to control a water solenoid valve that controls the flow of water over the media. The control system is set up so that the humidifier can operate only when the furnace fan is running. This type of humidifier usually does not require much maintenance because the water is not recirculated and does not sit in a sump. The minerals left behind from evaporation are washed away with the drain water. However, it does use more water than other types with similar capacities because the water that is not evaporated washes down the drain.

Fan Powered Evaporative Humidifier

The fan powered evaporative humidifier is similar to the bypass type, except that it does not require bypassing air. It can be mounted on the return or supply air plenum, but its capacity is greater on the supply plenum. Air is drawn in by the fan, forced over the wetted core, and delivered back into the plenum, Figure 63-44. The control system is set up so that the humidifier can operate only when the furnace fan is running. The wiring for a fan operated humidifier is shown in the diagram shown in Figure 63-45.

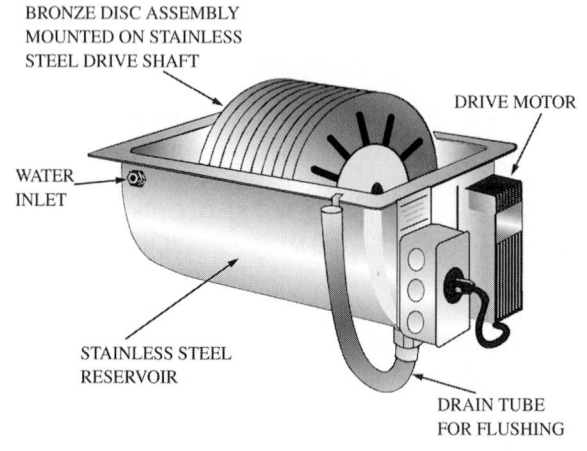

BRONZE DISC ASSEMBLY MOUNTED ON STAINLESS STEEL DRIVE SHAFT

DRIVE MOTOR

WATER INLET

STAINLESS STEEL RESERVOIR

DRAIN TUBE FOR FLUSHING

Figure 63-41 Rotating plate evaporative humidifier

Figure 63-42 In a bypass humidifier installation air flows from the supply plenum, through the humidifier into the return plenum

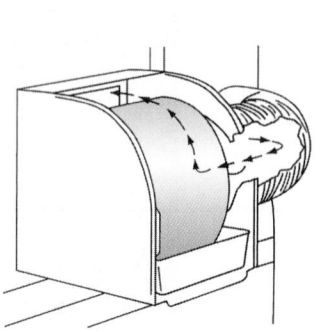

TYPICAL INSTALLATIONS

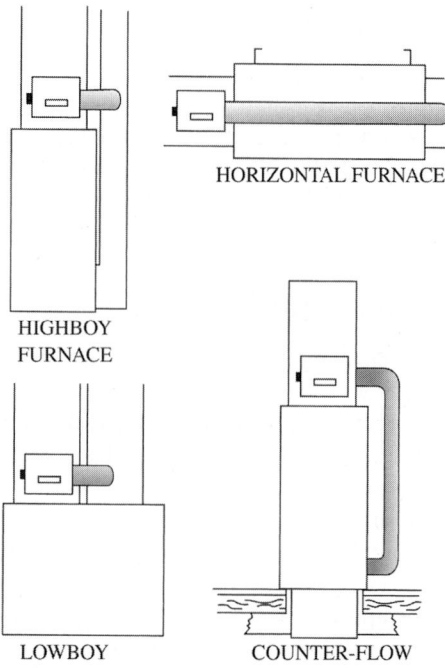

HORIZONTAL FURNACE

HIGHBOY FURNACE

LOWBOY FURNACE

COUNTER-FLOW FURNACE

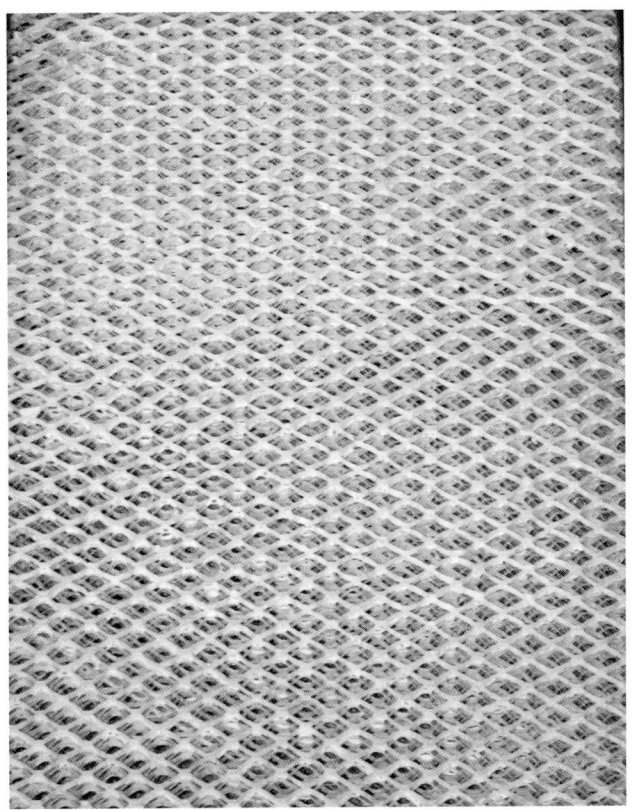

Figure 63-43 Expanded metal pad used in a bypass humidifier

Figure 63-44 Air is drawn in by the fan, forced over the wetted core, and delivered back into the plenum

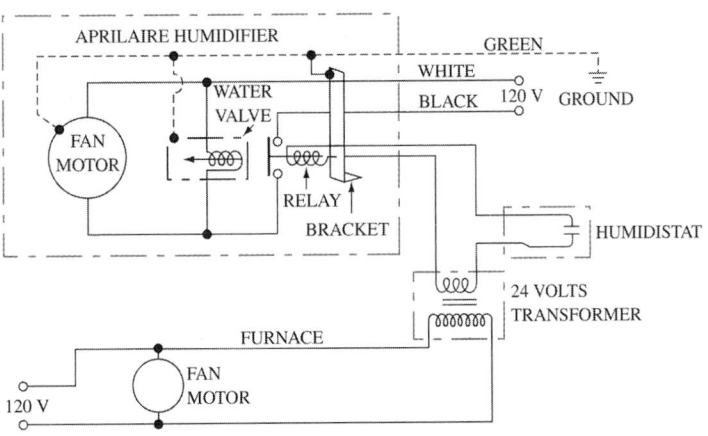

Figure 63-45 Wiring diagram for a fan powered evaporative humidifier

63.17 VAPORIZING HUMIDIFIERS

The vaporizing humidifier uses an electrical heating element immersed in a water reservoir to evaporate moisture into the furnace supply air plenum, as shown in Figure 63-46. A constant level of water is maintained in the reservoir. These humidifiers can operate even though the furnace is not supplying heat. The humidistat not only starts the water heater but also turns the furnace fan on if it is not running.

These humidifiers have among the highest capacities of any type humidifier. They require more electricity than other types because the electrical element is boiling water. Minerals from the water deposit on the element and in the sump, necessitating frequent cleaning. This type of humidifier often needs cleaning more than once a year. The heating element will burn out quickly if it is allowed to operate without water in the humidifier. These are both effective and simple, but frequent maintenance is absolutely essential.

(a)

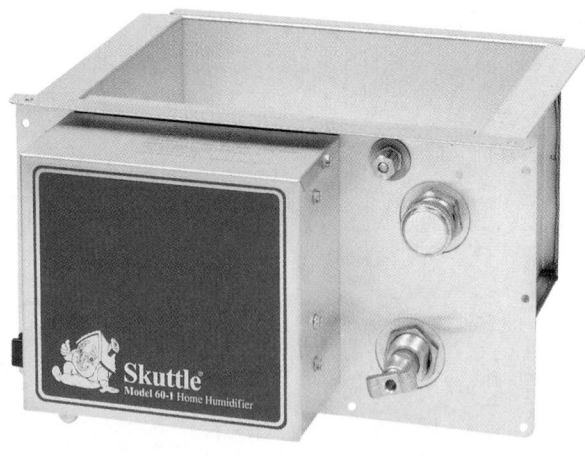

Figure 63-47 Steam humidifier
(Source: Skuttle Indoor Air Quality Products)

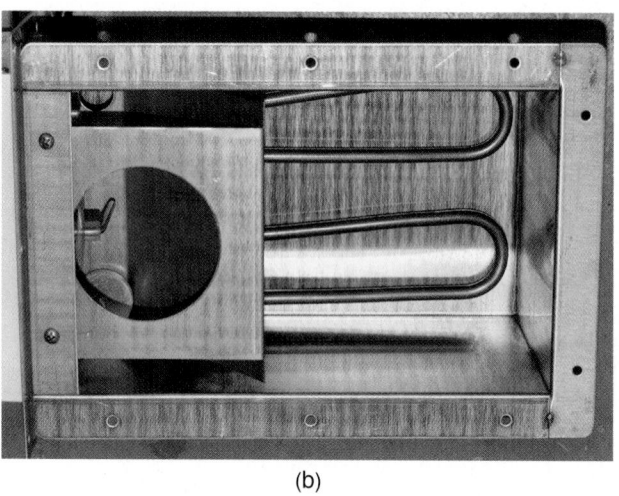

(b)

Figure 63-46 Vaporizing humidifier

SERVICE TIP

Mineral deposits are a problem with all types of humidifiers. When water evaporates, the minerals are left behind. This can be reduced by using filters in the water feeding the humidifier. Carbon filters can be used to remove chlorine from the water supply, thus eliminating the corrosive effects of chlorine on the unit. These filters also reduce mineral build-up.

SERVICE TIP

It is very important that humidifiers be checked for proper operation. It is especially important to ensure that excessive moisture is not released into the house or duct system. Excessive moisture has been associated with mold growth, and mold growth is associated with poor indoor air quality.

Steam Humidifiers

The steam humidifier is a type of vaporizing humidifier, pictured in Figure 63-47. Steam humidifiers are ideal for use with systems like heat pumps, electric furnaces, high efficiency furnaces, and furnaces using night setback thermostats that do not generate the high air temperatures necessary for evaporative humidifiers. The internal water temperature sensing device operates the fan independently of the heating system. To reduce scaling and mineral deposits, some steam humidifiers have a flushing timer and chlorine removal filters. The water in the unit is flushed out every 12 hr, removing accumulated solid materials.

63.18 HUMIDISTATS

A humidistat is used to control when the humidifier operates, Figure 63-48. Humidistats used with humidifiers open on an increase in humidity and close on a decrease in humidity. The setting of a humidistat can be changed to comply with changing outside air temperatures. If the setting on the humidistat is too high, it may cause sweating on interior walls and windows, Figure 63-49. As it gets colder outside, the humidistat setting may need to be lowered.

The least expensive and most common humidistats are mounted on the return air plenum. They typically use a nylon ribbon for sensing the humidity in the air, Figure 63-50. Better quality humidistats use hair to sense humidity change, Figure 63-51. Hair shrinks when it gets wet, and stretches when it dries. Several hundred hairs are stretched across a frame which controls the opening and closing of a set of points.

Some electronic humidity controls adjust themselves automatically to changing outdoor temperature. They sense

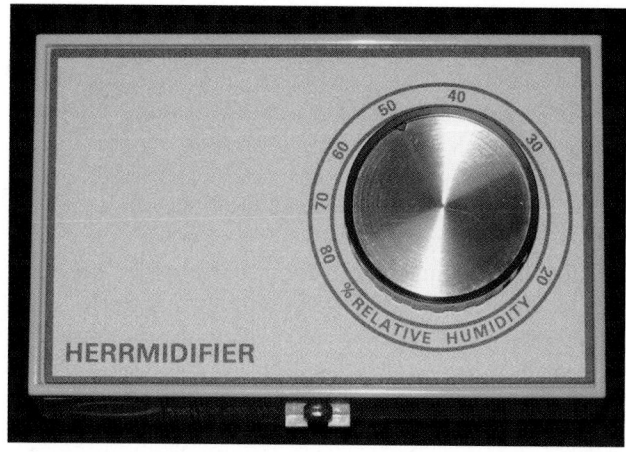

Figure 63-48 Typical humidistat for controlling a humidifier

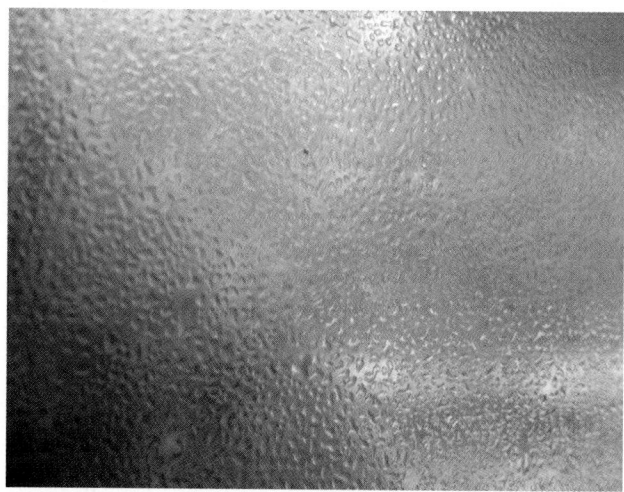

Figure 63-49 Water starts to condense on the windows when the relative humidity exceeds the maximum amount of moisture that the house can hold

Figure 63-50 The clear nylon ribbon is the controlling element in this humidistat

Figure 63-51 Hair is the controlling element of this humidistat

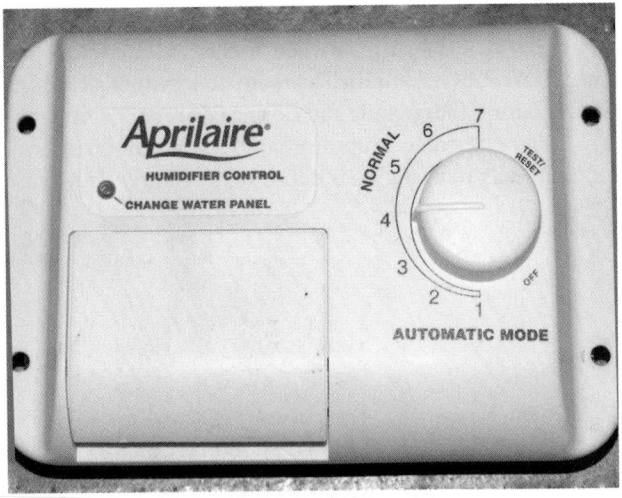

Figure 63-52 Advanced electronic humidity controller

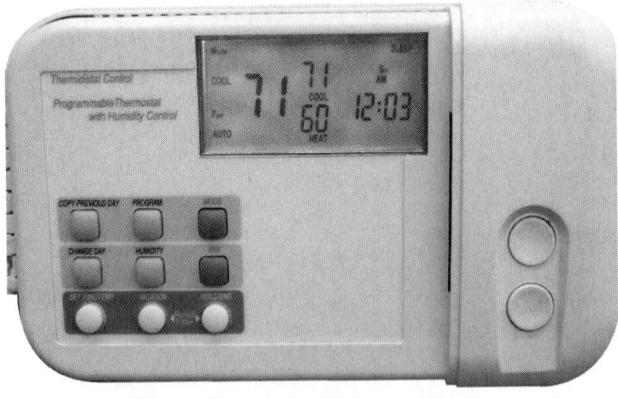

Figure 63-53 This thermostat incorporates humidity control in addition to temperature control

the outdoor temperature and reset the humidity to a safe level for the outdoor temperature, Figure 63-52.

A few advanced electronic thermostats also incorporate humidity control. These controls can be used to control the total system operation, including humidification, Figure 63-53.

UNIT 63—SUMMARY

Common air contaminants include dust, smoke, biological contaminants, and chemical contaminants. Contaminant particles are measured in microns. A micron is an SI unit of measurement equal to 1/1000 of a millimeter. Most of the particles in the air are below 1 micron in size. The most common filters use a media that traps the contaminants and lets the air pass through. These filters get more efficient as they get dirty. Filters have a recommended airflow rating which should not be exceeded. A filter's efficiency is stated

as its MERV rating. Higher MERV ratings mean higher efficiency filtration. When choosing a filter, it is important to select a filter that has the correct airflow rating and pressure drop for the application as well as a high efficiency. Electronic air cleaners use high DC voltage to attract dust particles to charged media or charged plates. Ultraviolet lights are used to sterilize air conditioning coils and the inside of system ducts.

Humidification is needed in the winter because heating the air reduces its relative humidity to desert levels. Humidifiers may be divided into two groups: those that rely on heat in the air to evaporate the water and those that supply their own energy for evaporating the water. Humidifiers that require heat from the air for water evaporation include atomizing, evaporative, and bypass humidifiers. Vaporizing and steam humidifiers supply their own energy to evaporate the water. Humidistats are used to control the operation of humidifiers. Mineral deposits are a common problem with many types of humidifiers. Humidifier service includes changing media and cleaning mineral deposits.

WORK ORDERS

Service Ticket 6301

Customer Complaint: Poor Cooling

Equipment Type: Split System Air Conditioner with a 1 in Electrostatic Air Filter

A customer calls because their unit runs continuously and does not cool. They also have noticed that very little air is coming out of the supply registers. The technician sees that the suction line at the outdoor condensing unit is iced over. Checking inside, the suction line is iced there as well. The filter is a relatively clean electrostatic air filter that the customer bought at the local home improvement store. The technician shows the homeowners on the filter packaging that its nominal pressure drop is 0.35 in wc when the filter is clean and explains that their system cannot move enough air with that much pressure drop across the filter. The low airflow caused the coil to freeze over. The technician replaces the filter with a lower efficiency and lower resistance panel filter and leaves the fan operating without the air conditioner to allow the coil to thaw. Once the coil has thawed out, the airflow returns to normal and the unit operates correctly. The technician advises the customer to consider a 5 in extended surface media filter if they want a truly high efficiency filter that will not severely impede the system airflow.

Service Ticket 6302

Customer Complaint: Poor Cooling

Equipment Type: Split System Air Conditioner with a 1 in Panel Filter

A customer calls because their unit runs continuously and does not cool. They also have noticed that very little air is coming out of the supply registers. The technician sees that the suction line at the outdoor condensing unit is iced over. Checking inside, the suction line is iced there as well. The filter is an inexpensive panel filter that is so dirty light will not pass through it. The customer is surprised because they remember changing the filter last year. The technician explains that the panel filters should be changed monthly and recommends cleaning the evaporator coil as well. After cleaning the evaporator coil and replacing the filter, the unit runs properly.

Service Ticket 6303

Customer Complaint: Popping Sound Coming From the System

Equipment Type: Split System Air Conditioner with an Electronic Air Cleaner

A customer calls because they hear a popping sound coming from their system and they are concerned that there may be a loose wire or electrical malfunction. The technician arrives, hears the sound, and realizes that it is coming from the electronic air cleaner. The technician explains that the sound is from the air cleaner arcing due to a large build up of dirt on the collector plates. The technician removes the cells and places them in the dishwasher to clean while they clean the prefilter. The technician allows the cells and prefilter to dry and then replaces them. And puts the unit back into operation. The popping sound is now gone.

Service Ticket 6304

Customer Complaint: Morning Dry Mouth and Irritated Sinuses

Equipment Type: Gas Furnace

A customer complains that the family wakes up in the morning with dry, cracked lips and irritated throat and sinus passages. They feel that the gas heat is to blame and ask if another form of heat would cause less drying. The technician explains that the dryness is from heating the air, not from the type of heat used and recommends installing a humidifier. The technician recommends an evaporative humidifier and installs it in the supply air plenum. The customer calls back a week later thanking the company saying that the parched morning conditions have disappeared.

Service Ticket 6305

Customer Complaint: Static Electricity

Equipment Type: Gas Furnace with a Plate Type Humidifier

A customer has noticed that the amount of static electricity in their home seems high. They suspect that their

humidifier is not working. The technician arrives and notices that the plates in the humidifier are hard and brittle, instead of soft. The technician explains to the customer that the plates are not very effective when they are calcified with mineral deposits. The humidifier is cleaned and the plates are replaced. The next day the static electricity in the house goes away.

UNIT 63—REVIEW QUESTIONS

1. How does mechanical filtration work?
2. What is the normal maximum air velocity across the face of a low efficiency panel filter?
3. How often should a low efficiency panel filter be changed?
4. How often should a renewable media, pleated surface be changed?
5. What factors should be considered when choosing an air filter?
6. Describe the MERV filter rating system.
7. Why are the highest MERV rating filters not used in residential applications?
8. Why is panel filter media sometimes coated with a viscous substance?
9. What is a HEPA filter?
10. How does increased airflow affect a filter's efficiency?
11. What is the purpose of expanded media area in pleated filters?
12. How does the increased pressure drop across a filter affect system operation?
13. List the three types of electronic air filter units.
14. What is the common operating voltage range on the cells of electronic air cleaners?
15. Describe the operation of an ionizing plate electronic air cleaner.
16. What advantages are there to adding humidity to heated air?
17. What is the desirable amount of relative humidity that should be maintained?
18. What are the two general categories of humidifiers?
19. What types of humidifiers work well with heat pump systems?
20. Which type of humidifiers require the least cleaning?
21. Why do most humidifiers require annual cleaning and media replacement?
22. Why should the humidity level in the house be reduced as the outdoor temperature drops?
23. Explain how a bypass humidifier works.
24. What are the two most common controlling elements in a mechanical humidistat?
25. How is steam humidifier operation different from evaporative humidifier operation?

UNIT 64

Residential Load Calculations

OBJECTIVES

After completing this unit you will be able to:

- discuss the importance of a heat load calculation.
- explain the difference between heat loss, sensible heat gain, and latent heat gain.
- construct a U factor for a building panel given the R values of the components.
- construct an HTM given a U factor and a design temperature difference.
- discuss the effect that daily temperature swings have on heat gain.
- explain the difference that house orientation has on solar heat gain.

64.1 INTRODUCTION

Heating and air conditioning equipment provides the most comfort at the least cost when it is properly sized. The calculations done to determine the amount of heating and cooling required for a particular building are called heat load calculations or a heat load study. In the winter, a load calculation is done to determine how fast the building loses heat. In the summer, the load calculation is done to determine how fast the building gains heat. The calculations determine the size of the equipment that will be used to condition the building. The load calculation is the first step in choosing the equipment and sizing the ductwork. The purpose of this unit is to raise the student's awareness of the factors involved in performing accurate heat load calculations, it is not intended as a complete calculation procedure.

64.2 WHY LOAD CALCULATIONS ARE NECESSARY

Heat load calculations are necessary to properly match the equipment capacity to the building requirement. The two primary reasons for doing a heat load study are to properly size the heating and cooling equipment, and to design the duct system to deliver the correct amount of air to each room or zone. A shell load is a calculation treating the entire house like one big room. This is fine for sizing the equipment, but is no help for sizing the ductwork. A room by room study is necessary to properly size the duct system because the duct design is based on the required heating and cooling load for each room or zone.

There are many variables to take into account when performing load calculations. The sheer number of factors to consider and the amount of number crunching involved can discourage contractors from performing accurate load calculations. One of the most common quick and dirty methods involves dividing the building's square footage by a factor to arrive at an equipment size. There are two obvious problems with this method: all buildings are not the same, and all rooms within a single building are not the same. The time spent doing a careful survey of the building and performing accurate load calculations will save time and money. It is time consuming and expensive to attempt to make an incorrectly sized and applied system work. This unit will concentrate on residential applications.

64.3 LOAD CALCULATION METHODS

Residential and commercial load calculations have unique characteristics that are best served by using a procedure especially designed for each specific system type. A few of the differences between residential and commercial load calculations are:

- **Ventilation**   Commercial buildings typically have much higher ventilation rates.
- **Lights**   The heat gain from lights in most commercial buildings is a major heat load.
- **People**   The people in many commercial buildings are a major source of heat gain.
- **Machinery**   The heat from equipment and machinery is often a major source of heat gain in commercial buildings.

The Air Conditioning Contractors of America, ACCA, has developed load calculation procedures that help organize the required information and simplify the process of performing an accurate load calculation. Current manuals include *Manual J, 8th edition* and *Manual J, 8th edition, Abridged* for residential calculations. *Manual N, 5th edition,* applies to commercial calculations. These calculation procedures provide tables with factors and data necessary to produce a handwritten spreadsheet. Many computer based solutions are now available to automate the process.

Manual J, 8th edition, provides tables and procedures for two types of load calculations: peak load procedure and average load procedure. The peak load procedure determines the peak load for each room or zone. Loads are calculated for each room or zone at the time of day in midsummer that represents the highest load for that exposure. Peak load procedure can be used for zoned systems, or for rooms with large exposures of glass. The average load procedure simplifies the calculations by averaging the factors over different times of the day to arrive at a single factor for each exposure, regardless of the time of day. The majority of residential load calculations can be done using the average load procedure. *Manual J, 8th edition, Abridged* only includes the average load procedure. The abridged edition also only has data on common forms of residential construction.

TECH TIP

There are many computer programs available that automate load calculation procedure. However, it is still necessary to collect all the relevant data from the plans or a building survey. The programs primarily save you the time required to look up factors in the tables and do the calculations. Probably the biggest advantage of computer aided load design is the ability to make changes and quickly see their effect. A customer might be better off spending more money on sealing and insulation than on purchasing a larger unit. This can be easily demonstrated using computer aided design.

64.4 RESIDENTIAL HEAT LOSS FACTORS

Heat loss occurs in the heating season when the building is warmer than the outside. Figure 64-1 illustrates common types of heat losses. The primary types of heat loss in a residential building are:

- Transmission losses.
- Infiltration losses.
- Ventilation losses.
- Duct losses.

Transmission Losses

Transmission losses occur because of a temperature difference between the inside and outside. Heat is transmitted through walls, windows, doors, floors, and ceilings from the inside to the outside.

The heat loss through these surfaces varies with

- The type of material.
- The thickness and thermal conductivity of the material.
- The area that is exposed to different temperatures.
- The temperature difference between the inside and the outside.

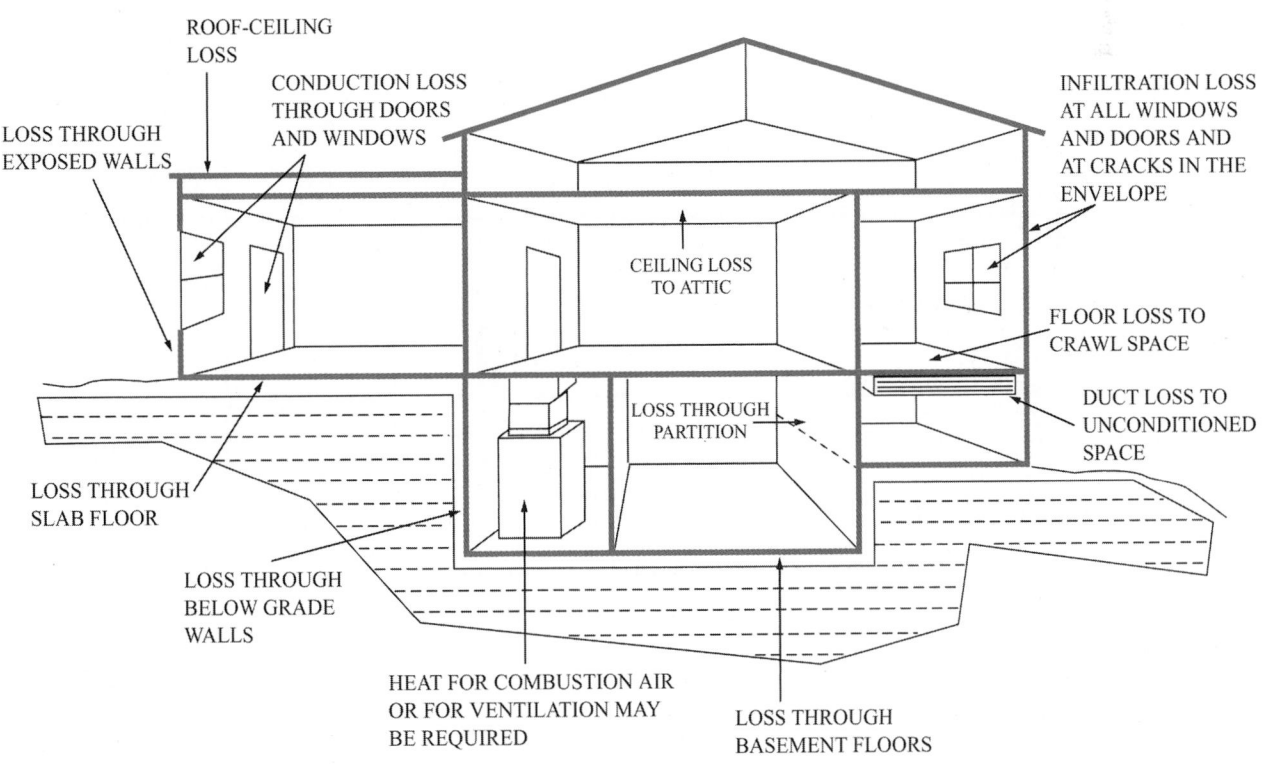

Figure 64-1 Winter heating loads
(Copyright by Air Conditioning Contractors of America [ACCA])

Infiltration Losses

Infiltration is air that leaks into the house through cracks and openings. Infiltration can be a significant heat loss because the warm, conditioned air is replaced with cold air from outside. The most obvious places where infiltration occurs are windows and doors. However, infiltration also occurs in walls between the sill and the foundation and in other openings, such as fireplaces.

Ventilation Losses

Ventilation air is air that is brought in on purpose. Like infiltration, ventilation is a heat loss because warm, conditioned air is replaced with cold, outdoor air. However, a big advantage of ventilation is that it can be controlled. Ventilation air can be filtered, and the amount entering can be controlled. Also, ventilation losses can be reduced by using an Energy Recovery Ventilator, ERV. Ventilation losses are significant in commercial structures, but play only a minor role in most residential buildings.

Duct Losses

There are really two types of duct losses: leaks and transmission losses through ducts located outside the conditioned area of the building. Duct leaks add to the overall infiltration in the building. The infiltration due to duct leaks can easily exceed the infiltration in the rest of the building. This can be addressed through proper duct installation. Duct transmission losses occur when the duct is located in an area exposed to outdoor temperatures, such as an attic or crawl space. These can be reduced by insulating the duct, but they cannot be eliminated. The only way to totally eliminate duct losses is to locate the duct inside the conditioned space, or use ductless systems.

64.5 RESIDENTIAL HEAT GAIN FACTORS

Heat gain occurs in the cooling season when the building is cooler than the outside. Figure 64-2 illustrates common types of heat gain. The same factors that affect heat loss also affect heat gain. They are:

- Transmission gains.
- Infiltration gains.
- Ventilation gains.
- Duct gains.

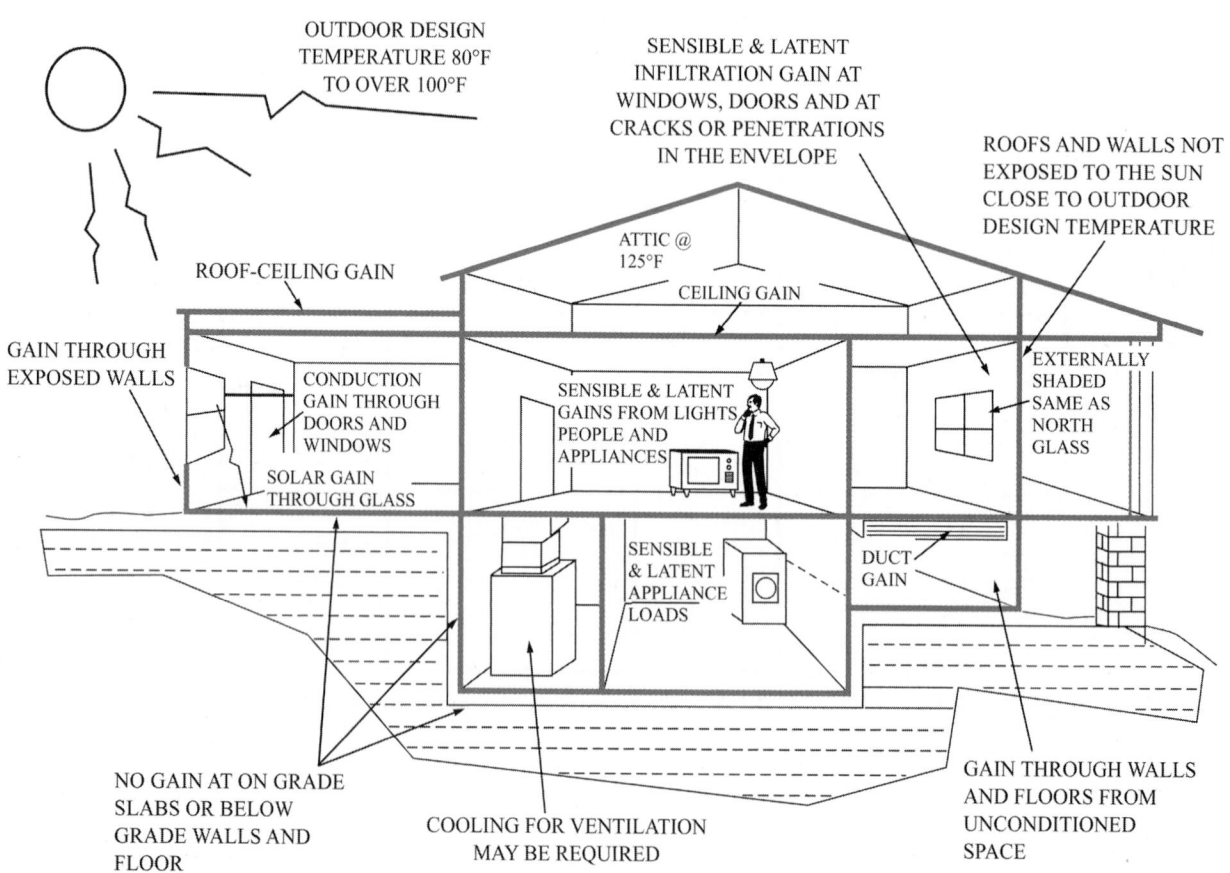

Figure 64-2 Summer cooling loads
(Copyright by Air Conditioning Contractors of America [ACCA])

Direction Windows Face	N	NE & NW	E & W	SE & SW	S	Horiz.
Clear glass (single or double), no protection	40	130	200	160	100	
Shaded completely by awnings	12	48	56	45	29	265
Light inside shades or Venetian blinds	24	77	122	95	58	
Glass brick, no protection	16	52	80	64	40	

Figure 64-3 Solar Heat Gain for Commercial Building Using Unitary Equipment (Btu/hr/sq ft Sash Area)
(The Trane Company)

However, there are additional factors that play an important role in heat gain. They are:

- Solar gain through glass.
- Internal heat gain from lights, machines, and appliances.
- Internal gain from people.
- Latent heat gain required for dehumidification.

Solar Gain

Solar gain is radiant heat gained from sun shining in through glass. Solar gain varies with the direction of the glass, the latitude of the building, the amount of external shade, and even the time of day. All directions have some solar gain. Northern facing glass has very little solar gain because the sun never shines directly into northern facing glass. In commercial load calculations, solar gain is determined separately from the transmissive gains through the windows. Figure 64-3 shows typical solar gains. Residential calculations, like *Manual J*, combine the transmissive and solar gains into a single factor.

Internal Gain from Lights, Machines, and Appliances

Lights, machines, and appliances all create heat. In many commercial applications the internal gain exceeds the gain from the walls, ceilings, and floors. Because of this, many commercial buildings need air conditioning even when it is cool outside. The internal light and appliance gains in a typical residence are much smaller. For years, these gains were estimated at 1,200 Btu/hr for a residence. Typically, this amount was added to the kitchen gain. *Manual J, 8th edition,* has a much more complete listing of appliances and their associated heat gain. The internal gain is still much smaller in residential buildings than in commercial buildings, but it is large enough to warrant a careful assessment.

Internal Gain from People

People produce heat. The gain from people in a theater is usually the major gain for that building. The gain from people in residential buildings is much smaller. The amount of heat produced by each person varies with activity level. Sedentary people add approximately 300 Btu/hr in total heat gain while people engaged in heavy work can produce approximately 1,500 Btu/hr in total heat gain. Figure 64-4 shows the heat gain from different types of activity.

Latent Heat Gain Required for Dehumidification

A big difference between heating loads and air conditioning loads is that air conditioning also involves dehumidification in most parts of the country. The amount of system capacity devoted to changing the air temperature is called sensible load. The amount of equipment capacity required to remove water from the air is called a latent load because the energy required for condensing water on the evaporator coil does not change the temperature of the air. When an air conditioner is operating with a large latent load, the temperature difference between the return and supply air is less than when it operates with a large sensible load.

In commercial buildings, the latent load from internal machines and people is often the major portion of the building's latent load. In residential buildings, the latent load is largely determined by the grains of water difference between the outdoor air and the indoor air, the amount of infiltration, and the amount of ventilation.

Air conditioning systems have both a sensible cooling capacity and a latent cooling capacity. Sizing a system to handle the latent load is extremely important in humid areas of the country. Mold and mildew problems can be created if a system with a low latent cooling capacity is installed in a humid area.

Degree of Activity	Typical Application	Sensible Heat (Btuh)	Latent Heat (Btuh)
Seated at rest	Theater—Matinee	225	105
	Theater—Evening	245	105
Seated, very light office work	Offices, Hotels Apartments	245	155
Moderately active office work	Offices, Hotels, Apartments	250	200
Standing; light work, walking slowly	Dept. Store, Retail Store	250	200
Walking; seated	Drug Store	250	250
Standing; walking slowly	Bank		
Sedentary work	Restaurants§	275	275
Light bench work	Factory	275	475
Moderate dancing	Dance Hall	305	545
Walking, 3 mph Moderately heavy work	Factory	375	625
Bowling§	Bowling Alley		
Heavy Work	Factory	580	870

*This table was extracted with permission from the 1993 ASHRAE Handbook: *Fundamentals*.
‡For *bowling*, figure one person per alley actually bowling and all others as sitting (400 Btuh) or standing (550 Btuh).
§The adjusted total heat value for *sedentary work, restaurant* includes 60 Btu per hour for food per individual (30 Btu sensible and 30 Btu latent).
NOTE: The above values are based on 75°F room dry-bulb temperature. For 80°F room dry-bulb temperature, the total heat gain remains the same, but the sensible heat values should be decreased by approximately 20 percent and the latent heat values increased accordingly.

Figure 64-4 Heat Gain from Occupants in a Commercial Building Using Unitary Equipment*
(The Trane Company)

TECH TIP

Oversizing an air conditioning unit reduces its latent cooling capacity. Units that operate for only short periods of time do not run long enough to remove much water from the air, so they have a lower effective latent cooling capacity.

64.6 HOUSE ORIENTATION AND SOLAR GAIN

East facing windows have a high solar heat gain in the morning, west facing windows have a high solar gain in the afternoon, and south facing windows receive solar radiation all day. Northern windows receive no direct solar gain. Figure 64-3 lists solar gain for different directions. Most houses have at least one side that has more windows and glass than the other sides. The direction the house is facing will significantly

affect the heat gain for cooling load calculations because of the difference in solar heat gain. The amount of heat gained from the floor and ceiling will not change as the house is rotated to face north, south, east, and west.

The effect of house orientation on heat gain will be demonstrated using the house floor plan shown in Figure 64-5. This house has 40 ft² of glass on the front, 75 ft² on the back, 13 ft² on the right side, and 24 ft² on the left side. The table in Figure 64-6 compares the solar load when the house faces south and when the house faces east. The solar gain nearly doubles from 13,400 Btu/hr when facing south to 25,920 Btu/hr when facing east.

64.7 THERMAL CONDUCTIVITY

All materials have different levels of thermal conductivity. The thermal conductivity of different materials is compared using k values. A k value states the amount of heat that will transfer through each square foot of material for each inch of thickness for every degree in temperature difference. It is expressed in Btu/hr, per square foot of area, per inch thickness,

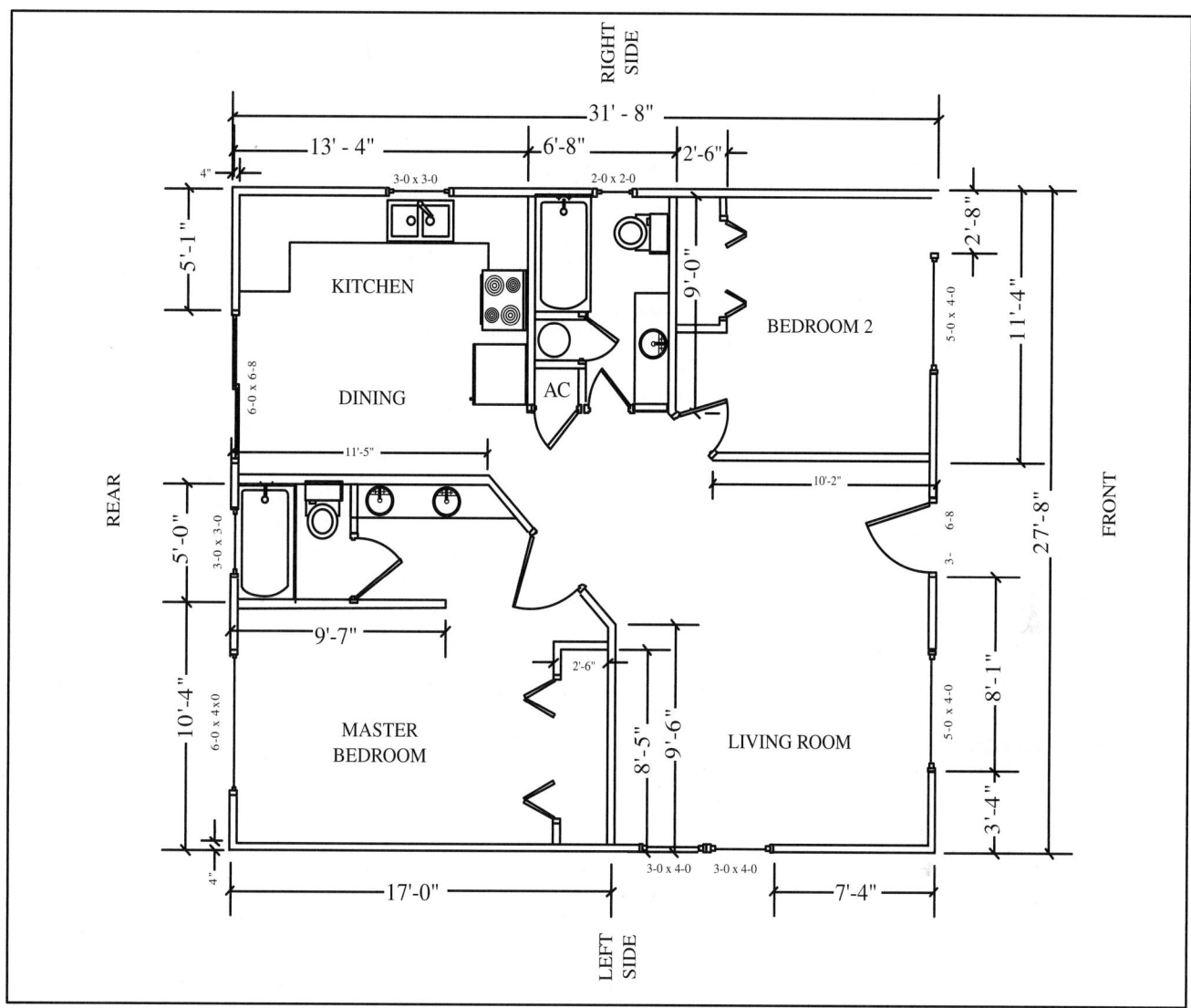

Figure 64-5 Basic residential floor plan

Facing Direction		South			East			
		Factor	Area	Btu gain	Direction	Factor	Area	Btu gain
Front	South	100	40	4,000	East	200	40	8,000
Right	East	200	13	2,600	North	40	13	520
Back	North	40	75	3,000	West	200	75	15,000
Left	West	200	24	4,800	South	100	24	2,400
Total Solar Gain				**13,400**	**Total Solar Gain**			**25,920**

Figure 64-6 The solar load for this house nearly doubles when it faces east instead of south

Figure 64-7 Thermal conductivity of common building materials

	Material	K value
Metal	Copper	223.00
	Aluminum	118.00
	Cast iron	40.00
Stone	Granite	24.29
	Marble	17.35
	Sandstone	11.10
Masonry	Concrete	12.00
	Brick	5.00
Wood	Kiln dried spruce	1.60
	Red oak	1.20
	Plywood	0.89
Insulation	Fiberglass blanket	0.32
	Expanded polystyrene	0.24
	Expanded urethane	0.17

per °F of temperature difference. Materials with high k values transmit heat more easily than materials with low k values. Figure 64-7 compares the thermal conductivities of common building materials.

64.8 THERMAL RESISTANCE

Thermal resistance is just the opposite of thermal conductance. A material with a low thermal conductance will have a high thermal resistance. The thermal resistance of materials is compared using R values. R is the number of hours it takes 1 Btu to pass through 1 ft^2 of material with a 1°F TD. R11 means it takes 11 hr for 1 Btu to pass through 1ft^2. R32 means it takes 32 hours for 1 Btu to pass through 1ft^2. A high R value indicates low heat flow rates.

R values are cumulative. The resistance of several components of a wall may be added together to obtain the total resistance. For example, a wall that has an exterior siding with an R value of 0.5, sheathing with an R value of 5.0, insulation with an R value of 11.0, and an interior surface with an R value of 0.5, would have a total R value of 17: 0.5 + 5 + 11 + 0.5 = 17. The R value is useful for comparing different types of insulation. Figure 64-8 lists the R values of some common building materials.

64.9 U VALUES

The U value of a material is defined as the quantity of heat in Btu that will flow through 1 ft^2 of material in 1 hr with a 1°F TD. The U value of any part of a structure is the total heat transfer coefficient for that component. The U value is the reciprocal of the component's R value. For example, if a material had a resistance of R-5, its U value would be 0.2: $^1/_5 = 0.2$. In the example of the wall with a total R value of 17, its U value is 0.06: $^1/_{17} = 0.06$ (rounded). The U value gives the Btu per hour per square foot of that component per

degree difference. In this case, 0.06 Btu/hr will transfer through each square foot of wall for every degree temperature difference.

64.10 HEAT TRANSFER MULTIPLIERS—HTM

U values give the heat transfer for each degree of temperature difference between the inside and outside temperatures. Heat transfer multipliers (HTMs) give the heat transfer for a specific temperature difference. As the temperature difference increases, so does the rate of heat transfer. HTMs are calculated by multiplying the U value times the temperature difference. In the example of the R-17 wall with the U value of 0.06, the HTM for heating with a 50°F temperature difference between outside and inside would be 3 Btu/hr: 0.06 Btu/hr/F° × 50°F = 3 Btu/hr.

64.11 STORAGE AND DAILY RANGE

The temperature difference used for determining most heat loss HTMs is simply the difference between the inside and outside temperature. The temperature difference used for determining heat gain HTMs is called the effective temperature difference (ETD). The effective temperature difference takes into account the temperature swings throughout the day and thermal storage in some parts of a building, such as attics.

Storage

When the sun shines in a window, its radiant heat is stored when it reaches the interior surfaces of the house and later gradually heats room air. The same kind of action occurs on the exterior of structures. Radiant heat from the sun warms the surfaces and is stored. Gradually, at a later time, the heat

Insulation Material	Kind	R value
Masonry	Brick, 4 in face	0.44
	Common 4 in	0.80
	Stone, lime/sand 1 in	0.08
	Stucco 1 in	0.20
	Concrete block, 8 in	1.04
	Concrete block, 8 in, cores filled	1.93
Concrete	Poured concrete 1 in	0.08
Wood	Fir, pine, other soft woods 1 in	1.25
	Maple oak, other hard woods 1 in	0.91
	Wood shavings or sawdust 1 in	2.20
	Plywood, $1/2$ in	0.63
Manufactured wood	Gypsum board $1/2$ in	0.45
products	Plywood, softwood, $1/4$ in	0.31
	Hardboard, underlayment $1/4$ in	0.31
Siding and roofing	Asphalt roofing shingles	0.44
	Wood bevel siding $1/2$ in	0.81
	Building paper, felt 15	0.06
Insulation	Glass fiber, batt 1 in	3.13
	Blown cellulose 1 in	3.4
	Expanded polystyrene 1 in	3.85
	Expanded polyurethane 1 in	6.64
	Extruded polystyrene 1 in (styrofoam blue board)	4.92

Various types of fiberglass insulation

R value	Applications(s)	Width (in)	Thickness (in)
R-11	Interior walls/noise control/basement walls	15, 23	3.5
R-13	Exterior walls/basement walls	15, 23	3.5
R-15	Exterior walls	15	3.5
R-19	Attics/exterior walls/crawl spaces	15, 23	6.25
R-21	Attics/Exterior walls	15, 23	5.5
R-30	Attics	16, 24	9.5
R-38	Attics	16, 24	12

Note: Insulation comes both faced and unfaced, in rolls and batts.

Figure 64-8 Value of common building materials

reaches the interior where it warms the interior air. The net effect of storage is to delay and smooth out solar loads. The delayed effect of the sun's load is incorporated in the procedures used for calculating heat gain.

Daily Range

The difference between the average high and low temperatures is the daily range. The high usually occurs late in the afternoon and the low at about daybreak. The daily range affects the cooling load since a low night temperature can reduce the daytime load due to the storage factor. The daily range factors are given for three ranges: low, medium, and high. The low daily range applies to climates where the difference between the high and low temperatures for the day is 15°F or less. This means there is less natural cooling effect to take advantage of. Areas with a low daily range have the highest effective temperature differences; and therefore, the highest heat gain HTMs. The medium daily range applies to climates where the difference between the high and low temperatures for the day is between 16°F and 25°F. These areas can take advantage of some natural cooling. The high daily range applies to climates where the difference between the high and low temperatures for the day is greater than 25°F. This means there is a large natural cooling effect to take advantage of. Areas with a high daily range have the lowest effective temperature differences; and therefore, the lowest heat gain HTMs.

Cooling Temperature Difference versus Design Temperature Difference

The design temperature difference is the difference between the outside and inside design temperatures. The outside design temperature is taken from weather data tables; the inside design temperature is typically 75°F for cooling. The cooling temperature difference is the temperature difference across a building component after taking into consideration factors like thermal storage and daily temperature range. The temperature of the surface of most roofs in the summer is considerably higher than the outdoor temperature. This makes the cooling temperature difference for most ceilings greater than the temperature difference between inside and outside. The cooling temperature difference across walls is often less than the difference between inside and outside because of the natural cooling effect of the daily range.

64.12 OUTSIDE DESIGN CONDITIONS

The outdoor temperature used for determining the temperature difference is not the coldest possible day in the winter or the hottest possible day in summer. The outside design conditions are selected from ASHRAE weather data. The data is assigned a percentage that represents the percentage of time during the year that the temperature exceeds that temperature. *Manual J* uses 99% for heating. This means that 99% of the time, the temperature will be above the heating design temperature. The temperature should dip below the heating design temperature for only 88 hr a year. *Manual J* uses 1% for cooling. This means that only 1% of the time will the temperature be above the cooling design temperature. The temperature should exceed the heating design temperature for only 88 hr a year. Using the 99% and 1% conditions prevents excessive oversizing of the equipment to handle a temporary high load. The recommended design temperatures are based on the average temperature of an entire day. Although people tend to think of the highs and lows they hear on the news, these temperatures typically only last for a few hours and do not represent the entire day.

TECH TIP

The design temperature for any locale is based on a 10 year average based on data provided by the US Weather Service. Over time, a design temperature for a locale may vary to match the data collected.

64.13 *MANUAL J, 8TH EDITION* WORKSHEET

The *Manual J* worksheet is like a computer spreadsheet, only in handwritten form, Figure 64-9. It helps organize the data and values for the many calculations required to perform an accurate heat load study. Rows 1–5 across the top contain information about the size of the house or room and the amount of exposed wall. This is shown in Figure 64-10 in yellow. The large block of columns on the left-hand side of the form are for listing the types of materials used and their corresponding heat transfer multipliers. This is shown in Figure 64-10 in blue. The materials are assigned construction numbers in *Manual J* to make referencing them easier. The next block over is for calculating the heat loss and heat gain for the entire house. This is shown in Figure 64-10 in green. The rest of the blocks are for calculating the heat loss and gain for each individual room. This is shown in Figure 64-10 in purple. Each of these blocks have columns for area, heating, and sensible cooling. The area of each material listed in the area column is multiplied by the HTMs for heating and cooling found on the left-hand side of the form. The answers are written in the heating and cooling columns. Totals are tabulated at the bottom of each column.

TECH TIP

There are many multipliers in *Manual J* that are decimal numbers with two digits to the right of the decimal. There is no reason to keep values in the Btu loss and gain columns in decimal form. A tenth of a Btu has no practical effect on the size of the equipment. For simplicity's sake, most designers round off the Btu loss and gain to whole numbers. Many round to the nearest hundred Btu because equipment is sized in thousands of Btu. For example, a Btu/hr loss of 2,517.6 would be rounded to either 2,518 for whole numbers, or simply 2,500 for even hundreds.

64.14 *MANUAL J* TABLES

At this point, the reader may be thinking that using a quick and dirty method is beginning to look pretty good. Keeping track of effective temperature differences, R values, U values, and heat transfer multipliers can appear to be a difficult task. The purpose of *Manual J* is to do most of the heavy lifting for you. The tables in *Manual J, 8th edition* list heat transfer multipliers for many different construction types. Factors like the direction that windows face, the daily range, and equivalent temperature differences have all been factored in for you. All you have to do is learn to use the tables. We are going to go through an example whole-house calculation using the plan in Figure 64-5. An abbreviated worksheet will be used which only shows the items being used. The necessary tables will be described along the way.

64.15 WEATHER DATA TABLES 1A AND 1B

Table 1A contains weather data for cities throughout the United States and Canada. The table is organized with cities in the United States in the first part of the table and cities in

		Const..Number	Panel Faces	HTM Htg.	HTM Clg.	Area or Length	Btuh Heating	Btuh S-Clg.	Btuh L-Clg.	Area or Length	Btuh Heating	Btuh S-Clg.

Figure 64-9 — Worksheet for Manual J, 8th edition table (lines 1–20):

1. Name of Room — Entire House
2. Running Feet of Exposed Wall
3. Ceiling Height At Walls (Ft) and Gross Wall Area (SqFt)
4. Room Dimensions (Feet) and Floor Plan Area (SqFT)
5. Ceiling Slope (Degrees) and Gross Ceiling Area
6a. Windows and Glass Doors (a, b, c)
6b. Skylights (a, b)
7. Metal Door (a, b)
8. Above Grade Walls (a, b, c)
9. Below Grade Walls (a, b, c)
10. Ceiling (a, b)
11b. Passive Floors (a, b)
12. Infiltration — Heat Loss (Btuh); Sensible Gain (Btuh); Latent Gain (Btuh); WAR
13. Internal — a Occupants at 230 and 200 Btuh (#); b Scenario Number; c Default Adjustments; d Individual Appliances; e Plants
14. Subtotals — Sum lines 6 through 11a + line 12 + line 13
15. Duct Loads — ELF-Loss and ELF-Gain; Latent Gain
16. Ventilation Loads   Vent CFM   Exh
17. Winter Humidification load   Gal / Day
18. Piping Load
19. Blower Heat
20. Total Load — Sum lines 11b + lines 14 through 19

Figure 64-9 Worksheet for *Manual J, 8th edition* (From Manual J 8th edition, Copyright Air Conditioning Contractors of America)

Canada in the second part. The states and provinces are listed in alphabetical order, and the cities are listed under their state in alphabetical order. The most important data found in this table is:

- **Latitude**   Latitude is used to calculate shade from overhangs above windows.
- **Heating 99% Dry Bulb**   Heating 99% dry bulb is used for the heating outdoor design temperature.
- **Cooling 1% Dry Bulb**   Cooling 1% dry bulb is used for the cooling outdoor design temperature.
- **Design Grains RH**   Design grains RH lists the grains of difference between inside and outside in the summer. This is used for calculating the latent cooling load. *Manual J* has three columns, one each for 55%, 50%, and 45% indoor relative humidity.

Table 1B lists the same information as Table 1A, but for more locations in the states of Arizona, California, Hawaii, and Nevada.

For our example, the house will be located in Selma, Alabama. The winter design for Selma is 26°F and the summer design temperature is 95°F, Figure 64-11. The design grains of difference will be 49 grains for 50% relative humidity. The winter design temperature difference will be 44°F: 70°F − 26°F = 44°F. The summer design temperature difference will be 20°F: 95°F − 75° = 20°F.

64.16 ROOM DIMENSIONS

The first line is for the room name, in this case it is the entire house. The running feet of exposed wall is the length of wall that is exposed to the outside. Only walls that are exposed to the outside are listed. For example, the master bathroom has only 5 ft of exposed wall. The house as a whole has two walls of 32 ft and two walls of 28 ft, for a total of 120 ft. The ceiling in our example will be a standard ceiling: 8 ft high with no slope. Figure 64-12 shows this part of the form completed.

Figure 64-10 Major sections of the *Manual J, 8th edition* worksheet *(From Manual J 8th edition, Copyright Air Conditioning Contractors of America)*

1	Name of Room						Entire House							
2	Running Feet of Exposed Wall													
3	Ceiling Height At Walls (Ft) and Gross Wall Area (SqFt)													
4	Room Dimensions (Feet) and Floor Plan Area (SqFT)													
5	Ceiling Slope (Degrees) and Gross Ceiling Area													
	Type of Exposure		Const.. Number	Panel Faces	HTM Htg.	HTM Clg.	Area or Length	Btuh Heating	Btuh S-Clg.	Btuh L-Clg.	Area or Length	Btuh Heating	Btuh S-Clg.	
6a	Windows and Glass Doors	a												
		b												
		c												
6b	Skylights	a												
		b												
7	Metal Door	a												
		b												
8	Above Grade Walls	a												
		b												
		c												
9	Below Grade Walls	a												
		b												
		c												
10	Ceiling	a												
		b												
11b	Passive Floors	a												
		b												
12	Infiltration	Heat Loss				Btuh	WAR				WAR			
		Sensible Gain				Btuh								
		Latent Gain				Btuh								
13	Internal	a	Occupants at 230 and 200 Btuh				#				#			
		b	Scenario Number											
		c	Default Adjustments											
		d	Individual Appliances											
		e	Plants											
14	Subtotals	Sum lines 6 through 11a + line 12 + line 13												
15	Duct Loads	ELF-Loss and ELF-Gain												
		Latent Gain												
16	Ventilation Loads	Vent CFM		Exh										
17	Winter Humidification load		Gal / Day											
18	Piping Load													
19	Blower Heat													
20	Total Load	Sum lines 11b + lines 14 through 19												

64.17 FENESTRATION HEAT LOSS TABLES 2A AND 2B

In *Manual J*, fenestration refers to anything that light can pass through, including windows, skylights, and glass doors. Table 2A lists U values for generic windows, skylights, and glass doors. These U values are used to construct heat loss HTMs.

In Table 2A, the column on the left describes the type of glass, the number of panes, and the general construction. The column on the right lists the type of frame. To use the table, locate the row in the left column that describes the type of glass and window construction. The U value is listed over on the right under the column that describes the frame style. The windows in our example house are fixed sash, wood frame, double pane window with a low e coating of 0.4 emissivity. Figure 64-13 shows the construction number is 3B and the U value is 0.51.

Once the U value has been determined, the HTM is calculated by multiplying the winter temperature difference times the U value. In this case, the HTM would be 23.5 Btu/hr for a winter temperature difference of 46°F: 0.51 Btu/hr°F × 46°F = 23.5 Btu/hr. The heat loss for the windows is calculated by multiplying this HTM by the area of all the windows, Figure 64-14.

Table 2B is for windows, glass doors, and skylights that are rated by the National Fenestration Rating Council, NFRC. NFRC rated items have a label that lists important energy performance data including the U value, solar heat gain coefficient, and air leakage. For typical windows and glass doors, the HTM can be calculated by multiplying the U value listed on the window by the winter temperature difference. Table 2B lists formulas to help determine the HTM values for more complicated fenestrations such as bay windows and skylights.

Table 1A
Outdoor Design Conditions For the United States and Canada

Location	Elevation Feet	Latitude Degrees North	Winter Heating 99% Dry Bulb	Summer Cooling 1% Dry Bulb	Coincident Wet Bulb	Design Grains 55% RH	Design Grains 50% RH	Design Grains 45% RH	Daily Range (DR)
Alabama									
Alexander City	686	33	22	93	76	39	46	52	M
Anniston AP	612	33	24	93	76	39	46	52	M
Auburn	776	32	22	93	76	39	46	52	M
Birmingham AP	644	33	23	92	75	34	41	47	M
Decatur	592	34	16	93	74	27	34	40	M
Dothan AP	401	31	32	93	76	39	46	52	M
Florence AP	581	34	21	94	75	31	38	44	M
Gadsden	569	34	20	94	75	31	38	44	M
Huntsville AP	629	34	20	92	74	28	35	41	M
Mobile AP	218	30	30	92	76	41	48	54	M
Mobile CO	26	30	29	93	77	46	53	59	M
Montgomery AP	221	32	27	93	76	39	46	52	M
Ozark, Fort Rucker	356	31	31	94	77	44	51	57	M
Selma-Craig AFB	166	32	26	95	77	42	49	55	M
Talladega	528	33	22	94	76	37	44	50	M
Tuscaloosa AP	170	33	24	94	77	44	51	57	M

Figure 64-11 Weather data selection from Table IA of *Manual J*, 8th edition
(From Manual J 8th edition, Copyright Air Conditioning Contractors of America)

1	Name of Room					Entire House			
2	Running Feet of Exposed Wall					120			
3	Ceiling Height and Gross Wall Area					8	120 × 8 = 960		
4	Room Dimensions and Floor Plan Area					32 × 28	32 × 28 = 896		
5	Ceiling Slope					0	896		

Type of Exposure		Const #	Facing	HTM Heating	HTM Cooling	Area or Length	BTU per Hour Heating	Sensible	Latent
6a	Windows and Glass Doors	a							
		b							
		c							
		d							
7	Wood and Metal Doors	a							
8	Above Grade Walls	a							
10	Ceilings	a							
11a	Passive Floors	a							
12	Infiltration	Heat Loss			WAR 1.0				
		Sensible Gain							
		Latent Gain							
13	Internal	a							
		b							
14	Subtotals	Sum lines 6−11a + lines 12 and 13							
15	Duct Loads	ELF Loss and ELF Gain							
		Latent Gain							
20	Total Load	Sum Lines 11b + lines 14−19							

Figure 64-12 Lines 1–5 completed on *Manual J* worksheet

Figure 64-13 Window construction number and U value from Table 2A of *Manual J, 8th edition*
(From Manual J 8th edition, Copyright Air Conditioning Contractors of America)

Construction Numbers 1 Though 7 Window and Glass Door Assemblies	Type of Frame Construction			
Reference Area = Area of Rough Opening (SqFt). **Bold Face** denotes U-Values used for Tables 3A, 3B, 3F and 3G.	Metal No Break	Metal With Break	Wood, Wood With Metal Clad or Vinyl	Insulated Fiberglass
Number 1 — Clear, Heat Absorbing or Reflective Glass	U-Value			
A. Single pane operable window or sliding glass door	1.27	1.08	0.90	0.81
B. Single pane window, fixed sash	1.13	1.07	0.98	0.94
C. Single pane operable window with storm	0.87	0.65	0.57	0.49
D. Double pane operable window or sliding glass door	0.87	0.65	0.57	0.49
E. Double pane window, fixed sash	0.69	0.63	0.56	0.53
F. Triple pane window, fixed sash	0.55	0.48	0.42	0.40
G. Products rated and labeled by the NFRC (see Table 2B-1)	Refer to label, NFRC Directory or manufacturer's engineering data.			
Number 2 — Double Pane Low-e Glass Designed For Cold Climate (Emissivity of Low-e coating = 0.60)	U-Value			
A. Operable window or sliding glass door	0.84	0.63	0.55	0.47
B. Window with fixed sash	0.67	0.60	0.54	0.51
C. Products rated and labeled by the NFRC (see Table 2B-1)	Refer to label, NFRC Directory or manufacturer's engineering data.			
Number 3 — Double Pane Low-e Glass Designed For Cold Climate (Emissivity of Low-e coating = 0.40)	U-Value			
A. Operable window or sliding glass door	0.82	0.61	0.53	0.45
B. Window with fixed sash	0.64	0.58	0.51	0.49
C. Products rated and labeled by the NFRC (see Table 2B-1)	Refer to label, NFRC Directory or manufacturer's engineering data.			
Number 4 — Double Pane Low-e Glass Designed For Cold Climate (Emissivity of Low-e coating = 0.20 or less)	U-Value			
A. Operable window or sliding glass door	0.77	0.56	0.47	0.41
B. Window with fixed sash	0.59	0.52	0.45	0.43
C. Products rated and labeled by the NFRC (see Table 2B-1)	Refer to label, NFRC Directory or manufacturer's engineering data.			
Number 5 — Jalousie Window	U-Value			
A. Jalousie window only	1.27	~	~	~
B. Jalousie window with storm	0.69	~	~	~
Number 6 — Projected Window Assemblies	U-Value			
A. Bay window with any fixed sash window listed above	Multiply flat panel, fixed sash U-Value by 1.15.			
B. Garden window with any fixed sash window listed above	Multiply flat panel, fixed sash U-Value by 2.75.			
C. Products rated and labeled by the NFRC (see Table 2B-1)	Refer to label, NFRC Directory or manufacturer's engineering data.			
Number 7 — Glass or Plastic Block	U-Value			
A. Glass block with mortar joints	Use 0.60 U-Value for all products.			
B. Products rated and labeled by the NFRC (see Table 2B-5)	Refer to label, NFRC Directory or manufacturer's engineering data.			

T2A-1

64.18 FENESTRATION HEAT GAIN TABLES 3A–3I

Tables 3A through 3I provide HTM values for heat gain, including solar gain. The large number of tables is for specifying the amount of external shade, the type of fenestration and the load procedure used. Tables 3A–3D are used for the Average Load Procedure. Tables 3F–3I are used for the Peak Load Procedure. Table 3E is used to adjust the HTM for factors such as overhang, foreground reflectance, and latitude. We will only be discussing tables 3A–3D. Briefly, the tables are:

- **3A** Generic windows and glass doors with no external sun screen.
- **3B** Generic windows and glass doors behind an external sun screen.
- **3C** Generic skylights.
- **3D** NFRC rated windows and doors.

Tables 3A and 3B both have multiple pages. In Table 3A, each page covers a different type of glass: clear, heat absorbing, reflective, and glass block. In Table 3B, each page covers a different amount of external sun screen: 15%, 25%, 35%, and 45%. Each page in both tables is organized into three columns: single pane, double pane, and triple pane. Each column is further divided into columns for temperature difference and rows for the direction the window faces. In our example, the HTM for a double pane window with no external sun screen, heat absorbing glass, and no internal shade would be found in Table 3A, page 2. To find the HTM for the east and west facing windows in the house, first look at the large row at the top of Table 3A, page 2 described as *No internal shade*. Find the column in the middle listed as *Double pane*. The HTM is at the intersection of the row for *East or west* and the *20* column. In this case the HTM is 52, Figure 64-15. The HTM values for the north facing and south facing windows are found in a similar manner. The HTM for the north facing windows is 20 and the HTM for the south facing windows is 29. The heat gain through the windows is then calculated by multiplying these HTM values by the area of the windows, Figure 64-16.

Commercial Environmental Systems

UNIT 65

Commercial Air Conditioning Systems

OBJECTIVES

After completing this unit you will be able to:

- explain the differences between residential, commercial, and industrial air conditioning applications.
- list the different types of commercial air conditioning applications.
- identify which type of equipment configuration best suits each commercial application.
- list the basic chilled-water system compressor and condenser types.
- describe the differences between single package conditioners and rooftop units.

65.1 INTRODUCTION

Air conditioning systems may vary widely depending on the size of the space to be conditioned, the geographical location, and specific applications required for the space. For example, a hospital operating room demands reduced room temperatures along with highly filtered dry air. The requirements for such a system are far different from a hotel room that requires only minor levels of filtration along with the ability to supply both heating and cooling through simple operation.

Most systems utilize the standard mechanical refrigeration cycle components of compressors, condenser, flow control, and evaporator; however the physical size and location of the components will differ. In addition, the air distribution systems for smaller units can be very simple by means of only a self-contained fan while larger systems could have a complex layout of ducting that may include an economizer or dehumidifier function.

A large building in a dry hot climate such as Arizona may be designed with an economizer that will use some outside air for cooling, particularly when the temperature begins to drop in the early evening. A supermarket in the northeast may use a heat reclaiming system to recirculate some of the heat removed by the condenser back into the store during the cold winter months. The air conditioning system for the control room of a power plant is designed to keep the computer systems dry and cool and therefore human comfort is only secondary to the needs of the equipment.

65.2 AIR CONDITIONING APPLICATIONS

Residential Air Conditioning Systems

This category generally includes single family, multifamily, and lowrise multifamily private household residences. The air conditioning type is typically central forced air, central hydronic, or zoned. The capacities of residential installations

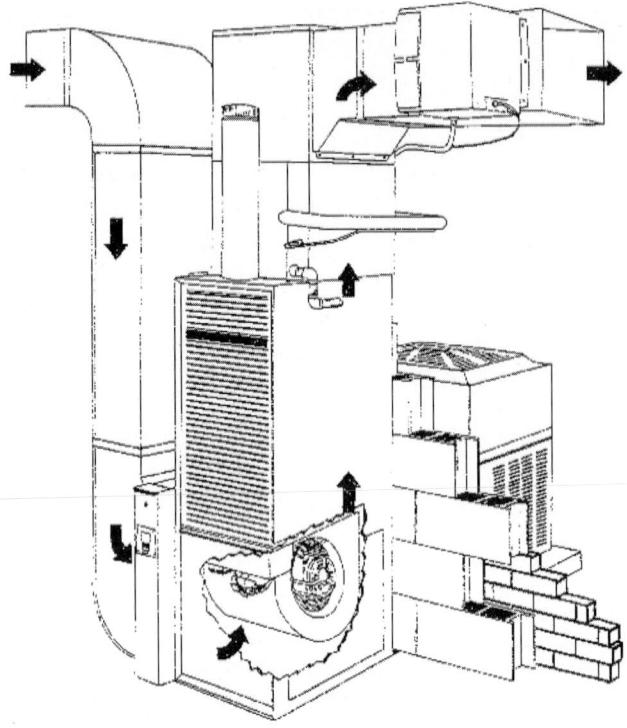

Figure 65-1 Residential installation of split system air cooled condensing unit with coil and upflow furnace
(© American Society of Heating, Refrigerating, and Air-Conditioning Engineers, Inc., www.ashrae.org)

Figure 65-2 Commercial rooftop single packaged unit

typically range from less than 1 ton up to about 5 tons. A typical residential split system is shown in Figure 65-1.

Commercial Air Conditioning Systems

The commercial sector is generally defined as nonmanufacturing business establishments, including hotels, motels, restaurants, wholesale businesses, retail stores, and health, social, and educational institutions. The air conditioning type varies considerably depending on the application. Systems can be as simple as a standard console through-the-wall conditioner for a hotel room. For conditioning multiple rooms or spaces in one building, single package conditioners, split system conditioners, and rooftop conditioners are most commonly used. Many of the smaller systems ranging from fractional tonnage room coolers up to about 20–30 tons are often referred to as "light commercial" systems, Figure 65-2. For substantial cooling loads, large central forced air systems and chiller systems with ratings of 100 tons and above may be required.

Industrial Air Conditioning Systems

Both residential and commercial air conditioning systems are designed primarily for comfort. Industrial air conditioning systems are designed for processes and environmental conditions that may require greater levels of filtration, more stringent humidity control, and special requirements for treatment of airborne contaminants that may result from a manufacturing process. Some examples of industrial facilities include laboratories, printing plants, textile processing plants, environmental control for animals and plants, wood and paper product facilities, nuclear facilities, and mine air conditioning and ventilation, Figure 65-3. Many of the system types are similar in arrangement and equipment requirements as compared to large commercial systems.

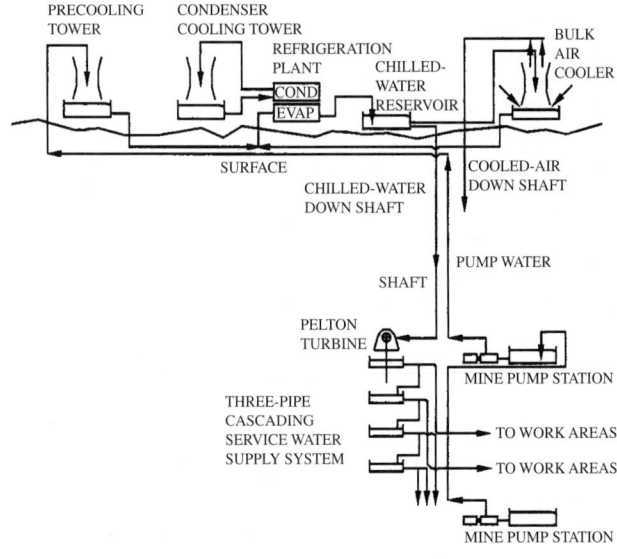

Figure 65-3 Air conditioning for a mine shaft
(© American Society of Heating, Refrigerating, and Air-Conditioning Engineers, Inc., www.ashrae.org)

65.3 COMMERCIAL AIR CONDITIONING APPLICATIONS

Hotels, Motels, and Dormitories

Very often each room will have its own unitary system such as a through the wall packaged terminal air conditioner (PTAC) for heating and cooling, Figure 65-4. This type of unit is generally simple to operate, and can be turned down or shut off since the room is not occupied at all times. The typical system consists of an indoor and outdoor coil, compressor, and refrigerant flow control. Electric heat is used either as a primary source or as an auxiliary source in the case of a heat pump application.

Restaurants, Nightclubs, and Casinos

Small cafeterias and bars with loads up to 10 tons will typically use direct expansion, self contained packaged units located within the space itself, Figure 65-5. Large establishments will use some form of central plant with either forced air or a chilled water system. These spaces require high ventilation rates to exhaust odors and fumes, which will require increased amounts of outside air. The increased air supply however should be admitted to the space without causing drafts for people who are dining. The considerable latent heat load from cooking, food, and people who may be active or dancing, requires a system with an increased cooling coil size to remove the excess moisture from the air. Special consideration needs to be given to odors. As an example, air should circulate from the dining area into the kitchen. This will keep odors out of the dining areas and serve to help the kitchen cool.

Supermarkets, Department Stores, and Malls

Supermarkets use large open refrigerated displays that will absorb heat from the room air in contact with them. This heat absorbed from the air by the refrigeration system must be taken into account as this will decrease the load on the air conditioning system. Energy costs can be extremely high if this is not taken into account. Many supermarkets utilize a heat reclaiming system that recovers the heat being rejected to the outside condenser by the refrigeration system, Figure 65-6. This heat is reintroduced to the air handler for the supply air circuit.

Department stores today are offering a number of conveniences including supermarket areas, lunch counters, auto service areas, and garden shops. This variety of merchandise will affect the air conditioning system type and requirements. Special ventilation requirements may be necessary if forklift trucks are entering the space. Major considerations to be taken into account for department store air conditioning systems are the installation cost, floor space requirements, and simplicity of control. For these reasons, rooftop mounted units are most commonly used. Usually the controls are operated by personnel who have little knowledge of air conditioning systems, so they should be simple and fully automatic.

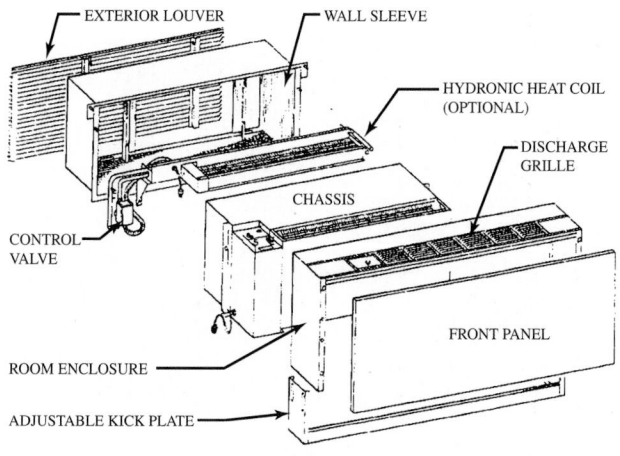

Figure 65-4 Packaged terminal air conditioner with heating section separate from cooling chassis
(© American Society of Heating, Refrigerating, and Air-Conditioning Engineers, Inc., www.ashrae.org)

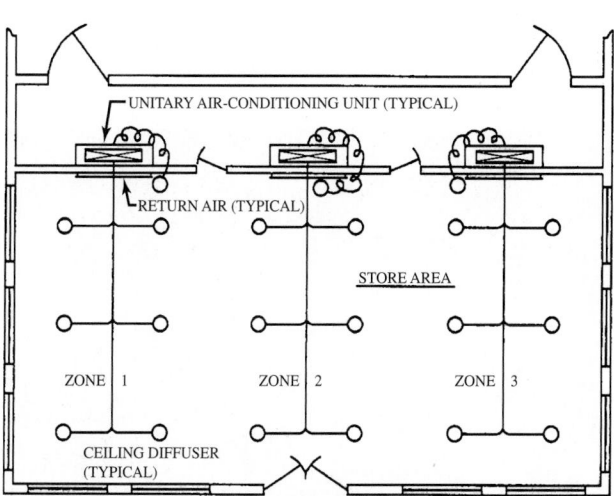

Figure 65-5 Multiple packaged units
(© American Society of Heating, Refrigerating, and Air-Conditioning Engineers, Inc., www.ashrae.org)

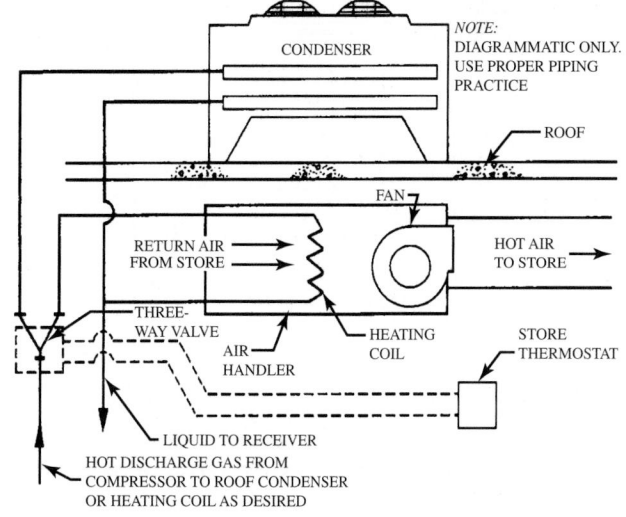

Figure 65-6 Supermarket heat reclaiming system
(© American Society of Heating, Refrigerating, and Air-Conditioning Engineers, Inc., www.ashrae.org)

Malls often utilize a central plant to distribute chilled air for the enclosed mall and then to the individual tenant stores. Variable volume control of the air supply and electric reheat is used for the temperature control of each individual space or store. Generally the enclosed mall will be at a slight positive air pressure relative to atmospheric. Individual stores will maintain an air pressure that is best suited for their use. As an example, a store may operate under a negative pressure for better odor control.

Office Buildings

The variety of office building configurations allows for the use of almost every type of available air conditioning system. A large office building will have some offices located near windows around the outer walls of the building, while others will be located on the interior of the building. The outer office's cooling load may vary considerably during the day as the sun rises and as the seasons change. The interior office's load will remain more uniform. Another consideration is the occupancy. Most office buildings are occupied from 8:00 AM until 6:00 PM. Lighting is also a consideration as it is a significant part of the cooling load.

Small one story office buildings may have individual unitary packaged systems for individual spaces, Figure 65-7. Multiple story buildings may use forced air with a rooftop central unit. This could be a rooftop forced air system as shown in Figure 65-8 or an air cooled chiller as shown in Figure 65-9. Very large multistory office buildings often use a large central chilled water system located in a mechanical equipment room, Figure 65-10. Each floor will have its own

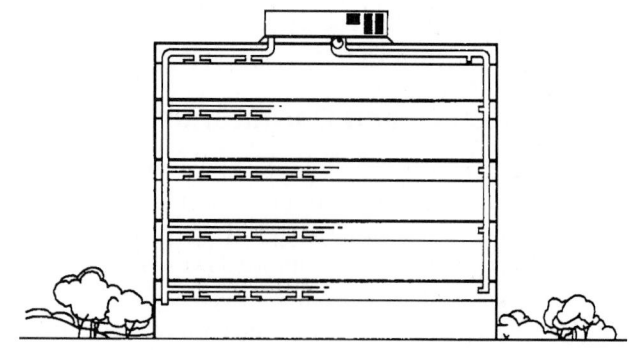

Figure 65-8 Multistory rooftop installation of single packaged unit
(© American Society of Heating, Refrigerating, and Air-Conditioning Engineers, Inc., www.ashrae.org)

Figure 65-9 Air cooled chiller

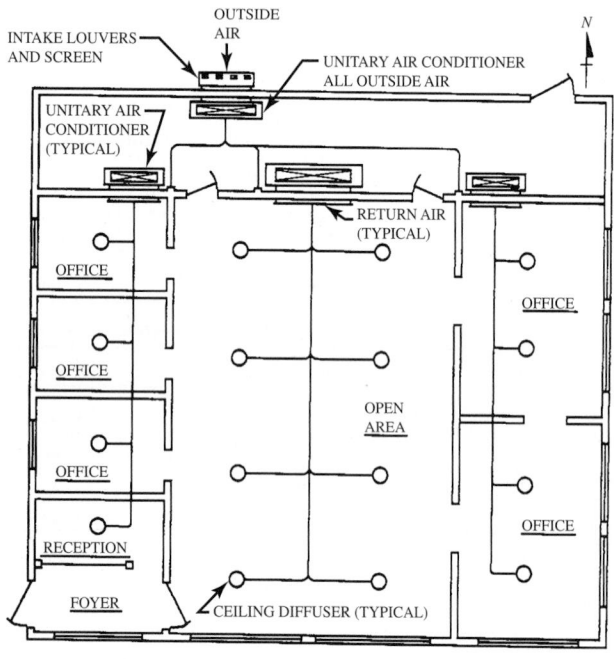

Figure 65-7 Multiple packaged units with separate outside air makeup unit
(© American Society of Heating, Refrigerating, and Air-Conditioning Engineers, Inc., www.ashrae.org)

Figure 65-10 Semi-hermetic centrifugal water cooled chiller

fan room where the chilled water supplied from the central system is used to indirectly cool the air. One mechanical equipment room usually services 8–20 floors. The fewer the floors served by an equipment room, the greater the flexibility in controlling the space temperatures. One equipment room per floor will allow for better control, however there will be more units that require maintenance and increased installation costs. There may be some savings in efficiency because equipment can be shut off in unoccupied areas.

Hospitals and Nursing Homes

Of all the commercial areas, hospital air conditioning is the most demanding in terms of the overall requirements necessary. For these systems, the air handling system can be very complex and sophisticated. Air circulation between spaces is often restricted. This is because many bacterial and viral infections such as Legionnaires' disease or chicken pox can be transported within the air. A good source of outside air will help to dilute viral and bacterial contaminants within a hospital. Special requirements for high-efficiency filters must be followed to make sure that the correct filters are installed and then replaced at regular intervals.

Temperature and humidity are of extreme concern for patient healing and recovery. Dry conditions can contribute to secondary infection and should be avoided. However, an increased relative humidity is not necessarily desired as some bacteria survive more readily in a humid environment. Therefore, general clinic areas of the entire hospital are typically maintained at 30–60% relative humidity. However, individual operating room, delivery room, recovery room, intensive care unit, and all other special treatment spaces will all have varying requirements that must be maintained.

Most hospitals will have a fairly large hot water central heating system utilizing steam boilers. Steam is also used for the sterilization of utensils, instruments, and equipment. Large centrifugal or screw type compressors are often used for the chilled water cooling plant. Most hospitals have backup emergency power in the event that the local power is disrupted. This backup power may be supplied by gasoline or diesel powered generators. Some of the newest systems use the combined cycle of gas and steam turbine driven generators. The gas turbine exhaust passes though a heat exchanger to boil water and produce steam. This steam, which is generated from heat that would normally be lost up the stack, is supplied to the steam turbine driven generator. Because there is an abundance of heat in this type of system, absorption type chillers can be used to reduce total operating costs. Figure 65-11 shows a gas turbine driven refrigeration compressor with the waste heat being used for an air conditioning absorption system.

Nursing homes have many of the same requirements as hospitals in regard to air quality, temperature, and humidity. However, since normally there are few special treatment spaces such as operating rooms, and so on, the overall demands for the system are far less complex. Individual room

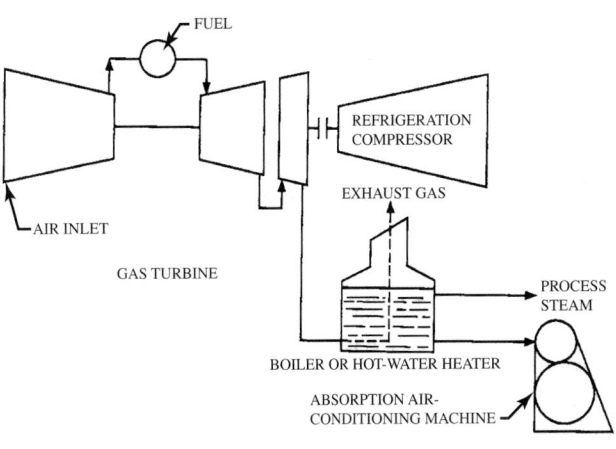

Figure 65-11 Gas turbine refrigeration system using exhaust heat
(© American Society of Heating, Refrigerating, and Air-Conditioning Engineers, Inc., www.ashrae.org)

temperature control should be allowed for and the registers should be located to reduce drafts. It is not uncommon for these systems to have large volumes of outside air admitted for odor control. To reduce operating costs, odor may be controlled with activated carbon or potassium permanganate-impregnated activated alumina filters.

Schools, Colleges, and Universities

The type of system normally found will vary depending whether the facility is new or existing and whether it is to be totally or partially renovated at some point. It should be a system that can be easily maintained by the institution's maintenance staff. Educational facilities typically have very limited budgets, therefore energy savings are often extremely important and this can affect the type of system that is installed. Schools that need to grow with new additions or wings, may not necessarily add new heating and cooling systems but instead may just upgrade and add on to the existing system.

There are a number of methods to reduce energy consumption that can be somewhat straightforward to incorporate. Outdoor economizer cycles use the cooler outdoor air whenever the outside air temperature begins to drop. This helps to offset the high inside load which has increased during the peak load part of the day. Night setback conserves energy by resetting the heating and cooling space temperatures during the evening hours when no one is in the building. Morning warmup and cooldown will reset the temperature back to normal with enough time allowed for the space to be comfortable when the students arrive at school.

The use of the facility is normally taken into account. As an example, a preschool should be configured to minimize drafts near the floor level. This is because the children are small and will most likely be playing on the floor a majority of the time. Large universities will have multiple buildings which may each utilize its own central cooling system. Many schools in northern climates will not have any air conditioning system at all. This is because during the summer months when it would be required, school is normally out of session. If summer sessions are held, windows are opened to provide for air circulation.

Airports, Bus Stations, Ship Docks, and Train Stations

These are generally large open areas one or more stories high. Heating and cooling is typically supplied from a central system through an air distribution system that has multiple zones. Some problems encountered relate to the air balancing of the space due to the many outside openings, high ceilings, and long, low passageways. The requirements for these spaces are different from office buildings in that often transportation centers are occupied on a 24-hour-a-day basis.

Auditoriums, Movie Theaters, Arenas, and Stadiums

These spaces are subject to high peak loads during an event and then very reduced loads at most other times. Many events are held in the evening rather than at the peak load portion of the day, which helps to minimize the cooling demand. The major cooling load results from the people in the space and relative humidity is a concern. Large systems will be designed to cool the air down below its dew point for the removal of moisture and then utilize some form of reheat. Often large central chilled water systems are used for these facilities. The air supply would be too noisy if located near the seating area, particularly for a theater where a performance is being held. In most cases, air is supplied from overhead at a high enough velocity to reach the seating area without being too noisy. The return air registers are located near the seats to

help circulate the air through the space. Many auditoriums and arenas are designed to operate on all outside air because during setup time trucks may be used to bring in equipment and supplies.

65.4 INDUSTRIAL AIR CONDITIONING APPLICATIONS

Manufacturing Plants

There are many different types of manufacturing facilities and each has its own needs and requirements for air conditioning. Some typical applications include the manufacture or processing of ceramics, plastics, leather, plywood, textiles, rubber dipped goods, floor coverings, and electrical products, Figure 65-12. Then there are consumer products such as tea, tobacco, and distilled liquors. Many applications require some form of painting process which requires special air filtration systems.

These facilities often require the use of large amounts of energy for the manufacturing processes involved and also for the air conditioning systems. Many processes require specific temperature and humidity levels. As an example, in the manufacture of rayon, temperature controls the rate of reaction and humidity maintains the solution at a constant strength. For varnish drying, the temperature is critical and proper humidity levels reduce the formation of bubbles on the surface.

Moisture regain is important for the processing of hygroscopic materials such as textiles, paper, wood, leather, and tobacco. A hygroscopic material readily absorbs moisture from the air. Moisture regain is the percentage of absorbed moisture in a material as compared to its bone-dry mass. Conditioning and drying are the typical processes utilized for removing or adding hygroscopic and free moisture. These two are combined to accurately regulate the final moisture content

Figure 65-12 Semiconductor manufacturing plant
(© American Society of Heating, Refrigerating, and Air-Conditioning Engineers, Inc., www.ashrae.org)

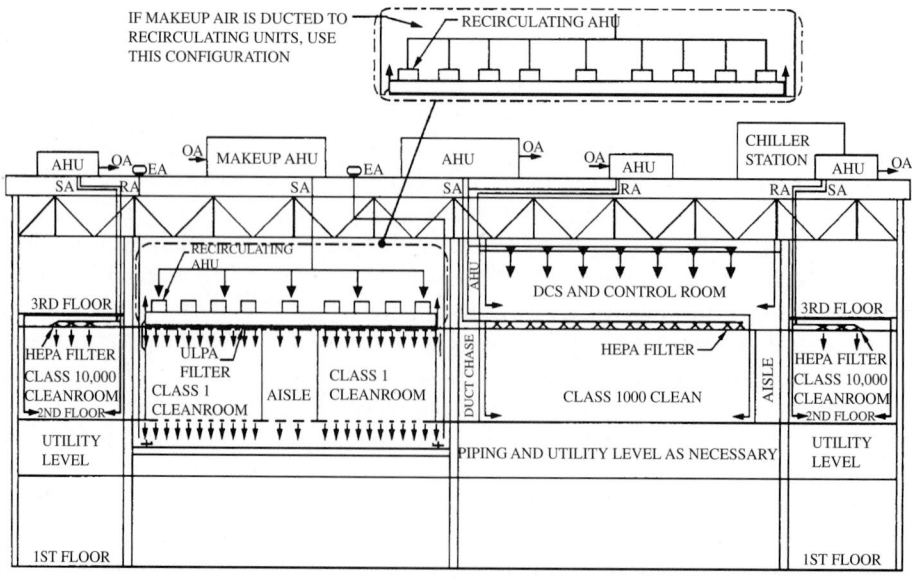

TYPICAL SEMICONDUCTOR MANUFACTURING PLANT SECTION VIEW

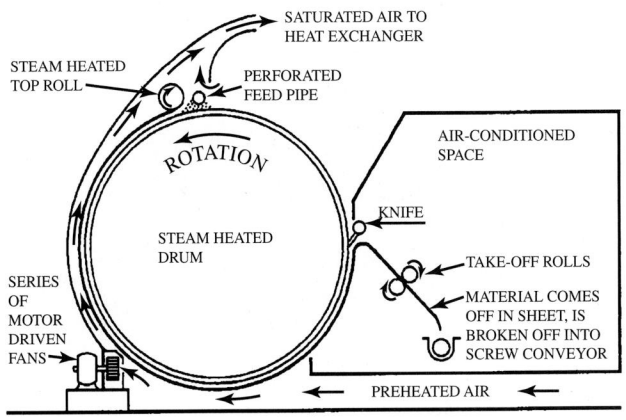

Figure 65-13 Drum dryer for paper-making machine
(© American Society of Heating, Refrigerating, and Air-Conditioning Engineers, Inc., www.ashrae.org)

in products such as textiles and tobacco. Figure 65-13 shows the large dryer drum used for the paper-making process.

In the manufacturing process, many airborne particles may be released. Some of these include dust, bacteria, smoke, spores, pollen, and radioactive particles. If left unfiltered, these may spoil perishable goods and clog small openings in precision machinery. Static electricity can be dangerous in explosive atmospheres and generally its effect is minimized at humidity levels above 35%.

The most important factor to be considered given all of these requirements is to also provide an environment that is suitable for employees working at the facility. High temperature and humidity levels can lead to worker fatigue. An employee who is sweating can leave fingerprints on finished metal products and the salt and acid from perspiration can cause corrosion and rust on metal surfaces. Most of the workplace standards are set and enforced by the Occupational Safety and Health Administration (OSHA). Industrial manufacturing plants are usually designed for an internal temperature of 60–90°F and a maximum of 60% relative humidity. One method of supplying ventilation with an air shower is shown in Figure 65-14.

With the many different types of requirements and the many diverse industrial manufacturing processes, there is no one common air conditioning system that is typically used. For

large facilities, central systems generally are the most cost-effective. Very often there will also be refrigeration systems and heating systems located within the plant that are required for the process. If there is a need for process heating with hot water or steam, then there may be waste heat available or conditions suited for a combined cycle application. Whenever this is the case, an absorption chiller system may prove to be the most cost-effective. As an example, steam may be used for a drying process. Once the steam has been used for heating it may need to be condensed back into water and then sent back to the boiler to be heated again. However, if there is still enough heat available in the steam to be used in an absorption chiller, this may be a better route. The steam condenses in the absorption chiller, giving off its latent heat before traveling back to the boiler.

65.5 TYPES OF COMMERCIAL AIR CONDITIONING EQUIPMENT

Commercial system air conditioning equipment varies from application to application. Very often to minimize the need for extensive field service work such as brazing connections, fitting together components, and evacuating and charging systems, unitary equipment is installed. The sizes of unitary equipment range from small fractional tonnage room coolers to large packaged rooftop units of 100 tons or more.

Hotels and small offices often use console through-the-wall conditioners also known as a packaged terminal air conditioners (PTAC). These units are generally easy to install and if sized correctly will adequately serve the needs of the conditioned space. They are also simple for the customer to operate.

For larger areas where a single PTAC cannot meet the load requirements, single packaged vertical and horizontal units are typically installed. A horizontal unit can come as one complete assembly, however the air cooled condenser section must be placed outside, Figure 65-15. If that is a problem,

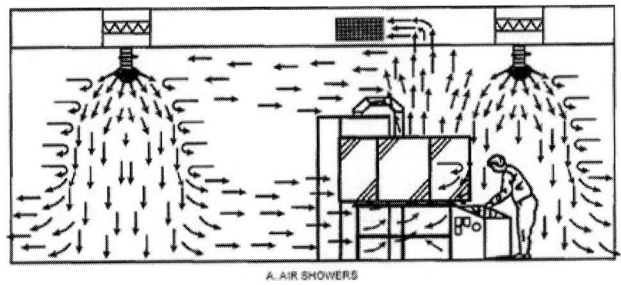

Figure 65-14 Air shower ventilation
(© American Society of Heating, Refrigerating, and Air-Conditioning Engineers, Inc., www.ashrae.org)

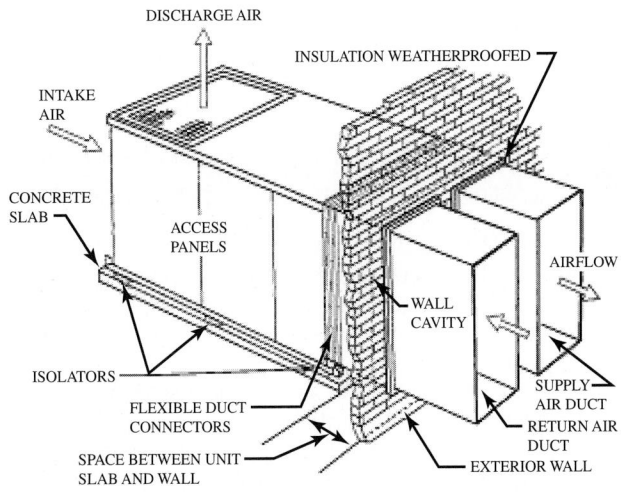

Figure 65-15 Through-the-wall installation of air cooled single packaged unit
(© American Society of Heating, Refrigerating, and Air-Conditioning Engineers, Inc., www.ashrae.org)

then a split system conditioner may be preferable. In this case the compressor and condenser are located outdoors, thereby saving some inside space and reducing noise inside the building. A vertical unit typically has a water cooled condenser and can be located totally indoors.

When the area outside the building is limited for the condenser and compressor section such as in a congested city location, then a rooftop unit may be the best choice. This type of unit is very popular and there are many systems available either as direct expansion or indirect expansion chilled water systems. The condenser and compressor section is located on the roof and out of sight. The proper installation of this type of unit is very important to ensure that rainwater does not leak into the building. Also to be considered are the roof design and the total weight load that that the roof can hold.

Central systems using chilled water loops are typically used for large office buildings, airport terminals, hospitals, and the like. These are generally indirect expansion systems that use a chilled water loop sent to fan rooms for cooling the air. They may be single compressor units that operate over a wide load range or they may be multiple compressor units that cycle on and off dependent on load. Compressor types typically range between reciprocating, centrifugal, and screw types. Absorption systems are popular where there is a readily available heat source, particularly if waste heat can be utilized.

65.6 CONSOLE THROUGH-THE-WALL CONDITIONERS

A console through-the-wall conditioner is a type of room cooler that is designed for permanent installation. It was developed to provide individual room conditioning for hotels, motels, and offices where it is impractical or uneconomical to install a central plant system. An opening needs to be made in the outside wall adjacent to the unit for condenser air and ventilation. These units are also known as packaged terminal air conditioners (PTAC), as shown in Figure 65-16a,b.

TECH TIP

Packaged terminal air conditioners (PTAC) are most commonly used in hotels, nursing homes, apartment complexes, and other such areas where the area being cooled is limited. PTAC units may be straight air conditioning, heat pumps, heat pumps with electric resistance supplemental heating, or straight air conditioning with electric resistance heating. All of these units are similar in appearance and most fit in a standard wall sleeve. These units are accessible from inside the occupied space and in most cases the condensate is simply allowed to drain outside the building. Some cities and municipalities have ordinances controlling condensate from PTAC units but many do not.

(a)

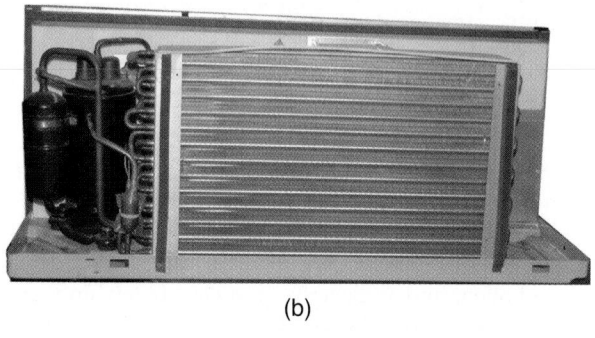

(b)

Figure 65-16 (a) Exterior view of a packaged terminal air conditioner (PTAC); (b) Interior view

PTAC units are efficient, quiet, and easy to install. Temperature efficiency is usually stated in terms of energy efficient ratio (EER). The EER is equal to the cooling output in Btu/hr divided by the power input in watts under standard rating conditions. Standard rating conditions set up by ARI are based on 80°F dry bulb temperature, 67°F wet bulb temperature for the indoor entering air and 95°F dry bulb temperature for the outdoor ambient air. For example, a unit with an output of 6,600 Btu/hr and 660 W input, under standard conditions, would have an EER of 10 (6,600/660), which is considered a good rating.

These units should comply with standards set up by the following associations:

- Canadian Standards Association (performance standards).
- Underwriters Laboratory (electrical and safety standards).
- Air-Conditioning and Refrigeration Institute (ARI): Standard #310 (for packaged terminal air conditioners and heat pumps), and Standard #380 (for refrigerant cooled liquid coolers, remote type).
- PTAC units should also meet ASTME (American Society of Testing and Materials Engineers) wind and rain infiltration standards.

Performance

The performance data for PTAC units are shown in Table 65-1. The sizes range from 6,800 to 14,900 Btu/hr at standard

Table 65-1 General Performance Data—Air Conditioner with Electric Heat Models

Model type	Air conditioner											
Model no.	PTEB 07			PTEB 09			PTEB 12			PTEB 15		
Voltage[1]	230	208	265	230	208	265	230	208	265	230	208	265
Capacity[2] (Btu/hr)	6800	6800	6800	9200	9100	9200	11900	11600	11800	14900	14600	14900
Indoor fan CFM												
High/low (wet coil)	240/210	215/185	240/210	240/210	215/185	240/210	280/260	260/240	280/260	280/260	260/240	280/260
High/low (dry coil)	300/260	280/240	300/260	300/260	280/240	300/260	350/325	325/300	350/325	350/325	325/300	350/325
Fresh air CFM (dry coil)[3]		40			40			55			55	
Approx. ship wt (lb)		129			133			148			157	
Refrig. charge (oz)		20.0			30.0			29.0			36.0	
Oil charge (oz)		8.8			7.4			10.8			13.9	

Minimum operating ambient temperature for cooling is 45°F.
[1]Minimum voltage on 230/280 V units is 197 V; maximum is 253 V.
[2]All capacities based on approved ARI rating point 80/67 entering air temperature, 95°F outdoor ambient.
[3]CFM rating is with the unit in the "fan only" setting.

rating conditions. The quantity of outside air that the units can admit ranges from 40 to 55 CFM depending on the size of the unit. Units are available for 115 and 208/230 V, single phase, AC power. Electric heat capacity from 1.5 to 5.0 kW can be installed in any size unit. Power receptacle configurations depend on the amperage drawn.

65.7 PTAC COMPONENTS AND INSTALLATION

Figure 65-17a–c shows the location of the following essential parts: (1) indoor fan cover; (2) temperature control; (3) heat/cool/fan switch; (4) evaporator; (5) temperature sensor; (6) compressor; (7) condenser; (8) metering device; (9) condensate level float/drain; and (10) condensate pan. The air filter is located behind the front return air panel and can be easily changed.

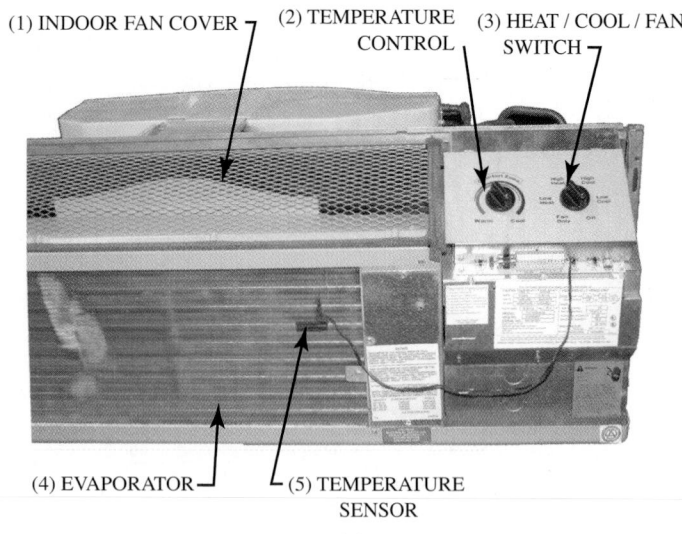

(a)

SERVICE TIP

Most PTAC units use rotary compressors and capillary tube metering devices. Rotary compressors have an excellent service life for this application provided that the condenser is kept clean. High compression ratios will cause refrigerant to break down and rotary compressors are unusually susceptible to damage from excessive heat because the motor is on the high side of the system.

An optional duct package that can be supplied for a PTAC unit is shown in Figure 65-18. This makes it possible to condition several rooms with one unit.

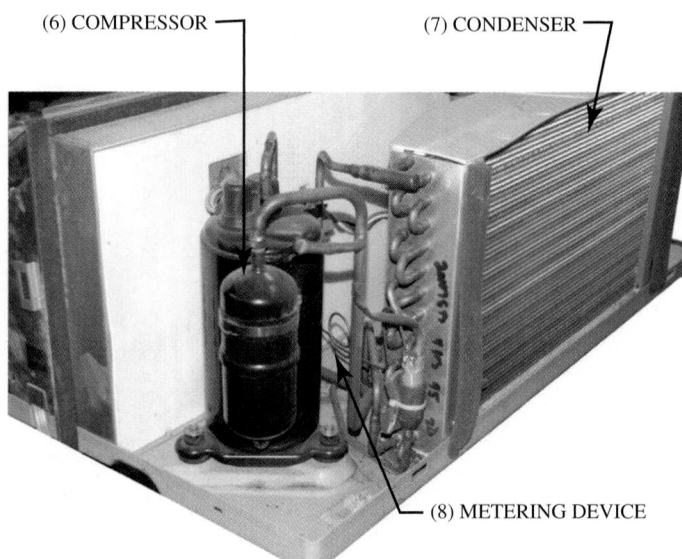

(b)

65.8 PTAC CONTROLS

A rotary switch is provided with the following choices:

OFF	turns unit off
FAN ONLY	indoor fan operates
COOL	provides cooling with indoor fan
HEAT	provides heating with indoor fan

A rocker switch provides the following choices:

HI	high fan speed
LOW	low fan speed

The following additional controls are provided:

- **Adjustable Temperature Limiting Device** Limits the range of the room thermostat.
- **Outside Air Damper** Control lever can be positioned to permit zero for fully open supply of outside air.
- **Fan Cycle Switch** Allows continuous or intermittent fan operation.

(c)

Figure 65-17 Expanded views of a PTAC unit listing major parts

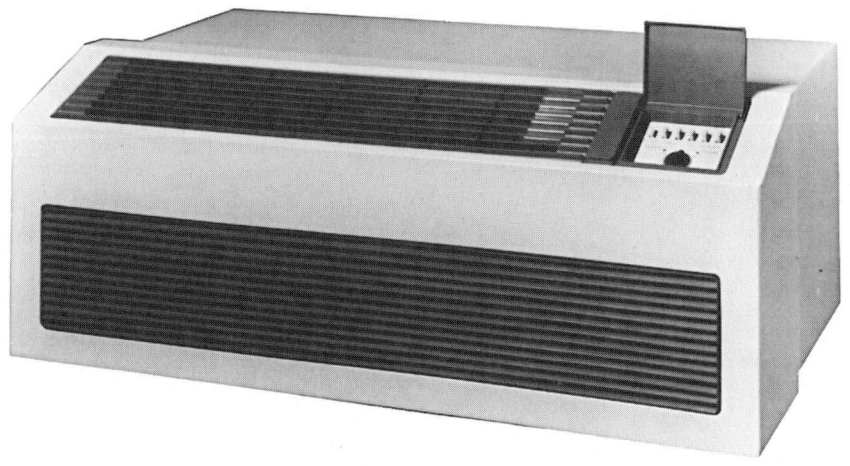

Figure 65-18 Duct package for PTAC units
(The Trane Company)

- **Remote Thermostat (Optional)** Unit can be wired to use a remote wall mounted thermostat rather than the one normally supplied in the unit.
- **Front Desk Control Interface (Optional)** Units may be individually started and stopped with an energy management panel from a central location.
- **Room Freeze Protection (Optional)** Overrides OFF signal when room thermostat goes below 40°F.

65.9 SINGLE PACKAGED CONDITIONERS

A single packaged conditioner, often called a Unitaire, is a complete self contained factory built unit, for permanent installation, to condition larger spaces than would be practical using single room conditioners. In this category there are two variations of available equipment:

- **Horizontal Conditioner** Horizontal packaged heating and cooling units, with integral air cooled condensers, in the size range of $1\frac{1}{2}$ to 5 tons.

- **Vertical Conditioner** Vertical self contained air conditioners, with water cooled or remote air cooled condensers, in the size range of 3 to 15 tons.

65.10 HORIZONTAL PACKAGE CONDITIONER

The horizontal unit usually uses ductwork for air distribution. The horizontal unit is completely self-contained, including the air cooled condenser. It therefore must be placed either entirely outside or at least with the condenser section outside. A schematic diagram for the arrangement of parts is shown in Figure 65-19.

The unit is primarily a cooling unit although electric heaters can be installed in the unit as shown in Figure 65-20. The unit can be equipped with supply and return air duct connections. Ducts can be entered from the side or bottom, depending on the application, Figure 65-21. The unit can be installed on the roof, as shown in Figure 65-22. This type of application is used for shopping malls, factories, and other commercial buildings.

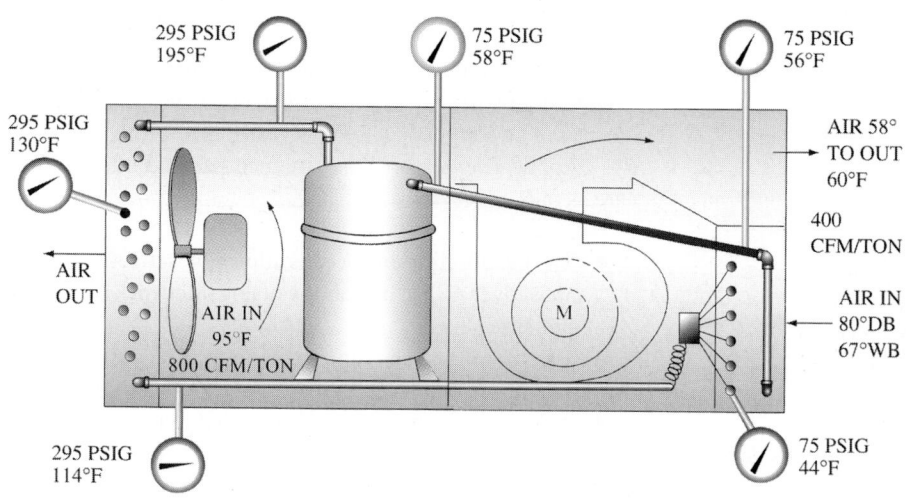

Figure 65-19 Component arrangement for a single-packaged conditioner

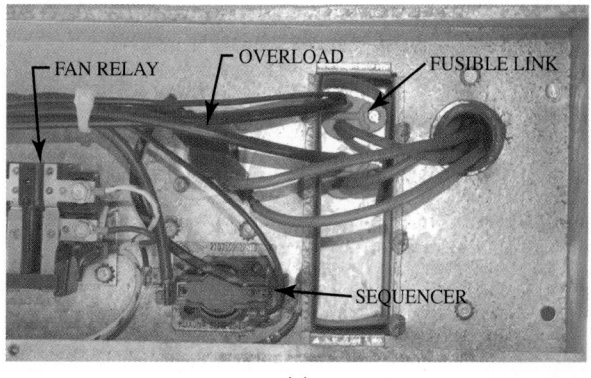

(a)

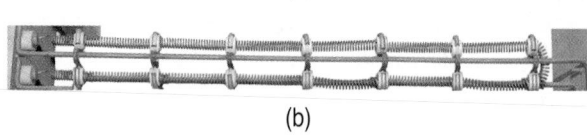

(b)

Figure 65-20 (a) Electric heaters for a packaged air conditioner; (b) Nichrome resistance heating wire

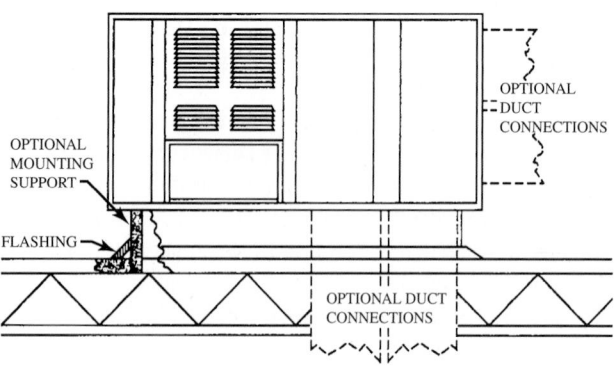

Figure 65-21 Rooftop installation of an air cooled single packaged unit
(© American Society of Heating, Refrigerating, and Air-Conditioning Engineers, Inc., www.ashrae.org)

Figure 65-22 Roof installation of a single packaged conditioner

Units range in capacity from 18,000 to 60,000 Btu/hr and range in air quantity from 600 to 2,000 CFM at standard rating conditions. All units are available for 208/230 V, single phase, 60 Hz power. Efficiencies range from 10.0 EER and higher depending on the size. Optional electric heaters range in size from 3.74 to 29.80 kW.

The horizontal unit comes equipped with the following features:

- **Water Protection** A weather resistant cabinet along with a water-shedding base pan with elevated downflow openings and a perimeter channel prevent water from draining into the ductwork.
- **Low Ambient Control (Optional)** Kits are available that control the condenser head pressure to permit the unit to cool even at low ambient temperatures.
- **Economizer (Optional)** An economizer and dry bulb temperature sensor can be supplied for downflow installations. This makes it possible to use outside air for cooling when outdoor temperatures and humidity permit.
- **Enthalpy Control Kit (Optional)** This can be supplied in place of the dry bulb sensor, or two enthalpy controls can be paired to provide differential enthalpy control.
- **Fresh Air (25%) Kit (Optional)** This kit can be mounted over the horizontal return air openings for downflow requirements. It also can be used on horizontal applications by cutting a hole in the return air duct or in the unit filter access panel.
- **Fan Delay Relay Kit (Optional)** This control keeps the indoor blower on for about 90 s after the unit stops to improve the EER.
- **Anti-Short Cycle Timer** A time-off device ensures a minimum of 5 min off between compressor cycles.

65.11 VERTICAL PACKAGED CONDITIONER

This is a packaged unit for installation, usually inside the space being conditioned, Figure 65-23. The condenser is water cooled. Water from a remotely located cooling tower needs to be piped in and out of a water cooled condenser.

Discharge air can either be free throw or ducted horizontally or vertically. An accessory plenum and grill that fits on top of the unit is supplied for the free throw arrangement. When ductwork is used, a number of discharge configurations can be supplied.

Application features that are incorporated into the unit are as follows:

- The evaporator fan speed is adjustable, affecting the air delivery CFM and the available ductwork static pressure.
- Thermostats can be supplied as an integral part of the unit or provision can be made for remote mounting.
- An anti-short cycle timer is provided to protect the compressor from excess cycling.

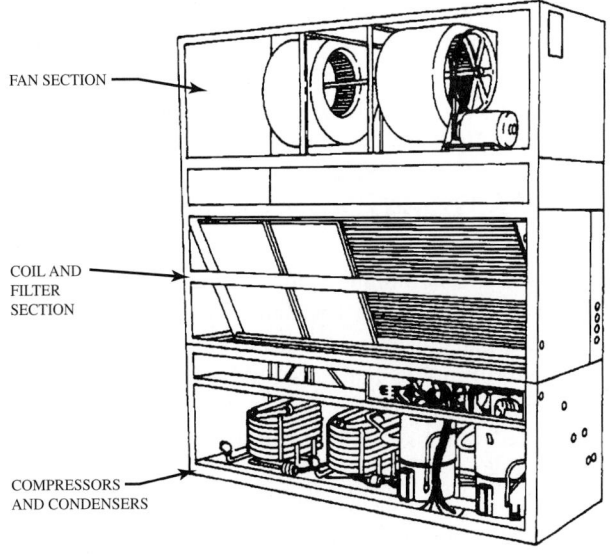

FAN SECTION

COIL AND FILTER SECTION

COMPRESSORS AND CONDENSERS

Figure 65-23 Vertical self-contained unit
(© American Society of Heating, Refrigerating, and Air-Conditioning Engineers, Inc., www.ashrae.org)

SERVICE TIP

One of the prime concerns and problems with all rooftop installations is water leakage. Most commercial buildings use flat roofs and water in a rainstorm can build up to several inches in depth. If the equipment panels are not properly reinstalled to provide an adequate water seal, rainwater can easily enter the building. In addition, if the proper curb is not provided for the unit, then the system will leak. Many commercial roofs are "bonded" which means that there is a specific insurance policy taken out on the roof by the roofing company at the time of installation. This provides the building owner with insurance that the roof will not leak. That roofing contractor is the only one who can do any work on the roof that would affect the integrity of that roof without violating that bond. Violating the bond on the roof by putting in a vent pipe could ultimately make you liable for any water damage resulting from leaks. Check with the building owner before any work is done on bonded roofs.

65.12 ROOFTOP CONDITIONERS

Rooftop conditioners are similar to single packaged conditioners except that they are thoroughly weatherproofed and provide for duct access at the bottom of the unit. They are popular for air conditioning low story commercial buildings because they offer a substantial savings of space within the building. They come in various sizes and configurations, Figure 65-24.

From the standpoint of the service technician, they are desirable because they offer plenty of access space around the unit for servicing. On many jobs, however, access to the roof is only by ladder and in bad weather the units may be difficult to reach and offer physical restraints in supplying needed tools and parts.

Rooftop self-contained air conditioning units are commonly used on commercial installations, Figure 65-25. The sizes range from 3 tons to 130 tons of cooling capacity under standard rating conditions. Besides the difference in size of the components, individual units differ in the type of heating supplied with the package.

For the units in the 3 to 25 ton range, gas fired or electric heat can be supplied, Figure 65-26a,b. Larger units can also be equipped with hot water or steam coils. When the units are located outside, adequate freeze protection needs to be provided where the unit contains water. Condensate drain pans must be free draining.

Reciprocating or scroll type, direct drive, hermetic compressors are used. Compressor motors are suction gas cooled, and are protected with temperature and current sensitive

Figure 65-24 Commercial rooftop packaged unit configurations from Lennox Landmark Commercial Packaged Rooftop Units Bulletin 36M72-02/08 PC 50992 page 6
(Courtesy of Lennox Industries)

Figure 65-25 Rooftop packaged system

overloads. Crankcase heaters are standard equipment. Dual compressor models are usually available starting at $7\frac{1}{2}$ tons and higher. When dual compressors are furnished, dual refrigeration circuits are also supplied. This arrangement makes possible better performance ratings and increased energy savings at partial loads.

Cabinets are constructed of zinc coated heavy gauge steel and are weathertight. All services can be performed through access panels on one side. Supply and return ductwork connections can be made at the bottom or side of the unit. Roof curb frames are available for roof mounting.

65.13 CENTRAL SYSTEM CHILLERS

For large air conditioning loads, central systems utilizing chill water are often used. There are many different configurations that can range from capacities of more than 700 tons for large absorption systems to as little as 15 tons for small reciprocating chillers.

Chilled water systems can utilize reciprocating, centrifugal, and screw type compressors. These can be configured as open or semi-hermetic systems. Condensers are often water cooled and if no ready source of water is available, then cooling water towers are used. Chillers can also come as air cooled units, however the compressor location is then limited. The compressor needs to be located relatively close to the condenser. With a water cooled unit, the compressor can be located most anywhere with the condenser water pumped to its location.

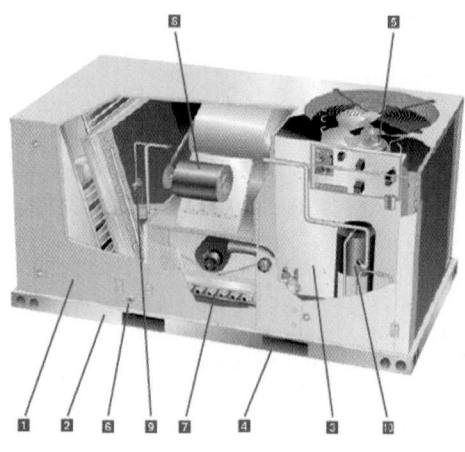

Easy to install and maintain

1 Hinged Access Panels—Factory option provides quick access to components and protects panels and roof from damage during servicing.

2 Full-Perimeter Base Rail (with Rigging Holes)—Provides greater structural integrity, so the unit is easier to handle when rigging and transporting.

3 Isolated Compressor Compartment—Allows performance check during normal compressor operation without disrupting airflow.

4 Fork Slots on Three Sides—Easy to pick up and transport units from almost any angle.

5 Independent Motor Mount—Allows for easy and efficient service access without removing the top panel.

6 Corrosion-Resistant Removable, Reversible Drain Pan—Provides application flexibility, durability and improved serviceability.

High-performance components

7 Direct-Spark Ignition—Electronic ignition eliminates standing pilot and enhances efficiency.

8 Pre-Defined Supply Fan Motor/Drive Combinations—Make selecting components to meet static and airflow requirements quick and easy.

9 Thermostatic Expansion Valves—Provide peak cooling performance across the entire application range.

10 Scroll Compressor—Standard on all units for reliable long-term operation.

(a)

(b)

Figure 65-26 (a) Commercial packaged rooftop unit 2–6 tons from Lennox Landmark Commercial Packaged Rooftop Units Bulletin 36M72-02/08 PC50992 page 1; (b) Component view for commercial packaged unit from Lennox Landmark Commercial Packaged Rooftop Units Bulletin 36M72-02/08 PC50992 page 4
(Courtesy of Lennox Industries)

Chillers can also be configured as absorption systems. A major advantage is that no compressor is required. Another advantage of this type is that waste heat can be utilized as the driving heat source, which provides for economical operation.

UNIT 65—SUMMARY

In this unit you have learned about different types of air conditioning systems such as console type through-the-wall conditioners, single packaged conditioners, rooftop conditioners, and chillers. Unitary equipment is factory built to be as complete as possible and fairly simple to install.

Packaged terminal air conditioners (PTAC) are most commonly used in hotels, nursing homes, and apartment complexes. Single packaged conditioners can be of the horizontal or vertical type and are permanently located in a separate space away from the room being cooled. Ductwork is often used for air distribution and horizontal units are generally sized from $1\frac{1}{2}$ to 5 tons while vertical units range from 3 to 15 tons.

Rooftop conditioners are similar to single packaged conditioners except that they are thoroughly waterproofed. In this way they can be conveniently located on the building's roof, thus conserving valuable inside building space. Large air conditioning load capacities often require chillers which can operate with mechanical compressors or as absorption type systems.

WORK ORDERS

Service Ticket 6501

Building Conversion: New Installation

Equipment Type: Rooftop Packaged Unit/PTAC

The company sales representative visited with the owner of a small business who was in the process of converting an older one-story building into office spaces. The old air distribution system was to be entirely replaced. The owner was wondering if through-the-wall individual packaged terminal units for each space would be sufficient.

The sales representative used information about the building dimensions, construction materials, and outside/inside design temperatures to determine the total heating and cooling load for the building. He then explained to the owner that a PTAC for each space would be sufficient to handle the load. Some advantages to the PTACs were that they could be turned down any time someone was not in that particular office space, and no new duct system would need to be installed during the building conversion. However the inner offices would require mini-split systems rather than using through-the-wall units.

Although a packaged rooftop unit would involve the installation of an air distribution system, this would be the best time to do that, while the building interior was being torn apart. The salesman recommended a cooling/heating rooftop unit with a gas furnace. This would prove much more economical over time for heating as compared to the electric resistance heat of a PTAC. The initial cost would be higher and the control system somewhat more complex, however the overall comfort for both the heating and cooling season would be better. The PTACs also could be noisy for the office space, so the owner decided on installing the rooftop packaged unit.

Service Ticket 6502

Customer Complaint: Cold Conference Room

Equipment Type: Central Chilled Water System

The technician answered a call at a large office building downtown. There was a problem with the cooling system in the conference room on the sixth floor. The 120 ton semi-hermetic centrifugal chiller located in a machinery room in the basement was operating normally. Everything also appeared normal in the sixth floor fan room with the chilled water supply temperature at 45°F and the return at 55°F.

When the service technician entered the conference room, it immediately felt cold. The supply register had cardboard taped over it and air was whistling through the cracks. The technician used a small stepladder and removed the ceiling panels from around the supply register. This system had steam reheat and the steam coil was now exposed. Without any reheat, cold air was being supplied regardless of the setting on the space thermostat. The supply damper was fixed in place and reheat was the only adjustment for space temperature. The technician found the steam regulating supply valve to the reheater was frozen shut. The steam supply to the line was secured and the valve was replaced. Soon after the space temperature started returning to a more comfortable level.

Service Ticket 6503

New Installation: System Replacement

Equipment Type: Packaged Rooftop Unit

The service technician arrived at the job site and found that the new packaged rooftop unit had already been lifted on to the roof of the building. Climbing up the fire escape to where the unit was located, the technician brought along a tape measure and the installation specifications for the new unit. Before even beginning to make measurements it was obvious that the footprint for the new unit was going to be quite a bit larger than the old unit. There were also structural members that would need to be reinforced for the rooftop foundation.

The service technician went back down and located the building superintendent. The roof was "bonded" and any new penetrations would need to be approved by the roofing contractor. The technician arranged for the installation to begin in coordination with a crew from the roofing company. They would need to work together to make sure that the old unit was properly removed and the new unit installed with adequate support.

UNIT 65—REVIEW QUESTIONS

1. Define residential air conditioning.

2. List at least five types commercial air conditioning applications.

3. What applications are best suited for console through-the-wall PTAC units?

4. If a PTAC unit had an output of 6,600 Btu/hr and 660 W input, what would be the SEER of the unit under standard conditions?

5. List the standards by which a PTAC unit is certified.

6. Name the metering device used on most PTAC units.

7. What is a special ventilation consideration for restaurants, nightclubs, and casinos?

8. Which commercial application would be most likely to use a heat reclaiming system that recovers the heat being rejected to the outside condenser?

9. What consideration should be given to office spaces when determining space heating and cooling loads?

10. State the two variations of single packaged conditioners and the tonnage capacity ranges of each.

11. The single packaged conditioner in the horizontal variation may come equipped with seven features. What are these?

12. What are the differences between a rooftop air conditioner and a single packaged air conditioner?

13. Why are rooftop units popular on small commercial buildings?

14. Explain what would happen if an HVAC/R contractor violated a bonded roof by putting in a vent pipe?

15. Could a packaged rooftop unit be adapted for both heating and cooling?

16. How are hermetic compressors cooled?

17. What types of compressors are commonly used for chillers?

18. Why do many central system chillers use water cooled condensers?

19. What is moisture regain?

20. List some of the airborne particles that may be released in an industrial manufacturing process.

UNIT 66

Air Handling Units and Accessories

OBJECTIVES

After completing this unit you will be able to:

- describe the different types of air handlers.
- explain the operation of a fan coil unit.
- list the different types of coils used for heating and cooling.
- explain the differences between centrifugal and axial fan arrangements.
- list the different types of air filters used in air handlers.
- explain how humidifiers operate.
- describe the operation of economizers and energy recovery ventilation sections.

66.1 INTRODUCTION

Air conditioning involves more than just cooling or heating air. The air also needs to be filtered, humidified or dehumidified, and distributed to the proper location in the appropriate amount at the designed velocity. Too little outside air will lead to an increase in the level of indoor pollutants. Too much outside air increases the load on the system and leads to lower efficiencies and higher operating costs. Air balance is important so that doors inside a building open easily and close without slamming shut. Too little exhaust air can lead to overpressurization of a space.

The air handler unit (AHU) should be selected and installed with all of the major requirements for the space taken into account. These include the air handler's location, type of coil design, and filtration ability. A central station air handling unit may offer economy of operation as compared to individual space fan coil units. However, individual units may provide for better temperature control and eliminate the mixing of airstreams between rooms such as may be required in a laboratory or hospital. Individual fan coil units can also be shut down when the space is unoccupied such as in a hotel room. The decision to install one large central air handler, multiple air handlers, or individual fan coil units requires careful planning and consideration of the building's main functions and requirements.

66.2 TYPES OF AIR HANDLING UNITS

Air handling units come in various sizes and configurations. These can be arranged as complete packaged systems for residential, light, and moderate commercial applications,

Large central air conditioning systems typically have built-up units that are assembled component by component. Sometimes these come as modular building blocks and can be arranged in a variety of configurations, Figure 66-1. Depending on the application, the air handler may be located in the conditioned area. However, installation in the basement, on a rooftop, or some other isolated area saves on valuable inside space and reduces the fan noise heard by the people indoors. Figure 66-2 shows the proper installation for ceiling mounted units that may be found in a large retail store or in warehouse

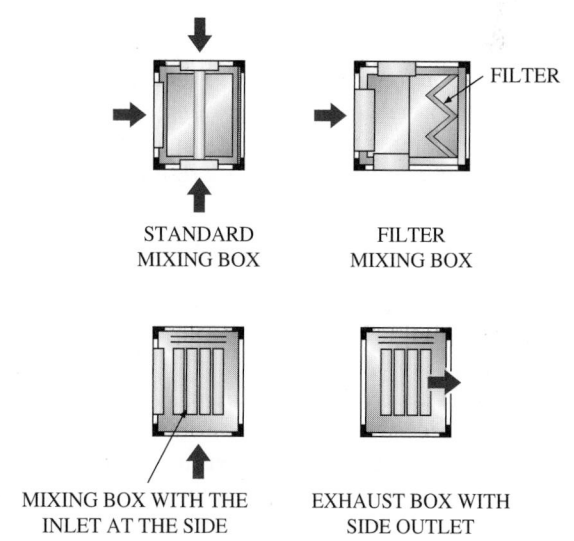

Figure 66-1 Modular air distribution components

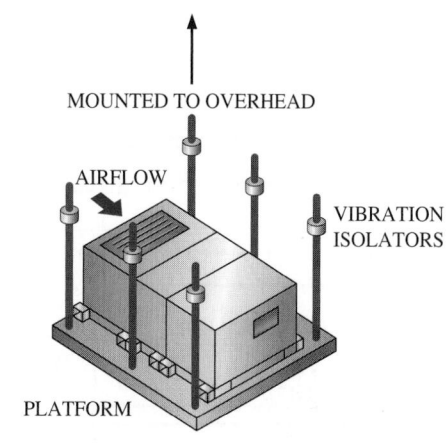

Figure 66-2 Ceiling mounted air handler

Figure 66-3 Indoor air handlers

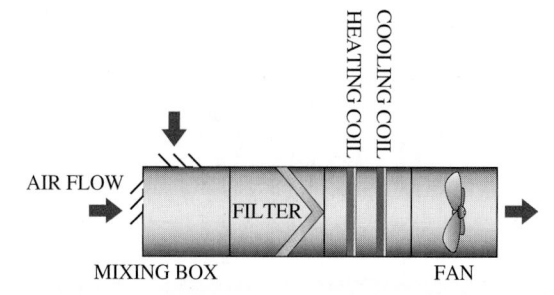

Figure 66-4 Draw-through horizontal air handler

applications. Many of these units have double wall insulation which reduces sweating on the outside surfaces and noise from the fan compartment.

The location for the air handler is usually flexible because it does not need to be located alongside the heating and cooling equipment. The handler can be as simple as a fan, a filter, and a coil. For example, a residential split system has refrigerant supplied from the outdoor unit to an air handler that may be located in the basement. This type of system would require just the basic components and would be considered a direct expansion system. However, for larger buildings that require more than one air handler, it would be impractical to deliver refrigerant to each one. In this case, a central plant will cool a secondary refrigerant (chilled water) that is then delivered to each air handler coil. This type of air handler may also have additional hot water or steam coils for heating and mixing and dampers for energy recovery applications. Figure 66-3 shows a large indoor air handler.

Most air handlers use a fan (or blower) to force the air at low, medium, or high velocity through the air distribution system. Draw through units are designed so that the fan is at the outlet of the air handler to draw the air across the coils,

Figure 66-4. This is more common than a blow-through type where the fan is located at the inlet to the coils. Sometimes blow-through type systems can be used if sound levels are a major consideration. Noise levels can be lowered because sound is absorbed by the coil section downstream from the fan. Less common are induction units that are designed to operate without any fan.

Air handlers can be designed to deliver a constant volume or a variable volume of air to a single zone or to multiple zones. A constant volume system always supplies the same amount of air and to control the temperature of the space, the supply air temperature has to be regulated. In contrast, a variable volume system will adjust to supply more or less air depending on the space temperature. In this case, the supply air temperature does not need to change.

66.3 FAN COIL UNITS

Fan coil units (FCUs) are supplied with chilled water directly from a central plant and can also include heating coils or electric heat. They are primarily designed to supply conditioned air to individual rooms, however larger fan coil units are capable of conditioning multiple spaces. Each one of these units has fans, cooling coils, filters, a fresh air supply, and a control system, Figure 66-5.

Fan coil units for combination heating and cooling come in a variety of designs, to fit under windowsills, above furred

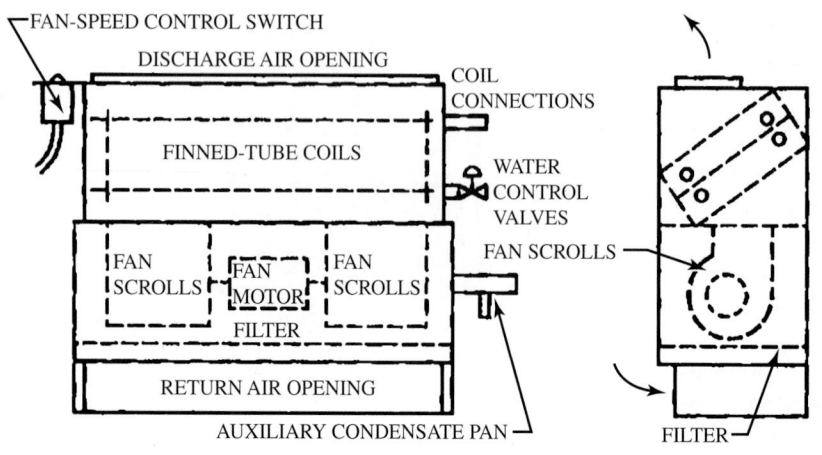

Figure 66-5 Fan coil unit
(© American Society of Heating, Refrigerating, and Air-Conditioning Engineers, Inc., www.ashrae.org)

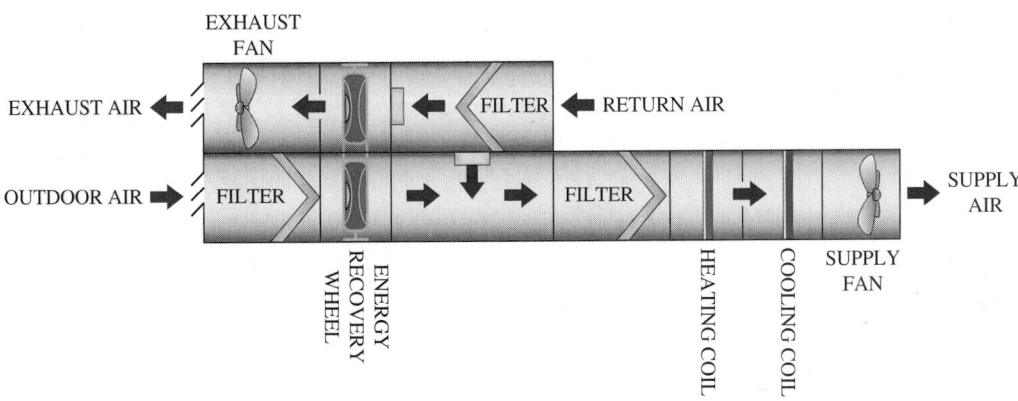

Figure 66-33 Draw-through air handler energy recovery section

The same system can be used to preheat and humidify the incoming outdoor air during the winter. On extremely cold days, an electric frost control operates an electric preheater to warm incoming air a few more degrees. Different heater sizes are available for different design temperature ranges.

UNIT 66—SUMMARY

Air handling units come in many sizes and configurations depending on the application. For individual space heating and cooling, fan coil units may be used supplied with hot or cold water from a central plant. Packaged air handlers can be factory assembled or put together as sections on the job site. Cooling coils can be of the indirect expansion type using chilled water or the direct expansion type with multiple expansion valves for capacity control.

The most common types of fans are centrifugal and axial. Centrifugal fans can utilize forward curved or backward curved blades and are often used for supplying air through duct systems. Axial fans develop lower static pressures but allow for higher volumes of airflow and are often used for ventilation. Filters in the airstream can be disposable or cleanable depending on their design. HEPA and electronic filters are used where high efficiency filtration is required.

Economizers and energy recovery systems increase the efficiency of a system. Humidification of the airstream allows for increased human comfort and reduces the drying out and shrinking of windowsills and doors. Microbial treatments and ultraviolet lamps are used to reduce the buildup of mold and mildew. Depending on the application, an air handler may include any arrangement of these accessories to provide for the proper distribution and treatment of air supplied to a building.

WORK ORDERS

Service Ticket 6601

Customer Complaint: AHU Supply Fan Motor Is Tripping

Equipment Type: 75 Ton AHU with Centrifugal Fan

The technician arrived at the site and spoke to the maintenance department supervisor. They recently replaced belts on the air handler supply fan and replaced a worn adjustable pulley sheave and now the AHU will not stay on line. First the technician started the unit and measured the amperage drawn by the supply fan motor and found it to be too high. Next the technician visually checked the supply fan belts and found that one of the new belts was already wearing on one side.

It was now obvious that the sheave-shaft alignment and overhang were not correct, Figure 66-34a,b. The belt tension was also too tight, Figure 66-35. When maintenance replaced the motor sheave they did not align it properly, causing the motor to overload. The technician removed the belts and adjusted the sheave alignment correctly. The technician reinstalled the belts, aligned the belts, and restarted the AHU. The unit is now operating within design specifications.

Service Ticket 6602

Customer Complaint: Humidifier Will Not Work

Equipment Type: Electric Powered Steam Pan Humidifier

The technician answered a complaint about very dry air in a dental office. The office had a small central station air handler located in a utility room in the back of the building. Opening the access panels to the unit, the technician found an electric powered steam pan humidifier. Measuring a zero voltage drop across the electric heater element indicated that it would need replacement.

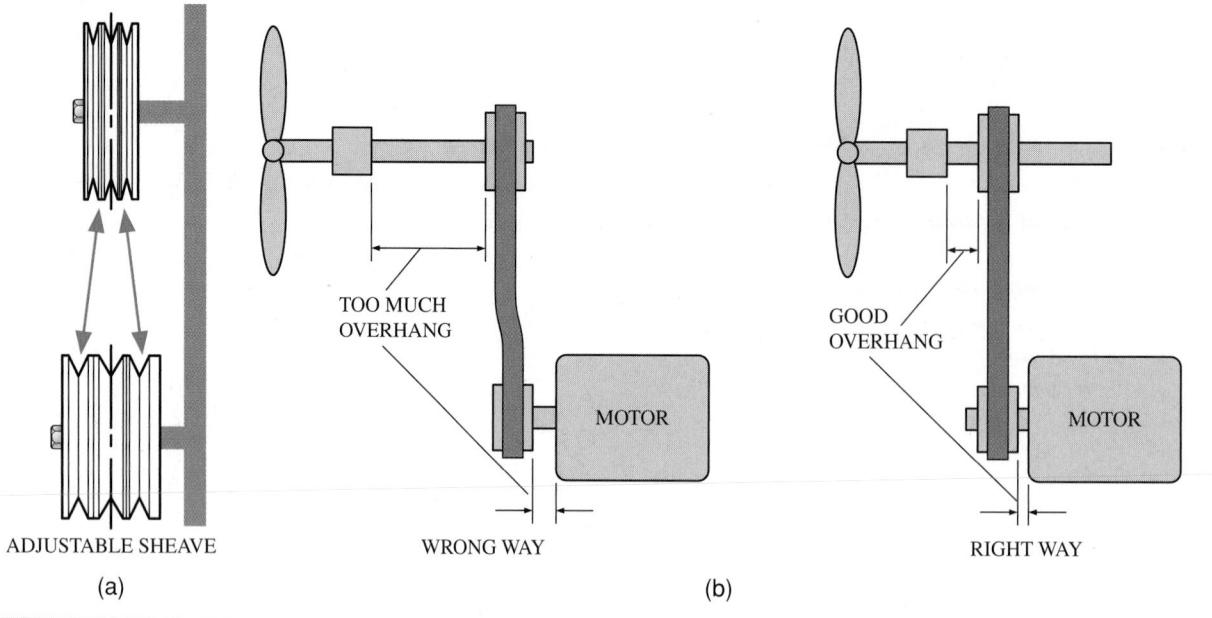

Figure 66-34 (a) sheave-shaft alignment; (b) sheave-shaft overhang

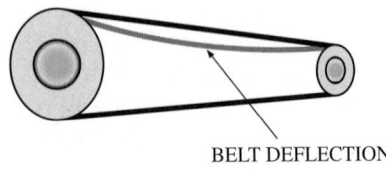

Figure 66-35 Supply fan belt deflection

The technician removed the old element and cleaned the pan of scale and mildew. The scale and mildew is the result of normal use and the minerals normally found in the makeup water tend to collect in the pan. The technician replaced the element with the exact factory replacement part and restarted the humidifier. The humidifier is now operating normally. The technician recommended regular maintenance and a water softener installed on the makeup water to the pan.

Service Ticket 6603

Customer Complaint: No Heat Equipment Type: Weathertight Central Station Air Handler

The technician answered an emergency no heat call at a large dry cleaning establishment. The central station air handler was a large weathertight unit located on the building's roof. The technician pulled hard to get the door to open as it was under a slight negative pressure inside the air handler. There were multiple fan and coil arrangements located inside supplying air individually to multiple zones. Each fan arrangement had its control mounted beside it. One of these was flashing an alarm signal. The alarm code manual was hanging by a small piece of chain next to the control panel and the technician looked up the fault code to find it was for a low air supply temperature.

The heating coil was easy to distinguish from the cooling coil because of the steam supply and return piping attached to it. The steam control valve was in the fully stroked wide open position as it should be calling for heat. The technician used a heat gun to check the surface temperature of the steam coil and found that it was no hotter than the airstream passing over it. The smaller steam preheat coil at the entrance to the air stream registered a temperature of over 200°F and was the only source of heat. The technician located the steam trap at the outlet of the heating coil and opened the bypass valve around it slowly to minimize any water hammer. Almost immediately the heating temperature began to increase. Next the technician closed the valves on either side of the steam trap and slowly broke the connection to make sure that there was no steam pressure remaining. The steam trap was replaced and put back into service and now the supply air temperature is normal.

UNIT 66—REVIEW QUESTIONS

1. Although air handler cabinets may be made of galvanized steel, there are still areas that may be subject to corrosion. Why?

2. Describe the two general types of AHU's.

3. List the components of an FCU.

4. Often around fluorescent lights in a dropped ceiling there is a narrow slit. What is the purpose and advantages of this application?

5. Where are larger FCU's most commonly used?

6. In FCU's that have cooling coils, how is the dehumidification condensate disposed of?

7. Explain the advantages unit ventilator type FCU's have in schools.

8. List the major components in most AHU's.

9. State the reason a properly sized AHU fan and motor usually requires field adjustment during the final startup/commissioning phase.

10. Name the two basic types of fans used in most AHU's.

11. On an AHU with a centrifugal fan, what are two advantages of backward curved airfoil blades?

12. State where axial fans are commonly used.

13. Tell why actual motor voltage and amperage should be field measured and logged under full load conditions.

14. In a heating coil, what advantage does heating water have over steam?

15. When referring to humidity, why is a cooling coil deeper (more rows) than a heating coil?

16. How should ultraviolet germicidal lamps be handled?

17. Describe the problems associated with poorly maintained humidifiers.

18. What is the principle of operation for an economizer?

19. If the inside temperature is 70°F and the RH is 50%, how low would the outside temperature have to be to form condensation on a double pane window? Refer to Table 66-1.

20. Why is the steam grid humidifier recommended?

UNIT 67

Packaged Unit Conditioned Air Control Systems

OBJECTIVES

After completing this unit you will be able to:

- explain how the outside air supply to a conditioned space is normally controlled.
- identify the differences between air distribution systems for core cooling as compared to perimeter cooling applications.
- describe how a constant air volume system is normally configured.
- explain how a variable air volume multiple zone air system is normally configured.
- list the common temperature input signals for a packaged air handler.
- describe the function of air quality and condition sensors.

67.1 INTRODUCTION

Air distribution control systems vary depending on the type of application, building design, and zone requirements. A single space maintained at one constant temperature would require the simplest form of control system. The amount of air supplied to the space can be allowed to remain constant with the control system configured to control the air temperature through the air handler. The duct static air pressure and the load on the supply fan remains relatively constant.

A large multistory building will have conditioned spaces of all different sizes. Some of these will be in the center core of the building while others will be around the outside located in the outer perimeter. The heating and cooling demands for one space will vary from another. For these reasons, a building of this type will require more complex control systems. Each space may require its own terminal unit with dampers that are adjusted to meet the individual space temperature requirements. As the position of air dampers changes throughout the system, the duct static pressure and loading of the supply fan also changes. Direct Digital Control (DDC) systems are sometimes used to manage the overall operation of all the individual terminal units. Variable frequency drive supply fans can be used that allow for speed variations to offset the changing duct static pressure.

67.2 AIR HANDLING

A typical air handling air distribution system is shown in Figure 67-1. This circuit has many different components. In tracing this circuit, we will start at the entrance to the air handling unit. Air that enters the unit is made up of both return air from the conditioned space and outside ventilation air. In the air handling unit, air passes through the filters, preheater, cooling coil, heating coil, reheater, and finally the fan. This type of system is referred to as a draw-through system because the fan is located after the coils and draws the air across them. A blow-through system would locate the fan before the coils.

Outside Air Supply

The air entering the handler will be a combination of outside air mixed with return air from the space being conditioned. If only outside air was used, then the load on the heating or cooling system would be excessive. To conserve energy, the outside air supply can be regulated to a minimum amount. Normally, the outside air supply is never completely shut off because some fresh air should always be supplied to the space. The amount required typically depends on the number of people occupying the space and the usage of the space. As the amount of outside air is reduced, the carbon dioxide (CO_2) levels in the space will increase, Figure 67-2. An air quality sensor can be installed in the conditioned space or the return air duct to detect levels of CO_2 in the air. The sensor can be used as an input for control of the outside air damper. This would allow only enough outside air to maintain the proper air quality while not oversupplying outside air, which would increase the total energy demand.

TECH TIP

Generally some outside air is always supplied to a space, however there are exceptions for fire containment. Fire dampers close off the supply of outside air completely so that the fire is not fed any additional oxygen. There are also exclusive systems for special applications that totally shut off the supply of outside air in the event of chemical or biological attack. These dampers should not interfere with normal operation.

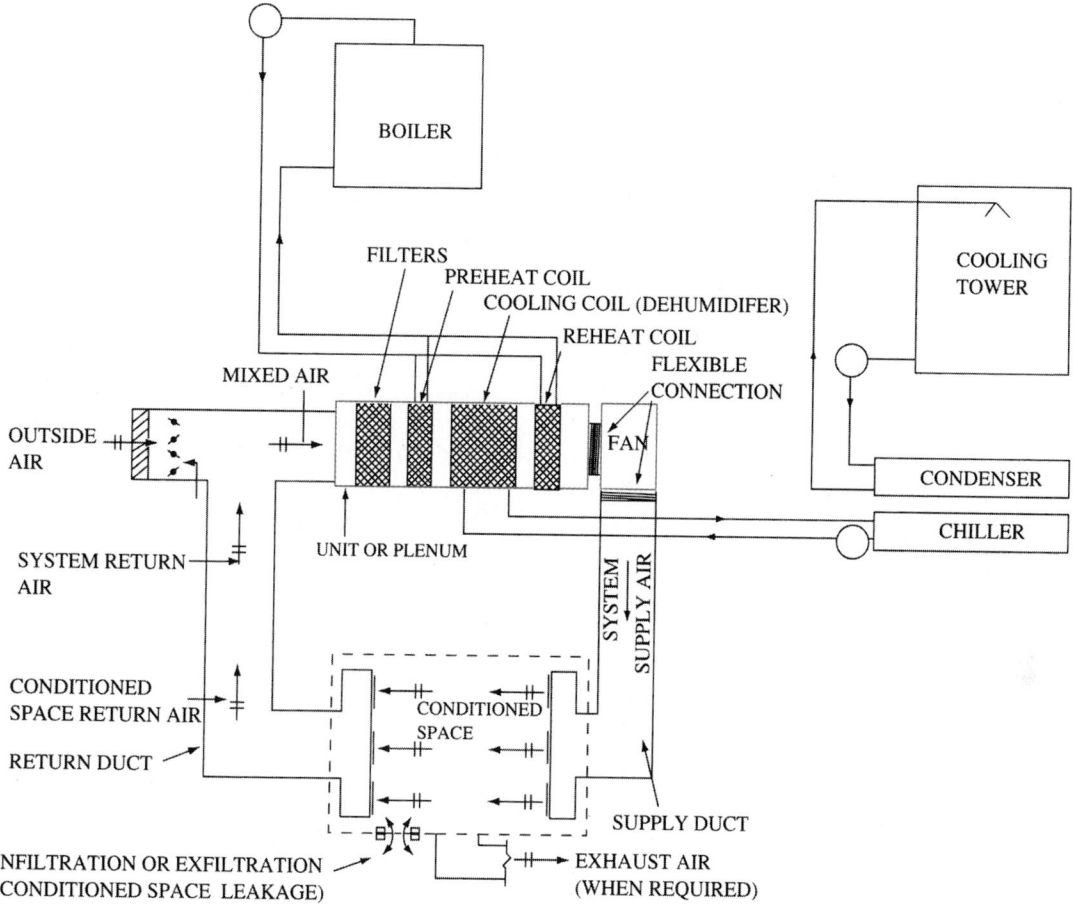

Figure 67-1 Typical central HVAC system showing air handler unit

Filters

Filters may vary greatly depending on the building type. On packaged air handlers, disposable type filters are often used. As the filters become dirty, the airflow will become restricted. This can lead to an increase in fan horsepower and fan instability. A filter status differential pressure switch can be used to trigger an alarm when the filters become dirty. Filter manufacturer literature should supply information on the differential pressure limits for dirty filters. Generally the differential pressure is set from 0.05 to 2.0 in wc depending on the filter type.

Cooling Coil

Cooling coils are typically direct or indirect expansion. The control of air temperature when using direct expansion coils is accomplished by regulating the refrigerant flow through the coil at the inlet. Coils may have multiple expansion valves and be staged to supply more or less cooling depending on the final air temperature. Indirect expansion coils use chilled water and typically the air temperature is controlled by regulating the water flow through the coil at the outlet. Face and bypass dampers can also be used to vary the airflow across the coil as an added control of the air temperature.

Figure 67-2 Ventilation air based on CO_2 setpoint

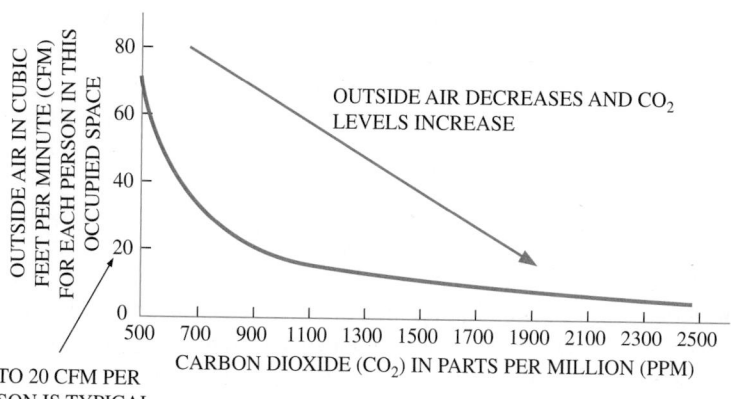

Preheater

The preheater is located in the airstream before the cooling coil. With indirect expansion chilled water coils, there is always a possibility of the coil freezing during cold weather conditions. This is because no matter how cold it may become outside, some outside air needs to enter the space for proper air quality. The low air temperature could freeze the water inside the coil, causing it to split and then leak. The coil would need to be repaired or replaced. To avoid this situation, one option is to drain the chilled water loop every time the outside air temperature drops, however this would be impractical. More commonly, preheaters are utilized. These may be electric, steam, or hot water. The preheater will turn on when the incoming air drops below a preset temperature. This should be well above the freezing temperature of the coil which may vary from system to system depending on the amount of glycol added to the chill water loop. In addition to protecting the cooling coil from freezing, the preheater also provides some heat to the conditioned space.

TECH TIP

Preheaters are used to prevent the cooling coil from freezing. Many systems also include a low temperature switch as a backup that will turn off the fan if the air temperature becomes too low.

Heating Coil

Heating coils may be electric, steam, or hot water. Electric heat is the most expensive but also the simplest. Hot water is also very common on small commercial systems. Many furnaces in this size category are forced hot air or hot water rather than steam. Hot water heating coils are also simpler and easier to control than steam coils. However, steam coils provide for increased heat transfer for large capacity systems and are preferable if an adequate steam supply is available.

Reheater

Reheaters can be electric, steam, or hot water. These are used on systems that require increased dehumidification. In geographical locations of high humidity, the air drops down below its dew point temperature as it passes across the cooling coil. The water vapor in the air will condense and be collected and drained away as condensate from a pan beneath the cooling coil. Although moisture has been removed from the air, it is now cold with a high relative humidity and will create drafts that could be uncomfortable for the people in the space. The reheater will increase the temperature of the air and reduce its relative humidity to more comfortable levels. This type of system is inefficient because the air is being cooled which requires energy and then it is heated back up again which requires additional energy. Instead of this form of reheat, it is preferable to use the warmer return air or outside air mixed with the cold air supply rather than a separate reheater whenever practical.

TECH TIP

In older building design, zone reheaters were used to control the final temperature of individual conditioned spaces. As an example, in a central system the air supplied to multiple spaces will be at the same temperature. However, individual thermostats can be used for each space. If a person is too cold in one space then he or she can adjust the thermostat setting. This does not affect the central system but only the reheater, turning it on for that particular space. Due to current energy codes, these types of systems are no longer used.

67.3 AIR DISTRIBUTION SYSTEMS

For simplicity, types of commercial air distribution may be classified as low, medium, or high velocity systems. The required velocity of the air is dependent on the length and configuration of the duct system along with the flow rate required for the space. Cool air is admitted to a space to absorb heat, thereby maintaining a comfortable temperature. The amount of cool air (i.e., the flow rate in CFM) required will depend on the total cooling load for the space (how much heat will need to be absorbed). Velocity should not be confused with flow rate. A large axial fan used for ventilation can deliver high flow rates of air, however this would be at a relatively low velocity. For a given flow rate (dependent on cooling load), if duct size decreases then the static pressure and the power required to deliver the air will increase.

Low velocity systems are often associated with the application of smaller unitary packaged and split system units. The use of limited ductwork or none at all (free blow) is typical of the classification. Where ductwork is used, the external static pressure is held down to the range of 0.25–0.50 in wc. The use of concentric supply and return ducts is a common application. The type of duct design is the same as that of the equal friction method, which permits the prediction or control of total static.

Medium to high pressure velocity systems are often used in large central air distribution systems. Smaller ducts use up less space and this can lead to installation cost savings. With smaller ducts, the ceiling height can be lowered by as much as 1 ft. For a large 12 floor multistory building with 10 ft ceilings, this will mean that one additional floor can be added that would have been occupied by the total sum of each floor's duct system. Smaller duct systems also provide for added installation choices. Older buildings with narrow areas and space limitations due to the structural design of the building can be better accommodated. Despite these space and installation savings, it should be realized that high velocity systems will have higher operating costs and higher noise levels.

T E C H   T I P

The higher the air distribution system's operating static pressure, the lower the system efficiency. This is because the blower has to work harder to move enough air. To reduce the static pressure, larger ducts are required. The savings from having a lower static pressure must be balanced against the higher cost of the larger duct system.

67.4 AIR DISTRIBUTION APPLICATIONS

Air distribution applications in central station systems fall into three broad areas: interior or core areas, exterior or perimeter areas or zones, and entire building applications.

Core areas have conditioning loads subject only to interior loads, such as lighting, people, and equipment. Consequently, they are basically cooling only loads, except for top floors and/or warmup cycles in extremely cold climates.

Perimeter zones are exposed to outer building skin variables, such as wall and window loads, wind effects, and exposure effects, as well as the items in the core areas. The perimeter zones have to handle a wide range of conditions, including such variances as high solar gain on a winter day requiring cooling, while shaded parts of the building require heating.

Entire building applications are a combination of these systems, the selection of which depends on building size and economics. Small buildings frequently cannot justify one system for the core and another for the perimeter. In these instances, any one of the perimeter systems can be used for the entire building.

The systems are all of the type that use primary (supply) air from the air conditioner, and the maximum quantity needed is based on the maximum load conditions of the area.

67.5 CORE AREA APPLICATIONS

If the interior core of a building is a large open area, a single zone constant volume system, Figure 67-3, can be used at a reasonable initial cost. The amount of air supplied is always the same. The desired supply air temperature is maintained by the heating and cooling coils only. A single HEAT/COOL thermostat with automatic changeover provides year-round control of the coil temperatures. Top floor and ground floor systems will have heating for morning warmup. Intermediate floors usually only have provisions for cooling. The duct design follows conventional practice, with room air distribution from the ceiling.

For core areas divided into smaller spaces, with variations in lighting and people loads, a variable air volume (VAV) single zone system has typically been used. Rather than always supplying the same amount of air to the space,

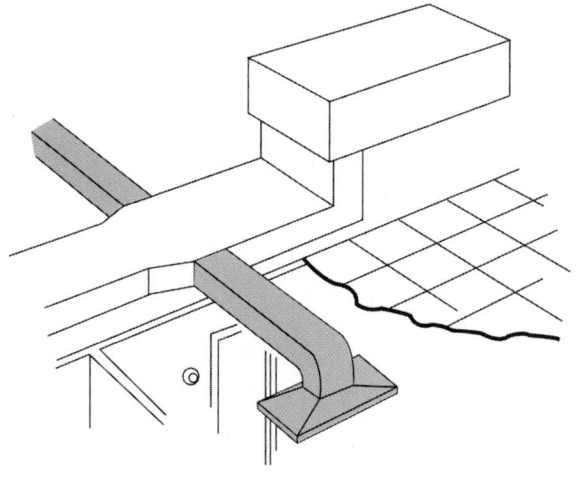

Figure 67-3 Single zone system using constant volume

the amount of air can be adjusted to better meet the load demands of the space. There are several approaches to this application.

Constant volume fans may be used with individual VAV terminals located for each space that increase or decrease the air supply with dampers, Figure 67-4. Terminal units can be designed to control air velocity, pressure, temperature, and flow rate. The final temperature is a result of mixing airstreams of different temperatures or humidity levels. Figure 67-5 shows a constant volume air handler connected to individual VAV terminals. The terminal may be an individual control box, a system air powered VAV slot diffuser, or a self contained temperature actuated VAV diffuser. In all these cases, the variable air volume is accomplished by throttling the airflow at the individual duct run, causing the constant volume air handler to "back up" the fan curve to a new balance point of lower CFM at a higher static pressure. The controls for this type of system are self contained within the air distribution system, and do not require any more control than the thermostat noted above.

Figure 67-4 VAV terminal unit
(Courtesy of the Trane Company)

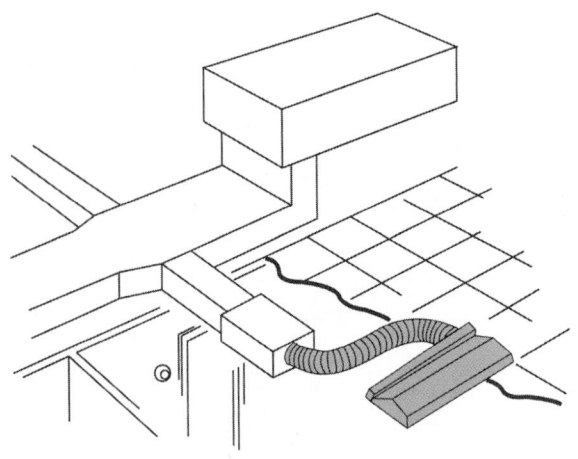

Figure 67-5 Single zone system using variable air volume (VAV)

TECH TIP

Constant volume supply fans can sometimes be used on variable air volume systems. However, as the demand for air decreases and dampers begin to close, the duct static pressure will increase as well as the load on the fan. This type of configuration should only be used in locations where heating and cooling loads are relatively steady.

Another approach for the core area is to use VAV terminals, with the capability of handling several duct runs from each terminal. In this case, the air handler is also constant volume, but the VAV terminal throttles the air supply to the ducts, and dumps the remainder back into the ceiling space return air plenum. The space is controlled with variable air volume, but the air handler is operating at constant volume. The control for this subsystem requires that the space thermostat controls an actuator on the VAV terminal, as well as controlling the cooling and heating demand.

In either of these cases, a single air handler is sufficient in the core zone and can provide proper comfort conditions. The air handler is typically constant volume because the loads are relatively steady, regardless of the season or ambient air temperature.

An approach often seen on older systems, but prohibited by current energy codes, is commonly called zone reheat. Reheat terminals differ from this basic mixing design by controlling the final temperature of the air with hot water coils, steam coils, or electric resistance heaters. As seen in Figure 67-6, an air handler delivers constant volume, constant temperature air to the distribution system. Individual zones or branches have heaters in them, which reheat the cool air to a comfort level for each space. These heaters may be individually controlled electric heaters, hot water coils, or steam coils. In many cases, these heaters are applied to a problem area in a system, to provide adequate heat where the original design was insufficient.

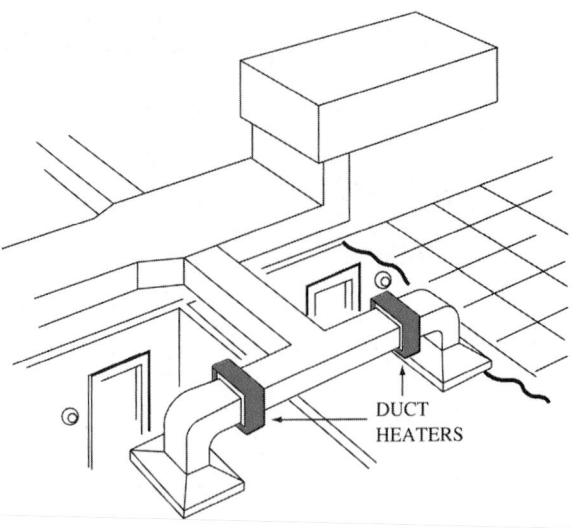

Figure 67-6 Constant volume system using zone duct heaters

67.6 PERIMETER ZONE APPLICATIONS

Perimeter zones require terminal systems that can handle the wide range of conditions, from the coldest morning warmup to the hottest solar gain cooling load. In many systems, this range was handled by providing perimeter radiant or forced air heat systems on the outer wall and under windows to furnish the necessary heat for the cold loads. A separate air system provided the necessary air movement, outside air requirements, and the cooling load responsibility. The air systems could be either constant or variable volume, but it has been found that only VAV really can provide the necessary control for comfort. In milder climates, the perimeter heating system is eliminated, without much loss of comfort.

TECH TIP

In some cases the entire perimeter heating and cooling load will not be controlled by the central system. Instead it may be handled by console units on the outside wall, with individual outside air sources and temperature controls.

The VAV systems for perimeter applications are generally provided with primary air from either a central air handler for the entire building, or an entire floor, depending on the size of the project, Figure 67-7. A single air handler may handle up to 40,000 ft^2 of occupied space, but in many cases the ductwork becomes unmanageable. Variable volume systems may be low velocity or high velocity, depending on the type of controller and the terminal units used. The volume of primary air is automatically adjusted to the total cooling demand by duct sensors controlling fan volume controls.

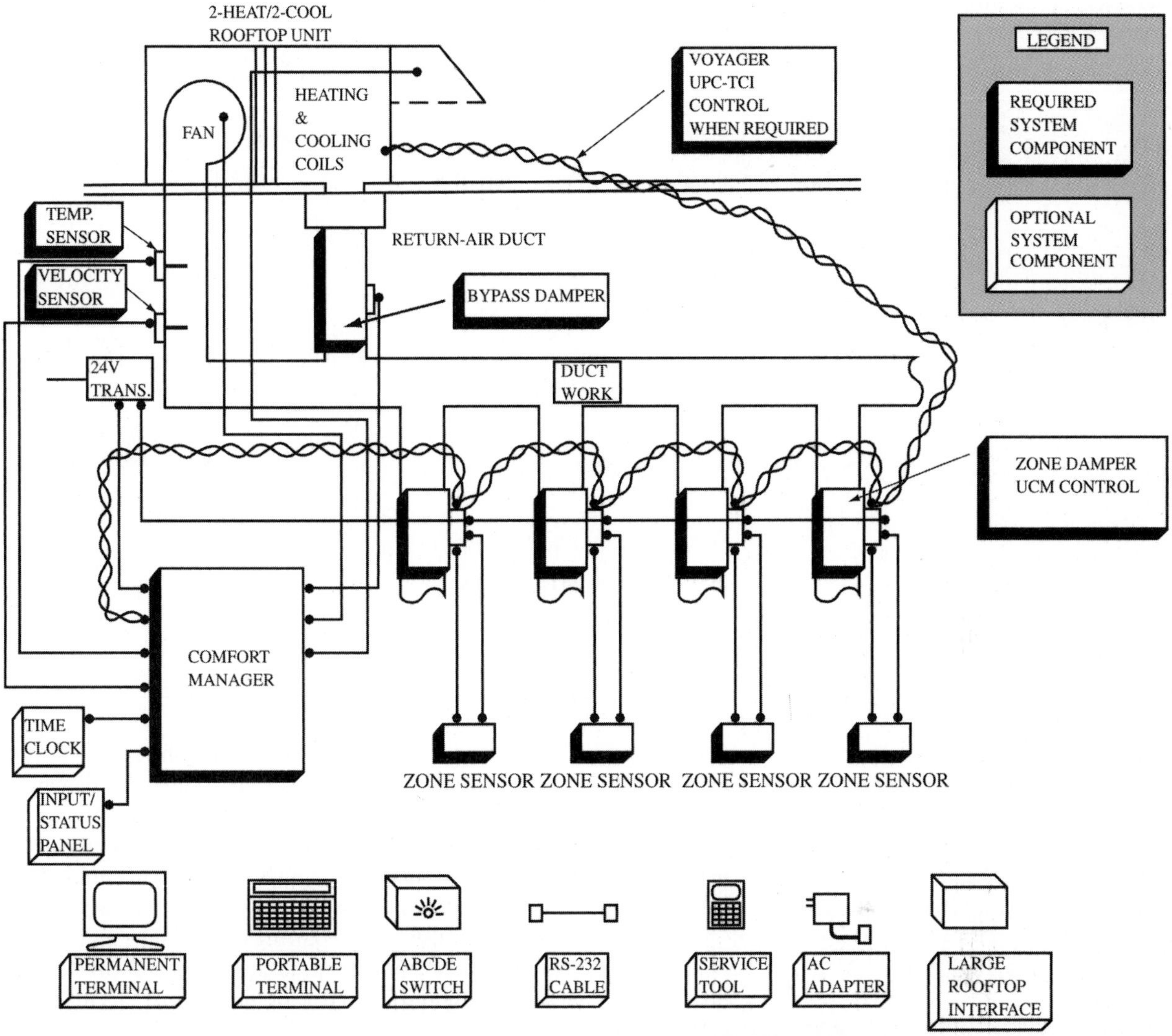

2-HEAT/2-COOL
ROOFTOP UNIT

FAN

HEATING
&
COOLING
COILS

VOYAGER
UPC-TCI
CONTROL
WHEN REQUIRED

LEGEND

REQUIRED
SYSTEM
COMPONENT

OPTIONAL
SYSTEM
COMPONENT

TEMP.
SENSOR

VELOCITY
SENSOR

RETURN-AIR DUCT

BYPASS DAMPER

24V
TRANS.

DUCT
WORK

ZONE DAMPER
UCM CONTROL

COMFORT
MANAGER

TIME
CLOCK

INPUT/
STATUS
PANEL

ZONE SENSOR ZONE SENSOR ZONE SENSOR ZONE SENSOR

PERMANENT
TERMINAL

PORTABLE
TERMINAL

ABCDE
SWITCH

RS-232
CABLE

SERVICE
TOOL

AC
ADAPTER

LARGE
ROOFTOP
INTERFACE

Figure 67-7 Schematic view of a typical variable air volume (VAV) system

The fan output may be adjusted by using variable inlet guide vanes. Throttling the air inlet to the fan is more efficient than reducing the airflow at the fan outlet which increases static pressure and fan power consumption. Another option is for stepped speed control settings such as slow, medium, and fast. Stepped speed control and inlet guide vanes may also be used in combination with one another. However, the most efficient method is for the use of a variable frequency drive (VFD) fan motor which allows for the full range of speed control. VFD's are considerably more expensive than most other alternatives; however, as the fan slows down under light loads less energy is used, reducing long term operating costs.

An older type of VAV perimeter zone system is the induction type. High velocity primary air is delivered to induction room terminals. This saves space, since the ductwork is much smaller than conventional ducting. The terminal unit takes the high velocity air through a nozzle arrangement, as shown in Figure 67-8. This induces room air into the unit

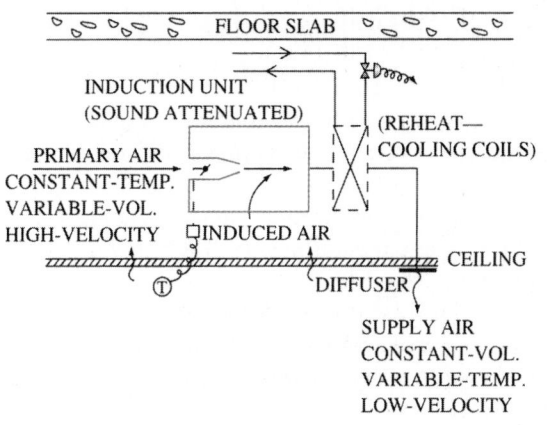

FLOOR SLAB

INDUCTION UNIT
(SOUND ATTENUATED)

(REHEAT—
COOLING COILS)

PRIMARY AIR
CONSTANT-TEMP.
VARIABLE-VOL.
HIGH-VELOCITY

INDUCED AIR

CEILING
DIFFUSER

SUPPLY AIR
CONSTANT-VOL.
VARIABLE-TEMP.
LOW-VELOCITY

Figure 67-8 Induction terminal

Figure 67-9 Sectional view of an induction type room terminal unit

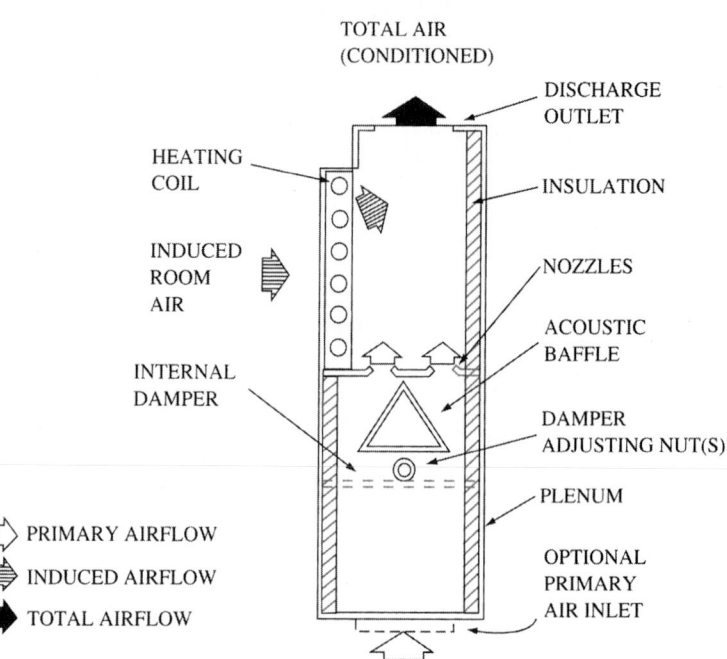

INDUCTION-ROOM TERMINAL

TOTAL AIR (CONDITIONED)

DISCHARGE OUTLET

HEATING COIL

INSULATION

INDUCED ROOM AIR

NOZZLES

ACOUSTIC BAFFLE

INTERNAL DAMPER

DAMPER ADJUSTING NUT(S)

PLENUM

OPTIONAL PRIMARY AIR INLET

▷ PRIMARY AIRFLOW

◈ INDUCED AIRFLOW

◆ TOTAL AIRFLOW

through a heating coil. The primary air may be unconditioned as there can be both heating and cooling coils located in the induction terminal. Figure 67-9 shows an induction room terminal that is constant volume, with temperature control achieved by reheat. Note that these terminal units do not rely on fans; the induced airflow provides the necessary secondary air.

SERVICE TIP

Induction air systems have many drawbacks. High pressure air requires very tight and sealed ductwork and air leaks are very noisy. These systems require considerable energy, since high duct static pressure requires increased fan power. VAV aspects are also limited because the induction effect falls off quickly with a reduction of airflow.

A type of VAV perimeter zone system operating at low pressure uses system powered boxes or diffusers. System air pressure controls the inflation of bladders that in turn, control the air volume in the unit. These are simple in concept and effective at a reasonable cost. They provide VAV space conditioning, but usually with constant volume supply fans. Some of these diffuser units use self contained, temperature powered actuators to modulate the diffuser openings. These can provide fairly simple, reasonable cost VAV to smaller systems.

Other systems provide cost effective zone control with a combination of VAV duct dampers and a sophisticated temperature control system. These allow the system to provide only heating or cooling at any given time. The demands of a number of zones are programmed to switch the system to that mode, for example, cooling. Any zones requiring heat are temporarily closed off. With a heating demand in place, the system controls will then switch the system back to heating, closing off the zones requiring cooling. The individual zone dampers are modulating, so there are no abrupt changes. A fan speed controller is part of the system, reducing airflow to a practical minimum, as allowable. These systems are generally designed for unitary equipment, but they can be used as part of a central system.

VAV systems can be used to provide minimum airflows to meet ventilation requirements. In this type of system, the terminal units are fan powered, providing constant volume in the conditioned zone. The primary air supply will vary from 100% down to about 20% of total air requirements. The primary air handler is variable volume, constant temperature, with the cooling plant demand proportional to the airflow. The low powered terminal fan provides terminal reheat at reduced air conditions for the zone, Figure 67-10. The individual zone controls can be stand alone systems, but usually are integrated through a Direct Digital Control (DDC) system which manages the overall operation of all terminal units.

67.7 ENTIRE BUILDING APPLICATIONS

Some older building designs utilized multizone or double duct applications. The major limitation for this type of system is the cost of energy to provide simultaneous heating and cooling. Different types of heat recovery methods were tried in an attempt to gain efficiency. As an example, the heat

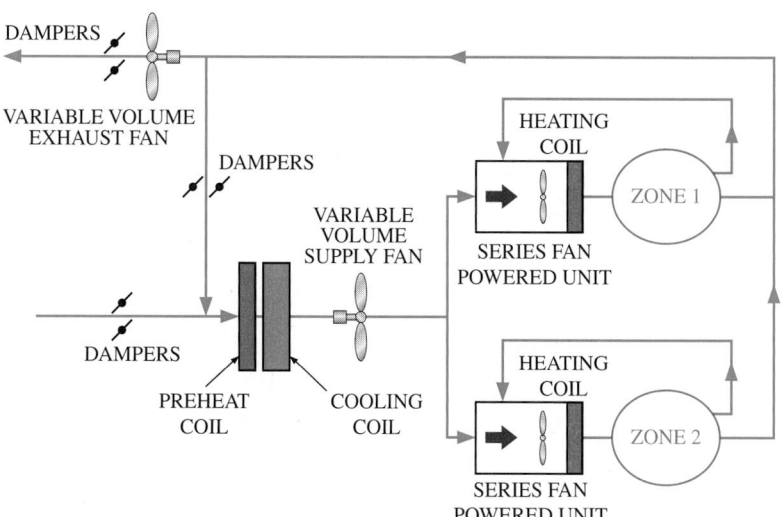

Figure 67-10 Series fan powered variable volume system

rejected from the chiller was used to provide warm water for heating. Other heat recovery approaches have been tried, but the fully energy efficient approaches were not always the simplest or most economical to install.

TECH TIP

Multizone and double duct applications were popular before energy codes were enacted, these were the ultimate in zoned comfort systems. By providing a blend of always available heated and cooled air to any zone, with the addition of good pneumatic control systems, these systems supplied excellent building comfort.

Multizone systems provide one trunk duct to each zone from the multizone air handler, Figure 67-11. The air handler is a blow-through design with a hot and a cold deck. The airflow from each of these decks is fed through a set of dampers, 90° opposed to each other on the same shaft. When the cooling damper is fully closed, the heating damper is fully open,

and vice versa. Most of the time, the dampers are modulating in response to a temperature signal from the zone. The overall system is low to medium pressure and constant volume. The multizone's limitations, from a design standpoint, are that only a limited number of zones are available on the air handler. Consequently, adjustments are always needed to get an even balance. The smallest zone is typically 8–10% of the full load.

Double duct systems are the ultimate in design flexibility, but are very high in initial cost. Double duct systems are high velocity, high pressure systems. Some are variable volume, but most are constant volume. Two full sized supply ducts are required for the system, one for cooling and one for heating, Figure 67-12. The major benefit of these systems is that the two ducts each serve one terminal mixing box, which controls the air temperature for each zone. The mixing boxes are available in very small sizes, down to 200 CFM, allowing for zones as small as $1/2$ ton. Zoning is limited by this small increment and the overall size of the system. The high pressure air in the main supply ducts (4–5 in wc) is reduced in the mixing boxes, so that the distribution ducting is normally low pressure design, with low noise levels.

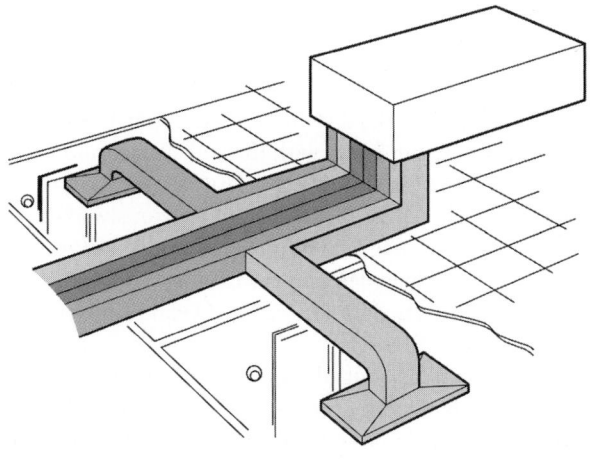

Figure 67-11 Constant volume multizone heating and cooling unit

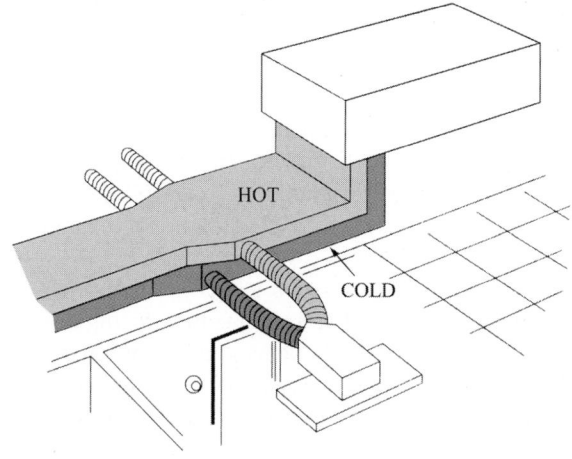

Figure 67-12 Double duct system

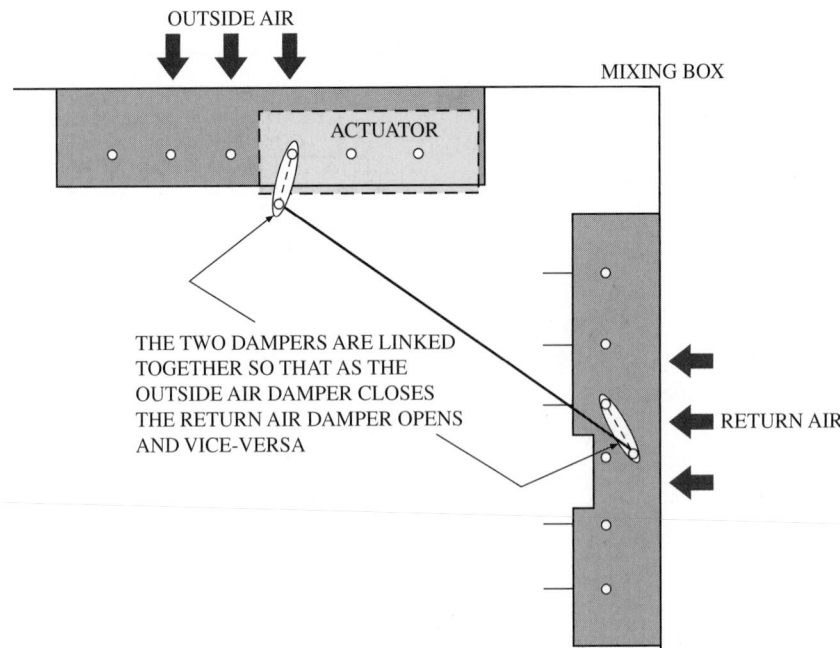

Figure 67-13 Mixing box parallel blade dampers

67.8 MIXING DAMPERS

Dampers installed on air handling units control the flow of air through various parts of the system. The function of dampers depends on the design of the system. There are two general types of multiple leaf dampers: parallel blade and opposing blade. Parallel blade dampers tend to direct the air as they open, whereas opposing blade dampers are usually constructed to more readily offer a positive close-off.

TECH TIP

The proper adjustment of mixing dampers is critical to maintaining an efficiently operating system that provides the proper air distribution within a building. Mixing dampers blend the air so that you have the proper temperature and are able to control humidity within the building. If these dampers are not set properly, then the building operating cost will go up dramatically.

Dampers can operate either in two positions, open or closed, or they can be modulated so that they can be positioned anywhere between fully open and fully closed, depending on the requirements of the control system. Most dampers on central station air handlers are of the modulating type.

Dampers can be linked together, so that when one opens the other closes. For example, in a mixing box such as shown in Figure 67-13, where the return air is mixed with outside air, the dampers can be linked and controlled so that when the outside air is increased, the return air is decreased (and vice versa). This provides the control of the airflow needed for the wide variety of conditioning requirements.

67.9 MIXED-AIR CONTROL

To illustrate some of the many uses of dampers, refer to Figure 67-14. Of primary importance is the mixing of return air and outside air. During normal operation only the return air and the minimum outside air dampers are involved. The minimum outside air damper is a two position damper. Normally it is fully open to provide ventilation air to meet code requirements. The only time it closes is when the building is unoccupied or the system is shut down.

Provision is made in the damper system and the control system to use additional outside air for free cooling (economizer cycle) when practical. A maximum outside air damper is modulated along with the return air and exhaust air damper to maintain a slightly positive pressure in the building. The total air quantity through the air handler does not change but the proportions of outside air to return air do change to meet the control requirements.

67.10 FACE AND BYPASS CONTROL

One way to control the amount of cooling or heating is to use a face damper in series with the coil surface and bypass dampers around the coil and in a duct connection for the return air as shown in Figure 67-14, previously. With this arrangement the total air volume remains constant even though the space load demand is changing. The air entering the fan can be adjusted for different load conditions by modifying the air mixture.

As an example, outside and return air are normally mixed in the air plenum chamber and passed through the filters, preheater, and cooling coil, and then to the fan. If the outside air temperature is low enough, the face dampers on the cooling coil can begin to close while the bypass dampers around the coil begin to open. This reduces the load on the

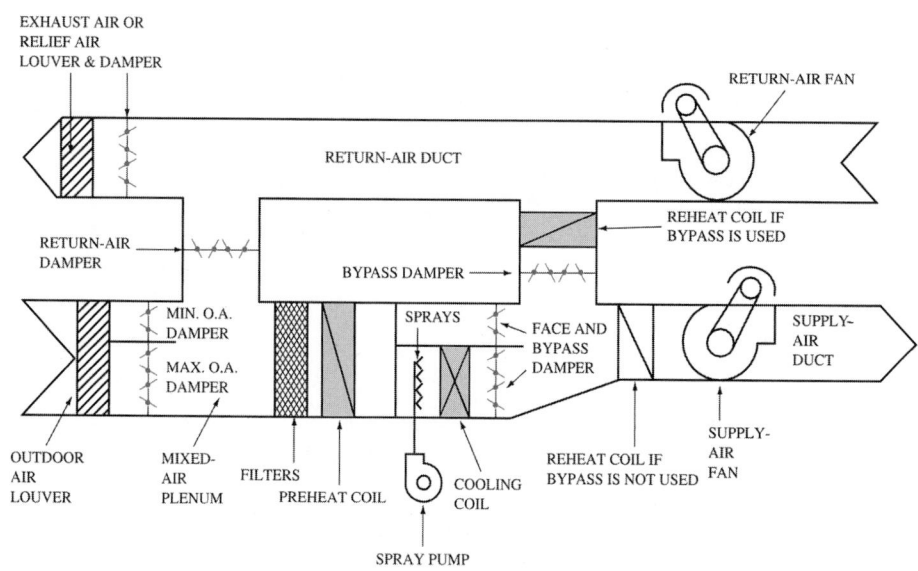

Figure 67-14 Schematic diagram of a typical air handling unit showing the various types of damper arrangements

cooling coil and utilizes the outside air to assist in cooling. The damper control modulates the air quantity from each source to match the load. The two sets of dampers are linked together either mechanically or electrically so that when one modulates toward the open position, the other modulates toward the closed position (and vice versa). Because the dampers are proportioned evenly, the flow of air through the fan remains unchanged.

67.11 PACKAGED AIR HANDLER CONTROL SYSTEM

Packaged air handlers can be factory assembled as one unit or field installed in multiple configurations. The best match of components for a specific application can be selected and located correctly. Once installed, the packaged air handler will have some type of control panel. Controllers are typically configured to accept hundreds of configuration settings and setpoints. A control module contains the software and microprocessor that controls the operation of the unit, Figure 67-15. The module will receive input from all of the different sensors located throughout the air handler that measure air temperature, quality, and condition. It will then regulate the supply fan, mixing dampers, and heating and cooling coils as necessary to achieve the programmed condition setpoints.

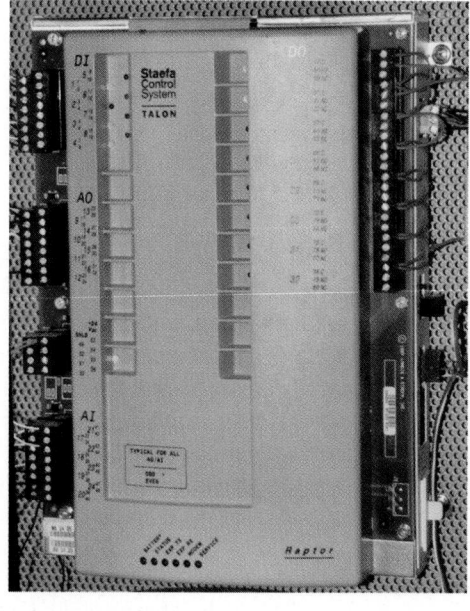

Figure 67-15 Air handler control module

67.12 CONSTANT AIR VOLUME CONTROL SYSTEM

Depending on the system configuration, there will be a variety of temperature, condition, and alarm sensors. These include supply air temperature, low temperature thermostat, filter differential pressure switch, mixed air temperature, airflow switch, and preheat temperature. Typical sensor locations are shown on the air handler in Figure 67-16.

These measured input signals are compared to the setpoints programmed into the controller and the appropriate actions will be taken on the supply fan relay (start/stop), mixed air damper actuator, heating coil valve/electric heater, cooling coil control valve or direct expansion control depending on the system, and the exhaust damper position.

SERVICE TIP

Most control panels will have a display for fault codes. When troubleshooting a unit always check this first. The manufacturer's literature will identify the fault code so that you can immediately begin correcting the problem.

Figure 67-16 Typical air handler actuator and sensor installation locations

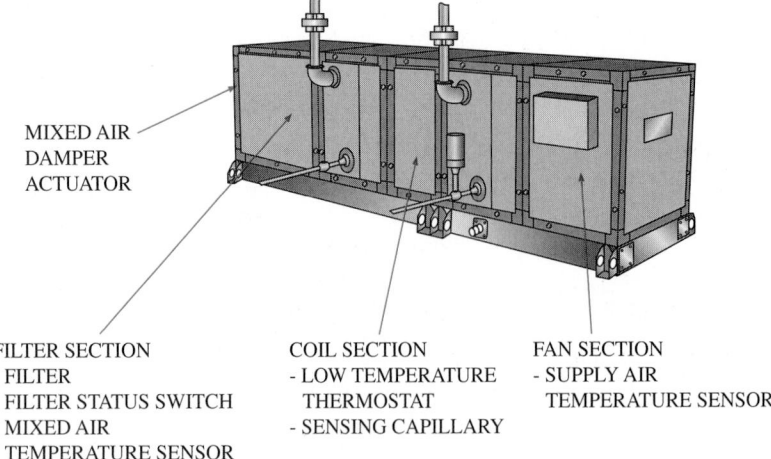

MIXED AIR
DAMPER
ACTUATOR

FILTER SECTION
- FILTER
- FILTER STATUS SWITCH
- MIXED AIR
  TEMPERATURE SENSOR

COIL SECTION
- LOW TEMPERATURE
  THERMOSTAT
- SENSING CAPILLARY

FAN SECTION
- SUPPLY AIR
  TEMPERATURE SENSOR

Figure 67-17 Capillary tube routing for low temperature thermostat on heating application only

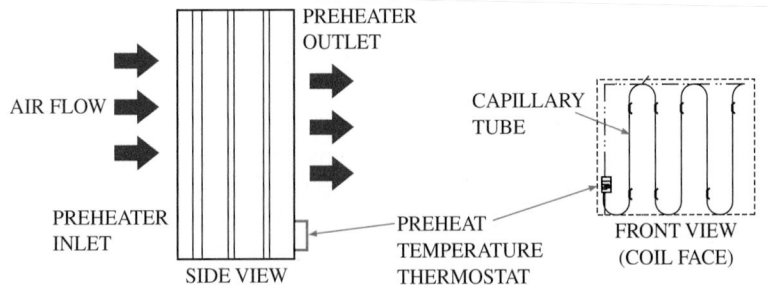

PREHEATER
OUTLET

AIR FLOW

CAPILLARY
TUBE

PREHEATER
INLET

SIDE VIEW

PREHEAT
TEMPERATURE
THERMOSTAT

FRONT VIEW
(COIL FACE)

Temperature Input Signals

A number of the input signals are temperature measurements. The supply air temperature sensor is installed on the discharge side of the air handler for measuring the supply air temperature for the conditioned space. The low temperature thermostat measures the temperature of the air as it passes across the cooling coil. The thermostat consists of a long length of serpentine capillary tubing that is installed on the inlet side of the coil. It will be set to shut down the fan and set off an alarm if the air temperature drops below 35°F. This is essentially a backup for the preheater which receives its signal from the preheat temperature sensor. This preheat sensor is also serpentine capillary tubing, however, it is located on the outlet of the preheater coil rather than at the inlet, Figure 67-17.

The mixed air temperature sensor is mounted in the mixing box, and has direct input for the spring return damper actuator, Figure 67-18. The damper control assembly will modulate the damper position through a linkage, Figure 67-19, based upon the input signal from the mixed air sensor.

SERVICE TIP

A malfunctioning sensor can sometimes be difficult to diagnose, however by logically working through a step-by-step sequence of operation, the different possible problems can be eliminated one by one. More difficult to troubleshoot is an improperly placed sensor. Always follow the manufacturer's recommendations when reinstalling sensors.

Airflow Input Signals

There are also airflow input signals. The airflow switch consists of a probe mounted in the fan discharge duct. This snap action switch verifies that the fan is either on or off. The filter status switch is set to alarm as the differential pressure increases once the filters become dirty.

Figure 67-18 Spring return damper actuator

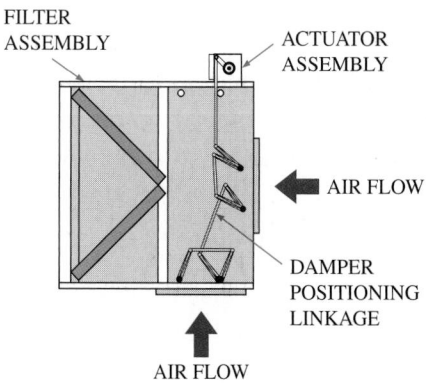

Figure 67-19 Assembled actuator and linkage

67.13 VARIABLE AIR VOLUME CONTROL SYSTEM

This system differs from the constant volume/variable temperature system since basically it maintains a nearly constant air temperature but matches the load by changing the air volume. This system became popular when attention was given to conserving energy without decreasing the comfort level during partial load conditions.

One of the features of these systems is the use of a variable frequency fan speed controller that is applied to the air handler fan, Figure 67-20. This electrical device, along with the necessary sensors, controls the speed of the central fan to match the total air volume required by the individual zone terminal units. As an example, a static pressure sensor can be installed in the airflow to reduce the speed of the fan as the air supply demand decreases and the static air pressure rises, Figure 67-21. Since the power required for driving the fan is proportional to the cube of the fan speed, tremendous power savings can result from slowing down the fan when the extra air is not needed.

Many of the input signals and controls are similar to the constant air volume system with some exceptions. The fan motor is a variable frequency drive unit (VFD). Because of this, a static pressure transducer and probe are installed rather than an airflow switch. The fan speed can be varied according to the static pressure in the system to supply more or less air as the system requires. There is also a temperature sensor located in the return air supply.

Also included in a VAV system is a high pressure switch. This switch will shut down the fan if the duct pressure exceeds the setpoint. Additional fan shutdowns are the low temperature thermostat and the fire shutdown relay.

67.14 AIR QUALITY AND CONDITION SENSORS

Air Quality

CO_2 levels are monitored in the conditioned air space and can also be monitored in the return air duct. These sensors use infrared technology with a range of 0–2000 parts per million (ppm). The amount of outside air admitted will be adjusted to control the setpoint level as shown previously in Figure 67-2.

Differential Enthalpy Control

Two individual sensors are used with one sensing the outside air enthalpy and the other sensing the return air enthalpy, Figure 67-22. This is used for the economizer section. The airstream with the lowest enthalpy will be directed by dampers through the economizer section.

Space Humidity

The humidity level is monitored in the conditioned space and is mounted in a location that is representative of the entire zone. This sensor can be used for adjusting the cooling coil face and bypass dampers to allow for sufficient cooling of the air for dehumidification.

Figure 67-20 Supply fan control

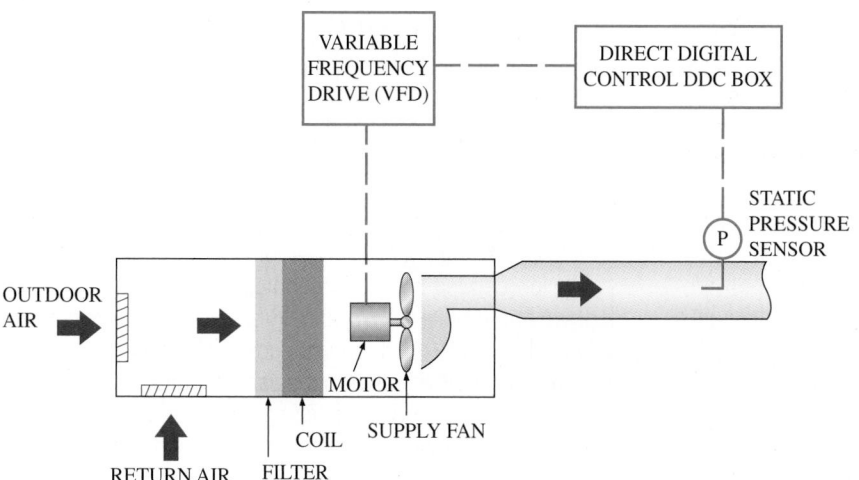

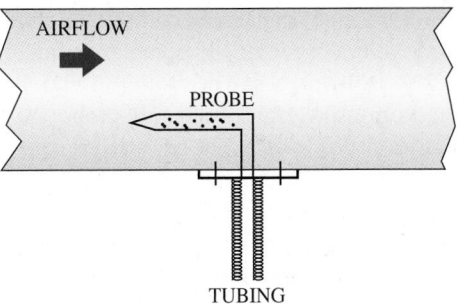

Figure 67-21 Duct static pressure probe

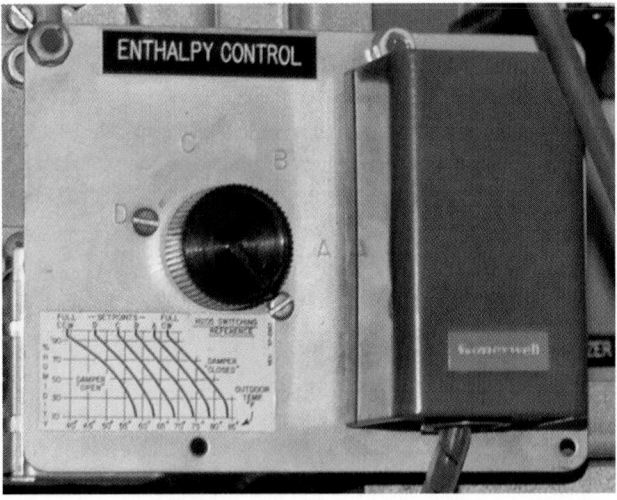

Figure 67-22 Differential enthalpy control sensor

UNIT 67—SUMMARY

Air distribution control systems use input from temperature, condition, and static air pressure sensors to position dampers for directing and mixing the airflow and/or control the supply fan. Some of these inputs are also used to regulate the temperature control of the preheater, cooling coil, heating coil, and reheater. Mixing dampers can be positioned to provide for the best mix of outside and return air through the handler. Variable air volume systems may also adjust the fan air supply. Inlet guide vanes are sometimes used on large supply fans that can be closed to reduce the air supply or can be opened to increase the air supply. This is a more efficient way to control the airflow through a fan as compared to regulating the airflow at the fan outlet. Variable frequency drive supply fans are becoming increasingly popular in variable air volume supply systems because they can be controlled to operate at the most efficient speed and load.

WORK ORDERS

Service Ticket 6701

Customer Complaint: Supply Air Pressure Low

Equipment Type: Packaged AHU with Centrifugal Fan

The service technician answered a call for a small office building with a recently installed packaged air handler. The owner complained that the space was too hot and that there did not seem to be very much air blowing from the supply registers in each space. The system had only been installed a couple of weeks ago and seemed to work properly, however the past few days the outside temperature was very hot. The owner was wondering if maybe the unit was undersized.

The air handler was located in the back of the building and the technician shut off the power and then removed the access covers for the fan section. The fan seemed to be mounted correctly and the drive belts appeared to be tensioned properly. Turning the fan on, it ran smoothly, however it had minimal airflow. With the fan running, the technician could see the problem was in the fan rotation. It was rotating backwards. The technician shut off the power supply and reversed two of the electrical leads to the fan motor. Once the unit was restarted, the air supply was more than adequate for the system.

Service Ticket 6702

Customer Complaint: Space Too Hot

Equipment Type: Packaged AHU Unit with Direct Expansion Cooling Coil

The service technician answered a service call for a veterinary building and spoke to the office receptionist. The receptionist explained that the waiting room and the lab areas were much warmer than they should be and this started a few hours ago. The system had been running fine prior to that. The technician was led to the back of the building where the air handler was located. The unit was rumbling and producing considerable vibration. The technician opened the access doors and immediately saw that the fan motor was loose on its mounting bolts. The unit was shut down and the drive belt tension adjusted as the motor mounting bolts were tightened. The technician replaced the original mounting nuts with lock nuts.

The unit was restarted and the vibration was eliminated and the unit was running smoothly. However, the mixing dampers did not seem to be operating. They were frozen in one position with the outside air supply almost wide open, placing a considerable load on the direct expansion cooling coil. The technician again shut the unit down and then tried to manually stroke the dampers and found they were not frozen into position. The locknut in the linkage from the actuator to the dampers had come off due to all of the vibration. The linkage was reconnected and the actuator stroked back and forth to confirm the damper

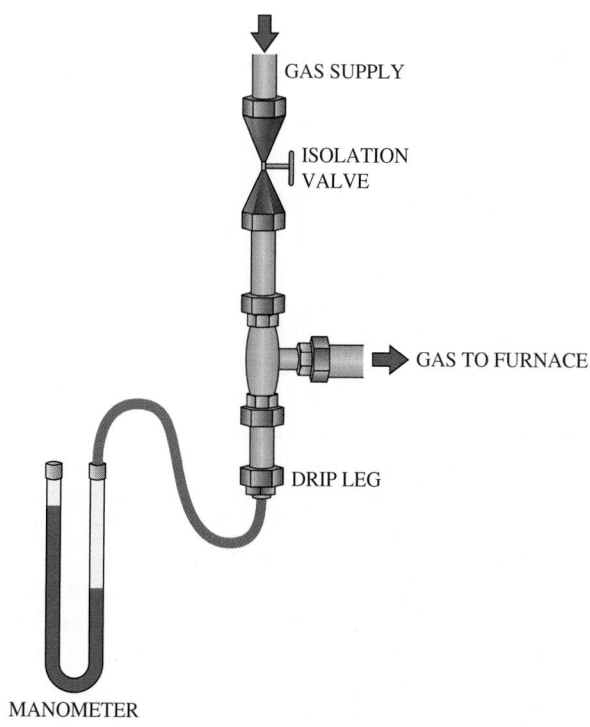

Figure 68-5 Measuring gas supply pressure at the clean out connection with a manometer

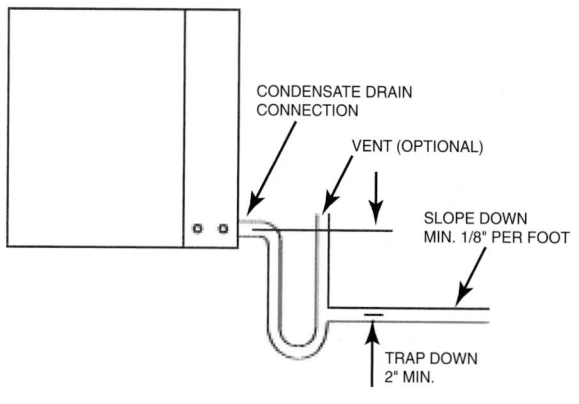

Figure 68-6 Condensate trap
(From Climate Master AP Series Installation & Maintenance Manual, page 3, Figure 3. Copyright Climate Master, Inc. By permission.)

68.9 CONDENSATE DRAIN

Part of the process of air conditioning is moisture removal from the air for dehumidification. The evaporator coil is below the dew point of the air being conditioned. Water in the air condenses on the cold coil, and follows the fins down into the drain pan located beneath it. From there, the condensate drains out into the drain line through the drain connection.

For this drain process to work properly, the condensate drain line should have a trap installed in it. The trap serves a couple of purposes. One is to prevent insects from finding their way into the rooftop unit where they could then enter the structure. The other purpose is so the condensate will drain properly.

Most packaged/rooftop units have draw-through evaporator coils. The blower is located downstream of the evaporator coil and creates a negative pressure across the coil. Therefore the drain will also be at a negative pressure whenever the blower is running. This can prevent the condensate from draining properly. A water-filled trap installed in the drain line will provide an air break. Because of the trap, water will not be pulled back up through the drain while the blower is running.

There is a formula that can be used for the design of the trap. It is related to the static pressure in the rooftop. From the outlet of the drain at the unit, to the outlet of the trap, there should be a distance of static pressure plus 1 in wc. The

depth of the trap, from the outlet to the bottom of the trap, should be equal to one-half of the distance from the inlet of the trap to the outlet of the trap. An alternative method is to simply follow the recommendations of the manufacturer. Normally a schematic with the proper drain trap dimensions is provided with the unit, Figure 68-6.

Although a condensate trap is a necessity, it can also create problems. One of these is the possibility of freezeup. There will be instances where the rooftop unit may be cooling in the afternoon but by morning the outside temperature has dropped below freezing. The condensate trap full of water from the cooling cycle will freeze and split. Now there will be a problem during the next cooling cycle. If this is a common occurrence then corrective steps can be taken. The trap can be insulated and if necessary heat tape can be installed around the outside of it.

Another problem with drain lines on rooftops is that they are exposed to ultraviolet radiation from the sun. UV light will break down PVC pipe. One way to correct this condition with PVC pipe is to insulate it. Another option is to use an alternative piping material such as copper tubing. However, this is generally a more expensive remedy.

SERVICE TIP

When installing the drain line for a rooftop unit, attention to detail will guarantee proper condensate removal. If the drain line is going to be run a considerable distance, an air vent should be installed. The location for the vent is important. It should be placed right after the trap at the point where the condensate exits. The vent will help prevent vapor locking of the water in the drain. It is also important to correctly pitch the drain line away from the unit, typically a 1 in drop for every 10 f of distance. There should also be no dips in the drain line.

68.10 VENTING

Rooftop units can be manufactured with cooling only or with cooling/heating. If the unit has electric heat or is a heat pump, then there are no considerations required for proper venting or combustion air supply. If the unit has gas heat, then there needs to be accommodation for venting and combustion air. Before the introduction of forced draft or induced draft rooftop units, the heating part of the unit was vented from the top through a vent pipe and cap. These older model rooftops used standing pilot ignition systems and nuisance blowouts of the pilot occurred frequently. Most of the units used today, which are forced or induced draft type systems with automatic ignitions, use only an exhaust/combustion air inlet hood. The exhaust/combustion hood normally comes with the unit uninstalled. After the initial setting of the rooftop unit, the hood is screwed into its proper place.

UNIT 68—SUMMARY

There is nothing that can replace the experience gained from working in the field, however even an experienced technician must still keep abreast of changes in installation procedures and equipment design. Reading current literature and trade journals, attending seminars and training sessions, and referring to the manufacturer's installation instructions are the keys for the HVAC/R installer/service technician to stay current with installation procedures. HVAC equipment manufacturers want their equipment installed correctly and operated properly and safely.

There are a number of important considerations to be taken into account when installing a rooftop unit. The strength of the roof to support the HVAC unit needs to be determined. The proper location of the unit has to be selected to minimize the chance of water leakage into the building and to avoid damage from poor quality corrosive outside air conditions. Proper voltage and phasing must be applied to the unit. Drain lines must be installed correctly for proper condensate removal. Clearances on top and around all sides of the unit must be adequate for correct operation, safety, and servicing. The correctly sized roof curb must be installed correctly.

Installing a rooftop unit is a multistep process. Any one improperly completed step can lead to poor performance from the system and premature failure of the unit. The manufacturer's installation instructions the relevant codes, and the use of common sense will go a long way in making sure a rooftop HVAC system runs like it was designed and in providing the customer with what has been paid for.

WORK ORDERS

Service Ticket 6801

Customer Complaint: Water Dripping Through Ceiling Tile

Equipment Type: Rooftop Package AC Unit

A business customer calls in a problem complaining of water dripping through the ceiling tile. There has not been a rain in several weeks, so the rooftop air conditioner is suspected. The service technician gets the call and arrives, goes inside the establishment, and locates the ceiling tile with the water damage and drip. Now the service technician has a good idea of where on the roof to start looking for the leak. Setting up a ladder and buckling on a tool belt, the technician climbs onto the roof. Just as suspected, a rooftop unit is directly above the spot in the ceiling where the leak is.

It is a spring day, warm and humid. The service technician knows the air conditioning unit will be condensing a lot of water from the air being conditioned. The condensate trap is found lying on the roof, detached from the main drain leaving the unit. It looks as though the trap broke at about the middle of an elbow, probably due to water being still in the trap and freezing during the winter.

The air conditioner is running, and the service technician hears the condensate gurgling as it tries to drain out but the negative pressure will not allow it. The service technician takes the panel off of the evaporator section and secures it. The condensate is flowing over the edges of the drain pan and through a gap between the return duct and the roof curb. Then the condensate is spilling down through the attic and on top of the ceiling tile.

The service technician installs a prefabricated trap to replace the damaged one. To help prevent the freezing problem from occurring again, the technician insulates the trap. Following the condensate drain line down along to the roof drain, the technician sees a steady stream of water running into the roof drain. The inside of the unit is checked one more time to make sure the condensate drain pan for the coil is not overflowing. The service technician reinstalls all panels securely and cleans up.

Service Ticket 6802

Customer Complaint: Compressor Noise on Startup Equipment Type: 3 Ton Rooftop Packaged AC

The 3 ton rooftop unit's installation is complete. It is now time to start the unit up. With the correct panels removed, the service technician has the proper refrigerant gauges installed and a voltmeter ready to check voltages. A clamp-on ammeter is placed around one of the power leads to the contactor. The system is a three phase, 240 V unit.

The service technician does one more check to make sure all the wiring has been done correctly. Taking out a set of jumper cords the technician carefully jumps R to Y and R to G, and then turns on the disconnect switch. The compressor contactor and fan relay energize. The blower comes on correctly, the condenser fan begins running, and the compressor starts up, but makes a terrible noise. The service technician looks at the gauges and notices that the suction pressure does not drop like it should if the compressor were pumping.

The unit is equipped with a scroll type compressor. Quickly turning off the electrical disconnect, the service technician notes that the compressor scroll is orbiting backward. The scroll compressor will only compress refrigerant if the rotor is running in the correct direction. The service technician disconnects two of the high voltage leads from the contactor and reverses them, tightening them securely. The disconnect switch is then turned back on and the unit starts up and begins running normally. The compressor runs smoothly, and the suction pressure starts to pull down like it should.

Service Ticket 6803

Customer Complaint: Several Offices Warmer Than Usual, Unit Not Cooling

Equipment Type: Rooftop AC Unit

The building manager calls in and explains that several offices are running warmer than usual. Contacted by the dispatcher, the service technician heads out to the location. This is a new account so there is no record of what kind of equipment will be involved. The only information received from the dispatcher was a no cool call, an address, and who to talk to.

Arriving on the job, and after finally locating the right contact person, the service technician finds out which offices are having problems. The HVAC unit is located on the roof. The service technician correctly sets up a ladder, buckles on a tool belt, and climbs up the ladder to the rooftop unit. The unit is running, so the disconnect switch is shut off to remove power to the unit.

The service technician pulls the panel to access the refrigerant service ports and secures the panel. The service port caps are unscrewed and a gauge manifold with low loss fittings is installed. The panel providing access to the evaporator coil is next removed and secured. One temperature thermister is positioned in the return air and another in the supply airstream. The service technician puts this panel back in place, so the airflow is correct through the coil. A temperature probe is positioned

on the suction line about 10 in before the line enters the compressor.

The service technician then powers the unit back up. All components seem to be running, so the panel removed to access the service ports is put back in place. If this panel is not in place, then the airflow would be around the condenser coil and not through it.

After the unit has run about 10 min, the service technician takes some readings. The discharge pressure appeared to be reasonable for R-22 at 275 psig as the outdoor ambient temperature was 94°F. The suction pressure of 80 psig was high. The service technician then checked the temperature difference across the evaporator coil and it was 10°F, which was too little. Upon further investigation, the service technician could feel hot air being pulled in from a gap between the rooftop unit and the curb. The evaporator coil could not overcome the 94°F air that was being pulled in from the roof.

This was a job for the installers to fix. The service technician called in to the dispatcher and filled in the details. The dispatcher said an installer would be over right away.

UNIT 68—REVIEW QUESTIONS

1. Describe one method to determine if a ladder is correctly set up.

2. Besides the manufacturer, where can the rooftop unit installer consult for proper unit installation?

3. If the rooftop unit is installed in a seacoast area, what is one consideration as to its location?

4. If the rooftop unit is subjected to a corrosive environment, and cannot be installed in an area away from the offending corrosion, what would be a possible alternative?

5. What is one of the main reasons the rooftop units has to be level?

6. Proper clearances are required for what purpose concerning the condenser?

7. What are the two possible duct configurations for a rooftop unit?

8. If using a heat pump rooftop unit, then proper height off of the roof is important why?

9. Why must the technician secure the rooftop unit's panels when servicing the unit?

10. Where can the weight for a rooftop unit be found?

11. The gasket material used between the rooftop unit and the roof curb is used for what purpose?

12. Why is it important for the roof curb to be square with the roof joists or rafters?

13. Utilities can be run to the rooftop unit in what two ways?

14. What code specifies the correct way for electrical connections to be made?

15. When installing units requiring three phase power, what is one of the concerns with the three phase installation?

16. What process allows for condensation of moisture on the evaporator coil?

17. What must be installed in the drain line to ensure proper condensate removal?

18. If PVC pipe is used for the construction of the drain line, what must be done to prevent deterioration of the pipe and what causes this deterioration?

19. If the rooftop unit utilizes gas heat, what two processes have to be considered in the installation of the unit?

20. What is the customer's number one concern relative to the rooftop unit?

UNIT 69

Air Handler Coils and Control Systems

OBJECTIVES

After completing this unit you will be able to:

- describe the general arrangement of a direct expansion coil in an air handling unit.
- explain how a chilled water system operates.
- list the different types of heating and cooling coils.
- select the proper coil for a given application.
- explain how an energy recovery wheel operates.
- describe how water or steam coil control valves operate.
- explain the differences and advantages of different types of control systems.

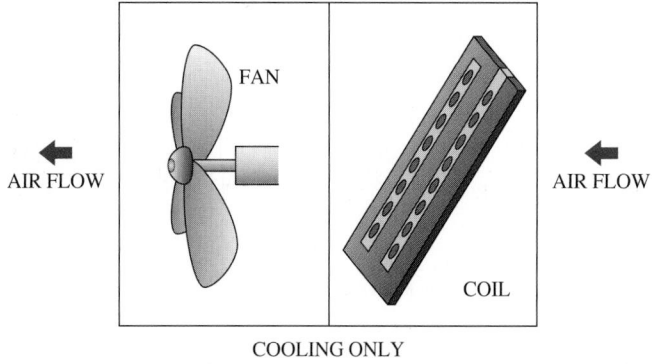

Figure 69-1 Cooling only horizontal flow air handler with DX coil

69.1 INTRODUCTION

Air handling units range greatly in size and application. Residential air handlers typically have a direct expansion (DX) coil and airflow rates in the range of 400 CFM per ton of air conditioning capacity. In comparison, large commercial air handlers may have airflow rates of 55,000 CFM or greater. These units often use cooling coils supplied with chill water from a central AC unit that may supply one or more air handlers.

Air handlers are often used for both cooling and heating. For the heating mode, smaller residential units may use electric resistance heat. Large air handlers have heating coils supplied with hot water or steam delivered from a furnace or a boiler. In addition to heating and cooling, air handlers may be specially equipped to improve dehumidification of the air in the cooling mode and to humidify the air in the heating mode. Many air handlers today also can be configured with energy recovery devices to increase the unit's efficiency without compromising comfort.

69.2 AIR HANDLING UNITS

A small residential horizontal air handler would have a DX coil and a blower as shown in Figure 69-1. This would be a fairly simple type air handler to install and service. Larger air handlers are more complex. The air handler shown in Figure 69-2 is the focal point of a number of subsystems that make up a typical central HVAC layout. In this installation the chiller supplies chilled water to the cooling coil located in the air handler assembly. This cooling circuit consists of a chiller, a pump, the cooling coil, and all necessary piping. Separate from the air handler, the compressor for the chiller

system utilizes a water cooled condenser. The condenser cooling water circuit consists of a cooling tower, a pump, and a water cooled condenser (part of the chiller). This is actually a subcircuit to the cooling circuit. This type of configuration will also have a heating circuit that generally consists of the boiler, a pump, and heating coil.

SERVICE TIP

A common maintenance item is the replacement of the filters at the inlet of the air handler chilled/heat coil. A building may have large and small air handler units (all usually located in relatively inaccessible locations and environments) with different filter demands. It is important to make sure that filters are changed when needed and not overlooked.

69.3 DIRECT EXPANSION (DX) COILS

Many residential and light commercial air handlers will have DX coils as shown in Figure 69-3. These may come from the factory without refrigerant and pressurized with nitrogen. If this is the case, they should be checked for pressure with the installed Schrader valve prior to installation. If no pressure is present, then the coil may have developed a leak during shipment and should be returned. Before installation, all of the nitrogen should be released and the ends of the connections cut off.

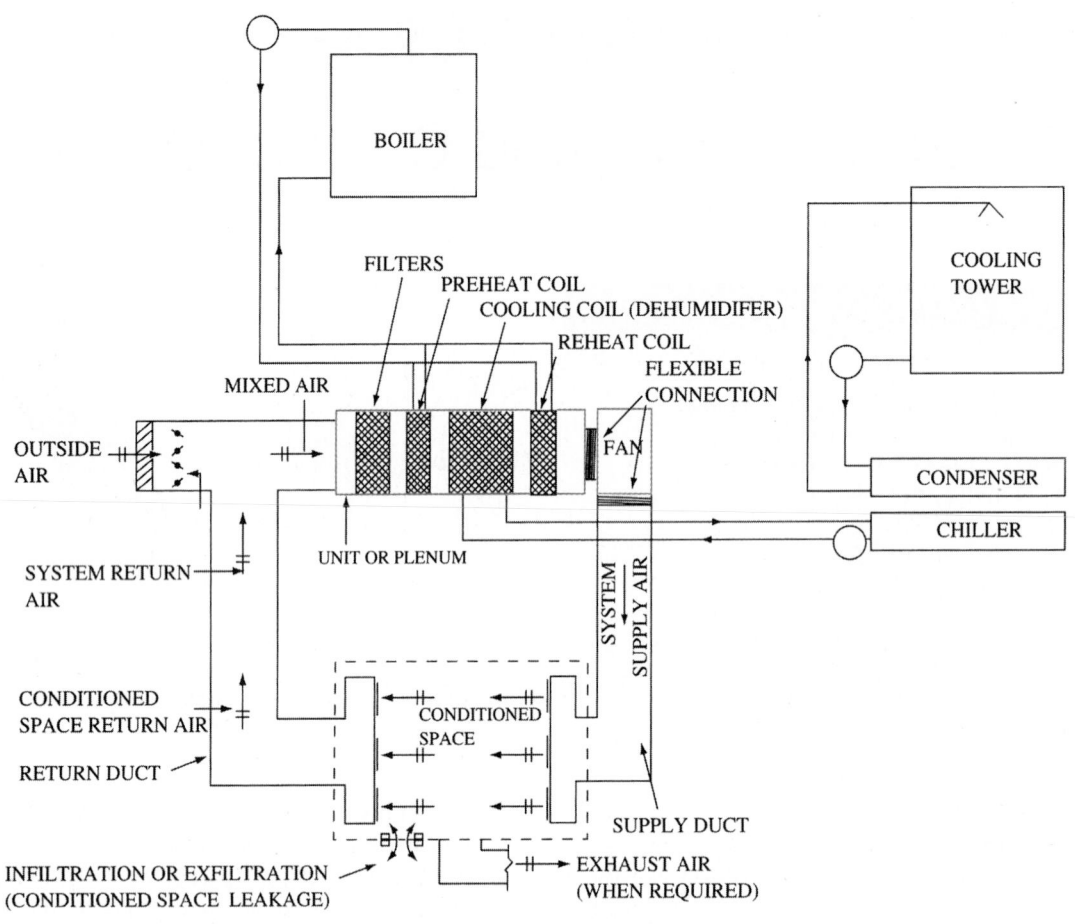

Figure 69-2 Typical central HVAC system showing air handler unit

---

SAFETY TIP

Make sure to bleed all the pressure from the DX coil before cutting off the end caps. Also make sure to protect your eyes and face while doing so.

Figure 69-3 DX coils for air handler applications

Once the connections have been cut off as shown in Figure 69-4, they should be prepared for flaring or soldering. A liquid line filter-drier should be installed as close to the coil as possible. When soldering a thermostatic expansion valve, always direct the flame away from the valve body. As an added precaution, a wet cloth should be wrapped around the

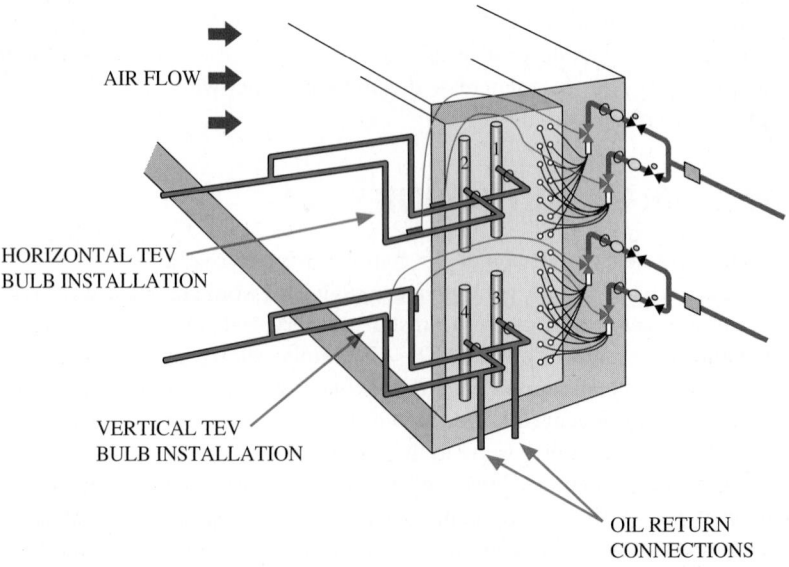

Figure 69-4 Connection after the end has been cut off

Figure 69-5 Wrap a wet cloth around the valve body when soldering

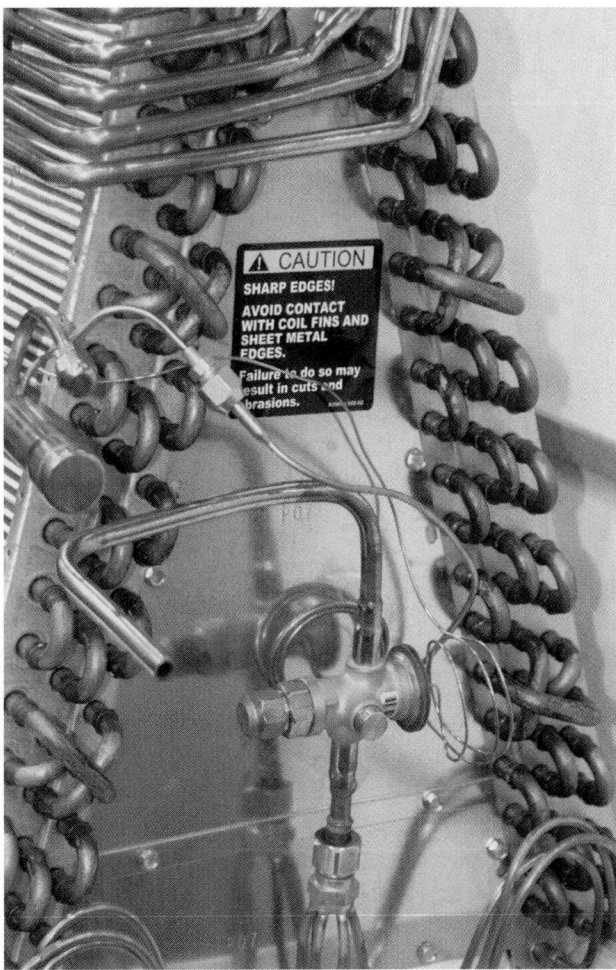

Figure 69-6 Route both the temperature sensing and pressure sensing lines

body and element during the soldering operation, Figure 69-5. After the proper fittings have been soldered, the thermostatic expansion valve can be installed. If the expansion valve is externally equalized, run both the temperature sensing and pressure sensing lines to the coil outlet, Figure 69-6.

Make sure that the TEV temperature sensing bulb is attached to the coil and properly insulated. The sensing bulb can be installed in a vertical or horizontal position as shown previously in Figure 69-3. The external equalizing connection is typically used on large evaporator sizes and should be located close to and downstream of the sensing bulb. On horizontal runs, the connection should be made to the top of the tube. On vertical runs, the connection should be made well above the beginning of the riser. Some DX coils have an oil return connection at the bottom of the suction header as shown previously in Figure 69-3. This is a small diameter line that will return oil to the compressor. Avoid installation techniques that allow for oil to collect in pockets that could lead to off cycle oil draining back and slugging of the compressor, Figure 69-7.

Staging and Hot Gas Bypass

Generally some type of staging control system is used. With a change in load demand, the compressor may be staged to start or stop. A liquid line solenoid valve can be used for capacity control. Another type of staging is unloading. Rather than allowing the compressor to continually cycle with demand, unloaders are often used to cut out individual compressor cylinders or banks of cylinders, Figure 69-8. Larger light commercial systems may require hot gas bypass for low load operation. The hot gas is introduced between the expansion valve and the distributor.

69.4 CHILLED WATER COOLING COILS

Chilled water systems are referred to as indirect expansion systems. A primary refrigerant will be used to remove heat from a secondary refrigerant in a chiller unit. The primary refrigerant remains in the chiller unit and operates on the normal refrigeration cycle. The secondary refrigerant (chilled water) will be pumped to the air handler cooling coils and

Figure 69-7 Compressor suction line connections to be avoided

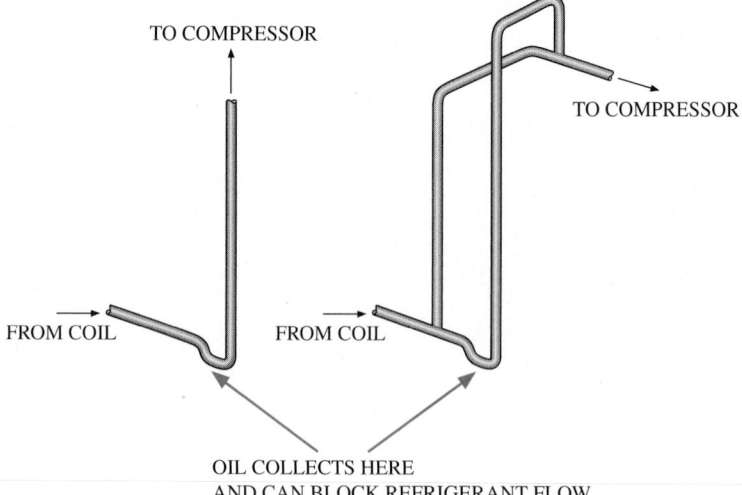

TO COMPRESSOR

TO COMPRESSOR

FROM COIL

FROM COIL

OIL COLLECTS HERE
AND CAN BLOCK REFRIGERANT FLOW

then return back to the chiller. An example of a chiller and air handler is shown in Figure 69-9.

The secondary refrigerant does not change state and expand when it removes heat from the air and so this type of system is known as indirect expansion. The secondary refrigerant is often a glycol and water mixture. The water should be of high quality, preferably distilled water, to avoid the build-up of scale on the inside tubing surfaces due to mineral deposits and sediments contained within the water. The glycol (antifreeze) will help to prevent freezing of the cooling coil if the outside air temperature drops too low. Coil freezeup thermostats can be installed to shut down the system if the air temperature drops below 36 °F. For cold weather winter conditions it is recommended that the coil be drained of water and flushed with antifreeze.

TECH TIP

In addition to protecting the cooling coil from freezing, glycol solutions generally have corrosion inhibitors added. These will protect the interior of the cooling coils and associated piping from prematurely rusting away. One drawback of glycol is that its specific heat is lower than that of water so it does not transfer heat as well.

Chilled water cooling coils are generally installed for counterflow. They should be piped so that the coldest water meets the coldest air. After installation, chilled water coils need to be purged of air through the bleed valve (vent).

69.5 HOT WATER COILS

Air handlers can be configured with both cooling and heating coils, Figure 69-10. The heating coil is located in the airstream before the cooling coil. This arrangement will help to reduce the possibility of the cooling coil freezing during cold weather conditions. Steam heating coils are more efficient than hot water heating coils, however furnaces that generate steam fall under stricter regulation and require more safety controls. Therefore many heating systems for residential and light commercial applications use circulated hot water rather than steam.

The hot water for the heating coil is normally supplied from a furnace and will circulate from the furnace to the air

Unloader

THIS UNIT CHARGED WITH
R-404A
CAUTION!

Figure 69-8 Compressor unloader solenoid

Figure 69-9 Chiller and air handler

handler and back again. This type of heating coil will have a bleed valve, Figure 69-11. Hot water coils should be piped for counterflow so that the warmest water meets the warmest air. The hot water loop will include an expansion tank and a fill connection. Similar to a cooling coil, high quality distilled water should be used for the circulated hot water to prevent scale formation on the inside of the coil surfaces.

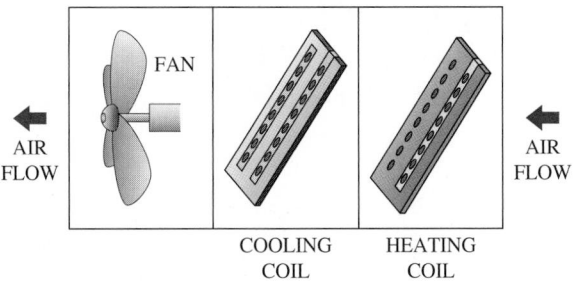

Figure 69-10 Horizontal flow configuration with heating and cooling coils

69.6 STEAM HEATING COILS

Steam heating coils will be smaller in physical size than a comparable hot water heating coil. This is because the coil not only transfers the sensible heat of the steam to the air but also the latent heat as the steam changes back to water within the heating coil. A steam trap is located at the outlet of the heating coil. To gain the most efficiency, it is important that the steam turn back to water, thereby giving up as much heat as possible before leaving the heating coil. The water formed from the steam condensing inside the heating coil is commonly referred to as condensate. The condensate will return to the boiler and be heated again to turn back into steam.

The water quality for this type of system is even more important than a chilled water or hot water loop. Since the water is boiling in the furnace, there is an even greater tendency for minerals and deposits to come out of the water and collect on the boiler heat transfer surfaces. It is essential that only high quality distilled water be used for this type of system.

Figure 69-11 Hot water coil with bleed vent

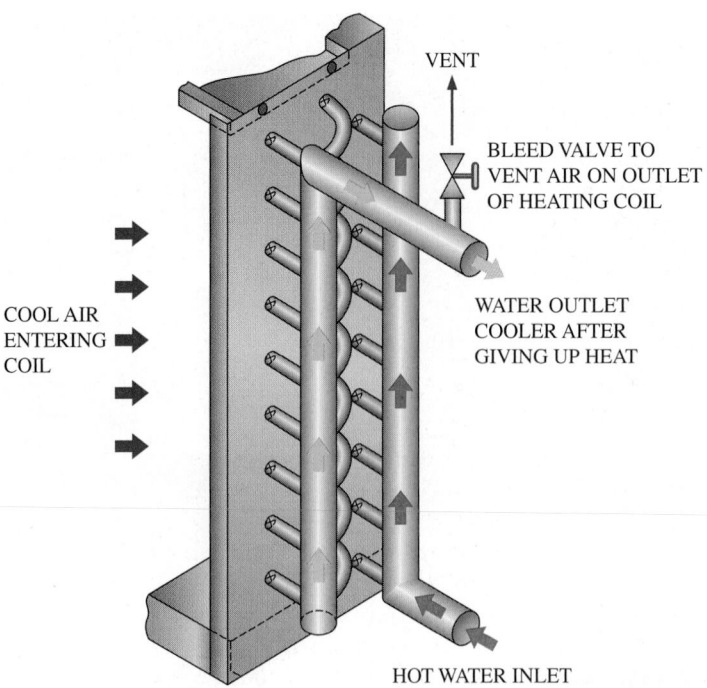

VENT

BLEED VALVE TO
VENT AIR ON OUTLET
OF HEATING COIL

COOL AIR
ENTERING
COIL

WATER OUTLET
COOLER AFTER
GIVING UP HEAT

HOT WATER INLET

SAFETY TIP

When working on a steam coil or steam trap, always make sure that the steam supply is shut off. Wear heavy gloves and a long sleeve shirt whenever disconnecting steam line components. Always bleed off any pressure in the line before opening or disconnecting components.

An advantage to a steam system is that circulating pumps are not required. In a hot water system, pumps must run to circulate the hot water to the heating coil and then back to the furnace. For steam systems, supply pumps are not required. The steam under pressure will travel through the piping and into the heating coil. The condensate leaves the heating coil through a steam trap. This is generally piped as a gravity or vacuum return to a condensate return tank, Figure 69-12. The condensate from the drain tank will be drawn off as feed water for the boiler by a feed water pump.

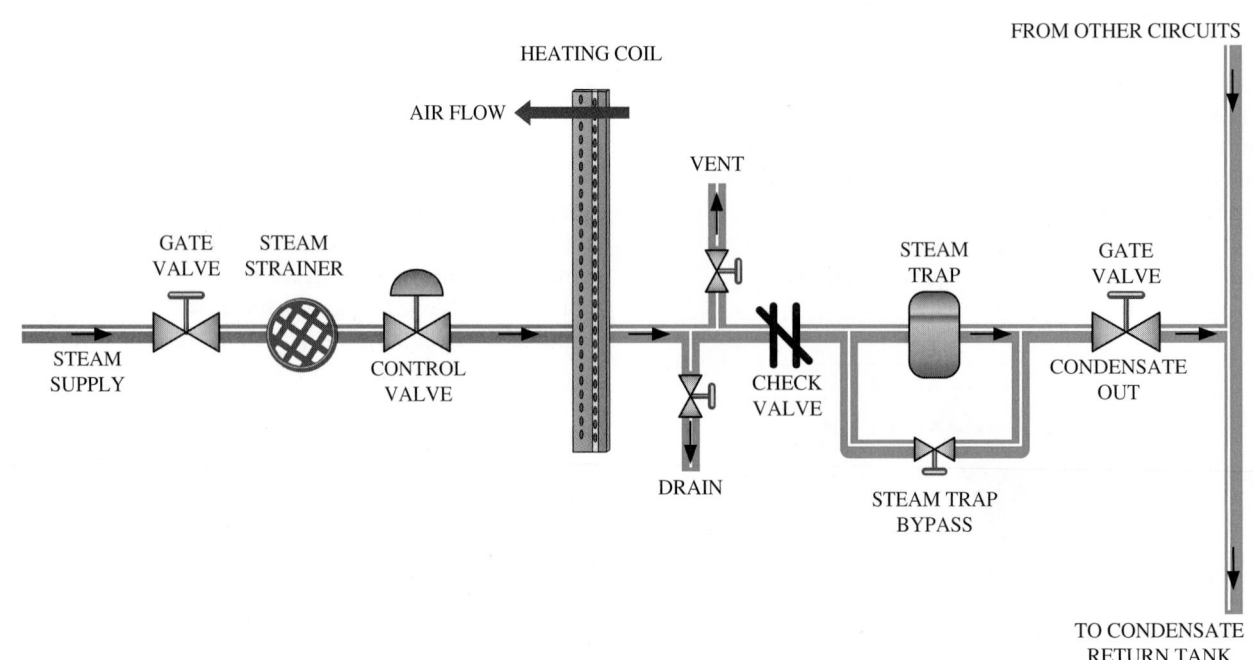

FROM OTHER CIRCUITS

HEATING COIL

AIR FLOW

VENT

STEAM
TRAP

GATE
VALVE

GATE
VALVE

STEAM
STRAINER

STEAM
SUPPLY

CONTROL
VALVE

CHECK
VALVE

CONDENSATE
OUT

DRAIN

STEAM TRAP
BYPASS

TO CONDENSATE
RETURN TANK

Figure 69-12 Steam coil supply and return

TECH TIP

Steam traps will generally have a bypass valve around them. If a steam trap happens to freeze in a stuck closed position, the steam flow through the coil will stop. The bypass valve can be opened to bring the coil temperature back up to normal and the trap can be isolated and replaced.

69.7 COIL CLEANING AND CORROSION

Chilled water, hot water, steam, and DX coil exterior surfaces must be cleaned regularly. The exterior surfaces of the coils are often finned to help increase the heat transfer surface area, Figure 69-13. The finned coils provide an opportunity for dirt and grime to collect. Dirty coils reduce heat transfer and lead to increased operating costs due to inefficiency. On direct expansion systems, a dirty coil can lead to liquid floodback and compressor slugging.

Water that forms and collects on the coil surface will drip off and fall into the drain pan located beneath the coil. Dirt and grease collecting on the fins and coil reduce the wettability of the coil surface. Rather than collecting on the coil and dripping into the drain pan, the water will be moved through the system with the air to potentially create moisture problems in other areas of the air distribution system. Surface grime and wet conditions can also lead to microbial growth (mold) which leads to foul odors and health related indoor air quality problems. Coils can be pressure cleaned with hot water and detergent or a commercial coil cleaner.

TECH TIP

If a chemical cleaning solution is used when cleaning the coil exterior surfaces, always make sure to rinse the coil surface thoroughly after the cleaning is complete.

Coil Corrosion

Corrosion can be caused by chemical, physical, or electrochemical reaction due to exposure from elements in the environment. Coils located in coastal and marine areas are subject to corrosion from sodium chloride (salt) that is carried by sea spray, mist, or fog. Units located near industrial areas may be exposed to corrosive emissions such as sulfur oxides (SO_2 and SO_3) and nitrogen oxides (NO_2) which lead to the formation of acid rain. In addition, dust particles containing harmful metal oxides, chlorides, sulfates, sulfuric acid, carbon, and carbon compounds may also be prevalent. Coils located in urban areas are susceptible to high sulfur oxide and nitrogen oxide levels generated from automobile and heating emissions.

The two common types of coil corrosion are galvanic and general corrosion. Galvanic corrosion occurs when two dissimilar metals are in contact with one another and an electrolyte is present. A coil with copper tubes and aluminum fins will be subject to galvanic corrosion in the presence of sodium or calcium chloride compounds. These are most commonly found in sea spray near coastal areas. Aluminum is a less noble metal than copper and so the fins will begin to deteriorate first.

General corrosion is caused by oxidation and chemical attack on the coil tubing surfaces. As an example, copper is susceptible to attack from gases containing sulfur. This leads to general corrosion that consumes some of the copper to form metal oxides on the tube surface. Eventually the copper tubing becomes thinner and thinner and turns brittle, resulting in tube failure, Figure 69-14.

There are a number of processes that can be applied to coils to reduce the potential for corrosion. Aluminum fin coils can be precoated with a durable epoxy coating for mildly corrosive environments. Aluminum fins may also be

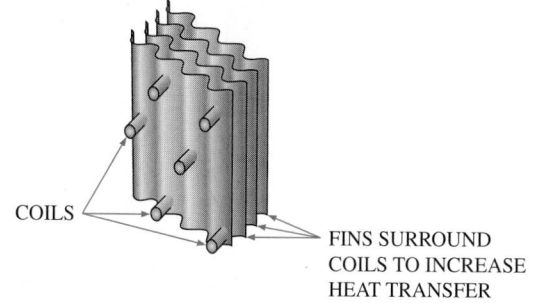

Figure 69-13 Standard finned coil construction

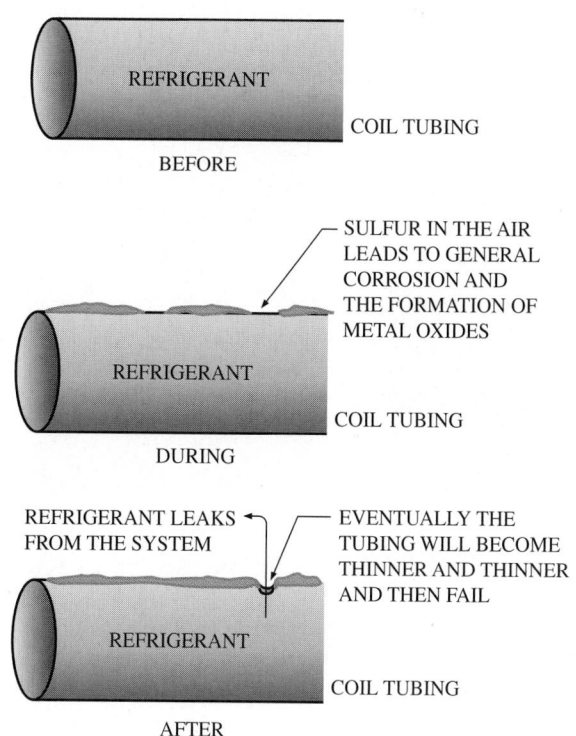

Figure 69-14 Coil tubing failure due to general corrosion

electrocoated through a multistep process that ensures the ultra clean coils are properly coated and cured. To reduce the chance of galvanic corrosion resulting from the use of dissimilar metals, copper fins rather than aluminum are mechanically bonded to copper tubes. A disadvantage, however, is that this type of coil can be rather expensive in comparison to standard aluminum fins. Manufacturers supply information to help determine which type of coil is best suited for any particular application.

69.8 ENERGY RECOVERY

Energy recovery units serve to precool and dehumidify the outdoor air during the cooling season and preheat and humidify it during the heating season. This provides for a cost savings while at the same time allowing for more outdoor air to be admitted to a space. Increased outdoor air will reduce the concentration of indoor pollutants and provide for better indoor air quality.

Air distribution systems are designed so that outdoor air is always admitted to the space being conditioned. The amount of outdoor air admitted is often directly related to the number of people that will normally be occupying the space. More outdoor air reduces indoor air contaminants, however increased outdoor air will require more energy for cooling or heating. As outdoor air is supplied to the space, an equal amount must be exhausted back outside to maintain a balance of air pressure within the space. An energy recovery system uses exhaust air leaving the building to preheat or precool the incoming outdoor air.

Most energy recovery units utilize an energy recovery wheel, Figure 69-15. The principal of operation is shown in

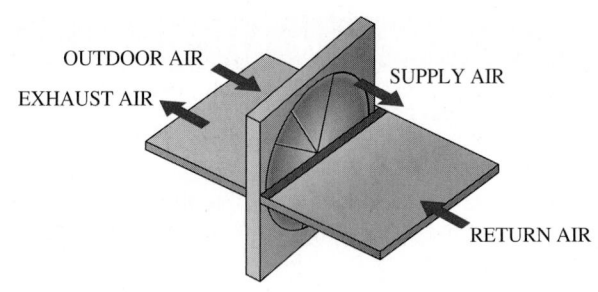

Figure 69-16 Flow through energy recovery wheel

Figure 69-16. The energy recovery wheel rotates and outdoor air passes across the top portion of the wheel while exhaust air passes across its bottom portion. During the summer months, the heat and moisture from the outdoor air will be transferred to the exhaust air. This is shown in Figure 69-17. For this particular application, the outdoor air temperature drops from 92°F to 79°F while the relative humidity still remains low. During the winter months, as shown for the application in Figure 69-18, the cold incoming outdoor air is preheated from 18°F to 59°F along with an increase in relative humidity.

Energy recovery sections for air handlers can be configured in a number of different ways. In colder climates, frost may form and eventually block the airflow through the energy

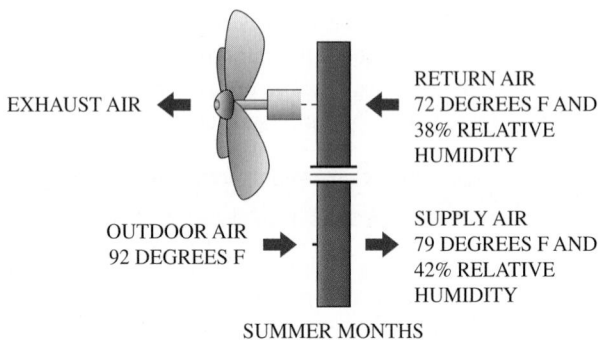

Figure 69-17 Energy wheel summer condition

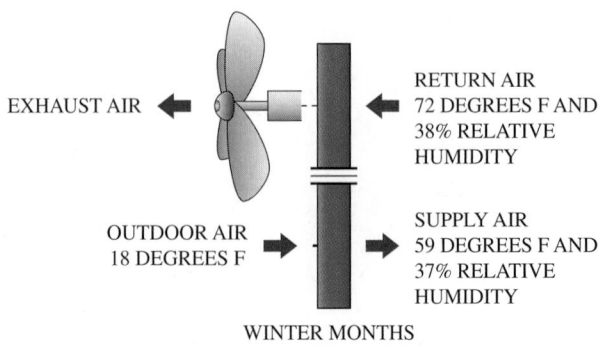

Figure 69-18 Energy wheel winter condition

Figure 69-15 Energy recovery wheel

recovery wheel. The methods for frost protection include the use of a preheat coil, a bypass for the wheel, on and off control, and exhaust only.

69.9 CONTROL SYSTEMS

The control system must direct the operation of all elements automatically. In large installations, the control system is usually separate from the air conditioning equipment. Controls may be electric, electronic, or pneumatic (air), or a combination of all three. The controls must be included in the initial construction stages to provide the total integration of the system.

CAUTION

Because these systems can be started and stopped automatically, you must make sure the power to the unit is off before beginning service to prevent the unit from starting while you are working on it.

Many air handlers will have an electronic control module installed in a control box located on the unit. The control module will continuously monitor inputs such as supply air temperature, return air temperature, air quality, space temperature, outdoor air temperature, duct static pressure, and space humidity. Dependent on the input, the control module is programmed to control outputs such as the supply fan, cooling and heating coil valves, mixed air dampers, electric heat, and direct expansion cooling. Multiple air handlers can be configured to be linked together.

Supply Fan Control

The supply fan can be started or stopped based upon a number of different programmable values. The fan can be set to turn on and off based upon the time the space is occupied, the temperature of the space, an unoccupied cool down or warm up period, and economizer cooling dependent on outside air conditions. Fans can be a constant speed constant volume, two speed variable volume, or variable frequency drive (VFD) variable volume.

Heating and Cooling Coil Control Valves

The heating or cooling coil control adjusts the steam, hot water, or chill water valve. Control valves are typically two way for steam and two way or three way for water. Control valves can come as normally open or normally closed. The correct sizing of proportional control valves is critical to proper system performance. An undersized valve will result in insufficient heating or cooling and damage from cavitation due to

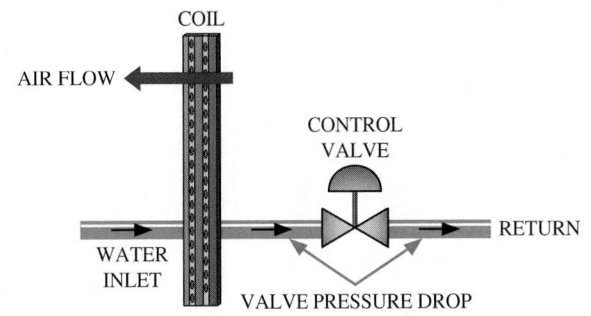

Figure 69-19 Coil two way valve

the excessive velocity through it. An oversized valve will also experience rapid wear of the seat and disc due to the increased velocity through a mostly closed valve. There will also be rapidly fluctuating temperatures and hunting especially at light loads for an oversized valve.

A typical installation for a two way control valve for a cooling coil chill water or a heating coil hot water loop is shown in Figure 69-19. The design pressure drop across the control valve is measured with the valve fully open. The recommended maximum pressure drop for two way and three way valves is 35 psig. Pressure drops in excess of this value can result in cavitation, erosion of discs, or wire drawing off the seat on a steam valve. Refer to the manufacturer's recommendations or valve sizing charts when selecting new valves or replacing existing valves in the system.

A three way valve installation is shown in Figure 69-20. The outlet from the coil is connected to the B port of the valve so that in this arrangement the valve will fail open allowing for full flow. Figure 69-21 shows an opposite arrangement where the control valve will fail closed thereby stopping all flow through the coil.

A two way steam control valve is shown in Figure 69-22. The steam valve modulates the flow of steam through the coil

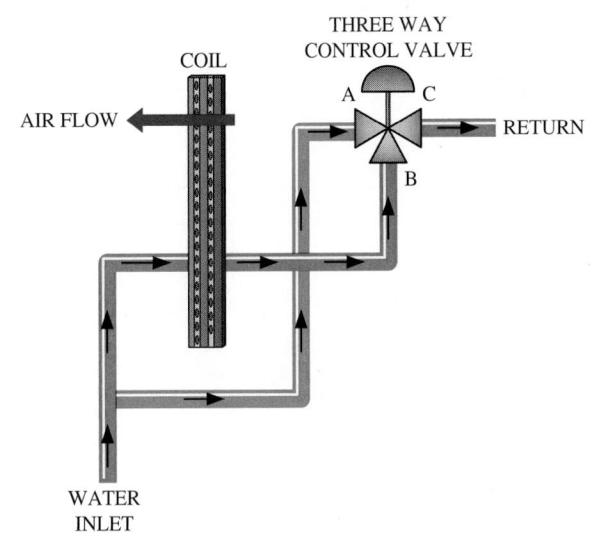

Figure 69-20 Coil three way valve—fails open as indicated in red

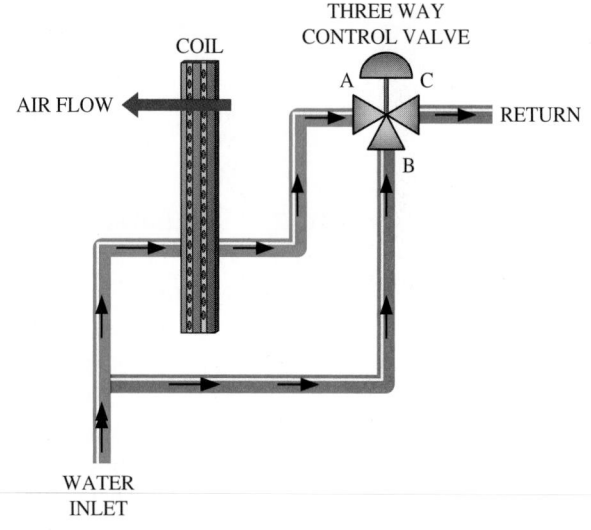

Figure 69-21 Coil three way valve—fails closed as indicated in red

based on the signal generated by the control. The pressure leaving the steam trap (system return pressure) is assumed to be zero. Low pressure steam applications are 15 psig or less. Medium steam pressure applications operate with steam pressures higher than 15 psig. Most steam control valves are designed to operate with steam pressure not exceeding 35 psig.

69.10 PNEUMATIC CONTROL SYSTEMS

In a basic control system for cooling, a thermostat sensing the chill water outlet temperature operates the chiller. Each air handler will have a control valve regulating the flow of chilled water through the cooling coil. The position of inlet, mixing, and bypass dampers will need to be controlled. The condenser cooling water pump will always be operating when the chiller is running. The cooling tower fan for the condenser

cooling water may cycle and often there may be a water bypass control.

For the heating system, boiler firing is activated by the hot water thermostat often referred to as an aquastat. Individual space thermostats and humidistats control the functions of the air handler.

Pneumatic control systems use compressed air to supply energy for the operation of valves, motors, relays, and other pneumatic control equipment. Consequently, the circuits consist of air piping, valves, orifices, and similar mechanical devices.

Pneumatic control systems offer some distinct advantages:

- They provide an excellent means of modulating control operation.
- They provide a wide variety of control sequences with relatively simple equipment.
- They are relatively free of operational problems.
- They cost less than electrical controls if the codes require electrical conduit.

Pneumatic controls are made up of the following elements:

- A constant supply of clean, dry, compressed air.
- Air lines consisting of mains and branches, usually copper or plastic, to connect the control devices.
- A series of controllers including thermostats, humidistats, humidity controllers, relays, and switches.
- A series of controlled devices including motors and valves called operators or actuators.

The air source is usually an electrically driven compressor, Figure 69-23, which is connected to a storage tank. The air pressure is maintained between fixed limits (usually between 20 and 35 psi for low pressure systems). Air leaving the tank is filtered to remove the oil and dust. Many installations use a small refrigeration system to dehumidify the air. Pressure reducing valves control the air pressure.

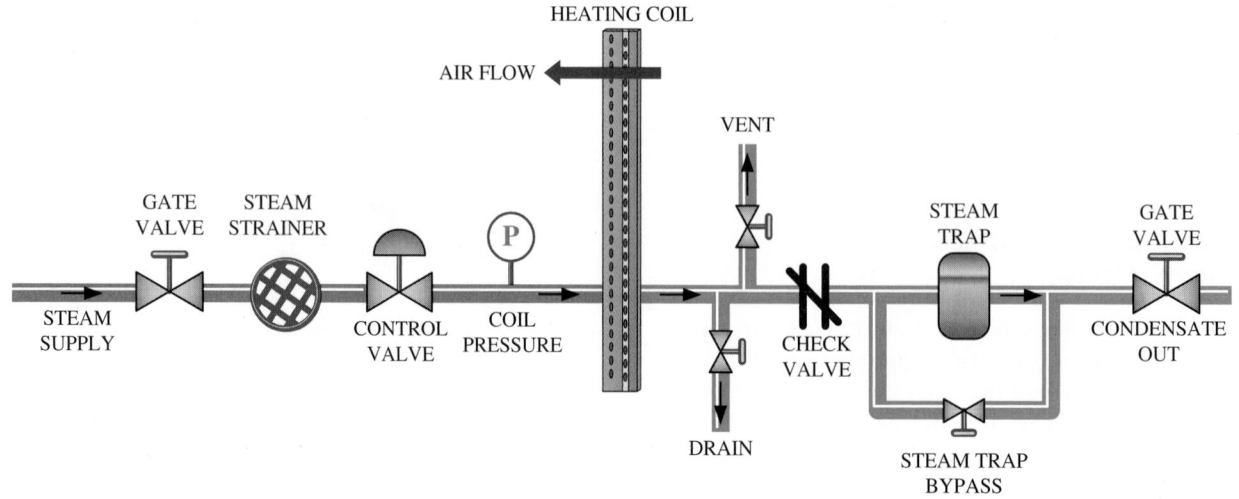

Figure 69-22 Heating coilsteam control valve

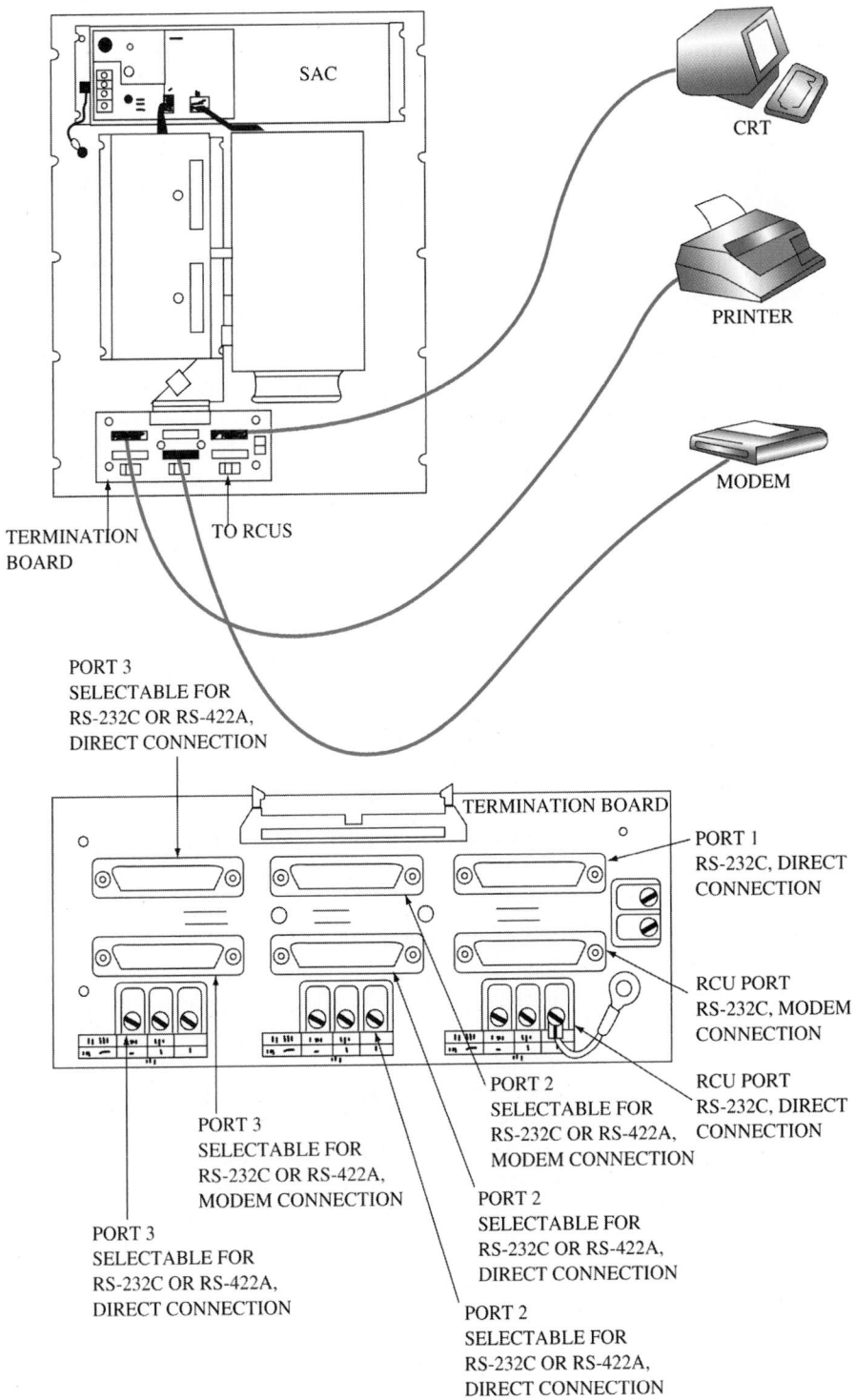

Figure 69-31 Stand alone controller (SAC)

between 0°F and 100°F. This input could be converted by the computer to produce an analog output signal to control a damper to any position between fully open and fully closed.

The digital function is a binary or two position function. For an input, the signal could monitor whether a switch is open or closed. For output, the binary signal could position the switch in either an ON or OFF position.

The SAC unit, RCU units, computer terminal, printer, and modem are all considered hardware. The control program,

which is programmed for an individual system, is called software. The software is installed in the SAC unit at the time that the DDC takes over the operation of the system. The operator periodically monitors the operation of the system through the computer, notes the reports and alarms, and makes any changes in the program that are considered advantageous.

The DDC systems are often called energy management systems since one of their main functions, and usually justification for their adoption, is saving energy. Special provision has been made in the selection of sensors to make possible continuous monitoring of the energy usage. The control system is set up to energize loads only when necessary and to use such features as free cooling (economizer operation) whenever possible.

The control center collects key operating data from the HVAC/R system and incorporates remote control devices to supervise the system's operation. The elaborateness of the data center is related to the type and size of the system and to economic considerations. Some control centers have continuous scanners with alarm indicators to monitor refrigeration machines, oil and refrigerant pressures, chilled water temperatures, air filter conditions, low water conditions in the boiler, and conventional space temperature and humidity conditions in each zone.

UNIT 69—SUMMARY

Air handlers come in many varied configurations and sizes. Many commercial and light commercial handlers are available in sectional units that can be put together like building blocks to meet the requirements for a specific application. All air handlers will have a fan and cooling/heating coils. However, the fan size, speed, and type of control will vary depending on the space requirements. There are also different types of coils. These can be direct expansion, chill water, hot water, or steam type. Energy recovery systems use the exhaust air leaving the space to preheat or precool the outside air being admitted to the space. Many control systems today are electronic; however, a combination of electric, electronic, and pneumatic controls can be used on large commercial systems.

WORK ORDERS

Service Ticket 6901

Customer Complaint: Compressors Run Constantly Even When the Outside Air Is Cool Enough for System to Be in Economizer Mode

Equipment Type: Light Commercial Air Handler with DX Coil and Economizer Package

The technician operated the system while doing a visual check. Even though the outside temperature was low enough for economizer operation, the compressor was not turning off and the outside air dampers (OA) were not opening. After examining the operation sequence and electrical diagram, the technician suspected a faulty economizer control thermostat. After testing, the technician proved that the control was defective. The technician replaced and set the thermostat. The technician then tested the system by placing the sensing bulb in icewater. The compressor cycled off and

the OA damper opened per the manufacturer's specifications. The system is now operating as designed.

Service Ticket 6902

Customer Complaint: System Has Shut Down Completely

Equipment Type: 100 Ton CHW and HW System with Pneumatic Control

The technician talks to the maintenance department and realizes there must be a complete shutdown of either the electrical power or the control system. The technician checked the electrical power and all the systems were energized. The technician checked the control system and found the control system air compressor was not running and the pressure was down to zero. Troubleshooting the air compressor revealed a bad pressure controller that would not allow the control air compressor to operate. After replacing the switch, the technician turned the compressor on and the system operated as designed.

Service Ticket 6903

Customer Complaint: The Third Floor of a Multistory Building Has Reported a "Cold Call"

Equipment Type: Air Handler with Heating and Cooling Operated From a Large Central Station Unit

The technician was taken to the area by a maintenance technician. The air handling unit was located in a third floor fan room. The technician connected the laptop computer to the ports furnished in the DDS controller located on the unit. The technician tried to cycle the unit from cool to heat and diagnosed a bad controller that would not cycle the damper, bring on the heating fan, or open the HW control valve. The technician replaced the DDS controller inside the control panel and the system now heats and cools as designed.

UNIT 69—REVIEW QUESTIONS

1. If a direct expansion coil delivered from the factory has lost its nitrogen pressure charge, what should be done?
2. How should an external equalizing line for a TEV be connected to a horizontal run?
3. List the different types of staging that can be used for air handler compressors using direct expansion coils.
4. What is the difference between a primary and a secondary refrigerant?
5. What type of water should be used in a chilled water system?
6. How should hot water heating coils be piped?

7. What happens if the steam trap at the outlet of a heating coil is stuck in the closed position?

8. Should heating and cooling coil exterior surfaces ever be cleaned?

9. What are the two common types of coil corrosion?

10. What happens when metal oxides are formed on the coil tube surfaces?

11. What is galvanic corrosion?

12. What is the function of an energy recovery unit?

13. What types of control valves are used for heating and cooling coils?

14. What can happen if the pressure drop through a heating or cooling coil control valve is excessive?

15. List some of the advantages of pneumatic control systems.

16. What is background power?

17. What are some of the advantages of electronic control systems?

18. List some electronic temperature sensing elements.

19. What acts as the primary control for all HVAC/R functions in a direct digital control (DDC) system?

20. What is a sensor?

UNIT 70
Chiller Water Systems

OBJECTIVES

After completing this unit you will be able to:

- describe the difference between a flooded and a dry (direct expansion) type chiller.
- explain why low pressure chillers need purge recovery.
- explain why some chillers are better suited for air cooled condensers while others operate with water cooled condensers.
- list the different types of compressor arrangements found on chillers.
- describe the function of a chiller economizer.
- describe the operation for an oil return system for a chiller.
- transfer refrigerant to and from a chiller.
- explain how an absorption chiller operates.

70.1 INTRODUCTION

In a large multistory building or complex it is impractical to deliver refrigerant long distances from a central air conditioning compressor and condensing unit. Excessive energy would be required for the compressor to deliver the refrigerant to different air handlers located on different levels of the building. Any leaks in the system could lead to a substantial loss of refrigerant before they could be detected.

The more common way to deliver refrigerant to individual air handlers is to use a secondary refrigerant such as chilled water. The chilled water is cooled in a central station chiller by a primary refrigerant. The chilled water is then delivered throughout the building to individual air handlers by circulating pumps, Figure 70-1. Any leaks in this system are easily detected. The primary refrigerant does not leave the central air conditioning unit.

70.2 FLOODED AND DRY TYPE WATER CHILLERS

The water in a chiller is cooled to approximately 43–45°F. The chilled water pump circulates the chilled water supply (CHWS) to the cooling coil in the air handler. The chilled water loop will have an expansion tank and fill connections for make-up water, and it will also have air vents, balancing valves, and cooling coil flow controls as shown in Figure 70-2. The heat absorbed from the air by the cooling coil warms the water about 10°F at full load, with a chilled water return (CHWR) temperature of 53–55°F.

The cooler section is the evaporator where the primary refrigerant changes state and absorbs heat from the chilled water. The cooler section, often referred to as the chiller, is often cylindrical in shape and of the shell and tube design. A "dry" direct expansion type cooler will circulate the refrigerant through the inside of the tubes and the chilled water will

Figure 70-1 Chill water cooling loop from central unit to multiple zones

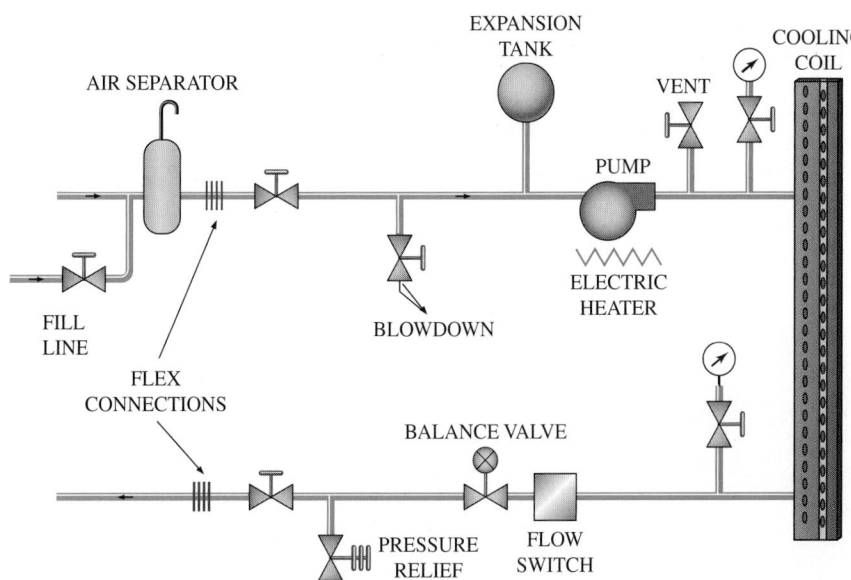

Figure 70-2 Chill water cooling loop for cooling coil

Figure 70-3 Centrifugal compressor chiller

surround the tubes. For larger tonnage units, flooded coolers are more commonly used. In a flooded cooler, the refrigerant surrounds the tubes and the chilled water is circulated through the inside of the tubes. Flooded coolers have greater cooling capacities, however they require more refrigerant and have a greater potential for freeze-up as compared to direct expansion coolers. Figure 70-3 shows a centrifugal compressor chiller with a flooded cooler and subcooler section.

70.3 LOW PRESSURE CHILLERS

The chilled water temperature for an air conditioning system should not fall much below 40°F. A temperature sensor located in the chill water circuit provides an input signal to the compressor operation and capacity controls. Many systems will automatically shut down if the chill water temperature drops to 35°F. Low pressure refrigerants are those that have boiling points of 50°F or above. This high boiling temperature would not be suitable for low temperature applica-

tions; however, it is suitable for chiller applications. To achieve the desired refrigerant temperature, many chillers operate with suction pressures below atmospheric pressure.

For large air conditioning loads, a considerable amount of refrigerant must be circulated by the compressor. Centrifugal compressors are able to pump large volumes of refrigerant as compared to reciprocating compressors. However, they do not develop the high side discharge pressures of a reciprocating compressor. Since low pressure refrigerants do not require such high discharge pressures, they are ideally suited for centrifugal chiller applications.

70.4 PURGE RECOVERY UNITS

A low pressure chiller will operate with a negative suction pressure below atmospheric. Any leaks in the system will draw in air. This air typically collects in the top section of the condenser. The air will increase the discharge pressure of the unit and lead to a higher power consumption of the compressor. The air will also contain water which will oxidize the oil in the system and lead to the formation of sludge and acids. Chillers of this type generally have some type of purge recovery unit. This unit will purge the air from the top of the condenser and recover the refrigerant on a continuous basis while the chiller is running.

70.5 LEAK TESTING LOW PRESSURE CHILLERS

Leak testing a low pressure chiller is difficult because air will be leaking in rather than refrigerant leaking out. One way to check for refrigerant leaks in a low pressure chiller is to raise the temperature of the chill water. The unit is shut down and the chill water is heated and circulated through the cooler. This will raise the pressure in the unit above atmospheric pressure so that a conventional leak detector can be used to find any refrigerant leaks.

CAUTION

Never allow a low pressure chiller to reach or exceed the rupture disk setting when testing for leaks. The rupture disk setting for low pressure chillers is normally set at 15 psig, however it is advisable not to exceed 10 psig. If this happens, then the chiller rupture disk will release and all of the refrigerant in the unit will be lost, Figure 70-4.

Figure 70-4 Centrifugal compressor suction side rupture disk

Figure 70-5 Package chiller with reciprocating compressor

70.6 RECIPROCATING COMPRESSOR CHILLERS

Air Cooled Condensers

Starting at the lower capacities, packaged water chillers use one or more reciprocating compressors. Figure 70-5 shows an example of a small air cooled chiller in the 30 ton range. This type of unit would be mounted directly outside or on a rooftop with supply and return connections for the chilled water piped into the building. For head (discharge) pressure control, the condenser fan control receives input from a pressure transducer, Figure 70-6. The fans are maintained at the lowest condensing pressure and temperature possible to maintain the highest unit efficiency.

The coolers for this type of unit are typically the "dry" direct expansion type. Refrigerant flows through the tubes and will generally make two passes for standard operation, which provides a counterflow arrangement, opposite to the typical chilled water flow pattern. The cooler shell is suspended beneath the condenser coil and fan section. The cooler shell (evaporator) must be protected from freezing. Electric heating elements are wrapped around the shell and then covered with a thick layer of insulation. Some manufacturers also add a final protective metal jacket that doubles as a good vapor barrier.

amount of oil collecting in the bottom of the cooler is allowed to pass to the vaporizer section. Hot gas from the condenser passes through a coil located in the vaporizer. This will vaporize any liquid refrigerant that has been carried over with the oil. The refrigerant vapor is allowed to pass through a mist eliminator to reduce the possibility of an oil slug before returning to the suction side of the compressor. The oil then passes from the vaporizer to the oil sump where an electric heater is utilized to further vaporize any refrigerant liquid entrained in the oil. A second mist eliminator directs the refrigerant vapor from the oil sump back to the suction side of the compressor.

70.17 CHILLER REFRIGERANT RECOVERY AND TRANSFER

Periodically chillers may need to be pumped down for servicing. Unlike some commercial systems that utilize receivers, there is no place to transfer the refrigerant other than an external storage tank. The external storage tank or receiver should be of sufficient size to hold the entire charge of refrigerant and it should be rated for the same or a higher maximum working pressure as the system. Some systems have external receivers that can be used for multiple chiller circuits.

> ### CAUTION
>
> Always begin the refrigerant transfer from a chiller unit using liquid recovery methods. If vapor is transferred from the chiller while liquid still remains, the chiller will freeze up and the tubes will crack to cause extensive damage to the chiller. Circulate chill water and condenser cooling water through the unit during the recovery process to reduce the possibility of freeze-up.

An example of a transfer arrangement is shown in Figure 70-19a,b. This system is permanently installed and can be used to transfer refrigerant from multiple chiller circuits. Chillers that do not have permanently installed transfer systems will require a portable unit. This is different from conventional portable recovery units because of the valve arrangement.

> ### CAUTION
>
> Do not mix refrigerants from chillers that use different compressor oils.

Always transfer liquid refrigerant first. Using Figure 70-19a as an example, the valve arrangement will be lined up with valves two and five open. This will allow the recovery compressor to draw suction from the top of the storage tank through valve five and deliver high pressure vapor to the top of the chiller cooler or condenser through valve two. Valves three and four will remain closed. During this liquid transfer, the recovery condenser will be inactive. The vapor entering the top of the chiller cooler or condenser will force liquid out of the bottom and to the storage tank.

> ### CAUTION
>
> During transfer, never fill a storage tank to more than 80% of capacity to allow room for expansion.

After all of the liquid has been removed from the chiller, the valve alignment will be changed for the vapor recovery portion of the transfer as shown in Figure 70-19b. Valves two and five will now be closed and valves three and four will be opened. Cooling water flow will be established to the recovery condenser. The recovery compressor will draw suction from the top of the chiller cooler or condenser through valve three. The vapor from the discharge of the recovery compressor will condense to liquid as it passes through the recovery condenser and continue through valve four and to the storage tank. The recovery compressor will shut down on the low pressure cutout once the refrigerant recovery is complete. The required evacuation level is 7 psia or 15 in Hg vacuum for high pressure chillers and 0.5 psia or 29 in Hg vacuum for low pressure chillers.

> ### CAUTION
>
> Never charge liquid into a chiller that is in a deep vacuum. The refrigerant will immediately flash and the chiller will freeze up and the tubes will crack to cause extensive damage to the chiller. During the initial charge, add vapor until the chiller pressure equates to a saturation temperature above 32°F. As an example, R-123 has a saturated pressure of 5.1 psia (19.5 in Hg vacuum) at 35°F. The chiller should be at that pressure or above before introducing liquid R-123. Circulate chill water and condenser cooling water through the unit during the charging process to reduce the possibility of freeze-up.

Figure 70-19 (a) Liquid recovery first (b) Vapor recovery follows liquid recovery

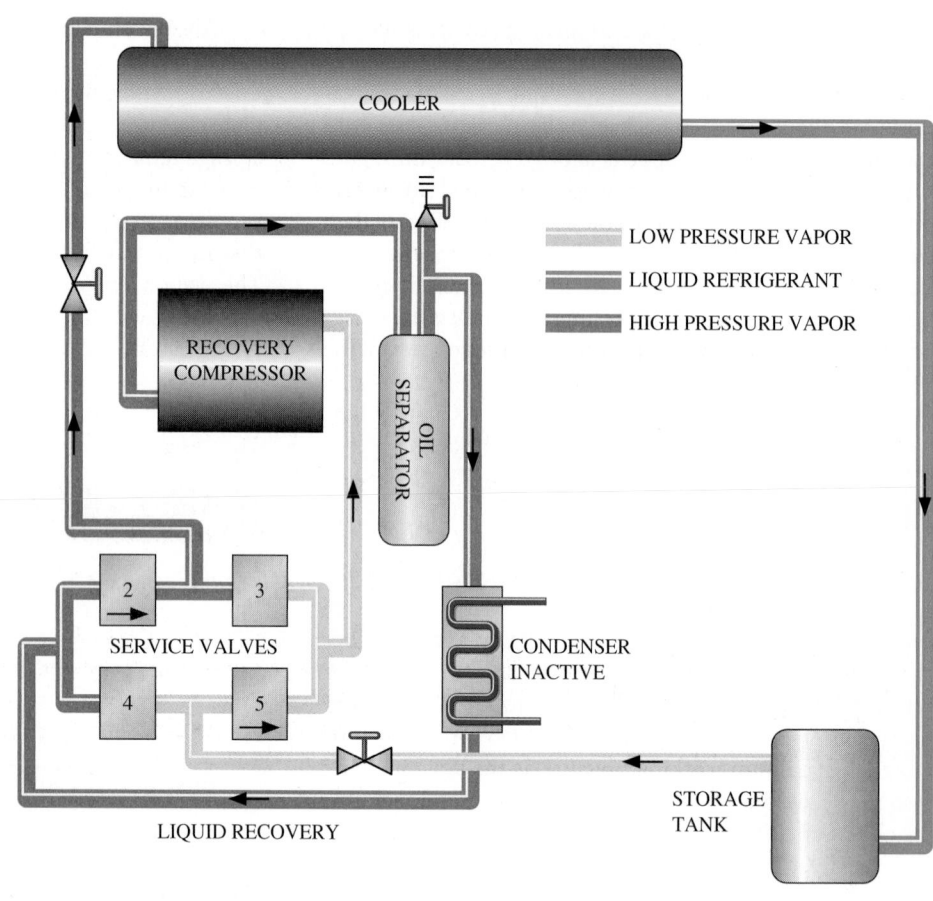

(a)

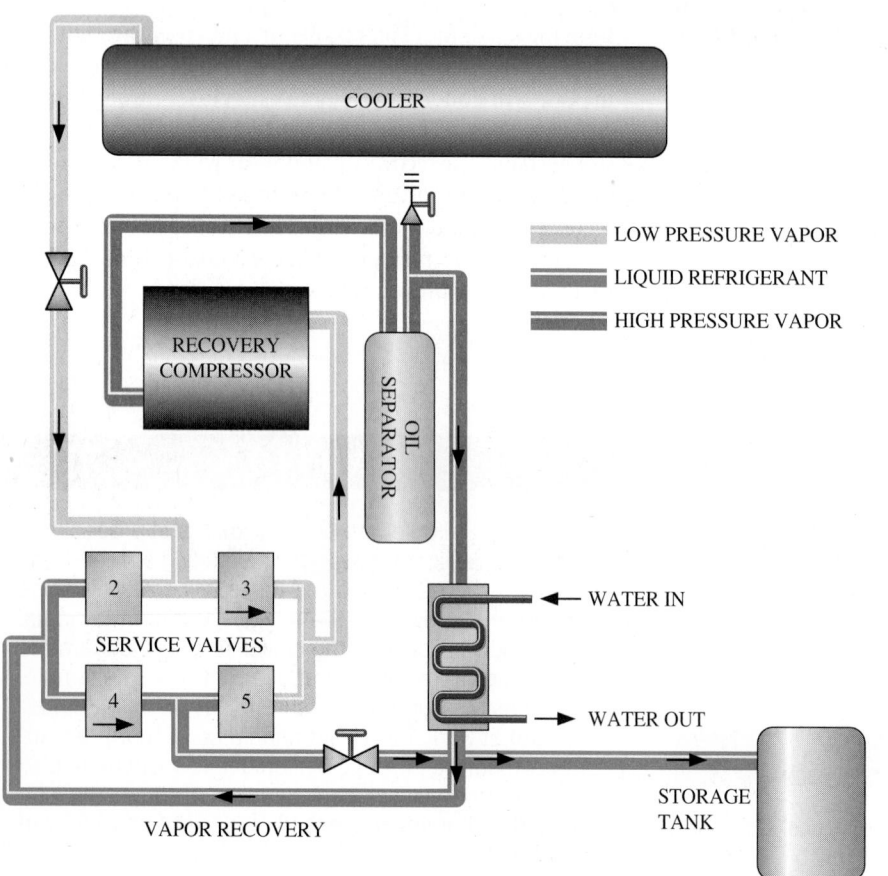

(b)

CAUTION

It is not easy to drain all of the fluid out of hydronic system pipes for service. Sometimes water can be trapped and then be released suddenly as the result of vibration from shaking the pipe or when air breaks the siphon. It is important when working on electrical components such as pump motors that you make certain that the power to the pump is off and all the water in the system has been removed. A sudden gush of water can create a major safety hazard from electric shock if these precautions are not taken.

71.4 HYDRONIC SYSTEM RESIDENTIAL APPLICATIONS

A hydronic heating system for residential use often includes a gas or oil fired boiler. The boiler will be piped with the proper accessories to allow for expansion, water make-up, and mixing valves for different types of zone heating applications. This typical arrangement is shown in Figure 71-1. The hot water leaves the boiler through a 2 in supply valve and is circulated throughout the building. The water returns to the boiler from a 2 in return line and through a circulating pump. In this example, the water is pressure fed into the boiler by the circulator pump. There are a number of different design types with another common example being a straight gravity return line without a circulating pump. Also note the expansion tank and an air vent located in the return line. The cold water inlet is for the make-up water. This will be connected to the house water supply plumbing. A pressure reducing valve is used to regulate the water admitted into the boiler. The boiler is equipped with a pressure relief valve. There are shut-off valves to isolate different parts of the system, as well as drain lines for use when servicing or repairing the system.

71.5 TERMINAL UNITS

Terminal units transfer heat from the hot water to the various building areas. The heat supplied by these units is controlled to provide comfortable conditions. Normally this equipment is rated in Btu/hr or MBtu/hr; however, these ratings can be stated in terms of equivalent direct radiation (EDR). For hot water systems 1 ft^2 EDR = 150 Btu, based on an average water temperature of 170°F. Hot water units are rated based on the water temperature drop through the unit, which can by 10–30°F. A number of types of terminal heating units are available, including: baseboard units, convectors, fan coil units, and radiators.

TECH TIP

The term radiator has been a commonly used term for heating systems. Although this term is commonly accepted, it is misleading because it implies that the heat transfer is through radiation, which is incorrect. Heat transfer from terminal units is through conduction (heat transfer through a solid substance) and convection (heat transfer through a fluid). This means that air circulation for convective heat transfer is critical for proper operation. Radiant floor heating also has this same type of misleading terminology; and heat transfer for this type of installation likewise depends on convection and conduction. A radiant floor heating system placed beneath a thick carpet will be less efficient than a radiant heating system placed beneath a tile floor due to the conductive heat transfer properties of the different materials.

Baseboard Units

Baseboard units are installed near the floor on the outside walls of each room. Heat is supplied by conduction and convection. The heating element is finned tube construction or cast

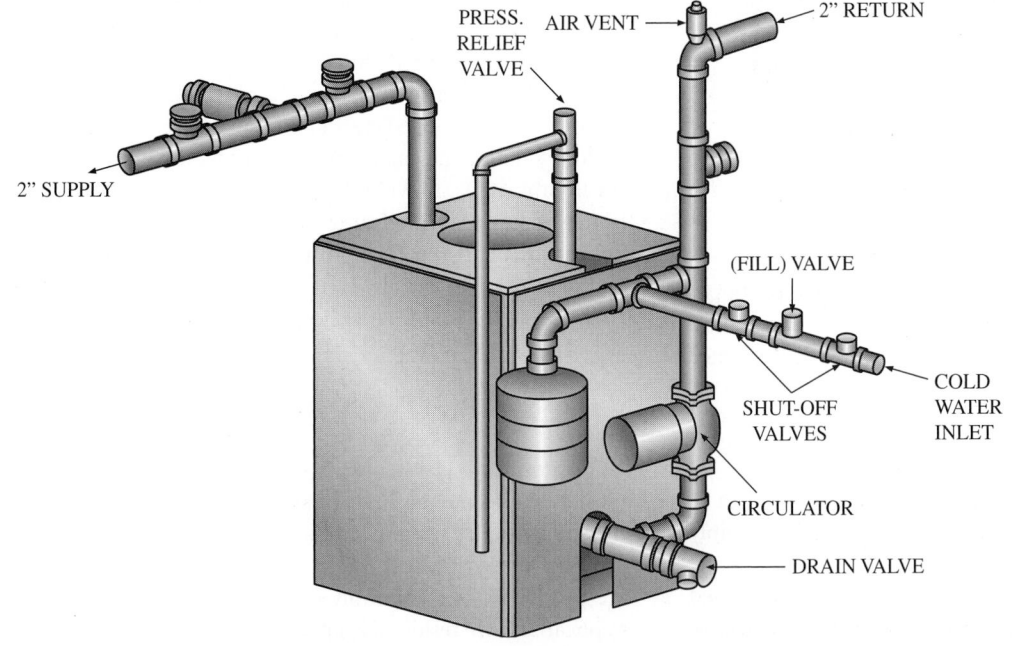

Figure 71-1 Hydronic boiler piping arrangement

PRESS. RELIEF VALVE

AIR VENT

2" RETURN

2" SUPPLY

(FILL) VALVE

COLD WATER INLET

SHUT-OFF VALVES

CIRCULATOR

DRAIN VALVE

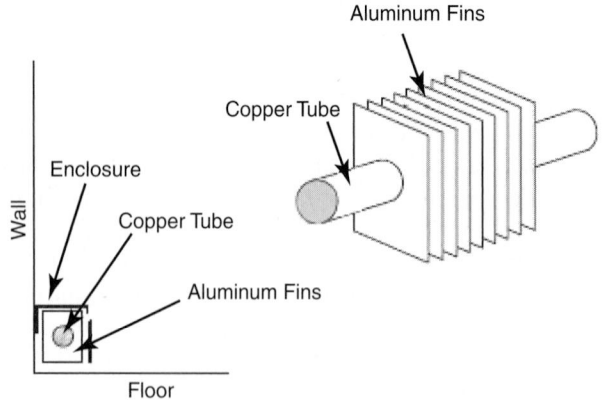

Figure 71-2 Baseboard radiation
(From Climate Master Water to Water System Design Guide, page 27, Figure 2-12. Copyright Climate Master, Inc. By permission.)

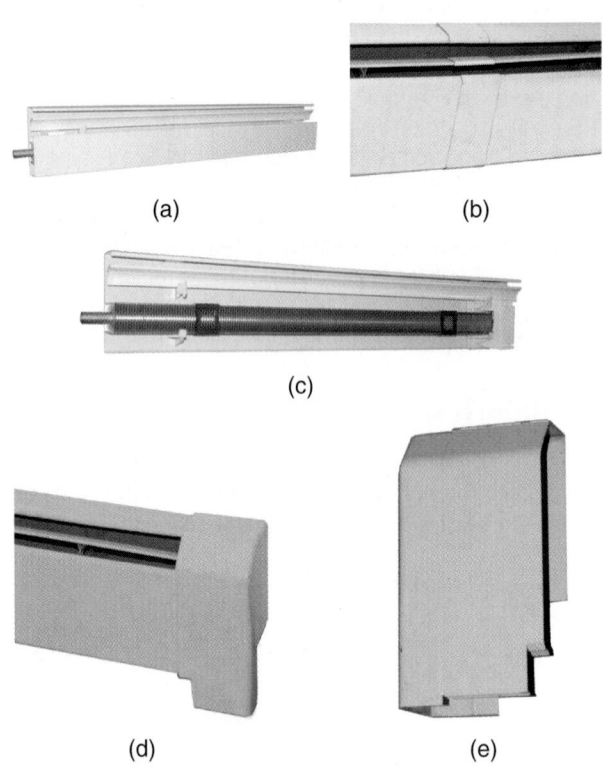

Figure 71-3 Trim pieces for baseboard enclosures

iron. The most common units have elements using copper tube and aluminum fins as shown in Figure 71-2. A typical finned tube along with accessory pieces for corners and ends is shown in Figure 71-3a–e.

Convector Units

Convector units such as the one shown in Figure 71-4 can be freestanding or recessed. These units heat the room mainly by convection, with the air entering the bottom and leaving from the upper front. The freestanding model is supplied either with a flat or slanting top. An adjustable damper can be supplied if desired.

Fan Coil Units

Fan coil units as shown in Figure 71-5 can serve the same function as convectors, but have additional features and increased efficiency. The unit has a centrifugal fan with manual speed control for circulating the room air through the unit. Air filters are standard equipment. The unit is often used for both heating and cooling. Outside air can be supplied through the back of the unit. Units are available with air volume ratings from 200–1200 CFM and hot water heating capacities from 7.6–112 MBtu/hr.

Radiators

Cast iron radiators are primarily used for steam installations, Figure 71-6. They were used more frequently in past years. Hydronic systems are sometimes configured to work with existing cast iron radiators. These typically operate with water temperatures of 125–200°F.

71.6 RADIANT FLOOR HEATING

Radiant floor heating has been recently growing in popularity although this type of heating has a long history. The Romans were the first to use this type of heating. The American architect Frank Lloyd Wright used radiant floor heating in many of his home designs from the 1930s. Radiant floor heating is more comfortable than conventional heating because it directs the heat to the occupant level and less heat is wasted up near the ceiling level as shown in Figure 71-7. There are also no baseboards or radiator panels offering obstruction to furniture. This allows for more effective use of wall space within the room. Radiant floor heating is also quiet when compared to the fan noise levels found with a forced hot air system.

Radiant heat piping will have a number of heating loops distributed through a manifold as shown in Figure 71-8. Often cross-linked polyethylene pipe is used because it is flexible and relatively easy to connect. The piping can be placed into the poured concrete slab for the building. This works well as the entire slab heats evenly to provide for a continuous and prolonged heat sink. For upper stories of the building, the piping can be installed under the floor through the floor joists as shown in Figure 71-9. This type of installation can be performed after the building is complete by drilling through the floor joists and installing the piping, Figure 71-10. This can also be installed during the initial construction of the building as shown in Figure 71-11.

71.7 TYPES OF PIPING SYSTEMS

Hot water heating systems can be installed with a variety of piping arrangements. Each of these arrangements controls the supply of hot water from the boiler to the terminal units (and the return) in such a way that comfortable conditions are produced. The common systems for hot water heating applications in residential and small commercial installations are each briefly explained.

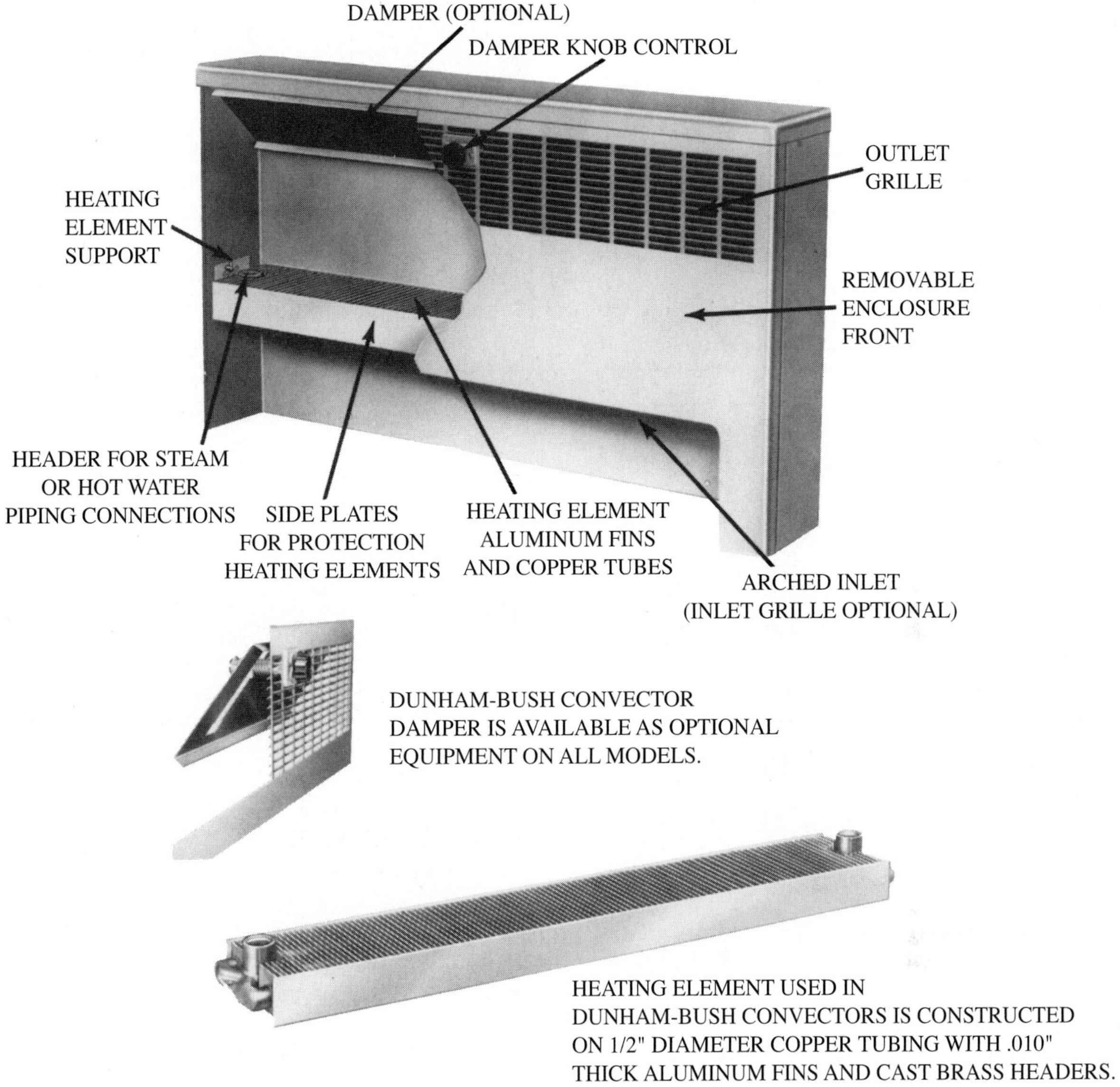

DAMPER (OPTIONAL)
DAMPER KNOB CONTROL
OUTLET GRILLE
HEATING ELEMENT SUPPORT
REMOVABLE ENCLOSURE FRONT
HEADER FOR STEAM OR HOT WATER PIPING CONNECTIONS
SIDE PLATES FOR PROTECTION HEATING ELEMENTS
HEATING ELEMENT ALUMINUM FINS AND COPPER TUBES
ARCHED INLET (INLET GRILLE OPTIONAL)
DUNHAM-BUSH CONVECTOR DAMPER IS AVAILABLE AS OPTIONAL EQUIPMENT ON ALL MODELS.
HEATING ELEMENT USED IN DUNHAM-BUSH CONVECTORS IS CONSTRUCTED ON 1/2" DIAMETER COPPER TUBING WITH .010" THICK ALUMINUM FINS AND CAST BRASS HEADERS.

Figure 71-4 Typical convector

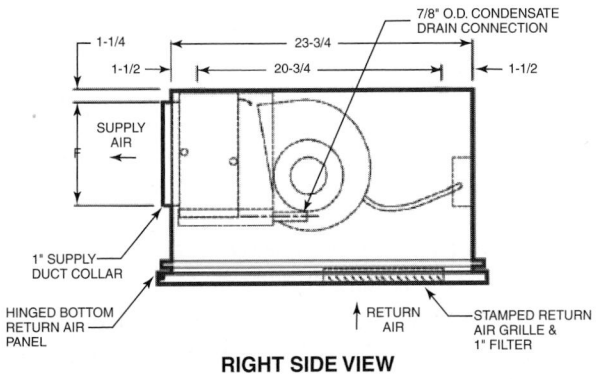

7/8" O.D. CONDENSATE DRAIN CONNECTION
1-1/4
23-3/4
1-1/2
20-3/4
1-1/2
SUPPLY AIR
F
1" SUPPLY DUCT COLLAR
HINGED BOTTOM RETURN AIR PANEL
RETURN AIR
STAMPED RETURN AIR GRILLE & 1" FILTER
RIGHT SIDE VIEW

Figure 71-5 Horizontal fan coil
(From Climate Master Water to Water System Design Guide, page 29, Figure 2-14. Copyright Climate Master, Inc. By permission.)

W
H

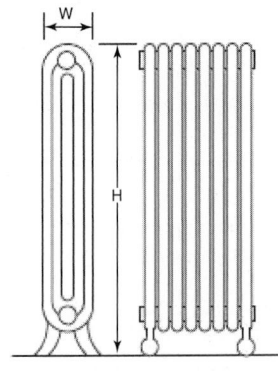

Figure 71-6 Cast iron radiator
(From Climate Master Water to Water System Design Guide, page 28, Figure 2-14. Copyright Climate Master, Inc. By permission.)

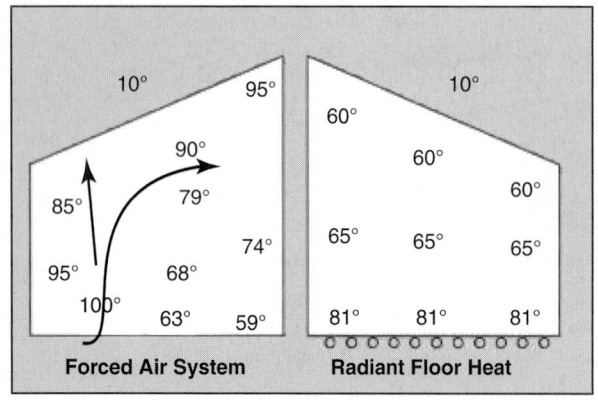

Figure 71-7 Radiant floor temperature comparison
(From Climate Master Water to Water System Design Guide, page 26, Figure 2-10a. Copyright Climate Master, Inc. By permission.)

Figure 71-8 Radiant floor manifold
(From Climate Master Water to Water System Design Guide, page 27, Figure 2-11. Copyright Climate Master, Inc. By permission.)

Figure 71-9 Radiant under floor heating
(Courtesy of MacDuffo Manufacturing)

Series Loop, Single Circuit

The series loop system is probably the simplest of all the piping arrangements. A schematic diagram of the single circuit piping layout is shown in Figure 71-12. In this pip-

Figure 71-10 Installing radiant under floor heating
(Courtesy of MacDuffo Manufacturing)

Figure 71-11 New construction installation of radiant floor heating
(Courtesy of MacDuffo Manufacturing)

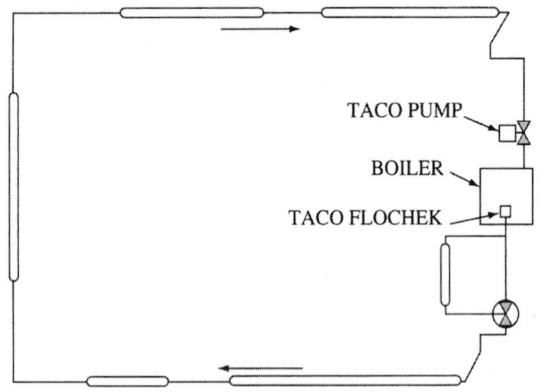

Figure 71-12 Series loop piping layout, single circuit
(Courtesy of Taco, Inc., Cranston, Rhode Island)

ing system, the main supply pipe from the boiler enters the first baseboard unit. The outlet from the first unit is connected directly to the inlet of the second unit. This arrangement is continued until all baseboard sections are connected in series. The outlet from the last section is connected to the circulator pump, which connects to the boiler. Thus, all the water flowing through the system passes through each unit.

In many cases the bathroom or kitchen does not have enough wall space for the proper length of baseboard heating. In this case a convector is used in place of the baseboard. The convector can be tied to the system using a venturi fitting as can be seen in Figure 71-12. The convector is the first terminal unit after the boiler. The venturi is simply a restriction in the line that ensures that some water will flow through the convector which is in parallel with the other terminal units in the circuit.

When these systems are installed, the entire perimeter of the building has baseboard enclosures. The amount of finned tube element placed in these enclosures is dependent on heat loss requirements. Where the main pipe passes a doorway, an offset is made in the piping to run it down below the floor until it passes the door opening to come up again on the other side.

With this piping arrangement, each downstream unit is supplied with cooler water than the preceding one. The actual hot water temperature drop between terminal units is about 2°F. To compensate for this, each successive unit is oversized by about 2%. The use of a series loop system reduces the cost of the installation to a minimum.

Series Loop, Double Circuit

On larger systems, better performance can be obtained by dividing the system into two (or more) approximately equal circuits, such as the example in Figure 71-13. When this is done, balancing valves are installed in each branch to permit adjustment of the flow.

One Pipe Venturi System, Single Circuit

The one pipe venturi fitting system has a single main line extending from the supply to the return connection of the

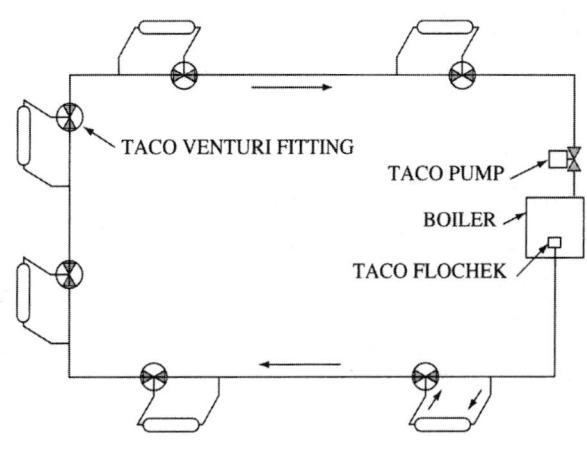

Figure 71-14 One pipe venturi system, single circuit
(Courtesy of Taco, Inc., Cranston, Rhode Island)

boiler. The terminal units are fed by a supply and return branch connected to the main as shown in Figure 71-14. The supply connection uses a standard tee and the return connection uses a special venturi fitting. The venturi creates a negative pressure at the main connection, drawing the necessary flow through the branch.

This system differs from the series loop in that only a portion of the total flow enters the terminal unit. There is still a temperature drop in the main line as it reaches the location of successive units. The reduced flow, however, improves the performance of the terminal units.

One Pipe Venturi Unit, Double Circuit

On larger systems using this piping arrangement, better performance can be obtained by dividing the system into two (or more) approximately equal circuits, as shown in Figure 71-15. When this is done, balancing valves are installed in each branch to permit adjusting flow.

Two Pipe System, Direct Return

In the two pipe system, separate supply and return mains are used. The return water from the terminal units is collected and returned to the boiler. With this piping arrangement, each unit will receive the same supply water temperature.

With the direct return, the two mains are run side by side with a supply branch run to each unit from the supply main and a return branch run from each unit to the return main. The first unit taken off the supply main is the first unit on the return main before it reaches the boiler, Figure 71-16. Obviously, the shortest piping is used on the unit nearest the boiler. The longest piping is used on the unit farthest from the boiler. This difference in piping pressure drop must be equalized by using a square head cock in either the supply or return branch to each unit.

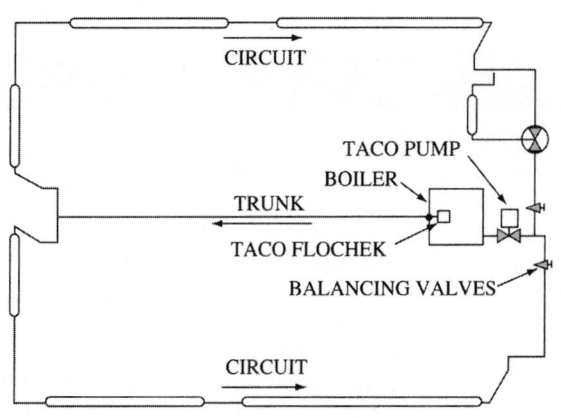

Figure 71-13 Series loop piping layout, double circuit
(Courtesy of Taco, Inc., Cranston, Rhode Island)

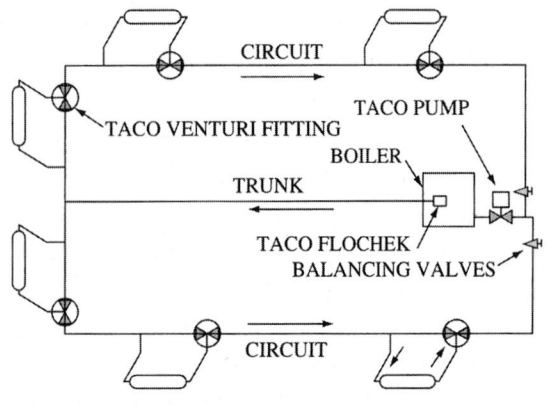

Figure 71-15 One pipe venturi system, double circuit
(Courtesy of Taco, Inc., Cranston, Rhode Island)

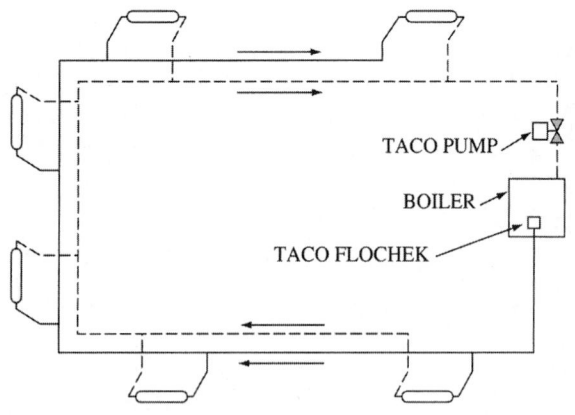

Figure 71-17 Two pipe reverse return system
(Courtesy of Taco, Inc., Cranston Rhode Island)

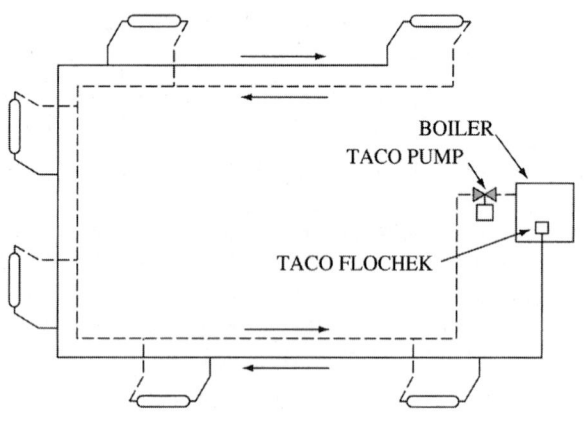

Figure 71-16 Two pipe direct return system
(Courtesy of Taco, Inc., Cranston, Rhode Island)

The two pipe direct system uses more pipe than the one pipe system; however, it is considered to be more efficient by providing better water distribution and better control. This system can also be designed using two or more circuits.

Two Pipe System, Reverse Return

The two pipe reverse return system is similar to the direct return system except that the piping is arranged so that the same length of pipe (supply + return) is used for each terminal unit. This is accomplished, as shown in Figure 71-17, by taking the unit nearest the boiler off the supply main first, connecting it to the return main last, and proceeding on this basis to equalize the piping lengths for all units. This equalization of the piping loss to each unit provides a balanced condition so that each unit receives its proper share of water.

71.8 ZONED SYSTEMS

Zoning is provided where it is desirable to control the supply of heat (hot water) to different areas of the building by separate thermostats. The areas selected can be determined by usage or building orientation. For example, to zone by usage, the living areas of a residence can be placed in one zone and the sleeping areas in another. To illustrate orientation zoning, a small commercial building can place all the rooms with southern exposure in one zone and the rooms with northern exposure in another. Whatever separation is made, allowance must be made in the piping and controls to provide this feature.

The piping needs to include a separate hot water supply circuit to the terminal units in each zone. The number of supply water circuits is the same as the number of zones. One way to control the flow of hot water in each zone is to provide a separate circulator for each zone as shown in Figure 71-18. Any one of the systems previously described can be provided with zoning. The circulator in each zone responds to the requirement of the thermostat in that zone.

TECH TIP

Zoning hydronic systems can have a significant energy savings in two ways. It provides heat only where it is needed; and the thermal mass of the water within the system will allow the heating unit to operate for longer periods of time even during light loads. As the water in the system is heated and the heat is used at a terminal unit located in a zoned area, the boiler may cut off and remain off for a period of time while the circulating pump still provides hot water to the zone. The boiler will not relight until the water temperature has dropped below the upper setpoint. This allows for longer boiler run times, which increases the overall operating efficiency.

Figure 71-18 Zoned system using separate circulators for each zone

71.9 RESIDENTIAL ZONE HEATING

Figure 71-19 shows the configuration for a multiple zone system. As an example, zone 1 could be the basement, zone 2 the first story of the house, and zone 3 the second floor. Each zone would have its own thermostat. The upstairs bedrooms

could be easily maintained at a lower temperature than the downstairs living spaces. This system has a separate circulator pump supplying water to each zone as well as a circulator on the return circuit to the hot water boiler.

The boiler shown in Figure 71-20a,b has a gravity return system. A circulator pump delivers the water from the boiler to the zone circulator pumps. When the zone calls for heat, the circulator pump for the zone will run. In this way, if zone 1 is running and then zone 2 comes on, there should be little reduction in the supply to zone 1.

The boiler in Figure 71-21 also has a gravity return system. However, instead of individual circulator pumps for the zones, there are zone control valves. One circulator pump will supply both zones. This type of system utilizes fewer pumps, thereby reducing installation costs and electricity usage. When the zone calls for heat, the zone control valve will open and the circulator pump will run. One apparent disadvantage should be evident. If zone 1 is running and then zone 2 comes on, there could be a reduction in the supply to zone 1.

The determination for the number of zones and the placement of circulator pumps depends on a number of factors. One is the personal preference of the homeowner. Every room could be a separate zone if desired. However this would involve a complex series of piping and zone valves or circulator pumps. It is not unusual for a house to have two zones. The first floor and second are often the two zones. One circulator pump with zone control valves may not be sufficient to deliver the water to both the first floor and second

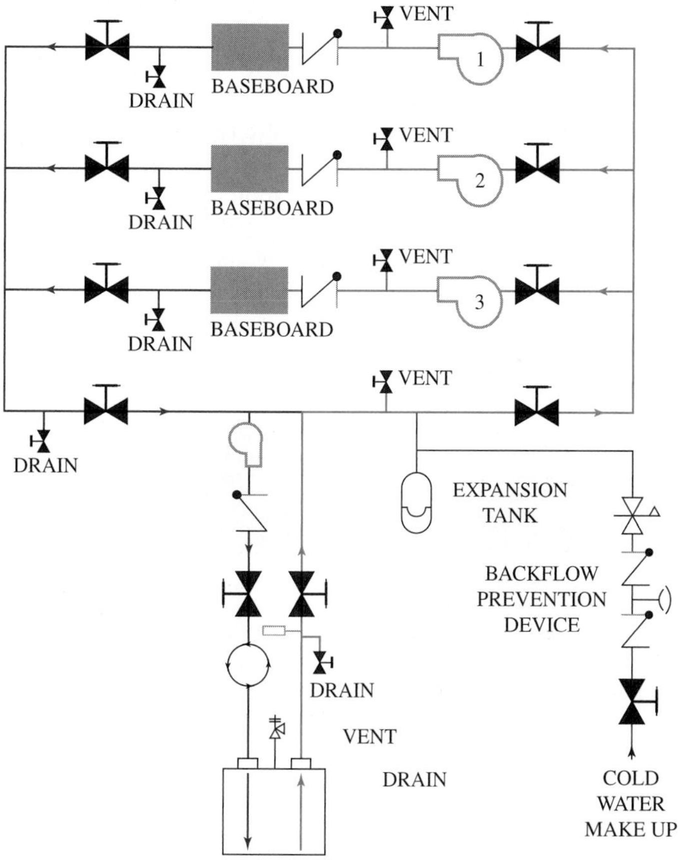

Figure 71-19 Multiple zones using circulators for supply and return

VENT

BASEBOARD

DRAIN

1

VENT

BASEBOARD

DRAIN

2

VENT

BASEBOARD

DRAIN

3

VENT

DRAIN

EXPANSION TANK

BACKFLOW PREVENTION DEVICE

DRAIN

VENT

DRAIN

COLD WATER MAKE UP

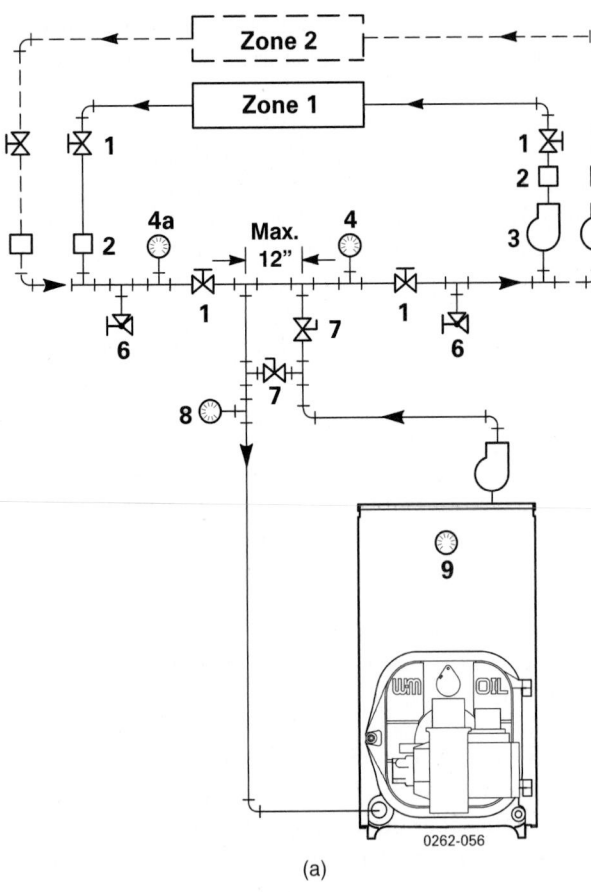

(a)

Legend:

1 Isolation Valve
2 Flow Control Valve
3 Circulator
4 System temperature gauge
5 Zone valve
6 Drain valve
7 System temperature valves
   Adjust these valves so that:
      - the temperature at gauge 8 is at least 140 °F
      - the temperature at gauge 9 is at least 160 °F

8 Blend temperature gauge
9 Boiler temperature gauge

(b)

Figure 71-20 (a) Multiple zones with circulator pumps and gravity return; (b) Schematic legend
(Courtesy Weil-McLain)

floor. In this case individual zone pumps may be required. If the house is a single story building with two zones on the first floor, then one circulator pump with zone control valves may prove to be sufficient.

71.10 ZONED SYSTEM, USING MOTORIZED VALVES

The zoning arrangement using motorized valves is similar to the system with pump zoning, with the exception that the motorized valves control the flow in each zone. Each supply

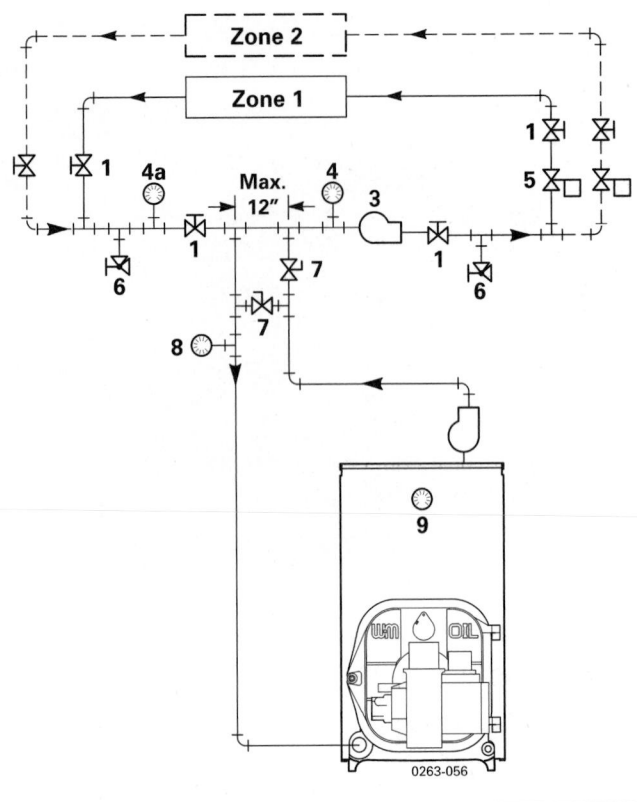

Figure 71-21 Multiple zones with zone control valves and gravity return
(Courtesy Weil-McLain)

circuit has a motorized valve controlled by the thermostat in that zone. A motorized valve can also be used as a bypass around the circulator pump to relieve the pressure when only one zone valve is open.

An example of motorized valve types is shown in Figure 71-22. The cross section view shown in Figure 71-23 can be used to describe the valve operation. When the thermostat contacts close on a call for heat the 120/24 V transformer is energized. The heating element wrapped around the wax filled element in the power head heats up. The heated expanding wax pushes down on the valve stem and water begins to flow through the valve to the zone. The stroking

Figure 71-22 Heat motor zone valves
(Courtesy of Taco, Inc., Cranston, Rhode Island)

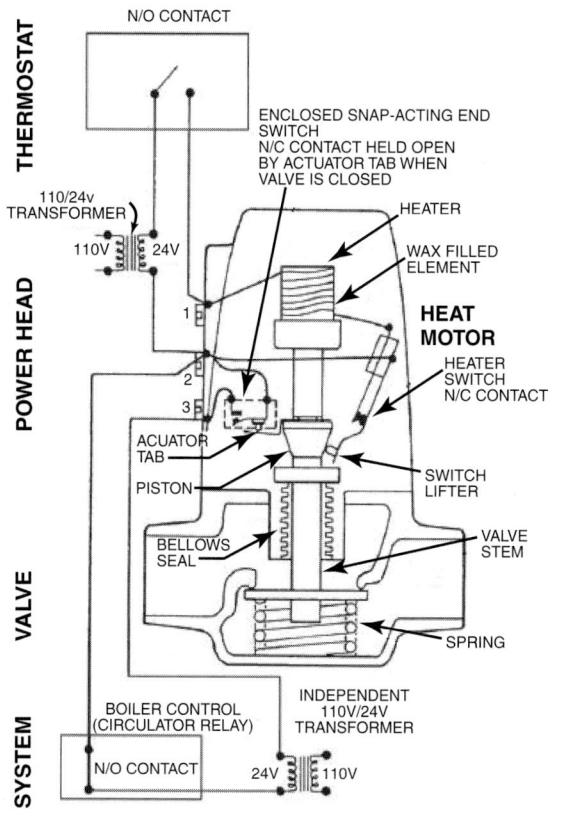

Figure 71-23 Heat motor valve cross section
(Courtesy of Taco, Inc., Cranston, Rhode Island)

action of the valve stem piston closes electrical contacts to complete the circuit through terminals 2 and 3. This triggers a relay to start the circulator pump. The opposite sequence occurs when the thermostat contacts open.

71.11 MIXING VALVES

Mixing valves are used to mix the hot boiler water with the cooler return water, Figure 71-24. These can be used for different purposes. As the outdoor temperature drops, the supply water temperature, can be increased due to the greater heating demand. The higher the water temperature, the higher the heat output at the terminal unit. At higher outside temperatures less heating is required and the mixed water temperature can be lowered providing energy savings. A three way mixing valve with outside temperature control is shown in Figure 71-25.

LOW TEMPERATURE OR RADIANT INSTALLATION

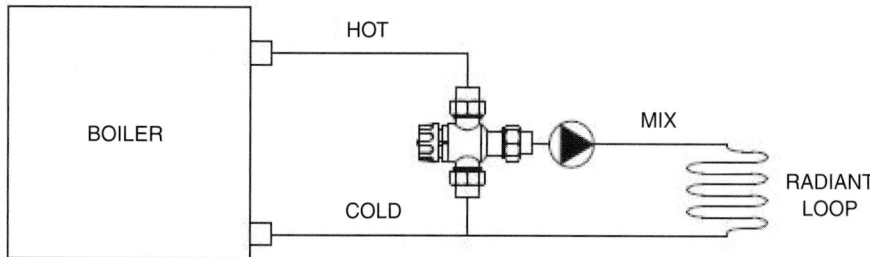

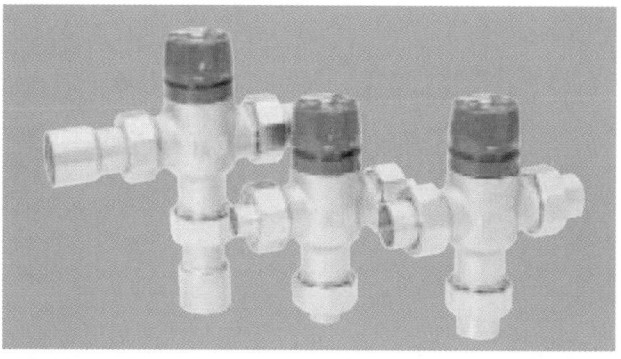

Figure 71-24 Mixing valves
(Courtesy of Taco, Inc., Cranston, Rhode Island)

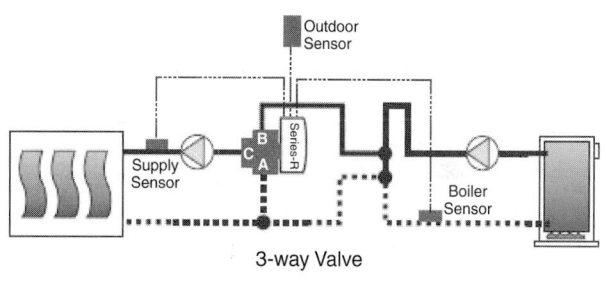

3-way Valve

Figure 71-25 Three way mixing valve
(Courtesy of Taco, Inc., Cranston, Rhode Island)

Another application of a three way mixing valve is for radiant floor heating. The temperature setpoint of the hot water boiler may be higher than the temperature required for the radiant loop. Generally, radiant floor heating loops operate at much lower temperatures than baseboard or convectors. The mixing valve will control the final temperature to the radiant loop as shown in Figure 71-26.

71.12 CIRCULATING WATER PUMPS

The major uses of pumps in an HVAC/R system are for: (1) pumping chilled or heated water, (2) pumping condenser water from the cooling tower, and (3) circulating water in a cooling tower or evaporative condenser water circuit. These pumps are generally centrifugal types with configurations as shown in Figure 71-27. It is common practice in central station systems to provide identical pumps operating in parallel, one of which is a spare for critical uses.

Figure 71-26 Three way mixing valve operation for radiant loop
(Courtesy of Taco, Inc., Cranston, Rhode Island)

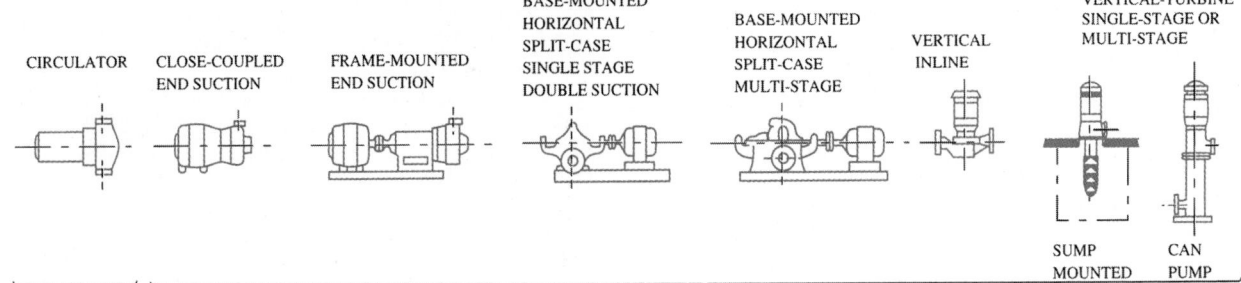

Figure 71-27 Typical centrifugal pumps
(© American Society of Heating, Refrigerating, and Air-Conditioning Engineers, Inc., www.ashrae.org)

SERVICE TIP

It is important to get all of the air out of the piping system before leaving the job. Air trapped in the system can cause noise and may result in the water pump losing its prime. The noise is a nuisance and the vibration can over time cause the pipe to fatigue and break. If one pump loses its prime, the impeller can overheat and become so damaged that the pump will not work. On large systems it may be necessary to connect an auxiliary pump in order to have sufficient flow velocity to remove all of the trapped air.

Pumps are selected to perform a specific purpose, providing the proper flow at a pressure to overcome the resistance of the circuit in which they are placed. They are selected from pump curves provided by the manufacturer, such as the sample in Figure 71-28. These curves show the flow in gallons per minute (gpm) for various head pressures measured in feet (1 ft = 2.31 psi). The curves also show the performance of the pump with different diameter impellers, as well as the required motor size, based on the desired performance. For example, using the pump curve in Figure 71-28, if 320 gpm is required at a 42 ft head, a 7.75 in impeller could be used with a 7.5 hp motor.

Figure 71-28 Typical pump performance curves provided by manufacturers
(© American Society of Heating, Refrigerating, and Air-Conditioning Engineers, Inc., www.ashrae.org)

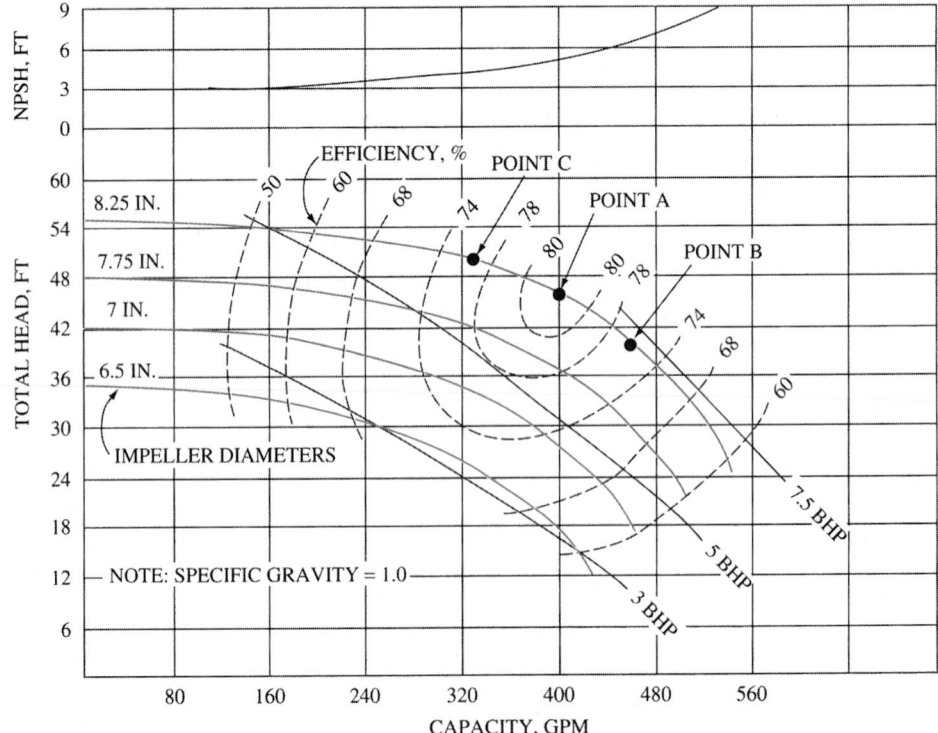

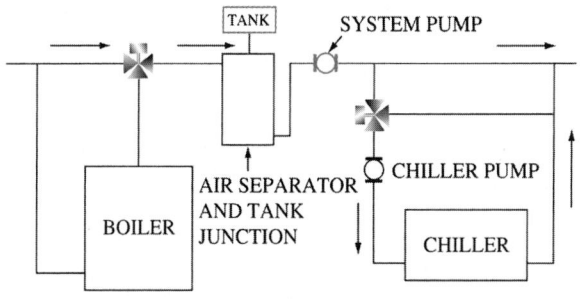

Figure 71-29 Correct expansion tank connection

Figure 71-30 Centrifugal pump used for hydronic systems
(Courtesy of Taco, Inc., Cranston, Rhode Island)

It is important to understand the difference between open and closed piping systems in working with pumps. An open system has some part of the circuit open to the atmosphere, such as a cooling tower pump water circuit. In this type of circuit the height that the water must be lifted must be added to the friction loss of the piping to determine the pump head. The suction lift of the pump is also limited.

In a closed system all piping is in series with the pump, such as in a circulating hot water heating system. The fluid pumped out returns to the suction side of the pump. An expansion tank is required in the circuit to allow for the volume change of the fluid due to variations in temperature. The location or the expansion tank and pump are important, as shown in Figure 71-29. In a closed system the system pressure can be regulated or limited by a pressure relief valve and an automatic make-up valve. Table 71-1 describes common pumping problems and presents solutions.

TECH TIP

Circulating pumps on closed loop systems only work against the vertical lift head when the system is initially being filled. Once the system is completely filled with water, the pump effective head (discharge head – suction head) is only the flow resistance of the piping system itself. The suction head developed from a height of 10 ft of water on the return side of the pump will balance the discharge head developed from a height of ten feet of water on the outlet side of the pump.

Circulator Pumps

The pumps used for hydronic heating systems are usually the centrifugal type. Some small circulator pumps used in hot water systems have replaceable cartridges, such as the one shown in Figure 71-30. The replacement cartridge contains all the moving parts and allows the pump to be serviced instead of replacing the entire unit. It is self lubricating and contains no mechanical seal. An example of

a pump performance chart for small circulator pumps is shown in Figure 71-31. Six curves are shown for various pumps. For example, a pump with model number 0010 would be able to deliver 18 gpm with 8 feet of total head.

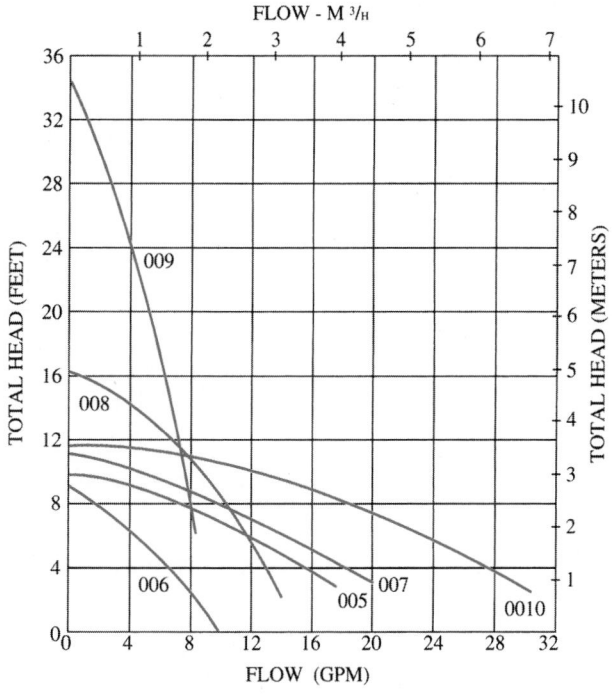

Figure 71-31 Typical performance of Taco "00" series centrifugal pumps
(Courtesy of Taco, Inc., Cranston, Rhode Island)

Table 71-1 Pumping System Trouble Analysis Guide

Complaint	Possible cause	Recommended action	Complaint	Possible cause	Recommended action
Pump or system noise	Shaft misalignment Worn coupling Worn pump/motor bearings	▪ Check and realign ▪ Replace and realign. ▪ Replace, check manufacturer's lubrication recommendations. ▪ Check and realign shafts.		Pump running backward (three-phase) Broken pump coupling Improper motor speed	▪ Reverse any two-motor leads. ▪ Replace and realign. ▪ Check motor nameplate wiring and voltage.
	Improper foundation or installation	▪ Check foundation bolting or proper grouting. ▪ Check possible shifting because of piping expansion/contraction. ▪ Realign shafts.		Pump (or impeller diameter) too small Clogged strainer(s)	▪ Check rump selection (impeller diameter) against specified system requirements. ▪ Inspect and clean screen.
	Pipe vibration and/or strain caused by pipe expansion/ contraction	▪ Inspect, alter, or add hangers and expansion provision to eliminate strain on pump(s).		Clogged impeller System not completely filled	▪ Inspect and clean. ▪ Check setting of PRV fill valve. ▪ Vent terminal units and piping high points.
	Water velocity	▪ Check actual pump performance against specified, and reduce impeller diameter as required.	Inadequate or no circulation	Balance valves or isolating valves improperly set	▪ Check settings and adjust as required.
		▪ Check for excessive throttling by balance valves or control valves.		Air-bound system	▪ Vent piping and terminal units.
	Pump operating close to or beyond end point of performance curve	▪ Check actual pump performance against specified, and reduce impeller diameter as required.			▪ Check location of expansion tank connection line relative to pump suction.
	Entrained air or low suction pressure	▪ Check expansion tank connection to system relative to pump suction. ▪ If pumping from cooling tower sump or reservoir, check line size. ▪ Check actual ability of pump against installation ▪ Check for vortex entraining air into suction line.		Air entrainment	▪ Review provision for air elimination. ▪ Check pump suction inlet conditions to determine if air is being entrained from suction tanks or sumps.
				Insufficient NPSHR	▪ Check NPSHR of pump. ▪ Inspect strainers and check pipe sizing and water temperature.

(Copyright by the American Society of Heating, Refrigerating, and Air-Conditioning Engineers, Inc.)

UNIT 71—SUMMARY

Hydronic heating systems require circulator pumps and piping loops for delivering hot water from a boiler to a terminal unit. The different types of terminal units include baseboard heaters, convectors, fan coil units, and radiators. Radiant floor heating is another popular application of a hydronic system.

There are a number of different types of piping arrangements such as series loops, one pipe venturi systems, two pipe systems, and zoned systems. These systems also require expansion tanks and many systems also require balancing valves, mixing valves, and motorized control valves. Most hot water heating systems do not come as packages and must be installed individually based upon the building floor plan and heating requirements.

WORK ORDERS

Service Ticket 7101

Customer Complaint: No Heat on Second Floor

Equipment Type: Gas Fired Boiler with Forced Hot Water—Two Zones

The technician arrived at a no heat call and spoke with the customer. The boiler appeared to be running fine but there was no heat on the second floor. The technician first checked the thermostat and found that it was calling for heat as it should, however the circulator for the zone was not operating. The motor circuit was tested with a multimeter for voltage and there was 120 V. The power was disconnected from the circuit and the circulator motor electrical leads measured infinite resistance indicating an open in the winding. The circulator was replaced as a unit and electrically wired. When the power was turned back on, the circulator began running as normal.

Service Ticket 7102

Customer Complaint: One Room Too Cold

Equipment Type: Radiant Floor Heating System

The technician met with the customer who explained that a newly installed radiant floor heating system worked well except for the bedroom. The system was an under floor system and all of the floors were tile except for the bedroom which had a thick wall to wall carpet. The technician located the supply manifold for the individual circuits and noted that the water temperature was mixed to be about 110°F. The technician adjusted the mixing valve for the bedroom to elevate the mixed temperature to 140°F. The technician told the customer that it may take a few hours before any difference was noticed but eventually the room should be warmer than it had been. The radiant heat temperature for the bedroom needed to be set slightly higher than the rest of the rooms because the wall to wall carpeting did not transfer the heat as well as the tile.

Service Ticket 7103

Customer Complaint: Banging Noise From Pipes

Equipment Type: Gas Fired Boiler—Three Zone Hot Water Heating System

The customer told the technician that the system had been fine until the heat was recently turned on to the upstairs bedrooms. Ever since that time, there had been an occasional banging in the pipes. The upstairs heat had been turned off to conserve energy and now that company had arrived it was back on again. The technician suspected that the water from the second floor had drained back to the boiler through a faulty check valve allowing air to enter the system. The technician turned up all the thermostats so that all of the circulators would be running and then went to each baseboard unit and vented air from each vent. After all the air was vented from the system, there seemed to be no more knocking noise.

The technician told the customer that the system would need to be shut off and drained to replace the check valve. The check valve may have just had something stuck underneath its seat and may not need replacement. The technician recommended leaving the check valve alone for now and replacing it when the heating season was over if the banging noise returned.

UNIT 71—REVIEW QUESTIONS

1. Define hydronics.
2. What was the common choice for hydronic piping in the past and how is that changing?
3. What are the advantages of hot water heating systems based on overall comfort?
4. What are the disadvantages of hot water heating systems?
5. What safety measures are used to allow for expansion in a hot water heating system?
6. What provisions should be made to prevent water from freezing during low temperature periods of operation for a hydronic heating system?
7. Why is it important when working on electrical components such as pump motors to make sure that all of the water in the system has been removed?
8. List the different types of terminal units used for hot water heating systems.
9. How does a fan coil unit differ from a convector?
10. What the advantages of radiant floor heating?
11. Describe a series loop, single circuit hot water piping system.
12. What does is the purpose of the venturi on a one pipe venturi system, single circuit?
13. What is the advantage to a two pipe system, direct return?
14. How does a two pipe system, reverse return differ from a two pipe system, direct return?
15. How is hot water controlled to a zone?
16. How is the water returned from a zone to the boiler?
17. How does a motorized zone control valve work?
18. What are mixing valves used for?
19. Why might mixing valves be used for radiant floor heating?
20. How does a radiant floor heating system transfer heat?
21. How does an open piping system differ from a closed type piping system?

UNIT 72

Boilers and Related Equipment

OBJECTIVES

After completing this unit you will be able to:

- explain the difference between steam boilers and hot water boilers.
- list the working pressures and temperatures for low pressure, medium pressure, and high pressure boilers.
- list the accessories required for a hot water boiler.
- vent air from a hot water boiler.
- describe the piping arrangements used for hot water boilers.

72.1 INTRODUCTION

All boilers are used to heat water. Where hot water is used to transfer heat, the output of the boiler maintains a temperature below the steaming temperature. At sea level atmospheric pressure, water boils at 212°F; at higher pressures the boiling point increases. Where large amounts of heat need to be transferred, the boiler is used to produce steam. This is due to the fact that about 970 Btu/lb of heat can be added to water at 212°F and atmospheric pressure to change it into steam at the same temperature. This same amount of heat will be transferred to the air passing across a heating coil as the steam turns back into condensate.

In general, for residential and small commercial installations, hot water boilers are used rather than steam due to the size of the installations and accuracy of control that can be provided.

72.2 BOILER CLASSIFICATION

A boiler is a pressure vessel designed to transfer heat (produced by combustion or by electrical resistance) to a fluid, usually water. If the fluid being heated is air, the unit is called a furnace. The heating surface of a boiler is the surface area with water on one side and the fire and exhaust gases on the other side. Boiler design provides for connections to a piping system that delivers heated fluid to the point of use and returns the fluid to the boiler.

A hot water boiler typically heats water to a final temperature of 180–200°F. The hot water pump delivers this hot water supply (HWS) to terminal units in the heating

circuit loop or to heating coils in an air handler. Water temperatures for most heating systems have a range of 130–180°F, while radiant floor heating systems are much lower at 85–140°F. Too low a temperature will result in inadequate heating while too high a temperature could be damaging to the piping or materials used in the heating loop. Because of this, there are different methods of mixing the supply and return water to achieve the desired supply temperatures.

The water will transfer its sensible heat in the terminal unit. The temperature difference from the supply to the return line is normally 20–40°F. In many boilers the return water is mixed with the supply water to maintain a temperature of at least 140°F returning to the boiler to reduce the chance of reaching the dew point in the boiler flue gases. Boilers are classified three ways: (1) working temperature/pressure, (2) fuel used, and (3) materials of construction.

72.3 WORKING TEMPERATURE/PRESSURE

Low pressure boilers have a working pressure of up to 15 psi steam and/or up to 160 psi water pressure at a maximum of 250°F operating temperature. Low pressure boilers are most commonly used for heating systems. Some are equipped with internal or external heat exchangers to supply domestic hot water. Residential heating boilers are gas and oil-fired boilers with inputs less than 300,000 Btu/hr. Commercial heating boilers are those with heating inputs of 300,000 Btu/hr and larger. Water boilers are available from outputs of 50,000 Btu to 50,000,000 Btu (50 MBH). Every steam and hot water boiler is rated at a maximum working pressure determined by the ASME code under which it is constructed and tested. Typical residential type boilers are shown in Figure 72-1a,b,c.

Medium and high pressure boilers operate above 15 psi steam and/or over 160 psi water pressure at temperatures above 250°F. Steam boilers are available for up to 50,000 lb/hr of steam. Many of them are used in central station systems for heating medium and large commercial buildings that are beyond the range of a hot water boiler. Often industrial boilers are used for the dual purposes of generating process steam and heating steam. As an example the process steam may be used in a hospital for sterilizing surgical equipment while the heating steam that is reduced to a lower pressure is used in the heating coils.

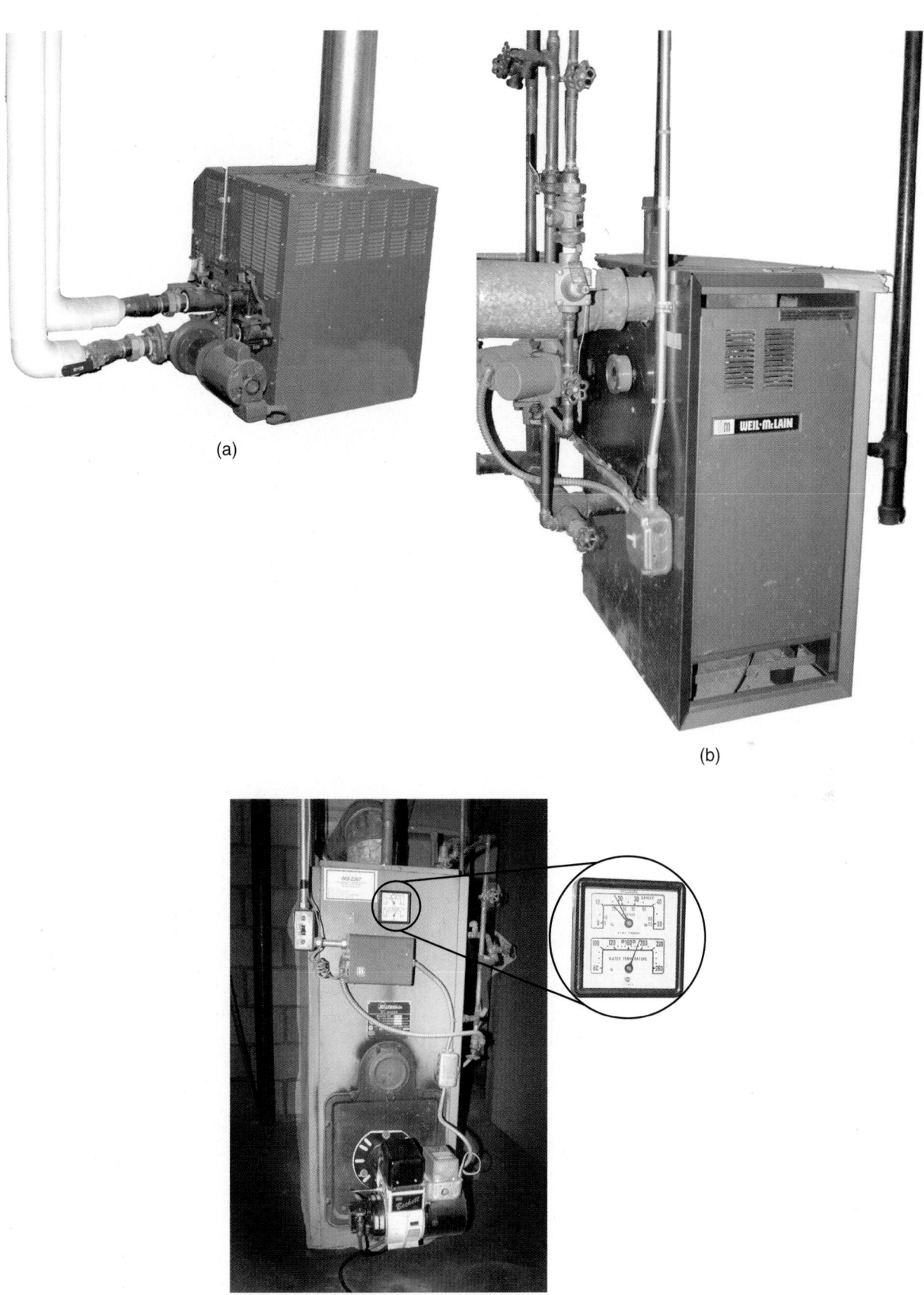

(a)

(b)

(c)

Figure 72-1 Types of residential boilers

CAUTION

Boiler operators are licensed and regulated by local, state, and federal agencies. This typically applies to commercial boilers and boilers located in public buildings. Only individuals holding appropriate licenses may be operating engineers in charge of boilers. Domestic hot water boilers are typically excluded from this category.

SAFETY TIP

All boilers must be routinely inspected and certified for operation. The boiler certification must be posted in plain view in the boiler room. This typically applies to commercial boilers and boilers located in public buildings. Domestic hot water boilers are typically excluded from this category.

72.4 BOILER FUELS

Boilers may be designed to burn coal, wood, various grades of fuel oil, various types of fuel gas, or operate as electric boilers. Heat recovery steam generators utilize the exhaust gas from a gas turbine to generate steam. Each fuel has its own special firing arrangement depending on the type of application.

By far the most common types of fuel for residential and light commercial applications are gas and oil. Natural gas is clean burning and convenient if it is readily available through a pipeline connection. The burner arrangement for a gas fired hot water boiler is very similar to a gas fired hot air furnace. Typically the return water temperature for a gas fired hot water boiler should not be below 140°F.

In rural areas where there is no gas pipe line connection, propane may be used; however, this requires a storage tank and regular delivery. The propane storage tank will be located outside the building and will be subject to proper installation to meet local codes. A common alternative is the use of #2 heating oil. The oil storage tank may be located within the building, typically in the basement. Similar to an oil fired hot air furnace, an oil fired hot water boiler will have a burner arrangement with an oil pump assembly.

72.5 MATERIALS OF CONSTRUCTION

Cast Iron Boilers

Hot water boilers are constructed using cast iron, steel, or stainless steel. A typical gas fired cast iron boiler is shown in Figure 72-2, link an oil fired cast iron boiler is shown in Figure 72-3. Both of these boilers are assembled and shipped as packaged units. The package usually includes the circulator pump and complete controls. The wall thermostat is shipped separately for field mounting and wiring. Some packages also include a diaphragm type expansion tank and a check valve piped into the

Figure 72-2 Typical cast iron gas boiler

Figure 72-3 Typical cast iron oil boiler

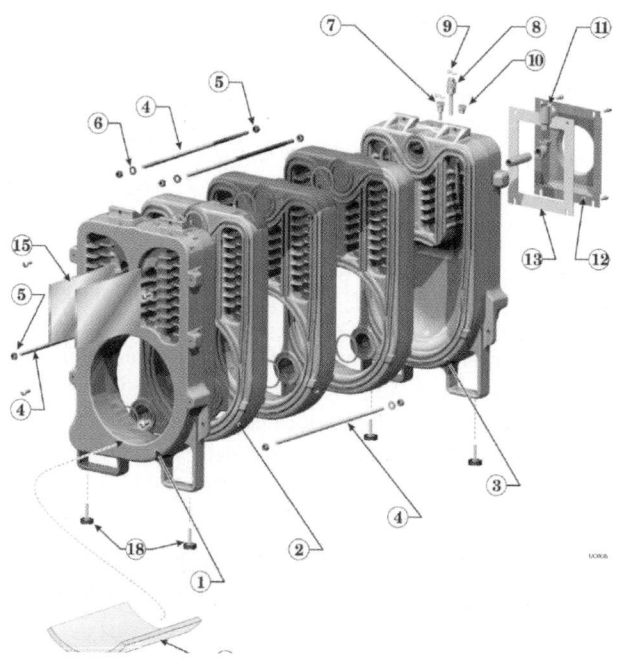

Figure 72-4 Cast iron boiling individual cast sections
(Courtesy Weil-McLain)

unit. Cast iron boilers are constructed of individually cast sections assembled in groups or sections, Figure 72-4. Push or screw nipples or an external header join the section pressure tight and provide passages for water, steam, and products of combustion.

Steel Boilers

A steel boiler is shown in Figure 72-5. This boiler is also shipped as a package with accessories and controls. The design illustrated is a high efficiency unit with a condensing type heat exchanger producing efficiencies in the AFUE 90+% range. Condensing boilers have recently been developed to improve the efficiency of boilers. Previously the flue gases were not allowed to condense in the boiler due to the corrosion that could cause. These new condensing boilers are constructed with heat exchangers made of materials to resist corrosion.

Figure 72-5 Steel boiler, gas fired

Steel boilers are fabricated into one assembly of a given size, usually by welding. The heat exchangers for steel boilers can be fire tube or water tube design. The fire tube construction, which is most common, has flue gas passage space between the water holding sections. The water tube construction uses water filled tubes for the heat exchanger with the flue gases in contact with the external surface of the tubes.

The surface of steel boilers can be electroplated or clad with nickel or other corrosion resistant material. Although this adds significant cost to the boiler, it significantly extends the unit operational life. Corrosion protection can also be provided by placing a sacrificial zinc rod in the tank. Zinc is more reactive than steel so it corrodes away first and can be easily replaced when it is gone.

For larger hot water installations, a high efficiency pulse type steel boiler is available, such as the examples shown in Figure 72-6a,b. These boilers produce efficiencies as high as AFUE 96%. Both combustion air and gas metering valves are standard equipment. A small fan is used to deliver combustion air on startup, but shuts off after ignition. The unit is primarily controlled by a microprocessor.

Other Boiler Types

Copper boilers are usually some variation of the water tube type. The two most common tube types are parallel finned copper tube coils with headers, and serpentine copper tube units. Some are offered as residential wall hung boilers. Electric boilers are in a separate class. No combustion takes place and no flue passages are needed. Electric elements can be immersed in the boiler water.

72.6 PIPING DETAILS

A number of accessory devices are used in piping hot water systems, such as shutoff valves, air purging fittings, automatic fill valves, flow control valves, expansion tanks, safety controls, and gauges. Each of these devices has a special function in the proper operation of the system.

One of the main concerns in the selection and use of these accessories is to maintain a system of piping that contains only water and is free from air pockets. Air in the system can prevent proper operation of the pump and interfere with the transfer of heat in the terminal units.

Any air that forms in the system must be either directed to the expansion tank or vented. The system must be properly filled with water and the pump pressure maintained to produce the required flow.

TECH TIP

To reduce the expense in piping for large water systems steel pipe is used. However, steel pipe has the potential problem of rusting. To reduce the rust or corrosion problem, steel pipes are treated with a "pickling" solution. This treatment forms a barrier to rust formation in the pipe. In addition, chemicals are added to the water circulating through the system that further retard rust. Check with the chemical manufacturer for the proper mixing ratio.

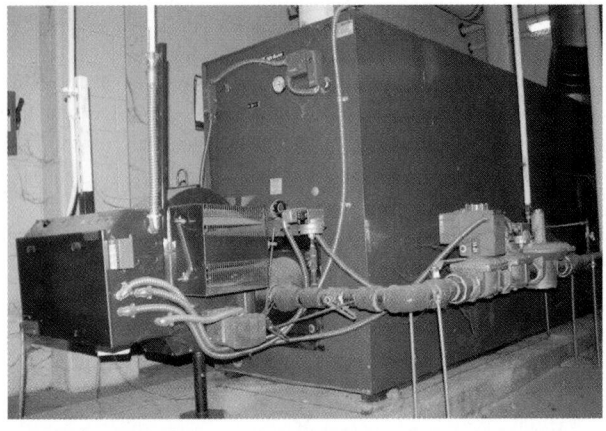

(a)

(b)

Figure 72-6 (a) Forced draft large high efficiency steel boiler; (b) Pulse high efficiency boiler

72.7 AIR PURGING ARRANGEMENT

Air must be eliminated from the piping system. Air vents need to be placed at high points of the system and on terminal units. Even if the system is free from air when filled, air can enter during normal operation. Depending on the selection of accessories, air that collects during operation can be vented at the expansion tank. Some air remains in the expansion tank to act as a cushion for the expansion and contraction of water during temperature change.

72.8 EXPANSION TANK

An expansion tank is placed in the piping to permit the expansion and contraction of the water volume. The tank holds both air and water. The air is compressed when the water volume expands and the air expands when the water volume decreases. An open type of expansion tank is located above the highest terminal unit, usually in the attic, and has a gauge glass and overflow pipe to a drain. These are not very common today.

SERVICE TIP

After installing or working on an expansion tank, watch the boiler pressure as the boiler heats up. If the pressure rises too high, this could be due to an expansion tank sizing or operational problem.

Closed type expansion tanks are welded gas tight and located above the boiler. The tank is partially filled with water to leave a cushion of air for expansion. Do not use an automatic air vent on this type of tank. The air will escape from the system rather than returning to the tank. Eventually the tank will waterlog. This type of tank should utilize a fitting that permits the air bubbles to rise directly into the tank, but restricts the flow of water back into the tank as shown in Figure 72-7.

Diaphragm type expansion tanks are also welded gas tight but have a flexible rubber membrane between the air space and the water space that moves during operation to allow for the changing volume of water. The air is precharged (usually 12 psig for residential units) into the expansion tank and unlike the closed type does not come in contact with the water in the system. An automatic air vent should be installed on top of a diaphragm expansion tank as shown in Figure 72-8.

SERVICE TIP

A weeping relief valve may be an indication of an expansion tank problem. If the tank is a closed type, it may be waterlogged. If the tank is a diaphragm type, the membrane may be damaged.

The expansion tank can be located on the suction side of the pump, as shown in Figure 72-9, or the discharge side of the boiler, as shown in Figure 72-10.

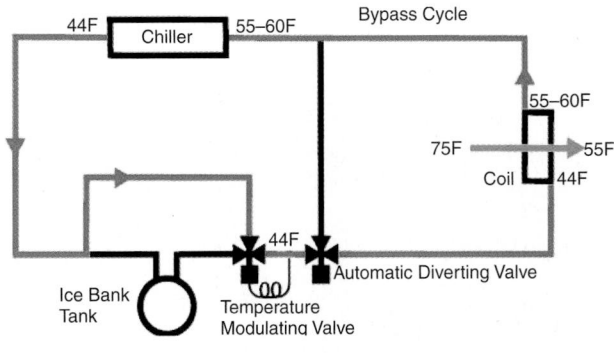

Figure 74-12 Live load chilling
(Courtesy of CALMAC Manufacturing Corporation)

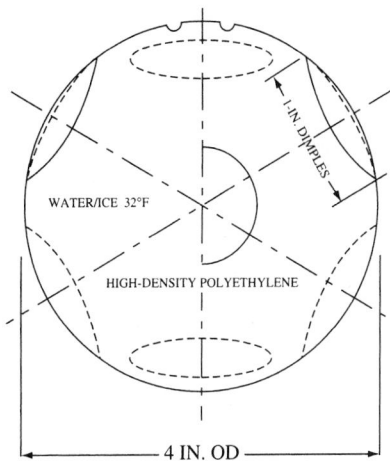

Figure 74-13 Spherical container for ice thermal storage

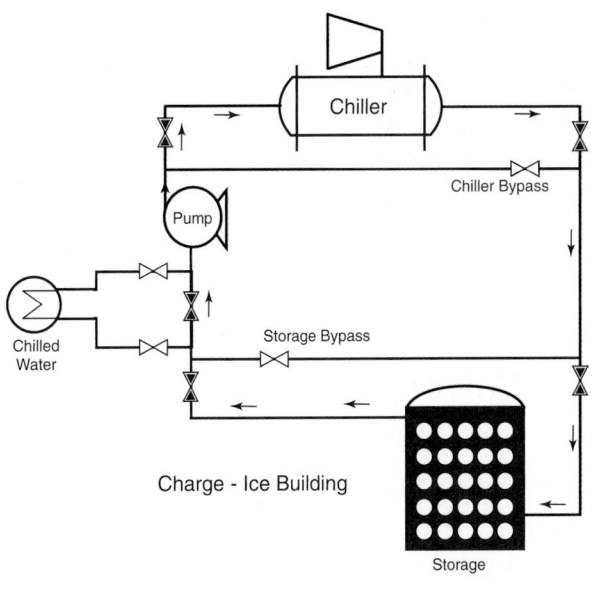

Figure 74-14 Encapsulated ice storage system—ice building

The full storage system ice-build phase occurs during the off-peak utility hours with the refrigeration chiller in operation. During the heat of the day, the refrigeration chiller is shut down. However, the glycol continues to circulate through the storage tank during the ice-melt phase to supply cooling for the building. Similar to the operation of the partial storage cycle, the modulating valve is used to mix a portion of the warmer glycol returning directly from the coil with the colder glycol passing through the storage tank to maintain the set temperature of the glycol supplied to the coil.

There may also be periods when the storage tank is bypassed altogether, referred to as live-load chilling. This may occur when electrical rates are low and the ice-storage tank is being conserved for later use or for mild temperature days in the spring and fall when cooling demand is relatively low. For live-load chilling, the thermal energy storage tank will be bypassed completely, and the refrigeration chiller will be used to meet the cooling demand as shown in Figure 74-12.

The polyethylene construction and seamless tank design result in a low-maintenance demand for this type of system. The water level of the storage tank is checked annually. A biocide is added to the water every two years. The concentration of the glycol solution is checked annually.

74.7 ENCAPSULATED ICE STORAGE SYSTEMS

In this type of system, a number of water-filled containers are placed inside a tank. A glycol solution fills the tank and circulates over and around the containers. Some containers are spherical, with dimples to allow for expansion on freezing, as shown in the diagram in Figure 74-13. Other containers are flat and rectangular like a giant hot-water bottle or annular, shaped like a donut. These containers are stacked in storage tanks that can vary in shape and design. In this type of system the ice is formed within each spherical container from contact with a cold glycol solution as shown in Figure 74-14.

The piping in and out of the tank must create a flow path that is effective for both charging and discharging. The control system monitors the liquid level of the tanks to determine the amount of ice formed. As ice is formed, the containers expand which raises the glycol level in the tank.

The tank level is monitored to determine when the system is fully charged.

The economic factors for this type of system include storage tank shape, configuration, and installation. The non-managed flow path of encapsulated ice storage systems does not offer repeatable performance. Because of this, there is a tendency for designers to oversize them. Also because of the design, encapsulated ice storage systems typically will use more glycol as compared to ice-on-coil systems.

74.8 ICE HARVESTING SYSTEMS

Ice harvesting systems are another application of industrial ice makers/water chillers. These types of systems require large and heavy equipment with limited configurations and so are becoming less common. These units build ice in sheets on the surface of vertical refrigerated plates. The ice is harvested by slightly warming the plates with refrigerant discharge gas, which causes the ice sheets to break away from the plates and fall into a water-filled storage tank. The sheets of ice break up when they hit the water, providing many exposed ice surfaces for heat transfer to the water. The thin sheets of ice provide a very even discharge cycle, with consistently low water temperatures. Monitoring of the tank level determines refrigeration operation.

The storage tank must be constructed with weirs (a weir is like a dam) to prevent the ice from getting into the circulation system. Since the ice floats and distributes itself in the tank, water flow distribution is less critical than with some of the other systems.

SERVICE TIP

Ice harvesting equipment is the most complex of the various thermal storage systems. However, it is often the most efficient method of ice production when properly set up. A major factor in the efficiency of ice harvesters is the actual harvesting cycle. Harvesting is typically performed by diverting the hot condenser gas back into the evaporator plate where the ice has formed. This momentary heating causes the ice to release, clearing the evaporator surface for more ice to form. Manufacturer guidelines list recommended harvest times to optimize ice production.

74.9 THERMAL STORAGE FOR HEATING

Heat Pump Applications

Applications of thermal storage for heating in the HVAC/R field are less common than cooling. Most ground and water source heat pumps take advantage of sources of heat without necessarily requiring a thermal storage tank. However, heat pumps can be used in combination with thermal storage systems. As an example, rooftop solar collector panels can be used during the day to heat water that is stored in a thermal storage tank. During the cooler evening hours, the heat pump can be used to remove heat from the storage tank and deliver it to the building.

Thermal Storage Under-Floor Heating

Some homes are designed with electric cables or heating panels buried 4–12 inches deep in a bed of sand. The cement slab for the building is then poured on top. During the low-cost off-peak hours, the sand is heated to create a thermal reservoir beneath the floor. During the cooler evening hours, the heat from the floor will be continually radiated into the building.

Coil-type mats are used for permanent and/or temporary ice applications such as skating rinks, Figure 74-15. Similar mats are also used for sub-floor heating and other

Figure 74-15 IceMat® during installation
(Courtesy of CALMAC Manufacturing Corporation)

applications such as turf warming for year-round plant growing at stadiums and greenhouses, snow melting for athletic fields and dog tracks, and permafrost prevention for refrigerated warehouses and ice-skating rinks. A heated liquid is circulated through a series of polyethylene tubes. Lake-coupled geothermal heating systems involve laying a series of plastic tubes near the bottom of a lake to be used in combination with a heat pump system. Standard-size preassembled mats are commonly available, as well as custom designs to meet almost any application.

Boreholes

For this application, an array of bored holes resembling standard drilled wells are spaced in a grid. A plastic pipe with a U bend is then inserted into the borehole. Solar heaters and a pumping system provide for a flow of hot water down into the borehole to heat the ground during the summer months. This heat is then recovered and sent to the building during the winter months.

UNIT 74—SUMMARY

Most thermal storage systems encountered in the HVAC/R are used for cooling. The storage of chilled water is popular, however this requires a large storage tank that is typically of the stratified design. Ice-storage systems require less space and are the most popular type. There are a number of different types of ice storage systems such as ice-on-coil internal melt, ice-on-coil external melt, ice harvesting, and encapsulated ice storage systems. Thermal storage systems allow for charging during periods of low cost electrical off-peak rates. This stored cooling capacity is then discharged during high-cost peak periods, which reduces or even eliminates the need to run the chiller units. Thermal storage systems therefore will reduce total operating costs.

WORK ORDERS

Service Ticket 7401

Customer Complaint: Ice Too Thin

Equipment Type: Ice-on-Coil System

The ice builder was charging very quickly and the ice formation was not very thick. During discharge periods, the total cooling period was short. The technician first checked the refrigeration chiller, and it was found to be operating normally. The ice formation was uniform across the coil, which indicated good refrigerant flow and water coverage. However, the layer of ice was thin. The technician located the ice sensors used to monitor the ice thickness and replaced them. Now the unit charged to the proper ice thickness and the discharge period was considerably longer.

Service Ticket 7402

Customer Complaint: Insufficient Ice Buildup

Equipment Type: Ice-on-Coil System

The glycol coil was not freezing the ice solid and the refrigeration unit was running for prolonged periods during the charging cycle. The technician first checked the refrigeration chiller and determined that the load on the unit was low, although the charging cycle was in progress. The glycol temperature difference into and out of the chiller was also low, indicating little heat transfer. The technician checked the glycol circulating pump and discovered a low suction pressure and a low discharge pressure. There was a restriction to flow somewhere in the glycol system. The technician was told that a glycol leak had been repaired a few days back. Because there was no glycol available, only water was added back into the system to replace the glycol that had leaked out. Evidently ice was forming inside the glycol circuit and restricting flow.

The technician recommended that the system be shut down to allow for the ice inside the circuit to melt. A glycol sample would be taken and tested for specific gravity. This would determine how much of the existing glycol solution would need to be drained and replaced with new glycol. When this was completed, the system should operate normally.

Service Ticket 7403

Customer Complaint: Ice Harvest Not Uniform

Equipment Type: Ice Harvesting System

The ice harvesting machine when working properly provided for uniform sheets of ice that would drop from the coil into the water filled storage tank. Now the ice was becoming too thick. To get the ice to drop off, the unit would need to be shut down until the sheet melted and fell. The technician checked the hot gas solenoid valve. This valve was set on a timer to automatically direct hot gas from the compressor through the evaporator coil so that the ice would melt and fall. The gas solenoid valve electromagnet solenoid coil was tested for electrical resistance and found to have infinite resistance, which indicated it would need to be replaced. The replacement was a fairly simple process of wiring in a new solenoid. The ice harvester was now working properly.

UNIT 74—REVIEW QUESTIONS

1. What are the advantages of thermal storage systems?
2. What is meant by a PCM when referring to thermal storage systems?
3. What is an advantage of ice storage systems as compared to water storage systems?
4. What is meant by a stratified thermal water storage tank?
5. What is meant by charging storage?
6. What is meant by discharging storage?
7. Would a system ever be charged and discharged at the same time?
8. What is meant by live load chilling?
9. What are the determining factors for when to charge and when discharge from thermal storage?
10. What is the difference between full and partial thermal storage systems?
11. What can happen if the ice sensor for an ice-on-coil system is faulty?
12. What type of regular maintenance is required for an ice-on-coil internal melt thermal energy system?
13. What percentage of ethylene glycol is commonly used for a solid-ice brine-coil system?
14. Why is clear ice formation on an ice-on-coil thermal storage system desired?
15. Why do spherical encapsulated ice containers have dimples on their exterior surface?
16. How does an encapsulated ice energy storage system compare to an ice-on-coil energy storage system?
17. How is the ice harvested from the evaporator plates in an ice harvesting system?
18. Of all the ice thermal storage systems, which is the most complex?
19. What are the advantages of water for use in a thermal energy storage system?
20. What melts the ice on an ice-on-coil external melt thermal energy storage system?

UNIT 75
Space Heaters

OBJECTIVES

After completing this unit you will be able to:

- list the different types of gas space heaters.
- list the different types of electric space heaters.
- explain which type of space heater is best suited for a specific application.
- determine the best location for an infrared type space heater.

TECH TIP

Many local codes do not allow unvented space heaters to be used in many occupied areas. This may mean that when replacing an unvented space heater with new equipment that a vented space heater may need to be used. The primary concern for unvented space heaters is the oxygen depletion and possible carbon monoxide buildup. For that reason it is strongly recommended and may be mandated by ordinance that carbon monoxide detectors be located in any area where unvented space heaters are being used.

75.1 INTRODUCTION

A space heater is used to heat a dedicated space rather than to supply heat for the entire building. There are a wide variety of types with some being portable while others are permanently installed in the space. Space heaters employ a combination of radiation, natural convection, and forced convection to transfer the heat produced. The energy source may be liquid, solid, gaseous, or electric. Space heaters are often used for garages, workshops, and utility rooms that may not be a part of the regular house heating circuit. They are also popular in applications where heat is to be used only on a periodic basis such as for a vacation home. Industrial space heaters can be used to heat a warehouse by staggering them at different locations throughout the building with each unit heating a specific area. Space heaters are designed to be easily installed and operated and due to the variation in their type and flexibility, they are commonly used for many different applications.

75.2 GAS ROOM HEATERS

Gas room heaters are self contained freestanding units that transfer the heat produced from fuel combustion to room air through a heat exchanger system. The heat is transferred by radiation and convection without mixing the flue gas with the circulating room air. Since air for combustion is supplied from the room air, these units must be installed in a space that has sufficient infiltration to supply the necessary combustion air. Room heaters are made in a number of different constructions: vented, unvented, and catalytic.

Vented Room Gas Heaters

Vented room gas heaters have an opening that is permanently connected to the chimney to convey the flue gas to the outdoors. The combustion gases pass through a heat exchanger that transfers the heat to the room air by radiation and convection. Cool room air enters the grill at the bottom of the unit and the heated air is distributed from the top. These heaters often have a glass panel on the front to supply radiant heat. Room air is completely separated from the combustion gases.

Some room heaters are operated entirely by gravity. Others use a fan to circulate the room air through the unit. The fan increases the efficiency of the heater and provides better distribution of the heated air. Since the air for combustion is taken from the room, applications are limited to spaces where there is sufficient infiltrated air to supply the required combustion air. These units are available in sizes of 10,000–75,000 Btu/hr.

Unvented Room Gas Heaters

Unvented room gas heaters discharge the products of combustion into the room. They are limited in application to commercial projects where the area is relatively open. They are often used during building construction to supply temporary heat. One type commonly used is called a "Salamander." It is portable and can be located where needed.

Catalytic Room Gas Heater

The catalytic heater transfers heat from a glowing heat exchanger. It has no flame. The heat exchanger is constructed of fibrous material impregnated with a catalytic substance that accelerates the oxidation of a gaseous fuel. Catalytic heaters transfer heat by radiation and convection. The surface temperature is below red heat, usually about 1,200°F.

UNIT 75—REVIEW QUESTIONS

1. What is a restriction to be considered when installing a gas room heater?

2. What safety device should be installed where unvented space heaters are being used?

3. How does a vented room gas heater differ from an unvented room gas heater?

4. What is a "Salamander"?

5. What type of gas space heater has no flame?

6. What is meant by a "direct vent" heater?

7. Why do some gas furnaces not require an electrical power supply?

8. How do infrared heaters transfer heat?

9. What type of fuel does a vaporizing oil pot heater use?

10. How is the oil vaporized in a vaporizing oil pot heater?

11. What happens to an electrical space heater if it sits for long periods of time unused?

12. What is an advantage of a forced air electric heater as compared to natural convection?

13. What type of electric space heater is used when large capacity and positive air circulation are important?

14. Where are cabinet type electrical space heaters typically installed?

15. What is the most frequently used type of electric space heater for residential and commercial buildings?

16. How does a standard convection baseboard electrical heater compare to a low density type?

17. How can electric infrared heaters be mounted?

18. What distance should an electric infrared heater be from any other surface?

19. How are mats for electric heat floor panels constructed?

20. What is mineral insulated (MI) heating cable?

Commercial Refrigeration Systems

UNIT 76

Commercial Refrigeration Systems

Commercial Refrigeration Systems

OBJECTIVES

After completing this unit you will be able to:

- describe the differences between high temperature, medium temperature, and low temperature refrigeration systems.
- list the various types of systems used in commercial refrigeration.
- explain how a multiple compressor system operates.
- describe how an evaporative cooling system operates.
- provide definitions for secondary and expendable refrigerants.
- explain the basic principles of operation for an absorption system.

76.1 INTRODUCTION

Commercial refrigeration systems serve a wide variety of purposes. Perhaps the most familiar systems are those used for food storage applications such as a walk in cooler at a grocery store, or a food display case. However, with the exception of air conditioning, refrigeration is used for almost everything else that needs to be cooled. Many commercial refrigeration systems are used to make large quantities of ice, while others may be used to quick freeze and store blueberries, potatoes, fish, and pizza. Refrigeration is also used in manufacturing, where it is referred to as process cooling.

There are many types of refrigeration systems and each type is suitable for specific applications. The equipment design must ensure that the quality of the product being cooled remains satisfactory. Additionally, a minimum amount of energy must be used to perform the operation. Finally, the process must be operated to comply with the laws relating to protecting the environment.

76.2 SYSTEMS

Refrigeration is divided into four broad areas based on the evaporator coil temperature. High temperature refrigeration coil temperatures range from +20°F to +55°F. Medium temperature refrigeration coil temperatures range from −10°F to +30°F. Low temperature refrigeration coils range from −40°F to +10°F. Cryogenics is a very low temperature process with temperatures of −250°F and below.

High temperature refrigeration is used for product storage above freezing. When we think of high temperature refrigeration, we usually think of food storage. Food items like milk, cheese, and fresh fruit and vegetables are stored at temperatures below 40°F and above 32°F. Storage temperatures within this range are also used for things like flowers or medicine.

Medium temperature refrigeration is used for storing frozen foods. The most common example of medium temperature refrigeration is a home refrigerator's freezer compartment.

Low temperature refrigeration is used to quickly freeze and store foods. Temperatures below 0°F freeze foods quickly to preserve their quality. Foods at these temperatures can be stored for long periods of time as compared to foods stored in the medium temperature range. The most common example of low temperature refrigeration is a deep freeze.

Cryogenic temperatures are used for the preservation of materials for an extremely long period of time. Materials stored at these temperatures are almost suspended in time. Maintaining cryogenic temperatures requires a lot of refrigeration and is very expensive, so this type of storage is mainly used to store medical and scientific materials.

TECH TIP

Generally, the colder a food product is stored, the longer its shelf life. For example, milk stored at 40°F in a refrigerator may only last a few days before souring, as compared to milk stored at 32°F, which may last two or more weeks before souring. Even foods that are frozen will remain at a higher quality longer the lower the storage temperature. Food in a refrigerator/freezer can be stored and used longer when the temperature in the freezer is closest to 0°F. A deep freeze temperature is below 0°F and foods at these temperatures can be stored for much longer periods of time while maintaining their quality.

76.3 TYPES OF SYSTEMS

The following are various types of systems used in commercial refrigeration, and are described in this section:

- Single component systems.
- Multiple evaporator systems.
- Multiple compressor systems.
- Multistage compressor systems.
  - Compound.
  - Cascade.
- Evaporative cooling systems.
- Secondary refrigerants.
- Thermoelectric refrigerators.
- Expendable refrigerants.
- Absorption refrigeration systems.

76.4 SINGLE COMPONENT SYSTEMS

The essential elements of a *single component system* as shown in Figure 76-1 are the: compressor, condenser, metering device, and evaporator. Also shown are some of the important accessories common to commercial refrigeration systems: a high/low pressure control, condenser fan, receiver tank, suction to liquid line heat exchanger, filter-drier, evaporator fan,

thermostat, and suction line accumulator. Each of these accessories helps maintain an efficient system.

There are many variations of these basic elements that are useful in a wide variety of applications. For example, Figure 76-2 shows a water-cooled condenser used in place of the air-cooled condenser and fan coil unit evaporator of an air conditioning system. Note also the additional accessories shown: compressor and receiver service valves, a liquid line solenoid, and a water-regulating valve for the condenser.

SERVICE TIP

Refrigeration systems require the addition of components not normally found on air conditioning systems. Each of these devices that are added create resistance to the flow of liquid or vapor refrigerant. Such resistance reduces the overall operating efficiency of a system. For that reason technicians must exercise good judgment when deciding whether to add additional accessories to an operating refrigeration system. They must weigh the advantages and necessity for such accessories to the proper operation of the system as compared to any detrimental effect it has on system capacity. This is of prime concern with systems that are marginally meeting current demand.

76.5 MULTIPLE EVAPORATOR SYSTEMS

Multiple evaporator systems are common in supermarkets. Multiple evaporators make it possible to use a single compressor to control a number of different case or fixture temperatures. Figure 76-3 shows a three-temperature system.

Evaporator pressure regulators (EPRs) are placed in the suction lines to the two higher temperature evaporators. These are adjusted to maintain the desired evaporator temperature.

A check valve, Figure 76-4, is installed in the suction line from the lowest temperature coil. This prevents migration of the refrigerant from the higher temperature coils to the low temperature coil when the compressor is producing cooling for the higher temperature coils.

When all of the coils require refrigeration, such as on startup, the compressor will operate at the suction pressure required to cool the highest temperature coil first, then the middle temperature coil, and last, the low temperature coil. The compressor must be sized to produce the entire cooling load at the evaporator pressure of the lowest temperature coil. The low temperature coil will receive very little refrigeration until the higher temperature coils are satisfied. For this reason, the load on the low temperature coil must account for 60% of the total load, otherwise it may not receive adequate refrigeration.

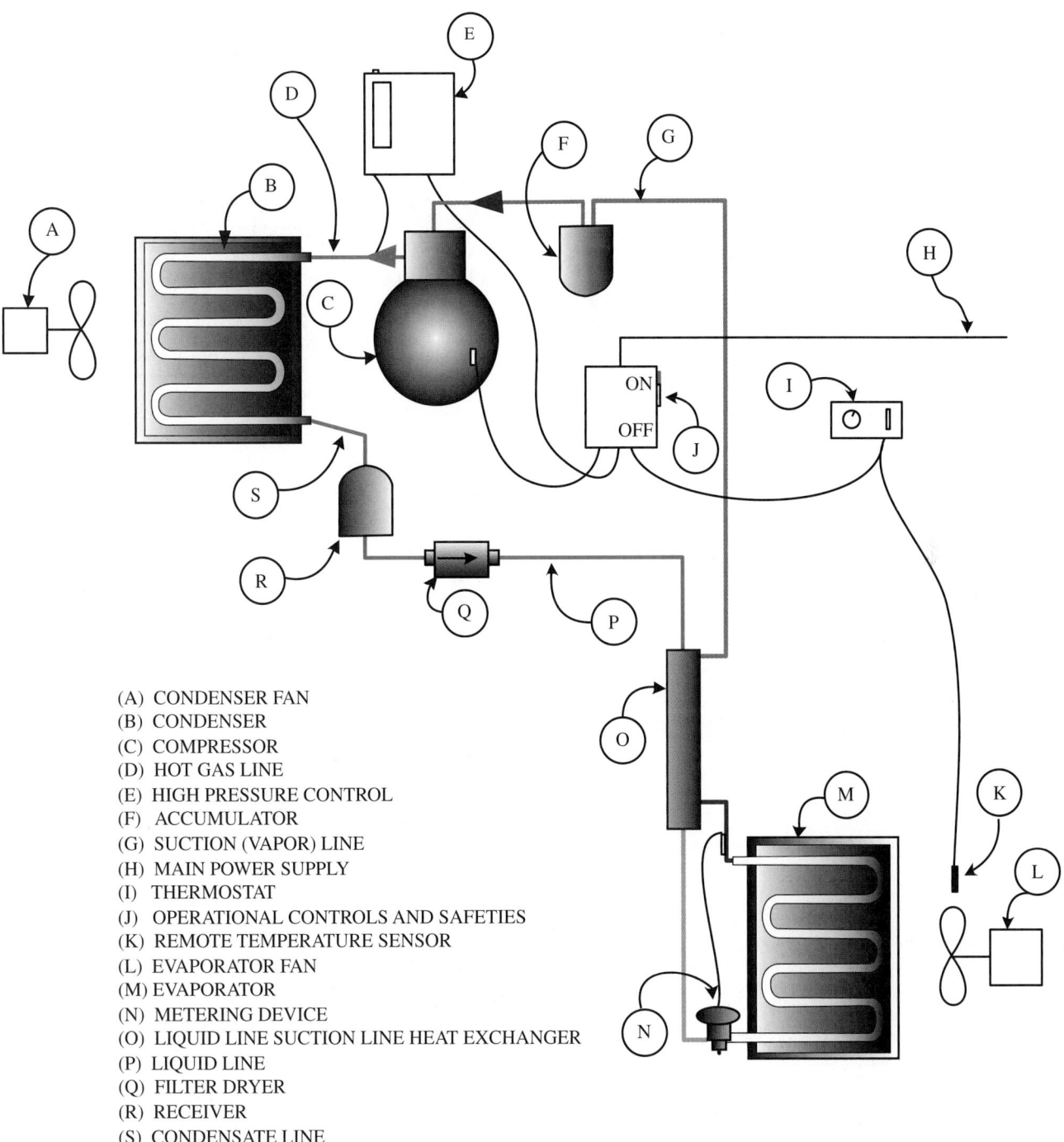

(A) CONDENSER FAN
(B) CONDENSER
(C) COMPRESSOR
(D) HOT GAS LINE
(E) HIGH PRESSURE CONTROL
(F) ACCUMULATOR
(G) SUCTION (VAPOR) LINE
(H) MAIN POWER SUPPLY
(I) THERMOSTAT
(J) OPERATIONAL CONTROLS AND SAFETIES
(K) REMOTE TEMPERATURE SENSOR
(L) EVAPORATOR FAN
(M) EVAPORATOR
(N) METERING DEVICE
(O) LIQUID LINE SUCTION LINE HEAT EXCHANGER
(P) LIQUID LINE
(Q) FILTER DRYER
(R) RECEIVER
(S) CONDENSATE LINE

Figure 76-1 A simple refrigeration system with a single compressor and air cooled condenser

On a small system it is general practice to install a surge tank in the suction line of the low temperature evaporator to prevent short cycling.

SERVICE TIP

Restaurants come and go, but the refrigeration equipment stays behind. Frequently refrigeration equipment designed for the original restaurant may not meet the needs of the new operation. When the primary loads change it is not possible simply to make adjustments to multiple evaporator systems to accommodate these changes. It is not possible to simply turn down or up the low temperature side of a system without adversely affecting the medium or high temperature side of a system. Restaurant managers are not always aware of this issue. It is in your best interest to take the time to explain to the manager what the difficulties can be for changing the load for refrigeration systems.

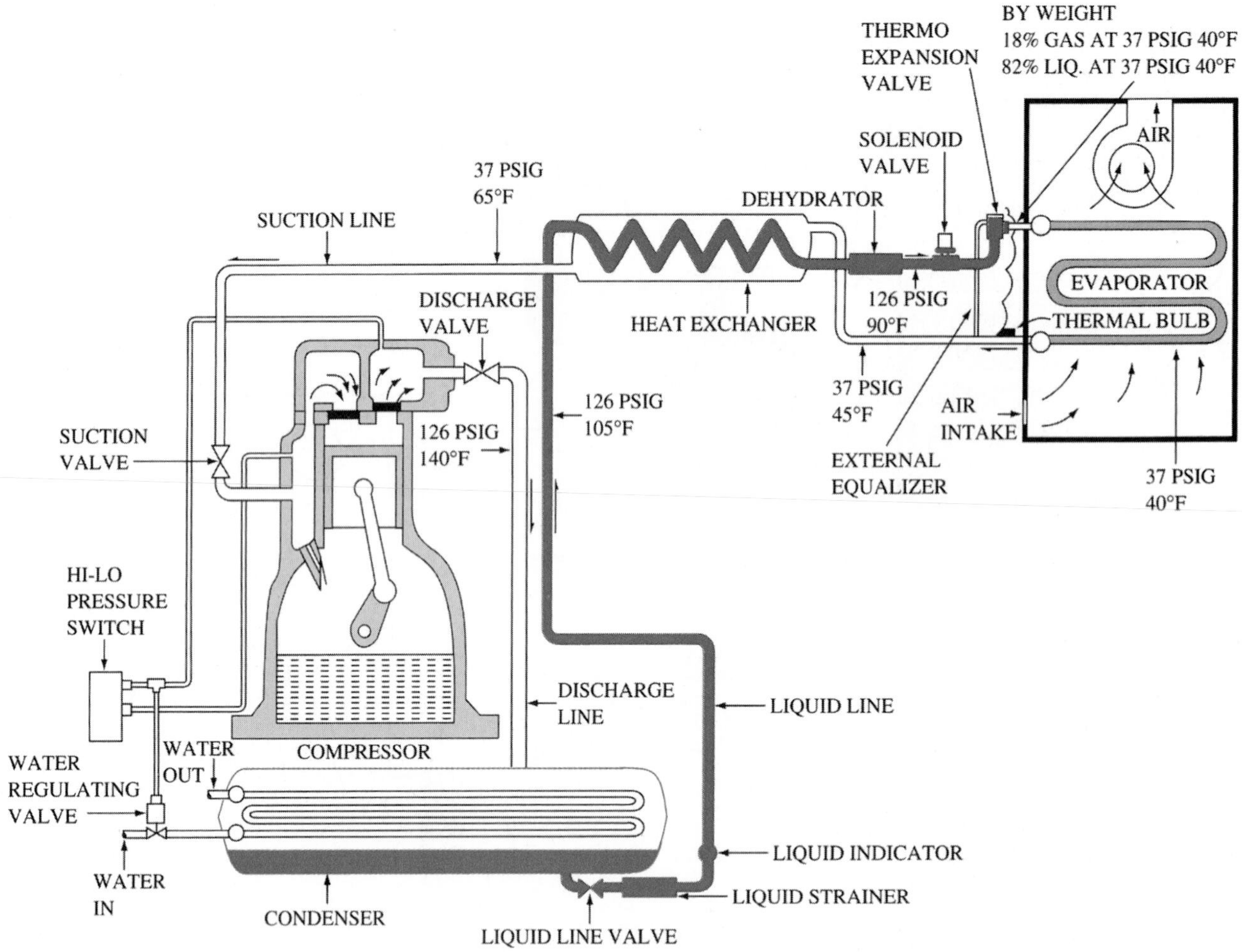

THERMO
EXPANSION
VALVE

BY WEIGHT
18% GAS AT 37 PSIG 40°F
82% LIQ. AT 37 PSIG 40°F

SOLENOID
VALVE

AIR

37 PSIG
65°F

SUCTION LINE

DEHYDRATOR

DISCHARGE
VALVE

HEAT EXCHANGER

EVAPORATOR

THERMAL BULB

126 PSIG
90°F

SUCTION
VALVE

126 PSIG
140°F

126 PSIG
105°F

37 PSIG
45°F

AIR
INTAKE

EXTERNAL
EQUALIZER

37 PSIG
40°F

HI-LO
PRESSURE
SWITCH

DISCHARGE
LINE

LIQUID LINE

WATER
REGULATING
VALVE

WATER
OUT

COMPRESSOR

LIQUID INDICATOR

WATER
IN

CONDENSER

LIQUID LINE VALVE

LIQUID STRAINER

Figure 76-2 A simple refrigeration system with a single compressor and water cooled condenser

Figure 76-3 Multiple evaporator system using evaporator pressure regulators to maintain different conditions in each box

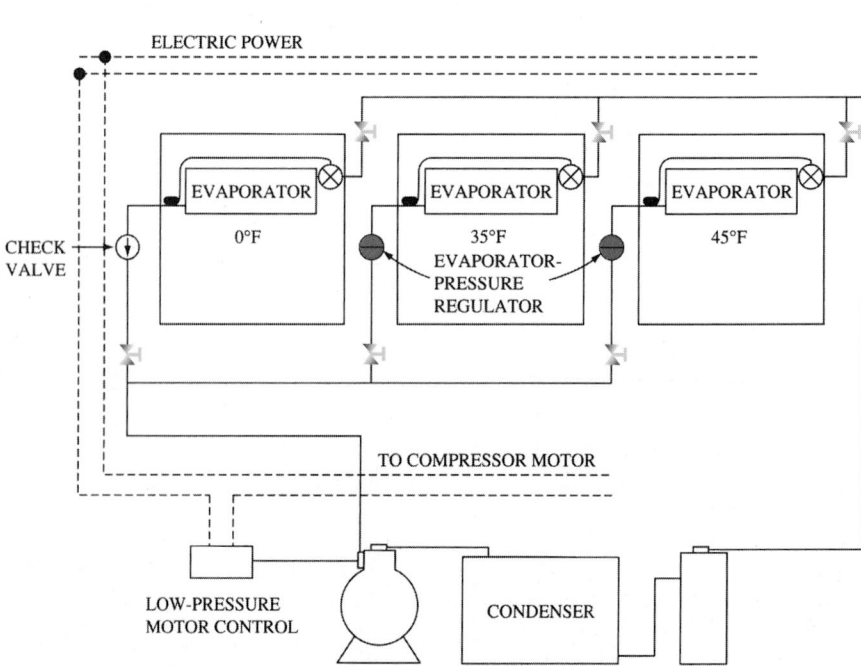

ELECTRIC POWER

EVAPORATOR
0°F

EVAPORATOR
35°F

EVAPORATOR
45°F

CHECK
VALVE

EVAPORATOR-
PRESSURE
REGULATOR

TO COMPRESSOR MOTOR

LOW-PRESSURE
MOTOR CONTROL

CONDENSER

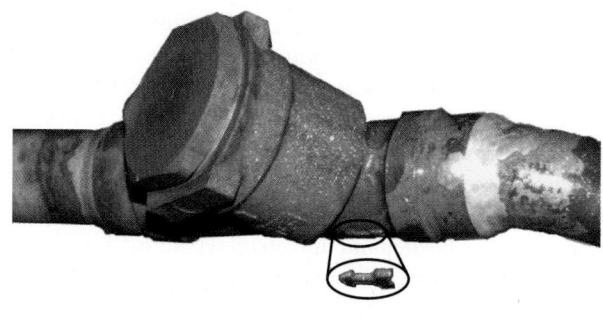

Figure 76-4 Refrigerant check valves have arrows showing the direction of flow

76.6 EVAPORATOR TEMPERATURE CONTROLS

Evaporator temperature can be controlled with a conventional thermostat, a suction pressure cutout control, or an evaporator pressure regulator. If the evaporator coil temperature is excessively low, the food stored in the space will be robbed of moisture and dry out. This is particularly true of vegetables and fruits. This moisture collects on the evaporator coil where it will freeze and lead to a build-up of ice.

An evaporator pressure regulator (EPR), Figure 76-5, maintains a steady refrigerant pressure in the evaporator coil. Since both liquid and vapor refrigerant fill the evaporator coil, the refrigerant is in its saturated state. For any given preset refrigerant pressure there will be a corresponding refrigerant saturation temperature. Regulating for a constant evaporator pressure provides a stable evaporator temperature.

Conventional thermostats and suction pressure cutout controls do not always maintain a constant evaporator pressure

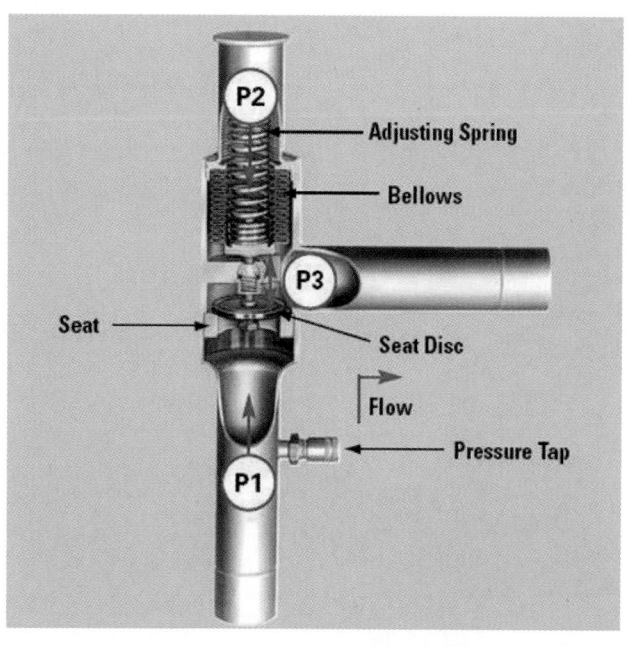

Figure 76-5 Evaporator pressure regulator (EPR) cutaway view *(Courtesy of Sporlan Division-Parker Hannifin Corporation)*

like an EPR. With these types of controls, the evaporator pressure is most likely to fall with a decrease in load. This can result in a lowering of the coil temperature to undesirable levels.

76.7 MULTIPLE COMPRESSOR SYSTEM

Where the refrigeration load varies over a wide range, such as in supermarkets, it is desirable to use multiple compressors connected in parallel, as shown in Figure 76-6. Suction pressure

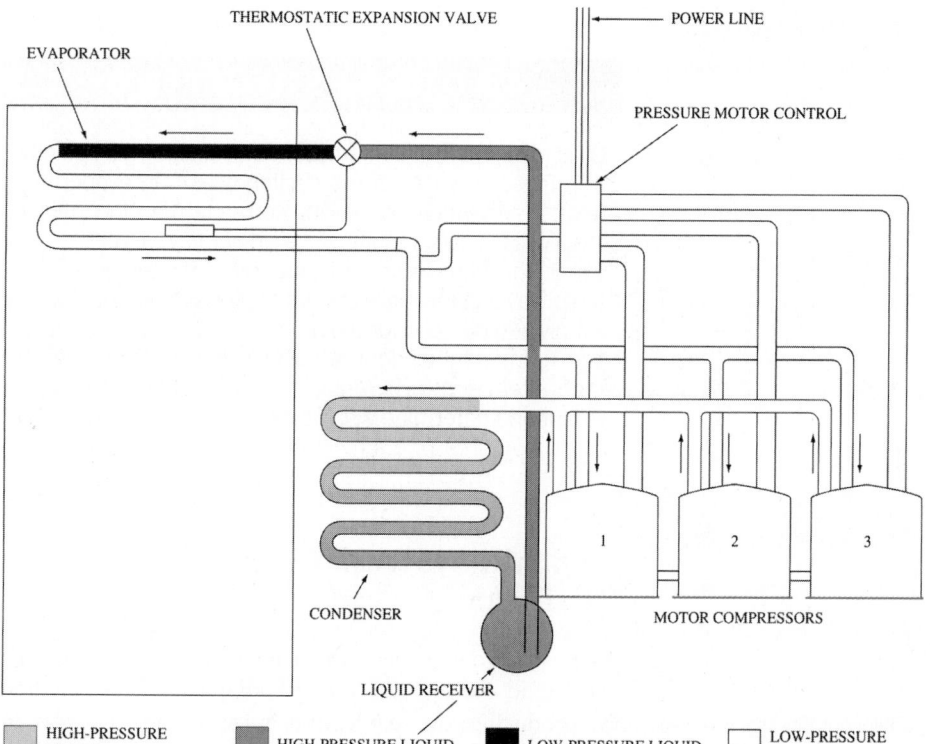

Figure 76-6 Multiple compressor system using three compressors connected in parallel

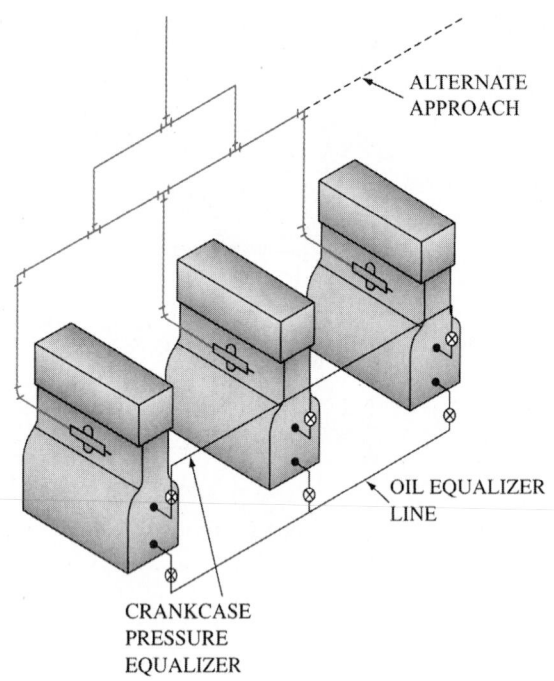

Figure 76-7 Suction line piping for parallel compressors

control is used to turn on and off individual compressors as required to match the load. These controls also have the ability to change the lead compressor to obtain approximately equal running time on each compressor. A single condenser and receiver is used for all units.

The refrigerant piping must be done properly, as shown in Figure 76-7 and Figure 76-8. Referring to Figure 76-7, the suction piping should be brought in above the level of the compressor. With multiple compressors, a common suction header should be used and the piping should be designed so that the oil return to several compressors is as nearly equal as possible.

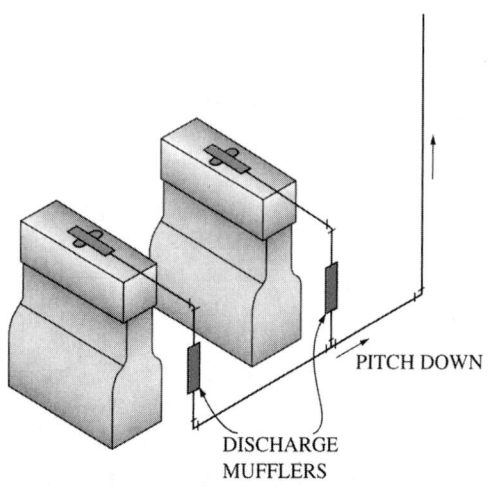

Figure 76-8 Discharge line piping for parallel compressors

If an oil level control is not used, the discharge piping as shown in 76-7 should be used with the discharge piping running to a header near to floor level. With this arrangement, a discharge line trap is not required since the header serves this purpose. It is also important to provide equalization of the oil level in all compressors using an arrangement such as shown in Figure 76-9. Oil is pumped by the compressor to a common discharge header and into an oil separator. Since the oil separator has a large holding capacity, oil is then transferred to an oil reservoir.

CAUTION

Maintaining proper oil level between multiple compressors is critical. If the compressor oil level drops, the system can be severely damaged or destroyed. Compressors have oil safety switches that are designed to trip and take the compressor offline when the oil pressure drops below a critical level. However, system owners and managers frequently see oil trips as a "nuisance" call and will push the reset button themselves. It is important that you stress to your customers that you must be notified each and every time a system shuts down as a result of an oil problem so that you are able to identify the root cause of the problem and correct it.

Pressure in the reservoir is reduced by boiling the refrigerant contained in the oil and relieving the pressure above the oil through a vent line to the suction header. An oil level control meters the oil to the compressors equal to the pumping rate and thereby maintains the oil level specified by the manufacturer.

TROUBLESHOOTING

Oil is returned to a compressor as a result of the velocity of refrigerant vapor in the suction line. If an evaporator defrost system is not working correctly, then the evaporator will ice over, resulting in a slower flow of refrigerant vapor. This can result in oil slugging of the evaporator. If the oil level in an entire system appears to be low, do not simply add oil. Look for the primary cause of the oil shortage. Refrigerant oil does not simply evaporate. It stays in the system somewhere and it is important that you locate it and determine what is necessary to have it return to the compressor during system operation.

76.8 MULTISTAGE COMPRESSOR SYSTEMS

There are two general methods of multistage compressors, compound and cascade. A *compound system* offers a method for producing low temperature refrigeration. In order to

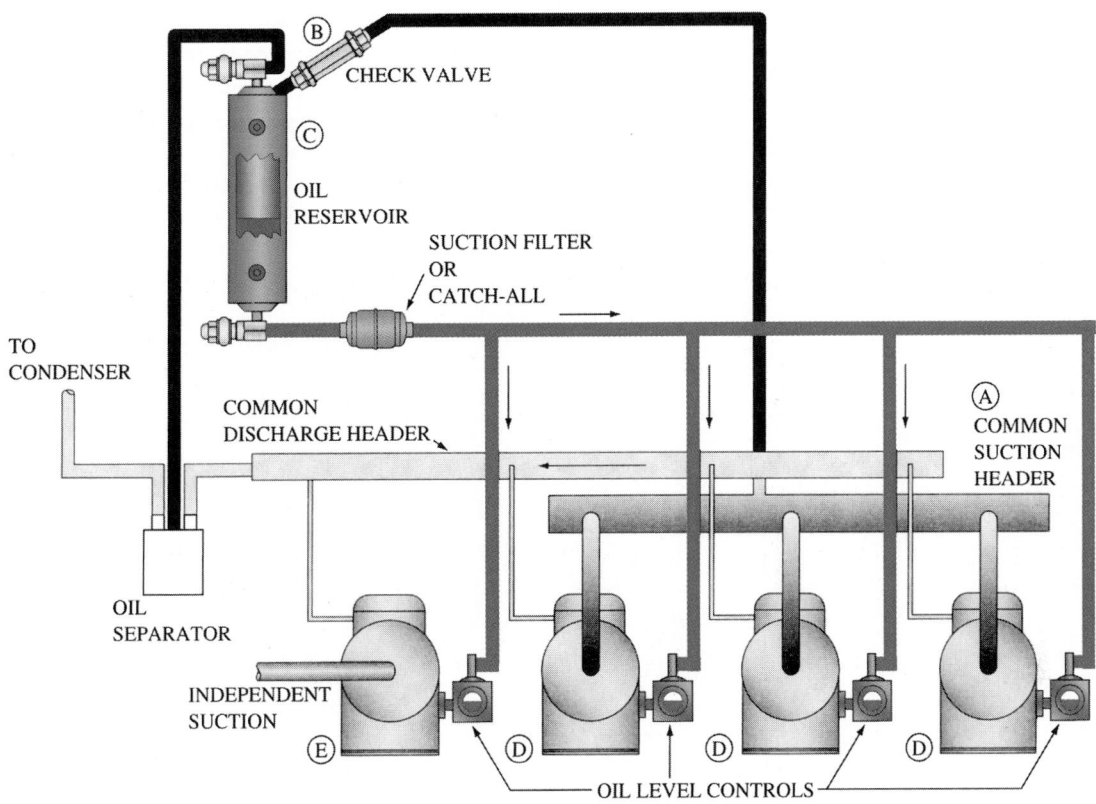

Figure 76-9 Oil level control system for multiple compressors
(Courtesy of Sporlan Valve Company)

achieve a low suction pressure, two compressors are connected in series as shown in Figure 76-10.

The suction line from the evaporator feeds the first compressor. Then the discharge from the first compressor enters the suction of the second compressor. The discharge from the second compressor goes to the condenser. Although both compressors handle about equal loads, the first compressor handles the greatest volume of gas, since the density of the gas in the first stage is less.

An important additional device in this system is the *intercooler* between the two stages that reduces the superheat in the discharge gas from the first compressor. This superheat, produced by the work done by the first compressor, must be removed to keep the gas temperature of the second compressor within limits. A single temperature control operates both compressor motors. On startup, both motors are started at the same time.

It would be possible to use a single compressor to achieve the multistage effect; however, the disadvantage of a single multistage compressor is that there is a fixed ratio between the high side and the low side volumes which only applies to applications where this ratio produces a satisfactory evaporating temperature. Compound systems using two compressors give the added flexibility of producing a wider range of low evaporating temperatures. Compound arrangements of compressors are seldom considered unless the desired evaporating temperature is below −20°F.

A single refrigerant is used throughout the entire compound system, in contrast to a cascade system which may use separate refrigerants for each compressor.

A *cascade system* is also used for low temperature refrigeration, but has the capability of reaching much lower temperatures than the compound system. The cascade system shown in Figure 76-11 uses two compressors; however, for lower temperatures, three or more stages (compressors) are used.

CAUTION

Because of the extreme load placed on low temperature compressors during startup, it may be necessary to use the suction line valve as a metering device to throttle the system capacity back so that it comes online more slowly. You can monitor the compressor amperage as the service valve is slowly opened so that it does not exceed the rated load by more than 10%. Failure to do this on large low temperature refrigeration systems, especially cascade system second stage compressors, can result in an almost immediate failure of the compressor.

The system has an interesting configuration. Each stage has a separate refrigeration circuit. Each stage can use a different refrigerant if there is an advantage in doing so. The

Figure 76-10 Compound refrigeration system using two compressors

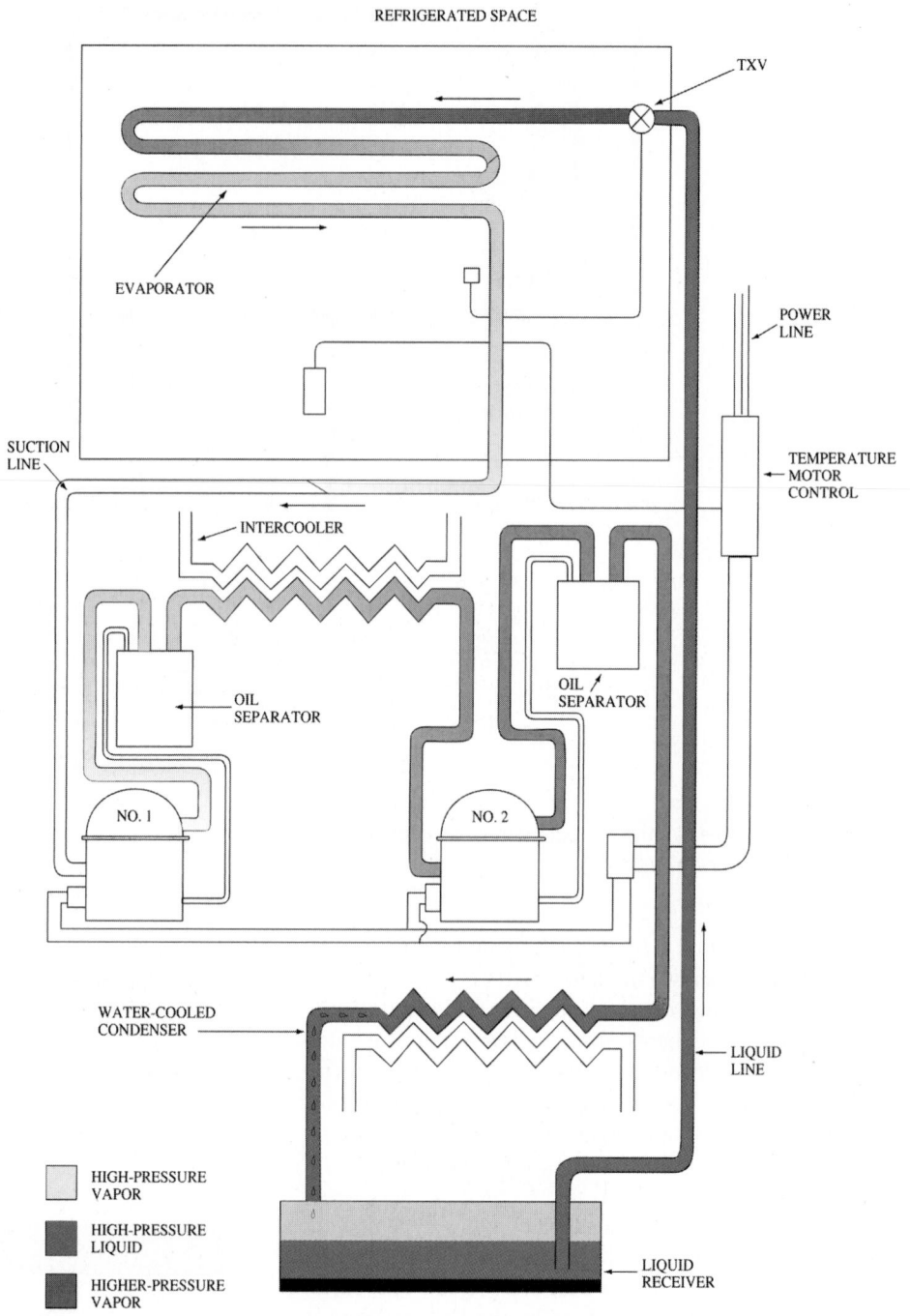

REFRIGERATED SPACE

TXV

EVAPORATOR

POWER LINE

SUCTION LINE

TEMPERATURE MOTOR CONTROL

INTERCOOLER

OIL SEPARATOR

OIL SEPARATOR

NO. 1

NO. 2

WATER-COOLED CONDENSER

LIQUID LINE

HIGH-PRESSURE VAPOR

HIGH-PRESSURE LIQUID

HIGHER-PRESSURE VAPOR

LIQUID RECEIVER

interconnection is through a common heat exchanger. In the system shown in Figure 76-11, the evaporator of the second stage machine cools the condenser of the first stage machine.

When the system is started up, the second (high) stage compressor is started first. After it lowers the evaporating temperature to the required level, the first (low) stage compressor is started. To facilitate shutdown, an expansion tank is added to the low stage circuit, as shown in Figure 76-12.

This is done to prevent the pressures from becoming excessive when the refrigerant is subjected to room temperatures. A relief valve on the high side circuit discharges into the expansion tank. Otherwise it would be necessary to transfer refrigerant to storage cylinders during shutdown.

76.9 EVAPORATIVE COOLING SYSTEMS

Evaporative cooling is the process of absorbing heat by the evaporation of water. Approximately 970 Btu of heat is required to evaporate a pound of water. Two general types of evaporative cooling are:

- An open system.
- A closed circuit system.

A diagram of an open system is shown in Figure 76-13.

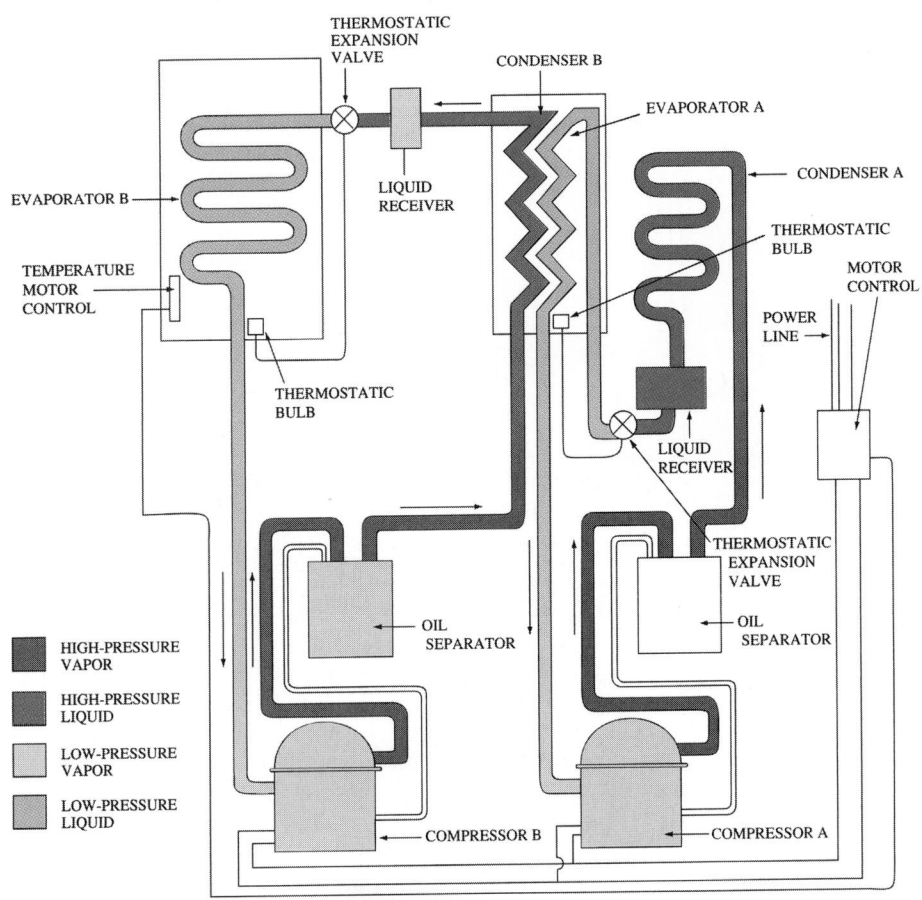

Figure 76-11 Cascade refrigeration system using two compressors

A cooling tower such as shown on top of the building in Figure 76-14 uses evaporative cooling to reduce the temperature of the hot water from the condenser so that it can be reused at a lower temperature.

Greenhouses, as shown in Figure 76-15, use evaporative cooling to provide a safe temperature for plants. Roof sprays are used to reduce roof temperatures to lower the building heat load. All of these systems are effective as long as the water temperature provided for evaporation is higher than the wet bulb temperature of the air.

TECH TIP

Because as water evaporates the dissolved minerals remain behind, evaporative cooling systems can be adversely affected by mineral deposits. An easy way to reduce the mineral deposit buildup in areas where water contains large quantities of dissolved minerals is to increase the water load to the system so that approximately 10% of the water in the pump flows into the waste water drain. This excessive water will keep the concentration of minerals in the basin low enough so that it does not pose as great a problem to system performance over time.

A *closed circuit* evaporative cooler is built like an evaporative condenser, as shown in Figure 76-16. Instead of refrigerant circulating through the coil, the coil is supplied with hot water from the condensers. The hot water entering the cooler is cooled by the evaporative action of the water on the outside of the tubes. This condensed water is pumped back to the condensers for reuse. The evaporative cooler coil, the circulating pump, the water cooled condensers, and an expansion tank are piped in series to form a closed loop.

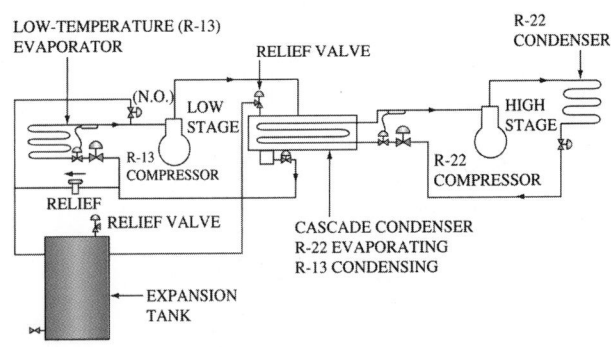

Figure 76-12 Cascade refrigeration system showing expansion tank added to the low stage circuit

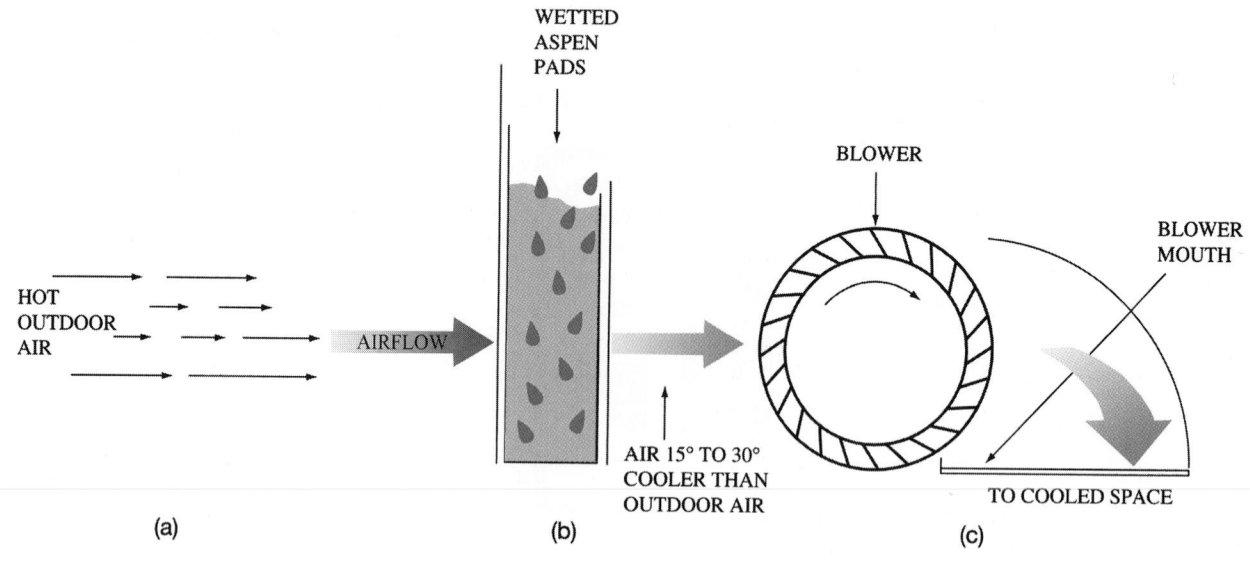

Figure 76-13 Schematic drawing of an evaporative cooling system

Figure 76-14 Cooling tower

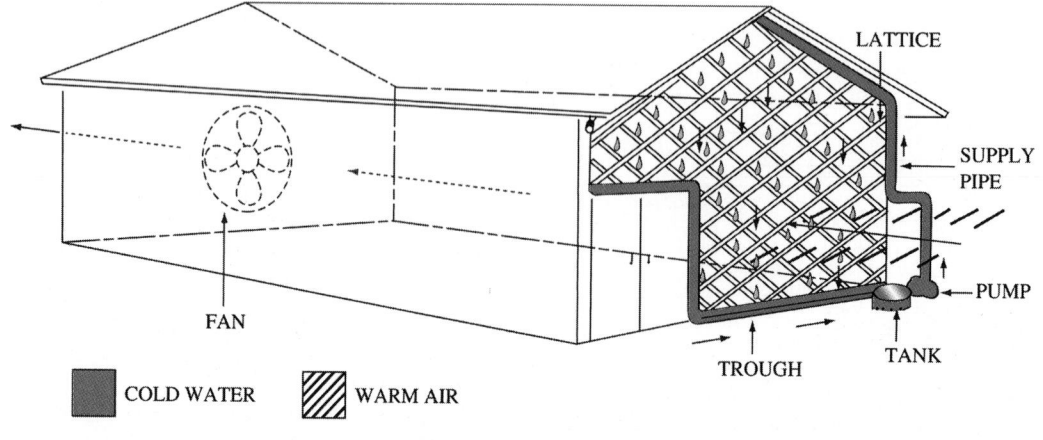

Figure 76-15 Application of evaporative cooling to a greenhouse

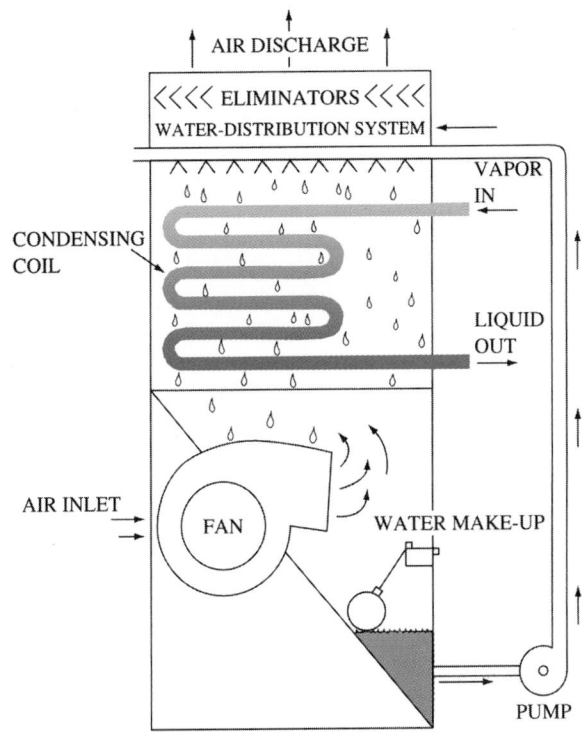

Figure 76-16 Diagram of a closed circuit evaporative cooler

76.10 SECONDARY REFRIGERANT

A secondary refrigerant is a fluid cooled by direct refrigeration and used to transfer cooling to a distant area where cooling is needed and long direct expansion lines are not practical or economical. A good example of the common use of a secondary refrigerant is in the application of *water chillers* to provide cooling for a large building.

A very effective use of water as the refrigerant for cooling is the *ice storage* application, as shown in Figure 76-17a,b.

These systems are used for comfort cooling installations where cooling is required only during the day. The refrigeration system builds up icy slurry during the night when electric rates are low. During the day, water is circulated through the icy slurry and through coils in the air conditioning system to provide cooling.

Where the secondary coolants are needed below the freezing temperature of water, a brine solution is used. *Brine* is the name given to a solution of a substance in water that lowers the freezing point of the water. Common additives are calcium chloride, sodium chloride, ethylene and propylene glycols, methyl alcohol, and glycerin. The amount of additive used affects the freezing point of the solution as shown in Table 76-1.

TECH TIP

The inventor of the mercury thermometer, Daniel Fahrenheit, used the lowest temperature that he could create using water, ice, and salt as the zero point on his

---

(a)

PNEUMATIC MOTOR AND PADDLES

(b)

Figure 76-17 (a) Ice storage used for cooling storage; (b) The pneumatic motor turns the paddles to "feel" when the ice storage tank is full so the compressor can be stopped

---

newly invented thermometer. The zero Fahrenheit point was the base point for his thermometer. The middle point was 32° or the freezing point of water, and the high point was 96° for the approximate temperature for the human body. These three fixed points were then used to calibrate and mark the scale for all of the thermometers Fahrenheit produced. During the 1720s it was important for scientists to be able to reproduce these scaled points so that thermometers manufactured in different parts of the world would have a uniform scale that could easily be related to temperature readings taken by other scientists in different parts of the globe. The 0°F point on the Fahrenheit scale therefore coincides with the lowest temperature a mixture of brine can be cooled to without the formation of ice crystals.

Table 76-1 Freezing Points of Aqueous Solution Used for Secondary Cooling

Alcohol		Glycerin		Ethylene glycol		Propylene glycol	
% by wt	°F	% by wt	°F	% by vol	°F	% by vol	°F
5	28.0	10	29.1	15	22.4	5	29.0
10	23.6	20	23.4	20	16.2	10	26.0
15	19.7	30	14.9	25	10.0	15	22.5
20	13.2	40	4.3	30	3.5	20	19.0
25	5.5	50	−9.4	35	−4.0	25	14.5
30	−2.5	60	−30.5	40	−12.5	30	9.0
35	−13.2	70	−38.0	45	−22.0	35	2.5
40	−21.0	80	−5.5	50	−32.5	40	−5.5
45	−27.5	90	+29.1			45	−15.0
50	−34.0	100	+62.6			50	−25.5
55	−40.5					55	−39.5
						59*	−57.0

*Above 60% fails to crystallize at −99.4°F.
(Copyright by the American Society of Heating, Refrigerating, and Air-Conditioning Engineers, Inc.)

A good example of the use of brine for secondary cooling is the ice rink application. The general plan for the piping is shown in Figure 76-18.

The brine used in modern rinks is a glycol solution. The layout includes supply and return headers with piping loops under the ice to carry the brine. The brine is pumped through the piping. It enters at a temperature of 12°F (−11°C) and returns to the chiller at 14°F (−10°C). Chillers are usually in the 100–125 hp range.

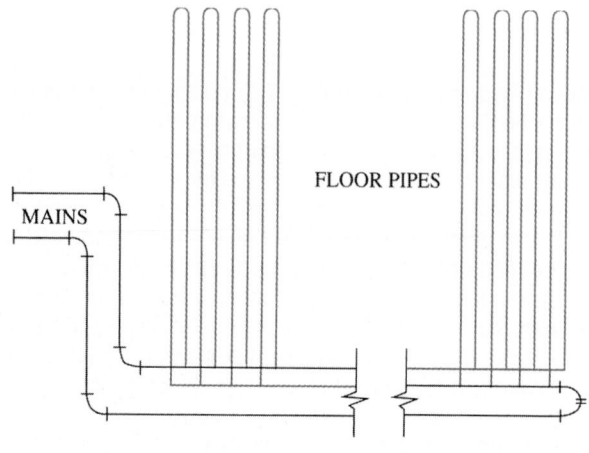

Figure 76-18 Piping schematic for an ice rink

76.11 THERMOELECTRIC REFRIGERATION

The thermoelectric refrigerator uses the *Peltier effect*, a physical principle discovered by Jean Peltier in 1834. He found that if direct current was passed through the junction of two dissimilar metals, the junction point would become hot or cold depending on the direction of current flow.

Figure 76-19 illustrates the construction of a thermoelectric refrigerator using semiconductors.

There are two types of semiconductors, the *N-type* which conducts electricity by the flow of negatively charged particles, and the *P-type* that conducts electricity by the flow of positively charged particles. When current flows from the N-type into the P-type, the junction absorbs heat. When current flows from the P-type to the N-type, the junction becomes warm and gives off heat. A single thermocouple produces a small amount of cooling, so a number of N-P junctions put in series produce a greater cooling effect. The diagram in Figure 76-19 shows a series of thermoelectric couples that pick up heat from the inside of the box and transfer the heat to the outside of the box.

Thermoelectric refrigerators are available in small portable units that can operate on 12 V automotive systems. Small electrically operated refrigerators can be found in hotel guest rooms and offices. Submarines and spaceships are often equipped with thermoelectric refrigerators.

One advantage of these units is that they have no moving parts requiring service. A disadvantage is that they are not as efficient as other types of electric refrigerators.

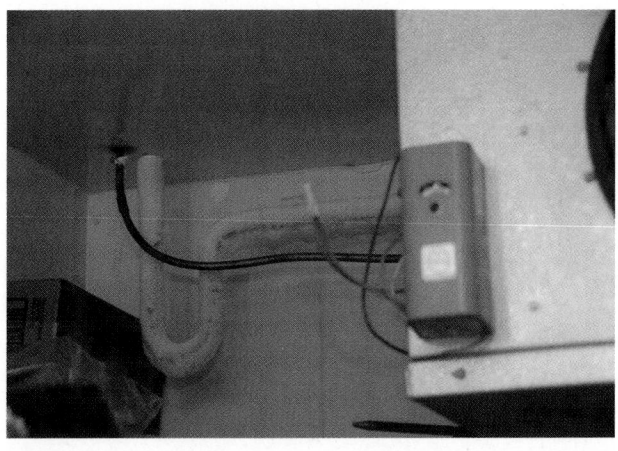

Figure 77-8 Adjustable temperature termination switch

pressure or temperature switch, if the termination switch fails, the defrost will be terminated by time. The fail-safe time should be set long enough to allow the system to terminate by the temperature or pressure switch, and short enough to prevent the system from over defrosting or creating a hazardous condition. Usually the fail-safe time is set to 35–45 min.

Terminating a defrost cycle by temperature is the most popular method. A temperature switch, such as one shown in Figure 77-8, is used to terminate a defrost cycle. It is installed on the evaporator at a location where the design engineers feel that frost will leave the coil last. At a specified temperature the defrost termination switch will close and energize the time-release solenoid (TRS), switching the system back into the refrigerating mode. The TRS is an electric solenoid located in the defrost timer. When the TRS is energized, it will mechanically switch the timer contacts: 2–4 will close and 1–3 will open. Many temperature termination switches are not adjustable and the temperature at which the switch closes may vary from design to design. It is best to check with the manufacturer of the system to determine the correct temperature setting. Some defrost termination switches will have the setting stamped onto the body of the device. A typical temperature cutin used on many systems is 60°F.

When the defrost cycle is terminated by pressure, a pressure control is used as the defrost termination switch. When the control senses a low side pressure that will ensure all the ice is removed from the evaporator, it will close and terminate the defrost cycle. Many times the pressure control and the defrost timer are combined into one unit. The pressure at which the switch closes will depend on the type of refrigerant used in the system. Check with the manufacturer for the recommended pressure setting.

The defrost timer can also be used to terminate defrost by time, although this method is not very popular. The time required to defrost an evaporator will vary depending on how much frost has developed on the coil. The ambient humidity level and the usage of the case will be a factor in how much frost develops on the coil. If the case is in a very humid location with heavy usage, a heavy accumulation of

frost will develop on the coil. If the case is installed in a location where the humidity level is low and has very little usage, the frost that develops on the coil will be less for the same time span.

Defrost systems can run into two problems: either the system will be over-defrosted or under-defrosted. Over-defrosting is when the defrost heaters stay energized too long, causing the case temperature to rise too high. The product may begin to melt and then refreeze. This problem can be identified by monitoring the box temperature during defrost or by examining the product in the case. Ice crystals forming on frozen product may be a sign of over-defrosting. Over-defrosting is normally caused by a malfunction in the termination of the defrost cycle. For time termination defrost systems, either the defrost time is set too long or the time clock is defective. On pressure terminated systems, either the terminating pressure control is set too high, the pressure control is defective, or the solenoid coil in the defrost timer is incorrectly wired or defective. On temperature terminated systems, either the temperature control is set too high, the control is defective, or the solenoid in the defrost timer is defective.

Systems that are under-defrosting will result in a frozen evaporator. The frost that normally develops on the evaporator coil will continue to build until the entire surface of the evaporator is iced over. This can be caused by a defective or incorrectly set time clock that does not initiate a defrost cycle. Or it can be caused by an open heater element or a defective defrost termination switch that continually terminates the defrost on each initiation of a new cycle.

Sizing Walk-in Coolers and Freezers

Sizing walk-in coolers and freezers generally is not a difficult procedure. There are many reference charts available that list the required refrigeration loads for different size walk-ins. Generally they provide two load estimates—one for average usage and one for heavy usage. It is important to remember that these load calculations are only estimates and the actual load requirements for a particular walk-in cooler or freezer may be different.

Heat load calculations for any walk-in cooler or freezer are based on four separate loads. These loads are:

- Heat transmission, which is the heat gained through the walls, floors, and ceiling of the walk-in structure.
- Air infiltration, which is heat gained due to the air entering the structure.
- Product load, which is the heat removed from a product to cool it from one temperature to a lower temperature. It also includes the heat of respiration from fruits and vegetables.
- Supplemental loads, which is the heat dissipated by people or mechanical equipment in the walk-in.

When sizing a walk-in cooler or freezer, a technician and/or salesperson must understand the application and environment in which the walk-in will be used. There are several situations where a person relying on the sizing chart alone could miscalculate the actual load for the walk-in.

If, for example, the walk-in were to be located outdoors rather than indoors, the heat gain through the walls would be much greater in the hot days of the summer than normally accounted for in many sizing charts. The size of the refrigeration equipment may need to be increased to remove this additional load. Two important questions a person sizing a walk-in cooler or freezer should ask are: Where is the walk-in going to be installed? What will the maximum ambient temperature outside of the box be?

Other important questions to ask concern the product going into the walk-in: How much and what type of product will be stored? What is the initial temperature of the product entering the walk-in? At what temperature does it need to be stored? Again, most charts are based on averages. If the temperature of the product entering the walk-in is higher than normal or if an unusual amount of product will be stored in the walk-in, the capacity of the refrigeration equipment may need to be increased.

Another potential problem with using generic sizing charts is with the supplemental loads. If the supplemental load is higher than the averages then the capacity as listed on a generic chart may need to be increased. For example, if many people will be working in the walk-in cooler, or if some type of major equipment will be running in the walk-in on a consistent basis, the load may need to be increased to handle this additional load.

There are other instances that may cause the actual load requirements to differ from the load as shown on a basic chart. Any person sizing walk-in coolers and freezers should know the process of calculating the actual load on a walk-in box. This will allow them to determine if a particular application falls outside the loads as stated on the charts and if a complete load calculation needs to be done.

77.6 STORAGE WAREHOUSES

Most modern refrigerated warehouses are one-story structures, as shown in Figure 77-9. The walls are constructed so that as few structural members as possible penetrate the insulated envelope. Insulated panels applied to the outside structural frame prevent conduction through the framing. It is usually convenient to locate the refrigeration equipment in a penthouse room.

77.7 REFRIGERATION EQUIPMENT SELECTION

Many field assembled refrigeration system installations require the installing contractor or sales engineer to select the proper system components. This involves selecting the correct condensing unit (compressor), unit cooler (evaporator), metering device, refrigerant, accessories, and piping. Before any of the system components can be selected, determine the required system Btu capacity by referring to a sizing chart or

Figure 77-9 Cold storage warehouse

performing a heat load calculation. Knowing the required Btu capacity for the project is the baseline for selecting the proper components for any installation. Many of the major system components are selected based on the Btu capacity of the system.

Normally the first major system component selected is the condensing unit, or compressor if the system will have a remote condenser. The Btu capacity of any compressor or condensing unit is based on the suction pressure of the refrigerant entering the compressor. Because of this, most manufacturers will provide the Btu capacity of their compressors or condensing units at a specific entering suction pressure, or more correctly, at a specific saturation temperature.

Determine the refrigerant saturation temperature by using a standard pressure/temperature (P/T) chart and convert the suction pressure to its equivalent saturation temperature. For example, if HFC-134a were the refrigerant and the entering suction pressure were 18.5 psig, the corresponding saturation temperature entering the compressor would be 20°F. First determine the design evaporator temperature to determine the saturation temperature entering a compressor. Many standard medium temperature applications use an evaporator temperature of 20–25°F, and many low temperature applications use an evaporating temperature of –10°F. Once the design evaporator temperature is determined, subtracting any suction line pressure losses will allow the approximated saturation temperature at the inlet of the compressor to be determined. For most applications a pressure loss equivalent to a 2°F reduction in saturation temperature is used. For example, if the design evaporating temperature were 22°F, the assumed saturation temperature entering the compressor would be 20°F.

The next component selected is the unit cooler or evaporator. The unit cooler must closely match the design Btu capacity of the compressor or condensing unit. Manufacturers of unit coolers will provide their Btu capacity at a specific temperature difference (TD), which is the difference between the air entering the unit cooler and the evaporating temperature of the refrigerant leaving the unit cooler. The desired TD of the unit cooler is selected to match the humidity requirements of the product being stored. For storage of general packaged products at a relative humidity of 85%, a TD of 10°F is normally used. Other types of products may require different relative humidity conditions, which will change the design TD.

Once the unit cooler has been selected, the metering device is next. Most field installed systems will use a thermostatic or electronic expansion valve. Capillary tubes and automatic expansion valves are normally used on self-contained systems that are completely assembled at the factory. The thermostatic expansion valve (TEV) is also selected based on the Btu capacity of the system. It is chosen to closely match the Btu capacity of both the condensing unit and unit cooler. The capacity of a TEV is based on several system characteristics. Always follow the selection guidelines of the TEV manufacturer for their recommendations.

Once all the major system components have been chosen, select the ACR tubing size. Size the tubing based on the Btu capacity of the system as well as the length of run. It is important to use correctly sized suction, discharge, and liquid lines on any application. Using an undersized suction line reduces overall system capacity. Using an oversized suction line leads to oil return problems. Always follow the equipment component manufacturer's guidelines for their recommendations.

77.8 LOCATING AIR COOLED CONDENSING UNITS

When installing walk-in coolers and freezers, the installing contractor will need to select the proper location of the condensing unit, such as shown in Figure 77-10. Location is an important consideration for the overall success of the installation. There are several items to consider when selecting the location of this type of condensing unit.

First, the location should be discussed with the customer. Be sure the customer is in agreement with the placement of the condensing unit. The customer may have a plan for the location different from where the installing contractor decides to place the unit. As retail space becomes more expensive, customers will want to take advantage of all the indoor space and may want the condensing unit located outdoors or in an indoor location that will not interfere with the retail operation.

If the condensing unit is to be placed indoors, make sure the location has adequate ventilation. Low temperature condensing units will require approximately 200 CFM per 1,000 Btu, and medium temperature units will require approximately 165 CFM per 1,000 Btu. Always check with the condensing unit manufacturer for ventilation requirements, as they may differ from these approximate values. Another consideration with air cooled units located indoors is the heat they may add to the space. This additional heat may be objectionable to the equipment owner.

An alternative to locating the condensing unit indoors is to place it outdoors. When installing outdoors there are several additional components that should installed on the condensing unit. The condensing unit should have a crankcase heater installed. This will help to prevent refrigerant migration during the off cycle when the condensing unit is exposed to temperatures that are colder than the evaporator. The condensing unit will also need some means of keeping the high side pressure above a minimum value during periods of low outdoor temperatures. This is normally accomplished with either a fan cycling control or a head pressure controller.

The method of controlling the case temperature may also need to be modified. The system should use a pump-down method to control the operation of the condensing unit. A standard air-sensing temperature controller should be used to control the operation of a liquid line solenoid. When the temperature controller is satisfied it will close the liquid line solenoid, causing the refrigerant to be trapped in the condenser and receiver. This will cause the low-side pressure to drop. The system's low-pressure control will then shut down the condensing unit when the low side pressure drops to an appropriate value.

The outdoor unit should also be covered to protect it from the outdoor environment, as shown in Figure 77-11. If the

Figure 77-10 Air cooled condensing unit
(Courtesy of Danfoss, Inc.)

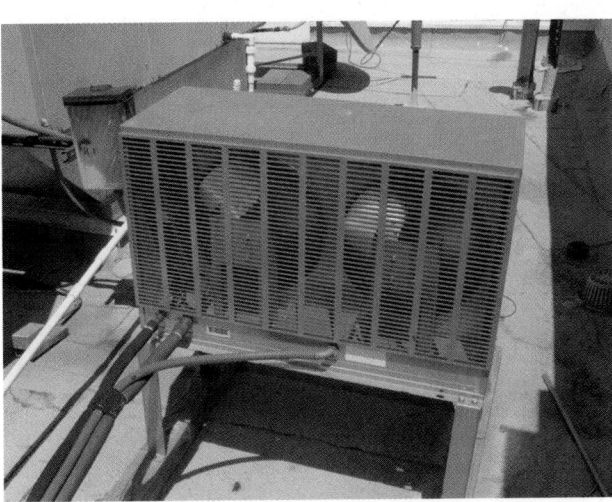

Figure 77-11 Outdoor condensing unit with enclosure

condensing unit is ordered for an outdoor application it will normally come with some type of enclosure. When moving an indoor condensing unit to the outdoors, make sure an adequate enclosure is constructed to properly protect the unit.

77.9 INSTALLING EVAPORATOR COILS IN A WALK-IN COOLER OR FREEZER

When installing a walk-in cooler or freezer, the installation of the evaporator coil is vital to the proper operation of the entire refrigeration system. A typical installation of an evaporator coil is shown in Figure 77-12. There are several general guidelines that apply to most installations; however, it is always best to check with the manufacturer of the evaporator for specific instructions. Below is a list of several guidelines:

- The air pattern of the evaporator must envelop the entire case. This is important in order to provide a more uniform temperature throughout the entire box. Do not install the coil where product could potentially be stacked that would block the airflow. Always allow for sufficient space between the rear and sides of the evaporator to permit free return air.
- Never install an evaporator above a door. This can cause the evaporator to draw warm, humid air through the coil each time the door is opened. This will cause the evaporator to frost up more quickly and may cause an icing problem.
- Do not install an evaporator coil in an area where it will interfere with the cooler's aisles or storage racks. This may cause a problem for the storeowner, which could result in the evaporator needing to be relocated. The location of the evaporator should allow for easy storage and removal of the refrigerated product.
- The evaporator should be installed in a location that will provide the shortest possible distance between it and the condensing unit. Excessive piping can increase the pressure drop between the evaporator and the

condensing unit. An excessive pressure drop will decrease the system's overall refrigeration capacity.

- The location of the condensate drains should provide for minimum pipe length. This will allow for proper drainage. In addition, the unit should be kept level for proper drainage and it should be trapped. When draining two or more evaporators into a common drain, always trap drain lines individually to prevent vapor migration. On low temperature evaporators, the traps should be located outside the case. If freezing of the traps is still a potential problem, they should be heated and wrapped.
- Supports for hanging the unit should be sufficient to hold its weight. For coils up to 250 lb, $5/16$ in bolts or threaded rods should be sufficient. For coils up to 500 lb, $3/8$ in bolts or threaded rods should be used. Coils over 500 lb should use $5/8$ in bolts or threaded rods. When using rod hangers, allow adequate space between the top of the unit and the ceiling for cleaning. If fastening the evaporator flush to the top of the cooler, seal the joint between the top and ceiling with an approved sealant.

77.10 PACKAGED LIQUID CHILLERS

Packaged water chillers, such as one shown in Figure 77-13, are used to cool water or brine, as a secondary refrigerant, for both air conditioning and refrigeration applications. They are available in capacity sizes ranging from 25 tons to 3,000 tons. A good example of this type of refrigeration system is its use for cooling the glycol brine used on many ice rinks. The basic

15 ton outdoor chiller

Figure 77-12 An installation of an evaporator coil in a walk-in cooler

Figure 77-13 Liquid package chiller
(Courtesy of Dimplex Thermal Solutions formerly Koolant Koolers.)

components include a motor driven compressor, a liquid cooler (evaporator), and either a water cooled or air cooled condenser, a refrigerant metering device, and a control system.

Liquid chillers are available with reciprocating, scroll, screw, or centrifugal compressors. The type of compressor used will depend on the overall capacity of the system. Reciprocating and scroll compressors are typically used on smaller capacity systems, and screw and centrifugal compressors are typically used on large capacity systems.

The type of control system used on these chillers will vary somewhat depending on the type of compressor used. These systems are typically designed to maintain a specific secondary refrigerant liquid temperature. They will have a sensor on the secondary refrigerant liquid line that will control the compressor's operation and maintain the desired secondary refrigerant liquid temperature. Most chillers have some arrangement for changing the capacity of the chiller to match the load. Screw compressors have capacity controls. Many screw compressors have a large range of capacity modulation. Secondary refrigerant temperature can be controlled to within 0.5°F from full load to 30% capacity. Reciprocating compressors use either multiple compressors or compressors with unloaders to vary capacity. The capacity of reciprocating compressors can only vary in defined steps. The steps in their capacity control will be determined by the number of compressors used and the arrangement of the unloaders used on each compressor.

The evaporators used on these liquid chillers are typically designed to reduce the returning secondary refrigerant temperature 10°F as the secondary refrigerant flows through the evaporator. For example, the secondary refrigerant could enter the chiller at 54°F and leave at approximately 44°F.

Figure 77-14 Refrigerated vending machine

77.11 VENDING MACHINES

Refrigerated vending machines, shown in Figure 77-14, allow businesses to sell refrigerated food products and beverages as a self-service option where there is no full-service cafeteria. They are available in both medium and low temperature applications.

These systems will normally use a fractional horsepower refrigeration system with a capillary tube metering device, an air cooled condenser, and a forced draft evaporator. Evaporator condensate is handled in the same way as in reach-in coolers. Time off defrost is normally used to defrost the evaporator since an off cycle defrost may not be long enough for a proper defrost. Since some machines may be located outdoors, they may have low ambient controls to maintain a minimum high side pressure.

Many have a health switch, which is a temperature switch that alerts a customer that the machine is operating above a safe operating temperature. For example, a sandwich dispenser operating above a temperature of 45°F for 30 min will shut off its lights and signal the customer not to buy the product.

Technicians working on these units must also be able to repair the coin and dispensing components of the machine. Normally a technician will receive training from the machine manufacturer on maintaining, servicing, and troubleshooting these components.

77.12 WATER COOLERS

Water coolers refrigerate drinking water in many commercial office buildings. There are two basic types of water coolers: one fed by city water and one in which an inverted water bottle is placed on top. A typical water cooler is pictured in Figure 77-15.

Water coolers that refrigerate city water will typically have a basin on top. These basins are generally made of porcelain-coated cast iron, porcelain-coated steel, or stainless steel. The water is dispensed through a fixture on the basin called a bubbler. Water coolers will also have a water regulator to control the water pressure at the bubbler. They will also have a permanent drain line attached to drain away any unconsumed water. Some water coolers will have a heat exchanger located between the drain line and either the incoming water or the liquid line of the refrigeration system to allow the system to operate more efficiently. The plumbing connection of these units must conform to local plumbing codes. These units can either be free standing or wall mounted systems.

Water coolers that have an inverted water bottle placed on top will typically dispense the water through a spout. They are normally freestanding and normally will not have a permanent drain system.

The refrigeration system is normally a self-contained, fractional horsepower, capillary tube system using an evaporator, and inside there is a small insulated tank to hold the water. This tank is made of nonferrous metal such as copper, brass, or stainless steel. They are thermostatically controlled to maintain

Figure 77-15 Refrigerated water cooler
(Courtesy of Halsey Taylor)

an approximate water temperature of 50°F. The cabinet is made so that one or more sides may be easily removed for access to the refrigeration system and waterside components.

77.13 REFRIGERATED AIR DRIERS

Some mechanical systems need dry compressed air to operate. When air is compressed it leaves the air compressor saturated with moisture. Some of this moisture condenses in the air storage tank and is exhausted through a float. However, the air is still very close to saturation when it leaves the tank. Refrigerated air driers are designed to lower the temperature of the air below its dew point temperature so water will condense out of it. A typical refrigerated air drier is shown in Figure 77-16a,b.

Refrigerated air dryers may run continuously with little to no load. If this is the case, then a hot gas bypass will be installed on the unit. As the load decreases on the evaporator the hot gas valve opens and allows hot gas to enter the suction line. This prevents the evaporator from operating at temperatures below 32°F and prevents the evaporator from icing up.

77.14 TRANSPORT REFRIGERATION

Many food products must be refrigerated when transported from their supplier to a local warehouse, or when being delivered from a warehouse to a local supermarket or restaurant. There are many different ways of transporting food

(a)

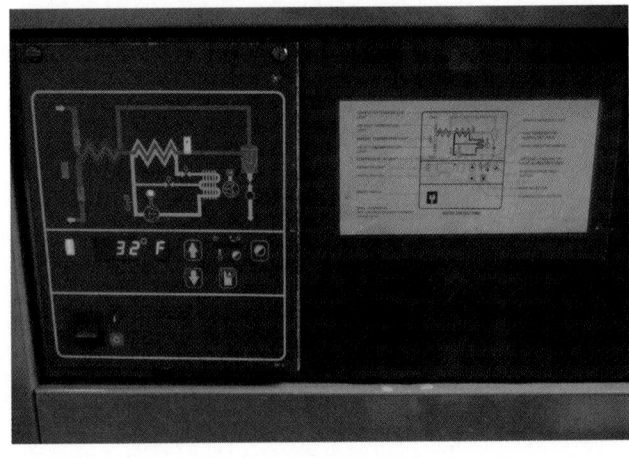

(b)

Figure 77-16 (a) Refrigerated air dryer; (b) air dryer control panel

products: by trucks, railroad containers, airplanes, or boats. Each of these vehicles will contain a refrigerated vessel that holds the product at a safe temperature. These vessels must be designed to maintain food products in either a frozen or a refrigerated state. Sometimes these vessels must also be able to heat the product to prevent it from dropping below a specific temperature.

Truck Refrigeration

Truck refrigeration requires special trailer bodies that are well insulated. The refrigerating system is similar to many other types of commercial refrigeration systems. A typical truck refrigeration unit is shown in Figure 77-17. One major difference is how power is supplied to operate the compressor and the other system components. These systems can use either a separate diesel or gas engine or the vehicle's engine to operate the compressor and an electric generator to operate any other system components or the entire system can be powered from a landline when not on the road.

Figure 78-14 Oil separators used to remove oil from the discharge gas
(Courtesy Danfoss Inc.)

78.15 HOT GAS LINE MUFFLERS

Mufflers are used on systems to reduce the noise that can be produced by the gas pulsations of the refrigerant being compressed and pumped by a compressor. Mufflers are normally installed on the discharge line of the compressor. A typical discharge line muffler is shown in Figure 78-15.

Figure 78-15 Hot gas line muffler

They are made of a brazed or welded cylinder with baffle plates mounted on the inside. Compressor manufacturers can also install a muffler interior to a compressor. When a muffler is added to a system, it will commonly be placed in the discharge line as close to the compressor as possible.

78.16 RECEIVERS

A receiver is a vessel that allows a system to store excess refrigerant that it does not currently need. A typical receiver is shown in Figure 78-16. A refrigeration system is designed to remove the maximum heat load as calculated by the system designer. When exposed to its maximum heat load, the entire amount of refrigerant needs to circulate throughout the system. When exposed to less than its maximum heat load, not all of the refrigerant needs to circulate and the system will store this excess refrigerant in its receiver. Only systems that have the ability to regulate the flow of refrigerant and are exposed to varying heat loads should have a receiver installed.

Receivers are normally installed in the liquid line of a system after the condenser and before the metering device. The inlet connection of the receiver will allow refrigerant to enter the top of the receiver. The outlet of the receiver will be connected to an internal dip tube connected to the bottom of the receiver. This ensures that only liquid refrigerant leaves the receiver and travels to the system's metering device.

Receivers are typically designed to hold 20% more than the entire system's refrigerant charge. This additional 20% allows a vapor cushion to exist within the receiver so that it cannot become overfilled with refrigerant.

The service valve installed at the outlet of the receiver is referred to as the king valve. This valve is very useful for a service technician. It allows a technician to read the system's pressure at the receiver as well as trap the system's refrigerant charge in the condenser and receiver. This allows a technician to work on any section of the system from the outlet of the king valve to the inlet of the compressor without having to recover the refrigerant charge.

78.17 DEFROST TIMERS

Defrost timers are used to initiate and terminate a defrost cycle on a refrigeration system. Depending on the type of defrost used, the defrost timer will either simply shut the refrigeration system down (time off defrost) or activate some type of supplementary heating circuit to mechanically defrost the evaporator.

When supplemental heat is used to defrost an evaporator, a defrost timer does not normally terminate the defrost cycle. The defrost cycle will then be terminated either by a temperature or pressure control. However, the defrost timer will serve as a backup and terminate the defrost, if the normal means of termination (temperature of pressure) does

Figure 78-16 Liquid receiver showing inlet and outlet valves and safety relief

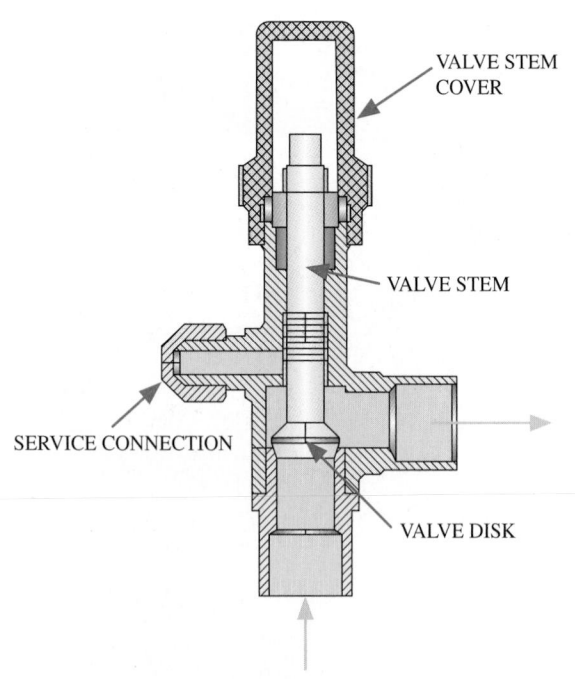

Figure 78-17 Suction service valve

not terminate defrost. This is a safety feature that will prevent the system from staying in defrost too long.

Many commercial defrost timers are field adjustable to vary the defrost times and number of defrosts that may be needed. Some systems may need to be defrosted only once a day, while others may need to be defrosted up to four times a day.

78.18 ELECTRIC DEFROST HEATERS

Many low temperature applications (freezers) use electric defrost heaters to supply the supplemental heat needed to defrost an evaporator coil. Electric defrost heaters are simply resistance heaters encased in a metal covering. Some smaller systems may encase the resistive heaters in a glass housing, but a metal housing is much more common. When voltage is applied to the heater, it converts electrical energy into heat energy and melts the frost off the evaporator. Electric defrost heaters are sized by wattage per foot. It is important to match the wattage of the heaters to the design of the system. A heater that is too small will not completely defrost the evaporator and a heater too large may overdefrost an evaporator. Overdefrosting may cause the product in the case to become too warm, causing it to defrost and spoil.

78.19 COMPRESSOR SERVICE VALVES

Many refrigeration compressors incorporate a suction service valve and a discharge service valve. A typical suction service valve is shown in Figure 78-17. These valves are used to allow refrigeration gauges to be attached to the system and, if needed, are used to isolate the compressor from the rest of system.

A typical compressor service valve is composed of four essential parts:

- Line connection.
- Compressor connection.
- Valve stem.
- Gauge port.

There are three positions in which the valve can be oriented. If the valve stem is all the way out, the valve is considered to be in the *back seated position*. The gauge port is closed and the valve is open, allowing refrigerant to flow through the system.

If the valve stem is all the way in, the valve is considered to be in the *front seated position*. The gauge port is open to the compressor connection and the refrigerant line (suction or discharge) connection is closed.

If the valve stem is between the front seated and back seated position, it is considered to be in the *mid seated position*. In this position all three connections—the gauge port, line, and compressor—are open. This allows the refrigerant to flow through the system and the system pressures to be read through the gauge port. When placing the valve in its mid seated position, it is best to have the valve in its back seated position first and then turn the valve stem only one or two turns into its mid seated position.

When opening a service valve, place it in a vise or attach it to the compressor to secure it. Also, look to see if the service valve has a packing gland nut—many will have this. The packing gland nut helps to ensure a leak-free seal. It is typically made of brass and is found at the base of the valve stem. It must be loosened by a quarter turn to a full turn before opening the valve stem. Not loosening the gland packing nut prior to turning the

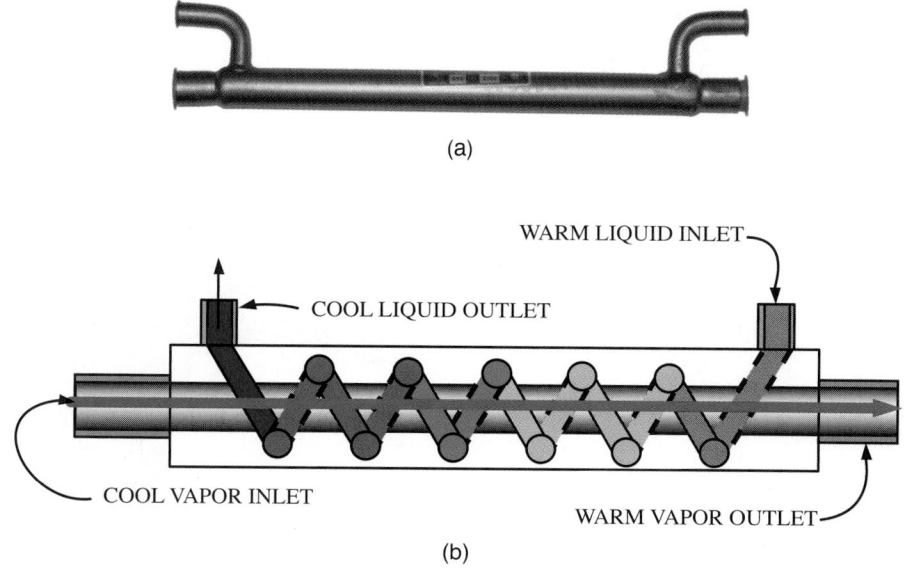

(a)

(b)

Figure 78-18 Suction to liquid line heat exchanger used to subcool the liquid and superheat the suction gas

valve stem may cause the valve to leak. Be sure to tighten the nut when you are finished manipulating the valve stem.

Make sure to use the right tools whenever opening and closing compressor service valves, such as an appropriately sized service wrench. Do not attempt to open a service valve with an adjustable wrench. You can easily round the valve stem edges and cause the valve to be useless.

78.20 SUCTION-TO-LIQUID HEAT EXCHANGER

In addition to the evaporator and condenser, there are other types of heat exchangers that can be added to a system. A suction-to-liquid line heat exchanger, shown in Figure 78-18, can be added to improve system efficiency and help prevent liquid from returning to the compressor. The liquid line is connected to the suction line, in such a way as to transfer heat from one fluid to the other through the tubing material. The cool vapor in the suction line returning to the compressor cools the liquid refrigerant entering the metering device. At the same time, the cool suction vapor is warmed by the liquid refrigerant to help boil off any liquid that might be flowing down the suction line.

78.21 HEAT RECLAIM COILS

Some larger refrigeration systems will reclaim the heat from the discharge vapor leaving a compressor and use this heat to either assist the heating of the building or assist in the heating of the domestic hot water for the building.

As the discharge vapor leaves the compressor it is piped to another heat exchanger, commonly referred to as a heat reclaim coil shown previously in Figure 78-11. This heat exchanger will extract some useful heat for this discharge

vapor and then the cooler discharge vapor will be piped to the system's condenser.

78.22 FILTER-DRIERS

Filter-driers are actually two devices incorporated into one housing. A cutaway view of a filter-drier is shown in Figure 78-19. An inside screen filters out any debris in the system that could potentially clog the small orifice in the metering device. It also has a desiccant inside that absorbs any water vapor in the system. Water vapor is very harmful to a refrigeration system. Even a very small amount—as little as 100 ppm—can cause serious system problems. Excessive amounts of water vapor can cause two problems: (1) it could freeze at the metering device causing a restriction; or (2) it could react with heat and oil inside the compressor to produce sludge and

Figure 78-19 Cutaway view of a filter-drier

potentially acids. The filter-drier is designed to help keep the system clean and dry. Any time a refrigeration system is opened for service, the filter-drier should be replaced.

78.23 STRAINERS

Strainers are similar to filter-driers except there is no desiccant inside to absorb the moisture in the system. Strainers are simply filters used to prevent solid particles from entering metering devices and causing a restriction.

78.24 WATER PRESSURE REGULATORS

A water cooled condenser that runs city water through its coils can use a water pressure regulator to control the water flow, as shown in Figure 78-20. This regulator will maintain a desired high side pressure and also provide a means of completely stopping the flow of water during the off cycle. The refrigerant pressure in the condenser is exposed to the underside of a diaphragm. As the condenser pressure increases, the diaphragm flexes and, through a mechanical linkage, opens the valve to let more water flow through it. As the condenser pressure decreases, less pressure is applied to the underside of the diaphragm and an opposing spring on the opposite side of the diaphragm closes the water valve. The spring pressure and the condenser pressure oppose one another to balance the correct amount of water flow through the valve. When the system shuts down the condenser, pressure is too low to oppose the spring pressure and the water valve completely shuts down.

78.25 SIGHT GLASSES/MOISTURE INDICATORS

A sight glass can be added to the liquid line to allow a technician to view the condition of the refrigerant in the liquid line at the point it is located. A typical liquid line sight glass is shown in Figure 78-21a, b. On a properly operating system the liquid line should contain only liquid refrigerant. A sight glass will show this condition, as only clear liquid will be seen flowing through the sight glass. If vapor exists along with the liquid refrigerant, it will be seen flowing through the sight glass along with the liquid refrigerant.

An indicator can also be added to a sight glass to help indicate the moisture content of the refrigerant. The indicator is a porous filter paper impregnated with chemical salt that is sensitive to moisture. A technician can view the indicator in the sight glass and the color of the paper will show the moisture content of the refrigerant. A common color-coding is green for a dry system and yellow for a wet system. Always check with the sight glass manufacturer to verify their color-coding system.

WATER VALVE

(a)

VALVE ADJUSTMENT

SPRING PRESSURE

WATER VALVE

REFRIGERANT PRESSURE

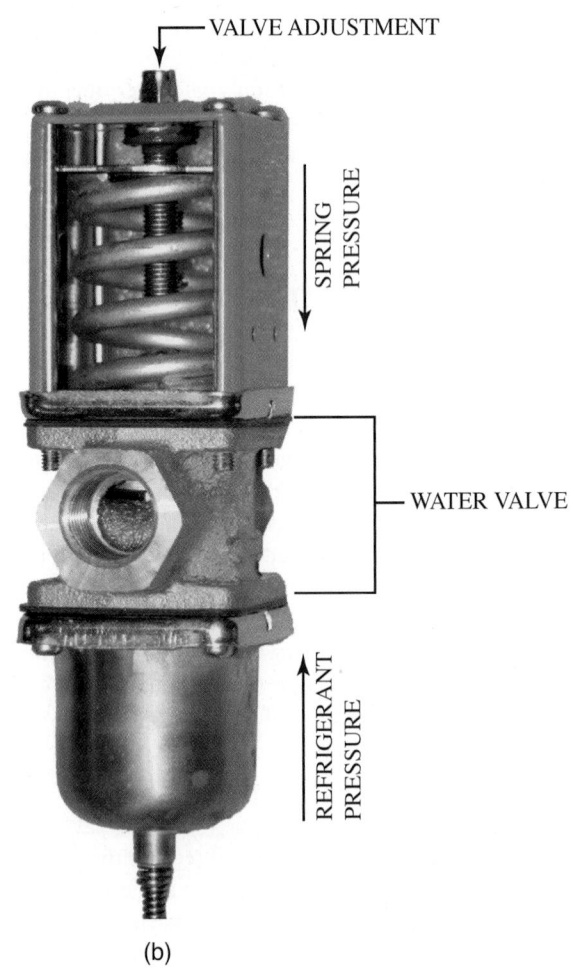

(b)

Figure 78-20 Condenser water regulating valve used for head pressure control
(Courtesy of Hampden Engineering Corporation)

(a)

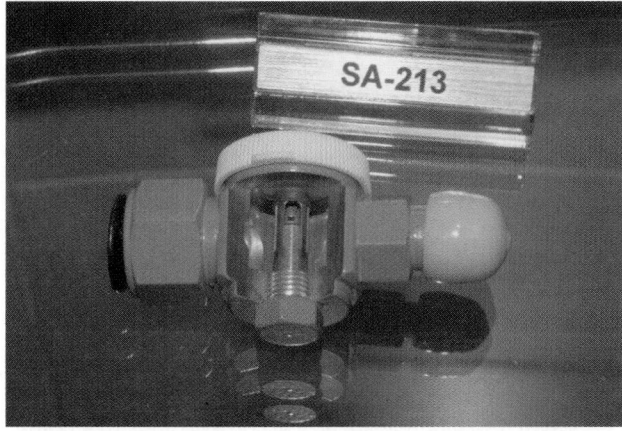

(b)

Figure 78-21 Liquid line sight glass moisture indicator (a) front view; (b) cross section

78.26 VIBRATION ELIMINATORS

As a compressor operates, it produces some vibrations in the suction line and discharge line. Figure 78-22 shows a vibration eliminator. On larger systems the vibration could cause

Figure 78-22 Suction line vibration eliminator

abnormal stress on the lines, which could lead to refrigerant leaks on those lines. Vibration eliminators are used to absorb some of the vibration created by the compressor. Typically they are made of flexible bronze tubing that expands and contracts like an accordion. Braided bronze strips with copper absorb the vibrations and prevent overstressing the copper lines leading to and from the compressor.

UNIT 78—SUMMARY

There are many components that could be added to the basic refrigeration system. Some of these components are designed to improve the operation of a system while others are safety components for the major system components and equipment owner.

An evaporator pressure regulator (EPR) is a refrigerant flow control device that prevents the refrigerant pressure in the evaporator from operating below a minimum value. A crankcase pressure regulator (CPR) is an outlet pressure regulator that will not allow the crankcase pressure to rise above a predetermined level, preventing the compressor from overloading.

A solenoid valve is a flow control device that stops or allows the flow of a refrigerant in a refrigeration system. Check valves are used on some larger refrigeration systems to ensure that the refrigerant flows in one direction only. Ball valves are used to isolate system components. Ball valves are preferred over other valves because they cause less restriction to the flow of refrigerant. Relief valves are used to release abnormally high pressure inside a vessel before the pressure causes it to burst.

High-pressure controls are normally used as safety controls. A low-pressure control is normally used to start and stop a compressor. It can be used as a safety control to stop the compressor in the event of a loss of refrigerant, or it can be used as a temperature control to cycle the compressor on and off to maintain a desired temperature. An oil pressure control is a safety control designed to stop a compressor if there is an insufficient amount of oil being fed to its bearings.

Fan cycling pressure controls are designed to cycle the condenser fan motor(s) on and off as needed to maintain a minimum discharge pressure. A temperature control is an electrical switch that opens and closes based on specific temperatures. Temperature controls can be divided into two major groups: mechanical and electronic. Low ambient controls are designed to maintain a minimum discharge pressure during low ambient conditions.

A suction line accumulator is a safety device that helps prevent liquid refrigerant from returning to the compressor. Oil separators are used to separate and collect some of the oil in the discharge line as it leaves the compressor and return it to the compressor's crankcase. Mufflers are used on systems to reduce the noise that can be produced by the gas pulsations of the refrigerant being compressed and pumped by a compressor. A receiver is a vessel that allows a system to store excess refrigerant that it does not currently need.

Defrost timers are used to initiate and terminate a defrost cycle on a refrigeration system. A suction-to-liquid line heat exchanger can be added to a system to improve its efficiency and help prevent liquid from returning to the compressor. A filter-drier is actually two devices incorporated into one housing. It has a screen inside that filters out any debris in the system and a desiccant that absorbs any water vapor in the system. Water pressure regulators are used to control the water flow through a water-cooled condenser. A sight glass allows a technician to view the condition of the refrigerant in the liquid line at the point it is located.

WORK ORDERS

Service Ticket 7801

Customer Complaint: Iced Evaporator Coil

Equipment: Walk-in Cooler

A technician is called out to service a walk-in cooler using R-134a refrigerant, an air cooled condenser, an externally equalized TEV, and operating at a case temperature of 52°F.

When the technician arrives on the job, the low-pressure control is being used to control the case temperature, the evaporator is iced over, and the compressor, condenser, and evaporator fans are running. After further investigation the technician observes the following conditions:

- The condenser coil is clean.
- The high pressure control is set to open at 195 psig.
- The cut in setting of the low pressure control is 26 psig.
- The differential setting of the low pressure control is 15 psig.
- The sight glass is clear.

The evaporator was defrosted, the system started, and the following conditions were observed:

- A suction pressure of 37 psig.
- A discharge pressure of 150 psig.
- A 52°F suction line temperature at the outlet of the evaporator.
- A 98°F liquid line temperature at the outlet of the condenser.

Based on the information the technician decides to readjust the low-pressure control.

Service Ticket 7802

Customer Complaint: Cooler Was Too Warm and the Compressor Was Cycling On and Off Too Often

Equipment Type: Walk-In Cooler

A technician is called out to service a walk-in cooler using R-134a refrigerant, an air cooled condenser, a TEV metering device, and a low pressure control to control case temperature. The case is operating at 65°F.

When the technician arrives on the job, the evaporator fans are running and the compressor and condenser are cycling on and off on the low-pressure control. The technician bypasses the low-pressure control and the following conditions are observed:

- An ambient temperature of 80°F.
- The suction pressure pulled down to 5 psig.
- A 125 psig pressure at the receiver.
- A 65°F suction line temperature at the outlet of the evaporator.
- A 80°F liquid line temperature at the outlet of the condensing unit.
- A 130°F discharge line temperature at the outlet of the compressor.
- The liquid line sight glass is clear (located before the filter-drier).
- A temperature drop of 10°F was measured across the filter-drier.

The technician then replaces the liquid line filter-drier.

Service Ticket 7803

Customer Complaint: Freezer Not Cooling Properly

Equipment Type: Walk-in Freezer

A technician is called out to service a walk-in freezer using R-404A refrigerant, an air cooled condenser, and a TEV metering device. It has pump down controls and a 208/230 V single phase, refrigerant cooled compressor. The compressor has failed three times in the last 12 months.

When the technician arrives on the job, the compressor is running, as are the condenser and evaporator fans. After further investigation, the technician observes the following conditions:

- Both the evaporator and condenser coils are clean.
- Ambient temperature is 75°F.
- An operating suction pressure of 24 psig.
- An operating discharge pressure of 252 psig.
- A –10°F suction line temperature at the outlet of the evaporator.
- An 89°F liquid line temperature at the outlet of the condenser.
- A 210°F discharge line temperature.
- The bulb of the TEV is located on the top of the suction line.

The technician then decides the reason that the compressor keeps failing is due to refrigerant floodback.

UNIT 78—REVIEW QUESTIONS

1. What is an evaporator pressure regulator?
2. What systems use crankcase pressure regulators?
3. How does a CPR work?
4. What is the purpose of a solenoid valve?
5. How can a technician tell which direction a solenoid valve should be installed?

Figure 79-5 A slip-clutch assembly
(Courtesy of Carpigiani)

Figure 79-4 A cutaway of a soft-serve freezing cylinder
(Courtesy of Carpigiani)

wrapped with copper tubing. The refrigerant will be fed from the metering device into the copper tubing wrapped around the cylinder.

Function of the Control System

There are several methods a manufacturer uses to determine when the ice cream mix is at the right consistency to be dispensed. Some machines will monitor the temperature of ice cream mix. When the mix is at the correct temperature the beater assembly and refrigeration system will be cycled off. Monitoring the low side pressure of the refrigeration system can also be used to determine when the ice cream mix is at the right consistency. A pressure control will be used to cycle the beater assembly and refrigeration system at a specific pressure. Another method used by manufacturers is to directly monitor the consistency of the product. As a product begins to freeze it requires greater force for the beater or auger to move through the ice cream mixture. This additional force, called torque, is measured by the control system so that as the product begins to freeze and thicken the refrigerant cycle can be terminated. This can be determined by

either mechanical means, such as a split clutch assembly, as shown in Figure 79-5, or by monitoring the amperage draw of the beater motor.

Function of the Beater Assembly

The beater assembly has three functions: (1) to scrape the frozen product from the cylinder; (2) to whip the product; and (3) to eject the product. A beater used by one manufacturer is shown in Figure 79-6. The beater blades must be kept in good condition and not be damaged during the cleaning operation. Some machines use a beater assembly with removable plastic blades. Care must be taken when removing and replacing these beater blades during cleaning. These blades wear in and should not be interchanged.

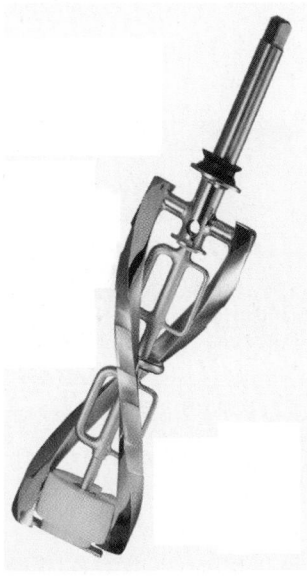

Figure 79-6 Beater
(Courtesy of Carpigiani)

SERVICE TIP

Scraping the frozen product in consistent even layers from the cylinder wall is essential for producing quality product. This requires that the beater and blade assembly be checked for alignment regularly. Misalignment will result in uneven wear of the evaporator wall which will produce inconsistent scraping of the product.

Function of the Mix Feed System

Mix feed systems automatically meter liquid mix into the freezing cylinder to replace that which has been drawn off. A mix feed system used by one manufacturer is shown in Figure 79-7. Most mix feed systems require some adjustment at the time of original startup and whenever a different mix is used. Some of the basic points relating to mix feed systems are as follows:

- Mechanical feed systems must be adjusted to meter an equivalent amount of liquid mix by weight into the cylinder to replace the product that has been drawn off.
- Gravity feed systems do not require such precise settings. An orifice size is selected that permits the proper flow of mix.
- Some models have different valve assemblies for soft ice cream and for milkshake makers. Milkshake machines require larger quantities of mix. These valve assemblies should not be interchanged.
- The freezer cylinder must be preloaded with the correct amount of mix at the start of the day's operation. Consult the service manual for the machine being used to obtain the initial loading and valve adjustment.

Figure 79-7 Mix feed system of soft-service freezer

Figure 79-8 A batch freezer
(Courtesy of Carpigiani)

Batch Freezers

Batch freezers are similar in operation to soft service freezers. A typical batch freezer is shown in Figure 79-8. They are designed to produce large quantities of ice cream instead of single servings as with a soft-serve freezer. They are used to make tubs of ice cream and multiple ice cream cakes. These machines have a freezing cylinder and a beater assembly to scrape the ice cream mix from the walls of the cylinder. However, they do not have a hopper or mix feed system. The operator pours the ice cream mix directly into the freezer. The consistency control for these machines is similar to those used on soft-service freezers.

TECH TIP

When possible, refer to the manufacturer's troubleshooting chart to isolate and resolve problems with equipment.

General Guide to Service

Always separate a problem into one of the following three categories: mix, operational, or mechanical problems. Solving these problems requires working jointly with the operator and mix supplier. Operational problems require actually observing the use and cleaning of the equipment. It is important to explain to the operator the necessity of following accepted procedures. Solving mechanical problems requires a thorough knowledge of the equipment being used. There are many different models—each having its own construction and service requirements. A careful study of the manufacturer's service manuals for the equipment being used makes the analysis of problems much easier.

79.5 SUPERMARKET SYSTEMS

Refrigeration systems used in supermarkets can be designed using several different configurations. Some supermarket systems will be designed to use a single condensing unit or compressor for each refrigerated case. Others are designed to use multiple refrigerated cases connected to a single condensing unit or compressor. Still other supermarkets may use a rack of multiple compressors (rack systems) piped together and connected to multiple refrigerated cases. The type of condenser used by supermarket designers will also vary. Single compressor applications may use individual air cooled or water cooled condensers. Sometimes single compressor applications will be piped into multi-circuited air cooled condensers (multiple condensers coils housed in one cabinet). Rack systems can use either one large air cooled condenser or a split condenser (a condenser split into two sections).

Single Condensing Unit per Refrigerated Case

In this system design, remote condensing units are connected to a single refrigerated case. A typical air cooled condensing unit feeding a single refrigerated case is shown in Figure 79-9. These single condensing units can be grouped together and located on a rack in an equipment room, normally in the back of the building, or they can be stand alone units. If air cooled condensers are used, controlled ventilation is provided to maintain a satisfactory ambient air temperature for the air cooled condensers. These systems may also be designed with remote outdoor air cooled condensers. This allows the compressor and all of the controls to be located indoors and the condenser outdoors. The heat from the condenser is rejected directly to the outdoor ambient. These systems may also be designed with water cooled condensers. In this design the heat from the condenser is transferred to the water running through its barrel. Both of these methods will require less ventilation for the equipment room.

Figure 79-9 An air cooled condensing unit connected to a single refrigerated case

Each individual refrigeration circuit will have its own electrical connections, refrigerant, refrigerant piping, temperature control, and defrost system. This is an advantage and a disadvantage at the same time. The advantage to this design is that when a problem arises with the system, such as a refrigerant leak, only that system is affected. The other refrigerated cases in the store, being completely separate systems, will continue to operate normally. There are also several disadvantages to this design: (1) many more compressors are need, usually resulting in higher operating costs; (2) the initial cost to install may be higher since it requires more equipment; (3) it is more difficult to reclaim some of the heat for use in the store, such as for space heating or for heating hot water.

Multiple Evaporators and Single Compressor Applications

In this system design, a remote condensing unit is connected to multiple evaporators or refrigerated cases. Normally, several evaporators operating at the same temperature will be grouped together and piped to the same condensing unit. However, it is possible to group evaporators operating at different temperatures with the use of evaporator pressure regulators. This design does require some type of compressor capacity control; as different cases may have different load requirements. Either compressor unloaders or a hot gas bypass system can be employed to regulate the capacity of the compressor.

These condensing units can also be grouped together and located on a rack in an equipment room. Controlled ventilation will also be provided to maintain a satisfactory ambient air temperature for the air cooled condensers. These systems may also be designed with remote outdoor air cooled condensers or water cooled condensers.

This design offers some of the same advantages and disadvantages as a single condensing unit serving single systems but not as dramatic. More systems will be affected when a problem arises with the condensing unit. However, fewer compressors are needed for the store operation and the compressor motors will be more efficient because they are larger. Also, the initial cost to install may be slightly lower and it may be easier to reclaim some of the heat for use in the store.

Parallel Systems

This system design consists of a bank of parallel-connected compressors and accessories mounted on a common base, piped and wired at the factory, ready for field connection to individual cases, as shown in Figure 79-10. The compressors could all be the same capacity or different capacities. When compressors of different capacities are used, the rack is referred to as an uneven rack system. The advantage of this type of arrangement is that individual compressors can be cycled on and off to provide the required capacity and in case of one compressor failure, the other compressors can carry the load. This equipment configuration is also advantageous for latent heat defrosting and heat recovery. Using this arrangement,

Figure 79-10 A parallel rack system

defrosting can be selective, with some units operating while others defrost. The operating units can provide the necessary heat for the units defrosting.

For maximum efficiency, a bank of compressors should be connected to evaporators operating at similar temperatures. From an operational standpoint, fixtures of different evaporating temperatures can be connected to the bank; however, this causes a substantial energy loss.

A typical supermarket system produces refrigeration in the low or medium temperature range. A low temperature rack maintains a suction temperature of –25°F with a satellite suction temperature of –33°F. A medium temperature rack maintains a suction temperature of +16°F and a satellite suction temperature of +7°F. A suction pressure controller is used to maintain a nearly constant suction pressure for the bank of compressors.

TECH TIP

One disadvantage of parallel systems is that a single leak can shut down a sizable number of cases. When possible, a refrigerant monitor should be used to alert the owner or service company of a refrigerant leak.

Rack systems are typically connected to a remote air cooled condenser (they could also be connected to an evaporative condenser). Typically the operation of the fans can be controlled to maintain a minimum high side pressure during low outdoor temperatures. The fans can either be cycled off and on as needed or the speed of the fans can be controlled. Some designs will use a split condenser, which is a condenser split into halves and piped in parallel. At a certain outdoor temperature, the cycling of the fans may not be sufficient to maintain a minimum high side pressure. In this design, with the use of solenoid controlled three way valve and a check valve, half of the condenser can be shut off from the system. This reduces the condensing

Figure 79-11 A three way valve used on a split condenser

area and will cause the high side pressure to increase. A typical piping arrangement is shown in Figure 79-11.

Piping from a rack system to the individual cases is carried in trenches underneath the floor or overhead using hangers. Piping must be properly insulated and isolated to prevent the possibility of electrolytic action as shown in Figure 79-12.

The Protocol System

The protocol system is an advanced approach to supermarket refrigeration. This system uses multiple compressor units located near the cases being cooled. A typical store might have as many as 10–15 protocol systems located throughout the entire store.

Figure 79-12 Piping arrangement of a rack system to several refrigerated cases

Each unit uses scroll compressors that provide quiet operation, and an HFC refrigerant that has a zero ODF to meet environmental requirements. A compact plate condenser is part of each package, and is cooled from a closed loop fluid cooler system. Each unit includes an electronic controller that manages both compressor cycling and scheduled defrosts. Compressors are cycled to match the load requirements.

A central pedestal mounted power distribution panel furnishes electrical power to each unit by means of a four wire drop cord that supplies power for the compressors, fans, lights, and antisweat heaters.

There are several advantages to using protocol systems:

- They reduce the total refrigerant charge for the store.
- They reduce the amount of refrigerant piping needed, which reduces the possibility of refrigerant leaks.
- They decrease or eliminate the need for EPR valves.
- They eliminate the need for a central area for refrigeration equipment.
- They lower initial installation costs.
- They provide load matching with multiplexed compressors.

79.6 SUPERMARKET REFRIGERATED CASES

The layout and style of refrigerated cases on the sales floor of a supermarket will vary depending on the size of the store, the food products being refrigerated, and the area in which the equipment is located. Generally speaking, there are two types of cases: (1) self-service equipment, where customers select their own products; and (2) service equipment, where the employee selects the products.

Open Display Cases

In order to maintain a more appealing shopping environment, most supermarkets will display some of their refrigerated merchandise in open display cases. While open display cases allow the product to be more sellable, they do present some additional service and maintenance problems.

There are several types of open display cases, which can be categorized into two general types: single deck and multi-deck. Single deck display cases, sometimes referred to as coffin cases, are refrigerated cabinets resembling a coffin in which the product is merchandised horizontally. On the other hand, multi-deck cases merchandise the product in a layered vertical fashion. This allows the product to be at eye level, making it more appealing to the customer.

Since there are no doors on open cases, they rely on an air curtain to provide a barrier between the store's environment and the product. The evaporator coil and its fans are located at the bottom of the cabinet with the fans located in front of the coil. The fans force air through the evaporator coil, up a channel at the rear and top of the case, through a set of honeycombs located on the top front of the case, and discharge the air down in front of the case's shelving. The honeycombs are designed to even out the airflow and develop a uniform air pattern down the front of the case.

Single deck cases are designed to provide an air curtain across the top of the case. These cases are less prone to problems since the colder air, which is heavier than the warmer store air, seems to stay in the case and not spill out. Multi-deck cases are a little different. The air curtain is directed down the front of the case opening with the discharge air on the top of the opening and the return on the bottom of the opening. These cases are more prone to problems since it is easy for the air curtain to become disturbed. Most service problem relating to the air curtain will be found on the multi-deck cases.

Both low and medium temperature single deck cases, as well as medium temperature multi-deck cases, will usually have a single air curtain. Low temperature multi-deck cases will usually have three separate air curtains. Since low temperature multi-deck cases are more prone to problems with heat leakage into the case, three air curtains are needed to provide a sufficient barrier: a primary air curtain, a secondary air curtains, and an ambient air curtain. The primary air curtain is the coldest air curtain and is closest to the product. The secondary air curtain is slightly warmer than the primary and is in front of it. The ambient air curtain is actually a blanket of store air that is directed straight down the front of the case. This air curtain is not circulated within the case.

Since open cases rely on an air curtain to seal the product from the store's environment, it is important to make sure it is sufficiently maintained. Otherwise, warmer and more humid store air will migrate into the case, causing the case temperature to rise and the evaporator coil to frost up more quickly. Measure the discharge velocity at the supply outlet to test an air curtain. This velocity can then be compared to the manufacturer's guidelines for the case. It is important to obtain the correct velocity from the manufacturer for a particular case. As a general guideline, medium temperature single deck cases will have an approximate discharge velocity of 120 to 140 feet per minute. Single deck low temperature cases will have a discharge velocity of approximately 200–250 fpm. Multi-deck medium temperature cases will have a discharge velocity of approximately 170–400 fpm. (This depends on the application and manufacturer.) The primary air curtain of a multi-deck low temperature case will have a discharge velocity of approximately 550 fpm; the secondary air curtain will have a velocity of approximately 400 fpm; and the ambient air curtain 250 fpm.

An air curtain can be disturbed by several factors. A technician needs to identify potential problems and correct them. A heating or air conditioning diffuser can disturb an air curtain. If a supply diffuser is directed toward a case it could disrupt its air curtain. Generally, velocities of over 20 fpm by the case are considered excessive.

Figure 79-13 Smoking a refrigerated meat case

Figure 79-14 Temperature sensor located at the discharge air honeycombs of an open display case

Another way an air curtain can be disturbed is by how the product is loaded in the case. Each case is normally marked with a load limit line. The product should not be loaded beyond this line; otherwise the air curtain will be disturbed and cause a problem.

If an air curtain is suspected of being disturbed, a technician can usually identify this in one of two methods. One method is to place a thin plastic bag in front of the case and its air curtain. (The bags used for fresh produce in a supermarket work very well.) If the plastic bag is drawn into the case so will the store air; the cause will need to be identified. Another method to test the integrity of an air curtain is to smoke the case, as shown in Figure 79-13. By using a smoke candle to introduce smoke into the return air grill, a technician can easily see if the air curtain is intact or is being disturbed. Smoke candles can usually be found at most local HVAC/R supply houses. These candles can be purchase to burn from 30–60 s. A 30-s burn is usually sufficient to test an air curtain.

Air curtains cannot totally eliminate all of the store air from migrating into a case. Small amounts of air will always migrate through the air curtains into the case. It is important to limit the store humidity level to 55% in order to keep these cases working properly. High store humidity will cause the case's evaporator to frost up more quickly, resulting in frost accumulating on the product and the system consuming more energy. A 10°F increase in the store wet bulb temperature will increase the compressor's power usage by 25%.

Another source of potential problems with these cases is the introduction of radiant heat into the case. Radiant heat can be introduced into a case from its own case lighting, the store's lighting, or, depending on its location, sunlight. This can be a major source of a load on the case and should be minimized when possible.

Another area of importance when troubleshooting open cases involves checking the discharge air temperature. It is standard practice for an open case to be controlled and monitored by its discharge air cemperature, shown in Figure 79-14, and *not* the interior case temperature or the return air temperature. This is different from other types of refrigeration equipment, which may be controlled and monitored by either the return air temperature or box temperature. Since there are major differences between the discharge air temperature, the box temperature, and the return air temperature, a technician should not confuse the three when servicing these cases.

The control system for open display cases can also be configured to set off an alarm if the discharge air temperature exceeds a predetermined temperature for a specific delay period. For example, an alarm temperature of 45°F with a 60-min delay could easily be used to signal a problem with the case. The alarm can be either a local or remote alarm. A local alarm will set off some type of light or buzzer in the store to notify personnel of a problem. A remote alarm will notify someone outside the store that there is a problem, such as a facilities manager, refrigeration contractor, or alarm company.

TECH TIP

Measuring various types of temperatures is a common task for HVAC/R technicians. The thermometers used must be accurate in order for a technician to be able to properly troubleshoot a system. Technicians should occasionally test the accuracy of their thermometers.

Place a thermometer in a solution of ice and water to do this. Fill a bucket with crushed ice and add water so that $3/4$ of the ice is immersed in the water. It is best to have a solution that has more ice than water. Let the temperature of the solution stabilize—it should stabilize close to 32°F.

Once the temperature of the solution has stabilized, place the thermometer in the ice/water solution. Let the temperature measured on the thermometer stabilize and observe its reading. If the thermometer measures a temperature relatively close to 32°F, then the thermometer is relatively accurate. If not, the thermometer needs to be adjusted, repaired, or discarded.

Verifying the correct defrost times is also an important check on open cases. When possible, always check with the manufacturer for the recommended settings. General defrost norms are: two to three defrosts a day for medium temperature single deck cases; three to four defrosts a day for medium temperature multi-deck cases; one to two defrosts per day for low temperature single deck cases; and two to four defrosts per day for low temperature multi-deck cases. Defrost times will depend greatly on the store's humidity level. The higher the store's humidity, the more defrosts the case might need.

An open case should not be installed tight to a wall as it may cause condensation to form on the back or bottom of the case. Always allow an air space at the back of the case. When joining cases together, be sure to follow the manufacturer's guidelines and procedures. A lineup of cases that defrost together should be sealed off from any adjoining cases that defrost at a different time.

Open display cases are designed and engineered to hold product at the temperature at which it enters the case. They are not designed to reduce a product's temperature. They are designed to primarily handle heat leakage into the case. They also are not designed to store product for a long period of time. Because of this, most case manufacturers recommend rotating product on a regular basis.

Regularly cleaning open cases is a very important maintenance task. They should be periodically shut down and cleaned out entirely to help prevent loss of product due to equipment failure. Without regular cleaning, drain lines can become clogged, causing ice to form in the drain pan and eventually rise up to stop the fans and shut the case down. Even with a properly tuned refrigeration system and proper defrost time settings, ice will develop on the ends of the evaporator coil and eventually grow large enough to where it may affect the operation of the case. Regular cleaning will prevent this from becoming a problem.

Produce is in general displayed in multi-deck cases. A commonly used produce case is shown in Figure 79-15. It is

Figure 79-16 A lineup of multideck dairy cases

sometimes referred to as a vision type case because mirrors are used to enhance the appearance of the product. Some of these cases will also have a misting system to wet down the produce as needed, as some produce products need to be kept moist. This increases the shelf life of the product and increases its appeal to the customer. A basic misting system consists of a water tube with multiple spray heads, a timer, a water filter, and a solenoid valve.

Dairy products are typically displayed in multi-deck cases. A typical dairy case is shown in Figure 79-16. These cases normally operate at a discharge air temperature of approximately 36°F.

Single deck or multi-deck cases can be used to display meat products and frozen food products. Figure 79-17 shows a typical multi-deck meat case. These cases normally operate at a discharge air temperature of approximately 26°F.

Figure 79-15 A typical produce case

Figure 79-17 A typical multideck meat case

Figure 79-18 A typical lineup of glass door frozen food cases

Supermarket Reach-in Freezers

When refrigeration engineers design supermarkets, they tend to use reach-in glass door cabinets for the low temperature display cases. A typical lineup of glass door freezers is shown in Figure 79-18. Although this makes shopping a little inconvenient for customers, they are less problematic than open display cases. Open display cases at low temperatures are more sensitive to the store's environment. The evaporator coils of open cases tend to freeze up more quickly, requiring longer and more frequent defrosting. Because of this, reach-in glass door freezers are more often chosen to display frozen food products since they are more reliable and less troublesome at low temperatures.

Although these cases are less prone to problems with fluctuations in the store's environment, they are still designed to work in a conditioned environment. The store's environment should not exceed a dry bulb temperature of 75°F and a relative humidity of 55%. Cases subjected to higher conditions may develop frosting and icing problems in the case, on its doors, and on the product. It is important that any supermarket have an adequate HVAC system to keep the store cool and dry. It is much less expensive for a supermarket to dehumidify with an air conditioning or desiccant system than modifying display case design.

Even though these cases have glass doors to seal the case from the store's environment, there is still a definite air pattern set up within them just as with open display cases. The discharge temperature usually operates in a range of –10°F to 0°F (–15°C to –5°C for ice cream applications). Many systems will use either mechanical or electronic temperature controls to regulate the case temperature, but electronic controllers are more often used today. Temperature controls are wired to control either a liquid line or suction line solenoid, depending on the design.

79.7 ICE MAKING UNITS

Restaurants and supermarkets use ice on a regular basis and will generally have their own ice machine instead of buying ice from an icehouse. Commercial ice machines are available to produce 60–2,000 lb each day. A typical ice machine is shown in Figure 79-19. There are several different styles of ice machines used by restaurant and supermarkets today; these include cubers, flakers, and nugget machines. Each of these produces a different style of ice cube.

The basic design of most cubed ice machines is to flow water into a trough and pump it over an evaporator. The evaporator is designed to produce the shape and size of the ice cube. The machine will sense when the correct size cube is formed and then drop the ice cubes into a bin. The exact procedure on how this is accomplished will vary from manufacturer to manufacturer. Installing, maintaining, and servicing these machines will require specific training from the equipment manufacturer.

The basic design of a flaker machine is to flow water into a refrigerated cylinder. Water will then freeze to the walls of the cylinder. An auger will then scrape the ice off the cylinder walls and dispense it into a bin. A nugget machine is similar in design to a flaker except the ice will be formed into nuggets as it is extruded from the machine.

Figure 79-19 A commercial ice machine

General Guidelines to Servicing Ice Machines

Repairing commercial ice machines can be a tedious experience. Since each manufacturer has a specific design, a technician servicing these systems needs to be versed in each different design. There are some general guidelines that a technician can use to service many of these machines.

Always check the installation of the machine; some problems can be traced back to the original installation. Where is the machine installed? Is it boxed in without any ventilation? This is especially important regarding machines with air cooled condensers because most manufacturers recommend at least a 6 in clearance on all sides of the machine. Is the ambient temperature too high or too low? Most ice machines should be installed in a room with temperatures ranging from 55°–95°F.

Next, check the water side of the system. Does the water pump operate? Is the water flowing properly over the evaporator? Turn the selector switch to the wash position and observing the water flow to check this. Does any water flow into the bin or down any overflow (dump) drains? Also make sure the ice machine is level. An unleveled machine may cause the water to dump into the bin or down a drain.

Commercial Ice Machine Capacities

A common complaint associated with commercial ice machines is that the machine is not producing enough ice for the customer. Each day the customer runs short of ice needed to operate his business. This can be the result of several different problems—not all necessarily related to a defect with the machine itself.

The ice machine's capacity may be too small for the customer's needs. The ice machine may have been sized properly when the customer's business first started, but now their business has grown and so has their need for ice.

When this occurs, it is often beneficial for a technician to calculate the ice production from a machine. This can be done by recording the cycle time and weight of ice produced from one cycle, and then using the following equation to determine the machine capacity:

$$\text{Ice production} = \left(\frac{1{,}440}{\text{cycle time}} \right) \times \text{wt}$$

where

Ice production = ice production in 24 hr
Cycle time = time in minutes that it takes to cycle through one complete ice cycle
1440 = number of minutes in 24 hr
wt = the weight in pounds of ice made in one complete cycle

This will yield the production of ice in a 24-hr period, which is how most ice machines are rated.

For example, let's say we measure a cycle time of 20 min and a weight of ice produced from one cycle of 6 lb.

$$\text{Ice production} = \left(\frac{1{,}440}{\text{cycle time}} \right) \times 6\,\text{lb}$$

$$\text{Ice production} = 432\,\text{lb}$$

This machine will produce 432 lb of ice in a 24-hr period. If this is relatively close to the stated capacity of the machine, it is working normally and the problem lies with the current needs of the customer and not the actual operation of the ice machine.

UNIT 79—SUMMARY

Even though restaurants and supermarkets use many different case and system designs, they all use the same basic refrigeration system. The differences in these cases and systems will depend upon their application. There are several kinds of draft beer dispensers. The three fundamentals common to each dispenser are the ability to satisfactorily clean the equipment, temperature control, and product pressure control.

The basic soft-serve freezer consists of a hopper, a mix feed system, a beater, and a freezing cylinder. The hopper is a refrigerated holding tank for the ice cream mix. As needed, the feed system injects mix into the freezing cylinder. A beater, sometimes referred to as an auger, will scrape the frozen mixture off the walls of the cylinder. There are several different methods that a manufacturer can use to determine when the ice cream mix is at the right consistency to be dispensed. Some machines will monitor the temperature of the ice cream mix; others will monitor the low side pressure of the refrigeration system; and others will directly monitor the consistency of the product.

Supermarket refrigeration systems can use several different designs, such as a single condensing unit for each refrigerated case, multiple refrigerated cases connected to a single condensing unit, or parallel rack systems. There are advantages and disadvantages to using single condensing units operating a single or multiple cases. When a problem arises with the system, only that system is affected; however, more compressors are needed to operate all the cases in a store. Piping from a rack system to the individual cases is carried in trenches underneath the floor or overhead using hangers.

There are several types of open display cases that can be categorized into two general types: single deck and multideck. Open display cases have no doors, and they rely on an air curtain to provide a barrier between the store's environment and the product. It is standard practice for an open case to be controlled and monitored by its discharge air temperature and *not* the interior case temperature or the return air temperature.

Each ice machine manufacturer has a specific design. A technician servicing these systems requires factory training and needs to be versed in the different machine designs.

— WORK ORDERS

Service Ticket 7901

Customer Complaint: Ice on Evaporator Coils

Equipment Type: Walk-in Freezer

A technician is called out to service a walk-in freezer with an air cooled condenser, R-404A refrigerant, and an external equalized thermostatic expansion valve operating at a 30°F case temperature.

When the technician arrives on the job, the evaporator has an excessive amount of ice on its coils and the compressor, condenser, and evaporator fans are running. The system incorporates electric defrost heaters and a time-temperature defrost arrangement with three defrost periods per day and a fail-safe time of 35 min. The system also uses a standard temperature controller to control case temperature. The technician decides to initiate a defrost cycle and then observes the following conditions:

- Compressor and evaporator fans shut down.
- Electric heaters were energized.
- Ice started to melt off the coils of the evaporator.
- The system stayed in defrost for 35 min and then the compressor cycled back on with the evaporator fan coming on after a slight delay.

A second defrost was initiated and the following conditions were observed:

- Compressor and evaporator fans shut down.
- Electric heaters were energized.
- The remaining ice melted off the coils of the evaporator.
- The system stayed in defrost for 30 minutes and then the compressor cycled back on with the evaporator fan coming on after a normal delay.

After running for approximately 45 min after the second defrost, the following conditions were observed:

- The operation of the time clock was observed and the time advanced normally.
- The case temperature was down to 10°F.

Based on these observations, the technician determines that the system is operating normally. After speaking with some employees working in the kitchen, it was discovered that the door was accidentally left slightly open for several hours, which most likely caused the elevated case temperature and the excessive ice on the evaporator.

Service Ticket 7902

Customer Complaint: Ice on Evaporator Coils

Equipment Type: Walk-in Freezer

A technician is called out to service a walk-in freezer using R-404A refrigerant, an air cooled condenser, TEV metering device, a time initiated-temperature terminated electric defrost strategy, and operating at a case temperature of 28°F and climbing.

When the technician arrives on the job, the compressor, condenser, and evaporator fans are running, and the evaporator is completely covered in ice. After further investigation the technician observes the following conditions:

- The condenser coil is clean.
- An ambient temperature of 78°F.
- An operating suction pressure of 20 psig.
- An operating discharge pressure of 229 psig.
- The resistances of the defrost heaters were measured and each heater had a measurable resistance.
- The defrost time clock was observed for 30 min and it seemed to advance normally.
- A manual defrost was initiated and the defrost time clock immediately jumps back into the refrigeration mode.

The technician then decides to replace the termination temperature switch.

Service Ticket 7903

Customer Complaint: Ice Production Low

Equipment Type: Commercial Ice Machine

A technician is called out to service a 400 lb commercial ice machine using R-404A refrigerant, an air cooled condenser, and a TEV metering device. The customer is complaining that the ice production from the machine is low.

When the technician arrives on the job the compressor, condenser, and evaporator fans are running. After further investigation the technician observes the following conditions:

- An ambient temperature of 83°F.
- An operating suction pressure at the beginning of the freeze cycle of 59 psig.
- An operating suction pressure at the end of the freeze cycle of 39 psig.
- An operating discharge pressure of 253 psig.
- Frost noticed on the suction line leaving the evaporator halfway through the freeze cycle.
- The condenser coil is clean.
- The freeze cycle is approximately 65 min.
- The harvest cycle is approximately 2 min.
- A small amount of water is continuously running down the drain.

The technician then decides to replace the inlet water float.

UNIT 79—REVIEW QUESTIONS

1. What are the advantages and disadvantages of using a remote condensing unit on restaurant refrigeration systems?

2. What are the three fundamentals common to each draft beer dispenser?

3. Why does some carbon dioxide gas need to be added in a beer system?

4. Explain the two methods to refrigerate the beer lines on a remote draft beer dispenser.

5. What is the average serving temperature of soft-serve ice cream?

6. What components does a basic soft-serve freezer contain?

7. Explain the function of the operator using a soft-serve freezer.

8. Explain the function of a mix feed system of a soft-serve freezer.

9. What is the difference between a batch freezer and soft-serve freezer?

10. What are the advantages and disadvantages of using single condensing units in supermarket applications?

11. What is a rack system named when compressors of different capacities are used?

12. What suction temperature does a typical low temperature rack system maintain in a supermarket?

13. What is the disadvantage of using a parallel rack system in a supermarket?

14. How is the refrigerant piping run from a rack system to the individual refrigerated cases?

15. What are the advantages of using a protocol refrigeration system?

16. How do open display cases maintain the temperature within the case without any doors?

17. Where is the temperature typically monitored in an open display case?

18. How many air curtains are used in a multi-deck open display freezer?

19. Why are glass door frozen food cases preferred over open display frozen food cases?

20. Explain the basic operation of commercial ice machines designed to produce cubes of ice.

UNIT 80

Refrigeration Applications

OBJECTIVES

After completing this unit you will be able to:

- describe the process for making ice cream.
- describe the cooling processes employed in bakeries for making bread.
- explain how ice is formed on an ice rink.
- list a variety of applications for cryogenic refrigeration.
- list the different categories of transportation refrigeration.
- provide examples of where cascade systems are used.
- explain how a drinking water cooler operates.

80.1 INTRODUCTION

Commercial systems vary in their configurations depending on the type of application requirements. A specialty area such as ice cream making varies significantly from the process of storing liquefied natural gas (LNG) onboard a ship. In both instances however, mechanical vapor compression systems are commonly employed.

In this unit you will be exposed to many of the varied commercial refrigeration applications that you may likely encounter in the field. This includes the areas of food service, ice making, and transportation.

Food service has wide ranging refrigeration demands from keeping vegetables fresh to quick freezing blueberries or fish. Ice is a general commodity found at most any convenience store and is an essential requirement for cooling where no suitable mechanical refrigeration system is available. The transportation sector continues to grow as food products travel from fair weather regions such as Florida and California to areas where the weather becomes too cold to grow crops. Climate controlled containers allow for grapes to be transported from Chile and bananas imported from Ecuador.

80.2 ICE CREAM

Hard ice cream is defined legally by its butterfat content. The minimum, set by federal standards, is 8% for bulk flavored ice cream mixes (chocolate) and 10% or above for other flavors (vanilla). For the specialty trade, the richer ice creams are 16–18% fat, but the average is 10–12%. Butterfat accounts for the rich flavor of the product. Refrigeration is a major cost in

the making of ice cream, and its effectiveness depends on how well it transfers heat throughout the production processes. The making of ice cream begins with making the mix, followed by freezing and storing the mix, and then using the mix to produce various kinds of ice cream. The service person should know the processes involved in order to recognize the source of problems that may arise, maintain efficient operations, avoid extra power use, and finish with a satisfactory product.

80.3 PASTEURIZING

The basic ingredients for a typical ice cream are milkfat (12.5%), serum solids (nonfat solids of milk, 10.5%), sugar (15.0%), a stabilizer/emulsifier (0.3%), and (optionally) egg solids. The ingredients are placed in a vat, mixed, and heated (pasteurized) at 155°F for 0.5 hr to dissolve the solids and to destroy any pathogenic organisms. They are then precooled in a plate section using cool water. The final cooling to just above the freezing point is done in a second plate section using chilled water or glycol.

SERVICE TIP

When working on equipment used in the manufacturing or sale of food and food products, you must wear the same types of hygienic protection required of other workers in the area. In some cases you must wear hair nets, beard nets, boot covers, jumpsuits, or other such items as a precaution to avoid possible contamination of the manufacturer's product as you are servicing their equipment.

In large plants having automated and computerized processes, all liquid ingredients are used. These are blended, preheated, homogenized, then heated with plate equipment, a heat exchanger, or a direct steam injector or infuser. This is followed by vacuum chamber treatment for precooling, which improves the flavor of the mix. It is then cooled through a regenerative plate section and additionally cooled indirectly to 40°F or less with chilled water.

80.4 HOMOGENIZING

The heated mix is blended to reduce the size of the fat globules so the fat will not churn out during freezing. Should this happen, the ice cream has a greasy taste.

80.5 COOLING AND HOLDING THE MIX

The mix should be as cold as possible. In smaller plants the vats are equipped with both precooling and final cooling sections. The mix is precooled to about 10°F warmer than the entering water temperature, using city, well, or cooling tower water. The final cooler using chilled water reduces the mix to about 40°F, and brine, or direct expansion refrigerant, reduces the mix temperature to 30–33°F.

Larger plants usually use separate equipment for the final cooling. An ammonia jacketed scraped surface chiller is often used. Where the mix can be held overnight, part of the final mix cooling is done by means of a refrigerated surface built into the tanks. The rate of cooling is about 1°F per hour.

80.6 FREEZING ICE CREAM

Two kinds of freezers, for making either batch or continuous ice cream, use a cylinder with annular space or coils around the cylinder for direct refrigerant cooling. The space is either flooded, with an accumulator, or the cooling controlled by a thermostatic expansion valve. A dasher inside the cylinder has sharp metal blades that scrape the ice cream off the sides as it freezes. For efficient operation the blades should be kept sharpened.

Small operations use batch freezers that have an average maximum output of eight batches per hour depending on: the sharpness of the blades, the refrigeration supplied, and the overrun desired. At optimum operation the ice cream is drawn from the freezer at about 24°F, with refrigerant temperature around the freezer cylinder of about −15°F.

Large operations use one or more continuous freezers. The ice cream is discharged from several machines connected together to facilitate packaging. The mix is continuously pumped into the freezer cylinder. Air pressure for the overrun is drawn into the cylinder at 20 to over 100 psig, either with the mix or from a separate air compressor. A dasher with freezer blades agitates the mix and air as it moves through the cylinder. The ice cream is discharged at the other end of the cylinder at an average temperature of 22°F. The flooded system surrounding the cylinder, when operating with ammonia, is −25°F. Ice cream temperatures as low as 16°F can be obtained with some mixes by regulating the evaporator temperature around the freezer cylinder using a suction pressure regulating valve.

80.7 HARDENING ICE CREAM

The semisolid ice cream leaving the cylinder is further refrigerated to a solid condition at 0°F for storage and distribution. Rapid freezing to obtain a smooth texture is achieved in hardening rooms kept at −30°F to −20°F. Forced air is circulated from a unit cooler or a remote bank of coils. Ice cream in containers up to 5 gal will harden in about 10 hr when spaced to allow air circulation. Systems using overhead coils or coil shelves with gravity circulation take twice this time.

Some larger plants use air blast type ice cream hardening tunnels with operating temperatures ranging from −50°F to −30°F to shorten hardening time to 4 hr.

> ### CAUTION
>
> Extremely low temperatures used in some refrigeration plants can cause skin burns and possible lung damage if you fail to wear proper protective clothing when working in these areas. Skin exposed to temperatures below −40°F can quickly freeze especially when working in an area that uses air blast type cooling.

Horizontal continuous plate hardening systems automatically load and unload ice cream packages, synchronized with the filler machines. They save space and power and eliminate package bulging, but can only be used for rectangular packages.

80.8 REFRIGERATION EQUIPMENT

Most of the larger commercial ice cream plants use ammonia systems while smaller operations use single stage halogen refrigerant compressors. These compressors are usually operated at conditions above the maximum compression ratio recommended by the manufacturer.

For maintaining −20°F freezer rooms, multistage compression is the most economical. One or more booster compressors are used at the same suction pressure, discharging into second stage compressors. Where a hardening tunnel is used, at least two booster compressors should be used for the tunnel and for the freezer/storage room. Both units discharge into the second stage compressor system. For plants with larger volumes, a three stage system may be the most economical. A low temperature booster is used for the tunnel and a second stage booster discharges into the third stage compressor system.

80.9 MAINTENANCE OF OPERATING EFFICIENCIES

The conditions that lower the efficiency and effectiveness of the refrigeration system in ice cream plants are related to the following:

- **Heat Transfer**   Efficiency is reduced by air films, frost and ice, scale, noncondensable gases, abnormal temperature differentials, clogged sprays, slow liquid circulation, poor air circulation, and foreign particles.
- **Ice Cream Mix**   Efficiency is reduced by viscous mix, low overrun percentage, high mix temperature, low ice cream discharge temperature, and high sugar content in the mix.

- **Dull Scraper Blades**
- **Refrigeration Equipment**   Low evaporator efficiency is caused by rapid frost and ice development and an oil film.

Automatic defrost is recommended. Regular oil purges and an oil separator in the discharge line of the compressor will minimize oil film.

Neglected condensers lead to high head pressures and higher electrical requirements. Condenser surfaces should be kept clean of mineral deposits and other forms of scale or debris. Noncondensable gases in compressor operation should be purged in order to avoid extra power use. Automatic purgers are available for this. Door and conveyor openings are the cause of significant refrigeration losses. Insulation in storage rooms should be sufficient.

Cold rooms and ice banks should be serviced when the ambient air temperature is 26°F or lower.

80.10 BAKERY REFRIGERATION

Proper refrigeration is an essential part of bakery production. Refrigeration is used primarily in three areas:

- Storage of the ingredients prior to use.
- Controlling the temperature of the dough during the mixing process.
- Storing and freezing the products.

80.11 STORING INGREDIENTS

Bulk quantities require temperature protection during shipment or storage. Certain items, such as corn syrup, liquid sugar, lard, and vegetable oil, are held at 125°F to prevent crystallization or congealing. Fructose syrups are often used because they can be stored at a lower temperature, 84°F, to maintain fluidity and require less refrigeration during mixing. Smaller amounts and specialized sugars and shortenings in drums, bags, or cartons are stored at conditions for preventing mold and rancidity. Yeast should always be stored below 45°F. Cocoa, milk products, spices, and other raw materials subject to insect infestation should be stored at the same temperature as yeast.

TECH TIP

Bulk wheat flour, rice flour, and corn meal along with other similar products are stored under refrigeration. These products, like all natural food products, contain insect eggs that when not stored under refrigerated conditions will hatch. If the eggs hatch, the insects will contaminate the product. Insect eggs are present in most raw food products as a result of the products being grown in a natural setting. There is no way of growing these products without some insect eggs being present. As the products are cooked they are sterilized.

Some food service programs that are only operated periodically such as those at summer camps should be encouraged to store their products in their walk in coolers during the off seasons as a way of ensuring the products remain insect free. Total plant air conditioning is often used in new plant construction and includes filters to protect the equipment from airborne flour dust.

80.12 MIXING PROCESS

During mixing, heat is produced in two ways: heat of friction from the electrical energy of the mixer and heat of hydration, produced when the material in the mixer absorbs water. The temperature rise in the dough is also dependent on the specific heat of each ingredient.

The temperature at which yeast is most active is quite critical. It is extremely active when mixed with water and fermentable sugars in a range of 80–100°F. The cells are killed at temperatures around 140°F and below 26°F, the freezing point of yeast. To maintain the proper mixing temperature, excess heat is removed by chilled water in contact with the dough.

For many years the principal refrigerant used in bakeries was ammonia. Other refrigerants are now in use for cooling the water to the desired temperature.

80.13 FERMENTATION

Two methods are used for processing the dough: the straight dough process and the sponge dough process.

In the straight dough process all the ingredients are mixed at once (yeast, flour, malt, and liquid) in an unjacketed tank at a temperature of 69–80°F and allowed to ferment for 1 hr. The second hour fermentation takes place in a jacketed tank at about 84°F. A continuous process allows the dough to be drawn from one tank while the other is fermenting.

In the sponge dough process, only part of the flour and water are mixed with the yeast for the first fermentation period. After fermentation takes place, the remaining flour and water are added. The total process takes $3\frac{1}{2}$ to 5 hr.

80.14 BREAD COOLING AND PROCESSING

Bread is cooled to 90–95°F for handling and slicing. This prevents condensation within the wrapper, which can cause mold to develop.

Refrigeration is required for the bread wrapping machine. The evaporator temperature is usually around 10°F. The plate surface temperature must be held to about 16°F. Refrigeration is not required if bags are used.

Bread is frozen at temperatures between 16–20°F and stored at temperatures below 0°F to prevent moisture loss and crystallization of the starch. Freezing rooms maintain storage temperatures between –30°F and 0°F. Two stage refrigeration equipment is generally used.

80.15 ICE RINKS

The category of ice rinks includes all types of ice sheets, indoors or outdoors, created for recreation such as skating, hockey, and curling.

The rinks are usually made by laying down a series of pipe coils below the level of the design surface of the ice. A secondary refrigerant (brine), such as glycol, methanol, or calcium chloride solution, circulates through the coils from a central chilling system. The system usually uses R-22, although other refrigerants have been used.

TECH TIP

The ice on skating rinks is produced in layers. The first layer is formed and then its top service is sprayed with white paint. This obscures the system's piping from view. Next, a thin layer of ice is formed and any markings such as hockey boundaries or logos are then painted on this ice layer's surface. Finally, the top layer is frozen. This is the layer the skaters are actually skating on. By producing the ice in multiple layers it is possible for rink operators to change the markings without having to allow the entire ice slab to melt.

The amount of refrigeration is usually dependent on the location of the rink (indoors or outdoors), the use of the rink, and the conditions of the building for indoor rinks, Table 80-1.

80.16 ICE RINK CONDITIONS

Indoor rinks are operated 6–11 months a year, depending mainly on profitability. Rooms for heated rinks are usually maintained at 50–60°F with relative humidity ranging from 60–90%.

The temperature of the ice is controlled closely either by the brine temperature or the ice surface temperature. The temperature of ice for hockey is 22°F, for figure skating 26°F, and for recreational skating 26–28°F. A 1 in thickness of ice is usually maintained.

Average brine temperatures are 10°F lower than the required ice temperature. Usually two compressors are used for pulldown and one for normal operation. The temperature differential between supply and return brine is approximately 2°F.

80.17 CONSTRUCTION AND EQUIPMENT

Brine systems generally use 1 in steel or polyethylene pipe 4 in on center. Pipes are set dead level, with sand fill around and over the pipes. A balanced flow distribution system is shown in Figure 80-1. An expansion tank must be installed in the piping.

The construction of the space below the rink is very important, Figure 80-2. There must be proper drainage to prevent "heaving" caused by water freezing below the rink. Many new rinks install heater cables below the floor of the rink or

---

Table 80-1 Ice Rink Refrigeration Requirements for a Variety of Applications

	ft²ton	mkW
Four to five winter months, above 37° latitude		
Outdoors, unshaded	85–300	2.2–7.8
Outdoors, covered	125–200	3.3–5.2
Indoors, uncontrolled atmosphere	175–300	4.6–7.8
Indoors, controlled atmosphere	150–350	4.0–9.1
Curling rinks, indoors	200–400	5.2–10.4
Year round (Indoors), controlled atmosphere		
Sports arena	100–150	2.6–4.0
Sports arena, accelerated ice making	50–100	1.3–2.6
Ice recreation center	130–175	3.4–4.6
Figure skating clubs and studios	135–185	3.5–4.8
Curling rinks	150–225	4.0–5.9
Ice shows	75–130	2.0–3.4

Copyright by the American Society of Heating, Refrigerating, and Air-Conditioning Engineers, Inc.

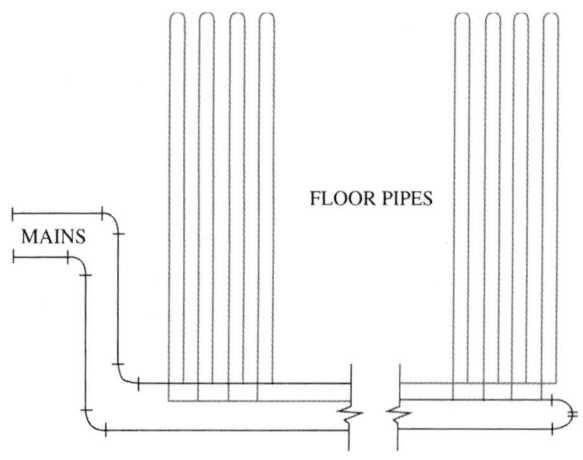

Figure 80-1 Piping diagram for ice rink to provide balanced flow

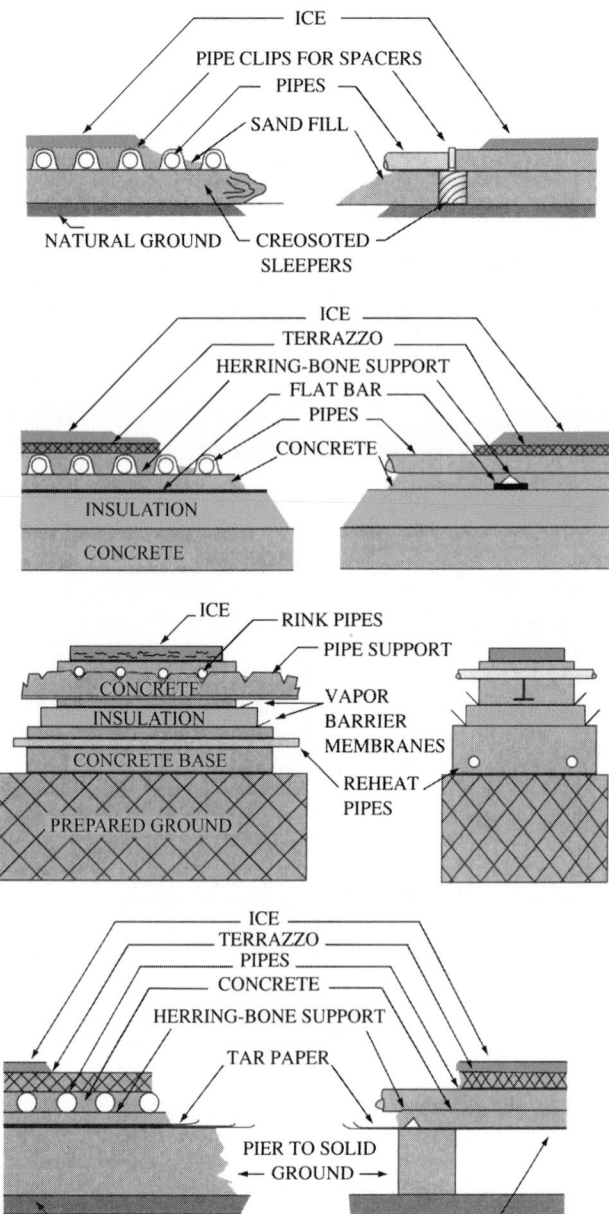

Figure 80-2 Types of ice rink surface floors

circulate warm brine to prevent heaving. A "header trench" is located at one end of the rink to house the piping header. A snow melting pipe is usually located at the opposite end of the rink for melting the scraped ice that is removed by scraping the surface of the rink.

80.18 INDUSTRIAL ICE PROCESSING

An industrial ice machine can produce up to 20,000 lb of cracked ice in 24 hr. Chilled water is continually recirculated over the surface of vertically suspended, double-walled cylindrical evaporators. Refrigerant passes through an annular space, allowing for 100% utilization of the evaporator surface.

To remove the ice that has been formed, the normal refrigerant flow stops and hot gas is allowed to flow through this space. As the ice evaporator surface warms slightly, the ice will slide from the cylinder and fall by gravity into the ice breaker/crusher assembly. This assembly rotates slowly to move the ice along and out of the unit into a storage bin. The ice thickness can be adjusted with a changeable gear rack.

80.19 INDUSTRIAL PROCESSING

Some of the industries where refrigeration is most prevalent are: commercial ice plants that produce large quantities of flake ice for refrigerating fresh fish and other perishable products, soil stabilization systems that prevent problems associated with "frost heave" encountered in cold climates such as Alaska, chemical processes that require refrigeration, usually for the removal of unwanted heat generated during manufacturing processes, and environmental test facilities that use refrigeration to simulate environments where their products will be used. For example, one of the large automobile factories tests car operation in a –40°F room.

TECH TIP

When a commercial facility is air conditioned for the purpose of aiding in the manufacturing of the company's products it is referred to as process cooling as opposed to an air conditioning system. Air conditioning is used for creature comfort. The EPA has different regulatory requirements relative to the allowable leak rate for air conditioning and process cooling. If you suspect the system is used for process cooling, verify that with the building owner before beginning work that would require recovering or recycling the refrigerant.

80.20 VERY LOW TEMPERATURE REFRIGERATION

Typical storage requirements for household foods range between high to medium refrigeration coil temperatures from 55°F down to 0°F. Applications for very low temperature refrigeration systems below 0°F are specialized. If a food product is to be stored for an extended period of time, temperatures below 0°F are preferred. The system utilized would be called a deep freeze. Prior to storage, many foods are quick frozen. This quick freezing of food also requires low temperature applications to be employed. Other applications for low temperature systems include industrial processes such as the production of oxygen and nitrogen and liquefied natural gas transport (LNG).

80.21 CRYOGENICS

The National Institute of Standards and Technology has suggested that the term cryogenics be applied to all temperatures below −238°F. At these low temperatures, materials will behave differently. Metals can become extremely brittle. Their specific heat and electrical resistance decreases. At these low temperatures, there is a possibility of the development of super conductive material.

A more established and important industrial application for cryogenics is the removal of oxygen and nitrogen from air. Oxygen is used in many daily activities from hospital operating rooms to oxyacetylene cutting torches. Nitrogen is used as a refrigerant for quick freezing foods and in agriculture as an important component of fertilizers.

Other applications include cryogenic hardening of metals similar to heat treatment, to increase their strength and hardness. Some cryogenic surgery techniques are being developed to remove tumors by selectively freezing and destroying tissue.

To achieve cryogenic temperatures, volatile liquids are rapidly evaporated such as through a valve. Temperatures as low as −458°F can be achieved through the evaporation of liquid helium. Adiabatic demagnetization that requires a magnetic field can be used to achieve even lower temperatures. Dewar flasks are used for storing liquids at cryogenic temperatures.

80.22 CASCADE SYSTEMS

A LNG (liquefied natural gas) tanker utilizes cryogenic cargo systems. LNG, which is principally methane, has a boiling point of −259°F. The two common processes used to liquefy gases at the gas liquefaction plants are the cascade process and the auto-refrigerated cascade (ARC) cycle. LNG is stored in large freestanding or membrane type cargo tanks where material requirements must be designed to withstand temperatures of −260°F. Stainless steel, aluminum alloys, and nickel steel are commonly used as materials for cargo tanks.

In order to maintain these subzero temperatures within the tanks, some of the liquid is allowed to gradually boil off, thus cooling the remaining liquid. This boil-off is often used in the ship's main engines as fuel. On some ships, nitrogen expander reliquefaction systems are installed. These are not as common due to the fact that these systems are expensive to install, operate, and maintain.

These systems will typically incorporate a traditional cascade system or an auto-refrigerated cascade (ARC) system. The cascade system consists of two or more refrigeration systems in series. The evaporator of the first cycle serves as the condenser for the second cycle and this can be repeated with multiple cycles. Commonly propane would be used as a refrigerant in the first cycle, ethylene in the second cycle, and methane in the third cycle.

The ARC system is a simplification of the cascade system with as many as six different types of refrigerants can be used. These include methane, ethane, propane, pentane, and nitrogen. The refrigerant is condensed in a series of condensers where it is sprayed in as a liquid. With compressors installed in parallel, system reliability and flexibility of operation are increased. The ARC system does however require comparably more power.

80.23 QUICK FREEZING METHODS

When a food product is frozen, the water contained within it will crystallize. These ice crystals will tend to break up the fiber of the product, particularly if they are large. When the product is thawed, a piece of cake as an example, it will not taste the same as when it was fresh. The slower the food is frozen, the larger are the ice crystals that form. A piece of beef may actually tenderize somewhat after freezing, however in general quick freezing methods are preferred to maintain product quality.

Very low temperature applications are used to quick freeze foods. A common method is the use of blast freezers. The product is placed on a conveyor belt that passes through the blast freezer. High velocity low temperature air is blown across the product so that it is frozen as it leaves the tunnel.

This method is commonly used for freezing blueberries. Once frozen, blueberries should not stick together in clumps but be separate from one another. A frozen container of blueberries should rattle when shaken. The blueberries will enter the tunnel shortly after harvesting, so they will be laden with moisture. If frozen in a container, the blueberries will all stick together. On the conveyor, they are spread out to allow the low temperature air to circulate up through them as they pass through the tunnel. After quick-freezing the blueberries are placed in large walk-in coolers for storage. The majority of blueberry processing plants use ammonia as a refrigerant with screw type compressors.

Cryogens such as liquid nitrogen and carbon dioxide are also used for quick freezing. The cryogen is injected into a tunnel type freezer to come in direct contact with the food

Figure 80-3 Spiral freezer
(Photograph Courtesy of Prazair, Inc.)

product. The spiral freezer shown in Figure 80-3 can be used for quick-freezing delicate and difficult to freeze products such as bakery products and entrees on trays. Internal freezer temperatures can reach −150°F.

Immersion freezing is the fastest method available for quick freezing. The product is passed through a shallow liquid nitrogen bath. This instant crust freeze locks in the natural flavors and moisture of the product.

80.24 TRANSPORTATION REFRIGERATION

The transportation of refrigerated products is a large and important aspect of commercial refrigeration. Many truck bodies are well insulated, and reliable refrigeration units are available to maintain the required temperatures. There are a number of types of refrigerated trucks and trailers. There is some difference between those used for long and short hauls, as well as for the different types of products being transported.

80.25 LONG HAUL SYSTEMS

Trailer trucks usually handle long distance hauls. These trailers can be detached from the engine or tractor portion of the assembly. The trailer is usually equipped with a standalone refrigeration system called a reefer. An illustration of a typical insulated trailer is shown in Figure 80-4. Notice the bulkhead in the front for return air coming back to the evaporator through a raised floor. This illustration shows a "piggyback" or clip on refrigeration unit.

Some trailers use refrigeration consisting of the evaporation of liquid nitrogen or liquid carbon dioxide Figure 80-5. In these systems the evaporated refrigerant is wasted to the outdoors.

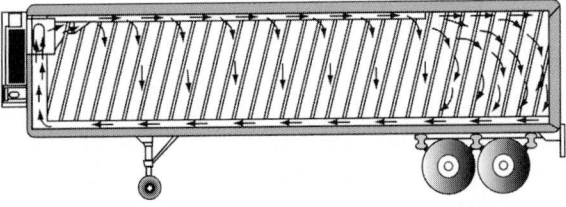

Figure 80-4 Section of a trailer showing air circulation

SERVICE TIP

It is relatively easy to adjust the temperature of a semi trailer refrigeration unit. This feature allows the trucking company to haul both frozen and refrigerated products.

The semi trailer with standalone refrigeration can be placed on a railroad flat car and transported. Upon arrival, the trailer is connected to a tractor to make the local delivery.

Four different temperature conditions are maintained in refrigerated transport, depending on the type of product being handled. These are:

Type of service	Temperature (°F)
Air conditioning for floral products, candy, etc.	55–70
Medium temperature for perishable foods	32–40
Fresh meats	28–32
Frozen foods	−5–0

Some systems that are used both winter and summer have heating equipment as well as cooling equipment. Reverse cycle refrigeration is popular for these applications. Reverse

Figure 80-5 Liquid nitrogen cylinders used for charging truck mounted refrigerant tanks

Figure 80-6 Front mount diesel powered cooling/heating unit for large trucks
(Courtesy of Thermo King Corporation)

Figure 80-8 Front mount cooling/heating unit
(Courtesy of Thermo King Corporation)

cycle refrigeration can also be used for defrosting evaporators where conditions cause the accumulation of ice on the coils.

There are basically two different types of transport refrigeration units: one type for trucks, Figure 80-6, and the other type for trailers, Figure 80-7.

The most common type of trailer unit is mounted at the top front of the trailer, Figure 80-8. Note that the complete unit is factory assembled, ready for installation. All units are available with diesel engine drive, a complete refrigeration system for cooling and heating, a control system, and accessories. Optional electric motors are available for stationary operation.

The net cooling capacity depends on the temperature maintained. Capacities range from 4,000–19,500 Btu/hr at

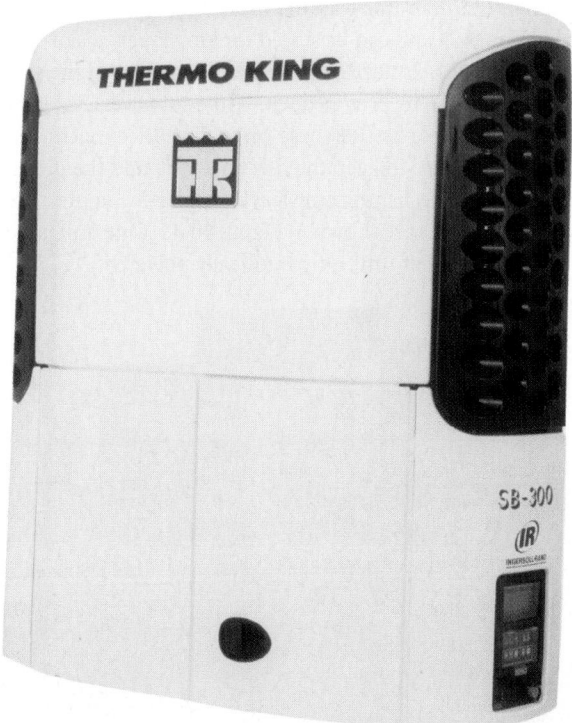

Figure 80-7 Fuel saver heating and cooling, high speed and low speed; runs continuously; automatic or manual defrost
(Courtesy of Thermo King Corporation)

0–100°F ambient. The fuel consumption varies from 0.13 gph to 5 gph, depending on the type of service.

Selection of the proper unit is based on the length of the truck body, the temperature maintained inside the body, the amount of insulation, and the number of door closings per day.

80.26 LOCAL DELIVERY EQUIPMENT

When smaller trucks are used for local deliveries, refrigeration systems with eutectic plates are advantageously used. Eutectic plates are constructed with a provision for refrigeration storage capacity. Plates are made with an interior volume that holds a special liquid called a eutectic solution. This liquid stores the cold by changing the state of the solution. Just as ice freezes at 32°F, these eutectic solutions freeze at various temperatures depending on the desired conditions in the truck. Plates are available for operating temperatures of −58°F, −29°F, −14°F, −12°F, −10°F, −8°F, −6°F, +18°F, +23°F, and +26°F.

The plates are usually connected to the refrigeration compressor at night, when the truck is not being used. The refrigeration capacity of the plates is sufficient to carry the load during the truck's next day use. Some trucks carry their own compressor so that they can be easily plugged into electric service wherever they may be. Illustrations of the eutectic plates are shown in Figure 80-9.

SERVICE TIP

The solution in delivery trucks' thermal banks does not lose its storage capacity over time. However, as a truck's refrigeration equipment wears it may lose enough capacity so that the thermal storage plates are not completely frozen during the overnight recharging cycle. If a vehicle's refrigerated compartment no longer maintains its temperature throughout the delivery day it may be necessary to do a complete compressor analysis to see if the compressor's capacity has diminished to the point where it can no longer provide enough refrigeration to keep the compartment cool.

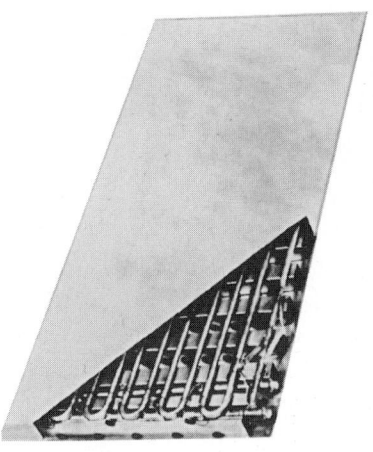

Figure 80-9 Plate evaporator with eutectic solution for holdover cooling capacity
(Courtesy of Dole Refrigerating Company)

Another arrangement for ice cream or frozen food service consists of equipping the truck with an auxiliary drive or an electric motor to operate the compressor while the truck is in service.

80.27 RAILWAY REFRIGERATION

Refrigerated railway boxcars are similar in design to the trailers found on long haul systems. They consist of a well-insulated box with a standalone refrigeration system run by a small diesel engine. Air is circulated across the evaporator coil and then throughout the boxcar as shown in Figure 80-10. These boxcars are designed for both frozen and fresh cargoes such as fruits and vegetables. Some systems allow for remote tracking and control by satellite. This allows for access of operating data and for the changing of settings. A standalone unit with a diesel engine, compressor, and condenser is typically used for cooling.

80.28 MARINE REFRIGERATION

Marine refrigeration applications vary depending on the type of ship or boat that the system is designed for. Mechanical refrigeration systems are used for refrigerated ship's stores, air conditioning, refrigerated cargo, and for the cooling of drinking water. Cruise ships have a requirement for food preservation and therefore will have a number of walk-in coolers for meats, fruits, vegetables, and beverages. A large central refrigeration system generally supplies this cooling requirement. In addition, the passengers must remain comfortable, so a large central air conditioning system with a chill water loop is common.

Food storage systems will generally consist of a number of walk-in coolers that operate at different temperatures. A chill box for fruits and vegetables would operate at temperatures above freezing. A separate box is sometimes utilized for dairy products and eggs. Frozen foods are sometimes separated between meats and fish. These systems generally operate with individual space control through the use of thermostats and solenoid valves. Evaporator pressure regulators are used for the higher temperature spaces.

Refrigerated cargo spaces at one time were dedicated holds onboard ship. Large quantities of bananas as an example were placed in large refrigerated cargo holds served by a central refrigeration system located in the ship's engine spaces. For cargo to be maintained at temperatures above freezing, chill water loops employing brine or glycol were frequently used.

With the advent of refrigerated containers and the ease with which the cargo can be transported from the ship to tractor-trailer or rail car, there is less need for large central refrigeration systems for refrigerated cargo. Refrigerated containers are placed on board the vessel and then plugged in to the onboard power supply system. If the onboard electrical capacity is too low, power packs equipped with diesel generators may be used.

Containers that require a controlled atmosphere for fruits and vegetables may employ a nitrogen and carbon dioxide flushing system. In this way, the fruits and vegetables will not ripen as quickly and can be stored for longer periods of time.

Fishing vessels need to maintain the quality of the product until the ship returns to dock. While some vessels load ice before leaving port, others rely on installed ice machines to supply enough ice to keep the fish holds full and the product chilled. On some fishing trawlers saltwater ice is produced. Two such systems are shown in Figure 80-11. One unit is electric while the other unit is hydraulically powered.

Figure 80-11 Electric and hydraulic powered saltwater ice makers
(Courtesy of Sea Ice)

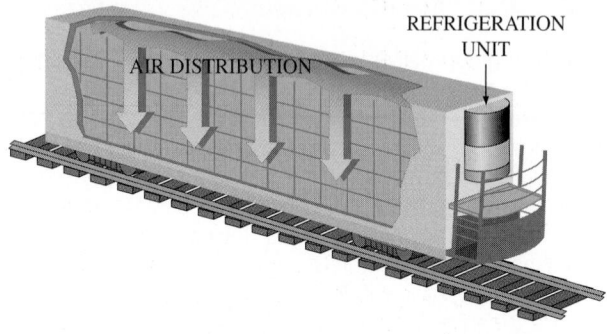

Figure 80-10 Railway boxcar

Some larger fishing vessels use refrigerated seawater chillers where seawater comes into direct contact with pipes containing refrigerant. The cold saltwater is then pumped into the fish holds. Large factory vessels will have a large centralized refrigeration system where the product can be quick frozen and then stored. A product such as shrimp is placed into a mesh bag and then placed into a brine solution (sodium chloride 18–23%) at a temperature of –4°F to 5°F for 12 to 15 min and once frozen they are transferred to dry hold evaporator plates.

80.29 AIR CARGO REFRIGERATION

FAA and IATA regulations impose strict performance specifications on airfreight equipment. The requirements for onboard power or standalone power systems are not practical due to weight restrictions and power demands. Until recently, refrigerated cargo on board airplanes has been limited to the use of dry ice and gel packs.

80.30 AIR CARGO HAULING

Systems are being developed for air cargo refrigeration hauling for those items that need to be transported quickly from overseas and shipping is not a viable alternative. Containers have been designed that operate on battery power. The temperature range for this unit is from –4°F to 104°F. It has a normal battery life of 100 hr down to 30 hr under extreme conditions. Its physical size is shown in Figure 80-12 and it can hold up to 2,101 lb of cargo. The unit will need to be plugged in for recharging once the aircraft lands.

80.31 TYPES OF TRANSPORTATION REFRIGERATION EQUIPMENT

Many types of systems are available for furnishing the power to drive the compressor, including:

- Independent gasoline (or propane or butane) engines.
- Independent diesel engines.
- Power takeoffs from vehicle engines.
- Electric motors.
- Batteries.

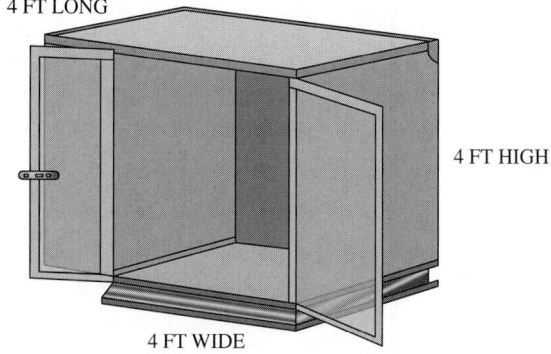

4 FT LONG

4 FT HIGH

4 FT WIDE

Figure 80-12 Dimensions of refrigerated container for air freight

80.32 MECHANICAL REFRIGERATION

The compressor may be either on board the vehicle or at the garage for out of service use only. Evaporators are of many types: finned and pipe coils for forced or gravity circulation, standard plates, or eutectic plates.

Equipment must be designed to withstand severe motion, shock, and vibration. Short, rigid lines are subject to cold working conditions. They become hard and brittle through continual motion. Thus, flexible hose connections are often used. Air cooled condensers need to be designed so that normal airflow due to movement of the truck does not prevent adequate air circulation. Units with independent engines require batteries for cranking, fuel tanks, and pumps.

The units are factory assembled with an engine compressor and condenser in the outside enclosure and the evaporator projecting inside the trailer. The engine runs continuously and the operator has the option of high speed or low speed cooling and high speed or low speed heating. When required, the unit will automatically defrost with hot gas. All units have an hour meter to determine service periods for the engine. The typical refrigeration cycle is shown in Figure 80-13 and Figure 80-14, and the typical heating and defrost cycle is shown in Figure 80-15 and Figure 80-16.

A typical diesel engine drive for a railway boxcar is shown in Figure 80-17. The compressor driven by this engine is shown in Figure 80-18.

80.33 DRINKING WATER COOLERS

There are two styles of free standing drinking water coolers: the bubbler, Figure 80-19, and the bottle, Figure 80-20. The uses of these two models are almost equal in popularity. Both coolers operate with a similar refrigeration cycle, with the exception that the bottle cooler has no precooler. The bottle cooler is more efficient, since all the cooled water is used.

The cutaway view, Figure 80-21, shows the component parts that make up the bubbler styles. The bubbler mechanism includes the shutoff valve and the stream height adjustment. The precooler is a heat exchanger located in the drain line, which effectively increases the capacity of the cooler about 40%. The cooling not only cools the incoming water but can also store cooling by creating an ice bank.

Many of these water coolers also provide a source of hot water for making tea or coffee, using a resistance heater accessory.

The capacities of water coolers are based on ARI standard conditions of 90°F room temperature, 90°F supply water temperature, and 50°F drinking water temperature.

The refrigerant systems are hermetically sealed using a capillary tube metering device and are normally not serviced in the field. The compressor motors are fractional horsepower, split phase, with a relay to cut out the start winding when the compressor is near full speed, as shown in Figure 80-22. The system is started and stopped by a water temperature thermostat.

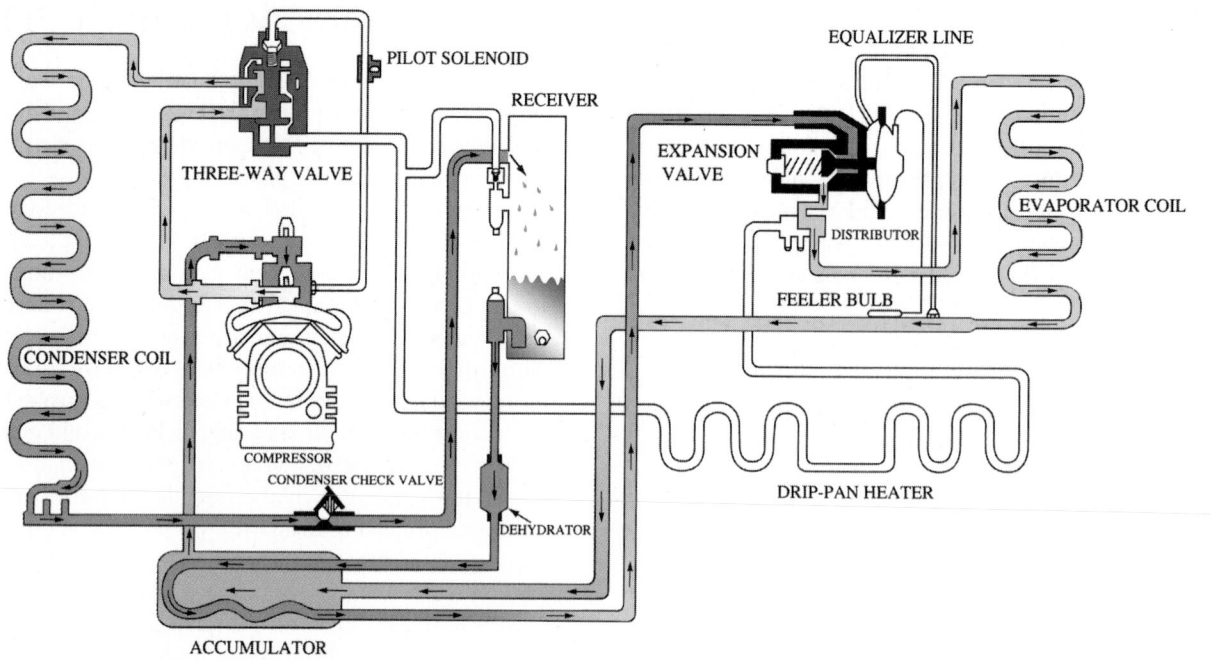

Figure 80-13 Cooling cycle for a truck refrigeration unit

Figure 80-14 Cooling cycle for an engine driven refrigeration unit

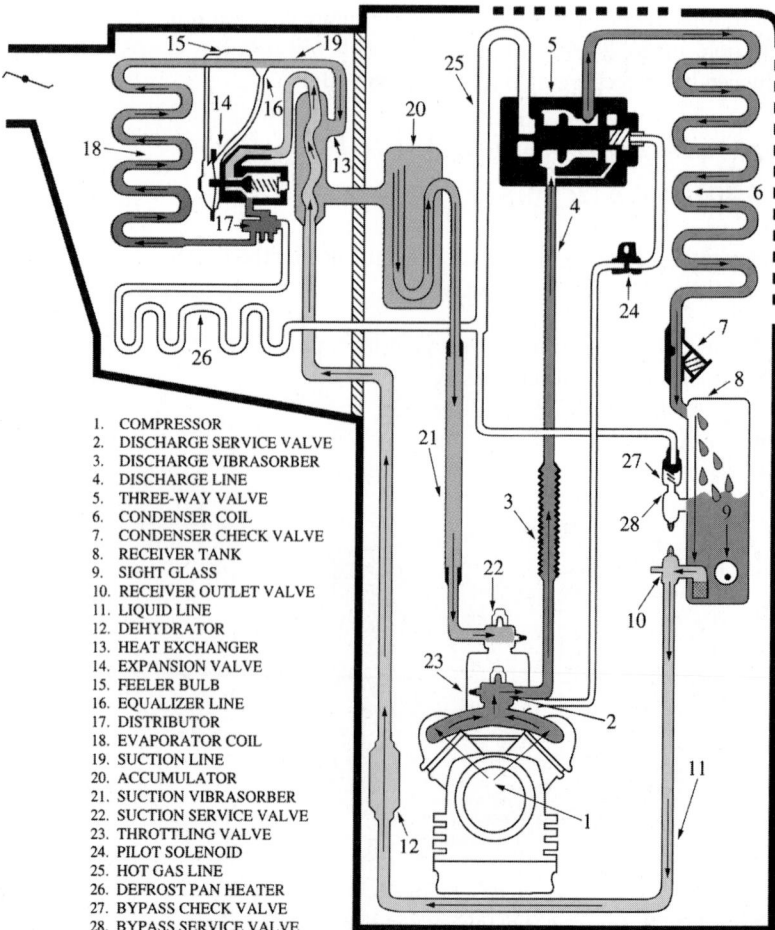

1. COMPRESSOR
2. DISCHARGE SERVICE VALVE
3. DISCHARGE VIBRASORBER
4. DISCHARGE LINE
5. THREE-WAY VALVE
6. CONDENSER COIL
7. CONDENSER CHECK VALVE
8. RECEIVER TANK
9. SIGHT GLASS
10. RECEIVER OUTLET VALVE
11. LIQUID LINE
12. DEHYDRATOR
13. HEAT EXCHANGER
14. EXPANSION VALVE
15. FEELER BULB
16. EQUALIZER LINE
17. DISTRIBUTOR
18. EVAPORATOR COIL
19. SUCTION LINE
20. ACCUMULATOR
21. SUCTION VIBRASORBER
22. SUCTION SERVICE VALVE
23. THROTTLING VALVE
24. PILOT SOLENOID
25. HOT GAS LINE
26. DEFROST PAN HEATER
27. BYPASS CHECK VALVE
28. BYPASS SERVICE VALVE

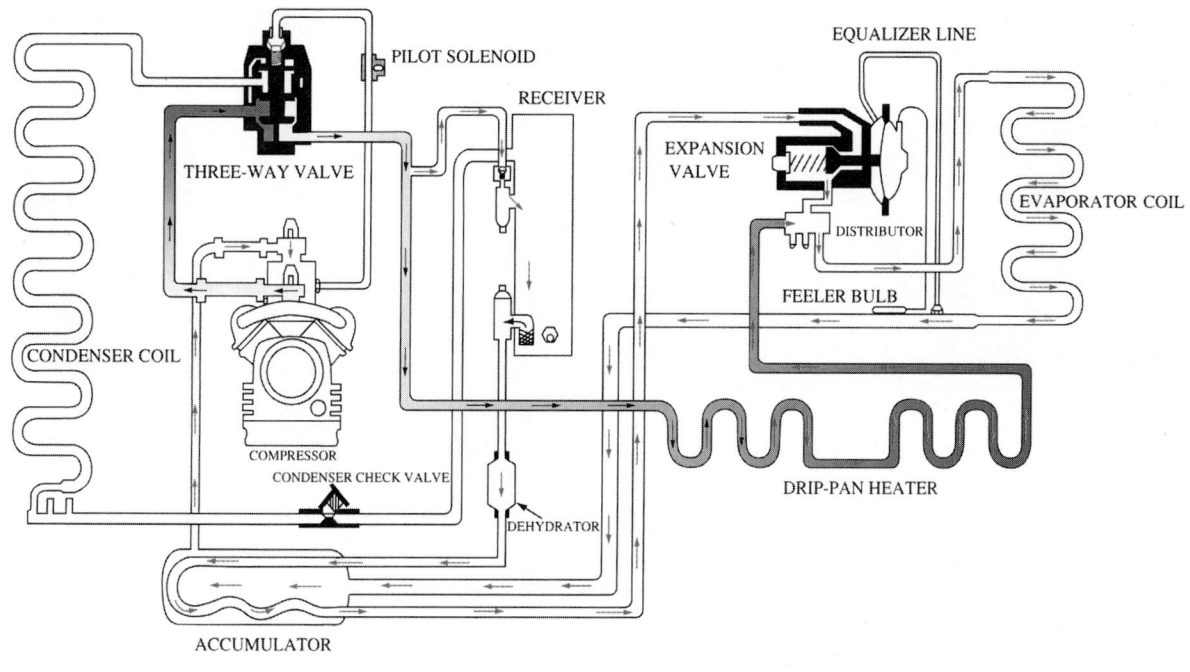

Figure 80-15 Heating and defrost cycle; heating is by reverse cycle principle using hot gas discharge from compressor

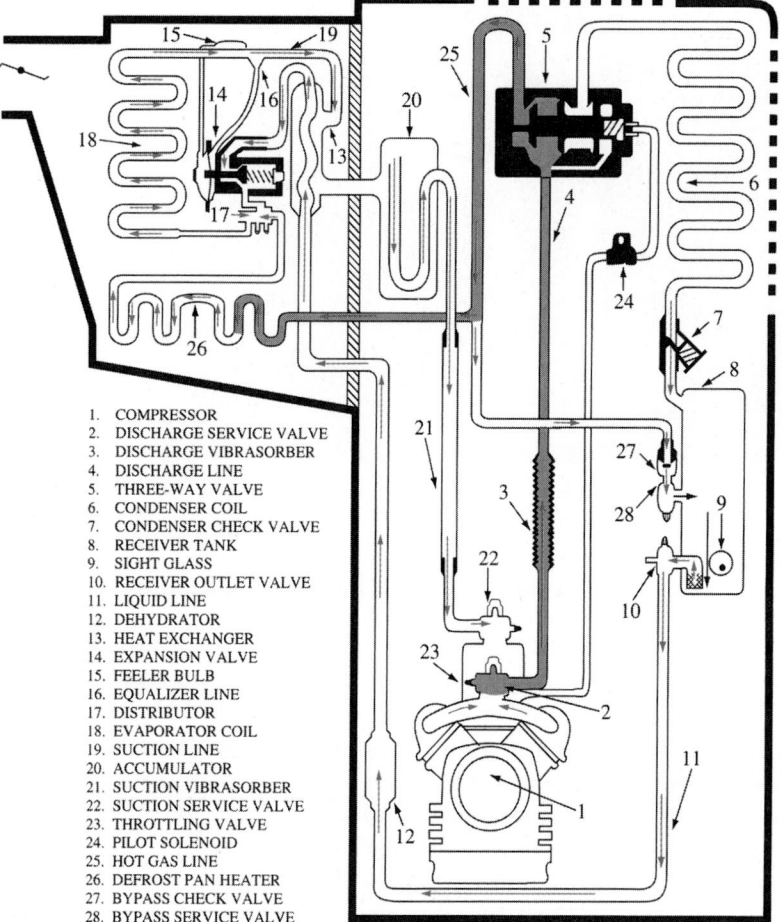

Figure 80-16 Heating/defrost cycle for an engine driven refrigeration unit

1. COMPRESSOR
2. DISCHARGE SERVICE VALVE
3. DISCHARGE VIBRASORBER
4. DISCHARGE LINE
5. THREE-WAY VALVE
6. CONDENSER COIL
7. CONDENSER CHECK VALVE
8. RECEIVER TANK
9. SIGHT GLASS
10. RECEIVER OUTLET VALVE
11. LIQUID LINE
12. DEHYDRATOR
13. HEAT EXCHANGER
14. EXPANSION VALVE
15. FEELER BULB
16. EQUALIZER LINE
17. DISTRIBUTOR
18. EVAPORATOR COIL
19. SUCTION LINE
20. ACCUMULATOR
21. SUCTION VIBRASORBER
22. SUCTION SERVICE VALVE
23. THROTTLING VALVE
24. PILOT SOLENOID
25. HOT GAS LINE
26. DEFROST PAN HEATER
27. BYPASS CHECK VALVE
28. BYPASS SERVICE VALVE

Figure 80-17 Diesel engine drive for a railway boxcar

The refrigerants used have been R-12 and R-500; however, most manufacturers now use an HFC type refrigerant, such as R-134a. The amount of the refrigerant charge is usually less than 1 lb. To meet environmental regulations, EPA requires the recovery of any CFC refrigerant if the unit is to be discarded or destroyed.

Figure 80-18 Compressor driven by railway boxcar diesel engine

Figure 80-19 Bubbler drinking water cooler

UNIT 80—SUMMARY

Ice cream making involves pasteurizing, homogenizing, cooling, freezing, and then hardening. For baking, ingredients must be stored and mixed at proper temperatures and then the finished baked product may be preserved by freezing. Very often ammonia is used as a refrigerant in these large food-processing plants.

Quick freezing of foods is accomplished through the use of blast freezers or running the product through a cryogen or very low temperature brine solution. This is done to seal in the moisture to maintain the natural flavors of the product.

Cryogens are also used for industrial processes for making oxygen and nitrogen and for treating metal surfaces. Liquefied natural gas, which is commonly used as a fuel, must be maintained at cryogenic temperature.

The transportation sector relies heavily on refrigerated methods for perishable food items. Refrigerated climate

Figure 80-20 Bottle drinking cooler

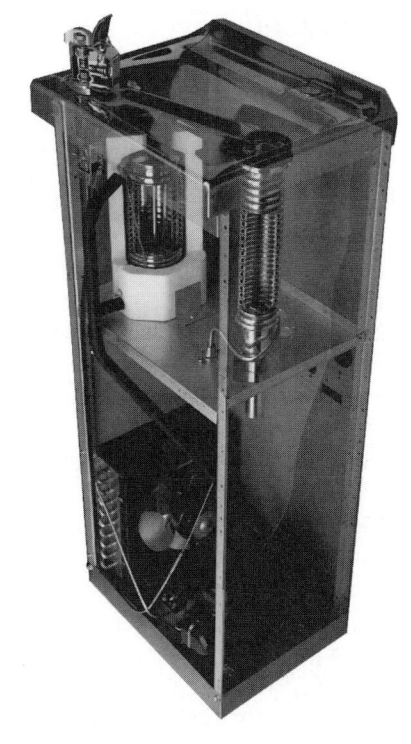

Figure 80-21 Cutaway view showing internal parts of a bubbler drinking water cooler
(Courtesy of Ebco Manufacturing Company)

controlled containers move fruits, vegetables, meats, and many other assorted products from ship to rail to truck. Airfreight relies primarily on dry ice and gel packs for cooling during transport. All of these refrigeration systems need to be monitored and periodically checked and repaired as necessary to ensure product quality upon delivery.

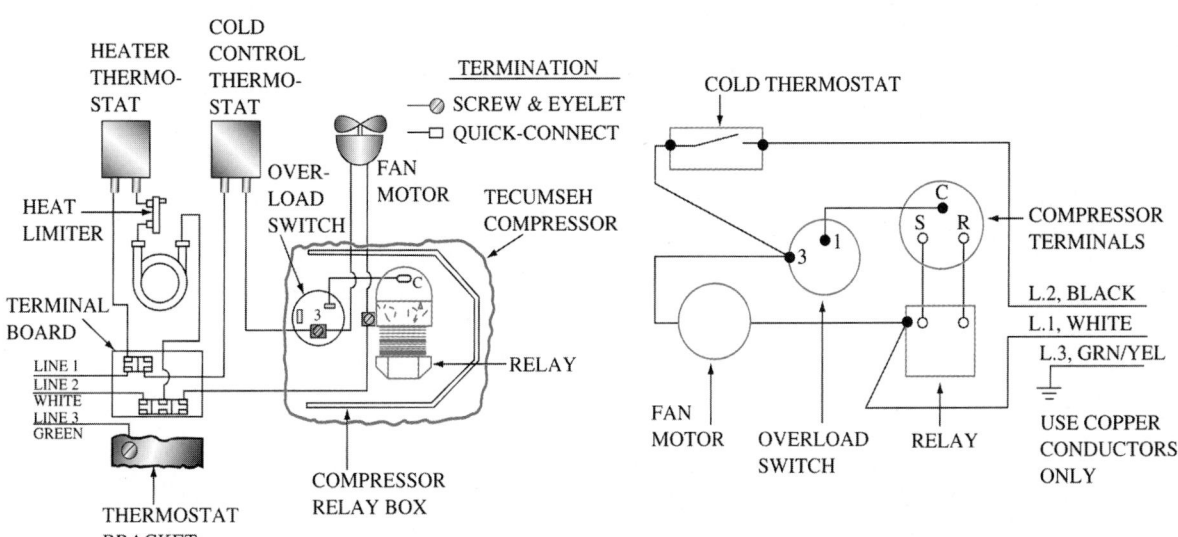

Figure 80-22 Wiring diagram for a drinking water cooler
(Courtesy of Ebco Manufacturing Company)

—— WORK ORDERS

Service Ticket 8001

Customer Complaint: Ice Cream Hardening Process Taking Too Much Time

Equipment Type: Ammonia System with Forced Air Evaporator

The service technician met with the production manager of the ice cream making facility who described the problem. During the past week, the ice cream was taking an unusually long time to harden. The hardening room temperature seemed to be OK and the central equipment was also operating properly.

The technician first made a general inspection of the central ammonia unit and determined that the discharge and suction pressures appeared normal. Next, the technician went to check the controls at the outside of the hardening room. The thermostatic expansion valve was fully iced over, as would have been expected. The box thermostat and EPR seemed to be functioning normally.

The technician then entered the hardening room to inspect the evaporator coils for ice. They appeared clear; however, the volume of airflow across the evaporator seemed low. Upon further inspection, one of the fans was not operating at all and a second one had a very hot motor. The technician would need to replace the two fan motors to increase the circulation across the evaporator coil to increase the heat transfer rate.

Service Ticket 8002

Customer Complaint: Refrigerated Container Temperature Rising

Equipment Type: 20 ft Refrigerated Container with Self Contained Unit

The service technician met with the trucking company dispatcher who was concerned about the temperature of one of the trucks that had just arrived. The product was frozen and very valuable and the temperature of the container was slowly rising.

The technician removed the cover from the self-contained refrigeration unit. A small diesel engine supplied power for the compressor and the unit controls. The belt drive was satisfactory and a check of the system operating pressures was also normal. Inspecting the upper section of the unit with a flashlight, the technician noticed a considerable amount of ice build-up on the evaporator coil.

The technician stopped the unit and carefully disconnected the electrical solenoid coil for the three way hot gas defrost valve and found that it had zero resistance indicating that it was burnt out. The technician replaced the solenoid coil and restarted the unit. The defrost cycle began to slowly melt away the ice.

Service Ticket 8003

Customer Complaint: Drinking Water Fountain Too Warm

Equipment Type: Drinking Water Bubbler with Sealed Hermetic Compressor

The service technician met with the receptionist in the lobby of the hospital. She explained that the bubbler type drinking water fountain was no longer producing cold water.

The technician checked the water flow and it appeared more than adequate as a nice arc was produced when the control handle was turned. However, the water was warm and at about room temperature and the compressor was not running. The technician removed the cover and felt the top of the compressor and it was hot to the touch. The technician suspected that the compressor was tripped on the thermal overload located on the shell.

The technician then secured the power to the unit and checked the condenser fan motor windings with a multimeter and discovered that the windings were shorted. The technician went out to the service van and found a replacement fan and wired it in place. By this time the compressor had cooled down enough for the thermal overload to reset itself. Once power was restored, the fan began to operate along with the compressor and now cold water was coming out from the fountain.

UNIT 80—REVIEW QUESTIONS

1. What are the major processes involved in making ice cream?
2. What temperature would you expect an ice cream hardening room to be maintained at?
3. What are nine items that can affect heat transfer in the ice cream making process?
4. At what three areas of bakery production is refrigeration used?
5. Why are bulk wheat flour, rice flour, and corn meal stored under refrigeration?
6. What are the two methods for processing dough?
7. What temperatures is bread frozen and stored at?
8. How is the ice on ice skating rinks produced?
9. What is the difference in ice temperature for different activities?
10. What is the term used to describe air conditioning a space for the purpose of aiding in the manufacturing of a company's products?
11. The National Institute of Standards and Technology has suggested that the term cryogenics be applied to all temperatures below what?
12. What can be used to store liquids at cryogenic temperatures?
13. What types of materials are commonly used for tanks that store liquefied natural gas?

UNIT 82

Domestic Refrigerators and Freezers

OBJECTIVES

After completing this unit you will be able to:

- describe the purposes behind refrigerator and freezer cabinet design.
- describe the refrigerant cycle components.
- describe the state of refrigerant throughout the refrigerant system.
- discuss the functions of mullion heaters.
- describe the function of temperature controls.
- follow the sequence of operation of a defrost timer.
- evaluate the convenience of frost free systems and discuss their operation.
- indicate the different applications of the vegetable, meat, and butter compartments.
- discuss the construction and operation of ice and water dispensers.
- perform maintenance for refrigerators and freezers.

TECH TIP

If food is kept cool or frozen, then it stays fresher longer for human consumption. The cooler temperatures slow the reproduction of bacteria, and the action of enzymes, which cause food to spoil. Over time humans have become aware of this fact, and refrigeration has evolved accordingly.

82.1 DOMESTIC REFRIGERATORS AND FREEZERS

The refrigerator has evolved from a simple cabinet to a complex operating system. The first refrigerator used a block of ice placed in the top section of the cabinet. Convection currents were relied on for the cool air from the ice to fall to the bottom of the cabinet and the warm air to rise to the top. This type of unit was simple, no moving parts, with not much of a need for skilled mechanics. Freezing temperatures were not achieved in this application.

These plain "ice boxes" have now advanced into complex electromechanical systems that require well-trained technicians for troubleshooting and repairing malfunctions. Units can now be purchased that are refrigerator/freezer combinations, straight refrigerators, and straight freezers. Cabinets come in different sizes to fit different applications. There are small units made for apartments or small rooms. There are high capacity units for the large household. The dreaded manual defrosting of freezer compartments has been replaced by automatic defrosting.

For the refrigerators of today to be correctly repaired, an understanding of their design and mechanics has to be undertaken and this process must continue as new models are introduced to the market. A refrigeration technician must be willing to continuously keep abreast of the field by reviewing trade journals and attending short courses.

82.2 REFRIGERATOR/FREEZER CABINET DESIGN

The design of the refrigerator/freezer serves several purposes. There is an insulated box, which is normally rectangular in design. A cooling only unit and a freezing only unit will have a single door, for access to the inside as shown in Figure 82-1. A combination refrigerator/freezer will have many configurations as shown in Figure 82-2. One door is for access to the cooling section, and the other door is for access to the freezer section.

Refrigerator/freezers come in many arrangements. One arrangement is called an upright, where the freezing section is on top, and the cooling section is below. There are some arrangements where the freezer section will be on the bottom. The other arrangement is called a side by side as shown in Figure 82-3, where the freezer section is on one side and the cooling section is on the other side.

Figure 82-1 Single door freezer

Figure 82-2 Combination two door upright refrigerator
(Photographs used with permission from Whirlpool Corporation)

Figure 82-4 Chest type freezer

Freezers come in different arrangements as well. One arrangement is called a chest type as shown in Figure 82-4, where the unit's long dimension is parallel with the ground, and the door is on top. The other arrangement is an upright as shown in Figure 82-5, where the freezer door opens in the front. The chest type freezer is more efficient in that when the door is opened, no spillage of cold air from the box occurs.

The upright freezer allows cold air to spill out every time the door is opened due to cold air being heavier than warm air.

Manufacturers also make available freezers and refrigerators for small areas such as apartments. These units are relatively little, holding only a small amount of food and drink.

Figure 82-3 Side by side refrigerator

Figure 82-5 Upright freezer

Figure 82-6 Adjustable refrigerator shelves
(Courtesy of Thermador)

The refrigerator/freezer cabinet will have brackets on the inside that provide places on which to rest shelves. These shelves are normally adjustable as shown in Figure 82-6. The shelves allow for the storage of food products and drinks. Some freezers utilize shelves that are not adjustable. The shelves in these freezers are actually the evaporator sections, and they cannot be moved as shown in Figure 82-7.

The cabinet provides spaces and support for the refrigerating mechanism. The refrigerating mechanism consists of mechanical components and is controlled by the electrical system. The mechanical side of the system is composed of the compressor, evaporator, condenser, and metering device. These four main components are connected by the hot gas line between the compressor and the condenser, the liquid line between the condenser and the metering device, the me-

tering device connects to the evaporator, and the suction line connects the evaporator to the compressor. This makes for a complete closed loop system.

The mechanical refrigeration process proceeds as follows:

- The compressor takes cool, low-pressure gas and compresses it into a high pressure, hot gas. The purpose is to raise the temperature of the refrigerant above the ambient temperature around the condenser so the heat in the refrigerant can be rejected. The heat will follow the second Law of Thermodynamics, which states that an object at a higher temperature will give up heat to an object at a lower temperature.
- The hot, high-pressure gas travels through the hot gas line, beginning the desuperheating process, and on to the condenser. In the condenser the latent heat of condensation occurs and the hot gas will condense to a high-pressure liquid. Heat that has been removed from inside the refrigerator/freezer cabinet, from produce in the cabinet, and from the compressor motor is rejected from the refrigerant at the condenser.
- The refrigerant leaving the condenser should be subcooled as it travels through the last passes of the condenser, and moves on through the liquid line and the filter-drier and on to the metering device. Sometimes the last pass of the condenser contains a strainer screen and desiccant. The tube is the drier.
- When the high-pressure liquid refrigerant encounters the metering device, which is normally a capillary tube, the refrigerant pressure is reduced to the low side pressure necessary for the correct evaporating temperature.
- As the low-pressure refrigerant, which is mainly liquid at this point, starts to boil due to the pressure drop caused by the metering device, latent heat of evaporation occurs. In other words, heat is absorbed by the refrigerant as it changes from a liquid to a vapor. A common low-side saturation temperature for refrigerator/freezers is −20°F.
- When the refrigerant leaves the evaporator, it should now be a superheated low-pressure gas that travels through the suction line to the compressor.

TECH TIP

The capillary tube and the suction line will normally be soldered together between the condenser and the evaporator. This allows for heat exchange between the cooler suction line and the warmer capillary tube. The heat exchange helps to subcool the liquid refrigerant as it passes through the capillary tube. This reduces flash gas and improves efficiency.

The compressor and condenser will normally be recessed in a space at the bottom of the cabinet as shown in Figure 82-8. In some higher end products, the compressor and condenser may be located on top of the unit.

Figure 82-7 Evaporator type freezer shelves

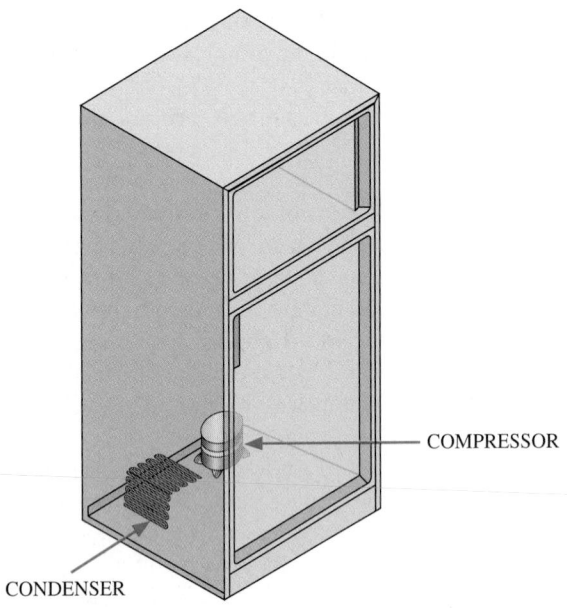

COMPRESSOR

CONDENSER

Figure 82-8 Compressor and condenser located in the bottom of the refrigerator cabinet

The compressor and the condenser are usually located together, and this arrangement is referred to as the condensing unit. An exception is the static fin type, where the condenser is located on the rear of the unit. With some freezing only and cooler/freezer combinations, the condenser will actually be underneath the outside skin of the unit. You will be able to determine this by feeling the outside of the unit while it is running and it will be warm. The refrigerant suction line and capillary tube will be located at the back of the refrigerator/freezer. On some units they are easily accessible while on others they may be recessed and underneath the outer skin of the unit.

SERVICE TIP

One problem the service tech will encounter in the field is a restricted capillary tube as shown in Figure 82-9. A restricted capillary tube indication is a warm suction line and a cool liquid line temperature. Be aware that a low refrigerant charge will give these indicators as well. To confirm a restricted capillary tube, a service tap will have to be installed on the low side of the system.

With the temporary tap in place and the unit running, suction pressure will be lower than normal. For example, a refrigerator/freezer using R-134a normally operates at about 4 in of vacuum on the low side. A deep vacuum indicates a total restriction. A small amount of refrigerant is then added to see if the suction pressure will rise. Since most refrigerators hold less than a pound of refrigerant, very little should be added to raise the pressure.

The technician must differentiate between a solid restriction and ice formation in the capillary tube. The ice restriction results from moisture in the sealed unit and will melt during the off cycle. In this case, the unit will start up

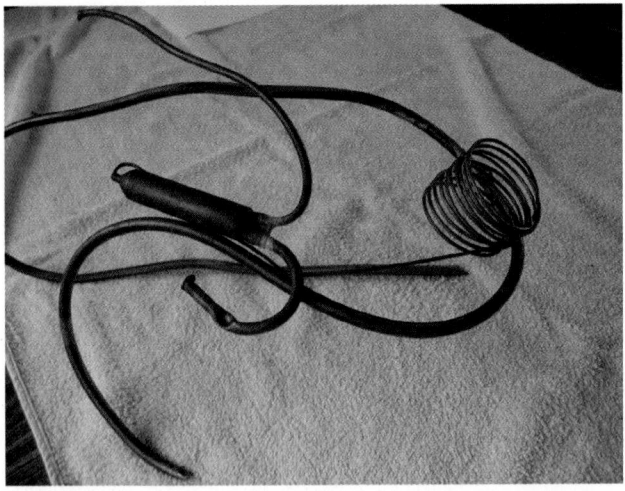

Figure 82-9 Capillary tube

and run properly for a short while with the correct pressures. The solid restriction will cause the suction pressure to drop as soon as the unit starts up.

CAUTION

If a restricted capillary tube is diagnosed, the practicality of replacement has to be judged for cost effectiveness. With the capillary tube being soldered to the suction line for heat exchange, installing a new capillary tube to achieve the same effectiveness is difficult. Even getting to the old capillary tube to pull it out can be time-consuming. The cost of a new refrigerator versus the cost of replacing the capillary tube will be the deciding factor.

The evaporator coil will be located inside the box, with several possible configurations. On an upright refrigerator/freezer, the evaporator coil will be in the upper section, either between the freezer compartment and the cooling compartment, or at the back of the freezing section as shown in Figure 82-10.

Top-freezer refrigerator with interior panel removed

Figure 82-10 Upright refrigerator evaporator coil

In a side by side, the evaporator coil will be in the freezer section normally at the back.

The cabinet also provides routes for the wiring of the electrical control circuits. The electrical systems can be very simple or complex. Examples of simple systems include cooling only or freezing only units. In this type there is only one thermostat control that interrupts one leg of power to the compressor. The thermostat is inside the box measuring box temperature. The electrical system is composed of the compressor windings, compressor overload, the thermostat, the connecting conductors, a current relay or PTC, and the plug or power cord. A typical wiring diagram is shown in Figure 82-11.

An example of a complex electrical system is a refrigerator/freezer combination unit. With this type of system there may be as many as two thermostats, defrost timer motor, an evaporator fan motor, a condenser fan motor, lights, mullion heaters, defrost heater, drain heater, defrost thermostat, door switch, compressor overload, compressor start components, water dispenser switches, ice making controls, as well as other components. Some refrigerator/freezers have thermostats and fans controlling humidity and temperature in the unit's crisper compartments. HVAC/R technicians must be able to read and understand wiring diagrams for these units to effectively troubleshoot a system as shown in Figure 82-12.

The design and function of the refrigerator/freezer cabinet determines where these electrical components will be located.

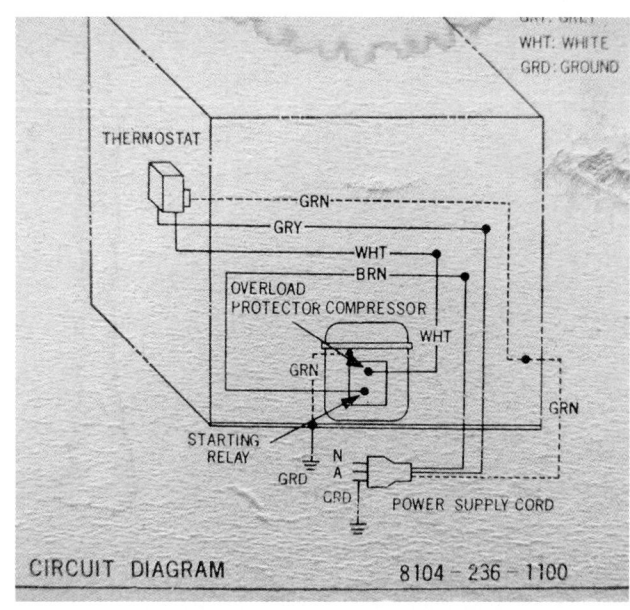

Figure 82-11 Refrigerator simple wiring diagram

82.3 CABINET INSULATION

The refrigerator/freezer cabinet has to be insulated or the unit will run continuously. The better the insulation, the less time the compressor will run, costing the homeowner less

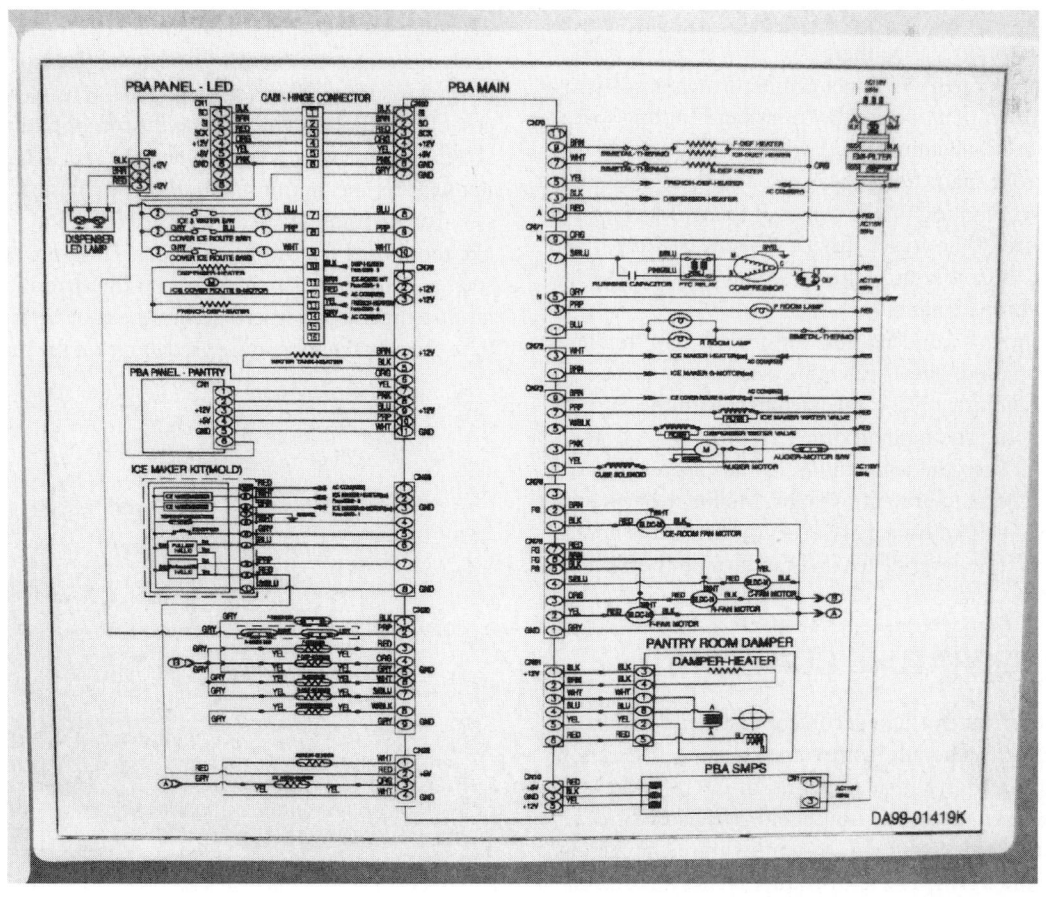

Figure 82-12 Refrigerator complex wiring diagram

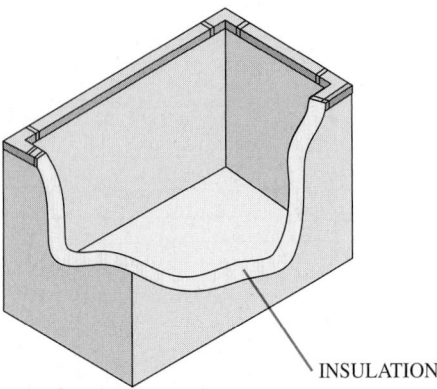

Figure 82-13 Chest type freezer insulation

Figure 82-14 Refrigerator thermostat

money. The insulation material is placed between the inner shell and the outer shell of the unit as shown in Figure 82-13.

The material normally used for insulation is expanding urethane foam. Initially the foam expands to fill all the nooks and crannies between the inner and outer shells. Be aware that if for any reason a puncture or tear occurs either to the inside or outside shell, moisture will collect between the two shells. As this moisture collects, it will absorb into the insulating foam, lowering the insulating value of the foam. If any damage to the inner or outer shell occurs, this should be repaired as soon as possible.

82.4 MULLION HEATERS

With refrigerators/freezers, there are two distinct conditioned spaces separated by a panel. Similar panels are also located on the doors that open to the freezer and cooling space. These panels are called mullions. Any time there is a mullion separating a cold space from a warm space, there exists the chance for condensation on the cooler of the two surfaces. If the temperature of the cooler surface is below freezing, then ice may form. In some cases, this ice could cause a door to freeze to the compartment.

To prevent this condensation from occurring, mullion heaters are employed. These heaters are placed close to the surface of the mullion that will come in contact with the warmer surface of a door. The mullion heater is a resistance-heating element. It will keep the temperature of the cabinet surfaces above the dew point to prevent sweating. Mullion heaters may be controlled by a thermostat that can be adjusted by the homeowner or by a power saver switch that can turn off the heater.

82.5 TEMPERATURE CONTROLS

All refrigeration systems have a control that starts and stops the compressor. Generally commercial type refrigeration units will have a control that responds, or opens and closes due to pressure changes. The household refrigerator/freezer uses a thermostat that responds to temperature changes, as shown in Figure 82-14. The temperature is measured in the space to be conditioned.

The unit type, whether it is a cooler, freezer, or a combination, will determine the temperature range of the thermostat and where it will be located. A refrigerator/freezer combination will have a thermostat located in the freezer compartment as shown in Figure 82-15 and a thermostat in the cooler. Thermostats used on refrigerator/freezers are designed to close with a rise in temperature in the box, and open with a fall in temperature in the box.

Thermostats allow for minor adjustment. The ideal temperature range for a cooling only box is 38–40°F. The ideal temperature range for a freezer is–10°F to 0°F. Any changes in the box temperature outside of the ideals should be made carefully. If the temperature is adjusted too low in the cooling only box, then there is a chance of the evaporator coil freezing up. Keeping the temperature in the box too warm may lead to product spoiling quicker. If the thermostat is set too low for a freezer, then the cost of operation will increase, as the compressor runs longer. It is recommended that a thermometer be kept in the box to monitor whether the thermostat needs to be adjusted.

The thermostats used for refrigerators and freezers are not like those used for comfort cooling. There are only numbers, such as 1 through 10, that have no direct relationship with a given temperature, where a comfort-cooling thermostat will have the actual temperature gradations on the thermostat. It is

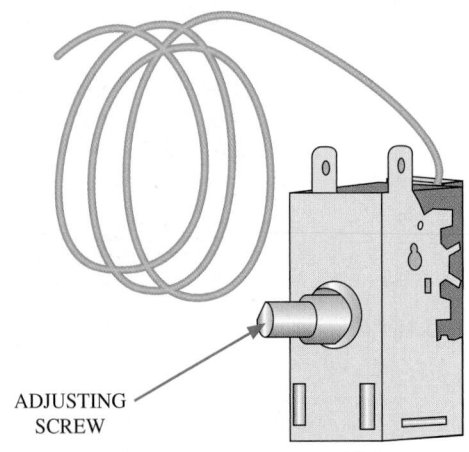

ADJUSTING
SCREW

Figure 82-15 Freezer thermostat

best to set the thermostat at a given number, and then monitor the thermometer located in the box. When the temperature is slightly below the desired temperature in the box, slowly turn up the thermostat until you hear the compressor shut off.

A combination cooler/freezing unit is more complicated. There are two separate conditioned spaces, each with a different temperature setpoint. Most units will have a thermostat monitoring the freezer compartment. When the setpoint temperature is reached, say 0°F, then the thermostat's contacts will open, breaking the circuit to the compressor.

The cooler section will have a thermostat as well, but it will only control a flapper door that allows cold air from the freezer section to flow into the cooler to maintain the temperature. Some units have a manually operated damper. These refrigerator/freezers have an evaporator fan in the freezer section that runs continuously, except during defrost, (which will be discussed later). Running the evaporator fan all the time keeps the air circulated throughout the refrigerated box, moving enough air from the freezer section to the cooler section to maintain the set temperature in the cooler.

The thermostats used in refrigerator/freezers must have line voltage rated contacts. These are single pole single throw contacts. Line voltage in most applications will be 115–120 V. The contact rating also has to be high enough for the application. Different size units will have different current draws. The thermostats are remote sensing. In other words, there is a temperature sensitive fluid filled bulb or capillary tube tip attached to the thermostat body by a capillary tube. The capillary tube transfers the pressure changes from the bulb or capillary tube tip to a bellows or diaphragm located in the thermostat. The bellows or diaphragm will then open or close a set of contacts.

These contacts allow current to flow to the compressor if closed. The cooler section thermostat will be attached to a flapper door by a wire or cable. The flapper door connects the freezer compartment to the cooler compartment.

The thermostats with the remote sensing will have a built in differential. This is the difference between the cutin setting and the cutout setting of the thermostat. As an example, if the thermostat is set at number 6 on the dial, and the thermostat opens its contacts at 38°F, this would be the cutout setting. If the temperature increases and the thermostat's contacts close at 42°F, this would be the cutin setting. The differential is 4°F. We would call the range of the thermostat 38–42°F.

SERVICE TIP

When replacing a faulty thermostat, be sure to match the temperature range of the new thermostat with the old one. Another important note is to match the type of sensing element. Some elements are designed to be in contact with the evaporator or an air register and others are designed to only come in contact with air.

82.6 HUMIDITY CONTROLS

One function of a refrigeration system is to dehumidify the space it is conditioning. Another function is to remove heat from the conditioned space. In comfort cooling, dehumidifying that results in the removal of moisture from the air as it flows through the evaporator coil is desirable. Drier air at a warmer temperature feels more comfortable than the same temperature air with higher relative humidity. However, product cooling for meats, vegetables, starches, and the like, is much different. Removing moisture from the ambient air around them takes away from their quality.

82.7 FROST FREE SYSTEMS

Anytime subfreezing temperatures are maintained in a conditioned space such as a refrigerator/freezer, frosting will occur on the evaporator. The evaporator surface temperature will be below 32°F and the moisture in the air being pulled through it will freeze on the coil surface. If 0°F is the desired temperature in the freezer, then the evaporator surface temperature will be around –10°F.

In older model refrigerator/freezers, the evaporator coil would have to be manually defrosted. This was accomplished by turning the unit off and letting the ice melt from the evaporator. This process could be sped up by putting a pan of hot water in the freezer or by using a hair drier.

CAUTION

Never use a pick or knife and chip the ice off of the coil. If a coil is punctured this will be followed by a hissing noise as refrigerant leaks out. Have patience with a manual defrost refrigerator/freezer and never try to remove the ice with something sharp.

Another disadvantage to manual defrost is the requirement to remove all the perishable produce and store it in a cool location until the defrosting is complete. Some under counter or dorm room sized refrigerators and freezer only units require manual defrost.

TECH TIP

Thawing and refreezing of a food product will decrease its quality. Ice crystals form inside the food product's cells when frozen. Repeated thawing and freezing could cause rupturing of cell walls, which degrades the food quality.

Most refrigerator/freezers have an automatic defrost. To accomplish automatic defrost, more controls are added to the refrigerating system. A defrost timer, defrost heater, and a defrost terminator or thermostat are the key components to the defrost circuit as shown in Figure 82-16.

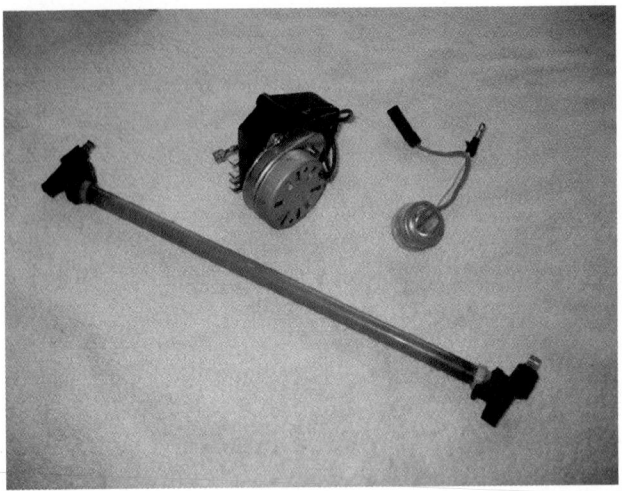

Figure 82-16 Key components of a defrost circuit

The defrost timer functions to initiate defrost. The majority of timers are clocks combined with a single pole double throw set of contacts. There are two basic styles of mechanical defrost timers. One style alternately places the timer motor in series with either the compressor or the defrost heater to keep each off while the other is in use. The defrost heater is a resistance heating element which applies heat to the evaporator coil when defrost is called for. The defrost thermostat is a normally open contact or thermistor attached to the evaporator. The defrost thermostat will close at approximately $28°F \pm 8°F$. The thermostat is in series with the defrost heater and when the evaporator coil has thawed out enough to raise its temperature to $50°F \pm 10°F$, the defrost thermostat opens and the circuit is broken to the heating element.

The sequence of events for an automatic defrost goes like this:

- Every time the compressor is energized, the defrost timer motor is energized. This way the defrost timer keeps track of compressor runtime. Accumulations of ice are formed every time the compressor runs.
- The defrost timer is designed so that after approximately 6–12 hr of accumulated compressor running time, the single pole double throw contacts will switch.
- When the 6 hr or more of running time is reached, the contacts switch, the circuit is broken to the compressor, condenser fan, and evaporator fan, turning them off.
- The switch also energizes the defrost heater.
- The defrost heater stays energized either until the defrost thermostat opens, or the defrost timer times out, usually around 28 min.
- After the unit has been in defrost for approximately 28 min, the defrost timer will switch its contacts back to their normal position, energizing the compressor, condenser fan motor, and evaporator fan motor.
- The condensate water from the defrosted evaporator coil will flow through a heated drain line into a pan normally located in the condenser area. Heat from the

hot gas line of the compressor or air drawn across the pan by the condenser fan motor will evaporate the water in between defrosts.

There are refrigerator/freezers that are designed to run more efficiently. This is accomplished by adaptive and preemptive defrost. The preemptive defrost prevents defrost cycles from happening during heavy use times, such as during mealtimes. The adaptive defrost only allows defrost when needed. Unlike the electromechanical timers, adaptive defrost systems do not defrost based upon regular timed sequences. Electronics are utilized to accomplish this type of defrost.

82.8 VEGETABLE, MEAT, BUTTER COMPARTMENTS

The refrigerator/freezer will have several separate compartments for keeping butter, meat, and vegetables. The butter compartment is designed to keep the butter at a slightly warmer temperature than the rest of the refrigerator. The slightly warmer temperature will make the spreading of the butter easier.

If vegetables are left out uncovered in the refrigerator, they will become dried out. Remember, as a refrigeration system cools a space, it also dehumidifies the space. A compartment called a crisper is located in the refrigerator to store vegetables and fruit as shown in Figure 82-17. Here the produce is in a closed compartment where the humidity will remain high, but the space will be cool. Some models of refrigerator/freezers will have vegetable and fruit compartments that have slide adjustments that can be moved to vary the humidity in the compartment as shown in Figure 82-18.

On some of the high-end cabinets, the crispers are complex units. They have their own circulating fan, independent damper, and a control that will have three settings. One setting maintains the same temperature as the fresh food compartment, one setting will maintain 38°F, and one setting will maintain 34°F. The

Figure 82-17 Crisper drawer
(Photographs used with permission from Whirlpool Corporation)

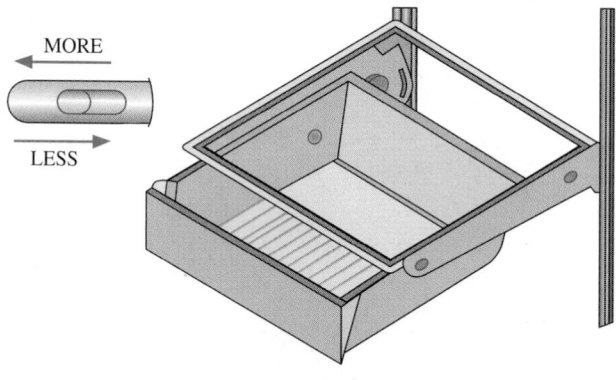

Figure 82-18 Crisper drawer humidity control

crisper can be maintained at a higher temperature than the fresh food section with the addition of a small heater. Humidity levels can be maintained in these crispers. The crispers have an inner layer of polymer. If the humidity gets too high in the crisper, the pores of the polymer expand, letting the humidity escape. If humidity decreases, the pores close up.

There may be a separate compartment for meats. It is important to keep meats separate from other produce so no cross contamination can occur.

82.9 ICE AND WATER DISPENSERS

One feature popular in the refrigerator/freezer is an ice and water dispenser as shown in Figure 82-19. Cold water can be provided at the push of a lever, and ice, crushed or cubed, is

also delivered at the push of a lever. Through the use of electronics, a simple push of a button can deliver the ice or water.

A recessed area on the outside of the refrigerator/freezer door will provide space for the water and ice dispenser. The ice is delivered when a lever or a button is pushed, the former by a glass normally, and the latter by the fingertip. The ice outlet is connected through a chute to the ice storage bin in the freezer. The water outlet is connected to a water storage compartment in the cooler section of the refrigerator. This allows for cool water to be dispensed when a glass depresses a lever or a button is pushed.

82.10 CABINET HARDWARE

Cabinet hardware associated with refrigerator/freezers includes hinges, door handles, and leveling feet. Hinges and door handles are designed on some refrigerator/freezers to be easily switched from one side to the other side of the door as shown in Figure 82-20. This arrangement will allow the doors to open either to the right or to the left. This kind of arrangement would only apply to over and under units where the freezer is on top and the cooler is on the bottom.

Refrigerator/freezer feet are adjustable to level the unit once it is in place. The refrigerator/freezer must be level to allow for the condensate from the evaporator to drain properly, to allow for the doors to open and close correctly, and to allow for the contents to rest on the shelves safely. If the unit is not level, there could be problems in the icemaker tray. When the tray fills up some of the water may spill out into the freezing section.

Some units have rollers for feet that can be adjusted to level the refrigerator/freezer. They enable the unit to be moved easily. Others will have leveling feet as shown in

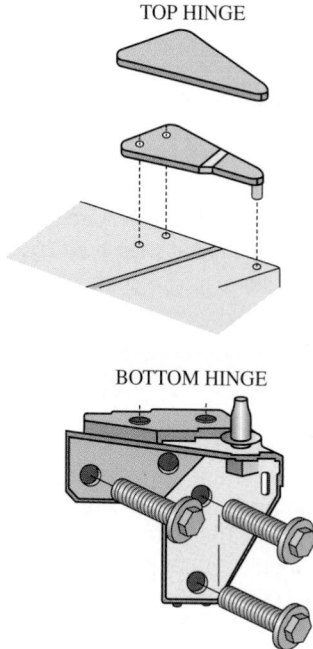

Figure 82-20 Refrigerator door hinge

Figure 82-19 Getting water from outside door of side-by-side Whirlpool refrigerator P080019_5z.tif ED5PBAXVQ
(Photograph used with permission from Whirlpool Corporation)

Figure 82-21 Refrigerator leveling feet

Figure 82-21, which can be adjusted to level the unit. If the unit is leveled properly, the doors will close by themselves when slowly let go. Installation instructions will describe how to adjust the level of the refrigerator for specific units.

Handles on modern units do not latch. Older refrigerator/freezers had handles that would latch to pull the door securely closed. Legislation was passed prohibiting this type of doors due to accidents involving small children who were trapped and the door could not be opened from the inside. Now the doors have to be able to be opened from the inside with a minimum force.

Doors for refrigerator/freezers use gaskets with magnetic strips inside them to pull and keep the doors closed. The low temperature inside the refrigerator also leads to a llow pressure area. This pressure difference between the outside and inside of the refrigerator helps to hold the door shut.

CAUTION

Whenever a refrigerator is not used and is stored in a place accessible to children, means should be undertaken to make sure the refrigerator is not a danger. Either taking the doors off or securing it so it cannot be readily opened will accomplish making the refrigerator child safe.

82.11 GASKETS

The refrigerator/freezer will have door gaskets to seal the inside from heat and moisture trying to get in from the outside. The gasket is made out of a flexible, waterproof material. The gaskets will have a magnetic strip built in to pull the door closed and keep it closed as shown in Figure 82-22.

TECH TIP

A simple test can be done to determine if the door gaskets are good. Open the refrigerator door for 10 s, and then close it. Approximately 15 s later, attempt to open the door once again. There should be resistance to opening the door. When the door was opened, cold air spilled out of the refrigerator and warm air replaced it. The introduced warm air begins to immediately cool thereby reducing its volume. This creates a lower pressure inside the unit. If the gaskets are not sealing effectively, then there will be minimal resistance to opening the door.

Figure 82-22 Refrigerator door gasket

82.12 PLANNED MAINTENANCE FOR REFRIGERATORS/FREEZERS

Defrosting

Low temperature refrigerator/freezer evaporator coils will develop frost on their surfaces over time. As frost builds on the coil, heat exchange between the refrigerant in the coil and the air in the box will decrease. If enough frost builds on the coil, the box temperature will begin to increase.

If the refrigerator/freezer requires manual defrost, then as the unit demands, it will have to be shut off and the door left open so the coil will warm to above 32°F. Any produce still in the box will have to be removed to a cooler or another freezer to prevent it from spoiling. A good time to defrost the unit is when the box is nearly empty. Some units may only need defrosting once a year. The number of times the box will need to be defrosted depends on the number of times the door is opened and also the humidity level of the surrounding area. Every time the refrigerator/freezer door is opened, warm air is introduced into the box along with the moisture it contains.

A cooling only box is designed to keep the interior of the cabinet between 38–40°F. This temperature range does require the evaporator to be below a freezing temperature. However it is not uncommon for the evaporator temperature to drop below freezing toward the end of the refrigerating cycle. When the unit is cycled off, the air in the cabinet that is above freezing will defrost any ice on the evaporator. If a large amount of frosting does occur on the evaporator coil leading to poor temperature control, the cause will have to be found and corrected.

A refrigerator/freezer with an automatic defrost will initiate automatically based upon a timed sequence. When compressor running time accumulates to the proper amount, and if the defrost thermostat is cold enough to close, the defrost will be initiated automatically. The compressor, condenser fan, and evaporator fan will shut off, and the defrost heater will be energized to defrost the coil.

An automatic defrost cycle can be tested. With units using an electromechanical timer, find the defrost timer as shown in Figure 82-23 and identify the power lead that goes to the defrost heater. Place the clamp-on ammeter jaws around this lead. Then

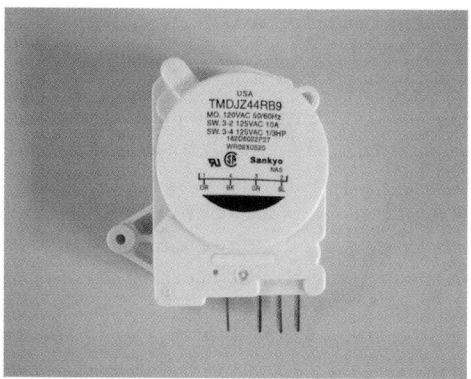

Figure 82-23 Refrigerator defrost timer cam
(Image courtesy of Nidec Sankyo America Corporation)

with a flat screwdriver rotate the defrost timer cam slowly. When the correct position is reached, the compressor, condenser fan, and evaporator fan should shut off, and the ammeter should show current draw to the defrost heater.

If the defrost thermostat is not closed, the heater will not draw current. But if the refrigerator/freezer has been running any length of time it should be closed. If the defrost test is successful, continue rotating the cam to bring the unit out of defrost.

Condenser

The condenser is where heat that has been absorbed from the refrigerator/freezer box, the heat of compression, and any superheat picked up in the suction line is rejected. If the condenser surface becomes restricted or clogged, as shown in Figure 82-24, then the heat rejection process decreases, raising the refrigeration system's head pressure, thus decreasing the unit's cooling ability. If the condenser becomes restricted enough, cooling can stop, and damage to the compressor may occur.

The condenser coil should be cleaned as often as needed. This may be once a year if the unit is in a low traffic flow area, or several times a year if in a high traffic flow area where lots of dust and debris such as dog or cat hair occurs.

Condenser coils come in different styles and each style may require a slightly different approach to cleaning. The coil can usually be cleaned with a brush, or if contaminants have been pulled deep into the coil, then air may need to be utilized to blow out the debris. Be careful, as blowing out the debris can really stir up the dust. To reduce this, a small vacuum can be used to first remove the heaviest layer.

Door Gaskets

Door gaskets serve the important purpose of keeping the refrigerator/freezer cabinet sealed to prevent warm and moist air from entering the box. Gaskets should be cleaned regularly. Sticky substances should be wiped off. These can cause the gasket surface to stick to the freezer cabinet. If this happens, the gasket could tear, which would keep the gasket material from sealing well. If gaskets do become torn or just worn out, they should be replaced.

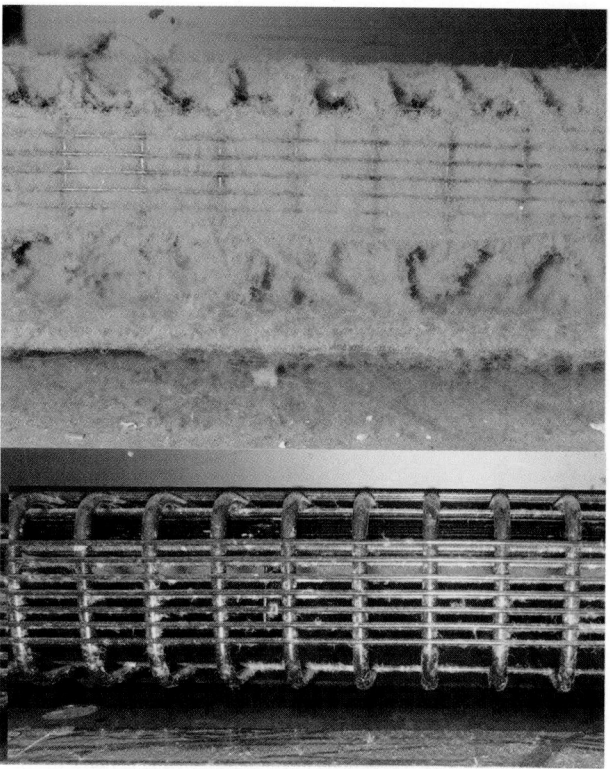

Figure 82-24 Refrigerator condenser

Exterior

The exterior shell of the refrigerator/freezer is normally metal with baked on enamel or porcelain. The shell serves to provide rigidity to the unit, keep moisture from entering into the conditioned space, provide attachment points for hardware, and provide support for the condenser. If the exterior becomes punctured, then moisture will flow into the space between the interior shell and exterior shell of the unit and soak into the insulation to decrease its efficiency. If any damage is done to the exterior such as a hole or cut, then it should be repaired. There are aftermarket repair kits that can be used to repair the exterior finishes.

Interior

The interior shell of the refrigerator/freezer is normally a plastic material that provides support for the shelves and the evaporator. This shell provides a barrier from moisture entering the cabinet space. Any damage should be repaired, as the efficiency of the unit will be decreased. The shell should also be cleaned regularly to prevent bacterial growth that can lead to foul odors and health dangers.

Evaporators

Evaporators normally do not require any maintenance. It is important to not rush into a manual defrost process. If manual defrost is required, then patience must be observed. Never chip ice off of the evaporator. This can lead to possible puncturing of the evaporator and the release of the refrigerant

Figure 82-25 Refrigerator condenser fan

from the system. Repairing evaporator refrigerant leaks is difficult. Some leaks cannot be repaired and the unit will be scrapped. Most evaporator coils for refrigerator/freezers are aluminum, which is very hard to weld.

Evaporator/Condenser Fan Motors

Some refrigerator/freezers rely on natural convection rather condenser or evaporator fan motors to transfer heat. If fan motors are used, as shown in Figure 82-25, they are usually shaded pole motors and there is little maintenance that can be performed on them. If the motor begins to squeal, it is an indication the bearings are damaged. In this case the motor should be replaced. Fan blades on the condenser motor can be cleaned if needed.

Refrigerant

Generally, household refrigerator/freezers are hermetically sealed without service taps for gauges. The refrigerant pressures therefore cannot be checked without installing service taps. If the refrigerant level or the pumping capacity of the compressor has to be checked, then service taps such as piercing valves can be purchased to install on the system. These taps are temporary and provide access to the sealed system. Taps can be installed on the low side and the high side of the system. These temporary taps are installed and the refrigerant level or compressor capacity is checked. Depending on the diagnosis, the temporary taps are to be removed and permanent taps are installed. For the temporary taps to be removed and replaced with sweat-on valves, all refrigerant in the system must be removed.

UNIT 82—SUMMARY

Refrigerator/freezers have advanced in design and so has the need for educated technicians to troubleshoot and make repairs. The refrigerator/freezer basics are the same for all makes and models, however they differ in the number of controls and added features.

The technician has to have an understanding of how the refrigeration system works. The technician also has to have an understanding of electricity: voltage, current, resistance, and how to use volt/ohm and ammeters correctly.

Staying current with manufacturer's changes and additions to components is critical for technicians. The basic elements of cabinet design, cabinet insulation, mullion heaters, temperature controls, humidity controls, automatic defrost controls, produce compartments, ice and water dispensers, cabinet hardware, door gaskets, and maintenance for refrigerator/freezers have not changed drastically. However, there are exceptions and many of these are related to increased efficiency. One major change is the use of electronics. Through electronics, three phase, variable speed compressors are now being used on some models. Three phase compressors run more efficiently than the split phase compressors commonly used.

Refrigerant types have also changed. Once commonly used, CFC R-12 refrigerant has been all but replaced by HFC R134-a. This is not the end of refrigerant changes. The methods used to preserve food have progressed from simple ice block boxes to units that incorporate sophisticated electronic controls. The technician who can learn and apply the basics of refrigeration and continually keep up with the manufacturers' changes is the technician who will excel in the HVAC/R field.

WORK ORDERS

Service Ticket 8201

Customer Complaint: Refrigerator Running Warm

Equipment Type: Domestic Refrigerator/Freezer

The customer called in complaining of the refrigerator running warm. The technician arrives and gets a temperature measurement of the refrigerator's freezer and cooler sections. The freezer was running at 42°F and the cooler was running at 55°F. The technician then measures the current draw at the compressor common and reads 2.4 A. This is within the manufacturer's specifications as read on the unit's data plate.

The compressor is running, but not maintaining the temperature in the box as it is supposed to. Upon checking the freezer compartment, the technician finds that there is no air movement even though the fan is running. The technician shuts the unit down and unloads the produce into a cooler provided by the customer. The panel covering the evaporator coil is removed and the evaporator coil is encased in ice. This indicates a defrost problem.

The technician then plugs the unit back in, clamps the ammeter around the circuit going to the number 2 terminal on the defrost timer, and turns the defrost timer cog until the compressor, condenser fan, and evaporator shut off. The circuit going to terminal 2 should now be drawing amperage but it is not. There are two possibilities, either the defrost thermostat is open or the heating element is open.

The technician has to be able to get to the evaporator coil to find out which problem the unit has. The technician first unplugs the unit, then plugs in a heat gun and carefully starts to thaw out the coil. Once the coil is free of ice, the technician carefully raises the coil to get to the defrost heater. Sure enough, it is burned in two. The technician calls it in and tells the customer it will take a trip back to the shop to pick up a new heater.

Service Ticket 8202

Customer Complaint: Refrigerator Running Warm

Equipment Type: Domestic Refrigerator/Freezer

The customer calls in that when she woke up and opened the refrigerator to prepare breakfast, everything was warm. When the technician arrived, the refrigerator had already been emptied, and the refrigerator had been unplugged. The first thing the tech noticed was there was no condensate in the drain pan as shown in Figure 82-26, at the bottom of the refrigerator. If an iced up evaporator had been the problem, it should have thawed by now and there would be condensate in the drain pan.

The technician pulls out the unit to gain access to the compressor area. First the technician takes a look to see if there were any visible wires burned off of the compressor terminals or anywhere else. Then the clamp-on ammeter jaws are connected around the common lead to the compressor and the unit is plugged in. The compressor pulls about half the locked rotor amperage on the compressor's tag and then trips the overload.

The technician then unplugs the refrigerator and pulls the current relay, as shown in Figure 82-27, from the run and start terminals at the compressor. The technician

Figure 82-27 Current relay

pulls the relay loose carefully, knowing that high pressure was just on the other side of the fusite plug in the compressor, as shown in Figure 82-28, and the terminals are easily damaged.

Using an auto ranging ohmmeter, one probe is touched to the S terminal on the fusite plug, the other probe is touched to the L terminal on the current relay. The relay is then turned upside down, and an infinity reading is measured. The technician knows with the current relay in the upright position, an infinity reading should be read, but turned upside down continuity should be read. The current relay contacts are designed to close when current flows to the run winding through the current relay coil during compressor startup. Then, as the current decreases once the compressor reaches about 75% of its speed, the current relay contacts open due to gravity pulling the contacts down and open.

The tech installs a new current relay from the truck stock, and plugs the unit in. On initial startup, the compressor pulls just under locked rotor amps and then the

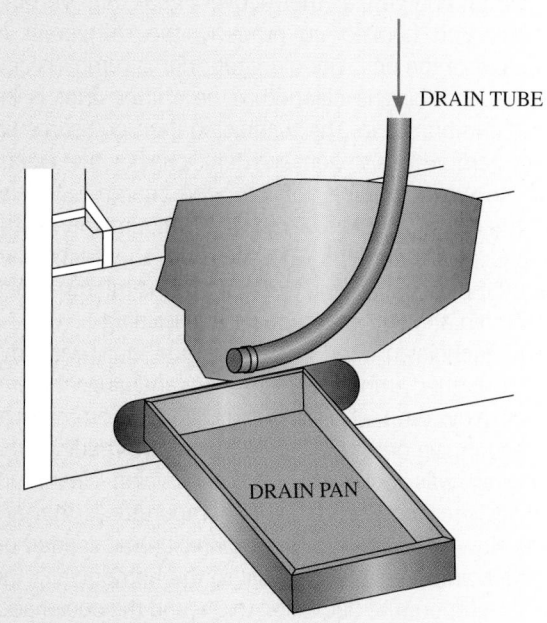

Figure 82-26 Drain pan for defrost

Figure 82-28 Fusite plug

current draw drops down to just under rated load amps. The technician reinstalls the compressor terminal cover and cleans up.

Service Ticket 8203

Customer Complaint: Refrigerator Running Warm

Equipment Type: Domestic Refrigerator/Freezer

A call comes in from the customer stating that all the refrigerator produce has spoiled, and the box was warm inside. When the technician arrives, luckily, the customer had already dumped everything and the box was left open to air out.

The refrigerator was still plugged in and the light inside the unit was on and the evaporator fan was running. This confirmed that the unit had power but the compressor was silent. The technician clamps the ammeter jaws around the common lead to the compressor and there is no current draw. The unit tag reads that the compressor rated load amperage is 1.8 A.

The technician checks with a voltmeter to the run and common terminals at the compressor and reads 120 V. That is the correct reading. Unplugging the unit, the current relay is disconnected from the compressor, and the common lead is also pulled. With an auto ranging ohmmeter, continuity is checked between common and run, common and start, and start and run. The meter shows $2 \, \Omega$ between run and common, but infinity between common and start. The technician knows that the ohms reading between common and run and between common and start, should equal start to run. The start winding has shorted out. The technician breaks the bad news to the customer, and orders a new compressor for the refrigerator.

Service Ticket 8204

Customer Complaint: Refrigerator Running Warm

Equipment Type: Domestic Refrigerator/Freezer

The homeowner called in the complaint that her refrigerator had been running great, but over the last few days the box temperature had been going up and now the freezer compartment was running about 38°F and the cooler was running around 50°F.

Upon arrival at the service call, the technician could hear the compressor running. Opening the refrigerator door, the evaporator fan was running and there was good air movement. The technician pulls out the refrigerator and reaches down and carefully touches the liquid line leaving the condenser. It was cool. The technician then carefully touches, for it should be hot, the hot gas line leaving the compressor. It was cool. Now there are a couple of possibilities for this scenario. The compressor is not pumping, due perhaps to a bad suction valve, a restriction in the filter-drier or metering device, or the system is low on refrigerant.

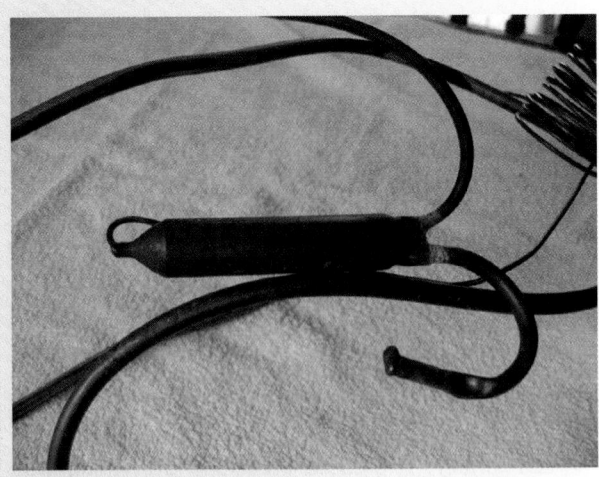

Figure 82-29 Filter-drier

The only way to know for sure is to install service taps. The technician installs temporary taps on the suction line and liquid line. After installing the gauges, there is 2 psig on the low side and 90 psig on the high side, with the unit running on R134-a refrigerant. The high side pressure should be running around 125 psig since the ambient temperature was 70°F. 70°F + 30°F = 100°F saturation temperature = 125 psig. The saturation temperature has to be above ambient and 30°F is a constant.

The refrigerant pressures show the unit to be low on refrigerant. As the technician was installing his gauges, there was an oily spot on the liquid line as it entered the filter-drier. A filter-drier is shown in Figure 82-29.

Getting out a soap solution, the technician dabs some on the oily spot and bubbles appear. The technician shuts the unit off and gets all the recovery gear out. With the recovery unit hooked up properly, the refrigerant is pulled out of the unit. The old filter-drier is removed and the copper tubing is cleaned. A new filter drier is installed and brazed in. The technician then pressures up the system with nitrogen and leak checks the welds. With the welds holding, the nitrogen charge is blown, and a vacuum is pulled. When the vacuum thermistor reaches and maintains 500 microns, the technician shut off the vacuum pump to see if the 500 microns hold. After 5 min, the 500 microns was still holding.

The technician then recharges the unit with the proper weighed amount of refrigerant and plugs the unit back in. Now the technician reads 125 psig on the high side and 4 psig on the low side. These are readings the technician was looking for. The technician cleans up, checking occasionally on the box temperatures, they are falling slowly. By the time the technician has loaded up the truck and presented the bill to the homeowner, the freezer temperature had fallen to 0°F and the cooler section had fallen to 38°F.

Service Ticket 8205

Customer Complaint: Standing Water in Refrigerator

Equipment Type: Domestic Refrigerator/Freezer Service

The service call comes in and the complaint is that the refrigerator has water standing in the bottom of it, below the crispers. The technician arrives and pulls out the crispers in the bottom of the box. There is about $1/2$ in of water standing there. pulling the front grill off of the unit, there is no water in the condensate drain pan.

The technician goes out to the truck, and brings in an air bottle. After shutting the unit off and unloading the produce in the freezer, the technician gains access to the evaporator coil. Finding the drain, the technician inserts the end of the air hose and opens up the bottle to blow through the drain. After an initial hesitation, the air flows through the drain. Some water is poured down the drain just to double-check for a clear drain. The panels are then reinstalled covering the evaporator coil. The drain line is now clear and should flow properly.

Service Ticket 8206

Customer Complaint: Freezer Running Warm

Equipment Type: Domestic Refrigerator/Freezer

The customer complaint is that the refrigerator is running warm in the freezer section as well as the cooler. The technician arrives, and puts a thermistor in the freezer and the cooler. Checking the temperature in both compartments shows 30°F in the freezer and 52°F in the cooler.

The technician rolls out the refrigerator, pulls the back cover off the condenser section, and immediately sees that the suction line is frosted all the way to the compressor. On opening the freezer door compartment, there is no sound of a fan. The technician unplugs the unit and gains access to the evaporator motor.

Once the panels are pulled and there is access for the voltmeter probes to get to the motor, the technician plugs the refrigerator back in. The compressor and condenser fan come on and run, but no evaporator fan motor. With the auto ranging voltmeter on, the technician puts one probe tip to one terminal at the fan motor and the other voltmeter probe is touched to the other electrical terminal at the fan motor. The voltmeter showed 115 V, which is good.

The technician unplugs the refrigerator again and spins the motor. The bearings are clear. The technician then disconnects both power leads to the evaporator fan motor, sets the multimeter on ohms, and checks, the continuity between the fan motor terminals. The meter shows OL or infinity, the motor winding is open. The tech-

nician goes out to the truck, gets a new fan motor, and has the refrigerator up and cooling in 30 min.

Without the evaporator fan motor running, the liquid refrigerant in the evaporator was not boiling off properly, causing the coil to run colder than it is supposed to, and ultimately leading to the coil freezing up.

UNIT 82—REVIEW QUESTIONS

1. How does freezing or cooling of food make it last longer without spoiling?

2. What principle allows an old fashioned refrigerator with a block of ice placed in the top compartment to cool?

3. Can freezing temperatures be achieved with just ice as the refrigerating mechanism?

4. Boxes for food preservation can be found in what temperature ranges?

5. Which freezer arrangement is most efficient?

6. Heat transfer in a refrigeration unit follows which law?

7. Where does subcooling occur in the refrigeration system?

8. Heat is absorbed by the refrigerant during which change of state?

9. What event could cause the insulation between the inner and outer shell of the refrigerator/freezer to lose its insulating capabilities?

10. What is the panel called between the freezer and cooler compartments?

11. Mullion heaters serve what purpose?

12. Refrigerator/freezer thermostats react to changes in _____.

13. What is one possibility if the homeowner sets the cooling only unit's thermostat too low?

14. What is the differential of a thermostat if its contacts open at 38°F and close at 42°F?

15. Why does frost form on the evaporator coil of a freezer?

16. What are the three main components of the defrost system?

17. The defrost timer keeps track of the _____ running time.

18. What one function of refrigerating is detrimental to produce such as lettuce?

19. What is the purpose of the crispers in a refrigerator/freezer?

20. What can occur if the refrigerator/freezer is not level?

21. What part of the door gasket is designed to pull and hold the refrigerator door closed?

22. Which electrical components shut off when defrost is initiated for a frost free refrigerator?

23. If the condenser becomes restricted, what happens to the head pressure?

24. What can be done to check the refrigerant pressures for a sealed system if there are no factory installed service valves?

UNIT 83

Troubleshooting Refrigeration Systems

OBJECTIVES

After completing this unit you will be able to:

- explain the different methods to electrically troubleshoot a refrigeration system.
- explain how to troubleshoot a defective compressor.
- explain how to troubleshoot a defective start relay.
- explain how to troubleshoot a defective capacitor.
- explain how to troubleshoot metering devices.
- explain how to troubleshoot common evaporator problems.
- explain how to troubleshoot common condenser problems.
- explain how to search for leaks in a refrigeration system.

83.1 INTRODUCTION

Patience is a requirement when troubleshooting refrigeration systems. It is important to take the time necessary to properly diagnose a system problem. Rushing to a quick diagnosis often leads to misdiagnosing the root cause of the problem.

A good service practice is to spend some time speaking to the customer before looking at the system. Listen to the customer's complaints and then ask some pertinent questions about the system, such as:

- How old is the unit?
- When was it last repaired, and what was done?
- Has the unit been working OK up until the time of the breakdown?
- Have you noticed any strange sounds or erratic operation lately?

After speaking with the customer, conduct a visual inspection of the system and look for any obvious system problems. This is another important part of the troubleshooting process. During the initial visual inspection try to determine the:

- Type of metering device used.
- Type of refrigerant in the system.
- Condition of the evaporator and condenser coils.
- Required supply voltage.
- Overall condition of the equipment.

A crucial part of the initial inspection is the examination of the evaporator and condenser coils. An iced up evaporator coil and dirty condenser coil are two common problems that can easily be identified during a visual inspection. The cause may not be as apparent but the symptom is easy to discover.

Identifying the refrigerant type helps to determine the correct operating pressure when it comes time to install a set of service gauges on the system to read its working pressures. Finding the correct supply voltage and whether it is a single or three phase system will also help when testing the circuit.

Another part of a visual inspection is to look for any oily pipes or parts, which is usually a good indication of a refrigerant leak. Also carefully (it may be hot) feel the head of the compressor to see if it is cold, warm, or hot. This helps determine if the compressor is the cause of the problem. For example, if the compressor is extremely hot and not running, it may be off due to an overload. You may want to start troubleshooting there to find out why this has happened.

Visually inspecting all the major components of a system takes a little extra time, but it is time well spent and is necessary to efficiently troubleshoot any refrigeration system.

SAFETY TIP

Taking shortcuts on a job may save time but may cause a technician to work in an unsafe manner. This is not a wise trade off. Do not take any shortcuts that may cause you to work in an unsafe manner. It is simply not worth the few extra minutes you may have gained.

83.2 ELECTRICAL TROUBLESHOOTING

Electrical troubleshooting can be divided into two areas: (1) electrically diagnosing controls (switches, relays, and contactors); and (2) electrically diagnosing loads (coils, fan motors, and compressors).

There are three major tools commonly used to troubleshoot the various electrical components of a refrigeration system: (1) voltmeter, (2) ammeter, and (3) ohmmeter. Each measures a different electrical characteristic in a circuit and is needed to properly diagnose an electrical fault within a system. Many technicians will use a multimeter, as shown in Figure 83-1, to measure all of these electrical characteristics.

Figure 83-1 A digital multimeter used to measure various electrical characteristics of a circuit
(UEi image is copyright © 2008 UEi. Used with permission. All rights reserved.)

SAFETY TIP

When replacing or repairing any electrical components, always verify that the voltage source is truly disconnected from the circuit. Test the circuit for the presence of voltage with some type of voltmeter or voltage indicator. Do not solely rely on the electrical disconnect to ensure the voltage is disengaged. Always verify this yourself.

A voltmeter measures electrical potential (voltage) at a switch or a load (such as motor or the coil of a contactor). In order for a load to operate properly, the correct voltage must be applied. Most units will have the required applied voltage stamped on a clearly marked name plate. If a load is not energized, one of the first steps in the troubleshooting process is to determine if the proper voltage is applied to the nonenergized load. For most loads, the applied voltage must be within ±10% of the name plate voltage. If no voltage or the incorrect voltage (outside the ±10% tolerance) is present at a load, then the problem lies in the voltage supply, controls, or wiring leading to that load. When checking the applied voltage to a load, always measure the voltage at the load and not

at an electrical junction before the load. There may be an issue with the wiring leading to the load, so it is more accurate to measure the applied voltage directly there.

SAFETY TIP

When working on electrical circuits, safety should always be first on your mind. Electrical circuits should always be deenergized before repairing or replacing any electrical component or wiring. Deenergize at the system's disconnect and then follow standard lock-out/tag-out procedures.

A voltmeter can also be used to check the operation of the various electrical controls in a circuit. Electrical controls fail in one of two ways: they fail to close or they fail to open. A voltmeter can be used to determine whether a control is electrically open or closed by measuring the line voltage across the control's contacts. A measured voltage indicates that the contacts are electrically open. If the contacts should be closed, then the circuit problem lies in the control.

A zero measured voltage would seem to indicate the control is closed. However, this is not always true. The absence of a line voltage across a contact does not always indicate the contact is closed. If two or more controls wired in series are electrically open in a circuit, then there will not be a line voltage drop across their contacts. Therefore this method of electrically troubleshooting a control is not always reliable.

A more reliable method of electrically troubleshooting controls is a procedure referred to by many technicians as hopscotching. This allows a technician to easily isolate an open electrical component. First, attach one probe of a voltmeter to a common point in the circuit as shown in Figure 83.2. The blue probe is attached to the L2 leg of the circuit and will stay attached at this point during the process. This is an electrically common point for all the loads in the circuit. Now the red probe can be moved around the circuit to help determine which switch is electrically open or closed.

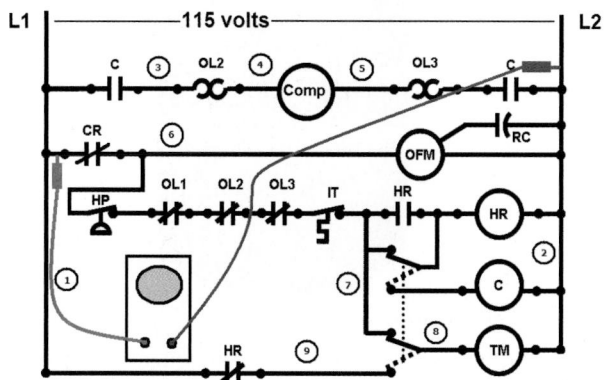

Figure 83-2 Hopscotching an electrical circuit

Here is an example of the process. As shown in Figure 83-2, the red probe of the voltmeter is initially connected before the CR contact and should read line voltage, which is 115 V in our example. When the red probe is moved to point 6 on the diagram, 115 V should again be read on the voltmeter if the CR contact is electrically closed. If the voltmeter reads 0 V, the CR contact is electrically open. This process can be repeated for all of the switches in the circuit. If line voltage is read before a switch and after the switch, the switch is electrically closed. If line voltage is read before a switch and not after the switch, the switch is electrically open.

An ammeter is another effective troubleshooting tool. A clamp-on ammeter is shown in Figure 83-3. It is used to measure how much current a load is drawing. This enables a technician to verify that a load is electrically energized. If a load is drawing current, it is electrically energized. However, the total amount of current being drawn will indicate whether the unit is operating properly. If a load is drawing current outside the specifications of the manufacturer of the component, then there is a problem with either its operation or application.

Always check with the manufacturer of the component to determine its correct operating current range. For many (but not all) fan motors, the current drawn by the fan motor should be within a range of –25%/+10% of its name plate full load amperage (FLA) rating. The amperage drawn by a compressor varies depending on its applied suction and discharge pressure and its applied voltage. Compressor manufacturers will publish the correct operating current draws for their compressors.

An ohmmeter is another useful tool for electrically troubleshooting electrical components. It can be used to check both controls (switches, relays, and contactors) and loads (coils, fan motors, and compressors). An ohmmeter measures the resistance of an electrical component. When using an ohmmeter it is necessary to electrically remove the component from the circuit. This means that if a voltage is applied to the circuit, it needs to be deenergized and then the wiring connecting the component to the electrical circuit removed. If voltage is applied to an ohmmeter, the meter could be damaged.

An ohmmeter can be used to check whether a control's contact is electrically open or closed. Once the component is disconnected from the circuit, the leads of an ohmmeter can be placed across the control's electrical contacts. If the ohmmeter measures a resistance of approximately 0 Ω, the contacts of the control are closed. If the ohmmeter measures an infinite resistance across the control's contacts, the contacts are open.

When using an ohmmeter to check the condition of a load, the leads are placed across the windings of the load. If the measured resistance agrees with the manufacturer's specifications, the windings of the load are OK. If a 0 Ω resistance is measured across the windings of the load, the windings are shorted. If an infinite resistance value is measured across the windings, the windings are open.

83.3 MECHANICAL REFRIGERATION TROUBLESHOOTING

Troubleshooting the mechanical side of a system involves analyzing or investigating the refrigerant flow either throughout the entire system or through any of the components. This requires being able to determine the refrigerant's pressure and temperature at various locations throughout a system.

When analyzing the entire system, the actual refrigerant conditions at various locations in a system are compared to the design conditions of a properly operating system. This will normally allow a technician to determine a system's defect. For example, if a system is discovered to be operating with both lower than normal suction and discharge pressures, and the superheat value of the refrigerant leaving the evaporator is higher than normal with a lower than normal subcooling value leaving the condenser, a technician can determine the system has a low refrigerant charge.

Figure 83-3 A digital clamp-on ammeter used to measure the amperage drawn of the load in a circuit
(UEi image is copyright © 2008 UEi. Used with permission. All rights reserved.)

Many times a technician will need to analyze the process through a component such as the compressor, condenser, or evaporator. This requires an understanding of the component and how it is designed to function in a system. For example, a refrigeration compressor is designed to pressurize a low-pressure refrigerant vapor to a higher-pressure refrigerant vapor. If a compressor is electrically operating but fails to sufficiently increase the pressure of the refrigerant from its inlet to its outlet, the compressor is mechanically defective and more than likely the compressor will need to be replaced.

In general a technician can analyze the operation of the evaporator as well. If the superheat value of the refrigerant leaving an evaporator is higher than normal, the evaporator is starved for refrigerant. If the superheat value of the refrigerant is lower than normal, the evaporator is flooded with refrigerant. Finding the reason why the evaporator is either being starved or flooded, however, will require looking at the entire system and analyzing other conditions.

When analyzing the condition of the refrigerant throughout a system or through a system component, a technician must allow the pressures and temperatures of the refrigerant to stabilize upon restarting if the system has been off. When troubleshooting, it is a good service practice to let a system run for about 10 min before recording any of the system's pressures or temperatures.

83.4 TROUBLESHOOTING A DEFECTIVE COMPRESSOR

Replacing a compressor on a refrigeration system is never an easy or inexpensive task. If a compressor is found to be defective, every effort should be made to verify that a correct diagnosis was made. Sometimes compressors that have been changed out in the field are later found to be operational.

Compressor problems can be divided into two groups: mechanical or electrical. Mechanical defects are problems that affect the operation inside the compressor, such as blown valve plates, a broken crankshaft, or worn pistons. These defects will either cause a compressor not to pump any refrigerant or pump to below its rated capacity.

It is generally easy to determine if a compressor is not pumping adequately. At startup, verify that the compressor is electrically energized, then measure its amperage draw. It will be lower than normal. Next, monitor the compressor's suction and discharge pressures. Neither the suction nor the discharge pressure will change dramatically. There may be a very slight change in pressure but the suction pressure will stay very high and the discharge will stay low.

To determine whether a compressor is pumping to its rated capacity is not quite as simple. A technician must measure the compressor's actual amperage draw and compare this to the amperage draw as stated by the manufacturer. The amperage should be within ±5% of the manufacturer's stated value. If it is drawing less than 5% of its rated amperage draw, it is not pumping to its rated capacity.

Compressors can fail to start as a result of either an electrical defect or a mechanical defect. Mechanically one or

more of the pistons within the compressor can become locked and fail to move. The compressor will attempt to start, but since the pistons will not move, the compressor draws high amperage causing it to shut down on overload.

There are three major electrical defects that will cause a compressor not to operate. One possibility is the motor windings of the compressor are open, shorted, or grounded. Another possibility is that the starting relay or capacitor as shown in Figure 83-4 are defective. The third possibility is that the incorrect voltage is applied to a compressor.

To check the condition of the compressor's motor windings, a technician will need to measure the resistance of the windings using a standard ohmmeter, as shown in Figure 83-5. For single phase compressors, measure the resistance value of both the run and start windings, and measure the resistance of each winding to ground. For three phase compressors, each of the three windings will need to be checked. If the

Figure 83-4 Starting components (relay and capacitor) used on a single phase compressor

Figure 83-5 Measuring the resistance of a compressor

correct resistance value is measured across its windings as shown in Figure 83-6 and an infinite resistance is measured from the windings to ground as shown in Figure 83-7, then the windings are satisfactory.

TECH TIP

The voltage applied to a three phase motor must be balanced, meaning the applied voltage to each leg must be relatively the same. The applied voltage must not deviate more than 2% from the average supplied voltage. A voltage imbalance of greater than 2% will cause the windings within a motor to generate heat beyond safe levels, leading to premature motor failure.

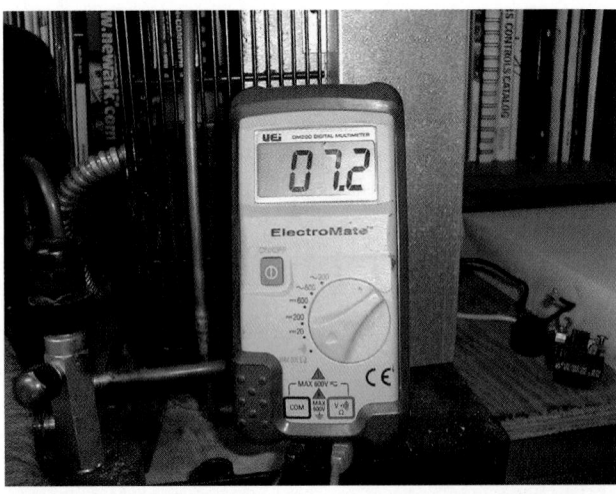

Figure 83-6 Measuring the resistance of a good compressor

Figure 83-7 Measuring the resistance of an open winding on a compressor

There is a common scenario where a compressor may appear to be defective when in fact it is not. A compressor with an *internal overload* that has overheated will shut down and will not restart until the compressor has cooled. If a technician performs a resistance check on the compressor, the first step will be to measure the resistance from common to run and common to start, which will be infinite resistance. The technician may interpret this to be an open winding in the compressor. However, if the compressor is allowed to cool down and the internal overload to reset, the technician may find the compressor will start normally and will not need to be replaced. The reason why the compressor overheated will need to be identified and resolved.

A compressor with a defective run capacitor will draw higher than normal amperage and cycle off on its overload or not start at all. If a compressor incorporates a start relay and a start capacitor and either is defective, the compressor will most likely not start.

Incorrect voltage applied to a compressor may cause it to run for a brief time then cycle off on its overload, or not start at all. A service technician must first verify the correct voltage for the compressor and then measure to see what actual voltage is applied. Most compressors are rated with a tolerance of ±10%. If the applied voltage is outside these limits or those stated by the manufacturer, it must be corrected before the compressor can be properly diagnosed.

Using a Compressor Analyzer

When troubleshooting a single phase hermetic compressor that does not start, it is good practice to use a compressor analyzer, as shown in Figure 83-8. This tool will allow a technician to start a single phase compressor directly without using any of the system's starting components. It will connect directly to the terminals of the compressor and use its own

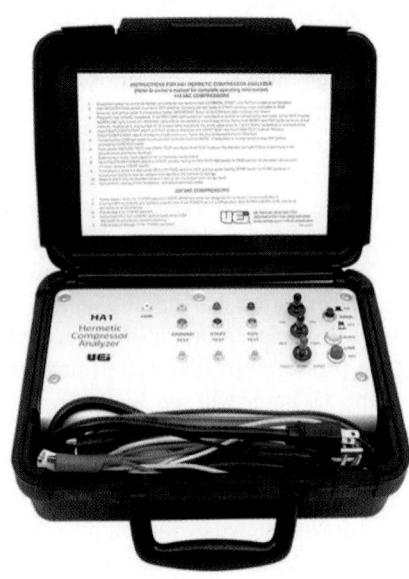

Figure 83-8 Hermetic compressor analyzer
(UEi image is copyright © 2008 UEi. Used with permission. All rights reserved.)

starting components to start the compressor. This will allow a technician to determine if the fault is with the compressor or with its starting components. Some compressor analyzers will also allow a technician to check the integrity of the compressor's windings and momentarily reverse the rotation of the rotor within the compressor.

Compressor Amperage Ratings

Compressor manufacturers will publish a rating chart for each compressor they manufacture. These charts are most often in a table, such as shown in Figure 83-9, or in graphic format. The compressor chart will list the correct amperage draw for the compressor under various operating conditions. To use the chart, a technician must know the evaporating temperature, condensing temperature, and voltage applied to the compressor. By using the compressor chart, a technician can determine the correct amperage draw for the compressor and use that information to accurately troubleshoot the compressor and the system.

Obtaining these charts can be time-consuming, but the extra time involved to find the correct amperage is worthwhile. With the use of the internet this information is now easier to obtain.

Most manufacturers will stamp the rated load amperage (RLA) on their compressors. However, a service technician cannot use this value to determine the correct operating amperage. RLA is a mathematical calculation required to meet Underwriters Laboratories (UL) approval. The compressor manufacturer must run a series of tests to determine the maximum continuous amperage before the overload trips. Once that has been determined, UL divides the MCC by 1.56 to determine the RLA. The primary value of the RLA is to determine at what amperage draw the compressor overload will trip. This will be used to determine the fuse/circuit breaker size and the wire size. Trying to determine if a compressor is good or bad using RLA is not correct. It has nothing to do with what the correct amperage draw should be under various load conditions.

When measuring the amperage draw of a compressor, make sure to read only the amperage drawn by the compressor. Choose a location on the wiring diagram that will isolate the compressor from any other loads such as the condensing fan motor. It is important to measure amperage draw of the *compressor only* when trying to determine if it is operating properly.

Compressor Overheating

A major cause of premature compressor failure is the compressor operating at elevated temperatures. Temperatures in the compressor head and cylinder become so hot that the oil thins and loses its ability to lubricate. This may cause rings, pistons, and cylinders to wear, resulting in blow by, leaking valves, and metal debris in the oil.

Cylinder temperatures exceeding 300°F will begin the breakdown of the oil, and at 350°F it will vaporize. When servicing a system, it is a good practice to check the operating temperature of the cylinders. To measure the cylinder temperature of a compressor, place a temperature gauge no more than 6 in out on the discharge line from the compressor and add 50–75°F to the measured pipe temperature. This will give an approximate temperature of the cylinders. For most applications, the discharge line temperature should be 225°F and below. A temperature of 250°F indicates a dangerous level. A temperature of 275°F and above indicates certain failure of the compressor.

Preventing Repeat Compressor Failure

When a compressor fails, its troubleshooting and replacement are relatively simple and common procedures. However, discovering *why* the original compressor failed may not be as simple. But it is extremely important for a technician to find this answer. Replacing the defective compressor without finding the cause will most likely result in the replacement compressor failing as well. Replacing the compressor a second, third, or fourth time is not advantageous to the service contractor or to the customer. It can cause the service contractor to lose money and quite possibly the customer. Figure 83-10 shows a compressor that has been changed four times within an 18 month period.

		CURRENT (AMPS)				@ 230 Volts (Multiply by 0.5 for 460 V)				
Condensing temperature		−40	−35	−30	−25	−20	−15	−10	−5	0
°F	(°C)	(−40.0)	(−37.2)	(−34.4)	(−31.7)	(−28.9)	(−26.1)	(−23.3)	(−20.6)	(−17.8)
70	(21.1)	4.5	4.7	4.8	4.9	5.0	5.1	5.3	5.4	5.6
80	(26.7)	4.7	4.8	5.0	5.1	5.2	5.4	5.5	5.7	5.8
90	(32.2)	4.7	4.9	5.1	5.2	5.4	5.5	5.7	5.8	6.0
100	(37.8)	4.7	4.9	5.1	5.3	5.5	5.6	5.8	6.0	6.1
105	(40.6)	4.7	4.9	5.1	5.3	5.5	5.7	5.8	6.0	6.2
110	(43.3)	4.6	4.9	5.1	5.3	5.5	5.7	5.9	6.1	6.3
120	(48.9)	4.5	4.7	5.0	5.3	5.5	5.7	5.9	6.1	6.4
130	(54.4)	4.2	4.6	4.9	5.2	5.5	5.7	6.0	6.2	6.5

Figure 83-9 Compressor amperage chart
(Table courtesy of Emerson Climate Technologies)

Figure 83-10 This compressor has been changed out four times

In most cases, upon original inspection of a defective compressor it is difficult to determine what caused the compressor to fail. The compressor is not normally running and the system is not refrigerating. After replacing the compressor, the technician should spend time discovering why the original compressor failed. With a detailed inspection the technician should be able to find the cause. The inspection should include checking: the operating suction and discharge pressures, the amount of superheat at the compressor inlet as shown in Figure 83-11, the return gas temperature, the discharge gas temperature, the amperage draw, and the applied voltage to the compressor. By comparing these readings to the manufacturer's specifications, the cause should be identifiable.

Some typical causes of a compressor failure are: liquid returning to the compressor, high return gas temperature, high discharge temperature, or incorrectly applied voltage to the compressor. Most of these causes can be found once the compressor is up and running.

There are times, however, when the apparent cause cannot be found upon startup. The technician should monitor the system's operation for a period of time to find the cause. The problem may develop after the system has been running for some time, for example, during or after a defrost cycle, or as the result of an iced evaporator coil.

Another helpful troubleshooting tool is to disassemble the defective compressor and examine the valve plates, pistons, crankshaft, bearing surfaces, and windings. Although this is time-consuming, it can significantly help to identify or confirm the cause of the original failure.

83.5 TESTING START RELAYS

Single-phase motors used with compressors sometimes require an external relay to assist in starting. The main purpose of this starting relay is to add an additional electrical circuit to provide the motor the extra torque it requires to start. This electrical circuit can be the addition of a start capacitor and the start winding of a motor, or it can simply be the addition of a start capacitor or start winding alone.

Many times a technician will need to determine if the capacitor or starting relay used on a compressor is the cause of the compressor not starting or operating properly. In order to properly inspect these components, they must be electrically removed from the system. Then using a standard ohmmeter or capacitance meter the component can be tested to see if it is electrically acceptable.

There are three types of starting relays used on single-phase compressors. They are the current relay, potential relay, and PTC relay. The current and potential relays can be tested with a standard ohmmeter. The PTC cannot easily be used with a standard ohmmeter.

The following procedure can be used to test a current relay using an ohmmeter:

1. Remove the relay from the circuit.
2. Set an ohmmeter to its lowest scale. Zero the ohmmeter (if using an analog).
3. Place the ohmmeter leads on the L and M terminals of the relay.
4. Hold the relay in the upright position.
5. Read the ohmmeter.
6. If the ohmmeter reads approximately 1Ω, the coil of the relay is electrically OK. If the meter reads an infinite reading, the coil is open and the relay needs to be replaced.
7. Next, place the ohmmeter leads on the M and S terminals of the relay.
8. If the ohmmeter reads an infinite resistance the contacts are open—as they should be. If the meter reads a resistance the contacts are stuck closed. The relay will need to be replaced.
9. Next, try turning the relay upside down and shake it. The contacts should be closed showing a zero resistance on the ohmmeter. Sometimes this test will fail even on a good relay, but it is worth trying.

Figure 83-11 Checking the superheat at the inlet of a compressor

Use the following procedure to test a potential relay using an ohmmeter:

1. Remove the relay from the circuit.
2. Set an ohmmeter to high scale. Zero the ohmmeter (if using an analog).
3. Place the ohmmeter leads on the 2 and 5 terminals of the relay.
4. If the ohmmeter reads a high resistance (approximately 6,000–14,000 Ω) the coil of the relay is electrically acceptable. If the coil reads infinite, it is electrically open and the relay needs to be replaced.
5. Next, place the ohmmeter leads on the 1 and 2 terminals on the relay.
6. If the ohmmeter reads zero, the contacts are closed—as they should be. If the ohmmeter reads a high resistance or an infinite resistance, the contacts are defective and the relay needs to be replaced.

83.6 TESTING CAPACITORS

Capacitors will normally fail open or shorted. They can be tested with an ohmmeter or a capacitor tester. Normally a visual inspection of a capacitor will indicate a defect. On run capacitors any sign of bulging of its body is a sign of a defect. Start capacitors will have a rubber membrane located on the top portion of the capacitor. If this membrane blows out, it is a sign of a defect.

The following procedure can be used to test a capacitor using an analog ohmmeter:

1. Remove the capacitor from the circuit.
2. Discharge the capacitor with a bleed resistor or a voltmeter.
3. Set an ohmmeter to its lowest scale. Zero the ohmmeter.
4. Place the ohmmeter leads on the capacitor terminals.
5. Watch for one of the following indications of the conditions of the capacitor:
   a. Good—needle will swing toward zero and then slowly return to infinity.
   b. Shorted—needle will swing toward zero and remain there.
   c. Open—needle will stay at infinity.
6. Make a second test by reversing the leads of the ohmmeter.
7. If the test shows an open or shorted capacitor, repeat the test on higher resistance scales to verify the capacitor is truly defective. Depending on the capacitance and the type of meter, higher resistance scales may need to be used for an accurate test.
8. For run capacitors, place one of the ohmmeter leads on a terminal of the capacitor and one lead on the body. If the ohmmeter reads a resistance, the capacitor is grounded and needs to be replaced. Next, test the other lead of the capacitor.

SAFETY TIP

Capacitors have the ability to store an electrical charge. Because of this, a technician should always discharge a capacitor before handling or checking it. A capacitor can be safely discharged using a 20,000 Ω, 5-W resistor with an insulated pair of pliers. Some start capacitors have a bleed resistor across the terminals designed to discharge the capacitor. It is still a good practice to discharge these capacitors with your own resistor. The resistor on the capacitor may be electrically open and may not have discharged the capacitor.

To test capacitors using a capacitance meter, simply discharge the capacitor and place the meter leads across the terminals of the capacitor. If the capacitor is OK, the actual capacitance (within 10% of its original value) will be displayed on the screen. If the capacitor is shorted, then the display will indicate a value close to zero. If the capacitor is open, it will normally show an O.L. on its display.

Alternate Method of Measuring the Microfarad Rating of a Capacitor

There is an alternate method of determining the microfarad rating of a capacitor. If the amperage draw and applied voltage of a capacitor are known, then its microfarad rating can be calculated. A simple circuit can be constructed as shown in Figure 83-12, making it easy to measure a capacitor's current draw and the applied voltage. Be sure to include a fuse in the circuit for protection. Only energize the circuit long enough to record the two values.

Once the amperage draw and the applied voltage have been measured, use the following formula to determine the microfarad rating:

$$\text{Microfarad rating} = (2{,}650 \times \text{amps})/\text{volts}$$

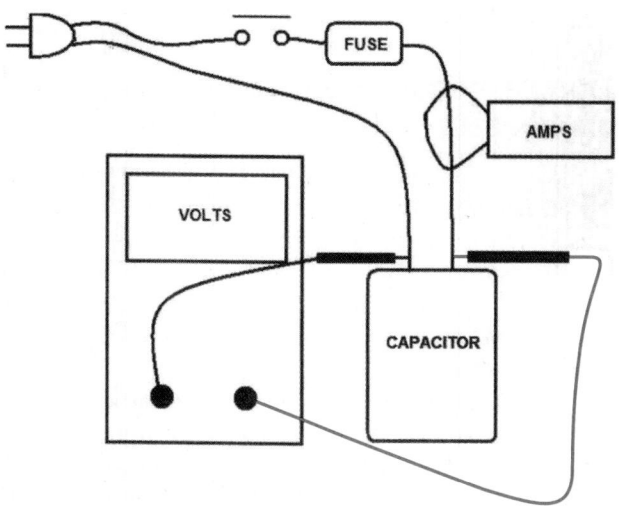

Figure 83-12 A simple circuit used to measure the capacitance of a circuit

For example, if a current of 0.45 A with an applied voltage of 118 V were measured, then the capacitor's microfarad rating would be:

Microfarad rating $= (2,650 \times 0.45)/118 = 10.11$ microfarads

83.7 TROUBLESHOOTING EVAPORATOR PROBLEMS

An evaporator is a heat exchanger used to absorb heat from the refrigerated product. Heat is transferred from the product through the tubing and fins of the evaporator to the refrigerant. If the evaporator's surface becomes insulated as the result of either being dirty or covered with ice, the amount of heat transfer will be dramatically reduced.

Ice buildup can occur when the heat load on the evaporator is reduced. As a result, the temperature of the evaporator drops and an excessive amount of frost and ice accumulates on its surface. For example, a blower-type evaporator needs the correct amount of airflow across its surface. If this airflow is restricted as a result of one or more defective fan motors, the surface of the evaporator will develop an excessive amount of ice and the system will not be able to absorb enough heat from the product to maintain the desired case temperature.

With an evaporator temperature below 32°F, frost will naturally develop on the surface of the evaporator even if the correct heat load is applied. The design of the refrigeration system must incorporate some means of defrosting the evaporator on a regular basis to prevent an excessive amount of frost from developing on the surface of the evaporator. Medium temperature refrigeration systems will use the case air to defrost the evaporator. When the refrigeration system shuts down, the evaporator fan continues to operate and will continue to draw case air across the evaporator to melt any frost that has accumulated. However, with low temperature systems the case temperature is well below 32°F and therefore the case air cannot be used to defrost the evaporator. Low temperature systems require some type of supplemental heat to defrost the evaporator surface.

Troubleshooting Defrost Problems on Freezers

A frozen evaporator coil is a common problem found when troubleshooting freezers. Although there are several possible causes for this problem, one common cause is the defrost system. The system is not properly defrosting the evaporator's coil on a regular basis. In order to effectively troubleshoot this problem, a technician must understand the design and operation of the defrost systems typically used.

Defrost system problems fall into two categories. The system may be *over-defrosted* or *under-defrosted*. Over-defrosting is when the defrost heater stays energized too long, causing the box temperature to rise too high during defrost. The product may begin to melt and then refreeze. This problem can be identified by monitoring the box temperature during defrost or by examining the product in the case. Ice crystals forming on frozen product may be an indication of melting and refreezing. Over-defrosting is normally caused by a malfunction in the defrost cycle termination. On time defrost systems, either the defrost time is set too long or the time clock is defective. On time-pressure systems, either the terminating pressure control is set too high, the pressure control is defective, or the solenoid coil in the defrost timer is incorrectly wired or defective. On time-temperature systems, either the temperature control is set too high, the control is defective, or the solenoid in the defrost timer is defective.

Systems that are under-defrosting will result in a frozen evaporator. The frost that normally develops on the evaporator coil will continue to build until the entire surface of the evaporator is iced over. This can be caused by a defective or incorrectly set time clock that does not initiate a defrost cycle. It can also be caused by an open heater element or a defective defrost termination switch that continually terminates defrost on each initiation of a new cycle.

When an evaporator ices over, a technician will need to defrost the coil. Sometimes this can be done by manually initiating a defrost cycle. This can be done on a mechanical defrost timer by rotating the inner knob clockwise. Many times, however, this cannot be done. The technician will have to manually defrost the coil. Extreme care must be taken when doing this. Do not use any sharp objects to chip away ice from the coil—this could easily puncture the coil and cause a refrigerant leak to develop in the evaporator. Using water is the best method, but is not always practical since the water will need to be drained away. If water cannot be used easily, a heat gun usually works well. Defrosting a coil manually is time-consuming. Do not rush this procedure. Making a careless mistake can be costly.

83.8 TROUBLESHOOTING CONDENSER PROBLEMS

A condenser is a heat exchange device used to reject heat energy from the refrigerant to its cooling medium. Heat energy from the refrigerant is rejected through the tubing and fins of the condenser and absorbed by the condensing medium. There are several problems that can occur that can impede this process. If the condenser's surface becomes insulated as a result of being dirty, it will reduce the ability of the cooling medium to absorb heat from the refrigerant. This will cause the discharge pressure of the system to rise beyond its normal operating range and cause the system to malfunction.

Determining Discharge Pressures

When troubleshooting commercial refrigeration systems, many times it is necessary to measure the discharge pressure of a system and determine if the pressure is normal, higher than normal, or lower than normal. In order to make this determination, the correct operating discharge pressure must be known. For systems utilizing an air cooled condenser, this can be determined by measuring the system's suction pressure and the temperature of the air entering the condenser.

Below are the general procedures for determining the correct operating discharge pressure of a commercial refrigeration system utilizing an air cooled condenser.

Step 1. Measure the dry bulb temperature of the air entering the condenser. (We will refer to this as the EAT—Entering Air Temperature.)

Step 2. Measure the system's operating suction pressure.

Step 3. Using a Pressure/Temperature (P/T) chart, convert the suction pressure to its equivalent saturation temperature.

Step 4. Determine the system's application for this procedure: low temperature, medium temperature, or high temperature. A low temperature system is one that operates at an evaporating temperature of −40°F to +10°F. A medium temperature system is one that operates at an evaporating temperature of between −10°F to +30°F. A high temperature system is one that operates at an evaporating temperature of between +20°F to +55°F.

Step 5. Using the chart in Table 83-1, determine the appropriate Temperature Rise (TR). The TR is the difference between the EAT and the condensing temperature of the refrigerant in the condenser.

Step 6. The Condensing Temperature (CT) can then be determined by adding the EAT and the TR. CT = EAT + TR.

Step 7. Once the condensing temperature is known, its equivalent saturation pressure can be determined using a P/T chart. This will be the correct operating discharge pressure of the system.

For example, suppose we are working on a walk-in cooler using R-134a refrigerant with an operating suction pressure of 18.4 psig and 76°F air temperature entering the condenser.

Step 1. The EAT in our example is 76°F.

Step 2. The system's operating suction pressure is 18.4 psig.

Step 3. Using a P/T chart we convert our suction pressure of 18.4 psig to a saturation temperature of 20°F.

Step 4. We determine the system's application to be medium temperature.

Step 5. Using Table 83-1, we determine the appropriate TR to be 32°F.

Step 6. The CT of our system will be 108°F (108°F = 76°F + 32°F).

Step 7. Again using a P/T chart we can conclude that our operating discharge pressure should be 142.8 psig.

Using this procedure should help determine if the discharge pressure of a commercial refrigeration system is normal, higher than normal, or lower than normal.

Checking for Noncondensable Gases

The only fluids circulating within a refrigeration system should be refrigerant and oil. Any other fluids contained in the system may reduce its capacity and cause harm to the system. One common contaminant that can enter a system is air. Air contains nitrogen and oxygen, both of which are harmful to a refrigeration system. When a system has been open to the atmosphere for servicing, it must be completely evacuated to remove the unwanted air before adding refrigerant.

One problem when air is contained in a system is that it will become trapped in the condenser and will not condense. It will take up space, causing less surface area for the refrigerant to condense. This will cause the high side pressure to elevate, causing further problems such as higher discharge temperatures and reduced system capacity.

Occasionally a technician may need to check whether noncondensables such as air are contained in a system. Use the following procedure to determine this in a refrigeration system with an air cooled condenser.

- Determine the type of refrigerant in the system.
- Electrically disable the compressor and allow the condenser fan to operate.
- Attach a temperature probe to both the discharge line and liquid line, shown as in Figure 83-13.
- Place a third temperature probe to measure the temperature of the air entering the condenser.
- Connect a pressure gauge on the system to measure the pressure of the refrigerant in the condenser.

Table 83-1 Temperature Rise for the Evaporator

	Evaporator temperature °F		
Temperature rise (TR) °F	Low temperature application	Medium temperature application	High temperature application
20	−25	0	—
23	−20	5	25
26	−15	10	30
29	−10	15	35
32	−5	20	40
35	0	25	45

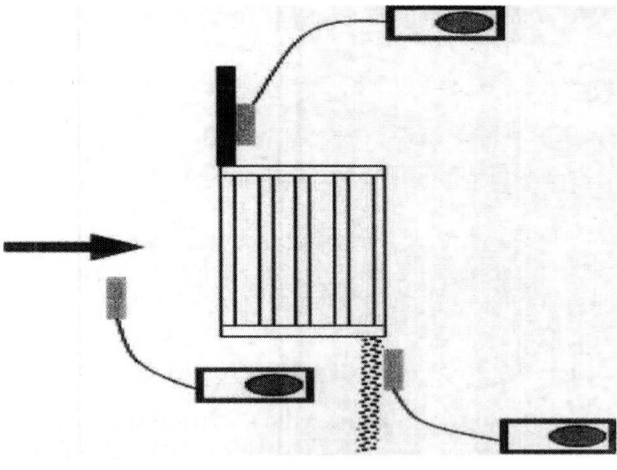

Figure 83-13 When checking for air in a refrigeration system, take temperatures at three locations: the discharge line at the inlet of the condenser, the liquid line at the outlet of the condenser, and the temperature of the air entering the condenser

- When all three temperature probes (discharge line, liquid line, and air entering the condenser) read the same temperature, record the pressure of the refrigerant in the condenser.
- Using a P/T chart, convert the measured pressure to its saturation temperature.
- The converted temperature should be within a few degrees of the measured discharge, liquid, and air entering temperatures.
- If the converted temperature is higher than the measured temperatures by more than a few degrees, there are noncondensables in the system that need to be removed.

83.9 TROUBLESHOOTING METERING DEVICES

Metering devices are refrigerant flow control devices that feed the proper amount of refrigerant into an evaporator. If a metering device is defective it will either feed too much or too little refrigerant into the evaporator. To determine if too much or too little is being fed into an evaporator, a technician must measure the superheat level of the refrigerant leaving the evaporator. If the superheat value is higher than recommended by the equipment manufacturer, too little refrigerant is being fed into the evaporator. If the superheat value is lower than recommended by the equipment manufacturer, too much refrigerant is being fed into the evaporator. Both of these conditions could be the result of a defective metering device. However, before deciding that the problem is the metering device, make sure all other possible causes are investigated and eliminated. Many times it may appear the metering device is not functioning properly but another system problem is the actual cause.

83.10 TROUBLESHOOTING THERMOSTATIC EXPANSION VALVES

A thermostatic expansion valve (TEV) is designed to maintain a specific amount of superheat at the outlet of the evaporator. If the superheat value is too high or too low at the outlet of the evaporator, the cause may be the TEV. However, as mentioned previously, make sure all other possible causes are investigated first before determining that it is the TEV.

If the TEV is the cause of the system problem, try adjusting the valve first. To increase the superheat setting of the valve, turn the adjustment stem clockwise. To decrease the superheat setting of the valve, turn the adjustment stem counterclockwise. If adjusting the valve does not resolve the problem, then the valve is defective and will need to be replaced.

Some common causes of an evaporator with a low superheat and a high suction pressure are:

- Oversized valve.
- TEV seat is leaking.
- Low superheat adjustment.
- Sensing bulb making poor thermal contact.
- Wrong thermostatic charge.
- Incorrectly located external equalizer.
- Restricted or capped external equalizer.

Some common causes of an evaporator with a high superheat and a low suction pressure are:

- Undersized valve.
- High superheat adjustment.
- Gas charge condensation.
- Dead thermostatic element charge.
- Wrong thermostatic charge.
- Evaporator pressure drop—no external equalizer.
- External equalizer location.

83.11 TROUBLESHOOTING CAPILLARY TUBES

Capillary tubes are simply a section of tubing with a very small inside diameter. A problem that does occur with these metering devices is that they can become restricted. Either they can be totally restricted where no refrigerant will pass through, or partially restricted where some refrigerant will pass through, but not enough to properly feed the evaporator. A system with a restricted capillary tube will have a low suction pressure and a discharge pressure that is slightly lower than normal.

Occasionally it may be difficult to determine the difference between a system with a low refrigerant charge, a restricted capillary tube, or a restricted filter-drier (or strainer). A system with a low refrigerant charge will have both a low suction pressure and a low discharge pressure. A system with a restricted capillary tube will have a low suction pressure and a discharge pressure that is lower than normal but not quite as low as a system with a low refrigerant charge. It may be difficult to determine the difference between a low discharge pressure and a slightly

84.9 NATIONAL ELECTRIC CODE

The National Electrical Code is developed by the National Fire Protection Association and is revised every three years. The most current code is 2008. Although the NFPA does not have the authority to enforce their code, the NEC is highly regarded and is adopted by nearly all code enforcement and governing agencies, giving it the force of law. The code specifies wiring methods and procedures necessary for the safe installation and service of electrical systems and equipment. Sections of the NEC that are particularly appropriate for air conditioning installation are sections 310 Conductors for General Wiring and 440 Air Conditioning and Refrigeration Equipment.

84.10 MAJOR PHASES OF INSTALLATION

Installations can be broken down into phases, based on the required skills and the work performed. The major phases of installations are:

- Equipment placement.
- Ductwork installation.
- Piping installation (both refrigerant and water).
- Electrical connection.
- Evacuation and charging.
- Start and check.

In larger companies, these phases are often performed by separate crews. The equipment placement and duct installation is typically done by the same crew. The erection of piping is sometimes performed by installers who specialize in piping. Electrical connections are frequently done by crews who primarily handle electrical wiring and installation. Frequently the wires are pulled in place by the equipment installers, but the connections are made by the wiring and controls crew. Evacuation, charging, and startup are usually performed by crews who specialize in refrigeration.

Any number of these phases can be performed by the same technicians in some companies. In smaller companies, a single installation crew is responsible for all phases of installation.

84.11 EQUIPMENT PLACEMENT

Despite what may seem to be a great many possibilities for positioning major components during installations, three factors must be considered in the placement of equipment if satisfactory installation and proper operation are to be ensured:

- Ample space must be provided for air movement around air cooled condensing equipment to and from the condenser.
- All major components must be installed so that they may be serviced readily. When an assembly is not easily accessible for service, the cost of service becomes excessive.

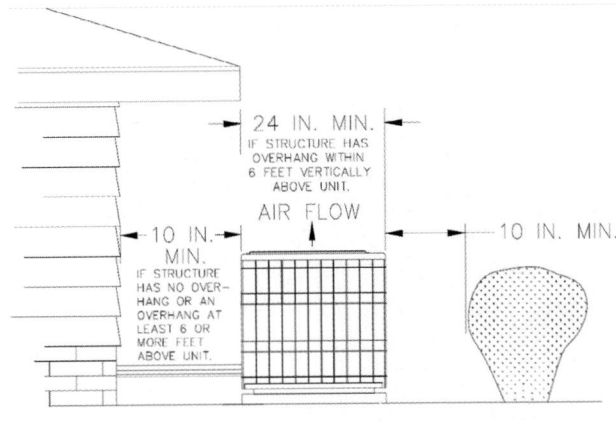

Figure 84-2 Air cooled condensing units must be placed so that their airflow is not restricted
(Courtesy of Thermo Products LLC)

- Vibration isolation must always be considered, not only in regard to the equipment itself, but also in relation to the interconnecting piping and sheet metal ductwork. All manufacturers supply recommendations of the space required; these recommendations should be followed.

Figure 84-2 shows a properly placed air cooled condensing unit. Sufficient room has been left for the passage of incoming air around and over the unit.

An example of a common error in positioning major system components is shown in Figure 84-3. A shell and tube water cooled condenser has been placed in such a position that the entire condensing unit must be moved to replace a single condenser tube. Be sure to allow room for replacement of items such as compressors, fan motors, fans, and filters. High service costs are often attributable to the poor placement of system components.

Noise is also an important factor in the placement of air cooled condensing equipment. The discharge air transmits noise generated within the unit. It is poor practice to "aim"

Figure 84-3 Service accessibility is important in positioning major system components

RUBBER ISOLATION BUSHINGS

(a)

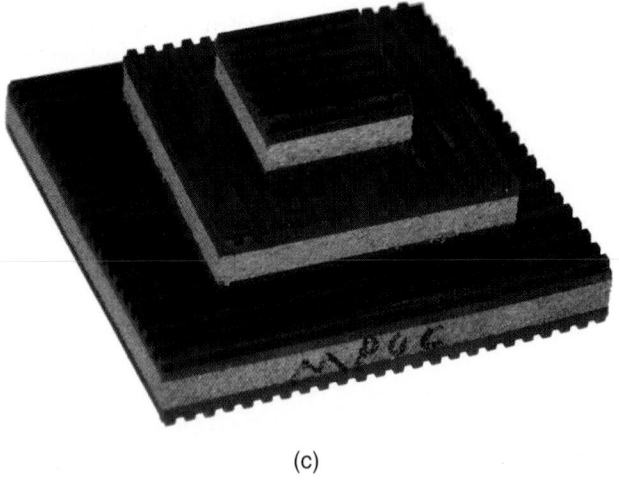

(c)

HANGING ISOLATION SPRINGS

(b)

(d)

Figure 84-4 Types of vibration isolators used for compressors: (a) Rubber isolation bushings; (b) Hanging spring mountings; (c) Isolation pads in various sizes; (d) Internal isolation springs

the condenser discharge air in a direction where noise may be disturbing, such as a neighboring window.

Vibrations set up by rotating assemblies such as compressors, fans, and fan motors can break refrigerant lines, cause structural building damage, and create noise. Vibration isolation is required on all refrigeration and air conditioning equipment where noise or vibration may be disturbing. Almost all manufacturers use some form of vibration isolation in the production of their equipment. This is usually enough for the average installation; however, individual conditions must be investigated to determine whether more stringent measures need to be taken.

TECH TIP

Some metropolitan areas have maximum noise level ordinances affecting HVAC/R equipment. These ordinances may affect the equipment selected and equipment placement in order to keep the sound level within the ordinance guidelines. Check with your local building office regarding noise level ordinances.

The compressor is considered the chief source of system vibration. Since it is good practice to isolate vibration at its source, compressor vibration isolation is essential during installation, as shown in Figure 84-4a–d.

When the compressor or condensing unit is to be installed on the roof or in the upper stories of a multistory building, vibration isolators as shown in Figure 84-4b may be used. This type of isolator is usually available from the manufacturer of the unit, and in many cases, it is standard equipment.

An isolation pad designed specifically for vibration dampening is shown in Figure 84-4c. This type of material is designed to dampen the vibration from a given amount of weight per square inch of area. Consult the manufacturer's installation recommendations when selecting vibration isolation materials. A final method of vibration isolation, used with small hermetic compressors, is shown in Figure 84-4d. The compressor is mounted on springs within the hermetic shell.

Figure 84-5a–c illustrates a vibration eliminator inserted in the discharge line of the compressor. This eliminator is designed to absorb compressor discharge line pulsation before it creates noise or breaks refrigerant lines. The eliminator consists of a flexible corrugated metal hose core with an overall metal braid. The braid will allow some linear movement of the flexible material, but no expansion or contraction. This type of eliminator is normally placed in the compressor discharge line as close to the compressor as practical. It is particularly effective on installations where the compressor and condenser are on different bases, yet quite close together. The vibration isolator should be placed in the line so that the movement it absorbs is in a plane at right angles to the device. Do not place this unit in a position that will put tension on it, as its useful life will be shortened.

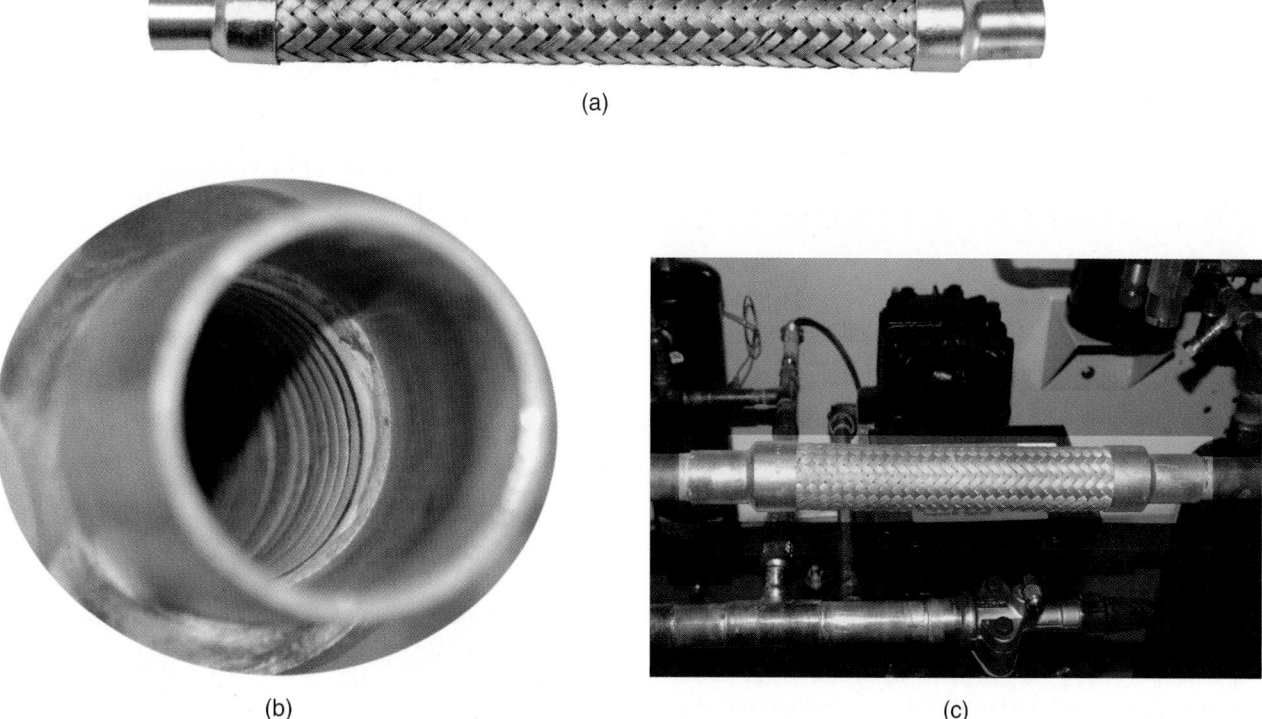

(a)

(b)   (c)

Figure 84-5 (a) Vibration eliminator; (b) Internal ribs that allow a vibration damper to flex; (c) Typical installation of a vibration damper as it is installed on a refrigeration system
(Courtesy of Hampden Engineering Corporation)

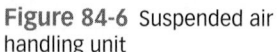

Figure 84-6 Suspended air handling unit

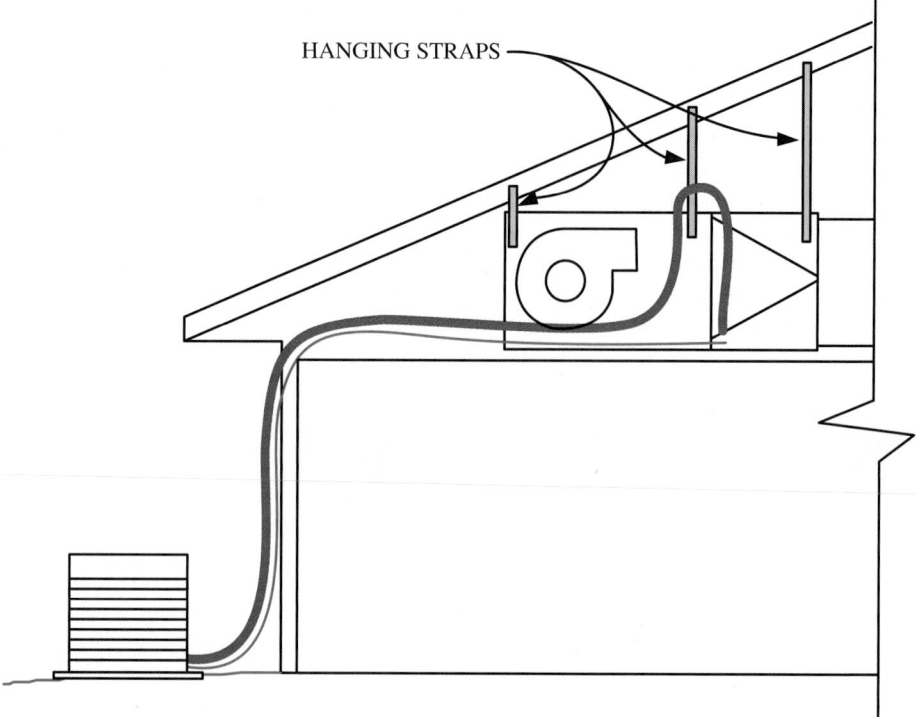

HANGING STRAPS

Some system components, such as the evaporator, may be suspended, as shown in Figure 84-6. As the air handling unit containing the evaporator will contain a fan and fan motor, it too is a possible source of vibration. Most manufacturers isolate the fan and fan motor inside the unit with rubber mounts. If this supplies sufficient vibration isolation, the unit may be directly connected to the ceiling. When more isolation is required, the same method used with compressors is effective. Coil springs support the air handling unit for additional isolation.

TECH TIP

When hanging an air handler from the attic rafters it can be set on wooden blocks first so it can be leveled before attaching the hanging straps. This will make leveling the unit much easier. In addition to the common sheet metal straps there are other hanging systems including cable and threaded rods, which make hanging and leveling much easier and faster.

84.12 PIPING

The art of making flared, soldered, and brazed connections in copper tubing has been discussed, as well as the procedures for sizing lines, installing traps, and so on, but several important points should be remembered while actually erecting the system piping.

When hard copper tubing is selected for refrigerant piping, it is recommended that low temperature silver alloy braz-

ing materials be used. These alloys have flow points in the range of 1,100–1,400°F. To attain these temperatures, oxyacetylene welding equipment is required. Figure 84-7 shows the equipment necessary for this type of brazing. Both oxygen and acetylene tanks with gauges and pressure regulating valves are needed. Also shown is the torch used with the tanks. At the right is a bottle of dry nitrogen also equipped with gauges and pressure regulating valves.

The use of nitrogen is recommended, since it serves to keep the interior of the pipe clean during the brazing process. During low temperature brazing, the surface of the copper will reach a temperature at which the metal will react with oxygen in the air to form a copper oxide scale. If this scale forms on the interior surface of the pipe, it might be washed off by the refrigerant and oil circulating in the system. The scale can clog strainers or capillary tubes and will plug orifices.

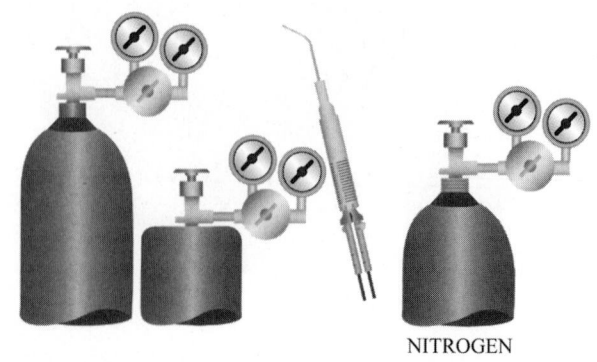

NITROGEN

Figure 84-7 Equipment necessary for oxyacetylene welding or brazing

This scaling can be prevented by replacing the air in the pipe with nitrogen or carbon dioxide. Flowing nitrogen or carbon dioxide through the pipe prevents scaling because the nitrogen and carbon dioxide are inert gases and will not combine with copper even under high temperature conditions. The pipe interior will remain clean during brazing and no scale is formed, though discoloration may occur with overheating.

TECH TIP

When using an inert gas as a purge to prevent oxide formation, only a very slight flow of gas is required. Excessively high flow rates may create enough internal pressure to cause pinholes during the brazing process as the gas is forced out through the joint.

Figure 84-8 shows a method by which nitrogen may be introduced into the refrigerant tubing during the brazing operation. Connect the nitrogen bottle to the liquid line service Schrader valve with a refrigeration hose. A slight pressure is admitted into the tubing using the pressure regulating valve on the nitrogen bottle. This is just enough pressure to ensure that air will be forced from the pipe. As shown in the inset, if the nitrogen flow can be felt on the palm of the hand, the flow is sufficient. This nitrogen pressure is kept in the tubing throughout the entire brazing operation, thus ensuring an oxygen free pipe.

CAUTION

Never use oxygen or acetylene to develop pressure when checking for leaks. Oxygen will cause an explosion in the presence of oil. Acetylene will decompose and explode if the regulator pressure is over 15–30 psig (30–45 psia or 210–310 kPa).

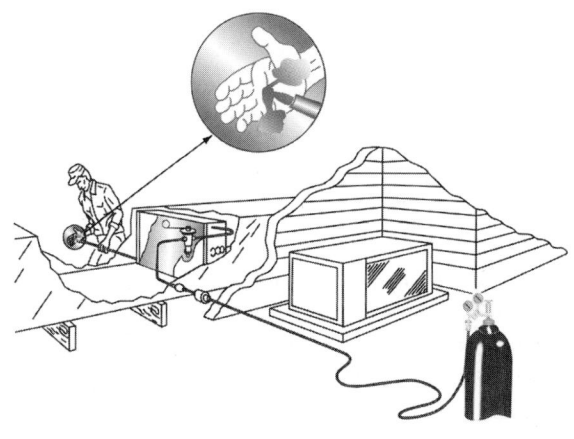

Figure 84-8 Brazing operation using nitrogen in the tube to eliminate scaling

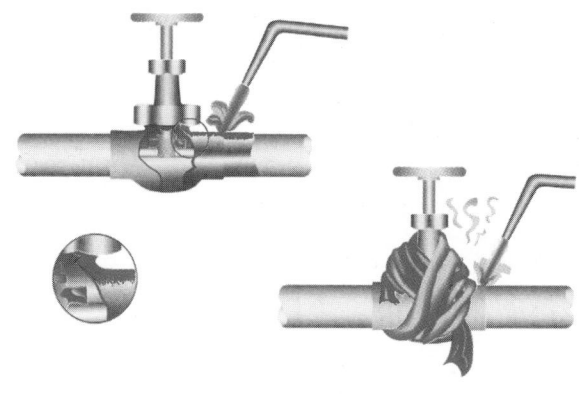

Figure 84-9 Protecting valves from overheating during brazing operation

Clean pipe is essential in refrigeration installation. Therefore, the use of nitrogen and carbon dioxide is extremely important in the brazing operation as it ensure scale free interior pipe walls.

The temperatures during brazing operations can warp metals and burn or distort plastic valve seats. It is important that metal and plastic components are not overheated during the brazing process. Figure 84-9 shows the result of brazing heat damage and also one method of ensuring this will not happen. The valve at the upper left was not protected from brazing heat; the plastic seat has been damaged. Also, the seat holder has been warped, as shown in the inset. The valve obviously will not operate properly and would require immediate replacement. The valve at the bottom right, however, has a wet rag wrapped around the body. The water absorbs the heat that flows to the valve body during the brazing operation. By keeping the rag wet, the valve and its component parts are protected from heat damage.

After all interconnecting tubing has been assembled, nitrogen is introduced into the system for leak testing. By using nitrogen, the pressure in the system may be built up to approximately 100 psig, at which pressure a true leak test can be made.

CAUTION

Never pressurize the system above the low side system test pressure, Figure 84-10, or above 150 psig for systems with hermetic compressors! Over-pressurizing a compressor shell can cause catastrophic shell failure, turning the compressor shell into a bomb!

Leaks may be detected with soap bubbles and ultrasonic leak detectors. Halide torches and electronic leak detectors will not work with nitrogen. A small amount of R-22 may be used with the nitrogen as a trace gas if you wish to use a halogen type leak detector. Since nitrogen is an inert gas, the nitrogen must be vented and the system evacuated after it has been determined to be leak free.

CONTAINS HCFC – 22		DESIGN PRESSURE		
FACTORY CHARGE		278	HI PSIG	
12 LBS	8 OZS	144	LO PSIG	
ELECTRICAL RATING		NOMINAL 208/230		VOLTS
1 PH	60 HZ	MIN 197	MAX 253	
COMPRESSOR(S):(1)		**FAN MOTOR(S): (1)**		
PH	1	PH	1	
RLA	23.8	FLA	1.7	
LRA	129	HP	1/4	
MIN.CKT AMPACITY AMPERAGE MINIMUM	31.5	MAX FUSE OR CKT.BKR. FUSIBLE/COUPE CIRCUIT (HACR PER NEC)	50	
FOR OUTDOOR USE				
VERIFIED	CSA	VERIFIE		

Figure 84-10 This system should not be pressurized past 144 psig when leak testing

TECH TIP

Venting mixtures of R-22 and nitrogen used as a holding charge or a leak test gas does not violate the prohibition on venting ozone depleting substances. However, other ozone depleting refrigerants may not be used as trace gases.

In many cases, the suction line of the refrigerant system will run through an unconditioned area. The outside surface temperature of this pipe is frequently below the dew point of the surrounding air. In this case the moisture in the air will condense on the exterior of the pipe. This will create problems where this continuous moisture drips and can be annoying. The pipe must be insulated to avoid condensation and excessive heat from being absorbed by the refrigerant Figure 84-11.

Figure 84-11 Suction lines should be insulated to avoid condensation and loss of system efficiency

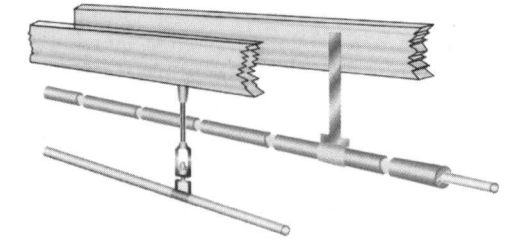

Figure 84-12 Pipe hangers used to support insulated pipes

TECH TIP

Moisture has been associated with the formation of mold and mildew in buildings. Condensate can be a significant source of moisture. It is very important that tubing insulation on refrigerant lines be sealed at the joints so that condensate cannot form.

The insulation must be of good quality so that the temperature of its exterior surface will never drop below the dew point of the surrounding area. It must also be well sealed, so that air and the moisture it contains cannot reach the pipe, thus causing condensation underneath the insulation.

An example of a typical pipe hanger that might be used on a small commercial refrigeration installation is shown on the right in Figure 84-12. This hanger serves as a vibration isolator as well as a pipe supporter. A short length of light gauge rustproof metal is used to form a cradle to support the insulated pipe. A metal strap has been attached to this length of metal. In some cases it is merely wrapped around the length of sheet metal. The free end of the strap is then fastened to the joist or ceiling. The insulation in such a hanger will act as the vibration isolator. The purpose of the short length of metal is to prevent the thin strap from cutting the insulation.

The hanger shown on the left in Figure 84-12 has a height adjustment feature for leveling or pitching the pipe if required for oil return. This type of hanger can be used with or without insulation.

84.13 ELECTRICAL CONNECTIONS

The service technician who installs the refrigeration equipment is sometimes responsible for the final wiring connections between the installed unit and the fused disconnect switch shown in Figure 84-13. All electrical power to the refrigeration unit must pass through this switch. When this switch is pulled, or opened, all electrical power to the unit must be disconnected. This same disconnect switch also contains fuses, that will interrupt the flow of current whenever a severe electrical overload occurs. This mechanism is a protection against fires and explosions and also against electrical shocks to people.

Figure 84-13 All equipment should have a disconnect switch within sight of the unit

CONTAINS HCFC – 22		DESIGN PRESSURE		
FACTORY CHARGE		278		HI PSIG
12 LBS 8 OZS		144		LO PSIG
ELECTRICAL RATING		NOMINAL 208/230		VOLTS
1 PH	60 HZ	MIN 197	MAX 253	
COMPRESSOR(S):(1)		FAN MOTOR(S): (1)		
PH	1	PH		1
RLA	23.8	FLA		1.7
LRA	129	HP		1/4
MIN. CKT AMPACITY AMPERAGE MINIMUM	31.5	MAX FUSE OR CKT.BKR. FUSIBLE/COUPE CIRCUIT (HACR PER NEC)		50
FOR OUTDOOR USE				
VERIFIED	CSA	VERIFIE		

Figure 84-14 The conductor for this unit should be sized to carry at least 31.5 A

nections are governed by national or local electrical codes. For example, electrical codes require that the fused disconnect switch always be placed within sight of the unit that receives the power passing through the switch, Figure 84-13.

CAUTION

Although codes require that all electricity to equipment be able to be disconnected at a single disconnect point, this is not always the case. Occasionally, host installation wiring may bring voltage into equipment that does not go through the disconnect. Before you begin working inside electrical panels on equipment, make certain that there is no voltage. Use your voltmeter to test all connections between each power connection and each power connection and a known ground.

Three components of the power wiring to the unit that must be properly sized are the

- Conductor.
- Disconnect.
- Overload protection device.

Conductors are sized by current carrying capacity and voltage drop. Voltage drop calculations are normally not necessary for runs under 100 ft if the minimum wire sizing charts in Section 310 of the NEC are followed. A conductor should be selected from the wire sizing charts whose current rating is equal to or greater than the minimum circuit ampacity listed on the unit data plate, Figure 84-14.

The disconnect current rating should be 115% of the minimum circuit ampacity. The overload protection should be no larger than the maximum fuse size shown on the data plate, Figure 84-15. Standard fuses and circuit breakers are subject to nuisance trips from the momentary high inrush current when compressors start. The over current protection for systems with compressors should be either time delay fuses or an HVAC/R rated circuit breaker because they allow the compressor to start without tripping.

Electrical codes, both national and local, are made to protect property and life, and should always be followed. All refrigeration equipment installations having electrical con-

CONTAINS HCFC – 22		DESIGN PRESSURE		
FACTORY CHARGE		278		HI PSIG
12 LBS 8 OZS		144		LO PSIG
ELECTRICAL RATING		NOMINAL 208/230		VOLTS
1 PH	60 HZ	MIN 197	MAX 253	
COMPRESSOR(S):(1)		FAN MOTOR(S): (1)		
PH	1	PH		1
RLA	23.8	FLA		1.7
LRA	129	HP		1/4
MIN. CKT AMPACITY AMPERAGE MINIMUM	31.5	MAX FUSE OR CKT.BKR. FUSIBLE/COUPE CIRCUIT (HACR PER NEC)		50
FOR OUTDOOR USE				
VERIFIED	CSA	VERIFIE		

Figure 84-15 The largest fuse of HVAC/R rated circuit breaker that can be used on this unit is 50 A

Secure electrical connections with good electrical contact are essential. Good electrical connections are made by stripping the wire to the correct length, using wire and wire connectors that are compatible, and using anti-oxidation paste for all aluminum wiring connections. Whenever possible, lug type connectors are recommended.

When stranded wire is used, a single wire may separate and create a potential electrical hazard. Loose wires might contact other wires or ground, causing electrical problems. Make sure there are no loose strands and that the connection is tight to ensure a good mechanical connection. This will ensure good contact and eliminate the hazard of wire separation.

84.14 DUCTWORK

The system installer is frequently required to make the final connection between the evaporator or air handling unit and the ductwork. This final connection for metal duct is made with a flexible connector, Figure 84-16, to eliminate vibration transmission from the air handler to the ductwork. It must be installed correctly. If, as shown in the upper left in the illustration, it is too loose, it will drop into the airstream and obstruct normal airflow. If too tight it will stretch, harden, and disintegrate over a period of time, causing leaks. If the canvas is damp and installed too tightly, the ductwork might be pulled out of alignment. The center of Figure 84-16 shows the proper application: the canvas is loose enough to absorb vibration and not so loose as to interfere with airflow. Blanket insulation should be installed over the flexible connection and properly sealed.

TECH TIP

Current codes and standards require that UL 181 mastic and pressure sensitive tapes be used to seal all ductwork to prevent air leaks.

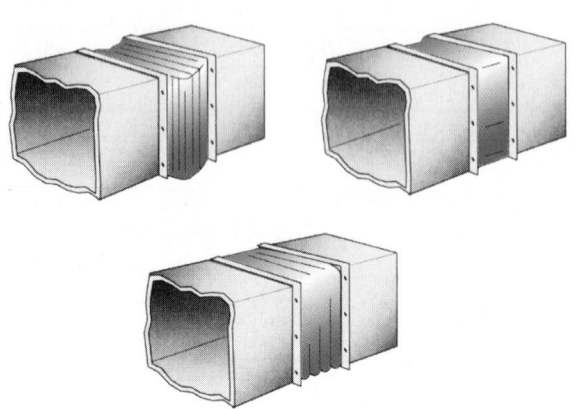

Figure 84-16 Flexible duct connector to eliminate vibration

84.15 SYSTEM EVACUATION

The refrigerant system needs to be leak tested and evacuated before it is charged. Nitrogen is commonly used as a leak test gas after making all the refrigerant piping connections. Any nitrogen left in the system from leak testing should be released before proceeding to evacuate the system. Connecting a vacuum pump to a system with a nitrogen charge will blow the oil out of the vacuum pump, making a mess and possibly damaging the vacuum pump.

TECH TIP

Since the air is 78% nitrogen it is perfectly legal to vent the nitrogen holding charge. Venting de minimus mixtures of R-22 and nitrogen used for leak testing is also permitted by the EPA. However, nitrogen mixed with other ozone depleting refrigerants may NOT be vented.

Be careful to only release nitrogen. Some systems, such as commercial refrigeration systems, come with only a nitrogen holding charge, which must be released before charging. The service valves on these units must be cracked to release the nitrogen. On the other hand, air conditioning systems usually have a factory refrigerant charge that should not be released. These valves are typically shipped front seated. They should not be turned until after the lines and coil have been evacuated. Read the installation instructions carefully to determine which type of system you are installing.

The system should be evacuated from both the high and low sides of the system to the vacuum level specified by the manufacturer, typically 500 microns or lower. The only way to ensure the proper level of evacuation is to use a vacuum gauge to verify the results. The amount of time required varies depending upon the size of the system and the length of refrigerant piping. However, clean systems rarely require longer than an hour unless they are very large.

SERVICE TIP

Many technicians save time by leak testing and evacuating the system before making the electrical connections. The system will typically be fully evacuated by the time they finish making all the electrical connections, so no additional installation time is required to properly evacuate the system.

84.16 CHARGING THE SYSTEM WITH REFRIGERANT

Liquid or Gas

The system may be charged with refrigerant as a liquid or gas. Although a number of factors may affect the method of charging, the most important is the quantity of refrigerant involved. Vapor charging is much slower than liquid charging. As vapor is removed from the cylinder, some of the liquid left in the cylinder boils to replace the vapor that left. The evaporating refrigerant cools the remaining liquid, reducing its pressure. After several minutes of vapor charging the cylinder temperature and pressure are much lower. Even with a full cylinder of refrigerant, charging will grind to a halt because the cylinder pressure drops to the same pressure as the system you are charging.

The relatively small outlet on refrigerant containers compounds this problem. In small units, sufficient gas vapor can pass through this outlet to complete the full charge of the unit in a reasonable length of time. On large units, however, the time required for the proper amount of vapor to pass through this small outlet may take so long that gas charging is impractical. When this is the case, liquid charging is used. The cylinder outlet will pass a much greater weight of liquid refrigerant in any given amount of time. Liquid charging is much faster than vapor charging, but it is much easier to overcharge a system while liquid charging. On the other hand, vapor charging is easier to control than liquid charging because the refrigerant transfer is much slower. When the amount of refrigerant needed exceeds 1 lb, liquid is charging is usually chosen. When the amount needed is less than 1 lb, vapor charging is the best choice.

Liquid must be used to charge a system when the refrigerant is a zeotrope because removing vapor from the cylinder will fractionate the blend. Zeotropic refrigerant must leave the cylinder as a liquid to maintain the integrity of the refrigerant. As vapor is drawn from the cylinder, more of one gas would be withdrawn than others, leaving an imbalance in the refrigerant charge. Some of these refrigerant cylinders have a dip tube that allows liquid to be withdrawn from the top of the cylinder in the upright position, while others must be inverted. The cylinders have arrows showing how to place the refrigerant for proper charging (Figure 84-17). Read the cylinder labels carefully to determine how to properly position the cylinder.

The point at which the refrigerant will actually enter the system is determined by one basic consideration: whether the unit is to be charged with refrigerant in a gas or liquid form. If the refrigerant is to be charged as a liquid, the charging should take place ahead of the metering device to protect the compressor from damage due to liquid flooding. Typically this would be at the king valve or liquid line service valve.

Packaged Units

Packaged units normally do not require charging for new installations because they are charged at the factory. In the event a packaged unit does require charging, you should first determine if the unit was shipped without a charge or if the charge leaked out. If the charge leaked out then the first step is to locate and repair all leaks. After the system is leak tight,

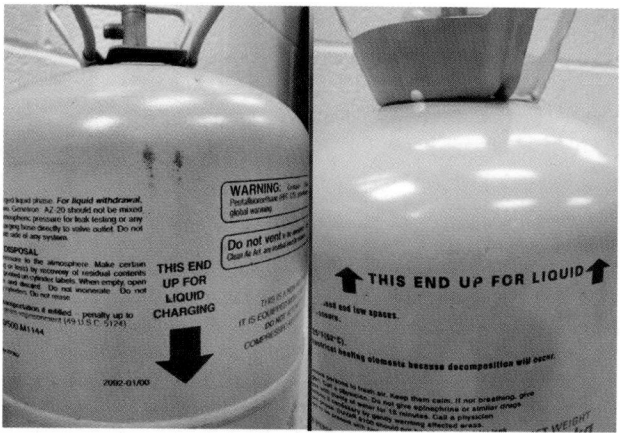

Figure 84-17 The cylinder on the left must be inverted to deliver liquid; the cylinder on the right delivers liquid while in the upright position

it should be evacuated and charged. The amount and type of refrigerant will be on the data plate (Figure 84-18). The unit should not be operating while the refrigerant is weighed in. For units that hold more than 1 lb of refrigerant the charge should be weighed in as a liquid into the king valve or liquid line service valve. For units that hold less than 1 lb, the refrigerant should be weighed in as a gas into both sides of the system at once.

Split Systems

Split systems usually do require some adjustment to the refrigerant charge to account for their refrigerant lines. Most manufacturers ship their condensing units with enough charge for the outdoor unit, the indoor coil, and a set length of refrigerant line. This charge is held in the

CONTAINS HCFC – 22		DESIGN PRESSURE		
FACTORY CHARGE		278	HI	PSIG
12 LBS	8 OZS	144	LO	PSIG
ELECTRICAL RATING		NOMINAL 208/230		VOLTS
1 PH	60 HZ	MIN 197	MAX	253
COMPRESSOR(S):(1)		FAN MOTOR(S): (1)		
PH	1	PH		1
RLA	23.8	FLA		1.7
LRA	129	HP		1/4
MIN.CKT AMPACITY AMPERAGE MINIMUM	31.5	MAX FUSE OR CKT.BKR. FUSIBLE/COUPE CIRCUIT (HACR PER NEC)		50
FOR OUTDOOR USE				
VERIFIED	CSA	VERIFIE		

Figure 84-18 This unit holds 12 lb 8 oz of HCFC 22 refrigerant

Figure 84-19 The unit arrives with the valves front seated, as shown on the left; turning the valves counterclockwise opens them and releases the refrigerant

condensing unit with split system shut-off valves, Figure 84-19.

These valves are front seated when the unit is shipped. The Schrader access fittings on these valves are always open to the refrigerant line regardless of the valve's position. The shut-off valves are opened only after

1. Installing the lines and coil.
2. Leak testing the lines and coil.
3. Evacuating the lines and coil.

CAUTION

Do not overtighten the installation valves when opening them. Stop turning the valve as soon as you feel increased resistance or see the top of the plug. A lock-ring is all that keeps the valve plug in. Overtightening it in the counterclockwise direction will result in the valve plug shooting out at a pressure exceeding 100 psig and all the refrigerant will come with it!

This allows the refrigerant that is trapped in the condenser to travel throughout the system. If the actual line length is exactly the same as the manufacturer's assumed line length, you are done. If the lines are longer than the assumed length, you will need to add refrigerant. If the lines are shorter, you will need to remove refrigerant. The amount of assumed line length varies from 15 ft to 30 ft depending upon the manufacturer. Many systems now include information on the unit that lists the assumed line length and gives the required per foot charge adjustment, Figure 84-20.

Table 84-1 Liquid Line Charge Allowance

Liquid line diameter (in)	Ounces per foot of liquid line
$1/4$	0.3
$5/16$	0.4
$3/8$	0.6
$1/2$	1.2
$5/8$	19

To calculate the amount of refrigerant needed:

1. Find the extra line length by subtracting the assumed length from the actual length.
2. Look up the per foot charge for the size liquid line used.
3. Multiply the extra line length by the charge per foot to find the amount of additional charge required.

Table 84-1 shows the per foot charge required for different size liquid lines. Note that an allowance is made only for the liquid line. There is not enough refrigerant in the suction line to calculate.

Under normal charging conditions, the refrigerant cylinder will be at ambient temperature and corresponding pressure. When the unit is operating, the refrigerant cylinder pressure will usually be below the head pressure of the condenser and above the back pressure of the evaporator. The easiest way to add the small amount of refrigerant needed for the line allowance is to add vapor to the suction side with the unit operating. For all refrigerants besides zeotropes, the refrigerant should be leaving the cylinder as a vapor with the cylinder in the upright position, Figure 84-21.

For zeotropes, the refrigerant must leave the cylinder as a liquid, Figure 84-17. This poses a problem because liquid should not be charged into the suction side of a system. The liquid refrigerant must be restricted between the cylinder and the system to safely add a zeotropic refrigerant with the unit operating. This can be accomplished with a charging device that is put in line with the cylinder (Figure 84-22) or by throttling the refrigerant using the hand valve on your gauges. Caution must be taken when charging a system with liquid refrigerant so that the compressor is not overloaded or slugged with liquid. Allowing too much liquid to enter the suction line is a fast way to kill a compressor.

SYSTEM TOTAL CHARGE

INSTALLER
DETERMINE COMPLETE SYSTEM TOTAL CHARGE BY USING PROPER ITEM BELOW. STAMP OR MARK THIS VALUE ON RATING PLATE IN "SYSTEM TOTAL CHARGE" BLOCK.

"OUTDOOR UNIT CHARGE"
ADD PER FT. VALUE SHOWN BELOW FOR EACH FOOT OVER 25 FT. LIQUID LINE TO FACTORY CHARGE. SUBTRACT PER FT. VALUE SHOWN BELOW FOR EACH FOOT UNDER 25 FT. LIQUID LINE FROM FACTORY CHARGE.

.3 OZ. PER FT. FOR 1/4 OD   .4 OZ. PER FT. FOR 5/16 OD
.6 OZ. PER FT. FOR 3/8 OD   1.2 OZ. PER FT. FOR 1/2 OD
1.9 OZ. PER FT. FOR 5/8 OD

92-23446-64-04

Figure 84-20 The assumed line length of 25 ft is included in the charging instruction that are included on this unit's service panel

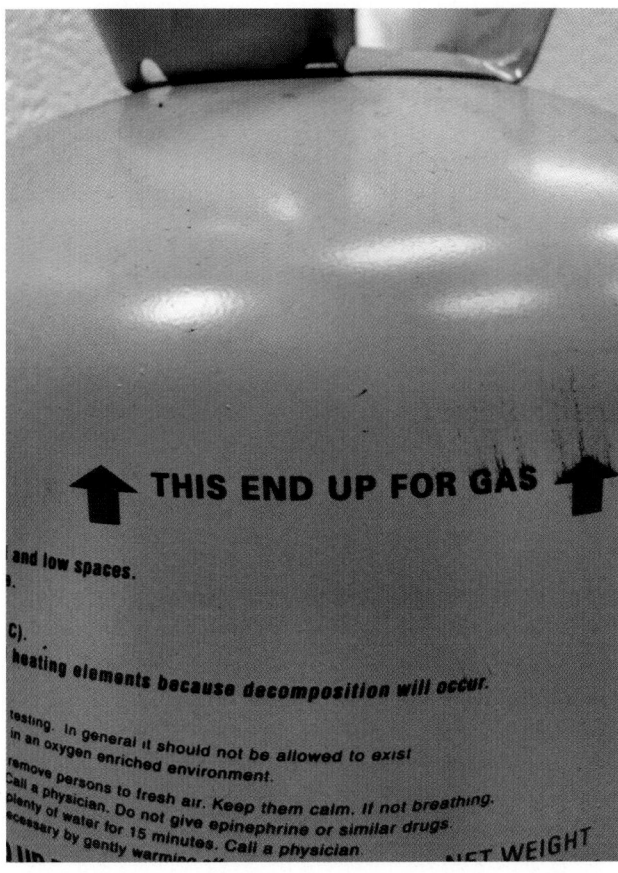

Figure 84-21 The refrigerant leaving this cylinder will be a gas when the cylinder is upright

---

TECH TIP

Some studies have shown that as many as 50% of the systems that are in service today are overcharged. There is a feeling among some technicians that a little extra refrigerant should be added to the system just in case there is a leak. If you suspect a leak, fix the leak, do not overcharge the system. Excessive refrigerant charges can be as detrimental to the equipment and to the equipment performance as undercharged equipment.

Figure 84-22 This device flashes off liquid to gas, allowing the refrigerant to leave the cylinder as a liquid even when charging into the suction line
(Courtesy of HVAC Department, Terra Community College, Fremont, Ohio)

84.17 CHARGING THE SYSTEM WITH OIL

New systems come with a correct charge of oil in them; adding oil when installing new equipment is unusual. However, if you have to add oil, the proper amount of oil can be determined by:

- Measuring in the oil by volume or weight.
- Observing the crankcase sight glass.

In a new system, oil can be measured or weighed in. Unit installation instructions include the compressor oil requirements in either weight or liquid volume measurements. This method is also applicable following a compressor overhaul, when all of the oil has been removed from the compressor; however, it should be used only when the system has no oil in it.

Some compressors have a sight glass in the crankcase for observing the oil level. The compressor crankcase sight glass is used after the system has operated for a period of time under normal conditions to determine the proper oil level. This procedure will ensure proper oil return to the crankcase. It will also allow the oil lines and reservoirs to fill and give the refrigerant an opportunity to absorb its normal operating oil content, if applicable.

As shown in Figure 84-23, oil is introduced into a refrigerant system by one of three methods:

- Oil may be poured in as shown on the left of Figure 84-23.
- Oil may be drawn in under vacuum as shown on the right of Figure 84-23.
- Oil may be forced in using an oil pump as shown in Figure 84-24.

To pour oil in, the compressor crankcase must be at atmospheric pressure. Otherwise, when the oil fill plug is removed any oil already in the compressor and will come flying out under pressure, giving the technician an oil bath. Besides being uncomfortable, this can also be dangerous. Oil in a contaminated system can be acidic and very hazardous. This method is normally used with a new compressor prior to system dehydration since it will expose the compressor crankcase interior to air and the moisture the air contains.

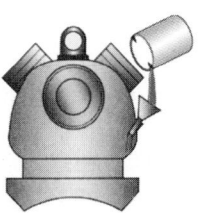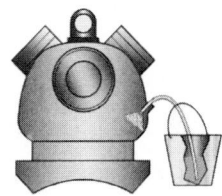

Figure 84-23 Two methods of charging oil into the compressor

Figure 84-24 An oil pump can be used to force oil in against system pressure

When using the vacuum method the crankcase is pumped down below atmospheric pressure and the oil is drawn in. The tube in the container should never be allowed to get close enough to the surface of the oil to draw in air. As shown in Figure 84-23, the tube is well below the level of the oil in the container.

An oil pump may also be used (Figure 84-24). The hand pump produces enough pressure to overcome the refrigerant pressure in the system and force the oil in. Care must be taken to purge the air from the pump and lines so that no air is pumped into the system.

The general precautions to take when charging or removing oil are as follows:

- Use clean, dry oil. Hermetically sealed oil containers are available and should be used.
- Do not keep open containers of oil on the shelf for use later, especially the new synthetic lubricants that are very hygroscopic. This invites contamination.
- Pressure must be controlled when the crankcase is opened to the atmosphere. Too much pressure can force oil out through the opening rapidly and create quite a mess.
- Overcharging the system with oil should be avoided. Not only will this create the possibility of oil slugs damaging the compressor, but it also can hinder the performance of the refrigerant in the evaporator. Oil overcharging may also cause liquid refrigerant to return to the compressor from the evaporator.

TECH TIP

Refrigerant oil can sometimes become acidic. Acid is formed as a result of water contamination and high heat. The oil acidity can be tested using an oil acid test kit. If the refrigeration oil in a semihermetic or open compressor is acidic, it should be changed. The oil in hermetic compressors can be cleaned using filter driers or acid neutralizing additives. However, most equipment manufacturers do not recommend using acid neutralizers.

84.18 PRESTART CHECKS

The initial startup is a critical time in a unit's life. Making certain that the installation meets all the manufacturer's specifications is a good way to prolong the life of the equipment. Installations that are not up to spec often lead to premature equipment failures that could have been avoided by taking a little extra time before starting the unit for the first time.

It is a good idea to have a routine to follow for initial startup. Using a routine saves time and ensures all necessary items are covered. If the manufacturer has supplied a suggested startup procedure, follow it! The installation and startup directions are normally inside the unit or shipping carton.

Clearances

Check to see that an adequate amount of space has been left on all sides of the unit. The specific distances for a particular unit can be found in the installation instructions. Clearances on air conditioning condensing units are required for proper airflow and adequate service access. Heat pump condensing units also require clearance from the ground in certain locations in order to elevate them above ice and snow. Also, all outdoor units should be protected from roof water runoff. This can be accomplished by locating the unit outside of the roof overhang, by using gutters to divert the water flow, or by using a strip of angled flashing installed on the edge of the roof above the unit. Furnaces require clearances from combustible materials. Tables 84-2 and 84-3 list typical clearances for air cooled condensers.

Mechanical Precheck

Prestart mechanical checks should include the following:

- Visually look for and remove all packing and shipping supports and bolts.
- Make sure that a clean air filter is in place inside.

Table 84-2 Vertical Discharge Air Cooled Condensing Units

Type of clearance	Distance (in)
Clearance above the top of the unit for airflow	48
Clearance from any side of the unit where air is drawn in	18
Clearance from any service access panel	24

Table 84-3 Horizontal Discharge Air Cooled Condensing Units

Type of clearance	Distance (in)
Clearance from all sides where air is discharged	48
Clearance from any side of the unit where air is drawn in	18
Clearance from any service access panel	24

- Check the thermostat with a small level.
- Use a level to check the level of the unit.
- Spin the condenser fan by hand to make sure it rotates freely.
- Check to see that the charging valves on the condensing unit are back-seated.
- If they are not, then you will need to evacuate the lines and evaporator coil *before* opening them.
- Check all line connections for leaks.

Electrical Precheck

Prestart electrical checks should include the following:

- The power wire should be *copper* (*not* aluminum).
- The power wire connections should be tight.
- Make certain that the unit is grounded.
- There should be a disconnect switch for each piece of equipment *in sight* of the equipment.
- Check that the over current protection is not more than the maximum size stated on the unit's name plate.
- Use the wiring diagram to check the low voltage connections. With the thermostat and disconnect switch turned off, check the voltage going into the disconnect. It should be within ± 10% of the nominal voltage rating on the name plate.
- Turn the disconnect switch on and check the voltage available to the unit. It should be within the minimum and maximum voltages stated on the unit data plate.

Gas Precheck for Combustion Appliances

- Check that gas line has a shut-off valve, drip tee, and union.
- Check to see that all gas piping is properly supported.
- Check for combustion air provisions.
- Check to see proper vent materials and connections.

84.19 INITIAL STARTUP

The equipment operational data should be checked against the manufacturer's specifications. This data is usually in the installation instructions. For systems with a refrigerant charge, connect the refrigerant gauges before stating the unit to ensure that it has a charge. For all types of systems, check the operating voltage and compare it to the system data plate. If the voltage was correct before startup, but drops below the unit's minimum voltage rating after starting, either the wire is too small or there is a bad connection. In either case, the unit must be shut off and the problem must be corrected. If the voltage is within the manufacturer's specifications, check the operating current against the data plate and make sure that it is not too high.

UNIT 84—SUMMARY

A successful installation begins with reading the instructions and applicable codes. National organizations that set installation standards include AHRI, ASHRAE, ASME, UL, and NFPA. Phases of installation include:

- Equipment placement.
- Ductwork installation.
- Piping installation (both refrigerant and water).
- Electrical connection.
- Evacuation and charging.
- Start and check.

Equipment should be located where it can be serviced. Air cooled condensers should be placed so that the airflow to them is not obstructed. All piping should be supported. Refrigerant lines should be purged with nitrogen during brazing to prevent oxidation. All equipment should have an electrical disconnect within sight of the equipment. Power wiring should be sized to carry the minimum circuit ampacity marked on the unit data plate. The circuit over current protection should not exceed the maximum fuse size listed on the unit data plate. Refrigeration systems should be evacuated to 500 microns before charging. A careful prestartup inspection and initial system performance check can help avoid future problems. Using a checklist to document the steps taken during the prestart inspection and initial startup can ensure that all steps have been taken. Regardless of equipment type, a good installation is the best way to ensure long equipment life, reliable operation, and energy efficiency.

WORK ORDERS

Service Ticket 8401

Initial System Startup

Equipment: Small Split System Air Conditioning Unit in Commercial Setting

A technician is performing a prestartup inspection and notices that the system's minimum circuit ampacity is listed as 15 A and the unit is wired with 14 gauge wire. The NEC wire sizing chart shows that 15 A is the most that wire will carry. The technician also notes that the power wire has been run a long way because the unit is over 200 ft from the power panel. The system nominal voltage rating is 208–230 V with a minimum of 190 V and a maximum of 250 V. The voltage check with the unit off shows 208 V available. The technician is wary because the voltage is in the lower end of the acceptable range. When the unit is started, the line voltage drops to 188 V and the technician shuts the system off. The technician recommends that the power wire be replaced with a larger gauge wire to reduce the voltage drop and keep the unit operating consistently above the minimum voltage rating.

Service Ticket 8402

Initial System Startup

Equipment: Split System Residential Air Conditioning Unit

A technician is sent to perform an initial system startup. During the prestart check the technician notices that the refrigerant line installation valves are still front seated. The technician decides to evacuate the lines and coil before opening the valves in case they were not evacuated properly. The lines and coil are blanked off after they are evacuated to 500 microns. The vacuum holds, so the technician opens the refrigeration line installation valves.

Service Ticket 8403

Packaged Unit Replacement

Equipment: Residential Packaged Air Conditioner with Vertical Condenser Air Discharge

An estimator is sent to collect information to bid a job replacing a packaged air conditioning unit. Upon arrival, the estimator notices that the old system is located under a porch, has an over-under duct configuration, and a horizontal discharge condenser. The systems their company normally sells have side by side duct connections and a vertical discharge condenser. The estimator returns and explains that either a different system must be used, or the system must be relocated to allow for proper condenser airflow and major duct modifications.

Service Ticket 8404

Heat Pump Installation

Equipment: Residential Split System Heat Pump in Northern Climate

A technician is sent to install a split system heat pump and notices that no provision has been made to keep the outdoor unit above the snow level in the winter. The company has never installed a heat pump before, and was planning on setting the outdoor unit on the concrete pad like an air conditioning condensing unit. The technician shows the foreman the installation instructions that show a metal frame elevating the unit above the top of the snow. The technician fabricates a galvanized metal frame that holds the outdoor unit 3 ft off the ground.

Service Ticket 8405

Gas Furnace Replacement

Equipment: 80% Induced Draft Furnace Replacing Existing Natural Draft Furnace

A technician is sent to replace an existing natural draft furnace with a new 80% induced draft furnace. The technician notices that the existing furnace uses a 7 in single wall metal vent connector leading to a masonry chimney. The new furnace has a vent collar of 5 in. The new furnace installation instructions clearly say that single wall pipe should not be used and that masonry chimneys should not be used unless a metal liner is used. The installer recommends lining the masonry chimney with a metal liner and replacing the old 7 in single wall vent connector with 5 in double wall pipe.

UNIT 84—REVIEW QUESTIONS

1. List the associations that establish national standards for the HVAC/R industry.
2. What is the function of AHRI?
3. What does the UL specialize in?
4. List all major phases of system installation.
5. What factors must be considered in equipment placement?
6. Outline the correct brazing procedure for hard copper refrigeration piping.
7. What electrical rating on a unit data plate is useful for sizing the power wire for the unit?
8. What electrical rating on the unit data plate is useful for sizing the circuit breaker for the unit?
9. Use the information on the data plate in Figure 84-14 to determine the minimum current rating for sizing the power wire to the unit.
10. Use the information on the data plate in Figure 84-14 to determine the minimum current rating for the unit disconnect.

11. Use the information on the data plate in Figure 84-15 to determine the maximum circuit breaker size for the unit.

12. What type of over current protection is used with air conditioning equipment?

13. How should ductwork be sealed against air leaks?

14. How can vibrations and sound transmission from the unit to the ductwork be minimized?

15. Use Figures 84-18, 84-20, and Table 84-1 to determine the correct amount of additional charge for a new split system with a 40 ft line set and a $^{3}/_{8}$ in liquid line.

16. List three methods of adding oil to a system.

17. What position are the unit installation valves in when the unit is shipped?

18. When installing a split system, what should be done prior to opening the installation valves?

UNIT 85

Planned Maintenance

OBJECTIVES

After completing this unit you will be able to:

- describe the four phases of a planned maintenance service call.
- discuss the advantages of planned maintenance.
- describe the planned maintenance process for refrigeration and air conditioning systems.
- describe the planned maintenance process for heating systems.
- list system operational safety concerns that should be addressed on a planned maintenance service call.
- discuss aspects of planned maintenance that are common to most systems.

85.1 INTRODUCTION

An often repeated bit of folk wisdom is "if it ain't broke, don't fix it." The problem with this philosophy is that it limits service work to emergency operations that are performed under duress after the worst has already happened. It makes life easier to keep things from breaking in the first place.

Planned maintenance enables efficient use of service labor resources. Regular maintenance is scheduled during slow periods, freeing service labor for more emergency service during peak seasons. Scheduling maintenance regularly helps catch small problems before they become big ones, saving both time and money. Keeping systems operating according to manufacturer's specifications saves both energy and money as well.

85.2 PLANNED MAINTENANCE

Scheduled maintenance calls include four important elements:

1. Routine maintenance on parts that need regular checking, cleaning, or replacing.
2. Prestart inspection of the equipment.
3. Operation check of the equipment.
4. Troubleshooting and correction when necessary.

Routine Maintenance

Maintenance schedules are developed according to the season and the system requirements. Seasonal maintenance on heating systems is typically done in the fall, and seasonal maintenance on air conditioning systems is usually done in the spring. These seasonal checkups are intended to ensure that the systems perform when needed. They are the customer's insurance policy against system malfunctions during the peak

season. However, some system components may need attention more than once a year. Air filters are a good example. Standard 1 in light duty filters need checking monthly in most houses. The maintenance schedule and services performed will vary depending upon the type of system. What remains constant is that neglecting the required maintenance will lead to increased operating costs and shorter equipment life.

Prestart Check

There are a few things that need to be checked before starting the system. The best time to discover that the voltage is incorrect is before you start the unit! First find the unit data plate (Figure 85-1) and note all information about the equipment operational requirements. These could include:

- The minimum and maximum voltage rating for the equipment.
- The current draw of all motors.

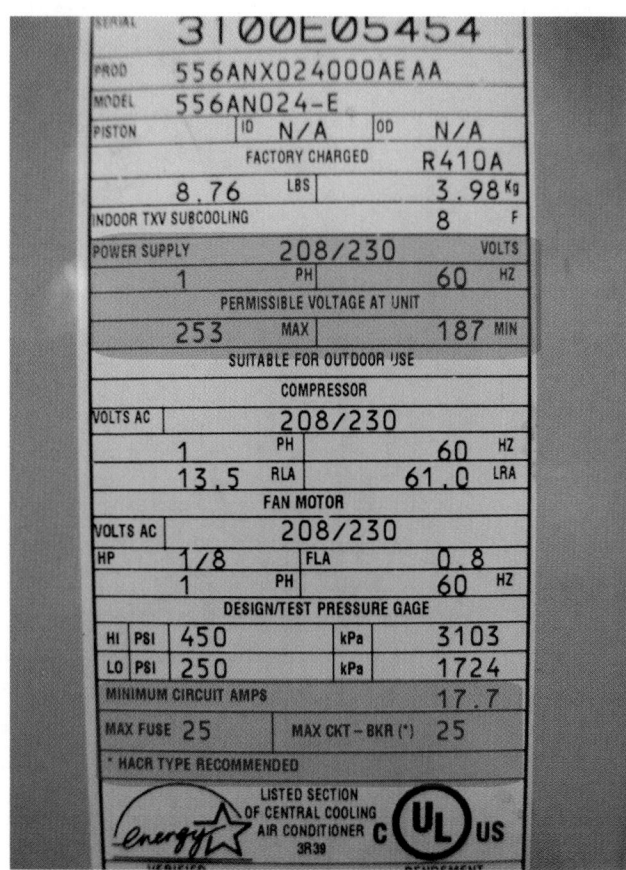

Figure 85-1 Unit data plate

IDB	Airflow		65°F 59	63	67	71	75°F 59	63	67	71	85°F 59	63	67	71	95°F 59	63	67	71	105°F 59	63	67	71	115°F 59	63	67	71
		MBh	39.6	41.1	45.0	–	38.7	40.1	43.9	–	37.8	39.2	42.9	–	36.9	38.2	41.9	–	35.0	36.3	39.8	–	32.4	33.6	36.8	–
		S/T	0.73	0.61	0.42	–	0.76	0.63	0.44	–	0.78	0.65	0.45	–	0.80	0.67	0.47	–	0.83	0.70	0.48	–	0.84	0.70	0.49	–
		ΔT	18	15	12	–	18	15	12	–	18	15	12	–	18	16	12	–	18	15	12	–	17	14	11	–
	1519	kW	2.79	2.85	2.93	–	3.00	3.06	3.16	–	3.18	3.25	3.35	–	3.34	3.42	3.53	–	3.48	3.56	3.67	–	3.60	3.68	3.80	–
		Amps	12.3	12.5	12.9	–	13.1	13.4	13.8	–	14.1	14.4	14.9	–	15.0	15.3	15.8	–	15.8	16.2	16.7	–	16.7	17.1	17.6	–
		Hi PR	222	239	252	–	249	268	283	–	283	305	322	–	322	347	366	–	363	390	412	–	401	431	455	–
		Lo PR	109	116	127	–	116	123	134	–	120	128	139	–	126	134	146	–	132	141	154	–	137	145	159	–
		MBh	38.5	39.9	43.7	–	37.6	38.9	42.7	–	36.7	38.0	41.6	–	35.8	37.1	40.6	–	34.0	35.2	38.6	–	31.5	32.6	35.8	–
		S/T	0.70	0.58	0.40	–	0.72	0.61	0.42	–	0.74	0.62	0.43	–	0.77	0.64	0.44	–	0.80	0.66	0.46	–	0.80	0.67	0.46	–
		ΔT	18	16	12	–	19	16	12	–	19	16	12	–	19	16	12	–	18	16	12	–	17	15	11	–
70	1350	kW	2.77	2.82	2.91	–	2.97	3.04	3.13	–	3.16	3.22	3.33	–	3.32	3.39	3.50	–	3.45	3.53	3.64	–	3.57	3.65	3.77	–
		Amps	12.2	12.5	12.8	–	13.0	13.3	13.7	–	14.0	14.3	14.7	–	14.9	15.2	15.6	–	15.7	16.1	16.5	–	16.5	16.9	17.4	–
		Hi PR	220	236	250	–	246	265	280	–	280	302	318	–	319	343	363	–	359	386	408	–	397	427	451	–
		Lo PR	108	115	126	–	114	122	133	–	119	126	138	–	125	133	145	–	131	139	152	–	135	144	157	–
		MBh	35.5	36.8	40.3	–	34.7	35.9	39.4	–	33.9	35.1	38.4	–	33.0	34.2	37.5	–	31.4	32.5	35.8	–	29.1	30.1	33.0	–
		S/T	0.67	0.56	0.39	–	0.70	0.58	0.40	–	0.72	0.60	0.41	–	0.74	0.62	0.43	–	0.77	0.64	0.44	–	0.77	0.65	0.45	–
		ΔT	19	16	12	–	19	16	12	–	19	16	12	–	19	16	12	–	19	16	12	–	18	15	12	–
	1181	kW	2.70	2.76	2.84	–	2.90	2.96	3.06	–	3.08	3.15	3.25	–	3.24	3.31	3.41	–	3.37	3.44	3.55	–	3.48	3.56	3.68	–
		Amps	11.9	12.2	12.5	–	12.7	13.0	13.4	–	13.7	14.0	14.4	–	14.5	14.8	15.3	–	15.3	15.7	16.1	–	16.1	16.5	17.0	–
		Hi PR	213	229	242	–	239	257	272	–	272	293	309	–	310	333	352	–	348	375	396	–	385	414	437	–
		Lo PR	105	112	122	–	111	118	129	–	115	123	134	–	121	129	141	–	127	135	147	–	131	140	153	–

Outdoor Ambient Temperature / Entering Indoor Wet Bulb Temperature

Figure 85-2 Manufacturer's refrigerant pressure chart

- The fuel source and fuel pressure for combustion appliances.
- The temperature rise for furnaces.

Operational Checks

The operation of the equipment should be checked against the manufacturer's specifications. Items to be checked could include:

- Operating voltage
- Operating current
- Refrigerant pressures (Figure 85-2)
- Gas manifold pressures
- Temperature rise (Figure 85-3)

85.3 REFRIGERATION/AIR CONDITIONING MAINTENANCE

Routine Maintenance

Air conditioning and refrigeration equipment should receive an annual checkup and cleaning. This is normally done in the spring. The first order of business is to inspect and clean the coils and filters. The condenser and evaporator should be checked and cleaned if necessary.

Lubrication and Adjustment

Now is a good time to lubricate all bearings and tighten any belts. Most residential blowers use sleeve bearings that need to be oiled. Many motors have lubrication instructions on the motor, Figure 85-4.

You should only apply oil to oiler tubes. Do not attempt to oil a motor that has no place for adding oil. Do not over oil, 5–10 drops are normally sufficient. Most residential equipment no longer uses belts. If you are working on a piece of equipment with a belt you should check the belt, the belt alignment, and the belt tension.

Prestart Inspection

Check the power supply to the unit with the unit off. It should fall between the minimum and maximum voltage ratings. Visually inspect the wiring for connections that appear discolored. Loose connections create heat, which makes the wires and insulation brittle and burned looking, Figure 85-5.

Inspect the contactor. Its armature should move freely without sticking. The contactor points should be smooth, not pitted. Some discoloration of the points is normal, Figure 85-6.

Figure 85-3 The temperature rise of gas fired heating equipment can be found on the unit data plate

Figure 85-4 The lubricating instructions for this motor are on its data plate

Figure 85-5 Overheating causes the terminal to discolor and could cause wire insulation to melt

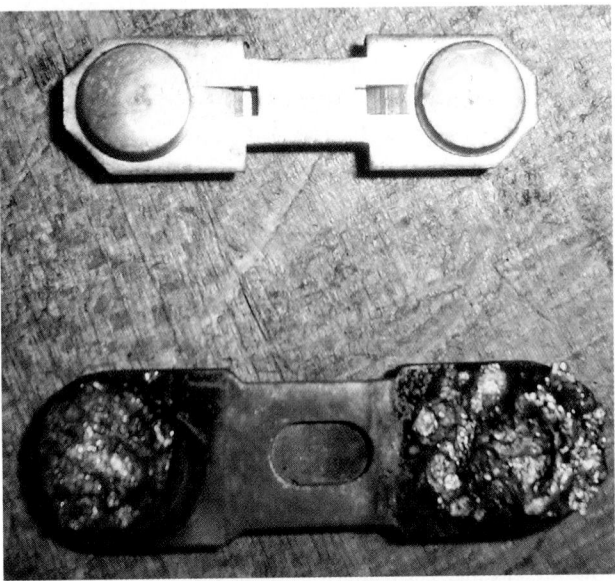

Figure 85-6 Burned and pitted contractor points, like the ones on the bottom, will create a voltage drop and cause motor overheating

SERVICE TIP

Do not try to sand or file the points, you will most likely do more harm than good. Filing removes the silver-cadmium outer plating which is much more resistant to oxidation than the copper underneath.

Install gauges on the equipment to make sure it has refrigerant. You should not operate equipment without a

Figure 85-7 Oil is a natural leak indicator; this vibrasorber has a leak at one end where it flexes
(Courtesy of HVAC Department, Terra Community College, Fremont, Ohio)

charge. Check for refrigerant leaks at all mechanical connections and visible braze joints. Particularly look for signs of oil on the lines or the pipe insulation, Figure 85-7.

If you find leaks, they should be repaired before proceeding.

Operational Checks

Start the system and check the incoming voltage with the unit operating. A significant drop in voltage indicates problems in the power supply. If the voltage drops below the minimum voltage, shut down the system. The contactor contacts should also be checked for voltage drop. The ideal voltage reading from one side of the contact to the other with current going though is 0 V. A reading of more than a few tenths of a volt indicates bad contacts on the contactor. If there is a significant voltage drop across the contacts, shut the system down and change the contactor. A voltage drop across the contactor contacts can kill the compressor.

With the unit operating check all operational characteristics including:

- Amp draw of all motors.
- Airflow.
- Low side and high side pressures.
- Superheat and subcooling.
- Temperature drop across the evaporator.

Compare your readings with the manufacturer's specifications, Figure 85-8.

SERVICE TIP

Most equipment has some operating specifications on the inside of the service panel, including refrigerant charging charts. The electrical specifications can be found on the unit name plate.

85.4 HEATING SYSTEMS MAINTENANCE

An annual heating system check should include checking the fuel source, performing prestart checks, and checking the air temperature rise. The combustion should be checked on gas and oil furnaces and boilers.

85.5 ELECTRIC HEATING

Routine Maintenance

The only routine maintenance necessary on an electric furnace would be changing or cleaning the air filter and

Figure 85-8 Manufacturer's system performance chart located on the equipment

lubricating the blower. In the rare cases of an electric furnace with a belt drive blower, you should also check the belt, belt alignment, and belt tension.

Prestart Inspection

The incoming voltage should be checked and compared to the name plate rating. Perform a visual inspection on all wires and wire connections. Overheating and degradation of wires, wire lugs, and fuse blocks are common problems in electric furnaces. The large current draw turns any small resistance into a small heater that degrades and discolors electrical connections over time. Any visibly discolored wires or wiring components should be replaced.

Operational Check

Checking the power source and all electrical connections is essential when performing annual maintenance. Because electric furnaces use large amounts of power, any resistance in any of the power handling components leads to heat and failure of that component. More seriously, heated wires, wiring lugs, or fuse blocks can be dangerous.

The voltage to the furnace should be checked before and after starting the furnace. A voltage drop indicates a problem with the power wiring to the furnace. The voltage at the heating elements should be checked and compared to the voltage entering the furnace; they should be the same. A voltage drop indicates that there is a problem in the furnace. This can be located by measuring the voltage across all the power handling components. An infrared thermometer can also help. The point of voltage drop will be hotter than the rest of the wires and components. The current draw of each heating element should be checked and compared to the name plate rating. A heat strip that does not draw any current indicates a problem. First check to

make sure it has voltage. If no voltage is being applied to the heat strip, the problem is in the controls to that strip. If voltage is being applied and it still has no current draw, then either the heat strip or its fusible link are open. After all heating elements are operating, check the temperature rise of the furnace. Measure the temperature of the air entering and leaving the furnace. The difference is the temperature rise. The temperature rise should fall within the range listed on the furnace name plate.

85.6 GAS HEATING

Routine Maintenance

As is the case for all forced air systems, the air filters should be cleaned or changed and the blower motor should be lubricated. For belt-drive systems the belt, belt alignment, and belt tension should all be checked. Ribbon, slotted, or drilled port burners should be removed so they can be inspected and cleaned. Burners with more than light surface rust should be replaced pending the outcome of the prestart inspection, Figure 85-9.

SERVICE TIP
Loose rust on the burners may not be from the burners, but from the heat exchanger. If the burners have large flakes of rust on them, the heat exchanger needs to be checked.

Inshot burners generally do not require cleaning but should be inspected for rust. This can usually be done with an inspection mirror without removing the burners. Extremely rusty burners could indicate a more serious problem that might require replacing the furnace. If you have removed the burners to clean them, leave them out for the prestart check.

Prestart Check

The heat exchanger should be visually inspected for holes, cracks, and rust. Some surface rust is normal, but flaky rust that comes off in chunks should be carefully inspected. The

Figure 85-9 These burners are no longer serviceable and should be replaced
(Courtesy of HVAC Department, Terra Community College, Fremont, Ohio)

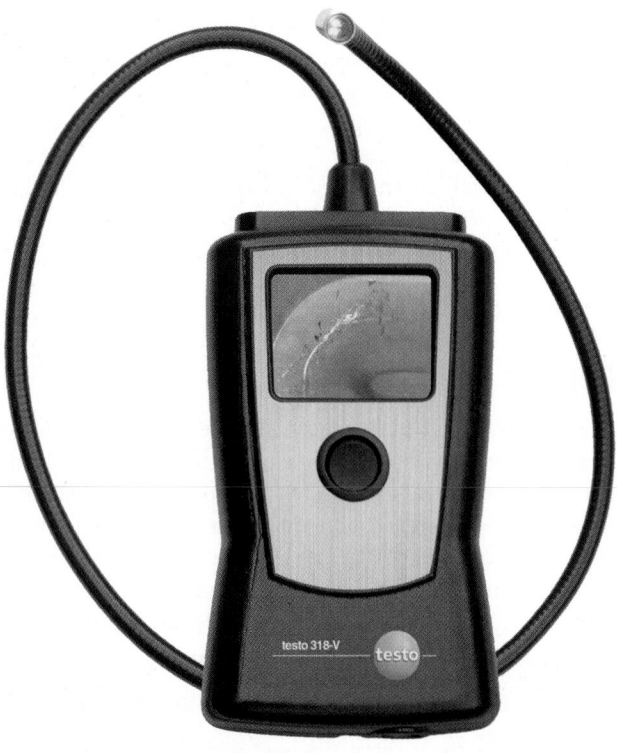

Figure 85-10 This Testo 318 inspection tool can be used to inspect heat exchangers for cracks
(Courtesy of Testo, Inc.)

heat exchanger may be viewed from the burner end and from the draft diverter end for older style natural draft furnaces. An inspection mirror can be helpful, but a flexible fiberoptic inspection tool is preferable, Figure 85-10.

SERVICE TIP

On noncondensing furnaces, a better view of the heat exchanger can be gained by removing the blower and looking through the furnace from the blower end. This will not work on condensing furnaces because the recuperative heat exchanger is in the way.

The heat exchanger will have a separate tube or clamshell for each burner. Each section needs to be inspected individually.

The vent system should be inspected for loose connections, signs of corrosion, or rust. A rusty or corroded vent indicates condensation in the vent, Figure 85-11.

The cause of the condensation should be determined and corrected. It could be using single wall vent in a cold ambient, an oversized vent, a vent with an excessively long horizontal run, a restricted vent, or lack of combustion air. A malfunctioning vent is dangerous; the cause should be found and corrected!

The combustion and venting processes cannot work correctly without adequate combustion and ventilation air. The room the furnace is in should normally be provided with combustion air somewhere near the floor and also near the ceiling. This can be a hole or grill to a ventilated crawl space or attic or through ducts that go outside. Locate the combustion air openings and verify that they are not blocked, Figure 85-12.

Figure 85-11 The water in the flue has been condensing in this vent causing the rust at the joints of the elbow
(Courtesy of HVAC Department, Terra Community College, Fremont, Ohio)

Find the name plate and write down:

- The type of gas.
- The minimum and maximum input gas pressure.
- The manifold gas pressure.
- The temperature rise.
- The operating voltage.

Check the incoming gas pressure to see if it falls between the minimum and maximum input pressures. Check the in-

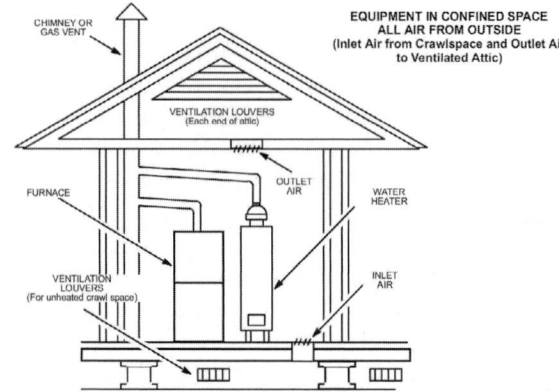

NOTE-The inlet and outlet air openings shall each have a free area of at least one square inch (645 mm²) per 4,000 Btu (1.17 kW) per hour of the total input rating of all equipment in the enclosure.

Figure 85-12 Gas fired equipment should have combustion air supplied near the floor and near the ceiling
(Courtesy of Lennox Industries)

coming voltage to see if it falls between the minimum and maximum voltage. Install the manometer on the manifold gas pressure port before turning on the system. Any reading other than 0 in wc indicates a leaking gas valve. This is a very rare but dangerous situation. If the gas valve leaks, it must be replaced. Turn off the gas supply and leave the area to let the accumulated gas dissipate before proceeding. Leave the manometer on for use during the operational check.

SAFETY TIP

Do not put your face directly in front of the burner area when the furnace first lights. Flame rollout and flashback can occur, causing flames to come out from the furnace.

Operational Check

For category I and II furnaces, place a draft gauge in the vent and check the draft with the burners operating. You should have a draft of at least –0.02 in wc. Watch the draft reading when the indoor blower comes on. A reduction in draft or an increase to a positive pressure indicates a leak in the heat exchanger. This is a serious safety issue that generally warrants replacing the furnace.

Check the manifold gas pressure after the burners light. The correct manifold gas pressure at sea level is indicated on the furnace name plate. The manifold pressure is usually slightly less at higher altitudes. The manufacturer's installation instructions are the best source of information for derating gas appliances. The chart in Figure 85-13 lists the typical manifold pressure and orifice sizes for different altitudes.

Figure 85-13 This chart shows the necessary adjustments to handle high altitude operation, including orifice changes and manifold pressure changes

TABLE 11—ORIFICE SIZE* AND MANIFOLD PRESSURES FOR GAS INPUT RATE
(TABULATED DATA BASED ON 20,000 BTUH HIGH-HEAT/13,000 BTUH LOW-HEAT PER BURNER,
DERATED 2%/1,000 FT ABOVE SEA LEVEL)

ALTITUDE RANGE (ft)	AVG. GAS HEAT VALUE AT ALTITUDE (Btu/cu ft)	SPECIFIC GRAVITY OF NATURAL GAS							
		0.58		0.60		0.62		0.64	
		Orifice No.	Mnfld Press High/Low	Orifice No.	Mnfld Press High/Low	Orifice No.	Mnfld Press High/Low	Orifice No.	Mnfld Press High/Low
U.S.A. and Canada 0 to 2000	900	43	3.5 / 1.5	43	3.6 / 1.5	43	3.8 / 1.6	42	3.2 / 1.3
	925	44	3.8 / 1.6	43	3.5 / 1.5	43	3.6 / 1.5	43	3.7 / 1.6
	950	44	3.6 / 1.5	44	3.8 / 1.6	43	3.4 / 1.4	43	3.5 / 1.5
	975	44	3.4 / 1.5	44	3.6 / 1.5	44	3.7 / 1.6	44	3.8 / 1.6
	1000	44	3.3 / 1.4	44	3.4 / 1.4	44	3.5 / 1.4	44	3.6 / 1.5
	1025	45	**3.8 / 1.6**	44	3.2 / 1.4	44	3.3 / 1.4	44	3.4 / 1.5
	1050	45	3.6 / 1.5	45	**3.7 / 1.6**	45	**3.8 / 1.6**	44	3.3 / 1.4
	1075	45	3.4 / 1.4	45	3.5 / 1.5	45	3.7 / 1.5	45	**3.8 / 1.6**
	1100	45	3.3 / 1.4	45	3.4 / 1.4	45	3.5 / 1.5	45	**3.6 / 1.5**
U.S.A Altitudes 2001 to 3000 or Canada Altitudes 2001 to 4500	800	43	3.8 / 1.6	42	3.2 / 1.4	42	3.3 / 1.4	42	3.5 / 1.5
	825	43	3.6 / 1.5	43	3.7 / 1.6	43	3.8 / 1.6	42	3.2 / 1.4
	850	43	3.4 / 1.4	43	3.5 / 1.5	43	3.6 / 1.5	43	3.7 / 1.6
	875	44	3.7 / 1.5	44	3.8 / 1.6	43	3.4 / 1.4	43	3.5 / 1.5
	900	44	3.5 / 1.5	44	3.6 / 1.5	44	3.7 / 1.6	44	3.8 / 1.6
	925	44	3.3 / 1.4	44	3.4 / 1.4	44	3.5 / 1.5	44	3.6 / 1.5
	950	45	**3.7 / 1.6**	44	3.2 / 1.4	44	3.3 / 1.4	44	3.4 / 1.4
	975	45	3.6 / 1.5	45	**3.7 / 1.6**	45	**3.8 / 1.6**	44	3.2 / 1.4
	1000	45	3.4 / 1.4	45	3.5 / 1.5	45	3.6 / 1.5	45	**3.7 / 1.6**
U.S.A. Only 3001 to 4000	775	43	3.7 / 1.6	42	3.2 / 1.3	42	3.3 / 1.4	42	3.4 / 1.4
	800	43	3.5 / 1.5	43	3.6 / 1.5	43	3.8 / 1.6	42	3.2 / 1.3
	825	44	3.8 / 1.6	43	3.4 / 1.4	43	3.5 / 1.5	43	3.7 / 1.5
	850	44	3.6 / 1.5	44	3.7 / 1.6	44	3.8 / 1.6	43	3.4 / 1.5
	875	44	3.4 / 1.4	44	3.5 / 1.5	44	3.6 / 1.5	44	3.7 / 1.6
	900	44	3.2 / 1.3	44	3.3 / 1.4	44	3.4 / 1.4	44	3.5 / 1.5
	925	45	**3.7 / 1.5**	45	**3.8 / 1.6**	44	3.2 / 1.4	44	3.3 / 1.4
	950	45	3.5 / 1.5	45	3.6 / 1.5	45	**3.7 / 1.6**	45	**3.8 / 1.6**
U.S.A. Only 4001 to 5000	750	43	3.7 / 1.6	43	3.8 / 1.6	42	3.2 / 1.4	42	3.3 / 1.4
	775	43	3.5 / 1.5	43	3.6 / 1.5	43	3.7 / 1.6	43	3.8 / 1.6
	800	44	3.7 / 1.6	43	3.4 / 1.4	43	3.5 / 1.5	43	3.6 / 1.5
	825	44	3.5 / 1.5	44	3.6 / 1.5	44	3.7 / 1.6	43	3.4 / 1.4
	850	44	3.3 / 1.4	44	3.4 / 1.4	44	3.5 / 1.5	44	3.6 / 1.5
	875	45	**3.8 / 1.6**	44	3.2 / 1.4	44	3.3 / 1.4	44	3.4 / 1.5
	900	45	3.6 / 1.5	45	**3.7 / 1.6**	45	**3.8 / 1.6**	44	3.2 / 1.4
	925	45	3.4 / 1.4	45	3.5 / 1.5	45	3.6 / 1.5	45	**3.7 / 1.6**
U.S.A. Only 5001 to 6000	725	43	3.6 / 1.5	43	3.8 / 1.6	42	3.2 / 1.4	42	3.3 / 1.4
	750	43	3.4 / 1.4	43	3.5 / 1.5	43	3.6 / 1.5	43	3.8 / 1.6
	775	44	3.7 / 1.5	44	3.8 / 1.6	43	3.4 / 1.4	43	3.5 / 1.5
	800	44	3.4 / 1.5	44	3.6 / 1.5	44	3.7 / 1.6	44	3.8 / 1.6
	825	44	3.2 / 1.4	44	3.3 / 1.4	44	3.4 / 1.4	44	3.6 / 1.5
	850	45	**3.7 / 1.6**	45	**3.8 / 1.6**	44	3.2 / 1.4	44	3.4 / 1.4
	875	45	3.5 / 1.5	45	3.6 / 1.5	45	**3.7 / 1.6**	45	**3.8 / 1.6**
	900	45	3.3 / 1.4	45	3.4 / 1.4	45	3.5 / 1.5	45	**3.6 / 1.5**
U.S.A. Only 6001 to 7000	675	42	3.2 / 1.3	42	3.3 / 1.4	42	3.4 / 1.4	42	3.5 / 1.5
	700	43	3.6 / 1.5	43	3.7 / 1.6	43	3.8 / 1.6	43	3.3 / 1.4
	725	44	3.8 / 1.6	43	3.5 / 1.5	43	3.6 / 1.5	43	3.7 / 1.6
	750	44	3.6 / 1.5	44	3.7 / 1.6	44	3.8 / 1.6	43	3.5 / 1.5
	775	44	3.4 / 1.4	44	3.5 / 1.5	44	3.6 / 1.5	44	3.7 / 1.6
	800	45	**3.8 / 1.6**	44	3.3 / 1.4	44	3.4 / 1.4	44	3.5 / 1.5
	825	45	3.6 / 1.5	45	**3.7 / 1.6**	45	**3.8 / 1.6**	44	3.3 / 1.4
	850	45	3.4 / 1.4	45	3.5 / 1.5	45	3.6 / 1.5	45	**3.7 / 1.6**

*Orifice numbers shown in **BOLD** are factory-installed.

Figure 85-14 The natural gas flame gives off both heat and light

Look at the color of the flames. The flames should be blue, Figure 85-14.

Yellow flames indicate incomplete combustion and the presence of carbon monoxide, Figure 85-15.

Yellow flames are the result of too much gas, too little air, or faulty burners. Older gas furnaces have adjustable primary air intakes, Figure 85-16.

The primary air can be adjusted until the yellow disappears. However, opening the shutters too far can cause delayed ignition, especially on cold days. Too much primary air also causes the flames to lift away from the burner face. In-shot burners like most modern furnaces use do not have any primary air adjustment. Yellow flames on these furnaces indicate a lack of combustion air in the room or too much gas. Check the orifice size against the manufacturer's specifications or an orifice chart to make certain the furnace has the correct size of gas orifices, Figures 85-17 and 85-18.

The combustion gases in the vent should be checked for carbon monoxide. Ideally the carbon monoxide level should be 0 ppm for complete combustion. Realistically, it is common

for some low level of CO to be present in the combustion gases. Levels of CO in the vent gases exceeding 50 parts per million warrant a closer look at the combustion process, Figure 85-19.

After the blower has been operating for a few minutes, check the temperature of the air entering and leaving the furnace. The difference is the temperature rise, Figure 85-20.

Be sure to check the leaving air temperature in a location that is not directly in the line of sight of the heat exchanger. If the thermometer can "see" the heat exchanger, it may read higher due to the heat exchanger's radiant heat. If the temperature rise is too high, the airflow needs to be increased. If the temperature rise is too low, the airflow needs to be reduced.

85.7 OIL FIRED HEATING

Routine Maintenance

Like all forced air systems, the air filters should be cleaned or changed and the blower motor should be lubricated. For belt-drive systems the belt, belt alignment, and belt tension should all be checked. Items unique to oil furnaces include changing the fuel oil filter, replacing the nozzle, lubricating the oil burner motor, inspecting the drive coupling, and inspecting the combustion chamber. All of these items should be done once a year. The fuel oil filter should be changed every time the oil tank is refilled, but no less than once a year.

Prestart Check

The oil burner will have to be removed to perform the annual maintenance and preseason check. After removing the oil burner you should:

- Change the nozzle. Make sure to replace it with the same spray pattern and angle, Figure 85-21
- Inspect the electrodes for cracks in the ceramic insulators, Figure 85-22.
- Clean the electrodes and set them to the correct angle and gap, Figure 85-23.
- Adjust the Z dimension of the burner tube, Figure 85-24.
- Inspect the drive coupling, Figure 85-25.
- Clean the cad cell sensor, Figure 85-26.

While the burner is removed, clean any accumulated debris out of the combustion chamber and inspect the combustion chamber liner. If it has deteriorated, it should be replaced. Replace the burner after these steps are completed.

SAFETY TIP

If the burner has not been firing, a dangerous accumulation of oil in the combustion chamber can result from pushing the reset button several times. The customer may have tried resetting the burner several times before calling for service. This oil needs to be cleaned from the combustion chamber as thoroughly as possible. Lighting the furnace with a soaked combustion chamber may lead to an explosion!

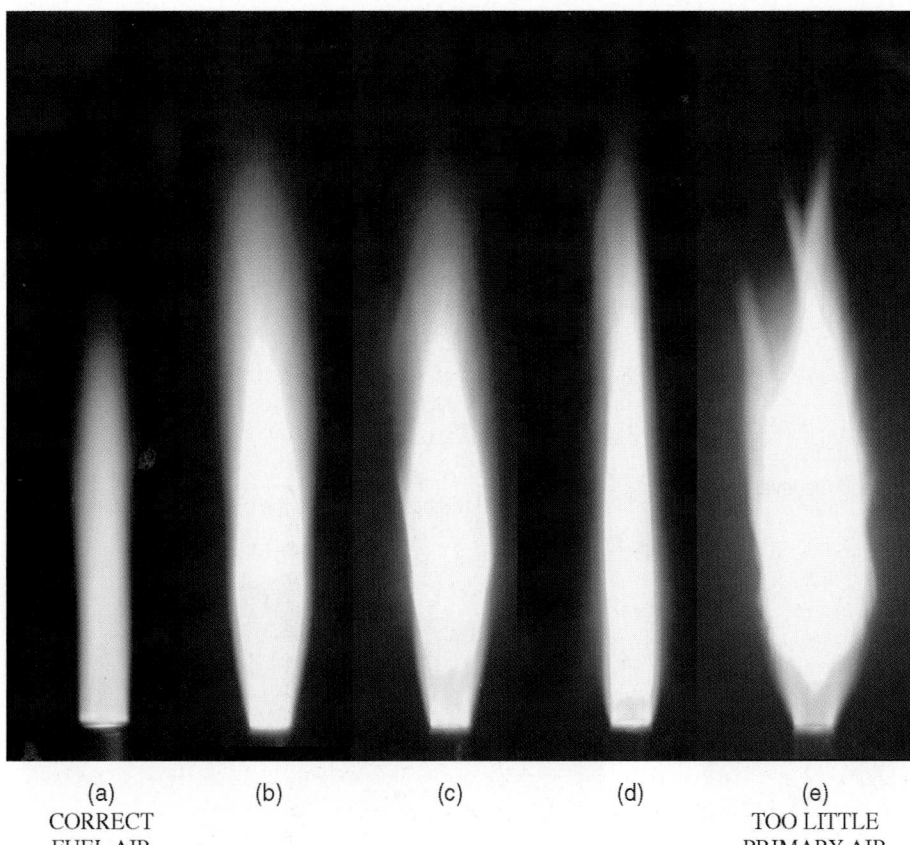

(a)
CORRECT
FUEL AIR
MIXTURE

(b)

(c)

(d)

(e)
TOO LITTLE
PRIMARY AIR

Figure 85-15 Natural gas flames: (a) Correct mixture of fuel and air; (b) Less primary air, cone reduced; (c) Less primary air, flame wider; (d) Less primary air, flame more irregular; (e) Too little primary air, irregular, wide flame

Figure 85-16 Some gas burners have primary air shutters for adjusting the amount of primary air to the burner

Figure 85-17 The orifice size is stamped on it; this is a #43

Figure 85-18 The same furnace may require four different orifices depending upon the type of gas and altitude

ORIFICE SIZE FOR 23,000 BTUH GAS FIRED BURNER				
Altitude	0 – 7,000	7,001 – 11,000	0 – 7,000	7,001 – 9,000	9,001 – 11,000
Type of Gas	LP	LP	Natural	Natural	Natural
Orifice Size	#55	#56	#43	#44	#45

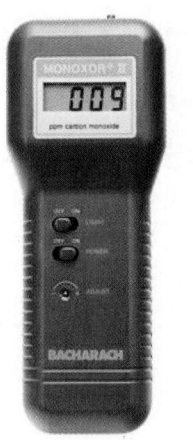

Figure 85-19 Carbon monoxide tester can read the level of CO in the flue gas

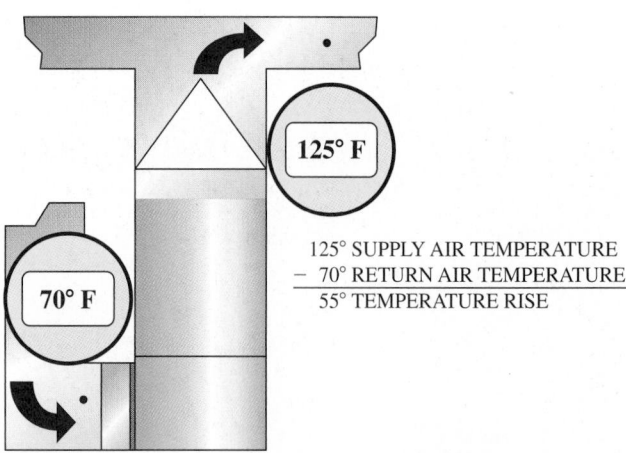

125° SUPPLY AIR TEMPERATURE
− 70° RETURN AIR TEMPERATURE
55° TEMPERATURE RISE

Figure 85-20 Temperature rise is the difference between the supply of return air temperatures

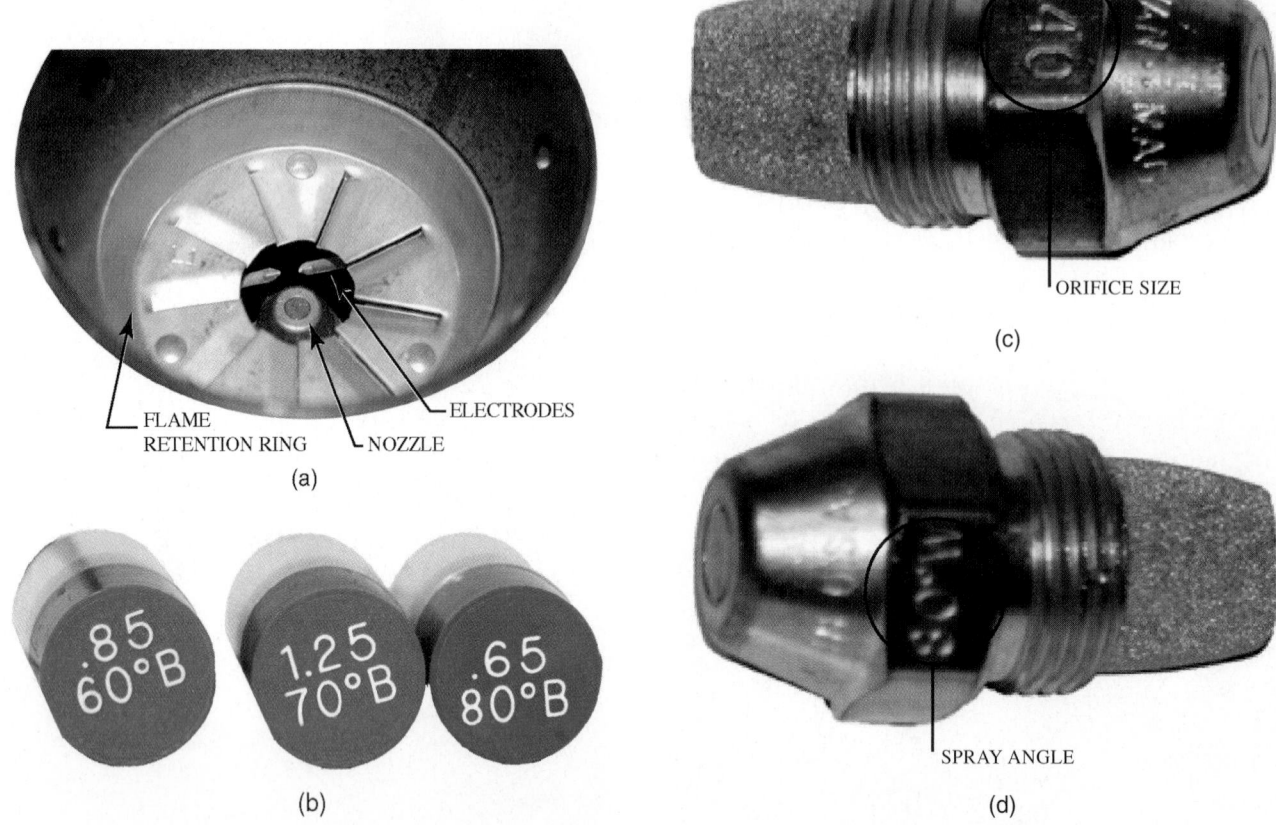

(a)

(b)

(c)

(d)

Figure 85-21 (a) Nozzle, electrodes, and air; (b) Various sizes and types of nozzles; (c) Nozzle size is stamped on the nozzle; (d) Nozzle angle is stamped on the nozzle

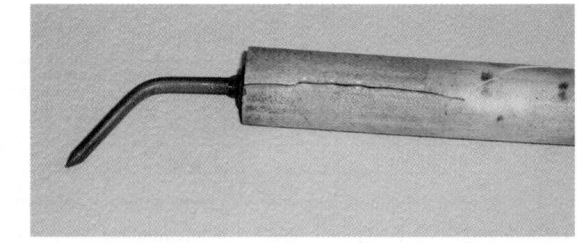

Figure 85-22 Cracks in the electrode porcelain can allow spark to arc at unwanted places and reduce the arc available at the electrode tip
(Courtesy of HVAC Department, Terra Community College, Fremont, Ohio)

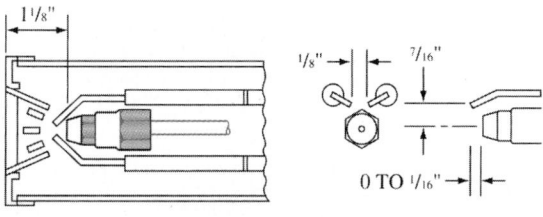

BECKET A-6 BURNER

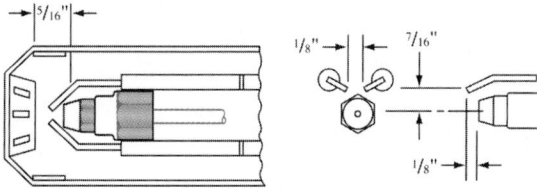

WAYNE MSR-6 BURNER

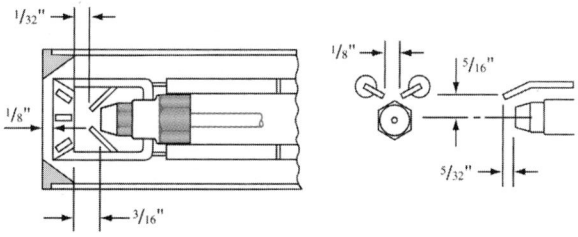

ABC/SUNRAY FC-134 BURNER

Figure 85-23 Oil burner electrode spacing dimensions
(Courtesy of Rheem Manufacturing Air Conditioning Division)

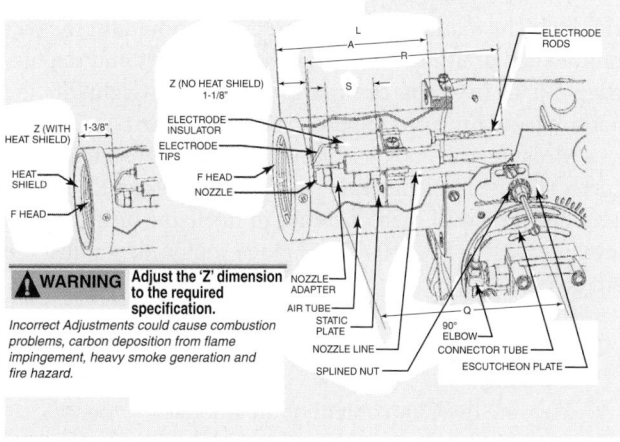

Figure 85-24 The "Z dimension" is the distance from the tip of the nozzle to the face on the burner head; an incorrect setting can cause incomplete combustion
(Courtesy of © R.W. Beckett Inc.)

Figure 85-25 The drive coupling makes the connection between the oil pump motor and the oil pump
(Courtesy of HVAC Department, Terra Community College, Fremont, Ohio)

Figure 85-26 Accumulated dirt and soot on the cad cell can keep it from seeing the flames
(Courtesy of HVAC Department, Terra Community College, Fremont, Ohio)

The vent system should be inspected for loose connections, signs of corrosion, or rust. The barometric damper should move freely, Figure 85-27.

Look to make sure adequate combustion air is provided. Find the name plate and write down the temperature rise and the minimum and maximum operating voltages. Check the incoming voltage to see if it falls between the minimum and maximum voltage.

Operational Check

To correctly adjust the burner it will be necessary to measure the oil pump pressure, stack temperature, and carbon diox-

Figure 85-29 The oil pressure is increased by turning the adjusting screw clockwise, and decreased by turning it counterclockwise
(Courtesy of HVAC Department, Terra Community College, Fremont, Ohio)

Figure 85-27 The barometric damper maintains the correct over fire draft in an oil furnace
(Courtesy of HVAC Department, Terra Community College, Fremont, Ohio)

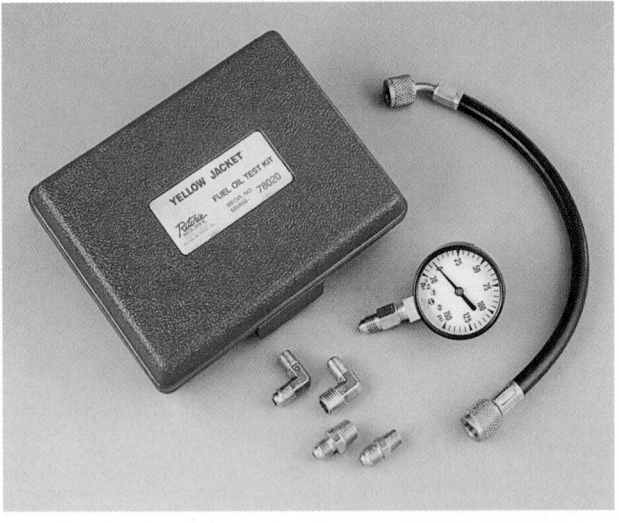

Figure 85-28 This fuel oil test kit can be used to check the operation oil pump pressure
(Courtesy of Ritchie Engineering Company, Inc.—YELLOW JACKET Products)

ide flue gas percentage. Install a pressure gauge on the pressure port of the oil pump, Figure 85-28.

Look in the manufacturer's literature or on the oil burner for the correct pump pressure. The most common pressure has been 100 psig for many years. However, most recent oil burners operate at higher pressures, 140–170

psig. Start the burner and compare the oil pump pressure to the recommended pressure. If the pressure is not correct, turn the adjusting screw clockwise to increase pressure or counterclockwise to decrease pressure, Figure 85-29.

The operation of the barometric damper should be checked. The manufacturer's instructions should list the recommended draft pressure between the damper and the furnace, −0.02 in wc is common. Adjust the weight on the barometric damper to achieve the correct draft.

Measure the smoke spot and the CO_2 percentage. The correct flame should have no smoke and a CO_2 level between 10% and 12.5%. If there is smoke in the flame or if the CO_2 level is outside of the 10–12.5% range you need to adjust the air. To do this:

1. Adjust the air inlet vane until you see a trace of smoke in the flame.
2. Measure the CO_2 content of the flue gas.
3. Open the air until you have lowered the CO_2 by 1 or 2%.
4. The correct flame should have no smoke and CO_2 between 10% and 12.5%.

Ideally the combustion efficiency should be measured and the flue gas should be checked for carbon monoxide. Measure the stack temperature and subtract the equipment ambient temperature from it to get the net stack temperature. The combustion efficiency can be calculated using the CO_2 percentage, the net stack temperature, and a combustion efficiency slide rule. The flue gas should have no carbon monoxide, but trace amounts of up to 50 ppm are acceptable.

Figure 85-30 The temperature and pressure relief valve is an extremely important safety item; it opens to relieve excessive pressure, preventing boiler explosion

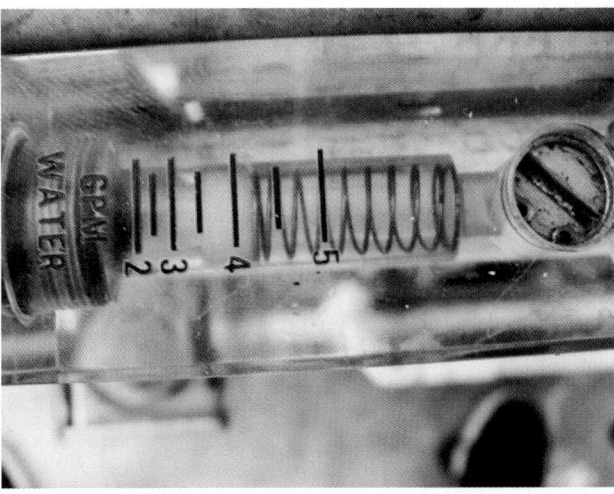

Figure 85-31 This system's water flow can easily be checked by looking at this water flow meter

Check the temperature rise and blower current draw once the indoor blower comes on.

85.8 HYDRONIC HEATING

One advantage of hydronic heating systems is their low maintenance requirements. Maintenance can be divided into three general areas:

- Boiler.
- Pump and controls.
- Piping, radiators, and convectors.

Hydronic boilers do not really boil the water; they are more like efficient hot water heaters for nonpotable water. The temperature-pressure relief valve should be checked annually, Figure 85-30.

Pull the lever on top of the valve and water should come out the discharge pipe connected to the temperature-pressure valve. Take caution, because this releases scalding hot water under pressure. Keep away from the discharge outlet and do not stand directly in front of the valve. The remaining maintenance requirements vary depending upon the fuel the boiler uses. They can operate on electricity, fuel oil, or gas.

Electric Boilers

Electric boilers require the least amount of maintenance because there is no combustion process. Because they use large amounts of current, the power source, all controls, and connections should be checked annually. Visually check for overheated wires and wire connections. Measure the element voltage and compare it to the name plate voltage and the

actual incoming voltage. Any voltage drop in the circuitry or controls should be located and eliminated. Finally, the current draw of each element should be checked against the name plate rating.

Gas Fired and Oil Fired Boilers

Gas fired and oil fired boilers should have their combustion air, combustion process, and vent system checked. These checks are similar to the checks used on gas and oil furnaces.

Water Pump

A water pump is used in hydronic heating systems to circulate the hot water. The vast majority of the pumps used today in residential systems are maintenance free. They have no seals to leak and they are typically cooled and lubricated by the water they pump. Checking the water pump consists of checking the amount of water it is pumping. This is done two ways. Some systems have water flow indicators that visually show the rate of water flow, Figure 85-31. Unfortunately, many systems do not have a water flow indicator. The other common method of checking the water flow is to measure the pressure drop across the pump and compare it to the pump specifications. This is quite accurate, but requires the pump specifications, Figure 85-32.

Piping and Fluid

The system should be inspected for water leaks. Systems that use a lot of makeup water have leaks. The system water pressure should also be checked, Figure 85-33.

Figure 85-32 Pump performance charts like this one can be used to determine water flow by comparing the pressure drop across the pump to the performance chart *(Courtesy of Taco, Inc., Cranston, Rhode Island)*

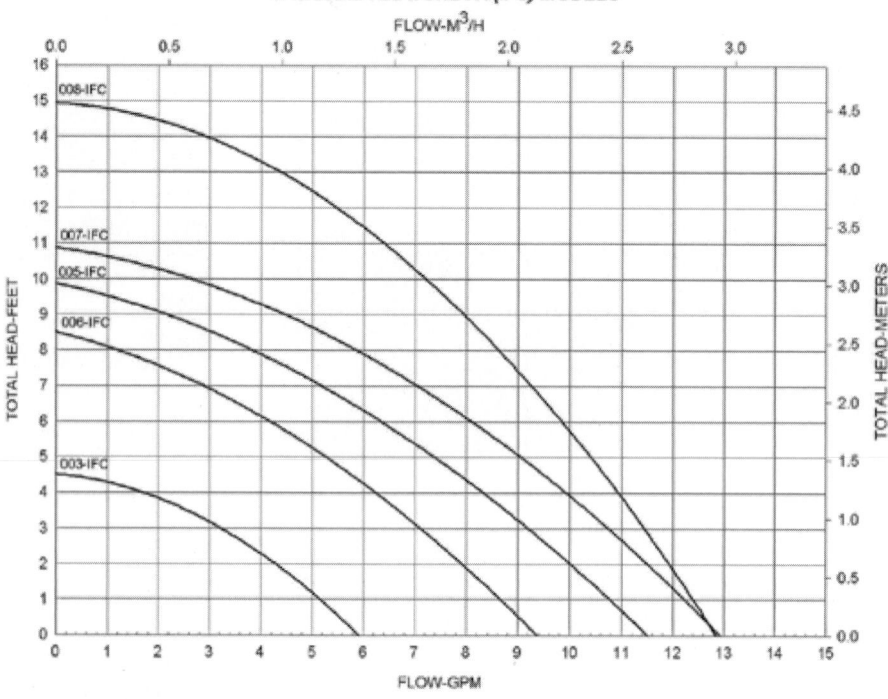

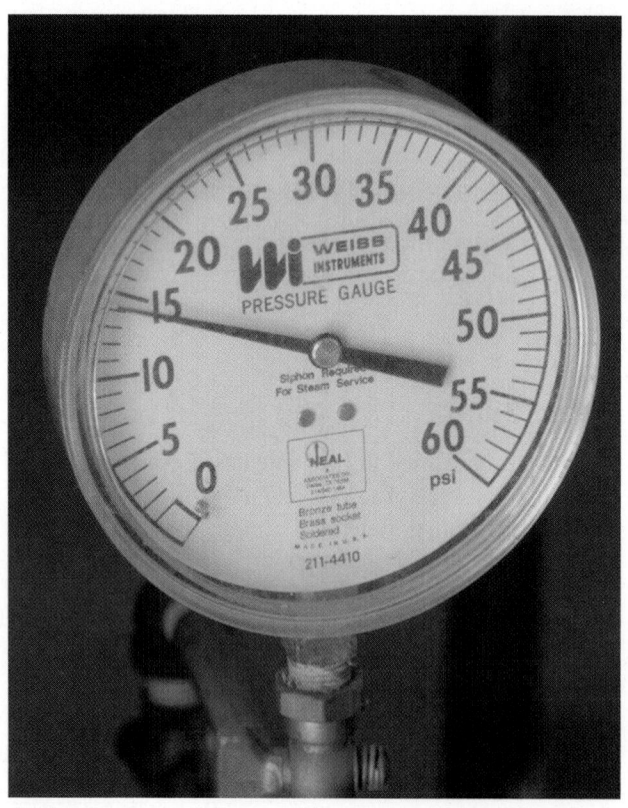

Figure 85-33 This dual pressure-temperature gauge shows both the pressure and temperature of the water loop

Most hydronic systems should be kept at a pressure of 10–20 psig. Below 10 psig systems experience more problems with air entrainment and corrosion. The pressure relief valve on most residential boilers opens at 30 psig, so the loop pres-sure should be kept enough below 30 psig to prevent opening the pressure relief valve.

Most hydronic systems are closed loops and use glycols and corrosion inhibitors in the water. The water pH level should be checked to ensure it is not corrosive to the system piping and components. This can be done with a pH meter, Figure 85-34.

Generally the pH should be between pH 8.5 and pH 10.5. The fluid's pH drops as the inhibitors wear. Adding inhibitor increases the water pH level. Check with the boiler manufacturer for the correct glycol and inhibitor solutions for the system.

TECH TIP

Generally speaking it is not a good idea to use automotive antifreeze. The inhibitors added are specific to the types of materials in the system. Because automobile engines contain different materials than hydronic heating systems, the antifreeze formulation is different.

85.9 HEAT PUMPS

During a heat pump planned service call, the cooling, heating, defrost, auxiliary heat, and emergency heat cycles should all be checked whenever possible. However, most heat pump systems should not be operated in the cooling cycle at temperatures below 50°F or in the heating and defrost cycles at temperatures above 70°F.

Cooling Cycle

In cooling, heat pumps are functionally very similar to air conditioning systems. Checking a heat pump in the cooling

Figure 85-34 A pH meter like this one can be used to check the water pH
(Courtesy of Extech Instruments Corporation)

cycle is essentially the same as checking an air conditioning system.

Heating Cycle

The routine maintenance for the heating cycle is also similar to air conditioning.

- Clean or change the air filter.
- Clean the outdoor coil.
- Check the indoor coil.
- Lubricate the motors.

The operational check should include:

- Amp draw of all motors.
- Airflow.
- Low side and high side pressures.
- Superheat and subcooling.
- Temperature rise across the indoor coil.

HEATING CHECK CHART FOR R-22 AIR SOURCE HEAT PUMP								
INDOOR TEMPERATURE	PRESSURE	OUTDOOR TEMPERATURE						
		60°F	50°F	40°F	30°F	20°F	10°F	0°F
60°F	HIGH	217	201	186	170	154	139	123
	LOW	68	50	41	53	35	27	17
70°F	HIGH	248	230	213	195	178	161	143
	LOW	71	62	53	44	36	27	17
80°F	HIGH	279	260	241	222	203	185	166
	LOW	74	65	55	46	36	27	17

USE OF CHART
Table indicates whether a correct relationship exists between system operating pressure and air temperature entering indoor and outdoor units. If pressure and temperature do not match on chart, system refrigerant charge may not be correct or other system abnormalities may exist. Do not use table to adjust refrigerant charge.

CHARGING
When charging is necessary during heating season, remove any refrigerant remaining in system, evacuate and recharge by weight. Weigh in total charge as indicated on unit rating plate. Rating plate charge is for systems with 15 ft. line-set. Adjust charge at rate of 0.6 oz/ft of 3/8" liquid line over 15 ft.

Figure 85-35 A check chart is used to check the heating operation but it is not used for adjusting the charge

Determining the correct charge in the heating cycle can be tricky because the system capacity varies with the operating conditions. Typically the heating capacity of most air source heat pumps at 45°F is similar to their cooling capacity at 95°F. But their heating capacity at 17°F is just a little more than half that. There is also about half the amount of refrigerant circulating. Manufacturers have different ways of handling this. It is essential that the equipment manufacturer's charge checking method be used for accurate results. The most common methods of checking the heating cycle operation are:

- Temperature rise across the indoor coil.
- Pressure-temperature charts, Figure 85-35.
- Subcooling, Figure 85-36.
- Ambient temperature approach, Figure 85-37.
- Suction superheat, Figure 85-38.
- Discharge line temperature.

The **temperature rise** method can be applied to any unit if you know the indoor airflow and the specified system Btu/hr capacity at the current outdoor temperature.

The expected temperature rise can be calculated using the formula

$$\text{temp rise} = \text{Btu}/(\text{CFM} \times 1.08)$$

The chart in Table 85-1 shows a calculated temperature rise for single speed systems whose airflow is 400 CFM per ton. The percentage capacity used for the calculations is shown in Table 85-1.

Some manufacturers provide heating cycle check charts. These are used to check the system pressures at specific operating conditions, but are not intended for use in charging systems. This is because it is possible to have enough refrigerant in the system to operate correctly at 25°F and still be

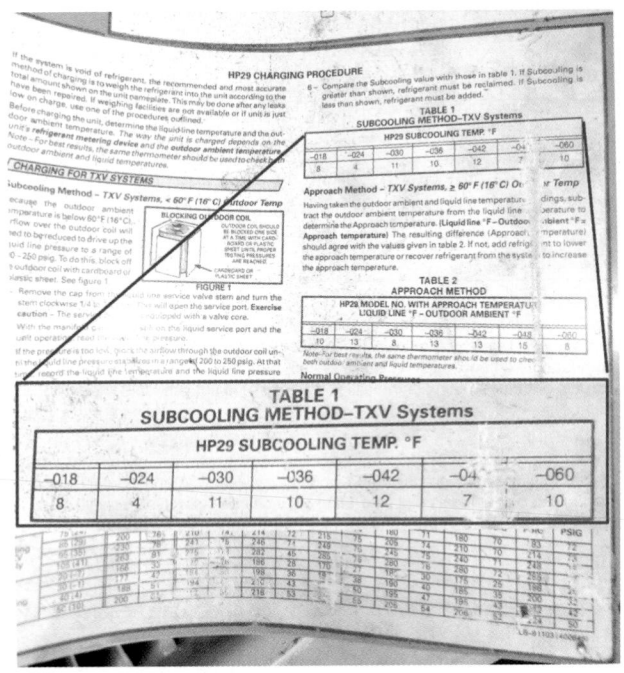

Figure 85-36 The charge may be checked using subcooling when the temperature is below 60°F: operate the unit in cooling and block the condenser to raise the liquid pressure to 200–250 psig (R-22)

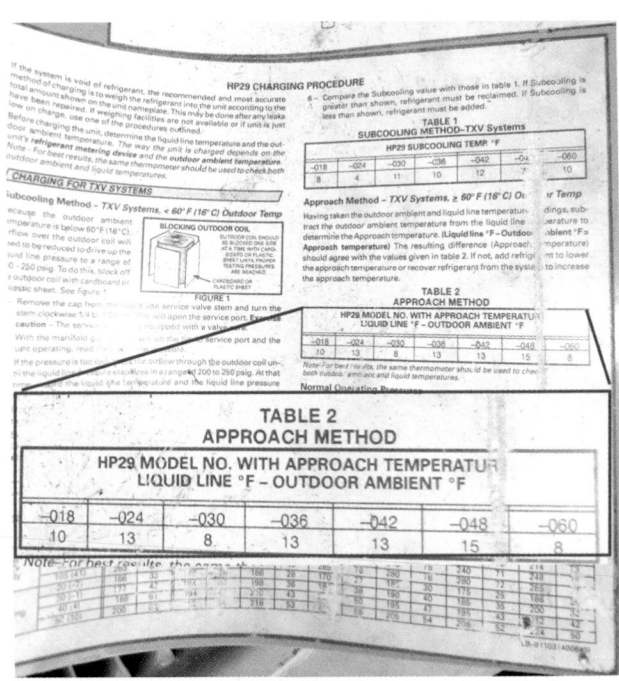

Figure 85-37 The approach method compares the outdoor temperature to the liquid line temperature while operating in cooling; the ambient temperature must be above 60°F

Superheat at Compressor Suction in Heating Operation

Figure 85-38 This chart gives the system's suction superheat in the heating cycle

Indoor Temperature	Outdoor Ambient Temperature							
	-10°F	0°F	10°F	20°F	30°F	40°F	50°F	60°F
55°F	NR	6	8	10	13	20	27	37
70°F	NR	NR	NR	NR	5	12	20	30
80°F	NR	NR	NR	NR	NR	8	16	26

Note: Chart values assume design airflow over both indoor and outdoor units

Table 85-1 Outdoor Temperature

	0°F	10°F	20°F	30°F	40°F	50°F
Temperature rise	9	11	14	18	23	28
Percent nominal capacity	33%	40%	50%	65%	82%	100%

undercharged at 45°. Typically these charts give you an expected high and low side pressure range for specific outdoor ambient temperatures.

The **discharge line temperature** method is used by one major manufacturer. It compares the discharge line temperature to the outdoor temperature. The discharge line temperature should be 110°F hotter than the outdoor ambient temperature. For example, a system operating in a 40°F ambient should have a discharge line temperature of 150°F: 40°F + 110°F = 150°F.

85.10 COIL MAINTENANCE

Air Cooled Condensers

Dirty condenser coils restrict airflow, raise the condenser temperature and pressure, reduce efficiency, and shorten equipment life, Figure 85-39. Air cooled condensers should be cleaned annually regardless of how clean they appear. A coil that appears clean can have dirt packed inside the fins where you cannot see.

Figure 85-39 Dirty air cooled condensers are a common problem

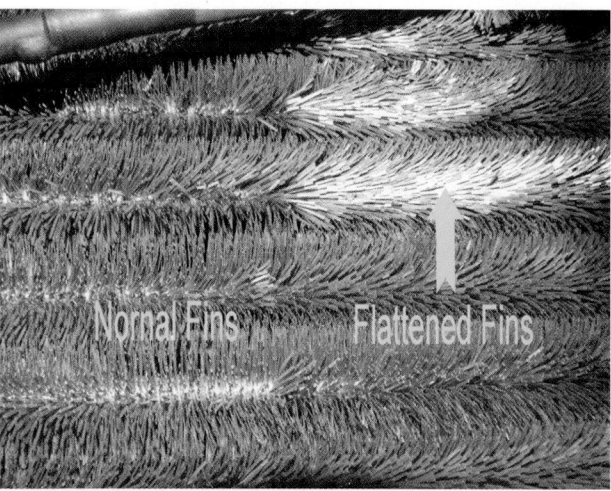

Figure 85-41 Be careful when cleaning spiney fins; they can be easily crushed

Always follow the equipment manufacturer's recommendations when selecting cleaning agents. Cleaning with the wrong chemicals or applying the chemicals incorrectly can do more harm than good. In particular, check that you have properly diluted the coil cleaner, Figure 85-40.

Many types of coil cleaner are sold concentrated and must be diluted with water before using. Care should be taken to rinse the coils thoroughly so that no cleaning chemicals remain on the coil. For spiney-fin coils that have the fins wrapped around the tubes, the amount of pressure used to apply both the cleaner and the water needs to be very low. These fins are quite thin and will crush easily. Flattening the fins essentially does the same thing as having them matted with dirt; the airflow is restricted, Figure 85-41. These coils cannot be straightened with a fin comb, so damaged coils are nearly impossible to repair.

Air Conditioning Evaporator Coils

Air conditioning evaporator coils should be protected by an air filter. You should always clean or replace the indoor air filter when servicing an air conditioner. If this filter is cleaned or changed regularly, then the evaporator will usually stay clean. If possible, you should visually inspect the evaporator to make certain that it is clean, but it is not necessary to clean the evaporator every year. However, if the filters are not kept clean, the evaporator can become matted with dirt, Figure 85-42.

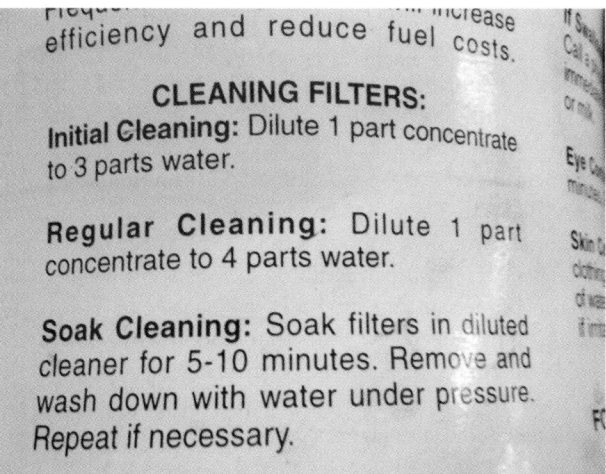

Figure 85-40 Make sure to dilute coil cleaner according to the manufacturer's directions

Figure 85-42 Dirty evaporators are a common problem that is often misdiagnosed as a refrigerant undercharge
(Courtesy of Nu-Calgon Wholesaler Inc. www.nucalgon.com)

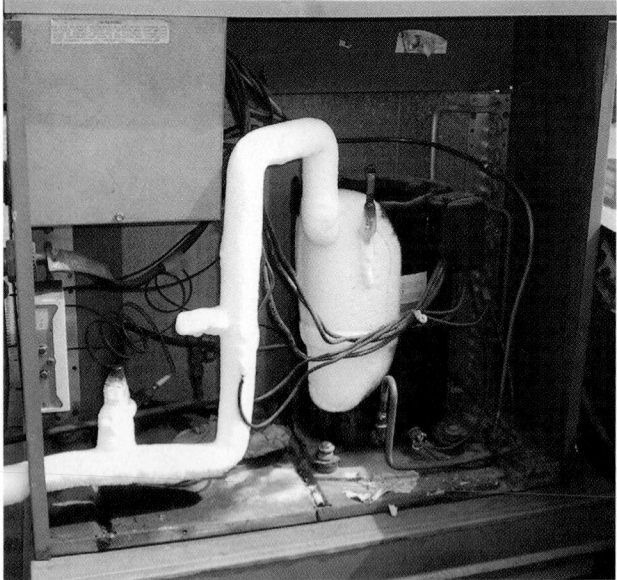

Figure 85-43 If a unit continues to operate after the evaporator coil freezes, the ice will travel down the suction line and even up onto the compressor
(Courtesy of HVAC Department, Terra Community College, Fremont, Ohio)

Since the evaporator is usually wet when it runs, dirt sticks to it. In severe cases this can reduce the airflow to the point that the evaporator freezes up. A frozen coil can be spotted by the ice around the suction line leaving the coil. If the unit runs long enough with a frozen evaporator, the suction line will freeze all the way back to the compressor, Figure 85-43.

The side of the coil that needs cleaning is where the air enters the coil. After removing the access door on an evaporator casing, what is usually visible is the side of the coil where the air leaves. You may have to remove interior sheet metal, cut into ductwork, or even entirely remove the evaporator coil to gain access to the side that needs cleaning, Figure 85-44.

Obviously it is easier to keep the coil clean in the first place! Another complication when cleaning evaporator coils is controlling the mess that is made. Condensers are usually outside, so the resulting mess is not as critical. But evaporators are normally inside and it just is not feasible to wash it down with a garden hose. Some cleaners are designed to be rinsed by the water that condenses on the evaporator as it operates. However, you should check with the equipment manufacturer before using them. A hand pump chemical sprayer is practical way to apply coil cleaner and control the amount and direction of the water spray when rinsing the coil.

To clean the evaporator coil you should:

1. Remove any visible dirt accumulation with a stiff brush.
2. Apply a properly diluted coil cleaner to both sides of the coil.
3. Thoroughly rinse the coil starting from the leaving air side.

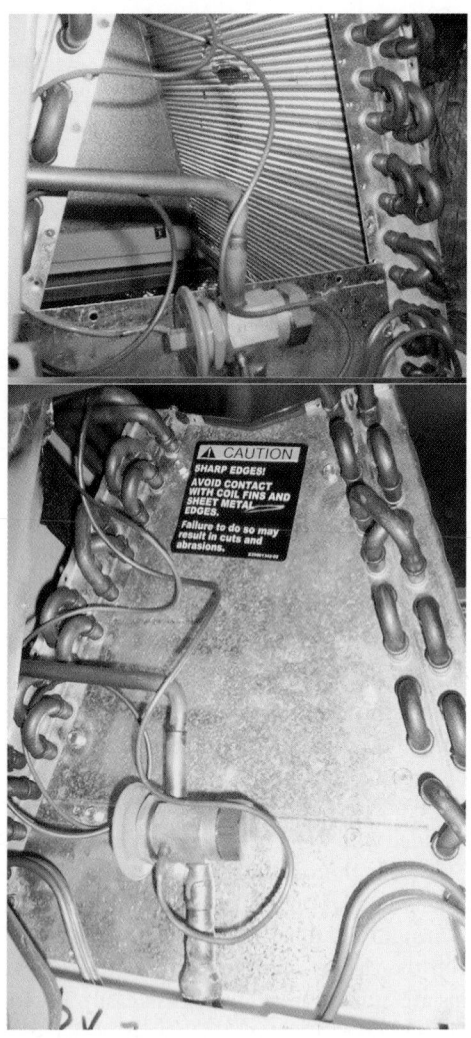

Figure 85-44 The triangle end plate must be removed from the coil to gain access to the underside of the coil where dirt collects

There are methods for cleaning the coil from the leaving air side. But without seeing the results, you cannot be certain you have properly completed the job. These methods include high-pressure air to blow backwards through the coil and chemical foams that are applied to the leaving air side. One problem with blowing the dirt off and leaving it is that the dirt is still there and could be trapped in the coil again. The foam cleaner works by expanding and pushing the dirt out the other way. The water condensing on the coil when the unit operates is then supposed to rinse off the foam.

Even though the evaporator coil does not always need cleaning, the drain pan and drain line usually do. The quickest and most effective way to clean a drain pan and drain is with a tool that uses air pressure or nitrogen pressure to create suction. This lets you suck the water and slime out of the drain pan and drain, Figure 85-45.

Water Coils

Systems that have water circulating in open loops should have the water checked weekly. Any water that is open to the air will grow things, Figure 85-46.

Figure 85-47 Example of mineral deposits on an ice machine water float

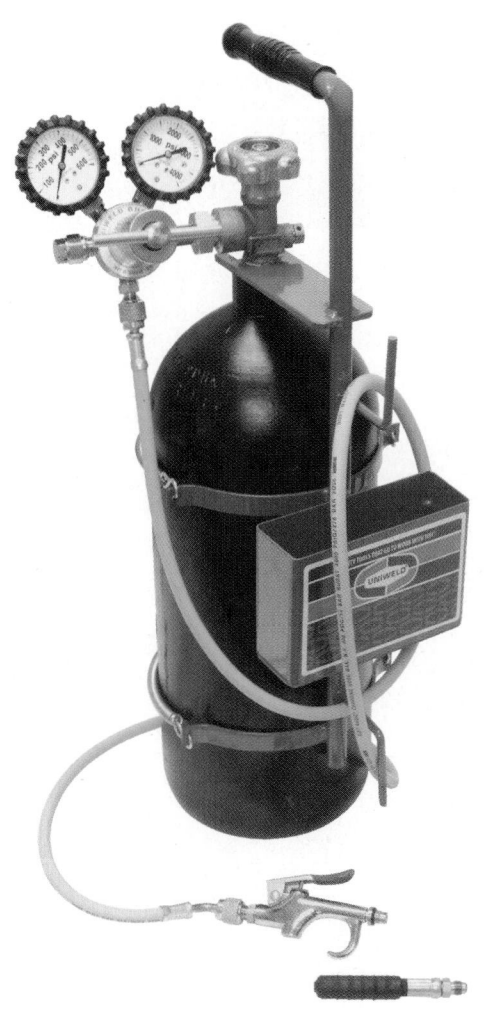

Figure 85-45 A sludge sucker can be used to clear a drain line from the outside
(Courtesy of Uniweld Products, Inc.)

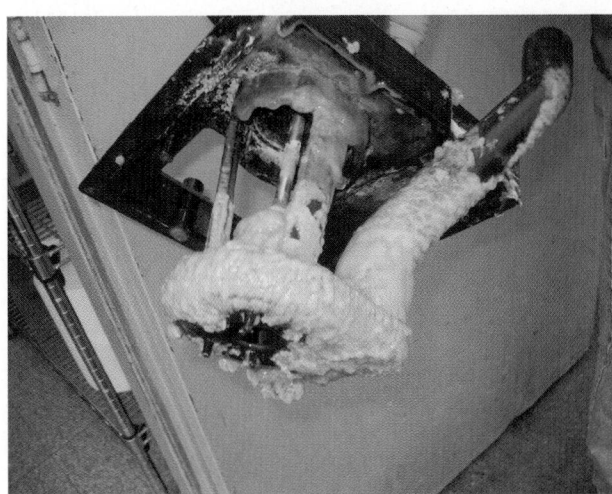

Figure 85-46 Example of ice machine slime collected around the base of the water base
(Courtesy of Mr. Ice Machines and Air Conditioning)

From ice machines to high temperature water jacketed heat exchangers; if the water is open to the air something will grow in the water. Evaporation of water in open loop systems leads to increased mineral concentration in the water. This leads to salting or calcification of all the water handling parts, Figure 85-47.

This can be controlled with regular maintenance. Regular maintenance on the water side of systems typically consists of testing the water and adding chemicals as needed to prevent biological fouling and mineral scaling. Regular cleaning is necessary for systems such as ice machines where chemicals cannot be present in the water during normal operation. Most ice machines should be cleaned monthly.

85.11 MAINTENANCE OF ELECTRONIC AIR FILTERS

Service on electronic air cleaners consists of:

1. Inspecting the air cleaner cells.
2. Checking the operation of the air cleaner.
3. Cleaning the prefilter.
4. Cleaning the collector plates.

Inspection

Turn off the power to the air cleaner. Normally there is a switch on the door or on top of the air cleaner. Most air cleaners have power indicator lights that will show when power is on. Remove the access door on the side of the air cleaner. The cells will slide out. Typically there will be one or two cells. Pay careful attention to how the cells are oriented so that you can reinsert them correctly. Many have arrows showing the direction of airflow or keyways to prevent misalignment, Figure 85-48.

Figure 85-48 The arrow on the side of the air cleaner cell indicates the airflow direction

Figure 85-49 The light at the top right is lit to indicate that the air cleaner is energized
(Courtesy of HVAC Department, Terra Community College, Fremont, Ohio)

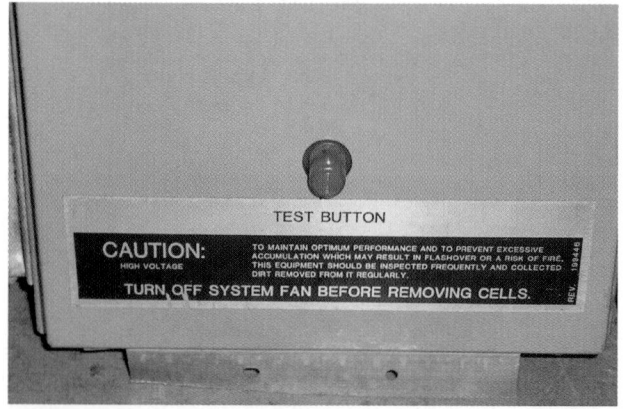

Figure 85-50 Pushing the test button at the bottom produces a snapping sound to indicate that the air cleaner is working
(Courtesy of HVAC Department, Terra Community College, Fremont, Ohio)

Visually check the fine wires on the front of the cells. There should be no loose wires. Reinsert the cells for the operational check.

Operational Check

Many electronic air cleaners have test buttons and/or test lights to indicate that the air cleaner is operating correctly. The test lights are wired to a transformer and tuned circuit in the air cleaner. They light when the air cleaner power supply is operating correctly, Figure 85-49.

The test button temporarily shorts across the positive and negative plates. This causes a loud zapping noise that indicates the air cleaner is working, Figure 85-50.

Do not try to short across the plates with anything else. The plates have 8,000 V DC on them and touching them during operation would literally be a shocking experience!

Some air cleaners have circuits that detect airflow and automatically energize the cells when airflow is detected. These usually have lights indicating when airflow is detected, Figure 85-51.

Make sure that the light comes on when the fan comes on and goes off when the fan goes off. These circuits are a common source of problems. If the circuit does not work, check to see that the air sensor tube is not plugged with debris, Figure 85-52.

Prefilter Cleaning

The prefilter is similar to a cleanable 1 in low efficiency air filter. Its job is to collect large dust particles and keep them out of the collector plates. When a large particle does occasionally make it into the air cleaner you will hear a loud zapping noise similar to a bug zapper. The prefilter should be cleaned monthly.

Cleaning the Air Cleaner Cells

The air cleaner cells should be cleaned once a year. They can be cleaned in a dishwasher, or they can be cleaned with coil cleaner and rinsed. They should be allowed to dry before

Figure 85-51 The green light on this air cleaner lights up whenever the air cleaner detects airflow and turns itself on

Figure 85-52 This sensor energizes the air cleaner whenever it senses airflow

being placed back into the air cleaner. It would not be good to apply 8,000 V to a dripping wet metal appliance.

85.12 AIR FILTERS

Air filters for residential systems are available in sizes from 1–5 in, in efficiencies from MERV 1 to MERV 12, and can be disposable or cleanable. The least expensive low efficiency filters are intended to protect your equipment while the higher efficiency filters are intended to protect the equipment and clean the air.

Figure 85-53 Filters have arrows on the sides to indicate the direction of airflow

Disposable 1 in Filters

Most 1 in filters should be changed monthly, including the standard 1 in disposable air filter. Disposable 1 in filters come in several efficiencies. As consumers become more concerned with indoor air quality high efficiency pleated 1 in filters are growing in popularity. Unfortunately, the higher efficiency 1 in disposable filters have a very high pressure drop, even when clean. The system airflow should be checked if lower efficiency 1 in filters are replaced with higher efficiency 1 in filters. It is essential that these filters be changed monthly. The cost of changing the filter monthly is far less than the cost of the extra energy consumed as a result of operating a system with dirty filters. In a worst case scenario, dirty air filters can lead to blocked indoor air coils and dead compressors. The cost of replacing a dead compressor will exceed the cost of replacing filters monthly for several years.

Pay attention to the directional arrows on the filter when inserting an air filter. The arrows point in the direction of airflow. This should be toward the unit, Figure 85-53.

Cleanable 1 in Filters

Most cleanable filters are 1 in thick. Cleanable low efficiency filters include hogs hair, expanded metal, and foam. These should be cleaned monthly. They may require more frequent cleaning in abnormally dirty conditions. Rinsing with water and mild detergent works well for these. Electrostatic air filters are a type of cleanable medium efficiency 1 in filters. These use materials that build up a static charge as air passes over them. Keeping these filters clean is critical. They have a higher pressure drop than standard air filters when they are clean. When they are dirty they restrict airflow to the point that most systems will not operate correctly. They are also very difficult to clean when they have become packed with dirt. These should be cleaned monthly.

High Efficiency Pleated Filters

Pleated disposable filters are available in 4 in and 5 in widths, Figure 85-54. These filters have MERV ratings from 8 to 12. The pleats provide more surface area for the air to pass through, so the filters can use a denser material. This allows

Figure 85-54 The combs in this filter separate the pleats; they must be removed and reinstalled when changing the filter media

Figure 85-55 These shafts are not in alignment; the straight edge does not rest straight across the faces of the pulleys

higher efficiency filtering without imposing large pressure drops. However, they do have a higher pressure drop than low efficiency 1 in filters. Large pleated filters have the added benefit of lasting longer between filter changes. Pleated high efficiency 5 in filters normally only need to be changed every 6 months. Some may go as long as a year depending upon the amount of material in the air. Two types are available, accordion fold filters that are assembled in the field and box filters that have a cardboard support around the pleats. The field assembled filters typically have combs that separate and support the pleats. Assembling these can be tricky if you have not done it before. Pay attention to the way the parts fit together when disassembling the old filter so that you will know how to reassemble the new one. Make certain the arrows indicating the airflow are facing the correct direction.

85.13 BELT-DRIVE ASSEMBLY CHECKING

Belt-drive assemblies are used to drive fans and compressors in commercial equipment. Some older residential equipment used belt drive fans, but residential equipment built after 1970 is all direct drive. When checking a belt-drive assembly you should check:

- Shaft alignment.
- Pulley alignment.
- Shaft bearings.
- Belt condition.
- Belt tension.

Safety

All work on belt-drive systems should be done with the system off and locked out. You should never try to adjust a belt drive system with the power on. An unexpected system startup could cause severe personal injury.

Shaft Alignment

The drive shaft and the driven shaft should be parallel in two axes. This can be checked by viewing the shafts from above and from the side. The shaft centers should be the same distance apart at the front and back of the shaft. Typically the motor mounts are adjustable and any shaft misalignment is corrected through adjustments to the motor mount, Figure 85-55.

Pulley Alignment

The two pulleys should be in line so that a straight edge will lay flat across the outside face of both pulleys, Figure 85-56.

Figure 85-56 These shafts are in alignment; the straight edge rests flat against the faces of the pulleys

Figure 85-57 These pulleys are out of alignment; the belt is pulling to the left

The pulley alignment can also be checked by looking at how the belt leaves the pulleys. If the belt appears to veer to the right or left after leaving the pulley, the pulleys are not properly aligned, Figure 85-57. This can be corrected by loosening the setscrew on the pulley and moving it until the belt comes off the pulley in a straight line.

Bearings

Belt-driven devices have bearings that should be checked and lubricated. Belt-drive fans typically use pillow-block bearings that are lubricated with a small amount of grease added through the grease fittings using a grease gun.

Belt Tension

The correct tension for any belt drive application is the minimum tension required to keep the belt from slipping at its maximum torque. For blowers, this is at startup. Belt manufacturers publish specifications for the design load of their belts, but a belt may not be operating at its maximum design load on any particular application. Tensioning a belt past the required torque can actually shorten its life. If a fan belt does not slip on startup it is tight enough.

Belt drive blowers typically use V-belts. New V-belts need to operate a while to settle in. They need to be retensioned after the first several hours of operation. This requires going back to the job to retension the belt. Some belt manufacturers specify different tensions for new belts and old belts. The new belt tension is higher to allow for the belt settling in. The intent is to avoid going back to retension the belt. Belt tensions should be checked every 6 months, Figure 85-58. There is no single tension specification that is accurate for all belts. The most common method is to check deflection of the belt while applying force to the center of the belt span, Figure 85-59.

Sheave Diameter - Inches
Deflection Force - Lbs.

Belt Cross Section	Smallest Sheave Diameter Range	RPM Range	Super Gripbelts and Unnotched Gripbands		Gripnotch Belts and Notched Gripbands	
			Used Belt	New Belt	Used Belt	New Belt
A,AX	3.0 - 3.6	1000-2500	3.7	5.5	4.1	6.1
		2501-4000	2.8	4.2	3.4	5.0
	3.8 - 4.8	1000-2500	4.5	6.8	5.0	7.4
		2501-4000	3.8	5.7	4.3	6.4
	5.0 - 7.0	1000-2500	5.4	8.0	5.7	8.4
		2501-4000	4.7	7.0	5.1	7.6
B,BX	3.4 - 4.2	860-2500	-	-	4.9	7.2
		2501-4000	-	-	4.2	6.2
	4.4 - 5.6	860-2500	5.3	7.9	7.1	10.5
		2501-4000	4.5	6.7	6.1	9.1
	5.8 - 8.6	860-2500	6.3	9.4	8.5	12.6
		2501-4000	6.0	8.9	7.3	10.9
C,CX	7.0 - 9.0	500-1740	11.5	17.0	14.7	21.8
		1741-3000	9.4	13.8	11.9	17.5
	9.5 - 16.0	500-1740	14.1	21.0	15.9	23.5
		1741-3000	12.5	18.5	14.6	21.6
D	12.0 - 16.0	200-850	24.9	37.0	-	-
		851-1500	21.2	31.3	-	-
	18.0 - 20.0	200-850	30.4	45.2	-	-
		851-1500	25.6	38.0	-	-
3V,3VX	2.2 - 2.4	1000-2500	-	-	3.3	4.9
		2501-4000	-	-	2.9	4.3
	2.65 - 3.65	1000-2500	3.6	5.1	4.2	6.2
		2501-4000	3.0	4.4	3.8	5.6
	4.12 - 6.90	1000-2500	4.9	7.3	5.3	7.9
		2501-4000	4.4	6.6	4.9	7.3
5V,5VX	4.4 - 6.7	500-1749	-	-	10.2	15.2
		1750-3000	-	-	8.8	13.2
		3001-4000	-	-	5.6	8.5
	7.1 - 10.9	500-1740	12.7	18.9	14.8	22.1
		1741-3000	11.2	16.7	13.7	20.1
	11.8 - 16.0	500-1740	15.5	23.4	17.1	25.5
		1741-3000	14.6	21.8	16.8	25.0
8V	12.5 - 17.0	200-850	33.0	49.3	-	-
		851-1500	26.8	39.9	-	-
	18.0 - 22.4	200-850	39.6	59.2	-	-
		851-1500	35.3	52.7	-	-

Figure 85-58 Belt tension chart
(Courtesy of Browning of Emerson Power Transmission Manufacturing)

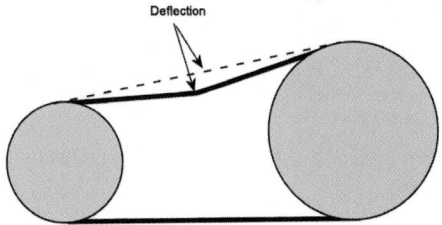

Figure 85-59 Belt tension gauges measure the amount of force required to produce belt deflection

The amount of force and amount of deflection differ from belt to belt. Belt manufacturers publish charts showing the proper amount of force and deflection for any given belt. In general longer belts will have more deflection than shorter belts.

Belt Condition

Belts wear out. They wear out more quickly if the alignment and tension are not correct, but even if all drive components are properly aligned and the belt is properly tensioned, it will still wear out. Worn belts will have one or more of the following characteristics:

- The sides on worn belts are hard and glazed, Figure 85-60.
- Dried and cracked, not soft and pliable.

Figure 85-60 The sides of this belt are shiny and glazed; this belt needs replacing

Figure 85-61 Belts should *not* be installed by rolling them over the pulley

- Deformed sides.
- Frayed.

Belt Replacement

Most belts will last for several years. When it is time to install a new belt it is important to do it correctly. A common, but incorrect method of installing a belt is to roll it over the outside edge of the pulley, Figure 85-61. This can damage the belt and shorten its life. The belt tension adjustment should be loosened until the belt fits easily over the pulley and then retightened after installing the belt. Be sure to check the pulley alignment and belt tension after installing a new belt.

Common Problems and Misconceptions

A sure sign of a belt-drive problem is vibration. Belt vibrations are caused by alignment problems or hardware problems. If the pulleys are misaligned, the belt has to jump over the side of the pulley, causing vibrations. Warped pulleys or shafts can do the same thing. This problem is frequently mistaken as a sign of a loose belt. Tightening the belt reduces the size of the arc in the belt vibration, but does not solve the problem. In fact, tightening a belt that is oscillating may actually increase belt wear.

Loose belts slip, causing a squealing noise. The proper fix is to ensure proper alignment and tighten the belt. Unfortunately a common "remedy" is lubricating the belt or treating it with belt dressing sprays. These only fix the sound. The lubricated belt slips even more, but it does so quietly. Usually just long enough for the technician to leave. Belt dressings are designed to make the belt tacky, and reduce slippage. However, that is also short lived. If the belt is loose it should be tightened; if it has glazed walls it should be replaced.

85.14 SOUND LEVEL MONITORING

Sound level monitoring is one technique used for predictive maintenance. The goal of predictive maintenance is to monitor system behavior, document changes in behavior, and repair or replace components that are on a predictable path toward failure. Machines all have their own sounds. When these sounds change, something has changed about the machine. Ultrasonic sound level meters can be used to hear sounds outside of human hearing. Increased friction leads to increased sound. When a machine changes its tune, it is trying to tell you something.

Ultrasonic detectors measure ultrasound in decibels relative to one millivolt, abbreviated dBmv, Figure 85-62. The ultrasonic output of a bearing should be relatively constant, ± 3–4 dBmv. Small increases in ultrasonic output indicate the need for bearing lubrication. Larger increases warn of the earliest stages of bearing failure.

85.15 LUBRICATION

There is really not a lot to lubricate on most modern heating and air conditioning systems. Only the fan motors need lubricating on most systems. Even many fan motors are now using sealed bearings that cannot be lubricated. Two types of bearings are used: ball bearings and sleeve bearings. Most residential applications use sleeve bearings.

Sleeve bearings are metal bushings whose inside diameter is just a few thousandths of an inch larger than the shaft diameter, Figure 85-63. An oil film separates the shaft from the bearing and the shaft hydroplanes on the bearing. The shaft does not touch the bearing when it is operating. In small motors a packing around the bearing holds oil like a sponge and releases it as the bearing heats up, Figure 84-63.

A slice is taken out of part of the bearing to allow the oil to reach the inside bearing surface, Figure 85-64. This type of bearing is oiled through the oiler ports on the motor, Figure 85-65. Ideally these should be pointing up, but they are sometimes on the side coming off at an angle. They should never be pointing down. Many motors have lubrication instructions on them.

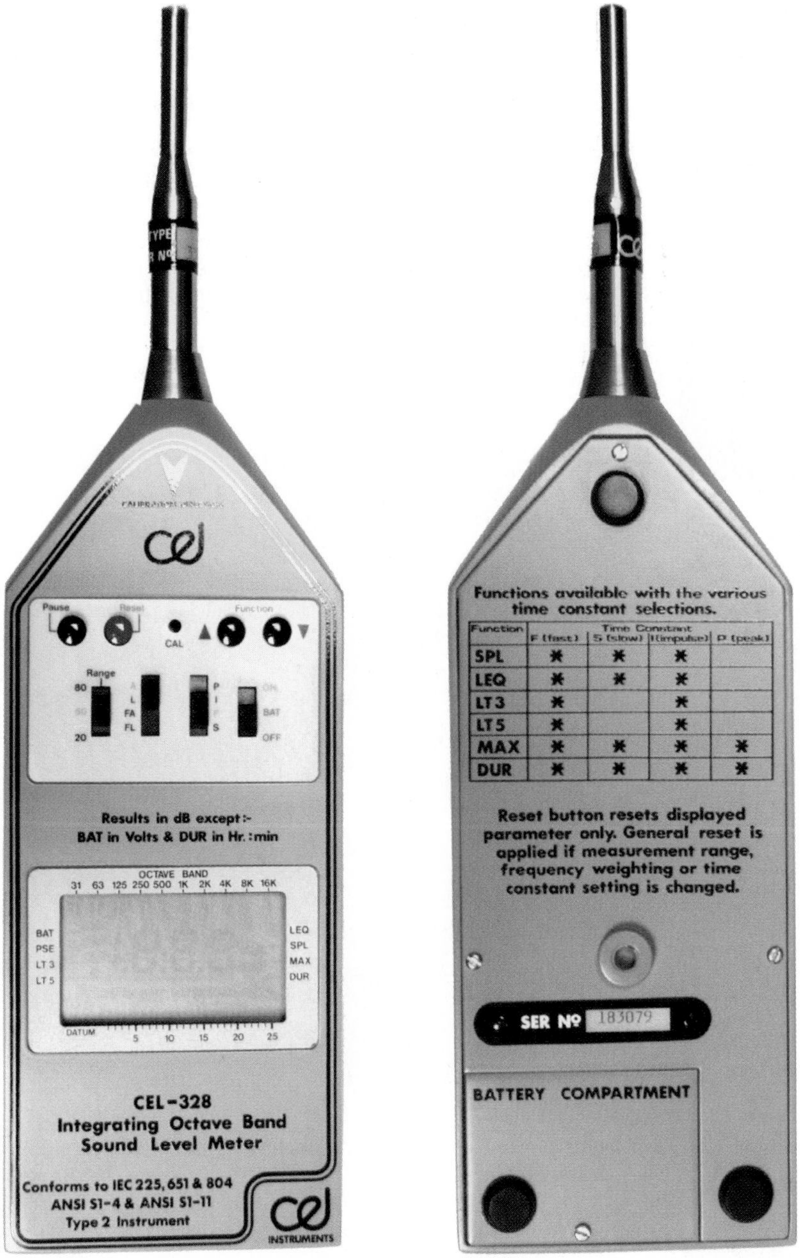

Figure 85-62 Noise dosimeter with data logger

(a)   (b)

Typically they use 5–10 drops of SAE 10 to 20 weight oil. Never use penetrating oils or spray lubricants. They are too thin and the solvents in them can attack the materials in the motor. The time period before the first lubrication is normally longer than subsequent lubrications. The initial operating period before lubrication is often as long as two years. The time between normal lubrications varies from 3 months to a year.

TECH TIP

Do not attempt to oil any part of an electric motor other than at the oiler holes. Spraying oil all around the motor will just accumulate dust faster and contribute to winding breakdown.

Larger motors typically use ball bearings or roller bearings. These are lubricated with grease. The grease should create a film over all the bearing components. It should not fill up all the space in the bearing, Figure 85-66. If the bearing is completely filled with grease, the balls have to push through it. This actually increases the bearing temperature. Further, the grease is whipped up and loses some of its ability to lubricate. Expansion of excess grease will force open the seals in the bearings and destroy the bearing. To lubricate a bearing with grease fittings you should:

1. Open both the fill and drain ports, Figure 85-67.
2. Operate the motor until the bearing is warm.
3. Add the manufacturer recommended amount of grease in the fill port.

Figure 85-63 The sleeve bearing is shown highlighted in blue

Figure 85-64 The slice at the top of the sleeve bearing allows oil to feed into the area between the shaft and the bearing

Figure 85-65 These oiler tubes carry oil to the packing around the sleeve bearing

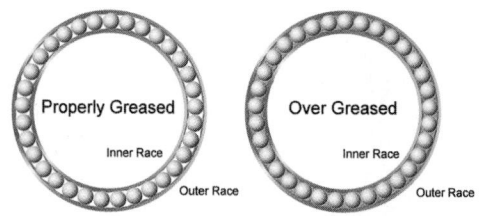

Figure 85-66 A properly lubricated ball bearing should not have grease packed in every space between the ball bearings, but just around the races

Figure 85-67 Many large motors have grease ports for greasing the bearings

4. Operate the motor with the ports still open until the bearing is warm.
5. Replace the port plugs.

If the manufacturer's recommendations are not available, use an ultrasonic tester to listen to the bearing and add small amounts until the bearing noise abates.

SERVICE TIP

A common misconception is that grease should be added until all the old grease is purged and new grease starts to exit the drain port. This will certainly fill all the bearing cavities with grease; thus this procedure is guaranteed to over-grease the bearing and shorten its life.

Troubleshooting Chart

Symptoms of Abnormal Operation	Associated LED Code[2]	Fault Description(s)	Possible Causes	Corrective Action	Cautions and Notes
• Furnace fails to operate. • Integrated control module diagnostic **LED** provides **no signal**.	NONE	• No 115 volt power to furnace, or no 24 volt power to integrated control module. • Blown fuse or circuit breaker. • No signal from thermostat.	• Manual disconnect switch OFF, door switch open, or 24 volt wires improperly connected or loose. • Blown fuse or circuit breaker. • Improper thermostat connection or setting.	• Assure 115 and 24 volt power to furnace integrated control module. • Check integrated control module fuse (3A). Replace if necessary. • Check for possible shorts in 115 and 24 volt circuits. Repair as necessary.	• Turn power OFF prior to repair. • Replace integrated control module fuse with 3A automotive fuse. • Improper thermostat connection or setting.
• Furnace fails to operate. • Integrated control module diagnostic **LED** is lit **continuously**.	ON CONTINUOUS ON	• Integrated control module has an internal fault.	• Integrated control module has an internal fault.	• Replace bad integrated control module.	• Turn power OFF prior to repair. • Read precautions in ìElectrostatic Dischargeî section of manual.
• Furnace fails to operate. • Integrated control module diagnostic **LED** is flashing **ONE** (1) flash.	1 1 FLASH	• Furnace lockout due to an excessive number of ignition ìretriesî (3 total) or ìrecyclesî (5 total)[1].	• Failure to establish flame. Cause may be no gas to burners, front cover pressure switch stuck open, bad igniter or igniter alignment, improper orifices, or coated/oxidized or improperly connected flame sensor. • Loss of flame after establishment. Cause may be interrupted gas supply, lazy burner flames (improper gas pressure or restriction in flue and/or combustion air piping), front cover pressure switch opening, or improper induced draft blower performance.	• Locate and correct gas interruption. • Check front cover pressure switch operation (hose, wiring, contact operation). Correct if necessary. • Replace or realign igniter. • Check flame sense signal. Sand sensor if coated and/or oxidized. • Check flue piping for blockage, proper length, elbows, and termination. • Verify proper induced draft blower performance.	• Turn power OFF prior to repair. • Igniter is fragile, handle with care. • Sand flame sensor with emery cloth. • See ìVent/Flue Pipeî section for piping details.
• Furnace fails to operate. • Integrated control module diagnostic **LED** is flashing **TWO** (2) flashes.	2 2 FLASHES	• Pressure switch circuit is closed. • Induced draft blower **is not** operating.	• Induced draft blower pressure switch contacts sticking. • Shorts in pressure switch circuit.	• Replace induced draft blower pressure switch. • Repair short.	
• Induced draft blower cycles ON for one minute and OFF for three minutes with no further furnace operation. • Integrated control module diagnostic **LED** is flashing **THREE** (3) flashes.	3 3 FLASHES	• Low stage pressure switch circuit does not close in response to induced draft blower operation.	• Pressure switch hose blocked, pinched or connected improperly. • Blocked flue and/or inlet air pipe, blocked drain system, or weak induced draft blower. • Incorrect low stage pressure switch setpoint or malfunctioning switch contacts. • Loose or improperly connected wiring.	• Inspect pressure switch hose. Repair, if necessary, • Inspect flue and/or inlet air piping for blockage, proper length, elbows, and termination. Check drain system. Correct as necessary. • Correct low stage pressure switch setpoint or contact motion. • Tighten or correct wiring connection.	• Turn power OFF prior to repair. • Replace pressure switch with proper replacement part. • Turn power OFF prior to repair. • Replace pressure switch with proper replacement part.

[1]Integrated control module will automatically attempt to reset from lockout after one hour.

Figure 86-6 Typical ignition board fault code from page 40 86-6.pdf Part No. 10759833. From Amana—"Two-stage Variable Speed Gas-Fired Furnace" installation instructions
(Used with permission from Whirlpool Corporation)

R-410A WATER SOURCE HEAT PUMP OPERATING DATA

ENTERING WATER	FLOW GPM	COOLING PERFORMANCE DATA				HEATING PERFORMANCE DATA			
		WATER TEMP RISE	SUCTION PRESSURE	DISCHARGE PRESSURE	AIR TEMP DROP	WATER TEMP DROP	SUCTION PRESSURE	DISCHARGE PRESSURE	AIR TEMP RISE
30°F	5	NR	NR	NR	NR	5-6	72-87	296-361	21-25
	7	NR	NR	NR	NR	3-4	75-92	301-368	22-26
40°F	5	14-17	114-139	155-190	22-27	6-7	88-107	314-384	24-29
	7	10-12	108-132	147-180	23-28	4-5	92-112	321-392	25-30
50°F	5	13-16	116-142	192-234	21-26	7-9	104-127	333-407	27-33
	7	9-12	111-135	182-222	22-27	5-6	109-133	340-415	28-34
60°F	5	13-16	119-146	228-279	21-26	8-10	120-146	352-430	30-37
	7	9-11	113-138	217-265	22-27	6-7	125-153	359-439	32-39
70°F	5	13-15	122-149	262-323	20-25	9-12	136-166	371-453	33-41
	7	9-11	116-142	251-307	21-26	7-8	142-174	378-462	35-43
80°F	5	12-15	125-152	301-368	20-24	11-13	152-185	389-476	36-44
	7	9-11	118-145	286-349	21-26	8-9	159-194	397-485	38-47
90°F	5	12-15	127-156	337-412	19-24	12-15	168-205	408-499	39-48
	7	9-10	121-148	320-392	20-25	8-10	176-215	416-509	41-51

NOTE: CHART VALUES ASSUME 80°F DRY BULB/ 67°F WET BULB ENTERING AIR IN COOLING, 70°F DRY BULB ENTERING AIR IN HEATING.

Figure 86-7 Water source heat pump performance data

86.10 TESTING TO ISOLATE THE CAUSE

Many people think of this part of the process as troubleshooting. Indeed, the majority of a technician's troubleshooting time is spent tracking down the cause of the problem. However, technicians should avoid the temptation to jump straight into solving a problem that is not clearly defined. Jumping straight to determining the cause can waste time by looking for the cause of nonexistent problems.

Proceed from General to Specific

Try to resist the temptation of starting immediately to diagnose specific components. The slowest way to solve a problem is by jumping from one component to the next looking for the specific cause before you have a good idea of exactly what the system is doing. First make sure you understand what the system is supposed to do. Next, determine what the system is actually doing, and then determine what it is doing incorrectly. Once you know what the system is doing wrong, start with more general investigations like system line voltage or control voltage.

The Process of Elimination

The key to determining the root cause in a reasonable amount of time is to follow a logical pattern of investigation and use the process of elimination. You should have a purpose for each test performed. For example, if a system is not operating at all, a logical question is whether or not it has voltage available. Taking a voltage reading at the power source will help decide where to look next. If no voltage is available, then the reason for the loss of power must be investigated. On the other hand, if voltage is present, then it would make sense to look at the controls. Each test should eliminate some avenues of investigation and help narrow the focus of further tests.

86.11 LOGICAL ELECTRICAL TROUBLESHOOTING PROCEDURE

Electrical problems are by far the most common problems encountered in the field. A general procedure for quickly isolating the cause of an electrical failure is to check:

1. Line voltage to the unit.
2. Control voltage.
3. Voltage to the nonfunctional component.
4. Circuit to the nonfunctional component.

Line Voltage to the Unit

A significant number of problems are solved at this point. If the system does not operate at all, check to see that it has the correct voltage. If a fuse is blown or a breaker is tripped, look for the reason. Overload devices can open because of reasons other than problems in the unit, like power interruptions. However, any time a fuse is replaced or a breaker is reset, the operation of the system should be checked carefully. Before operating the system, check all major loads for shorts or grounds and check the main power wire connections. Run the system and check the amp draw on the circuit to the unit and at each major load.

Control Voltage

If a system has no control voltage, the controls can not operate the system. Control voltage can be out because the part of the system that houses the transformer has no line voltage, or it can be an issue with the transformer that supplies the control voltage. If a low voltage fuse is blown, or if the transformer needs replacing, be sure to look for shorts and grounds in the low voltage components. Check the secondary voltage immediately after the fuse or transformer is replaced. If a short is causing the transformer to overheat, the secondary voltage will drop very low, possibly close to 0 V. The transformer cannot take this for more than a few seconds, so it must be recognized immediately. If there are no problems at power up, monitor the secondary voltage while running the system through all its operating cycles.

Voltage to Nonfunctional Component(s)

If there are nonfunctional components and the system has both line voltage and control voltage, the next step is to determine if these components are receiving voltage. At this point, you are trying to determine if the problem is in the component or in the circuit to the component.

If the component is receiving the correct voltage and is not operating, the problem is most likely that component. However, be careful with single phase motors. Most single phase motors have some sort of starting components: run capacitor, start capacitor, or starting relay. Failure of the starting components will keep a single phase motor from operating. It is more common for these starting components to fail than for the actual motors to fail.

If the nonfunctional component is not receiving voltage, the circuit to the component needs to be checked. The most effective method of locating a break in a circuit is a technique called hopscotching.

86.12 HOPSCOTCHING

This technique works by starting at a point where there is correct voltage, and moving one lead at a time from point to point in the circuit toward the nonfunctional load until the voltage is lost. Most circuits put all the controls on one side of a load. Use the schematic diagram to identify all the controls in series with the load and the path that voltage takes to get to the load.

Place the leads at a point in the circuit before the controls, where the correct voltage will be read. Follow the schematic and move the meter lead on the control side of the circuit from one control to the next, checking the voltage in and out of the control. The voltage will drop to 0 immediately after the control that is opening the circuit.

Next, you need to determine why the control is open. For example, if the control is a pressure switch, check the system pressures. If the control is a relay, check to see if the relay coil is receiving voltage. If it is not receiving voltage, then you need to investigate the circuit to the coil using the same hopscotching technique. If the control is receiving the correct input and is not closing, it needs to be replaced.

For example, Figure 86-8 shows the low voltage schematic for an air conditioning unit with a contactor that is not closing. The contactor coil is shown in blue. Three controls are

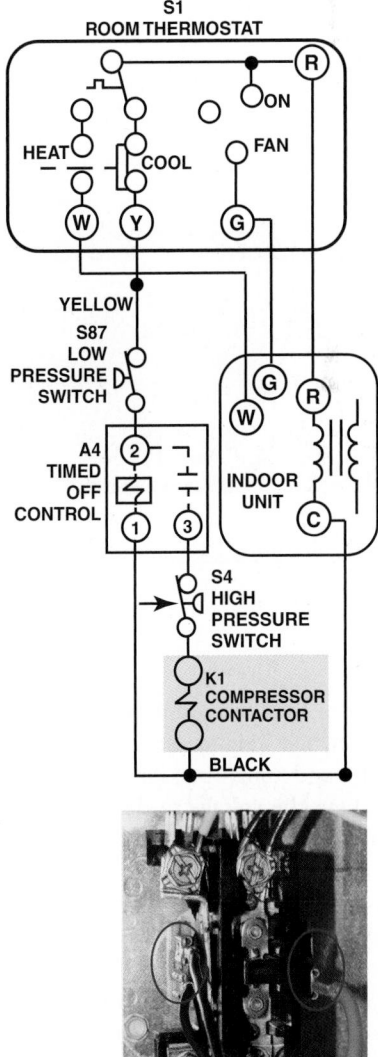

Figure 86-8 Schematic of low voltage circuits in air conditioning condensing unit

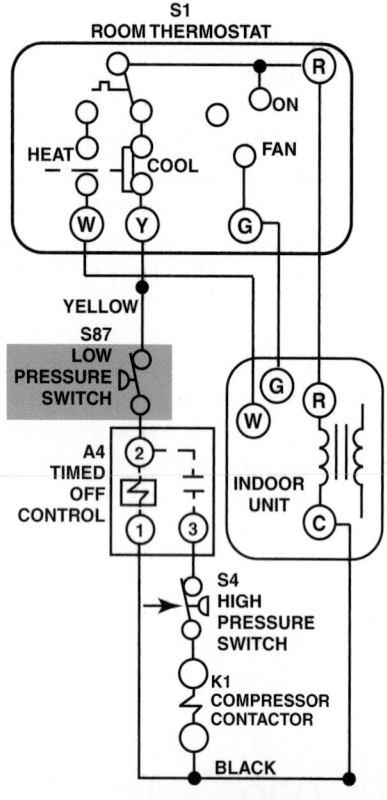

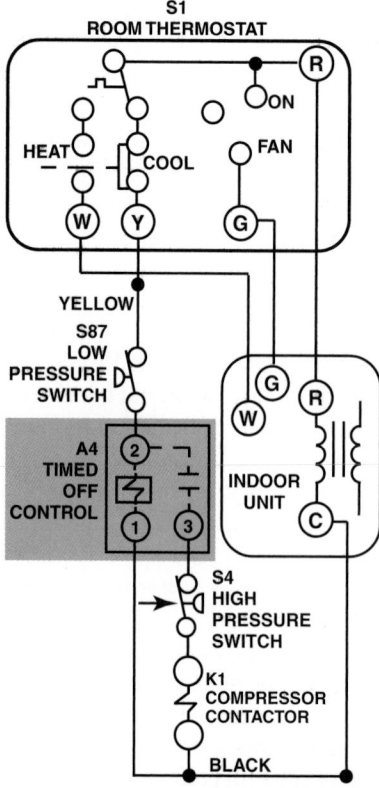

Figure 86-9 The low pressure switch is in series with the contactor coil

Figure 86-10 The timed off circuit board is in series with the contactor coil

in series between the thermostat and the contactor coil: a low pressure switch (Figure 86-9), a timed off control (Figure 86-10), and a high pressure switch (Figure 86-11). Start by checking the voltage to the circuit, Figure 86-12. The meter shows that the unit is receiving a control voltage of 25 V. Place one meter lead on the side of the load that is not fed through controls. In this case, the side of the coil wired with black wires, Figure 86-13. The schematic shows that the first control in the circuit is the low pressure switch, Figure 86-9. We know it is receiving voltage. The low pressure switch feeds the time delay circuit board. Checking voltage at the input of the time delay board will check the voltage leaving the low pressure switch, Figure 86-14. The meter shows that there is 25 V between the low pressure switch and common, indicating that the low pressure switch is not

breaking the circuit. Next, check the voltage leaving the timer, Figure 86-15. The meter shows that there are 25 V at the timer out terminal, indicating that the timer is not breaking the circuit. The diagram shows that the high pressure switch is next in the circuit, Figure 86-11. The leads for the high pressure switch are wired directly to the timer and the contactor coil. The meter reading drops to near 0 V when checking the voltage at the contactor coil, indicating

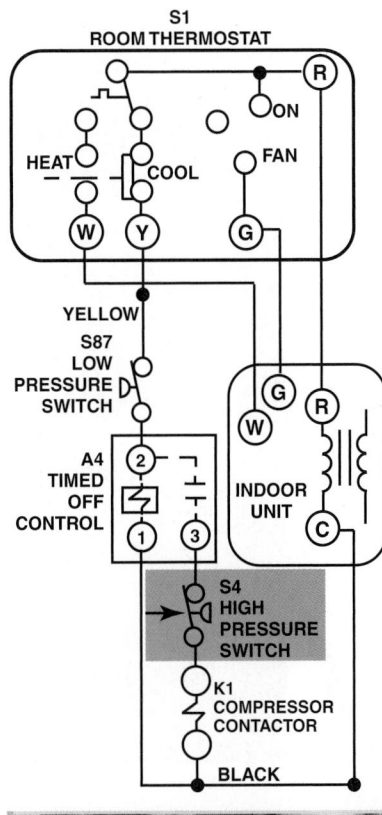

Figure 86-11 The high pressure switch is in series with the contactor coil

its coils. The majority of refrigeration problems can be solved by establishing a proper flow across both the condenser and evaporator.

Once proper flow is established, system operating data can be collected. As always, the best benchmarks are those provided by the manufacturer. However, technicians should be able to recognize many common refrigeration cycle problems even without the manufacturer's data. Many problems can be identified by looking at these system performance indicators:

- Low side pressure.
- High side pressures.
- Suction line temperature.
- Discharge line temperature.
- Liquid line temperature.
- Air or water temperature rise across the condenser.
- Air or water temperature drop across the evaporator.

Four of the most important indicators require a comparison of data:

- Suction line superheat.
- Liquid line subcooling.
- Condenser temperature difference (delta T).
- Evaporator temperature difference (delta T).

Suction line superheat is the difference between the actual suction line temperature and the refrigerant saturation temperature. The saturation temperature is obtained from the suction pressure using a refrigerant pressure-temperature chart. Liquid line subcooling is the difference between the saturation temperature obtained from the discharge pressure using a pressure temperature chart and the actual liquid line temperature.

TECH TIP

Many technical manuals use the word "delta" when talking about the difference in a condition. For example, delta-T is used for temperature difference and delta-P is used for pressure difference. Sometimes the Greek letter delta is used, which looks like a triangle: Δ. So temperature difference is abbreviated as ΔT and pressure difference is abbreviated as ΔP. These are simply shorthand ways of writing temperature difference or pressure difference.

---

that the high pressure switch is open, Figure 86-16. The next step would be to check the system high side pressure to determine whether or not the pressure switch should be open. If the system pressure is high, then the technician should look for causes of high discharge pressure.

86.13 REFRIGERATION CYCLE TROUBLESHOOTING

The first thing to check with any refrigeration problem is the flow across the evaporator and condenser. There is no point in taking pressure and temperature readings on a system that does not have the correct airflow or water flow across one of

The condenser temperature difference is simply the difference between the temperature of the air or water entering the condenser and the temperature of the air or water leaving the condenser. The evaporator temperature difference is the difference between the temperature of the air or water entering the evaporator and the temperature of the air or water leaving the evaporator.

Figure 86-12 Checking the low voltage control signal coming into the unit

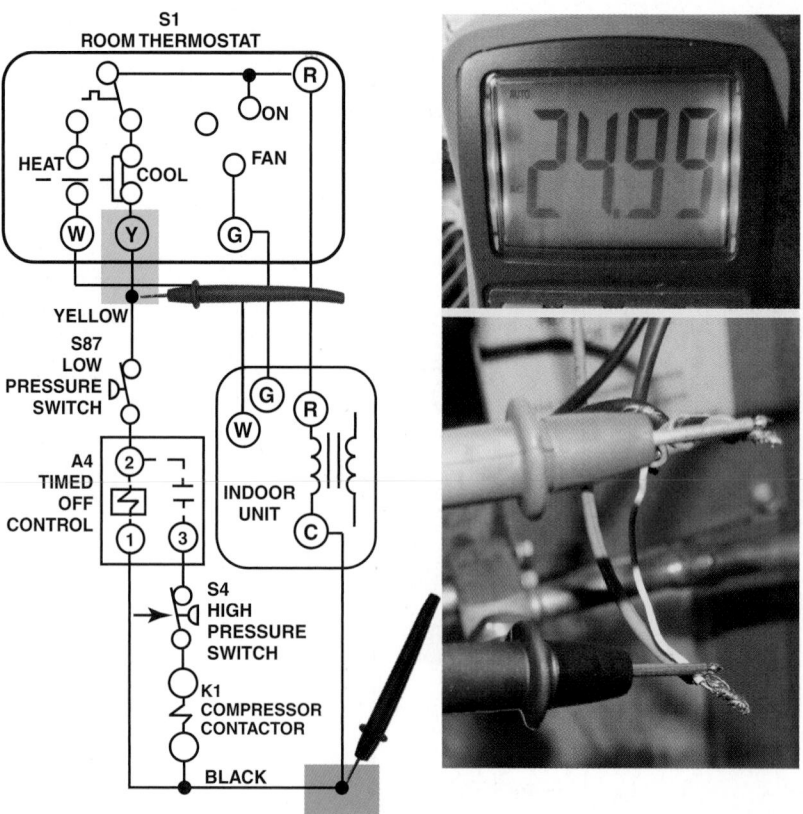

Figure 86-13 The common side of low voltage can be read at the common side of the contactor coil

The chart in Figure 86-17 summarizes the effect common problems will have on the important refrigeration cycle indicators. There are no numbers on the chart, only arrows. The arrows show if a system performance indicator will increase or decrease from normal as a result of a particular problem. The technician still must know what normal is to use the chart.

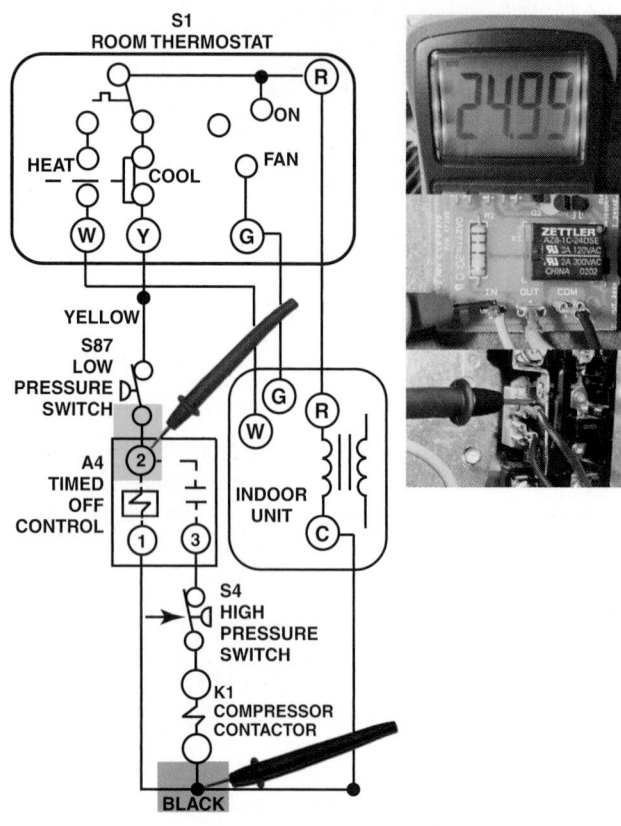

Figure 86-14 Checking the voltage leaving the low pressure switch and entering the timed off board

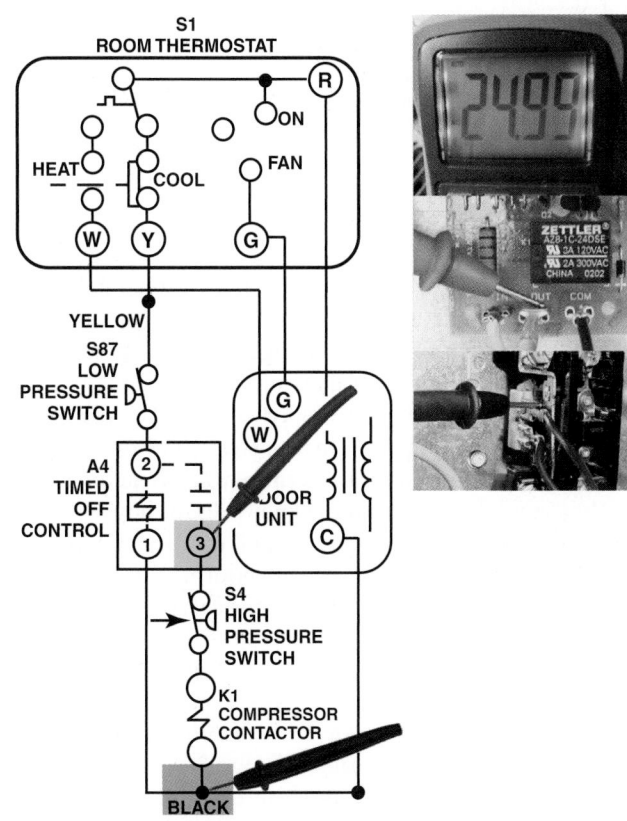

Figure 86-15 Checking the voltage leaving the timed off board and centering the high pressure switch

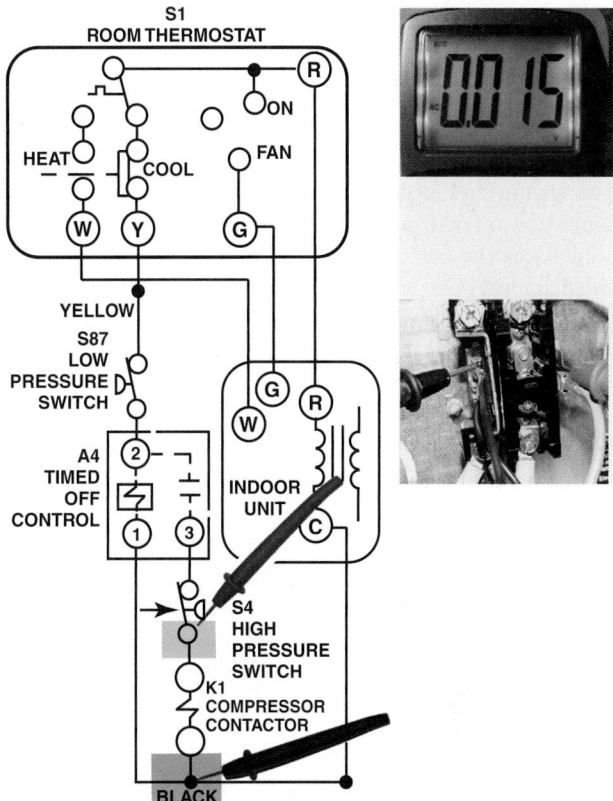

Figure 86-16 Checking the voltage leaving the high pressure switch and entering the contactor coil

Problem	Discharge pressure	Subcooling	Condenser delta T	Suction pressure	Superheat	Evaporator delta T	Compressor amps
Low flow of evaporator air or water	⇓	⇑	⇓	⇓	⇓	⇑	⇓
Dirty evaporator	⇓	⇑	⇓	⇓	⇓	⇑	⇓
Liquid line restriction	⇓	⇑	⇓	⇓	⇑	⇓	⇓
Underfeeding expansion device	⇓	⇑	⇓	⇓	⇑	⇓	⇓
Undercharge	⇓	⇓	⇓	⇓	⇑	⇓	⇓
Low capacity compressor	⇓	⇑	⇓	⇑	⇑	⇓	⇓
Low flow of condenser air or water	⇑	⇓	⇑	⇑	⇓	⇓	⇑
Dirty air cooled condenser	⇑	⇓	⇑	⇑	⇓	⇓	⇑
Scaled water cooled condenser	⇑	⇓	⇓	⇑	⇓	⇓	⇑
Overcharge	⇑	⇑	⇓	⇑	⇓	⇓	⇑
Overfeeding expansion device	⇑	⇓	⇓	⇑	⇓	⇓	⇑

Figure 86-17 Refrigeration cycle troubleshooting chart

86.14 RECOMMENDING CORRECTIVE ACTION

The technician's job is to solve problems, so the customer should be offered at least one solution to their problem. Sometimes the corrective action is obvious. If a part has failed, it must be replaced. However, make sure that you solve the problem and not the symptoms. If a part has failed because of abuse or lack of maintenance, be sure to include correcting the cause of the failure as part of the solution.

When possible, it is best to keep the customer informed as you proceed. They will have a much easier time accepting a large repair bill if they had an opportunity to choose not to implement the repair. Again, understanding how the system works and being able to logically explain your solution are crucial at this point. If the solution being proposed involves replacing parts, be prepared to explain why each of the parts is necessary. If the solution involves customer education, be patient. It is never helpful to be condescending towards customers.

86.15 USING MANUFACTURER'S TROUBLESHOOTING CHARTS

Most manufacturers supply some form of troubleshooting chart in the service manuals for their equipment. These tend to take three general forms: logical troubleshooting flow-charts, lists of common symptoms and causes, and references to fault codes provided by diagnostic LEDs on the system controls.

Logic Flowcharts

A logic flowchart provides pass/fail tests to help guide the technician in using the process of elimination to locate the cause of a system malfunction, Figure 86-18. These charts can be especially useful for determining if proprietary control boards are functioning properly or not. The danger of these troubleshooting aids is that answering one question incorrectly can send you off in an entirely incorrect direction. Technicians who have too little knowledge of how a system actually works may not understand why tests are being performed or even exactly how to perform them. Incorrect readings cause misinterpretation of the chart.

Symptom Lists

Many manufacturers provide a list of common symptoms and their most common causes, Figure 86-19. These troubleshooting aids can help speed up diagnosis of common problems. These are generally easier for people to follow and require less testing. However, it is not really possible to make a complete list of all possible symptoms, or even a complete list of all the possible causes of any particular symptom. Another issue is the temptation to simply go down the list of

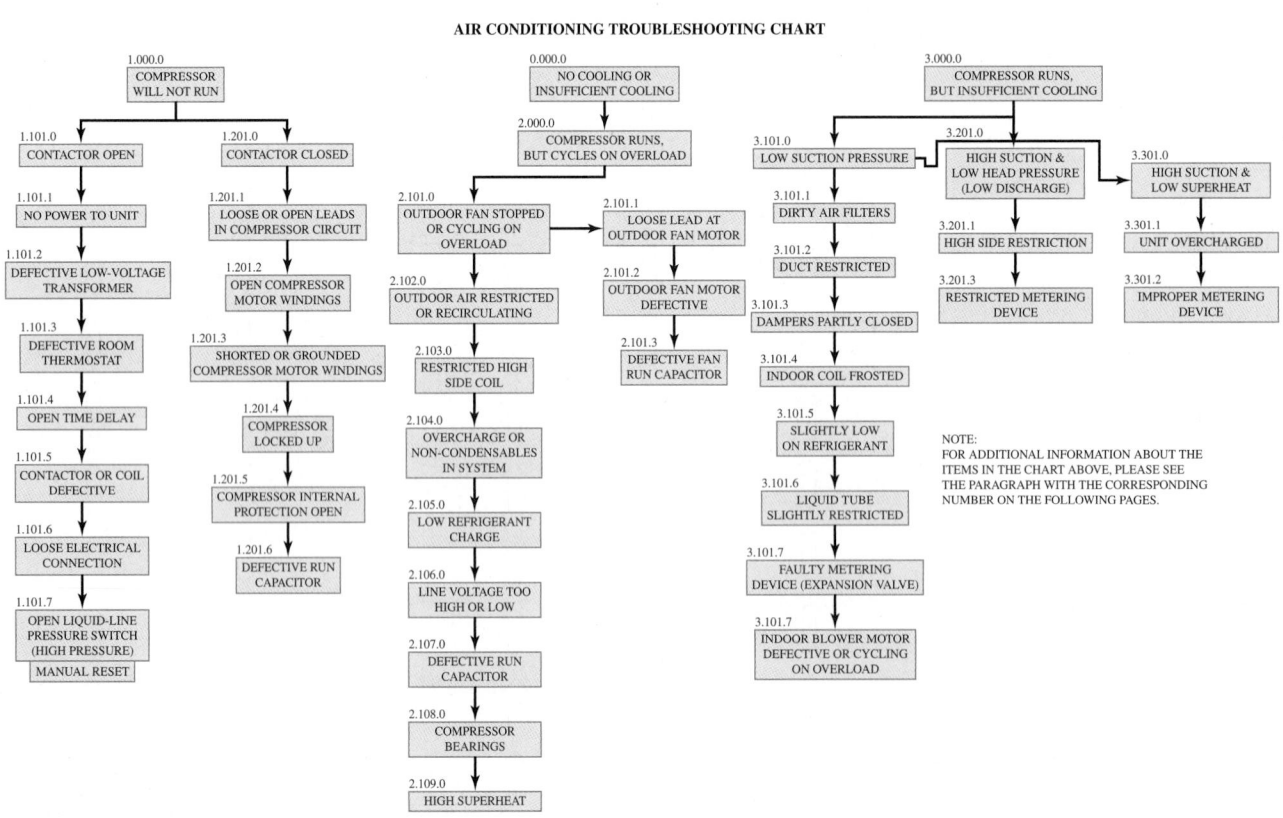

Figure 86-18 Example of a troubleshooting logic flowchart

WATER SOURCE HEAT PUMP TROUBLESHOOTING CHART		
PROBLEM	**CAUSE**	**CORRECTION**
Nothing operates in any thermostat setting	No power to unit	Check circuit breaker or fuses
	Defective control transformer	Replace defective transformer
	Loose connection	Repair connection
	Defective thermostat	Replace thermostat
Unit short cycles	Thermostat location	Move thermostat
Blower operates but compressor does not operate	Defective compressor overload	Replace (if external)
	Defective compressor contactor	Replace
	Supply voltage too low	Check power wire size
	Defective compressor capacitor	Replace capacitor
	Defective windings	Replace compressor
	Limit switches open	Check cause and replace
Insufficient system capacity	Dirty air filter	Replace air filter
	Blower RPM too low	Increase blower RPM
	Leaky duct work	Repair and/or seal ductwork
	Low refrigerant charge	Locate leak, recover charge, repair leak, evacuate and recharge system
	Restricted expansion valve	Replace expansion valve
	Defective reversing valve	Replace reversing valve
	Thermostat located in supply air	Move thermostat
	Undersized system	Perform load calculation
	Insufficient water flow	Increase water flow
	Scaled or fouled water coil	Clean or replace water coil
	Water temperature outside of manufacturer's specified operating limits	Correct water temperature
High pressure switch open or high head pressure	Inadequate water flow	Increase water flow
	Water too hot	Decrease water temperature
	Dirty or fouled water coil	Clean or replace water coil
	Inadequate airflow	Increase airflow
	Dirty air filter	Replace air filter
	Overcharged with refrigerant	Recover charge
	Defective pressure switch	Replace pressure switch
	Non-condensables in system	Recover refrigerant, evacuate and recharge
Low pressure switch open or low suction pressure	Inadequate airflow	Increase airflow
	Dirty air filter	Replace air filter
	Inadequate water flow	Increase water flow
	Water too cold	Increase water temperature
	Undercharged with refrigerant	Add refrigerant charge
	Defective pressure switch	Replace pressure switch
	Restricted expansion valve	Replace expansion valve

Note: Items in blue apply only to cooling cycle, items in red apply only to heating cycle.

Figure 86-19 Example of a troubleshooting systems list

Ignition Control Board Diagnostic Codes

DIAGNOSTIC CODES
Make sure to Identify LED'S Correctly.
Refer to Installation Instructions for control board layout.

DS1 (Red or Green)	DS2 (Green)	DESCRIPTION
SIMULTANEOUS SLOW FLASH	SIMULTANEOUS SLOW FLASH	Power on Normal operation. Also signaled during cooling and continuous fan.
SIMULTANEOUS FAST FLASH	SIMULTANEOUS FAST FLASH	Normal operation Signaled when heating demand initiated at thermostat.
SLOW FLASH	ON	Primary or secondary limit switch open. Limit must close within 3 minutes or unit goes into 1 hour Watchguard.
OFF	SLOW FLASH	Pressure switch open; OR: Blocked inlet/exhaust vent; OR: Condensate line blocked; OR: Pressure switch closed prior to activation of combustion air inducer.
ALTERNATING SLOW FLASH	ALTERNATING SLOW FLASH	Watchguard Burners failed to ignite, limit open longer than 3 minutes, or flame sense lost 5 times in one heating cycle.
SLOW FLASH	OFF	Flame sensed without gas valve energized.
ON	SLOW FLASH	Rollout switch open.
ON ON OFF	ON OFF ON	Circuit board failure or control wired incorrectly. Check 24 volt and 115 volt connections to board.
FAST FLASH	SLOW FLASH	Main power polarity reversed. Switch line and neutral. Improper main ground.
SLOW FLASH	FAST FLASH	Low flame signal. Check flame sensor.
ALTERNATING FAST FLASH	ALTERNATING FAST FLASH	The following conditions are sensed during the ignitor warm up period only: 1) Improper main ground; 2) Broken ignitor; OR: Open ignitor circuit; 3) Line voltage below 75 volts.

NOTE Slow flash rate equals 1 Hz (one flash per second). Fast flash rate equals 3 Hz (three flashes per second). Drop out flame sense current = 0.15 0.24 microAmps.

Figure 86-20 Fault code from a service manual from page 30 of 86-20.pdf Lennox 504,957M *(Courtesy of Lennox Industries)*

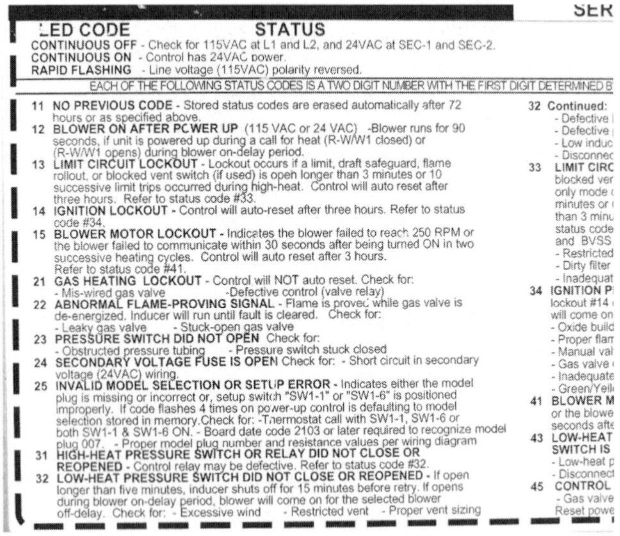
SER
LED CODE STATUS
CONTINUOUS OFF - Check for 115VAC at L1 and L2, and 24VAC at SEC-1 and SEC-2.
CONTINUOUS ON - Control has 24VAC power.
RAPID FLASHING - Line voltage (115VAC) polarity reversed.
EACH OF THE FOLLOWING STATUS CODES IS A TWO DIGIT NUMBER WITH THE FIRST DIGIT DETERMINED B

11 NO PREVIOUS CODE - Stored status codes are erased automatically after 72 hours or as specified above.
12 BLOWER ON AFTER POWER UP (115 VAC or 24 VAC) -Blower runs for 90 seconds, if unit is powered up during a call for heat (R-W/W1 closed) or (R-W/W1 opens) during blower on-delay period.
13 LIMIT CIRCUIT LOCKOUT - Lockout occurs if a limit, draft safeguard, flame rollout, or blocked vent switch (if used) is open longer than 3 minutes or 10 successive limit trips occurred during high-heat. Control will auto reset after three hours. Refer to status code #33.
14 IGNITION LOCKOUT - Control will auto-reset after three hours. Refer to status code #34.
15 BLOWER MOTOR LOCKOUT - Indicates the blower failed to reach 250 RPM or the blower failed to communicate within 30 seconds after being turned ON in two successive heating cycles. Control will auto reset after 3 hours. Refer to status code #41.
21 GAS HEATING LOCKOUT - Control will NOT auto reset. Check for: - Mis-wired gas valve -Defective control (valve relay)
22 ABNORMAL FLAME-PROVING SIGNAL - Flame is proved while gas valve is de-energized. Inducer will run until fault is cleared. Check for: - Leaky gas valve - Stuck-open gas valve
23 PRESSURE SWITCH DID NOT OPEN Check for: - Obstructed pressure tubing - Pressure switch stuck closed
24 SECONDARY VOLTAGE FUSE IS OPEN Check for: - Short circuit in secondary voltage (24VAC) wiring.
25 INVALID MODEL SELECTION OR SETUP ERROR - Indicates either the model plug is missing or incorrect or, setup switch "SW1-1" or "SW1-6" is positioned improperly. If code flashes 4 times on power-up control is defaulting to model selection stored in memory.Check for: -Thermostat call with SW1-1, SW1-6 or both SW1-1 & SW1-6 ON. - Board date code 2103 or later required to recognize model plug 007. - Proper model plug number and resistance values per wiring diagram
31 HIGH-HEAT PRESSURE SWITCH OR RELAY DID NOT CLOSE OR REOPENED - Control relay may be defective. Refer to status code #32.
32 LOW-HEAT PRESSURE SWITCH DID NOT CLOSE OR REOPENED - If open longer than five minutes, inducer shuts off for 15 minutes before retry. If opens during blower on-delay period, blower will come on for the selected blower off-delay. Check for: - Excessive wind - Restricted vent - Proper vent sizing

32 Continued:
- Defective
- Defective
- Low induc
- Disconnec
33 LIMIT CIRC
blocked ver
only mode
minutes or
than 3 minu
status code
and BVSS
- Restricted
- Dirty filter
- Inadequat
34 IGNITION P
lockout #14
will come on
- Oxide build
- Proper flam
- Manual val
- Gas valve
- Inadequate
- Green/Yell
41 BLOWER M
or the blowe
seconds afte
43 LOW-HEAT
SWITCH IS
- Low-heat p
- Disconnect
45 CONTROL
- Gas valve
Reset powe

Figure 86-21 Fault code located on an equipment panel

causes for a particular symptom. If more than one component can cause the same symptom, multiple components may be replaced by someone who is just running the list and does not really know how to check each component.

Fault Code Reference List

Most units today employ some type of electronic control. Many of these have built-in diagnostics. Typically, these diagnostics will tell the technician what the control is "thinking." A list of fault conditions are typically located in the service manual (Figure 86-20), and also frequently on the unit (Figure 86-21). The explanation can be a short description, such as "open pressure switch," or it can be a more detailed explanation of the problem including a fault history of the system.

Technicians need to understand the limitations of on board diagnostics. On board diagnostics can only report on issues that there are inputs for. Also, all the board knows is that an input is incorrect. The accompanying chart can suggest what the cause is, but it does not really know. Verifying the cause is still the service technician's job. Although diagnostics greatly simplify locating system malfunctions, they do not replace understanding how a system operates or knowing how to diagnose faulty components.

UNIT 86—SUMMARY

Troubleshooting is the process of identifying the problems, determining their cause, and correcting the cause of the problem. Technicians should view units as systems, keeping in mind the interrelationship between the electrical, refrigeration, and airflow system components. Troubleshooting can be broken down into the following steps:

- Understanding system operational sequence.
- Preliminary system inspection.
- Collecting operational data.

- Recognizing what is operating incorrectly.
- Testing to isolate the cause.
- Recommending corrective action.

Technicians must understand exactly how equipment operates so they can analyze the cause of improper operation. Understanding the operating sequence of the most common types of systems is important. Sources of information on system operation include the manufacturer's installation and operation and manuals, unit wiring diagrams, unit charging charts, and general textbooks. Preliminary system checks should include checking the thermostat setting, air filter, airflow and/ or water flow, line voltage, and control voltage. Operational data can come from the homeowner, general observation, diagnostic boards, and system performance tests. Troubleshooting logic flowcharts, common symptom lists, and diagnostic codes can all be helpful in identifying the cause of system malfunction. The hopscotching technique is useful for identifying the problem in a malfunctioning electrical circuit. When troubleshooting the refrigeration cycle in a system, key performance indicators include:

- Low side pressure.
- High side pressures.
- Suction line temperature.
- Discharge line temperature.
- Liquid line temperature.
- Air or water temperature rise across the condenser.
- Air or water temperature drop across the evaporator.
- Suction line superheat.
- Liquid line subcooling.
- Condenser delta T.
- Evaporator delta T.

The technician should be able to explain to the customer exactly what is causing the problem and recommend a solution.

WORK ORDERS

Service tickets 8601–8604 all start with the same symptoms, but they each have a different root cause. The beginning of each call starts out as follows:

A customer calls because their air conditioning system is not cooling properly. The system is operating when technician arrives. The technician notices that the condensing fan motor outside is running, but that the compressor is not running. The compressor line voltage wires on the contactor have the correct voltage. The compressor shell is very hot. The technician turns off the power to the unit and measures the resistance of the compressor terminals. There is no continuity between common and either run or start, but there is continuity

between start and run. This indicates that the internal overload is open.

Each service ticket picks up from this point.

Service Ticket 8601

Customer Complaint: Poor Cooling

R-410a Residential Split System Air Conditioner

. . . The condenser coil appears clean. The technician checks the compressor starting components and finds that the compressor run capacitor is open. The run capacitor is replaced. The compressor starts and runs correctly after it cools down and the internal overload resets. The technician checks the system performance against the manufacturer's specifications on the service panel to verify that it is operating correctly.

Service Ticket 8602

Customer Complaint: Poor Cooling

R-410a Residential Split System Air Conditioner

. . . The condenser coil appears clean. The technician checks the compressor starting components and finds that they are all good. Next, the technician checks the system pressure and finds the equalized pressure is 100 psig. The technician concludes that the system is undercharged, leading the compressor to overheat. A leak inspection reveals a leak at the mechanical fitting on the suction line. The technician tightens this fitting, stopping the leak. The unit is charged according to the manufacturer's performance chart after the compressor cools and is able to operate.

Service Ticket 8603

Customer Complaint: Poor Cooling

R-410a Residential Split System Air Conditioner

. . . The condenser coil appears to be clogged with debris. The technician concludes that poor condenser airflow has caused the compressor to overheat, turns off the power to the unit, and cleans the condenser coil. The compressor starts and runs correctly after it cools down and the internal overload resets. The technician checks the system performance against the manufacturer's specifications on the service panel to verify that it is operating correctly.

Service Ticket 8604

Customer Complaint: Poor Cooling

R-410a Residential Split System Air Conditioner

. . . The condenser coil appears clean. The technician checks the compressor starting components and finds that they are all good. Next, the technician checks the system pressure and finds the equalized pressure is

200 psig. The technician decides that the system will have to operate to make any further diagnosis. The compressor starts and runs after it cools down and the internal overload resets. The high side pressure climbs quickly to close to the manufacturer's specification. The low side, however, drops to around 50 psig, much lower than the manufacturer's specification. The superheat and subcooling are both high, and the air temperature exchange across the condenser is lower than normal. The technician begins looking for a temperature drop in the liquid line that would indicate a restriction. None is found. The expansion device is an expansion valve. The technician removes the thermal bulb and holds it, looking for a change in the low side pressure or superheat. There is no change. The technician concludes that the thermostatic expansion valve is underfeeding, causing the compressor to overheat. The refrigerant is recovered, the expansion valve changed, and the system is evacuated and recharged according to the manufacturer's specifications. The technician operates the system and compares the system performance to the manufacturer's specifications to verify that the system is performing correctly.

Service Ticket 8605

Customer Complaint: No Cooling

Residential Packaged Heat Pump

. . . A customer complains that they have no cooling. The technician arrives, makes sure the thermostat is set to COOL, and checks the line voltage to the unit. The line voltage is 0 V. The technician finds a blown fuse in the outdoor disconnect switch. Next, all major loads are checked for shorts and grounds. None are found. The technician notes that the fuses in the disconnect box are one-time fuses and replaces both fuses with time delay fuses. The unit comes on and runs after the fuses are replaced. The technician checks the system amp draw and the amp draw of each component and finds them at or below the data plate specifications. Next, the system performance is checked against the manufacturer's specifications to verify correct operation.

Service Ticket 8606

Customer Complaint: No Cooling

Residential Packaged Heat Pump

. . . A customer complains that they have no cooling. The technician arrives, makes sure the thermostat is set to COOL, and checks the line voltage to the unit. The line voltage is 240 V. The technician checks the control voltage and finds 0 V. The technician finds 24 V fuse to the R terminal is blown. The fuse is replaced and it immediately blows again. The technician starts checking the low

voltage controls for shorts and finds that the compressor contactor coil has a resistance reading of $\frac{1}{2}$ ohm. The contactor is replaced and the system is turned on again. This time the system starts and operates. Next, the system performance is checked against the manufacturer's specifications to verify correct operation.

Service Ticket 8607

Customer Complaint: Noisy Unit

R-22 Residential Split System Air Conditioner

. . . A customer calls complaining about their condensing unit making a lot of noise. The customer states that all their neighbors have the same systems, and they are all noisy. However, they cannot stand the noise any longer, and are ready to change out the unit if necessary. The customer also asks for the "extra cooling" option, explaining that they paid the original contractor $100 to add extra refrigerant to improve the system's performance. The technician explains that adding extra charge does not help the unit cool better. If anything, it makes it cool worse. The technician checks the system performance characteristics and finds the both pressures are high, the superheat is essentially 0°F, and the subcooling is 30°F. The technician suspects that the system charge was not done correctly at installation and elects to start from scratch. So all the charge is recovered, the system evacuated, and a full charge weighed in according to the manufacturer's data plate information, including line allowances. The system starts and runs much more quietly, and the pressures fall to within the manufacturer's specifications.

UNIT 86—REVIEW QESTIONS

1. List some common questions customers ask service technicians.
2. Explain what is meant by a systems approach to troubleshooting.
3. Give an example of an airflow problem that can look like a refrigerant charge problem if a service technician is only looking at system pressures.
4. List the stages of troubleshooting.
5. What checks are typically performed during the preliminary inspection?
6. What should a service technician do if there is a blown fuse in the unit disconnect switch during the preliminary inspection?
7. What should a service technician do if there is a blown fuse in series with the low voltage side of the transformer?
8. Outline a method of isolating an electrical fault using the process of elimination.
9. Describe the process of hopscotching.
10. Using the logic flowchart in Figure 86-18, what is the first condition listed to check for a compressor that will not run when the contactor is closed?

11. Using the symptoms list in Figure 86-19, what possible causes are listed for a unit that experiences high pressure switch tripping only during the cooling cycle?

12. Using the chart in Figure 86-20, what conditions cause both lights to display an alternating fast flash?

13. Using the air source heat pump sequence chart in Figure 86-2, list the devices in order that control the outdoor fan.

14. Using the chart in Figure 86-17, what problems can cause both a high superheat and a high subcooling?

15. Using the induced draft sequence chart in Figure 86-6, what should be checked if the induced draft fan comes on but the igniter is never energized?

16. List some resources the air conditioning technician can use to learn about the system operational sequence.

17. List some sources the air conditioning technician can use to get system operational data.

18. Using Figure 86-7, what should the approximate suction pressure be for an EC015 system operating in heating with an entering water temperature of 50°F and a water flow of 2.8 GPM?

19. Why are diagnostic codes not always able to identify the system problem?

20. Why should service technicians be familiar with company pricing policies?

Refrigerant Data

Low Pressure Refrigerants for Centrifugal Chillers

ASHRAE #	Name	Type	Formula	Boiling Point	Safety	ODP	GWP
11	Trichlorofluoromethane	CFC Compound	CCl_3F	74.7 °F	A1	1	4750
113	Trichlorotrifluoroethane	CFC Compound	$C_2Cl_3F_3$	117.7 °F	A1	1	6130
123	Dichlorotrifluoroethane	HCFC Compound	$CHCl_2CF_3$	82.1 °F	B1	0.002	77

Very High Pressure Cryogenic Refrigerants for Cascade Systems

ASHRAE #	Name	Type	Formula	Boiling Point	Safety	ODP	GWP
13	Chlorotrifluoromethane	CFC Compound	$CCIF_3$	-114.6°F	A1	1	14,000
23	Trifluoromethane	HFC Compound	CHF_3	-115.8°F	A1	0	27,000
503	Trifluoromethane Chlorotrifluoromethane	HFC/HCFC Azeotrope	CHF_3 and $CCIF_3$	-125.5	A1	0.6	47,000

High Pressure Refrigerants for Commercial Refrigeration

ASHRAE #	Name	Type	Formula	Boiling Point	Safety	ODP	GWP
12	Dichlorodifluoromethane	CFC Compound	CCl_2F_2	-21.6°F	A1	1	10890
134a	Tetrafluoroethane	HFC Compound	CF_3CH_2F	-14.9°F	A1	0	1330
502	Chlorodifluoromethane Chloropentafluoroethane	CFC Azeotrope	$CHClF_2$ $CClF_2CF_3$	-49.5°F	A1	0.6	7900
404A	Pentafluoroethane Trifluoroethane Tetrafluoroethane	HFC Zeotrope	CF_3CHF_2 CF_3CH_3 CF_3CH_2F	-51.8°F	A1/A1	0	3800
507	Pentafluoroethane Trifluoroethane	HFC Azeotrope	CF_3CHF_2 CF_3CH_3	-52.8°F	A1	0	3900

High Pressure Refrigerants for Air Conditioning

ASHRAE #	Name	Type	Formula	Boiling Point	Safety	ODP	GWP
22	Chlorodifluoromethane	HCFC Compound	$CHClF_2$	-41.6°F	A1	0.034	1700
407C	Difluoromethane Pentafluoroethane Tetrafluoroethane	HFC Zeotrope	CH_2F_2 CF_3CHF_2 CF_3CH_2F	-46.9°F	A1/A1	0	1700
410A	Difluoromethane Pentafluoroethane	HFC Zeotrope	CH_2F_2 CF_3CHF_2	-60.9°F	A1/A1	0	2000

APPENDIX B
Commonly Used HVAC/R Formulas

1. **Formula for area (common math formula)**
   area = length × width
2. **Formula for volume (common math formula)**
   volume = length × width × height
3. **Formula to measure density (Unit 4)**

   $$\text{density} = \frac{\text{weight}}{\text{volume}}$$

4. **Formula to measure specific volume (Unit 4)**

   $$\text{specific volume} = \frac{\text{volume}}{\text{weight}}$$

5. **Formula to measure specific gravity of solids and liquids in English Units (Unit 4)**

   $$\text{specific gravity} = \frac{\text{density in lb ft}^3}{62.4}$$

6. **Formula to measure specific gravity of gases in English Units (Unit 4)**

   $$\text{specific gravity} = \frac{\text{density in lb ft}^3}{0.075}$$

7. **Formula to convert degrees Celsius to degrees Fahrenheit (Unit 6)**

   Method 1 $°F = (9/5 × °C) + 32$
   Method 2 $°F = (1.8 × °C) + 32$
   Method 3 $°F = ((°C + 40) × 1.8) − 40$

8. **Formula to convert degrees Fahrenheit to degrees Celsius (Unit 6)**

   Method 1 $°C = (°F − 32) × 5/9$
   Method 2 $°C = (°F − 32) ÷ 1.8$
   Method 3 $°C = ((°F + 40) ÷ 1.8) − 40$

9. **Formula to calculate sensible heat added or removed from a substance in English units (Unit 7)**

   Btu = lb × °FΔT × specific heat capacity in Btu per lb

10. **Formula to calculate sensible heat added or removed from a substance in SI units (Unit 7)**

    kilojoules = kilograms × °KΔT × specific heat capacity in kilojoules per kilogram

11. **Formula to determine the latent heat added or removed from a substance (Unit 7)**
    Btu = weight × latent heat factor
12. **Formula to measure pressure (Unit 8)**

    $$\text{pressure} = \frac{\text{force}}{\text{area}}$$

13. **Formula to measure head pressure (Unit 8)**

    $$p = 0.433 × h$$

    where
    p = pressure, psi
    h = head, feet of water

14. **Formula to calculate changes in gas volume, temperature, and pressure (Ideal Gas Law) (Unit 8)**

    $$\frac{P_1 V_1}{T_1} = \frac{P_2 V_2}{T_2}$$

    where
    V_1 = the starting volume
    V_2 = the ending volume
    P_1 = the starting pressure
    P_2 = the ending pressure
    T_1 = the starting temperature
    T_2 = the ending temperature

15. **Formula to determine refrigeration effect (Unit 18)**

    $$\text{net refrigeration effect} = W × \Delta h$$

    where
    W = refrigerant mass flow in pounds per minute
    Δh = refrigerant enthalpy change

16. **Formula to measure refrigerant coefficient of performance (RCOP) (Unit 18)**

    $$R_{COP} = \frac{\text{refrigerating effect}}{\text{heat of compression}}$$

17. **Formulas to calculate series circuits (Unit 28)**

    $$I_T = I_1 = I_2 = I_3 = I_4$$
    $$R_T = R_1 + R_2 + R_3 + R_4$$
    $$E_T = E_1 + E_2 + E_3 + E_4$$

    where
    E = volts
    I = amps
    R = resistance

18. **Formulas to calculate parallel circuits (Unit 28)**

$$I_T = I_1 + I_2 + I_3 + I_4$$

$$R_T = \frac{R_1 \times R_2}{R_1 \times R_2}$$

$$\frac{1}{R_T} = \frac{1}{R_1} + \frac{1}{R_2} + \frac{1}{R_3} + \frac{1}{R_4}$$

$$E_T = E_1 = E_2 = E_3 = E_4$$

where
E = volts
I = amps
R = resistance

19. **Formula for direct current electrical power (Unit 28)**

Method 1   Watts = volts × amps
Method 2 $P = EI$
Method 3 $P = I^2R$

Method 4 $P = \dfrac{E^2}{R}$

where
P = watts
E = volts
I = amps
R = resistance

20. **Formula for single phase alternating current electrical power (Unit 28)**

$$\text{watts} = \text{volts} \times \text{amps} \times \text{power factor}$$
$$P = EI(\text{PF})$$

where
P = watts
E = volts
I = amps
PF = power factor

21. **Formula for three phase alternating current electrical power (Unit 28)**

$$P = \sqrt{3}EI(\text{PF})$$

where
P = watts
E = volts
I = amps
PF = power factor

22. **Formulas to measure power factor (Unit 29)**

$$\text{power factor} = \frac{(\text{true power})}{(\text{apparent power})}$$

or

$$\text{power factor} = \frac{(\text{wattmeter reading})}{(E \times I)}$$

23. **Formula to calculate impedance in an inductive circuit (Unit 29)**

$$Z = E/I$$

where
Z = impedance

24. **Formula to calculate synchronous motor speed (Unit 30)**

$$\text{rpm} = \frac{\text{Hz} \times 60 \text{ sec/min}}{\frac{1}{2}p} \quad \text{or} \quad \frac{\text{Hz} \times 120}{p}$$

where
rpm = revolutions per minute
Hz = frequency in cycles/sec
p = number of poles

25. **Formula to calculate total airflow through a unit (Unit 35)**

$$\text{CFM} = \frac{\text{furnace output in Btu/hr}}{(\text{TD} \times 1.08)}$$

where TD is the temperature rise in °F

26. **Formula to determine coil operating temperatures (Unit 36)**

$$COT = \left(\frac{EAT + LAT}{2}\right) - \text{split}$$

where
COT = coil operating temperature
EAT = temperature of air entering the coil
LAT = temperature of air leaving the coil

27. **Formula to find the condensing temperature (Unit 36)**

$$RCT = EAT + \text{split}$$

where
RCT = refrigerant condensing temperature
EAT = temperature of the air entering the condenser
split = design temperature difference between the entering air temperature and the condensing temperatures of the hot high-pressure vapor from the compressor

28. **Formula to measure gas flow through the meter (Unit 40)**

$$\text{time (sec/ft}^3) = \frac{\text{seconds per hour}}{\text{ft}^3/\text{hr of gas}}$$

29. **Formula to determine the system capacity (Unit 35)**

$$Q_t = 4.45 \times \text{CFM} \times \Delta h$$

where
Q_t = the total (sensible and latent) cooling being done
CFM = airflow across the evaporator coil
Δh = the change of enthalpy of the air across the coil

30. **Formula to measure airflow through the furnace (cubic feet per minute) (Unit 48)**

$$CFM = \frac{V \times A \times 3.412}{\Delta T \times 1.08}$$

31. **Formula to measure energy efficiency ratio in a heat pump (Unit 49)**

$$SEER = \frac{\text{total cooling season Btu}}{\text{total watts consumed}}$$

32. **Formula to measure coefficient of performance (Unit 49)**

$$COP = \frac{\text{Btu heat output}}{\text{electric heat equivalent}}$$

33. **Formula to measure heating seasonal performance factor of a heat pump (Unit 49)**

$$HSPF = \frac{\text{total Btu heating season output}}{\text{total heating season watts}}$$

34. **Formula to calculate gross heating capacity (Unit 51)**

$$H_s = CFM \times TD \times 1.08$$

35. **Formulas to calculate for fan operation (Fan Laws) (Unit 56)**

$$\text{New CFM} = \text{Old CFM} \times \frac{\text{New rpm}}{\text{Old rpm}}$$

$$\text{New rpm} = \text{Old RPM} \times \frac{\text{New CFM}}{\text{Old CFM}}$$

$$\text{New SP} = \text{Old SP} \times \left[\frac{\text{New rpm}}{\text{Old rpm}}\right]^2$$

$$\text{New BHP} = \text{Old BHP} \times \left[\frac{\text{New rpm}}{\text{Old rpm}}\right]^3$$

where
  CFM = cubic feet per minute
  rpm = revolutions per minute
  BHP = brake horsepower

36. **Formula to determine CFM (Unit 56)**

$$CFM = \text{free area of grill (ft}^2) \times fpm$$

37. **Formula to determine adjusted friction rate (Unit 57)**

adjusted friction rate =
design friction rate $\times$ (100/equivalent length)

38. **Formula for determining mixed air temperature (Unit 61)**

mixed air temperature = (makup air temperature
$\times$ %outdoor air) + (return air
temperature $\times$ %return air)

39. **Formula to calculate U value (Unit 64)**

$$U \text{ value} = 1/R \text{ value}$$

40. **Formula to calculate heat transfer multiplier, HTM (Unit 64)**

$$HTM = U \text{ value} \times \text{temperature difference}$$

41. **Formula to calculate rate of heat transfer (Unit 64)**

$$\text{heat transfer rate} = HTM \times \text{area}$$

42. **Formula to calculate heat (Unit 73)**

$$Q = gpm \times 500 \times TD$$

where
  Q = heat rejection in Btu/hr
  gpm = flow in gallons per minute
  500 = factor derived from, specific heat of water (1)
    $\times$ 60 min/hr $\times$ 8.33 lb/gal
  TD = temperature difference in °F

APPENDIX C
Abbreviations and Acronyms

AC   alternating current
ACR   air conditioning and refrigeration tubing
AEV   automatic expansion valve
AFUE   Annual Fuel Utilization Efficiency
AHRI   Air Conditioning, Heating and Refrigeration Institute
ANSI   American National Standards Institute
ASHRAE   American Society of Heating, Refrigeration, and Air Conditioning Engineers
ASME   American Society of Mechanical Engineers
ASTME   American Society for Testing and Materials Engineers
AT   ampere turn
AWG   American wire gauge
BEMF   back electromotive force
BRI   building related illness
C   capacitance
C   kilocalorie
C   thermal conductance
CAE   combined annual efficiency
CFC   chlorofluorocarbon
CFM   cubic feet per minute
CO   carbon monoxide
CO$_2$ carbon dioxide
COP   coefficient of performance
CS   capacitor start motor
CSR   capacitor start-run motor
CPR   crankcase pressure regulator
CPVC   chlorinated polyvinyl chloride
DA   direct acting control
DC   direct current
DDC   direct digital control
DIP   dual inline pair switch
DOT   Department of Transportation
DSI   direct spark ignition
E   electromotive force
ECM   electronically commutated motor
EEPROM   electrical erasable programmable read-only memory
EER   energy efficiency ratio
EMF   electromotive force
EPA   Environmental Protection Agency
EPR   evaporator pressure regulator
EUI   energy utilization index
ERV   energy recovery ventilator
EXV   electronic expansion valve
FLA   full load amperage
GFCI   ground fault circuit interrupter

GWP   global warming potential
H   Henry (inductance)
HCFC   hydrochlorofluorocabon
HEPA   high efficiency particulate air filter
HFC   hydrofluorocarbon
Hg   mercury
HSPF   heating season performance factor
Hz   hertz (frequency)
I   electric current
IAQ   indoor air quality
ICC   Interstate Commerce Commission
k   thermal conductivity (single material)
k   SI prefix for 1,000
K   Kelvin scale
km   kilometer
kPa   kilopascal
kVA   kilovoltampere
kW   kilowatt
kWh   kilowatt hour
L   liter
LED   light emitting diode
LP   liquefied petroleum gases
LPG   liquefied petroleum gases
LN$_2$ liquid nitrogen
LNG   liquefied natural gas
LRA   locked rotor amperage
m   milli, SI prefix for one thousandth
M   mega, SI prefix for one million
MΩ   megohm
MBH   one thousand Btu/hr
MERV   minimum efficiency reporting value
MFD   microfarad
MO   mineral oil
MOP   maximum operating pressure
N   Newton
NC   normally closed
NEBB   National Environmental Balancing Bureau
NEC   National Electrical Code
NFPA   National Fire Protection Association
NFPA 54   National Fuel Gas Code
NI   ampere turn
NIST   National Institute of Standards and Technology
NO   normally open
NPT   national pipe taper
NTC   negative temperature coefficient thermistor
ODP   ozone depletion potential
P   power
Pa   pascal

PAG   polyalkylene glycol
PAT   powder actuated tool
PB   polybutylene
PCB   polychlorinated biphenyl
PE   polyethylene
PEX   polyethylene, cross linked
pH   scale used to measure acid/base
PH diagram   pressure-enthalpy diagram
POA Valve   Pressure Operated Altitude Valve
POE   polyol ester
ppm   parts per million
$\mathbf{P_s}$ static pressure
PSC   permanent split capacitor motor
psi   pounds per square inch
psia   pounds per square inch absolute
psig   pounds per square inch gauge
$\mathbf{P_t}$ total pressure
PTAC   packaged terminal air conditioner
PTC   positive temperature coefficient thermistor
PT chart   pressure-temperature chart
PT plugs   pressure-temperature plugs
$\mathbf{P_v}$ velocity pressure
PVC   polyvinyl chloride
PWM   pulse width modulation
Q   heat transfer rate
R   Rankine
R   electrical resistance
R value, SI   thermal resistance of a building material in ($K \cdot m^2/W$)
R value, US   thermal resistance of a building material in ($ft^2 \cdot °F \cdot h/Btu$).
RA   reverse acting control
RH   relative humidity
RLA   rated-load amperage
RMS   root mean square voltage
S lock   an S shaped metal strip

SEER   seasonal energy efficiency ratio
SBS   sick building syndrome
SF   service factor
SG   specific gravity
SI   international system of units
SPDT   single pole double throw switch
SPST   single pole single throw switch
SSU, SUS   Saybolt universal seconds
T   earth temperature minimum
TAB   testing, adjusting, and balancing
TABB   Testing, Adjusting and Balancing Bureau
TEM   total energy management
TEV   thermostatic expansion valve
TEWI   total equivalent warming impact
TP chart   temperature-pressure chart
TPR   temperature-pressure relief valve
TXV   thermostatic expansion valve
***U* Factor**   unit of measure of thermal conductivity
***U* Value**   another name for *U* factor
UL   Underwriters Laboratories
UV   ultraviolet light
UVA   ultraviolet A
UVB   ultraviolet B
UVC   ultraviolet C
v   velocity
V   volt
VAV   variable air volume
VFD   variable frequency drive
VOM   volt ohm milliammeter
W   Watt
wc   water column
wbt   wet bulb temperature
Wh   Watt-hour
ΔP   pressure drop
ΔT   temperature change
Ω   ohm

English Language Glossary

A Coil   Evaporator consisting of two coils joined together forming the shape of the letter A.

Absolute Humidity   The actual amount of moisture in a given volume of air.

Absolute Pressure   Gauge pressure plus atmospheric pressure.

Absolute Temperature   Temperature measured from absolute zero.

Absolute Zero   Temperature at which all molecular motion ceases (−460°F and −273°C).

Absorbent   Substance that has the ability to take up or absorb another substance.

Absorber   A device containing liquid for absorbing refrigerant vapor or other vapors.

Absorption   Diffusion of one substance into the inner composition of another substance.

Absorption Chiller   Device used to produce chill water using the absorption cycle.

Absorption Cycle   Refrigeration cycle based upon the absorption of the refrigerant by a chemical substance rather than by mechanical compression.

Absorption Refrigerator   A refrigerator that utilizes the principles of the absorption cycle.

Accessible Hermetic   A hermetically sealed unit that can be opened for repair and maintenance, also referred to as semi-hermetic.

Accumulator   A storage vessel located in the suction line before the compressor. Used to limit liquid refrigerant return to the compressor and store excess refrigerant in the heating mode.

Acetylene   Gas commonly used with oxygen for brazing and soldering.

ACR Tubing   Air conditioning and refrigeration tubing sealed on each end to keep the tubing clean and dry.

Activated Alumina   An aluminum oxide desiccant used in refrigeration system driers to absorb moisture.

Activated Carbon   Specially processed carbon commonly used to clean air.

Active Refrigerant Recovery Device   A self contained recovery unit that is not an integral part of the refrigeration system.

Active Solar System   A system designed to utilize solar energy.

Actuator   A device used to convert fluid power, thermal energy, and electrical energy into mechanical motion.

Adiabatic Compression   Compressing refrigerant gas without removing or adding heat.

Adsorbent   Substance that has the property to hold molecules of fluids without causing a chemical or physical change.

Air   The fluid surrounding us composed mainly of oxygen and nitrogen.

Air-Acetylene   Brazing torch that draws in the surrounding air rather than requiring a separate oxygen supply.

Air Binding   A condition in which a bubble or other pocket of air is present in a pipeline that prevents the desired flow in the pipeline.

Air Break   An inverted opening placed in a chimney to prevent a downdraft from affecting the furnace flame.

Air Changes   The amount of air leakage through a building in terms of the number of building volumes exchanged.

Air Cleaner   A filtration system used to remove airborne impurities.

Air Coil   A refrigeration heat exchanger that has air passing across its outer surface.

Air Conditioner   Device used to control temperature, humidity, cleanliness, and movement of air in conditioned space.

Air Conditioning   The process to control temperature, humidity, cleanliness, and movement of air in conditioned space.

Air Conditioning Heating and Refrigeration Institute (AHRI)   A national trade association representing manufacturers of over 90% of U.S.-produced central air conditioning, gas appliances, and commercial refrigeration equipment.

Air Cooled Condenser   A heat exchanger that uses air passing across it to condense refrigerant from vapor to liquid.

Air Core Solenoid   A solenoid that has a hollow center.

Air Curtain   Forced air used to shield the food product in an uncovered display case.

Air Cushion Tank   (see Expansion Tank)

Air Defrosting   A defrost method of shutting the unit off while allowing the warm air to circulate.

Air Diffuser   An air register designed to distribute air in a specific arrangement.

Air Friction Chart   A chart used for sizing round ducts.

Air Gap   The air space between the rotating and stationary components of a motor or generator.

Air Handler   A unit housing a blower and heating/cooling coils that is used for delivering air to a space.

Air Heat Exchanger   A heat exchanger that allows for air to be drawn across its exterior surface.

Air Loop   The ducted air side on a heat pump system.

Air Pressure Switch   Measures air pressure drop across an outdoor heat pump coil to determine frost build-up.

Air Sensor   Installed in air handlers to measure conditions such as temperature, pressure, velocity, and humidity.

Air Shutter   An adjustable shutter on the primary air openings of a burner that is used to control the amount of combustion air.

Air Source Heat Pump   Heat pump that transfers heat from outdoor air to an indoor air circulation system.

Air Standard   The ASHRAE standard designation for dry air at 70°F and atmospheric pressure.

Air-to-Air Heat Pump   (see Air Source Heat Pump)

Air Vent   A valve installed at the high points in a hot water system to remove air from the system.

Air Washer   Filtration of air using water or other liquid.

Aldehyde   A class of compounds that can be produced during incomplete combustion of a fuel gas.

Algae   A light to dark green plant growth that can develop in water systems.

Alkylbenzene   A synthetic oil compatible with CFC and HCFC refrigerants.

Allen Head Screw   Screw with recessed head designed to be turned with a hex shaped wrench.

Alternating Current (AC)   Current that reverses polarity or direction with regular frequency. It can be single phase, two phase, three phase, or polyphase.

Alternative Refrigerant   A replacement refrigerant that is different from the existing system refrigerant.

Alternator   A machine that converts mechanical energy into alternating current.

Altitude   The measured distance above sea level.

Altitude Adjustment   Thermostat adjustment to account for changes in elevation dependent on geographical location.

Ambient Compensator   An electronic device that provides enough heat to cycle the refrigeration unit when ambient temperatures are low.

Ambient Temperature   Temperature of the air that surrounds an object.

American National Standards Institute (ANSI)   Institute that determines refrigeration standards along with ASHRAE.

American Society of Heating, Refrigeration, and Air Conditioning Engineers (ASHRAE)   Its membership is composed of thousands of professional engineers and technicians from all phases of the HVAC/R industry. ASHRAE also creates equipment standards for the industry.

American Society for Testing and Materials Engineers (ASTME)   Society that in addition to materials testing determines wind and rain infiltration standards.

American Standard Pipe Thread   Identifies the standard pipe thread size encountered in the field for installation purposes.

American Wire Gauge (AWG)   A system of numbers that designate cross-sectional area of wire. As the diameter gets smaller, the number gets larger, for example, AWG #14 = 0.0641 in, AWG #12 = 0.0808 in.

Ammeter   An electric meter used to measure current.

Ammonia   A widely used refrigerant for large commercial systems due to its high latent heat value.

Amperage   The measured flow of electrical current.

Ampere   Unit of electric current equivalent to the flow of one coulomb per second.

Ampere Turn (AT) (NI)   Unit of magnetizing force produced by a current flow of one ampere through one turn of wire in a coil.

Amplitude   The maximum instantaneous value of alternating current or voltage. It can be in either a positive or negative direction.

Analog Electronic Device   A device that delivers a modulated signal.

Analog Signal   A modulated signal as compared to a digital signal, which is binary.

Analog VOM   A volt-ohm meter using a needle measurement scale rather than a digital display.

Anemometer   Instrument for measuring the flow rate of air.

Aneroid Barometer   An instrument used for measuring barometric pressure.

Angle Valve   A valve that is constructed with a 90° bend.

Angle of Lag or Lead   Phase angle difference between two sinusoidal waveforms having the same frequency.

Annealing   Process of heat treating metal to obtain desired properties of softness and ductility.

Annual Fuel Utilization Efficiency (AFUE)   A furnace efficiency comparison for consumers.

Anode   The positive electrode in an electrolytic cell.

Anticipator   A heater used to adjust thermostat operation to produce a closer temperature differential than the mechanical capability of the control.

Antifreeze Solution   A mixture of glycol and water with a freezing point below 32°F.

Approach   Term used for cooling water towers to determine effectiveness. A measure of the cooling air ambient wet bulb compared to the temperature of the cooling water.

Approach Temperature   Chilled water leaving temperature compared to refrigerant temperature.

Arcing   Sparking discharge between two electrodes or contacts.

Armature   The moving or rotating component of a motor, generator, relay, or other electromagnetic device.

ASME   American Society of Mechanical Engineers.

Aspect Ratio   Ratio of length to width of a rectangular duct.

Aspirating Psychrometer   A device that draws in a sample of air to measure for humidity.

Aspiration   To draw a fluid by creating a suction.

Atmospheric Dust Spot Efficiency   A measure of the ability for a filter to remove atmospheric dust from a test sample of air.

Atmospheric Pressure   The envelope of atmospheric gases creating a pressure equal to approximately 14.7 psi at a temperature of 70°F at sea level.

Atom   Smallest particle of an element.

Atomic Weight   The number of protons in an atom of a material.

Atomize   Process of changing a liquid to a fine spray.

Atomization   (see Atomize)

Atomizing Humidifier   A humidifier that supplies finely atomized water into the airstream.

Attenuate   Decrease or lessen in intensity.

Auger   Rotating device resembling a huge corkscrew used in ice machines.

Authorized Dealer   A dealer authorized to install heat pumps by the manufacturer.

Automatic Changeover Thermostat   A thermostat that automatically changes modes dependent on the room temperature.

Automatic Defrost   System of removing ice and frost from evaporators automatically.

Automatic Expansion Valve (AEV)   Pressure controlled valve used as a metering device.

Automatic Pumpdown System   A system designed to pump down refrigerant to the receiver prior to shutting down.

Autotransformer   A transformer in which both primary and secondary coils have turns in common. Stepup or stepdown of voltage is accomplished by taps on a common winding.

Auxiliary Drain Pan   Located beneath the evaporator coil to collect and drain away water that condenses from the air.

Azeotrope   Two or more refrigerants mixed together by the refrigerant manufacturer that have the combined properties of a single refrigerant.

B Vent   Double walled vent pipe used for gas furnace applications.

BW Vent   Double walled vent pipe used with wall type gas furnaces.

Back Electromotive Force (BEMF)   Voltage generating effect of an electrical motor's rotor.

Back Pressure   Pressure in the low side of the refrigeration system. Also called low side pressure or suction pressure.

Back Seat   The position of a service valve that is all the way counterclockwise or fully open.

Bacteria   Microscopic organisms found almost everywhere; while some types can be useful, other types can cause disease.

Baffle   Similar to a damper used to regulate the flow of a fluid.

Balance Fitting   A pipe fitting or valve designed so that its resistance to flow may be varied. This type of fitting is used to obtain the desired flow rate through parallel circuits.

Balance Point   The outdoor temperature at which the heating capacity of a heat pump in a particular installation is equal to the heat loss of the conditioned area. Below the balance point, supplementary heat is needed to maintain indoor comfort.

Balance Point, Initial   The outdoor ambient temperature at which the heating capacity of the heat pump only balances the heat loss of the conditioned area.

Balance Point, Second   The outdoor temperature at which the heating capacity of the heat pump plus the auxiliary heat capacity balances the heat loss of the conditioned area.

Balanced-Port TEV   A thermostatic expansion valve that compensates for wide variations in high to low side pressure and evaporator loads.

Ball Check Valve   A check valve that uses a ball against a seat as a shut-off means.

Ball Valve   A valve in which modulation or shut-off is accomplished by a one quarter turn of a ball that has an opening through it.

Bar   One bar is 100 kilopascals (kPa) with 101.3 kPa equal to standard atmospheric pressure.

Barometer   Instrument for measuring atmospheric pressure.

Base   Semiconductor terminal.

Baseboard   A terminal unit resembling the base trim of a house.

Bath   A container holding a liquid where a component can be washed or heated.

Battery   Two or more primary or secondary electrically interconnected cells.

Baudelot Cooler   Heat exchanger in which water flows by gravity over the outside of the tubes or plates.

Bearing   Ball bearings are used in pumps and motors to hold the rotating shaft in alignment with the casing.

Bellows   Corrugated cylindrical container that moves as pressures change.

Bellows Seal   A crankshaft seal made tight by a bellows arrangement.

Belly-Band-Mount Motor   An electric motor held in place with a metal strap.

Belt   A flexible material used to connect rotating shafts through a pulley arrangement such as a motor driving a fan.

Bending Spring   Coil spring that is used to keep a tube from collapsing while being bent.

Bio-aerosol   An airborne microbial contaminant, such as a virus, bacteria, fungus, or algae.

Bimetal Strip   Two dissimilar metals with unequal expansion rates fused together.

Blast Freezer   A unit that deep freezes the product faster than conventional freezers.

Bleeding   Slowly draining pressure from a system.

Bleed Off   The continuous or intermittent wasting of a small fraction of the water in the basin of a cooling tower to prevent the buildup of scale-forming minerals.

Bleed Valve   Valve that permits a minimum fluid flow when valve is closed.

Blend   A mixture of two or more refrigerants.

Blocked Suction   A method for unloading a reciprocating compressor.

Blowdown   Draining a controlled amount of water from a cooling water tower to reduce the level of dissolved solids.

Blown   Building insulation can be applied to a structure using this method. A melted fuse can be considered blown.

Blower   A centrifugal fan.

Boiler   A furnace that generates either hot water or steam.

Boiler, High Pressure   A boiler that operates at a pressure higher than 15 psig.

Boiler, Low Pressure   A boiler that operates at a pressure below 15 psig.

Boiler Horsepower   The equivalent evaporation of 34.5 lb of water per hour at 212°F. This is equal to a heat output of $970.3 \times 34.5 = 33,475$ Btu/hr.

Boiling Point   Temperature at a given pressure at which a fluid changes from a liquid to a gas.

Boiling Temperature   Temperature at which a fluid changes from a liquid to a gas.

Bonnet   The sheet metal chamber in a furnace where heat collects.

Booster Pump   A second pump used to raise the pressure in the system higher than created by the first pump.

Boot   Connection between a floor register and a branch duct.

Bore   Inside diameter of a cylindrical hole.

Bourdon Tube   Thin walled tube of circular shape that tends to straighten as pressure inside is increased.

Boyle's Law   Law stating the pressure-volume relationship of gases.

Brazing   Soldering with a filler material whose melting temperature is higher than 840°F.

Break   Electrical discontinuity in the circuit generally resulting from the operation of a switch or circuit breaker.

Breaker   (see Circuit Breaker)

Breaker Strip   Strip of plastic used to cover the joint between the outside case and the inside liner of a refrigerator.

Breeching   Transition piece located between furnace and stack.

Bubble Point   The formation of bubbles in a saturated liquid refrigerant zeotrope will begin at this temperature.

Building Related Illness (BRI)   Health disorders linked to the environment of modern airtight buildings.

Built Up System   Unit is not packaged but instead the individual components (condenser, compressor, etc.) are installed together at the job site.

Brine   Water saturated with a chemical such as salt.

British Thermal Unit (Btu)   The amount of heat required to raise the temperature of 1 lb of water (about one pint) by 1°F.

Bulb   Used as a sensing element for valves and controls.

Bull Head   The installation of a pipe tee in such a way that water enters (or leaves) the tee at both ends of the run (the straight through section of the tee) and leaves (or enters) through the side connection only.

Bunsen Burner   A gas burner in which combustion air is premixed with the gas supply within the burner body before the gas burns at the burner port.

Burner   A device for the final conveyance of gas, or a mixture of gas and air, to the combustion zone.

Burnout   Accidental passage of high voltage through an electrical circuit or device that causes damage.

Burr   Raised edges left behind from cutting tubing or a pipe. This burr must be removed before installation.

Butane   A highly flammable, colorless, odorless, easily liquefied gas.

Butterfly Valve   A valve with a handle that can be positioned 90° to be either parallel (open) or perpendicular (closed) to the fluid flow.

Bypass   A connection that diverts the fluid flow around a valve or component.

Cadmium Cell   A device whose resistance changes according to the amount of light sensed.

Calibrate   To adjust an indicator so that it correctly indicates the variable sensed.

Calorie   Heat required to raise the temperature of 1g of water 1°C.

Calorimeter   A device for measuring the heat of chemical reactions.

Cam   A projection on a rotating disc that can be used to operate defrost timers as the cam slowly turns.

Capacitance   A measure of the amount of energy stored by a capacitor.

Capacitive Reactance   The capacitive electrical impedance opposing the alternating current in a circuit.

Capacitor   Type of electrical storage device used in starting and/or running circuits on many electric motors.

Capacitor Start Motor (CSR)   A single-phase motor that has a capacitor in series with the start winding.

Capacity   The rating of a unit generally based on size, power, and refrigerant amount.

Capillary Attraction   The ability of one substance to draw another substance into it.

Capillary Tube   A fixed restriction pressure reducing device. Usually consists of lengths of small inside diameter tubing. The flow restriction produces the necessary reduction in pressure and boiling point of the liquid refrigerant before entering the evaporator.

Capillary Tube System   A refrigeration unit that utilizes a capillary tube type of flow control device.

Carbon Dioxide (CO_2)   A nontoxic product of combustion.

Carbon Dioxide Indicator   Device used to measure carbon dioxide levels.

Carbon Filter   Activated charcoal filter used for adsorption purposes.

Carbon Monoxide (CO)   A chemical resulting from incomplete combustion. It is odorless, colorless, and toxic.

Cascade System   One having two or more refrigerant circuits, each with a compressor, condenser, and evaporator, where the evaporator of one circuit cools the condenser of the other (lower temperature) circuit.

Cathode   Electrode through which positive electric current flows.

Cavitation   Vapor bubbles forming in a liquid region due to a drop in pressure that creates turbulence.

Celsius   The metric system temperature scale.

Cellulose   Is used as an environmentally preferable material for building insulation.

Centigrade   An earlier name for the Celsius scale.

Centimeter   Metric unit of linear measurement, equals 0.3937 in.

Central Air Conditioning   Air is treated at a central station and then distributed to the conditioned spaces by a series of ducts.

Central Station   The equipment required for treating the air is all located together at one location.

Centrifugal Compressor   Compressor that compresses gaseous refrigerants by centrifugal force.

Centrifugal Force   The outward force created by the circular motion of an object.

Centrifugal Pump   A pump with a rotating impeller that utilizes centrifugal force to pump a liquid.

Centrifugal Switch   A switch that opens or closes due to the action of centrifugal force.

Ceramic Ignitor   Ignitor used for gas stoves and heaters.

Change of State   (see Phase Change)

CFM   Cubic feet per minute (ft^3/min).

Charge   The amount of refrigerant in a system.

Charging Cylinder   A device for charging a predetermined weight of refrigerant into a system.

Charging Scale   Digital scale that measures the weight of refrigerant in a cylinder.

Charging the Loop   Filling the earth loop with the correct mixture and purging all the air from the loop.

Charles' Law   The ideal gas law.

Check Valve   A flow control valve that permits flow in one direction only.

Chemical Refrigeration   (see Absorption Cycle)

Chill Factor   (see Wind Chill Factor)

Chiller   Refrigeration system designed to cool water, glycol, or brine.

Chilled Water System   The series of pumps and heat exchangers used to deliver chilled water to a conditioned space.

Chimney   Stack used for venting hot flue gases from a boiler or furnace.

Chimney Connector   Connecting pipe to connect the furnace to the chimney.

Chimney Effect   The tendency of air or gas in a duct or other vertical passage to rise when heated.

Chimney Flue   Chimney stack.

Chlorinated Polyvinyl Chloride (CPVC)   A thermoplastic used for hot and cold water pipes.

Chlorofluorocarbon (CFC)   Refrigerant composed of chlorine, fluorine, and carbon.

Circuit   A tubing, piping, or electrical wire installation that permits flow from the energy source back to energy source.

Circuit Breaker   A device that senses current flow and opens when its rated current flow is exceeded.

Circuit, Parallel   (see Parallel Circuit)

Circuit, Pilot   A device used to initiate a circuit.

Circuit, Series   (see Series)

Circulator   A pump used for hydronic heating systems.

Clamp-on Ammeter   Current measuring device that is not connected directly to the circuit but instead temporarily clamps around the electrical wire.

Clearance Space   Amount of access space required on all sides and above and below an installed unit.

Clean Room   Found in semiconductor manufacturing plants to maintain a perfectly clean environment.

Clearance   Space in cylinder not occupied by the piston at the end of the compression stroke.

Climate   Weather conditions for a specific geographical region established over long periods of time.

Climate Control   HVAC is often referred to as a method of climate control.

Closed Circuit   Completed path for current flow with no open switches.

Closed Circuit Cooling Tower   The process cooling fluid is completely isolated from the atmosphere.

Closed Loop   Any cycle in which the primary medium is always enclosed and repeats the same sequence of events.

Closed-Loop Control Configuration   A sensor monitors the output and provides feedback to maintain setpoint conditions.

Closed-Loop Heat Pump   A geothermal heat pump that circulates a glycol solution through a ground coil.

Clutch, Magnetic   Transmits torque and speed without contact.

Clutch, Centrifugal   The driving shaft nested inside the driven shaft uses centrifugal force for engagement.

Coaxial Fitting   A fitting that connects to a single port of a hot water storage tank. Or, tube in a fitting. The hot water goes through the tube into the tank, and the cold water comes out of the fitting surrounding the tube.

Coaxial Heat Exchanger   A spiral shaped heat exchanger consisting of an inner and outer tube for counterflow applications.

Code   Local, state, and national rules and regulations.

Coefficient of Conductivity   Thermal conductivity of a substance (k).

Coefficient of Expansion   Change in length per degree of temperature change of a substance.

Coefficient of Performance (COP)   A ratio calculated by dividing the total heating capacity provided by the refrigeration system, including circulating fan heat but excluding supplementary resistance heat (Btu/hr), by the total electrical input (watts) $\times$ 3.412.

Cogeneration   Combined heat and power.

Coil   A wound conductor that creates a strong magnetic field when current passes through it.

Coil, Device Subcooler   A section in the outdoor evaporator coil used to increase the liquid subcooling during the cooling mode as well as act as an extra defrost surface during the defrost mode.

Coil, Inside   The coil located in the inside portion of the heat pump system. Performs as the evaporator in the cooling mode and the condenser in the heating mode.

Coil, Outside   The coil located in the outside portion of an air-to-air heat pump system. Performs as an evaporator in the heating mode and as the condenser in the cooling mode.

Cold   The absence of heat.

Cold Anticipator   (see Cooling Anticipator)

Cold Junction   The part of the thermoelectric system that absorbs heat.

Cold Trap   Used with vacuum pumps to collect condensation.

Collector   Semiconductor terminal.

Combined Annual Efficiency (CAE)   Annual performance of combination appliances such as space and water heaters.

Combustible Liquids   Class II and Class III liquids with closed cup flash points at or above 100°F.

Combustion   The rapid oxidation of fuel gases accompanied by the production of heat.

Combustion Air   Air supplied for the combustion of a fuel.

Combustion Analyzer   Device used for analysis of flue gases for optimizing combustion efficiency.

Combustion Products   Constituents resulting from the combustion of a fuel gas with the oxygen in air, including the inerts, but excluding excess air.

Comfort   Those conditions that are most suitable for human well being.

Comfort Chart   Chart used in air conditioning that shows the dry bulb temperature and humidity for human comfort.

Comfort Zone   The temperature and humidity range within which one is comfortable.

Commercial Buildings   Such buildings as stores, shops, restaurants, motels, and large apartment buildings.

Commercial System   Systems designed for nonmanufacturing business establishments.

Commutator   A ring of copper segments insulated from each other and connecting the armature and brushes of a motor or generator. It passes power into or from the brushes.

Compound Gauge   Pressure gauge that has scales both above and below atmospheric pressure.

Compound Pump   A two stage pump.

Compound Refrigerating System   System that has several compressors in series.

Compression   A reduction of gas volume resulting in an increase in pressure.

Compression Gauge   A gauge used to measure compression pressure.

Compression Ratio   The absolute discharge pressure divided by the absolute suction pressure for a compressor.

Compression Ring   Piston ring closest to the cylinder head on a reciprocating compressor.

Compression Tank   (see Air Cushion Tank)

Compressor   The pump of a refrigerating mechanism that draws a vacuum or low pressure on the cooling side of refrigerant cycle and squeezes or compresses the gas into the high pressure or condensing side of the cycle.

Compressor Crankcase   Location for the crankshaft and oil sump.

Compressor Displacement   The volume discharged by a compressor in one rotation of the crankshaft.

Compressor, External Drive   A compressor that requires a crankshaft seal because it is externally coupled to a motor.

Compressor Head   (see Cylinder Head)

Compressor, Hermetic   A sealed unit with the compressor and motor located within the same casing.

Compressor, Multiple Stage   Compressor with more than one stage of compression.

Compressor Oil Cooler   Heat exchanger used to cool the oil in a compressor crankcase.

Compressor, Open   (see Compressor, External Drive)

Compressor, Reciprocating   Compressor that uses pistons driven by a crankshaft.

Compressor, Rotary Screw   Compressor that utilizes two meshed rotating positive-displacement helical screws.

Compressor Seal   Leakproof seal between crankshaft and compressor body.

Compressor Shaft Seal   (see Shaft Seal)

Compressor, Single Stage   Compressor with only one stage of compression.

Condensate   Water that has condensed on the surface of a cooling coil.

Condensate Drain Trap   A pipe arrangement that provides a water seal in the drain line to prevent airflow through the drain line.

Condensate Pan   A pan located under an evaporator to collect condensate from the coil and carry it to the drain line.

Condensate Pump   Device used to remove fluid condensate.

Condensation   Liquid that forms when a vapor is cooled below its condensing temperature or dew point.

Condense   The action of changing a saturated vapor to a saturated liquid.

Condenser   The part of the refrigeration system that receives the high pressure superheated vapor from the compressor and extracts the heat in the vapor reducing it to a high pressure saturated liquid.

Condenser, Air Cooled   A heat exchanger that transfers heat energy from the refrigerant vapor to air.

Condenser Fan   A fan used to deliver air across the surface of an air cooled condenser.

Condenser Flooding   Condenser containing excessive liquid refrigerant.

Condenser, Liquid Cooled   A heat exchanger that transfers heat energy from the refrigerant vapor to the liquid heat sink.

Condenser Water Pump   A device used to supply cooling water to the condenser.

Condensible   A gas that can be easily converted to liquid form.

Condensing Boiler   Boiler where the flue gas is allowed to drop below the dew point temperature and condense.

Condensing Furnace   (see Condensing Boiler)

Condensing Pressure   The refrigerant pressure inside the condenser coil.

Condensing Temperature   The temperature at which a vapor changes to a liquid at a given pressure.

Condensing Unit   The portion of the refrigeration system that converts high pressure superheated vapor to high pressure saturated liquid. Commonly called the high side.

Conductance, Thermal (C)   The time rate of heat flow per unit area through a material.

Conduction, Thermal   Particle to particle transmission of heat.

Conductivity   The ability of a substance to allow the flow of heat or electricity.

Conductor   Material or substance that readily passes electricity.

Connected Load   The sum of the capacities or continuous ratings of the load-consuming apparatus connected to a supplying system.

Connecting Rod   The part of a compressor that connects the piston to the crankshaft.

Console   An interface to operate computers and control systems.

Constant   A known and unchanging value.

Constrictor   Tube or orifice used to restrict flow.

Contact   The part of a switch or relay that carries current.

Contactor   A device for making or breaking load carrying contacts by a pilot circuit through a magnetic coil.

Contaminant   A substance (dirt, moisture, etc.) foreign to refrigerant or refrigerant oil in a system.

Continuous Absorption Cycle   An absorption cycle that uses a limited amount of heat with no moving parts.

Continuous Operation   Unit that is always running.

Contractual Agreement   Agreed to by both parties and legally binding.

Control   Switches and other devices to run HVAC/R equipment.

Control Motor   Motor used to control an action such as the positioning of a damper.

Control, High Pressure   Shuts down the unit if the high pressure setpoint is reached.

Control Loop   Control system with sensors and feedback.

Control, Low Pressure   A pressure operated control connected to the suction side of the refrigeration system to prevent unit operation below a set pressure or coil operating boiling point.

Control Module   Component that contains the control system inputs and outputs.

Control Point   The actual value as compared to the setpoint.

Control, Refrigerant   A device used to provide the necessary pressure reduction of the liquid refrigerant to obtain the proper boiling point of the refrigerant in the evaporator.

Control System   System used to manage, command, direct, or regulate other devices.

Control, Temperature   A device that uses changes in temperature to operate contacts in an electrical circuit.

Control Valve   Valve used for directing flow.

Controlled Environment   (see Climate Control)

Controlled Medium   The conditioned air or water distributed through an HVAC/R system.

Controller   Measures the difference between sensed output and desired output and initiates a response to correct the difference.

Convection   Transfer of heat by means of movement of a fluid, either liquid or air.

Convection, Forced   Transfer of convective heat assisted by a pump or fan rather than natural circulation.

Convection, Natural   Transfer of convective heat by natural circulation with warm air rising and cold air falling.

Conversion Factor   Constant value used to change from one scale to another such as from Celsius to Fahrenheit.

Cooler   A walk-in or reach-in refrigerated compartment.

Cooling Anticipator   A resistor in a room thermostat that causes the cooling cycle to begin prematurely.

Cooling Coil   An evaporator coil.

Cooling Tower   Device that cools water by evaporation in air. Water is cooled to the wet bulb temperature of air.

Copper Plating   Electrolysis process that leads to copper deposits on the compressor internals.

Core, Air   (see Air Core Solenoid)

Core, Magnetic   (see Solenoid)

Core Valve   (see Schrader Valve)

Corrosion   The breakdown of material such as the weakening of iron due to oxidation known as rust.

Cotter Pin   Split type fastener also called a cotter key or split pin.

Coulomb   An electrical unit of charge; one coulomb per second (C/s) equals one ampere (A) or 6.25×10^{23} electrons past a given point in 1s.

Counter EMF   Counterelectromotive force. The EMF induced in a coil that opposes applied voltage.

Counterflow   Two liquids and/or vapors flowing in directions opposite to each other.

Coupling   Device used to connect two shafts together.

Cracking a Valve   Opening a valve a small amount.

Cradle-Mounted Motor   A motor cradled on each end and held down with a bracket.

Crankcase Heater   A heating device fastened to the crankcase or lower portion of the compressor housing intended to keep the oil in the compressor at a higher temperature than the rest of the system to reduce the migration of the refrigerant.

Crankcase Pressure Regulating Valve (CPR)   Device to limit the compressor suction pressure to reduce the load at startup.

Crankshaft   Converts rotating motion to reciprocating motion through the connecting rod to the piston.

Crankshaft Seal   Leakproof joint between crankshaft and compressor body.

Crank Throw   Location where the connecting rod is attached to the crankshaft.

Creosote   The buildup of carbon deposits in chimneys from wood-burning fires.

Crisper   The enclosed vegetable compartment in a refrigerator.

Critical Pressure   The vapor pressure at the critical temperature.

Critical Temperature   The temperature above which liquid and gas phases do not exist.

Cross-Charged   A TEV sensing bulb charged with a fluid that is different from the refrigerant used in the system.

Cryogenic   Temperatures typically below −238°F.

Cryogenic Fluid   Liquid nitrogen and liquid helium are commonly used in cryogenic applications.

Cryogenic Food Freezing   Liquid nitrogen is used in blast freezing or immersion freezing systems.

Cryogenics   The branches of physics and engineering that involve the study of very low temperatures.

Crystallization   A highly concentrated brine solution that precipitates as salt.

Cupronickel   An alloy of copper and nickel that does not corrode in seawater.

Current   The flow of electrons through a conductor.

Current Relay   Opens or closes contacts with a change in current flow through it.

Current Limiting Fuse   Opens the circuit if the current is above the setpoint.

Current Transformer   Provides current in its secondary winding proportional to the current flow through its primary winding.

Customer Relations   The evaluation of the technician by the customer as a result of the job performance and attitude.

Cut In   The temperature or pressure at which an automatic control switch closes.

Cut Out   The temperature or pressure at which an automatic control switch opens.

Cycle   A repeated series of events from start to end such as the refrigeration cycle.

Cylinder, Compressor   Compression chamber that houses the piston in a reciprocating compressor.

Cylinder Head   Part that encloses compression end of compressor cylinder.

Cylinder, Refrigerant   Rigid container holding refrigerant which may be of the disposable type or reusable type such as a recovery cylinder.

Cylinder Unloading   Method of reducing compressor load by cutting out individual cylinders.

Cylindrical Commutator   Armature for a motor.

Dalton's Law   Law of partial pressures.

Damper   Movable plate or louver for controlling airflow.

Damper, Return Air   Positioned to control air flow through the return air duct.

Damper, Outdoor Air   Positioned to control airflow through the outdoor air duct.

DC Motor   Direct current motor.

Dead Band   A range of temperature in a heating/cooling system in which no heating or cooling is supplied.

Decibel   Unit used for measuring relative loudness of sounds.

Deck, Cold   Air directed over a cooling coil located in separate cool air duct for a large zone system.

Deck, Hot   Air directed over a heating coil located in separate hot air duct for a large zone system.

Dedicated Geothermal Well   Water is drawn from the top of the well and returned to the bottom of the well. The well supplies only the heat pump.

Deep Vacuum   A vacuum of 500 microns or less.

Defrost Control   A control system used to detect frost or ice buildup on the outside coil of an air-to-air heat pump during the heating mode and causes the system to reverse in order to remove the frost or ice from the coil.

Defrost Cycle   Refrigerating cycle in which evaporator frost and ice accumulation is melted.

Defrosting   Method of removing frost and ice from an evaporator coil.

Defrosting Evaporator   An evaporator that utilizes hot gas defrost.

Defrost Mode   The portion of system operation when the evaporator frost or ice is removed.

Defrost Timer   A device connected into the electronic control system that controls the frequency and duration of the defrost operating mode.

Degreaser   Cleaning solvent used to remove grease.

Degreasing   Using degreaser to remove grease buildup.

Degree Day   Unit that represents one degree of difference from a standard average outdoor temperature of one day.

Dehumidify   Lowering air temperature below its dew point to remove moisture.

Dehumidifier   Device such as a cooling coil used for dehumidification.

Dehydrate   To remove water in all forms from a material or system.

Dehydrated Oil   Moisture free oil.

Dehydrator   Removes moisture in a refrigeration system and is often referred to as a drier.

Deice   To remove ice such as in defrosting.

Deice Control   (see Defrost Control)

Delta Connection   The connection in a three phase system in which terminal connections are triangular, similar to the Greek letter delta (Δ).

Delta-*P*   Change in pressure.

Delta-*T*   Change in temperature.

Delta Connected Motor   (see Delta Connection)

Demand   The size of any load generally averaged over a specified interval of time.

Demand (Billing)   The demand upon which billing to a customer is based.

Demand Meter   An instrument used to measure peak kilowatt hour consumption.

Density   Weight per unit volume.

Deodorizer   Substance used to inhibit the growth of bacteria that causes odors.

Department of Transportation   Name for the government agency in North America devoted to transportation.

Desert Bag   Watertight bag that may be used for storage. A bag used to keep water cool in the desert.

Desiccant   Substance used to collect and hold moisture.

Desiccant Drier   Usually located in the liquid line, a drier charged with desiccant.

Design Load   The amount of heating or cooling required to maintain inside conditions when the outdoor conditions are at design temperature.

Design Pressure   Rated pressure the system is normally designed to operate at.

Design Temperature Difference   The difference between the design indoor and outdoor temperatures.

Design Water Temperature Difference   The difference between the temperature of the water leaving the unit and entering the unit when the system is operating at design conditions.

Desuperheater   A heat exchanger in the hot gas line between the compressor discharge and reversing valve. Used to heat domestic water by removing the superheat from the hot refrigerant vapor.

Detector, Leak   A test instrument used to detect and locate refrigerant leaks.

Detent   Allows for a controlled hesitation in movement.

Dew   Water that has condensed out of air.

Dew Point   Temperature at which water vapor begins to condense out of air. Air at the dew point—100% relative humidity—is referred to as saturated air.

Diagnostics   Methodical identification of symptoms to identify problems with operating equipment.

Diagnostic Thermostat   A thermostat that can receive input to diagnose problems.

Diaphragm   Flexible membrane.

Diaphragm Valve   The valve stem acts on a diaphragm to open or close the valve.

Dielectric   An insulator or nonconductor.

Dies (Thread)   Tool used to cut external threads.

Differential   As applied to controls, the differential between the cut in and cut out temperature or pressure setpoints of a control.

Diffuser   Air distribution outlet designed to direct airflow into a room.

Diffuse Radiation   Solar radiation reaching the earth's surface after having been scattered by molecules in the atmosphere.

Digital Electronic Devices   Devices that send or receive bit stream digital signals

Digital Electronic Signal   A waveform that switches between two voltage levels representing two states (0 and 1).

Digital Volt Ohm Milliammeter (VOM)   A multimeter with a digital output.

Dilution Air   Air that enters a draft hood and mixes with the flue gases.

Diode   A device that will carry current in one direction but not the reverse direction.

Dual Inline Pair Switch (DIP)   A small low amperage single-pole, double-throw switch used in electronic circuits.

Direct Current (DC)   Electric current that flows only in one direction.

Direct Digital Control (DDC)   The ability to control HVAC devices via microprocessors.

Direct Drive Compressor   Compressor directly connected and driven at motor speed.

Direct Drive Motor   Motor directly connected to device it is driving.

Direct Expansion Evaporator   The primary refrigerant expands and absorbs heat from the air as opposed to an indirect expansion system that uses a secondary refrigerant such as chill water.

Direct Return   A two pipe system in which the first terminal unit taken off the supply main is the first unit connected to the return main.

Direct Spark Ignition (DSI)   The gas burner is lit by a direct spark rather than a pilot.

Direct Vent   Flue gases can be vented directly outside the building without the use of a chimney.

Discharge Pressure   Refrigerant pressure on the high side at the compressor outlet of a system.

Discharge Valve   A valve located directly at the outlet of the compressor.

Disconnecting Switch   A knife switch that opens a circuit.

Discus Compressor   A compressor with discus valve design to allow for capacity modulation to reduce cycling.

Discus Valve   A valve designed to allow for less clearance volume vapors to be trapped when the piston is at top dead center.

Dispensing Freezers   Units that process and freeze previously pasteurized product such as soft ice cream.

Displacement   The total volume of refrigerant that a compressor can draw in during the intake stroke.

Distributed Controls   The controls are not in a central location but rather distributed throughout the system.

Distributor   Allows for distribution of refrigerant to individual refrigerant circuits in an evaporator coil.

District Heating and Cooling   A system for distributing heat generated in a centralized location for residential and commercial use.

Disturbed Earth Effect   Denotes the heat content change that affects the earth's temperature by the addition or removal of heat energy by the heat pump system.

Diverter Tee   Fitting used for a hydronic system to direct water through a terminal unit branch circuit.

Dome Hat   Compressor housing for a hermetically sealed refrigeration unit.

Domestic Hot Water   Heated water used for cooking, washing, and so on.

Domestic Geothermal Well   Water is drawn from the top of the well. Only the water from the heat pump is returned to the bottom of the well. The difference is used for building requirements.

Door Heater   A heater located around the opening of a refrigerator door to prevent the door from freezing closed.

Downflow Furnace   Furnace where the return air enters at the top, flows down through the heat exchanger, and exits out the bottom.

Double Pole Switch   Simultaneously opens and closes two connections of a circuit.

Double Thickness Flare   Tubing end that has been formed into a two-wall thickness.

Dowel Pin   Pin pressed through two assembled parts to ensure accurate alignment.

Downdraft   Downward flow of flue gas.

Draft Gauge   Instrument used to measure air pressure.

Draft Indicator   Instrument used to measure chimney draft.

Draft Regulator   Device used to automatically control chimney draft.

Drier   A substance or a device used to absorb moisture within a refrigeration system.

Drift   Entrained water carried from a cooling tower by wind.

Drilled Port Burner   A burner in which the ports have been formed by drilled holes.

Drilled Well   A water supply for a geothermal water source heat pump.

Drip Pan   Pan shaped panel or trough used to collect condensate from evaporator coil.

Drip Proof Motor   A motor typically designed for outdoor use or a wet environment.

Drive Clip   Steel fastener for connecting ductwork.

Dry Bulb Temperature   The actual (physical) temperature of a substance. Usually refers to air.

Dry Cell Battery   Common standard battery with a paste low-moisture electrolyte as compared to a wet cell type.

Dry Ice   Solid carbon dioxide.

Dry System   Refrigerant is metered into the evaporator coil rather than flooding the coil.

Dry Well   A water return for a geothermal water source heat pump open loop.

Dual Pressure Regulator   A high and low pressure control mounted together.

Duct   Round or rectangular sheet metal or fiberglass pipe that carries the air between the conditioning unit and the conditioned area.

Duct Sweeper   A cleaning tool used to remove dirt and debris from the inside of air ducts.

Dust Mites   Microscopic bug often found in bedding and one of the most common allergens that trigger asthma.

Dynamometer   Device for measuring power.

E   Symbol for volts. From the term "electromotive force."

Earth Coupled Heat Pump   Geothermal heat pump.

Earth Temperature, Minimum (*T*)   The lowest temperature the earth will become in the winter season. Used for heat pump design. Will vary with location and weather conditions.

Eccentric   A circle or disk mounted off center on a shaft.

Economizer, Air Conditioning   Multiple flash chamber for air conditioning chiller designed to gain efficiency.

Economizer, Air Supply   Adjusts for optimum outside air supply designed to maintain maximum efficiency.

Economizer, Evaporator   Heat exchanger used to reduce flash gas through the metering device.

Eddy Currents   Circulating flow of current within a conductor that can generate heat.

Effective Area   The actual opening in a grill or register through which air can pass. The effective area is the gross (overall) area of the grill face minus the area of the deflector vanes or bars.

Effective Latent Heat   (see Net Refrigeration)

Effective Temperature   Calculated nonmeasured temperature based upon temperature, humidity, and air movement.

Effectiveness, Absorption Systems   Method to evaluate absorption systems using heat input and cooling effect.

Efficiency, Electrical   A percentage value denoting the ratio of power output to power input.

Ejector   A venturi arrangement used as a pump with no moving parts.

Electric Defrosting   An electric resistance strip heater attached to the evaporator coil used for defrosting.

Electric Field   A magnetic region in space.

Electric Forced Air Furnace   Return air is blown across electric resistance strip heaters.

Electric Heating   A heating system that uses electric resistance elements as the heat energy source.

Electric Heating Element   A unit consisting of resistance wire, insulated supports, and connection terminals for connecting wire to a source of electrical power.

Electric Hydronic Boiler   Electric resistance heating elements used to heat water.

Electric Water Valve   Electrically operated valve to control water flow.

Electrical Circuit   Electrical wire installation that permits flow from the energy source back to energy source.

Electrical Erasable Programmable Read-Only Memory (EEPROM)   Memory used in computers and electronic devices to store small amounts of data.

Electrical Power   Measured in units of watts, equal to voltage × amperage.

Electrical Resistance   The degree to which an object opposes the flow of electric current through it.

Electrical Shock   Contact with a voltage source allowing current to flow through the body.

Electricity   The presence and flow of an electric charge.

Electrodes   Used with high voltage applications for lighting oil and gas burners.

Electrolyte   A solution of a substance (liquid or paste) that is capable of conducting electricity.

Electrolytic Capacitor   Capacitor using a paper spacer soaked in electrolyte in one of its plates.

Electromagnet   A magnet created by the flow of electricity through a coil of wire.

Electromagnetic Energy   Energy derived from an electromagnet.

Electromechanical Controls   Mechanical movement controlled through electrical input or motors.

Electromotive Force (EMF)   The difference in potential or voltage of electrical energy between two points.

Heat Recovery System   System utilizing an energy recovery ventilator.

Heat Recovery Ventilator   (see Energy Recovery Ventilator)

Heat, Sensible   The heat energy used to change the temperature of a material—solid, liquid, or vapor—without a change in state.

Heat Sink   A place or material into which heat energy is placed. In a heat pump, the air outside the house is used as a heat sink during the cooling cycle.

Heat Source   A place or material from which heat energy is obtained. In an air source heat pump, the air outside the house is used as a heat source during the heating cycle.

Heat, Total   The sum of both the sensible and latent heat energy in air. Expressed as Btu/lb of air.

Heat Tape   Electrical resistance heating wire that is wrapped around drain piping to prevent freezing.

Heat Transfer   Movement of heat energy from one body or substance to another. Heat may be transferred by any combination of or all of the three methods radiation, conduction, and convection.

Heat Transfer Coefficient (U)   Value assigned to designate heat transfer through a combination of given materials.

Heat Transfer Rate (Q)   Amount of heat transferred per unit of time.

Helix Coil   Bimetal coil used for dial thermometers.

Henry (H)   The unit of inductance.

Hermetic   Completely sealed.

Hermetic Motor   Compressor drive motor sealed within the same casing that contains the compressor.

Hertz (Hz)   Measure of frequency.

Hg   Symbol for mercury.

High Glide Blend   The range from the bubble point to the dew point is greater than 1°F at constant pressure.

High Efficiency Gas Furnace   Furnace rated at 90% AFUE or better.

High Efficiency Particulate Air Filter (HEPA)   Removes at least 99.97% of airborne particles 0.3 micrometers in diameter.

High Limit Control   Safety that shuts off the furnace burner if the bonnet temperature is too high.

High Pressure Cutout   An electrical pressure control switch operated by the high side pressure that is set to stop the compressor if the pressure safety limit is reached.

High Side   Parts of a refrigerating system that are under condensing or discharge pressure.

High Side Float   Refrigerant flow control located in the condenser.

High Temperature Refrigeration   System with evaporator temperatures above 35°F.

High Vacuum Pump   (see Deep Vacuum)

High Velocity System   Usually large commercial or industrial air distribution systems designed to operate with static pressures of 6–9 in WC.

Horizontal Furnace   The air flows horizontally through the furnace.

Horsepower   A unit of power equal to 33,000 ft-lb of work per minute.

Hot Gas   Compressor discharge vapor.

Hot Gas Bypass   Method of compressor capacity control.

Hot Gas Defrost   A defrosting system in which hot refrigerant gas from the compressor is directed through the evaporator to remove frost or ice from the evaporator.

Hot Gas Line   The refrigerant tube that carries the high pressure, high temperature refrigerant vapor from the compressor to the condenser.

Hot Junction   That part of a thermoelectric circuit that releases heat.

Hot Pulldown   Lowering the temperature of a warm space.

Hot Surface Ignition   A silicon carbide element is heated for the purpose of lighting the main burner.

Hot Water Heating System   System that distributes hot water with pumps for heating a building.

Hot Wire   Live wire with voltage potential to ground.

Humidifiers   Device that directs water spray or mist into an airstream for humidification.

Humidistat   A control that is affected by changes in the relative humidity in air. It is often used to control the operation of a humidifier.

Humidity   Related to the amount of water vapor in the air.

Hunting   Cycling above and below a setpoint such as a valve continuously opening and closing.

Hydraulics   The use of fluid properties for the purpose of fluid power.

Hydrocarbon   Any of a number of compounds composed of carbon and hydrogen.

Hydrochlorofluorocarbon (HCFC)   Refrigerant composed of hydrogen, chlorine, fluorine, and carbon.

Hydrofluorocarbon (HFC)   Refrigerant composed of hydrogen, fluorine, and carbon.

Hydrogen   A colorless, odorless, highly flammable gas. It is the lightest of all elements.

Hydrometer   Floating instrument used to measure specific gravity of a liquid.

Hydronics   Pertaining to heating or cooling with water.

Hygrometer   An instrument used to measure the percentage of moisture (relative humidity) in air.

Hygroscopic   Ability of a substance to absorb and retain moisture.

Ice Bank   A thermal accumulator in which ice is formed or charged during off peak periods of refrigeration demand, and used during peak demand for refrigeration to supplement the compressor capacity by melting the ice.

Ice Harvest Switch   A device located at the end of the water plate. It resets the timer on the status indicator control card after each ice harvest.

Ice Maker   A cyclic-type automatic ice making machine that has separate and sequential water fill, freezing, and ice harvesting phases for the production of ice.

Ice Ring   An accumulation of ice at the bottom of the outdoor coil due to incomplete defrost operation.

Identification Plate   Equipment data or name plate.

Idler   A pulley used on some belt drives to provide the proper belt tension.

Ignition System   Method of lighting a furnace.

Ignition Temperature   The minimum temperature at which combustion can be started.

Ignition Transformer   A transformer designed to provide a high voltage current for furnace electrodes.

Impedance   A type of electrical resistance that is only present in alternating current circuits.

Impeller   Rotating part of a centrifugal pump.

Impingement   (see Flame Impingement)

Incandescent Heat driven light emissions allowing an object to glow from the heat.

Inches Hg Pressure Measurement of pressure in inches of mercury (in Hg) absolute.

Inches Hg Vacuum Measurement of vacuum in inches of mercury (in Hg) vacuum.

Inclined Water Manometer (see Manometer, Inclined)

Incomplete Combustion A condition where a portion of the fuel passing through a furnace remains unburned.

Indoor Air Quality A measurement of the factors attributing to the air quality condition within a building.

Indoor Coil The portion of a heat pump that is located in the house and functions as the heat transfer point for warming or cooling indoor air.

Induced Draft Burner A burner that depends on draft induced by a fan or blower at the flue outlet to draw in combustion air and vent flue gases.

Induced Magnetism Ability of a magnetic field to induce magnetism in a metal.

Inductance The characteristic of an alternating current circuit to oppose a change in current flow.

Induction The act that produces induced voltage in an object by exposure to a magnetic field.

Induction Motor An AC motor that operates on the principle of the rotating magnetic field. The rotor has no electrical connection, but receives electrical energy by transformer action from field windings.

Inductive Circuit Electrical circuit where the current lags the voltage.

Inductive Load A device that uses electrical energy to produce motion.

Inductive Reactance Opposition, measured in ohms, to an alternating or pulsating current.

Inerts Noncombustible substances in a fuel, or in flue gases, such as nitrogen or carbon dioxide.

Infiltration The air that leaks into the refrigerated or air conditioned space.

Infrared Unnoticeable rays just below red in the visible spectrum that transfer heat by radiation.

Infrared Humidifier A humidifier that utilizes infrared lamps to evaporate the water into the airstream.

Infrared Lamp An electrical device that emits infrared rays.

Inherent Motor Protection Built in motor protection such as a thermal overload located in the winding.

Inhibitor Substance that prevents a chemical reaction.

Injection Term used for a hydronic system circulating pump forcing water into a secondary heating loop.

In Phase The condition existing when two waves of the same frequency have their maximum and minimum values of like polarity at the same instant.

Input/Output Board Circuit board with measured inputs and controlled outputs.

Inspection To examine equipment and installation and compare to established guidelines and codes.

Instrument The addition of sensors with feedback and control loops to an existing system.

Insulation, Electric A substance that is a poor conductor of electricity with few free electrons.

Insulation, Thermal Substance used to retard or slow the flow of heat through a wall or partition.

Insulator Nonconductive material such as glass, rubber, or plastic used to shield bare wires and electrical connections.

Integrated Circuit A miniaturized electronic circuit consisting of mainly semiconductor devices.

Integrated Circuit Board Electronic circuits are manufactured on a thin surface of semiconductor material that is also referred to as microchip or just chip.

Interlock A safety device that allows power to a circuit only after a predetermined function has taken place.

Intermittent Absorption Cycle Closed system charged with ammonia and water and activated by a gas burner.

Intermittent Ignition Furnace ignition system that operates only as required.

Internal Motor Overload (see Inherent Motor Protection)

Interstate Commerce Commission (ICC) Federal regulatory body to oversee common carriers such as railroads and trucking.

Inverter An electrical device for converting DC to AC.

Ion An ion is an atom that is either negatively (anion) or positively (cation) charged.

Ion Generator A device that charges particles.

IR Drop Voltage drop resulting from current flow through a resistor.

Isolation Relays A relay designed to prevent undesirable electrical feedback.

Isothermal At constant temperature.

Joints, Brazed A solder type connection or joint obtained by the joining of the metal parts with metallic mixtures or alloys that have a melting temperature above 1,000°F and up to 1,500°F.

Joint, Soldered A solder type connection or joint obtained by the joining of the metal parts with metallic mixtures or alloys that have a melting temperature below 1,000°F.

Joint, Welded A solder type pipe connection or joint obtained by the joining of the metal parts with metallic mixtures or alloys that have a melting temperature above 1,500°F.

Joule A measure of heat in the metric system.

Joule-Thomson Effect A drop in gas temperature due to a sudden increase in its volume

Journal, Crankshaft Part of the shaft that contacts the bearing.

Junction Box Group of electrical terminals housed in protective box or container.

Kelvin Scale (K) Thermometer scale on which the unit of measurement equals the centigrade degree and according to which absolute zero is 0°K, the equivalent of −273.16°C.

Kilocalorie (C) Measure of heat equal to 1,000 calories.

Kilometer (km) Measure of distance equal to 1,000 m.

Kilopascal (kPa) A measure of pressure in the metric system.

Kilovoltampere (kVA) Measure of electrical work equal to 1,000 voltamperes.

Kilowatt (kW) A unit of electrical energy equal to 1,000 W.

Kilowatt Hour (kWh) A unit for measuring electrical energy equal to 3,413 Btu.

Kinetic Energy Energy in motion.

King Valve The valve located at the outlet of the receiver.

Lacquer Clear coating on wire that provides insulation for electric windings.

Ladder Diagram Electrical diagram that shows a circuit by circuit arrangement. The power lines are the "rails" of the ladder, and each individual circuit is a "rung" of the ladder.

Lagging Thermal insulation around pipes and boiler jackets.

Psychrometrics The study of the thermodynamic and physical properties of air.

Puffback An explosion in the firebox of an oil burner accompanied by a puff of smoke created by delayed ignition. Potentially very hazardous.

Pulley A wheel with a groove around its circumference used for transmitting mechanical power using a belt designed to fit in the groove.

Pulse Combustion A series of small explosions that produces extremely efficient combustion.

Pulse Furnace A Furnace that uses pulse combustion for high operating efficiency.

Pulse Width Modulation (PWM) A pulsing electronic signal that communicates based on the length of the pulses and the time intervals in between the pulses. Used in some types of electronic control systems.

Pump A motor driven device used to mechanically circulate water in the system.

Pump, Centrifugal A pump that works by taking water into the center of a high-rpm impellar and throwing it to the outside of the wheel using centrifugal force.

Pump, Screw Moves liquid using two intermeshing, auger shaped screws turning in opposite directions

Pumpdown A service procedure where the refrigerant is pumped into the receiver.

Pump Head The difference in pressure on the supply and intake sides of the pump created by the operation of the pump.

Purging Releasing compressed gas to atmosphere through some part or parts for the purpose of removing contaminants from that part or parts.

Pyrometer Instrument for measuring temperatures.

Quenching Submerging hot solid object in cooling fluid.

Quench Valve A valve used on transport refrigeration units to meter small amounts of liquid refrigerant into the suction side of the compressor to reduce the compressor discharge temperature.

Quick Connect Coupling A device that permits an easy and fast means of connecting two fluid lines or fittings together without the use of solder.

R Value, SI The thermal resistance of a building material in units of $K \cdot m^2/W$.

R Value, U.S. The thermal resistance of a building material in units of $ft^2 \cdot °F \cdot h/Btu$.

Rack System A commercial refrigeration system with multiple compressors manifolded together on a rack.

Radiant Heating A heating system in which only the heat radiated from panels is effective.

Radiation Transfer of heat by heat rays.

Radiator A heating unit exposed to view within the room or space to be heated.

Radiator Valve A valve installed on a terminal unit to manually control the flow of water through the unit.

Radon A naturally occurring radioactive gas sometimes found in basements and crawl spaces.

Range Pressure or temperature settings of a control.

Rankine (R) Absolute Fahrenheit scale.

Rated-Load Amperage (RLA) The current that a motor draws when it is operating at its rating condition.

Reactance Opposition to alternating current by either inductance or capacitance, or both.

Reamer A tool for removing the burr left by a tubing cutter.

Receiver A refrigeration component located after the condenser that stores high pressure liquid refrigerant.

Receiver-drier A refrigerant receiver that incorporates a desiccant bag for dehydrating the refrigerant.

Reciprocal The result of dividing any number into 1 is its reciprocal.

Reciprocating Action in which the motion is back and forth in a straight line.

Reciprocating Compressor A compressor that uses pistons, cylinders, and valves to compress gas.

Recirculated Air Return air passed through the conditioner before being again supplied to the conditioned space.

Recirculated Water System A heating or cooling system that reuses the same water by circulating the water through a closed loop.

Reclaim To reprocess refrigerant so that it meets the AHRI 700-2006 standard for new refrigerant.

Recording Ammeter An ammeter that can record the amp draw over a period of time either on paper or in the meter's memory.

Recording Thermometer A thermometer that can record the temperature over a period of time either on paper or in its memory.

Recording Voltmeter A voltmeter that can record voltage over a period of time either on paper or in the meter's memory.

Recovery Removing refrigerant from a system and storing it in an external container without cleaning or processing the refrigerant.

Recovery Cylinder A DOT approved cylinder for storing recovered refrigerant.

Rectifier, Electric An electrical device for converting AC into DC.

Rectifier, Refrigeration A component in an absorption system that condenses water vapor and returns it to the generator to improve ammonia concentration to the condenser.

Recuperative Heat Exchanger A secondary heat exchanger on high efficiency gas and oil furnaces that recovers heat from the combustion gases through condensation.

Recycling Removing refrigerant from a system, processing it using filters and oil separators, and storing it in an external container.

Reducing Fitting A pipe fitting designed to change from one pipe size to another.

Reed Valve Thin flat tempered steel plate fastened at one end.

Reference Point A specific known condition used for calibrating instruments.

Reference Pressure The pressure that data in a chart or table are based on.

Reference Temperature The temperature that the data in a chart or table are based on.

Refractory A material that can withstand very high temperature that is used to line the combustion chamber of furnaces.

Refrigerant Substance used in a refrigerating mechanism to absorb heat in an evaporator coil and to release its heat in a condenser.

Refrigerant Blend A mixture of two or more refrigerants that do not chemically combine.

Refrigerant Charge Quantity of refrigerant in a system.

Refrigerant Control Another name for the refrigerant expansion device or metering device in a refrigeration system.

Refrigerant Quality The percentage of liquid and vapor in a saturated mixture.

Refrigerant Reclaim (see Reclaim)

Refrigerant Recovery (see Recovery)

Refrigerant Recycling (see Recycling)

Refrigerating Effect The amount of heat in Btu/hr the system is capable of transferring.

Refrigerant Expansion Device Another name for the metering device or refrigerant control in a refrigeration system.

Refrigerated Air Drier Reduces the dew point of compressed air using a refrigeration system.

Refrigeration The process of transferring heat from one place to another.

Refrigeration Cycle A process during which a refrigerant absorbs heat at a relatively low temperature and reflects heat at a relatively higher temperature.

Refrigeration Oil Specially prepared oil used in refrigerator mechanism. It circulates with refrigerant.

Refrigeration System The combination of interconnecting devices, tubes, and/or pipes in which the refrigerant is circulated for the purpose of exchanging heat to produce cooling.

Register Combination grill and damper assembly on an air opening or at the end of an air duct.

Regulator A device that controls the flow through it to control the downstream pressure.

Relative Humidity (RH) The ratio of the weight of moisture that air actually contains at a certain temperature as compared to the amount that it could contain if it were saturated.

Relay Electrical mechanism that uses small current in the control circuit to operate a valve switch in the operating circuit.

Relief Opening The opening in a draft hood to permit ready escape to the atmosphere of flue products.

Relief Valve Safety device designed to open before a dangerous pressure is reached.

Reluctance The opposition to magnetic lines of force passing through a magnetic material.

Remote Bulb A temperature sensing element that works by pressure change which is transmitted through a capillary tube to the control. It is located in a different location from the component it controls.

Remote Condenser A condenser that is located by itself in a different location from the compressor.

Repulsion Start Induction Motor Type of motor that has an electrical winding on the rotor for starting purposes.

Resilient Motor Mount A motor mount that contains flexible material such as rubber to reduce transmission of vibration and noise.

Refrigerant Control Another name for the refrigerant expansion device or metering device in a refrigeration system.

Refrigerant Dye Used to locate difficult to find leaks in refrigeration systems. It actually dyes the refrigerant oil, not the refrigerant.

Refrigerant Management System An accounting system to document refrigerant use.

Resistance The opposition to current flow by a physical conductor.

Resistor An electronic component with a fixed electrical resistance that opposes current flow.

Resonance The pipe organ effect produced by a gas furnace when the frequency of the burner flame combustion and the pressure wave distance in the burner pouch are in exact synchronization.

Restrictor A refrigerant metering device with a small orifice that creates a pressure drop because of its restriction

Retrofit, Mechanical Reworking existing equipment to meet current efficiency or code requirements.

Retrofit, Refrigerant Reworking an existing system to replace an older ozone depleting refrigerant with a newer environmentally friendly refrigerant.

Return Air Air returned from conditioned or refrigerated space.

Return Well The well that water from an open loop water source heat pump is returned to.

Return Piping That portion of the piping system that carries water from the terminal units back to the boiler.

Reverse Acting Control (RA) A switch controlled by temperature and designed to open on temperature drop and close on temperature rise.

Reverse Cycle Defrost A method of defrosting the evaporator by means of flow valve(s) to move hot vapor from the compressor into the evaporator.

Reverse Cycle Refrigeration System Commonly called a heat pump. A refrigeration system capable of reversing its operation and direction of heat transfer.

Reverse Return A two pipe system in which the return connections from the terminal units into the return main are made in the reverse order from that in which the supply connections are made.

Reversing Valve A device used to change the direction of refrigerant vapor flow between the evaporator to compressor and from the compressor to the condenser depending on the heating or cooling effect desired.

Rheostat An adjustable or variable resistor.

Rich Mixture A mixture of gas and air containing too much fuel or too little air for complete combustion of the gas.

Riser A vertical pipe carrying gas or fluid up against gravity.

Rod and Tube Consists of a rod with a low expansion rate inside a tube with a high expansion rate. Thermal change produces linear movement for operating switches.

Rollout A condition where flame rolls out of a combustion chamber when the burner is turned on.

Roof Mounted The unit is mounted on a platform designed to distribute the weight of the unit over as wide an area of the roof as possible.

Root Mean Square Voltage (RMS) An accurate method of determining the effective voltage of an alternating current waveform.

Rotary Compressor Mechanism that compresses by trapping gas in a cylinder between an offset disc and one or more blades.

Rotating Blade Rotary Compressor A rotary compressor with blades housed in the offset disc that rotate with the compressor shaft.

Rotor Rotating part of a mechanism.

Run Capacitor   A capacitor designed to stay in the circuit all the time in a permanent split capacitor motor.

Running Winding   Electrical winding of motor which has current flowing through it during normal operation of the motor.

Runout   This term generally applies to the horizontal portion of branch duct between the main trunk and the diffuser.

Rupture Disk   A disk on a low pressure chiller that breaks to keep the pressure of the chiller from exceeding 15 psig.

S Lock   An S shaped metal strip used to hold the long sides of rectangular metal duct together.

SI System   The international system of units based on the metric system.

Saddle Valve   Valve body shaped so it may be silver brazed to refrigerant tubing surface.

Safety Control   Device that will stop the refrigerating unit if unsafe pressures and/or temperatures are reached.

Safety Interlock Switch   A switch that prevents the operation of a machine at an unsafe condition, such as with a panel removed.

Safety Plug   Device that will release the contents of a container above normal pressure conditions and before rupture pressures are reached.

Sail Switch   A switch that detects airflow in ductwork using a "sail".

Satellite Compressor   A compressor on a rack system that is dedicated to the lowest temperature and pressure evaporators.

Saturated Vapor   A vapor condition that will result in condensation into droplets of liquid as vapor temperature is reduced.

Saturation   Condition when both liquid and vapor are present or either phase is just about to appear or disappear.

Saybolt Universal Seconds (SUS, SSU)   Used to measure oil viscosity. It is the time required for 60 ml of oil to flow through the calibrated orifice.

Scaling   The formation of lime and other deposits on the water side surfaces of heat exchangers.

Schematic Wiring Diagram   Another name for ladder or line diagram.

Schrader Valve   Spring loaded device that permits fluid flow when a center pin is depressed.

Scotch Yoke   Mechanism used to change reciprocating motion into rotary motion or vice versa.

Screw Compressor   Compresses gas using two intermeshing, auger shaped screws turning in opposite directions.

Scroll Compressor   Reduces the gas volume using a fixed and an orbiting scroll (spiral) to move gas from the outside of the scrolls to the inside.

Sealed Combustion   Provides combustion air for a furnace, water heater, or boiler through a pipe, sealing off the combustion process from the air surrounding the equipment.

Seasonal Energy Efficiency Ratio (SEER)   The total cooling of a central air conditioner in Btu during its normal annual usage period for cooling divided by the total electric input in watt-hours during the same period.

Seat   The part of a valve body that the moveable portion of the valve rests against when sealing off.

Secondary Air   Combustion air externally supplied to a burner flame at the point of combustion.

Secondary Refrigerant   The water or brine that is circulated in a chiller system from the chiller to the heat load.

Secondary Refrigeration System   Uses a primary refrigerant in a compression refrigeration system to cool a fluid that is circulated to the actual heat load. The secondary refrigerant uses all sensible cooling and does not change state.

Secondary Voltage   The output, or load supply voltage, of a transformer.

Second Law of Thermodynamics   Heat will flow only from material at a certain temperature to material at a lower temperature.

Seebeck Effect   The generation of electrical current when a temperature difference exists between the two ends of a thermocouple.

Semiconductor   A material that conducts electricity better than an insulator but not as well as a conductor.

Semihermetic Compressor   A serviceable hermetic compressor.

Sensible Heat   Heat energy added to or removed from a material that causes a change in temperature of the material without a change in state of the material.

Sensor   A material or device that changes characteristics (electrical or mechanical) with a change in temperature and pressure.

Sequencer   A control device used to control electrical circuits that use a heat motor for time delay of the operation of the device (see Heat Motor).

Series   A circuit with one continuous path for current flow.

Series Wound Motor   A brush-type motor with a wound armature that is wired in series with the field windings. It can operate on either DC or AC current.

Serviceable Hermetic   Hermetic unit housing containing motor and compressor assembled by use of bolts or threads.

Service Factor (SF)   A decimal factor that produces the maximum safe motor output when multiplied by the motor's nominal capacity rating.

Service Valve   Device used by service technicians to check pressures and change refrigerating units.

Setpoint   The temperature setting on a thermostat.

Shaded Pole Motor   A small AC motor used for light start loads.

Shaft Seal   A device used to prevent leakage between shaft and housing.

Shell and Coil Condenser   A water cooled condenser consisting of a coil of tubing inside a shell. Water runs through the coil, and the refrigerant is in the shell.

Shell and Tube   A water cooled condenser consisting of straight tubes passing through a shell. Water runs through the tubes, and the refrigerant is in the shell.

Short Circuit   A low resistance connection (usually accidental and undesirable) between two parts of an electrical circuit.

Short Cycling   Refrigerating system that starts and stops more frequently than it should.

Shroud   A baffle around a propeller fan that separates the intake air from the exhaust air.

Sick Building Syndrome (SBS)   A combination of ailments associated with an individual's exposure to a particular building.

Sight Glass   Glass tube or glass window in refrigerating mechanism that shows the amount of refrigerant or oil in the system.

Silica Gel   Chemical compound used as a drier that has ability to absorb moisture.

Silicon   A semiconductor material used in the manufacture of electronic components.

Silver Brazing   Brazing process in which brazing alloy contains some silver as part of the joining alloy.

Sine Wave   The shape created when the voltage of an alternating current is graphed. It appears like a regular set of repeating peaks and valleys connected by a single smooth curve.

Single Package Heat Pump   A system that has all components completely contained in one unit.

Single Phase   An alternating current with a single sine waveform supplied by two wires.

Single-Phase Motor   An electric motor designed to operate on single phase alternating current.

Single Phasing   Occurs when a three phase motor is suddenly operating on a single phase of current instead of three because one of the three legs of power drops out. The current in the remaining two legs increases and the motor windings rapidly overheat.

Single Pipe System, Steam Heat   A method of piping that allows a single pipe to carry both the steam to the radiators and the condensate back to the boiler.

Single Pipe System, Oil Heat   Using a single pipe to carry the oil from the tank to the oil burner.

Single Pole Double Throw Switch (SPDT)   A switch that can connect a center post to one of two circuits.

Single Pole Single Throw Switch (SPST)   A switch that can open or close a single circuit.

Skin Condenser   A condenser commonly found on chest type freezers that uses the outer surface of the cabinet to radiate heat.

Slinger Ring   A ring around the outside of the condenser fan on window units that throws evaporator condensate water onto the condenser, causing the water to evaporate.

Sling Psychrometer   Humidity measuring device with wet and dry bulb thermometers.

Slinky Loop   A type of loop used in ground source heat pump installations in which a coil of tubing is stretched out in a ditch a flattened slinky.

Slip   The difference between the synchronous speed and the actual speed of an induction motor.

Slug   A quantity of liquid in the compressor clearance space that causes a hydraulic hammer.

Slugging   A condition where liquid refrigerant is entering an operating compressor.

Smoke Test   Test made to determine completeness of combustion.

Snap Action   A means of ensuring positive closure of a mechanically operated electrical switch.

Snap-Disc   A warped bimetal disc that snaps at a particular temperature to operate switches.

Soft Flame   A flame partially deprived of primary air such that the combustion zone is extended and the inner cone is ill defined.

Solar Cell   (see Photovoltaic Cell)

Solar Collector   Typically, an insulated box that converts solar energy into thermal energy using a black surface.

Solar Heat   Heat from visible and invisible energy waves from the sun.

Solder   An alloy with a low melting temperature used for joining metals.

Soldering   Joining two metals by adhesion of a low melting temperature metal (less than 840°F).

Solderless Terminals   Wire terminals that connect to the wires using mechanical crimping rather than solder.

Solenoid   A movable plunger activated by an electromagnetic coil.

Solenoid Valve   Valve actuated by magnetic action by means of an electrically energized coil.

Solid   The physical state of matter that has both a definite shape and volume.

Solid Fuel   Combustible material such as wood, coal, or corn pellets.

Solubility   The ability of one substance to be dissolved in another.

Solution, Chemical   A liquid with another solid, liquid, or gas dissolved in it.

Solution, Refrigeration   A mixture of absorbent and refrigerant in an absorption system.

Solution, Strong   The solution leaving the absorber with a high percentage of refrigerant.

Solution, Weak   The solution leaving the generator with a low percentage of refrigerant.

Sone   A sound rating used for rating ventilation fans.

Soot   A black substance, mostly consisting of small particles of carbon, that can result from incomplete combustion.

South Pole   The Pole on a magnet that magnetic lines of force flow into.

Space Heater   A small heater designed to sit in the area that it heats.

Specific Gravity (SG)   For a liquid or solid, the ratio of its density compared to water. For a vapor, the ratio of its density to air.

Specific Heat   The amount of heat energy needed to change the temperature of a material at a given pressure as compared to an equal quantity of water or air at the same pressure.

Specific Volume   The volume of a substance per unit mass; the reciprocal of density units; cubic feet per pound, cubic centimeters per gram, and so on.

Splash Lubrication   Lubrication based on compressor components dipping into the oil in the crankcase.

Split Phase Motor   Motor with two stator windings.

Split System   Refrigeration or air conditioning installation that places condensing unit remote from evaporator.

Split System Heat Pump   A heat pump with components located both inside and outside of a building—the most common type of heat pump installed in a home.

Spray Pond   Used for cooling condenser water through evaporation by spraying water into the air.

Squirrel Cage   Fan that has blades parallel to fan axis and moves air at right angle to fan axis.

Stack Switch   A type of primary control and safety for oil furnaces that senses the temperature of the flue for operation.

Standard Air   Air at standard conditions.

Standard Atmosphere   Air at a pressure of 14.696 psia, 59°F, with a relative humidity of 30%.

Standard Conditions   68°F and 14.696 psia atmospheric pressure.

Standard Rating Conditions   The conditions used for AHRI performance ratings. For cooling, 80°F dry bulb, 67°F wet bulb return air, and 95°F dry bulb outside air.

Standing Pilot   A small flame that burns continuously that is used to light the main burners of a gas fired appliance.

Start Capacitor   A capacitor that is used only during startup to increase the starting torque of a single phase motor

Start Relay   An electrical device that connects and/or disconnects the start winding of electric motor.

Starting Winding   Winding in electric motor used for only the brief period when the motor is starting.

Starved Evaporator   A term used to describe a condition where less refrigerant flows into the evaporator than is required for the heat load.

Static Condenser   A natural draft condenser that depends more on radiation than convection for its cooling effect.

Static Electricity   Electrical potential that results from the physical displacement of electrons from one object to another.

Static Head   The amount of pressure difference a pump must overcome before it can move any water.

Static Pressure (P$_s$)   The pressure exerted against the inside surfaces of a container or duct. Sometimes defined as burst pressure.

Stationary Blade Rotary Compressor   A rotary compressor with a single blade housed in the compressor body that does not rotate with the compressor shaft.

Stator   Stationary part of electric motor.

Steady State Condition   The voltage and current levels of the controls on a gas furnace after ignition has been achieved and the indoor blower is operating.

Steam Jet Refrigeration   Refrigerating system that uses a steam venturi to create high vacuum (low pressure) on a water container causing water to evaporate at low temperature.

Steam   Water in a vapor state.

Steam Heating   A heating system in which water absorbs heat in a boiler where it boils and gives off heat from radiators where it condenses.

Steam Trap   A device that will prevent the flow of steam, but will allow the flow of condensate.

Step Motor   A motor used for precisely positioning valves that moves in small repeatable steps.

Strainer   A screen used to retain solid particles while liquid passes through.

Stratification   Condition in which air lies in temperature layers.

Stratosphere   The portion of the atmosphere approximately 12–30 mi above the earth. The ozone layer is in the stratosphere.

Stroke, Actuator   The distance that an actuator for a damper or valve can move.

Stroke, Compressor   The distance that a piston travels in the cylinder of a reciprocating compressor.

Subbase   The mounting base for a low voltage thermostat where electrical connections are made.

Subcooled Liquid   Liquid at a temperature lower than is possible when it is in equilibrium with its vapor. The pressure is higher than the vapor pressure.

Subcooling   The reduction of the temperature of a liquid below its condensing temperature.

Sublimation   Condition where a substance changes from a solid to a gas without becoming a liquid.

Suction Line   Tubing or pipe used to carry refrigerant vapor from the evaporator to the compressor in single function systems or from the reversing valve to the compressor in dual function systems.

Suction Line Accumulator   (see Accumulator)

Suction Pressure   Pressure in the low side of the refrigeration system. Also called low side pressure or suction pressure.

Suction Service Valve   A two way manually operated valve located at the inlet to the compressor.

Suction Valves   The valves on the underside of the valve plate of a reciprocating compressor that allow gas to enter the cylinder on the downstroke.

Sump   A reservoir at the bottom of a piece of equipment that circulates water, such as a cooling tower.

Superheat   Heat energy added to a gas so that the enthalpy is higher than for saturated vapor at the same pressure. The heat added to a vapor to raise the sensible temperature of the vapor above its boiling point.

Supplementary Heat   The auxiliary heat provided at temperatures below the heat pump balance point. In most cases this is done with electric heating elements that are part of the heat pump system installation. A gas or oil furnace also can be used to provide supplementary heat when a heat pump is added to an existing fossil fuel heating system.

Surge Tank   Container connected to a refrigerating system that increases gas volume and reduces the rate of pressure change.

Swaging   Enlarging a tube end so that another tube of the same size will fit inside it.

Swaging, Tool   A tool for swaging tubing.

Swamp Cooler   An air conditioner that uses water evaporation to reduce the temperature of the air.

Swash Plate   Wobble plate. Device used to change rotary motion to reciprocating motion.

Sweating   This term has two definitions in air conditioning or heat pump work: (1) formation of moisture on the outside of cold pipes or ducts; and (2) joining of two metals by the adhesive action of a third metal.

Sweet Water   Tap water.

Synchronous Speed   The theoretical speed that an alternating current induction motor would turn if the rotor turned at the same speed as the magnetic pulses in the motor windings.

Synthetic   Not naturally occurring, manmade.

Synthetic Lubricant   A synthetically derived chemical such as polyol ester that is used for lubrication.

Synthyetic Dust Weight Arrestance   A method of testing air cleaner efficiency using manufactured "dust" whose size is carefully controlled.

System Charge   The type and amount of refrigerant in a system, usually stated on the data plate.

System Lag   Time delay between when a condition is sensed and when a system begins to act on the condition.

System Overshoot   Space temperature exceeding the thermostat setpoint in a heating system.

Tankless Water Heater   An indirect water heater designed to operate without a hot water storage tank.

Tap (Screw Thread)   Tool used to cut internal threads.

Temperature   Degree of hotness or coldness as measured by a thermometer.

Temperature Glide   The temperature difference between the dew point and the bubble point of a zeotropic refrigerant.

Temperature-Humidity Index   An index that combines air temperature and humidity to describe levels of comfort.

Temperature-Pressure Relationship   (see Pressure-Temperature Relationship)

Temperature-Pressure Chart (TP Chart)   (see Pressure-Temperature Chart)

Temperature-Pressure Relief Valve (TPR)   A valve that opens to relieve the pressure on a closed water system if the pressure or temperature exceeds a safe level.

Temperature Sensing Bulb   A bulb filled with a volatile fluid or gas with a capillary tube that transmits pressure from the bulb to the controlled device. Used with thermostatic expansion valves or thermostats.

Temperature Swing   The difference between the low temperature and the high temperature in a controlled space.

Terminal Units   Radiators, convectors, baseboard, unit heaters, finned tube, and so on.

Terminal Velocity   The speed of the airstream leaving a diffuser when it has slowed to a point that it no longer effectively mixes with room air. Typically between 50–150 fpm.

Test Light   An electrical test instrument that indicates the presence of voltage by illuminating a light.

Testing, Adjusting, and Balancing (TAB)   Testing system performance and making adjustments in the system to make actual system operation match design specification. The term is often used to refer to airflow adjustments, but all aspects of system performance should be evaluated.

Testing, Adjusting and Balancing Bureau (TABB)   An organization affiliated with the sheet metal industry that certifies TAB technicians.

Therm   A unit of heat having a value of 100,000 Btu.

Thermal Conductivity   The ability of a material to transmit heat.

Thermal Conductivity, Earth   The rate at which heat energy flows through an earth material. Expressed in Btu/ft^2 of the material surface times the temperature difference per thickness in feet of the material.

Thermal Cutout   An overcurrent protection device that contains a heater element that affects a bimetal element designed to open a circuit in the event of electrical current flow above the rated amount of the device.

Thermal Resistance   The resistance a material offers to the transmission of heat.

Thermistor   An electrical device that changes electrical resistance with a change in temperature of the device.

Thermocouple   Device that generates electricity using the principle that if two dissimilar metals are welded together and the junction is heated, a voltage will develop across the open ends.

Thermodynamics   The study of heat and heat flow.

Thermoelectric Refrigeration   A refrigerator mechanism that depends on the Peltier effect.

Thermometer   Device for measuring temperatures.

Thermopile   A pilot generator.

Thermostat   A control device that responds to surrounding air temperatures.

Thermostat, Outdoor Ambient   A control used to limit the amount of auxiliary electric heat according to the outdoor ambient temperature to reduce electrical surge and cost.

Thermostat, Termination   A thermostat mounted on the outdoor coil that interrupts the defrost mode when the temperature of the coil reaches the cutout setpoint of the control.

Thermostat Droop   Maintaining temperature lower than the setpoint.

Thermostatic Control   A device that controls the operation of equipment according to the temperature of the air surrounding the control.

Thermal Expansion Valve   (see Thermostatic Expansion Valve)

Thermostatic Expansion Valve (TEV, TXV)   A valve operated by temperature and pressure within the evaporator coil.

Thermostatic Valve   Valve controlled by thermostatic elements.

Thermostatic Water Valve   A water regulating valve controlled by temperature used on water cooled systems.

Three Phase   An alternating current with three sine waveforms separated by 120°, supplied by three wires.

Three Phase Motor   An electric motor designed to operate on three phase alternating current.

Three Way Valve, Control   A valve that controls flow from one inlet to two outlets.

Three Way Valve, Manual   A manual valve with three ports and two seats often used as a manual refrigeration service valve.

Throttling   Expansion of gas through an orifice.

Throw   The distance that air travels from an air diffuser or register before reaching terminal velocity.

Thrust Bearing   A bearing designed to withstand force pushing against the bearing in parallel with the shaft. Vertical mount fans require thrust bearings.

Timed Off Control   A timer that begins timing when the unit cycles off to ensure a minimum off cycle time before allowing the unit to restart.

Time Delay   A delay between when a control is energized and when it acts.

Time Delay Fuse   A fuse that can withstand momentary overload. Commonly used with motors.

Time Delay Relay   A relay whose coil is energized for a time period before its contacts open or close.

Timers   Mechanism used to control the time cycling of an electrical circuit.

Timer, Defrost   A timer that operates at the same time as the refrigeration system. After a set period of operating time, the timer trips to initiate a defrost operation if the termination thermostat is closed.

Ton   Refrigerating effect equal to the melting of one ton of ice in 24 hr.

Torque   Turning or twisting force.

Torque, Full Load   The maximum torque that a motor can provide at its rated output.

Torque, Stall   The amount of torque that a motor produces when energized and mechanically locked. This is the highest torque that a motor can produce.

Torque, Starting   The amount of torque a motor produces when starting, typically much higher than full load torque.

Torque Wrenches   Wrenches that may be used to measure the torque applied.

Torr   A non-SI unit of vacuum equal to 1/760 of standard atmospheric pressure. A perfect vacuum is 760 Torr.

Total Energy Management (TEM)   An energy management strategy that looks at the total energy use of a building rather than concentrating on specific components or systems.

Total Equivalent Warming Impact (TEWI)   An index of global warming that takes into account both the direct an indirect global warming impact of a refrigerant.

Total Heat   The sum of sensible heat and latent heat, referred to as enthalpy.

Total Pressure (P_t)   The sum of the static pressure and the velocity pressure at the point of measurement.

Toxicity   The degree to which something is poisonous. Refrigerants that are harmful in concentrations of 400 ppm or less are listed as higher toxicity.

Transducer   A device that produces an electronic signal based on a physical property such as temperature or pressure.

Transformer   A device designed to change voltage.

Transmission, Heat   Heat loss or gain through building components.

Triple Point   The temperature and pressure where a substance can exist as a solid, liquid, and gas simultaneously.

Troposphere   The lowest portion of the atmosphere, close to the earth's surface.

True RMS Meter   Uses frequent value sampling and the root mean square formula to determine alternating current values.

Tube in a Tube Coaxial   A heat exchanger constructed of a tube inside a tube sealed off from each other. Usually liquid is in the inner tube and refrigerant is in the outer tube.

Tubing   Used for conveying fluids. Tubing has a consistent outside diameter and relatively thin walls compared to pipe.

Turbulent Flow   The movement of a liquid or vapor in a pipe in a constantly churning and mixing fashion.

Turndown   The ratio of maximum to minimum input rates.

Twinning   Installing and wiring two furnaces to operate simultaneously as one larger unit.

Two Pipe System   A hot water heating system using one pipe to supply heated water to the terminal units, and a second pipe to return the water from the terminal units.

Two Position Control   A control that is either on or off.

Two Stage Air Conditioner   Can operate at two separate capacities to better match unit capacity to load.

Two Stage Compressor   Can operate at two separate capacities to better match the compressor capacity to the load. Used in two stage air conditioners and heat pumps.

Two Stage Vacuum Pump   Produces a lower pressure and deeper vacuum by having two vacuum pumps in series; the discharge of the low stage feeds the suction of the high stage.

Two Stage Furnace   Has a low firing rate and a high firing rate that can better match furnace capacity to the load.

Two Stage Heat Pump   Can operate at two separate capacities to better match unit capacity to load. Allows increased heating capacity without oversizing the air conditioning.

Two Temperature Valve   Another name for evaporator pressure regulator.

Two Way Valve   A valve with one inlet and one outlet that has two positions: opened and closed.

U Factor   Unit of measure of thermal conductivity.

U Value   Another name for U factor.

Ultrasonic Leak Detector   Detects gas leaks in refrigeration systems by hearing the ultrasonic whistle of the gas escaping.

Ultraviolet (UV)   Invisible radiation waves with frequencies shorter than wavelengths of visible light and longer than X-ray.

Ultraviolet A (UVA)   Long wavelength ultraviolet light with wavelengths of 400–315 nm.

Ultraviolet B (UVB)   Medium wavelength ultraviolet light with wavelengths of 315–280 nm.

Ultraviolet C (UVC)   Short wavelength ultraviolet light with wavelengths of 280–100 nm.

Underwriters Laboratories (UL)   Independent standards and testing laboratory for the examination and testing of devices.

Unit Heater   A fan and motor, a heating element, and an enclosure hung from a ceiling or wall.

Unit Ventilator   A terminal unit in which a fan is used to mechanically circulate air over the heating coil.

Universal Motor   A series wound DC motor that can operate on either AC or DC current.

Unvented Space Heater   A gas fired space heater that releases all the products of combustion into the space it is heating.

Universal Motor   A series wound motor used for small electric appliances and power tools. Universal motors can operate on either AC or DC current.

Unloader   Device that reduces the capacity of a compressor by preventing some cylinders from compressing.

Upflow   Furnaces and air handlers with airflow that is up vertically, entering at the bottom of the unit and leaving at the top.

Urethane Foam   Type of insulation that is foamed in between inner and outer walls of a display case.

U-Tube Manometer   measures pressure by the height of liquid column that it will support in a U-shaped tube. Low pressure manometers are filled with water, higher pressure manometers are filled with mercury.

V Belt   Drive belt with a V-shaped cross section.

Vacuum   Reduction in pressure below atmospheric.

Vacuum Gauge   Measures the level of a deep vacuum, usually in microns.

Vacuum Pump   A high efficiency vapor pump used for creating deep vacuum in refrigeration systems for testing and/or drying purposes.

Valve   Device used for controlling fluid flow.

Valve, Check   A valve that will permit fluid flow in only one direction. Sometimes called a one way valve.

Valve, Expansion   A modulating refrigerant metering device.

Valve Plate   Part of compressor located between the top of the compressor body and the head that contains the compressor valves.

Valve, Reversing   A valve used to change the direction of refrigerant flow in a heat pump system. Because there are four pipe connections, it is also called a four way valve.

Valve Seat   (see Seat)

Valve, Service   A device used by service technicians to connect pressure gauges into the refrigeration system.

Valve, Slide   The slide valve portion of the reversing valve that shifts the refrigerant flow.

Valve, Solenoid A flow control valve controlled by an electromagnetic coil actuating a plunger off its seat.

Valve, Suction (see Suction Valves)

Valve, TXV, Bi-Flow A thermostatic expansion valve that is designed to provide pressure reduction and refrigerant flow control in either direction.

Valve Stem Depressor The part on the end of a refrigeration hose that pushes in the valve core when connecting to a Schrader valve.

Vapor The gas form of a substance. It takes the shape and volume of its container.

Vapor Barrier Thin plastic or metal foil sheet used to prevent water vapor from penetrating insulating material.

Vapor Charge Bulb Also called gas charge or limited charge. A temperature sensing bulb that has a limited amount of liquid so that all the liquid will be vaporized at the upper end of the bulb's operating temperature range.

Vapor Line Found only in dual action heat pumps. It is the suction line in the cooling mode and the hot gas line in the heating mode.

Vapor Lock The restriction or blockage of flow in a liquid line due to the presence of vapor in the line.

Vapor, Saturated A vapor whose temperature has been reduced to the point of condensation but condensation has not started.

Vapor Pressure The pressure exerted by a vapor on its surroundings.

Vapor Refrigerant Charging Adding refrigerant to a system in gas form.

Vapor Refrigerant Recovery Removing refrigerant from a system in vapor form.

Vaporization Changing physical state from a liquid to a gas.

Variable Air Volume (VAV) A method of zone control that varies the volume of air to the zone depending upon the load.

Variable Frequency Drive (VFD) A control for an AC electric motor that changes the speed of the motor by varying the frequency of the current to the motor

Variable Pitch Pulley Pulley that can be adjusted to provide different pulley ratios.

Variable Resistor A resistor whose value can be adjusted, typically between 0 Ω and its maximum value.

Variable-Speed Motor A motor whose speed can be adjusted to meet varying load requirements

Velocimeter Instrument used to measure air velocities.

Velocity (ν) Speed.

Velocity Pressure (P_v) The pressure exerted in the direction of flow.

Vent-Free A gas fired appliance that is designed to operate without a vent whose combustion products are released into the area it is in.

Vented Space Heater A gas fired space heater whose combustion products are vented through a flue to the outside.

Vent Gases Products of combustion.

Ventilation The introduction of outdoor air into a building by mechanical means.

Venturi A section in a pipe or a burner body that narrows down and then flares out again.

Vibrasorber A refrigeration component for reducing vibration in refrigerant piping consisting of a corrugated inner tube and a woven metal outer casing.

Viscosity Measure of a fluid's ability to flow. Typically measured in Saybolt universal seconds.

Volatile A fluid that evaporates readily.

Volt (V) The unit of electrical potential or pressure.

Voltage The potential difference between two points.

Voltage, Effective A measure of AC voltage that states its effect in a resistive circuit.

Voltage, RMS Root mean square voltage is used to calculate the effective AC voltage. The instantaneous voltage is measured many times each cycle. Each of these values are squared, the average of the squares is found, and finally the square root of the average is the effective voltage.

Voltage, Minimum The minimum supply voltage to a piece of equipment.

Voltage, Maximum The maximum supply voltage to a piece of equipment.

Voltage, Nominal The standard AHRI voltage rating for a piece of equipment.

Voltage, Peak The voltage at the peak of an AC sine waveform.

Voltage Relay One that functions at a predetermined voltage value.

Voltmeter A meter that reads voltage.

Volt Ohm Milliammeter (VOM) A meter that measures voltage, resistance (ohms), and milliamps.

Volumetric Efficiency Ratio of the actual performance of a compressor and calculated performance.

Walk-in Cooler Large commercial refrigerated room.

Wastewater System A water cooled refrigeration system that does not recirculate the condenser cooling water.

Water Box The water manifolding portion of a chiller or boiler.

Water Coil A heat transfer coil designed for water.

Water Column (wc) A unit of pressure comparing the height of water column it will support.

Water Cooled Condenser A heat exchanger that uses water to remove the heat from the high temperature compressor discharge vapor.

Water Cooled Condensing Unit A condensing unit (high side) that is cooled by the use of water.

Water Cooler An appliance that cools drinking water.

Water Hammer A pounding sound made by the sudden increase in static pressure in the pipes when flowing water is stopped suddenly by the closing of a valve.

Water Loop The piping and components in a closed circuit.

Water Regulating Valve A valve that regulates the water flow through a water cooled condenser in response to condenser pressure.

Water Tube Boiler A hot water boiler in which the water is circulated through the tubes and the hot gases from combustion of the fuel are circulated around the tubes.

Watt (W) A unit of electrical power.

Watt-Hour (Wh) Using electrical power at the rate of 1 W for a period of 1 hr.

Welded Hermetic Compressor A compressor with both the compressor and motor inside a welded shell.

Well Water Source, Closed Loop A system that removes water from the earth by means of a drilled well and returns it to the earth by means of a separate drilled well.

Well Water Source, Open Loop A system that removes water from the earth by means of a drilled or bored well and returns the water to the earth through a separate disposal system.

Wet Bulb Temperature (wbt)   A temperature taken with a wet bulb thermometer.

Wet Bulb Depression   The difference between the dry bulb and wet bulb temperatures.

Wet Bulb Thermometer   A thermometer that uses a wet sac on the bulb to measure the evaporation rate of the air sample.

Wet Cell Battery   A battery with a liquid electrolyte solution.

Wet Heat   Heating system using hot water or steam.

Wind Chill Factor   The reduction in perceived temperature because of wind.

Wind Effect   The increase in evaporation rate due to air travel over a water surface.

Winding Thermostat   A temperature sensor that opens if the motor winding temperature exceeds a safe level.

Windmilling   Backward fan rotation caused by wind blowing through outdoor fans when they are off.

Window Unit   An air conditioner designed to be installed in a window.

Wire Connectors   Electrical terminals that are fastened to wires by soldering or crimping that facilitate wire connection to components.

Wobble Plate Compressor   A compressor with pistons that are parallel to the crankshaft that uses an offset disc to create reciprocating motion.

Work   The transfer of energy.

Work Hardening   Metal becoming brittle as a result of being repeatedly flexed.

Wye Connected Motor   A three phase motor whose windings are joined at the center to form a wye.

WYE Transformer   A three phase transformer whose windings are joined at the center to form a wye.

Zeotropic   A blend that changes in composition as it boils.

Zone   That portion of a building whose temperature is controlled by a single thermostat.

Zone Control   The controller that coordinates operation of the dampers or valves in a zone control system.

Zone Damper   A damper that controls the airflow to a particular zone in a zoned system.

Zone Control System   A control system that maintains the condition of separate zones within a building.

Zone Valve   A valve that controls water flow to a zone in a zoned hydronic heating system.

Spanish Language Glossary

A Coil Serpentín A. Evaporador consistente en dos serpentines de cobre que unidos tienen la forma de la letra A.

Absorption Absorción. Diseminación de una sustancia en la composición interna de otra sustancia.

Absorption Chiller Enfriador de agua. Máquina de refrigeración usada para producir agua fría utilizando el ciclo de absorción.

Absorption Cycle Ciclo de absorción. Ciclo de refrigeración basado en la absorción del refrigerante lograda por una sustancia química en vez de la compresión mecánica.

Absorption Refrigerator Refrigerador por absorción. Un refrigerador en el que se utilizan los principios del ciclo de absorción.

Accessible Hermetic Hermético accesible. Una unidad sellada herméticamente que puede abrirse para reparaciones y mantenimiento, también conocido como semihermético.

Acetylene Acetileno. Gas utilizado con oxígeno en equipos de soldadura tradicional y soldadura en frío.

Activated Alumina Alúmina activada. Un óxido de aluminio desecante utilizado en las secadoras de los sistemas de refrigeración para absorber humedad.

Active Refrigerant Recovery Device Dispositivo de recuperación de refrigerante. Una unidad de recuperación independiente que no forma parte integral de un sistema de refrigeración.

Active Solar System Sistema de energía solar. Un sistema diseñado para el aprovechamiento de la energía solar.

Actuator Actuador. Dispositivo capaz de generar movimiento mecánico a partir de líquidos, de energía eléctrica y térmica.

Air-Acetylene Llama de aire-acetileno. Soplete de soldadura que extrae lo que necesita del entorno en vez de necesitar un suministro separado de oxígeno.

Air Break Paso de aire. Una abertura invertida en el interior de la chimenea para prevenir que los gases o humos regresen a la cámara de combustión.

Air Cleaner Filtro de aire. Sistema de filtración utilizado para quitar las impurezas que transporta el viento.

Air Coil Serpentín de tubos. Intercambiador de calor de un sistema de refrigeración en el cual pasa aire a través de su parte externa.

Air Conditioning Acondicionamiento de aire. El proceso de controlar la temperatura, humedad, limpieza y movimiento de aire en el espacio acondicionado.

Air Conditioning, Heating, and Refrigeration Institute (AHRI) Instituto de acondicionamiento de aire, calefacción y refrigeración (AHRI). Una asociación nacional de comercio que representa a fabricantes de más del 90% de la producción de aire acondicionado central, electrodomésticos a gas y equipamiento comercial de refrigeración en los EE.UU.

Air Cooled Condenser Condensador refrigerado por aire. Intercambiador que utiliza aire que pasa a través de él para condensar el refrigerante de vapor a líquido.

Air Core Solenoid Solenoide de núcleo hueco. Solenoide que tiene un centro hueco.

Air Curtain Cortina de aire. Aire forzado que se utiliza para proteger productos alimenticios expuestos en un exhibidor abierto.

Air Defrosting Descongelación por aire. Método de descongelación que consiste en apagar la unidad mientras se permite la circulación de aire cálido.

Air Diffuser Difusor de aire. Un registro de aire diseñado para distribuir aire de una manera determinada.

Air Friction Chart Tabla de coeficientes de fricción. Tabla utilizada para medir conductos redondos.

Air Gap Entrehierro. El espacio entre los componentes móviles y fijos de un motor o de un generador.

Air Handler Unidad de tratamiento de aire. Una unidad que contiene un ventilador y serpentines calentadores y refrigerantes, la cual es utilizada para transportar aire a un espacio determinado.

Air Heat Exchanger Intercambiador de paso simple. Un intercambiador de calor que permite que el aire sea succionado a través de su parte externa.

Air Loop Captador. La parte de equipamiento con aire entubado en un sistema de calor por bomba de calor.

Air Pressure Switch Interruptor de presión. Mide el descenso de la presión de aire en el serpentín exterior de una bomba de calor para determinar la formación de escarcha.

Air Sensor Sensor de aire. Sensor instalado en unidades de tratamiento de aire para medir condiciones tales como temperatura, presión, velocidad y humedad.

Air Standard Estándar de aire. La designación de la ASHRAE para aire seco a 70° F y presión atmosférica.

Air-to-Air Heat Pump Bomba térmica aire a aire. (Ver Bomba térmica de alimentación de aire)

Air Washer Purificador de aire. Filtración de aire utilizando agua u otro líquido.

Algae Alga. Vegetación cuyo color va del verde claro al verde oscuro que se desarrolla en sistemas de agua.

Alkylbenzene Alquilbenceno Aceite sintético compatible con refrigerantes CFC y HCFC.

Alternative Refrigerant Refrigerante alternativo. Refrigerante sustituto distinto del sistema refrigerante existente.

Alternator Alternador. Máquina que convierte energía mecánica en corriente alterna.

Altitude Altitud. La distancia medida sobre el nivel del mar.

Altitude Adjustment Ajuste de altitud. Ajuste del termostato para dar razón de los cambios de elevación dependientes de la ubicación geográfica.

Ambient Compensator Compensador de ambiente. Dispositivo electrónico que provee calor suficiente para alternar la unidad de refrigeración cuando las temperaturas de ambiente son bajas.

Ambient Temperature Temperatura Ambiente. Temperatura del aire que rodea a un objeto.

American National Standards Institute (ANSI) Instituto de Estándar Nacional Americano (ANSI). Instituto que junto con ASHRAE determina estándares de refrigeración.

American Society of Heating, Refrigeration, and Air Conditioning Engineers (ASHRAE) Sociedad Americana de Ingenieros de Calefacción, Refrigeración y Aire Acondicionado (ASHRAE). Su membresía está compuesta por cientos de profesionales ingenieros y técnicos de todas las fases de la industria HVAC/R. ASHRAE además fabrica equipos estándares para la industria.

American Society for Testing and Materials Engineers (ASTME) Sociedad Americana de Materiales y Pruebas de Ingeniería (ASTME). Sociedad que además de probar materiales, determina estándares de infiltración de lluvia y viento.

American Standard Pipe Thread Rosca para tubos normalizada en América. Identifica el tamaño de la rosca para tubos normalizada y encontrada en el sector, con el propósito de instalarla.

Ammonia Amoníaco. Refrigerante generalmente usado para grandes sistemas comerciales, debido a su alto valor de calor latente.

Amperage Amperaje. Medida del flujo de la corriente eléctrica.

Analog Electronic Device Dispositivo electrónico analógico. Dispositivo que envía una señal modulada.

Analog Signal Señal analógica. Señal modulada, comparada a una señal digital binaria.

Analog VOM VOM analógico. Voltímetro ohmetro que utiliza una aguja como escala de medición, en lugar de una visualización digital.

Aneroid Barometer Barómetro aneroide. Instrumento usado para medir la presión barométrica.

Angle Valve Válvula angular. Válvula formada por una curva de 90°.

Annual Fuel Utilization Efficiency (AFUE) Eficiencia de Utilización de Combustible Anual (AFUE). Comparación de la eficiencia de un horno para consumidores.

Anode Ánodo. Electrodo positivo de una célula electrolítica.

Antifreeze Solution Solución anticongelante. Mezcla de glicol y agua, con un punto de congelación de 32° F bajo cero.

Approach Aproximación. Período usado para refrigerar depósitos de agua elevados, con el objetivo de determinar efectividad. Medida del interruptor de refrigeración de la humedad del aire en el ambiente, comparado con la temperatura de la refrigeración líquida.

Approach Temperature Temperaturas de aproximación. Temperatura refrigerada despedida, comparada con la temperatura refrigerante.

Arcing Formación de arco. Descarga chispeante entre dos contactos o electrodos.

Aspiration Aspiración. Extraer un fluido mediante una succión.

Atmospheric Dust Spot Efficiency Eficiencia de una mancha de polvo atmosférico. Medición de la habilidad de un filtro para remover polvo atmosférico de una prueba de muestra de aire.

Atmospheric Pressure Presión atmosférica. Gases atmosféricos que rodean un planeta creando una presión equivalente a 14.7 PSI aproximadamente, a una temperatura de 70° F a nivel del mar.

Atomization Atomización o Pulverización. (ver Atomizar)

Atomizing Humidifier Humidificadores de pulverización. Humidificador que abastece a la corriente de aire con agua finamente atomizada.

Auger Barrena. Instrumento giratorio semejante a un inmenso sacacorchos que se utiliza en máquinas de hielo.

Automatic Changeover Thermostat Termostato de cambio automático. Termostato que cambia de modo automáticamente, dependiendo de la temperatura de la habitación.

Automatic Pumpdown System Sistema de bombeo automático. Sistema diseñado para bombear refrigerante al receptor antes del cierre.

Auxiliary Drain Pan Bandeja colectora auxiliar. Ubicada debajo del serpentín evaporador, para colectar y escurrir agua que se condensa en el aire.

Azeotrope Azeótropo. Dos o más refrigerantes mezclados por el fabricante, que poseen las propiedades combinadas de un refrigerante simple.

B Vent Tiro Natural. Conducto de ventilación de doble pared que se utiliza para aplicaciones de horno de gas.

BW Vent Tiro de retorno. Conducto de ventilación de doble pared que se utiliza con los hornos de gas de pared.

Back Electromotive Force (BEMF) Fuerza Electromotriz (BEMF). Efecto generador de voltaje de un rotor de motor eléctrico.

Bacteria Bacteria. Organismos microscópicos que se hallan en casi todos lados. Algunos tipos de bacterias pueden ser útiles, pero otros pueden causar enfermedades.

Baffle Reductor de circulación. Similar a un volquete. Se utiliza para regular el flujo de un fluido.

Balanced-Port TEV Puerto Balanceado TEV. Válvula termostática de expansión que compensa por las amplias variaciones de alta y baja presión y por las cargas de evaporación.

Bar Bar. Un bar equivale a 100 kilopascales (kPa) con 101.3 kPa equivalentes a una presión atmosférica estándar.

Base Base. Terminal de semiconducción.

Bath Bañera. Recipiente que contiene un líquido, en el que se puede lavar o calentar un componente.

Bearing Cojinete. Cojinetes de bolas que se utilizan en bombas y motores para mantener el eje giratorio en alineación con la cubierta.

Bellows Seal Sello de fuelle. Sello de cigüeñal ajustado por una colocación de fuelle.

Belly-Band-Mount Motor Motor de banda de soporte de tapa de convertidor. Motor eléctrico sujetado por una correa de metal.

Belt Correa. Material flexible utilizado para conectar ejes giratorios a través de una polea, como un motor que propulsa un ventilador.

Bio-aerosols Bioaerosol. Contaminante microbiano transmitido por el aire, tal como un virus, una bacteria, un hongo o algas.

Blast Freezer Congelador a explosión. Unidad que congela profundamente un producto con mayor rapidez que los congeladores convencionales.

Bleeding Purgar. Drenar presión de un sistema lentamente.

Blend Mezcla. Mezcla de dos o más refrigerantes.

Blocked Suction Bloqueo de succión. Método para descargar un compresor alternante.

Blowdown Escape. Drenaje de una controlada cantidad de agua, desde un depósito elevado de agua de enfriamiento, para reducir el nivel de sólidos disueltos.

Blown   Soplado. La fabricación de material aislante puede aplicarse a una estructura utilizando este método. Un fusible fundido puede considerarse soplado.

Boiler   Caldera. Horno que genera tanto agua caliente, como vapor.

Boiler, High Pressure   Caldera de alta presión. Caldera que opera a una presión mayor a 15 psi.

Boiler, Low Pressure   Caldera de baja presión. Caldera que opera a menos de 15 psi.

Boiling Point   Punto de ebullición. Temperatura a una determinada presión, a la que un fluido cambia de líquido a gas.

Bonnet   Tapa de válvula de compuerta. Cámara de hoja de metal de un horno, en el que se acumula calor.

Booster Pump   Bomba elevadora de presión. Segunda bomba que se utiliza para elevar más la presión en el sistema, que la presión creada por la primera bomba.

Boot   Arranque. Conexión entre un registro de piso y un conducto de ramificación.

Boyle's Law   Ley de Boyle. Ley que pone de manifiesto la relación del volumen de presión de los gases.

Breaker   Interruptor. (ver Cortocircuito)

Breeching   Calzón de chimenea. Pieza de transición ubicada entre el horno y la chimenea embudo.

Bubble Point   Punto de burbujeo. La formación de burbujas de un líquido zoótropo refrigerante saturado dará comienzo a esta temperatura.

Building Related Illness (BRI)   Enfermedades relacionadas con la construcción. Desórdenes en la salud, relacionados con el medio ambiente de edificios herméticos modernos.

Build Up System   Sistema de reparaciones. En lugar de que se envuelva la unidad, los elementos individuales (condensador, compresor, etc.) se instalan juntos en la obra.

Bulb   Lámpara. Se utiliza como elemento sensor para válvulas y controles.

Burr   Rebaba. Extremos elevados que sobresalen del cortado de tubería o de un caño. Esta rebaba debe quitarse antes de la instalación.

Butane   Butano. Gas sencillamente licuado, inodoro, incoloro y altamente inflamable.

Butterfly Valve   Válvula de mariposa. Válvula que posee un mango que puede posicionarse a 90°, para estar ya sea en forma paralela (abierta), o perpendicular (cerrada), en relación al flujo de fluidos.

Bypass   Desviación. Conexión que desvía el flujo de fluidos alrededor de un componente o una válvula.

Calorimeter   Calorímetro. Instrumento para medir el calor de las reacciones químicas.

Cam   Leva. Proyección sobre un disco rotativo, que puede utilizarse para operar temporizadores de deshielo a medida que la leva gira lentamente.

Capacitance   Capacitancia. Medida de la cantidad de energía almacenada por un condensador.

Capacitive Reactance   Reactancia capacitiva. La impedancia eléctrica capacitiva, en oposición a la corriente alterna de un circuito.

Capacitor Start Motor (CSR)   Motor de arranque por condensador (CSR). Motor monofásico, que contiene un condensador en serie con el bobinado de arranque.

Capacity   Capacidad. La capacidad de una unidad basada en su tamaño, poder y cantidad de refrigeración.

Capillary Attraction   Atracción capilar. Habilidad de una sustancia de atraer a otra sustancia hacia su interior.

Capillary Tube System   Sistema de tubo capilar. Unidad de refrigeración que utiliza un tubo capilar de tipo dispositivo de control de flujo.

Carbon Dioxide Indicator   Indicador de gas carbónico. Dispositivo que se utiliza para medir niveles de dióxido de carbono.

Carbon Filter   Filtro del Carbón. Filtro activado de carbón vegetal, que se utiliza para propósitos de adsorción.

Cathode   Cátodo. Electrodo a través del cual fluye la corriente eléctrica positiva.

Cavitation   Cavitación. Burbujas de vapor que se forman en una región líquida debido a una caída de presión que produce turbulencia.

Cellulose   Celulosa. Se utiliza como material ambientalmente preferible para aislamiento en edificios.

Centigrade   Centígrado. Nombre antiguo con el que se denominaba la Escala Celsius.

Central Air Conditioning   Aire acondicionado central. El aire se trata en una estación central y es luego enviado a espacios condicionados a través de una serie de ductos.

Central Station   Estación central. El equipamiento requerido para el tratamiento del aire está ubicado conjuntamente en una única locación.

Centrifugal Force   Fuerza centrífuga. Fuerza externa creada por el movimiento circular de un objeto.

Centrifugal Pump   Bomba centrífuga. Bomba con un impulsor rotatorio, que utiliza fuerza centrífuga para bombear un líquido.

Centrifugal Switch   Interruptor centrífugo. Interruptor que se abre o cierra, debido a la acción de la fuerza centrífuga.

Ceramic Ignitor   Bujía de encendido de cerámica. Bujía de encendido, que se utiliza para cocinas de gas y estufas.

Change of State   Cambio de estado. (ver Cambio de fase).

Charging Scale   Escala para carga o báscula de plancha. Escala digital que mide el peso del refrigerante en un cilindro.

Charles' Law   Ley de Charles. Ley de gas ideal.

Chill Factor   Sensación térmica. (ver Temperatura de sensación)

Chiller   Enfriador. Sistema de refrigeración diseñado para enfriar agua, glicol o salmuera.

Chilled Water System   Sistema de agua refrigerada. Serie de bombas e intercambiadores de calor, que se utilizan para enviar agua refrigerada a un espacio acondicionado.

Chimney   Chimenea. Conducto que se utiliza para evacuar gases de combustión calientes, desde una caldera u horno.

Chimney Connector   Conector de chimenea. Tubo conector, que une el horno a la chimenea.

Chimney Flue   Tubo de chimenea. Pila de chimenea.

Chlorinated Polyvinyl Chloride (CPVC)   Cloruro de polivinilo clorado (PVC-C). Termoplástico que se utiliza para tuberías de agua caliente y fría.

Chlorofluorocarbon (CFC)   Clorofluorocarbono. Refrigerante compuesto por cloro, flúor y carbón.

Circuit Breaker   Disyuntor. Dispositivo que detecta el flujo de la corriente y que se abre cuando se excede su capacidad de flujo de corriente.

Circuit, Parallel   Circuito en paralelo. (ver Circuito en paralelo).

Circuit, Pilot   Guía de circuito. Dispositivo que se utiliza para iniciar un circuito.

Circuit, Series   Circuito en serie. (Ver en serie.)

Clamp-on Ammeter   Pinza amperimétrica. Dispositivo de medición de corriente, que no se halla directamente conectado al circuito, sino que abraza temporalmente el cable de corriente.

Clearance Space   Espacio libre. Cantidad de acceso de espacio requerido por encima, por debajo y en todos los lados de una unidad instalada.

Clean Room   Sala blanca. Creado en fábricas de semiconductores para mantener un ambiente perfectamente limpio.

Climate   Clima. Condiciones meteorológicas establecidas a través de largos periodos de tiempo, para una región geográfica específica.

Climate Control   Control climático. HVAC se refiere frecuentemente a un método de control climático.

Closed Circuit   Circuito cerrado. Ruta completada del flujo de corriente, con ningún interruptor abierto.

Closed Circuit Cooling Tower   Torre de enfriamiento de circuito cerrado. El proceso de enfriamiento del líquido se encuentra completamente aislado de la atmósfera.

Closed-Loop Control Configuration   Configuración de control de bucle cerrado. Un sensor monitorea la salida y proporciona retroalimentación para mantener las condiciones del valor de referencia.

Closed-Loop Heat Pump   Bomba de calor de bucle cerrado. Bomba de calor geotérmica, que pone en circulación una solución de glicol a través de un serpentín de suelo.

Clutch, Magnetic   Embrague magnético. Transmite torque y velocidad sin contacto.

Clutch, Centrifugal   Embrague centrífugo. El eje impulsor anidado dentro del eje impulsado utiliza fuerza centrífuga para transmitir la fuerza.

Coaxial Heat Exchanger   Intercambiador de calor coaxial. Intercambiador de calor en forma de espiral, que consiste en un tubo interno y externo para aplicaciones a contracorriente.

Code   Código. Reglas y regulaciones locales, estatales y nacionales.

Coefficient of Conductivity   Coeficiente de conductividad. Conductividad térmica de una sustancia (k).

Coefficient of Expansion   Coeficiente de expansión. Cambio en la longitud por cambio de grado de temperatura de una sustancia.

Cogeneration   Cogeneración. Calor y poder combinados.

Cold Anticipator   Anticipador de frío. (ver Anticipador de enfriamiento).

Cold Trap   Dispositivo de absorción en frío. Utilizado con bombas de vacío para acumular condensación.

Collector   Colector. Terminal semiconductora.

Combined Annual Efficiency (CAE)   Eficiencia anual combinada. Rendimiento anual de aparatos en combinación, como calentadores de agua y ambiente.

Combustible Liquids   Líquidos inflamables. Líquidos de clase II y clase III, con puntos de inflamabilidad de copa cerrada a 100°F o más.

Combustion Analyzer   Analizador de combustión. Dispositivo utilizado para el análisis de gases de combustión, con el objetivo de optimizar la eficiencia de combustión.

Comfort   Bienestar. Aquellas condiciones que son más apropiadas para el bienestar del ser humano.

Comfort Zone   Zona de bienestar. Rango de humedad y temperatura al que uno se encuentra cómodo.

Commercial System   Sistema comercial. Sistemas diseñados para establecimientos de negocios de no manufactura.

Compound Pump   Bomba compuesta. Bomba de dos fases.

Compression   Compresión. Reducción de volumen de gas resultante en un aumento de presión.

Compression Gauge   Indicador de compresión. Indicador utilizado para medir la presión de compresión.

Compression Ring   Segmento de compresión. Anillo del pistón más cercano a la cabeza del cilindro de un compresor alternativo.

Compressor Crankcase   Compresor del cárter de cigüeñal. Ubicación del cárter de cigüeñal y del cárter de aceite.

Compressor, External Drive   Compresor de impulso externo. Compresor que requiere de un sello de cigüeñal debido a que se halla externamente acoplado a un motor.

Compressor Head   Cabeza del compresor. (ver Cabeza de cilindro)

Compressor, Hermetic   Compresor hermético. Unidad sellada con el motor y el compresor ubicado dentro de la misma carcasa.

Compressor, Multiple Stage   Compresor de múltiples etapas. Compresor que contiene más de una etapa de compresión.

Compressor Oil Cooler   Enfriador de aceite para compresores. Intercambiador de calor, que se utiliza para enfriar el aceite en un compresor de cárter de cigüeñal.

Compressor, Open   Compresor abierto. (ver Compresor de conducción externa)

Compressor, Reciprocating   Compresor alternativo. Compresor que utiliza pistones accionados por un cigueñal.

Compressor, Rotary Screw   Compresor de tornillo rotativo. Compresor que utiliza dos tornillos rotatorios helicoidales de engranaje de desplazamiento positivo.

Compressor Shaft Seal   Sello del eje del compresor. (ver Sello del vástago o eje)

Compressor, Single Stage   Compresor de una sola etapa. Compresor que sólo posee una etapa de compresión.

Condensate   Condensación. Agua que se ha condensado en la superficie de una bobina de enfriamiento.

Condenser Fan   Ventilador condensador. Ventilador que se utiliza para enviar aire a través de la superficie de un condensador de enfriamiento de aire.

Condenser Flooding   Inundación de un condensador. Condensador que contiene exceso de refrigerante líquido.

Condensing Boiler   Caldera de condensación. Caldera en donde se permite que el gas de combustión descienda por debajo de la temperatura del punto de condensación y que condense.

Condensing Furnace   (ver Caldera de condensación)

Conductance, Thermal (C)   Conductancia térmica. Tasa de tiempo de flujo calorífico por unidad de área que atraviesa un material.

Console   Consola. Interfaz para operar computadoras y sistemas de control.

Constant   Constante. Valor invariable y conocido.

Continuous Absorption Cycle   Ciclo de absorción continuo. Ciclo de absorción que utiliza una cantidad de calor limitada y que no posee piezas movibles.

Continuous Operation   Funcionamiento continuo. Unidad que se halla siempre en funcionamiento.

Contractual Agreement   Acuerdo contractual. Acuerdo realizado por ambas partes con fuerza jurídica obligatoria.

Control   Control. Interruptores y otros dispositivos que se requieren para operar un equipo HVAC/R.

Control Motor   Motor de control. Motor utilizado para llevar el control de una acción, tal como la colocación de un amortiguador.

Control, High Pressure   Control de alta presión. Detiene la unidad si ésta alcanza el punto de alta presión fijada.

Control Loop   Bucle de control. Sistema de control que posee retroalimentación y sensores.

Control Module   Módulo de control. Componente que contiene entradas y salidas del sistema de control.

Control Point   Punto de control. Valor actual comparado al punto fijado.

Control System   Sistema de control. Sistema que se utiliza para manejar, comandar, dirigir o regular otros dispositivos.

Control Valve   Válvula de control. Válvula que se utiliza para dirigir el flujo.

Controlled Environment   Ambiente controlado. (ver control climático)

Controlled Medium   Medio ambiente controlado. Acondicionamiento de aire o agua, distribuído a través de un sistema HVAC.

Convection, Forced   Convección forzada. Transferencia de calor de convección asistida por una bomba o ventilador en lugar de una circulación natural.

Convection, Natural   Convección natural. Transferencia de calor de convección en el que se da una circulación natural, en la que el aire cálido asciende y el aire frio desciende.

Conversion Factor   Factor de conversión. Valor constante que se utiliza para cambiar de una escala a otra, como por ejemplo de Celsius a Fahrenheit.

Cooler   Enfriador. Entrada o alcance de un compartimento de refrigeración.

Cooling Oil   Aceite refrigerante. Serpentín de evaporación.

Copper Plating   Encobrado. Proceso de electrólisis que conduce depósitos de cobre al interior del compresor.

Core, Air   Núcleo hueco. (ver selenoide de núcleo hueco)

Core, Magnetic   Núcleo magnético. (ver selenoide)

Core Valve   Válvula de núcleo. (ver válvula Schrader)

Corrosion   Corrosión. Deterioro de un material, como el debilitamiento del hierro, debido a la oxidación conocida como herrumbre.

Cotter Pin   Pasador de chaveta. Sujetador de tipo dividido también denominado chaveta de cuña o pasador hendido.

Coupling   Condensador de acoplamiento. Dispositivo que se utiliza para unir dos ejes entre si.

Cradle-Mounted Motor   Motor de cuna montada. Motor acunado en cada extremo y sujetado por un soporte.

Crankcase Pressure Regulating Valve (CPR)   Válvula reguladora de presión de cigüeñal. Dispositivo que limita la presión de succión del compresor para reducir la carga en el arranque.

Crankshaft   Cigüeñal. Convierte el movimiento rotatorio en movimiento alternativa desde la varilla de acoplamiento hasta el pistón.

Crank Throw   Codo del cigüeñal. Lugar en el que la varilla de acoplamiento se halla sujeta al cigüeñal.

Creosote   Creosota. Acumulación de depósitos de carbón en chimeneas provenientes de la quema de leña.

Crisper   Compartimento para vegetales. Espacio en un refrigerador destinado al almacenamiento de vegetales.

Critical Pressure   Presión crítica. Presión de vapor a una temperatura crítica.

Critical Temperature   Temperatura crítica. Temperatura sobre la cual no existen fases gaseosas ni líquidas.

Cross-Charged   Carga cruzada. Bulbo de detección TEV, cargado con un fluido diferente al del refrigerante que se utiliza en el sistema.

Cryogenic   Criogénico. Temperaturas comúnmente inferiores a 238° F.

Cryogenic Fluid   Fluido criogénico. Nitrógeno líquido y helio líquido que se utilizan comúnmente en aplicaciones criogénicas.

Cryogenic Food Freezing   Congelamiento criogénico de alimento. El nitrógeno líquido se utiliza en la congelación por corriente de aire o en sistemas de congelado de inmersión.

Cryogenics   Criogenia. Rama de la física e ingeniería que supone el estudio de muy bajas temperaturas.

Crystallization   Cristalización. Solución de salmuera altamente concentrada que se precipita como sal.

Cupronickel   Cuproníquel. Aleación de cobre y níquel que no se corroe en el agua de mar.

Current Relay   Relé de corriente. Abre o cierra contactos a través de un cambio en el flujo de corriente.

Current Limiting Fuse   Fusible limitador de corriente. Abre el circuito si la corriente supera el valor de referencia.

Current Transformer   Transformador de corriente. Proporciona corriente a su bobinado secundario en forma proporcional al flujo de corriente que proporciona a través de su bobinado primario.

Customer Relations   Relaciones con el cliente. Evaluación del técnico por un cliente como resultado de su desempeño y actitud en el trabajo.

Cycle   Ciclo. Serie de eventos que se repiten desde el comienzo hasta el final, tal como el ciclo de refrigeración.

Cylinder, Compressor   Cilindro de compresor. Cámara de compresión que alberga el pistón en un compresor alternativo.

Cylinder Head   Cabeza de cilindro. Pieza que encierra el final de compresión de un cilindro de compresor.

Cylinder, Refrigerant   Cilindro refrigerante. Contenedor rígido que sujeta al refrigerante, el cual puede ser de tipo desechable o reutilizable, tal como un cilindro de recuperación.

Cylinder Unloading   Descarga de cilindro. Método para reducir la carga del compresor mediante el corte de cilindros individuales.

Cylindrical Commutator   Conmutador cilíndrico. Inducido de un motor.

Dalton's Law   Ley de Dalton. Ley de presiones parciales.

Damper, Return Air   Amortiguador de aire de retorno. Se halla posicionado para controlar el flujo de aire a través del conducto de aire de retorno.

Damper, Outdoor Air   Amortiguador de aire externo. Se halla posicionado para controlar el flujo de aire a través del conducto de aire externo.

DC Motor   Motor DC. Motor de corriente continua.

Deck, Cold   Corriente de enfriamiento. Aire dirigido sobre un serpentín de enfriamiento ubicado en un conducto separado de aire frio para un sistema de una gran zona.

Endothermal Endotérmica. Reacción química donde el calor se transforma en energía química.

Energized Electrificado. Que tiene corriente eléctrica.

Energy Energía. La capacidad de realizar un trabajo.

Energy Management Manejo de la energía. Sistema de instrumentos informáticos para verificar y controlar más eficientemente las funciones del sistema de calefacción, ventilación y aire acondicionado (CVAA).

Energy Management Control System Sistema de control del manejo de la energía. (ver manejo de la energía)

Energy Recovery Ventilator (ERV) Ventilador para recuperación de energía (ERV). Intercambiador de aire y calor, con método "aire y aire," instalado en un sistema de conductos para aumentar la eficiencia.

Energy Utilization Index (EUI) Índice de utilización de energía (EUI). Comparación del uso de la energía dentro de diferentes áreas de un mismo edificio.

Entropy Entropía. Energía que no puede utilizarse para realizar un trabajo externo.

Environment Ambiente. Las condiciones del entorno.

Environmental Protection Agency (EPA) Agencia de Protección Ambiental (EPA). Agencia del gobierno federal responsable de salvaguardar el medio ambiente natural.

Equalizer Tube Tubo equilibrador. Dispositivo utilizado para mantener la misma presión o los mismos niveles de líquido en dos contenedores.

Equivalent Length Longitud equivalente. Longitud no medida de la tubería que se calcula tomando en cuenta las pérdidas por fricción.

Error Codes Códigos de error. Códigos numéricos utilizados en el sistema de control para indicar fallas.

Ester Lubricant Lubricante ester. Aceite sintético para refrigeración.

Ethane Etano. Gas incoloro e inodoro utilizado como refrigerante en los sistemas de refrigeración criogénica.

Eutectic Eutéctica. Solución utilizada para el almacenaje en frío dentro de los serpentines de evaporación.

Eutectic Point Punto eutéctico. Temperatura a la cual la solución eutéctica pasa de estado líquido a sólido.

Eutectic Solution Solución eutéctica. Mezcla de dos sólidos en la cual el punto de fusión es el más bajo posible.

Evacuate Vaciar. Acción de eliminar el agua, en todas las formas posibles, de un material o un sistema.

Evacuation Vaciamiento. Remoción de los gases no condensables y de la humedad de un sistema de refrigeración.

Evaporation Evaporación. Término utilizado para describir el cambio de un líquido a vapor cuando se añade energía calorífica. Paso de un líquido a vapor a una velocidad relativamente muy baja.

Evaporative Condenser Condensador por evaporación. Un dispositivo que emplea un pulverizador de agua para enfriar un condensador.

Evaporative Cooling Enfriamiento por formación de vapor. El uso de vapor o gotas de agua para enfriar el aire.

Evaporative Humidifier Humidificador por evaporación. Acción de añadir humedad a la corriente de aire usando vapor de agua o rociando agua.

Evaporator Evaporador. El componente de un mecanismo de refrigeración en el cual el refrigerante se evapora y absorbe el calor.

Evaporator Coil Serpentín del evaporador. (ver evaporador)

Evaporator, Dry Type Evaporador de tipo seco. Un evaporador en el cual el refrigerante es proporcionado a través de un dispositivo de reducción de la presión.

Evaporator Fan Ventilador del evaporador. Ventilador que mueve el aire a través del evaporador.

Evaporator, Flooded Evaporador inundado. Un evaporador que contiene líquido refrigerante en todo momento.

Excess Air Exceso de aire. Aire que excede la cantidad requerida para que se realice la combustión completa de un gas combustible.

Exfiltration Exfiltración. Flujo del aire desde un área ocupada hacia el exterior a través de los orificios en la estructura del edificio.

Exhaust Opening Apertura de escape. Cualquier apertura a través de la cual se elimina aire de un espacio.

Exhaust Valve Válvula de escape. Válvula de descarga para un compresor de desplazamiento positivo.

Exothermal Exotérmica. Reacción química en la cual se libera calor.

Explosion Proof Motor Motor a prueba de explosiones. Motor que no provoca chispas, diseñado para funcionar en ubicaciones donde hay explosivos.

External Drive Conducción externa. (ver Compresor de conducción externa)

External Motor Protection Protección externa del motor. Sobrecarga instalada en la parte exterior de un motor.

Fail-Safe A prueba de fallo. Diseñado para afianzar la seguridad de la unidad en caso de que un componente falle en su funcionamiento.

Fan Relay Relé del ventilador. Relé utilizado para poner en marcha y para detener un ventilador.

Faraday Experiment Experimento de Faraday. Un experimento sobre la inducción electromagnética.

Fast Acting Fuse Fusible de actuación rápida. Un fusible que abre el circuito inmediatamente si se excede la corriente nominal.

Feedback Control System Sistema de control de la realimentación. Sistema de control en lazo cerrado con sensores que proporcionan realimentación sobre el punto de ajuste.

Fiberduct Conducto de fibra de vidrio. Conducto hecho de fibra de vidrio.

Fiberglass Fibra de vidrio. Compuesto de fibra de vidrio fino y resina.

Field Pole Polo de campo. Localizado como parte del bobinado del estátor del motor.

Fill Relleno. Material con forma de panal usado en las torres de enfriamiento de agua para disminuir la caída de agua y aumentar la superficie de exposición.

Film Factor Factor pelicular. Valor que representa la resistencia a la transferencia de calor a través de la película de la superficie de un material.

Filter Drier Secador de filtro. Una combinación de secador de refrigerante y filtro en un mismo componente.

Finned-Tube Evaporator Evaporador de tubos de aletas. Tipo de evaporador que tiene tubos con aletas para aumentar el área de la superficie y la transferencia de calor.

Firepot Hornillo. Cámara de combustión con revestimiento refractario.

Fixed-Bore Device Refrigerant Refrigerante con dispositivo de diámetro interior fijo. Dispositivo de dosificación con orificios de entrada fijos.

Fixed Resistor   Resistor fijo o no regulable. Un resistor en el cual el valor no cambia.

Flame Impingement   Choque de la llama. Una llama de quemador excesivamente ancho o dentado que hace contacto con las paredes laterales de un horno.

Flame Rectification   Rectificación de la llama. La corriente alterna se convierte en corriente continua debido a la llama de un horno de gas.

Flammability   Combustibilidad. La facilidad con la que arderá una sustancia.

Flapper Valve   Válvula de charnela. Una válvula liviana, del tipo de lengüetas o láminas, abisagrada en un extremo para permitir que éste gire abriéndose y cerrándose.

Flash Weld   Soldadura por calentamiento eléctrico. Una soldadura por resistencia o un punto de soldadura donde las secciones metálicas bajo presión se funden juntas a causa de la corriente eléctrica.

Flexible Duct   Conducto flexible. Diseñado para permitir un cierto movimiento y algo de flexión para acomodar la instalación.

Flexible Lines   Líneas flexibles. Líneas diseñadas para acomodar la flexión.

Floating Head Pressure   Presión principal flotante. (ver control de la presión principal)

Flooding   Inundación. Término utilizado para describir un exceso de refrigerante líquido en el evaporador o condensador.

Fluorescent   Fluorescente. Capaz de emitir fluorescencia, como en el caso de los tubos de luz fría.

Flow Check Piston   Pistón de control del flujo. Dispositivo dosificador con orificio fijo y pistón ensamblado, que sirve como mecanismo de control para el flujo invertido.

Force   Fuerza. Empuje o atracción que causará que un objeto comience a moverse.

Force Feed Oiling   Lubricación con alimentación a presión. El aceite se proporciona a los puntos de lubricación mediante una bomba.

Forced Air   Aire forzado. Movimiento de aire producido por un ventilador.

Forced Circulation Evaporator   Evaporador de circulación forzada. Evaporador con aire forzado que fluye a través de él.

Forced Draft Cooling Tower   Torre de enfriamiento de tiro forzado. Una torre de enfriamiento que utiliza un ventilador para hacer circular el aire en lugar de una corriente de aire natural.

Forced Draft Evaporator   Evaporador de tiro forzado. (ver evaporador de circulación forzada)

Fossil Fuels   Combustibles fósiles. Combustibles minerales, principalmente hidrocarburos, como el petróleo que se halla en la capa superior de la corteza terrestre.

Four-Way Valve   Válvula con cuatro vías. Válvula con varias aperturas usada para cambiar el ciclo de calentamiento de las bombas de calor.

Fractionation   Fraccionamiento. Tendencia de los refrigerantes contenidos en una mezcla zeotrópica a vaporizarse y separarse.

Free Wheeling   Viraje libre. Que puede moverse o rotar sin obstáculos.

Freeze Drying   Secado por congelación o liofilización. Proceso de deshidratación que supone congelar primero el material.

Freezer Burn   Quemadura del congelador. Daño ocasionado por la pérdida de humedad a un producto alimenticio incorrectamente envasado.

Freezing Point Depression   Depresión de la temperatura de congelación. El descenso de la temperatura a la cual se solidifica un líquido al mezclarlo con un aditivo.

Friction   Fricción. Fuerza que se opone al movimiento relativo de dos superficies en contacto, sólidas o líquidas.

Front Seated   Posición delantera. Una válvula cerrada en un sistema de refrigeración se considera en posición delantera.

Frostbite   Congelación de un tejido. Daño causado a la piel y al tejido debido al frío extremo.

Frozen   Congelado. Cuando un líquido se ha solidificado.

Fuel Oil   Aceite combustible. Combustible fósil de petróleo líquido usado en un horno alimentado con aceite.

Fusible Link   Cartucho de fusible. Fusible dentro de un circuito eléctrico que se fundirá y abrirá debido a una temperatura excesiva.

Gain   Ganancia. Incremento en la amplificación electrónica de una señal.

Gas Valve   Válvula de gas. Válvula utilizada para controlar el flujo de gas.

Gate Valve   Válvula de compuerta. Válvula que se abre mediante el levantamiento de una compuerta vertical que se halla normalmente completamente abierta o completamente cerrada, no se emplea para regulación.

Gauge Port   Orificio de manómetro. Conexión de entrada para instalar manómetros.

Geothermal   Geotérmico. Calor que proviene del interior de la Tierra.

Germanium   Germanio. Material semiconductor usado para fabricar transistores.

Global Warming   Calentamiento global. Aumento en la temperatura promedio de la Tierra.

Global Warming Potential (GWVP)   Potencial de calentamiento global (GWVP). Escala relativa usada para determinar el aumento en el calentamiento global atribuido a un equipo en operación.

Globe Valve   Válvula de globo. Válvula con un disco esférico y un asiento que puede usarse para regulación o estrangulamiento.

Glow Coil   Bobina encendedora. Dispositivo que automáticamente vuelve a encender la llama del piloto, si ésta se apaga, en un quemador de gas.

Glycol   Glicol. Anticongelante.

Graduated Cylinder   Cilindro graduado. (ver cilindro de carga)

Grain   Grano. Unidad de medida de peso. 7,000 granos equivalen a una libra.

Gram   Gramo. Unidad de peso en el sistema métrico.

Gravity Flow   Flujo gravitacional. (ver sistema de calefacción por gravedad)

Grommet   Guardaojal. Protector de caucho, plástico o metal, redondo u ovalado, utilizado para proteger los lugares por donde entran los cables, alambres o tubos a través de una base de metal.

Ground Fault   Fuga a tierra. Una fuga eléctrica desde un circuito a la tierra.

Ground Fault Circuit Interrupter (GFCI)   Disyuntor por pérdidas a tierra (GFCI). Disyuntor diseñado específicamente para abrir el circuito en caso de una fuga a tierra.

Guide Vanes, Inlet, Prerotation Paletas directrices para prerotación. Ubicadas en la toma de los compresores centrífugos y de los ventiladores para variar la capacidad.

Gun Burner Quemador de pistola. El aceite inducido a través del orificio del quemador se atomiza cuando entra al horno.

Halogens Halógenos. Compuestos químicos que constan de flúor, cloro, bromo, yodo y ástato.

Hand Truck Vagoneta para mano. Vagón pequeño con dos ruedas utilizado para trasladar objetos pesados.

Hanger Soporte colgante. Dispositivo utilizado para apoyar tuberías, tubos, conductos, etc.

Head, Static Presión estática. Presión de un líquido o de un vapor expresada en términos de la altura de una columna de un líquido o de mercurio.

Heat Coil Serpentín de calentamiento. (ver serpentín térmico)

Heat Gain Ganancia de calor. Cantidad total de calor que absorbe un edificio, utilizada para determinar las cargas del sistema de calefacción, ventilación y aire acondicionado (CVAA).

Heat Pipe Tubería de calefacción. Tubos llenos de líquido usados en los hornos de gas de alta eficiencia.

Heat Reclaim Reclamación de calor. La utilización del calor rechazado por el condensador para otros propósitos de calefacción.

Heat Recovery System Sistema de recuperación de calor. Sistema que utiliza un ventilador de recuperación de energía.

Heat Recovery Ventilator Ventilador de recuperación de calor. (ver ventilador para recuperación de energía)

Heat Tape Cinta calefactora. Hilo térmico con resistencia eléctrica que se bobina alrededor de la tubería de desagüe para evitar su congelación.

Heat Transfer Rate (Q) Tasa de transferencia de calor. Cantidad de calor transferida por unidad de tiempo.

Heating Control Control de calentamiento. Dispositivo para controlar la función térmica.

Helix Coil Bobina en forma de hélice. Bobina bimetálica usada en los termómetros con dial.

Hertz (Hz) Hercio (Hz) Medida de frecuencia. Unidad de frecuencia del Sistema Internacional, que equivale a la frecuencia de un fenómeno cuyo período es un segundo.

Hg Símbolo del mercurio.

High Glide Blend Mezcla de alto deslizamiento. El rango entre la temperatura de burbujeo y la temperatura de condensación es mayor que 1 °F a una presión constante.

High Efficiency Gas Furnace Horno de gas de alta eficiencia. Horno calificado con un 90%, o más, de eficiencia anual de utilización de combustible.

High Efficiency Particulate Air Filter (HEPA) Filtro HEPA (Filtro de alta eficiencia en el control de partículas suspendidas). Elimina al menos 99.97% de las partículas aéreas que tienen 0.3 micrómetros de diámetro.

High Limit Control Control de tolerancia máxima. Mecanismo de seguridad que apaga el quemador del horno si la temperatura del casquete es demasiado alta.

High Side Float Flotador del lado alto. Control del flujo de refrigerante ubicado en el condensador.

High Temperature Refrigeration Refrigeración a temperatura alta. Sistema con temperaturas por encima de los 35 °F en el evaporador.

High Vacuum Pump Bomba de vacío alto. (ver vacío profundo)

Horizontal Furnace Horno horizontal. El aire fluye horizontalmente a través del horno.

Hot Gas Gas caliente. Vapor de descarga del compresor.

Hot Gas Bypass Desviación de gas caliente. Método de regulación de la capacidad del compresor.

Hot Pulldown Descenso caliente. Proceso de bajar la temperatura de un espacio caliente.

Hot Surface Ignition Encendido por superficie caliente. Un elemento de carburo de silicona se calienta con el fin de encender el quemador principal.

Hot Water Heating System Sistema de calefacción con agua caliente. Sistema que distribuye agua caliente mediante bombas para calentar un edificio.

Hot Wire Conductor electrizado. Alambre electrificado con potencial de voltaje a tierra.

Hunting Oscilación. Ciclado arriba y debajo de un punto de ajuste, como una válvula que se abre y cierra continuamente.

Hydraulics Hidráulica. El estudio y el uso de las propiedades de los fluidos con el fin de obtener energía de los fluidos.

Hydrochlorofluorocarbon (HICFC) Hidroclorofluorocarburo. Refrigerante compuesto por hidrógeno, cloro, flúor y carbono.

Hydrofluorocarbon (HFC) Hidroflurocarbono. Refrigerante compuesto por hidrógeno, flúor y carbono.

Hydrogen Hidrógeno. Un gas incoloro, inodoro y muy inflamable. Es el más liviano de todos los elementos.

Identification Plate Placa de identificación. Placa con los datos del equipo o placa con inscripción.

Ignition System Sistema de encendido. Método para encender un horno.

Impingement Choque. (ver choque de la llama)

Incandescent Incandescente. Calor producido por las emisiones de luz que hacen que un objeto brille al rojo vivo por la acción del calor.

Inches Hg Pressure Presión Hg en pulgadas. Medida de la presión en pulgadas de mercurio absoluto.

Inches Hg Vacuum Vacío Hg en pulgadas. Medida del vacío en pulgadas de vacío de mercurio.

Inclined Water Manometer Manómetro inclinado de agua. (ver manómetro inclinado)

Incomplete Combustion Combustión incompleta. Una situación en la cual no se quema una parte del combustible que pasa a través de un horno.

Indoor Air Quality Calidad del aire interior. Una medida de los factores que contribuyen a la calidad del aire en el interior de un edificio.

Induced Magnetism Magnetismo inducido. Capacidad que tiene un campo magnético de inducir magnetismo en un metal.

Inductive Circuit Circuito inductivo. Circuito eléctrico donde la corriente desfasa al voltaje.

Infrared Infrarrojos. Rayos no visibles, ubicados justo por debajo del rojo en el espectro visible, que transfieren calor mediante radiación.

Infrared Humidifier Humidificador infrarrojo. Un humidificador que utiliza lámparas infrarrojas para evaporar el agua en la corriente de aire.

Inherent Motor Protection Protección inherente del motor. Protección incorporada al motor como una sobrecarga calorífica ubicada en el bobinado.

Inhibitor   Inhibidor. Sustancia que impide una reacción química.

Injection   Inyección. Término utilizado para una bomba de circulación de un sistema hidrónico que obliga al agua a fluir por un circuito de calefacción secundario.

Input/Output Board   Tablero de entrada/salida. Tablero del circuito que mide las entradas y controla las salidas.

Inspection   Inspección. Examinar y comparar el equipo y la instalación según las pautas establecidas y los Códigos vigentes.

Instrument   Instrumentar. Añadir sensores con realimentación y circuitos de control a un sistema existente.

Insulation, Electric   Aislamiento eléctrico. Sustancia que es un conductor pobre de la electricidad con pocos electrones libres.

Insulator   Aislante. Material no conductor, como el vidrio, la goma o el plástico, usado para revestir los cables pelados y las conexiones eléctricas.

Integrated Circuit   Circuito integrado. Un circuito electrónico diminuto que consiste principalmente en dispositivos semiconductores.

Integrated Circuit Board   Tablero de circuito integrado. Conjunto de circuitos electrónicos fabricados sobre una superficie delgada de un material semiconductor, también se lo llama microchip o simplemente chip.

Intermittent Absorption Cycle   Ciclo de absorción intermitente o interrumpida. Sistema cerrado cargado con amoníaco y agua y activado mediante un quemador de gas.

Intermittent Ignition   Ignición intermitente. Sistema de ignición de hornos que opera sólo de la manera requerida.

Internal Motor Overload   Sobrecarga interna del motor.

Interstate Commerce Commission (ICC)   Comisión Interestatal de Comercio (ICC). Organismo federal regulatorio que supervisa las empresas de transporte comunes, tales como las de ferrocarriles y camiones.

Inverter   Inversor. Un dispositivo eléctrico para convertir DC en AC.

Ion   Ión. Un ión es un átomo que no tiene carga negativa (anión) ni positiva (catión).

Ion Generator   Generador de iones. Un dispositivo que carga partículas.

Isolation Relays   Relés de aislamiento. Un relé diseñado para evitar realimentaciones eléctricas no deseadas.

Joule-Thomson Effect   Efecto Joule-Thomson. Descenso de la temperatura de un gas debido a un aumento repentino de su volumen.

Kilocalorie (C)   Kilocaloría (C). Medida de calor equivalente a 1.000 calorías.

Kilometer (km)   Kilómetro (km). Medida de distancia equivalente a 1.000 m.

Kilovoltampere (kVA)   Kilovoltamperio (kVA). Medida de trabajo eléctrico equivalente a 1.000 voltamperios.

Kinetic Energy   Energía cinética. Energía en movimiento.

Lacquer   Laca. Recubrimiento de color claro sobre un cable, que provee aislamiento para bobinados eléctricos.

Ladder Diagram   Diagrama de escalera. Diagrama eléctrico que muestra una disposición circuito por circuito. Las líneas eléctricas son las "barandillas" de la escalera y cada circuito individual es un "peldaño" de la misma.

Lagging   Calorifugado. Aislación térmica usada alrededor de las cañerías y envolturas de calderas.

Latent Heat of Condensation   Calor latente de condensación. Calor liberado cuando un gas se condensa, transformándose en líquido.

Latent Heat of Deposition   Calor latente de deposición. Calor liberado cuando un gas se congela, transformándose en sólido.

Latent Heat of Sublimation   Calor latente de sublimación. Calor absorbido cuando un sólido se transforma directamente en gas sin convertirse primero en líquido.

Leads, Meter   Cables conductores de medidor. Los cables que se usan para conectar un aparato eléctrico de medición al circuito que se encuentra a prueba.

Leads, Motor   Cables conductores de motor. El cableado de conexión en un motor.

Light Emitting Diode (LED)   Diodo emisor de luz (LED). Un diodo que emite luz cuando fluye a través de él una corriente eléctrica.

Legionella   Legionella. La bacteria que puede crecer con fuerza en torres de refrigeración y provoca la enfermedad del legionario o Legionelosis.

Legionnaire's Disease   Enfermedad del legionario o Legionelosis. Una neumonía bacteriana cuyo nombre proviene de un brote ocurrido en la convención de la Legión Americana en Filadelfia en julio de 1976.

Limit Switch   Interruptor límite. Un interruptor normalmente cerrado en un horno que se abre si la temperatura del horno excede el punto límite fijado.

Line Diagram   Diagrama de línea. Otro nombre dado al diagrama de escalera o esquemático.

Line Set   Equipo de líneas. Cañería de cobre usada en las líneas de líquido y vapor para conectar las dos partes de equipos de aire acondicionado y bombas térmicas de sistema dividido.

Line Tap Valve   Vávula de llave de paso de línea. (Ver Válvula perforadora).

Line Voltage Thermostat   Termostato de voltaje de línea. Termostato diseñado para ser usado con voltajes de 120 voltios o más.

Liquefied Natural Gas (LNG)   Gas natural licuado (GNL). Gas natural que ha sido enfriado hasta que se convierte en líquido.

Liquid   Líquido. Un estado fluido de la materia que adopta la forma del recipiente que lo contiene pero cuyo volumen no está determinado por el volumen del recipiente.

Liquid Charge Bulb   Bulbo de carga líquida. Un bulbo sensor de temperatura que contiene suficiente refrigerante para asegurar que siempre haya cierta cantidad de líquido en el bulbo.

Liquid Floodback   Retorno líquido. Refrigerante líquido que regresa a la línea de succión de un compresor durante la operación.

Liquid Hammer   Martillo líquido. Sonido palpitante producido por el aumento repentino de la presión estática en las cañerías cuando el líquido que fluye se detiene súbitamente debido al cierre de una válvula.

Liquid Injection   Inyección líquida. Enfriar compresores de baja temperatura introduciendo pequeñas cantidades de refrigerante líquido en el armazón del compresor.

Liquid Refrigerant Charging   Carga de refrigerante líquido. Agregar refrigerante a un sistema de refrigeración en estado líquido.

Liquid Refrigerant Recovery   Recuperación del refrigerante líquido. Retirar refrigerante de un sistema en estado líquido.

Liquid Slugging   Acumulación de líquido. Presiones hidráulicas creadas por el líquido que queda atrapado en el bolsillo de eliminación de un compresor alternativo durante la operación.

Liquid-Vapor Valve   Válvula de líquido-vapor. La válvula que se encuentra en los cilindros refrigerantes recargables, que permite retirar líquido o vapor del cilindro.

Lithium Bromide   Bromuro de litio. El absorbente que se encuentra en refrigeradores por absorción de gran tamaño que usan agua como refrigerante.

Load Matching   Adaptación de la carga. Ajustar la capacidad del sistema a la carga de calor.

Load Shedding   Reducción energética. Retirar cargas eléctricas en un edificio por ciertos periodos de tiempo, como parte de una estrategia de manejo de la energía.

Lock Out Relay   Relé de cierre. Un esquema de control que evita el reinicio de un compresor una vez abierto el control de seguridad, incluso luego de que el control de seguridad se reinicie.

Low Ambient Control   Control de baja temperatura. Un dispositivo utilizado para permitir la operación adecuada de condensación en condiciones de baja temperatura ambiente en el exterior.

Lowboy Furnace   Horno tipo gabinete. Un horno que tiene el fuelle y el intercambiador de calor uno junto al otro y las conexiones de retorno y provisión de aire en la parte superior.

Low Glide Blend   Mezcla de bajo deslizamiento. Un refrigerante zeotrópico con una diferencia típica de temperatura entre el punto de burbujeo y el punto de rocío menor a 3.

Low-Loss Fitting   Accesorio de baja pérdida. Un accesorio ubicado al final de una manguera de refrigeración, diseñado para evitar que el refrigerante abandone la manguera cuando está desconectada del sistema.

Low Side Float   Flotador de zona baja. Controla el flujo que ingresa al evaporador usando un flotador ubicado en la zona baja del sistema.

Low-Temperature Refrigeration   Refrigeración de baja temperatura. Un sistema de refrigeración comercial que tiene una temperatura de saturación del evaporador de entre $-30°F$ y $10°F$ y un punto nominal del compresor de $-10°F$.

Low Voltage   Baja tension. Un sistema de tensión de AC que no tiene más de 30 V con una clasificación máxima de 100 VA. Comúnmente tiene 24 V en sistemas de control de aire acondicionado.

Low-Voltage Thermostat   Termostato de baja tensión. Termostato diseñado para un sistema de control de baja tensión.

MBH   Abreviatura de 1.000 Btu/hr.

Machine Room   Sala de máquinas. La sala donde se encuentra el equipo mecánico en un edificio.

Machine Screw   Tornillo para máquina. Tornillo compuesto por una cabeza, un cuerpo cilíndrico y roscas delgadas.

McLeod Gauge   Vacuómetro McLeod. Un instrumento usado para la medición precisa de presiones muy bajas.

Magnetic Clutch   Embrague magnético. Montaje que transfiere energía desde una polea externa a un compresor abierto al recibir impulso energético.

Magnetic Flux   Flujo magnético. Las líneas de fuerza que se generan alrededor de un campo magnético.

Magnetic Gasket   Junta magnética. El cierre de la puerta de una nevera o congelador que utiliza un imán para asegurar un cerramiento ajustado.

Magnetic Overload Protection   Protección de sobrecarga magnética. Allana el circuito a un motor eléctrico cuando una alta corriente de atracción produce un campo magnético fuerte.

Magnetism   Magnetismo. Una fuerza que atrae a ciertos metales como el hierro y lasaleaciones de níquel y cobalto.

Manifold   Colector. Un tubo con varias salidas para la distribución de fluido.

Manometer   Manómetro. Un instrumento utilizado para medir la presión de gases o vapores. La presión de un gas se mide en relación a una columna de líquido, que puede ser agua o mercurio por ejemplo, en un tubo con forma de U abierto a la presión atmosférica.

Manometer, Inclined   Manómetro inclinado. Un manómetro en el cual el tubo de líquido está inclinado con respecto al eje horizontal a fin de proveer mediciones más amplias y precisas en base a una gama más reducida de mediciones.

Manual Reset   Reinicio manual. Un dispositivo de seguridad con un botón o estandarte que debe apretarse para restaurar la operación normal de un sistema.

Mapp Gas   Gas Mapp. Marca de metilacetileno propadieno de Dow Chemical, un gas licuado de petróleo que emite más calor al quemarse que el propano y se usa a veces para soldar y estañar.

Marine Water Box   Caja marina para agua. La parte que corresponde al colector de agua de una caldera o máquina frigorífica, que cuenta con una cubierta desmontable.

Matched Belts   Correas de transmisión superpuestas. Un conjunto de correas de transmisión cuyo tamaño está adaptado con precisión a la misma circunferencia para ser usadas en una transmisión de correas múltiples.

Matched System   Sistema combinado. Un equipo de aire acondicionado o bomba térmica de sistema dividido cuyos componentes internos y externos están diseñados para usarse en forma conjunta.

Matter   Materia. La sustancia de la que están compuestos los objetos físicos. La materia tiene peso y ocupa espacio.

Maximum Operating Pressure (MOP)   Máxima presión de operación (MOP). La presión máxima que una válvula de expansión termostática con limitación de presión permitirá en el evaporador.

Mechanical Controls   Controles mecánicos. Controles que operan solamente a través de medios mecánicos, tales como las válvulas reguladoras de presión.

Medium-Temperature Refrigeration   Refrigeración de temperatura media. Un sistema de refrigeración comercial cuya temperatura de saturación del evaporador se encuentra entre $-10°F$ y $30°F$ y su punto nominal del compresor es de $-10°F$.

Megohmmeter   Megóhmetro. Un instrumento que puede medir millones de ohms de resistencia.

Metering Device   Dispositivo de medición. Controla el flujo de refrigerante hacia el evaporador de un sistema de refrigeración.

Metric System   Sistema métrico. El sistema de medición usado a nivel mundial, basado en unidades decimales.

Micro   Micro. Un elemento compositivo que denota una millonésima parte.

Micrometer   Micrómetro. Un dispositivo para hacer mediciones precisas del orden de milésimas de pulgadas.

Microprocessor   Microprocesador. Un chip integrado único que combina todas las funciones de una unidad central de procesamiento de computación.

Midposition   Posición media. Descripción de la posición de una válvula de servicio de refrigeración cuando se encuentra entre el asiento delantero y el asiento posterior de la válvula.

Migration of Refrigerant   Migración del refrigerante. Refrigerante que se traslada de una parte a otra de un sistema de refrigeración durante el ciclo de parade.

Mineral Oil (MO)   Aceite mineral (MO). Lubricante elaborado a través del refinamiento de petróleo crudo. Se usa en sistemas de CFC y HCFC.

Minimum Efficiency Reporting Value (MERV)   Valor reportado de eficiencia mínima (MERV). Sistema utilizado para comparar la eficiencia relativa de los filtros de aire.

Miscibility   Miscibilidad. La capacidad de mezclarse de un refrigerante y un lubricante.

Module   Módulo. Un grupo de componentes o circuitos en una vivienda individual. Normalmente electrónico.

Mold   Moho. Un hongo que prospera en ambientes húmedos y puede contribuir a causar problemas de calidad del aire en interiores.

Molecular Motion   Movimiento molecular. Vibración y movimiento de las moléculas individuales de una sustancia, que aumentan a medida que aumenta el nivel de energía molecular.

Montreal Protocol   Protocolo de Montreal. Un tratado internacional destinado a controlar la producción y emisión de sustancias que agotan la capa de ozono.

Motor   Motor. Convierte la energía eléctrica en movimiento mecánico rotativo usando el electromagnetismo.

Motor, Permanent Split Capacitor   Condensador dividido permanente de motor. Un motor de inducción monofásico que usa bobinado de marcha y bobinado de arranque en el modo de marcha. El bobinado de arranque está conectado en serie con un condensador para modificar las características eléctricas del bobinado.

Muffler   Silenciador. Un componente de los equipos de refrigeración ubicado inmediatamente después del compresor. Reduce el sonido y la vibración producidos por el flujo pulsante del refrigerante.

Mullion Heater   Calentador del partaluz. Un calentador que mantiene la temperatura del partaluz por encima del punto de rocío.

Multiple Circuit Coil   Bobina de circuito múltiple. Una bobina que tiene más de un recorrido para el flujo fluido simultáneo.

Multiple Evacuation   Evacuación múltiple. Evacuar un sistema, cargarlo de nitrógeno seco, liberar el nitrógeno y luego evacuar el sistema nuevamente.

Multistage System   Sistema multietapa. Un sistema que provee calefacción o refrigeración en dos o más pasos o etapas.

Naphthenic Oil   Aceite nafténico. Aceite mineral que tiene un bajo contenido de cera.

National Environmental Balancing Bureau (NEBB)   Departamento Nacional de Regulación Ambiental (NEBB). Un organismo que otorga certificación a las empresas y técnicos del área de servicios de las ciencias de la construcción, incluyendo la instalación, evaluación, ajuste y regulación de edificaciones y las salas blancas.

National Fuel Gas Code (NFPA 54)   Código Nacional de Gas Combustible (NFPA 54). Un código de seguridad para la instalación y uso de sistemas y equipos de cañerías de gas combustible.

National Fire Protection Association (NFPA)   Asociación Nacional de Protección contra Incendios (NFPA). Organismo dedicado a la prevención de incendios que redacta el Código Eléctrico Nacional y el Código Nacional de Gas Combustible.

National Institute of Standards and Technology (NIST)   Instituto Nacional de Normas y Tecnología (NIST). Una agencia federal no reglamentaria enmarcada dentro del Departamento de Comercio de los Estados Unidos que se encarga de establecer las normas para mediciones y tecnología.

National Pipe Taper (NPT)   Rosca de cañería cónica nacional (NPT). La especificación normativa para las roscas de cañería.

Natural Draft   Corriente natural de aire. Flujo de aire creado por la convección natural.

Natural Draft Cooling Tower   Torre de enfriamiento de corriente natural de aire. Una torre de enfriamiento que depende de la convección natural y no de un ventilador.

Negative Electrical Charge   Carga eléctrica negativa. Una carga eléctrica generada a partir de un átomo u objeto con más electrones que protones.

Negative Temperature Coefficient Thermistor (NTC)   Termistor de coeficiente de temperatura negativo (NTC). Un semiconductor cuya Resistencia eléctrica aumenta al disminuir su temperatura. Se usa comúnmente para medir la temperatura de serpentines exteriores en bombas de calor para iniciar y concluir ciclos de descongelación.

Net Oil Pressure   Presión neta de aceite. La diferencia entre la presión en la salida de la bomba de aceite y la presión del cárter en un compresor.

Net Stack Temperature   Temperatura neta de chimenea. La diferencia entre la temperatura de los gases de escape y la temperatura del aire de combustión.

Neutralizer   Neutralizador. Un químico agregado a un sistema para contrarrestar el efecto de los ácidos.

Neutron   Neutrón. Una partícula subatómica ubicada en el núcleo de un átomo que no tiene carga eléctrica.

Newton (N)   Newton (N). Una medida de fuerza empleada en el sistema SI. Un Newton acelera un kilogramo un metro por segundo cuadrado.

Nichrome   Nicromo. Una aleación de níquel y cromo utilizada en la construcción de elementos de calefacción eléctrica.

Nitrogen   Nitrógeno. Un gas común, inerte. El aire está compuesto por 78% de nitrógeno.

No-Frost Freezer   Congelador libre de escarcha. Un congelador que cuenta con un ciclo automático de descongelación.

Noise Dosimeter   Dosímetro de ruido. Un instrumento utilizado para medir la exposición a determinados niveles de sonido.

Nominal   Nominal. La clasificación estandarizada para cantidades y dimensiones cuyo valor real es variable.

Nominal Voltage   Voltaje nominal. El voltaje que aparece en la placa de un electrodoméstico. La norma 110-2002 de AHRI establece los voltajes nominales para equipos de aire acondicionado.

Non-Frosting Evaporator   Evaporador libre de escarcha. Evaporador de refrigeración comercial que opera por encima de la temperatura de congelación.

Non-Inductive Load   Carga no inductiva. Una carga eléctrica que no posee componentes electromagnéticos.

North Pole   Polo norte. El polo de un imán desde el cual fluyen hacia afuera las líneas magnéticas de fuerza.

NOx   NOx. Un término que hace referencia a varios compuestos de nitrógeno y oxígeno que son subproductos de la combustión.

Nut Driver   Destornillador de tubo. Una herramienta que cuenta con un mango, un vástago y una cabeza en el extremo para ajustar y desajustar tuercas y tornillos hexagonales.

Off-Cycle Defrost   Descongelación de ciclo de parade. Una descongelación que sucede naturalmente en equipos comerciales de refrigeración con una temperatura del evaporador por debajo del punto de congelación y una temperatura en caja por encima del punto de congelación.

Offset   Offset. La diferencia entre el valor de control al que se apunta (setpoint) y la condición real sostenida.

Ohmmeter   Óhmetro. Un instrumento de medición de la resistencia eléctrica.

Ohm's Law   Ley de Ohm. Enuncia la relación entre el voltaje, la corriente y la Resistencia en un circuito puramente resistivo.

Oil Burner   Quemador de aceite. La parte de un horno o caldera de aceite que produce calor al quemar fueloil.

Oil Level Regulator   Regulador de nivel de aceite. Controla el nivel de aceite en un compresor de un sistema de múltiples compresores.

Oil Pressure, Compressor   Presión de aceite del compresor. La presión creada por la bomba de aceite de un compresor con sistema de lubricación por presión positiva.

Oil Pressure, Oil Burner   Presión de aceite del quemador de aceite. La presión creada por la bomba de aceite en un quemador de aceite.

Oil Pressure Safety Switch   Interruptor de seguridad de presión de aceite. Un interruptor de tiempo controlado de diferencial de presión de aceite que abre el circuito de control a un compresor si la presión de aceite desciende por debajo de los niveles seguros.

Oil Reservoir   Depósito de aceite. El recipiente que contiene la reserva de aceite en un sistema de control del nivel de aceite utilizado por un sistema de múltiples compresores

Oil Slugging   Acumulación de aceite. Presiones hidráulicas creadas por el aceite que queda atrapado en el bolsillo de eliminación de un compresor alternativo durante la operación.

One-Time Relief Valve   Válvula de descarga de único uso. Un dispositivo de alivio de la presión que debe ser reemplazado luego de haberse abierto.

One-Time Fuse   Fusible de único uso. Un fusible con poca demora para abrirse y baja tolerancia para picos de corriente.

Open Display Case   Exhibidor abierto. Un refrigerador o congelador comercial que está diseñado para permanecer abierto en el extremo superior o en el frente.

Open-Loop, Control System   Sistema de control de circuito abierto. Un sistema de control donde la salida del controlador no afecta la condición que el controlador está detectando.

Open-Loop, Water System   Sistema de agua de circuito abierto. Un sistema de agua con recirculación que se encuentra abierto a la atmósfera en algún punto del sistema.

Open-Loop, Heat Pump   Bomba de calor de circuito abierto. Bomba de calor alimentada por agua que utiliza agua subterránea.

Open Refrigeration System   Sistema de refrigeración abierto. Un sistema de refrigeración que isa un compresor abierto.

Open Winding   Bobinado abierto. Un bobinado de motor que cuenta con un corte.

Operating Control   Control opertativo. Conduce el ciclo de los componentes del sistema durante la operación normal. Comúnmente empleado para hacer referencia al control que conduce los ciclos del compresor en un sistema de refrigeración.

Operating Pressures   Presiones operativas. Las presiones mínimas y máximas en un sistema de refrigeración en operación.

O-Ring   Junta tórica. Un elemento de cierre elástico con forma de círculo utilizado para sellar partes mecánicas.

Overload   Sobrecarga. Carga mayor a la carga para la cual el sistema fue ideado.

Oxidation   Oxidación. Una reacción química entre el oxígeno y otros materiales que forman nuevos compuestos. La herrumbre u óxido es la oxidación del hierro.

Oxygen   Oxígeno. Un elemento normalmente hallado en estado gaseoso que compone aproximadamente 21% de la atmósfera. Se requiere para la combustión.

Ozone Depletion   Agotamiento del ozono. Reducción de la concentración de ozono en la estratósfera.

Ozone Depletion Potential (ODP)   Potencial de agotamiento del ozono (ODP). Una categorización del potencial que un químico tiene de agotar el ozono estratosférico. Por definición, el potencial de agotamiento del ozono de un CFC 11 es 1.

Packaged Terminal Air Conditioner (PTAC)   Paquete terminal de aire acondicionado (PTAC). Un paquete de aire acondicionado de poca capacidad instalado a través de la pared, diseñado para ser usado en moteles, habitaciones de residencias estudiantiles y departamentos monoambientes.

Packing   Empaquetadura. El material que se envuelve alrededor del vástago de una válvula manual para sellarla.

Paraffinic Oil   Aceite parafínico. Un aceite mineral con alto contenido de cera.

Parts per Million (ppm)   Partes por millón (ppm). Una medida de la concentración de gases y contaminantes en niveles relativamente bajos.

Part Winding Start   Arranque de bobina parcial. Arrancar un motor trifásico de voltaje dual usando solamente la mitad de los bobinados del motor cuando se usa en bajo voltaje, a fin de reducir la corriente de irrupción del motor.

Pascal (Pa)   Pascal (Pa). Medida de presión del Sistema Internacional de Unidades equivalente a 1 Newton de fuerza aplicado sobre un área de un metro cuadrado.

Passive Refrigerant Recovery Device   Dispositivo pasivo de recuperación del refrigerante. Un dispositivo de recuperación del refrigerante que no posee componentes operativos.

Passive Solar Heating   Calefacción solar pasiva. Calefacción solar que depende del diseño arquitectónico en vez de basarse en componentes mecánicos y eléctricos.

Peltier Effect   Efecto Peltier. El principio que determina el funcionamiento de la refrigeración termoeléctrica. Cuando la corriente fluye a través de un termopar, un extremo se calienta y el otro se enfría.

Permanent Magnet   Imán permanente. Un imán que mantiene su efecto magnético y produce su propio campo magnético.

Permanent Split Capacitor Motor (PSC)   Motor de condensador dividido permanente (PSC). (Ver Motor, Condensador dividido permanente).

Phase, Electrical   Fase eléctrica. El número de formas de ondas senoidales separadas que suministran energía a un aparato de corriente alterna.

Phase, Physics   Fase física. El estado físico de una sustancia: sólido, líquido, gas o plasma.

Phase Change   Cambio de fase. Una sustancia que cambia de un estado físico a otro.

Phase Loss Monitor   Monitor de pérdida de fase. Un dispositivo de seguridad que monitorea la corriente trifásica y apaga un sistema o componente si una de las tres fases se retira.

Phase Reversal   Inversión de fase. Una nueva disposición de las tres líneas de energía de un circuito trifásico que hace que los motores trifásicos inviertan su rotación.

Photovoltaic Cell   Célula fotovoltaica. Un dispositivo semiconductor que convierte la luz solar en electricidad.

Pictorial Wiring Diagram   Diagrama de cableado. Muestra los componentes eléctricos tal como aparecen en el equipo y muestra los recorridos y colores reales de todos los cables interconectados.

Piercing Valve   Válvula perforadora. Una válvula que se atornilla o estaña a la parte exterior de una cañería y que la perfora para obtener acceso al sistema.

Piezoelectric   Piezoelectricidad. Una propiedad de algunos cristales que produce potencial eléctrico cuando se los golpea.

Pilot Duty Relay   Relé piloto. Un relé usado como interruptor de otros controles. Sólo calificado para cantidades reducidas de corriente.

Pipe   Cañería. Se usa para transportar fluidos. Se mide según su diámetro interno aproximado y tiene paredes relativamente gruesas comparadas con la tubería.

Pneumatic Controls   Controles neumáticos. Controles operados por presión de aire.

Pollen Count   Recuento de polen. Un índice que da cuenta del número de granos de polen en un metro cúbico de aire.

Polyalkylene Glycol (PAG)   Glicol polialquileno (PAG). Un lubricante sintético utilizado con refrigerantes HFC.

Polychlorinated Biphenyl (PCB)   Bifenilo policlorado (PCB). Un aceite dieléctrico que solía usarse en transformadores y condensadores. Ya no se usa debido a que es cancerígeno.

Polyethylene (PE)   Polietileno (PE). Un plástico utilizado para tuberías en sistemas de bucle de tierra, líneas de agua fría y cañerías de bombas de calor.

Polyethylene, Cross Linked (PEX)   Polietileno con formación de red (PEX). Un derivado del polietileno que es más fuerte, más elástico y puede tolerar temperaturas más elevadas.

Polyol Ester (POE)   Polioléster (POE). Un lubricante sintético que puede usarse con la mayoría de los refrigerantes en base a CFC, HCFC y HFC.

Polyphase   Polifase. Un dispositivo o sistema eléctrico diseñado para operar con más de una fase de corriente alterna.

Polyphase Motor   Motor polifásico. Un motor eléctrico diseñado para operar con más de una fase de corriente alterna.

Polyvinyl Chloride (PVC)   Policloruro de Vinilo (PVC). Un material termoplástico utilizado para hacer cañerías de agua fría y líneas de drenaje.

Positive Displacement   Compresor de desplazamiento positivo. Un compresor que comprime gas llenando el espacio ocupado por el gar con una pieza física como un pistón.

Positive Electrical Charge   Carga eléctrica positiva. Una carga eléctrica producto de un átomo u objeto que tiene más protones que electrones.

Positive Pressure   Presión positiva. Una presión cuyo valor está por encima de la presión atmosférica.

Positive Temperature Coefficient Thermistor (PTC)   Termistor de coeficiente de temperatura positivo (PTC). Un semiconductor cuya resistencia eléctrica aumenta al aumentar su temperatura. A veces se usa como relé de arranque electrónico en los circuitos de arranque para compresores.

Potential Energy   Energía potencial. Energía almacenada.

Potential Relay   Relé potencial. Un relé que detecta el emf trasero del bobinado de arranque y desconecta los componentes de arranque de un compresor.

Pounds per Square Inch (psi)   Libras por pulgada cuadrada (psi). Unidad de medida de presión.

Pounds per Square Inch Absolute (psia)   Libras por pulgada cuadrada absoluta (psi). Presión medida en libras por pulgada cuadrada absoluta.

Pounds per Square Inch Gauge (psig)   Libras por pulgada cuadrada manométrica (psig). Un símbolo o iniciales utilizados para indicar presión medida en libras por pulgada cuadrada manométrica.

Powder Actuated Tool (PAT)   Herramienta activada por pólvora (PAT). Una herramienta que desatornilla clavos y realiza anclajes en cemento y acero usando pólvora.

Power Burner   Quemador eléctrico. Un quemador que usa un soplador para hacer entrar aire y controlar la mezcla de combustible y aire.

Predictive Maintenance   Mantenimiento predictivo. Realizar pruebas calibradas en equipos en operación y compararlas con las mediciones de línea de base de modo que los equipos pueden ser reparados o reemplazados cuando se desgastan, antes de que se produzcan fallas.

Pressure, Absolute (psia)   Presión absoluta (psia). (Ver Presión absoluta).

Pressure, Atmospheric   Presión atmosférica. Presión ejercida por la atmósfera.

Pressure, Gauge (psig) Presión manométrica (psig). Presión medida por encima de la presión atmosférica.

Pressure, Static (PS) Presión estática (PS). La presión en el sistema cuando la bomba se encuentra inactiva.

Pressure, Suction Presión de succión. La presión en la sección de baja presión o evaporador del sistema de refrigeración.

Pressure-Enthalpy Diagram (PH) Diagrama presión-entalpía (PH). (Ver Diagrama de Mollier).

Pressure Gauge Manómetro. Instrumento para medir la presión en libras por pulgada cuadrada manométrica (psig).

Pressure Limiting Thermostatic Expansion Valve Válvula de expansión termostática limitadora de presión. Una válvula de expansión termostática que dejará de proveer refrigerante una vez que ha alcanzado la máxima presión operativa.

Pressure Switch Interruptor de presión. Un interruptor eléctrico que se abre y se cierra según los cambios de presión.

Pressure-Temperature Chart (PT Chart) Tabla de presión-temperatura (tabla PT). Muestra las presiones y temperaturas de saturación del refrigerante.

Pressure-Temperature Plugs (P/T) Conectores de presión-temperatura (P/T). Permiten la entrada de termómetros y manómetros al sistema de agua sin desagotar el agua o retirar la presión del sistema.

Pressure-Temperature Relationship Relación presión-temperatura. La relación predecible entre la presión y la temperatura de una mezcla saturada.

Pressure Transducer Transductor de presión. Produce una señal eléctrica variable basada en la presión aplicada.

Pressure Vessel Recipiente a presión. Un envase diseñado para contener presión.

Pressure Water Valve Válvula reguladora de presión para agua. Una válvula que controla el flujo de agua a través de un condensador refrigerado por agua en base a la presión del condensador.

Preventative Maintenance Mantenimiento preventivo. Realizar tareas de mantenimiento programadas regularmente a fin de prevenir fallas o cortes en el equipo.

Primary Winding Devanado primario. El bobinado de entrada de un transformador.

Product Producto. El material que está siendo refrigerado en un sistema de refrigeración comercial.

Product Heat Load Carga de calor del producto. El calor añadido al sistema de refrigeración por el producto que se está refrigerando.

Programmable Thermostat Termostato programable. Un termostato que puede programarse para cambiar automáticamente los niveles requeridos en base al tiempo.

Propeller Fan Ventilador helicoidal. Un ventilador con paletas montadas de forma perpendicular al eje y dispuestas en círculo. El flujo de aire es paralelo al eje.

Proportional Controller Controlador proporcional. Un controlador que puede combinar dos corrientes de aire o agua en proporciones variadas.

Propylene Glycol Glicol de propileno. Un químico no tóxico utilizado para soluciones anticongelantes en aplicaciones HVAC/R.

Proton Protón. Una partícula subatómica de carga positiva hallada en el núcleo de los átomos.

Psychrometrics Psicrometría. El estudio de las propiedades termodinámicas y físicas del aire.

Puffback Explosión con nube de humo (Puffback). Una explosión en la chimenea de un quemador de aceite, acompañada por una nube de humo creada por la ignición retardada. Es muy peligrosa en potencia.

Pulley Polea. Una rueda con una ranura rodeando su circunferencia, utilizada para transmitir energía mecánica usando una correa diseñada para encajar en la ranura.

Pulse Combustion Combustión de pulso. Una serie de pequeñas explosiones que producen una combustión extremadamente eficiente.

Pulse Furnace Horno de pulso. Un horno que emplea la combustión de pulso para lograr una alta eficiencia operativa.

Pulse Width Modulation (PWM) Modulación de la anchura del impulso (PWM). Una señal electrónica pulsante que se comunica en base a la duración de los impulsos y los intervalos de tiempo entre impulsos. Usada en algunos tipos de sistemas de control electrónicos.

Pump, Centrifugal Bomba centrífuga. Una bomba que funciona llevando agua hacia el centro de un impulsor alto y lanzándola al exterior a través de la rueda usando fuerza centrífuga.

Pump, Screw Bomba espiral. Transporta líquido usando dos tornillos ensamblados en forma de taladro que giran en direcciones opuestas.

Quench Valve Válvula de templamiento. Una válvula usada en unidades de transporte con refrigeración para administrar cantidades reducidas de refrigerante líquido en el área de succión del compresor para reducir la temperatura de emisión del compresor.

R Value, SI Valor R, SI. La resistencia térmica de un material de construcción en unidades de K·m²/W.

R Value, U.S. Valor R, Estados Unidos. La resistencia térmica de un material de construcción en unidades de ft²·°F·h/Btu.

Rack System Sistema de parrilla. Un sistema de refrigeración comercial con múltiples compresores ensamblados juntos en una parrilla.

Radiation Radiación. Transferencia de calor a través de rayos térmicos.

Radon Radón. Es un gas radioactivo de generación natural hallado en los sótanos y conductos subterráneos.

Rankine (R) Rankine (R). Escala Fahrenheit de cero absoluto.

Rated-Load Amperage (RLA) Amperaje de carga nominal (RLA). La corriente que atrae un motor cuando se encuentra en operación en su condición nominal.

Reactance Reactancia. Oposición a la corriente alterna por parte de la inductancia o la capacitancia, o de ambas.

Reamer Escariador. Una herramienta usada para retirar el excedente de metal dejado por un cortador de tubos.

Receiver Receptor. Un componente de refrigeración ubicado luego del condensador que almacena refrigerante líquido de alta presión.

Receiver-Drier Receptor-Secador. Un receptor de refrigeración que incorpora un desecante para deshidratar el refrigerante.

Reciprocal   Recíproco. El resultado obtenido al dividir cualquier número por 1 es su recíproco.

Reciprocating Compressor   Compresor alternativo. Un compresor que usa pistones, cilindros y válvulas para comprimir gas.

Recirculated Water System   Sistema de agua recirculada. Un sistema de calefacción o refrigeración que reutiliza la misma agua al hacerla circular una y otra vez a través de un circuito cerrado.

Reclaim   Reprocesar. Volver a procesar un refrigerante para que cumpla con la norma AHRI 700-2006 para refrigerante nuevo.

Recording Ammeter   Amperímetro registrador. Un amperímetro que puede registrar la corriente de amperios a lo largo de un periodo de tiempo, en papel o en la memoria del aparato.

Recording Thermometer   Termómetro registrador. Un termómetro que puede registrar la temperatura a lo largo de un periodo de tiempo, en papel o en su memoria.

Recording Voltmeter   Voltímetro registrador. Un voltímetro que puede registrar el voltaje a lo largo de un periodo de tiempo, en papel o en la memoria del aparato.

Recovery   Recuperar. Retirar refrigerante de un sistema y almacenarlo en un recipiente externo sin limpiarlo o procesarlo.

Recovery Cylinder   Cilindro de recuperación. Un cilindro con especificación DOT utilizado para recuperar refrigerante.

Rectifier, Refrigeration   Rectificador para refrigeración. Un componente de un sistema de absorción que condensa vapor de agua y lo regresa al generador para mejorar la concentración de amoníaco en el condensador.

Recuperative Heat Exchanger   Intercambiador de calor recuperador. Un intercambiador de calor secundario presente en hornos de gas y de aceite de alta eficiencia que recupera calor de los gases de combustión por medio de la condensación.

Recycling   Reciclado. Retirar refrigerante de un sistema, procesarlo usando filtros y separadores de aceite y almacenarlo en un recipiente externo.

Reference Point   Punto de referencia. Una condición específica conocida utilizada para calibrar instrumentos.

Reference Pressure   Presión de referencia. La presión sobre la cual se basan los datos deun gráfico o tabla.

Reference Temperature   Temperatura de referencia. La temperatura sobre la cual se basan los datos de un gráfico o tabla.

Refrigerant Blend   Mezcla de refrigerante. Una mezcla de dos o más refrigerantes que no se combinan químicamente.

Refrigerant Control   Control de refrigerante. Otro nombre utilizado para denominar al dispositivo de expansión o de medición en un sistema de refrigeración.

Refrigerant Quality   Calidad del refrigerante. El porcentaje de líquido y vapor en una mezcla saturada.

Refrigerant Reclaim   Reprocesamiento del refrigerante. (Ver Reprocesar).

Refrigerant Recovery   Recuperación del refrigerante. (Ver Recuperar).

Refrigerant Recycling   Reciclaje del refrigerante. (Ver Reciclado).

Refrigerant Expansion Device   Dispositivo de expansión del refrigerante. Otro nombre utilizado para denominar al dispositivo de medición o al control del refrigerante en un sistema de refrigeración.

Refrigerated Air Drier   Secador de aire refrigerado. Reduce el punto de rocío del aire comprimido utilizando un sistema de refrigeración.

Regulator   Regulador. Un dispositivo que controla el flujo que lo atraviesa para controlar la presión corriente abajo.

Reluctance   Reluctancia. La oposición a líneas de fuerza magnéticas que pasan a través de un material magnético.

Remote Bulb   Bulbo remoto. Un elemento de percepción de temperatura que funciona por medio de cambios de presión que son transmitidos al control a través de un tubo capilar. Está ubicado en un lugar diferente al del componente que controla.

Remote Condenser   Condensador remoto. Condensador ubicado solo, en un sitio diferente al que se encuentra el compresor.

Resilient Motor Mount   Soportes de motor elástico. Soporte de motor que contiene un material flexible como goma, que reduce la transmisión de vibración y sonido.

Refrigerant Control   Control de refrigeración. Otra expresión para dispositivo de expansión de refrigeración o dispositivo de medición en un sistema de refrigeración.

Refrigerant Dye   Tintura de refrigeración. Se utiliza para localizar fugas difíciles de encontrar en sistemas de refrigeración. La tintura tiñe el aceite refrigerante, no el refrigerante.

Refrigerant Management System   Sistema de gestión de refrigerantes. Sistema contable que se utiliza para documentar el uso del refrigerante.

Resistor   Reóstato. Componente electrónico con una resistencia eléctrica determinada opuesta al flujo de corriente.

Restrictor   Restrictor. Dispositivo de medición de refrigerantes que contiene un pequeño orificio el cual crea un descenso de presión debido a su restricción.

Retrofit, Mechanical   Readaptación mecánica. Actualización del equipamiento existente para cumplir con la eficiencia actual o las exigencias del código.

Retrofit, Refrigerant   Readaptación de refrigerante. Actualización de un sistema existente para reemplazar un refrigerante reductor de ozono viejo, por un refrigerante ecológico nuevo.

Return Well   Pozo de retorno. El pozo al cual regresa el agua de una bomba de calor de fuente natural de agua de circuito abierto.

Riser   Columna ascendente. Caño vertical que transporta gas o fluido hacia arriba en contra de la gravedad.

Rod and Tube   Barra y tubo. Consiste en una barra con un índice de baja expansión, dentro de un tubo con un índice de alta expansión. El cambio termal produce un movimiento lineal necesario para el funcionamiento de los interruptores.

Root Mean Square Voltage (RMS)   Valor Eficaz (RMS). Método exacto que se utiliza para determinar el voltaje eficaz de una onda de corriente alterna.

Rotating Blade Rotary Compressor   Compresor rotativo de aspas giratorias. Compresor rotativo con aspas ubicadas en el disco descentrado, que rota con el eje del compresor.

Run Capacitor Condensador para el funcionamiento de motores. Dispositivo diseñado para permanecer en el circuito todo el tiempo, en un motor de condensador dividido permanente.

Rupture Disc Disco de ruptura. Disco de una máquina frigorífica de baja presión, que se rompe para mantener la presión de la máquina frigorífica por debajo de 15 psig.

S Lock Sistema de bloqueo S. Cinta de metal en forma de S que se utiliza para mantener unidos los lados largos del conducto de metal rectangular.

SI System Sistema SI. Sistema internacional de unidades, basado en el sistema métrico.

Safety Interlock Switch Interruptor del mecanismo de interbloqueo de seguridad. Interruptor que evita que una máquina en condiciones inseguras opere, como en el caso de un panel removido.

Sail Switch Interruptor de paleta. Dispositivo que detecta el aire en una red de conductos utilizando una "paleta."

Satellite Compressor Compresor satélite. Compresor en un sistema de soporte dedicado a la temperatura más baja y a los evaporadores de presión.

Saybolt Univesal Seconds (SUS - SSU) Segundos saybolts universales (SSU). Unidad de medida que se utiliza para medir la viscosidad del aceite. Tiempo que demora 60 ml de aceite, en fluir a través de un orificio calibrado.

Schematic Wiring Diagram Diagrama de cableado esquematizado. Otra expresión para diagrama de escalera o diagrama de escala.

Screw Compressor Compresor de tornillo. Comprime gas utilizando dos husillos que engranan, girando en sentido contrario.

Scroll Compressor Compresor espiral. Reduce el volumen de gas, usando un espiral fijo y un espiral giratorio, que se encargan de trasladar el gas desde el exterior del espiral hacia el interior.

Sealed Combustion Combustión estanca. Provee aire de combustión a un horno, calentador de agua o caldera a través de un conducto, cerrando el proceso de combustión del aire que rodea el equipo.

Seat Asiento. Parte de una válvula cuya pieza movible de la misma se acomoda en contra al cerrar.

Secondary Refrigerant Refrigerante secundario. Agua o salmuera que circula en un sistema de máquina frigorífica desde la máquina frigorífica hasta la carga de calor.

Secondary Refrigeration System Sistema de refrigeración secundaria. Utiliza un refrigerante primario en un sistema de refrigeración por compresión, para enfriar un líquido que circula hasta la carga de calor existente. El refrigerante secundario utiliza todo el enfriamiento sensible y no cambia el estado.

Seebeck Effect Efecto Seebeck. Generación de una corriente eléctrica, cuando existe una diferencia de temperatura entre los dos extremos de un termopar.

Semiconductor Semiconductor. Material que conduce electricidad de una mejor manera que un aislante, pero no tan bien como un conductor.

Series Wound Motor Motor serie. Motor tipo escoba con una armadura bobinada, que se cablea en series con los arrollamientos inductores. Puede operar tanto con corriente continua (CC) como con corriente alterna (CA).

Service Factor (SF) Factor de servicio (FS). Factor decimal que produce motores de máxima seguridad al multiplicarlo por la evaluación de la capacidad nominal del motor.

Setpoint Valor de referencia. La temperatura de encendido de un termostato.

Shell and Coil Condenser Condensador de casco y serpentín. Condensador enfriado por agua que consiste en un serpentín de tubería dentro de un casco. El agua pasa a través del serpentín y el refrigerante se encuentra en el casco.

Shell and Tube Condensador de casco y tubo. Condensador enfriado por agua que consiste en tubos rectos que pasan a través de un casco. El agua fluye por los tubos y el refrigerante se encuentra en el casco.

Shroud Aro de refuerzo. Deflector alrededor de un ventilador helicoidal que separa el aire de entrada del aire de escape.

Sick Building Syndrome (SBS) Síndrome del edificio enfermo (SEE). Conjunto de molestias y enfermedades asociadas a la exposición de un individuo en un espacio cerrado en particular.

Silicon Silicio. Material semiconductor que se utiliza en la fabricación de componentes electrónicos.

Sine Wave Onda sinusoidal. Forma creada cuando se grafica un voltaje de una corriente alterna. Aparece como un conjunto regular de picos y valles consecutivos, conectados en una curva suave.

Single Phase Monofásico. Corriente alterna con una única forma de onda sinusoidal suministrada por dos cables.

Single-Phase Motor Motor monofásico. Motor eléctrico diseñado para operar con corriente alterna monofásica.

Single Phasing De una sola fase. Ocurre cuando un motor trifásico está operando en forma repentina en una corriente monofásica en vez de trifásica, debido a que una de las tres piernas de potencia dejó de funcionar. La corriente en las dos piernas restantes aumenta y el bobinado de motor se recalienta rápidamente.

Single Pipe System, Steam Heat de sistema monotubular, Calefacción de vapor. Método en el que se aplica un sistema de tuberías que permite que un sólo caño transporte tanto el vapor hacia los radiadores, como el retorno condensado hacia la caldera.

Single Pipe System, Oil Heat de sistema monotubular, Calefacción de aceite. Utiliza un solo caño para transportar el aceite desde el tanque hasta el quemador.

Single Pole Double Throw Switch (SPDT) Conmutador unipolar de dos vías (SPDT). Interruptor que puede conectar un puesto central a uno de los dos circuitos.

Single Pole Single Throw Switch (SPST) Conmutador unipolar de una vía (SPST). Interruptor que puede abrir o cerrar un circuito monofásico.

Skin Condenser Condensador oculto. Condensador que se encuentra comúnmente en congeladores horizontales, que utiliza la superficie exterior de la cabina para emitir calor.

Slinger Ring Anillo deflector. Anillo en la parte exterior del ventilador condensador en conjunto con cristales, que despide agua condensada de evaporador hacia el condensador, causando la evaporación del agua.

Slinky Loop Espiral. Tipo de circuito cerrado que se utiliza en instalaciones de sistemas geométricos superficiales, en el que un serpentín de la tubería es estirado en un canal como si fuera un resorte helicoidal aplanado.

Slip   Deslizamiento. Diferencia entre la velocidad sincrónica y la velocidad real de un motor eléctrico.

Slug   Relleno. Cantidad de líquido en el espacio libre del compresor que produce un martillo hidráulico.

Snap Action   De fijación a presión. Una manera de asegurar el cierre positivo de un interruptor eléctrico activado en forma mecánica.

Snap-Disc   Disco de acción rápida. Disco bimetálico deformado, que se rompe a una determinada temperatura para accionar interruptores.

Solar Cell   Célula solar. (ver célula fotovoltaica)

Solar Collector   Colector solar. Generalmente, una caja aisladora que convierte la energía solar en energía termal utilizando una superficie de color negra.

Solder   Soldadura. Aleación a una temperatura de fundición baja, utilizada para unir metales.

Solderless Terminals   Terminales sin soldadura. Terminales de cables que se conectan a los cables, utilizando el engastado mecánico en vez de la soldadura.

Solid   Sólido. Estado físico de la materia que posee volumen y forma definida.

Solid Fuel   Combustible Sólido. Material combustible como la madera, el carbón o los pellets de maíz.

Solubility   Solubilidad. Capacidad de una sustancia para disolverse en otra.

Solution, Chemical   Solución química. Un líquido con otro sólido, líquido o gas disuelto en él.

Solution, Refrigeration   Solución de refrigeración. Mezcla de absorbente y refrigerante en un sistema de absorción.

Solution, Strong   Solución concentrada. Solución que deja un alto porcentaje de refrigerante en el absorbente.

Solution, Weak   Solución de baja concentración. Solución que deja un bajo porcentaje de refrigerante en el generador.

Sone   Sonio. Unidad de medida del sonido utilizada para clasificar ventiladores de ventilación.

South Pole   Polo sur. Polo en un imán donde las líneas magnéticas fluyen hacia adentro.

Space Heater   Calentador ambiental. Calentador pequeño diseñado para permanecer en el área que calefacciona.

Splash Lubrication   Lubricación por salpicado. Método de lubricación en el que los componentes del compresor se sumergen en el líquido lubricante del cigüeñal.

Spray Pond   Condensador evaporativo. Se utiliza para refrigerar agua condensada a través de la evaporación mediante la pulverización de agua en el aire.

Stack Switch   Interruptor de salida de humos. Tipo de control de seguridad primario para hornos de aceite pesado, que perciben la temperatura en la salida de humos para su funcionamiento.

Standard Air   Aire normal. Aire en condiciones normales.

Standard Atmosphere   Atmósfera normal. Aire a una presión de 14.696 psia, 59 °F con una humedad relativa de 30%.

Standard Rating Conditions   Condiciones de evaluación estándar. Condiciones que utiliza la clasificación de resultados AHRI. Para el enfriamiento, 80 °F de bulbo seco, 67 °F de bulbo húmedo de aire de retorno y 95 °F de bulbo seco de aire exterior.

Standing Pilot   Piloto permanente. Pequeña llama que quema continuamente y se utiliza para iluminar los principales quemadores en artefactos calentados con gas.

Start Capacitor   Condensador de arranque. Condensador que se utiliza sólo durante el arranque para aumentar el torque de arranque de un motor monofásico.

Starved Evaporator   Evaporador con falta de refrigerante. Término que se utiliza para describir una condición en el evaporador cuando fluye menos refrigerante del necesario para la descarga de calor.

Static Condenser   Condensador estático. Condensador de corriente natural que depende más de la radiación que de la convección, para su efecto de enfriamiento.

Static Electricity   Electricidad estática. Tensión potencial eléctrica que resulta del desplazamiento de electrones de un objeto a otro.

Static Head   Caída estática. La diferencia de presión que debe superar una bomba antes de poder mover agua.

Stationary Blade Rotary Compressor   Compresor rotativo de álabe fijo. Compresor rotativo que contiene un único álabe ubicado dentro del cuerpo del compresor. Este álabe no gira junto con el eje del compresor.

Steady State Condition   Condición de régimen estable. Situación después del encendido de un horno de gas, que se logra cuando se han alcanzado los niveles de corriente y voltaje de los controles y el ventilador interior está en funcionamiento.

Steam   Vapor. Agua en estado gaseoso.

Steam Heating   Calefacción de vapor. Sistema de calefacción en el que el agua absorbe calor en una caldera, donde se evapora y emite calor desde los radiadores, donde se condensa.

Step Motor   Motor a pasos. Motor que se utiliza para el posicionamiento preciso de válvulas cuyos movimientos son pequeños pasos repetibles.

Stratosphere   Estratósfera. Capa de la atmósfera que se sitúa aproximadamente entre 12 y 30 mi encima de la Tierra. La capa de ozono se encuentra en la estratósfera.

Stroke, Actuator   Recorrido del actuador. Distancia que puede mover un actuador, por un amortiguador o válvula.

Stroke, Compressor   Recorrido de compresor. Distancia recorrida por un pistón en el cilindro de un compresor de pistón.

Subbase   Subbase. La base instalada para un termostato de bajo voltaje, donde se realizan las conexiones eléctricas.

Suction Line Accumulator   Acumulador de la línea de succión. (ver acumulador)

Suction Valves   Válvulas de succión. Válvulas que se encuentran en la parte inferior del platillo de válvula de un compresor, que permiten que el gas entre al cilindro en la carrera descendente del pistón.

Sump   Sumidero. Tanque que se encuentra en el fondo de una máquina, como una torre de refrigeración, que hace circular agua.

Swaging Tool   Herramienta para abocardar. Herramienta que se utiliza para aumentar el diámetro de un tubo.

Swamp Cooler   Enfriador evaporativo. Acondicionador de aire que utiliza evaporación de agua para reducir la temperatura del aire.

Synchronous Speed   Velocidad de sincronismo. Velocidad teórica a la que giraría un motor de inducción de corriente alterna, si el rotor girara a la misma velocidad que los pulsos magnéticos en los embobinados de motor.

Synthetic   Sintético. No se encuentra en la naturaleza, artificial.

Synthetic Lubricant Lubricante sintético. Producto químico obtenido sintéticamente como el poliolester que se utiliza para lubricación.

Synthetic Dust Weight Arrestance Prueba de colección de masa de la ASHRAE. Método para probar la eficiencia de un filtro de aire, mediante la utilización de "polvo" fabricado, cuyo tamaño es cuidadosamente controlado.

System Charge Carga del sistema. Tipo y cantidad de refrigerante en un sistema, usualmente indicado en la chapa con instrucciones.

System Lag Retardo del sistema. Tiempo de demora que existe entre el momento en el que se detecta una condición y el momento en el que el sistema comienza a actuar en base a esa condición.

System Overshoot Exceso del sistema. Temperatura de espacio que excede el punto de trabajo de un termostato en un sistema de calefacción.

Temperature Glide Deslizamiento de temperatura. Diferencia de temperatura entre el punto de rocío y el punto de burbuja en un refrigerante zeotrópico.

Temperature-Humidity Index Índice de humedad de la temperatura. Índice que combina la temperatura del aire con la humedad para describir niveles de bienestar.

Temperature-Pressure Relationship Relación temperatura-presión. (ver relación presión-temperatura)

Temperature-Pressure Chart (TP Chart) Tabla de temperatura-presión (Tabla TP) (ver tabla de presión-temperatura)

Temperature-Pressure Relief Valve (TPR) Válvula de alivio de presión y temperatura (VPT). Válvula que se abre para liberar la presión en un sistema de agua cerrado, si la presión o la temperatura exceden el nivel seguro.

Temperature Sensing Bulb Bulbo detector de temperatura. Bulbo llenado con un fluido volátil o gas que contiene un tubo capilar cuya función es transmitir presión desde el bulbo hasta el dispositivo de control. Se utiliza con válvulas de expansión termostática o termostatos.

Temperature Swing Oscilación de temperatura. Diferencia entre la temperatura baja y la temperatura alta en un espacio controlado.

Terminal Velocity Velocidad terminal. Velocidad de la corriente de aire al salir de un difusor, cuando éste ha reducido la velocidad a un punto en el que ya no se mezcla con la habitación de aire. Normalmente entre 50 y 150 ppm.

Test Light Lámpara de prueba. Instrumento eléctrico de prueba que indica la presencia de voltaje mediante la iluminación de una lámpara.

Testing, Adjusting and Balancing (TAB) Prueba de compensación y ajuste (TAB). Prueba del rendimiento del sistema y ajustes hechos en el sistema para que el funcionamiento del sistema existente, corresponda a los requisitos del diseño. Este término también se utiliza para referirse a los ajustes de flujo de aire. Sin embargo, todos los aspectos del funcionamiento del sistema deben ser evaluados.

Testing, Adjusting and Balancing Bureau (TABB) Organismo de prueba de compensación y ajuste (TABB). Organización afiliada a la industria de láminas metálicas que certifica a los técnicos TAB.

Thermodynamics Termodinámica. Estudio del calor y del flujo del calor.

Thermostat Droop Valor establecido. Mantener la temperatura por debajo del valor establecido.

Thermostatic Expansion Valve (TXV) Válvulas de expansión termostática (VET). Válvula que funciona por la temperatura y la presión dentro de un serpentín evaporador.

Thermostatic Water Valve Válvula de agua termostática. Válvula reguladora de agua controlada por la temperatura que se utiliza en los sistemas de refrigerado por agua.

Three Phase Trifásico. Corriente alterna de forma sinusoidal separada por 120°, alimentada por tres cables.

Three Phase Motor Motor trifásico. Motor eléctrico diseñado para funcionar con una corriente alterna trifásica.

Three Way Valve, Control Válvula de control de tres vías. Válvula que regula el flujo desde una entrada hacia dos salidas.

Three Way Valve, Manual Válvula manual de tres vías. Válvula manual que contiene tres puertos y dos asientos de válvula, que se utiliza frecuentemente como una válvula de servicio de refrigeración manual.

Throw Carrera. Distancia que recorre el aire desde un difusor de aire o registro, antes de alcanzar la velocidad terminal.

Thrust Bearing Cojinete de empuje. Rodamiento diseñado para resistir una fuerza que empuja contra el cojinete en paralelo con el eje. Los ventiladores de montaje vertical requieren de cojinetes de empuje.

Timed Off Control Control de tiempo de retardo. Temporizador que comienza la medición del tiempo cuando la unidad ciclos fuera para asegurar un tiempo mínimo de retardo antes de permitir que la unidad se reinicie.

Time Delay Demora. Espacio de tiempo entre el momento en el que se energiza un control y el momento en el que actúa.

Time Delay Fuse Fusible de retardo. Fusible que tiene la capacidad de resistir sobrecarga momentánea. Se utiliza comúnmente en motores.

Time Delay Relay Relé de retardo. Relé cuyo serpentín se energiza por un período de tiempo antes de que sus contactos se abran o se cierren.

Torque, Full Load Momento de torsión a plena carga. Par de torsión máximo que un motor le puede dar a su potencia nominal.

Torque, Stall Momento de torsión a la velocidad crítica. Momento de torsión total que produce un motor cuando se energiza y se cierra mecánicamente. Éste es el máximo momento de torsión que puede producir un motor.

Torque, Starting Momento de torsión de arranque. Momento de torsión total que produce un motor cuando arranca, normalmente mucho más alto que el momento de torsión a plena carga.

Torr Torr. Unidad de presión que no pertenece al Sistema Internacional de Medidas (SI) y es equivalente a 1/760 de una presión atmosférica normal. Una presión ideal es 760 Torr.

Total Energy Management (TEM) Sistema de Gestión Total de la Energía (SGTE) Estrategia de gestión de energía que analiza el total de energía que se utiliza en una construcción en vez de concentrarse en sistemas o componentes específicos.

Total Equivalent Warming Impact (TEWI) Impacto total equivalente de calentamiento (TEWI). Índice de calentamiento global que tiene en cuenta el impacto de refrigerantes en el calentamiento global, tanto en forma directa como indirecta.

Total Heat   Calor total. Cantidad de calor sensible y calor latente. Se denomina entalpía.

Toxicity   Toxicidad. Grado en que una sustancia es venenosa. Los refrigerantes dañinos a concentraciones de 400 ppm o menos, se clasifican como refrigerantes de mayor toxicidad.

Transducer   Transductor. Dispositivo que produce una señal electrónica basada en una propiedad física, como la temperatura o la presión.

Transmission, Heat   Transmisión calorífica. Pérdida de calor o aumento de temperatura a través de los componente de construcción.

Triple Point   Punto triple. La temperatura y la presión en donde coexisten el estado sólido, el estado líquido y el estado gaseoso.

Troposphere   Troposfera. Zona inferior de la atmósfera y más cercana a la superficie terrestre.

True RMS meter   Medidor de verdadero valor eficaz. Utiliza muestreo de valores frecuentes y la fórmula de la media cuadrática para determinar los valores de corriente alterna.

Tubing   Tubería. Se utiliza para transportar fluidos. La tubería tiene un diámetro exterior uniforme y paredes relativamente delgadas comparadas a las de un caño.

Twinning   Maclaje Instalación o cableado eléctrico de dos hornos para que funcionen en forma simultánea como si fueran una sola unidad mayor.

Two Position Control   Control de dos posiciones. Control que está encendido o apagado.

Two Stage Air Conditioner   Acondicionador de aire de dos etapas. Puede funcionar a dos capacidades separadas, de manera que la capacidad de la unidad se ajuste mejor a la carga.

Two Stage Compressor   Compresor de dos etapas. Puede funcionar a dos capacidades separadas, de manera que la capacidad del compresor se ajuste mejor a la carga. Se utiliza en acondicionadores de aire y bombas de calor de dos etapas.

Two Stage Vacuum Pump   Bomba de vacío de dos etapas. Produce un vacío más profundo y de baja presión al tener dos bombas de vacío en serie. La descarga de la etapa inferior alimenta la succión de la etapa superior.

Two Stage Furnace   Horno de dos etapas. Contiene un índice de fuego bajo y un índice de fuego alto, de manera que la capacidad del horno se ajuste mejor a la carga.

Two Stage Heat Pump   Bomba de calor de dos etapas. Puede funcionar a dos capacidades separadas, de manera que la capacidad de la unidad se ajuste mejor a la carga. Permite una capacidad de calefacción elevada, sin superar al acondicionador de aire.

Two Temperature Valve   Válvula de dos temperaturas. Otra expresión para válvula reguladora de la presión del evaporador.

Two Way Valve   Válvula de dos vías. Válvula que contiene una entrada y una salida y que tiene dos posiciones, una abierta y una cerrada.

U-Value   Conducción de calor. Otra expresión para conductividad térmica.

Ultrasonic Leak Detector   Detector de fuga ultrasónico. Detecta fugas de gas en sistemas de refrigeración al percibir el sonido del silbido ultrasónico del gas al escapar

Ultraviolet A (UVA)   Radiación ultravioleta A (UVA). Radiación ultravioleta de larga longitud de onda que comprende longitudes de onda entre 315 y 400 nm.

Ultraviolet B (UVB)   Radiación ultravioleta B (UVB). Radiación ultravioleta de longitud de onda mediana que comprende longitudes de onda entre 280 y 315 nm.

Ultraviolet C (UVC)   Radiación ultravioleta C (UVC). Radiación ultravioleta de corta longitud de onda que comprende longitudes de onda entre 100 y 280 nm.

Universal Motor   Motor universal. Motor de CD con embobinado en serie que puede funcionar tanto con corriente alterna como con corriente continua.

Unvented Space Heater   Calentador ambiental sin ventilación. Calentador alimentado por gas que despide todos los productos de combustión dentro del espacio que calefacciona.

Universal Motor   Motor universal. Motor con embobinado en serie que se utiliza para artefactos y herramientas eléctricas. Los motores universales pueden funcionar tanto con corriente alterna como con corriente continua.

Unloader   Descargador. Dispositivo que reduce la capacidad de un compresor evitando que algunos cilindros se compriman.

Upflow   De tiro ascendente. Hornos y gestores de aire cuyo flujo de aire se halla arriba en forma vertical, entrando por la parte inferior de la unidad y saliendo por la parte superior.

U-Tube Manometer   Manómetro de tubo en U. Instrumento que mide la presión mediante la altura de la columna líquida que soporta en un tubo en forma de U. Los manómetros de baja presión se llenan con agua. Los manómetros de mayor presión se llenan con mercurio.

V Belt   Correa trapezoidal. Correa de transmisión con una sección transversal en forma de V.

Vacuum Gauge   Vacuómetro. Instrumento que mide el nivel de un vacío profundo, usualmente en micrones.

Valve, Expansion   Válvula de expansión. Dispositivo de medición de refrigerante modulador.

Valve Seat   Asiento de válvula. (ver asiento)

Valve, Suction   Válvula de succión (ver válvulas de succión)

Valve Stem Depressor   Depresor de vástago de válvula. Parte en el extremo de una manguera de refrigeración que deprime la base de la válvula cuando se conecta a una válvula Schrader.

Vapor   Vapor. Estado gaseoso de una sustancia. Toma la forma y volumen de su recipiente.

Vapor Charge Bulb   Bulbo de carga de vapor. También denominado carga de gas o carga limitada. Bulbo detector de temperatura que contiene una cantidad limitada de líquido para que todo el líquido sea vaporizado al límite máximo de temperatura utilizada en el bulbo.

Vapor Lock   Traba de vapor. Interrupción u obstrucción del flujo en una línea de líquido debido a la presencia de vapor en la línea.

Vapor Pressure   Presión de vapor. Presión ejercida por un vapor sobre sus alrededores.

Vapor Refrigerant Charging   Carga de refrigerante de vapor. Agregar refrigerante a un sistema en forma de gas.

Vapor Refrigerant Recovery   Recuperación de refrigerante de vapor. El refrigerante es removido del sistema en forma de vapor.

Vaporization   Vaporización. Cambio de estado físico de líquido a vapor.

Variable Air Volume (VAV)   Volumen de aire variable (VAV). Método de control de zona que varía la cantidad de aire que se suministra a la zona, dependiendo de la carga.

Variable Frequency Drive (VFD)   Impulsor de frecuencia variable (IFV). Control de un motor de CA que cambia la velocidad del motor, variando la frecuencia de la corriente que va al motor.

Variable Resistor   Reóstato variable. Reóstato cuyo valor se puede adaptar, normalmente entre 0 ohm y su máximo valor.

Variable-Speed Motor   Motor de velocidad regulable. Motor cuya velocidad se puede adaptar para cumplir con los distintos requerimientos de carga.

Velocity (v)   Velocidad (v). Aceleración.

Vent-Free   Chimenea a gas sin conductos de ventilación. Artefacto alimentado por gas diseñado para operar sin un conducto de ventilación y cuyos productos de combustión se despiden dentro del mismo área en donde se encuentra el artefacto.

Vented Space Heater   Calentador de espacio con salida de humo. Calentador de espacio alimentado por gas, cuyos productos de combustión son despedidos hacia el exterior a través de un tubo de chimenea.

Vibrasorber   Absorbente de vibración. Componente de refrigeración que sirve para reducir la vibración en el sistema de tuberías de un refrigerante y consiste en un tubo interno corrugado y una carcasa de tejido metálico en el exterior.

Volatile   Volátil. Fluido que se evapora rápidamente.

Voltage   Tensión. La diferencia potencial entre dos puntos.

Voltage, Effective   Tensión eficaz. Medida de la corriente alterna que establece su efecto en un circuito resistivo.

Voltage, RMS   Tensión RMS. El valor eficaz de la tensión se utiliza para calcular la corriente alterna eficaz. El voltaje instantáneo se mide varias veces cada ciclo. Cada uno de estos valores se elevan al cuadrado, se halla el promedio de los cuadrados y finalmente la raíz cuadrada del promedio es el voltaje efectivo.

Voltage, Minimum   Tensión mínima. Suministro mínimo de voltaje a un determinado aparato.

Voltage, Maximum   Tensión máxima. Suministro máximo de voltaje a un determinado aparato.

Voltage, Nominal   Tensión nominal. Rango de voltaje normal para un aparato determinado.

Voltage, Peak   Voltaje pico. Voltaje en el punto máximo de una forma de onda sinusoidal de una CA.

Voltmeter   Voltímetro. Medidor que lee la tensión.

Volt Ohm Milliammeter (VOM)   Voltio-ohmio-miliamperímetro (VOM). Instrumento que mide tensión, resistencia y corriente en miliamperios.

Wastewater System   Sistema de agua séptica. Sistema de refrigeración enfriado por agua que no recicla el agua de refrigeración del condensador.

Water Box   Caja de agua. Parte colectora de agua en un enfriador o caldera.

Water Coil   Serpentín de agua. Serpentín de transferencia de calor diseñado para el agua.

Water Cooler   Enfriador de agua. Aparato que enfría agua potable.

Water Hammer   Martillo de agua. Fuerte sonido originado por un aumento repentino de la presión estática en las tuberías cuando el agua corriente se detiene bruscamente al cerrar una válvula.

Water Loop   Circuito de agua. Sistema de tuberías y componentes en un circuito cerrado.

Water Regulating Valve   Válvula reguladora de agua. Válvula que regula la corriente de agua a través de un condensador refrigerado por agua, en respuesta a la presión del refrigerante.

Watt-Hour (Wh)   Vatio hora. Uso de potencia eléctrica de 1 vatio durante 1 hora.

Welded Hermetic Compressor   Compresor hermético soldado. Compresor que tiene tanto el compresor como el motor, dentro de una carcasa soldada.

Wet Bulb Temperature (wbt)   Temperatura de una bombilla húmeda (tbh). Temperatura obtenida con un termómetro de bulbo húmedo.

Wet Bulb Depression   Depresión del bulbo mojado. Diferencia entre la temperatura de bulbo seco y la temperatura de bulbo húmedo.

Wet Bulb Thermometer   Termómetro de bulbo húmedo. Termómetro que tiene un saco en el bulbo para medir la tasa de evaporación en una muestra de aire.

Wet Cell Battery   Batería de celda húmeda. Dispositivo que contiene una solución de electrolito líquido.

Wet Heat   Calor húmedo. Sistema de calentamiento que utiliza agua o vapor.

Wind Chill Factor   Temperatura de sensación. Reducción en la temperatura percibida a causa del viento.

Winding Thermostat   Termostato de bobina. Sensor de temperatura que se abre si la temperatura de la bobina del motor excede el nivel seguro. A temperature sensor that opens if the motor winding temperature exceeds a safe level.

Windmilling   En molinete. Rotación al revés del ventilador a causa del soplo del viento que pasa a través de los ventiladores exteriores cuando se encuentran apagados.

Window Unit   Acondicionador de aire para la ventana. Acondicionador de aire diseñado para ser instalado en una ventana.

Wire Connectors   Conectores de cables. Terminales eléctricas que se unen a los cables mediante la soldadura o engastado que facilita la conexión de cables a los componentes.

Wobble Plate Compressor   Compresor de disco oscilante. Compresor con pistones que se hallan en forma paralela al cigüeñal, que utiliza un disco hiperbólico para crear movimiento alterno.

Work   Trabajo. Transferencia de energía.

Work Hardening   Endurecimiento mecánico por deformación. Metal que se vuelve frágil como consecuencia de haber sido flexionado repetidamente.

Wye Connected Motor   Motor conectado en estrella. Motor trifásico cuyos bobinados están unidos en el centro para adoptar forma de estrella.

WYE Transformer   Transformador en estrella. Transformador trifásico cuyos bobinados están unidos en el centro para adoptar forma de estrella.

Zeotropic   Zeotrópico. Mezcla que cambia su composición al bullir.

Zone Control   Control de zona. Regulador que coordina el funcionamiento de los amortiguadores y válvulas en un sistema de control de zona.

Zone Damper   Amortiguador de zona. Amortiguador que controla el flujo del aire en una zona determinada en un sistema divido en zonas.

Zone Control System   Sistema de control de zona. Sistema de control que mantiene la condición de zonas separadas en una misma construcción.

Zone Valve   Válvula de sector. Válvula que controla el flujo de agua hacia una zona en un sistema de calefacción hidrónica dividido en zonas.

Index